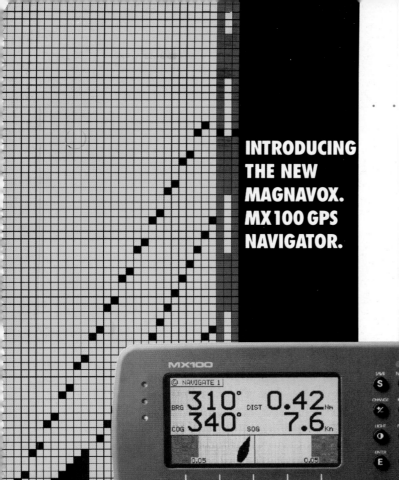

INTRODUCING THE NEW MAGNAVOX. MX100 GPS NAVIGATOR.

NAVIGATION FOR THE 21st CENTURY.

You already have DECCA. Possibly a SatNav system. Maybe even a GPS receiver.

None of which could have prepared you for your first experience with the new MX100 GPS Navigator. Hardware at the cutting edge of technology. Software of astonishing power. At your command.

GO AHEAD. PRESS THE ON BUTTON.

In moments you're locked onto a constellation of GPS satellites with the unerring accuracy of six-channel continuous tracking.

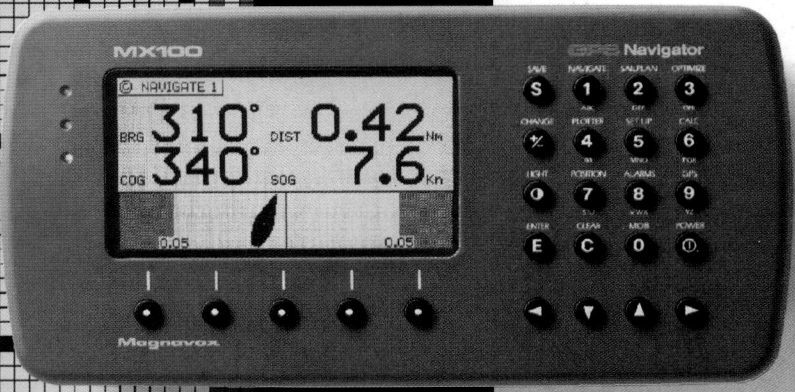

MX100
GPS Navigator
NAVIGATE 1
BRG 310°
DIST 0.42 Nm
COG 340°
SOG 7.6 Kn
0.05
0.05
Magnavox

The advanced backlit, double super-twist LCD screen fills with bright, high-resolution data. Position. Speed. Heading. Cross-track error. Time and distance to the next waypoint. All updated at one-second intervals.

You're impressed.

BUT YOU'VE ONLY SCRATCHED THE SURFACE.

For yacht skippers, blue water sailors, competition fishermen, sailboat racers, and those who just won't compromise, the MX100 GPS Navigator gives you instant access to more and better information.

For example, a PLOTTER display of your course, cross-track and upcoming waypoints.

A SAILPLAN function that lets you enter up to 200 waypoints with complete descriptions. Plus 20 routes with as many as 20 waypoints each.

There's even a Man Over Board button that records your position and instantly displays a return course to the exact spot.

The MX100 GPS Navigator. Incredible. And it's at your dealer now.

Magnavox GPS

Engineering The Evolution.

TORRANCE, CALIFORNIA 90503 U.S.A.
TELEPHONE (213) 618-1200, FAX (213) 618-7001

MAGNAVOX SYSTEMS LTD.
7 CHURCH STREET, SLOUGH, BERKS. SL1 1TL
TEL 0753-538025, FAX 0753-824633

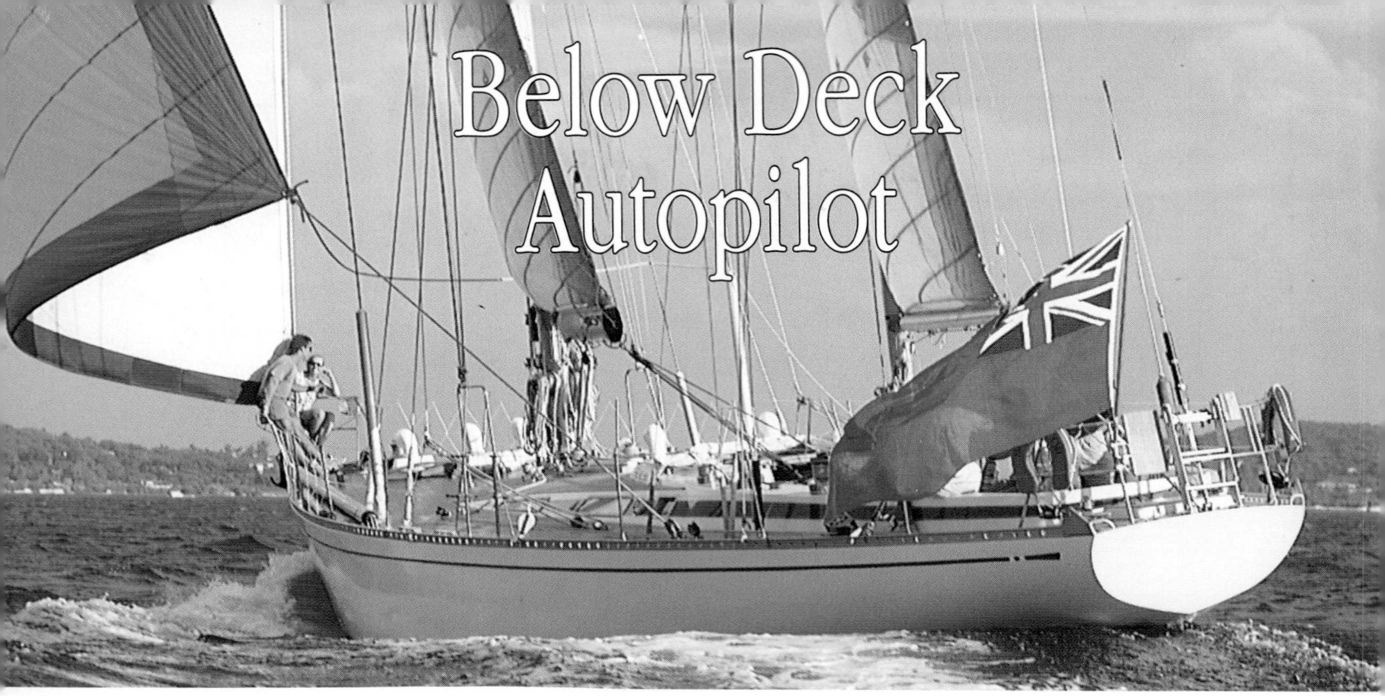
Below Deck
Autopilot

Photo by Rick Tomlinson

Upper Hand Control

Navico, world class manufacturers of autopilots, introduce the 8000 range of Below Deck pilots following two seasons of extensive seatrials and system optimisation. Two actuator options (hydraulic pump or linear drive) are available to suit most steering configurations.

The Navico 8000 is not just another autopilot. It combines unparallelled performance with economy of current consumption. For a fully integrated system, interface your 8000 pilot to virtually all modern navigational aids, including Decca, Loran and GPS receivers.

The 8000 "lock on course" controller simplifies basic operation. Add the popular Hand Programmer HP8000 for greater sophistication, flexibility, and a whole host of features.

For the Upper Hand in autopilot control, contact us now! Navico Ltd, Star Lane, Margate, Kent CT9 4NP.
Tel: 0843 290290 Fax: 0843 290471

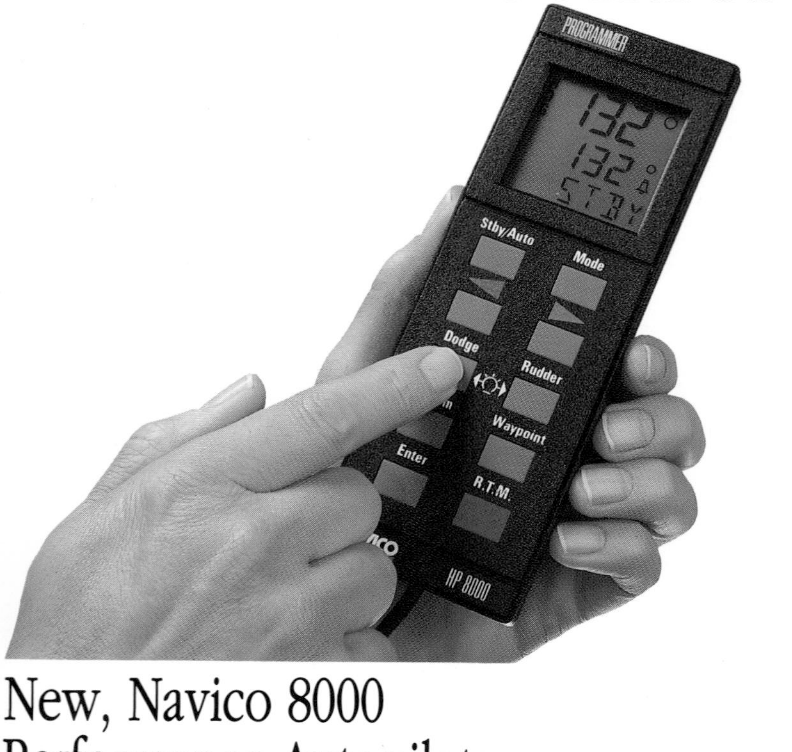
PROGRAMMER
132°
132°
STBY
Stby/Auto
Mode
Dodge
Rudder
Waypoint
Enter
R.T.M.
HP 8000

New, Navico 8000 Performance Autopilots

NAVICO®

Available from leading marine electronic specialists at prices starting from £695 RRP + VAT

First published 1980
This edition published 1992 by Macmillan Press Ltd
a division of MACMILLAN PUBLISHERS LTD
London and Basingstoke

Associated Companies in Auckland, Delhi, Dublin, Gaborone, Hamburg, Harare, Hong Kong, Johannesburg, Kuala Lumpur, Lagos, Manzini, Melbourne, Mexico City, Nairobi, New York, Singapore and Tokyo.

This book is sold under the standard conditions of the Net Book Agreement.

British Cataloguing In Publication Data
A CIP catalogue record for this book is available for this book from the British Library.

ISBN 0–333–54975–9

MACMILLAN CONSULTANT EDITOR
Klaus Boehm

IMPORTANT NOTE
Whilst every care has been taken in compiling the information contained in this Almanac, the Publishers and Editors accept no responsibility for any errors or omissions, or for any accidents or mishaps which may arise from its use.

CORRESPONDENCE
Letters on editorial matters should be addressed to:
The Editors, The Macmillan & Silk Cut Nautical Almanac, 41 Arbor Lane, Winnersh, Wokingham, Berks RG11 5JE or Edington House, Trent, Sherborne, Dorset DT9 4SR.
See also Chapter 1 paragraph 1.2.1.

Enquiries about despatch, invoicing or commercial matters should be addressed to:

Customer Services Department,
Macmillan Press Ltd, Houndmills, Basingstoke,
Hampshire RG21 2XS

Enquiries about advertising space should be addressed to:
Communications Management International,
Chiltern House, 120 Eskdale Avenue, Chesham,
Buckinghamshire HP5 3BD

Chapters 1–9 Page preparation by
Wyvern Typesetting Limited, Bristol
Chapter 10 Cartography and page preparation by
Lovell Johns Ltd, Oxford
Colour artwork by Dick Vine
Editorial colour separations by Excel Photolit Ltd, Slough

Printed and bound in Hong Kong

THE MACMILLAN & SILK CUT NAUTICAL ALMANAC

1992

EDITORS Wing Commander B.D'Oliveira OBE, FRIN

Rear Admiral I.J. Lees-Spalding CB

CONSULTANT EDITORS Commander R.L. Hewitt LVO, RN MIMechE, MRINA, FRIN

M.W. Richey MBE, Hon MRIN

W. Nicholson BSc, FRAS

K.E. Best

Dr B.D. Yallop PhD, BSc, ARCS

M

MACMILLAN

Our support team is the best in the business

With an Autohelm, you've invested in an autopilot that's designed and built to give years of outstanding service.

However, should it ever need attention we want you to know that there is a network of Service Centres to get you back in action quickly – if you're on a holiday cruise that's a really important point.

Each Service Centre has factory trained staff and comprehensive stocks of parts. Service Centres are located conveniently in every major sailing area and each one is a leading marine electronics specialist.

As part of the best team in the business they are ready to give you their help – when you need it – wherever you sail.

Autohelm Service Centres – UK, Eire & Channel Islands

Factory Service
Nautech Ltd, Portsmouth
0705 693611

Hampshire
Emsworth
Greenham Marine Ltd
0243 378314
Hamble
BK Electro Marine
0703 455112
Hamble
Hudson Marine Electronics
0703 455129
Hamble
Greenham Marine Ltd
0703 455044
Hamble
Maricom
0703 454263
Hamble
Marine Technology
0703 455743
Southampton
Regis Marine Electronics
0703 636555
Fareham
Paul Waite
0329 233306/0836 775590
Cowes
Regis Marine Electronics
0983 293996
Lymington
Greenham Marine Ltd
0590 671144

Dorset
Poole
Fleet Marine
0202 673880
Poole
Greenham Marine Ltd
0202 676363
Broadstone
Tolley Marine
0202 632644

Devon
Salcombe
Burwin Marine
0548 843321
Dartmouth
Burwin Marine
0804 25417
Plymouth
Ocean Marine Services
0752 223922
Plymouth
Sutton Marine
0752 662129
Plymouth
Tolley Marine
0752 222530
Kingswear
J W & A Upham
0804 25242

Cornwall
Falmouth
Mylor Marine Electronics
0326 74001
Falmouth
Seacom Electronics Ltd
0326 76565
Penzance
Seacom Electronics Ltd
0736 69695

Avon & Gloucestershire
Avonmouth
A N D Electronics
0272 821441

Wales
Newport
Aquascan International
0633 841117
Dyffes
Dyffed Electronics
0646 694572
Pwllmeli
Rowlands Marine
0758 613193

Lancashire
Fleetwood
John N Jones
0391 75241

Merseyside
Liverpool
Robbins Marine Radio
051 709 5431

Humberside
Hull
Electronics Marine Ltd
0482 25163

Northumberland
Seahouses
Seatron
0665 720182

Norfolk
Norwich
R & J Marine Electronics
0603 897855

Suffolk
Lowestoft
Navtronics
0502 589 159
Levington
R & J Marine Electronics
0473 659737
Ipswich
Foxes Marine Electronics
0473 689111

Essex
Maldon
Mantsbrite Marine
0621 853003

Kent
Herne Bay
Heron Marine
0227 361255

Sussex
Brighton
FAM Enterprises
0273 684385
Itchenor
Regis Electronics
0243 511070
Peacehaven
LD Electronics
0273 586179

Scotland
Oban
A & B Marine
0631 66670
Aryshire
Boat Electrics & Electronics
0292 315355
Argyll
Forth Area Marine Electronics
085 25622
Ayrshire
Yacht Electrical & Electronics
0475 686463
Aberdeen
Land & Sea Electronics Ltd
0224 593281

Isle of Man & Eire
Ramsey
Bevan Ltd
0624 812583
Dublin
BJ Marine
0001 831353
Dublin
Eddie Brunker
0001 342590
Cork
Rider Services
021 841176

Channel Islands
St Peter Port
Boatworks +
0481 26071
St Peter Port
Radio & Electronic Services Ltd
0481 728837
St Helier
Jersey Marine Electronics
0534 21603
Braye
Mainbrayce Ltd
0481 22772

Autohelm Service Centres – France

Local Service Centres

Grand Fort Philippe
Dieppe
Baude Electronique
28 23 10 92
Dunkerque
E.G.E.F.
28 59 34 56
Boulogne sur Mer
Ocel
21 31 75 92
Lille
C.N.N.
20 04 94 60
Saint Valery sur Somme
Lattitude 50
22 26 82 06
Port en Bessin
L.K.E.
31 21 93 79
Carentan
Gam Marine
33 71 17 02
Saint Vaast La Hougue
Marelec
33 54 63 82
Cherbourg
Ergelin
33 53 20 26
Saint Malo
S.E.E.
99 82 68 48
Saint Guenole
St Gue Electronique
98 58 74 98
Le Guilvinec
Cariou
98 58 12 90
Loctudy
E.B.S.
98 87 91 33
Concarneau
St Gue Electronique
98 27 50 86
Concarneau
C.E.S.
98 50 51 09
Lorient
Celtec
97 83 06 07
Port Louis
E.D.E.
97 82 46 17
La Trinite sur Mer
S.E.E.M.A.
97 55 78 06
Les Sables d'Olonne
Masson
51 32 01 07
La Rochelle
Pochon
46 41 30 53
Dieppe
E.E.M.
35 84 54 24
Le Havre
Electronique Equipement
35 48 64 02
Honfleur
Labarriere
31 89 05 17
Deauville
Serra Marine
31 98 50 92
Ouistreham
Nauti Plaisance
31 97 16 21
St Brieu
L'Habitat de la Mer
96 33 71 68
Granville
Nautilec
33 50 04 96
Paimpol
Le Lionnais
96 20 79 25
Brest
S.E.N
98 42 10 35
Douarnenez
Poenot
98 92 02 98
Vannes
Seema
97 42 58 75
La Turballe
Hudault
40 23 30 77
Arzal
Erelec
97 45 05 92
Pornichet
Emtec
40 61 25 01
Saint Nazaire
Emtec
40 66 42 10
St Gilles Croix de Vie
Masson
51 32 01 07

Head straight for the best

Autohelm™

LIT 122/3

Contents

SOME USEFUL ADDRESSES

Amateur Yacht Research Society.
10 Boringdon Terrace, Turnchapel,
Plymouth PL9 9TQ.
Tel: Plymouth (0752) 592646.

Association of Brokers and Yacht Agents.
The Wheelhouse, 5 Station Road, Liphook,
Hants GU30 7DW.
Tel: Liphook ((0428) 722322.

British Marine Industries Federation (BMIF).
Boating Industry House, Vale Road, Oatlands Park,
Weybridge, Surrey KT13 9NS.
Tel: Weybridge (0932) 854511.

British Sub-Aqua Club.
16 Upper Woburn Place, London WC1H 0QW.
Tel: 071-387 9302.

British Telecom Maritime Radio Services.
43, Bartholomew Close, London EC1A 7HP.
Tel: 071-583- 9416.

British Waterways Board.
Greycaine Road, Watford, Herts WD2 4JR.
Tel: (0923) 226 422.

Clyde Cruising Club.
S.V. Carrick, Clyde Street, Glasgow G1 4LN.
Tel: 041-552 2183.

Cowes Combined Clubs.
Secretary, 18 Bath Road, Cowes, Isle of Wight
PO31 7QN.
Tel: Cowes (0983) 295744.

Cruising Association (CA).
Ivory House, St Katherine's Dock, World Trade
Centre, London E1 9AT.
Tel: 071-481 0881.

HM Customs and Excise.
Dorset House, Stamford Street, London SE1 9PS.
Tel: 071-865 4743.

International Maritime Organisation (IMO).
4, Albert Embankment, London SE1 7SR.
Tel: 071-735 7611.

International Maritime Satellite Organisation (INMARSAT).
40, Melton Street, London NW1 2EQ.
Tel: 071-387 9089.

Junior Offshore Group.
59, Queen's Road, Cowes, Isle of Wight.
Tel: Cowes (0983) 291572).

Little Ship Club.
At the Naval Club, 38 Hill Street, London W1X 8DP.
Tel: 071-236 7729.

Lloyd's Register of Shipping.
Yacht and Small Craft Services, 69 Oxford Street,
Southampton, Hants S01 1DL.
Tel: Southampton (0703) 220353.

Maritime Trust.
16, Ebury Street, London SW1H 0LH.
Tel: 071-730 0096.

Meteorological Office.
London Road, Bracknell, Berkshire RG12 2SZ.
Tel: Bracknell (0344) 420242.

Royal Cruising Club (RCC).
42 Half Moon Street, London W1.
Tel: 071-499 2103.

Royal Institute of Navigation.
At the Royal Geographical Society,
1 Kensington Gore, London SW7 2AT.
Tel: 071-589 5021.

Royal National Lifeboat Institution (RNLI).
West Quay Road, Poole, Dorset BH15 1HZ.
Tel: Poole (0202) 671133.

Royal Naval Sailing Association (RNSA).
c/o Royal Naval Club, Pembroke Road, Portsmouth,
Hants PO1 2NT.
Tel: Portsmouth (0705) 23524.

Royal Ocean Racing Club (RORC).
20, St James Place, London SW1A 1NN.
Tel: 071-493 5252.

Royal Thames Yacht Club (RTYC).
60 Knightsbridge, London SW1A 7LF.
Tel: 071-235 2121.

Royal Yachting Association (RYA).
RYA House, Romsey Road, Eastleigh,
Hants S05 4YA.
Tel: Eastleigh (0703) 629962.

Royal Yachting Association (Scotland).
Caledonia House, South Gyle,
Edinburgh EH12 9DQ.
Tel: 031-317 7388.

Solent Cruising and Racing Association.
18 Bath Road, Cowes, Isle of Wight PO31 7QN.
Tel: Cowes (0983) 295744.

Sports Council.
16 Upper Woburn Place, London WC1H 0QP.
Tel: 071-388 1277.

Trinity House, Corporation of.
Trinity House, Tower Hill, London EC3N 4DH.
Tel: 071-480 6601.

UK Civil Satnav Group (UK CSG).
c/o The Royal Institution of Navigation, at the Royal
Geographical Society, 1 Kensington Gore,
London SW7 2AT.
Tel: 071-589 5021. Fax: 071-823 8671.

UK Offshore Boating Association.
Burn's House, 144 Holdenhurst Road,
Bournemouth, Hants BH8 8AS.
Tel: Bournemouth (0202) 298555.

Yacht Brokers, Designers and Surveyors Association.
Wheel House, Petersfield Road, Whitehill,
Bordon, Hants GU35 8BU.
Tel: Bordon (0420) 473862.

QUICK PAGE REFERENCE
(for main index see page 854)

PERSONAL INDEX OF IMPORTANT PAGES

LET'S SEE THE

Silk Cut Nautical Awards

These awards were launched in 1983 to reward and to recognise outstanding achievements in the sailing world: namely, nautical skill, bravery and seamanship.

To date, 4,000 nominations have been received through monitoring press, radio and TV coverage, as well as recommendations from HM Services, the Police and members of the public.

Chay Blyth is at the helm of the judging panel again with representatives from HM Coastguard, the RNLI, the RYA Seamanship Foundation and other experienced and noteworthy master mariners.

They will be awarding prizes in five main areas. These being, Rescue, Seamanship, Club and Yachting Service, Yacht Racing and Original Design.

All winners will be presented with awards at an exclusive lunch at a top London hotel. For more information and nomination forms please contact the Awards' Secretary, 11A West Halkin Street, London SW1X 8JL. Or telephone 071-333 0333.

BEATING.
Punishment for missing the Southampton Boat Show.

BEARING AWAY.
Alter course away from your present activities and get down to Southampton.

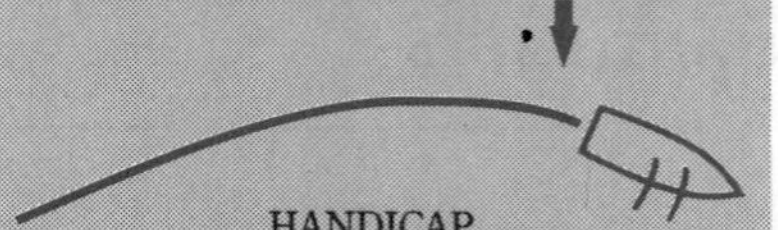

HANDICAP.
The time allowance you have to get down to Southampton.

GYBING.
The practice of taunting or jibing sailors who arrive late.

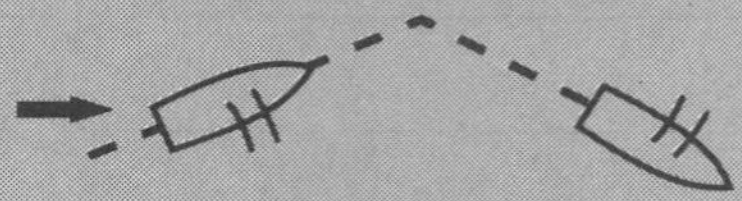

LEEWARD.
You'll be away from the wind in our nice cosy hall.

LUFFING.
A mixture of laughing and guffawing at those who miss out by not turning up.

OBSTRUCTION TO SEE ROOM.
This is a popular Boat Show, make sure you arrive early.

Silk Cut Cut 'N' Sail Challenge

Once again, designers and boat builders will be pitting their talents against each other at the Southampton Boat Show.

It's the ultimate challenge because the sixteen teams of two will have to design and construct a boat out of limited materials.

And what's more daunting is the fact that they'll have to battle against the clock as well.

On the last day of the show the completed craft will take to the water and attempt to navigate a set course.

After this 'trial by water', prizes will be awarded

UT OF YOUR JIB.

for fast building, elegance, and outrageous design as well as to the winning craft. If you're an aspiring designer whose ideas hold water, why not apply for an entry form from:- Silk Cut 'N' Sail, 11A West Halkin Street, London SW1X 8JL or telephone 071-333 0333.

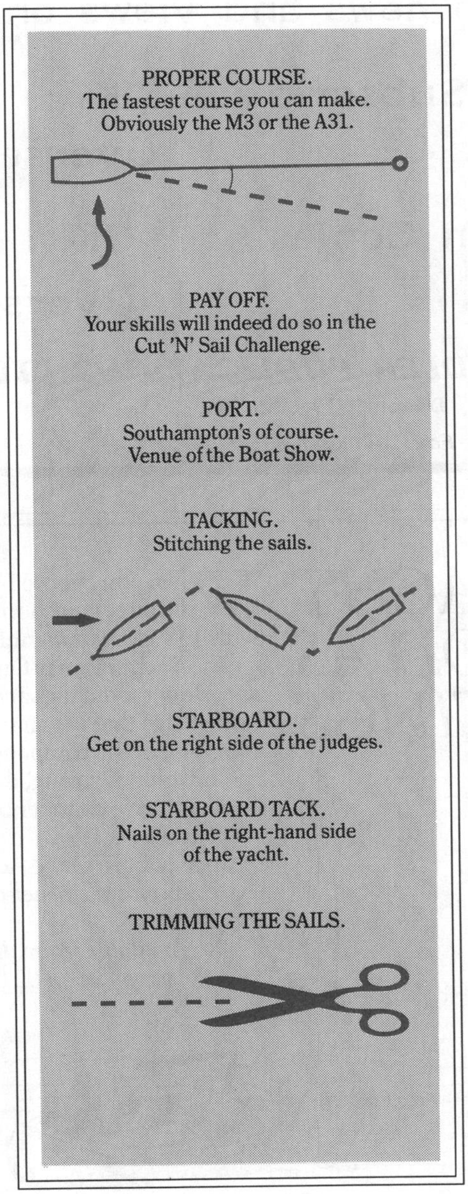
PROPER COURSE.
The fastest course you can make.
Obviously the M3 or the A31.
PAY OFF.
Your skills will indeed do so in the
Cut 'N' Sail Challenge.
PORT.
Southampton's of course.
Venue of the Boat Show.
TACKING.
Stitching the sails.
STARBOARD.
Get on the right side of the judges.
STARBOARD TACK.
Nails on the right-hand side
of the yacht.
TRIMMING THE SAILS.

MACMILLAN AND SILK CUT NAUTICAL ALMANAC AND YACHTSMAN'S HANDBOOK

When sailing in the waters of the British Isles there are no better books to have onboard.

For the novice and accomplished sailor alike, the Almanac contains all the standard information as well as updated navigational data and the rules and regulations for all seafarers. The handbook contains detailed information on owning, maintaining and operating a yacht. Meticulously researched and fully illustrated it's an indispensible companion to the Almanac.

Steer a course towards your local bookseller and order now. You're scuppered without them.

MACMILLAN
SILK CUT
Yachtsman's
HANDBOOK
NEW EDITION

SILK CUT HALL

The Silk Cut Hall at the Southampton Boat Show has been a feature since 1985.

Sponsored by Silk Cut, the hall offers exhibitors the opportunity to display nautical equipment to visiting mariners.

Every September the hall is visited by thousands of people. And it also provides a large lounge bar area where visitors can relax away from the crowds.

Quick Reference Marine Products and Services Guide

The following guide gives readers a quick reference to companies and organisations currently offering supplies or services to boat owners and the boating industry. Where possible, each entry carries a concise description and while every care is taken to ensure accuracy, the publisher does not necessarily endorse the information supplied.

- BOAT BUILDERS & REPAIRS
- BOOKS & CHARTS
- CHANDLERS
- CLOTHING
- COMMUNICATIONS EQUIPMENT
- ELECTRONIC EQUIPMENT
- ELECTRONIC & ELECTRICAL ENGINEERS
- ENGINES
- FLAGS & PENNANTS
- GENERAL MARINE EQUIPMENT & MACHINERY
- GRAPHICS & BOAT NAMING SYSTEMS
- INSTRUMENTATION & POSITION FIXING
- MAIL ORDER
- MARINAS
- MARINE INSURANCE & FINANCE
- MARINE TRANSPORT & YACHT DELIVERIES
- MOTOR CRUISER SCHOOLS
- OSMOSIS TREATMENT
- PAINT
- REPAIR MATERIALS
- SAFETY EQUIPMENT
- SAILING SCHOOLS
- SAILS
- SPECIALIST RESPRAYS
- VIDEOS
- WEATHER INFORMATION
- YACHT BROKERS

BOAT BUILDERS & REPAIRS

BOATWORKS + LTD
Castle Emplacement,
St Peter Port, Guernsey
Tel: (0481) 726071
Fax: (0481) 714224
Boatworks + provides a comprehensive range of services including electronics, chandlery, boatbuilding and repairs, engine sales and services, yacht brokerage, clothing and fuel supplies.

CAMBRIAN & WESTFLEET
The Boatyard,
Portway Village Marina,
Penarth, South Glamorgan
Tel: (0222) 709983
Boatbuilders and repairers, marine engineers, riggers, marine clothing specialists, chart agents, nautical booksellers, and yacht chandlers.

CAMUS MARINE SERVICES
Craobh Haven,
Craignish,
By Lochgilphead, Argyll
Tel: (08525) 225/622/222
Fax: (08525) 252
200 marina berths. Water. Electricity. Diesel fuel. Gas. Yacht repairs, fitting-out and engineering. Storage ashore. Chandlery. Brokerage. Insurance. Nearby facilities include: pub, shops, sailing school, dive centre, launderette, riding centre, hotels/guest houses, self-catering accommodation. Electronic & electric installation & service. Agents for Yanmar, Bukl, L/P diesels, Honda & Mariner outboards, Autolink RT, Easyreef furling systems.

CRINAN BOATS LTD
Crinan, By Lochgilphead,
Argyll PA31 8SP
Tel: (054 683) 232
Boatbuilders, chandlers, engineers, slipping, repairs, charts, electricians, pontoon, moorings, shower, laundry, basic stores.

EEL PIE MARINE CENTRE
Eel Pie Island,
Twickenham,
Middlesex TW1 3DY
Tel: 081-892 3626
Fax: 081-744 1312
Eel Pie Marine Centre offers full marina services with boatyard and full repair and maintenance facilities. Visitors welcome.

EVERSON AND SONS LTD
Phoenix Works,
Riverside, Woodbridge,
Suffolk
Tel: (03943) 4358
Boatbuilding and marine engineers; chandlers and riggers; insurance and brokerage arranged. Full yard facilities.

FALMOUTH BOAT CONSTRUCTION LTD
Little Falmouth Yacht Yard,
Flushing,
Falmouth, Cornwall TR11 5TJ
Tel: (0326) 74309
Fax: (0326) 77679
Repairs, refits, storage undercover and quayside, osmosis treatment specialists, resprays. Slipways to 100 ton. Commercial craft repairs. Specialist one-off builds. Full engineering shop for all diesel and petrol engines.

MITCHELL MOULDINGS LTD
Unit 10, Essex Marina,
Wallasea Island,
Canewdon, Essex SS4 2HG
Tel/Fax: (0702) 258112
Mitchell Mouldings Ltd boatbuilders and repairers, produce 4 versions of the Mitchell 31ft, suitable for Workboat, Patrol Boat, Passenger Launch, Leisure Boat, and a 23 Fast Fisherman (FF700). We also produce contract mouldings, at present the Coaster 33, Duellist 32 and Sapphire Launch.

A H MOODY & SON LTD
Swanwick Shore Road,
Swanwick,
Southampton SO3 7ZL
Tel: (0489) 885000
Fax: (0489) 885509
Sail and motor new boat sales. New construction. Brokerage. Major refits, repair facilities. Winterlay-up, marina. Chandlery, bunkering, valeting. Insurance.

NEWHAVEN MARINA LTD
The Yacht Harbour,
Newhaven,
East Sussex BN9 9BY
Tel: (0273) 513881
Fax: (0273) 517990

Newhaven Marina has comprehensive facilities including marine workshops, fuel, yacht brokerage, chandlery, pleasure and business charter, superb yacht club with hotel accommodation and riverside restaurant (open to non-members), 4 Gold Anchor Award. (0273) 513881.

PADSTOW HARBOUR
Padstow Harbour Commissioners,
Harbour Office, West Quay,
Padstow, Cornwall PL28 8AQ
Tel: (0841) 532239
Fax: (0841) 533346

Small West Country port having a vigorous fishing fleet and enjoying an excellent reputation for waterborne recreation. General cargo capability extends up to vessels 1500/2000 GRT.

SEAWARD MARINE ENTERPRISES
Southdown Quay,
Millbrook, Cornwall PL10 1EZ
Tel: (0752) 823084

32 berth marina on edge of River Tamar in quiet location behind Rame Peninsula. Plymouth just across river. Quayside berths available for large vessels. Winter storage. Good security. DIY facilities available.

BOOKS & CHARTS

CAMBRIAN & WESTFLEET
The Boatyard,
Portway Village Marina,
Penarth, South Glamorgan
Tel: (0222) 709983

Boatbuilders and repairers, marine engineers, riggers, marine clothing specialists, chart agents, nautical booksellers, and yacht chandlers.

CAMBRIAN SMALL BOATS & CHANDLERY LTD
14 Cambrian Place,
South Dock, Swansea,
West Glamorgan
Tel: (0792) 467263

Yacht chandlers, riggers, marine clothing specialists, nautical booksellers and THE ONLY ADMIRALTY 'A' CLASS CHART AGENT IN WALES.

DUBOIS PHILLIPS & McCALLUM LTD
Oriel Chambers,
Covent Garden,
Liverpool L2 8UD
Tel: 051-236 2776
Fax: 051-236 4577

Admiralty chart agents and nautical booksellers. Chart correction service. Worldwide mail order service.

HYDROGRAPHIC OFFICE
Taunton,
Somerset TA1 2DN
Tel: (0823) 337900

Admiralty charts and hydrographic publications - worldwide coverage corrected to date of issue. Available from appointed admiralty agents together with notices to mariners.

KELVIN HUGHES CHARTS & MARITIME SUPPLIES
New North Road,
Hainault,
Ilford, Essex IG6 2UR
Tel: 081-500 6166

Kelvin Hughes is the world's largest supplier of navigational charts and one of the U.K.'s leading nautical booksellers. They have retail outlets in the City of London, Southampton, Glasgow and Aberdeen and offer a worldwide mail order service.

TODD CHART AGENCY LTD
North Quay,
The Harbour, Portrush,
Northern Ireland BT56 8DF
Tel: (0265) 824176
Fax: (0265) 823077

Admiralty Class 'A' chart agent for Northern Ireland. Chart correction service and nautical booksellers. Stockist of navigation and chartroom instruments, binoculars, clocks, etc. Mail order service available. Visa and Access accepted.

WARSASH NAUTICAL BOOKSHOP
31 Newtown Road,
Warsash, Southampton
Tel: (0489) 572384
Fax: (0489) 885756

Nautical bookseller and chart agent. Callers and mail order. New and secondhand books. Free lists. Credit cards taken. Publishers of the bibliography of nautical books.

CHANDLERS

ABINGDON BOAT CENTRE
The Bridge,
Abingdon, Oxon OX14 3HX
Tel: (0235) 21125

The main chandlery on Upper Thames, supplying a large range of equipment and clothing for offshore and inland cruising and sailing. Admiralty Chart agents. Talurit and Roll Swage rigging. Trailers, inflatables.

BOATWORKS + LTD
Castle Emplacement,
St Peter Port, Guernsey
Tel: (0481) 726071
Fax: (0481) 714224

Boatworks + provides a comprehensive range of services including electronics, chandlery, boatbuilding and repairs, engine sales and services, yacht brokerage, clothing and fuel supplies.

BRENTFORD MARINE SERVICES
The Boathouse,
Brentford Dock Marina,
Justin Close, Brentford,
Middlesex TW8 8QA
Tel: 081-568 0287

Well stocked chandlery.

BRIXHAM YACHT SUPPLIES LTD
72 Middle Street,
Brixham, Devon
Tel: (0803) 882290

We stock a complete range of sailing and leisure clothing. English and continental pure wool traditional knitwear. Admiralty charts. Camping accessories.

BROMLEY BOATS
109-123 Southlands Road,
Bromley, Kent BR2 9QX
Tel: 081-464 8685
Fax: 081-313 0583

Chandlery - s/s wire - bolts - SP Systems - chain - shackles - rope - paints - trailer spares - charts - books - Navigational aids - dinghy equipment - Sniper boats - PLS wood.

CALEY MARINA
Canal Road,
Inverness, Scotland IV3 6NF
Tel: (0463) 236539
Fax: (0463) 238323

Open 08.30 - 17.30. Berths: 50 Pontoon (visitors available). Facilities: fuel, water, provisions (nearby shops), repair, cranage, storage afloat and ashore. Comprehensive chandlery, showers, workshop. Situated at eastern end of Caledonian canal above Muirtown Locks. Access via sea locks four hours either side of high water.

CAMBRIAN & WESTFLEET
The Boatyard,
Portway Village Marina,
Penarth, South Glamorgan
Tel: (0222) 709983
Boatbuilders and repairers, marine engineers, riggers, marine clothing specialists, chart agents, nautical booksellers, and yacht chandlers.

CAMBRIAN SMALL BOATS & CHANDLERY LTD
14 Cambrian Place,
South Dock, Swansea,
West Glamorgan
Tel: (0792) 467263
Yacht chandlers, riggers, marine clothing specialists, nautical booksellers and THE ONLY ADMIRALTY 'A' CLASS CHART AGENT IN WALES.

COMPASS POINT CHANDLERY
The Quay, Hamble,
Southampton S03 5HA
Tel: (0703) 452388
Fax: (0703) 456942
Compass Point is adjacent to the new quay at Hamble. It stocks an attractive selection of leisure clothing and foulweather gear as well as a wide range of chandlery including British Seagull spares and Calor gas.

CRINAN BOATS LTD
Crinan, By Lochgilphead,
Argyll PA31 8SP
Tel: (054 683) 232
Boatbuilders, chandlers, engineers, slipping, repairs, charts, electricians, pontoon, moorings, shower, laundry, basic stores.

CRUISING GEAR
Unit 4,
Cable Street, Northam,
Southampton,
Hants SO1 1RJ
Tel: (0703) 232772
Tel: (0860) 709396
Fax: (0703) 230735
Yacht services consultants and supply, new and second hand quality cruising gear, general chandlery, electronics - repairs and fitting, engineering works. Marine and engineering fasteners.

THE DINGHY STORE AND WHITSTABLE MARINE
Sea Wall,
Whitstable, Kent CT5 1BX
Tel: (0227) 274168/262525
Fax: (0227) 770938
Chandlers -wet suits, buoyancy, clothing, paint, boots, electrical, books. Main agents for Johnson Outboards. Full workshop facilities, Orkney fishing boats, Narwhal inflatables. Main agents for Fletchers. Main dealer for Mercury. All outboards serviced.

EVERSON AND SONS LTD
Phoenix Works, Riverside,
Woodbridge, Suffolk
Tel: (03943) 4358
Boatbuilding and marine engineers; chandlers and riggers; insurance and brokerage arranged. Full yard facilities.

MARQUAND BROS LTD
North Quay, Guernsey
Tel: (0481) 720962
Fax: (0481) 713974
Yacht chandlers, stockists of a comprehensive range of marine products.

MAYFLOWER INTERNATIONAL MARINA (SAILPORT) PLC
Ocean Quay, Richmond Walk,
Plymouth PL1 4LS
Tel: (0752) 556633
Fax: (0752) 606896
Marina operators with boat-hoist (25-ton) facility. Restaurant, clubroom, launderette, fuel, chandlery, shop and off-licence. Winter storage. Owned by berth holders and operated to a very high standard.

PADSTOW HARBOUR
Padstow Harbour Commissioners,
Harbour Office, West Quay,
Padstow, Cornwall PL28 8AQ
Tel: (0841) 532239
Fax: (0841) 533346
Small West Country port having a vigorous fishing fleet and enjoying an excellent reputation for waterborne recreation. General cargo capability extends up to vessels 1500/2000 GRT.

SOLENT TRADING CO
Mercury Yacht Harbour,
Satchell Lane,
Hamble SO3 5HQ
Tel: (0703) 454849 (& FAX)
Chandlery charts and books, clothing, oilskins - boots and shoes. Avon agent. Liferaft sales, hire and service safety equipment. Paint, varnish and anti-fouling. Groceries and off licence sales.

WYATTS CHANDLERY
110 & 128 Coast Road,
West Mersea,
Nr Colchester, Essex
Tel: (0206) 384745
Fax: (0206) 384455
Wyatts Chandlery, well stocked and competitively priced.

CLOTHING

CAMBRIAN SMALL BOATS & CHANDLERY LTD
14 Cambrian Place,
South Dock, Swansea,
West Glamorgan
Tel: (0792) 467263
Yacht chandlers, riggers, marine clothing specialists, nautical booksellers and THE ONLY ADMIRALTY 'A' CLASS CHART AGENT IN WALES.

DOWNSOUTH (TORQUAY) LTD
Kents Lane, Wellswood,
Torquay, Devon
Tel: (0803) 297715
Fax: (0803) 200449
Manufacturers and suppliers of the Downsouth range of buoyancy aids, offering a buoyancy aid for most water sports. A bespoke service is also catered for.

COMMUNICATIONS EQUIPMENT

COMMUNICATION AERIALS LTD
Unit 1A,
Woodland Industrial Estate,
Eden Vale Road, Westbury,
Wiltshire BA13 3QS
Tel: (0373) 822835
Fax: (0373) 858081
We have antennas and accessories to meet most applications. We use high quality cable and connectors to ensure your antenna operates efficiently. Ask for details on the comprehensive range of products that we now have to offer for VHF, cellular and Active Antenna installations.

ROWLANDS MARINE ELECTRONICS LTD
The Outer Harbour,
Pwllheli, Gwynedd LL53 5HD
Tel: (0758) 613193
Marine Electronic Trade Association member, dealer for Autohelm, Brookes and Gatehouse, Cetrek, ICOM, Kelvin Hughes,

Marconi, Nasa, Navico, Navstar, Neco, Seafarer, Shipmate, Stowe, Racal-Decca, V-Tronix, Ampro, Walker. Equipment supplied installed and serviced.

ELECTRONIC EQUIPMENT

W & H CHINA
Howley Properties Ltd,
Howley Tannery,
Howley Lane, Warrington,
Cheshire WA1 2DN
Tel: (0925) 34621
Telex: 94013565 Chin G

Manufacturers of China chart dividers. Agents for LINEX navigational aids, slide rules etc.

KELVIN HUGHES
(BOAT ELECTRONICS)
New North Road, Hainault,
Ilford, Essex IG6 2UR
Tel: 081-500 1020

A supplier of electronic equipment to the leisure and fishing industries. Kelvin Hughes Boat Electronics can provide Radar systems, Echo sounders, Fish finders, Plotters, navigators and radio systems to suit all budgets.

LOKATA LTD
Falmouth,
Cornwall TR10 8AE
Tel: (0326) 73636
Fax: (0326) 73941

Manufacturer of type approved 406 MHZ EPIRBs including automatic float-free and personal models for rapid detection and location by rescue services. In addition: NAVTEX Receivers.

NAVICO LTD
Star Lane,
Margate CT9 4NP
Tel: (0843) 290290
Fax: +44 843 290471

Navico Limited manufacture a complete range of high quality marine electronics for yachts, powerboats, work and fishing vessels. The world's most advanced and high performance cockpit and below deck autopilots to suit most steering configurations. Stylish and reliable instruments, including echosounders, wind direction/speed, close hauled and VMG indicators, log and digital compasses.Quality marine VHF radios.

REGIS ELECTRONICS
LIMITED
Regis House, Quay Hill,
Lymington, Hants SO41 9AR
Tel: (0590) 679251/679176
Fax: (0590) 679910

(also at COWES, SOUTHAMPTON, CHICHESTER & GUERNSEY) Sales, service and installation of Marine Electronic equipment. Leading south coast agents for AUTOHELM, FURUNO, RAYTHEON, CETREK, STOWE, ROBERTSON, A.P. NAVIGATOR, PRO-NAV, KELVIN HUGHES and other manufacturers of quality marine electronic equipment. Competitively-priced quotations (incl. owner familiarisation & seatrials) forwarded by return of post.

ROWLANDS MARINE
ELECTRONICS LTD
The Outer Harbour,
Pwllheli, Gwynedd LL53 5HD
Tel: (0758) 613193

Marine Electronic Trade Association member, dealer for Autohelm, Brookes and Gatehouse, Cetrek, ICOM, Kelvin Hughes, Marconi, Nasa, Navico, Navstar, Neco, Seafarer, Shipmate, Stowe, Racal-Decca, V-Tronix, Ampro, Walker. Equipment supplied installed and serviced.

STOWE MARINE
EQUIPMENT LTD
Parklands Business Park,
Forest Road, Denmead,
Hants PO7 6XP
Tel: (0705) 241313

Leading manufacturers of electronic instrument systems for yachts and powerboats. A proven range of rugged reliable products, widely available throughout the UK and backed by service second to none.

TOLLEY MARINE
ELECTRONIC COMPANY
Blackhill Road,
Holton Heath Trading Park,
Poole, Dorset BH16 6LS
Tel: (0202) 632644
Fax: (0202) 632622

(Also at: 13 Commercial Road, Coxside, Plymouth, Devon) Tel: (0752) 222530. Agents of sales and service for Autohelm, Brookes & Gatehouse, Cetrek, Furuno, Icom, Kelvin Hughes, Lo-Kata, Navstar, Neco, Robertson, Sailor, Shipmate.

ELECTRONIC & ELECTRICAL ENGINEERS

AMBERLEY MARINE
ELECTRONICS LTD
'Hurley Cottage',
Henley Road, Hurley,
Berkshire SL6 5LW
Tel: (0628) 826104

Suppliers, installers and service agents of the finest marine electronics. Our service includes the design, supply and fitting of all woodwork and steelwork relevant to bespoke electronic installations. Customer training and after-sales service.

CRUISING GEAR
Unit 4,
Cable Street, Northam,
Southampton,
Hants SO1 1RJ
Tel: (0703) 232772
Tel: (0860) 709396
Fax: (0703) 230735

Yacht services consultants and supply, new and second hand quality cruising gear, general chandlery, electronics - repairs and fitting, engineering works. Marine and engineering fasteners.

NEWHAVEN MARINA LTD
The Yacht Harbour,
Newhaven,
East Sussex BN9 9BY
Tel: (0273) 513881

Newhaven Marina has comprehensive facilities including marine workshops, fuel, yacht brokerage, chandlery, pleasure and business charter, superb yacht club with hotel accommodation and riverside restaurant (open to non-members) 4 Gold Anchor Award. (0273) 513881.

REGIS ELECTRONICS
LIMITED
Regis House, Quay Hill,
Lymington, Hants SO41 9AR
Tel: (0590) 679251/679176
Fax: (0590) 679910

(also at COWES, SOUTHAMPTON, CHICHESTER & GUERNSEY) Sales, service and installation of Marine Electronic equipment. Leading south coast agents for AUTOHELM, FURUNO, RAYTHEON, CETREK, STOWE, ROBERTSON, A.P. NAVIGATOR, PRO-NAV, KELVIN HUGHES and other manufacturers of quality marine electronic equipment. Competatively-priced quotations (incl. owner familiarisation & seatrials) forwarded by return of post.

WEST MERSEA MARINE
ENGINEERING
110 & 128 Coast Road,
West Mersea,
Nr Colchester, Essex
Tel: (0206) 384350
Fax: (0206) 384455

Providing full marine engineering facilities. There are also undercover facilities for those vessels being worked on by our staff. Shipwrights, GRP specialists, painters and riggers are also available. There is a sailmaker and an outboard repair and service workshop nearby, and liferaft hire, sales and service, together with inflatable dinghy repairs and service are also available locally.

ENGINES

BRITISH SEAGULL OUTBOARD ENGINES
Engine Manufacturing Division of Chillington Marine Ltd, Unit 1, Newtown Industrial Estate, Ringwood Road, Poole, Dorset BH12 3PF
Tel: (0202) 747400

Pure bred marine engines, designed to last. The new series are quieter, cleaner and run on unleaded petrol. Our worldwide dealer network and spares back up is legendary. Ring Mike, Jacky or Lindsay for details.

CAMBRIAN & WESTFLEET
The Boatyard, Portway Village Marina, Penarth, South Glamorgan
Tel: (0222) 709983

Boatbuilders and repairers, marine engineers, riggers, marine clothing specialists, chart agents, nautical booksellers, and yacht chandlers.

FALMOUTH BOAT CONSTRUCTION LTD
Little Falmouth Yacht Yard, Flushing, Falmouth, Cornwall TR11 5TJ
Tel: (0326) 74309
Fax: (0326) 77679

Repairs, refits, storage undercover and quayside, osmosis treatment specialists, resprays. Slipways to 100 ton. Commercial craft repairs. Specialist one-off builds. Full engineering shop for all diesel and petrol engines.

VOLVO PENTA UK LTD
Otterspool Way, Watford, Herts WD2 8HW.
Tel: (0923) 28544.

Volvo Pentas leading marine power-petrol and diesel for leisure craft and workboats - is supported by an extensive network of parts and service dealers.

FLAGS & PENNANTS

LOVELL LOGOS LTD
Ringcroft Farm, Cranfield Road, North Crawley, Bucks MK16 9HP
Tel: (0234) 750735
Fax: (0234) 751369

We manufacture flags/pennants of all sizes. They can be personalised with your boat name, family crest, company logo etc. We supply sweatshirts, tee-shirts. rugby shirts, jogging suits, yachting scarves also personalised.

GENERAL MARINE EQUIPMENT & MACHINERY

AQUA-MARINE MANUFACTURING (UK) LTD
216 Fair Oak Road, Bishopstoke, Eastleigh, Hants SO5 6NJ
Tel: (0703) 694949
Fax: (0703) 601381

Manufacturers and distributors of chandlery, incl: Engel refrigeration; Dutton-Lainson and Muir winches; Anchor fenders; Rule pumps; Aquaflow water systems; Sierra engine spares; Flexatrol controls; Ritchie compasses; RWO and Holt fittings; Danforth anchors; Aqua-Signal lights.

ARISAIG MARINE LTD
Arisaig Harbour, Inverness-shire PH39 4NH
Tel: (06875) 224

Boatyard/Slipway/Pier with power, fuel and water/moorings for rent and large anchorage/ample parking. Easy access road and rail. Good village facilities. Restaurant - Hotels -Shop - Post Office - All grades accommodation.

BLAKES & TAYLORS:
Toilets, cookers & heaters, Equipment Manufacturing Divison of Chillington Marine Limited, Unit 1, Newtown Industrial Estate, Ringwood Road, Poole, Dorset BH12 3PF.
Tel: (0202) 747400.

Blake's toilets and seacocks, and Taylor's cookers and heaters are the classic definition of hand-assembled, traditional marine equipment. Essential if considerations of reliable and simple working over a long life outweigh those of low initial price.

BOATWORKS + LTD
Castle Emplacement, St Peter Port, Guernsey
Tel: (0481) 726071
Fax: (0481) 714224

Boatworks + provides a comprehensive range of services including electronics, chandlery, boatbuilding and repairs, engine sales and services, yacht brokerage, clothing and fuel supplies.

BROOKES & ADAMS LTD
Shady Lane, Kingstanding, Birmingham B44 9DX
Tel: 021-360 1588

Manufacturers of bronze and brass deck and interior fittings, rigging screws, shackles, snap shackles, berthlights and many other articles. Suppliers to the marine industry, the admiralty and other government departments.

C T HARWOOD LIMITED
Ashley House, Hurlands Close, Farnham, Surrey GU9 9JF.
Tel: (0252) 733312
Fax: (0252) 733346.

Manufacturers of water separators and filters to remove harmful water from diesel fuel. Also a range of cold starting aids for diesel engines. Contact: M Barcy.

DOWNSOUTH (TORQUAY) LTD
Kents Lane, Wellswood, Torquay, Devon
Tel: (0803) 297715
Fax: (0803) 200449

Manufacturers and suppliers of the Downsouth range of buoyancy aids, offering a buoyancy aid for most water sports. A bespoke service is also catered for.

GREENHAM MARINE LTD
King's Saltern Road, Lymington, Hampshire
Tel: (0590) 671144
Fax: (0590) 679517

Greenham Marine can offer yachtsmen one of the most comprehensive selections of marine electronic equipment currently available.

E C SMITH & SONS (MARINE FACTORS) LTD
Units H & J Kingsway Industrial Estate, Kingsway, Luton, Beds LU1 1LP
Tel: (0582) 29721
Fax: (0582) 458893
Telex: 825473 ECSLTN G

Manufacturers and distributors: Lofrans Windlasses. Professional Mariner battery chargers, sealants, ECS ventilators, toilets, hardware, Quartz/other lighting, Firemaster fire extinguishers, table/seat pedestals, skin fittings, Shurflo water pumps, teak mouldings and general chandlery.

SOLENT TRADING CO
Mercury Yacht Harbour, Satchell Lane, Hamble SO3 5HQ
Tel: (0703) 454849 (& FAX)

Chandlery charts and books, clothing, oilskins - boots and shoes. Avon agent. Liferaft sales, hire and service safety equipment. Paint, varnish and anti-fouling. Groceries and off licence sales.

SOUTH WESTERN MARINE FACTORS LTD
43 Pottery Road, Poole, Dorset BH14 8RE
Tel: (0202) 745414
Fax: Company (0202) 743931
Chandlery (0202) 731598

The Sowester group offers the most comprehensive range of marine equipment, engines, steering and control systems in the UK, distributing Mercury outboards, MerCruiser sterndrives and inboard engines, Morse controls, Achilles inflatables, Maxwell winches, Bruce anchors, and many other well known products.

GRAPHICS & BOAT NAMING SYSTEMS

GRAPHICRAFT LTD
15 The Manton Centre, Bedford MK41 7PX
Tel: (0234) 340058

Graphicraft manufactures tailormade graphics, names and striping systems for many production boatbuilders. Additionally, their CRAFTNAME boat naming system provides the same quality and application simplicity to individual boat owners.

INSTRUMENTATION & POSITION FIXING

AUTOHELM Nautech Ltd
Anchorage Park, Portsmouth, Hants PO3 5TD
Tel: (0705) 693611
Fax: (0705) 694642
Telex: 86384 Nautec G.

Maufacturers of the Autohelm range of instruments, compasses and autopilots for power and sail craft from 22' to 125'. Manufacturer of the Autohelm personal compass.

CETREK LTD
1 Factory Road, Upton, Poole, Dorset BH16 5SJ
Tel: (0202) 632116

World famous for autopilots and electronic compass systems as well as being one of the biggest UK suppliers of hydraulic and mechanical steering systems, battery chargers and trim tabs.

GREENHAM MARINE LTD
King's Saltern Road, Lymington, Hampshire
Tel: (0590) 671144
Fax: (0590) 679517

Greenham Marine can offer yachtsmen one of the most comprehensive selections of marine electronic equipment currently available.

MARITEK LTD
B5 D2
Templeton Business Centre, Glasgow G40 1DA, Scotland
Tel: 041- 554 2492/041- 942 0430

Computer programs for coastal/celestial navigation/tidal height prediction, using Psion organiser pocket computer. Yacht race management systems. Large computer systems and projects using 4th generation languages.

RIGEL COMPASSES LTD
1 Factory Road, Upton, Poole, Dorset BH16 5SJ
Tel: (0202) 632116

Manufacturers and suppliers of a comprehensive range of magnetic compasses, hand bearing compasses, electronic compasses and electronic chart-plotter. The Rigel name is renowned for quality.

ROWLANDS MARINE ELECTRONICS LTD
The Outer Harbour, Pwllheli, Gwynedd LL53 5HD
Tel: (0758) 613193

Marine Electronic Trade Association member, dealer for Autohelm, Brookes and Gatehouse, Cetrek, ICOM, Kelvin Hughes, Marconi, Nasa, Navico, Navstar, Neco, Seafarer, Shipmate, Stowe, Racal-Decca, V-Tronix, Ampro, Walker. Equipment supplied installed and serviced.

STOWE MARINE EQUIPMENT LTD
Parklands Business Park, Forest Road, Denmead, Hants PO7 6XP
Tel: (0705) 241313

Leading manufacturers of electronic instrument systems for yachts and powerboats. A proven range of rugged reliable products, widely available throughout the UK and backed by service second to none.

MAIL ORDER

DUBOIS PHILLIPS & McCALLUM LTD
Oriel Chambers, Covent Garden, Liverpool L2 8UD
Tel: 051- 236 2776
Fax: 051- 236 4577

Admiralty chart agents and nautical booksellers. Chart correction service. World-wide mail order service.

MARINAS

ARDFERN YACHT CENTRE LTD
Ardfern By Lochgilphead, Argyll, Scotland PA31 8QN
Tel: (08525) 247/636
Fax: (08525) 624

Boatyard with full repair and maintenance facilities. Timber and GRP repairs, painting and engineering. Sheltered moorings and pontoon berthing. Winter storage, chandlery, showers, fuel calor, brokerage. Hotel, bars and restaurant.

ARDORAN MARINE
Lerags, By Oban, Argyll PA34 4SE
Tel: (0631) 66123
Fax: (0631) 66611

Swinging moorings, pontoons, diesel, gas, water, toilets, hot showers, slip and cranage for winter storage, engine sales and repairs, Suzuki/mariner outboards, Zodiac inflatables, Orkney boats, chain/shackles in stock.

ARISAIG MARINE LTD
Arisaig Harbour, Inverness-shire PH39 4NH
Tel: (06875) 224

Boatyard/Slipway/Pier with power, fuel and water/Moorings for rent and large anchorage/Ample parking. Easy access road and rail. Good village facilities. Restaurant - Hotels -Shop - Post Office - All grades accommodation.

THE BRIGHTON MARINA COMPANY LTD
Brighton Marina Village, Brighton BN2 5UF
Tel: (0273) 693636

Britain's largest marina (1800 pontoon berths) with marina village under development. NYHA five gold anchors. Full boatyard and shore facilities. Brokerage and boat sales. Club racing throughout the year. Group visits, rallies welcome.

CALEY MARINA
Canal Road, Inverness, Scotland IV3 6NF
Tel: (0463) 236539
Fax: (0463) 238323

Open 08.30 - 17.30. Berths: 50 Pontoon (visitors available). Facilities: Fuel, water, provisions (nearby shops), repair, cranage, storage afloat and ashore. Comprehensive chandlery, showers, workshop. Situated at eastern end of Caledonian canal above Muirtown Locks. Access via sea locks four hours either side of high water.

I N S I S T   O N   I N T E R N A T I O N A L

If boating ever becomes an indoor sport, we'll stop making yacht varnish.

LOOK OUT FOR THE SPECIAL OFFER PACKS IN YOUR LOCAL CHANDLERY WHILE STOCKS LAST

Frankly, the advent of indoor boating is about as likely as a monsoon in your front room. Which is why a varnish that's adequate for the dining room table is unlikely to be of much use on a boat.

A yacht varnish has to do so much more than simply look pretty. It has to stand up to extremely hard use, as well as protecting the wood against salt, sun, sea and rain – and that means water, lots of water!

And because boating means different things to different people, we don't produce just one Blue Peter yacht varnish, we produce six.

For example Blue Peter Original, a traditional varnish much-loved by devotees of classic cruisers, has the sort of flexibility that's essential to a wooden boat built the old-fashioned way.

Whereas two-pot Blue Peter Crystal, the dinghy sailor's favourite, gives an incredibly hard and durable high gloss finish, but is only suitable for reasonably stable substrates such as moulded wood or ply.

For help in choosing Blue Peter varnishes, ask your chandler, or pick up a copy of the International leaflet on varnishing.

And as for using it on the dining room table? Fine. At least then it'll be protected if the bath ever overflows!

International
DeLUXE
Blue Peter
Quick Drying Polyurethane Yacht Varnish
International
ORIGINAL
Blue Peter
Full Gloss U.V. Resistant Yacht Varnish
International
DeLUXE SATIN
Blue Peter
Quick Drying Satin
CRYSTAL
Blue Peter
Varnish Curing Agent
International
CRYSTAL FOR TEAK
Blue Peter
High performance varnish for oily timbers (Base)
International
CRYSTAL
Blue Peter
High Performance Polyurethane Yacht Varnish
International
INTERTOX
Blue Peter
Wood Preservative
INTERSTAIN
Blue Peter
Non-Drip Woodstain MAHOGANY

International

No.1 in yacht paints-worldwide.

TERNATIONAL PAINT LTD, YACHT DIVISION, 24-30 CANUTE ROAD, SOUTHAMPTON SO9 3AS, UNITED KINGDOM. TELEPHONE (0703) 226722

COURTAULDS COATINGS

and 'International' are trademarks of Courtaulds Coatings (Holdings) Limited.

DESIGN LINE *from* SUUNTO

Marine Compasses

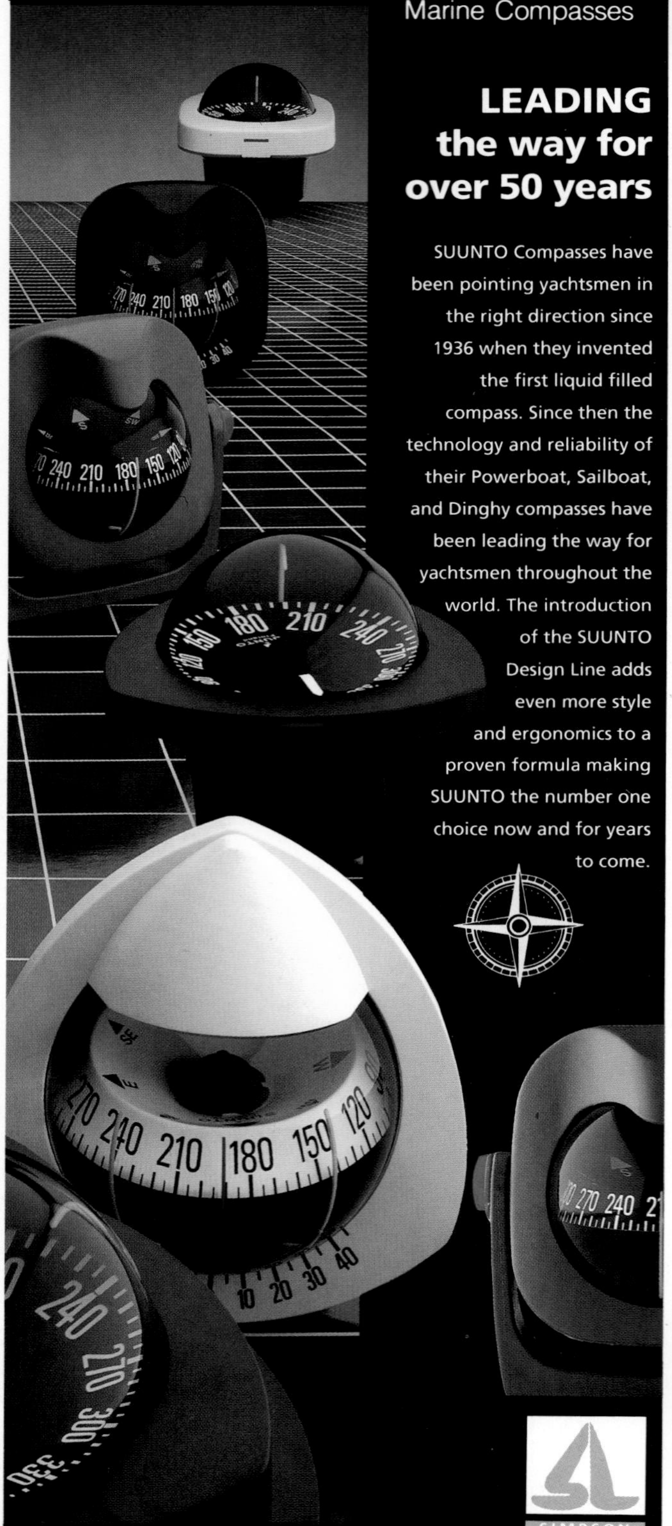

LEADING the way for over 50 years

SUUNTO Compasses have been pointing yachtsmen in the right direction since 1936 when they invented the first liquid filled compass. Since then the technology and reliability of their Powerboat, Sailboat, and Dinghy compasses have been leading the way for yachtsmen throughout the world. The introduction of the SUUNTO Design Line adds even more style and ergonomics to a proven formula making SUUNTO the number one choice now and for years to come.

ANOTHER QUALITY PRODUCT *from* SIMPSON LAWRENCE

Please Tel. 041-427 5331 for our free colour brochure, or write to Simpson Lawrence 218-228 Edmiston Drive, Glasgow G51 2YT.

PROFURL®

The ULTIMATE headsail furling system for racing and cruising

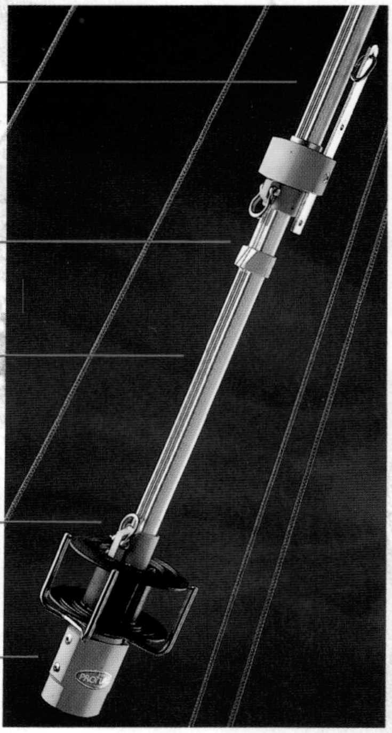

1. PATENTED WRAPSTOP, ENSURES NO HALYARD FOUL UP.

RACING/CRUISING, AND RACING VERSIONS WITH REMOVABLE DRUM AND TWIN GROOVE HEADFOIL.

2. EXTRUDED SECTION, FOR OPTIMUM SAIL SHAPE.

3. EASY ASSEMBLY- FITS OVER EXISTING FORESTAY WITHOUT REMOVAL.

4. PATENTED SEALED GUNMETAL BEARING SYSTEM FOR MAINTENANCE FREE LIFE.

Profurl is one of the toughest and most reliable headsail furling systems that money can buy. Designed originally for round the world single-handed yachtsmen, the Profurl system has been engineered to withstand the toughest tests, whilst maintaining race winning sail shape throughout varying wind strengths.
Profurl is the perfect solution for the owner who likes to cruise in comfort and race in the points.

-Profurl was chosen by Phillipe Jeantot, winner of two single handed round the world races.

ANOTHER QUALITY PRODUCT *from* SIMPSON LAWRENCE

Please Tel. 0329-823300 for our free colour brochure, or write to Tony Hill

CAMUS MARINE SERVICES
Craobh Haven, Craignish,
By Lochgilphead, Argyll
Tel: (08525) 225/622/222
Fax: (08525) 252
200 marina berths. Water. Electricity. Diesel fuel. Gas. Yacht repairs, fitting-out and engineering. Storage ashore. Chandlery. Brokerage. Insurance. Nearby facilities include: pub, shops, sailing school, dive centre, launderette, riding centre, hotels/guest houses, self-catering accommodation. Electronic & electric installation & service. Agents for Yanmar, Bukl, L/P diesels, Honda & Mariner outboards, Autolink RT, Easyreef furling systems.

CARRICKFERGUS MARINA
Rodger's Quay, Carrickfergus,
Northern Ireland BT38 8BU
Tel: (09603) 66666
300 fully serviced pontoon berths with full on shore facilities (half a mile from town centre). Steeped in a wealth of historical legend, Carrickfergus has excellent restaurants, hotels, pubs, shops and a host of recreational leisure facilities.

CHICHESTER YACHT BASIN
Birdham, Chichester,
Sussex PO20 7EJ
Tel: (0243) 512731
A very attractive marina offering superb services and shore installations, welcoming long and short-term visitors.

CLARKE & CARTER BOATYARD
110 & 128 Coast Road,
West Mersea,
Nr Colchester, Essex
Tel: (0206) 382244
Fax: (0206) 384455
The Clarke & Carter boatyard is a division of West Mersea Marine Ltd. The yard is situated on the main waterfront at West Mersea. The anchorage, which has retained its traditional character, offers both swinging and post moorings for vessels up to about 50' LOA. Access is at all states of the tide to the River Blackwater. There are also some edge moorings available.

THE CLOVELLY BAY COMPANY LTD
The Quay, Turnchapel,
Plymouth PL9 9TF
Tel: (0752) 404231
MARINA - totally sheltered from prevailing winds, minutes from Plymouth Sound. Showers, laundry, chandlery. 24 hour security. Electricity, water, phonelines on pontoons. Vessels up to 150 feet. Some fore and afts available. Two local pubs. Visitors welcome.

DAN WEBB & FEESEY
Shipways,
North Street, Maldon,
Essex CM9 7HN
Tel: (0621) 854280 & 856829
(Also Marine Parade, Maylandsea, Essex CM3 6AN Tel: (0621) 740264/741267) On the River Blackwater, 600 moorings, excellent shore-based facilities. Shipwright repairs and GRP. Chandlery. Rigging.

DARTHAVEN MARINA
Kingswear Quay, Kingswear,
Dartmouth, Devon
Tel: (080 425) 545/242
All services at Darthaven Marina and J W & A Upham Ltd: engineer, electricians, chandlery, brokerage, boat repairs, 30-ton travel hoist.

EEL PIE MARINE CENTRE
Eel Pie Island,
Twickenham,
Middlesex TW1 3DY
Tel: 081-892 3626
Fax: 081-744 1312
Eel Pie Marine Centre offers full marina services with boatyard and full repair and maintenance facilities. Visitors welcome.

ELMHAVEN MARINA
Rochester Road, Halling, Kent
Tel: (0634) 240489
Elmhaven provides a peaceful setting combined with good facilities including toilets, shower, power on pontoons, mud berths, hard standing, boat lifting up to 5 tons max. Scand boat sales with Volvo Penta repairs and parts by (John Hawkins Marine).

ESSEX MARINA LTD
Wallasea Island, Nr Rochford,
Essex SS4 2HG
Tel: (0702) 258531
Fax: (0702) 258227
Deep water marina. Berths for yachts up to 150 feet. Swinging moorings at attractive rates. All ancillary services. Visitors welcome.

FALMOUTH YACHT MARINA
North Parade, Falmouth,
Cornwall TR11 2TD
Tel: (0326) 316620
The most westerly marina in England, strategically placed for transatlantic departures and arrivals. Fully serviced permanent and visitor berths. Diesel fuel. Chandlery, 30-ton hoist. Famous friendly service.

GILLINGHAM MARINA
173 Pier Road, Gillingham,
Kent ME7 1UB
Tel: (0634) 280022
Gillingham Marina offers 5 Gold Anchor berthing, brokerage, boat hoist and mast stepping facilities, chandlery, fuel and extensive workshop facilities including gelshield centre. A complete range of marina services integrated under our mangement.

GRANARY YACHT HARBOUR LTD
Dock Lane, Melton,
Woodbridge, Suffolk IP12 1PE
Tel:(03943) 6327
Pontoon berths (long or short term) laying-up facilities. Slipping and cranage. Craft maintenance/repairs and engineering. Chandlery.

HAFAN PWLLHELI
Glan Don, Pwllheli,
Gwynedd LL53 5YT
Tel: (0758) 701219
Brand new marina facilities opened in April 1991. 260 alongside berths with full facilities. Keen active racing and good cruising on this beautiful North Wales coastline. Visitors welcome.

HARTLEPOOL YACHT HAVEN
Lock Office, Slake Terrace,
Hartlepool, Cleveland
Tel: (0429) 865 744
Brand new marina facilities on the North East coast protected by lock gates operational 18 hours per day. Full services ashore and afloat. Good racing with local clubs. Visitors always welcome.

HOO MARINA MEDWAY LTD
Vicarage Lane, Hoo, Rochester, Kent ME3 9LE
Tel: (0634) 250311

Pontoon berthing afloat at all states of the tide. All facilities available. Visitors welcome.

KILMELFORD YACHT HAVEN
Kilmelford, Oban, Argyll PA34 4XD
Tel: (08522) 248/279
Fax: (08522) 343

VHF CH.37/80 Full boatyard facilities.

KIP MARINA
The Yacht Harbour, Inverkip, Renfrewshire PA16 0AS
Tel: (0475) 521485

Scotland's premier marina with over 700 berths - visitors always welcome. Full facility yard, 40-ton boat hoist, chandlery, yacht sales and superb new club house.

LANGSTONE MARINA
Fort Cumberland Road, Eastney, Portsmouth, Hants PO4 9RU
Tel: (0705) 822719
Fax: (0705) 822220

Langstone Marina is a 300 berth marina on the western side of the entrance to Langstone Harbour. Facilities include: hoist, brokerage, showers, toilets, chandlery, hard standing. Access over the sill is available approximately 3 hours either side of high water.

LARGS YACHT HAVEN LTD
Irvine Road, Largs, Ayrshire KA30 8EZ
Tel: (0475) 675333

Perfectly situated in the Firth of Clyde for the best cruising grounds in Britain. 600 berths with first class shore facilities. 45-ton hoist. Regular racing off the marina. Visitors always welcome. Excellent shore facilities including pub.

LITTLEHAMPTON MARINA LTD
Ferry Road, Littlehampton, Sussex
Tel: (0903) 713553

Marina and boatyard with storing ashore for all types of craft. Full marina amenities on site. Compressed air for diving cylinders with large slipway for visitors.

LYMINGTON YACHT HAVEN LTD
King's Saltern Road, Lymington, Hants SO4 9XY
Tel: (0590) 677071

Established 700 berth marina with all the boatyard and shore facilities required by visiting yachtsmen. 50-ton hoist and emergency call out engineer.

MAYFLOWER INTERNATIONAL MARINA (SAILPORT) PLC
Ocean Quay, Richmond Walk, Plymouth PL1 4LS
Tel: (0752) 556633
Fax: (0752) 606896

Marina operators with boat-hoist (25-ton) facility. Restaurant, clubroom, launderette, fuel, chandlery, shop and off-licence. Winter storage. Owned by berth holders and operated to a very high standard.

NEWHAVEN MARINA LTD
The Yacht Harbour, Newhaven, East Sussex BN9 9BY
Tel: (0273) 513881
Fax: (0273) 517990

Newhaven Marina has comprehensive facilities including marine workshops, fuel, yacht brokerage, chandlery, pleasure and business charter, superb yacht club with hotel accommodation and riverside restaurant (open to non-members), 4 Gold Anchor Award. (0273) 513881.

PORT FLAIR LTD
Bradwell Marina, Waterside, Bradwell-on-Sea, Essex CM0 7RB
Tel: (0621) 76235/76391

300 pontoon berths with water and electricity, petrol and diesel, chandlery, marine slip/hoistage to 20 ton; repairs, winter lay-ups, licensed club, yacht brokerage.

PORT SOLENT LTD
The Port House, Port Solent, Portsmouth, Hants PO6 4TH
Tel: (0705) 210765
Fax: (0705) 324241

Port Solent is a developing community of houses, apartments, restaurants and shops encompassing 900 berths. This includes 500 public berths with facilities for visitors, including travel hoist and club.

SALTERNS MARINA
40 Salterns Way, Lilliput, Poole, Dorset BH14 8JR
Tel: (0202) 707321

Marina berths, swinging moorings, 5 ton hoist. Boatyard with 40 tonne hoist, full services, engineers, shipwrights. Engine and boat sales. Brokerage. Poole Harbour Yacht Club and Salterns Hotel with bar and excellent restaurant.

SEAWARD MARINE ENTERPRISES
Southdown Quay, Millbrook, Cornwall PL10 1EZ
Tel: (0752) 823084

32 berth marina on edge of river Tamar in quiet location behind Rame Peninsula. Plymouth just across river. Quayside berths available for large vessels. Winter storage. Good security. DIY facilities available.

THE MARINA AT SOUTH DOCK
South Lock Office, Rope Street, Plough Way, London SE16 1AA
Tel: 071-252 2244

London's newest and largest marina with full boatyard facility and liftout to 20 tonnes. Welcomes visitors.

SWANSEA YACHT HAVEN LTD
Lockside, Maritime Quarter, Swansea, West Glamorgan SA1 1WN
Tel: (0792) 470310

Centre piece of a multi-million development. Locked marina with 360 berths and good facilities. Tidal access HW+/- 3 hrs. Excellent motorway/rail communications. Ideal for day-sailing cruising, racing.

MARINE INSURANCE & FINANCE

BOWRING CAMPER AND NICHOLSONS LTD
Havelock Chambers, Queens Terrace, Southampton SO9 4NS
Tel: (0703) 634333
Fax: (0703) 211188

Leading specialists for arranging yacht insurance and covers required by yacht builders, yards and marinas. Also advise with yacht registration and transfer of ownership.

CAMUS MARINE SERVICES
Craobh Haven, Craignish,
By Lochgilphead, Argyll.
Tel: (08525) 225/622/222
Fax: (08525) 252
200 marina berths. Water. Electricity. Diesel fuel. Gas. Yacht repairs, fitting-out and engineering. Storage ashore. Chandlery. Brokerage. Insurance. Nearby facilities include: pub, shops, sailing school, dive centre, launderette, riding centre, hotels/guest houses, self-catering accommodation. Electronic & electric installation & service. Agents for Yanmar, Bukl, L/P diesels, Honda & Mariner outboards, Autolink RT, Easyreef furling systems.

CRAVEN HODGSON ASSOCIATES
Suite 15, 30-38 Dock Street,
Leeds LS10 1JF
Tel: (0532) 438443
Independent insurance and investment consultants and intermediaries. We recommend and advise in relation to all major experienced marine insurers.

KNOX-JOHNSTON INSURANCE BROKERS
St Clare House,
30-33 Minories,
London EC3N 1DD
Tel: 071-488 9607
Specialist pleasure craft insurance and finance brokers with unique 'Plus Plan' and 'Inland Plus Plan' policies plus fast friendly service based on experience.

MARINE TRANSPORT & YACHT DELIVERIES

PADSTOW HARBOUR
Padstow Harbour Commissioners,
Harbour Office, West Quay,
Padstow, Cornwall PL28 8AQ
Tel: (0841) 532239
Fax: (0841) 533346
Small West Country port having a vigorous fishing fleet and enjoying an excellent reputation for waterborne recreation. General cargo capability extends up to vessels 1500/2000 GRT.

MOTOR CRUISER SCHOOLS

MIKE REEDER SCHOOL OF SEAMANSHIP
13 Courtenay Place,
Lymington,
Hampshire SO41 9NQ
Tel: (0590) 674560
Motor Cruising courses, from beginner to Yachtmaster standard, arranged throughout the year home and abroad. Personal tuition by Commander Mike Reeder, who is a Master Mariner and RYA Yachtmaster Instructor of many years experience.

OSMOSIS TREATMENT

FALMOUTH BOAT CONSTRUCTION LTD
Little Falmouth Yacht Yard,
Flushing, Falmouth,
Cornwall TR11 5TJ
Tel: (0326) 74309
Fax: (0326) 77679
Repairs, refits, storage undercover and quayside, osmosis treatment specialists, resprays. Slipways to 100 ton. Commercial craft repairs. Specialist one-off builds. Full engineering shop for all diesel and petrol engines.

PAINT

EXTENSOR AB
24-30 Canute Road,
Southampton SO9 3AS
Tel: (0703) 226722
Fax: (0703) 335975
Extensor provides a comprehensive range of yacht paint products designed for first class boat maintenance. This range includes the well known antifoulings, VC17M and VC-offshore (with Teflon) and a range of epoxies, fillers, boat care and accessory products.

INTERNATIONAL YACHT PAINTS
24-30 Canute Road,
Southampton SO9 3AS
Tel: (0703) 226722
Fax: (0703) 335975
Yachtpaint and antifouling manufacturers.

REPAIR MATERIALS

SOLENT TRADING CO
Mercury Yacht Harbour,
Satchell Lane,
Hamble SO3 5HQ
Tel: (0703) 454849 (& FAX)
Chandlery charts and books, clothing, oilskins - boots and shoes. Avon agent. Liferaft sales, hire and service safety equipment. Paint, varnish and anti-fouling. Groceries and off licence sales.

SAFETY EQUIPMENT

ANGLO DUTCH ENGINEERING CO LTD
4 Masons Avenue,
Croydon, Surrey CR0 1EH
Tel: 081-686 9717
Approved liferaft service station for South East UK. Additionally we hire and sell new rafts and sell a complete range of safety equipment for yachts including pyrotechnics/fire extinguishers/lifejackets/buoys and a buoyancy bag system.

CREWSAVER LTD
Mumby Road, Gosport,
Hampshire PO12 1AQ
Tel: (0705) 528621
Crewsaver - leading UK manufacturers of lifejackets, buoyancy aids and personal safety equipment. Crewsaver is able to offer a complete range designed to meet your individual water sport needs.

DOWNSOUTH (TORQUAY) LTD
Kents Lane, Wellswood,
Torquay, Devon
Tel: (0803) 297715
Fax: (0803) 200449
Manufacturers and suppliers of the Downsouth range of buoyancy aids, offering a buoyancy aid for most water sports. A bespoke service is also catered for.

LOKATA LTD
Falmouth, Cornwall TR10 8AE
Tel: (0326) 73636
Fax: (0326) 73941
Manufacturer of type approved 406 MHZ EPIRBs including automatic float-free and personal models for rapid detection and location by rescue services. In addition: NAVTEX Receivers.

SAILING SCHOOLS

CITY YACHT SCHOOL
The Elms, Bellevue Road,
Minster, Sheerness,
Kent ME12 2JF
Tel: (0795) 873395
(evenings only)
The City Yacht School provides a service to the marine commercial and leisure fields. We specialise in short intensive courses, private tuition and consultancy in many aspects of the maritime area.

FOWEY CRUISING SCHOOL (MALTA & UK)
32 Fore Street, Fowey,
Cornwall PL23 1AQ
Tel: (0726) 832129
All RYA cruising courses and shorebased exam courses; plus skippered charters and cruises available in the West Country. Skippered charters, bareboat charters, luxury cruises and RYA Competent Crew or Keelboat courses all year round in Malta.

PADSTOW HARBOUR
Padstow Harbour Commissioners,
Harbour Office, West Quay,
Padstow Cornwall PL28 8AQ
Tel: (0841) 532239
Fax: (0841) 533346
Small West Country port having a vigorous fishing fleet and enjoying an excellent reputation for waterborne recreation. General cargo capability extends up to vessels 1500/2000 GRT.

SOLENT COASTAL & OFFSHORE SAILING SCHOOL
Archipelagoes,
South Mundham, Chichester,
Sussex PO20 6NA
Tel: (0243) 262724
We are an RYA recognised sailing school, based on the River Hamble. We offer a wide range of courses. All shorebased theory courses. Families, groups, couples and singles welcome. Ladies only - 5 day courses with lady instructor. Please write or telephone Philip or Julie Hawes for brochure or to discuss your requirements.

SAILS

BANKS SAILS
Bruce Banks Sails Ltd
372 Brook Lane, Sarisbury,
Nr Southampton,
Hampshire SO3 6ZA
Tel: (0489) 582444
Fax: (0489) 589789
Manufacturers of all types of sails, racing, cruising, one design, plus accessories and covers. Specialist repair and servicing department. Ideally positioned close to the Hamble River and 10 minutes from Southampton and Portsmouth.

SPECIALIST RESPRAYS

FALMOUTH BOAT CONSTRUCTION LTD
Little Falmouth Yacht Yard,
Flushing, Falmouth,
Cornwall TR11 5TJ
Tel: (0326) 74309
Fax: (0326) 77679
Repairs, refits, storage undercover and quayside, osmosis treatment specialists, resprays. Slipways to 100 ton. Commercial craft repairs. Specialist one-off builds. Full engineering shop for all diesel and petrol engines.

VIDEOS

AMBERLEY MARINE ELECTRONICS LTD
'Hurley Cottage' Henley Road,
Hurley, Berkshire SL6 5LW
Tel: (0628) 826104
Video programme makers and suppliers of the largest range of marine video titles in the U.K. Covering sail and power, navigation, radar, VHF radio, boat handling, fishing, weather and general interest.

WEATHER INFORMATION

MARINECALL
24/30 West Smithfield,
London EC1A 9DL
Tel: 071-975 9000
Marinecall offers detailed coastal weather forecasts for 15 different regions, for up to 5 days ahead, from The Met Office.

YACHT BROKERS

BOATWORKS + LTD
Castle Emplacement,
St Peter Port, Guernsey
Tel: (0481) 726071
Fax: (0481) 714224
Boatworks + provides a comprehensive range of services including electronics, chandlery, boatbuilding and repairs, engine sales and services, yacht brokerage, clothing and fuel supplies.

BRENTFORD MARINE SERVICES
The Boathouse,
Brentford Dock Marina,
Justin Close, Brentford,
Middlesex TW8 8QA
Tel: 081-568 0287
Yacht brokers and well stocked chandlery.

CAMUS MARINE SERVICES
Craobh Haven, Craignish,
By Lochgilphead, Argyll
Tel: (08525) 225/622/222
Fax: (08525) 252
200 marina berths. Water. Electricity. Diesel fuel. Gas. Yacht repairs, fitting-out and engineering. Storage ashore. Chandlery. Brokerage. Insurance. Nearby facilities include: pub, shops, sailing school, dive centre, launderette, riding centre, hotels/guest houses, self-catering accommodation. Electronic & electric installation & service. Agents for Yanmar, Bukl, L/P diesels, Honda & Mariner outboards, Autolink RT, Easyreef furling system.

ESSEX MARINA LTD
Wallasea Island, Nr Rochford,
Essex SS4 2HG
Tel: (0702) 258531
Fax: (0702) 258227
Yacht marina. Pontoon and swinging moorings. Fuel sales. Yacht brokerage. Night security. Hauling and launching. Engineering and shipwrights. Bars and restaurant. One hour from London.

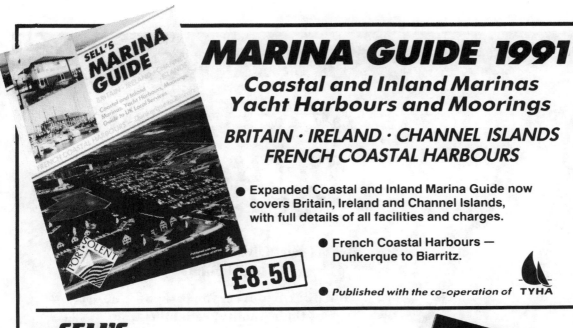

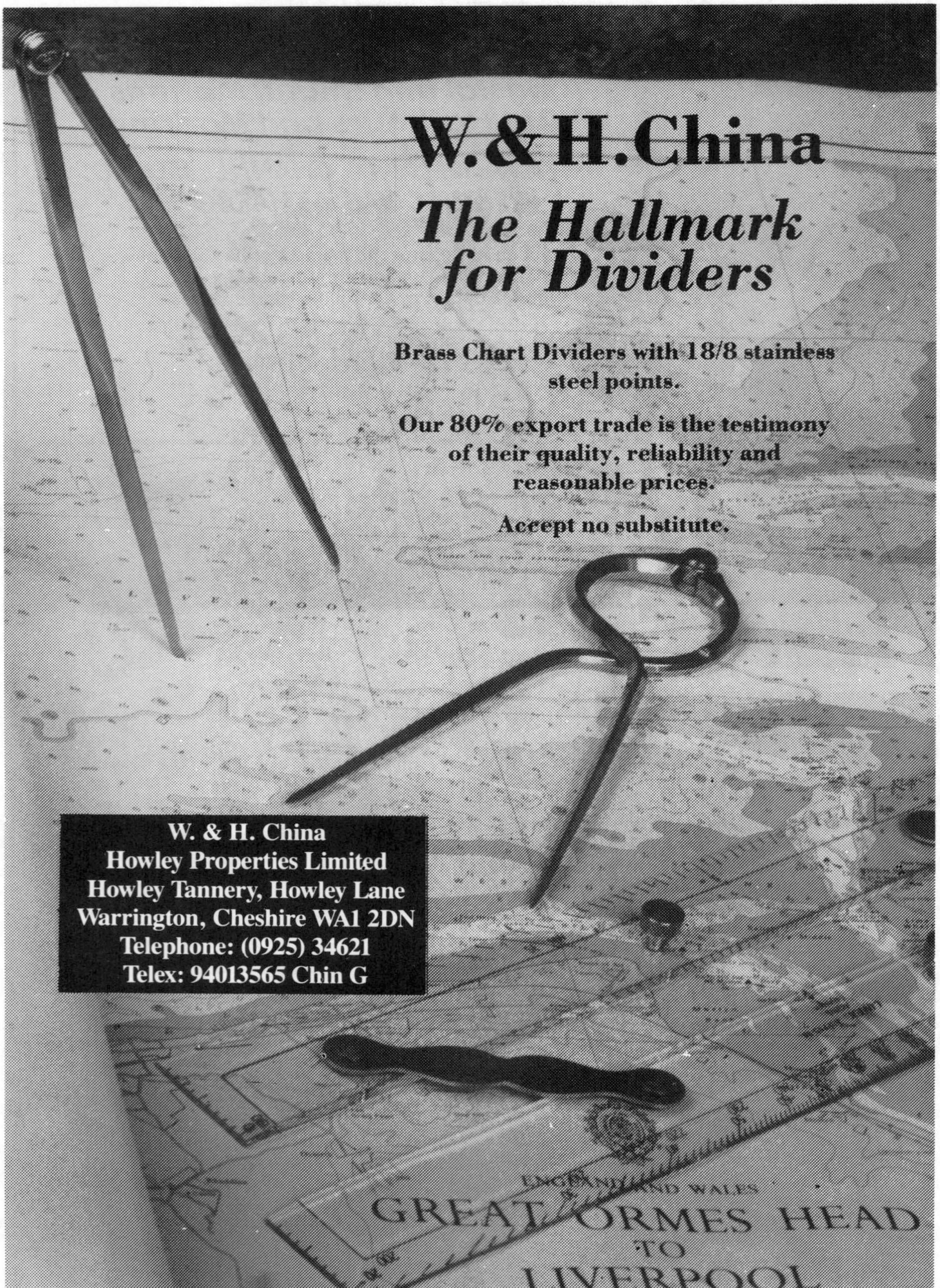
W. & H. China
The Hallmark for Dividers
Brass Chart Dividers with 18/8 stainless steel points.
Our 80% export trade is the testimony of their quality, reliability and reasonable prices.
Accept no substitute.
W. & H. China
Howley Properties Limited
Howley Tannery, Howley Lane
Warrington, Cheshire WA1 2DN
Telephone: (0925) 34621
Telex: 94013565 Chin G
ENGLAND AND WALES
GREAT ORMES HEAD
TO
LIVERPOOL

Chapter 1

About this Almanac

1

Contents

IMPROVEMENTS TO THIS EDITION

- All abbreviations and Symbols are now grouped in Chapter 1.
- French, Dutch and German glossaries are in relevant geographical areas.
- New Customs regulations and telephone numbers are in Chapter 2.
- Extended North Sea Traffic Separation Scheme is also in Chapter 2.
- The boundaries of Areas 1, 10 and 11 have been adjusted for clarity.
- Improved sequence of information in Area 2.
- New port entries for Ploumanach and Pontreux in Area 16.
- New port entries for Dahouet and River Rance/Dinan in Area 18.
- The Channel Islands alone now comprise Area 17, with more detail.
- The adjacent French Coast is in a revised Area 18.
- The former Areas 18–20 are therefore re-numbered 19–21.

Explanation

The 1992 edition of *The Macmillan & Silk Cut Nautical Almanac* follows the pattern established in 1985, when much of the standing information which does not alter from year to year was transferred to a new companion volume — *The Macmillan & Silk Cut Yachtsman's Handbook*. This will not be republished on an annual basis. A new and revised edition was published in 1990.

The 1992 *Almanac* contains the essential navigational data needed by yachtsmen for the waters round the United Kingdom, Ireland, and the coast of Europe from the border of Spain and France on the Atlantic coast to the North Sea border of Germany and Denmark.

Chapters 2–9 of the *Almanac* deal with the same subjects as Chapters 2–9 of the *Handbook*. Matters which are not likely to change, or which are of a permanent nature, are in the *Handbook*; things which are liable to alter from year to year (or which change completely, such as the tide tables and the ephemeris) are in this *Almanac*. Chapters 2–9 of the *Almanac* and the *Handbook* are cross-referenced where this is helpful to the user.

Chapter 10 — the bulk of the *Almanac* — contains harbour, coastal and tidal information, arranged area by area. A map of the twenty areas is shown on page 188.

1.1 INTRODUCTION

1.1.1 Numbering system

There are ten chapters. For ease of reference each chapter is divided into numbered sections, prefaced by the number of the chapter. Thus the sections in Chapter 7, for example, are numbered 7.1, 7.2 etc.

Within each section the key paragraphs are numbered. Thus in section 7.2 (say) the main paragraphs are numbered 7.2.1, 7.2.2, 7.2.3 etc.

Diagrams carry the chapter number and a figure in brackets, thus: Fig. 7(1), Fig. 7(2), Fig. 7(3) etc.

Tables carry the chapter number and a figure in brackets, thus Table 3(1), Table 3(2) etc.

1.1.2 Index

The main paragraph headings and the page number of each section are listed on the contents page at the start of each chapter. At the back of the book is a full page index, while at the front is a quick reference and personal index for important items.

1.1.3 General acknowledgments

The Editors wish to record their thanks to the many individuals and official bodies who have assisted by providing essential information and much advice in the preparation of this almanac. They include the Hydrographic Office of the Ministry of Defence (Navy) at Taunton, the Proudman Oceanographic Laboratory at Bidston, HM Nautical Almanac Office, HM Stationery Office, HM Customs, the Meteorological Office, HM Coastguard, British Telecom, Trinity House, the National Maritime Museum, the BBC and IBA, the Department of Transport, the Royal National Lifeboat Institution, the Port of London Authority, Associated British Ports, countless Harbour Masters, and our many individual agents.

Chartlets, tidal stream diagrams and tidal curves are produced from British Admiralty Charts and from Hydrographic Publications with the permission of the Controller of HM Stationery Office and of the Hydrographer of the Navy, and from French publications by permission of the Service Hydrographique et Océanographique de la Marine.

Information from the *Admiralty Lists of Lights*, *Admiralty Sailing Directions* and from the *Admiralty List of Radio Signals* is reproduced with the sanction of the Controller HM Stationery Office, and of the Hydrographer of the Navy.

Extracts from the following are published by permission of the Controller of HM Stationery Office: *International Code of Signals, 1969*; *Meteorological Office Weather Services for Shipping.*

Astronomical data is derived from the current edition of *The Nautical Almanac*, and is included by permission of HM Nautical Almanac Office and of the Science and Engineering Research Council.

Material from the *Handbook for Radio Operators* is by permission of British Telecom.

1.1.4 Acknowledgments — tidal information

Tidal predictions for Southampton, Dover, Sheerness, London Bridge, Harwich, Lowestoft, Immingham, River Tees, Leith, Aberdeen, Liverpool, Holyhead, Milford Haven, Avonmouth, Shoreham, Galway, Cobh, Belfast and St Helier are computed by the Proudman Oceanographic Laboratory, copyright reserved. Predictions for Dublin are prepared by the Proudman Oceanographic Laboratory for the Dublin Port and Docks Board, copyright reserved. Phases of the Moon are supplied by the Science and Engineering Research Council.

Tidal predictions for Devonport, Dartmouth, Poole, Portsmouth, Lerwick, Ullapool, Oban and Greenock are Crown Copyright and are supplied by permission of the Controller of HM Stationery Office, and the Hydrographer of the Navy.

Acknowledgment is made to the following authorities for permission to use the tidal predictions stated. Service Hydrographique et Océanographique de la Marine, France: Pointe de Grave, Brest, St Malo, Cherbourg, Le Havre and Dieppe. Department van Waterstaat, Netherlands: Flushing and Hook of Holland. Deutsches Hydrographisches Institut: Helgoland.

1.1.5 Standard terms

All bearings given in this Almanac are 'True', from seaward. For example, the sector of a light shown as G (Green) from 090°–180° is visible over an arc of 90° from the moment that the observer is due west of the light until he is due north of it.

Dimensions, in general, are stated in metric terms, the Imperial equivalent being included where appropriate. Distances, unless otherwise stated, are in International nautical (sea) miles, abbreviated as M. All depths and heights are shown in metres (m) unless otherwise indicated.

Times are given in UT, unless stated otherwise (e.g. LT or local time), and are reckoned from 0000 (midnight) to 2400. DST refers to Daylight Saving Time (e.g. BST — British Summer Time). For BST and for standard time (in winter) in France, Belgium, Netherlands and West Germany — add one hour to UT. For Daylight Saving (DST) from last Sunday in March to last Saturday in September in France, Belgium, Netherlands and West Germany — add two hours to UT. Tidal predictions are given in UT for the United Kingdom and Zone −0100 for the Continent. (See 9.1.2.)

VHF frequencies are identified throughout by their International Maritime VHF series channel (Ch) designator. Frequencies used for calling and working may be separated thus Ch 16; 12.

1.2 IMPROVING THE ALMANAC

1.2.1 Suggestions for improvements

The Editors would be particularly grateful for suggestions for improving the content of the Almanac. Ideas based on experience with its practical use afloat would be specially welcome. It is not always feasible to implement suggestions received, but all will be carefully considered. Even minor ideas are welcome. Please send any ideas or comments to:

For Chapters 1 to 9 inclusive, and in Chapter 10 for pages listing Coastal Lights, Fog Signals, and Waypoints; Passage Information; or Area Waypoints: The Editor, *The Macmillan & Silk Cut Nautical Almanac*, 41, Arbor Lane, Winnersh, Wokingham, Berks RG11 5JE. (Fax 0734 772717).

For Chapter 10, Areas 1 to 21 inclusive: The Editor, *The Macmillan & Silk Cut Nautical Almanac*, Edington House, Trent, Sherborne, Dorset DT9 4SR. (Fax 0935 850737).

1.2.2 Notification of errors

Although very great care has been taken in compiling all the information from innumerable sources, it is recognised that in a publication of this nature some errors may occur. The Editors would be extremely grateful if their attention could be called to any such lapses, by writing to them at the address in 1.2.1 above.

1.3 KEEPING IT UP TO DATE

1.3.1 Late corrections

Late corrections are at the back of the Almanac, in front of the index.

1.3.2 Sources of amendments

It is most important that charts and other navigational publications — such as this Almanac — are kept up to date. Corrections to Admiralty charts and publications are issued weekly in *Admiralty Notices to Mariners.* These are obtainable from Admiralty Chart Agents (by post if required), or they can be sighted at Customs Houses or Mercantile Marine Offices.

An alternative, but less frequent, service is given by the *Admiralty Notices to Mariners, Small Craft Edition.* This contains reprinted Notices for the British Isles and the European coast from the Gironde to the Elbe. Notices concerning depths greater in general than 7 metres (23ft), or which do not affect small craft for some other reason, are not included. They are available from Admiralty Chart Agents, or through the Royal Yachting Association.

1.3.3 Our free supplements

Important navigational information in this Almanac is corrected up to and including Admiralty Notices to Mariners, Weekly Edition No. 14 of 1991. Late amendments are at the back of the almanac, before the index. Inserted into the almanac is a postcard application for two free supplements.

The first, to be published in January 1992, will contain corrections up to November 1991. The second, to be published in May 1992, will contain corrections up to March 1992.

Please enter your name and address clearly in block capitals where indicated on the postcard.

Affix a stamp and return it to: Penny Warren, *The Macmillan & Silk Cut Nautical Almanac*, Macmillan Press Ltd, Stockton House, 1 Melbourne Place, London WC2B 4LF.

The supplements will then be posted to you in due course, as they are published. Postage for the supplements will be paid by the publishers.

The Editors are grateful for any comments or suggestions. If you have any comments, please write them on the postcard in the space provided.

Supplements also include important corrections to *The Macmillan & Silk Cut Yachtsman's Handbook*.

1.3.4 Record of amendments

The amendment sheet below is intended to assist you in keeping the Almanac up to date, although it can also be used to record corrections to charts or other publications. Tick where indicated when the appropriate amendments have been made.

Weekly Notices to Mariners

1	....	27	....
2	....	28	....
3	....	29	....
4	....	30	....
5	....	31	....
6	....	32	....
7	....	33	....
8	....	34	....
9	....	35	....
10	....	36	....
11	....	37	....
12	....	38	....
13	....	39	....
14	....	40	....
15	....	41	....
16	....	42	....
17	....	43	....
18	....	44	....
19	....	45	....
20	....	46	....
21	....	47	....
22	....	48	....
23	....	49	....
24	....	50	....
25	....	51	....
26	....	52	....

Small Craft Editions

1 Feb 1991	....
1 May 1991	....
1 July 1991	....
1 Sept 1991	....
1 Feb 1992	....
1 May 1992	....
1 July 1992	....
1 Sept 1992	....

Late corrections
(see back of Almanac, before index)

Macmillan Supplements

First (Jan 1992)	....
Second (May 1992)	....

1.4.1 Abbreviations & Symbols

The following selected abbreviations and symbols may be encountered in this Almanac, in Supplements, in Admiralty Publications, or on Charts.

AB*	Alongside berth
abt	About
AC	220v AC electrical supplies
AC	Admiralty Chart
ACA	Admiralty Chart Agent
✈	Airport
Aero	Aeronautical
ALRS	Admiralty List of Radio Signals
Alt	Altitude
Al, Alt	Alternating Lt
AM	Amplitude Modulation
anch, ⚓	Anchorage
anct	Ancient
annly	Annually
App	Apparent
Appr.	Approaches
approx	Approximate
ATT	Admiralty Tide Tables
Az	Azimuth

B	Bay
B	Black
Ⓑ	Bank (£)
Bar	Licensed bar
Bcst	Broadcast
BFO	Beat Frequency Oscillator
BH	Boat Hoist (tons)
Bk	Bank (shoal)
bk	Broken
Bn(s)	Beacon(s)
Bldg	Building
Bo	Boulders
Bol	Bollard
brg	Bearing
BS	British Standard
BST	British Summer Time
Bu	Blue
By(s)	Buoy(s)
BY	Boatyard

°C	Degrees Celsius
C.	Cape
C	Crane (tons)
c	Coarse
ca	Cable
Calib	Calibration
Cas	Castle
Cath	Cathedral
Cemy	Cemetery
CG	Coastguard
CH	Chandlery
Ch	Channel (VHF)
Ch, ✠	Church, chapel
chan	Channel (navigational)
Chy	Chimney
Ck	Chalk
cm	Centimetre(s)
Col	Column, pillar, obelisk
conspic	Conspicuous
const	Construction
cont	Continuous
Corr	Correction
cov	Covers
Cr	Creek
CRS	Coast Radio Station
CS	Calibration Station
Cup	Cupola
⋕	Customs
Cy	Clay

D, ⛽	Diesel fuel
Dec	Declination
decrg	Decreasing
dest	Destroyed
DF	Direction finding
DG Range	Degaussing Range
Dia	Diaphone
◆	Diamond
Dir	Direction
Dir Lt	Directional light
discont	Discontinued
dist	Distance, Distant
Dk	Dock
dm	Decimetre(s)
Dn	Dolphin
Dr	Doctor
dr	Dries
DST	Daylight Saving Time
DW	Deep Water, Deep-draught Route
DZ	Danger Zone (buoy)

E	East
EC	Early closing
ECM	East Cardinal Mark
ECM	Editions Cartographiques Maritimes
ED	Existence doubtful
ED	European datum
El	Electrical repairs
Ⓔ	Electronics repairs

Ent.	Entrance
Est.	Estuary
ETA	Estimated Time of Arrival
ETD	Estimated Time of Departure
exper	Experimental
explos	Explosive
ext	Extension
°F	Degrees Fahrenheit
F	Fixed Light
f	Fine
Fax	Facsimile
Fcst	Forecast
F Fl	Fixed and Flashing light
Fl	Flashing light
FM	Frequency Modulation
Fm	Farm
Fog Det Lt	Fog Detector Light
Freq, Fx	Frequency
FS	Flagstaff
ft	Foot, feet
Ft	Fort
FW,	Fresh water supply
G	Gravel
G	Green
Gas	Calor Gas
Gaz	Camping Gaz
GC	Great-circle
Gd	Ground
GHA	Greenwich Hour Angle
GMT	Greenwich Mean Time
Gp	Group
GPS	Global Positioning System
Grt	Gross Registered Tonnage
Gt	Great
Gy	Grey
h	Hard
H+, H-	Minutes past/before each hour
H24	Continuous
HAT	Highest Astronomical Tide
Hbr(s)	Harbour(s)
Hd.	Head, Headland
HF	High Frequency
HFP	High Focal Plane Buoy
HIDB	Highlands & Islands Development Board
HJ	Day Service only
HMSO	Her Majesty's Stationery Office
HN	Night Service only
Hn.	Haven
Ho	House
(hor)	Horizontally disposed
H	Hospital
Hrs	Hours
Hr Mr	Harbour Master
ht	Height
HW	High Water
HX	No fixed hrs
Hz	Hertz
IALA	International Association of Lighthouse Authorities
Ident	Identification signal
IDM	Isolated Danger Mark
IHO	International Hydrographic Organization
illum	Illuminated
IMO	International Maritime Organization
in	Inch, inches
incrg	Increasing
INMARSAT	International Maritime Satellite Organization
inop	Inoperative
Int	Interrupted, International
intens	Intensified
IQ	Interrupted quick flashing light
Is	Island, Islet
Iso	Isophase
ITU	International Telecommunications Union
ITZ	Inshore Traffic Zone
IUQ	Interrupted ultra quick flashing light
IVQ	Interrupted very quick flashing light
kHz	Kilohertz
km	Kilometre(s)
kn	knot(s)
Kos	Kosangas
kW	Kilowatts
L	Loch, Lough, Lake
L*,Lndg,	Landing place
	Launderette
l	Large
Lat	Latitude
LAT	Lowest Astronomical Tide
LANBY	Large Automatic Navigational Buoy
LB	Lifeboat
Ldg	Leading
Le.	Ledge
LF	Low frequency
LHA	Local Hour Angle
Lit	Little
LL	Admiralty List of Lights
LOA	Length overall
Long	Longitude
Lr	Lower
LT	Local time

Lt	Light
Lt By	Light buoy
Lt F	Light Float
Lt Ho	Lighthouse
Lt V	Light vessel
LW	Low Water
M*	Moorings available
M	International nautical mile
M	Mud
m	Metre(s)
mm	Millimetre(s)
Mag	Magnetic, magnitude (of Star)
ME	Marine engineering repairs
MF	Medium Frequency
MHWN	Mean High Water Neaps
MHWS	Mean High Water Springs
MHz	Megahertz
min(s)	Minute(s) of time
ML	Mean Level
MLWN	Mean Low Water Neaps
MLWS	Mean Low Water Springs
Mo	Morse
Mon	Monument, memorial
MRCC	Maritime Rescue Co-ordination Centre
MRSC	Maritime Rescue Sub-Centre
Ms	Mussels
ms	Millisecond(s)
μs	Microseconds
MSL	Mean Sea Level
Mt.	Mountain, Mount
N	North
Nauto	Nautophone
NAVTEX	Navigational telex service
NB	Notice Board
NCM	North Cardinal Mark
NM	Notices to Mariners
No.	Number
NON	Unmodulated continuous wave emission
np	Neap tides
NRT	Net registered tonnage
Obstn	Obstruction
Obsy	Observatory
Oc	Occulting Light
occas	Occasional
Off	Office
Or	Orange
OSGB	Ordnance Survey Great Britain Datum (1936)

Oz	Ooze
P, ⛽	Petrol
P.	Port (harbour)
P	Pebbles
(P)	Provisional, Preliminary
PA	Position approximate
Pass.	Passage
PD	Position doubtful
PHM	Port-hand Mark
Pk.	Peak
✉	Post Office
pos(n)	Position
priv	Private
Prog	Prognosis
prohib	Prohibited
proj	Projected
prom	Prominent
Pt.	Point
PV	Pilot Vessel
Q, Qk Fl	Quick flashing light
R	Red
R.	River
R, Rk(s),Rky	Rock(s), Rocky
Ra	Coast Radar Station
Racon	Radar Transponder Beacon
Ramark	Radar Beacon
RC	Non-directional radiobeacon
RD	Directional radiobeacon
Rds	Roads, Roadstead
Rep, Repd.	Reported
R, ✕	Restaurant
Rf.	Reef
RG	Radio Direction Finding Station
Rly, ⇌	Railway station
RNLI	Royal National Lifeboat Institution
Ro Ro	Roll-on Roll-off (ferry terminal)
●	Round, circular
RT	Radio Telephony
Ru	Ruins
RW	VHF Radio Lighthouse
Rx	Receiver
S	South
S	Sand
S, St, Ste	Saint(s)
SAR	Search and Rescue
SC	Sailing Club
Sch	School
SCM	South Cardinal Mark
Sd.	Sound
SD	Semi-Diameter
SD	Sailing Directions

SD	Sounding of doubtful depth
sec(s)	Second(s) (of time)
Sem	Semaphore
Seq	Sequence
sf	Stiff
Sh	Shells
Sh	Shipwright, hull repairs etc
SHA	Sidereal Hour Angle
SHM	Starboard-Hand Mark
SHOM	Charts issued by French Hydrographer
Si	Silt
Sig	Signal
Sig Stn	Signal station
SM	Sailmaker
◣	Slip for launching, scrubbing
sm	Small
sn	Shingle
so	Soft
Sp	Spire
sp	Spring tides
SPM	Special Mark
■	Square
SS	Signal Station
SS (Storm)	Storm Signal station
SSB	Single Sideband
St	Stones
Stbd	Starboard
Stn	Station
Str.	Strait
subm	Submerged
sum	Summer
SWM	Safe Water Mark
sy	Sticky
(T), temp	Temporary
t	Ton, tonne
TD	Fog signal temp discontinued
TE	Light temp extinguished
☎, Tel	Telephone
Tr	Tower
▼, ▲	Triangle
TSS	Traffic Separation Scheme
TV Tr	Television Tower
Twi	Twilight
Tx	Transmitter, Transmission
ufn	Until further notice
uncov	Uncovers
unexam	Unexamined
UQ	Ultra Quick flashing Light
UT	Universal Time

V	Victuals, food stores etc
Ⓥ ⛵ ⚓	Visitor's berth/mooring, or where to report
Var	Variation
Vel	Velocity
vert	Vertically disposed
VHF	Very High Frequency
Vi	Violet
vis	visibility, visible
Volmet	Weather broadcasts for aviation
VTM	Vessel Traffic Management
VTS	Vessel Traffic Service
VQ	Very Quick flashing light
W	West
W	White
Water Tr	Water tower
WCM	West Cardinal Mark
Wd	Weed
wef	With effect from
WGS	World Geodetic System datum
Whf	Wharf
Whis	Whistle
win	Winter
Wk	Wreck
WMO	World Meteorological Organisation
WPT, ⊕	Waypoint
W/T	Wireless Telegraphy
Wx	Weather
Y	Yellow, Amber, Orange
YC, ⚑	Yacht Club
Yd(s)	Yard(s)

NOTE: * Not shown for Marinas

MIAMI SHOW
50-FOOT SCENE
BOAT
INTERNATIONAL
APACHE
STEVE CURTIS & COUGAR MARINE PROFILES • MIAMI BOAT SHOW • 50-FOOT SCENE • BOARDSAILING: LOCATION HAWAII • ON BOARD: SILVER SHALIS • ON BOARD: MAYA
£2
NUMBER 24 APRIL 1988

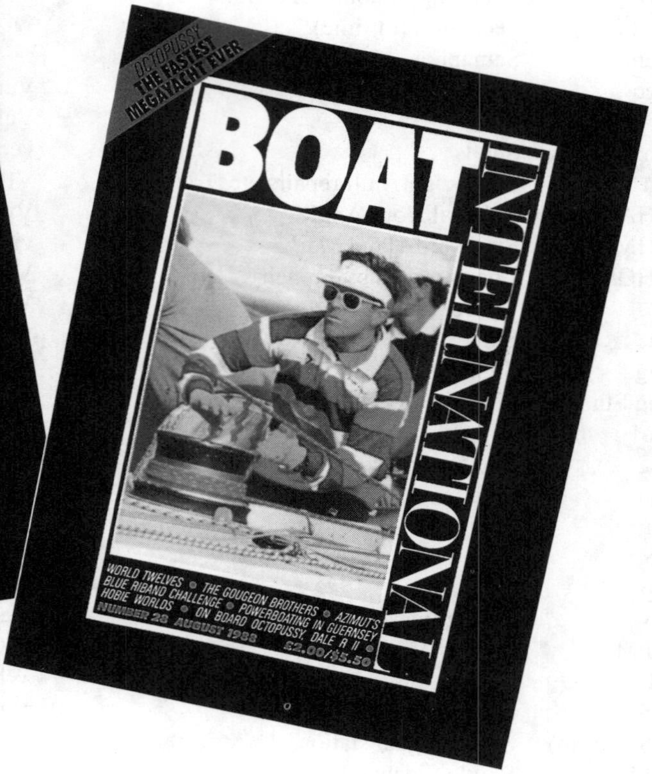
OCTOPUSSY
THE FASTEST
MEGAYACHT EVER
BOAT
INTERNATIONAL
WORLD TWELVES • THE GOUGEON BROTHERS • AZIMUT'S BLUE RIBAND CHALLENGE • POWERBOATING IN GUERNSEY • HOBIE WORLDS • ON BOARD OCTOPUSSY, DALE A II •
NUMBER 28 AUGUST 1988
£2.00/$5.50

For the connoisseur

Keep up to date with top international yacht racing action, colourful waterborne adventure, and the latest news from the high-society world of the Superyachts with a subscription to BOAT INTERNATIONAL the world's best presented yachting magazine.

Subscribe to *Boat International*

SUBSCRIPTION RATES: UK £22.00 · EUROPE & EIRE (AIRMAIL) £35.00 · REST OF WORLD (AIRSPEEDED) £40.00

I would like a one-year (12 issue) subscription to *Boat International* commencing with the ________ (month) issue.

Pleae charge my Visa/Access/American Express/Mastercharge/Diners Club No ________

Credit Card expiry date ________ Signature ________

I enclose cheque/money order value £ ________

Please send a proforma invoice ☐

Cheques must be in sterling drawn on a UK bank and made payable to SF Publications Ltd.

Name ________ Address ________

Boat International Subs Dept. Sterling House 5-7 Kingston Hill Kingston-upon-Thames Surrey KT2 7PW

Chapter 2

General Information

Contents

General information — introduction

The following subjects are described in detail in Chapter 2 of *The Macmillan & Silk Cut Yachtsman's Handbook*:

Limits and dangers — e.g. territorial waters; fishing limits; measured distances; hovercraft; warships on exercises; practice and exercise areas; submarines; minefields; wrecks; offshore oil and gas fields; power cables; traffic schemes. HM Customs — notice of departure; immigration; full and quick reports. Customs regulations in European countries. Yacht tonnage measurement — Net and Gross Tonnages; Lloyd's Register Tonnage; Deadweight Tonnage; One Ton Cup etc. Units and conversions. Glossaries of nautical terms. Yachting organisations — Royal Yachting Association; Seamanship Foundation; British Marine Industries Federation; Trinity House; useful addresses.

Here in the Almanac are given brief notes on the *International Regulations for Preventing Collisions at Sea*, traffic separation schemes, useful conversion factors, a summary of documentation and Customs procedures. For further details of these items, and of the subjects listed above, reference should be made to *The Macmillan & Silk Cut Yachtsman's Handbook*.

2.1 INTERNATIONAL REGULATIONS FOR PREVENTING COLLISIONS AT SEA

2.1.1 General

The regulations are stated in full, with diagrams and explanatory notes, in *The Macmillan & Silk Cut Yachtsman's Handbook* (2.1). The following are notes on provisions of special concern to yachtsmen. The numbers of the rules quoted are given for reference.

The rules must be interpreted in a seamanlike way if collisions are to be avoided (Rule 2). A vessel does not have right of way over another regardless of special factors — such as other vessels under way or at anchor, shallow water or other hazards, poor visibility, traffic schemes, fishing boats etc — or the handling characteristics of the vessels concerned in the prevailing conditions. Sometimes vessels must depart from the rules to avoid a collision. See Plate 4 on page 120.

A sailing vessel is so defined (Rule 3) when she is under sail only. When under power she must show the lights for a power-driven vessel, and when under sail and power a cone point down forward (Rule 25).

Keep a good lookout, using eyes and ears, particularly at night or in poor visibility (Rule 5).

Safe speed is dictated by visibility, traffic, depth of water, navigational dangers, and the manoeuvrability of the boat (Rule 6). Excess speed gives less time to appreciate the situation, less time to take avoiding action, and produces a worse collision if such action fails.

Risk of collision must be assessed by all available means (Rule 7). A yacht should take a series of compass bearings of a converging ship. Unless the bearings change appreciably, there is risk of collision. Take special care with large ships.

Take early and positive action to avoid collision (Rule 8). Large alterations of course and/or speed are more evident to the other skipper, particularly at night or on radar. Do not hesitate to slow down, stop (or even go astern, under power). While keeping clear of one vessel, watch out for others.

In narrow channels, keep to starboard whether under power or sail (Rule 9). A yacht under 20m in length must not impede larger vessels confined to a channel.

2.1.2 Traffic separation schemes

Yachts, like other vessels, must conform to traffic schemes (Rule 10). Traffic schemes are essential for the safety of larger vessels and, while inconvenient for yachtsmen, must be accepted as another element of passage planning, and be avoided where possible. They are shown on charts, and those around the British Isles are summarised in Figs 2(1)–2(8) on pages 11–18

Proceed in the correct lane, and in the general direction of traffic. Normally join or leave a lane at its extremity, but when joining or leaving at the side, do so at as small an angle as possible. Boats under 20m in length, and any sailing yacht, may use inshore traffic zones — often the most sensible action for a yacht. If essential to cross a traffic lane, do so heading at as near right angles as possible to the lane, and do not impede vessels using the lane. If under sail, start the engine if speed falls below about three knots or if a reasonable course cannot be maintained.

Rule 10 does not modify the Collision Regulations when two vessels meet or converge in a traffic scheme and are in risk of collision. Some traffic schemes are under surveillance by radar, aircraft or patrol vessels. There are heavy penalties for breaking the rules. 'YG' in the International Code means 'You appear not to be complying with the traffic separation scheme'. See Plates 6 and 7 on pages 122 and 123.

2.1.3 Vessels in sight of each other

When two sailing vessels are in risk of collision and on opposite tacks, the port tack one keeps clear. If on the same tack, the windward one keeps clear (Rule 12).

Any overtaking vessel, whether power or sail, keeps clear of a vessel she is overtaking (Rule 13). Overtaking means approaching the other vessel from a direction more than $22\frac{1}{2}°$ abaft her beam (in the sector of her sternlight by night). An overtaken vessel must not hamper one overtaking: always look astern before altering course.

When two power-driven vessels approach head-on, each must alter course to starboard, to pass port to port (Rule 14). A substantial alteration may be needed, with the appropriate sound signal (see page 20 and Rule 34), to make intentions clear.

When two power-driven vessels are crossing and in risk of collision, the one with the other on her starboard side must keep clear and, if possible, avoid passing ahead of the other (Rule 15). The give-way vessel should normally alter to starboard; exceptionally, an alteration to port may be justified, in which case a large alteration may be needed to avoid crossing ahead of the other.

When one vessel has to keep clear, the other shall hold her course and speed. But if she realises that the give-way vessel is failing to keep clear, she must take independent action to avoid collision (Rule 17).

Under Rule 18, except where Rules 9 (Narrow Channels), 10 (Traffic Schemes) and 13 (Overtaking) otherwise require:

continued on page 19

Fig. 2(1) Traffic Separation Schemes (TSS) and Routeing Measures – Western Channel

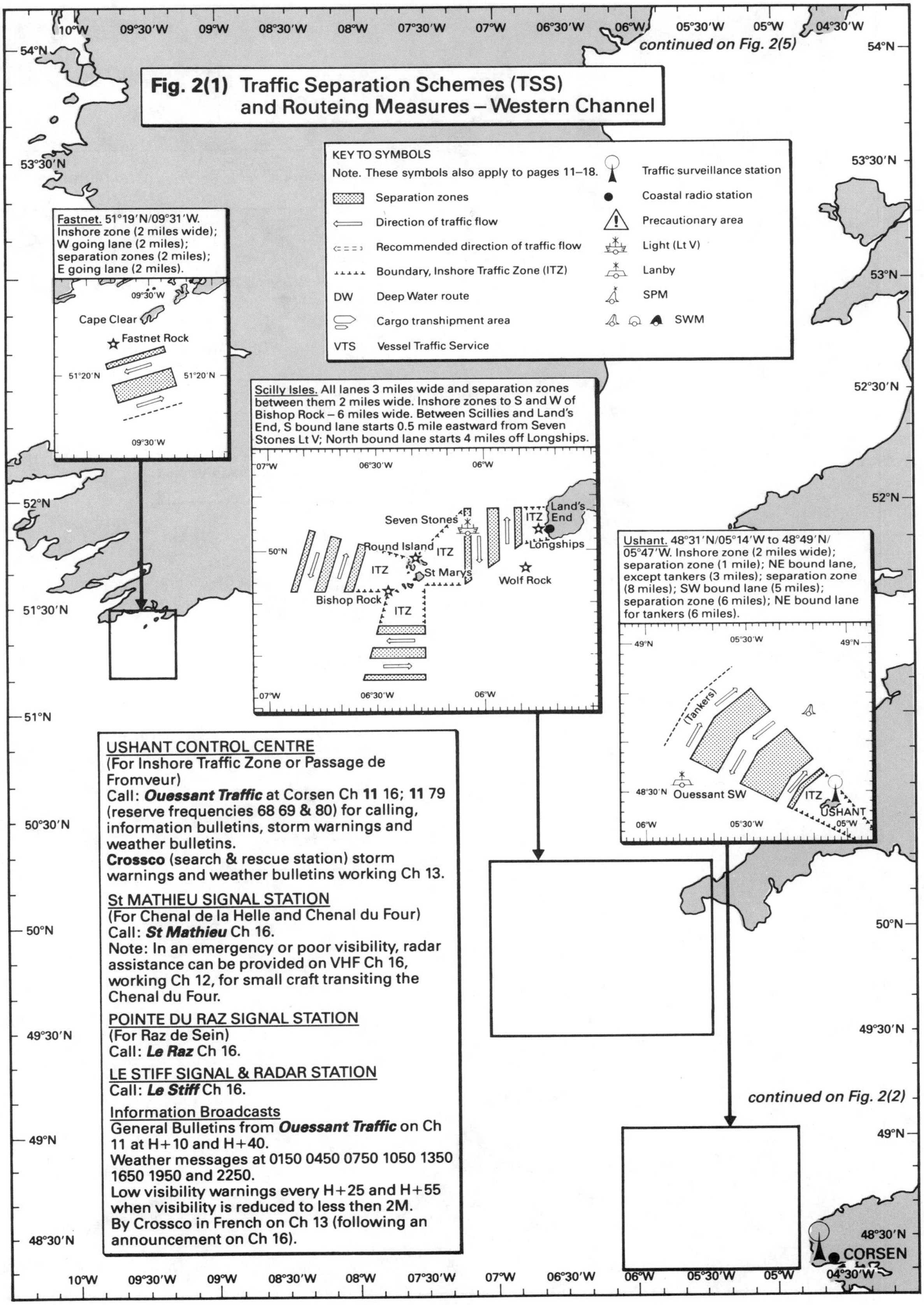
10°W
09°30′W
09°W
08°30′W
08°W
07°30′W
07°W
06°30′W
06°W
05°30′W
05°W
04°30′W
continued on Fig. 2(5)
54°N
53°30′N
53°N
52°30′N
52°N
51°30′N
51°N
50°30′N
50°N
49°30′N
49°N
48°30′N
KEY TO SYMBOLS
Note. These symbols also apply to pages 11–18.
Separation zones
Direction of traffic flow
Recommended direction of traffic flow
Boundary, Inshore Traffic Zone (ITZ)
DW Deep Water route
Cargo transhipment area
VTS Vessel Traffic Service
Traffic surveillance station
Coastal radio station
Precautionary area
Light (Lt V)
Lanby
SPM
SWM
Fastnet. 51°19′N/09°31′W. Inshore zone (2 miles wide); W going lane (2 miles); separation zones (2 miles); E going lane (2 miles).
09°30′W
Cape Clear
Fastnet Rock
51°20′N
51°20′N
09°30′W
Scilly Isles. All lanes 3 miles wide and separation zones between them 2 miles wide. Inshore zones to S and W of Bishop Rock – 6 miles wide. Between Scillies and Land's End, S bound lane starts 0.5 mile eastward from Seven Stones Lt V; North bound lane starts 4 miles off Longships.
07°W
06°30′W
06°W
50°N
Seven Stones
Round Island
ITZ
ITZ
St Marys
Bishop Rock
ITZ
ITZ
Land's End
Longships
Wolf Rock
07°W
06°30′W
06°W
Ushant. 48°31′N/05°14′W to 48°49′N/05°47′W. Inshore zone (2 miles wide); separation zone (1 mile); NE bound lane, except tankers (3 miles); separation zone (8 miles); SW bound lane (5 miles); separation zone (6 miles); NE bound lane for tankers (6 miles).
49°N
05°30′W
49°N
(Tankers)
48°30′N
Ouessant SW
ITZ
USHANT
06°W
05°30′W
05°W
continued on Fig. 2(2)
48°30′N
CORSEN

USHANT CONTROL CENTRE
(For Inshore Traffic Zone or Passage de Fromveur)
Call: ***Ouessant Traffic*** at Corsen Ch **11** 16; **11** 79 (reserve frequencies 68 69 & 80) for calling, information bulletins, storm warnings and weather bulletins.
Crossco (search & rescue station) storm warnings and weather bulletins working Ch 13.

St MATHIEU SIGNAL STATION
(For Chenal de la Helle and Chenal du Four)
Call: ***St Mathieu*** Ch 16.
Note: In an emergency or poor visibility, radar assistance can be provided on VHF Ch 16, working Ch 12, for small craft transiting the Chenal du Four.

POINTE DU RAZ SIGNAL STATION
(For Raz de Sein)
Call: ***Le Raz*** Ch 16.

LE STIFF SIGNAL & RADAR STATION
Call: ***Le Stiff*** Ch 16.

Information Broadcasts
General Bulletins from ***Ouessant Traffic*** on Ch 11 at H+10 and H+40.
Weather messages at 0150 0450 0750 1050 1350 1650 1950 and 2250.
Low visibility warnings every H+25 and H+55 when visibility is reduced to less then 2M.
By Crossco in French on Ch 13 (following an announcement on Ch 16).

Fig. 2(2) Traffic Separation Schemes (TSS) and Routeing Measures – English Channel

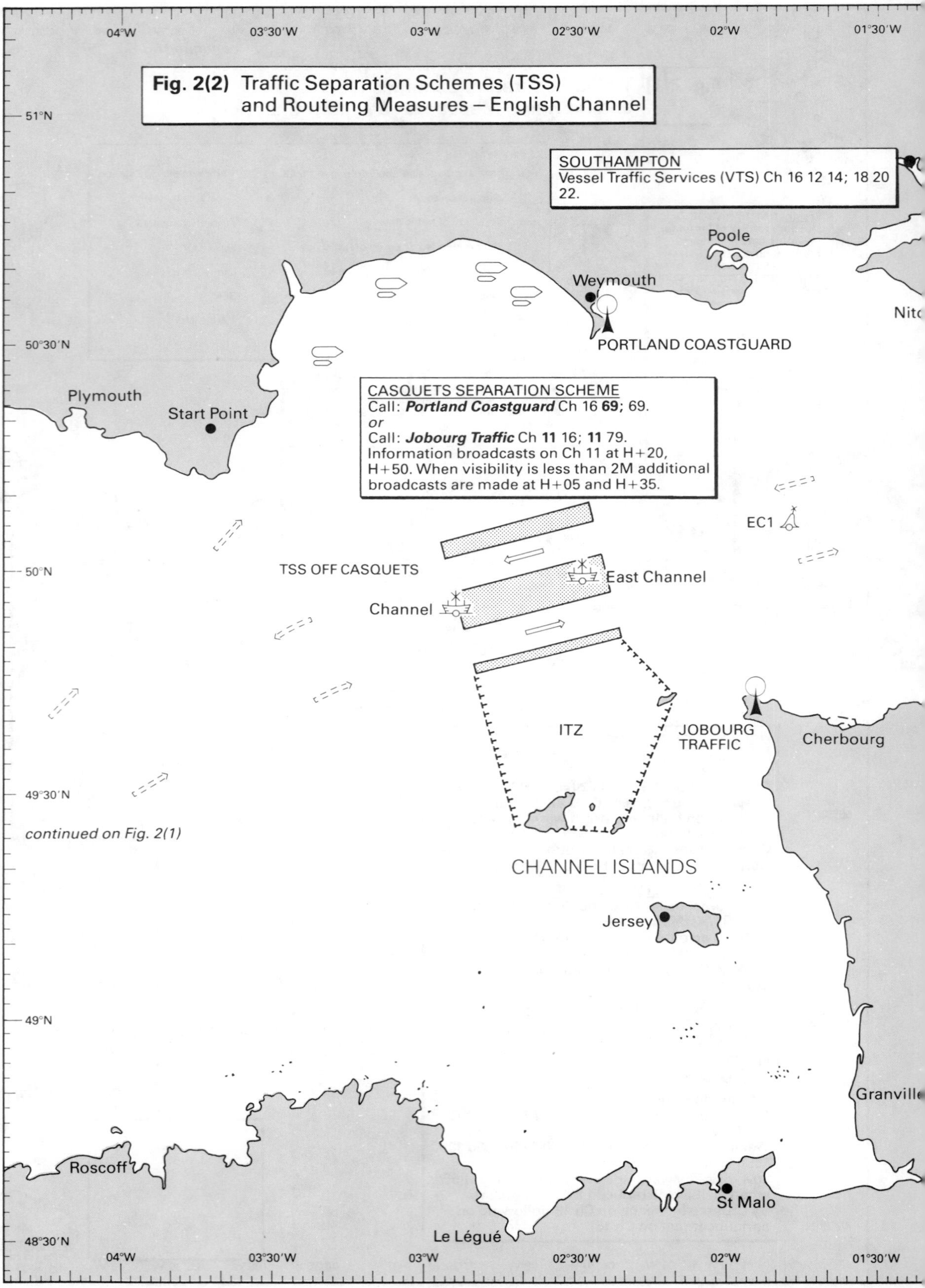
04°W
03°30′W
03°W
02°30′W
02°W
01°30′W
51°N
50°30′N
50°N
49°30′N
49°N
48°30′N
SOUTHAMPTON
Vessel Traffic Services (VTS) Ch 16 12 14; 18 20 22.
Poole
Weymouth
PORTLAND COASTGUARD
Plymouth
Start Point
CASQUETS SEPARATION SCHEME
Call: ***Portland Coastguard*** Ch 16 **69**; 69.
or
Call: ***Jobourg Traffic*** Ch **11** 16; **11** 79.
Information broadcasts on Ch 11 at H+20, H+50. When visibility is less than 2M additional broadcasts are made at H+05 and H+35.
EC1
TSS OFF CASQUETS
East Channel
Channel
ITZ
JOBOURG TRAFFIC
Cherbourg
CHANNEL ISLANDS
Jersey
Granville
Roscoff
St Malo
Le Légué

continued on Fig. 2(1)

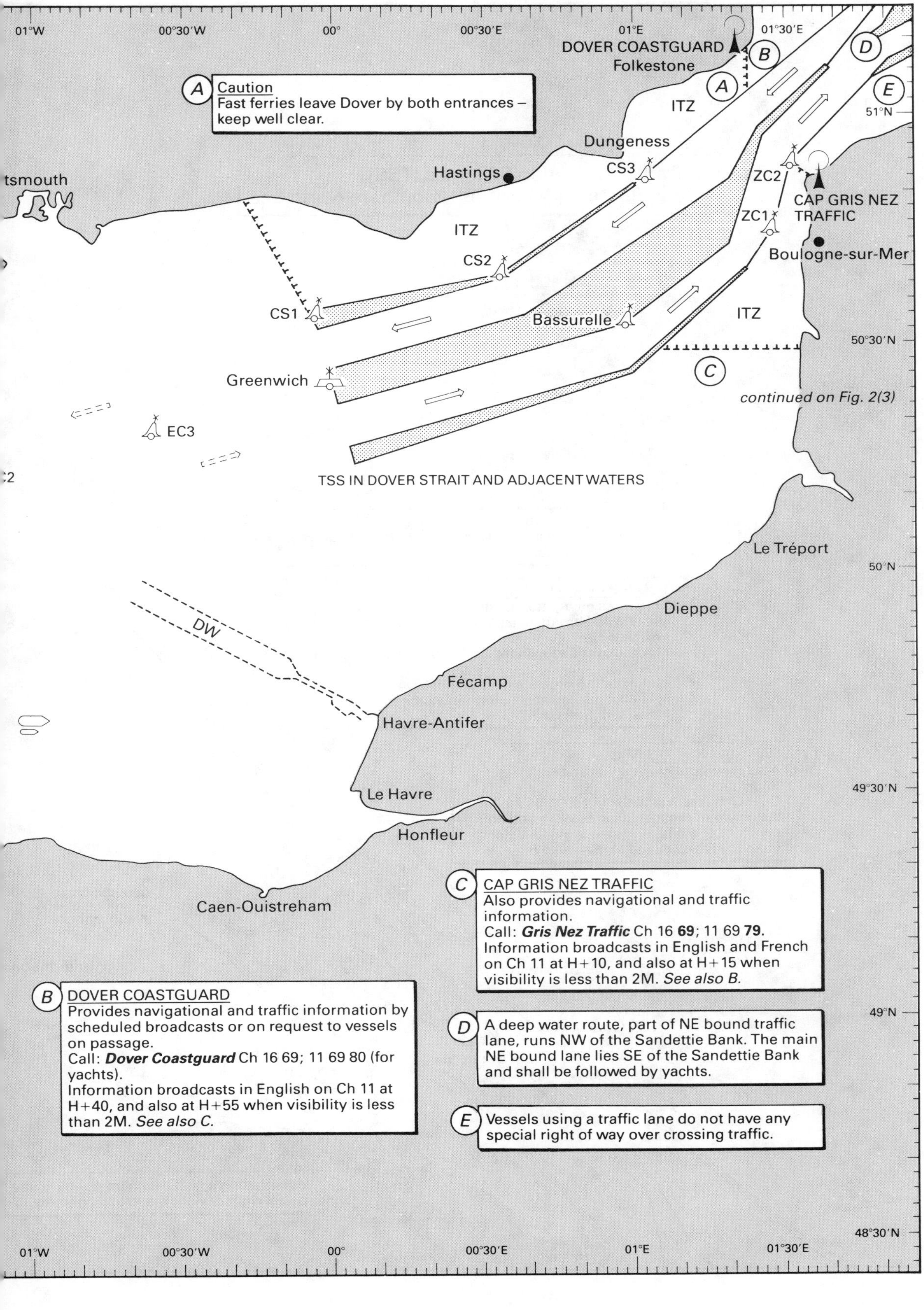
01°W
00°30′W
00°
00°30′E
01°E
01°30′E
DOVER COASTGUARD
Folkestone
A
B
D
E
Caution
Fast ferries leave Dover by both entrances – keep well clear.
ITZ
51°N
Dungeness
Hastings
CS3
ZC2
tsmouth
CAP GRIS NEZ TRAFFIC
ZC1
ITZ
CS2
Boulogne-sur-Mer
CS1
Bassurelle
ITZ
50°30′N
C
Greenwich
continued on Fig. 2(3)
EC3
TSS IN DOVER STRAIT AND ADJACENT WATERS
Le Tréport
50°N
Dieppe
DW
Fécamp
Havre-Antifer
49°30′N
Le Havre
Honfleur
Caen-Ouistreham
CAP GRIS NEZ TRAFFIC
Also provides navigational and traffic information.
Call: Gris Nez Traffic Ch 16 69; 11 69 79.
Information broadcasts in English and French on Ch 11 at H+10, and also at H+15 when visibility is less than 2M. See also B.
DOVER COASTGUARD
Provides navigational and traffic information by scheduled broadcasts or on request to vessels on passage.
Call: Dover Coastguard Ch 16 69; 11 69 80 (for yachts).
Information broadcasts in English on Ch 11 at H+40, and also at H+55 when visibility is less than 2M. See also C.
49°N
A deep water route, part of NE bound traffic lane, runs NW of the Sandettie Bank. The main NE bound lane lies SE of the Sandettie Bank and shall be followed by yachts.
Vessels using a traffic lane do not have any special right of way over crossing traffic.
48°30′N
01°W
00°30′W
00°
00°30′E
01°E
01°30′E

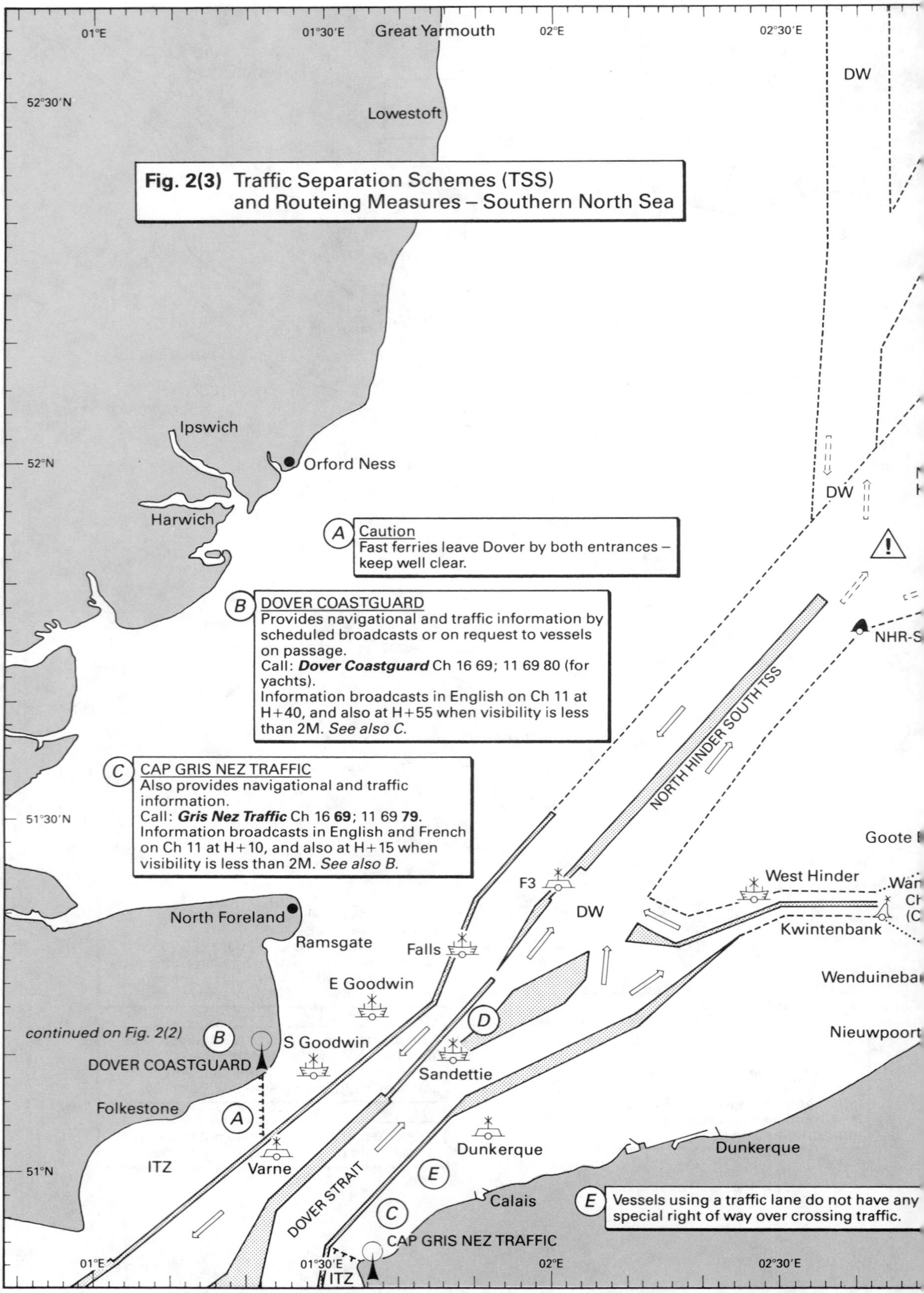

Great Yarmouth
Lowestoft
Ipswich
Orford Ness
Harwich
01°E
01°30′E
02°E
02°30′E
52°30′N
52°N
51°30′N
51°N
DW
A Caution
Fast ferries leave Dover by both entrances – keep well clear.
B DOVER COASTGUARD
Provides navigational and traffic information by scheduled broadcasts or on request to vessels on passage.
Call: Dover Coastguard Ch 16 69; 11 69 80 (for yachts).
Information broadcasts in English on Ch 11 at H+40, and also at H+55 when visibility is less than 2M. See also C.
C CAP GRIS NEZ TRAFFIC
Also provides navigational and traffic information.
Call: Gris Nez Traffic Ch 16 69; 11 69 79.
Information broadcasts in English and French on Ch 11 at H+10, and also at H+15 when visibility is less than 2M. See also B.
NORTH HINDER SOUTH TSS
NHR-S
Goote
West Hinder
Kwintenbank
Wenduineba
Nieuwpoort
F3
DW
North Foreland
Ramsgate
Falls
E Goodwin
continued on Fig. 2(2)
B
DOVER COASTGUARD
S Goodwin
D
Sandettie
Folkestone
A
ITZ
Varne
Dunkerque
Dunkerque
DOVER STRAIT
E
Calais
C
CAP GRIS NEZ TRAFFIC
ITZ
E Vessels using a traffic lane do not have any special right of way over crossing traffic.

Fig. 2(3) Traffic Separation Schemes (TSS) and Routeing Measures – Southern North Sea

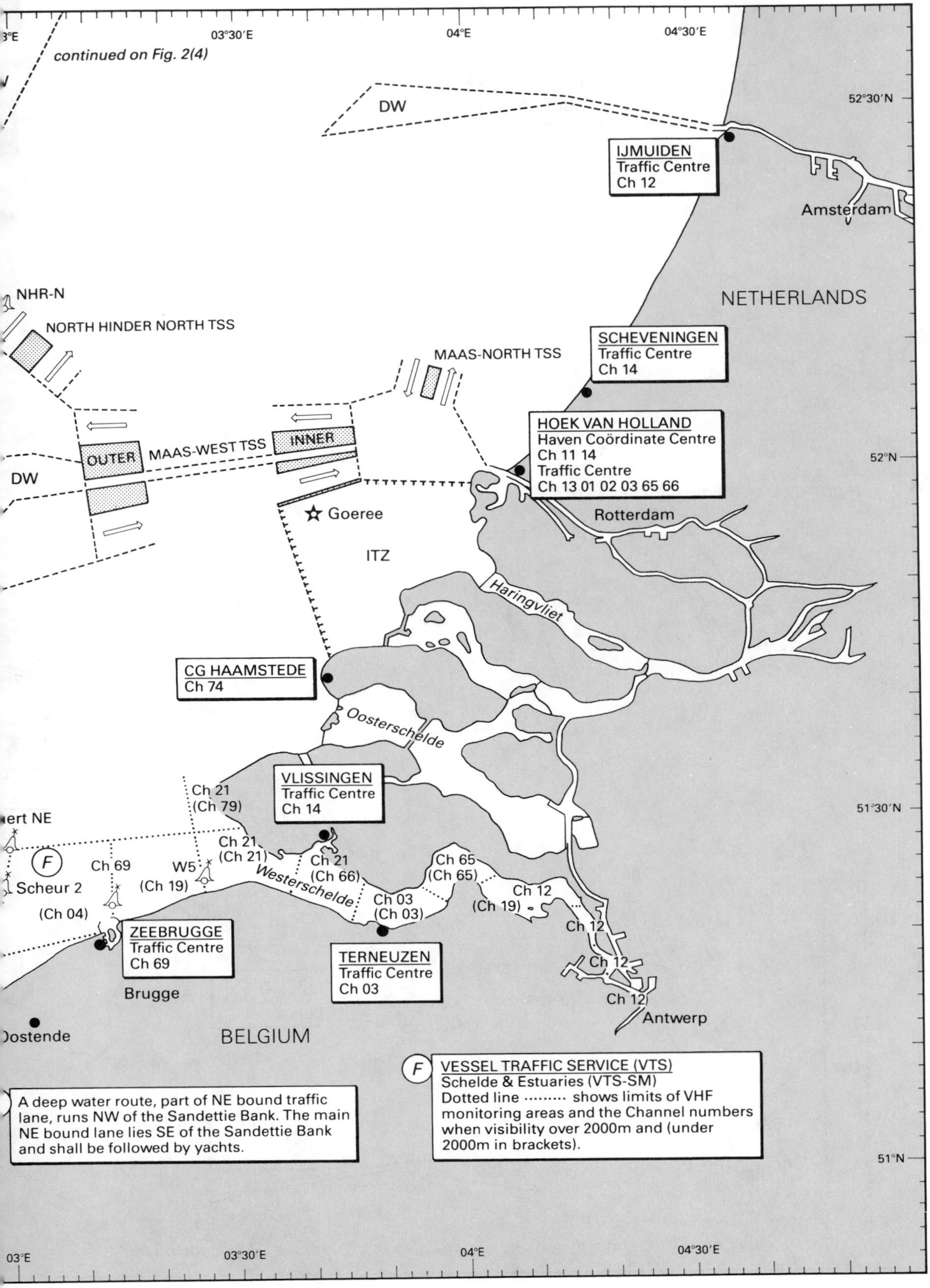
continued on Fig. 2(4)
03°30′E
04°E
04°30′E
52°30′N
DW
IJMUIDEN
Traffic Centre
Ch 12
Amsterdam
NETHERLANDS
NHR-N
NORTH HINDER NORTH TSS
MAAS-NORTH TSS
SCHEVENINGEN
Traffic Centre
Ch 14
HOEK VAN HOLLAND
Haven Coördinate Centre
Ch 11 14
Traffic Centre
Ch 13 01 02 03 65 66
52°N
OUTER
MAAS-WEST TSS
INNER
DW
Goeree
Rotterdam
ITZ
Haringvliet
CG HAAMSTEDE
Ch 74
Oosterschelde
VLISSINGEN
Traffic Centre
Ch 14
Ch 21
(Ch 79)
51°30′N
ert NE
Ch 21
(Ch 21)
F
Ch 69
W5
(Ch 19)
Ch 21
(Ch 66)
Ch 65
(Ch 65)
Westerschelde
Ch 03
(Ch 03)
Ch 12
(Ch 19)
Scheur 2
(Ch 04)
ZEEBRUGGE
Traffic Centre
Ch 69
TERNEUZEN
Traffic Centre
Ch 03
Ch 12
Ch 12
Ch 12
Antwerp
Brugge
Oostende
BELGIUM
F
VESSEL TRAFFIC SERVICE (VTS)
Schelde & Estuaries (VTS-SM)
Dotted line ········ shows limits of VHF monitoring areas and the Channel numbers when visibility over 2000m and (under 2000m in brackets).
A deep water route, part of NE bound traffic lane, runs NW of the Sandettie Bank. The main NE bound lane lies SE of the Sandettie Bank and shall be followed by yachts.
51°N
03°E
03°30′E
04°E
04°30′E

2

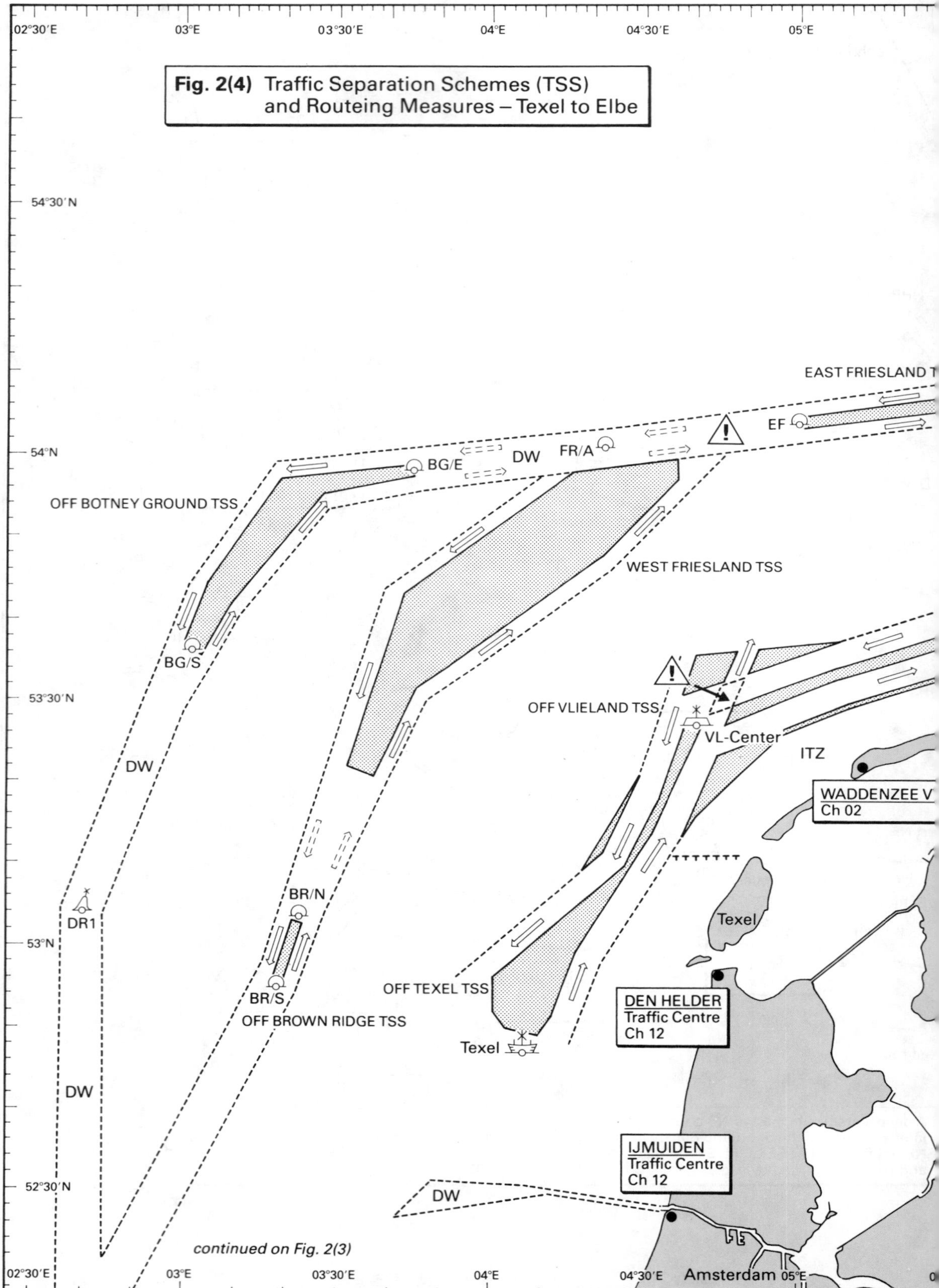

Fig. 2(4) Traffic Separation Schemes (TSS) and Routeing Measures – Texel to Elbe
02°30′E
03°E
03°30′E
04°E
04°30′E
05°E
54°30′N
54°N
53°30′N
53°N
52°30′N
EAST FRIESLAND T
EF
FR/A
DW
BG/E
OFF BOTNEY GROUND TSS
WEST FRIESLAND TSS
BG/S
OFF VLIELAND TSS
VL-Center
ITZ
WADDENZEE V
Ch 02
DR1
BR/N
BR/S
OFF BROWN RIDGE TSS
OFF TEXEL TSS
Texel
DEN HELDER
Traffic Centre
Ch 12
IJMUIDEN
Traffic Centre
Ch 12
Amsterdam

continued on Fig. 2(3)

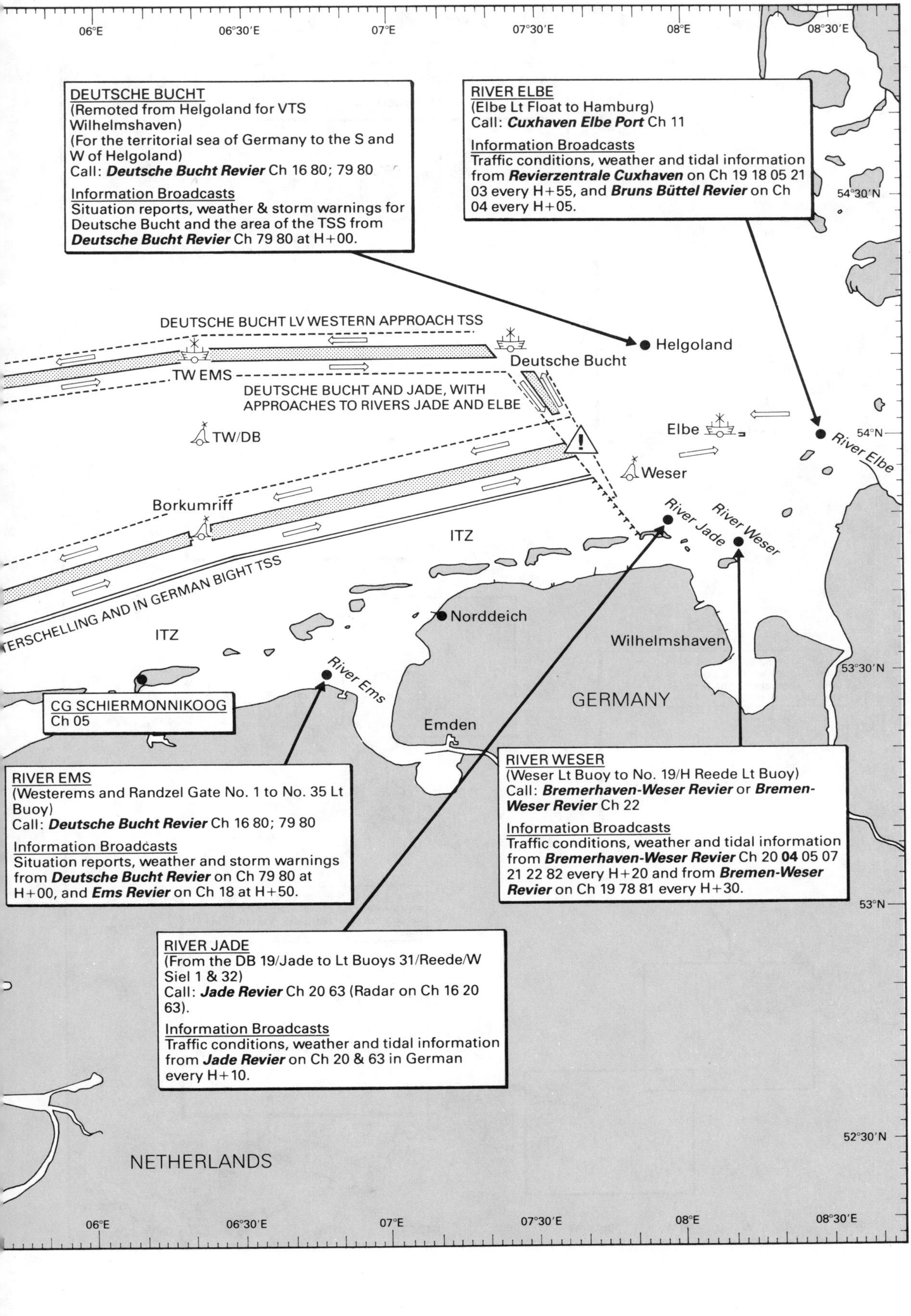
DEUTSCHE BUCHT
(Remoted from Helgoland for VTS Wilhelmshaven)
(For the territorial sea of Germany to the S and W of Helgoland)
Call: ***Deutsche Bucht Revier*** Ch 16 80; 79 80
Information Broadcasts
Situation reports, weather & storm warnings for Deutsche Bucht and the area of the TSS from ***Deutsche Bucht Revier*** Ch 79 80 at H+00.
RIVER ELBE
(Elbe Lt Float to Hamburg)
Call: ***Cuxhaven Elbe Port*** Ch 11
Information Broadcasts
Traffic conditions, weather and tidal information from ***Revierzentrale Cuxhaven*** on Ch 19 18 05 21 03 every H+55, and ***Bruns Büttel Revier*** on Ch 04 every H+05.
06°E
06°30′E
07°E
07°30′E
08°E
08°30′E
54°30′N
54°N
53°30′N
53°N
52°30′N
DEUTSCHE BUCHT LV WESTERN APPROACH TSS
Helgoland
Deutsche Bucht
TW EMS
DEUTSCHE BUCHT AND JADE, WITH APPROACHES TO RIVERS JADE AND ELBE
TW/DB
Elbe
Weser
River Elbe
Borkumriff
River Jade
River Weser
ITZ
ERSCHELLING AND IN GERMAN BIGHT TSS
ITZ
Norddeich
Wilhelmshaven
River Ems
GERMANY
CG SCHIERMONNIKOOG
Ch 05
Emden
RIVER EMS
(Westerems and Randzel Gate No. 1 to No. 35 Lt Buoy)
Call: ***Deutsche Bucht Revier*** Ch 16 80; 79 80
Information Broadcasts
Situation reports, weather and storm warnings from ***Deutsche Bucht Revier*** on Ch 79 80 at H+00, and ***Ems Revier*** on Ch 18 at H+50.
RIVER WESER
(Weser Lt Buoy to No. 19/H Reede Lt Buoy)
Call: ***Bremerhaven-Weser Revier*** or ***Bremen-Weser Revier*** Ch 22
Information Broadcasts
Traffic conditions, weather and tidal information from ***Bremerhaven-Weser Revier*** Ch 20 **04** 05 07 21 22 82 every H+20 and from ***Bremen-Weser Revier*** on Ch 19 78 81 every H+30.
RIVER JADE
(From the DB 19/Jade to Lt Buoys 31/Reede/W Siel 1 & 32)
Call: ***Jade Revier*** Ch 20 63 (Radar on Ch 16 20 63).
Information Broadcasts
Traffic conditions, weather and tidal information from ***Jade Revier*** on Ch 20 & 63 in German every H+10.
NETHERLANDS

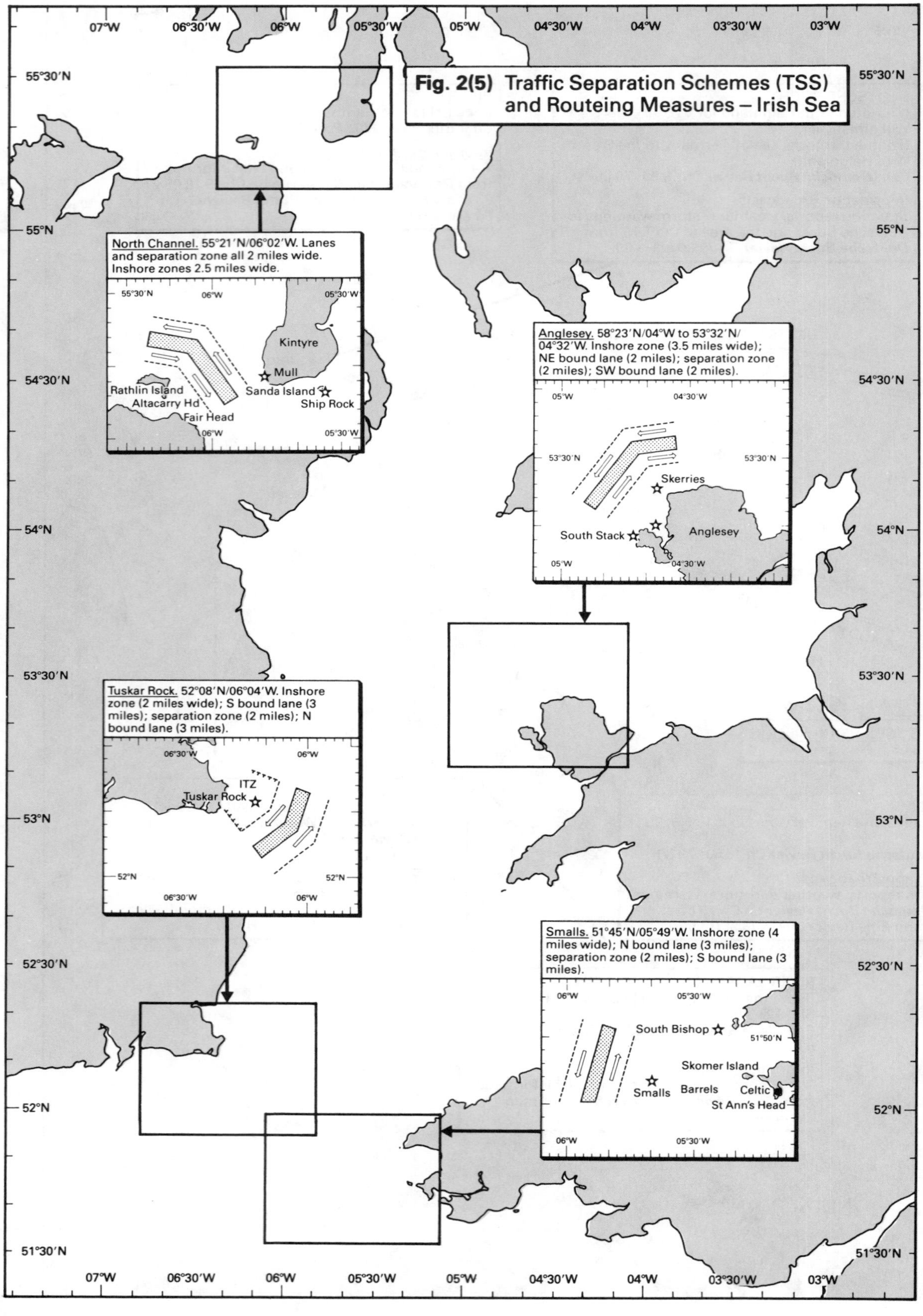
07°W
06°30'W
06°W
05°30'W
05°W
04°30'W
04°W
03°30'W
03°W
55°30'N
55°N
54°30'N
54°N
53°30'N
53°N
52°30'N
52°N
51°30'N
North Channel. 55°21'N/06°02'W. Lanes and separation zone all 2 miles wide. Inshore zones 2.5 miles wide.
Kintyre
Mull
Rathlin Island
Altacarry Hd
Fair Head
Sanda Island
Ship Rock
Anglesey. 58°23'N/04°W to 53°32'N/04°32'W. Inshore zone (3.5 miles wide); NE bound lane (2 miles); separation zone (2 miles); SW bound lane (2 miles).
Skerries
South Stack
Anglesey
Tuskar Rock. 52°08'N/06°04'W. Inshore zone (2 miles wide); S bound lane (3 miles); separation zone (2 miles); N bound lane (3 miles).
ITZ
Tuskar Rock
Smalls. 51°45'N/05°49'W. Inshore zone (4 miles wide); N bound lane (3 miles); separation zone (2 miles); S bound lane (3 miles).
South Bishop
51°50'N
Skomer Island
Smalls
Barrels
Celtic
St Ann's Head

Fig. 2(5) Traffic Separation Schemes (TSS) and Routeing Measures – Irish Sea

(a) A power-driven vessel underway keeps clear of:
 (i) a vessel not under command;
 (ii) a vessel restricted in manoeuvrability;
 (iii) a vessel engaged in fishing;
 (iv) a sailing vessel.

(b) A sailing vessel underway keeps clear of: (i), (ii) and (iii) in (a) above.

(c) A vessel engaged in fishing, underway, keeps clear of: (i) and (ii) in (a) above.

(d) (i) Any vessel, except one not under command or one not restricted in her ability to manoeuvre, shall if possible avoid impeding a vessel constrained by her draught, showing the signals prescribed in Rule 28 (see page 120).
 (ii) A vessel constrained by her draught shall navigate with particular caution.

2.1.4 Restricted visibility

In poor visibility vessels must proceed at a safe speed (Rule 19). On hearing a fog signal ahead of the beam, be prepared to reduce speed or stop. If a vessel is detected by radar, take early action to avoid collision: if the other vessel is ahead of the beam avoid altering course to port, unless the other vessel is being overtaken: if the other vessel is abaft the beam, do not alter course towards. Sound the appropriate fog signal; keep a good lookout; have an efficient radar reflector; keep clear of shipping lanes; and be ready to take avoiding action. In thick fog it is best to anchor in shallow water, out of the shipping channels.

2.1.5 Lights and shapes

The required lights must be shown from sunset to sunrise, and by day in restricted visibility. The required shapes must be shown by day (Rule 20). See Plate 4 on page 120.

The types of navigation light are defined in Rule 21, and are shown in Plate 1 on page 117, together with illustrations of the lights to be shown by power-driven vessels and sailing vessels underway. A summary of the lights and shapes to be shown by various classes of vessel is given in Plate 4 on page 120.

A yacht, even with sails set, which is under engine must show the lights of a power-driven vessel. By day, a boat which is motor-sailing must show a cone, point down, forward.

In a sailing yacht up to 20m in length, the sidelights and sternlight may be combined in one tricolour lantern at the masthead. This gives excellent visibility for the lights, and maximum brightness for minimum battery drain, but must not be used when under power.

A sailing vessel underway may, in addition to her normal sidelights and sternlight, show near the masthead two all-round lights in a vertical line, red over green. But these lights must not be shown in conjunction with the tricolour lantern described in the previous paragraph (Rule 25).

Lights required for vessels towing and being towed (Rule 24) include a special yellow towing light above the sternlight of the towing vessel. But this is not required by a yacht or other small craft not normally used for towing.

The rules for vessels not under command, or restricted in their ability to manoeuvre (Rule 27) do not apply to vessels under 12m in length, except for showing flag 'A' International Code when engaged in diving operations. See Plates 6–7 on pages 122 and 123.

A power-driven vessel under 12m in length may combine her masthead light and sternlight in one all-round white light (Rule 23).

A yacht less than 7m in length is not required to show an anchor light or ball when she is not anchored in or near a narrow channel, fairway or anchorage, or where other vessels normally navigate (Rule 30). A vessel under 12m in length is not required to show the lights or shapes prescribed by that rule when she is aground.

2

2.1.6 Distress signals

Distress signals are listed below. See Plates 6 and 7 on pages 122 and 123. Those applicable to yachts are described in more detail in Chapter 8 (8.1.4). A DISTRESS SIGNAL MUST ONLY BE USED WHEN A VESSEL OR PERSON IS IN SERIOUS AND IMMEDIATE DANGER AND URGENT HELP IS NEEDED. For lesser emergencies use 'V' International Code — 'I require assistance'. See 6.1.5 for other signals of an emergency nature.

1. The following, together or separately, indicate distress and need of help:

(a) a gun or other explosive signal fired at intervals of about a minute;

(b) a continuous sounding with any fog-signalling apparatus;

(c) rockets or shells, throwing red stars fired one at a time at short intervals;

(d) a signal made by radiotelegraphy or by any other signalling method consisting of the group ··· ——— ··· (SOS) in the Morse Code;

(e) a signal sent by radiotelephony consisting of the spoken word 'Mayday';

(f) the International Code Signal of distress indicated by N.C.; see Plate 6 and 7 on pages 122 and 123;

(g) a signal consisting of a square flag having above or below it a ball or anything resembling a ball;

(h) flames on the vessel (as from a burning tar barrel, oil barrel, etc.);

(i) a rocket parachute flare or a hand flare showing a red light;

(j) a smoke signal giving off orange-coloured smoke;
(k) slowly and repeatedly raising and lowering arms outstretched to each side;
(l) the radiotelegraph alarm signal;
(m) the radiotelephone alarm signal;
(n) signals transmitted by emergency position-indicating radio beacons.

2. The use or exhibition of any of the foregoing signals except for the purpose of indicating distress and need of assistance and the use of other signals which may be confused with any of the above signals is prohibited.
3. Attention is drawn to the relevant sections of the *International Code of Signals*, the *Merchant Ship Search and Rescue Manual* and the following signals:

(a) a piece of orange-coloured canvas with either a black square and circle or other appropriate symbol (for identification from the air);
(b) a dye marker.

2.1.7 Sound signals

Sound signals required (by Rules 34 and 35) are summarised in the table below. Vessels over 12m in length must be provided with a whistle (foghorn) and a bell. A boat under 12m is not obliged to carry these sound signalling appliances, but must have some means of making an efficient sound signal. The effectiveness of a yacht's sound signal should be judged against its audibility from the bridge of a large ship, with conflicting noises from other sources.

Note that a short blast is about one second, and a prolonged blast four to six seconds in duration. A sailing vessel underway in fog sounds one prolonged blast, followed by two short blasts ('D'). The maximum intervals between sound signals for vessels underway in restricted visibility is two minutes, but they should be sounded more frequently if other craft are near.

Summary of important sound signals — Rules 34 and 35

Note: • indicates a short blast of foghorn, of about one second's duration.
— indicates a prolonged blast of foghorn, of four to six seconds' duration.

Vessels in sight of each other (Rule 34)

•	I am altering course to starboard (power-driven vessel)
••	I am altering course to port (power-driven vessel)
•••	I am operating astern propulsion (power-driven vessel)
——•	(In a narrow channel) I intend to overtake you on your starboard side
——••	(In a narrow channel) I intend to overtake you on your port side
—•—•	Agreement with the overtaking signal above
•••••	I fail to understand your intentions or actions/I doubt if you are taking sufficient action to avoid collision
—	Warning signal by vessel(s) approaching a bend in channel

Sound signals in restricted visibility (Rule 35)

—	Power-driven vessel making way through the water
——	Power-driven vessel under way, but stopped and not making way through the water
—••	Vessel not under command, or restricted in her ability to manoeuvre, or constrained by her draught, or engaged in fishing, or towing or pushing, or a sailing vessel
—•••	Vessel being towed, or if more than one vessel is towed the last vessel in the tow
••••	Pilot vessel engaged on pilotage duties
Bell rung rapidly for about 5 seconds, every minute	Vessel at anchor
Gong rung rapidly for about 5 seconds following above signal, every minute	Vessel of 100 metres or more in length at anchor: the bell being sounded in the fore part of the vessel and the gong aft
•—•	Vessel at anchor (optional additional signal)
Bell rung rapidly for about 5 seconds, with three separate and distinct strokes before and after	Vessel aground

2.2.1 Conversion factors

To convert	*Multiply by*	*To convert*	*Multiply by*
sq in to sq mm	645.16	sq mm to sq in	0.00155
sq ft to sq m	0.0929	sq m to sq ft	10.76
lb/hp/hr to gram/hp/hr	447.4	gram/hp/hr to lb/hp/hr	0.0022
in to mm	25.40	mm to in	0.0394
ft to m	0.3048	m to ft	3.2808
fathoms to m	1.8288	m to fathoms	0.5468
naut miles to statute	1.1515	statute miles to naut	0.8684
lbf to N	4.4482	N to lbf	0.2248
kgf to N	9.8066	N to kgf	0.101972
lb to kg	0.4536	kg to lb	2.205
tons to tonnes (1000 kg)	1.016	tonnes to tons (2240 lb)	0.9842
horsepower to kW	0.7457	kW to hp	1.341
hp to metric hp	1.014	metric hp to hp	0.9862
metric hp to kW	0.735	kW to metric hp	1.359
lb/sq in to kg/sq cm	0.0703	kg/sq cm to lb/sq in	14.22
lb/sq in to ft of water	2.31	ft of water to lb/sq in	0.433
lb/sq in to atmospheres	0.0680	atmospheres to lb/sq in	14.7
ft/sec to m/sec	0.3048	m/sec to ft/sec	3.281
ft/sec to miles/hr	0.682	miles/hr to ft/sec	1.467
ft/min to m/sec	0.0051	m/sec to ft/min	196.8
knots to miles/hr	1.1515	miles/hr to knots	0.868
knots to km/hr	1.8520	km/hr to knots	0.5400
lbf ft to Nm	1.3558	Nm to lbf ft	0.7376
kgf m to Nm	9.8066	Nm to kgf m	0.1020
lbf ft to kgf m	0.1383	kgf m to lbf ft	7.2330
cu ft to galls	6.25	galls to cu ft	0.16
cu ft to litres	28.33	litres to cu ft	0.035
pints to litres	0.568	litres to pints	1.76
galls to litres	4.546	litres to galls	0.22
Imp galls to US galls	1.2	US galls to Imp galls	0.833

2

2.2.2 Feet to metres, metres to feet

Explanation: The central columns of figures in bold type can be referred in either direction. To the left to convert metres into feet, or to the right to convert feet into metres. For example, five lines down: 5 feet = 1·52 metres, and 5 metres = 16·40 feet.

Feet		*Metres*	*Feet*		*Metres*	*Feet*		*Metres*	*Feet*		*Metres*
3.28	**1**	0.30	45.93	**14**	4.27	88.58	**27**	8.23	131.23	**40**	12.19
6.56	**2**	0.61	49.21	**15**	4.57	91.86	**28**	8.53	134.51	**41**	12.50
9.84	**3**	0.91	52.49	**16**	4.88	95.14	**29**	8.84	137.80	**42**	12.80
13.12	**4**	1.22	55.77	**17**	5.18	98.43	**30**	9.14	141.08	**43**	13.11
16.40	**5**	1.52	59.06	**18**	5.49	101.71	**31**	9.45	144.36	**44**	13.41
19.69	**6**	1.83	62.34	**19**	5.79	104.99	**32**	9.75	147.64	**45**	13.72
22.97	**7**	2.13	65.62	**20**	6.10	108.27	**33**	10.06	150.92	**46**	14.02
26.25	**8**	2.44	68.90	**21**	6.40	111.55	**34**	10.36	154.20	**47**	14.33
29.53	**9**	2.74	72.18	**22**	6.71	114.83	**35**	10.67	157.48	**48**	14.63
32.81	**10**	3.05	75.46	**23**	7.01	118.11	**36**	10.97	160.76	**49**	14.94
36.09	**11**	3.55	78.74	**24**	7.32	121.39	**37**	11.28	164.04	**50**	15.24
39.37	**12**	3.66	82.02	**25**	7.62	124.67	**38**	11.58			
42.65	**13**	3.96	85.30	**26**	7.92	127.95	**39**	11.89			

2.3 DOCUMENTATION

2.3.1 Registration

Two forms of registration are available for British owned yachts. Both are described more fully in section 1.5 of *The Macmillan & Silk Cut Yachtsman's Handbook.*

Full registration, under the Merchant Shipping Act of 1894, is a relatively complex and expensive business since a yacht has to follow the same procedure as a large merchant vessel. It does however have the advantage of establishing title (ownership), and is also required for recording a marine mortgage. The procedure is described in Customs Notice No. 382, obtainable from any Registrar of British Ships, who can normally be located at the Custom House in major ports.

The Small Ships Register, established in 1983, is sufficient for most purposes. It satisfies the law that a British yacht proceeding abroad must be registered, and it also meets the registration requirement for a privileged ensign. The cost is only £10 for a five year period, and measurement is a simple matter of taking the overall length of the boat — well described in the instructions which accompany the application form, obtainable from the Royal Yachting Association, RYA House, Romsey Road, Eastleigh, Hants SO5 4YA.

2.3.2 International Certificate for Pleasure Navigation

With the introduction of the Small Ships Register, this certificate has no relevance for yachts owned by UK or Commonwealth citizens resident in the UK. It is however available for other persons.

2.3.3 Helmsman's (Overseas) Certificate of Competence

Some countries require a skipper to have a certificate of competence. If a suitable RYA Certificate (e.g. Yachtmaster Offshore) is not held, the above certificate can be issued by the RYA to UK residents on receipt of the appropriate application form, endorsed by the secretary or flag officer of an RYA club or the principal of an RYA recognised teaching establishment.

2.3.4 Licences

A licence is required to operate a boat on most inland waterways (e.g. the River Thames above Teddington Lock, the Norfolk Broads, Yorkshire Ouse above Naburn Lock, and canals or rivers controlled by the British Waterways Board).

2.3.5 Insurance

Any cruising boat represents a large capital investment, which should be protected against possible loss or damage by adequate insurance. It is also essential to insure against third-party risks, and cover for at least £500,000 is recommended.

The value for which a boat is insured should be the replacement cost of the boat and all equipment. Read the proposal form carefully, and fill in the details required as accurately as possible. Take care to abide by the nominated period in commission and cruising area. Note the various warranties which are implied or expressed in the policy. For example, the owner is required to keep the boat in good, seaworthy condition; insurance does not cover charter, unless specially arranged; prompt notice must be given of any claim; a reduction may be made for fair wear and tear for items such as outboards, sails and rigging; theft is only covered if forcible entry or removal can be shown; engines and other mechanical items are only covered in exceptional circumstances; personal effects are not covered, unless specially arranged; and motor boats with speeds of 17 knots or more are subject to special clauses and often to extra premiums.

2.3.6 Classification

Lloyd's Register of Shipping provides an advisory and consultancy service to owners, builders, moulders and designers, and publishes rules for the construction of yachts in various materials. Experienced surveyors approve drawings, supervise moulding, inspect fitting out, check the machinery, and certify the completed yacht. To remain 'in class' a yacht must be subjected to periodical surveys.

As an alternative to full classification, Lloyd's Register Building Certificate is provided to newly-built yachts which have been constructed of any approved material in accordance with the Society's rules, and under the supervision of its surveyors, without the requirement for periodical survey.

2.3.7 Cruising formalities

Before, or while cruising abroad, certain formalities are necessary, as summarised below:

(1) Conform to HM Customs regulations, see 2.4.

(2) The yacht must be registered, see 2.3.1.

(3) Take valid passports for all the crew, and conform to health regulations (e.g. by reporting any infectious disease): exceptionally vaccination certificates may be needed.

(4) Conform to Customs regulations in countries visited. Brief notes are given in section 2.5, but if in doubt about specific items or procedures, ask. All countries are sensitive to the importation (including carriage on board) of illegal quantities of alcohol and tobacco, and drugs of any kind.

(5) Make sure the yacht is covered by insurance for the intended cruising area, including third party cover.

(6) It is wise for the skipper to carry a Certificate of Competence or similar document (e.g. Yachtmaster Certificate).
(7) The yacht should wear the Red Ensign (or a Special Ensign, if so authorised), and fly a courtesy ensign of the country concerned at starboard crosstree. Flag 'Q' must be carried to comply with Customs procedures.
(8) In most countries it is illegal to use a visiting cruising yacht for any commercial purpose (e.g. charter).

2.4 HM CUSTOMS

2.4.1 General information

Yachts arriving in or departing from the UK from or to places abroad must conform to the regulations in Customs Notice No. 8 summarised below. This Notice, the forms mentioned, and further information may be obtained from any Customs and Excise office or from HM Customs and Excise, CDE 1, Dorset House, Stamford Street, London SE1 9PS (Tel: 071-865 4743). Foreign yachts are subject to Customs Notice No. 8A.

Yachtsmen are warned that a boat may be searched at any time. The commonest offences, which may result in fining, are failure to clear outwards and inwards, including not hoisting Flag 'Q' on arrival. Non-declaration of excess, prohibited or restricted goods will be dealt with more seriously; whilst carriage and non-declaration of prohibited drugs or firearms will incur the forfeiture of the boat and all its equipment. It is clearly in the yachtsman's interests to have an up to date copy of Customs Notice No. 8 aboard.

2.4.2 Notice of departure

Each intended departure from the UK must be notified to HM Customs on Part I of Form C1328, copies of which are available at Customs offices and from most yacht clubs etc. The form is in three parts. When completed Part I should be delivered to the Customs office nearest the place of departure, so as to arrive before departure or put in a Customs post box. It is valid for up to 48 hours after the stated time of departure. Should the voyage be abandoned, Parts II and III should be delivered to the same office marked 'voyage abandoned'. Failure to give notice of departure may result in delay and inconvenience on return, and possible prosecution.

2.4.3 Stores

In general there is no restriction on reasonable quantities of food, fuel and other stores on which all duties and VAT have been paid. Duty-free stores may be allowed on vessels proceeding south of Brest or north of the Eider — details may be obtained from any Customs office.

2.4.4 Immigration

The skipper must inform a Customs Officer if there is any person on board who is not a national of the European Community (EC) and who is arriving in the UK from anywhere other than the Channel Is, Republic of Ireland and the Isle of Man.

2.4.5 Arrivals

On arrival from abroad (including the Channel Is and the Republic of Ireland) yachts are subject to Customs control. As soon as UK Territorial Waters are entered, i.e., the 12-mile limit, complete Form C1328 (C1329 for foreign yachts) and fly Flag 'Q' where it can easily be seen (illuminated at night) until formalities are complete. The signal 'OQ' means 'I require health clearance'.

2

2.4.6 Full report

The full report procedure is applicable if duty and/or VAT is payable on the vessel; or if the vessel has goods on which duty and/or VAT is payable; or has had repairs/modifications done abroad; or has on board any animal or bird, or goods which are prohibited or restricted; or non-EC nationals without entry permit (except from Channel Islands or Ireland); or the vessel left UK more than one year previously; or was not cleared outwards on Part I of form C1328, notifying the nearest Customs office by telephone or RT and awaiting the arrival of a Customs Officer; or has any death or notifiable illness on board. Under the above circumstances the skipper must make a full report by completing Parts II and III of Form C1328 and awaiting the arrival of a Customs Officer.

2.4.7 Report with Nothing To Declare

When none of the conditions in the previous paragraph apply, and animal and health clearance is not required, the skipper is to complete Parts II and III of Form C1328. If the yacht is not visited by a Customs Officer, deliver Part II to the Customs office concerned (or post it in a Customs post box) and retain Part III for reference. The crew may then proceed ashore. This procedure is not available to foreign yachts.

2.4.8 Customs offices — telephone numbers

The telephone number of the appropriate Customs office (HMC) is given under the heading 'Telephone' for each British harbour in Chapter 10.

2.5 FOREIGN CUSTOMS PROCEDURES

2.5.1 General

It is the skipper's responsibility to find out and to observe the Customs formalities which vary from country to country. In some cases it is obligatory to fly flag 'Q' on arrival, but in others only when carrying dutiable stores above the normal 'tourist' allowances. It is useful to have duplicated lists of those people on board, with their passport numbers.

2.5.2 Irish Republic

It is preferable for yachts to clear Customs at a harbour where there are Customs facilities – Dublin, Dun Laoghaire, Dunmore East, Waterford, New Ross, Dungarvan, Cobh, Cork, Kinsale, Baltimore (summer only), Crookhaven, Bantry, Castletownbere, Cahirciveen, Fenit, Kilrush, Foynes, Limerick, Galway, Westport, Sligo or Killybegs. But yachts may arrive at any port, and if the correct procedure is followed may report to the Civil Guard if there is no Customs officer present.

On arrival therefore, all yachts from abroad (whether carrying dutiable stores or not) must fly flag 'Q' by day, or show a red light over a white light by night, and report to the local Customs (or Civil Guard). Dutiable, prohibited or restricted goods must be declared. United Kingdom citizens do not require passports or visas.

2.5.3 France

Provided that a boat which is on a temporary visit from Great Britain, Northern Ireland or the Channel Islands is only carrying effects of the crew, authorised goods intended for personal use which are within duty-free allowances (and not for commercial purposes) and foreign currency which does not exceed 5000 French francs, there are no Customs formalities on arriving in French waters.

If, for whatever reason, it is required to clear Customs, a yacht should berth in a port which has Customs facilities (*Douanes*), and must fly flag 'Q' by day, or show a red light over a white light by night. It is a requirement that a boat is registered, either under the full registration procedure or on the Small Ships Register (see 2.3.1), or equivalent documentation for the Channel Islands.

A private owner taking his yacht to France qualifies for six months *Importation en Franchise Temporaire* (IFT), with no duty payable. To qualify for IFT the yacht should normally be skippered by the owner: while in France the boat must not be chartered, or even lent to somebody else, and the owner and crew must not pursue any paid activity. There should not be a change of skipper. Nor should the crew contribute to running expenses, which might be construed by the authorities as a charter operation.

The six month period may be unbroken, or it may be split into two or more visits within one year. After that, the boat becomes liable to TVA (French VAT) and to an annual tax called *Droit de Passeport.* Details should be obtained from the French Customs. Special regulations apply to yachts chartered from outside France, and to yacht deliveries in and out of the country.

2.5.4 Belgium

Foreign yachts are temporarily admitted duty-free, and there are no arduous formalities unless a stay of more than two months is contemplated, in which case it is necessary to apply for a *plaque d'immatriculation.*

In normal circumstances, fly flag 'Q' at the port of entry, where the yacht will be boarded by Customs officers (in light blue uniform) and possibly by marine police (in blue uniform) for immigration control.

2.5.5 Netherlands

On arrival the skipper must report to Customs with documentation of the yacht and the passports of the crew, to obtain an entry certificate which is then valid for 12 months. Flag 'Q' need only be flown if dutiable stores are carried. Yachts are expected to carry, and to obey, the *Binnenvaart Politie Reglement* contained in part 1 of the Almanaak voor Watertoerisme (collision regulations etc.), and also, where applicable, the special regulations which apply to the Rivers Rhine, Lek and Waal. It is possible that on these rivers and other inland waterways a Certificate of Competence or equivalent documentation may have to be produced.

2.5.6 Federal Republic of Germany

On arrival it is necessary to clear Customs at one of the main ports of entry — Borkum, Norderney, Norddeich, Wilhelmshaven, Bremerhaven or Cuxhaven. It is not possible to clear Customs at Heligoland. Yachts arriving from EC or Scandinavian harbours need not fly flag 'Q'. If the yacht is not boarded by Customs officers, go ashore and report to the Customs office (*Zoll*).

There are special arrangements for yachts arriving in the Elbe and which only intend to transit the Kiel Canal: they are not required to clear Customs, but should fly the Third Substitute flag. Special regulations governing the canal and giving details of signals etc are available at the locks.

It is probable that a Certificate of Competence or equivalent document will have to be produced for navigation on the rivers and inland waterways.

BOAT MART INTERNATIONAL

TAKE OUT A SUBSCRIPTION NOW! FOR YOU OR YOUR FRIENDS

FOR ONLY £14.40* YOU CAN HAVE YOUR COPIES POSTED PROMPTLY TO YOUR HOME

*12 ISSUES/1 YEAR

BOAT MART
API
FLETCHER 210
Sports cruiser for the 90s
RYA COURSES —
A practical experience
TEPCO
Built to last
Fitting and maintaining
SAFE AN
PREVE
QUIET
AVOID

- ★ BOAT TESTS
- ★ NEW PRODUCT REVIEWS
- ★ SPECIALIST FEATURES
- ★ REGIONAL REPORTS
- ★ BOAT SHOW PREVIEWS
- ★ 40 PAGES OF INFORMATIVE EDITORIAL
- ★ MARINE MARKETPLACE FOR SERVICES AND ACCESSORIES

Please send me my copy of the magazine each month.
I enclose my remittance of £14.40 to commence Month . . . .

NAME: ______________________ TELEPHONE: ______________________

ADDRESS: ____

____ POST CODE: __________

PAYMENT BY:

☐ CHEQUE ☐ POSTAL ORDER

OR

DEBIT MY ACCESS/VISA ACCOUNT NO:

EXPIRY DATE: __________

Please make Cheques/Postal Orders payable to *Boat Mart International*

SEND WITH REMITTANCE TO: BOAT MART INTERNATIONAL (SUBSCRIPTIONS)
89 EAST HILL, COLCHESTER, ESSEX CO1 2QN (0255) 676815

RABIES PREVENTION

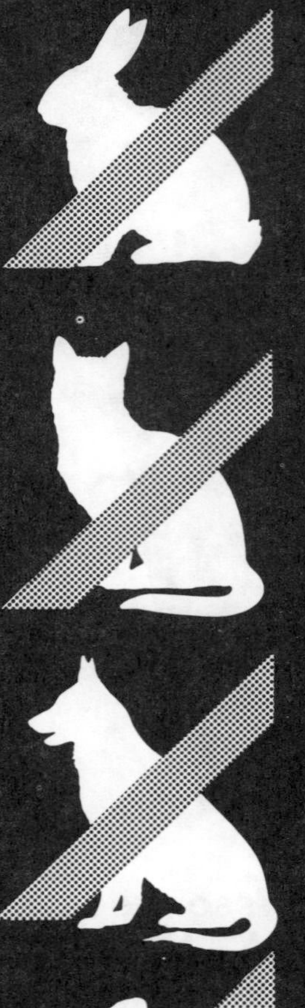

NEVER SAIL ABROAD WITH ANIMALS ON BOARD

Sailing overseas? If you're travelling to any place outside territorial waters, always leave pets at home and never bring back any animals. The reason, in a word, is rabies.

A horrifying disease, rabies is invariably fatal in humans, once symptoms develop. It is usually caused by the bite of a pet that has been infected by a wild or stray animal. With the sea as a natural barrier, Britain has been free of the disease for over 60 years. But this situation can only be maintained by the observance of strict animal import and quarantine controls. In other words, the care and common-sense of us all.

Any animal shipped overseas is automatically liable to quarantine regulations, whether or not it has stepped ashore. So you should consider, before deciding to take pets abroad, the expense and separation of six-months quarantine on return.

Moreover, the penalties for evading regulations are severe. So-called 'pet-lovers' attempting to break the rules face an unlimited fine or up to a year's imprisonment. In addition, the animal may be destroyed, and at best will have to undergo the full six-months quarantine.

Just one infected animal would endanger humans and animals throughout Britain.

IT'S JUST NOT WORTH THE RISK.

MAFF Ministry of Agriculture Fisheries and Food

Contents

Coastal Navigation

Chapter 3

Coastal navigation — introduction

The following subjects are described in detail in Chapter 3 of *The Macmillan & Silk Cut Yachtsman's Handbook*:

> *The terms and definitions used in coastal navigation; magnetic variation and deviation; compass checks; compass adjusting and compass swinging; charts and their symbols; lights and fog signals; methods of laying off courses and position fixing; time, speed and distance; measured mile table; pilotage; IALA buoyage system; passage planning; the use of calculators; practical passage making; sailing directions.*

Here in the Almanac is provided basic information, in the form of tables and other data, needed for coastal navigation. Some brief descriptions on how to use the tables etc are included, but for a fuller explanation of these matters or of the subjects listed above, reference should be made to Chapter 3 of *The Macmillan & Silk Cut Yachtsman's Handbook.*

3.1.1 Compass variation and deviation

The compass is the most vital navigational instrument in a cruising boat. It is affected by variation (the amount magnetic North is displaced from True North, and which varies from place to place) and by deviation (caused by the boat's local magnetic field). Variation, which alters slightly from year to year, is shown on the chart — normally at the compass rose. Deviation varies according to the boat's heading: it should be shown, for different headings, on a deviation card — produced as a result of adjusting and swinging the compass. With a properly adjusted compass, deviation should not be more than about 2° on any heading — in which case it can often be ignored except on long passages.

When converting a True course or a True bearing to Magnetic: add Westerly variation or deviation and subtract Easterly.

When converting a Magnetic course or bearing to True: subtract Westerly variation or deviation, and add Easterly.

Bearings given on charts and in Sailing Directions are normally True bearings, from seaward.

3.1.2 Tables — explanations

The tables listed below are given on pages 27–34. Here are brief explanations of their use. For greater detail see Chapter 3 of *The Macmillan & Silk Cut Yachtsman's Handbook.*

Table 3(1) — True bearing of Sun at sunrise and sunset

Enter with approximate latitude and with declination (extracted from the ephemeris in Chapter 5). The tabulated figure is the True bearing, measured from North if declination is North or from South if declination is South, towards the East if rising or towards the West if setting. Having extracted the True bearing, apply variation before comparing with compass to determine deviation on course steered. The bearing of the Sun should be taken when its lower limb is a little over half a diameter above the horizon.

Table 3(2) — Distance off by Vertical Sextant Angle

Enter with the height of the body (in metres or feet) and read across the page until the required sextant angle (corrected for index error) is met. Take out the distance of the object (in nautical miles) at the head of the column. Caution is needed when the base of the object (e.g. a lighthouse) is below the horizon. For precise ranges the distance that sea level is below MHWS must be added to the height of the object (above MHWS) before entering the table.

Table 3(3) — Distance of horizon for various heights of eye

Enter with height of eye (in metres or feet), and extract distance of horizon (in Ms). The actual distance may be affected by abnormal refraction.

Table 3(4) — Lights — distance off when rising or dipping

This table combines selected heights of eye with selected heights of lights, to give the range at which a light dips below or rises above the horizon.

Table 3(5) — Time, speed and distance table

Enter with time (in decimals of an hour, or in minutes) and speed (in knots) to determine distance run (in Ms).

Table 3(6) — Measured mile table

Enter with time (in minutes at the head of columns, and in seconds down the side of the table) to extract speed (in knots).

3.1.3 Navigation by electronic calculator

Speed, time and distance

$$\text{Speed (in knots)} = \frac{\text{Distance (Ms)} \times 60}{\text{Time (mins)}}$$

$$\text{Time (in mins)} = \frac{\text{Distance (Ms)} \times 60}{\text{Speed (knots)}}$$

$$\text{Distance (in M)} = \frac{\text{Speed (knots)} \times \text{Time (mins)}}{60}$$

Distances and speed

Distance of horizon (in Ms) =

$$1.144 \times \sqrt{\text{Ht of eye}} \text{ (in ft)}$$

or

$$2.072 \times \sqrt{\text{Ht of eye}} \text{ (in m)}$$

Distance a light is visible (in Ms)=

$$1.144 \times (\sqrt{h_o} + \sqrt{h_e})$$

where h_o and h_e are heights of light and eye (ft)

or $= 2.072 \times (\sqrt{h_o} + \sqrt{h_e})$

where heights are in metres.

Distance of mountains etc beyond horizon, in Ms = $\sqrt{1.13(h_o - h_e) + (a - .972 \times \sqrt{h_e})^2} - (a - .972 \times \sqrt{h_e})$ where h_o is height of mountain (ft), h_e is height of eye (ft), and a is the sextant angle in minutes; or = $\sqrt{3.71(h_o - h_e) + (a - 1.76 \times \sqrt{h_e})^2} - (a - 1.76 \times \sqrt{h_e})$ where the heights are in metres.

(Continued on page 35)

TABLE 3(1) True bearing of sun at sunrise and sunset.

LAT	DECLINATION 0°	1°	2°	3°	4°	5°	6°	7°	8°	9°	10°	11°	LAT
	°	°	°	°	°	°	°	°	°	°	°	°	
30°	90	88.8	87.7	86.5	85.4	84.2	83.1	81.9	80.7	79.6	78.4	77.3	30°
31°	90	88.8	87.7	86.5	85.3	84.2	83.0	81.9	80.6	79.5	78.3	77.1	31°
32°	90	88.8	87.6	86.5	85.3	84.1	82.9	81.7	80.5	79.4	78.2	77.0	32°
33°	90	88.8	87.6	86.4	85.2	84.0	82.8	81.6	80.4	79.2	78.0	76.8	33°
34°	90	88.8	87.6	86.4	85.2	84.0	82.7	81.5	80.3	79.1	77.9	76.7	34°
35°	90	88.8	87.5	86.3	85.1	83.9	82.7	81.4	80.2	79.0	77.8	76.5	35°
36°	90	88.8	87.5	86.3	85.0	83.8	82.6	81.3	80.1	78.8	77.6	76.3	36°
37°	90	88.7	87.5	86.2	85.0	83.7	82.5	81.2	80.0	78.7	77.4	76.2	37°
38°	90	88.7	87.5	86.2	84.9	83.6	82.4	81.1	79.8	78.5	77.3	76.0	38°
39°	90	88.7	87.4	86.1	84.8	83.6	82.3	81.0	79.7	78.4	77.1	75.8	39°
40°	90	88.7	87.4	86.1	84.8	83.5	82.1	80.8	79.5	78.2	76.9	75.6	40°
41°	90	88.7	87.3	86.0	84.7	83.4	82.0	80.7	79.4	78.0	76.7	75.3	41°
42°	90	88.6	87.3	86.0	84.6	83.3	81.9	80.6	79.2	77.8	76.5	75.1	42°
43°	90	88.6	87.3	85.9	84.5	83.1	81.8	80.4	79.0	77.6	76.3	74.9	43°
44°	90	88.6	87.2	85.8	84.4	83.0	81.6	80.2	78.8	77.4	76.0	74.6	44°
45°	90	88.6	87.2	85.7	84.3	82.9	81.5	80.1	78.6	77.2	75.8	74.3	45°
46°	90	88.6	87.1	85.7	84.2	82.8	81.3	79.9	78.4	77.0	75.5	74.0	46°
47°	90	88.5	87.1	85.6	84.1	82.6	81.2	79.7	78.2	76.7	75.2	73.7	47°
48°	90	88.5	87.0	85.5	84.0	82.5	81.0	79.5	78.0	76.5	75.0	73.4	48°
49°	90	88.5	86.9	85.4	83.9	82.4	80.8	79.3	77.7	76.2	74.6	73.1	49°
50°	90	88.4	86.9	85.3	83.8	82.2	80.6	79.1	77.5	75.9	74.3	72.7	50°
51°	90	88.4	86.8	85.2	83.6	82.0	80.4	78.8	77.2	75.6	74.0	72.4	51°
52°	90	88.4	86.7	85.1	83.5	81.9	80.2	78.6	76.9	75.3	73.6	71.9	52°
53°	90	88.3	86.7	85.0	83.3	81.7	80.0	78.3	76.6	74.9	73.2	71.5	53°
54°	90	88.3	86.6	84.9	83.2	81.5	79.8	78.0	76.3	74.6	72.8	71.1	54°
55°	90	88.2	86.5	84.8	83.0	81.3	79.5	77.7	76.0	74.2	72.4	70.6	55°
56°	90	88.2	86.4	84.6	82.8	81.0	79.2	77.4	75.6	73.8	71.9	70.0	56°
57°	90	88.2	86.3	84.5	82.6	80.8	78.9	77.0	75.2	73.3	71.4	69.5	57°
58°	90	88.1	86.2	84.3	82.4	80.5	78.6	76.7	74.8	72.8	70.9	68.9	58°
59°	90	88.1	86.1	84.2	82.2	80.3	78.3	76.3	74.3	72.3	70.3	68.3	59°
60°	90	88.0	86.0	84.0	82.0	80.0	77.9	75.9	73.8	71.8	69.7	67.6	60°

LAT	DECLINATION 12°	13°	14°	15°	16°	17°	18°	19°	20°	21°	22°	23°	LAT
	°	°	°	°	°	°	°	°	°	°	°	°	
30°	76.1	74.9	73.8	72.6	71.4	70.3	69.1	67.9	66.7	65.5	64.4	63.2	30°
31°	76.0	74.8	73.6	72.4	71.2	70.0	68.9	67.7	66.5	65.3	64.1	62.9	31°
32°	75.8	74.6	73.4	72.2	71.0	69.8	68.6	67.4	66.2	65.0	63.8	62.6	32°
33°	75.6	74.4	73.2	72.1	70.8	69.6	68.4	67.1	65.9	64.7	63.5	62.2	33°
34°	75.5	74.2	73.0	71.8	70.6	69.3	68.1	66.9	65.6	64.4	63.1	61.9	34°
35°	75.3	74.1	72.8	71.6	70.3	69.1	67.8	66.6	65.3	64.1	62.8	61.5	35°
36°	75.1	73.8	72.6	71.3	70.1	68.8	67.5	66.3	65.0	63.7	62.4	61.1	36°
37°	74.9	73.6	72.4	71.1	69.8	68.5	67.2	65.9	64.6	63.3	62.0	60.7	37°
38°	74.7	73.4	72.0	70.8	69.5	68.2	66.9	65.6	64.3	62.9	61.6	60.3	38°
39°	74.5	73.2	71.9	70.5	69.2	67.9	66.6	65.2	63.9	62.5	61.2	59.8	39°
40°	74.2	72.9	71.6	70.2	68.9	67.6	66.2	64.8	63.5	62.1	60.7	59.3	40°
41°	74.0	72.7	71.3	69.9	68.6	67.2	65.8	64.4	63.0	61.6	60.2	58.8	41°
42°	73.7	72.4	71.0	69.6	68.2	66.8	65.4	64.0	62.6	61.2	59.7	58.3	42°
43°	73.5	72.1	70.7	69.3	67.9	66.4	65.0	63.6	62.1	60.7	59.2	57.7	43°
44°	73.2	71.8	70.3	68.9	67.5	66.0	64.6	63.1	61.6	60.1	58.6	57.1	44°
45°	72.9	71.4	70.0	68.5	67.0	65.6	64.1	62.6	61.1	59.5	58.0	56.4	45°
46°	72.6	71.1	69.6	68.1	66.6	65.1	63.6	62.0	60.5	58.9	57.4	55.8	46°
47°	72.2	70.7	69.2	67.7	66.2	64.6	63.1	61.5	59.9	58.3	56.7	55.0	47°
48°	71.9	70.3	68.8	67.2	65.7	64.1	62.5	60.9	59.3	57.6	55.9	54.3	48°
49°	71.5	69.9	68.4	66.8	65.1	63.5	61.9	60.2	58.6	56.9	55.2	53.4	49°
50°	71.1	69.5	67.9	66.2	64.6	62.9	61.3	59.6	57.8	56.1	54.3	52.6	50°
51°	70.7	69.1	67.4	65.7	64.0	62.3	60.6	58.8	57.1	55.3	53.5	51.6	51°
52°	70.3	68.6	66.9	65.1	63.4	61.6	59.9	58.1	56.3	54.4	52.5	50.6	52°
53°	69.8	68.1	66.3	64.5	62.7	60.9	59.1	57.3	55.4	53.5	51.5	49.5	53°
54°	69.3	67.5	65.7	63.9	62.0	60.2	58.3	56.4	54.4	52.4	50.4	48.3	54°
55°	68.7	66.9	65.1	63.2	61.3	59.4	57.4	55.4	53.4	51.3	49.2	47.1	55°
56°	68.2	66.3	64.4	62.4	60.5	58.5	56.5	54.4	52.3	50.1	47.9	45.7	56°
57°	67.6	65.6	63.6	61.6	59.6	57.5	55.4	53.3	51.1	48.9	46.5	44.2	57°
58°	66.9	64.9	62.8	60.8	58.7	56.5	54.3	52.1	49.8	47.4	45.0	42.5	58°
59°	66.2	64.1	62.0	59.8	57.6	55.4	53.1	50.8	48.4	45.9	43.3	40.7	59°
60°	65.4	63.3	61.1	58.8	56.5	54.2	51.8	49.4	46.8	44.2	41.5	38.6	60°

TABLE 3(2) Distance off by Vertical Sextant Angle

Height of object ft	m	Distance of object (nautical miles) 0.1	0.2	0.3	0.4	0.5	0.6	0.7	0.8	0.9	1.0	1.1	1.2	1.3	1.4	1.5	Height of object m	ft
		° ′	° ′	° ′	° ′	° ′	° ′	° ′	° ′	° ′	° ′	° ′	° ′	° ′	° ′	° ′		
33	**10**	3 05	1 33	1 02	0 46	0 37	0 31	0 27	0 23	0 21	0 19	0 17	0 15	0 14	0 13	0 12	**10**	33
39	**12**	3 42	1 51	1 14	0 56	0 45	0 37	0 32	0 28	0 25	0 22	0 20	0 19	0 17	0 16	0 15	**12**	39
46	**14**	4 19	2 10	1 27	1 05	0 52	0 43	0 37	0 32	0 29	0 26	0 24	0 22	0 20	0 19	0 17	**14**	46
53	**16**	4 56	2 28	1 39	1 14	0 59	0 49	0 42	0 37	0 33	0 30	0 27	0 25	0 23	0 21	0 20	**16**	53
59	**18**	5 33	2 47	1 51	1 24	1 07	0 56	0 48	0 42	0 37	0 33	0 30	0 28	0 26	0 24	0 22	**18**	59
66	**20**	6 10	3 05	2 04	1 33	1 14	1 02	0 53	0 46	0 41	0 37	0 34	0 31	0 29	0 27	0 25	**20**	66
72	**22**	6 46	3 24	2 16	1 42	1 22	1 08	0 58	0 51	0 45	0 41	0 37	0 34	0 31	0 29	0 27	**22**	72
79	**24**	7 23	3 42	2 28	1 51	1 29	1 14	1 04	0 56	0 49	0 45	0 40	0 37	0 34	0 32	0 30	**24**	79
85	**26**	7 59	4 01	2 41	2 01	1 36	1 20	1 09	1 00	0 54	0 48	0 44	0 40	0 37	0 34	0 32	**26**	85
92	**28**	8 36	4 19	2 53	2 10	1 44	1 27	1 14	1 05	0 58	0 52	0 47	0 43	0 40	0 37	0 35	**28**	92
98	**30**	9 12	4 38	3 05	2 19	1 51	1 33	1 20	1 10	1 02	0 56	0 51	0 46	0 43	0 40	0 37	**30**	98
105	**32**	9 48	4 56	3 18	2 28	1 58	1 39	1 25	1 14	1 06	0 59	0 54	0 49	0 46	0 42	0 40	**32**	105
112	**34**	10 24	5 15	3 30	2 38	2 06	1 45	1 30	1 19	1 10	1 03	0 57	0 53	0 49	0 45	0 42	**34**	112
118	**36**	11 00	5 33	3 42	2 47	2 14	1 51	1 35	1 24	1 14	1 07	1 01	0 56	0 51	0 48	0 45	**36**	118
125	**38**	11 36	5 41	3 55	2 56	2 21	1 58	1 41	1 28	1 18	1 11	1 04	0 59	0 54	0 50	0 47	**38**	125
131	**40**	12 11	6 10	4 07	3 05	2 28	2 04	1 46	1 33	1 22	1 14	1 07	1 02	0 57	0 53	0 49	**40**	131
138	**42**	12 47	6 28	4 19	3 15	2 36	2 10	1 51	1 37	1 27	1 18	1 11	1 05	1 00	0 56	0 52	**42**	138
144	**44**	13 22	6 46	4 32	3 24	2 43	2 16	1 57	1 42	1 31	1 22	1 14	1 08	1 03	0 58	0 54	**44**	144
151	**46**	13 57	7 05	4 44	3 33	2 51	2 22	2 02	1 47	1 35	1 25	1 18	1 11	1 06	1 01	0 57	**46**	151
157	**48**	14 32	7 23	4 56	3 42	2 58	2 28	2 07	1 51	1 39	1 29	1 21	1 14	1 09	1 04	0 59	**48**	157
164	**50**	15 07	7 41	5 09	3 52	3 05	2 35	2 13	1 56	1 43	1 33	1 24	1 17	1 11	1 06	1 02	**50**	164
171	**52**	15 41	7 59	5 21	4 01	3 13	2 41	2 18	2 01	1 47	1 36	1 28	1 20	1 14	1 09	1 04	**52**	171
177	**54**	16 15	8 18	5 33	4 10	3 20	2 47	2 23	2 05	1 51	1 40	1 31	1 23	1 17	1 12	1 07	**54**	177
184	**56**	16 49	8 36	5 45	4 19	3 28	2 53	2 28	2 10	1 55	1 44	1 34	1 27	1 20	1 14	1 09	**56**	184
190	**58**	17 23	8 54	5 58	4 29	3 35	2 59	2 34	2 15	2 00	1 48	1 38	1 30	1 23	1 17	1 12	**58**	190
197	**60**	17 57	9 12	6 10	4 38	3 42	3 05	2 39	2 19	2 04	1 51	1 41	1 33	1 26	1 20	1 14	**60**	197
203	**62**	18 31	9 30	6 22	4 47	3 50	3 12	2 44	2 24	2 08	1 55	1 45	1 36	1 29	1 22	1 17	**62**	203
210	**64**	19 04	9 48	6 34	4 56	3 57	3 18	2 50	2 28	2 12	1 59	1 48	1 39	1 31	1 25	1 19	**64**	210
217	**66**	19 37	10 06	6 46	5 05	4 05	3 24	2 53	2 33	2 16	2 02	1 51	1 42	1 34	1 27	1 22	**66**	217
223	**68**	20 10	10 24	6 59	5 15	4 12	3 30	3 00	2 38	2 20	2 06	1 55	1 45	1 37	1 30	1 24	**68**	223
230	**70**	20 42	10 42	7 11	5 24	4 19	3 36	3 05	2 42	2 24	2 09	1 58	1 48	1 40	1 33	1 27	**70**	230
236	**72**	21 15	11 00	7 23	5 33	4 27	3 42	3 11	2 47	2 48	2 14	2 01	1 51	1 43	1 35	1 29	**72**	236
246	**75**	22 03	11 27	7 41	5 47	4 38	3 52	3 19	2 54	2 35	2 19	2 07	1 56	1 47	1 39	1 33	**75**	246
256	**78**	22 50	11 54	7 59	6 01	4 49	4 01	3 27	3 01	2 41	2 24	2 12	2 01	1 51	1 43	1 36	**78**	256
266	**81**	23 37	12 20	8 18	6 14	5 00	4 10	3 35	3 08	2 47	2 30	2 17	2 05	1 56	1 47	1 40	**81**	266
276	**84**	24 24	12 47	8 36	6 28	5 11	4 19	3 42	3 15	2 53	2 36	2 22	2 10	2 00	1 51	1 44	**84**	276
289	**88**	25 25	13 22	9 00	6 46	5 26	4 32	3 53	3 24	3 01	2 43	2 28	2 16	2 06	1 57	1 49	**88**	289
302	**92**	26 25	13 57	9 24	7 05	5 40	4 44	4 04	3 33	3 10	2 51	2 35	2 22	2 11	2 02	1 54	**92**	302
315	**96**	27 24	14 32	9 48	7 23	5 55	4 56	4 14	3 42	3 18	2 58	2 42	2 28	2 17	2 07	1 59	**96**	315
328	**100**	28 22	15 07	10 12	7 41	6 10	5 09	4 25	3 52	3 26	3 05	2 49	2 35	2 23	2 13	2 04	**100**	328
341	**104**	29 19	15 41	10 36	7 59	6 24	5 21	4 35	4 01	3 34	3 13	2 55	2 41	2 28	2 18	2 09	**104**	341
358	**109**	30 29	16 24	11 06	8 22	6 43	5 36	4 48	4 12	3 44	3 22	3 04	2 48	2 36	2 24	2 15	**109**	358
374	**114**	31 37	17 06	11 36	8 45	7 01	5 51	5 02	4 24	3 55	3 31	3 12	2 56	2 43	2 31	2 21	**114**	374
394	**120**	32 56	17 57	12 11	9 12	7 23	6 10	5 17	4 38	4 07	3 42	3 22	3 05	2 51	2 39	2 28	**120**	394
427	**130**	35 04	19 20	13 10	9 57	8 00	6 40	5 44	5 01	4 28	4 01	3 39	3 21	3 05	2 52	2 41	**130**	427
459	**140**	37 05	20 42	14 09	10 42	8 36	7 11	6 10	5 24	4 48	4 19	3 56	3 36	3 20	3 05	2 53	**140**	459
492	**150**	39 00	22 03	15 07	11 27	9 12	7 41	6 36	5 47	5 09	4 38	4 13	3 52	3 34	3 19	3 05	**150**	492
574	**175**		25 17	17 29	13 17	10 42	8 57	7 41	6 44	6 00	5 24	4 55	4 30	4 09	3 52	3 36	**175**	574
656	**200**		28 22	19 48	15 07	12 11	10 12	8 46	7 41	6 51	6 10	5 36	5 09	4 45	4 25	4 07	**200**	656
738	**225**			22 03	16 54	13 39	11 27	9 51	8 38	7 41	6 56	6 18	5 47	5 20	4 58	4 38	**225**	738
820	**250**			24 14	18 39	15 07	12 41	10 55	9 35	8 32	7 41	7 00	6 25	5 56	5 30	5 09	**250**	820
902	**275**			26 20	20 22	16 32	13 54	11 59	10 31	9 22	8 27	7 41	7 03	6 31	6 03	5 39	**275**	902
984	**300**				22 03	17 57	15 07	13 02	11 27	10 12	9 12	8 23	7 41	7 06	6 36	6 10	**300**	984
1148	**350**					20 42	17 29	15 07	13 17	11 51	10 42	9 45	8 57	8 16	7 41	7 11	**350**	1148
1312	**400**						19 48	17 09	15 07	13 30	12 11	11 07	10 12	9 26	8 46	8 12	**400**	1312
ft	m Height of object	0.1	0.2	0.3	0.4	0.5	0.6	0.7	0.8	0.9	1.0 Distance of object (nautical miles)	1.1	1.2	1.3	1.4	1.5	m Height of object	ft

TABLE 3(2) Distance off by Vertical Sextant Angle (continued)

Height of object ft	m	1.6	1.7	1.8	1.9	2.0	2.1	2.2	2.3	2.4	2.5	2.6	2.7	2.8	2.9	3.0	Height of object m	ft
		Distance of object (nautical miles)																
		° ′	° ′	° ′	° ′	° ′	° ′	° ′	° ′	° ′	° ′	° ′	° ′	° ′	° ′	° ′		
33	**10**	0 12	0 11	0 10	0 10												**10**	33
39	**12**	0 14	0 13	0 12	0 12	0 11	0 11	0 10	0 10	0 10							**12**	39
46	**14**	0 16	0 15	0 14	0 14	0 13	0 12	0 12	0 11	0 11	0 10	0 10	0 10				**14**	46
53	**16**	0 19	0 17	0 16	0 16	0 15	0 14	0 13	0 13	0 12	0 12	0 11	0 11	0 11	0 10	0 10	**16**	53
59	**18**	0 21	0 20	0 19	0 18	0 17	0 16	0 15	0 15	0 14	0 13	0 13	0 12	0 12	0 12	0 11	**18**	59
66	**20**	0 23	0 22	0 21	0 20	0 19	0 18	0 17	0 16	0 15	0 15	0 14	0 14	0 13	0 13	0 12	**20**	66
72	**22**	0 26	0 24	0 23	0 21	0 20	0 19	0 19	0 18	0 17	0 16	0 16	0 15	0 15	0 14	0 14	**22**	72
79	**24**	0 28	0 26	0 25	0 23	0 22	0 21	0 20	0 19	0 19	0 18	0 17	0 16	0 16	0 15	0 15	**24**	79
85	**26**	0 30	0 28	0 27	0 25	0 24	0 23	0 22	0 21	0 20	0 19	0 19	0 18	0 17	0 17	0 16	**26**	85
92	**28**	0 32	0 31	0 29	0 27	0 26	0 25	0 24	0 23	0 22	0 21	0 20	0 19	0 19	0 18	0 17	**28**	92
98	**30**	0 35	0 33	0 31	0 29	0 28	0 27	0 25	0 24	0 23	0 22	0 21	0 21	0 20	0 19	0 19	**30**	98
105	**32**	0 37	0 35	0 33	0 31	0 30	0 28	0 27	0 26	0 25	0 24	0 23	0 22	0 21	0 20	0 20	**32**	105
112	**34**	0 39	0 37	0 35	0 33	0 31	0 30	0 29	0 27	0 26	0 25	0 24	0 23	0 23	0 22	0 21	**34**	112
118	**36**	0 42	0 39	0 37	0 35	0 33	0 32	0 30	0 29	0 28	0 27	0 26	0 25	0 24	0 23	0 22	**36**	118
125	**38**	0 44	0 41	0 39	0 37	0 35	0 34	0 32	0 31	0 29	0 28	0 27	0 26	0 25	0 24	0 24	**38**	125
131	**40**	0 46	0 44	0 41	0 39	0 37	0 35	0 34	0 32	0 31	0 30	0 29	0 27	0 27	0 26	0 25	**40**	131
138	**42**	0 49	0 46	0 43	0 41	0 40	0 37	0 35	0 34	0 32	0 31	0 30	0 29	0 28	0 27	0 26	**42**	138
144	**44**	0 51	0 48	0 45	0 43	0 41	0 39	0 37	0 36	0 34	0 33	0 31	0 30	0 29	0 28	0 27	**44**	144
151	**46**	0 53	0 50	0 47	0 45	0 43	0 41	0 39	0 37	0 36	0 34	0 33	0 32	0 30	0 29	0 28	**46**	151
157	**48**	0 56	0 52	0 49	0 47	0 45	0 42	0 40	0 39	0 37	0 36	0 34	0 33	0 32	0 31	0 30	**48**	157
164	**50**	0 58	0 55	0 52	0 49	0 46	0 44	0 42	0 40	0 39	0 37	0 36	0 34	0 33	0 32	0 31	**50**	164
171	**52**	1 00	0 57	0 54	0 51	0 48	0 46	0 44	0 42	0 40	0 39	0 37	0 36	0 34	0 33	0 32	**52**	171
177	**54**	1 03	0 59	0 56	0 53	0 50	0 48	0 46	0 44	0 42	0 40	0 39	0 37	0 36	0 35	0 33	**54**	177
184	**56**	1 05	1 01	0 58	0 55	0 52	0 49	0 47	0 45	0 43	0 42	0 40	0 38	0 37	0 36	0 35	**56**	184
190	**58**	1 07	1 03	1 00	0 57	0 54	0 51	0 49	0 47	0 45	0 43	0 41	0 40	0 38	0 37	0 36	**58**	190
197	**60**	1 10	1 06	1 02	0 59	0 56	0 53	0 51	0 48	0 46	0 45	0 43	0 41	0 40	0 38	0 37	**60**	197
203	**62**	1 12	1 08	1 04	1 01	0 58	0 55	0 52	0 50	0 48	0 46	0 44	0 43	0 41	0 40	0 38	**62**	203
210	**64**	1 14	1 10	1 06	1 03	0 59	0 57	0 54	0 52	0 49	0 48	0 46	0 44	0 42	0 41	0 40	**64**	210
217	**66**	1 17	1 12	1 08	1 05	1 01	0 58	0 56	0 53	0 51	0 49	0 47	0 45	0 44	0 42	0 41	**66**	217
223	**68**	1 19	1 14	1 10	1 06	1 03	1 00	0 57	0 55	0 53	0 50	0 49	0 47	0 45	0 44	0 42	**68**	223
230	**70**	1 21	1 16	1 12	1 08	1 05	1 02	0 59	0 56	0 54	0 52	0 50	0 48	0 46	0 45	0 43	**70**	230
236	**72**	1 24	1 19	1 14	1 10	1 07	1 04	1 01	0 58	0 56	0 53	0 51	0 49	0 48	0 46	0 45	**72**	236
246	**75**	1 27	1 22	1 17	1 13	1 10	1 06	1 03	1 01	0 58	0 56	0 54	0 51	0 50	0 48	0 46	**75**	246
256	**78**	1 30	1 25	1 20	1 16	1 12	1 09	1 06	1 03	1 00	0 58	0 56	0 54	0 52	0 50	0 48	**78**	256
266	**81**	1 34	1 28	1 23	1 19	1 15	1 12	1 08	1 05	1 03	1 00	0 58	0 56	0 54	0 52	0 50	**81**	266
276	**84**	1 37	1 32	1 27	1 22	1 18	1 14	1 11	1 08	1 05	1 02	1 00	0 58	0 56	0 54	0 52	**84**	276
289	**88**	1 42	1 36	1 31	1 26	1 22	1 18	1 14	1 11	1 08	1 05	1 03	1 00	0 58	0 56	0 54	**88**	289
302	**92**	1 47	1 40	1 35	1 30	1 25	1 21	1 18	1 14	1 11	1 08	1 06	1 03	1 01	0 59	0 57	**92**	302
315	**96**	1 51	1 45	1 39	1 34	1 29	1 25	1 21	1 17	1 14	1 11	1 09	1 06	1 04	1 01	0 59	**96**	315
328	**100**	1 56	1 49	1 43	1 38	1 33	1 28	1 24	1 21	1 17	1 14	1 11	1 09	1 06	1 04	1 02	**100**	328
341	**104**	2 01	1 54	1 47	1 42	1 36	1 32	1 28	1 24	1 20	1 17	1 14	1 11	1 09	1 07	1 04	**104**	341
358	**109**	2 06	1 59	1 52	1 46	1 41	1 36	1 32	1 28	1 24	1 21	1 18	1 15	1 12	1 10	1 07	**109**	358
374	**114**	2 12	2 04	1 58	1 51	1 46	1 41	1 36	1 32	1 28	1 25	1 21	1 18	1 16	1 13	1 11	**114**	374
394	**120**	2 19	2 11	2 04	1 57	1 51	1 46	1 41	1 37	1 33	1 29	1 26	1 22	1 20	1 17	1 14	**120**	394
427	**130**	2 31	2 22	2 14	2 07	2 01	1 55	1 50	1 45	1 41	1 36	1 33	1 29	1 26	1 23	1 20	**130**	427
459	**140**	2 42	2 33	2 24	2 17	2 10	2 04	1 58	1 53	1 48	1 44	1 40	1 36	1 33	1 30	1 27	**140**	459
492	**150**	2 54	2 44	2 35	2 26	2 19	2 13	2 07	2 01	1 56	1 51	1 47	1 43	1 39	1 36	1 33	**150**	492
574	**175**	3 23	3 11	3 00	2 51	2 42	2 35	2 28	2 21	2 15	2 10	2 05	2 00	1 56	1 52	1 48	**175**	574
656	**200**	3 52	3 38	3 26	3 15	3 05	2 57	2 49	2 41	2 35	2 28	2 23	2 17	2 13	2 08	2 04	**200**	656
738	**225**	4 21	4 05	3 52	3 40	3 29	3 19	3 10	3 01	2 54	2 47	2 41	2 36	2 29	2 24	2 19	**225**	738
820	**250**	4 49	4 32	4 17	4 04	3 52	3 41	3 31	3 22	3 13	3 05	2 58	2 52	2 46	2 40	2 35	**250**	820
902	**275**	5 18	5 00	4 43	4 28	4 15	4 03	3 52	3 42	3 32	3 24	3 16	3 09	3 02	2 56	2 50	**275**	902
984	**300**	5 47	5 27	5 09	4 52	4 38	4 25	4 13	4 02	3 52	3 42	3 34	3 26	3 19	3 12	3 05	**300**	984
1148	**350**	6 44	6 21	6 00	5 41	5 24	5 09	4 55	4 42	4 30	4 19	4 09	4 00	3 52	3 44	3 36	**350**	1148
1312	**400**	7 41	7 14	6 51	6 29	6 10	5 52	5 36	5 22	5 09	4 56	4 45	4 34	4 25	4 16	4 07	**400**	1312
ft	m	1.6	1.7	1.8	1.9	2.0	2.1	2.2	2.3	2.4	2.5	2.6	2.7	2.8	2.9	3.0	m	ft
Height of object		Distance of object (nautical miles)															Height of object	

3

TABLE 3(2) Distance off by Vertical Sextant Angle (continued)

Height of object ft	m	3.1	3.2	3.3	3.4	3.5	3.6	3.7	3.8	3.9	4.0	4.2	4.4	4.6	4.8	5.0	Height of object m	ft
		Distance of object (nautical miles)																
		° ′	° ′	° ′	° ′	° ′	° ′	° ′	° ′	° ′	° ′	° ′	° ′	° ′	° ′	° ′		
33	**10**																**10**	33
39	**12**																**12**	39
46	**14**																**14**	46
53	**16**	0 10															**16**	53
59	**18**	0 11	0 10	0 10	0 10	0 10											**18**	59
66	**20**	0 12	0 12	0 11	0 11	0 11	0 10	0 10	0 10	0 10							**20**	66
72	**22**	0 13	0 13	0 12	0 12	0 12	0 11	0 11	0 11	0 10	0 10						**22**	72
79	**24**	0 14	0 14	0 13	0 13	0 13	0 12	0 12	0 12	0 11	0 11	0 11	0 10				**24**	79
85	**26**	0 16	0 15	0 15	0 14	0 14	0 13	0 13	0 13	0 12	0 12	0 11	0 11	0 10	0 10		**26**	85
92	**28**	0 17	0 16	0 16	0 15	0 15	0 14	0 14	0 14	0 13	0 13	0 12	0 12	0 11	0 11	0 10	**28**	92
98	**30**	0 18	0 17	0 17	0 16	0 16	0 15	0 15	0 15	0 14	0 14	0 13	0 13	0 12	0 12	0 11	**30**	98
105	**32**	0 19	0 19	0 18	0 17	0 17	0 16	0 16	0 16	0 15	0 15	0 14	0 13	0 13	0 12	0 12	**32**	105
112	**34**	0 20	0 20	0 19	0 19	0 18	0 17	0 17	0 17	0 16	0 16	0 15	0 14	0 14	0 13	0 13	**34**	112
118	**36**	0 22	0 21	0 20	0 20	0 19	0 19	0 18	0 18	0 17	0 17	0 16	0 15	0 14	0 14	0 13	**36**	118
125	**38**	0 23	0 22	0 21	0 21	0 20	0 20	0 19	0 19	0 18	0 18	0 17	0 16	0 15	0 15	0 14	**38**	125
131	**40**	0 24	0 23	0 22	0 22	0 21	0 21	0 20	0 20	0 19	0 19	0 18	0 17	0 16	0 15	0 15	**40**	131
138	**42**	0 25	0 24	0 24	0 23	0 22	0 22	0 21	0 21	0 20	0 19	0 19	0 18	0 17	0 16	0 16	**42**	138
144	**44**	0 26	0 25	0 25	0 24	0 23	0 23	0 22	0 22	0 21	0 20	0 19	0 19	0 18	0 17	0 16	**44**	144
151	**46**	0 28	0 27	0 26	0 25	0 24	0 24	0 23	0 22	0 22	0 21	0 20	0 19	0 19	0 18	0 17	**46**	151
157	**48**	0 29	0 28	0 27	0 26	0 25	0 25	0 24	0 23	0 23	0 22	0 21	0 20	0 19	0 19	0 18	**48**	157
164	**50**	0 30	0 29	0 28	0 27	0 27	0 26	0 25	0 24	0 24	0 23	0 22	0 21	0 20	0 19	0 19	**50**	164
171	**52**	0 31	0 30	0 29	0 28	0 28	0 27	0 26	0 25	0 25	0 24	0 23	0 22	0 21	0 20	0 19	**52**	171
177	**54**	0 32	0 31	0 30	0 29	0 29	0 28	0 27	0 26	0 26	0 25	0 24	0 23	0 22	0 21	0 20	**54**	177
184	**56**	0 34	0 32	0 31	0 31	0 30	0 29	0 28	0 27	0 27	0 26	0 25	0 24	0 23	0 22	0 21	**56**	184
190	**58**	0 35	0 34	0 33	0 32	0 31	0 30	0 29	0 28	0 28	0 27	0 26	0 24	0 23	0 22	0 21	**58**	190
197	**60**	0 36	0 35	0 34	0 33	0 32	0 31	0 30	0 29	0 29	0 28	0 26	0 25	0 24	0 23	0 22	**60**	197
203	**62**	0 37	0 36	0 35	0 34	0 33	0 32	0 31	0 30	0 30	0 29	0 27	0 26	0 25	0 24	0 23	**62**	203
210	**64**	0 38	0 37	0 36	0 35	0 34	0 33	0 32	0 31	0 30	0 30	0 28	0 27	0 26	0 25	0 24	**64**	210
217	**66**	0 40	0 38	0 37	0 36	0 35	0 34	0 33	0 32	0 31	0 31	0 29	0 28	0 27	0 26	0 25	**66**	217
223	**68**	0 41	0 39	0 38	0 37	0 36	0 35	0 34	0 33	0 32	0 32	0 30	0 29	0 27	0 26	0 25	**68**	223
230	**70**	0 42	0 41	0 39	0 38	0 37	0 36	0 35	0 34	0 33	0 32	0 31	0 29	0 28	0 27	0 26	**70**	230
236	**72**	0 43	0 42	0 40	0 39	0 38	0 37	0 36	0 35	0 34	0 33	0 32	0 30	0 29	0 28	0 27	**72**	236
246	**75**	0 45	0 44	0 42	0 41	0 40	0 39	0 38	0 37	0 36	0 35	0 33	0 32	0 30	0 29	0 28	**75**	246
256	**78**	0 47	0 45	0 44	0 43	0 41	0 40	0 39	0 38	0 37	0 36	0 34	0 33	0 31	0 30	0 29	**78**	256
266	**81**	0 48	0 47	0 46	0 44	0 43	0 42	0 41	0 40	0 39	0 38	0 36	0 34	0 33	0 31	0 30	**81**	266
276	**84**	0 50	0 49	0 47	0 46	0 45	0 43	0 42	0 41	0 40	0 39	0 37	0 35	0 34	0 32	0 31	**84**	276
289	**88**	0 53	0 51	0 49	0 48	0 47	0 45	0 44	0 43	0 42	0 41	0 39	0 37	0 36	0 34	0 33	**88**	289
302	**92**	0 55	0 53	0 52	0 50	0 49	0 47	0 46	0 45	0 44	0 43	0 41	0 39	0 37	0 36	0 34	**92**	302
315	**96**	0 57	0 56	0 54	0 52	0 51	0 49	0 48	0 47	0 46	0 45	0 42	0 41	0 39	0 37	0 36	**96**	315
328	**100**	1 00	0 58	0 56	0 55	0 53	0 52	0 50	0 49	0 48	0 46	0 44	0 42	0 40	0 39	0 37	**100**	328
341	**104**	1 02	1 00	0 58	0 57	0 55	0 54	0 52	0 51	0 49	0 48	0 46	0 44	0 42	0 40	0 39	**104**	341
358	**109**	1 05	1 03	1 01	1 00	0 58	0 56	0 55	0 53	0 52	0 51	0 48	0 46	0 44	0 42	0 40	**109**	358
374	**114**	1 08	1 06	1 04	1 02	1 00	0 59	0 57	0 56	0 54	0 53	0 50	0 48	0 46	0 44	0 42	**114**	374
394	**120**	1 12	1 10	1 07	1 06	1 04	1 02	1 00	0 59	0 57	0 56	0 53	0 51	0 48	0 46	0 45	**120**	394
427	**130**	1 18	1 15	1 13	1 11	1 09	1 07	1 05	1 03	1 02	1 00	0 57	0 55	0 52	0 50	0 48	**130**	427
459	**140**	1 24	1 21	1 19	1 16	1 14	1 12	1 10	1 08	1 07	1 05	1 02	0 59	0 56	0 54	0 52	**140**	459
492	**150**	1 30	1 27	1 24	1 22	1 20	1 17	1 15	1 13	1 11	1 10	1 06	1 03	1 01	0 58	0 56	**150**	492
574	**175**	1 45	1 41	1 38	1 36	1 33	1 30	1 28	1 25	1 23	1 21	1 17	1 14	1 11	1 08	1 05	**175**	574
656	**200**	2 00	1 56	1 52	1 49	1 46	1 43	1 40	1 38	1 35	1 33	1 28	1 24	1 21	1 17	1 14	**200**	656
738	**225**	2 15	2 10	2 06	2 03	1 59	1 56	1 53	1 50	1 47	1 44	1 39	1 35	1 31	1 27	1 24	**225**	738
820	**250**	2 30	2 25	2 20	2 16	2 13	2 09	2 05	2 02	1 59	1 56	1 50	1 45	1 41	1 37	1 33	**250**	820
902	**275**	2 45	2 39	2 34	2 30	2 26	2 22	2 18	2 14	2 11	2 08	2 01	1 56	1 51	1 46	1 42	**275**	902
984	**300**	2 59	2 54	2 48	2 44	2 39	2 35	2 30	2 26	2 23	2 19	2 13	2 07	2 01	1 56	1 51	**300**	984
1148	**350**	3 29	3 23	3 16	3 11	3 05	3 00	2 55	2 51	2 46	2 42	2 35	2 28	2 21	2 15	2 10	**350**	1148
1312	**400**	3 59	3 52	3 44	3 38	3 32	3 26	3 20	3 15	3 10	3 05	2 57	2 49	2 41	2 35	2 28	**400**	1312
ft Height of object	**m**	**3.1**	**3.2**	**3.3**	**3.4**	**3.5**	**3.6**	**3.7**	**3.8**	**3.9**	**4.0**	**4.2**	**4.4**	**4.6**	**4.8**	**5.0**	**m Height of object**	**ft**
		Distance of object (nautical miles)																

TABLE 3(3) Distance of horizon for various heights of eye

Height of eye		Horizon distance	Height of eye		Horizon distance	Height of eye		Horizon distance
metres	feet	M	metres	feet	M	metres	feet	M
1	3.3	2.1	21	68.9	9.5	41	134.5	13.3
2	6.6	2.9	22	72.2	9.8	42	137.8	13.5
3	9.8	3.6	23	75.5	10.0	43	141.1	13.7
4	13.1	4.1	24	78.7	10.2	44	144.4	13.8
5	16.4	4.7	25	82.0	10.4	45	147.6	14.0
6	19.7	5.1	26	85.3	10.6	46	150.9	14.1
7	23.0	5.5	27	88.6	10.8	47	154.2	14.3
8	26.2	5.9	28	91.9	11.0	48	157.5	14.4
9	29.6	6.2	29	95.1	11.2	49	160.8	14.6
10	32.8	6.6	30	98.4	11.4	50	164.0	14.7
11	36.1	6.9	31	101.7	11.6	51	167.3	14.9
12	39.4	7.2	32	105.0	11.8	52	170.6	15.0
13	42.7	7.5	33	108.3	12.0	53	173.9	15.2
14	45.9	7.8	34	111.6	12.1	54	177.2	15.3
15	49.2	8.1	35	114.8	12.3	55	180.4	15.4
16	52.5	8.3	36	118.1	12.5	56	183.7	15.6
17	55.8	8.6	37	121.4	12.7	57	187.0	15.7
18	59.1	8.8	38	124.7	12.8	58	190.3	15.9
19	62.3	9.1	39	128.0	13.0	59	193.6	16.0
20	65.6	9.3	40	131.2	13.2	60	196.9	16.1

TABLE 3 (4) Lights — distance off when rising or dipping (M)

Height of light		Height of eye										
		metres	1	2	3	4	5	6	7	8	9	10
metres	feet	feet	3	7	10	13	16	20	23	26	30	33
10	33		8.7	9.5	10.2	10.8	11.3	11.7	12.1	12.5	12.8	13.2
12	39		9.3	10.1	10.8	11.4	11.9	12.3	12.7	13.1	13.4	13.8
14	46		9.9	10.7	11.4	12.0	12.5	12.9	13.3	13.7	14.0	14.4
16	53		10.4	11.2	11.9	12.5	13.0	13.4	13.8	14.2	14.5	14.9
18	59		10.9	11.7	12.4	13.0	13.5	13.9	14.3	14.7	15.0	15.4
20	66		11.4	12.2	12.9	13.5	14.0	14.4	14.8	15.2	15.5	15.9
22	72		11.9	12.7	13.4	14.0	14.5	14.9	15.3	15.7	16.0	16.4
24	79		12.3	13.1	13.8	14.4	14.9	15.3	15.7	16.1	16.4	17.0
26	85		12.7	13.5	14.2	14.8	15.3	15.7	16.1	16.5	16.8	17.2
28	92		13.1	13.9	14.6	15.2	15.7	16.1	16.5	16.9	17.2	17.6
30	98		13.5	14.3	15.0	15.6	16.1	16.5	16.9	17.3	17.6	18.0
32	105		13.9	14.7	15.4	16.0	16.5	16.9	17.3	17.7	18.0	18.4
34	112		14.2	15.0	15.7	16.3	16.8	17.2	17.6	18.0	18.3	18.7
36	118		14.6	15.4	16.1	16.7	17.2	17.6	18.0	18.4	18.7	19.1
38	125		14.9	15.7	16.4	17.0	17.5	17.9	18.3	18.7	19.0	19.4
40	131		15.3	16.1	16.8	17.4	17.9	18.3	18.7	19.1	19.4	19.8
42	138		15.6	16.4	17.1	17.7	18.2	18.6	19.0	19.4	19.7	20.1
44	144		15.9	16.7	17.4	18.0	18.5	18.9	19.3	19.7	20.0	20.4
46	151		16.2	17.0	17.7	18.3	18.8	19.2	19.6	20.0	20.3	20.7
48	157		16.5	17.3	18.0	18.6	19.1	19.5	19.9	20.3	20.6	21.0
50	164		16.8	17.6	18.3	18.9	19.4	19.8	20.2	20.6	20.9	21.3
55	180		17.5	18.3	19.0	19.6	20.1	20.5	20.9	21.3	21.6	22.0
60	197		18.2	19.0	19.7	20.3	20.8	21.2	21.6	22.0	22.3	22.7
65	213		18.9	19.7	20.4	21.0	21.5	21.9	22.3	22.7	23.0	23.4
70	230		19.5	20.3	21.0	21.6	22.1	22.5	22.9	23.2	23.6	24.0
75	246		20.1	20.9	21.6	22.2	22.7	23.1	23.5	23.9	24.2	24.6
80	262		20.7	21.5	22.2	22.8	23.3	23.7	24.1	24.5	24.8	25.2
85	279		21.3	22.1	22.8	23.4	23.9	24.3	24.7	25.1	25.4	25.8
90	295		21.8	22.6	23.3	23.9	24.4	24.8	25.2	25.6	25.9	26.3
95	312		22.4	23.2	23.9	24.5	25.0	25.4	25.8	26.2	26.5	26.9
metres	feet	metres	1	2	3	4	5	6	7	8	9	10
Height of light		feet	3	7	10	13	16	20	23	26	30	33
		Height of eye										

TABLE 3(5) Time, Speed and Distance Table

Time: Decimal of hr.	Time: Mins	2.5	3	3.5	4	4.5	5	5.5	6	6.5	7	7.5	8	8.5	9	9.5	10	Time: Mins	Time: Decimal of hr.
		Speed in knots																	
.0167	1				0.1	0.1	0.1	0.1	0.1	0.1	0.1	0.1	0.1	0.1	0.2	0.2	0.2	1	.0167
.0333	2	0.1	0.1	0.1	0.1	0.1	0.2	0.2	0.2	0.2	0.2	0.2	0.3	0.3	0.3	0.3	0.3	2	.0333
.0500	3	0.1	0.1	0.2	0.2	0.2	0.2	0.3	0.3	0.3	0.3	0.4	0.4	0.4	0.4	0.5	0.5	3	.0500
.0667	4	0.1	0.2	0.2	0.3	0.3	0.3	0.4	0.4	0.4	0.5	0.5	0.5	0.6	0.6	0.6	0.7	4	.0667
.0833	5	0.2	0.2	0.3	0.3	0.4	0.4	0.5	0.5	0.5	0.6	0.6	0.7	0.7	0.7	0.8	0.8	5	.0833
.1000	6	0.2	0.3	0.3	0.4	0.4	0.5	0.5	0.6	0.6	0.7	0.7	0.8	0.8	0.9	0.9	1.0	6	.1000
.1167	7	0.3	0.4	0.4	0.5	0.5	0.6	0.6	0.7	0.8	0.8	0.9	0.9	1.0	1.1	1.1	1.2	7	.1167
.1333	8	0.3	0.4	0.5	0.5	0.6	0.7	0.7	0.8	0.9	0.9	1.0	1.1	1.1	1.2	1.3	1.3	8	.1333
.1500	9	0.4	0.4	0.5	0.6	0.7	0.7	0.8	0.9	1.0	1.0	1.1	1.2	1.3	1.3	1.4	1.5	9	.1500
.1667	10	0.4	0.5	0.6	0.7	0.8	0.8	0.9	1.0	1.1	1.2	1.3	1.3	1.4	1.5	1.6	1.7	10	.1667
.1833	11	0.5	0.5	0.6	0.7	0.8	0.9	1.0	1.1	1.2	1.3	1.4	1.5	1.6	1.6	1.7	1.8	11	.1833
.2000	12	0.5	0.6	0.7	0.8	0.9	1.0	1.1	1.2	1.3	1.4	1.5	1.6	1.7	1.8	1.9	2.0	12	.2000
.2167	13	0.5	0.6	0.8	0.9	1.0	1.1	1.2	1.3	1.4	1.5	1.6	1.7	1.8	2.0	2.0	2.2	13	.2167
.2333	14	0.6	0.7	0.8	0.9	1.0	1.2	1.3	1.4	1.5	1.6	1.7	1.9	2.0	2.1	2.2	2.3	14	.2333
.2500	15	0.6	0.7	0.9	1.0	1.1	1.2	1.4	1.5	1.6	1.8	1.9	2.0	2.1	2.2	2.4	2.5	15	.2500
.2667	16	0.7	0.8	0.9	1.1	1.2	1.3	1.5	1.6	1.7	1.9	2.0	2.1	2.3	2.4	2.5	2.7	16	.2667
.2833	17	0.7	0.8	1.0	1.1	1.3	1.4	1.6	1.7	1.8	2.0	2.1	2.3	2.4	2.5	2.7	2.8	17	.2833
.3000	18	0.7	0.9	1.0	1.2	1.3	1.5	1.6	1.8	1.9	2.1	2.2	2.4	2.5	2.7	2.8	3.0	18	.3000
.3167	19	0.8	1.0	1.1	1.3	1.4	1.6	1.7	1.9	2.1	2.1	2.4	2.5	2.7	2.9	3.0	3.2	19	.3167
.3333	20	0.8	1.0	1.2	1.3	1.5	1.7	1.8	2.0	2.2	2.3	2.5	2.7	2.8	3.0	3.2	3.3	20	.3333
.3500	21	0.9	1.0	1.2	1.4	1.6	1.7	1.9	2.1	2.3	2.4	2.6	2.8	3.0	3.1	3.3	3.5	21	.3500
.3667	22	0.9	1.1	1.3	1.5	1.7	1.8	2.1	2.2	2.4	2.6	2.8	2.9	3.1	3.3	3.5	3.7	22	.3667
.3833	23	1.0	1.1	1.3	1.5	1.7	1.9	2.1	2.3	2.5	2.7	2.9	3.1	3.3	3.4	3.6	3.8	23	.3833
.4000	24	1.0	1.2	1.4	1.6	1.8	2.0	2.2	2.4	2.6	2.8	3.0	3.2	3.4	3.6	3.8	4.0	24	.4000
.4167	25	1.0	1.3	1.5	1.7	1.9	2.1	2.3	2.5	2.7	2.9	3.1	3.3	3.5	3.8	4.0	4.2	25	.4167
.4333	26	1.1	1.3	1.5	1.7	1.9	2.2	2.4	2.6	2.8	3.0	3.2	3.5	3.7	3.9	4.1	4.3	26	.4333
.4500	27	1.1	1.3	1.6	1.8	2.0	2.2	2.5	2.7	2.9	3.1	3.4	3.6	3.8	4.0	4.3	4.5	27	.4500
.4667	28	1.2	1.4	1.6	1.9	2.1	2.3	2.6	2.8	3.0	3.3	3.5	3.7	4.0	4.2	4.4	4.7	28	.4667
.4833	29	1.2	1.5	1.7	1.9	2.2	2.4	2.7	2.9	3.1	3.4	3.6	3.9	4.1	4.3	4.6	4.8	29	.4833
.5000	30	1.2	1.5	1.7	2.0	2.2	2.5	2.7	3.0	3.2	3.5	3.7	4.0	4.2	4.5	4.7	5.0	30	.5000
.5167	31	1.3	1.6	1.8	2.1	2.3	2.6	2.8	3.1	3.4	3.6	3.9	4.1	4.4	4.7	4.9	5.2	31	.5167
.5333	32	1.3	1.6	1.9	2.1	2.4	2.7	2.9	3.2	3.5	3.7	4.0	4.3	4.5	4.8	5.1	5.3	32	.5333
.5500	33	1.4	1.6	1.9	2.2	2.5	2.7	3.0	3.3	3.6	3.8	4.1	4.4	4.7	4.9	5.2	5.5	33	.5500
.5667	34	1.4	1.7	2.0	2.3	2.6	2.8	3.1	3.4	3.7	4.0	4.3	4.5	4.8	5.1	5.4	5.7	34	.5667
.5833	35	1.5	1.7	2.0	2.3	2.6	2.9	3.2	3.5	3.8	4.1	4.4	4.7	5.0	5.2	5.5	5.8	35	.5833
.6000	36	1.5	1.8	2.1	2.4	2.7	3.0	3.3	3.6	3.9	4.2	4.5	4.8	5.1	5.4	5.7	6.0	36	.6000
.6117	37	1.6	1.8	2.1	2.4	2.8	3.1	3.4	3.7	4.0	4.3	4.6	4.9	5.2	5.5	5.8	6.1	37	.6117
.6333	38	1.6	1.9	2.2	2.5	2.8	3.2	3.5	3.8	4.1	4.4	4.7	5.1	5.4	5.7	6.0	6.3	38	.6333
.6500	39	1.6	1.9	2.3	2.6	2.9	3.2	3.6	3.9	4.2	4.5	4.9	5.2	5.5	5.8	6.2	6.5	39	.6500
.6667	40	1.7	2.0	2.3	2.7	3.0	3.3	3.7	4.0	4.3	4.7	5.0	5.3	5.7	6.0	6.3	6.7	40	.6667
.6833	41	1.7	2.0	2.4	2.7	3.1	3.4	3.8	4.1	4.4	4.8	5.1	5.5	5.8	6.1	6.5	6.8	41	.6833
.7000	42	1.7	2.1	2.4	2.8	3.1	3.5	3.8	4.2	4.5	4.9	5.2	5.6	5.9	6.3	6.6	7.0	42	.7000
.7167	43	1.8	2.2	2.5	2.9	3.2	3.6	3.9	4.3	4.7	5.0	5.4	5.7	6.1	6.5	6.8	7.2	43	.7167
.7333	44	1.8	2.2	2.6	2.9	3.3	3.7	4.0	4.4	4.8	5.1	5.5	5.9	6.2	6.6	7.0	7.3	44	.7333
.7500	45	1.9	2.2	2.6	3.0	3.4	3.7	4.1	4.5	4.9	5.2	5.6	6.0	6.4	6.7	7.1	7.5	45	.7500
.7667	46	1.9	2.3	2.7	3.1	3.5	3.8	4.2	4.6	5.0	5.4	5.8	6.1	6.5	6.9	7.3	7.7	46	.7667
.7833	47	2.0	2.3	2.7	3.1	3.5	3.9	4.3	4.7	5.1	5.5	5.9	6.3	6.7	7.0	7.4	7.8	47	.7833
.8000	48	2.0	2.4	2.8	3.2	3.6	4.0	4.4	4.8	5.2	5.6	6.0	6.4	6.8	7.2	7.6	8.0	48	.8000
.8167	49	2.0	2.5	2.9	3.3	3.7	4.1	4.5	4.9	5.3	5.7	6.1	6.5	6.9	7.4	7.8	8.2	49	.8167
.8333	50	2.1	2.5	2.9	3.3	3.7	4.2	4.6	5.0	5.4	5.8	6.2	6.7	7.1	7.5	7.9	8.3	50	.8333
.8500	51	2.1	2.5	3.0	3.4	3.8	4.2	4.7	5.1	5.5	5.9	6.4	6.8	7.2	7.6	8.1	8.5	51	.8500
.8667	52	2.2	2.6	3.0	3.5	3.9	4.3	4.8	5.2	5.6	6.1	6.5	6.9	7.4	7.8	8.2	8.7	52	.8667
.8833	53	2.2	2.6	3.1	3.5	4.0	4.4	4.9	5.3	5.7	6.2	6.6	7.1	7.5	7.9	8.4	8.8	53	.8833
.9000	54	2.2	2.7	3.1	3.6	4.0	4.5	4.9	5.4	5.8	6.3	6.7	7.2	7.6	8.1	8.5	9.0	54	.9000
.9167	55	2.3	2.8	3.2	3.7	4.1	4.6	5.0	5.5	6.0	6.4	6.9	7.3	7.8	8.3	8.7	9.2	55	.9167
.9333	56	2.3	2.8	3.3	3.7	4.2	4.7	5.1	5.6	6.1	6.5	7.0	7.5	7.9	8.4	8.9	9.3	56	.9333
.9500	57	2.4	2.8	3.3	3.8	4.3	4.7	5.2	5.7	6.2	6.6	7.1	7.6	8.1	8.5	9.0	9.5	57	.9500
.9667	58	2.4	2.9	3.4	3.9	4.4	4.8	5.3	5.8	6.3	6.8	7.3	7.7	8.2	8.7	9.2	9.7	58	.9667
.9833	59	2.5	2.9	3.4	3.9	4.4	4.9	5.4	5.9	6.4	6.9	7.4	7.9	8.4	8.8	9.3	9.8	59	.9833
1.0000	60	2.5	3.0	3.5	4.0	4.5	5.0	5.5	6.0	6.5	7.0	7.5	8.0	8.5	9.0	9.5	10.0	60	1.0000
Decimal of hr.	Mins.	2.5	3	3.5	4	4.5	5	5.5	6	6.5	7	7.5	8	8.5	9	9.5	10	Mins.	Decimal of hr.
Time		Speed in knots																Time	

TABLE 3(5) Time, Speed and Distance Table (continued)

Time: Decimal of hr.	Time: Mins	Speed in knots: 10.5	11.0	11.5	12.0	12.5	13.0	13.5	14.0	14.5	15.0	15.5	16.0	17.0	18.0	19.0	20.0	Time: Mins	Time: Decimal of hr.
.0167	**1**	0.2	0.2	0.2	0.2	0.2	0.2	0.2	0.2	0.2	0.3	0.3	0.3	0.3	0.3	0.3	0.3	**1**	.0167
.0333	**2**	0.3	0.4	0.4	0.4	0.4	0.4	0.4	0.5	0.5	0.5	0.5	0.5	0.6	0.6	0.6	0.7	**2**	.0333
.0500	**3**	0.5	0.5	0.6	0.6	0.6	0.6	0.7	0.7	0.7	0.7	0.8	0.8	0.8	0.8	0.9	1.0	**3**	.0500
.0667	**4**	0.7	0.7	0.8	0.8	0.8	0.9	0.9	0.9	1.0	1.0	1.0	1.1	1.1	1.2	1.3	1.3	**4**	.0667
.0833	**5**	0.9	0.9	1.0	1.0	1.0	1.1	1.1	1.2	1.2	1.2	1.3	1.3	1.4	1.5	1.6	1.7	**5**	.0833
.1000	**6**	1.0	1.1	1.1	1.2	1.2	1.3	1.3	1.4	1.4	1.5	1.5	1.6	1.7	1.8	1.9	2.0	**6**	.1000
.1167	**7**	1.2	1.3	1.3	1.4	1.5	1.5	1.6	1.6	1.7	1.8	1.8	1.9	2.0	2.1	2.2	2.3	**7**	.1167
.1333	**8**	1.4	1.5	1.5	1.6	1.7	1.7	1.8	1.9	1.9	2.0	2.1	2.1	2.3	2.4	2.5	2.7	**8**	.1333
.1500	**9**	1.6	1.6	1.7	1.8	1.9	1.9	2.0	2.1	2.1	2.2	2.3	2.4	2.5	2.7	2.8	3.0	**9**	.1500
.1667	**10**	1.8	1.8	1.9	2.0	2.1	2.2	2.3	2.3	2.4	2.5	2.6	2.7	2.8	3.0	3.2	3.3	**10**	.1667
.1833	**11**	1.9	2.0	2.1	2.2	2.3	2.4	2.5	2.6	2.7	2.7	2.8	2.9	3.1	3.3	3.5	3.7	**11**	.1833
.2000	**12**	2.1	2.2	2.3	2.4	2.5	2.6	2.7	2.8	2.9	3.0	3.1	3.2	3.4	3.6	3.8	4.0	**12**	.2000
.2167	**13**	2.3	2.4	2.5	2.6	2.7	2.8	2.9	3.0	3.1	3.2	3.3	3.5	3.7	3.9	4.1	4.3	**13**	.2167
.2333	**14**	2.4	2.6	2.7	2.8	2.9	3.0	3.1	3.3	3.4	3.5	3.6	3.7	4.0	4.2	4.4	4.7	**14**	.2333
.2500	**15**	2.6	2.7	2.9	3.0	3.1	3.2	3.4	3.5	3.6	3.7	3.9	4.0	4.2	4.5	4.7	5.0	**15**	.2500
.2667	**16**	2.8	2.9	3.1	3.2	3.3	3.5	3.6	3.7	3.9	4.0	4.1	4.3	4.5	4.8	5.1	5.3	**16**	.2667
.2833	**17**	3.0	3.1	3.3	3.4	3.5	3.7	3.8	4.0	4.1	4.2	4.4	4.5	4.8	5.1	5.4	5.7	**17**	.2833
.3000	**18**	3.1	3.3	3.4	3.6	3.7	3.9	4.0	4.2	4.3	4.5	4.6	4.8	5.1	5.4	5.7	6.0	**18**	.3000
.3167	**19**	3.3	3.5	3.6	3.8	4.0	4.1	4.3	4.4	4.6	4.8	4.9	5.1	5.4	5.7	6.0	6.3	**19**	.3167
.3333	**20**	3.5	3.7	3.8	4.0	4.2	4.3	4.5	4.7	4.8	5.0	5.2	5.3	5.7	6.0	6.3	6.7	**20**	.3333
.3500	**21**	3.7	3.8	4.0	4.2	4.4	4.5	4.7	4.9	5.1	5.2	5.4	5.6	5.9	6.3	6.6	7.0	**21**	.3500
.3667	**22**	3.9	4.0	4.2	4.4	4.6	4.8	5.0	5.1	5.3	5.5	5.7	5.9	6.2	6.6	7.0	7.3	**22**	.3667
.3833	**23**	4.0	4.2	4.4	4.6	4.8	5.0	5.2	5.4	5.6	5.7	5.9	6.1	6.5	6.9	7.3	7.7	**23**	.3833
.4000	**24**	4.2	4.4	4.6	4.8	5.0	5.2	5.4	5.6	5.8	6.0	6.2	6.4	6.8	7.2	7.6	8.0	**24**	.4000
.4167	**25**	4.4	4.6	4.8	5.0	5.2	5.4	5.6	5.8	6.0	6.3	6.5	6.7	7.1	7.5	7.9	8.3	**25**	.4167
.4333	**26**	4.5	4.8	5.0	5.2	5.4	5.6	5.8	6.1	6.3	6.5	6.7	6.9	7.4	7.8	8.2	8.7	**26**	.4333
.4500	**27**	4.7	4.9	5.2	5.4	5.6	5.8	6.1	6.3	6.5	6.7	7.0	7.2	7.6	8.1	8.5	9.0	**27**	.4500
.4667	**28**	4.9	5.1	5.4	5.6	5.8	6.1	6.3	6.5	6.8	7.0	7.2	7.5	7.9	8.4	8.9	9.3	**28**	.4667
.4833	**29**	5.1	5.3	5.6	5.8	6.0	6.3	6.5	6.8	7.0	7.2	7.5	7.7	8.2	8.7	9.2	9.7	**29**	.4833
.5000	**30**	5.2	5.5	5.7	6.0	6.2	6.5	6.7	7.0	7.2	7.5	7.7	8.0	8.5	9.0	9.5	10.0	**30**	.5000
.5167	**31**	5.4	5.7	5.9	6.2	6.5	6.7	7.0	7.2	7.5	7.8	8.0	8.3	8.8	9.3	9.8	10.3	**31**	.5167
.5333	**32**	5.6	5.9	6.1	6.4	6.7	6.9	7.2	7.5	7.7	8.0	8.3	8.5	9.1	9.6	10.1	10.7	**32**	.5333
.5500	**33**	5.8	6.0	6.3	6.6	6.9	7.1	7.4	7.7	8.0	8.2	8.5	8.8	9.3	9.9	10.4	11.0	**33**	.5500
.5667	**34**	6.0	6.2	6.5	6.8	7.1	7.4	7.7	7.9	8.2	8.5	8.8	9.1	9.6	10.2	10.8	11.3	**34**	.5667
.5833	**35**	6.1	6.4	6.7	7.0	7.3	7.6	7.9	8.2	8.5	8.7	9.0	9.3	9.9	10.5	11.1	11.7	**35**	.5833
.6000	**36**	6.3	6.6	6.9	7.2	7.5	7.8	8.1	8.4	8.7	9.0	9.3	9.6	10.2	10.8	11.4	12.0	**36**	.6000
.6117	**37**	6.4	6.7	7.0	7.3	7.6	8.0	8.3	8.6	8.9	9.2	9.5	9.8	10.4	11.0	11.6	12.2	**37**	.6117
.6333	**38**	6.6	7.0	7.3	7.6	7.9	8.2	8.5	8.9	9.2	9.5	9.8	10.1	10.8	11.4	12.0	12.7	**38**	.6333
.6500	**39**	6.8	7.1	7.5	7.8	8.1	8.4	8.8	9.1	9.4	9.7	10.1	10.4	11.0	11.7	12.3	13.0	**39**	.6500
.6667	**40**	7.0	7.3	7.7	8.0	8.3	8.7	9.0	9.3	9.7	10.0	10.3	10.7	11.3	12.0	12.7	13.3	**40**	.6667
.6833	**41**	7.2	7.5	7.9	8.2	8.5	8.9	9.2	9.6	9.9	10.2	10.6	10.9	11.6	12.3	13.0	13.7	**41**	.6833
.7000	**42**	7.3	7.7	8.0	8.4	8.7	9.1	9.4	9.8	10.1	10.5	10.8	11.2	11.9	12.6	13.3	14.0	**42**	.7000
.7167	**43**	7.5	7.9	8.2	8.6	9.0	9.3	9.7	10.0	10.4	10.8	11.1	11.5	12.2	12.9	13.6	14.3	**43**	.7167
.7333	**44**	7.7	8.1	8.4	8.8	9.2	9.5	10.0	10.3	10.6	11.0	11.4	11.7	12.5	13.2	13.9	14.7	**44**	.7333
.7500	**45**	7.9	8.2	8.6	9.0	9.4	9.7	10.1	10.5	10.9	11.2	11.6	12.0	12.7	13.5	14.2	15.0	**45**	.7500
.7667	**46**	8.1	8.4	8.8	9.2	9.6	10.0	10.4	10.7	11.1	11.5	11.9	12.3	13.0	13.8	14.6	15.3	**46**	.7667
.7833	**47**	8.2	8.6	9.0	9.4	9.8	10.2	10.6	11.0	11.4	11.7	12.1	12.5	13.3	14.1	14.9	15.7	**47**	.7833
.8000	**48**	8.4	8.8	9.2	9.6	10.0	10.4	10.8	11.2	11.6	12.0	12.4	12.8	13.6	14.4	15.2	16.0	**48**	.8000
.8167	**49**	8.6	9.0	9.4	9.8	10.2	10.6	11.0	11.4	11.8	12.2	12.7	13.1	13.9	14.7	15.5	16.3	**49**	.8167
.8333	**50**	8.7	9.2	9.6	10.0	10.4	10.8	11.2	11.7	12.1	12.5	12.9	13.3	14.2	15.0	15.8	16.7	**50**	.8333
.8500	**51**	8.9	9.3	9.8	10.2	10.6	11.0	11.5	11.9	12.3	12.7	13.2	13.6	14.4	15.3	16.1	17.0	**51**	.8500
.8667	**52**	9.1	9.5	10.0	10.4	10.8	11.3	11.7	12.1	12.6	13.0	13.4	13.9	14.7	15.6	16.5	17.3	**52**	.8667
.8833	**53**	9.3	9.7	10.2	10.6	11.0	11.5	11.9	12.4	12.8	13.2	13.7	14.1	15.0	15.9	16.8	17.7	**53**	.8833
.9000	**54**	9.4	9.9	10.3	10.8	11.2	11.7	12.1	12.6	13.0	13.5	13.9	14.4	15.3	16.2	17.1	18.0	**54**	.9000
.9167	**55**	9.6	10.1	10.5	11.0	11.5	11.9	12.4	12.8	13.3	13.8	14.2	14.7	15.6	16.5	17.4	18.3	**55**	.9167
.9333	**56**	9.8	10.3	10.7	11.2	11.7	12.1	12.6	13.1	13.5	14.0	14.5	14.9	15.9	16.8	17.7	18.7	**56**	.9333
.9500	**57**	10.0	10.4	10.9	11.4	11.9	12.3	12.8	13.3	13.8	14.2	14.7	15.2	16.1	17.1	18.0	19.0	**57**	.9500
.9667	**58**	10.2	10.6	11.1	11.6	12.1	12.6	13.1	13.5	14.0	14.5	15.0	15.5	16.4	17.4	18.4	19.3	**58**	.9667
.9833	**59**	10.3	10.8	11.3	11.8	12.3	12.8	13.3	13.8	14.3	14.7	15.2	15.7	16.7	17.7	18.7	19.7	**59**	.9833
1.0000	**60**	10.5	11.0	11.5	12.0	12.5	13.0	13.5	14.0	14.5	15.0	15.5	16.0	17.0	18.0	19.0	20.0	**60**	1.0000
Decimal of hr.	**Mins**	**10.5**	**11.0**	**11.5**	**12.0**	**12.5**	**13.0**	**13.5**	**14.0**	**14.5**	**15.0**	**15.5**	**16.0**	**17.0**	**18.0**	**19.0**	**20.0**	**Mins**	**Decimal of hr.**
Time		**Speed in knots**																**Time**	

TABLE 3(6) Measured Mile Table – Knots related to time over one nautical mile

Secs	1 min	2 min	3 min	4 min	5 min	6 min	7 min	8 min	9 min	10 min	11 min
0	60.00	30.00	20.00	15.00	12.00	10.00	8.57	7.50	6.67	6.00	5.45
1	59.02	29.75	19.89	14.94	11.96	9.97	8.55	7.48	6.66	5.99	5.45
2	58.06	29.51	19.78	14.88	11.92	9.94	8.53	7.47	6.64	5.98	5.44
3	57.14	29.27	19.67	14.81	11.88	9.92	8.51	7.45	6.63	5.97	5.43
4	56.25	29.03	19.57	14.75	11.84	9.89	8.49	7.44	6.62	5.96	5.42
5	55.38	28.80	19.46	14.69	11.80	9.86	8.47	7.42	6.61	5.95	5.41
6	54.55	28.57	19.35	14.63	11.76	9.84	8.45	7.41	6.59	5.94	5.41
7	53.73	28.35	19.25	14.57	11.73	9.81	8.43	7.39	6.58	5.93	5.40
8	52.94	28.12	19.15	14.52	11.69	9.78	8.41	7.38	6.57	5.92	5.39
9	52.17	27.91	19.05	14.46	11.65	9.76	8.39	7.36	6.56	5.91	5.38
10	51.43	27.69	18.95	14.40	11.61	9.73	8.37	7.35	6.55	5.90	5.37
11	50.70	27.48	18.85	14.34	11.58	9.70	8.35	7.33	6.53	5.89	5.37
12	50.00	27.27	18.75	14.29	11.54	9.68	8.33	7.32	6.52	5.88	5.36
13	49.32	27.07	18.65	14.23	11.50	9.65	8.31	7.30	6.51	5.87	5.35
14	48.65	26.87	18.56	14.17	11.46	9.63	8.29	7.29	6.50	5.86	5.34
15	48.00	26.67	18.46	14.12	11.43	9.60	8.28	7.27	6.49	5.85	5.33
16	47.37	26.47	18.37	14.06	11.39	9.58	8.26	7.26	6.47	5.84	5.33
17	46.75	26.28	18.27	14.01	11.36	9.55	8.24	7.24	6.46	5.83	5.32
18	46.15	26.09	18.18	13.95	11.32	9.52	8.22	7.23	6.45	5.83	5.31
19	45.57	25.90	18.09	13.90	11.29	9.50	8.20	7.21	6.44	5.82	5.30
20	45.00	25.71	18.00	13.85	11.25	9.47	8.18	7.20	6.43	5.81	5.29
21	44.44	25.53	17.91	13.79	11.21	9.45	8.16	7.19	6.42	5.80	5.29
22	43.90	25.35	17.82	13.74	11.18	9.42	8.14	7.17	6.41	5.79	5.28
23	43.37	25.17	17.73	13.69	11.15	9.40	8.13	7.16	6.39	5.78	5.27
24	42.86	25.00	17.65	13.64	11.11	9.37	8.11	7.14	6.38	5.77	5.26
25	42.35	24.83	17.56	13.58	11.08	9.35	8.09	7.13	6.37	5.76	5.26
26	41.86	24.66	17.48	13.53	11.04	9.33	8.07	7.11	6.36	5.75	5.25
27	41.38	24.49	17.39	13.48	11.01	9.30	8.05	7.10	6.35	5.74	5.24
28	40.91	24.32	17.31	13.43	10.98	9.28	8.04	7.09	6.34	5.73	5.23
29	40.45	24.16	17.22	13.38	10.94	9.25	8.02	7.07	6.33	5.72	5.22
30	40.00	24.00	17.14	13.33	10.91	9.23	8.00	7.06	6.32	5.71	5.22
31	39.56	23.84	17.06	13.28	10.88	9.21	7.98	7.04	6.30	5.71	5.21
32	39.13	23.68	16.98	13.24	10.84	9.18	7.96	7.03	6.29	5.70	5.20
33	38.71	23.53	16.90	13.19	10.81	9.16	7.95	7.02	6.28	5.69	5.19
34	38.30	23.38	16.82	13.14	10.78	9.14	7.93	7.00	6.27	5.68	5.19
35	37.89	23.23	16.74	13.09	10.75	9.11	7.91	6.99	6.26	5.67	5.18
36	37.50	23.08	16.67	13.04	10.71	9.09	7.89	6.98	6.25	5.66	5.17
37	37.11	22.93	16.59	13.00	10.68	9.07	7.88	6.96	6.24	5.65	5.16
38	36.73	22.78	16.51	12.95	10.65	9.05	7.86	6.95	6.23	5.64	5.16
39	36.36	22.64	16.44	12.90	10.62	9.02	7.84	6.94	6.22	5.63	5.15
40	36.00	22.50	16.36	12.86	10.59	9.00	7.83	6.92	6.21	5.62	5.14
41	35.64	22.36	16.29	12.81	10.56	8.98	7.81	6.91	6.20	5.62	5.13
42	35.29	22.22	16.22	12.77	10.53	8.96	7.79	6.90	6.19	5.61	5.13
43	34.95	22.09	16.14	12.72	10.50	8.93	7.78	6.89	6.17	5.60	5.12
44	34.62	21.95	16.07	12.68	10.47	8.91	7.76	6.87	6.16	5.59	5.11
45	34.29	21.82	16.00	12.63	10.43	8.89	7.74	6.86	6.15	5.58	5.10
46	33.96	21.69	15.93	12.59	10.40	8.87	7.72	6.84	6.14	5.57	5.10
47	33.64	21.56	15.86	12.54	10.37	8.85	7.71	6.83	6.13	5.56	5.09
48	33.33	21.43	15.79	12.50	10.34	8.82	7.69	6.82	6.12	5.56	5.08
49	33.03	21.30	15.72	12.46	10.32	8.80	7.68	6.80	6.11	5.55	5.08
50	32.73	21.18	15.65	12.41	10.29	8.78	7.66	6.79	6.10	5.54	5.07
51	32.43	21.05	15.58	12.37	10.26	8.76	7.64	6.78	6.09	5.53	5.06
52	32.14	20.93	15.52	12.33	10.23	8.74	7.63	6.77	6.08	5.52	5.06
53	31.86	20.81	15.45	12.29	10.20	8.72	7.61	6.75	6.07	5.51	5.05
54	31.58	20.69	15.38	12.24	19.17	8.70	7.59	6.74	6.06	5.50	5.04
55	31.30	20.57	15.32	12.20	10.14	8.67	7.58	6.73	6.05	5.50	5.04
56	31.03	20.45	15.25	12.16	10.11	8.65	7.56	6.72	6.04	5.49	5.03
57	30.77	20.34	15.19	12.12	10.08	8.63	7.55	6.70	6.03	5.48	5.02
58	30.51	20.22	15.13	12.08	10.06	8.61	7.53	6.69	6.02	5.47	5.01
59	30.25	20.11	15.06	12.04	10.03	8.59	7.52	6.68	6.01	5.46	5.00
Secs	1 min	2 min	3 min	4 min	5 min	6 min	7 min	8 min	9 min	10 min	11 min

(Continued from page 26)

Distance to radar horizon (in M) =

$$1.22 \times \sqrt{\text{Ht of scanner (in ft)}},$$

or

$$2.21 \times \sqrt{\text{Ht of scanner (in m)}}$$

Boat speed over measured distance of 1 M =

$$\frac{3600}{\text{time in seconds}} \text{ (knots)}$$

Horizontal sextant angle
Radius of position circle (in Ms) =

$$\frac{D}{2 \times \sin A}$$

where D is distance between objects in Ms, and A is the angle between them in degrees.

Vertical sextant angles

$$\text{Distance off (in Ms)} = \frac{\text{Ht of object (above MHWS, in ft)}}{6076 \times \tan\text{ (sextant angle)}}$$

$$\text{or} = \frac{\text{Ht of object (above MHWS, in m)}}{1852 \times \tan\text{ (sextant angle)}}$$

Note: sextant angle above is in degrees and minutes, and must be corrected for index error.

An approximate distance off, in Ms, adequate for most purposes is given by:

$$\text{Distance (Ms)} = \frac{\text{Ht of object (in feet)} \times 0.565}{\text{Sextant angle (in minutes)}}$$

$$\text{or} = \frac{\text{Ht of object (in metres)} \times 1.854}{\text{Sextant angle (in minutes)}}$$

Coastal navigation
To find the DR/EP, as bearing and distance from start position; example using TI.57. Key in:

1st distance run	5.2	x⇌t
1st course (°T)	230	→R STO 0 x⇌t STO 6
2nd distance run	1.9	x⇌t
2nd course (°T)	255	→R SUM 0 x⇌t SUM 6

Repeat for each subsequent Co(°T) and distance. For EP, treat Set/Drift as for Co(°T) and distance.

To display bearing and distance from start:

RCL 6 x⇌t RCL 0 → P	236.6	(°T)
x⇌t	6.97	(nm)

Note: To find EP, treat Set/Drift as for Co(°T) and distance run.
Example: Using RPN calculator. Key in:

1st course (°T)	230	ENTER
1st distance run	5.2	→R Σ+
2nd course (°T)	255	ENTER
2nd distance run	1.9	→R Σ+

Repeat for each subsequent Co (°T) and distance.

To display distance and bearing from start:

RCL 13(1) RCL 11(1) → P	6.97	M
x⇌y	236.6(2)	(°T)

Notes: (1) Check the actual stores used for vector summation in your calculator.
(2) If display negative (−), add 360

To find EP, treat Set/Drift as for Co(°T) and distance run.

Distance (D, in M) of object at second bearing

$$= \frac{R \times \sin A}{\sin (B - A)}$$

Predicted distance (in Ms) object will be off when abeam = D × sin B, where R is distance run (M) between two relative bearings of an object, first A degrees and then B degrees.

Course to steer and speed made good

$$\text{Co(°T)} = \text{Tr(°T)} - \sin^{-1} (\text{Drift} \div \text{Speed}) \times \sin (\text{Set} - \text{Track})$$

$$\text{SMG} = \text{Speed} \times \cos (\text{Co.T} - \text{Track}) + \text{Drift} \times \cos (\text{Set} - \text{Track})$$

Note: The Drift must be less than yacht's speed.

Conversion angle (half convergency)
Radio bearings follow great circles, and become curved lines when plotted on a Mercator chart, see 4.1.10. A correction may be needed for bearings of beacons more than about 60 Ms away, and can be calculated from the formula:
Conversion angle = ½ d.Long × sin mid Latitude

A great circle always lies on the polar side of the rhumb line, and conversion angle is applied towards the equator.

Short distance sailing
(Note: These formulae should not be used for distances over 600 Ms).

Departure = Distance × sin Course
= d.Long × cos Mean Latitude
= tan Course × d.Lat
d.Lat = Distance × cos Course
d.Long = Departure ÷ cos Mean Latitude
Distance = Departure ÷ sin Course
= d.Lat × sec Course
sin Course = Departure ÷ Distance
cos Course = d.Lat ÷ Distance
tan Course = Departure ÷ d.Lat

Further explanation of the use of calculators, and formulae for the calculation of tracks and distances for distances over 600 Ms are contained in Chapter 3 of *The Macmillan & Silk Cut Yachtsman's Handbook*.

3.1.4 LIGHT CHARACTERS (Fathoms and Metric Charts)

CLASS OF LIGHT		International abbreviations	Older form (where different)	Illustration Period shown
Fixed *(steady light)*		F		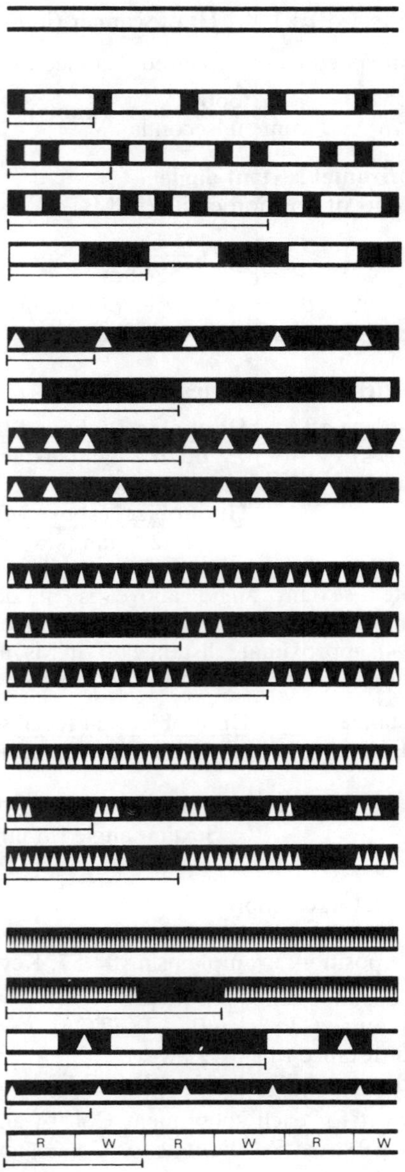
Occulting *(total duration of light more than dark)*				
Single-occulting		Oc	Occ	
Group-occulting	*e.g.*	Oc(2)	Gp Occ(2)	
Composite group-occulting	*e.g.*	Oc(2+3)	Gp Occ(2+3)	
Isophase *(light and dark equal)*		Iso		
Flashing *(total duration of light less than dark)*				
Single-flashing		Fl		
Long-flashing (flash 2s or longer)		L Fl		
Group-flashing	*e.g.*	Fl(3)	Gp Fl(3)	
Composite group-flashing	*e.g.*	Fl(2+1)	Gp Fl(2+1)	
Quick *(50 to 79—usually either 50 or 60—flashes per minute)*				
Continuous quick		Q	Qk Fl	
Group quick	*e.g.*	Q(3)	Qk Fl(3)	
Interrupted quick		IQ	Int Qk Fl	
Very Quick *(80 to 159—usually either 100 or 120—flashes per minute)*				
Continuous very quick		V Q	V Qk Fl	
Group very quick	*e.g.*	V Q(3)	V Qk Fl(3)	
Interrupted very quick		IV Q	Int V Qk Fl	
Ultra Quick *(160 or more—usually 240 to 300—flashes per minute)*				
Continuous ultra quick		UQ		
Interrupted ultra quick		IUQ		
Morse Code	*e.g.*	Mo(K)		
Fixed and Flashing		F Fl		
Alternating	*e.g.*	Al.WR	Alt.WR	

COLOUR	International abbreviations	Older form (where different)
White	W *(may be omitted)*	
Red	R	
Green	G	
Yellow	Y	
Orange	Y	Or
Blue	Bu	Bl
Violet	Vi	

RANGE in sea miles		International abbreviations	Older form
Single range	*e.g.*	15M	
2 ranges	*e.g.*	14/12M	14.12M
3 or more ranges	*e.g.*	22–18M	22,20,18M

ELEVATION is given in metres **(m)** or feet **(ft)**

PERIOD in seconds *e.g.*	International abbreviations	Older form
	5s	5sec

3.1.5 IALA Buoyage System (Region A)

(See also Plate 5 on page 121.)

International buoyage is harmonized into a single system which, applied to Regions A and B, differs only in the use of red and green lateral marks. In Region A (which includes all Europe) lateral marks are red on the port hand, and in Region B red on the starboard hand, related to direction of buoyage. Five types of marks are used, as illustrated in Plate 5, on page 121.

(1) *Lateral marks* are used in conjunction with a direction of buoyage, shown by a special arrow on the chart. In and around the British Isles its general direction is from SW to NE in open waters, but from seaward when approaching a harbour, river or estuary. Where port or starboard lateral marks do not rely on can or conical buoy shapes for identification they carry, where practicable, the appropriate topmarks. Any numbering or lettering follows the direction of buoyage.

In Region A, port hand marks are coloured red, and port hand buoys are can or spar shaped. Any topmark fitted is a single red can. Any light fitted is red, any rhythm. Starboard hand marks are coloured green, and starboard hand buoys are conical or spar shaped. Any topmark fitted is a single green cone, point up. Any light fitted is green, any rhythm. In exceptional cases starboard hand marks may be coloured black.

At a division, the preferred channel may be shown by lateral marks with red or green stripes:

Preferred channel	**Indicated by**	**Light (if any)**
To starboard	Port lateral mark with green stripe	Flashing red (2 + 1)
To port	Starboard lateral mark with red stripe	Flashing green (2 + 1)

(2) *Cardinal marks* are used in conjunction with a compass to show where dangers exist or where the mariner may find navigable water. They are named after the quadrant in which the mark is placed, in relation to the danger or point indicated. The four quadrants (North, East, South and West) are bounded by the true bearings NW–NE, NE–SE, SE–SW and SW–NW, taken from the point of interest. The name of a cardinal mark indicates that it should be passed on the named side.

A cardinal mark may indicate the safe side on which to pass a danger, or that the deepest water is on the named side of the mark, or it may draw attention to a feature in a channel such as a bend, junction or fork, or the end of a shoal.

Cardinal marks are pillar or spar shaped, painted black and yellow, and always carry black double cone topmarks, one cone above the other. Their lights are white, either very quick flashing (VQ or VQkFl) 120 to 100 flashes per minute, or quick flashing (Q or QkFl) 60 to 50 flashes per minute. A long flash is one of not less than two seconds duration.

North cardinal mark

Two black cones —	Points up
Colour —	Black above yellow
Light (if fitted) —	White; VQ or Q

East cardinal mark

Two black cones —	Base to base
Colour —	Black, with horizontal yellow band
Light (if fitted) —	White; VQ(3) 5 sec or Q(3) 10 sec

South cardinal mark

Two black cones —	Points down
Colour —	Yellow above black
Light (if fitted) —	White; VQ(6) plus long flash 10 sec or Q(6) plus long flash 15 sec

West cardinal mark

Two black cones —	Point to point
Colour —	Yellow, with horizontal black band
Light (if fitted) —	White; VQ(9) 10 sec or Q(9) 15 sec

(3) *Isolated danger marks* are placed on or above an isolated danger such as a rock or a wreck which has navigable water all around it. The marks are black, with one or more broad horizontal red bands. Buoys are pillar or spar shaped. Any light is white, flashing (2). Topmark—two black spheres.

(4) *Safe water marks* indicate that there is navigable water all round the mark, and are used for mid-channel or landfall marks. Buoys are spherical, pillar, with spherical topmark or spar, and are coloured with red and white vertical stripes. Any topmark fitted is a single red sphere. Any light fitted is white — either isophase, occulting or long flash every 10 seconds.

(5) *Special marks* do not primarily assist navigation, but indicate a special area or feature (e.g. spoil grounds, exercise areas, water ski areas, cable or pipeline marks, outfalls, Ocean Data Acquisition Systems (ODAS), or traffic separation marks where conventional channel marks may cause confusion). Special marks are yellow, and any shape not conflicting with lateral or safe water marks. If can, spherical or conical are used they indicate the side on which to pass. Any topmark fitted is a yellow X. Any light fitted is yellow, and may have any rhythm not used for white lights.

New dangers (which may be natural obstructions such as a sandbank, or a wreck for example) are marked in accordance with the rules above, and lit accordingly. For a very grave danger one of the marks may be duplicated.

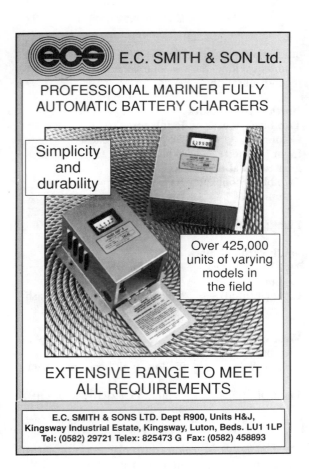

Chapter 4

Radio Navigational Aids

Contents

4

Radio navigational aids – introduction

The following subjects are described in detail in Chapter 4 of *The Macmillan & Silk Cut Yachtsman's Handbook:*

Marine radiobeacons; DF receiving sets; grouping and sequence of beacons; directional radiobeacons; beacons incorporating distance finding; Aero radiobeacons; types of emissions; operating procedures; errors in radio bearings; calibration; QTG service from Coast Radio Stations; VHF emergency direction finding service; half convergency; Consol; Decca Navigator; Loran-C; Omega; satellite navigation; radar; radar beacons (Racons).

The necessary detail about individual radiobeacons and Racons for navigational use is provided here in the *Almanac*, but for information on procedures and possible errors, together with the other subjects listed above, reference should be made to Chapter 4 of *The Macmillan & Silk Cut Yachtsman's Handbook.*

IMPORTANT NOTE: A major reorganisation of Marine Radiobeacons is planned for implementation commencing February 1992. The changes will affect both radiobeacons and frequencies. Details on the changes are not expected to be available before December 1991 and will be notified in the first available Supplement.

4.1 RADIOBEACONS

4.1.1 Marine radiobeacons — general

This widely-used system of direction finding allows a yachtsman to obtain a bearing from a non-directional radiobeacon, using a receiving set with an aerial which has directional qualities. This is useful in poor visibility, or when out of sight of land, but the effective range is limited, and few beacons give bearings of reasonable accuracy at distances of more than 50 miles.

Details of marine and aero radiobeacons in the area covered by this *Almanac* are given in Table 4(2), commencing on page 45. Often up to six marine beacons are grouped together to share the same frequency, and these groupings are also listed and shown diagrammatically in Table 4(2).

On Admiralty charts, marine radiobeacons are shown by a magenta circle with the letters 'RC'.

To obtain a bearing from a beacon, the yachtsman must tune his receiver to the frequency listed for that beacon in Table 4(2), positively identify its Morse callsign and then rotate the receiver aerial until a minimum, or null, signal is obtained.

4.1.2 DF receiving sets

Most sets have ferrite rod aerials, which give a minimum signal when in line with the direction of the beacon. Often the aerial incorporates a small compass, so that the operator can read the bearing at the moment that he identifies the null in his earphones. Such compasses are just as liable to error as any other magnetic compass, and must not be held close to magnetic objects.

With some sets the receiver itself is fixed, and the aerial rotates against a graduated scale, which shows the bearing relative to the ship's head. In this case it is necessary to record the course steered at the same moment as the null and the relative bearing.

An Automatic Direction Finding (ADF) set is tuned to the required frequency, and will then lock on to any transmission automatically, indicating the bearing. If there is a sequence of beacons on one frequency it will point to each in turn. Some sets even assess the reliability of individual bearings taken.

A quartz clock may be incorporated, to allow beacons to be identified by their time sequence, but this should only be considered an aid. A beacon should always be positively identified by its call (ident) sign in order to avoid possible errors.

4.1.3 Grouping and sequence of beacons

Where two or more beacons share a common frequency, they transmit on a strict time schedule, for one minute in turn. The minutes past each hour at which a beacon transmits, depending on its sequence number, is shown in the table at the foot of each relevant page of Table 4(2).

4.1.4 Beacons incorporating distance finding

A few beacons allow radio and sound signals to be synchronised for distance finding. The two signals are synchronised at an easily identifiable point in the cycle, e.g. at the start or end of a long dash. Using a stopwatch, the difference between the two times in seconds, multiplied by 0·18, gives the distance in nautical miles.

Another system involves the transmission of a number of measuring signals, started when the fog signal is sounded. The number of measuring signals received before the fog signal is heard indicates the distance. An interval of 5·5 seconds between measuring signals is equivalent to a unit distance of one nautical mile.

4.1.5 Aero Radiobeacons

Although intended for aircraft, some of those near the coast are useful to yachtsmen. They are shown on a chart by a small magenta circle, and the letters 'Aero RC'. These beacons transmit continuously during operational hours. They must be used with care, because the land effect (see 4.1.7) is unpredictable. Details of those beacons which may be of use to yachtsmen, in the area covered by this *Almanac*, are included in Table 4(2).

4.1.6 Types of emission (Modes)

There are several different types of radio emission from radiobeacons, and these are identified under the heading of 'Mode' in Table 4(2). If the receiver on board is fitted with a separate Beat Frequency Oscillator (BFO), this control should be adjusted as follows when taking radio bearings:

Mode		BFO setting	
Old style	New style	For DF use	For ident.
A1	A1A	ON	ON
AOA1	NON A1A	ON	ON
AOA2	NON A2A	ON	OFF[2]
A2	A2A	ON or OFF[1]	OFF[2]
A2*		ON or OFF[1]	OFF[2]
A3	A3E	ON or OFF[1]	OFF[2]

Notes: (1) For best performance consult the maker's handbook.
(2) If BFO cannot be switched off, it may be difficult to hear the Morse identification.

4.1.7 Errors in radio bearings

The various errors to which radio bearings are subject are described in Chapter 4 of *The Macmillan & Silk Cut Yachtsman's Handbook* (4.2.9). They fall into two categories — signal errors (caused by distance from the beacon, night or sky-wave effect particularly near sunset and sunrise, land effect or coastal refraction where the beam passes over high ground or along the coast, and synchronised transmissions of two beacons), and errors on board the boat (caused by quadrantal error due to magnetic objects re-radiating the incoming signal, compass error, the possibility of inadvertently taking a reciprocal bearing, and operating error due to inexperience or bad weather). Do not rely on radio bearings exclusively, unless three or more give an acceptable cocked hat.

4.1.8 Radiobeacons — calibration

A DF set can be calibrated for quadrantal error by taking simultaneous radio and visual bearings of a beacon on different headings. Alternatively radio bearings may be taken from a known position, and the bearing of the beacon taken from the chart. To save time it is helpful if the beacon transmits continuously. Beacons which provide a calibration service are shown in Table 4(3).

4.1.9 Half convergency

Half convergency is a correction to be applied to a radio bearing — which always follows a great circle path — to enable it to be plotted as a straight line on a Mercator chart. The correction does not become significant until the difference in longitude between the radio station and the yacht is 3 degrees or more. Half convergency is therefore unlikely to be of concern to most yachtsmen.

In North latitudes, for bearings taken from a yacht — if the yacht is East of the station, half convergency must be subtracted; if West of the station it must be added. For bearings provided by a DF station — if the yacht is East of the station, half convergency must be added; if West of the station, it must be subtracted. The opposite applies in the Southern hemisphere.

For practical purposes the values of half convergency given in Table 4(1) can be used for distances up to 1000 M.

4.2 POSITION FIXING SYSTEMS

4.2.1 Types of systems

Five systems are available for yachtsmen: Decca, Loran-C and Omega (all hyperbolic systems) and satellite navigation from the American Transit and GPS satellites. Each has its merits for particular applications, and they are described in *The Macmillan & Silk Cut Yachtsman's Handbook* (4.5).

The Decca Yacht Navigator uses the established

4

TABLE 4(1) Half convergency

Enter with difference in longitude between the station and the boat (along the top), and mid latitude between the station and the boat (down the side). The figures extracted are half convergency, in degrees.

Mid Lat	Difference in longitude (degrees) 3°	6°	9°	12°	15°	18°	21°	24°	27°	30°
5°	0.1	0.3	0.4	0.5	0.7	0.8	0.9	1.0	1.2	1.3
10°	0.3	0.5	0.8	1.0	1.3	1.6	1.8	2.1	2.3	2.6
15°	0.4	0.8	1.2	1.6	1.9	2.3	2.7	3.1	3.5	3.9
20°	0.5	1.0	1.5	2.1	2.6	3.1	3.6	4.1	4.6	5.1
25°	0.6	1.3	1.9	2.5	3.2	3.8	4.4	5.1	5.7	6.3
30°	0.7	1.5	2.2	3.0	3.7	4.5	5.2	6.0	6.7	7.5
35°	0.9	1.7	2.6	3.4	4.3	5.2	6.0	6.9	7.7	8.6
40°	1.0	1.9	2.9	3.9	4.8	5.8	6.7	7.7	8.7	9.6
45°	1.1	2.1	3.2	4.2	5.3	6.4	7.4	8.5	9.5	10.6
50°	1.1	2.3	3.4	4.6	5.7	6.9	8.0	9.2	10.3	11.5
55°	1.2	2.5	3.7	4.9	6.1	7.4	8.6	9.8	11.0	12.3
60°	1.3	2.6	3.9	5.2	6.5	7.8	9.1	10.4	11.7	13.0

Example. A yacht in DR position 42°N, 2°W obtains a radio bearing from a powerful station in position 58°N, 7°E. The difference in longitude between the two positions is 9°. The mid latitude is 50°. From inspection, the half convergency is 3·4°. Because the yacht is to the west of the station, this figure should be added to the bearing taken before it is plotted on the chart.

chains of Decca Navigator transmitting stations, and provides good coverage in NW Europe and in some other parts of the world (but not the Mediterranean). Loran-C covers the United States and much of the Northern hemisphere, but coverage of European waters is poor. Omega gives extensive global coverage, but the accuracy is not so good as Decca or Loran-C. Transit satellites give world-wide coverage, but a fix can only be obtained when there is a suitable satellite pass – about every 1½ hours in British waters. GPS gives better coverage and accuracy and is planned to become fully operational in 1992/1993. Currently GPS provides over 16 hours a day two dimensional fixing (latitude/longitude) in European waters.

4.2.2 Waypoints

For use with position fixing systems, over 2100 waypoints are given in Chapter 10 — for individual harbours (under the heading of 'Navigation' in each area), in section 4 of each Area (where they are underlined in the lists of 'Lights, Fog Signals and Waypoints'), for the Solent area (10.2.18), for cross-Channel passages (10.1.7), SE England (10.3.8), S North Sea (10.4.6) and for the Clyde (10.9.7).

Latitudes and longitudes are normally stated to one-hundredth of a minute, as taken from a large scale chart. But it should be realised that a chart using a different datum or based on another survey may give a slightly different position. Charts may contain small errors, just like the read-out from an electronic instrument.

Electronic systems are only aids to navigation and are subject to fixed and variable errors – or sometimes total failure. It is essential to maintain a DR plot, not only as a stand-by but to make sure that the boat's track is well clear of all dangers. Take great care when using waypoints on shore.

4.3 RADIO DIRECTION FINDING AND RADIO LIGHTHOUSES

4.3.1 Principle of operation — radio direction finding

Radio direction finding stations are shown on charts by the letters 'RG', and are equipped with apparatus to determine the direction of signals transmitted by a vessel. The vessel calls the station, and is requested to transmit a series of long dashes, followed by her callsign. There are no stations in the United Kingdom except as shown in 4.3.2, where the procedure is modified.

4.3.2 VHF emergency DF service

The stations below operate a VHF DF service for emergency use only. See Fig. 4(1). They are controlled by a Coastguard MRCC or MRSC as shown in brackets. On request from a yacht in distress, the station transmits her bearing *from the DF site*. Watch is kept on Ch 16. A yacht should transmit on Ch 16 (Distress Only) or on Ch 67 (Ch 67 or 82 for Jersey, and Ch 11 for French stations) to allow the station to obtain the bearing, which is transmitted on the same frequency.

St Mary's	(Falmouth)	49°55′.7N	06°18′.2W
Pendeen	(Falmouth)	50°08′.1N	05°38′.2W
Pendennis	(Falmouth)	50°08′.7N	05°02′.7W
Rame Head	(Brixham)	50°19′.0N	04°13′.1W
East Prawle	(Brixham)	50°13′.1N	03°42′.5W
Berry Head	(Brixham)	50°23′.9N	03°29′.0W
Grove Point	(Portland)	50°32′.9N	02°25′.2W
Hengistbury Head	(Portland)	50°42′.9N	01°45′.6W
Stenbury Down	(Solent)	50°36′.8N	01°14′.5W
Selsey Bill	(Solent)	50°43′.8N	00°48′.1W
Newhaven	(Solent)	50°46′.9N	00°03′.1E
Fairlight	(Dover)	50°52′.2N	00°38′.8E
Dover	(Dover)	51°07′.9N	01°20′.7E
North Foreland	(Dover)	51°22′.5N	01°26′.8E
Bawdsey	(Thames)	51°59′.5N	01°24′.6E
Trimingham	(Yarmouth)	52°54′.5N	01°20′.7E
Hunstanton	(Yarmouth)	52°56′.9N	00°29′.7E
Easington	(Humber)	53°39′.1N	00°05′.9E
Flamborough	(Humber)	54°07′.0N	00°05′.0W
Whitby	(Humber)	54°29′.4N	00°36′.2W
Tynemouth	(Tyne Tees)	55°01′.1N	01°24′.9W
Newton-by-the-Sea	(Tyne Tees)	55°31′.0N	01°37′.1W
St Abb's Head	(Forth)	55°54′.9N	02°12′.2W
Fife Ness	(Forth)	56°16′.7N	02°35′.2W
Inverbervie	(Aberdeen)	56°51′.1N	02°15′.7W
Windyheads Hill	(Aberdeen)	57°38′.9N	02°14′.5W
Compass Head	(Shetland)	59°52′.0N	01°16′.3W
Thrumster	(Pentland)	58°23′.5N	03°07′.2W
Dunnett Head	(Pentland)	58°40′.3N	03°22′.5W
Wideford Hill	(Pentland)	58°59′.3N	03°01′.4W
Sandwick	(Stornoway)	58°12′.6N	06°21′.2W
Barra	(Stornoway)	57°00′.8N	07°30′.4W
Rodel	(Stornoway)	57°44′.9N	06°57′.5W
Tiree	(Oban)	56°30′.3N	06°57′.8W
Kilchiaran	(Clyde)	56°46′.0N	06°27′.1W
Snaefell	(Liverpool)	54°15′.8N	04°27′.6W
Walney Island	(Liverpool)	54°06′.6N	03°15′.9W
Great Ormes Head	(Holyhead)	53°20′.0N	03°51′.2W
Mynydd Rhiw	(Holyhead)	52°50′.0N	04°37′.7W
St Ann's Head	(Milford Haven)	51°41′.0N	05°10′.5W
Hartland	(Swansea)	51°01′.1N	04°31′.3W
Trevose Head	(Falmouth)	50°32′.9N	05°01′.9W
Orlock Point	(Belfast)	54°40′.4N	05°35′.0W
West Torr	(Belfast)	55°11′.9N	06°05′.6W
Guernsey	—	49°26′.3N	02°35′.8W
Jersey	—	49°10′.8N	02°14′.3W
Etel	(CROSS)	47°39′.8N	03°12′.0W
Créac'h	(CROSS)	48°27′.6N	05°07′.7W
Roches Douvres	(CROSS)	49°06′.5N	02°48′.8W
Jobourg	(CROSS)	49°41′.1N	01°54′.6W
Griz-Nez	(CROSS)	50°52′.1N	01°35′.0E

For 4.3.3, details of VHF Radio Lighthouses, see pp. 64–65.

FIG. 4(1) VHF EMERGENCY DF SERVICE

VHF EMERGENCY DF SERVICE
United Kingdom Ch 16 (Distress only) Ch 67
Jersey Ch 67 or 82
France Ch 11
Compass Head
Wideford Hill
Dunnett Head
Thrumster
Sandwick
Windyheads Hill
Rodel
Barra
Inverbervie
Tiree
Kilchiaran
Fife Ness
St Abb's Head
Newton-by-the-Sea
West Torr
Tynemouth
Orlock Point
Whitby
Snaefell
Walney Island
Flamborough
Easington
Great Ormes Head
Hunstanton
Trimingham
Mynydd Rhiw
Bawdsey
St Ann's Head
North Foreland
Dover
Selsey Bill
Fairlight
Hartland
Hengistbury Head
Griz Nez
Trevose Head
Berry Head
Newhaven
Rame Head
Grove Point
Stenbury Down
Pendennis
East Prawle
Pendeen
St Mary's
Jobourg
Guernsey
Jersey
Roches Douvres
60°
58°
56°
54°
52°
50°
8°W
6°W
4°W
2°W
0°
2°E

FIG. 4(2) DECCA CHAINS — WESTERN EUROPE

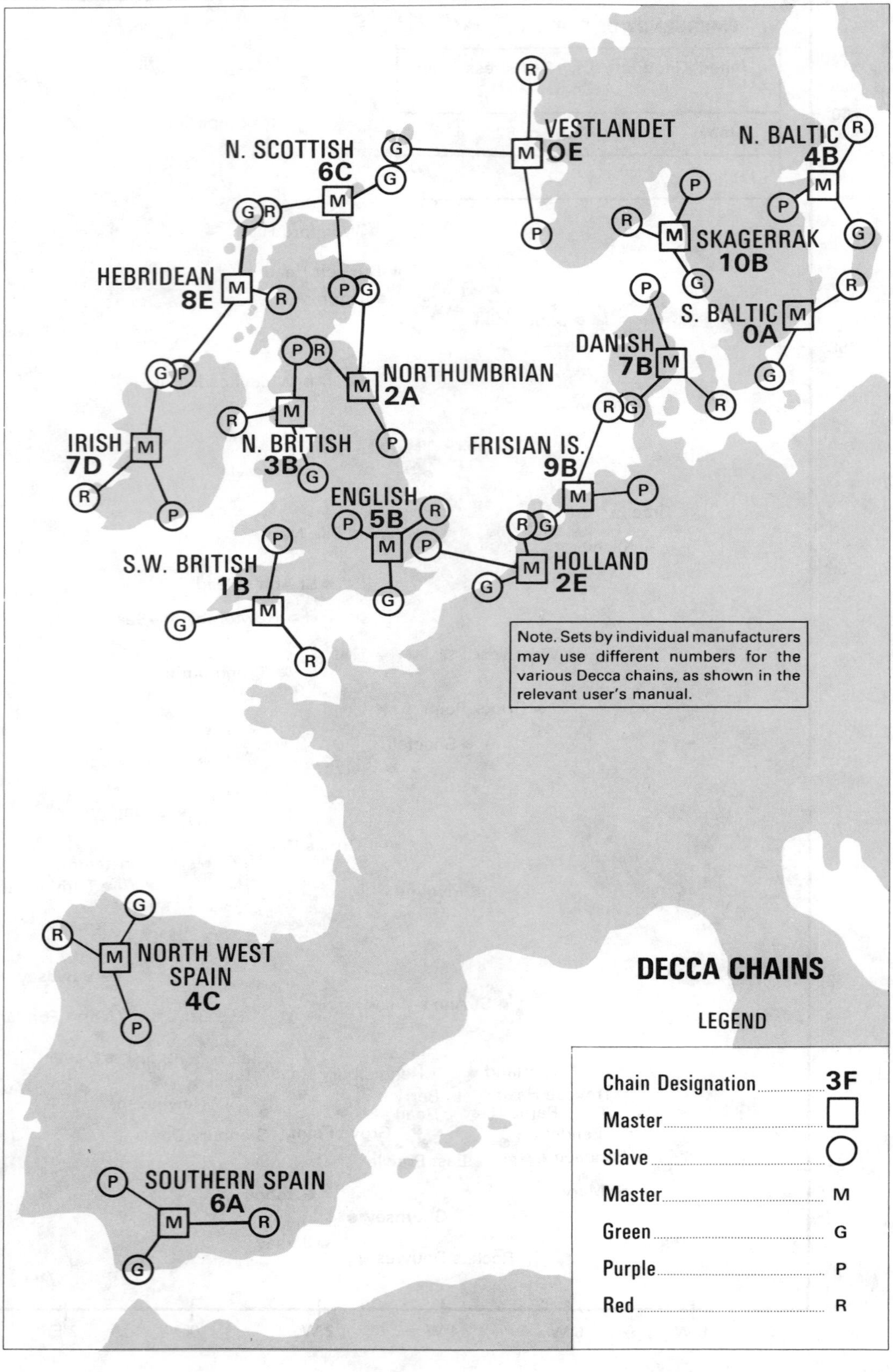
VESTLANDET
0E
N. BALTIC
4B
N. SCOTTISH
6C
SKAGERRAK
10B
HEBRIDEAN
8E
S. BALTIC
0A
DANISH
7B
NORTHUMBRIAN
2A
IRISH
7D
N. BRITISH
3B
FRISIAN IS.
9B
ENGLISH
5B
S.W. BRITISH
1B
HOLLAND
2E
Note. Sets by individual manufacturers may use different numbers for the various Decca chains, as shown in the relevant user's manual.
NORTH WEST
SPAIN
4C
SOUTHERN SPAIN
6A
DECCA CHAINS
LEGEND
Chain Designation 3F
Master
Slave
Master M
Green G
Purple P
Red R

IMPORTANT NOTE: A major reorganisation of Marine Radiobeacons is planned for implementation commencing February 1992. The changes will affect both radiobeacons and frequencies. Details on the changes are not expected to be available before December 1991 and will be notified in the first available Supplement.

TABLE 4(2) MARINE AND AERONAUTICAL RADIOBEACONS

Note: Beacon numbers prefixed with A are Aeronautical Radiobeacons

ENGLAND — SOUTH COAST

No	Name	Lat/Long	Ident	Freq	Mode	Range	Notes
1	**Round Island Lt** (grouped with 181)	49°58′.7N 06°19′.3W	**RR** •—• •—•	308	A2A	200/100 M	
A1	**St Mary's, Scilly**	49°54′.8N 06°17′.4W	**STM** ••• — ——	321	NonA2A	15 M	Day service
A2	**Penzance Heliport**	50°07′.7N 05°31′.0W	**PH** •——• ••••	333	Non A2A	15 M	Day service: Mon–Sat
5	**Lizard Lt** (grouped with 9)	49°57′.6N 05°12′.1W	**LZ** •—•• ——••	298.8	A2A	70 M	
9	**Penlee Point**	50°19′.1N 04°11′.3W	**PE** •——• •	298.8	A2A	50 M	

No	*Name*	*Ident*		*Range*	*Seq*	*Mode*	*Fog*	*Clear*
9	Penlee Point	PE	•——• •	50	1	A2A	Cont	Cont
13	Start Point	SP	••• •——•	70	2	A2A	Cont	Cont
255	Casquets	QS	——•— •••	50	3	A2A	Cont	Cont
635	Roches Douvres	RD	•—• —••	70	4	A2A	Cont	Cont
623	Ile Vierge	VG	•••— ——•	70	5	A2A	Cont	Cont
5	Lizard	LZ	•—•• ——••	70	6	A2A	Cont	Cont

No	Name	Lat/Long	Ident	Freq	Mode	Range	Notes
A6	**Plymouth**	50.25′.4N 04°06′.7W	**PY** •——• —•——	396.5	Non A2A	20 M	
13	**Start Point Lt.** (grouped with 9)	50°13′.3N 03°38′.5W	**SP** ••• •——•	298.8	A2A	70 M	
A10	**Berry Head**	50°23′.9N 03°29′.6W	**BHD** —••• •••• —••	318	NonA2A	25 M	
A14	**Exeter**	50°45′.1N 03°17′.6W	**EX** • —••—	337	NonA2A	15 M	Day service
17	**Portland Bill**	50°30′.8N 02°27′.3W	**PB** •——• —•••	291.9	A2A	50 M	

No	*Name*	*Ident*		*Range*	*Seq*	*Mode*	*Fog*	*Clear*
17	Portland Bill	PB	•——• —•••	50	1	A2A	Cont	Cont
25	St Catherine's Pt	CP	—•—• •——•	50	2	A2A	Cont	Cont
667	C d'Antifer	TI	— ••	50	3	A2A	Cont	Cont
663	Le Havre Lanby	LH	•—•• ••••	30	4	A2A	Cont	Cont
659	P de Ver	ÉR	••——•• •—•	20	5	A2A	Cont	Cont
651	P de Barfleur	FG	••—• ——•	70	6	A2A	Cont	Cont

No	Name	Lat/Long	Ident	Freq	Mode	Range	Notes
A18	**Bournemouth/Hurn**	50°48′.0N 01°43′.7W	**HRN** •••• •—• —•	401.5	NonA2A	30 M	
A20	**Bournemouth/Hurn**	50°45′.7N 01°56′.6W	**BMH** —••• —— ••••	339	NonA2A	15 M	
21	**Poole Harbour** (grouped with 29)	50°40′.9N 01°56′.7W	**PO** •——• ———	303.4	A2A	10 M	
25	**St Catherine's Pt Lt** (grouped with 17)	50°34′.5N 01°17′.8W	**CP** —•—• •——•	291.9	A2A	50 M	
A26	**Bembridge**	50°40′.6N 01°05′.9W	**IW** •• •——	274.5	Non A2A	15 M	
A30	**Lee-on-Solent**	50°52′.9N 01°06′.7W	**LS** •—•• •••	323	Non A2A	10 M	
29	**Chichester Bar Bn**	50°45′.9N 00°56′.3W	**CH** —•—• ••••	303.4	A2A	10 M	Coded wind info as below

CH 4 times: 4s dash: up to 8 dashes (direction; 1 dash = NE, 8 dashes = N): 4s dash: up to 8 dots (speed: Beaufort 1–8): 12s dash: CH twice: 5s silence.

No	*Name*	*Ident*		*Range*	*Seq*	*Mode*	*Fog*	*Clear*
29	Chichester	CH	—•—• ••••	10	1,4	A2A	Cont	Cont
37	Brighton	BM	—••• ——	10	2,5	A2A	Cont	Cont
41	Newhaven	NH	—• ••••	10	3,6	A2A	Cont	Cont
21	Poole	PO	•——• ———	10	3,6	A2A	Cont	Cont

4

IMPORTANT NOTE: A major reorganisation of Marine Radiobeacons is planned for implementation commencing February 1992. The changes will affect both radiobeacons and frequencies. Details on the changes are not expected to be available before December 1991 and will be notified in the first available Supplement.

No	Name	Lat/Long	Ident	Freq	Mode	Range	Notes
33	**Nab Tower Lt**	50°40′.0N 00°57′.1W	**NB** —• —•••	312.6	A2A	10 M	

No	*Name*	*Ident*		*Range*	*Seq*	*Mode*	*Fog*	*Clear*
33	Nab	NB	—• —•••	10	1,3,5	A2A	Cont	Cont
647	Cherbourg	RB	•—• —•••	20	2,4,6	A2A	Cont	Cont

No	Name	Lat/Long	Ident	Freq	Mode	Range	Notes
A38	**Shoreham**	50°49′.9N 00°17′.6W	**SHM** ••• •••• ——	332	Non A2A	10 M	Day service
37	**Brighton Marina** (grouped with 29)	50°48′.7N 00°05′.9W	**BM** —••• ——	303.4	A2A	10 M	
41	**Newhaven** (grouped with 29)	50°46′.9N 00°03′.5E	**NH** —• ••••	303.4	A2A	10 M	
45	**Royal Sovereign Lt** (grouped with 679)	50°43′.4N 00°26′.2E	**RY** •—• —•——	310.3	A2A	50 M	
A42	**Lydd**	50°58′.2N 00°57′.3E	**LYX** •—•• —•—— —••—	397	Non A2A	15 M	
49	**Dungeness Lt** (grouped with 679)	50°54′.8N 00°58′.7E	**DU** —•• ••—	310.3	A2A	30 M	
57	**North Foreland Lt**	51°22′.5N 01°26′.8E	**NF** —• ••—•	301.1	A2A	50 M	
61	**Falls Lt V**	51°18′.1N 01°48′.5E	**FS** ••—• •••	305.7	A2A	50 M	

No	*Name*	*Ident*		*Range*	*Seq*	*Mode*	*Fog*	*Clear*
61	Falls Lt V	FS	••—• •••	50	1	A2A	Cont	Cont
701	W Hinder Lt V	WH	•—— ••••	20	3	A2A	Cont	Cont
713	Oostende	OE	——— •	30	4	A2A	Cont	Cont
691	Calais Main Lt	CS	—•—• •••	20	5	A2A	Cont	Cont

ENGLAND — EAST COAST

No	Name	Lat/Long	Ident	Freq	Mode	Range	Notes
A46	**Southend**	51°34′.5N 00°42′.1E	**SND** ••• —• —••	362.5	Non A2A	20 M	
A48	**Clacton**	51°50′.9N 01°09′.0E	**CLN** —•—• •—•• —•	295.0	NonA2A	30 M	
69	**Sunk Lt F**	51°51′.0N 01°35′.0E	**UK** ••— —•—	312.6	A2A	10 M	
73	**Outer Gabbard Lt V** (grouped with 77)	51°59′.4N 02°04′.6E	**GA** ——• •—	287.3	A2A	50 M	
77	**Smith's Knoll Lt V**	52°43′.5N 02°18′.0E	**SK** ••• —•—	287.3	A2A	50 M	

No	*Name*	*Ident*		*Range*	*Seq*	*Mode*	*Fog*	*Clear*
77	Smith's Knoll Lt V	SK	••• —•—	50	1	A2A	Cont	Cont
721	Goeree Lt	GR	——• •—•	50	2	A2A	Cont	Cont
85	Dudgeon Lt V	LV	•—•• •••—	50	3	A2A	Cont	Cont
73	Outer Gabbard Lt V	GA	——• •—	50	4	A2A	Cont	Cont
81	Cromer	CM	—•—• ——	50	5	A2A	Cont	Cont
709	N Hinder Lt V	NR	—• •—•	50	6	A2A	Cont	Cont

BEACON SEQUENCE NUMBERS Commence transmission at the following minutes past the hour:

1 00 06 12 18 24 30 36 42 48 54	**2** 01 07 13 19 25 31 37 43 49 55	**3** 02 08 14 20 26 32 38 44 50 56
4 03 09 15 21 27 33 39 45 51 57	**5** 04 10 16 22 28 34 40 46 52 58	**6** 05 11 17 23 29 35 41 47 53 59

IMPORTANT NOTE: A major reorganisation of Marine Radiobeacons is planned for implementation commencing February 1992. The changes will affect both radiobeacons and frequencies. Details on the changes are not expected to be available before December 1991 and will be notified in the first available Supplement.

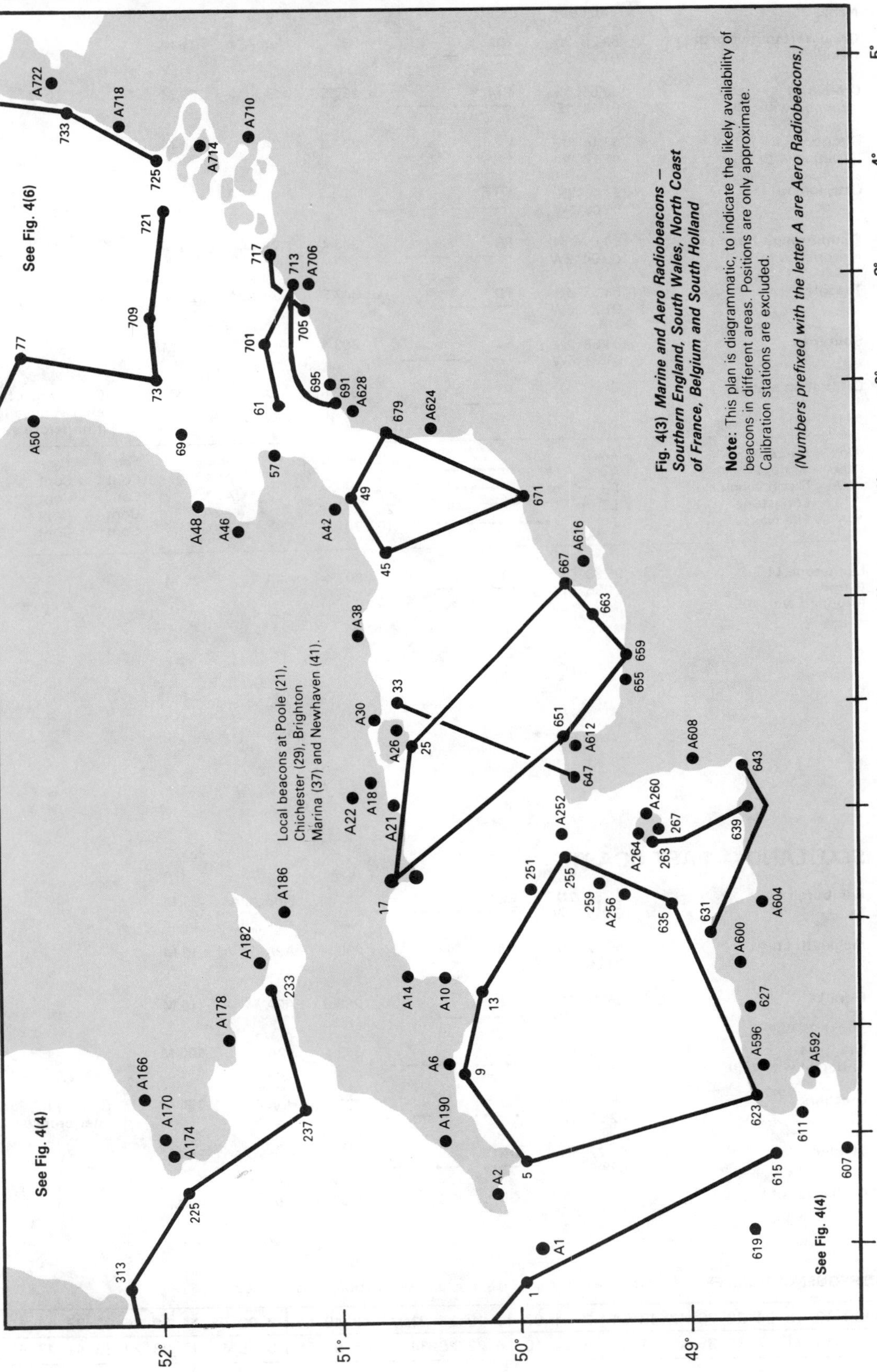

See Fig. 4(6)
See Fig. 4(4)
See Fig. 4(4)
Local beacons at Poole (21), Chichester (29), Brighton Marina (37) and Newhaven (41).
52°
51°
50°
49°
6°
5°
4°
3°
2°
1°
0°
1°
2°
3°
4°
5°

Fig. 4(3) Marine and Aero Radiobeacons – Southern England, South Wales, North Coast of France, Belgium and South Holland

Note: This plan is diagrammatic, to indicate the likely availability of beacons in different areas. Positions are only approximate. Calibration stations are excluded.

(Numbers prefixed with the letter A are Aero Radiobeacons.)

IMPORTANT NOTE: A major reorganisation of Marine Radiobeacons is planned for implementation commencing February 1992. The changes will affect both radiobeacons and frequencies. Details on the changes are not expected to be available before December 1991 and will be notified in the first available Supplement.

No	Name	Lat/Long	Ident	Freq	Mode	Range	Notes
A50	**Great Yarmouth/North Denes**	52°38′.2N 01°43′.5E	**ND** —• —••	397	Non A2A	15 M	
81	**Cromer Lt** (grouped with 77)	52°55′.5N 01°19′.1E	**CM** —•—• ——	287.3	A2A	50 M	
85	**Dudgeon Lt V** (grouped with 77)	53°16′.6N 01°17′.0E	**LV** •—•• •••—	287.3	A2A	50 M	
A54	**Ottringham**	53°41′.9N 00°06′.1W	**OTR** ——— — •—•	398.5	Non A2A	30 M	
97	**Flamborough Head Lt** (grouped with 109)	54°07′.0N 00°04′.9W	**FB** ••—• —•••	303.4	A2A	70 M	
A58	**Teeside**	54°33′.6N 01°20′.0W	**TD** — —••	347.5	Non A2A	25 M	
109	**Souter Lt**	54°58′.2N 01°21′.8W	**SJ** ••• •———	303.4	A2A	70 M	
	Calibration station		**PT** •——• —	312.6	A2A	5 M	Cont from 1 hour after sunrise to 1 hr before sunset

No	*Name*	*Ident*		*Range*	*Seq*	*Mode*	*Fog*	*Clear*
109	Souter Lt	SJ	••• •———	70	1,4	A2A	Cont	Cont
97	Flamborough Hd	FB	••—• —•••	70	2	A2A	Cont	Cont
113	Longstone	LT	•—•• —	20	5	A2A	Cont	Cont
125	Fife Ness	FP	••—• •——•	100/70	6	A2A	Cont	Cont

No	Name	Lat/Long	Ident	Freq	Mode	Range	Notes
113	**Longstone Lt** (Farne I) (grouped with 109)	55°38′.6N 01°36′.5W	**LT** •—•• —	303.4	A2A	20 M	

SCOTLAND — EAST COAST

No	Name	Lat/Long	Ident	Freq	Mode	Range	Notes
A70	**Edinburgh**	55°58′.7N 03°17′.0W	**EDN** • —•• —•	341	Non A2A	35 M	
117	**Inchkeith Lt**	56°02′.0N 03°08′.1W	**NK** —• —•—	296.5	A2A	10 M	
119	**Fidra Lt**	56°04′.4N 02°47′.0W	**FD** ••—• —••	289.6	A2A	10 M	
125	**Fife Ness** (grouped with 109)	56°16′.7N 02°35′.1W	**FP** ••—• •——•	303.4	A2A	100 M	
A74	**Leuchars**	56°22′.3N 02°51′.4W	**LU** •—•• ••—	330	Non A2A	100 M	Subject to night interference
A78	**Dundee**	56°27′.3N 03°06′.6W	**DND** —•• —• —••	394	Non A2A	25 M	
133	**Girdle Ness Lt**	57°08′.3N 02°02′.8W	**GD** ——• —••	310.3	A2A	50 M	

BEACON SEQUENCE NUMBERS Commence transmission at the following minutes past the hour:

1 00 06 12 18 24 30 36 42 48 54	**2** 01 07 13 19 25 31 37 43 49 55	**3** 02 08 14 20 26 32 38 44 50 56
4 03 09 15 21 27 33 39 45 51 57	**5** 04 10 16 22 28 34 40 46 52 58	**6** 05 11 17 23 29 35 41 47 53 59

IMPORTANT NOTE: A major reorganisation of Marine Radiobeacons is planned for implementation commencing February 1992. The changes will affect both radiobeacons and frequencies. Details on the changes are not expected to be available before December 1991 and will be notified in the first available Supplement.

No	Name	Lat/Long	Ident	Freq	Mode	Range	Notes
A82	**Aberdeen**	57°16′.1N 02°14′.7W	**AOS** •— ——— •••	377	Non A2A	50 M	
A86	**Scotstown Head**	57°33′.6N 01°48′.9W	**SHD** ••• •••• —••	383	Non A2A	80 M	
137	**Kinnairds Head**	57°41′.9N 02°00′.1W	**KD** —•— —••	291.9	A2A	100/70 M	

No	*Name*	*Ident*		*Range*	*Seq*	*Mode*	*Fog*	*Clear*
137	Kinnairds Hd	KD	—•— —••	100/70	1,4	A2A	Cont	Cont
145	N Ronaldsay	NR	—• •—•	100/70	2	A2A	Cont	Cont
141	Stroma (Swilkie Pt)	OM	——— ——	50	3,6	A2A	Cont	Cont
149	Sumburgh Hd	SB	••• —•••	70	5	A2A	Cont	Cont

No	Name	Lat/Long	Ident	Freq	Mode	Range	Notes
A90	**Kinloss**	57°39′.0N 03°35′.0W	**KS** —•— •••	370	Non A2A	50 M	
A94	**Wick**	58°26′.8N 03°03′.7W	**WIK** •—— •• —•—	344	Non A2A	40 M	
141	**Stroma, Swilkie Pt Lt** (grouped with 137)	58°41′.8N 03°06′.9W	**OM** ——— ——	291.9	A2A	50 M	
A98	**Kirkwall, Orkney**	58°57′.6N 02°54′.6W	**KW** —•— •——	395	Non A2A	30 M	
145	**North Ronaldsay Lt** (grouped with 137)	59°23′.4N 02°22′.8W	**NR** —• •—•	291.9	A2A	100/70 M	
A102	**Sumburgh**	59°52′.1N 01°16′.3W	**SUM** ••• ••— ——	351	Non A2A	75 M	
149	**Sumburgh Hd Lt** (grouped with 137)	59°51′.3N 01°16′.4W	**SB** ••• —•••	291.9	A2A	70 M	
153	**Bressay Lt, Shetland I**	60°07′.2N 01°07′.2W	**BY** —••• —•——	287.3	A2A	30 M	
A106	**Lerwick/Tingwall**	60°11′.3N 01°14′.7W	**TL** — •—••	376	Non A2A	25 M	
A110	**Scatsa**	60°27′.7N 01°12′.8W	**SS** ••• •••	315.5	Non A2A	25 M	
A114	**Unst**	60°44′.3N 00°49′.2W	**UT** ••— —	325	Non A2A	20 M	
157	**Muckle Flugga (N Unst Lt)** (grouped with 165)	60°51′.3N 00°53′.0W	**MF** —— ••—•	298.8	A2A	150/70 M	
161	**Sule Skerry Lt** (grouped with 165)	59°05′.1N 04°24′.3W	**LK** •—•• —•—	298.8	A2A	100/70 M	

SCOTLAND — WEST COAST

No	Name	Lat/Long	Ident	Freq	Mode	Range	Notes
A118	**Dounreay/Thurso**	58°34′.9N 03°43′.6W	**DO** —•• ———	364.5	Non A2A	15 M	
165	**Cape Wrath Lt**	58°37′.5N 04°59′.9W	**CW** —•—• •——	298.8	A2A	50 M	

No	*Name*	*Ident*		*Range*	*Seq*	*Mode*	*Fog*	*Clear*
165	Cape Wrath	CW	—•—• •——	50	1	A2A	Cont	Cont
169	Butt of Lewis	BL	—••• •—••	150	2,5	A2A	Cont	Cont
157	Muckle Flugga	MF	—— ••—•	150/70	3,6	A2A	Cont	Cont
161	Sule Skerry	LK	•—•• —•—	100/70	4	A2A	Cont	Cont

4

IMPORTANT NOTE: A major reorganisation of Marine Radiobeacons is planned for implementation commencing February 1992. The changes will affect both radiobeacons and frequencies. Details on the changes are not expected to be available before December 1991 and will be notified in the first available Supplement.

No	Name	Lat/Long	Ident	Freq	Mode	Range	Notes
169	**Butt of Lewis Lt** (grouped with 165)	58°30′.9N 06°15′.7W	**BL** —••• •—••	299.8	A2A	150 M	
A120	**Stornoway**	58°17′.2N 06°20′.6W	**SWY** ••• •—— —•——	669.5	Non A2A	60 M	
173	**Eilean Glas Lt** (grouped with 189)	57°51′.4N 06°38′.4W	**LG** •—•• ——•	294.2	A2A	50 M	
177	**Hyskeir Lt, Oigh Sgeir** (grouped with 189)	56°58′.1N 06°40′.8W	**OR** ——— •—•	294.2	A2A	50 M	
A122	**St Kilda**	57°49′.0N 08°35′.0W	**KL** —•— •—••	338	A2A	30 M	
A124	**Barra**	57°01′.4N 07°26′.4W	**BRR** —••• •—• •—•	316	Non A2A	20 M	Occas
181	**Barra Head Lt, Berneray**	56°47′.1N 07°39′.2W	**BD** —••• —••	308	A2A	200/70 M	

No	*Name*	*Ident*		*Range*	*Seq*	*Mode*	*Fog*	*Clear*
181	Barra Hd	BD	—••• —••	200/70	1	A2A	Cont	Cont
337	Tory I	TY	— —•——	100/70	2	A2A	Cont	Cont
341	Eagle I	GL	——• •—••	200/100	3	A2A	Cont	Cont
301	Mizen Hd	MZ	—— ——••	200/100	4	A2A	Cont	Cont
1	Round I	RR	•—• •—•	200/100	5	A2A	Cont	Cont
615	Pte de Créac'h	CA	—•—• •—	100	6	A2A	Cont	Cont

No	Name	Lat/Long	Ident	Freq	Mode	Range	Notes
A126	**Connel/Oban**	56°28′.0N 05°24′.0W	CNL —•—• —• •—••	404	Non A2A	15 M	
185	**Rhinns of Islay Lt** (grouped with 189)	55°40′.4N 06°30′.7W	**RN** •—• —•	294.2	A2A	70 M	
A128	**Islay/Port Ellen**	55°41′.0N 06°14′.9N	**LAY** •—•• •— —•——	395	A2A	20 M	Day service
189	**Pladda Lt, Arran I**	55°25′.5N 05°07′.1W	**DA** —•• •—	294.2	A2A	30 M	

No	*Name*	*Ident*		*Range*	*Seq*	*Mode*	*Fog*	*Clear*
189	Pladda	DA	—•• •—	30	1	A2A	Cont	Cont
329	Mew I	MW	—— •——	50	2	A2A	Cont	Cont
333	Altacarry Hd	AH	•— ••••	50	3	A2A	Cont	Cont
185	Rhinns of Islay	RN	•—• —•	70	4	A2A	Cont	Cont
177	Hyskeir	OR	——— •—•	50	5	A2A	Cont	Cont
173	Eilean Glas	LG	•—•• ——•	50	6	A2A	Cont	Cont

No	Name	Lat/Long	Ident	Freq	Mode	Range	Notes
193	**Cloch Pt Lt** (calibration station)	55°56′.5N 04°52′.7W	**CL** —•—• •—••	308		8 M	On request Tel: (0475) 26221 (6 hrs notice)
A138	**Turnberry**	55°18′.8N 04°47′.0W	**TRN** — •—• —•	355	Non A2A	25 M	
A142	**New Galloway**	55°10′.6N 04°10′.0W	**NGY** —• ——• —•——	399	Non A2A	35 M	

ENGLAND (WEST COAST), ISLE OF MAN, WALES

No	Name	Lat/Long	Ident	Freq	Mode	Range	Notes
197	**Point of Ayre High Light** (grouped with 217)	54°24′.9N 04°22′.0W	**PY** •——• —•——	301.1	A2A	50 M	
201	**Douglas, Victoria Pier Lt** (grouped with 209)	54°08′.8N 04°28′.0W	**DG** —•• ——•	287.3	A2A	50 M	

BEACON SEQUENCE NUMBERS Commence transmission at the following minutes past the hour:

1 00 06 12 18 24 30 36 42 48 54	**2** 01 07 13 19 25 31 37 43 49 55	**3** 02 08 14 20 26 32 38 44 50 56
4 03 09 15 21 27 33 39 45 51 57	**5** 04 10 16 22 28 34 40 46 52 58	**6** 05 11 17 23 29 35 41 47 53 59

IMPORTANT NOTE: A major reorganisation of Marine Radiobeacons is planned for implementation commencing February 1992. The changes will affect both radiobeacons and frequencies. Details on the changes are not expected to be available before December 1991 and will be notified in the first available Supplement.

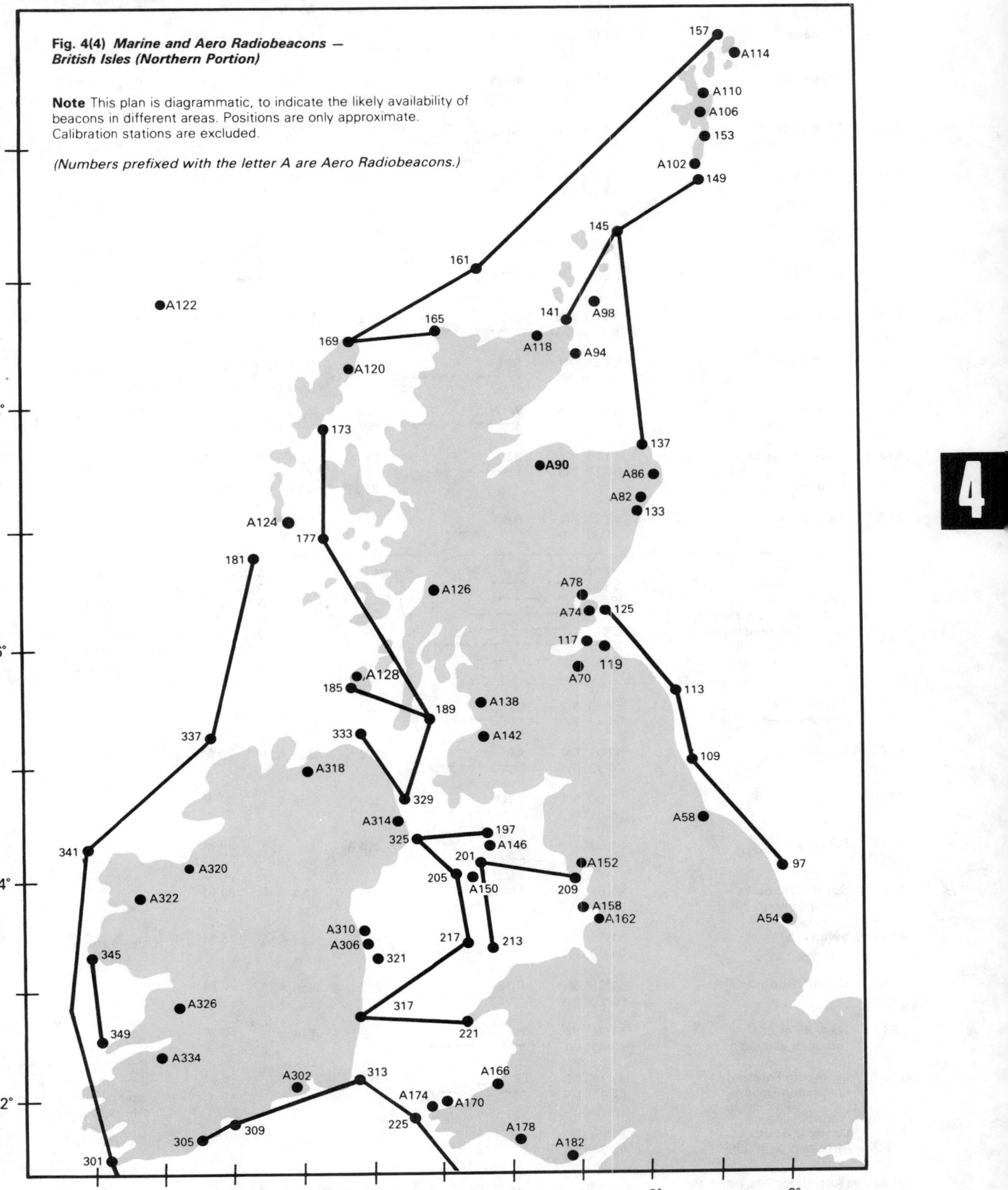
157
A114
A110
A106
153
A102
149
145
161
A122
141
A98
165
169
A118
A94
A120
173
137
A90
A86
A82
133
A124
177
181
A78
A126
A74
125
117
119
A70
A128
185
113
189
A138
333
337
A142
109
A318
329
A314
A58
325
197
A146
341
201
A152
97
A320
205
A150
209
A322
A158
A162
A54
A310
A306
217
213
321
345
317
A326
221
349
A334
A166
A302
313
A174
A170
309
225
A178
305
A182
301
60°
58°
56°
54°
52°
10°
8°
6°
4°
2°
0°
4

Fig. 4(4) Marine and Aero Radiobeacons — British Isles (Northern Portion)

Note This plan is diagrammatic, to indicate the likely availability of beacons in different areas. Positions are only approximate. Calibration stations are excluded.

(Numbers prefixed with the letter A are Aero Radiobeacons.)

IMPORTANT NOTE: A major reorganisation of Marine Radiobeacons is planned for implementation commencing February 1992. The changes will affect both radiobeacons and frequencies. Details on the changes are not expected to be available before December 1991 and will be notified in the first available Supplement.

No	Name	Lat/Long	Ident	Freq	Mode	Range	Notes
A146	**Carnane**	54°08′.5N 04°29′.4W	**CAR** —·—· ·— ·—·	366.5	Non A2A	25 M	
A150	**IOM/Ronaldsway**	54°05′.1N 04°36′.4W	**RWY** ·—· ·—— —·——	359	Non A2A	20 M	Day service
205	**Cregneish, IOM** (grouped with 217)	54°03′.9N 04°45′.9W	**CN** —·—· —·	301.1	A2A	50 M	
209	**Walney Island Lt**	54°02′.9N 03°10′.5W	**FN** ··—· —·	287.3	A2A	30 M	

No	*Name*	*Ident*		*Range*	*Seq*	*Mode*	*Fog*	*Clear*
209	Walney I	FN	··—· —·	30	1,4	A2A	Cont	Cont
213	Point Lynas	PS	·——· ···	40	2,5	A2A	Cont	Cont
201	Douglas	DG	—·· ——·	50	3,6	A2A	Cont	Cont

No	Name	Lat/Long	Ident	Freq	Mode	Range	Notes
A152	**Walney Island**	54°07′.6N 03°15′.8W	**WL** ·—— ·—··	385	A2A	15 M	Day service
A158	**Blackpool**	53°46′.2N 02°59′.3W	**BPL** —··· ·——· ·—··	276.5	Non A2A	15 M	Day service
A162	**Warton**	53°45′.1N 02°51′.1W	**WTN** ·—— — —·	337	A2A	15 M	Day service
213	**Point Lynas Lt** (grouped with 209) Calibration station	53°25′.0N 04°17′.3W	**PS** ·——· ···	287.3 310.3	A2A A2A	40 M 5 M	 H24
217	**Skerries Lt**	53°25′.3N 04°36′.5W	**SR** ··· ·—·	301.1	A2A	50 M	

No	*Name*	*Ident*		*Range*	*Seq*	*Mode*	*Fog*	*Clear*
217	Skerries	SR	··· ·—·	50	1	A2A	Cont	Cont
221	Bardsey Lt	IB	·· —···	30	2	A2A	Cont	Cont
317	Wicklow Hd	WK	·—— —·—	70	3	A2A	Cont	Cont
205	Cregneish	CN	—·—· —·	50	4	A2A	Cont	Cont
197	Point of Ayre	PY	·——· —·——	50	5	A2A	Cont	Cont
325	South Rock Lt F	SU	··· ··—	50	6	A2A	Cont	Cont

No	Name	Lat/Long	Ident	Freq	Mode	Range	Notes
221	**Bardsey Lt** (grouped with 217)	52°45′.0N 04°47′.9W	**IB** ·· —···	301.1	A2A	30 M	
A166	**Aberporth**	52°07′.0N 04°33′.6W	**AP** ·— ·——·	370.5	Non A2A	20 M	
A170	**Strumble**	52°00′.5N 05°01′.0W	**STU** ··· — ··—	400	Non A2A	40 M	
A174	**Brawdy**	51°53′.4N 05°07′.3W	**BY** —··· —·——	414.5	Non A2A	30 M	
225	**South Bishop Lt** (grouped with 309)	51°51′.1N 05°24′.6W	**SB** ··· —···	296.5	A2A	50 M	
A178	**Swansea**	51°36′.1N 04°03′.9W	**SWN** ··· ·—— —·	320.5	Non A2A	15 M	Day service
A182	**Cardiff/Rhoose**	51°23′.6N 03°20′.2W	**CDF** —·—· —·· ··—·	363.5	Non A2A	20 M	
233	**Nash Point Lt** (grouped with 309)	51°24′.0N 03°33′.1W	**NP** —· ·——·	296.5	A2A	50 M	
235	**Lynmouth Foreland Lt** Calibration station	51°14′.7N 03°47′.1W	**FP** ··—· ·——·	312.6	A2A	5 M	Cont from 1 hr after sunrise to 1 hr before sunset
237	**Lundy I, South Lt** (grouped with 309)	51°09′.7N 04°39′.3W	**LS** ·—·· ···	296.5	A2A	50 M	Reliable 234°–216°

BEACON SEQUENCE NUMBERS Commence transmission at the following minutes past the hour:

1 00 06 12 18 24 30 36 42 48 54	**2** 01 07 13 19 25 31 37 43 49 55	**3** 02 08 14 20 26 32 38 44 50 56
4 03 09 15 21 27 33 39 45 51 57	**5** 04 10 16 22 28 34 40 46 52 58	**6** 05 11 17 23 29 35 41 47 53 59

IMPORTANT NOTE: A major reorganisation of Marine Radiobeacons is planned for implementation commencing February 1992. The changes will affect both radiobeacons and frequencies. Details on the changes are not expected to be available before December 1991 and will be notified in the first available Supplement.

No	Name	Lat/Long	Ident	Freq	Mode	Range	Notes
A190	**St Mawgan**	50°26′.8N 04°59′.6W	**SM** ••• — —	356.5	Non A2A	50 M	

CHANNEL ISLANDS

No	Name	Lat/Long	Ident	Freq	Mode	Range	Notes
251	**Channel Lt V**	49°54′.4N 02°53′.7W	**CR** —•—• •—•	287.3	A2A	10 M	
255	**Casquets Lt** (grouped with 9)	49°43′.4N 02°22′.5W	**QS** ——•— •••	298.8	A2A	50 M	
A252	**Alderney**	49°42′.6N 02°11′.9W	**ALD** •— •—•• —••	383	Non A2A	50 M	Day service
259	**Castle Breakwater, St Peter Port**[1]	49°27′.4N 02°31′.4W	**GY** ——• —•——	285	A2A	10 M	

[1] Synchronised with horn for distance finding. Horn begins simultaneously with 27 sec long dash after the four GY ident signals. Time in secs from start of long dash until horn is heard, multiplied by 0.18, gives distance in nm

No	Name	Lat/Long	Ident	Freq	Mode	Range	Notes
A256	**Guernsey**	49°26′.1N 02°38′.3W	**GUR** ——• ••— •—•	361	Non A2A	30 M	Day service
263	**La Corbière**[1,2] (grouped with 639)	49°10′.9N 02°14′.9W	**CB** —•—• —•••	305.7	A2A	20 M	

[1] For details of coded wind information see 7.2.13. [2] Synchronised for distance finding. Horn blast (Morse 'C') begins with end of 18 sec long dash. Each pip heard before the blast corresponds to a distance of 335m from the light.

No	Name	Lat/Long	Ident	Freq	Mode	Range	Notes
267	**St Helier Harbour**	49°10′.6N 02°07′.5W	**EC** • —•—•	287.3	A2A	10 M	
A260	**Jersey East**	49°13′.2N 02°02′.1W	**JEY** •——— • —•——	367	Non A2A	75 M	
A264	**Jersey West**	49°12′.4N 02°13′.3W	**JW** •——— •——	329	Non A2A	25 M	

IRELAND — SOUTH AND EAST COASTS

No	Name	Lat/Long	Ident	Freq	Mode	Range	Notes
301	**Mizen Head Lt** (grouped with 181)	51°27′.0N 09°48′.8W	**MZ** —— ——••	308	A2A	200/100 M	070° 475m from Lt.
305	**Old Head of Kinsale Lt** (grouped with 309)	51°36′.3N 08°32′.0W	**OH** ——— ••••	296.5	A2A	50 M	
309	**Ballycotton Lt**	51°49′.5N 07°59′.0W	**BN** —••• —•	296.5	A2A	50 M	
	Calibration station		**BC** —••• —•—•	312.6	A2A	5 M	On request

No	*Name*	*Ident*		*Range*	*Seq*	*Mode*	*Fog*	*Clear*
309	Ballycotton Lt	BN	—••• —•	50	1	A2A	Cont	Cont
305	Kinsale	OH	——— ••••	50	2	A2A	Cont	Cont
237	Lundy	LS	•—•• •••	50	3	A2A	Cont	Cont
233	Nash Point	NP	—• •——•	50	4	A2A	Cont	Cont
225	South Bishop	SB	••• —•••	50	5	A2A	Cont	Cont
313	Tuskar Rock	TR	— •—•	50	6	A2A	Cont	Cont

No	Name	Lat/Long	Ident	Freq	Mode	Range	Notes
A302	**Waterford**	52°11′.8N 07°05′.3W	**WTD** •—— — —••	368	Non A2A	25 M	
313	**Tuskar Rock Lt** (grouped with 309)	52°12′.1N 06°12′.4W	**TR** — •—•	296.5	A2A	50 M	
317	**Wicklow Hd Lt** (grouped with 217)	52°57′.9N 05°59′.8W	**WK** •—— —•—	301.1	A2A	70 M	
A306	**Killiney**	53°16′.2N 06°06′.3W	**KLY** —•— •—•• —•——	378	Non A2A	50 M	
A310	**Dublin/Rush**	53°30′.7N 06°06′.6W	**RSH** •—• ••• ••••	326	Non A2A	30 M	
321	**Kish Bank Lt**	53°18′.7N 05°55′.4W	**KH** —•— ••••	312.6	A2A	20 M	
	Calibration station		**KH** —•— ••••	312.6	A2A	5 M	On request

4

IMPORTANT NOTE: A major reorganisation of Marine Radiobeacons is planned for implementation commencing February 1992. The changes will affect both radiobeacons and frequencies. Details on the changes are not expected to be available before December 1991 and will be notified in the first available Supplement.

No	Name	Lat/Long	Ident	Freq	Mode	Range	Notes
325	**South Rock Lt F** (grouped with 217)	54°24′.5N 05°21′.9W	SU ••• ••—	301.1	A2A	50 M	
A314	**Belfast Harbour**	54°37′.0N 05°52′.9W	HB •••• —•••	275	Non A2A	15 M	
329	**Mew Island Lt** (grouped with 189)	54°41′.9N 05°30′.7W	MW —— •——	294.2	A2A	50 M	
	Calibration station		MC —— —•—•	312.6	A2A	5 M	On request
333	**Altacarry Head Lt** (grouped with 189)	55°18′.1N 06°10′.2W	AH •— ••••	294.2	A2A	50 M	

IRELAND — WEST COAST

No	Name	Lat/Long	Ident	Freq	Mode	Range	Notes
A318	**Eglinton/Londonderry**	55°02′.7N 07°09′.2W	EGT • ——• —	328.5	Non A2A	25 M	Occasional
337	**Tory Island Lt** (grouped with 181)	55°16′.3N 08°14′.9W	TY — —•——	308	A2A	100/70 M	
341	**Eagle Island Lt** (grouped with 181)	54°17′.0N 10°05′.5W	GL ——• •—••	308	A2A	200/100 M	
A320	**Sligo**	54°16′.5N 08°36′.0W	SL ••• •—••	384	Non A2A	25 M	
345	**Slyne Head Lt**	53°24′.0N 10°14′.0W	SN ••• —•	289.6	A2A	50 M	

No	*Name*	*Ident*		*Range*	*Seq*	*Mode*	*Fog*	*Clear*
345	Slyne Head	SN	••• —•	50	1,3,5	A2A	Cont	Cont
349	Loop Head	LP	•—•• •——•	50	2,4,6	A2A	Cont	Cont

No	Name	Lat/Long	Ident	Freq	Mode	Range	Notes
A322	**Carnmore/Galway**	53°18′.0N 08°57′.0W	CRN —•—• •—• —•	321	Non A2A	——	
A326	**Ennis**	52°54′.3N 08°55′.6W	ENS • —• •••	352	Non A2A	80 M	
A334	**Foynes**	52°34′.0N 09°11′.7W	FOY ••—• ——— —•——	395	Non A2A	50 M	
349	**Loop Head Lt** (grouped with 345)	52°33′.6N 09°55′.9W	LP •—•• •——•	289.6	A2A	50 M	

SPAIN — NORTH COAST

No	Name	Lat/Long	Ident	Freq	Mode	Range	Notes
543	**Cabo Mayor Lt** (grouped with 551)	43°29′.5N 03°47′.4W	MY —— —•——	296.5	A2A	50 M	
A548	**Bilbao**	43°19′.4N 02°58′.4W	BLO —••• •—•• ———	370	Non A2A	70 M	
547	**Cabo Machichaco Lt** (grouped with 551)	43°27′.4N 02°45′.1W	MA —— •—	296.5	A2A	100 M	Reliable sector 110°–220°
A552	**San Sebastian**	43°23′.3N 01°47′.7W	HIG •••• •• ——•	328	Non A2A	50 M	

BEACON SEQUENCE NUMBERS Commence transmission at the following minutes past the hour:

1	00	06	12	18	24	30	36	42	48	54	**2**	01	07	13	19	25	31	37	43	49	55	**3**	02	08	14	20	26	32	38	44	50	56
4	03	09	15	21	27	33	39	45	51	57	**5**	04	10	16	22	28	34	40	46	52	58	**6**	05	11	17	23	29	35	41	47	53	59

IMPORTANT NOTE: A major reorganisation of Marine Radiobeacons is planned for implementation commencing February 1992. The changes will affect both radiobeacons and frequencies. Details on the changes are not expected to be available before December 1991 and will be notified in the first available Supplement.

FRANCE

No	Name	Lat/Long	Ident	Freq	Mode	Range	Notes
A556	Biarritz	43°28′.2N 01°24′.2W	BZ —··· ——··	341	A1A	35 M	
A560	Cazaux	44°33′.1N 01°07′.1W	CAA —·—· ·— ·—	382	A1A	80 M	
551	Cap Ferret Lt	44°38′.8N 01°15′.0W	FT ··—· —	296.5	A2A	100 M	

No	*Name*	*Ident*		*Range*	*Seq*	*Mode*	*Fog*	*Clear*
551	Cap Ferret	FT	··—· —	100	1,2	A2A	Cont	Cont
547	Cabo Machichaco	MA	—— ·—	100	3,4	A2A	Cont	Cont
543	Cabo Mayor	MY	—— —·——	50	5,6	A2A	Cont	Cont

No	Name	Lat/Long	Ident	Freq	Mode	Range	Notes
A564	Bordeaux/Merignac	44°55′.9N 00°33′.9W	BD —··· —··	393	A1A	30 M	
A568	Cognac/Chateaubernard	45°40′.1N 00°18′.5W	CGC —·—· ——· —·—·	354	A1A	75 M	
559	Pointe de la Coubre (grouped with 607)	45°41′.9N 01°13′.9W	LK ·—·· —·—	303.4	A2A	100 M	
563	La Rochelle, Tour Richelieu Lt	46°09′.0N 1°10′.3W	RE ·—· ·	291.9	A1A	5 M	
571	Les Baleines Lt (Île de Ré) (grouped with 607)	46°14′.7N 01°33′6W	BN —··· —·	303.4	A2A	50 M	
575	Les Sables d'Olonne Tour de la Chaume Lt	46°29′.6N 01°47′.8W	SO ··· ———	291.9	A2A	5 M	Temp inop (Aug 1988)
579	Île d'Yeu Main Lt	46°43′.1N 02°22′.9W	YE —·—— ·	312.6	A2A	70 M	Sequence 3
583	Île du Pilier Lt	47°02′.6N 02°21′.5W	PR ·——· ·—·	298.8	A2A	10 M	Temp inop (Aug 1988)
587	St Nazaire, Pointe de St Gildas Lt	47°08′.1N 02°14′.7W	NZ —· ——··	298.8	A1A	10 M	
A572	St Nazaire/Montoir	47°20′.0N 02°02′.6W	MT —— —	398	A1A	50 M	
A580	Lorient/Lann-Bihoué	47°45′.7N 03°26′.4W	LOR ·—·· ——— ·—·	294.2	A1A	80 M	

BEACON SEQUENCE NUMBERS Commence transmission at the following minutes past the hour:

1 00 06 12 18 24 30 36 42 48 54	**2** 01 07 13 19 25 31 37 43 49 55	**3** 02 08 14 20 26 32 38 44 50 56
4 03 09 15 21 27 33 39 45 51 57	**5** 04 10 16 22 28 34 40 46 52 58	**6** 05 11 17 23 29 35 41 47 53 59

IMPORTANT NOTE: A major reorganisation of Marine Radiobeacons is planned for implementation commencing February 1992. The changes will affect both radiobeacons and frequencies. Details on the changes are not expected to be available before December 1991 and will be notified in the first available Supplement.

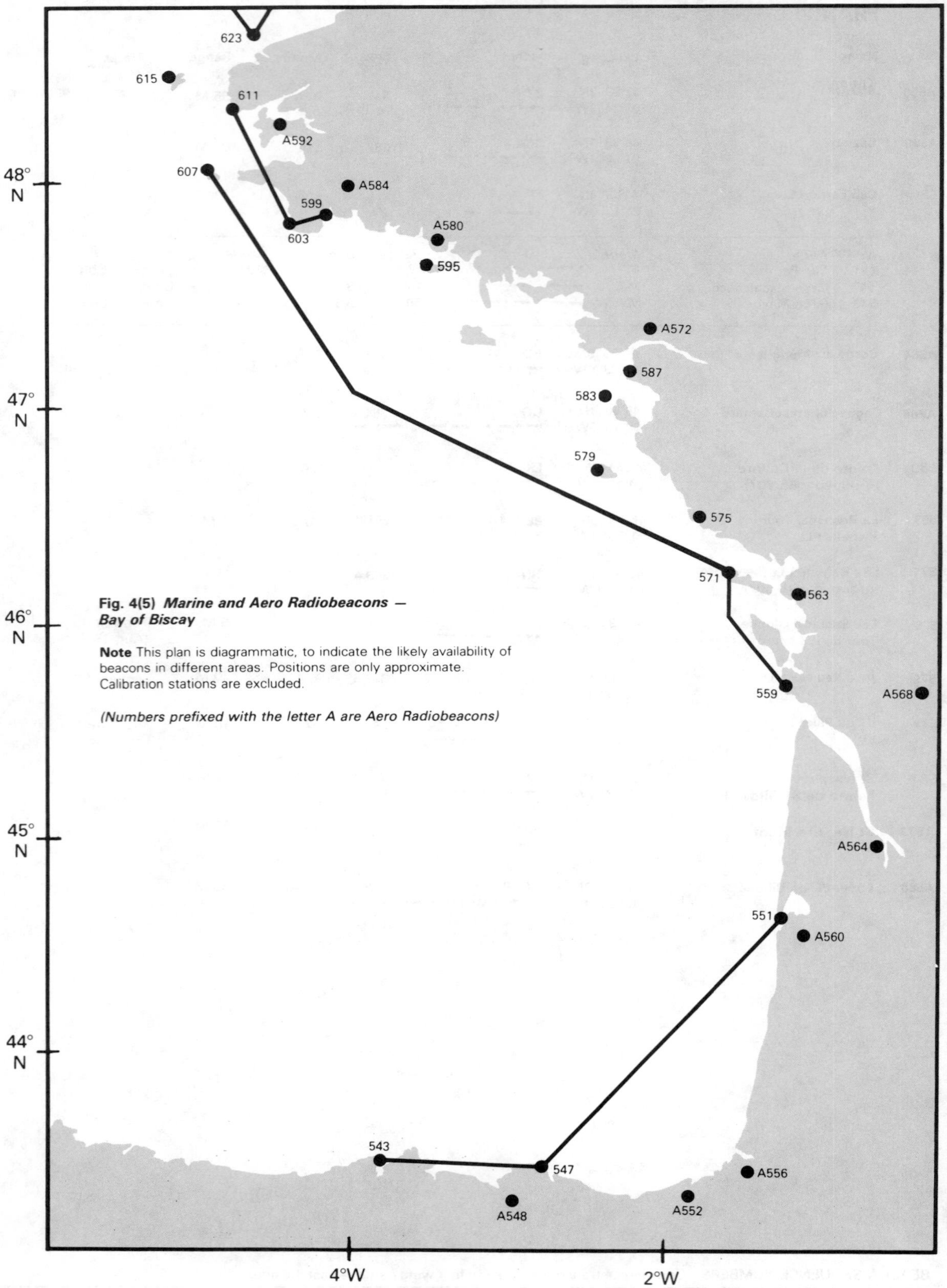

623
615
611
A592
607
48° N
A584
599
603
A580
595
A572
587
583
47° N
579
575
571
563
46° N
559
A568
45° N
A564
551
A560
44° N
543
547
A556
A548
A552
4°W
2°W

Fig. 4(5) ***Marine and Aero Radiobeacons — Bay of Biscay***

Note This plan is diagrammatic, to indicate the likely availability of beacons in different areas. Positions are only approximate. Calibration stations are excluded.

(Numbers prefixed with the letter A are Aero Radiobeacons)

IMPORTANT NOTE: A major reorganisation of Marine Radiobeacons is planned for implementation commencing February 1992. The changes will affect both radiobeacons and frequencies. Details on the changes are not expected to be available before December 1991 and will be notified in the first available Supplement.

No	Name	Lat/Long	Ident	Freq	Mode	Range	Notes
595	**Pen Men Lt, Île de Groix**	47°38′.9N 03°30′.5W	**GX** — — • — • • —	301.1	A1A	10 M	
A584	**Quimper/Pluguffan**	47°58′.1N 03°59′.8W	**QR** — — • — • — •	380	A1A		
599	**Pointe de Combrit Lt** (grouped with 603)	47°51′.9N 04°06′.7W	**CT** — • — • —	289.6	A2A	20 M	
603	**Eckmühl Lt, Pointe de Penmarc'h**	47°47′.9N 04°22′.4W	**ÜH** • • — — • • • •	289.6	A2A	50 M	

No	*Name*	*Ident*		*Range*	*Seq*	*Mode*	*Fog*	*Clear*
603	Eckmühl	ÜH	• • — — • • • •	50	1	A2A	Cont	Cont
611	Pte St Mathieu	SM	• • • — —	20	3	A2A	Cont	Cont
599	Pte de Combrit	CT	— • — • —	20	4	A2A	Cont	Cont

No	Name	Lat/Long	Ident	Freq	Mode	Range	Notes
607	**Île de Sein NW Lt**	48°02′.7N 04°52′.0W	**SN** • • • — •	303.4	A2A	70 M	

No	*Name*	*Ident*		*Range*	*Seq*	*Mode*	*Fog*	*Clear*
607	Île de Sein	SN	• • • — •	100	3	A2A	Cont	Cont
559	Pte de la Coubre	LK	• — • • — • —	100	4	A2A	Cont	Cont
571	Les Baleines	BN	— • • • — •	50	6	A2A	Cont	Cont

No	Name	Lat/Long	Ident	Freq	Mode	Range	Notes
A592	**Lanvéoc, Poulmic**	48°17′.1N 04°26′.0W	**BST** — • • • • • • —	316	A1A	80 M	
611	**Pte St Mathieu Lt** (grouped with 603)	48°19′.8N 04°46′.2W	**SM** • • • — —	289.6	A2A	20 M	
615	**Pte de Créac'h Lt** (grouped with 181)	48°27′.6N 05°07′.6W	**CA** — • — • • —	308	A2A	100 M	
619	**Ouessant SW Lanby**	48°31′.7N 05°49′.1W	**SW** • • • • — —	294.2	A2A	10 M	
623	**Île Vierge Lt** (grouped with 9)	48°38′.4N 04°34′.0W	**VG** • • • — — — •	298.8	A2A	70 M	
A596	**Landivisiau**	48°32′.8N 04°08′.2W	**LDV** • — • • — • • • • • —	324	A1A	60 M	
627	**Roscoff-Bloscon Jetty Lt**	48°43′.3N 03°57′.6W	**BC** — • • • — • — •	287.3	A2A	10 M	
A600	**Lannion**	48°43′.3N 03°18′.4W	**LN** • — • • — •	345.5	A1A	50 M	
631	**Rosédo Lt, Île Bréhat**	48°51′.5N 03°00′.3W	**DO** — • • — — —	294.2	A2A	10 M	

No	*Name*	*Ident*		*Range*	*Seq*	*Mode*	*Fog*	*Clear*
631	Rosédo	DO	— • • — — —	10	1,5	A2A	Cont	Cont
643	Le Grand Jardin	GJ	— — • • — — —	10	2,6	A2A	Cont	Cont

No	Name	Lat/Long	Ident	Freq	Mode	Range	Notes
635	**Roches-Douvres Lt** (grouped with 9)	49°06′.5N 02°48′.8W	**RD** • — • — • •	298.8	A2A	70 M	
A604	**St Brieuc**	48°34′.1N 02°46′.9W	**SB** • • • — • • •	353	A1A	25 M	
639	**Cap Fréhel Lt**	48°41′.1N 02°19′.1W	**FÉ** • • — • • • — • •	305.7	A2A	20 M	

IMPORTANT NOTE: A major reorganisation of Marine Radiobeacons is planned for implementation commencing February 1992. The changes will affect both radiobeacons and frequencies. Details on the changes are not expected to be available before December 1991 and will be notified in the first available Supplement.

No	Name	Lat/Long	Ident	Freq	Mode	Range	Notes

No	*Name*	*Ident*		*Range*	*Seq*	*Mode*	*Fog*	*Clear*
639	Cap Fréhel	FÉ	••—• ••—••	20	1,3,5	A2A	Cont	Cont
263	La Corbière	CB	—•—• —•••	20	2,4,6	A2A	Cont	Cont

No	Name	Lat/Long	Ident	Freq	Mode	Range	Notes
643	**Le Grand Jardin Lt** (grouped with 631)	48°40′.3N 02°04′.9W	**GJ** ——• •———	294.2	A2A	10 M	
A608	**Granville**	48°55′.1N 01°28′.9W	**GV** ——• •••—	321	A1A	25 M	
647	**Cherbourg W Fort Lt** (grouped with 33)	49°40′.5N 01°38′.9W	**RB** •—• —•••	312.6	A2A	20 M	
651	**Pte de Barfleur Lt** (grouped with 17)	49°41′.9N 01°15′.9W	**FG** ••—• ——•	291.9	A2A	70 M	
655	**Port en Bessin Rear Lt**	49°21′.0N 00°45′.6W	**BS** —••• •••	313.5	A2A	5 M	
A612	**Cherbourg**	49°38′.3N 01°22′.3W	**MP** —— •——•	373	A1A	——	
659	**Pte de Ver Lt** (grouped with 17)	49°20′.5N 00°31′.1W	**ÉR** ••—•• •—•	291.9	A2A	20 M	
663	**Le Havre Lanby** (grouped with 17)	49°31′.7N 00°09′.8W	**LH** •—•• ••••	291.9	A2A	30 M	
A616	**Le Havre/Octeville**	49°35′.7N 00°11′.0E	**LHO** •—•• •••• ———	346	A2A	15 M	
667	**Cap d'Antifer Lt** (grouped with 17)	49°41′.1N 00°10′.0E	**TI** — ••	291.9	A2A	50 M	
671	**Pte d'Ailly Lt** (grouped with 679)	49°55′.0N 00°57′.6E	**AL** •— •—••	310.3	A2A	50 M	
A624	**Le Touquet/Paris Plage**	50°32′.2N 01°35′.4E	**LT** •—•• —	358	A2A	20 M	
679	**Cap d'Alprech Lt**	50°41′.95N 01°33′.83E	**PH** •——• ••••	310.3	A2A	20 M	

No	*Name*	*Ident*		*Range*	*Seq*	*Mode*	*Fog*	*Clear*
679	Cap d'Alprech	PH	•——• ••••	20	1,3,5	A2A	Cont	Cont
45	Royal Sovereign	RY	•—• —•——	50	2	A2A	Cont	Cont
671	Pointe d'Ailly	AL	•— •—••	50	4	A2A	Cont	Cont
49	Dungeness	DU	—•• ••—	30	6	A2A	Cont	Cont

No	Name	Lat/Long	Ident	Freq	Mode	Range	Notes
691	**Calais Main Lt** (grouped with 61)	50°57′.7N 01°51′.3E	**CS** —•—• •••	305.7	A2A	20 M	
A628	**Saint Inglevert**	50°53′.0N 01°44′.6E	**ING** •• —• ——•	387.5	A1A	50 M	
695	**Dunkerque Lanby**	51°03′.1N 01°51′.8E	**DK** —•• —•—	294.2	A2A	10 M	Temp inop (Mar 1989)
A632	**Calais/Dunkerque**	50°59′.8N 02°03′.3E	**MK** —— —•—	275	A1A	15 M	

BEACON SEQUENCE NUMBERS Commence transmission at the following minutes past the hour:

1 00 06 12 18 24 30 36 42 48 54	**2** 01 07 13 19 25 31 37 43 49 55	**3** 02 08 14 20 26 32 38 44 50 56
4 03 09 15 21 27 33 39 45 51 57	**5** 04 10 16 22 28 34 40 46 52 58	**6** 05 11 17 23 29 35 41 47 53 59

IMPORTANT NOTE: A major reorganisation of Marine Radiobeacons is planned for implementation commencing February 1992. The changes will affect both radiobeacons and frequencies. Details on the changes are not expected to be available before December 1991 and will be notified in the first available Supplement.

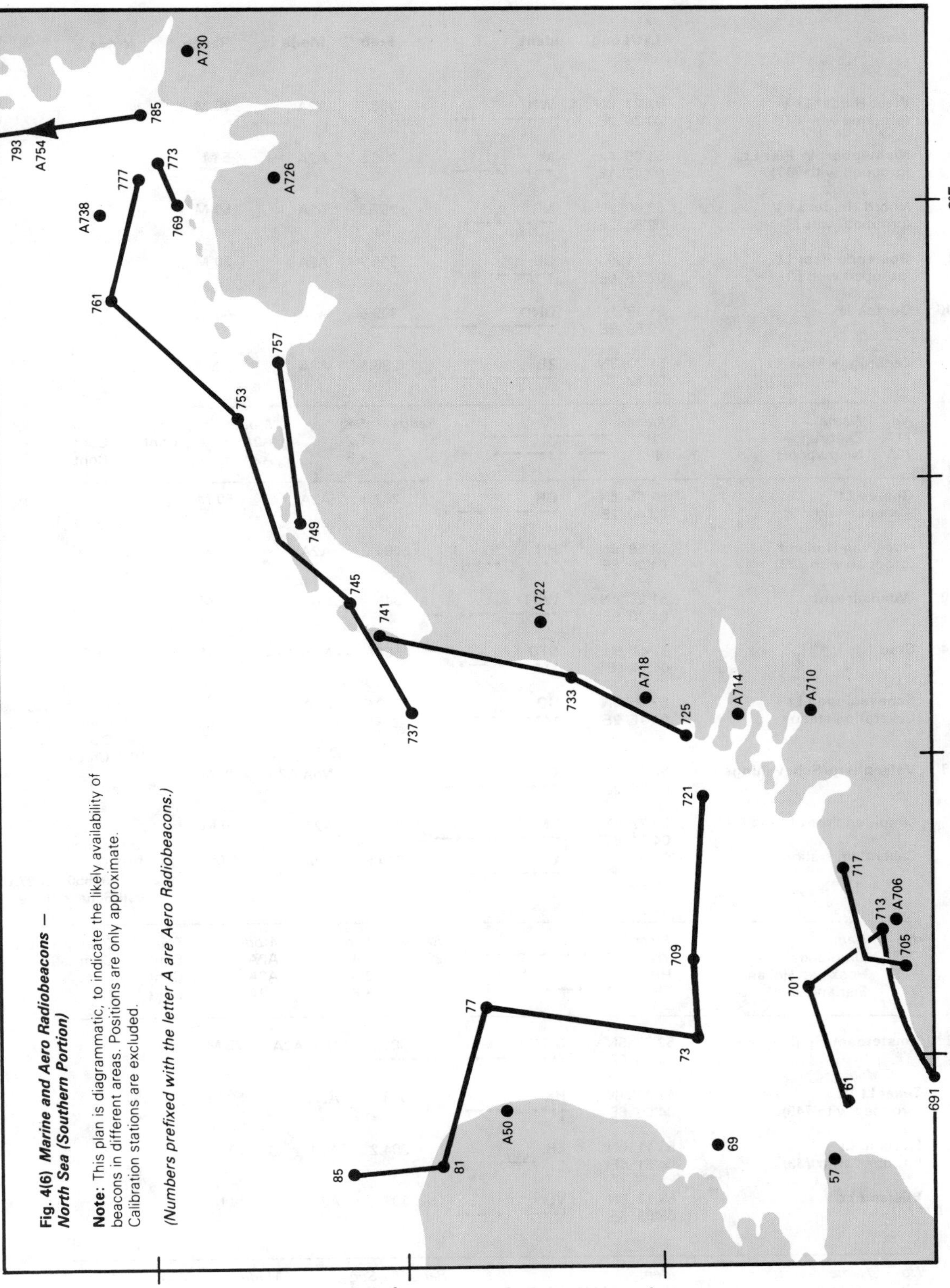

793
A754
785
A730
777
773
A738
769
A726
8°E
761
757
753
6°E
749
745
A722
741
733
A718
A714
A710
737
725
4°E
721
717
713
A706
709
705
701
77
73
2°E
691
61
A50
69
85
81
57
54° N
53° N
52° N

Fig. 4(6) ***Marine and Aero Radiobeacons – North Sea (Southern Portion)***

Note: This plan is diagrammatic, to indicate the likely availability of beacons in different areas. Positions are only approximate. Calibration stations are excluded.

(Numbers prefixed with the letter A are Aero Radiobeacons.)

IMPORTANT NOTE: A major reorganisation of Marine Radiobeacons is planned for implementation commencing February 1992. The changes will affect both radiobeacons and frequencies. Details on the changes are not expected to be available before December 1991 and will be notified in the first available Supplement.

BELGIUM, NETHERLANDS AND GERMANY

No	Name	Lat/Long	Ident	Freq	Mode	Range	Notes
701	**West Hinder Lt V** (grouped with 61)	51°23′.0N 20°26′.3E	**WH** •—— ••••	305.7	A2A	20 M	
705	**Nieuwpoort W Pier Lt** (grouped with 717)	51°09′.4N 02°43′.1E	**NP** —• •——•	296.5	A2A	5 M	
709	**Noord Hinder Lt V** (grouped with 77)	52°00′.2N 02°51′.2E	**NR** —• •—•	287.3	A2A	50 M	
713	**Oostende Rear Lt** (grouped with 61)	51°14′.6N 02°56′.0E	**OE** ——— •	305.7	A2A	30 M	
A706	**Oostende**	51°13′.1N 02°59′.9E	**ONO** ——— —• ———	399.5	A2A	50 M	
717	**Zeebrugge Mole Lt**	51°20′.9N 03°12′.2E	**ZB** ——•• —•••	296.5	A2A	5 M	

No	*Name*	*Ident*		*Range*	*Seq*	*Mode*	*Fog*	*Clear*
717	Zeebrugge	ZB	——•• —•••	5	1,2	A2A	Cont	Cont
705	Nieuwpoort	NP	—• •——•	5	4,5	A2A	Cont	Cont

No	Name	Lat/Long	Ident	Freq	Mode	Range	Notes
721	**Goeree Lt** (grouped with 77)	51°55′.5N 03°40′.2E	**GR** ——• •—•	287.3	A2A	50 M	
725	**Hoek van Holland** (grouped with 733)	51°58′.9N 04°06′.8E	**HH** •••• ••••	294.2	A2A	20 M	
A710	**Woensdrecht**	51°26′.4N 04°20′.9E	**WDT** •—— —•• —	345	Non A2A	25 M	
A714	**Stad**	51°44′.5N 04°14′.6E	**STD** ••• — —••	386	Non A2A	15 M	
729	**Scheveningen Lt** Calibration station	52°06′.3N 04°16′.2E	**HO** •••• ———	312.6	A2A		On request Tel: 01747 4840 or call Centralepost van DGSM on VHF Ch 01
A718	**Valkenberg/Scheveningen**	52°05′.6N 04°15′.2E	**GV** ——• •••—	364	Non A2A	25 M	
733	**IJmuiden Front Lt**	52°27′.8N 04°34′.6E	**YM** —•—— ——	294.2	A2A	20 M	
	Calibration station		**YC** —•—— —•—•	314.5	A2A	5 M	On request VHF Ch 12 Tel: 02550 19027 or call Scheveningen

No	*Name*	*Ident*		*Range*	*Seq*	*Mode*	*Fog*	*Clear*
733	IJmuiden	YM	—•—— ——	20	1,4	A2A	Cont	Cont
725	Hoek van Holland	HH	•••• ••••	20	2,5	A2A	Cont	Cont
741	Eierland	ER	• •—•	20	3,6	A2A	Cont	Nil

No	Name	Lat/Long	Ident	Freq	Mode	Range	Notes
A722	**Amsterdam/Spijkerboor**	52°32′.5N 04°50′.5E	**SPY** ••• •——• —•——	381	Non A2A	75 M	
737	**Texel Lt V** (grouped with 745)	52°47′.1N 04°06′.6E	**HK** •••• —•—	308	A2A	50 M	
741	**Eierland Lt** (grouped with 733)	53°11′.0N 04°51′.4E	**ER** • •—•	294.2	A2A	20 M	
745	**Vlieland Lt**	53°17′.8N 05°03′.6E	**VL** •••— •—••	308	A2A	70 M	

No	*Name*	*Ident*		*Range*	*Seq*	*Mode*	*Fog*	*Clear*
745	Vlieland	VL	•••— •—••	70	1	A2A	Cont	Cont
761	Deutsche Bucht Lt F	DB	—•• —•••	50	4	A2A	Cont	Cont
737	Texel Lt V	HK	•••• —•—	50	5	A2A	Cont	Cont
777	Elbe No 1 Lt F	EL	• •—••	50	6	A2A	Cont	Cont

IMPORTANT NOTE: A major reorganisation of Marine Radiobeacons is planned for implementation commencing February 1992. The changes will affect both radiobeacons and frequencies. Details on the changes are not expected to be available before December 1991 and will be notified in the first available Supplement.

No	Name	Lat/Long	Ident	Freq	Mode	Range	Notes
749	**Ameland Lt**	53°27′.0N 05°37′.6E	**AD** ·— —··	298.8	A2A	20 M	

No	*Name*	*Ident*		*Range*	*Seq*	*Mode*	*Fog*	*Clear*
749	Ameland	AD	·— —··	20	1,3,5	A2A	Cont	Nil
757	Borkum Little	BE	—··· ·	20	2,4,6	A2A	Cont	Cont

No	Name	Lat/Long	Ident	Freq	Mode	Range	Notes
757	**Borkum Little Lt** (grouped with 749)	53°34′.8N 06°40′.1E	**BE** —··· ·	298.8	A2A	20 M	
761	**Deutsche Bucht Lt F** (grouped with 745)	54°10′.7N 07°26′.1E	**DB** —·· —···	308	A2A	50 M	
769	**Wangerooge Lt**	53°47′.4N 07°51′.5E	**WE** ·—— ·	291.9	A2A	30 M	

No	*Name*	*Ident*		*Range*	*Seq*	*Mode*	*Fog*	*Clear*
769	Wangerooge	WE	·—— ·	30	1,3,5	A2A	Cont	Cont
773	Alte Weser	AR	·— ·—·	10	2,4,6	A2A	Cont	Cont

No	Name	Lat/Long	Ident	Freq	Mode	Range	Notes
773	**Alte Weser Lt** (grouped with 769)	53°51′.9N 08°07′.7E	**AR** ·— ·—·	291.9	A2A	10 M	
777	**Elbe No 1 Lt Float** (grouped with 745)	54°00′.0N 08°06′.6E	**EL** · ·—··	308	A2A	50 M	
A726	**Jever**	53°31′.2N 08°00′.9E	**JEV** ·——— · ···—	390	Non A2A	50 M	
779	**Wilhelmshaven** Calibration station	53°31′.0N 08°08′.8E	**JB** ·——— —···	312.6	A2A		On request, call Jade Revier Ch 16 20
781	**Bremerhaven** Calibration station	53°32′.4N 08°34′.9E	**GB** ——· —···	312.6	A2A		On request, call West Revier Ch 05 07
785	**Grosser Vogelsand Lt** (grouped with 793)	53°59′.8N 08°28′.7E	**VS** ···— ···	301.1	A2A	10 M	
A730	**Nordholz**	53°47′.2N 08°48′.5E	**NDO** —· —·· ———	372	Non A2A	30 M	
789	**Hollerwettern Lt** Calibration station	53°50′.4N 09°21′.3E	**HB** ···· —···	313.5	A2A		On request, Tel 04852 8011–16 Ext 393
791	**Krautsand** Calibration station	53°45′.6N 09°22′.6E	**KB** —·— —···	312.6	A2A		On request, Tel 04852 8400
A734	**Glukstadt**	53°51′.1N 09°27′.3E	**GLX** ——· ·—·· —··—	365	Non A2A	30 M	
A738	**Helgoland Lt**	54°11′.0N 07°53′.0E	**DHE** —·· ···· ·	397.2	A1A	100 M	Aeromarine beacon
	Calibration station		**NB** —· —···	313.5	A2A		On request, Eider Lock Radio Ch 14
A754	**Westerland/Sylt**	54°51′.4N 08°24′.7E	**SLT** ··· ·—·· —	286	Non A2A	25 M	
793	**Kampen/Rote Kliff Lt, Sylt**	54°56′.9N 08°20′.5E	**RF** ·—· ··—·	301.1	A2A	20 M	

No	*Name*	*Ident*		*Range*	*Seq*	*Mode*	*Fog*	*Clear*
793	Kampen	RF	·—· ··—·	20	1,3,5	A2A	Cont	Cont
785	Gr Vogelsand	VS	···— ···	10	2,4,6	A2A	Cont	Cont

BEACON SEQUENCE NUMBERS Commence transmission at the following minutes past the hour:

1 00 06 12 18 24 30 36 42 48 54	**2** 01 07 13 19 25 31 37 43 49 55	**3** 02 08 14 20 26 32 38 44 50 56
4 03 09 15 21 27 33 39 45 51 57	**5** 04 10 16 22 28 34 40 46 52 58	**6** 05 11 17 23 29 35 41 47 53 59

4

TABLE 4(3)

RADIOBEACONS —
CALL SIGNS AND STATION NUMBERS

(Numbers prefixed with the letter A are Aero Radiobeacons)

(CS) = Calibration Station

Call Sign	Station	No
AD	Ameland Lt	749
AH	Altacarry Hd Lt	333
AL	Pte d'Ailly Lt	671
ALD	Alderney	A252
AOS	Aberdeen	A82
AP	Aberporth	A166
AR	Alte Weser Lt	773
BC	Bloscon	627
BC	Ballycotton (CS)	309
BD	Barra Hd Lt	181
BD	Bordeaux/Merignac	A564
BE	Borkum Little	757
BHD	Berry Hd	A10
BL	Butt of Lewis Lt	169
BLO	Bilbao	A548
BM	Brighton Marina	37
BMH	Bournemouth/Hurn	A20
BN	Ballycotton Lt	309
BN	Les Baleines Lt	571
BPL	Blackpool	A158
BRR	Barra	A124
BS	Port en Bessin	655
BST	Lanvéoc/Poulmic	A592
BY	Bressay Lt	153
BY	Brawdy	A174
BZ	Biarritz	A556
CA	Pte de Creac'h Lt	615
CAA	Cazaux	A560
CAR	Isle of Man/Carnane	A146
CB	La Corbière	263
CDF	Cardiff/Rhoose	A182
CGC	Cognac/Chateaubernard	A568
CH	Chichester Bar	29
CL	Cloch Pt Lt (CS)	193
CLN	Clacton	A48
CM	Cromer Lt	81
CN	Cregneish, IOM	205
CNL	Connel/Oban	A126
CP	St Catherine's Pt Lt	25
CR	Channel Lt V	251
CRN	Carnmore	A322
CS	Calais Main Lt	691
CT	Pte de Combrit Lt	599
CW	Cape Wrath Lt	165
DA	Pladda Lt	189
DB	Deutsche Bucht Lt V	761
DG	Douglas	201
DHE	Helgoland	A738

Call Sign	Station	No
DK	Dunkerque Lt Buoy	695
DND	Dundee	A78
DO	Rosédo Lt (Brehat)	631
DO	Dounreay	A118
DU	Dungeness Lt	49
EC	St Helier	267
EDN	Edinburgh	A70
EGT	Eglington	A318
EL	Elbe No 1 Lt V	777
ENS	Ennis	A326
ER	Eierland Lt	741
ÉR	Pte der Ver Lt	659
EX	Exeter	A14
FB	Flamborough Hd	97
FD	Fidra Lt	119
FÉ	Cap Fréhel	639
FG	Pte de Barfleur Lt	651
FN	Walney Island Lt	209
FOY	Foynes	A334
FP	Fife Ness Lt	125
FS	Falls Lt V	61
FT	Cap Ferret Lt	551
GA	Outer Gabbard Lt V	73
GB	Bremerhaven (CS)	781
GD	Girdle Ness Lt	133
GJ	Grand Jardin Lt	643
GL	Eagle Island Lt	341
GLX	Gluckstadt	A734
GN	Cap Gris Nez Lt	687
GR	Goeree Lt	721
GUR	Guernsey	A256
GV	Granville	A608
GV	Valkenburg	A718
GX	Ile de Groix, Pen Men	595
GY	St Peter Port	259
HB	Hollerwettern (CS)	789
HB	Belfast Harbour	A314
HH	Hoek van Holland	725
HIG	San Sebastian	A552
HK	Texel Lt V	737
HO	Scheveningen (CS)	729
HRN	Hurn	A18
IB	Bardsey Lt	221
ING	St Inglevert	A628
IW	Bembridge	A26

TABLE 4(3) continued
(Numbers prefixed with the letter A are Aero Radiobeacons)
(CS) = Calibration Station

Call Sign	Station	No
JB	Wilhelmshaven (CS)	779
JEV	Jever	A726
JEY	Jersey East	A260
JW	Jersey West	A264
KB	Krautsand (CS)	791
KD	Kinnairds Hd	137
KH	Kish Bank Lt	321
KL	St Kilda	A122
KLY	Killiney	A306
KS	Kinloss	A90
KW	Kirkwall	A98
LAY	Islay/Port Ellen	A128
LDV	Landivisiau	A596
LG	Eilean Glas Lt	173
LH	Le Havre Lanby	663
LHO	Le Havre/Octeville	A616
LK	Sule Skerry Lt	161
LK	Pointe de la Coubre	559
LM	Isle of May	121
LN	Lannion	A600
LOR	Lorient/Lann-Bihoué	A580
LP	Loop Head Lt	349
LS	Lundy Island, S Lt	237
LS	Lee-on-Solent	A30
LT	Longstone Lt	113
LT	Le Touquet	A624
LU	Leuchars	A74
LV	Dudgeon Lt V	85
LYX	Lydd	A42
LZ	Lizard Lt	5
MA	Cabo Machichaco Lt	547
MC	Mew Island (CS)	329
MF	Muckle Flugga	157
MK	Calais/Dunkerque	A632
MP	Cherbourg	A612
MT	St Nazaire/Montoir	A572
MW	Mew Island Lt	329
MY	Cabo Mayor Lt	543
MZ	Mizen Head Lt	301
NB	Nab Tower Lt	33
NB	Helgoland Lt (CS)	A738
ND	Gt Yarmouth	A50
NDO	Nordholz	A730
NF	N Foreland Lt	57
NGY	New Galloway	A142
NH	Newhaven	41
NK	Inchkeith Lt	117

Call Sign	Station	No
NP	Nash Point Lt	233
NP	Nieuwpoort	705
NR	N Ronaldsay	145
NR	Noord Hinder Lt V	709
NZ	St Nazaire	587
OE	Oostende Rear Lt	713
OH	Kinsale	305
OM	Stroma	141
ONO	Oostende	A706
OR	Hyskeir Lt	177
OTR	Ottringham	A54
PB	Portland Bill	17
PE	Penlee Point	9
PH	Penzance	A2
PH	Cap d'Alprech Lt	679
PO	Poole Harbour	21
PR	Ile du Pilier Lt	583
PS	Point Lynas Lt	213
PT	Souter Lt (CS)	109
PY	Point of Ayre	197
PY	Plymouth	A6
QR	Quimper/Pluguffan	A584
QS	Casquets Lt	255
RB	Cherbourg	647
RD	Roches Douvres Lt	635
RE	La Rochelle	563
RF	Kampen/Rote Kliff Lt	793
RN	Rhinns of Islay Lt	185
RR	Round Island Lt	1
RSH	Dublin (Rush)	A310
RWY	Ronaldsway, IOM	A150
RY	Royal Sovereign Lt	45
SB	Sumburgh Hd Lt	149
SB	South Bishop Lt	225
SHD	Scotstown Hd	A86
SHM	Shoreham	A38
SJ	Souter Lt	109
SK	Smiths Knoll Lt V	77
SL	Sligo	A320
SLT	Westerland/Sylt	A754
SM	St Mawgan	A190
SM	Pt de St Mathieu Lt	611
SN	Slyne Head Lt	345
SN	Ile de Sein	607
SND	Southend	A46
SO	Les Sables d'Olonne	575
SP	Start Point Lt	13
SPY	Amsterdam	A722

4

TABLE 4(3) continued
(Numbers prefixed with the letter A are Aero Radiobeacons)
(CS) = Calibration Station

Call Sign	Station	No
SR	Skerries Lt	217
SS	Scatsa	A110
STD	Stad	A714
STM	St Mary's Scilly	A1
STU	Strumble	A170
SU	South Rock Lt F	325
SUM	Sumburgh	A102
SW	Ouessant SW Lanby	619
SWN	Swansea	A178
SWY	Stornoway	A122
TD	Teeside	A58
TI	Cap d'Antifer Lt	667
TL	Lerwick	A106
TR	Tuskar Rock Lt	313
TRN	Turnberry	A138
TY	Tory Island Lt	337
ÜH	Eckmühl Lt, Penmarc'h	603
UK	Sunk Lt F	69
UT	Unst	A114
VA	Vannes/Meucon	A576
VG	Ile Vierge Lt	623
VL	Vlieland Lt	745
VS	Gr Vogelsand Lt	785
WDT	Woensdrecht	A710
WE	Wangerooge Lt	769
WH	West Hinder Lt V	701
WIK	Wick	A94
WK	Wicklow Head Lt	317
WL	Walney Is	A152
WTD	Waterford	A302
WTN	Warton	A162
YC	IJmuiden (CS)	733
YE	Ile d'Yeu Main Lt	579
YM	IJmuiden	733
ZB	Zeebrugge Mole Lt	717

4.3.3 VHF Radio Lighthouses

This is a beacon which transmits a rotating directional signal that can be received by a VHF set capable of receiving frequency modulated signals. The signals are modulated with an audio tone varying between a maximum and a null. The 'null radial' rotates at a uniform speed of 4° per second, and the bearing of the beacon is determined by measuring the time that the null radial takes to reach the observer from a known starting point. To measure the time interval, the tone is broken into a number of half-second beats, each beat being the equivalent of 2° of bearing. The observer simply counts the number of beats from the start of each transmission, until the tone disappears, and then refers to Table 4(3).

The signal composition is as follows: Pause 0.1s; Morse ident. 3.2s; Pause 1.0s; Digital data 0.3s; Pause 1.0s; 70 Nav. beats 35.0s; Pause 1.0s; Morse ident. 3.2s; Pause 1.0s; Digital data 0.1s; Pause 12.1s; Static gap 2.0s. Total 60.0s.

The digital data is of no navigational significance, and is transmitted for the use of test equipment.

Beat numbers 10, 20, 30, 40, 50 and 60 are marked by a change in audio tone frequency.

All the VHF Radio Lighthouses currently in service transmit on VHF Ch 88 (162.025 MHz). The mode of emission used is designated as FXX, in which the main carrier is frequency modulated.

In the event of a transmitting equipment fault, a warbling tone will be transmitted, rendering the preceding beats invalid.

In the absence of a table, the bearing can be found from the formula:

$$\text{Bearing} = A + 2(N - 7)$$

where N is the number of beats counted, and A is the start bearing for 7 beats.

Alternatively, the time (T) in seconds can be taken with a stopwatch between beat 7 and the null. Then:

$$\text{Bearing} = A + 4T$$

The overall bearing accuracy is estimated as ±2° (root mean square error) or better.

The stations are experimental, and transmissions may be altered or discontinued without warning.

TABLE 4(4) VHF RADIO LIGHTHOUSES

ANVIL POINT LT 50°35′·47N 01°57′·52W

Morse ident: **AL** ·— ·—··
Frequency: Ch 88 (162·025 MHz)
Range: 14 M
Times: H24 (transmits alternately with Scratchell's Bay)

Count of beats	Bearing of Lt Ho from seaward (degrees) 0	1	2	3	4	5	6	7	8	9
0	—	—	—	—	—	—	—	247	249	251
10	253	255	257	259	261	263	265	267	269	271
20	273	275	277	279	281	283	285	287	289	291
30	293	295	297	299	301	303	305	307	309	311
40	313	315	317	319	321	323	325	327	329	331
50	333	335	337	339	341	343	345	347	349	351
60	353	355	357	359	001	003	005	007	—	—

HIGH DOWN (Scratchell's Bay) 50°39′·70N 01°34′·60W

Morse ident: **HD** ···· —··
Frequency: Ch 88 (162·025 MHz)
Range: 30 M
Times: H24 (transmits alternately with Anvil Point Lt)

Count of beats	Bearing of Lt Ho from seaward (degrees) 0	1	2	3	4	5	6	7	8	9
0	—	—	—	—	—	—	—	337	339	341
10	343	345	347	349	351	353	355	357	359	001
20	003	005	007	009	011	013	015	017	019	021
30	023	025	027	029	031	033	035	037	039	041
40	043	045	047	049	051	053	055	057	059	061
50	063	065	067	069	071	073	075	077	079	081
60	083	085	087	089	091	093	095	097	—	—

CALAIS MAIN LT 50°57′·73N 01°51′·30E

Morse ident: **CL** —·—· ·—··
Frequency: Ch 88 (162·025 MHz)
Range: 20 M
Times: H24

Count of beats	Bearing of Lt Ho from seaward (degrees) 0	1	2	3	4	5	6	7	8	9
0	—	—	—	—	—	—	—	090	092	094
10	096	098	100	102	104	106	108	110	112	114
20	116	118	120	122	124	126	128	130	132	134
30	136	138	140	142	144	146	148	150	152	154
40	156	158	160	162	164	166	168	170	172	174
50	176	178	180	182	184	186	188	190	192	194
60	196	198	200	202	204	206	208	210	—	—

4.4 RADAR

4.4.1 Radar in yachts

Radar is useful both for navigation and for collision avoidance, but to take full advantage of it and to use it in safety demands a proper understanding of its operation and of its limitations. Read the instruction book carefully, and practise using and adjusting the set so as to get optimum performance in different conditions. It is important to learn how to interpret what is actually seen on the display.

Radar beams do not discriminate so well in bearing as they do in range — so an accurate fix is sometimes best obtained by a radar range and a visual bearing of the same object.

The effective range of radar is approximately line of sight, but this can be decreased or increased by abnormal conditions. It is necessary to be aware that radar will not detect a low-lying coastline which is over the radar horizon.

The details of radar, and its use in yachts, are described in *The Macmillan & Silk Cut Yachtsman's Handbook* (4.6).

4.4.2 Radar for collision avoidance

Yacht radars invariably have a 'ship's head up display', with the boat at the centre, apparently stationary. If a target is moving in the same direction and at the same speed, it is stationary relative to own ship, and its echo should be sharp and well defined. If it is on a reciprocal course, it paints an echo with a long tail.

If an echo is on a steady bearing, and the range is decreasing, there is risk of collision. But to determine the proper action to take it is necessary to plot an approaching echo three or four times, in order to determine her actual course and speed, and how close she will actually approach.

4.4.3 Radar as a navigation aid

Radar cannot see behind other objects, or round corners; it may not pick up small objects, or differentiate between two targets that are close together. As already stated, radar ranges are more accurate than radar bearings. Objects with sharp features such as buildings give a better reflection than those with curved or sloping surfaces. High cliffs make a good target, but low coastlines should be approached with extreme caution as the first thing to show on radar may be hills some distance inland.

4.4.4 Radar beacons (Racons)

A Racon is a transponder beacon which, when triggered by a transmission from a vessel's radar, sends back a distinctive signal which appears on the vessel's radar display. Racons are fitted to some light-vessels, buoys and lighthouses, and are marked on charts by a magenta circle and the word Racon.

In most cases the Racon flash on the display is a line extending radially outwards from a point slightly beyond the actual position of the Racon, due to the slight delay in the response of the beacon apparatus. Thus the distance to the mark of the Racon flash is a little more than the vessel's real distance from the Racon. Some Racons give a flash composed of a Morse identification signal, often with a tail to it, the length of the tail depending on the number of Morse characters.

The maximum range of a radar beacon is usually about 10 nautical miles, but may be more. In practice, picking up a Racon at greater distances depends also on the effective range of the boat's radar. With abnormal radio propagation, a spurious Racon flash may be seen at much greater distances than the beacon's normal range, appearing at any random position along the correct bearing on the display. Only rely on a Racon flash if its appearance is consistent, and the boat is believed to be within its range. At short range a Racon sometimes causes unwelcome interference on the radar display, and this may be reduced by adjusting the rain clutter control on the set.

The characteristics of Radar beacons around the coasts of Great Britain are given in Table 4(4). Details are arranged in the following columns:

(1) Reference number.
(2) The type of Radar beacon. Unless otherwise stated, all radar beacons sweep the frequency range of marine 3cm (X-band) radar emissions. The older type of radar beacon (swept frequency Racons) take 30 to 90 seconds to sweep the band and the period of sweep is adjusted during installation to suit the individual location. The newer type of radar beacon (agile frequency Racon) responds immediately to radar interrogations. However, in order that wanted echoes should not be obscured by the racon signal, the agile response is switched 'on' and 'off' at a pre-determined rate to suit the installation. Where indicated (marked by an asterisk), radar beacons respond to both 10cm (S-band) and 3cm (X-band) emissions and are usually agile frequency Racons.
(3) Name of the station.
(4) Latitude and longitude.
(5) The sector within which signals may be received, bearings being towards the beacon, clockwise from 000° to 359°. 360° indicates all round operation.
(6) Approximate range, in nautical miles. This also depends on the range of the yacht's radar set.
(7) The form of the beacon's flash on the radar display. Morse signals are shown alphabetically, and are often followed by a 'tail'. Racons coded 'D' are used to mark new dangers.

Table 4(5) LIST OF RADAR BEACONS
(For heading details see 4.4.4)

(1) No.	(2) Type	(3) Name	(4) Lat	Long	(5) Sector	(6) Approx range	(7) Form of flash
GREAT BRITAIN							
1	3 & 10 cm*	**Bishop Rock Lt**	49°52′.3N	6°26′.7W	245°–215°	18 M	T
3	3 & 10 cm*	**Seven Stones Lt V**	50°03′.6N	6°04′.3W	360°	15 M	O
5	3 & 10 cm*	**Wolf Rock Lt**	49°56′.7N	5°48′.5W	360°	10 M	T
7	3 & 10 cm	**Eddystone Lt**	50°10′.8N	4°15′.9W	360°	10 M	T
9	3 cm	**West Bramble Lt By**	50°47′.2N	1°18′.6W	360°	3 M	T
11	3 cm	**Nab Tower Lt**	50°40′.1N	0°57′.1W	360°	10 M	T
13	3 & 10 cm*	**Greenwich Lanby**	50°24′.5N	0°00′.0	360°	15 M	T
15	3 & 10 cm*	**Varne Lanby**	51°01′.3N	1°24′.0E	360°	10 M	T
17	3 & 10 cm*	**East Goodwin Lt F**	51°13′.0N	1°36′.3E	360°	10 M	T
19	3 & 10 cm	**Falls Lt F**	51°18′.1N	1°48′.5E	360°	10 M	O
21	3 & 10 cm*	**NE Goodwin Lt By**	51°20′.3N	1°34′.3E	360°	10 M	G
23	3 & 10 cm*	**Dover Strait TSS, F3 Lanby**	51°23′.8N	2°00′.6E	360°	10 M	T
25	3 cm	**Sea Reach Lt By No 1**	51°29′.4N	0°52′.7E	360°	10 M	T
27	3 cm	**Sea Reach Lt By No 7**	51°30′.1N	0°37′.1E	360°	10 M	T
29	3 & 10 cm*	**Outer Tongue Lt By**	51°30′.8N	1°26′.5E	360°	10 M	T
31	3 & 10 cm*	**Barrow No 3 Lt By**	51°42′.0N	1°19′.9E	360°	10 M	B
33	3 & 10 cm	**S Galloper Lt By**	51°43′.9N	1°56′.5E	360°	10 M	T
35	3 & 10 cm	**Sunk Lt V**	51°51′.0N	1°35′.0E	360°	10 M	T
37	3 & 10 cm*	**Harwich Channel Lt By No 1**	51°56′.1N	1°27′.3E	360°	10 M	T
39	3 & 10 cm*	**Outer Gabbard Lt V**	51°59′.4N	2°04′.6E	360°	10 M	T
40		**Orfordness Lt**	**52°05′.0N**	**1°34′.6E**	**360°**	10 M	**T**
41	3 cm	**Cross Sand Lt By**	52°37′.0N	1°59′.2E	360°	10 M	T
43	3 cm	**Winterton Old Lighthouse**	52°42′.8N	1°41′.8E	360°	10 M	T
45	3 & 10 cm*	**Smiths Knoll Lt F**	52°43′.5N	2°18′.0E	360°	10 M	T
47	3 & 10 cm	**Newarp Lt F**	52°48′.4N	1°55′.8E	360°	10 M	O
49	3 & 10 cm	**Cromer Lt**	52°55′.4N	1°19′.1E	360°	25 M	C
51	3 & 10 cm	**North Haisbro Lt By**	53°00′.2N	1°32′.4E	360°	10 M	T
53	3 cm	**North Well Lt By**	53°03′.0N	0°28′.0E	360°	10 M	T
55	3 9 10 cm*	**Dudgeon Lt V**	53°16′.6N	1°17′.0E	360°	10 M	O
57	3 & 10 cm*	**Inner Dowsing Lt**	53°19′.7N	0°34′.0E	360°	25 M	T
59	3 & 10 cm	**Spurn Lt F**	53°33′.5N	0°14′.3E	360°	5M	M
60		**Dowsing Lt V**	**53°34′.0N**	**0°50′.2W**	**360°**	10 M	**T**
61	3 & 10 cm	**Humber Lt By**	53°36′.7N	0°21′.6E	360°	7 M	T
63	3 cm	**Tees Fairway By**	54°40′.9N	1°06′.4W	360°		B
65	3 cm	**St Abbs' Head Lt**	55°55′.0N	2°03′.2W	360°	18 M	T
67	3 cm	**Inchkeith Fairway By**	56°03′.5N	3°00′.0W	360°	5 M	T
69	3 cm	**Forth North Channel Lt By 7**	56°02′.8N	3°10′.9W	360°	5 M	T
71	3 & 10 cm	**Bell Rock Lt**	56°26′.0N	2°23′.1W	360°	18 M	M
73	3 cm	**Abertay Lt By**	56°27′.4N	2°40′.6W	360°	8 M	T
75	3 cm	**Scurdie Ness Lt**	56°42′.1N	2°26′.1W	360°	15 M	T
77	**3 & 10 cm**	**Girdle Ness Lt**	57°08′.3N	2°02′.8W	165°–055°[1]	25 M	G
	[1] Reduced coverage within sector 055°–165°						
79	3 cm	**Aberdeen Fairway By**	57°09′.3N	2°01′.8W	360°	7 M	T
81	3 cm	**Buchan Ness Lt**	57°28′.2N	1°46′.4W	155°–045°[1]	25 M	O
	[1] Reduced coverage within sector 045°–155°						
82	3 & 10 cm	**Rattray Ho Lt Ho**	57°36′.6N	1°48′.9W	110°–340°	**15 M**	**M**
83	3 cm	**Cromarty Firth Fairway By**	57°40′.0N	3°54′.1W	360°	5 M	**M**
85	3 cm	**Tarbat Ness Lt**	57°51′.9N	3°46′.5W	360°	12 M	T
87	3 cm	**Duncansby Head Lt**	58°38′.7N	3°01′.4W	360°	20 M	T
89	3 cm	**Lother Rock Lt**	58°43′.8N	2°58′.6W	360°	10 M	M
91	3 cm	**North Ronaldsay Lt**	59°23′.4N	2°22′.8W	360°	10 M	T
93	3 cm	**Rumble Rock Bn**	60°28′.2N	1°07′.1W	360°	10 M	O

(1) No.	(2) Type	(3) Name	(4) Lat	Long	(5) Sector	(6) Approx range	(7) Form of flash
95	3 cm	**Gruney Island Lt**	60°39′.2N	1°18′.0W	360°	18 M	T
97	3 & 10 cm	**Ve Skerries Lt**	60°22′.4N	1°48′.7W	360°	15 M	T
99	3 cm	**Sule Skerry Lt**	59°05′.1N	4°24′.3W	360°	20 M	T
101	3 cm	**Eilean Glas Lt**	57°51′.4N	6°38′.5W	360°	12 M	T
103	3 cm	**Castlebay South By**	56°56′.1N	7°27′.2W	360°	7 M	T
105	3 cm	**Monach Lt Ho**	57°31′.5N	7°41′.6W	360°	16 M	T
109	3 cm	**Kyleakin Lt**	57°16′.7N	5°44′.5W	360°	16 M	T
111	3 cm	**Skerryvore Lt**	56°19′.4N	7°06′.7W	360°	25 M	M
113	3 cm	**Sanda Lt**	56°16′.5N	5°34′.9W	360°	20 M	T
115	3 cm	**Point of Ayre Lt**	54°24′.9N	4°22′.0W	360°	15 M	M
117	3 & 10 cm*	**Lune Deep Lt By**	53°55′.8N	3°11′.0W	360°	10 M	T
119	3 cm	**Bar Lanby**	53°32′.0N	3°20′.9W	360°	10 M	T
121	3 & 10 cm*	**Skerries Lt**	53°25′.3N	4°36′.4W	360°	25 M	T
123	3 & 10 cm*	**The Smalls Lt**	51°43′.2N	5°40′.1W	360°	25 M	T
125	3 & 10 cm*	**St Gowan Lt V**	51°30′.5N	4°59′.8W	360°	15 M	T
127	3 & 10 cm*	**W Helwick Lt By**	51°31′.4N	4°23′.6W	360°	10 M	T
129	3 & 10 cm*	**W Scar Lt Buoy**	51°28′.3N	3°55′.5W	360°	10 M	T
131	3 & 10 cm*	**English and Welsh Grounds Lt By**	51°26′.9N	3°00′.1W	360°	10 M	O
133	3 & 10 cm*	**Breaksea Lt F**	51°19′.9N	3°19′.0W	360°	10 M	T

CHANNEL/CHANNEL ISLANDS (see also No 13)

No.	Type	Name	Lat	Long	Sector	Approx range	Form of flash
151	3 cm	**Lt By EC1**	50°05′.9N	1°48′.3W	360°	10 M	T
153	3 cm	**Lt By EC2**	50°12′.1N	1°12′.4W	360°	10 M	T
155	3 cm	**Lt By EC3**	50°18′.3N	0°36′.1W	360°	10 M	T
157	3 cm	**East Channel Lt F**	49°58′.7N	2°28′.9W	360°	10 M	T
159	3 & 10 cm*	**Channel Lt V**	49°54′.4N	2°53′.7W	360°	15 M	O
161	3 & 10 cm*	**Casquets Lt**	49°43′.4N	2°22′.5W	360°	25 M	T
163	3 cm	**Platte Fougère Lt**	49°30′.9N	2°29′0W			P
165	3 cm	**St Helier — Demie de Pas Lt**	49°09′.1N	2°06′.0W	360°	10 M	T
167	3 cm	**St Helier — Mount Ubé Lt**	49°10°.3N	2°03′.5W	360°	14 M	T

IRELAND

No.	Type	Name	Lat	Long	Sector	Approx range	Form of flash
201	3 cm	**Mizzen Head Lt**	51°27′.0N	9°49′.2W	360°	24 M	T
203	3 cm	**Cork Lt By**	51°42′.9N	8°15′.5W	360°	7 M	T
205	3 & 10 cm	**Hook Head Lt**	52°07′.4N	6°55′.7W	237°–177°	10 M	K
207	3 cm	**Coningbeg Lt F**	52°02′.4N	6°39′.4W	360°	13 M	M
209	3 cm	**Tuskar Rock Lt**	52°12′.2N	6°12′.4W	360°	18 M	T
211	3 cm	**Arklow Lanby**	52°39′.5N	5°58′.1W	360°	10 M	O
213	3 cm	**Codling Lanby**	53°03′.0N	5°40′.7W	360°	10 M	G
215	3 cm	**Kish Bank Lt**	53°18′.7N	5°55′.4W	360°	15 M	T
217	3 cm	**South Rock Lt V**	54°24′.5N	5°21′.9W	360°	13 M	T
219	3 & 10 cm*	**Inishtrahull Lt**	55°25′.9N	7°14′.6W	060°–310°[1]	24 M	T

[1] Reduced or no signal 310°–060°

FRANCE

No.	Type	Name	Lat	Long	Sector	Approx range	Form of flash
301	3 cm	**BXA Lanby**	45°37′.6N	1°28′.6W	360°		B
303	3 cm	**St Nazaire La Couronnée Lt By No 10**	47°07′.7N	2°20′.0W	360°	3–5 M	See [1]
		[1] Signals appear as a series of dots, the distance between each dot corresponding to 0.2 M.					T
305	3 cm	**St Nazaire Lt By SN1**	47°00′.0N	2°39′.9W	360°	3–8 M	Z
307	3 cm	**Chausée de Sein Lt By**	48°03′.8N	5°07′.7W	360°	10 M	O
309	3 cm	**Pointe de Créac'h Lt**	48°27′.6N	5°07′.6W	030°–248°	20 M	C

(1) No.	(2) Type	(3) Name	(4) Lat	Long	(5) Sector	(6) Approx range	(7) Form of flash
311	3 & 10 cm	**Ouessant SW Lanby**	48°31′.7N	5°49′.1W	360°	20 M	**M**
313	3 cm	**Ouessant NE Lt By**	48°45′.9N	5°11′.6W	360°	20 M	**B**
315	3 & 10 cm	**Le Havre LHA Lanby**	49°31′.7N	0°09′.8W	360°	8–10 M	See [1]
	[1] Signals appear as a series of 8 dots or 8 groups of dots, the distance between each dot or groups of dots corresponding to 0.3 M.						
317	3 cm	**Antifer Approach Lt By A5**	49°45′.9N	0°17′.4W	360°		**K**
319	3 cm	**Brassurelle Lt By**	50°32′.7N	0°57′.8E	360°	6–10 M	**B**
321	3 & 10 cm	**Vergoyer Lt By N**	50°39′.7N	1°22′.3E	360°	5–8 M	**C**
323	3 cm	**Sangatte**	50°57′.2N	1°46′.6E	360°	11 M	See [1]
	[1] Signal appears as 3 successions of 3 dots, the distance between each dot corresponding to 0.3 M.						
325	3 cm	**Dunkerque Lt By**	51°03′.1N	1°51′.8E	360°		See [1]
	[1] Signal appears as a series of 8 dots, the distance between each dot corresponding to 0.3 M						
327	3 & 10 cm	**Sandettié Lt V**	51°09′.4N	1°47′.2E	360°	4–10 M	**T**
BELGIUM AND NETHERLANDS							
375	3 & 10 cm	**Wandelaar Lt MOW 0**	51°23′.7N	3°02′.8E	360°	10 M	**W**
377	3 & 10 cm	**Bol Van Heist Lt MOW 3**	51°23′.4N	3°12′.0E	360°	10 M	**H**
379	3 cm	**Keeten B Lt By**	51°36′.4N	3°58′.1E	360°	—	**K**
399	3 & 10 cm	**Zuid Vlije Lt By ZV15/SRK28**	51°38′.2N	4°14′.5E	360°		**K**
401	3 cm	**Noord Hinder By NHR-SE**	51°45′.5N	2°40′.0E	360°	10 M	**N**
403	3 & 10 cm	**Noord Hinder Lt V**	52°00′.2N	2°51′.2E	360°	12–15 M	**T**
405	3 cm	**Noord Hinder Lt By NHR-N**	52°13′.3N	2°59′.5E	360°	10 M	**K**
407	3 cm	**Schouwenbank Lt By**	51°45′.0N	3°14′.4E	360°	10 M	**O**
409	3 & 10 cm	**Goeree Lt**	51°55′.5N	3°40′.2E	360°	12–15 M	**T**
411	3 cm	**Maas Center Lt By MC**	52°01′.2N	3°53′.6E	360°	10 M	**M**
413	3 & 10 cm	**Rijn Field Platform P15-B**	52°18′.5N	3°46′.7E	30°–270°	12–15 M	**B**
415	3 cm	**IJmuiden Lt By**	52°28′.7N	4°23′.9E	360°	10 M	**Y**
417	3 & 10 cm	**Texel Lt V**	52°47′.1N	4°06′.6E	360°	12–15 M	**T**
419	3 & 10 cm	**Logger Platform**	53°00′.9N	4°13′.0E	060°–270°	12–15 M	**X**
420	3 & 10 cm*	**Nam Field Platform K14-FA-1**	53°16′.2N	3°37′.7E	360°	**7 M**	
421	3 & 10 cm	**Vlieland Lanby VL-CENTER**	53°27′.0N	4°40′.0E	360°	12–15 M	**C**
423	3 & 10 cm	**Terschelling Bank, Platform L8-G**	53°34′.9N	4°36′.3E	000°–160°	12–15 M	**G**
425	3 & 10 cm	**Placid Field Platform PL-K9C-PA**	53°39′.2N	3°52′.4E	360°	8 M	**B**
427	3 cm	**DW Route Lt By**	54°00′.3N	4°21′.4E	360°	6–10 M	**M**
GERMANY (North Sea Coast)							
503	3 cm	**Westerems Lt By**	53°37′.1N	6°19′.5E	360°	8 M	**G**
505	3 cm	**TW/EMS Lt F**	54°10′.0N	6°20′.8E	360°	6–10 M	**T**
507	3 cm	**Deutsche Bucht Lt F**	54°10′.7N	7°26′.1E	360°	8 M	**T**
509	3 cm	**DB/Weser Lt By**	54°02′.4N	7°43′.0E	360°	6 M	**K**
511	3 cm	**Weser Lt By**	53°54′.2N	7°50′.0E	360°	7 M	**T**
513	3 cm	**Elbe No 1 Lt F**	54°00′.0N	8°06′.6E	360°	6–8 M	**T**

4

Chapter 5

Astro-Navigation

Contents

5

Astro-Navigation — introduction

The following subjects are described in detail in Chapter 5 of *The Macmillan & Silk Cut Yachtsman's Handbook*

A general introduction to astro-navigation; the sextant; sextant errors and adjustments; sextant handling. The principles of nautical astronomy — angular and geographical distances; time and hour angle; glossary of terms. Altitude corrections — dip; refraction; semi-diameter; parallax. Theory into practice — the astronomical triangle; sight reduction methods. Practical sight taking — notes on observation; the accuracy of sights; Sun sights; Moon sights; star sights. Sight reduction — tables; latitude by meridian altitude; latitude by Polaris; plotting the Sun's geographical position; equal altitudes. The use of calculators — dip; refraction; amplitudes; sight reduction. The position line — the use of a single position line; angle of cut; rate of change of bearing and altitude. Plotting and evaluating the sight. Sight reduction table — description; notation, method, equations and rules; instructions and illustrative examples; table. Bibliography.

Here in the Almanac are given the necessary astronomical data for determining position at sea — the Greenwich Hour Angle of the first point of Aries, the Greenwich Hour Angle and the Declination of the Sun, Moon, planets and selected stars for any instant of Greenwich Mean Time, together with auxiliary data comprising corrections to observed altitude, times of rising and setting of the Sun and Moon, times of twilight, planning data, star diagrams and azimuth diagrams.

5.1 THE USE OF CALCULATORS

5.1.1 General

For sight reduction either a 'dedicated' calculator (designed for the purpose) or a calculator offering program capability, and adequate memory storage together with polar-rectangular conversion and statistical functions should be used. Further information on this subject, and on the formulae below, is given in Chapter 5 (section 5.7) of *The Macmillan & Silk Cut Yachtsman's Handbook.*

5.1.2 Dip

Dip corrections to the observed altitude are always negative (—), and may be calculated from:

$$\text{Dip (in mins)} = 1'{\cdot}76 \times \sqrt{\text{HE}} \text{ (in metres)}$$
or
$$= 0'{\cdot}97 \times \sqrt{\text{HE}} \text{ (in feet)}$$

where HE is height of eye above sea level.

5.1.3 Refraction

The correction for refraction is always subtractive (—), and may be calculated from the formula:

$$R_M = \left(\frac{74}{h+2}\right) - 0{\cdot}7$$

where R_M is mean refraction in minutes of arc
h is observed altitude in degrees at sea level air temperature 10°C and atmospheric pressure 1010 millibars

5.1.4 Amplitudes

Amplitude is the bearing of a body measured from true east or west when it is on the horizon (i.e. rising or setting), and is useful for checking the accuracy of the compass.

$$\sin \text{Amplitude} = \frac{\sin \text{Declination}}{\cos \text{Latitude}}$$

Amplitudes should not be used in high latitudes.

5.1.5 Sight reduction

Several different methods can be used for the reduction of sights. The following are two basic formulae upon which most of these are based.

$$\sin \text{Alt} = (\sin \text{Lat} \times \sin \text{Dec}) + (\cos \text{Lat} \times \cos \text{Dec} \times \cos \text{LHA})$$

where: Dec is positive if the SAME name as Lat, and negative if CONTRARY name.

For the Azimuth Angle (Z): tan Z =

$$\frac{\sin \text{LHA}}{(\cos \text{Lat} \times \tan \text{Dec}) - (\sin \text{Lat} \times \cos \text{LHA})}$$

where the sign conventions are:

(a) If Lat or Dec are SOUTH change their sign to minus (−).

(b) If Z and sin LHA have the same sign, Zn = Z + 180°; if Z is minus (−) and LHA is less than 180°, Zn = Z + 360°; if Z is plus (+) and LHA is greater than 180°, Zn = Z.

5.2 ASTRONOMICAL DATA (EPHEMERIS) – EXPLANATION

5.2.1 Summary of contents

The object of this Almanac is to provide, in a condensed form, the data needed to determine position at sea to an accuracy of one or two minutes of arc. It is designed for European waters between latitudes N.30° and N.60°.

The presentation of the daily ephemerides has been changed from decimals of a degree to the more usual degrees and minutes of arc.

The ephemerides are derived from data supplied by Her Majesty's Nautical Almanac Office, but if comparisons are made with their publication, *'The Nautical Almanac'*, it will be seen that there are occasional differences in the tabulated values—this is because the end figures in this almanac have been adjusted to allow linear interpolation to be used with a minimum of error.

For the Sun and planets this adjustment is rarely significant, with a maximum value (for Venus) of 0′·1. However, for the Moon it is more significant, with a maximum value of 0′·8. Such large adjustments then become inconsistent with end-figures of 0′·1 and hence the tabulation for the Moon has been reduced to 1′.

The main contents consist of data from which the *Greenwich Hour Angle* (GHA) and the *Declination* (Dec) of the Sun, Moon and planets (Venus, Mars, Jupiter and Saturn) can be determined for any instant of *Universal Time* (UT). The *Local Hour*

Angle (LHA) can then be obtained from:

$$\text{LHA} = \text{GHA} \begin{matrix} -\text{west} \\ +\text{east} \end{matrix} \text{ longitude}$$

Auxiliary data consist of: corrections to observed altitude, calendarial data, times of rising and setting of the Sun and Moon, times of twilight, planning data, star diagrams and azimuth diagrams.

For the Sun and planets, the GHA and Dec are tabulated directly for 00^h of each day throughout the year. For the Moon the tabulations are for 00^h, 08^h and 16^h each day. For the stars the *Sidereal Hour Angle* (SHA) is given, and the GHA is obtained from:

$$\text{GHA Star} = \text{GHA Aries} + \text{SHA Star}$$

The SHA and Dec of the stars change slowly but, to the accuracy required, mean values are adequate and are given for use throughout the year. The errors in the tabulated coordinates can rise to $\pm0'\cdot6$ in SHA and $\pm0'\cdot4$ in Dec. GHA Aries, or the Greenwich Hour Angle of the first point of Aries, is tabulated for 00^h each day. Permanent tables give the increments and corrections to the tabulated daily values of GHA and Dec for hours, minutes and seconds of UT.

The tabular accuracy of GHA and Dec of the Sun and planets, GHA Aries and of the SHA and Dec of the stars is $0'\cdot1$; for the Moon the tabular accuracy has been reduced to $1'$.

The ephemeral data for two months are given on an opening of two pages; the left-hand page contains data for Aries and the planets and the right-hand page data for the Sun and Moon. Separate tabulations give Local Mean Times (LMT), for every third day, of Morning Nautical Twilight, Sunrise, Sunset and Evening Civil Twilight for latitude N.50°, together with variations (v) which, with the aid of auxiliary tables, enable the LMT for other latitudes in the range N.30° to N.60° to be found. Tabulations for Moonrise and Moonset for each day for latitude N.50° are given together with variations (v) which, with the auxiliary tables, enable the LMT of Moonrise and Moonset to be found for latitudes N.30° to N.60°.

5.2.2 Main data

Monthly pages. These give on each left-hand page the GHA of Aries and the GHA and Dec of the four navigational planets at 00^h UT each day. On the right-hand page, the GHA and Dec of the Sun are given each day for 00^h UT, and the mean semi-diameter (SD) is shown each month; for the Moon the GHA and Dec are given each day for 00^h, 08^h and 16^h UT, and horizontal parallax (HP) for 12^h. Values of the variations (v) in GHA and (d) in Declination allow the GHA and Dec of Sun, Moon or planets to be found at any instant of UT. South declinations are treated as negative.

Stars. The SHA and Dec of 48 selected stars are tabulated in numerical order in 5.3.3 on page 81 and are intended for use throughout the year; an alphabetical list of star names and numbers is also given.

Interpolation tables. These tables provide the increments for hours, minutes and seconds to be applied to the tabular values of GHA and Dec; the tables for Aries, Sun and planets comprise six pages, and those for the Moon four pages. The increment for GHA Aries is taken out in two parts, the first with argument UT in units of 12 minutes and the second part, with argument the remainder, in minutes and seconds, is given on the left-hand side of the opening. For the GHA of the Sun and planets the increment is found in three parts: the first with argument UT in units of 12 minutes, the second is for the remainder in minutes and seconds, given on the right hand side of the opening and the third with vertical argument UT (in units of 12 minutes) and horizontal argument v. The increments for Dec are found with vertical argument UT (in units of 12 minutes) and horizontal argument d.

For the Moon, the increment of GHA is found in three parts. First with argument UT in units of 4 minutes, second with argument the remainder of UT in minutes and seconds, and third with vertical argument UT (in units of 4 minutes) and horizontal argument v. The increments for Dec are found with vertical argument UT (in units of 4 minutes) and horizontal argument d.

The increments are based on the following adopted hourly rates of increase: Aries $15°\cdot0411$; Sun and planets 15° precisely; Moon $14°\cdot25$. The values of v are the differences (in minutes of arc) of the actual changes in GHA minus the adopted changes over the tabular interval, i.e. for the Sun and planets v is the daily change minus 360° and can be either positive or negative; for the Moon v is the change over eight hours minus 114° and is always positive. The values of d are the changes in Dec over the tabular interval. For the Sun and planets the full values (to $0'\cdot1$) of v and d should be obtained by inspection before using the interpolation tables.

The errors introduced by using the tables may amount to $0'\cdot15$ for Aries, $0'\cdot2$ for the Sun and planets, and $1'\cdot5$ for the Moon. If direct interpolation is used (see page 78) these errors can be reduced slightly, to $0'\cdot1$ for Aries, Sun and planets, and $1'\cdot0$ for the Moon.

5.2.3 Rising and setting phenomena

These tabulations give for every third day of the year, Local Mean Times (LMT) of Morning Nautical Twilight, Sunrise, Sunset and Evening Civil Twilight for latitude N.50°, together with variations (v) which, with the aid of auxiliary tables, enable the LMT for other latitudes (in the range N.30° to N.60°) to be found. The tabulations for Moonrise and Moonset are given for each day for latitude N.50°, together with variations (v) which, with the aid of auxiliary tables, enable the LMT to be found for latitudes N.30° to N.60°. The tabular values are for the Greenwich Meridian, but are approximately the Local Mean Times of the corresponding phenomena for the other meridians; only for the Moon phenomena need a correction for longitude be applied and a note of this correction is given in 5.3.7 on page 87. The UT of a phenomenon is obtained from the LMT by

$$\text{UT} = \text{LMT} \begin{matrix} +\text{west} \\ -\text{east} \end{matrix} \text{ longitude}$$

in which the longitude must first be converted to time by the table in 5.3.12 on page 116.

At Sunrise and Sunset 16′ is allowed for semi-diameter and 34′ for horizontal refraction, so that at the times given the Sun's upper limb is on the visible horizon; all times refer to phenomena as seen from sea level with a clear horizon.

At the times given for the beginning and end of twilight, the Sun's zenith distance is 96° for Civil, and 102° for Nautical Twilight. The degree of illumination at the times given for Civil Twilight (in good conditions and in the absence of other illumination) is such that the brightest stars are visible and the horizon is clearly defined. At the times given for Nautical Twilight the horizon is in general not visible, and it is too dark for observation with a marine sextant.

At Moonrise and Moonset allowance is made for semi-diameter, parallax and refraction (34′), so that at the times given the Moon's upper limb is on the visible horizon as seen from sea level.

5.2.4 Altitude correction tables

Tables for the correction of dip of the horizon, due to height of eye above sea level, are given in 5.3.2 on page 80; this correction should be applied to the sextant altitude to give apparent altitude, which is the correct argument for the other tables.

The dip table is arranged as a critical table, where an interval of height of eye corresponds to a single value of dip. No interpolation is required. At a 'critical' entry the upper of the two possible values of the correction is to be used.

Separate tables for refraction are given for the Sun, stars and planets, and Moon. With the Sun and Moon, to allow for semi-diameter, separate corrections are given for the lower and upper limbs. For the Moon, corrections are also given for parallax.

The altitude correction tables are given to one decimal of a minute of arc so that the addition of several corrections does not lead to any significant error.

5.2.5 Polaris table

The table in 5.3.4 on page 81 provides means by which the latitude can be deduced from an observed altitude of *Polaris*; the azimuth of *Polaris* is also given. The correction Q, to be applied to the apparent altitude, corrected for refraction, is given corresponding to an argument of LHA Aries (LHA♈).

5.2.6 Auxiliary and planning data

Pages 82 and 83 (5.3.5) give the times of meridian passage (mer pass) of the Sun; symbols, approximate SHA and Dec, magnitude (mag) and meridian passage of the planets; an explanation of the symbols used and planet notes are given on page 83. Phases of the Moon, with brief eclipse notes, are also given on page 83.

Star diagrams. Star diagrams are given on pages 110–112; these have been drawn for latitude N.45° and show the approximate positions in altitude and azimuth, of stars in the Selected list for each range of 15° of LHA Aries; indications are also given of the horizons for latitude N.30° (shown as ··· ···) and N.60° (shown as ·—·—); these will enable the user to estimate the approximate altitude and azimuth of any particular star and will indicate stars suitable for observation at a given value of LHA Aries.

Symbols indicate the magnitude of the stars as follows:

- • Mag 2·1 to 3·1
- ○ Mag 1·1 to 2·0 note that the larger symbols
- ● Mag 0·0 to 1·0 indicate greater brilliance
- ⊙ Mag −1·6 to 0·0

The symbol for any star indicates its position at the beginning of the range of LHA Aries and the arrow point the end of the range.

Azimuth diagrams are given on pages 113–115; they are used as follows: a point is plotted on the diagrams corresponding to the LHA and Dec of the object observed; the plotted point is then moved horizontally to the *left* corresponding to the co-latitude (90° — latitude) of the observer; the background graticule and the scale along the top of the diagram will assist in this movement; at the new position the corresponding value of LHA is read and is converted to azimuth according to the rules given below the diagrams.

5.2.7 Illustrations

Example (a) Required the GHA and Dec of the Sun on 1992 January 22 at UT $15^h\ 47^m\ 13^s$.

			GHA	v	Dec	d
			° ′		° ′	
Page 89	Jan 22		177 10·4	−4	S19 53·5	+14
Interpolation	UT	$15^h\ 36^m$	234			
Tables	UT	$11^m\ 13^s$	2 48·2			
Page 101	UT	$15^h\ 47^m\ 13^s$ ($v = -4{\cdot}1\ d = +13{\cdot}5$)	−2·7		+8·9	
			413 55·9		S19 44·6	
	Remove 360°		−360			
			53 55·9			

Note that, in this case, the declination is south (i.e. negative) and the correction for d is positive, so that the correction must be subtracted.

Example (b) Required the GHA and Dec of the Moon on 1992 January 13 at UT $15^h\ 47^m\ 13^s$.

			GHA	v	Dec	d
			° ′		° ′	
Page 89	Jan 13 08^h–16^h		210 44	127	N14 28	+88
Interpolation	UT	$07^h\ 44^m$	110 12			
Tables	UT	$3^m\ 13^s$	0 46			
Pages 108, 109	UT	$07^h\ 47^m\ 13^s$ ($v = 127\ \ d = +88$)	2 04		+1 26	
			323 46		N15 54	

Note that the correction for v and d are taken from the interpolation tables as +124 and +86 respectively.

Example (c) Required the LHA and Dec of Venus on 1992 January 3 at UT $07^h\ 47^m\ 13^s$ for longitude E 5° 15′.

			GHA	v	Dec	d
			° ′		° ′	
Page 88	Jan 3		220 39·7	−16	S18 42·1	−15
Interpolation	UT	$07^h\ 36^m$	114			
Tables	UT	$11^m\ 13^s$	2 48·2			
Pages 102, 103	UT	$07^h\ 47^m\ 13^s$ ($v = -15{\cdot}7\ \ d = -15{\cdot}3$)	−5·1		−5·0	
			337 22·8		S18 47·1	
Longitude East			+5 15·0			
	LHA		342 37·8			

The first correction for the GHA of the planets is taken from the column headed Sun/Planet.

Here, the declination is south (i.e. negative) and the correction for d is negative, so that the correction must be added.

Example (d) Required the GHA and Dec of *Aldebaran* on 1992 January 22 at UT $15^h\ 55^m\ 13^s$.

		GHA	Dec
		° ′	° ′
Page 81	SHA and Dec	291 07·2	N16 29·7
Page 88	GHA Aries	120 36·5	
Interpolation	UT $15^h\ 48^m$	237 38·9	
Tables	UT $7^m\ 13^s$	1 48·2	
Pages 100, 101			
		651 10·8	
	Remove 360°	−360	
	GHA at UT $15^h\ 55^m\ 13^s$	291 10·8	

Example (e) Required the UT at the beginning of nautical twilight and sunrise on 1992 January 22 for latitude N30° 50′, longitude W7° 25′.

		Naut Twi	*v*	Sunrise	*v*
		h m		h m	
Page 84	Jan 22	06 31	+30	07 47	+52
Page 85	Corrections for N 30°50′	−29		−50	
	LMT	06 02		06 57	
Page 116	Long. equivalent in time	+30		+30	
	UT	06 32		07 27	

Example (f) Required the UT of sunset and evening civil twilight on 1992 January 22 for latitude N36° 07′, longitude E18° 20′.

		Sunset	*v*	Civil Twi	*v*
		h m		h m	
Page 84	Jan 22	16 36	−52	17 12	−41
Page 85	Corrections for N 36°07′	+39		+31	
	LMT	17 15		17 43	
Page 116	Long. equivalent in time	−1 13		−1 13	
	UT	16 02		16 30	

Example (g) Required the UT of moonrise and moonset on 1992 January 16 for latitude N36° 07′, longitude W6° 30′.

		Moonrise	*v*	Moonset	*v*
		h m		h m	
Page 86	Jan 16	12 35	−73	04 32	+71
Page 87	Corrections for N 36°07′	+55		−54	
	LMT	13 30		03 38	
Page 116	Long. equivalent in time	+26		+ 26	
	UT	13 56		04 04	

These times can be increased by $+1^m$ to allow for the effect of longitude on the LMT of the phenomena (see page 87).

Example (h) Required the correction to an observed altitude of *Polaris*, made on 1992 January 22 at UT 16ʰ 45ᵐ in DR longitude E18° 20′ the sextant angle being 37° 05′5, height of eye 15ft.

		° ′
Page 88	Jan 22 GHA Aries	120 36·5
Page 101	Correction for 16ʰ 36ᵐ	249 40·9
Page 100	Correction for 9ᵐ	2 15·4
		372 32·8
	Correction for Long E.18°20′	+18 20·0
		390 52·8
	Remove 360°	−360
	LHA Aries	30 52·8

		° ′
Sextant altitude		37 05·5
Page 80	Dip, for 15ft	−3·8
	Apparent altitude	37 01·7
Page 80	Refraction, stars	−1·3
	Corrected observed altitude	37 00·4
Page 81	Q for LHA Aries 31°	−46
	Latitude	36 14

From page 81 azimuth of *Polaris* at LHA Aries of 31° is seen to be 0°.

The following examples illustrate the use of the altitude correction tables on page 80. The sextant altitudes are assumed to be taken on 1992 December 3 with a marine sextant at height 5·4 metres (18ft).

	SUN lower limb	SUN upper limb	MOON lower limb	MOON upper limb	VENUS	POLARIS
	° ′	° ′	° ′	° ′	° ′	° ′
Sextant altitude	21 19·7	3 20·2	33 27·6	26 06·7	4 32·6	49 36·5
Dip, height 5.4 metres (18ft)	−4·1	−4·1	−4·1	−4·1	−4·1	−4·1
Apparent altitude	21 15·6	3 16·1	33 23·5	26 02·6	4 28·5	49 32·4
Main correction	+13·7	−29·5	+58·5	+31·7	−10·7	−0·8
Parallax correction for Moon (HP = 54′5, from page 99)			+0·5	+0·3		
Corrected sextant altitude	21 29·3	2 46·6	34 22·5	26 34·6	4 17·8	49 31·6

The following example illustrates the use of the Star Diagrams: on 1992 January 22 an observer in an approximate position of latitude N51°, longitude W7° wishes to determine which stars are suitable for observation at about UT 7ʰ 20ᵐ, and determines LHA Aries as follows.

			° ′
Page 88	Jan 22	GHA Aries	120 36·5
Interpolation	UT	7ʰ 12ᵐ	108 17·7
Tables	UT	8ᵐ	2 00·3
Page 100			
GHA Aries	UT	7ʰ 20ᵐ	230 54·5
	Correction for Long W7°		− 7 00·0
	LHA Aries		223 54·5

Inspection of the Star Diagram for LHA Aries 210° to 225° on page 111 indicates that stars 53, 49, and 46 are visible towards the east, 39, 37, and 33 are towards the south, 28 and 26 are westerly and 3 (rather low) and 40 (rather high) are northerly; *Polaris* will also be available. The names of the stars corresponding to the numbers can be found on page 81 and also at the foot of page 111.

5.2.8 The use of a calculator for interpolation

When using a calculator the tabular values of GHA, *v*, Dec and *d* should be extracted from the monthly pages for the date of observation (and in the case of the Moon, the nearest 8^h before the UT of observation). The UT must be converted to hours and decimals, i.e. hours + (minutes ÷ 60) + (seconds ÷ 3600). The GHA and Dec should also be converted to decimal units, i.e. degrees + (minutes ÷ 60), then the required values are found as follows. Southern declinations are treated as negative.

Stars

GHA star = Tabular GHA Aries + (15°·0411 × UT) + SHA star
Dec star = Tabular Dec (from Star list)

Sun

GHA Sun = Tabular GHA Sun + (15° + (*v* ÷ 1440)) × UT
Dec Sun = Tabular Dec Sun + (*d* ÷ 1440) × UT

Planets

GHA Planet = Tabular GHA Planet + (15° + (*v* ÷ 1440)) × UT
Dec Planet = Tabular Dec Planet + (*d* ÷ 1440) × UT

Moon

GHA Moon = Tabular GHA Moon + (14·25 + (*v* ÷ 480)) × UT*
Dec Moon = Tabular Dec Moon + (*d* ÷ 480) × UT*

* For the Moon, multiples of 8 hours must be subtracted from the UT.

5.2.9 Standard Times

List 1 — Places fast on UT

The times given below should be { *added* to UT to give Standard Time / *subtracted* from Standard Time to give UT }

	h		h		h
Albania*	01	France*	01	Netherlands, The*	01
Algeria	01	Germany*	01	Norway*	01
Austria*	01	Gibraltar*	01	Poland*	01
Balearic Islands*	01	Greece*	02	Romania*	02
Belgium*	01	Hungary*	01	Sardinia*	01
Bulgaria*	02	Israel*	02	Sicily*	01
Corsica*	01	Italy*	01	Spain*	01
Crete*	02	Latvia	03	Sweden*	01
Cyprus, Ercan*	02	Lebanon*	02	Switzerland*	01
Cyprus, Larnaca*	02	Libya*	01	Syria*	02
Czechoslovakia*	01	Liechtenstein*	01	Tunisia*	01
Denmark*	01	Lithuania	03	Turkey*	02
Egypt*	02	Luxembourg*	01	USSR west of 40°E*	03
Estonia	03	Malta*	01	Yugoslavia*	01
Finland*	02	Monaco*	01		

List 2 — Places normally keeping UT

Canary Islands*	Great Britain[1]	Irish Republic*
Channel Islands[1]	Iceland	Morocco*
Faeroes, The*	Ireland, Northern[1]	Portugal*

* Summer time may be kept in these countries.

[1] Summer time, one hour in advance of UT, is kept from March 29 01^h to October 25 01^h UT (1992).

5.3.1 CALENDAR, 1992

DAYS OF THE WEEK AND DAYS OF THE YEAR

DAY	JAN	FEB	MAR	APR	MAY	JUN	JUL	AUG	SEP	OCT	NOV	DEC
1	W 1	S 32	**Su** 61	W 92	F 122	M 153	W 183	S 214	Tu 245	Th 275	**Su** 306	Tu 336
2	Th 2	**Su** 33	M 62	Th 93	S 123	Tu 154	Th 184	**Su** 215	W 246	F 276	M 307	W 337
3	F 3	M 34	Tu 63	F 94	**Su** 124	W 155	F 185	M 216	Th 247	S 277	Tu 308	Th 338
4	S 4	Tu 35	W 64	S 95	M 125	Th 156	S 186	Tu 217	F 248	**Su** 278	W 309	F 339
5	**Su** 5	W 36	Th 65	**Su** 96	Tu 126	F 157	**Su** 187	W 218	S 249	M 279	Th 310	S 340
6	M 6	Th 37	F 66	M 97	W 127	S 158	M 188	Th 219	**Su** 250	Tu 280	F 311	**Su** 341
7	Tu 7	F 38	S 67	Tu 98	Th 128	**Su** 159	Tu 189	F 220	M 251	W 281	S 312	M 342
8	W 8	S 39	**Su** 68	W 99	F 129	M 160	W 190	S 221	Tu 252	Th 282	**Su** 313	Tu 343
9	Th 9	**Su** 40	M 69	Th 100	S 130	Tu 161	Th 191	**Su** 222	W 253	F 283	M 314	W 344
10	F 10	M 41	Tu 70	F 101	**Su** 131	W 162	F 192	M 223	Th 254	S 284	Tu 315	Th 345
11	S 11	Tu 42	W 71	S 102	M 132	Th 163	S 193	Tu 224	F 255	**Su** 285	W 316	F 346
12	**Su** 12	W 43	Th 72	**Su** 103	Tu 133	F 164	**Su** 194	W 225	S 256	M 286	Th 317	S 347
13	M 13	Th 44	F 73	M 104	W 134	S 165	M 195	Th 226	**Su** 257	Tu 287	F 318	**Su** 348
14	Tu 14	F 45	S 74	Tu 105	Th 135	**Su** 166	Tu 196	F 227	M 258	W 288	S 319	M 349
15	W 15	S 46	**Su** 75	W 106	F 136	M 167	W 197	S 228	Tu 259	Th 289	**Su** 320	Tu 350
16	Th 16	**Su** 47	M 76	Th 107	S 137	Tu 168	Th 198	**Su** 229	W 260	F 290	M 321	W 351
17	F 17	M 48	Tu 77	F 108	**Su** 138	W 169	F 199	M 230	Th 261	S 291	Tu 322	Th 352
18	S 18	Tu 49	W 78	S 109	M 139	Th 170	S 200	Tu 231	F 262	**Su** 292	W 323	F 353
19	**Su** 19	W 50	Th 79	**Su** 110	Tu 140	F 171	**Su** 201	W 232	S 263	M 293	Th 324	S 354
20	M 20	Th 51	F 80	M 111	W 141	S 172	M 202	Th 233	**Su** 264	Tu 294	F 325	**Su** 355
21	Tu 21	F 52	S 81	Tu 112	Th 142	**Su** 173	Tu 203	F 234	M 265	W 295	S 326	M 356
22	W 22	S 53	**Su** 82	W 113	F 143	M 174	W 204	S 235	Tu 266	Th 296	**Su** 327	Tu 357
23	Th 23	**Su** 54	M 83	Th 114	S 144	Tu 175	Th 205	**Su** 236	W 267	F 297	M 328	W 358
24	F 24	M 55	Tu 84	F 115	**Su** 145	W 176	F 206	M 237	Th 268	S 298	Tu 329	Th 359
25	S 25	Tu 56	W 85	S 116	M 146	Th 177	S 207	Tu 238	F 269	**Su** 299	W 330	F 360
26	**Su** 26	W 57	Th 86	**Su** 117	Tu 147	F 178	**Su** 208	W 239	S 270	M 300	Th 331	S 361
27	M 27	Th 58	F 87	M 118	W 148	S 179	M 209	Th 240	**Su** 271	Tu 301	F 332	**Su** 362
28	Tu 28	F 59	S 88	Tu 119	Th 149	**Su** 180	Tu 210	F 241	M 272	W 302	S 333	M 363
29	W 29	S 60	**Su** 89	W 120	F 150	M 181	W 211	S 242	Tu 273	Th 303	**Su** 334	Tu 364
30	Th 30		M 90	Th 121	S 151	T 182	Th 212	**Su** 243	W 274	F 304	M 335	W 365
31	F 31		Tu 91		**Su** 152		F 213	M 244		S 305		Th 366

RELIGIOUS CALENDARS

Epiphany	Jan 6
Septuagesima Sunday	Feb 16
Ash Wednesday	Mar 4
Good Friday	Apr 17
Easter Day	Apr 19
Low Sunday	Apr 26
Ascension Day	May 28
Whit Sunday	Jun 7
Christmas Day	Dec 25
Jewish New Year (5753)	Sep 28
Islamic New Year (1413)	Jul 2

CIVIL CALENDAR

Accession of the Queen	Feb 6
St David (Wales)	Mar 1
Commonwealth Day	Mar 9
St Patrick (Ireland)	Mar 17
Birthday of the Queen	Apr 21
St George (England)	Apr 23
Coronation Day	Jun 2
Birthday of Prince Philip	Jun 10
The Queen's Official Birthday	Jun 13
Remembrance Sunday	Nov 8
Birthday of the Prince of Wales	Nov 14
St Andrew (Scotland)	Nov 30

BANK HOLIDAYS

ENGLAND & WALES
Jan 1, Apr 17, Apr 20, May 4, May 25, Aug 31, Dec 25, Dec 28

NORTHERN IRELAND
Jan 1, Mar 17, Apr 17, Apr 20, May 4, May 25, July 13, Aug 31, Dec 25, Dec 28

SCOTLAND
Jan 1, Jan 2, Apr 17, May 4, May 25, Aug 3, Dec 25, Dec 28

5

5.3.2 ALTITUDE CORRECTION TABLES

DIP

Ht of eye (m)	Corr (′)	Ht of eye (ft)
1.6		5.3
	−2.3	
1.7		5.8
	−2.4	
1.9		6.3
	−2.5	
2.1		6.9
	−2.6	
2.2		7.4
	−2.7	
2.4		8.0
	−2.8	
2.6		8.6
	−2.9	
2.8		9.2
	−3.0	
3.0		9.8
	−3.1	
3.2		10.5
	−3.2	
3.4		11.2
	−3.3	
3.6		11.9
	−3.4	
3.8		12.6
	−3.5	
4.0		13.3
	−3.6	
4.3		14.1
	−3.7	
4.5		14.9
	−3.8	
4.7		15.7
	−3.9	
5.0		16.5
	−4.0	
5.2		17.4
	−4.1	
5.5		18.3
	−4.2	
5.8		19.1
	−4.3	
6.1		20.1
	−4.4	
6.3		21.0
	−4.5	
6.6		22.0
	−4.6	
6.9		22.9
	−4.7	
7.2		23.9
	−4.8	
7.5		24.9
	−4.9	
7.9		26.0
	−5.0	
8.2		27.1
	−5.1	
8.5		28.1
	−5.2	
8.8		29.2
	−5.3	
9.2		30.4
	−5.4	
9.5		31.5
	−5.5	
9.9		32.7
	−5.6	
10.3		33.9
	−5.7	
10.6		35.1
	−5.8	
11.0		36.3
	−5.9	
11.4		37.6
	−6.0	
11.8		38.9
	−6.1	
12.2		40.1
	−6.2	
12.6		41.5
	−6.3	
13.0		42.8
	−6.4	
13.4		44.2
	−6.5	
13.8		45.5
	−6.6	
14.2		46.9
	−6.7	
14.7		48.4
	−6.8	
15.1		49.8
	−6.9	
15.5		51.3
	−7.0	
16.0		52.8
	−7.1	
16.5		54.3
	−7.2	
16.9		55.8
	−7.3	
17.4		57.4
	−7.4	
17.9		58.9
	−7.5	
18.4		60.5
	−7.6	
18.8		62.1

SUN / STARS and PLANETS

App Alt (°)	SUN Lower limb (′)	SUN Upper limb (′)	STARS and PLANETS (′)
2.5	+ 0.1	−32.0	−16.1
3.0	1.8	30.2	14.4
3.5	3.2	28.8	13.0
4.0	4.4	27.7	11.8
4.5	5.4	26.6	10.7
5	+ 6.3	−25.8	− 9.9
6	7.7	24.3	8.5
7	8.7	23.3	7.4
8	9.6	22.4	6.6
9	10.3	21.8	5.9
10	+ 10.8	−21.2	− 5.3
12	11.7	20.4	4.5
14	12.4	19.7	3.8
16	12.8	19.2	3.3
18	13.2	18.8	3.0
20	+ 13.5	−18.5	− 2.6
25	14.1	18.0	2.1
30	14.5	17.6	1.7
35	14.8	17.3	1.4
40	15.0	17.0	1.2
45	+ 15.2	−16.9	− 1.0
50	15.3	16.8	0.8
55	15.5	16.6	0.7
60	15.6	16.5	0.6
70	15.7	16.3	0.4
80	+ 15.8	−16.1	− 0.2

MOON

App Alt (°)	Lower limb (′)	Upper limb (′)	App Alt (°)	Lower limb (′)	Upper limb (′)
2.5	+ 52.5	+ 23.1	40	+ 55.1	+ 25.3
3.0	54.2	24.8	42	53.9	24.2
3.5	55.7	26.2	44	52.7	23.0
4.0	56.8	27.4	46	51.5	21.7
4.5	57.8	28.4	48	50.2	20.4
5	+ 58.6	+ 29.2	50	+ 48.8	+ 19.0
6	60.0	30.5	52	47.4	17.6
7	60.9	31.5	54	46.0	16.1
8	61.7	32.2	56	44.5	14.6
9	62.2	32.7	58	42.9	13.1
10	+ 62.6	+ 33.1	60	+ 41.4	+ 11.5
12	63.1	33.6	62	39.8	9.9
14	63.3	33.8	64	38.1	8.3
16	63.3	33.7	66	36.5	6.6
18	63.2	33.6	68	34.8	4.9
20	+ 62.9	+ 33.3	70	+ 33.1	+ 3.2
22	62.5	32.9	71	32.2	+ 2.3
24	62.0	32.3	72	31.3	+ 1.4
26	61.4	31.7	73	30.4	+ 0.5
28	60.7	31.0	74	29.6	− 0.3
30	+ 59.9	+ 30.3	75	+ 28.7	− 1.2
32	59.1	29.4	76	27.8	− 2.1
34	58.2	28.5	77	26.9	− 3.0
36	57.2	27.5	78	26.0	− 3.9
38	56.2	26.4	79	25.1	− 4.8
40	+ 55.1	+ 25.3	80	+ 24.2	− 5.7

CORRECTION FOR MOON'S PARALLAX

App Alt	0°		20°		40°		50°		60°		70°		80°	
HP	L	U	L	U	L	U	L	U	L	U	L	U	L	U
	+	+	+	+	+	+	+	+	+	+	+	+	+	
′	′	′	′	′	′	′	′	′	′	′	′	′	′	′
54.0	0.0	0.0	0.0	0.0	0.0	0.0	0.0	0.0	0.0	0.0	0.0	0.0	0.0	0.0
54.5	0.6	0.4	0.6	0.3	0.5	0.2	0.4	0.2	0.4	0.1	0.3	0.0	0.2	0.0
55.0	1.3	0.7	1.2	0.7	1.0	0.5	0.9	0.4	0.8	0.2	0.6	0.0	0.4	−0.1
55.5	1.9	1.1	1.8	1.0	1.5	0.7	1.3	0.6	1.1	0.3	0.9	0.1	0.6	−0.1
56.0	2.5	1.5	2.4	1.3	2.1	1.0	1.8	0.7	1.5	0.5	1.2	0.1	0.9	−0.2
56.5	3.1	1.8	3.0	1.7	2.6	1.2	2.2	0.9	1.9	0.6	1.5	0.2	1.1	−0.2
57.0	3.8	2.2	3.6	2.0	3.1	1.5	2.7	1.1	2.3	0.7	1.8	0.2	1.3	−0.3
57.5	4.5	2.5	4.2	2.3	3.6	1.7	3.2	1.3	2.7	0.8	2.1	0.2	1.5	−0.3
58.0	5.1	2.9	4.8	2.7	4.1	2.0	3.6	1.5	3.1	1.0	2.4	0.3	1.8	−0.4
58.5	5.7	3.3	5.4	3.0	4.7	2.2	4.1	1.7	3.4	1.1	2.8	0.3	2.0	−0.4
59.0	6.3	3.6	6.0	3.3	5.2	2.5	4.6	1.8	3.8	1.2	3.1	0.3	2.3	−0.5
59.5	7.0	4.0	6.6	3.7	5.7	2.7	5.0	2.0	4.2	1.3	3.4	0.4	2.5	−0.5
60.0	7.6	4.4	7.2	4.0	6.2	3.0	5.5	2.2	4.6	1.4	3.7	0.4	2.7	−0.6
60.5	8.2	4.8	7.8	4.3	6.7	3.2	6.0	2.4	4.9	1.5	4.0	0.4	2.9	−0.6
61.0	8.9	5.1	8.4	4.7	7.2	3.5	6.4	2.6	5.2	1.6	4.3	0.5	3.1	−0.7
61.5	9.5	5.5	9.0	5.0	7.7	3.7	6.8	2.7	5.5	1.7	4.6	0.5	3.4	−0.7

ALTITUDE CORRECTION TABLES

App Alt = Apparent altitude
= Sextant altitude corrected for index error and dip.

The correction for the Sun's lower or upper limbs can be taken out directly as also can the corrections for the stars and planets.

The correction for the Moon is in two parts; the first correction is taken from the upper table with argument apparent altitude, and the second correction from the lower table with arguments apparent altitude and HP.

Separate corrections are given for lower (L) and upper (U) limbs.

5.3.3 SELECTED STARS, 1992

No	Name	Mag	SHA	Dec	Name	No
			° ′	° ′		
1	*Alpheratz*	2.2	357 59.8	N29 03.2	*Acamar*	7
2	*Ankaa*	2.4	353 31.0	S42 20.8	*Adhara*	19
3	*Schedar*	2.5	349 58.6	N56 29.9	*Aldebaran*	10
4	*Diphda*	2.2	349 11.6	S18 01.6	*Alioth*	32
6	*Hamal*	2.2	328 18.4	N23 25.8	*Alkaid*	34
7	*Acamar*	3.1	315 30.1	S40 20.0	*Al Na'ir*	55
8	*Menkar*	2.8	314 31.4	N 4 03.7	*Alnilam*	15
9	*Mirfak*	1.9	309 02.8	N49 50.2	*Alphard*	25
10	*Aldebaran*	1.1	291 07.2	N16 29.7	*Alphecca*	41
11	*Rigel*	0.3	281 27.0	S 8 12.6	*Alpheratz*	1
12	*Capella*	0.2	280 57.4	N45 59.5	*Altair*	51
13	*Bellatrix*	1.7	278 48.7	N 6 20.6	*Ankaa*	2
14	*Elnath*	1.8	278 32.3	N28 36.1	*Antares*	42
15	*Alnilam*	1.8	276 02.1	S 1 12.4	*Arcturus*	37
16	*Betelgeuse*	*	271 18.1	N 7 24.4	*Bellatrix*	13
17	*Canopus*	−0.9	264 03.0	S52 41.5	*Betelgeuse*	16
18	*Sirius*	−1.6	258 47.5	S16 42.4	*Canopus*	17
19	*Adhara*	1.6	255 24.7	S28 57.7	*Capella*	12
20	*Procyon*	0.5	245 15.9	N 5 14.6	*Deneb*	53
21	*Pollux*	1.2	243 46.7	N28 02.6	*Denebola*	28
23	*Suhail*	2.2	223 04.0	S43 24.2	*Diphda*	4
25	*Alphard*	2.2	218 11.3	S 8 37.7	*Dubhe*	27
26	*Regulus*	1.3	208 00.0	N12 00.1	*Elnath*	14
27	*Dubhe*	2.0	194 10.7	N61 47.3	*Eltanin*	47
28	*Denebola*	2.2	182 49.6	N14 36.8	*Enif*	54
29	*Gienah*	2.8	176 08.5	S17 30.1	*Fomalhaut*	56
32	*Alioth*	1.7	166 34.3	N55 59.9	*Gienah*	29
33	*Spica*	1.2	158 47.8	S11 07.4	*Hamal*	6
34	*Alkaid*	1.9	153 11.1	N49 20.9	*Kaus Aust*	48
36	*Menkent*	2.3	148 26.3	S36 20.1	*Kochab*	40
37	*Arcturus*	0.2	146 10.1	N19 13.1	*Markab*	57
39	*Zuben'ubi*	2.9	137 23.0	S16 00.8	*Menkar*	8
40	*Kochab*	2.2	137 19.3	N74 11.1	*Menkent*	36
41	*Alphecca*	2.3	126 24.3	N26 44.3	*Mirfak*	9
42	*Antares*	1.2	112 45.7	S26 25.0	*Nunki*	50
44	*Sabik*	2.6	102 30.7	S15 43.0	*Pollux*	21
45	*Shaula*	1.7	96 43.4	S37 06.0	*Procyon*	20
46	*Rasalhague*	2.1	96 21.1	N12 33.9	*Rasalhague*	46
47	*Eltanin*	2.4	90 53.5	N51 29.4	*Regulus*	26
48	*Kaus Aust*	2.0	84 04.8	S34 23.3	*Rigel*	11
49	*Vega*	0.1	80 49.7	N38 46.6	*Sabik*	44
50	*Nunki*	2.1	76 17.9	S26 18.4	*Schedar*	3
51	*Altair*	0.9	62 23.7	N 8 51.0	*Shaula*	45
53	*Deneb*	1.3	49 42.3	N45 15.3	*Sirius*	18
54	*Enif*	2.5	34 02.6	N 9 50.6	*Spica*	33
55	*Al Na'ir*	2.2	28 03.3	S46 59.8	*Suhail*	23
56	*Fomalhaut*	1.3	15 41.2	S29 39.6	*Vega*	49
57	*Markab*	2.6	13 54.7	N15 10.0	*Zuben'ubi*	39

* Variable 0.1 – 1.2

5.3.4 POLARIS TABLE, 1992

LHA ♈	Q	LHA ♈	Q	LHA ♈	Q
°	′	°	′	°	′
0	−37	**120**	− 4	**240**	+42
3	39	**123**	− 2	**243**	41
6	40	**126**	0	**246**	40
9	41	**129**	+ 3	**249**	39
12	42	**132**	5	**252**	37
15	−43	**135**	+ 8	**255**	+36
18	44	**138**	10	**258**	34
21	44	**141**	12	**261**	33
24	45	**144**	15	**264**	31
27	45	**147**	17	**267**	29
30	−46	**150**	+19	**270**	+27
33	46	**153**	21	**273**	25
36	46	**156**	23	**276**	23
39	46	**159**	25	**279**	21
42	46	**162**	27	**282**	19
45	−45	**165**	+29	**285**	+17
48	45	**168**	31	**288**	15
51	44	**171**	33	**291**	12
54	44	**174**	34	**294**	10
57	43	**177**	36	**297**	8
60	−42	**180**	+37	**300**	+ 5
63	41	**183**	39	**303**	+ 3
66	40	**186**	40	**306**	0
69	39	**189**	41	**309**	− 2
72	37	**192**	42	**312**	4
75	−36	**195**	+43	**315**	− 7
78	34	**198**	44	**318**	9
81	32	**201**	45	**321**	12
84	31	**204**	45	**324**	14
87	29	**207**	45	**327**	16
90	−27	**210**	+46	**330**	−18
93	25	**213**	46	**333**	21
96	23	**216**	46	**336**	23
99	21	**219**	46	**339**	25
102	18	**222**	46	**342**	27
105	−16	**225**	+46	**345**	−29
108	14	**228**	45	**348**	31
111	12	**231**	45	**351**	32
114	9	**234**	44	**354**	34
117	7	**237**	43	**357**	36
120	− 4	**240**	+42	**360**	−37

Azimuth of Polaris

LHA ♈	**0°**		**11°**		**60°**		**190°**
Az		1°		0°		359°	

LHA ♈	**190°**		**241°**		**360°**
Az		0°		1°	

Latitude = Apparent altitude (corrected for refraction)+Q

5.3.5 PLANET PLANNING DATA, 1992

Date	SUN Mer Pass	VENUS Symbol	VENUS SHA	VENUS Dec	VENUS Mag	VENUS Mer Pass	MARS Symbol	MARS SHA	MARS Dec	MARS Mag	MARS Mer Pass	JUPITER Symbol	JUPITER SHA	JUPITER Dec	JUPITER Mag	JUPITER Mer Pass	SATURN Symbol	SATURN SHA	SATURN Dec	SATURN Mag	SATURN Mer Pass
	h m		°	°		h m		°	°		h m		°	°		h m		°	°		h m
Jan 1	12 03	EB	121	S18	−4.1	09 16	Eb	97	S24	+1.4	10 53	MB	194	N 7	−2.2	04 25	Wa	52	S19	+0.7	13 52
6	12 06		115	19	4.1	09 21		93	24	1.4	10 49	WB	194	7	2.3	04 05		51	19	0.7	13 35
11	12 08		109	21	4.1	09 27		89	24	1.4	10 46		194	7	2.3	03 45	Wa	50	19	0.6	13 17
16	12 10		102	21	4.0	09 33		85	24	1.4	10 42		194	7	2.3	03 24	⊙	50	19	0.6	13 00
21	12 11	EB	96	22	4.0	09 39		81	24	1.4	10 39		194	7	2.4	03 04		49	19	0.6	12 43
26	12 12	Eb	89	S22	−4.0	09 46	Eb	76	S24	+1.4	10 36	WB	195	N 8	−2.4	02 43	⊙	49	S19	+0.6	12 25
31	12 13		82	22	4.0	09 53		72	23	1.4	10 32	WB	195	8	2.4	02 21		48	19	0.6	12 08
Feb 5	12 14		76	22	4.0	10 00		68	23	1.3	10 29	V	196	8	2.4	02 00		47	18	0.6	11 51
10	12 14		69	22	4.0	10 06		64	22	1.3	10 25		196	8	2.5	01 38	⊙	47	18	0.7	11 34
15	12 14		63	21	4.0	10 13		60	22	1.3	10 22		197	9	2.5	01 16	Eb	46	18	0.7	11 16
20	12 14	Eb	56	S20	−3.9	10 19	Eb	56	S21	+1.3	10 18	V	197	N 9	−2.5	00 54	Eb	46	S18	+0.7	10 59
25	12 13		50	19	3.9	10 25		52	20	1.3	10 15		198	9	2.5	00 32		45	18	0.7	10 42
Mar 1	12 12		43	17	3.9	10 31		48	19	1.3	10 11		198	9	2.5	00 10		44	18	0.7	10 24
6	12 11		37	16	3.9	10 36		44	18	1.3	10 07		199	10	2.5	23 44		44	17	0.7	10 07
11	12 10		31	14	3.9	10 40		40	17	1.2	10 02		200	10	2.5	23 22	Eb	43	17	0.8	09 49
16	12 09	Eb	25	S12	−3.9	10 44	Eb	37	S16	+1.2	09 58	V	200	N10	−2.5	23 00	EB	43	S17	+0.8	09 32
21	12 07		19	9	3.9	10 48		33	14	1.2	09 53		201	10	2.5	22 38		42	17	0.8	09 14
26	12 06		13	7	3.9	10 52		29	13	1.2	09 49	V	201	10	2.4	22 16		42	17	0.8	08 56
31	12 04		8	5	3.9	10 55		25	12	1.2	09 44	EA	202	11	2.4	21 55		41	17	0.8	08 38
Apr 5	12 03		2	2	3.9	10 58		22	10	1.2	09 39		202	11	2.4	21 34		41	17	0.8	08 20
10	12 01	Eb	356	S 0	−3.9	11 01	Eb	18	S 9	+1.1	09 34	EA	202	N11	−2.4	21 13	EB	41	S17	+0.8	08 02
15	12 00		351	N 2	3.9	11 04	EB	14	8	1.1	09 29		203	11	2.3	20 52		40	16	0.8	07 44
20	11 59	Eb	345	5	3.9	11 07		11	6	1.1	09 23	EA	203	11	2.3	20 32		40	16	0.8	07 25
25	11 58	⊙	339	7	3.9	11 10		7	5	1.1	09 18	MA	203	11	2.3	20 12		40	16	0.8	07 07
30	11 57		334	10	3.9	11 13		4	3	1.1	09 12		203	11	2.2	19 52		39	16	0.8	06 48
May 5	11 57	⊙	328	N12	−3.9	11 17	EB	0	S 2	+1.1	09 07	MA	203	N11	−2.2	19 32	EB	39	S16	+0.7	06 29
10	11 56		322	14	3.9	11 21		357	0	1.1	09 01		203	11	2.2	19 13	EB	39	16	0.7	06 10
15	11 56		316	16	3.9	11 25		353	N 2	1.0	08 55		203	11	2.1	18 54	MB	39	16	0.7	05 51
20	11 56		310	18	3.9	11 30		350	3	1.0	08 50	MA	203	11	2.1	18 35		39	16	0.7	05 32
25	11 57		303	19	3.9	11 36		346	5	1.0	08 44	WA	202	11	2.1	18 17		39	16	0.7	05 13
30	11 58	⊙	297	N21	−3.9	11 41	EB	343	N 6	+1.0	08 38	WA	202	N10	−2.0	17 59	MB	39	S16	+0.6	04 53
June 4	11 58		291	22	3.9	11 48		339	7	1.0	08 32		201	10	2.0	17 41		39	16	0.6	04 33
9	11 59		284	23	3.9	11 54		336	9	1.0	08 27		201	10	2.0	17 23	MB	39	16	0.6	04 13
14	12 00		277	23	3.9	12 01		332	10	0.9	08 21		200	10	1.9	17 06	WB	39	16	0.6	03 53
19	12 01		271	24	3.9	12 08		329	11	0.9	08 15		200	10	1.9	16 48		39	16	0.5	03 33
24	12 02	⊙	264	N24	−3.9	12 15	EB	325	N13	+0.9	08 10	WA	199	N 9	−1.9	16 31	WB	39	S16	+0.5	03 13
29	12 03		257	24	3.9	12 23		322	14	0.9	08 04		199	9	1.9	16 14		40	16	0.5	02 52
Jul 4	12 04		251	23	3.9	12 30		318	15	0.9	07 58		198	9	1.8	15 57		40	17	0.4	02 31
9	12 05		244	22	3.9	12 36		315	16	0.9	07 53		197	8	1.8	15 41	WB	40	17	0.4	02 11
14	12 06		237	21	3.9	12 43		311	17	0.8	07 47		196	8	1.8	15 24	V	40	17	0.4	01 50
19	12 06	⊙	231	N20	−3.9	12 49	EB	307	N18	+0.8	07 42	WA	196	N 8	−1.8	15 08	V	41	S17	+0.3	01 29
24	12 06	⊙	225	18	3.9	12 54		304	19	0.8	07 36	WA	195	7	1.8	14 51		41	17	0.3	01 08
29	12 06	Wa	219	17	3.9	12 59		300	20	0.8	07 30	Wa	194	7	1.7	14 35		41	17	0.3	00 47
Aug 3	12 06		212	15	3.9	13 03		297	20	0.8	07 25		193	7	1.7	14 19		42	17	0.2	00 26
8	12 06		207	13	3.9	13 07		293	21	0.7	07 19		192	6	1.7	14 03		42	17	0.2	00 04
13	12 05	Wa	201	N10	−3.9	13 11	EB	290	N22	+0.7	07 13	Wa	191	N 6	−1.7	13 47	V	43	S17	+0.2	23 39
18	12 04		195	8	3.9	13 14		287	22	0.7	07 07		190	6	1.7	13 31		43	18	0.2	23 18
23	12 03		189	5	3.9	13 17		283	22	0.6	07 01		189	5	1.7	13 15		43	18	0.3	22 57
28	12 01		184	N 3	3.9	13 20		280	23	0.6	06 54	Wa	188	5	1.7	13 00		44	18	0.3	22 36
Sep 2	12 00		178	S 0	3.9	13 22		277	23	0.6	06 48	⊙	187	4	1.7	12 44	V	44	18	0.3	22 15
7	11 58	Wa	172	S 2	−3.9	13 25	EB	273	N23	+0.5	06 41	⊙	186	N 4	−1.7	12 28	EA	44	S18	+0.3	21 54
12	11 56		167	5	3.9	13 28		270	23	0.5	06 34		185	3	1.7	12 13		44	18	0.4	21 33
17	11 54		161	7	3.9	13 30		267	23	0.5	06 27		184	3	1.7	11 57		45	18	0.4	21 13
22	11 53		156	10	3.9	13 33		264	23	0.4	06 19		183	3	1.7	11 41		45	18	0.4	20 52
27	11 51		150	12	3.9	13 37		261	23	0.4	06 11		182	2	1.7	11 25	EA	45	18	0.4	20 32
Oct 2	11 49	Wa	144	S14	−3.9	13 40	EB	258	N23	+0.3	06 02	⊙	181	N 2	−1.7	11 10	MA	45	S18	+0.5	20 12

PLANET PLANNING DATA — PHASES OF THE MOON, 1992

Date	SUN Mer Pass	VENUS Symbol	VENUS SHA	VENUS Dec	VENUS Mag	VENUS Mer Pass	MARS Symbol	MARS SHA	MARS Dec	MARS Mag	MARS Mer Pass	JUPITER Symbol	JUPITER SHA	JUPITER Dec	JUPITER Mag	JUPITER Mer Pass	SATURN Symbol	SATURN SHA	SATURN Dec	SATURN Mag	SATURN Mer Pass
			°	°		h m		°	°		h m		°	°		h m		°	°		h m
Oct 2	11 49	Wa	144	S14	−3.9	13 40	EB	258	N23	+0.3	06 02	⊙	181	N 2	−1.7	11 10	MA	45	S18	+0.5	20 12
7	11 48		138	17	3.9	13 45	EB	256	23	0.2	05 53	Eb	180	1	1.7	10 54		45	18	0.5	19 52
12	11 46		132	19	3.9	13 49	MB	253	23	0.2	05 43		179	1	1.7	10 38		45	18	0.5	19 32
17	11 45		126	20	4.0	13 54		251	23	0.1	05 33		178	S 0	1.7	10 22		45	18	0.5	19 12
22	11 44		120	22	4.0	14 00		249	23	0.0	05 22		177	0	1.7	10 06		45	18	0.6	18 53
27	11 44	Wa	113	S23	−4.0	14 06	MB	247	N23	−0.1	05 10	Eb	176	S 0	−1.7	09 50	MA	45	S18	+0.6	18 33
Nov 1	11 44	Wa	107	24	4.0	14 12		245	23	0.1	04 57		176	1	1.7	09 34	WA	45	18	0.6	18 14
6	11 44	WA	100	25	4.0	14 19		243	23	0.2	04 44	Eb	175	1	1.7	09 18		45	18	0.6	17 55
11	11 44		93	25	4.0	14 26		242	23	0.3	04 29	EB	174	1	1.7	09 02		45	18	0.7	17 36
16	11 45		87	26	4.1	14 33		241	23	0.4	04 14		173	2	1.8	08 46		45	18	0.7	17 18
21	11 46	WA	80	S25	−4.1	14 39	MB	240	N23	−0.5	03 57	EB	172	S 2	−1.8	08 29	WA	44	S18	+0.7	16 59
26	11 47		74	25	4.1	14 46	WB	240	23	0.7	03 39		171	2	1.8	08 13		44	18	0.7	16 41
Dec 1	11 49		67	24	4.1	14 52		240	23	0.8	03 20		171	3	1.8	07 56		44	18	0.7	16 22
6	11 51		61	23	4.1	14 58		240	23	0.9	02 59		170	3	1.9	07 39		43	18	0.7	16 04
11	11 53		55	22	4.2	15 03		241	24	1.0	02 37		169	3	1.9	07 22		43	18	0.7	15 46
16	11 56	WA	49	S20	−4.2	15 07	WB	242	N24	−1.1	02 13	EB	169	S 4	−1.9	07 05	WA	42	S17	+0.7	15 28
21	11 58		43	19	4.2	15 10	V	243	25	1.2	01 48		168	4	1.9	06 47		42	17	0.7	15 11
26	12 01		37	17	4.3	15 13		245	25	1.3	01 21		168	4	2.0	06 30		41	17	0.7	14 53
31	12 03	WA	32	S15	−4.3	15 15	V	247	26	−1.4	00 54	EB	167	4	−2.0	06 12	WA	41	S17	+0.8	14 35

The symbols indicate the position of the planet as follows:

⊙	Too close to the Sun for observation.		
Eb	Low in the east before sunrise.	Wa	Low in the west after sunset.
EB	Well placed in the east before sunrise.	WA	Well placed in the west after sunset.
MB	Well placed near the meridian before sunrise.	MA	Well placed near the meridian after sunset.
WB	Well placed in the west before sunrise.	EA	Well placed in the east after sunset.
V	Visible all night or most of the night, in the east after sunset or in the west before sunrise.		

PLANET NOTES 1992

The approximate SHA and Dec of the planets as tabulated above can be used for plotting the positions of the planets on a star chart, or for determining their positions amongst the stars in a star list.

Venus, the most brilliant of the planets, is visible in the morning sky until May when it becomes too close to the Sun for observation, reappearing as an evening object from mid-July to the end of the year. In conjunction with Mars on February 19, Saturn on February 29 and December 21 and with Jupiter on August 23.

Mars is a morning object at the beginning of the year, its distance from the Sun increasing until at the end of the year it is visible all night. In conjunction with Venus on February 19 and with Saturn on March 6.

Jupiter, initially a morning star, becomes visible all night during February and March, then it becomes an evening star. By September it is too close to the Sun for observation, reappearing in early October it remains a morning star for the rest of the year. In conjunction with Venus on August 23.

Saturn, initially an evening object until mid-January, when it becomes too close to the Sun for observation, it returns as a morning object in mid-February, moving steadily away from the Sun until July and August when it becomes visible all night and thereafter is an evening object until the end of the year. In conjunction with Venus on February 29 and December 21 and with Mars on March 6.

Do not confuse — Mercury with Mars (reddish tint) in the first half of January.
— Venus with Mars from late February to early March;
with Saturn in February–March and late December;
with Mercury early April and late May;
with Jupiter in late August.
— Mars (the brighter) with Saturn in early March.

PHASES OF THE MOON

New Moon	d h m	First Quarter	d h m	Full Moon	d h m	Last Quarter	d h m
Jan	4 23 10	Jan	13 02 32	Jan	19 21 28	Jan	26 15 27
Feb	3 19 00	Feb	11 16 15	Feb	18 08 04	Feb	25 07 56
Mar	4 13 22	Mar	12 02 36	Mar	18 18 18	Mar	26 02 30
Apr	3 05 01	Apr	10 10 06	Apr	17 04 42	Apr	24 21 40
May	2 17 44	May	9 15 43	May	16 16 03	May	24 15 53
Jun	1 03 57	Jun	7 20 47	Jun	15 04 50	Jun	23 08 11
Jun	30 12 18	Jul	7 02 43	Jul	14 19 06	Jul	22 22 12
Jul	29 19 35	Aug	5 10 58	Aug	13 10 27	Aug	21 10 01
Aug	28 02 42	Sep	3 22 39	Sep	12 02 17	Sep	19 19 53
Sep	26 10 40	Oct	3 14 12	Oct	11 18 03	Oct	19 04 12
Oct	25 20 34	Nov	2 09 11	Nov	10 09 20	Nov	17 11 12
Nov	24 09 11	Dec	2 06 17	Dec	9 23 41	Dec	16 19 13
Dec	24 00 43						

ECLIPSES

1. Annular eclipse of the Sun, January 4–5. Not visible from Europe.
2. Partial eclipse of the Moon, June 15. Not visible from Europe.
3. Total eclipse of the Sun, June 30. Not visible from Europe except Eastern Spain.
4. Total eclipse of the Moon, December 9–10. Visible from Europe.
5. Partial eclipse of the Sun, December 23–24. Not visible from Europe.

5.3.6 SUNRISE, SUNSET AND TWILIGHT — 1992

Date	Naut Twi	ν	Sun-rise	ν	Sun-set	Civil Twi	ν
	h m		h m		h m	h m	
Jan 1	06 39	+39	07 59	+63−	16 08	16 46	−51
4	06 39	38	07 58	62	16 11	16 49	50
7	06 39	38	07 58	61	16 15	16 53	48
10	06 38	37	07 56	59	16 19	16 56	48
13	06 37	36	07 55	58	16 23	17 00	46
16	06 35	+34	07 53	+56−	16 27	17 04	−45
19	06 33	32	07 50	54	16 32	17 08	43
22	06 31	30	07 47	52	16 36	17 12	41
25	06 28	28	07 44	49	16 41	17 17	39
28	06 25	26	07 40	47	16 46	17 22	36
31	06 22	+24	07 36	+45−	16 51	17 26	−35
Feb 3	06 18	22	07 32	42	16 56	17 31	32
6	06 14	20	07 27	39	17 02	17 36	30
9	06 10	18	07 22	37	17 07	17 41	27
12	06 06	16	07 17	34	17 12	17 46	24
15	06 01	+13	07 12	+31−	17 17	17 51	−22
18	05 56	10	07 07	28	17 22	17 55	20
21	05 50	7	07 01	26	17 27	18 00	17
24	05 45	5	06 55	23	17 32	18 05	14
27	05 39	+ 2	06 49	20	17 37	18 10	11
Mar 1	05 33	− 1	06 43	+17−	17 42	18 15	− 8
4	05 27	4	06 37	14	17 47	18 20	5
7	05 21	7	06 30	11	17 52	18 25	2
10	05 15	9	06 24	8	17 57	18 29	0
13	05 08	13	06 18	5	18 02	18 34	+ 3
16	05 01	−16	06 11	+ 2−	18 07	18 39	+ 6
19	04 55	18	06 05	− 1+	18 12	18 44	9
22	04 48	22	05 58	3	18 16	18 49	12
25	04 41	25	05 52	6	18 21	18 54	15
28	04 34	28	05 45	9	18 26	18 59	19
31	04 27	−31	05 39	−12+	18 31	19 03	+21
Apr 3	04 20	34	05 32	15	18 35	19 08	24
6	04 12	39	05 26	18	18 40	19 13	27
9	04 05	42	05 19	21	18 45	19 18	30
12	03 58	45	05 13	24	18 49	19 23	33
15	03 51	−49	05 07	−27+	18 54	19 28	+36
18	03 43	53	05 01	29	18 59	19 34	40
21	03 36	56	04 55	32	19 03	19 39	43
24	03 29	60	04 49	35	19 08	19 44	46
27	03 22	64	04 43	38	19 13	19 49	49
30	03 15	−68	04 38	−40+	19 17	19 54	+52
May 3	03 08	72	04 33	43	19 22	19 59	55
6	03 01	76	04 28	46	19 27	20 04	58
9	02 55	79	04 23	48	19 31	20 09	60
12	02 48	83	04 18	51	19 35	20 14	63
15	02 42	−87	04 14	−53+	19 40	20 19	+66
18	02 36	91	04 10	55	19 44	20 24	69
21	02 30	95	04 06	57	19 48	20 29	72
24	02 25	98	04 03	59	19 52	20 33	74
27	02 20	102	04 00	61	19 55	20 37	76
30	02 15	−105	03 57	−63+	19 58	20 41	+79
Jun 2	02 11	108	03 55	64	20 02	20 45	81
5	02 08	110	03 53	66	20 04	20 48	82
8	02 05	113	03 52	67	20 07	20 51	84
11	02 02	116	03 51	68	20 09	20 53	84
14	02 01	−117	03 50	−68+	20 11	20 55	+85
17	02 00	118	03 50	69	20 12	20 56	85
20	02 00	118	03 50	69	20 13	20 57	86
23	02 01	118	03 51	69	20 13	20 58	86
26	02 02	118	03 52	68	20 13	20 58	86
29	02 05	−116	03 54	−68+	20 13	20 57	+85
Jul 2	02 08	−114	03 56	−67+	20 12	20 56	+84

Date	Naut Twi	ν	Sun-rise	ν	Sun-set	Civil Twi	ν
	h m		h m		h m	h m	
Jul 2	02 08	−114	03 56	−67+	20 12	20 56	+84
5	02 11	113	03 58	66	20 11	20 54	82
8	02 15	110	04 01	65	20 09	20 52	80
11	02 20	107	04 03	63	20 07	20 50	79
14	02 25	104	04 07	62	20 05	20 47	77
17	02 30	−101	04 10	−60+	20 02	20 43	+75
20	02 36	97	04 13	58	19 58	20 39	72
23	02 42	93	04 17	56	19 55	20 35	70
26	02 48	90	04 21	54	19 51	20 31	68
29	02 54	86	04 25	52	19 47	20 26	65
Aug 1	03 00	− 82	04 29	−49+	19 42	20 21	+62
4	03 06	78	04 34	47	19 37	20 15	58
7	03 12	74	04 38	44	19 32	20 10	56
10	03 18	71	04 42	42	19 27	20 04	53
13	03 24	67	04 47	39	19 22	19 58	50
16	03 30	− 63	04 51	−36+	19 16	19 52	+47
19	03 36	59	04 56	34	19 10	19 45	43
22	03 42	55	05 00	31	19 04	19 39	41
25	03 47	52	05 05	28	18 58	19 33	38
28	03 53	48	05 09	25	18 52	19 26	35
31	03 59	− 44	05 14	−23+	18 46	19 19	+31
Sep 3	04 04	41	05 18	20	18 39	19 13	29
6	04 09	38	05 23	17	18 33	19 06	26
9	04 14	35	05 27	14	18 26	18 59	22
12	04 20	31	05 32	11	18 20	18 52	19
15	04 25	− 28	05 36	− 8+	18 13	18 46	+17
18	04 30	24	05 40	5	18 07	18 39	14
21	04 34	22	05 45	− 3+	18 00	18 32	10
24	04 39	19	05 50	0	17 53	18 26	8
27	04 44	15	05 54	+ 3−	17 47	18 19	5
30	04 49	− 12	05 59	+ 6−	17 40	18 12	+ 2
Oct 3	04 54	9	06 03	9	17 34	18 06	− 1
6	04 58	7	06 08	12	17 27	17 59	4
9	05 03	3	06 13	15	17 21	17 53	7
12	05 07	− 1	06 17	18	17 15	17 47	9
15	05 12	+ 2	06 22	+20−	17 09	17 41	−12
18	05 17	5	06 27	23	17 02	17 35	15
21	05 21	7	06 32	26	16 57	17 30	17
24	05 26	10	06 37	29	16 51	17 24	20
27	05 30	12	06 42	32	16 45	17 19	23
30	05 35	+ 15	06 47	+34−	16 40	17 14	−25
Nov 2	05 39	17	06 52	37	16 35	17 09	28
5	05 44	20	06 57	40	16 30	17 04	31
8	05 48	22	07 02	42	16 25	17 00	33
11	05 52	24	07 07	45	16 21	16 56	35
14	05 57	+ 27	07 11	+47−	16 17	16 52	−38
17	06 01	29	07 16	50	16 13	16 49	39
20	06 05	30	07 21	52	16 10	16 46	41
23	06 09	32	07 26	54	16 07	16 43	44
26	06 13	34	07 30	56	16 04	16 41	45
29	06 16	+ 35	07 34	+58−	16 02	16 39	−47
Dec 2	06 20	36	07 38	59	16 00	16 38	48
5	06 23	37	07 42	61	15 59	16 37	49
8	06 26	38	07 45	62	15 58	16 36	51
11	06 29	39	07 49	63	15 58	16 36	51
14	06 31	+ 39	07 51	+63−	15 58	16 36	−52
17	06 34	41	07 54	64	15 59	16 37	52
20	06 35	40	07 56	64	16 00	16 39	52
23	06 37	40	07 57	64	16 02	16 40	52
26	06 38	40	07 58	64	16 04	16 42	52
29	06 39	+ 40	07 59	+63−	16 06	16 44	−52
Jan 1	06 39	+ 39	07 59	+63−	16 09	16 47	−51

SUNRISE, SUNSET AND TWILIGHT — 1992

Corrections to Sunrise or Sunset

N.Lat	30°	35°	40°	45°	50°	52°	54°	56°	58°	60°
v	m	m	m	m	m	m	m	m	m	m
0	0	0	0	0	0	0	0	0	0	0
2	− 2	− 1	− 1	0	0	+ 1	+ 1	+ 1	+ 2	+ 2
4	4	3	2	− 1	0	1	1	1	2	3
6	6	5	3	2	0	1	2	3	4	5
8	8	6	5	2	0	1	2	3	5	6
10	−10	− 8	− 6	− 3	0	+ 1	+ 3	+ 4	+ 6	+ 8
12	12	10	7	4	0	2	4	6	8	10
14	14	11	8	5	0	2	4	6	9	12
16	16	13	9	5	0	2	5	8	11	14
18	18	14	10	6	0	2	5	9	12	16
20	−20	−16	−11	− 6	0	+ 3	+ 6	+10	+14	+18
22	22	17	12	7	0	3	7	11	15	20
24	24	19	14	8	0	3	7	12	16	22
26	26	21	15	8	0	4	8	13	18	24
28	28	22	16	9	0	4	9	14	19	26
30	−30	−24	−17	− 9	0	+ 5	+10	+15	+21	+28
32	32	26	19	10	0	5	10	16	22	30
34	34	27	20	10	0	5	11	17	24	32
36	36	29	21	11	0	5	11	17	25	33
38	38	31	22	12	0	5	11	18	26	35
40	−40	−32	−23	−13	0	+ 6	+12	+20	+28	+37
42	42	34	24	13	0	6	13	21	30	40
44	44	36	26	14	0	6	13	22	31	42
46	46	37	27	15	0	7	14	23	33	44
48	48	39	28	15	0	7	15	25	35	46
50	−50	−40	−29	−16	0	+ 7	+16	+26	+36	+48
52	52	42	30	16	0	8	17	27	38	51
54	54	43	31	17	0	8	17	27	39	53
56	56	45	33	18	0	8	17	28	40	55
58	58	47	34	19	0	9	18	30	42	57
60	−60	−48	−35	−20	0	+ 9	+19	+31	+45	+61
62	62	50	37	21	0	9	20	32	47	64
64	64	52	38	21	0	10	21	34	49	67
66	66	53	39	21	0	11	22	35	51	70
68	68	55	41	22	0	11	23	37	54	73
70	−70	−57	−42	−23	0	+11	+24	+38	+56	+76

Corrections to Nautical Twilight

N. Lat	30°	35°	40°	45°	50°	52°	54°	56°	58°	60°
v	m	m	m	m	m	m	m	m	m	m
+ 40	−40	−31	−22	−12	0	+ 5	+11	+17	+23	+30
30	30	23	16	9	0	3	7	12	16	21
20	20	15	10	6	0	2	4	7	10	13
+ 10	−10	− 7	− 5	− 2	0	+ 1	+ 2	+ 3	+ 4	+ 5
0	0	+ 1	+ 1	0	0	0	− 1	− 2	− 3	− 5
− 10	+10	+ 8	+ 6	+ 4	0	− 2	− 4	− 6	− 9	−13
20	20	17	13	7	0	3	7	12	17	23
30	30	25	19	11	0	4	10	16	24	32
40	40	33	24	14	0	6	14	22	32	44
50	50	41	30	17	0	9	18	29	42	58
− 60	+60	+49	+37	+21	0	−11	−22	−36	−53	−74
70	70	58	43	24	0	13	27	45	67	96
80	80	66	50	29	0	14	32	53	83	−134
90	90	75	56	32	0	18	39	68	−118	TAN
100	100	84	63	37	0	20	46	−87	TAN	TAN
−110	+110	+92	+70	+41	0	−25	−60	TAN	TAN	TAN
−120	+120	+100	+78	+46	0	−29	−83	TAN	TAN	TAN

Corrections to Civil Twilight

N. Lat	30°	35°	40°	45°	50°	52°	54°	56°	58°	60°
v	m	m	m	m	m	m	m	m	m	m
−50	+50	+40	+29	+16	0	− 7	−15	−23	−33	−44
40	40	32	22	12	0	6	12	19	26	35
30	30	24	17	10	0	4	8	13	18	24
20	20	16	11	7	0	3	6	9	12	16
−10	+10	+ 8	+ 5	+ 3	0	− 1	− 3	− 4	− 5	− 7
0	0	0	0	0	0	0	0	+ 1	+ 1	+ 2
+10	−10	− 8	− 6	− 4	0	+ 1	+ 3	5	8	11
20	20	16	12	7	0	3	7	11	15	20
30	30	24	18	10	0	5	10	16	22	30
40	40	32	24	13	0	6	13	21	30	41
+50	−50	−41	−30	−16	0	+ 8	+17	+27	+39	+53
60	60	49	36	20	0	9	20	33	47	65
70	70	57	42	23	0	12	25	41	60	85
80	80	65	48	27	0	14	30	50	75	111
83	83	68	50	28	0	15	32	52	80	121
+86	−86	−71	−52	−30	0	+15	+33	+55	+85	+135

The times given on the opposite page are the local mean times (LMT) of nautical twilight, sunrise, sunset and civil twilight for latitude N.50°, together with variations v. The variations are the differences in time between the times for latitude N.50° and those for latitude N.30°. The sign on the left-hand side of v (between sunrise and sunset) applies to sunrise, and the right-hand sign applies to sunset. The LMT for any latitude from N.30° to N.60° can be found by applying corrections, taken from the tables above, to the tabulated times.

To determine the LMT of sunrise or sunset, take out the tabulated time and v corresponding to the required date and, using v and latitude as arguments in the table of "Corrections to Sunrise or Sunset", extract the correction and apply it to the tabulated time as follows. If v is positive, apply the correction with the sign as tabulated. If v is negative, apply the correction with the opposite sign to that which is tabulated.

To determine LMT of nautical twilight the correction to the tabulated time must be taken from the table of "Corrections to Nautical Twilight" using as argument latitude and v; in entering the correction table the correct sign of v must be used, and in applying the correction to the tabulated time its sign must be used as given in the table. When TAN (Twilight All Night) is given, the Sun does not reach a zenith distance of 102°.

The corrections to civil twilight must be found in the same manner as those for nautical twilight.

LMT can be converted to UT by adding the longitude (in time) if west or subtracting if east.

Examples of the use of these tables are given on page 76.

5.3.7 MOONRISE AND MOONSET – 1992

Date	JANUARY Rise	ν	Set	ν	MARCH Rise	ν	Set	ν	MAY Rise	ν	Set	ν	JULY Rise	ν	Set	ν
	h m		h m		h m		h m		h m		h m		h m		h m	
1	05 07	+69	13 11	−70	05 13	+46	14 46	−42	03 32	−34	18 20	+42	05 01	−57	20 51	−48
2	06 07	74	13 55	75	05 34	34	15 53	29	03 57	47	19 35	55	06 25	44	21 21	34
3	06 59	75	14 48	74	05 53	22	17 00	16	04 29	58	20 49	65	07 51	28	21 46	19
4	07 41	70	15 48	68	06 09	+ 8	18 08	− 2	05 10	67	21 57	71	09 14	−12	22 08	+ 4
5	08 14	61	16 53	58	06 26	− 4	19 16	+11	06 02	72	22 56	70	10 35	+ 4	22 29	−11
6	08 41	+50	17 59	−46	06 43	−17	20 25	+25	07 07	−69	23 44	+64	11 54	+19	22 50	−26
7	09 03	38	19 06	34	07 02	30	21 37	39	08 21	60	24 21	52	13 12	35	23 14	39
8	09 21	25	20 13	20	07 25	43	22 50	52	09 41	47	00 21	52	14 27	48	23 41	52
9	09 38	+13	21 19	− 7	07 52	56	24 02	63	11 01	33	00 50	38	15 40	60	24 14	63
10	09 54	0	22 27	+ 7	08 28	66	00 02	63	12 22	17	01 15	24	16 47	68	00 14	63
11	10 10	−13	23 35	+20	09 14	−72	01 11	+71	13 41	− 1	01 36	+ 9	17 46	+72	00 55	−69
12	10 28	26	24 47	35	10 13	72	02 13	73	14 59	+14	01 57	− 5	18 35	70	01 44	71
13	10 49	40	00 47	35	11 24	66	03 05	68	16 17	29	02 17	20	19 15	64	02 41	68
14	11 15	53	02 01	48	12 44	54	03 46	58	17 35	44	02 40	34	19 47	55	03 43	62
15	11 49	65	03 17	61	14 08	39	04 18	44	18 50	56	03 06	48	20 12	43	04 49	51
16	12 35	−73	04 32	+71	15 32	−23	04 45	+29	20 01	+66	03 38	−59	20 33	+31	05 55	−40
17	13 36	75	05 41	75	16 57	− 6	05 08	+14	21 05	72	04 17	67	20 52	19	07 01	27
18	14 52	68	06 38	71	18 20	+11	05 29	− 2	21 58	71	05 04	72	21 09	+ 7	08 07	14
19	16 18	55	07 22	59	19 42	27	05 50	18	22 41	66	06 00	70	21 26	− 5	09 12	− 1
20	17 46	39	07 56	44	21 02	41	06 13	32	23 15	58	07 02	64	21 43	17	10 18	+12
21	19 14	−22	08 23	+29	22 20	+56	06 39	−46	23 42	+47	08 07	−54	22 02	−30	11 25	+25
22	20 38	− 5	08 46	+13	23 32	66	07 09	59	24 04	35	09 14	42	22 25	42	12 34	38
23	22 00	+12	09 06	− 3	24 36	72	07 47	68	00 04	35	10 20	30	22 53	54	13 45	51
24	23 19	28	09 26	18	00 36	72	08 32	73	00 23	23	11 26	17	23 29	64	14 56	61
25	24 35	42	09 47	32	01 30	73	09 25	72	00 40	+10	12 32	− 4	24 16	70	16 06	69
26	00 35	+42	10 10	−46	02 13	+68	10 25	−66	00 57	− 2	13 39	+ 9	00 16	−70	17 09	+71
27	01 49	56	10 38	58	02 48	60	11 29	57	01 15	15	14 48	23	01 17	70	18 02	66
28	02 58	66	11 11	69	03 15	49	12 35	46	01 34	28	15 59	36	02 31	63	18 45	55
29	04 01	73	11 53	74	03 38	38	13 41	34	01 57	41	17 13	49	03 54	51	19 19	41
30	04 56	75	12 43	74	03 57	25	14 48	20	02 25	54	18 28	61	05 20	36	19 47	26
31	05 41	+72	13 41	−69	04 15	+13	15 55	− 7	03 02	−64	19 40	+69	06 47	−20	20 11	+11
	FEBRUARY				APRIL				JUNE				AUGUST			
1	06 17	+64	14 44	−61	04 32	+ 1	17 03	+ 6	03 51	−70	20 45	+71	08 12	− 3	20 33	− 5
2	06 45	54	15 50	50	04 49	−13	18 13	20	04 52	70	21 38	66	09 35	+13	20 55	20
3	07 09	43	16 56	38	05 08	26	19 24	34	06 05	64	22 20	56	10 56	29	21 18	35
4	07 28	29	18 03	25	05 30	38	20 38	48	07 26	52	22 53	43	12 14	43	21 45	48
5	07 46	17	19 10	−12	05 56	52	21 51	59	08 48	38	23 19	28	13 29	56	22 17	59
6	08 02	+ 4	20 17	+ 2	06 30	−62	23 03	+69	10 10	−22	23 42	+13	14 39	+66	22 55	−67
7	08 18	− 9	21 25	15	07 13	70	24 07	72	11 30	− 6	24 03	− 1	15 40	70	23 41	71
8	08 35	22	22 35	30	08 08	72	00 07	72	12 48	+ 9	00 03	1	16 33	71	24 35	70
9	08 55	34	23 47	43	09 15	68	01 01	69	14 06	25	00 23	16	17 15	66	00 35	70
10	09 18	48	25 00	56	10 31	57	01 45	61	15 22	39	00 45	29	17 49	57	01 36	64
11	09 48	−60	01 00	+56	11 51	−44	02 19	+49	16 37	+52	01 09	−43	18 17	+47	02 40	−55
12	10 27	69	02 14	68	13 13	28	02 47	35	17 49	63	01 38	55	18 39	35	03 46	43
13	11 19	74	03 23	74	14 34	−13	03 10	19	18 54	70	02 13	66	18 59	24	04 52	31
14	12 25	72	04 23	73	15 55	+ 3	03 32	+ 5	19 51	72	02 57	71	19 17	+12	05 58	18
15	13 44	62	05 12	66	17 16	19	03 52	−11	20 37	68	03 50	71	19 34	0	07 03	− 6
16	15 09	−48	05 50	+53	18 36	+35	04 14	−25	21 14	+60	04 49	−67	19 51	−13	08 09	+ 8
17	16 37	32	06 21	38	19 54	49	04 38	40	21 44	51	05 54	58	20 09	25	09 15	20
18	18 04	−14	06 45	21	21 10	61	05 07	52	22 08	40	07 00	47	20 30	38	10 22	33
19	19 29	+ 3	07 07	+ 5	22 18	69	05 41	64	22 28	28	08 07	34	20 55	50	11 31	45
20	20 52	20	07 28	−10	23 18	72	06 24	70	22 46	16	09 12	23	21 27	60	12 41	57
21	22 12	+35	07 49	−26	24 06	+69	07 14	−72	23 02	+ 2	10 18	− 9	22 08	−68	13 50	+66
22	23 30	50	08 12	41	00 06	69	08 13	68	23 19	−10	11 24	+ 4	23 01	70	14 54	71
23	24 43	61	08 39	54	00 45	23	09 16	60	23 37	23	12 31	17	24 07	67	15 50	69
24	00 43	61	09 11	65	01 15	53	10 21	50	23 58	35	13 40	31	00 07	67	16 36	61
25	01 50	70	09 51	71	01 40	42	11 28	38	24 23	48	14 51	43	01 23	58	17 14	49
26	02 49	+74	10 38	−74	02 01	+31	12 34	−25	00 23	−48	16 05	+56	02 47	−44	17 45	+35
27	03 38	73	11 34	71	02 19	18	13 40	−13	00 55	59	17 18	66	04 13	29	18 11	19
28	04 17	67	12 35	64	02 36	+ 5	14 47	+ 1	01 37	68	18 26	71	05 40	−12	18 34	+ 3
29	04 48	+57	13 40	−54	02 53	− 8	15 56	14	02 32	72	19 26	70	07 06	+ 6	18 57	−12
30					03 12	−20	17 07	+28	03 41	−68	20 14	+61	08 30	22	19 20	28
31													09 52	+37	19 47	−41

MOONRISE AND MOONSET — 1992

Date	SEPTEMBER Rise	ν	SEPTEMBER Set	ν	NOVEMBER Rise	ν	NOVEMBER Set	ν
	h m		h m		h m		h m	
1	11 11	+51	20 17	−55	12 48	+46	22 21	−42
2	12 25	62	20 54	64	13 12	35	23 26	31
3	13 31	69	21 38	70	13 33	24	24 31	19
4	14 27	70	22 30	70	13 51	+12	00 31	19
5	15 14	67	23 29	66	14 09	0	01 36	− 6
6	15 51	+60	24 32	−58	14 27	−12	02 42	+ 7
7	16 20	50	00 32	58	14 46	25	03 48	19
8	16 44	39	01 38	46	15 08	37	04 56	31
9	17 05	27	02 43	35	15 35	48	06 06	44
10	17 24	16	03 49	22	16 09	58	07 17	56
11	17 41	+ 3	04 54	−10	16 51	−65	08 25	+63
12	17 58	− 9	06 00	+ 3	17 44	68	09 29	68
13	18 17	21	07 06	16	18 47	65	10 23	66
14	18 37	33	08 13	28	20 00	56	11 08	59
15	19 01	45	09 22	41	21 17	44	11 44	48
16	19 30	−56	10 31	+53	22 36	−29	12 14	+36
17	20 08	64	11 39	62	23 55	−15	12 39	21
18	20 55	69	12 44	69	25 14	0	13 02	+ 8
19	21 54	68	13 41	69	01 14	0	13 23	− 8
20	23 04	61	14 30	64	02 33	+15	13 46	22
21	24 22	−50	15 09	+53	03 52	+30	14 11	−36
22	00 22	50	15 42	41	05 11	44	14 41	48
23	01 44	36	16 09	26	06 28	56	15 16	60
24	03 08	20	16 34	+11	07 39	65	16 00	66
25	04 33	− 4	16 57	− 4	08 42	68	16 53	68
26	05 57	+12	17 20	−20	09 34	+67	17 53	−65
27	07 21	28	17 46	34	10 15	60	18 58	57
28	08 43	43	18 15	48	10 48	51	20 05	47
29	10 02	56	18 50	59	11 14	40	21 11	36
30	11 14	+66	19 32	−67	11 36	28	22 17	23

Date	OCTOBER Rise	ν	OCTOBER Set	ν	DECEMBER Rise	ν	DECEMBER Set	ν
1	12 16	+69	20 23	−69	11 55	+16	23 22	−11
2	13 08	68	21 20	67	12 13	+ 5	24 27	+ 2
3	13 49	62	22 23	60	12 31	− 7	00 27	2
4	14 21	53	23 28	50	12 49	19	01 32	14
5	14 47	42	24 33	39	13 10	31	02 39	27
6	15 09	+31	00 33	−39	13 34	−43	03 47	+39
7	15 29	20	01 39	26	14 04	55	04 48	51
8	15 47	+ 8	02 44	14	14 43	63	06 08	61
9	16 04	− 5	03 49	− 2	15 32	68	07 14	67
10	16 23	16	04 55	+11	16 33	67	08 14	67
11	16 43	−29	06 03	+25	17 45	−59	09 04	+62
12	17 06	41	07 11	37	19 02	49	09 44	52
13	17 34	53	08 21	49	20 23	34	10 17	40
14	18 10	61	09 30	59	21 44	19	10 44	26
15	18 54	67	10 36	66	23 03	− 4	11 07	+11
16	19 49	−68	11 36	+69	24 22	+11	11 29	− 3
17	20 55	63	12 26	64	00 22	11	11 51	18
18	22 09	53	13 08	56	01 40	26	12 15	31
19	23 27	40	13 42	45	02 57	40	12 42	44
20	24 47	26	14 10	31	04 13	52	13 14	56
21	00 47	−26	14 35	+17	05 25	+62	13 54	−64
22	02 08	−11	14 58	+ 3	06 30	68	14 42	68
23	03 30	+ 5	15 20	−13	07 25	67	15 39	67
24	04 52	21	15 44	28	08 11	63	16 42	61
25	06 14	36	16 12	41	08 47	55	17 48	52
26	07 34	+50	16 44	−54	09 16	+45	18 55	+41
27	08 51	62	17 24	63	09 39	33	20 02	28
28	09 59	68	18 11	69	10 00	22	21 08	16
29	10 56	68	19 07	68	10 18	+10	22 12	− 4
30	11 43	65	20 09	63	10 35	− 3	23 17	+ 9
31	12 19	+56	21 14	−54	10 53	−15	24 22	+21

Corrections to Moonrise or Moonset

N Lat / ν	30°	35°	40°	45°	50°	52°	54°	56°	58°	60°
	m	m	m	m	m	m	m	m	m	m
0	0	0	0	0	0	0	0	0	0	0
2	− 2	− 1	− 1	0	0	0	+ 1	+ 1	+ 2	+ 2
4	4	3	2	− 1	0	0	1	2	3	3
6	6	5	3	2	0	+ 1	2	3	4	5
8	8	6	5	2	0	1	2	3	5	6
10	−10	− 8	− 6	− 3	0	+ 1	+ 3	+ 4	+ 6	+ 8
12	12	10	7	4	0	2	4	5	8	10
14	14	11	8	5	0	2	4	6	9	12
16	16	13	9	5	0	2	5	8	11	14
18	18	14	10	6	0	2	5	9	12	16
20	−20	−16	−11	− 6	0	+ 3	+ 6	+10	+14	+18
22	22	17	12	7	0	3	7	11	15	20
24	24	19	14	8	0	3	7	12	16	22
26	26	21	15	8	0	4	8	13	18	24
28	28	22	16	9	0	4	9	14	19	26
30	−30	−24	−17	− 9	0	+ 5	+10	+15	+21	+28
32	32	26	19	10	0	5	10	16	22	30
34	34	27	20	10	0	5	11	17	24	32
36	36	29	21	11	0	5	11	17	25	33
38	38	31	22	12	0	5	11	18	26	35
40	−40	−32	−23	−13	0	+ 6	+12	+20	+28	+37
42	42	34	24	13	0	6	13	21	30	40
44	44	36	26	14	0	6	13	22	31	42
46	46	37	27	15	0	7	14	23	33	44
48	48	39	28	15	0	7	15	25	35	46
50	−50	−40	−29	−16	0	+ 7	+16	+26	+36	+48
52	52	42	30	16	0	8	17	27	38	51
54	54	43	31	17	0	8	17	27	39	53
56	56	45	33	18	0	8	17	28	40	55
58	58	47	34	19	0	9	18	30	42	57
60	−60	−48	−35	−20	0	+ 9	+19	+31	+45	+61
62	62	50	37	21	0	9	20	32	47	64
64	64	52	38	21	0	10	21	34	49	67
66	66	53	39	21	0	11	22	35	51	70
68	68	55	41	22	0	11	23	37	54	73
70	−70	−57	−42	−23	0	+11	+24	+38	+56	+76
72	72	58	43	24	0	12	25	40	58	80
74	74	60	44	24	0	12	26	41	60	84
76	76	62	45	25	0	12	27	43	62	87
78	78	63	46	26	0	12	27	44	64	90
80	−80	−65	−48	−27	0	+12	+27	+45	+67	+94
82	82	67	49	28	0	13	28	47	70	100
84	84	68	50	28	0	14	30	49	73	106
86	86	70	51	29	0	14	31	50	76	112
88	88	72	53	30	0	15	32	52	80	119
90	−90	−73	−54	−30	0	+16	+33	+55	+84	+127

The times given on the opposite page and alongside are the Local Mean Times (LMT) of moonrise and moonset for latitude N.50° and their variations ν from the times for N.30°.

To find the times for any latitude between N.30° and N.60°, enter the table with arguments latitude and ν, and apply the correction found to the tabulated time, *using the tabulated sign of the correction if ν is positive, and the opposite sign of the correction if ν is negative.* A very small extra correction due to the daily difference of the times has a mean value of $+3^m$ in longitude W.20° and -3^m in longitude E.20°.

The LMT can be converted to UT by adding the longitude (in time) if west or subtracting if east.

Examples of the use of this table are given on page 76.

5

5.3.8 1992 JANUARY, FEBRUARY — ARIES AND PLANETS

0ʰ UT	ARIES GHA	VENUS GHA	v	Dec	d	MARS GHA	v	Dec	d	JUPITER GHA	v	Dec	d	SATURN GHA	v	Dec	d
Jan						JANUARY											
	° ′	° ′		° ′		° ′		° ′		° ′		° ′		° ′		° ′	
1	99 54.7	221 10.2	−15	S18 10.0	−16	196 41.9	+11	S23 45.4	− 3	293 36.7	+59	N 7 08.1	0	151 31.9	+52	S19 22.4	+ 2
2	100 53.8	220 55.1	15	18 26.2	16	196 52.9	11	23 48.0	2	294 36.1	60	7 08.5	0	152 24.1	52	19 20.8	2
3	101 52.9	220 39.7	16	18 42.1	15	197 03.7	11	23 50.3	2	295 35.6	60	7 08.9	+1	153 16.3	52	19 19.2	2
4	102 52.1	220 24.0	16	18 57.4	15	197 14.5	11	23 52.4	2	296 35.2	60	7 09.4	1	154 08.5	52	19 17.6	2
5	103 51.2	220 08.0	16	19 12.3	15	197 25.3	11	23 54.2	2	297 35.1	60	7 10.0	1	155 00.6	52	19 15.9	2
6	104 50.3	219 51.7	−17	S19 26.8	−14	197 35.9	+11	S23 55.8	− 1	298 35.1	+60	N 7 10.7	+ 1	155 52.7	+52	S19 14.3	+ 2
7	105 49.5	219 35.2	17	19 40.7	13	197 46.6	11	23 57.1	1	299 35.4	60	7 11.5	1	156 44.8	52	19 12.6	2
8	106 48.6	219 18.4	17	19 54.1	13	197 57.1	11	23 58.2	1	300 35.8	61	7 12.3	1	157 36.9	52	19 10.9	2
9	107 47.8	219 01.3	17	20 07.0	12	198 07.6	10	23 59.1	− 1	301 36.4	61	7 13.2	1	158 28.9	52	19 09.2	2
10	108 46.9	218 43.9	18	20 19.4	12	198 18.0	10	23 59.7	0	302 37.1	61	7 14.2	1	159 20.9	52	19 07.5	2
11	109 46.0	218 26.3	−18	S20 31.2	−11	198 28.4	+10	S24 00.0	0	303 38.1	+61	N 7 15.2	+ 1	160 13.0	+52	S19 05.8	+ 2
12	110 45.2	218 08.4	18	20 42.5	11	198 38.8	10	24 00.1	0	304 39.2	61	7 16.3	1	161 04.9	52	19 04.1	2
13	111 44.3	217 50.4	18	20 53.2	10	198 49.1	10	23 59.9	0	305 40.5	62	7 17.5	1	161 56.9	52	19 02.3	2
14	112 43.4	217 32.0	19	21 03.4	10	198 59.3	10	23 59.5	+ 1	306 42.0	62	7 18.8	1	162 48.8	52	19 00.6	2
15	113 42.6	217 13.5	19	21 12.9	9	199 09.5	10	23 58.8	1	307 43.7	62	7 20.1	1	163 40.7	52	18 58.9	2
16	114 41.7	216 54.7	−19	S21 21.9	− 8	199 19.7	+10	S23 57.9	+ 1	308 45.5	+62	N 7 21.5	+ 2	164 32.6	+52	S18 57.1	+ 2
17	115 40.9	216 35.7	19	21 30.3	8	199 29.9	10	23 56.7	2	309 47.5	62	7 23.0	2	165 24.5	52	18 55.4	2
18	116 40.0	216 16.6	19	21 38.1	7	199 40.0	10	23 55.2	2	310 49.7	62	7 24.5	2	166 16.4	52	18 53.6	2
19	117 39.1	215 57.2	20	21 45.3	7	199 50.2	10	23 53.5	2	311 51.9	63	7 26.1	2	167 08.3	52	18 51.8	2
20	118 38.3	215 37.7	20	21 51.9	6	200 00.2	10	23 51.6	2	312 54.5	63	7 27.8	2	168 00.2	52	18 50.0	2
21	119 37.4	215 18.0	−20	S21 57.9	− 5	200 10.3	+10	S23 49.3	+ 2	313 57.2	+63	N 7 29.5	+ 2	168 52.0	+52	S18 48.2	+ 2
22	120 36.5	214 58.1	20	22 03.2	5	200 20.3	10	23 46.9	3	315 00.0	63	7 31.3	2	169 43.9	52	18 46.4	2
23	121 35.7	214 38.2	20	22 07.9	4	200 30.4	10	23 44.1	3	316 03.0	63	7 33.2	2	170 35.7	52	18 44.6	2
24	122 34.9	214 18.1	20	22 12.0	3	200 40.4	10	23 41.1	3	317 06.1	63	7 35.1	2	171 27.5	52	18 42.8	2
25	123 34.0	213 57.9	20	22 15.3	3	200 50.5	10	23 37.9	4	318 09.4	64	7 37.1	2	172 19.3	52	18 41.0	2
26	124 33.1	213 37.6	−20	S22 18.1	− 2	201 00.5	+10	S23 34.4	+ 4	319 12.9	+64	N 7 39.1	+ 2	173 11.2	+52	S18 39.2	+ 2
27	125 32.2	213 17.2	21	22 20.3	1	201 10.6	10	23 30.7	4	320 16.6	64	7 41.3	2	174 02.9	52	18 37.4	2
28	126 31.4	212 56.7	21	22 21.7	− 1	201 20.6	10	23 26.7	4	321 20.3	64	7 43.4	2	174 54.8	52	18 35.6	2
29	127 30.5	212 36.2	21	22 22.5	0	201 30.6	10	23 22.4	5	322 24.2	64	7 45.7	2	175 46.6	52	18 33.7	2
30	128 29.6	212 15.7	21	22 22.7	+ 1	201 40.7	10	23 17.9	5	323 28.2	64	7 47.9	2	176 38.4	52	18 31.9	2
31	129 28.8	211 55.1	−21	S22 22.1	+ 1	201 50.8	+10	S23 13.2	+ 5	324 32.5	+64	N 7 50.2	+ 2	177 30.2	+52	S18 30.1	+ 2
Feb						FEBRUARY											
1	130 28.0	211 34.5	−21	S22 20.9	+ 2	202 00.9	+10	S23 08.1	+ 5	325 36.8	+65	N 7 52.6	+ 3	178 22.0	+52	S18 28.2	+ 2
2	131 27.1	211 13.9	21	22 19.1	3	202 11.0	10	23 02.8	6	326 41.3	65	7 55.1	2	179 13.9	52	18 26.3	2
3	132 26.2	210 53.3	21	22 16.6	3	202 21.2	10	22 57.3	6	327 45.9	65	7 57.5	3	180 05.7	52	18 24.5	2
4	133 25.4	210 32.8	21	22 13.4	4	202 31.4	10	22 51.6	6	328 50.6	65	8 00.1	3	180 57.5	52	18 22.7	2
5	134 24.5	210 12.3	21	22 09 6	5	202 41.6	10	22 45.6	6	329 55.5	65	8 02.6	3	181 49.4	52	18 20.8	2
6	135 23.6	209 51.8	−20	S22 05.1	+ 5	202 51.8	+10	S22 39.3	+ 7	331 00.5	+65	N 8 05.2	+ 3	182 41.3	+52	S18 19.0	+ 2
7	136 22.8	209 31.5	20	21 59.9	6	203 02.2	10	22 32.8	7	332 05.6	65	8 07.9	3	183 33.1	52	18 17.1	2
8	137.21.9	209 11.2	20	21 54.1	6	203 12.5	10	22 26.1	7	333 10.8	65	8 10.6	3	184 25.0	52	18 15.2	2
9	138 21.1	208 51.0	20	21 47.7	7	203 22.9	11	22 19.1	7	334 16.1	65	8 13.3	3	185 16.9	52	18 13.4	2
10	139 20.2	208 31.0	20	21 40.5	8	203 33.4	11	22 11.8	8	335 21.5	66	8 16.1	3	186 08.8	52	18 11.5	2
11	140 19.3	208 11.0	−20	S21 32.8	+ 8	203 43.9	+11	S22 04.3	+ 8	336 27.1	+66	N 8 18.9	+ 3	187 00.7	+52	S18 09.7	+ 2
12	141 18.5	207 51.2	20	21 24.4	9	203 54.4	11	21 56.7	8	337 32.6	66	8 21.7	3	187 52.7	52	18 07.8	2
13	142 17.6	207 31.5	20	21 15.4	10	204 05.0	11	21 48.7	8	338 38.3	66	8 24.5	3	188 44.6	52	18 05.9	2
14	143 16.7	207 12.0	19	21 05.7	10	204 15.7	11	21 40.5	8	339 44.2	66	8 27.5	3	189 36.6	52	18 04.1	2
15	144 15.9	206 52.7	19	20 55.4	11	204 26.4	11	21 32.1	9	340 50.0	66	8 30.4	3	190 28.6	52	18 02.2	2
16	145 15.0	206 33.5	−19	S20 44.6	+12	204 37.2	+11	S21 23.5	+ 9	341 56.0	+66	N 8 33.3	+ 3	191 20.6	+52	S18 00.4	+ 2
17	146 14.2	206 14.5	19	20 33.0	12	204 48.1	11	21 14.6	9	343 02 0	66	8 36.2	3	192 12.7	52	17 58.5	2
18	147 13.3	205 55.7	19	20 20.9	13	204 59.0	11	21 05.5	9	344 08.1	66	8 39.2	3	193 04.7	52	17 56.7	2
19	148 12.4	205 37.1	18	20 08.2	13	205 10.0	11	20 56.1	10	345 14.2	66	8 42.2	3	193 56.8	52	17 54.8	2
20	149 11.6	205 18.7	18	19 54.9	14	205 21.1	11	20 46.6	10	346 20.5	66	8 45.2	3	194 48.9	52	17 53.0	2
21	150 10.7	205 00.5	−18	S19 41.0	+15	205 32.2	+11	S20 36.8	+10	347 26.7	+66	N 8 48.3	+ 3	195 41.0	+52	S17 51.1	+ 2
22	151 09.8	204 42.6	18	19 26.5	15	205 43.4	11	20 26.8	10	348 33.0	66	8 51.3	3	196 33.2	52	17 49.3	2
23	152 09.0	204 24.9	18	19 11.4	16	205 54.8	11	20 16.6	11	349 39.4	66	8 54.4	3	197 25.4	52	17 47.5	2
24	153 08.2	204 07.4	17	18 55.8	16	206 06.1	12	20 06.1	11	350 45.8	66	8 57.4	3	198 17.6	52	17 45.7	2
25	154 07.3	203 50.2	17	18 39.7	17	206 17.6	12	19 55.5	11	351 52.2	66	9 00.5	3	199 09.8	52	17 43.9	2
26	155 06.4	203 33.2	−17	S18 23.0	+17	206 29.1	+12	S19 44.7	+11	352 58.6	+67	N 9 03.5	+ 3	200 02.1	+52	S17 42.0	+ 2
27	156 05.6	203 16.4	17	18 05.9	18	206 40.7	12	19 33.6	11	354 05.1	67	9 06.5	3	200 54.4	52	17 40.2	2
28	157 04.7	202 59.9	16	17 48.1	18	206 52.4	12	19 22.3	12	355 11.6	67	9 09.6	3	201 46.8	52	17 38.4	2
29	158 03.8	202 43.7	−16	S17 29.9	+19	207 04.2	+12	S19 10.8	+12	356 18.1	+66	N 9 12.7	+ 3	202 39.2	+52	S17 36.6	+ 2

1992 JANUARY, FEBRUARY — SUN AND MOON

0^h UT	SUN GHA	v	SUN Dec	d	MOON 0^h–8^h GHA	v	Dec	d	MOON 8^h–16^h GHA	v	Dec	d	MOON 16^h–24^h GHA	v	Dec	d	HP
Jan	(SD 16′.3)				JANUARY												
	° ′		° ′		° ′		° ′		° ′		° ′		° ′		° ′		′
1	179 14.2	– 7	S23 04.7	+ 5	227 00	116	S22 52	– 39	342 56	114	S23 31	– 32	98 50	114	S24 03	– 24	55.0
2	179 07.1	7	23 00.0	5	214 44	113	24 27	– 16	330 37	113	24 43	– 9	86 30	114	24 52	0	54.6
3	179 00.0	7	22 54.7	6	202 24	115	24 52	+ 7	318 19	116	24 45	+ 15	74 15	119	24 30	+ 23	54.3
4	178 53.0	7	22 49.1	6	190 14	120	24 07	30	306 14	124	23 37	37	62 18	126	23 00	43	54.1
5	178 46.1	7	22 43.0	7	178 24	130	22 17	50	294 34	133	21 27	56	50 47	136	20 31	62	54.0
6	178 39.4	– 7	S22 36.4	+ 7	167 03	140	S19 29	+ 67	283 23	143	S18 22	+ 72	39 46	146	S17 10	+ 76	53.9
7	178 32.7	7	22 29.4	7	156 12	150	15 54	81	272 42	152	14 33	84	29 14	154	13 09	87	54.0
8	178 26.2	7	22 22.0	8	145 48	157	11 42	91	262 25	158	10 11	93	19 03	160	8 38	96	54.1
9	178 19.7	6	22 14.1	8	135 43	161	7 02	97	252 24	161	5 25	99	9 05	161	S 3 46	101	54.4
10	178 13.4	6	22 05.8	9	125 46	161	S 2 05	101	242 27	160	S 0 24	102	359 07	158	N 1 18	102	54.8
11	178 07.3	– 6	S21 57.0	+ 9	115 45	156	N 3 00	+102	232 21	154	N 4 42	+102	348 55	150	N 6 24	+100	55.4
12	178 01.3	6	21 47.8	10	105 25	147	8 04	99	221 52	143	9 43	98	338 15	137	11 21	95	56.1
13	177 55.5	6	21 38.2	10	94 32	132	12 56	92	210 44	127	14 28	88	326 51	119	15 56	85	56.9
14	177 49.8	6	21 28.2	10	82 50	113	17 21	79	198 43	106	18 40	74	314 29	99	19 54	68	57.8
15	177 44.3	5	21 17.8	11	70 08	91	21 02	61	185 39	84	22 03	52	301 03	77	22 55	44	58.8
16	177 38.9	– 5	S21 06.9	+11	56 20	71	N23 39	+ 34	171 31	64	N24 13	+ 24	286 35	60	N24 37	+ 13	59.7
17	177 33.7	5	20 55.6	12	41 35	56	24 50	+ 2	156 31	54	24 52	– 11	271 25	52	24 41	– 22	60.5
18	177 28.7	5	20 44.0	12	26 17	52	24 19	– 34	141 09	53	23 45	45	256 02	56	23 00	57	61.1
19	177 23.9	5	20 31.9	12	10 58	60	22 03	68	125 58	64	20 55	77	241 02	69	19 38	87	61.5
20	177 19.2	5	20 19.5	13	356 11	74	18 11	95	111 25	80	16 36	102	226 45	86	14 54	108	61.4
21	177 14.7	– 4	S20 06.7	+13	342 11	91	N13 06	–113	97 42	97	N11 13	–117	213 19	102	N 9 16	–120	61.1
22	177 10.4	4	19 53.5	14	329 01	106	7 16	121	84 47	110	N 5 15	123	200 37	114	N 3 12	122	60.4
23	177 06.3	4	19 40.0	14	316 31	117	N 1 10	122	72 28	120	S 0 52	120	188 28	121	S 2 52	118	59.6
24	177 02.4	4	19 26.1	14	304 29	123	S 4 50	114	60 32	124	6 44	112	176 36	124	8 36	107	58.6
25	176 58.7	4	19 11.7	15	292 40	125	10 23	102	48 45	124	12 05	98	164 49	123	13 43	92	57.7
26	176 55.2	– 3	S18 57.1	+15	280 52	123	S15 15	– 87	36 55	121	S16 42	– 80	152 56	120	S18 02	– 74	56.8
27	176 51.8	3	18 42.1	15	268 56	119	19 16	67	24 55	118	20 23	59	140 53	116	21 22	53	56.0
28	176 48.7	3	18 26.8	16	256 49	116	22 15	45	12 45	114	23 00	38	128 39	114	23 38	30	55.3
29	176 45.8	3	18 11.1	16	244 33	114	24 08	– 22	0 27	114	24 30	– 14	116 21	114	24 44	– 6	54.8
30	176 43.1	3	17 55.1	16	232 15	116	24 50	+ 1	348 11	116	24 49	+ 10	104 07	118	24 39	+ 16	54.4
31	176 40.5	– 2	S17 38.8	+17	220 05	120	S24 23	+ 24	336 05	123	S23 59	+ 32	92 08	125	S23 27	+ 38	54.1
Feb	(SD 16′.2)				FEBRUARY												
1	176 38.2	– 2	S17 22.2	+17	208 13	128	S22 49	+ 44	324 21	131	S22 05	+ 51	80 32	135	S21 14	+ 57	54.0
2	176 36.0	2	17 05.2	17	196 47	137	20 17	63	313 04	141	19 14	67	69 25	143	18 07	73	53.9
3	176 34.1	2	16 48.0	18	185 48	147	16 54	77	302 15	149	15 37	81	58 44	151	14 16	85	54.0
4	176 32.4	2	16 30.4	18	175 15	154	12 51	89	291 49	156	11 22	91	48 25	158	9 51	94	54.1
5	176 30.9	1	16 12.6	18	165 03	159	8 17	96	281 42	160	6 41	98	38 22	160	5 03	99	54.3
6	176 29.6	– 1	S15 54.6	+19	155 02	160	S 3 24	+101	271 42	160	S 1 43	+101	28 22	159	S 0 02	+102	54.6
7	176 28.5	1	15 36.1	19	145 01	158	N 1 40	102	261 39	156	N 3 22	101	18 15	154	N 5 03	100	55.0
8	176 27.5	1	15 17.5	19	134 49	151	6 43	100	251 20	149	8 23	97	7 49	144	10 00	96	55.5
9	176 26.9	– 1	14 58.6	19	124 13	140	11 36	92	240 33	136	13 08	90	356 49	130	14 38	86	56.1
10	176 26.3	0	14 39.5	19	112 59	125	16 04	81	229 04	119	17 25	77	345 03	113	18 42	71	56.7
11	176 26.0	0	S14 20.1	+20	100 56	107	N19 53	+ 65	216 43	100	N20 58	+ 58	332 23	95	N21 56	+ 51	57.5
12	176 25.9	0	14 00.4	20	87 58	88	22 47	42	203 26	82	23 29	34	318 48	77	24 03	+ 24	58.4
13	176 26.0	0	13 40.6	20	74 05	73	24 27	+ 14	189 18	69	24 41	+ 4	304 27	65	24 45	– 7	59.2
14	176 26.3	0	13 20.5	20	59 32	64	24 38	– 18	174 36	63	24 20	– 29	289 39	63	23 51	40	60.0
15	176 26.7	+ 1	13 00.2	21	44 42	65	23 11	52	159 47	66	22 19	61	274 53	69	21 18	72	60.7
16	176 27.4	+ 1	S12 39.7	+21	30 02	72	N20 06	– 81	145 14	77	N18 45	– 89	260 31	80	N17 16	– 98	61.1
17	176 28.2	1	12 19.0	21	15 51	85	15 38	104	131 16	88	13 54	110	246 44	94	12 04	115	61.2
18	176 29.3	1	11 58.1	21	2 18	97	10 09	119	117 55	101	8 10	121	233 36	104	N 6 09	124	61.1
19	176 30.5	1	11 37.0	21	349 20	107	N 4 05	124	105 07	109	N 2 01	124	220 56	112	S 0 03	123	60.6
20	176 31.9	1	11 15.7	21	336 48	113	S 2 06	121	92 41	114	S 4 07	119	208 35	115	6 06	115	59.8
21	176 33.3	+ 2	S10 54.3	+22	324 30	116	S 8 01	–112	80 26	115	S 9 53	–106	196 21	116	S11 39	–102	58.9
22	176 35.0	2	10 32.6	22	312 17	114	13 21	96	68 11	114	14 57	89	184 05	113	16 26	83	58.0
23	176 36.9	2	10 10.8	22	299 58	113	17 49	76	55 51	111	19 05	68	171 42	111	20 13	61	57.0
24	176 38.9	2	9 48.8	22	287 33	110	21 14	54	43 23	109	22 08	45	159 12	109	22 53	38	56.2
25	176 41.1	2	9 26.8	22	275 01	110	23 31	– 29	30 51	110	24 00	– 21	146 41	111	24 21	– 14	55.4
26	176 43.4	+ 2	S 9 04.5	+22	262 32	112	S24 35	– 5	18 24	113	S24 40	+ 3	134 17	116	S24 37	+ 10	54.8
27	176 45.8	3	8 42.1	22	250 13	118	24 27	+ 18	6 11	120	24 09	25	122 11	123	23 44	32	54.4
28	176 48.4	3	8 19.6	23	238 14	126	23 12	39	354 20	128	22 33	46	110 28	133	21 47	51	54.1
29	176 51.1	+ 3	S 7 57.0	+23	226 41	135	S20 56	+ 57	342 56	138	S19 59	+ 63	99 14	141	S18 56	+ 68	54.0

5

1992 MARCH, APRIL — ARIES AND PLANETS

0h UT	ARIES GHA	VENUS GHA	v	Dec	d	MARS GHA	v	Dec	d	JUPITER GHA	v	Dec	d	SATURN GHA	v	Dec	d
Mar	° ′	° ′		° ′		° ′		° ′		° ′		° ′		° ′		° ′	
						MARCH											
1	159 03.0	202 27.7	−16	S17 11.1	+19	207 16.1	+12	S18 59.2	+12	357 24.5	+67	N 9 15.7	+ 3	203 31.6	+53	S17 34.8	+ 2
2	160 02.1	202 12.0	16	16 51.9	20	207 28.0	12	18 47.3	12	358 31.1	67	9 18.7	3	204 24.1	53	17 33.0	2
3	161 01.3	201 56.5	15	16 32.2	20	207 40.1	12	18 35.2	12	359 37.6	66	9 21.7	3	205 16.6	53	17 31.3	2
4	162 00.4	201 41.3	15	16 12.0	21	207 52.2	12	18 22.9	12	0 44.0	66	9 24.7	3	206 09.1	53	17 29.5	2
5	162 59.5	201 26.4	15	15 51.4	21	208 04.4	12	18 10.5	13	1 50.5	66	9 27.7	3	207 01.6	53	17 27.7	2
6	163 58.7	201 11.7	−14	S15 30.3	+22	208 16.8	+12	S17 57.8	+13	2 56.9	+66	N 9 30.7	+ 3	207 54.2	+53	S17 26.0	+ 2
7	164 57.8	200 57.3	14	15 08.8	22	208 29.2	13	17 45.0	13	4 03.4	66	9 33.6	3	208 46.9	53	17 24.2	2
8	165 56.9	200 43.1	14	14 46.9	22	208 41.7	13	17 32.1	13	5 09.7	66	9 36.5	3	209 39.6	53	17 22.5	2
9	166 56.1	200 29.2	14	14 24.6	23	208 54.3	13	17 18.8	13	6 16.1	66	9 39.4	3	210 32.3	53	17 20.8	2
10	167 55.2	200 15.6	13	14 01.9	23	209 07.0	13	17 05.5	14	7 22.4	66	9 42.3	3	211 25.1	53	17 19.0	2
11	168 54.4	200 02.2	−13	S13 38.8	+24	209 19.8	+13	S16 52.0	+14	8 28.6	+66	N 9 45.2	+ 3	212 18.0	+53	S17 17.3	+ 2
12	169 53.5	199 49.1	13	13 15.3	24	209 32.7	13	16 38.2	14	9 34.8	66	9 48.0	3	213 10.9	53	17 15.7	2
13	170 52.6	199 36.2	13	12 51.4	24	209 45.7	13	16 24.4	14	10 40.9	66	9 50.8	3	214 03.8	53	17 14.0	2
14	171 51.8	199 23.6	13	12 27.2	25	209 58.8	13	16 10.3	14	11 47.0	66	9 53.5	3	214 56.8	53	17 12.3	2
15	172 50.9	199 11.1	12	12 02.7	25	210 12.0	13	15 56.1	14	12 53.0	66	9 56.2	3	215 49.9	53	17 10.6	2
16	173 50.0	198 59.0	−12	S11 37.8	+25	210 25.3	+13	S15 41.8	+15	13 59.0	+66	N 9 58.9	+ 3	216 42.9	+53	S17 09 0	+ 2
17	174 49.2	198 47.0	12	11 12.6	26	210 38.6	14	15 27.2	15	15 04.8	66	10 01.5	3	217 36.1	53	17 07.4	2
18	175 48.4	198 35.3	11	10 47.1	26	210 52.1	14	15 12.6	15	16 10.6	66	10 04.1	3	218 29.2	53	17 05.8	2
19	176 47.5	198 23.9	11	10 21.4	26	211 05.7	14	14 57.8	15	17 16.3	66	10 06.7	2	219 22.5	53	17 04.1	2
20	177 46.6	198 12.5	11	9 55.3	26	211 19.3	14	14 42.8	15	18 21.8	66	10 09.1	2	220 15.8	53	17 02.6	2
21	178 45.7	198 01.5	−11	S 9 28.9	+27	211 33.1	+14	S14 27.7	+15	19 27.4	+65	N10 11.6	+ 2	221 09.2	+53	S17 01.0	+ 2
22	179 44,9	197 50.6	11	9 02.4	27	211 46.9	14	14 12.4	15	20 32.8	65	10 14.0	2	222 02.6	53	16 59.4	2
23	180 44.0	197 39.8	11	8 35.5	27	212 00.9	14	13 57.1	16	21 38.0	65	10 16.4	2	222 56.0	54	16 57.9	2
24	181 43.1	197 29.3	10	8 08.5	27	212 14.9	14	13 41.5	16	22 43.2	65	10 18.7	2	223 49.6	54	16 56.3	2
25	182 42.3	197 19.0	10	7 41.2	28	212 29.0	14	13 25.9	16	23 48.3	65	10 20.9	2	224 43.2	54	16 54.8	2
26	183 41.5	197 08.7	−10	S 7 13.6	+28	212 43.2	+14	S13 10.1	+16	24 53.2	+65	N10 23.2	+ 2	225 36.8	+54	S16 53.3	+ 2
27	184 40.6	196 58.7	10	6 45.9	28	212 57.5	14	12 54.2	16	25 58.1	65	10 25.3	2	226 30.5	54	16 51.8	1
28	185 39.7	196 48.8	10	6 18.0	28	213 11.9	14	12 38.1	16	27 02.8	65	10 27.4	2	227 24.4	54	16 50.4	1
29	186 38.9	196 39.0	10	5 50.0	28	213 26.3	15	12 22.0	16	28 07.4	65	10 29.5	2	228 18.2	54	16 48.9	1
30	187 38.0	196 29.3	9	5 21.7	28	213 40.9	15	12 05.7	16	29 11.9	64	10 31.4	2	229 12.1	54	16 47.5	1
31	188 37.1	196 19.9	−10	S 4 53.3	+29	213 55.6	+15	S11 49.3	+17	30 16.2	+64	N10 33.4	+ 2	230 06.1	+54	S16 46.1	+ 1
Apr						APRIL											
1	189 36.3	196 10.4	− 9	S 4 24.8	+29	214 10.3	+15	S11 32.8	+17	31 20.4	+64	N10 35.3	+ 2	231 00.1	+54	S16 44.8	+ 1
2	190 35.4	196 01.1	9	3 56.2	29	214 25.1	15	11 16.3	17	32 24.4	64	10 37.1	2	231 54.2	54	16 43.4	1
3	191 34.6	195 52.0	9	3 27.4	29	214 40.0	15	10 59.5	17	33 28.4	64	10 38.8	2	232 48.4	54	16 42.0	1
4	192 33.7	195 42.8	9	2 58.5	29	214 55.0	15	10 42.7	17	34 32.1	64	10 40.5	2	233 42.7	54	16 40.7	1
5	193 32.8	195 33.8	9	2 29.5	29	215 10.0	15	10 25.9	17	35 35.8	63	10 42.1	2	234 37.0	54	16 39.4	1
6	194 32.0	195 24.8	− 9	S 2 00.5	+29	215 25.1	+15	S10 08.9	+17	36 39.2	+63	N10 43.7	+ 2	235 31.4	+54	S16 38.1	+ 1
7	195 31.1	195 15.9	9	1 31.4	29	215 40.4	15	9 51.8	17	37 42.6	63	10 45.2	1	236 25.8	55	16 36.8	1
8	196 30.2	195 07.0	9	1 02.2	29	215 55.7	15	9 34.6	17	38 45.7	63	10 46.6	1	237 20.3	55	16 35.6	1
9	197 29.4	194 58.2	9	0 33.0	29	216 11.1	15	9 17.4	17	39 48.7	63	10 47.9	1	238 15.0	55	16 34.3	1
10	198 28.5	194 49.4	9	S 0 03.8	29	216 26.5	16	9 00.1	17	40 51.6	63	10 49.3	1	239 09.7	55	16 33.1	1
11	199 27.7	194 40.6	− 9	N 0 25.5	+29	216 42.1	+16	S 8 42.7	+18	41 54.2	+63	N10 50.5	+ 1	240 04.4	+55	S16 31.9	+ 1
12	200 26.8	194 31.9	9	0 54.8	29	216 57.7	16	8 25.2	18	42 56.7	62	10 51.7	1	240 59.3	55	16 30.8	1
13	201 25.9	194 23.1	9	1 24.1	29	217 13.4	16	8 07.6	18	43 59.1	62	10 52.7	1	241 54.2	55	16 29.6	1
14	202 25.1	194 14.3	9	1 53.3	29	217 29.2	16	7 50.0	18	45 01.3	62	10 53.8	1	242 49.1	55	16 28.5	1
15	203 24.2	194 05.5	9	2 22.6	29	217 45.0	16	7 32.3	18	46 03.3	62	10 54.7	1	243 44.2	55	16 27.4	1
16	204 23.3	193 56.7	− 9	N 2 51.8	+29	218 00.8	+16	S 7 14.6	+18	47 05.2	+62	N10 55.6	+ 1	244 39.4	+55	S16 26.3	+ 1
17	205 22.5	193 47.8	9	3 20.9	29	218 16.8	16	6 56.8	18	48 06.8	62	10 56.5	1	245 34.6	55	16 25.3	1
18	206 21.7	193 38.9	9	3 50.0	29	218 32.8	16	6 38.9	18	49 08.4	61	10 57.2	1	246 29.9	55	16 24.2	1
19	207 20.8	193 29.9	9	4 19.1	29	218 48.9	16	6 21.1	18	50 09.7	61	10 57.9	1	247 25.3	56	16 23.3	1
20	208 19.9	193 20.8	9	4 48.0	29	219 05.0	16	6 03.1	18	51 10.9	61	10 58.5	1	248 20.8	56	16 22.3	1
21	209 19.1	193 11.7	− 9	N 5 16.9	+29	219 21.2	+16	S 5 45.1	+18	52 11.9	+61	N10 59.0	+ 1	249 16.3	+56	S16 21.4	+ 1
22	210 18.2	193 02.5	9	5 45.6	29	219 37.4	16	5 27.1	18	53 12.7	61	10 59.5	0	250 11.9	56	16 20.4	1
23	211 17.3	192 53.1	9	6 14.2	29	219 53.8	16	5 09.0	18	54 13.3	61	10 59.9	0	251 07.7	56	16 19.5	1
24	212 16.4	192 43.7	10	6 42.7	28	220 10.1	16	4 50.9	18	55 13.8	60	11 00.2	0	252 03.5	56	16 18.7	1
25	213 15.6	192 34.1	10	7 11.1	28	220 26.5	17	4 32.8	18	56 14.2	60	11 00.5	0	252 59.4	56	16 17.8	1
26	214 14.8	192 24.4	−10	N 7 39.3	+28	220 43.0	+17	S 4 14.6	+18	57 14.3	+60	N11 00.7	0	253 55.4	+56	S16 17.0	+ 1
27	215 13.9	192 14.5	10	8 07.3	28	220 59.5	17	3 56.4	18	58 14.2	60	11 00.9	0	254 51.4	56	16 16.2	1
28	216 13.0	192 04.6	10	8 35.2	28	221 16.0	17	3 38.2	18	59 14.0	60	11 01.0	0	255 47.6	56	16 15.4	1
29	217 12.2	191 54.4	10	9 02.9	28	221 32.6	17	3 19.9	18	60 13.6	59	11 01.0	0	256 43.9	56	16 14.7	1
30	218 11.3	191 44.1	−11	N 9 30.4	+27	221 49.3	+17	S 3 01.7	+18	61 13.0	+59	N11 00.8	0	257 40.2	+56	S16 14.0	+ 1

1992 MARCH, APRIL — SUN AND MOON

0^h UT	SUN GHA	v	SUN Dec	d	MOON 0^h–8^h GHA	v	Dec	d	MOON 8^h–16^h GHA	v	Dec	d	MOON 16^h–24^h GHA	v	Dec	d	HP
Mar	(SD 16′.1)				MARCH												
	° ′		° ′		° ′		° ′		° ′		° ′		° ′		° ′		′
1	176 54.0	+ 3	S 7 34.2	+23	215 35	145	S17 48	+ 73	332 00	147	S16 35	+ 77	88 27	149	S15 18	+ 81	54.0
2	176 56.9	3	7 11.3	23	204 56	152	13 57	85	321 28	153	12 32	89	78 01	156	11 03	91	54.2
3	177 00.0	3	6 48.4	23	194 37	156	9 32	94	311 13	158	7 58	96	67 51	158	6 22	99	54.4
4	177 03.2	3	6 25.3	23	184 29	158	S 4 43	99	301 07	159	S 3 04	101	57 46	157	S 1 23	102	54.7
5	177 06.5	3	6 02.2	23	174 23	157	N 0 19	102	291 00	155	N 2 01	102	47 35	153	N 3 43	101	55.1
6	177 09.9	+ 4	S 5 38.9	+23	164 08	151	N 5 24	+100	280 39	148	N 7 04	+ 99	37 07	145	N 8 43	+ 97	55.5
7	177 13.4	4	5 15.7	23	153 32	141	10 20	95	269 53	137	11 55	91	26 10	133	13 26	89	55.9
8	177 17.0	4	4 52.3	24	142 23	129	14 55	84	258 32	123	16 19	79	14 35	118	17 38	74	56.4
9	177 20.8	4	4 28.8	23	130 33	113	18 52	69	246 26	108	20 01	62	2 14	102	21 03	55	57.0
10	177 24.6	4	4 05.3	24	117 56	97	21 58	47	233 33	92	22 45	40	349 05	88	23 25	30	57.6
11	177 28.4	+ 4	S 3 41.8	+24	104 33	83	N23 55	+ 22	219 56	81	N24 17	+ 12	335 17	77	N24 29	+ 2	58.2
12	177 32.5	4	3 18.2	24	90 34	76	24 31	− 8	205 50	74	24 23	− 19	321 04	75	24 04	− 28	58.8
13	177 36.5	4	2 54.5	24	76 19	74	23 36	39	191 33	76	22 57	49	306 49	78	22 08	58	59.4
14	177 40.6	4	2 30.9	24	62 07	80	21 10	68	177 27	83	20 02	76	292 50	86	18 46	85	60.0
15	177 44.8	4	2 07.3	24	48 16	89	17 21	92	163 45	93	15 49	98	279 18	96	14 11	105	60.3
16	177 49.1	+ 4	S 1 43.6	+24	34 54	99	N12 26	−110	150 33	102	N10 36	−114	266 15	105	N 8 42	−117	60.5
17	177 53.4	4	1 19.9	24	22 00	107	6 45	120	137 47	109	N 4 45	121	253 36	111	N 2 44	122	60.4
18	177 57.8	4	0 56.1	24	9 27	111	N 0 42	122	125 18	113	S 1 20	121	241 11	112	S 3 21	119	60.1
19	178 02.2	5	0 32.4	24	357 03	113	S 5 20	116	112 56	112	7 16	113	228 48	112	9 09	109	59.6
20	178 06.7	5	0 08.7	24	344 40	111	10 58	104	100 31	109	12 42	98	216 20	108	14 20	93	58.8
21	178 11.2	+ 5	N 0 15.0	+24	332 08	107	S15 53	− 85	87 55	106	S17 18	− 79	203 41	105	S18 37	− 71	58.0
22	178 15.7	5	0 38.7	24	319 26	104	19 48	64	75 10	103	20 52	55	190 53	103	21 47	47	57.1
23	178 20.2	5	1 02.3	24	306 36	102	22 34	39	62 18	104	23 13	30	178 02	104	23 43	− 22	56.3
24	178 24.7	5	1 26.0	24	293 46	105	24 05	− 14	49 31	107	24 19	− 5	165 18	109	24 24	+ 3	55.6
25	178 29.3	5	1 49.6	24	281 07	112	24 21	+ 10	36 59	114	24 11	+ 19	152 53	118	23 52	25	55.0
26	178 33.8	+ 5	N 2 13,1	+24	268 51	121	S23 27	+ 33	24 52	124	S22 54	+ 40	140 56	128	S22 14	+ 45	54.5
27	178 38.3	5	2 36.7	23	257 04	131	21 29	52	13 15	135	20 37	58	129 30	139	19 39	63	54.3
28	178 42.9	5	3 00.1	23	245 49	141	18 36	68	2 10	145	17 28	72	118 35	147	16 16	77	54.2
29	178 47.4	5	3 23.5	23	235 02	150	14 59	81	351 32	152	13 38	84	108 04	154	12 14	88	54.2
30	178 52.0	4	3 46.9	23	224 38	156	10 46	91	341 14	156	9 15	93	97 50	158	7 42	96	54.4
31	178 56.4	+ 5	N 4 10.1	+23	214 28	157	S 6 06	+ 98	331 05	158	S 4 28	+ 99	87 43	156	S 2 49	+100	54.7
Apr	(SD 16′.0)				APRIL												
1	179 00.9	+ 4	N 4 33.4	+23	204 19	156	S 1 09	+101	320 55	155	N 0 32	+102	77 30	152	N 2 14	+102	55.2
2	179 05.3	5	4 56.5	23	194 02	151	N 3 56	101	310 33	147	5 37	100	67 00	145	7 17	99	55.6
3	179 09.8	4	5 19.5	23	183 25	141	8 56	97	299 46	136	10 33	94	56 02	133	12 07	92	56.1
4	179 14.1	4	5 42.4	23	172 15	128	13 39	88	288 23	123	15 07	83	44 26	118	16 30	78	56.6
5	179 18.5	4	6 05.3	23	160 24	113	17 48	74	276 17	107	19 02	66	32 04	103	20 08	60	57.1
6	179 22.7	+ 4	N 6 28.0	+23	147 47	97	N21 08	+ 53	263 24	93	N22 01	+ 45	18 57	89	N22 46	+ 36	57.6
7	179 26.9	4	6 50.6	23	134 26	85	23 22	+ 27	249 51	82	23 49	+ 18	5 13	79	24 07	+ 08	58.1
8	179 31.1	4	7 13.1	22	120 32	78	24 15	− 1	235 50	78	24 14	− 12	351 08	77	24 02	− 21	58.5
9	179 35.3	4	7 35.5	22	106 25	79	23 41	32	221 44	80	23 09	41	337 04	82	22 28	50	58.9
10	179 39.4	4	7 57.7	22	92 26	85	21 38	60	207 51	88	20 38	67	323 19	91	19 31	76	59.2
11	179 43.3	+ 4	N 8 19.8	+22	78 50	95	N18 15	− 83	194 25	98	N16 52	− 90	310 03	102	N15 22	− 96	59.4
12	179 47.3	4	8 41.8	22	65 45	105	13 46	101	181 30	108	12 05	106	297 18	111	10 19	109	59.6
13	179 51.2	4	9 03.6	22	53 09	113	8 30	113	169 02	115	6 37	115	284 57	116	N 4 42	117	59.6
14	179 55.0	4	9 25.3	22	40 53	117	N 2 45	118	156 50	118	N 0 47	118	272 48	119	S 1 11	117	59.5
15	179 58.7	4	9 46.8	21	28 47	117	S 3 08	116	144 44	118	S 5 04	113	260 42	116	6 57	111	59.2
16	180 02.3	+ 4	N10 08.2	+21	16 38	114	S 8 48	−107	132 32	113	S10 35	−103	248 25	111	S12 18	− 98	58.8
17	180 05.8	4	10 29.4	21	4 16	109	13 56	92	120 05	108	15 28	86	235 53	105	16 54	80	58.2
18	180 09.3	3	10 50.3	21	351 38	103	18 14	72	107 21	102	19 26	65	223 03	100	20 31	56	57.6
19	180 12.6	3	11 11.2	21	338 43	100	21 27	49	94 23	99	22 16	40	210 02	99	22 56	31	56.9
20	180 15.8	3	11 31.9	20	325 41	100	23 27	− 23	81 21	101	23 50	− 14	197 02	102	24 04	− 6	56.2
21	180 19.0	+ 3	N11 52.3	+20	312 44	105	S24 10	+ 2	68 29	108	S24 08	+ 11	184 17	110	S23 57	+ 18	55.5
22	180 22.0	3	12 12.6	20	300 07	114	23 39	26	56 01	118	23 13	33	171 59	121	22 40	40	55.0
23	180 24.9	3	12 32.7	20	288 00	126	22 00	46	44 06	129	21 14	52	160 15	134	20 22	58	54.6
24	180 27.7	3	12 52.5	20	276 29	137	19 24	63	32 46	141	18 21	68	149 07	144	17 13	73	54.3
25	180 30.3	3	13 12.1	20	265 31	147	16 00	77	21 58	150	14 43	80	138 28	153	13 23	84	54.2
26	180 32.9	+ 2	N13 31.6	+19	255 01	155	S11 59	+ 87	11 36	156	S10 32	+ 90	128 12	157	S 9 02	+ 92	54.4
27	180 35.3	2	13 50.8	19	244 49	159	7 30	95	1 28	158	5 55	97	118 06	158	S 4 18	98	54.6
28	180 37.5	2	14 09.8	19	234 44	158	S 2 40	99	351 22	157	S 1 01	100	107 59	154	N 0 39	101	55.0
29	180 39.7	2	14 28.5	19	224 33	153	N 2 20	100	341 06	150	N 4 00	101	97 36	147	5 41	99	55.5
30	180 41.6	+ 2	N14 47.1	+18	214 03	144	N 7 20	+ 98	330 27	139	N 8 58	+ 97	86 46	135	N10 35	+ 94	56.2

5

1992 MAY, JUNE — ARIES AND PLANETS

0ʰ UT	ARIES GHA	VENUS GHA	v	VENUS Dec	d	MARS GHA	v	MARS Dec	d	JUPITER GHA	v	JUPITER Dec	d	SATURN GHA	v	SATURN Dec	d
May								**MAY**									
	° ′	° ′		° ′		° ′		° ′		° ′		° ′		° ′		° ′	
1	219 10.4	191 33.6	−11	N 9 57.6	+27	222 05.9	+17	S 2 43.4	+18	62 12.3	+59	N11 00.7	0	258 36.6	+57	S16 13.3	+ 1
2	220 09.6	191 22.9	11	10 24.7	27	222 22.6	17	2 25.1	18	63 11.4	59	11 00.5	0	259 33.1	57	16 12.6	1
3	221 08.7	191 12.1	11	10 51.5	27	222 39.4	17	2 06.8	18	64 10.3	59	11 00.2	0	260 29.7	57	16 12.0	1
4	222 07.9	191 01.0	11	11 18.0	26	222 56.2	17	1 48.5	18	65 09.0	59	10 59.9	0	261 26.4	57	16 11.4	1
5	223 07.0	190 49.7	12	11 44.4	26	223 13.1	17	1 30.2	18	66 07.6	58	10 59.5	− 1	262 23.2	57	16 10.9	1
6	224 06.1	190 38.2	−12	N12 10.3	+26	223 29.9	+17	S 1 11.9	+18	67 06.0	+58	N10 59.0	− 1	263 20.0	+57	S16 10.3	+ 1
7	225 05.3	190 26.5	12	12 36.1	25	223 46.9	17	0 53.6	18	68 04.2	58	10 58.4	1	264 17.0	57	16 09.8	+ 1
8	226 04.4	190 14.7	12	13 01.5	25	224 03.8	17	0 35.4	18	69 02.2	58	10 57.8	1	265 14.1	57	16 09.3	0
9	227 03.5	190 02.5	12	13 26.7	25	224 20.8	17	S 0 17.1	18	70 00.1	58	10 57.2	1	266 11.3	57	16 08.9	0
10	228 02.7	189 50.1	13	13 51.4	25	224 37.8	17	N 0 01.1	18	70 57.8	58	10 56.4	1	267 08.5	57	16 08.5	0
11	229 01.8	189 37.5	−13	N14 15.9	+24	224 54.8	+17	N 0 19.4	+18	71 55.3	+57	N10 55.6	− 1	268 05.9	+57	S16 08.0	0
12	230 01.0	189 24.6	13	14 40.0	24	225 11.9	17	0 37.6	18	72 52.7	57	10 54.7	1	269 03.3	58	16 07.7	0
13	231 00.1	189 11.5	13	15 03.8	23	225 29.0	17	0 55.8	18	73 49.9	57	10 53.8	1	270 00.8	58	16 07.3	0
14	231 59.2	188 58.1	14	15 27.2	23	225 46.1	17	1 13.9	18	74 46.9	57	10 52.8	1	270 58.4	58	16 07.0	0
15	232 58.4	188 44.5	14	15 50.2	23	226 03.2	17	1 32.1	18	75 43.8	57	10 51.7	1	271 56.2	58	16 06.8	0
16	233 57.5	188 30.6	−14	N16 12.8	+22	226 20.3	+17	N 1 50.2	+18	76 40.5	+57	N10 50.6	− 1	272 54.0	+58	S16 06.5	0
17	234 56.6	188 16.4	15	16 35.0	22	226 37.4	17	2 08.3	18	77 37.0	56	10 49.4	1	273 51.9	58	16 06.3	0
18	235 55.8	188 01.9	15	16 56.9	21	226 54.7	17	2 26.3	18	78 33.4	56	10 48.1	1	274 49.9	58	16 06.1	0
19	236 55.0	187 47.2	15	17 18.2	21	227 11.8	17	2 44.3	18	79 29.6	56	10 46.8	1	275 48.1	58	16 06.0	0
20	237 54.1	187 32.2	15	17 39.1	20	227 29.0	17	3 02.2	18	80 25.6	56	10 45.4	1	276 46.3	58	16 05.9	0
21	238 53.2	187 16.9	−16	N17 59.5	+20	227 46.2	+17	N 3 20.1	+18	81 21.6	+56	N10 44.0	− 2	277 44.5	+59	S16 05.8	0
22	239 52.4	187 01.3	16	18 19.5	20	228 03.4	17	3 38.0	18	82 17.3	56	10 42.4	2	278 43.0	59	16 05.7	0
23	240 51.5	186 45.4	16	18 39.1	19	228 20.6	17	3 55.7	18	83 12.8	56	10 40.9	2	279 41.5	59	16 05.7	0
24	241 50.6	186 29.3	16	18 58.1	19	228 37.9	17	4 13.5	18	84 08.3	55	10 39.2	2	280 40.0	59	16 05.7	0
25	242 49.7	186 12.9	17	19 16.7	18	228 55.1	17	4 31.2	18	85 03.5	55	10 37.6	2	281 38.7	59	16 05.7	0
26	243 48.9	185 56.2	−17	N19 34.7	+17	229 12.4	+17	N 4 48.8	+18	85 58.7	+55	N10 35.8	− 2	282 37.5	+59	S16 05.8	0
27	244 48.1	185 39.2	17	19 52.1	17	229 29.6	17	5 06.4	18	86 53.6	55	10 34.0	2	283 36.4	59	16 05.9	0
28	245 47.2	185 22.0	18	20 09.1	16	229 46.8	17	5 23.9	17	87 48.5	55	10 32.1	2	284 35.4	59	16 06.0	0
29	246 46.3	185 04.5	18	20 25.5	16	230 04.0	17	5 41.3	17	88 43.1	55	10 30.2	2	285 34.4	59	16 06.2	0
30	247 45.5	184 46.6	18	20 41.4	15	230 21.3	17	5 58.6	17	89 37.7	54	10 28.2	2	286 33.7	59	16 06.4	0
31	248 44.6	184 28.6	−18	N20 56.7	+15	230 38.5	+17	N 6 15.9	+17	90 32.1	+54	N10 26.2	− 2	287 32.9	+59	S16 06.5	0
Jun								**JUNE**									
1	249 43.7	184 10.3	−19	N21 11.4	+14	230 55.7	+17	N 6 33.1	+17	91 26.3	+54	N10 24.1	− 2	288 32.3	+59	S16 06.8	0
2	250 42.9	183 51.7	19	21 25.5	14	231 13.0	17	6 50.2	17	92 20.4	54	10 22.0	2	289 31.7	60	16 07.1	0
3	251 42.0	183 32.9	19	21 39.0	13	231 30.2	17	7 07.3	17	93 14.4	54	10 19.7	2	290 31.3	60	16 07.4	0
4	252 41.2	183 13.9	19	21 51.9	12	231 47.5	17	7 24.2	17	94 08.2	54	10 17.5	2	291 31.0	60	16 07.7	0
5	253 40.3	182 54.6	20	22 04.3	12	232 04.7	17	7 41.1	17	95 01.9	54	10 15.2	2	292 30.7	60	16 08.1	0
6	254 39.4	182 35.1	−20	N22 15.9	+11	232 21.9	+17	N 7 57.8	+17	95 55.4	+54	N10 12.8	− 2	293 30.6	+60	S16 08.5	0
7	255 38.6	182 15.4	20	22 27.0	11	232 39.1	17	8 14.5	17	96 48.9	53	10 10.4	3	294 30.5	60	16 08.9	0
8	256 37.7	181 55.5	20	22 37.5	10	232 56.3	17	8 31.1	16	97 42.2	53	10 07.9	3	295 30.5	60	16 09.4	0
9	257 36.8	181 35.4	20	22 47.3	9	233 13.5	17	8 47.6	16	98 35.3	53	10 05.4	3	296 30.7	60	16 09.8	− 1
10	258 36.0	181 15.1	20	22 56.4	8	233 30.7	17	9 04.0	16	99 28.4	53	10 02.8	3	297 30.9	60	16 10.3	− 1
11	259 35.1	180 54.7	−21	N23 04.8	+ 8	233 47.9	+17	N 9 20.3	+16	100 21.2	+53	N10 00.2	− 3	298 31.3	+60	S16 10.9	− 1
12	260 34.3	180 34.1	21	23 12.6	7	234 05.0	17	9 36.4	16	101 14.0	53	9 57.5	3	299 31.7	61	16 11.5	1
13	261 33.4	180 13.3	21	23 19.7	7	234 22.2	17	9 52.5	16	102 06.7	53	9 54.8	3	300 32.2	61	16 12.0	1
14	262 32.5	179 52.4	21	23 26.2	6	234 39.3	17	10 08.5	16	102 59.2	53	9 52.0	3	301 32.8	61	16 12.7	1
15	263 31.7	179 31.4	21	23 32.0	5	234 56.5	17	10 24.3	16	103 51.7	52	9 49.2	3	302 33.5	61	16 13.3	1
16	264 30.8	179 10.3	−21	N23 37.0	+ 4	235 13.6	+17	N10 40.0	+16	104 43.9	+52	N 9 46.3	− 3	303 34.3	+61	S16 14.0	− 1
17	265 29.9	178 49.1	21	23 41.4	4	235 30.7	17	10 55.7	16	105 36.1	52	9 43.4	3	304 35.1	61	16 14.7	1
18	266 29.1	178 27.8	21	23 45.1	3	235 47.8	17	11 11.2	15	106 28.1	52	9 40.4	3	305 36.1	61	16 15.4	1
19	267 28.3	178 06.4	21	23 48.1	2	236 04.8	17	11 26.5	15	107 20.1	52	9 37.4	3	306 37.1	61	16 16.1	1
20	268 27.4	177 45.0	22	23 50.4	2	236 21.8	17	11 41.8	15	108 11.9	52	9 34.4	3	307 38.3	61	16 16.9	1
21	269 26.5	177 23.5	−22	N23 51.9	+ 1	236 38.9	+17	N11 56.9	+15	109 03.7	+52	N 9 31.3	− 3	308 39.5	+61	S16 17.8	− 1
22	270 25.7	177 02.0	22	23 52.8	0	236 55.9	17	12 11.9	15	109 55.3	52	9 28.1	3	309 40.8	61	16 18.6	1
23	271 24.8	176 40.5	22	23 53.0	− 1	237 12.9	17	12 26.8	15	110 46.8	51	9 24.9	3	310 42.2	61	16 19.4	1
24	272 23.9	176 19.0	22	23 52.4	1	237 29.9	17	12 41.5	15	111 38.2	51	9 21.7	3	311 43.6	62	16 20.3	1
25	273 23.0	175 57.5	22	23 51.2	2	237 46.9	17	12 56.0	15	112 29.5	51	9 18.4	3	312 45.2	62	16 21.2	1
26	274 22.2	175 36.0	−22	N23 49.2	− 3	238 03.8	+17	N13 10.5	+14	113 20.6	+51	N 9 15.1	− 3	313 46.9	+62	S16 22.2	− 1
27	275 21.4	175 14.5	21	23 46.5	3	238 20.7	17	13 24.8	14	114 11.8	51	9 11.7	3	314 48.5	62	16 23.1	1
28	276 20.5	174 53.2	21	23 43.1	4	238 37.6	17	13 39.0	14	115 02.8	51	9 08.3	3	315 50.3	62	16 24.1	1
29	277 19.6	174 31.9	21	23 39.0	5	238 54.5	17	13 53.0	14	115 53.6	51	9 04.9	4	316 52.3	62	16 25.1	1
30	278 18.8	174 10.7	−21	N23 34.2	− 5	239 11.4	+17	N14 07.0	+14	116 44.4	+51	N 9 01.4	− 4	317 54.2	+62	S16 26.2	− 1

1992 MAY, JUNE — SUN AND MOON

0^h UT	SUN GHA	v	Dec	d	MOON 0^h–8^h GHA	v	Dec	d	MOON 8^h–16^h GHA	v	Dec	d	MOON 16^h–24^h GHA	v	Dec	d	HP
May	(SD 15′.8)				MAY												
	° ′		° ′		° ′		° ′		° ′		° ′		° ′		° ′		′
1	180 43.6	+ 2	N15 05.3	+18	203 01	130	N12 09	+ 91	319 11	125	N13 40	+ 88	75 16	120	N15 08	+ 83	56.8
2	180 45.3	2	15 23.4	18	191 16	113	16 31	79	307 09	108	17 50	73	62 57	102	19 03	67	57.4
3	180 46.9	2	15 41.1	18	178 39	97	20 10	59	294 16	91	21 09	52	49 47	86	22 01	44	58.0
4	180 48.4	1	15 58.6	17	165 13	82	22 45	35	280 35	78	23 20	+ 25	35 53	75	23 45	+ 16	58.5
5	180 49.7	1	16 15.9	17	151 08	74	24 01	+ 5	266 22	72	24 06	− 4	21 34	72	24 02	− 15	58.9
6	180 50.9	+ 1	N16 32.8	+17	136 46	72	N23 47	− 26	251 58	75	N23 21	− 35	7 13	77	N22 46	− 45	59.1
7	180 51.9	1	16 49.5	16	122 30	80	22 01	54	237 50	84	21 07	62	353 14	88	20 05	71	59.3
8	180 52.9	1	17 05.9	16	108 42	92	18 54	79	224 14	97	17 35	85	339 51	101	16 10	91	59.3
9	180 53.6	1	17 22.0	16	95 32	105	14 39	97	211 17	109	13 02	101	327 06	112	11 21	105	59.3
10	180 54.2	+ 1	17 37.9	16	82 58	116	9 36	109	198 54	118	7 47	111	314 52	121	5 56	113	59.2
11	180 54.8	0	N17 53.4	+15	70 53	122	N 4 03	−114	186 55	123	N 2 09	−114	302 58	125	N 0 15	−115	59.0
12	180 55.1	0	18 08.7	15	59 03	124	S 1 40	113	175 07	124	S 3 33	112	291 11	123	S 5 25	110	58.7
13	180 55.3	0	18 23.6	15	47 14	122	7 15	107	163 16	120	9 02	103	279 16	119	10 45	100	58.3
14	180 55.5	0	18 38.2	14	35 15	116	12 25	95	151 11	114	14 00	90	267 05	112	15 30	84	57.9
15	180 55.4	0	18 52.5	14	22 57	109	16 54	77	138 46	107	18 11	71	254 33	105	19 22	64	57.4
16	180 55.1	0	N19 06.6	+14	10 18	102	S20 26	− 56	126 00	102	S21 22	− 48	241 42	100	S22 10	− 39	56.9
17	180 54.9	− 1	19 20.2	13	357 22	100	22 49	32	113 02	100	23 21	− 23	228 42	100	23 44	− 14	56.3
18	180 54.4	1	19 33.6	13	344 22	102	23 58	− 6	100 04	103	24 04	+ 3	215 47	106	24 01	+ 10	55.7
19	180 53.7	1	19 46.5	13	331 33	108	23 51	+ 19	87 21	112	23 32	26	203 13	116	23 06	33	55.2
20	180 53.0	1	19 59.2	12	319 09	120	22 33	40	75 09	123	21 53	47	191 12	128	21 06	53	54.8
21	180 52.1	− 1	N20 11.5	+12	307 20	132	S20 13	+ 58	63 32	136	S19 15	+ 64	179 48	139	S18 11	+ 68	54.5
22	180 51.1	1	20 23.5	12	296 07	144	17 03	73	52 31	147	15 50	77	168 58	150	14 33	80	54.3
23	180 49.9	1	20 35.2	11	285 28	153	13 13	84	42 01	155	11 49	87	158 36	157	10 22	89	54.2
24	180 48.6	1	20 46.5	11	275 13	159	8 53	92	31 52	159	7 21	94	148 31	161	5 47	95	54.4
25	180 47.2	2	20 57.4	11	265 12	160	S 4 12	97	21 52	160	S 2 35	98	138 32	159	S 0 57	99	54.7
26	180 45.6	− 2	N21 07.9	+10	255 11	157	N 0 42	+ 99	11 48	155	N 2 21	+ 99	128 23	153	N 4 00	+ 99	55.2
27	180 43.9	2	21 18.1	10	244 56	150	5 39	98	1 26	146	7 17	97	117 52	142	8 54	96	55.8
28	180 42.1	2	21 28.0	10	234 14	137	10 30	93	350 31	132	12 03	90	106 43	127	13 33	88	56.5
29	180 40.2	2	21 37.5	9	222 50	120	15 01	83	338 50	115	16 24	78	94 45	108	17 42	74	57.3
30	180 38.2	2	21 46.5	9	210 33	102	18 56	67	326 15	95	20 03	60	81 50	89	21 03	53	58.0
31	180 36.1	− 2	N21 55.2	+ 8	197 19	83	N21 56	+ 45	312 42	78	N22 41	+ 35	68 00	73	N23 16	+ 26	58.8
Jun	(SD 15′.8)				JUNE												
1	180 33.8	− 2	N22 03.6	+ 8	183 13	69	N23 42	+ 16	298 22	67	N23 58	+ 6	53 29	65	N24 04	− 5	59.3
2	180 31.4	2	22 11.5	8	168 34	64	23 59	− 16	283 38	65	23 43	− 27	38 43	67	23 16	37	59.8
3	180 29.0	3	22 19.0	7	153 50	69	22 39	47	268 59	73	21 52	57	24 12	76	20 55	66	60.0
4	180 26.5	3	22 26.2	7	139 28	81	19 49	75	254 49	86	18 34	82	10 15	91	17 12	88	60.0
5	180 23.9	3	22 33.0	6	125 46	96	15 44	95	241 22	101	14 09	100	357 03	106	12 29	105	59.8
6	180 21.2	− 3	N22 39.4	+ 6	112 49	109	N10 44	−107	228 38	114	N 8 57	−111	344 32	117	N 7 06	−113	59.5
7	180 18.4	3	22 45.3	6	100 29	119	N 5 13	114	216 28	122	N 3 19	114	332 30	124	N 1 25	114	59.1
8	180 15.5	3	22 50.9	5	88 34	125	S 0 29	114	204 39	125	S 2 23	112	320 44	126	S 4 15	110	58.7
9	180 12.7	3	22 56.1	5	76 50	125	6 05	108	192 55	125	7 53	104	309 00	123	9 37	101	58.2
10	180 09.7	3	23 00.9	4	65 03	122	11 18	96	181 05	120	12 54	92	297 05	118	14 26	87	57.6
11	180 06.7	− 3	N23 05.2	+ 4	53 03	116	S15 53	− 81	168 59	113	S17 14	− 74	284 52	111	S18 28	− 68	57.1
12	180 03.7	3	23 09.2	4	40 43	109	19 36	61	156 32	107	20 37	54	272 19	106	21 31	45	56.6
13	180 00.5	3	23 12.8	3	28 05	104	22 16	38	143 49	103	22 54	30	259 32	103	23 24	− 22	56.1
14	179 57.4	3	23 15.9	3	15 15	103	23 46	− 13	130 58	104	23 59	− 5	246 42	106	24 04	+ 4	55.7
15	179 54.3	3	23 18.7	2	2 28	107	24 00	+ 11	118 15	110	23 49	+ 19	234 05	113	23 30	27	55.2
16	179 51.1	− 3	N23 21.0	+ 2	349 58	116	S23 03	+ 34	105 54	120	S22 29	+ 40	221 54	124	S21 49	+ 48	54.8
17	179 47.9	3	23 22.9	2	337 58	127	21 01	53	94 05	132	20 08	59	210 17	136	19 09	64	54.5
18	179 44.6	3	23 24.4	1	326 33	139	18 05	69	82 52	143	16 56	73	199 15	147	15 43	78	54.3
19	179 41.5	3	23 25.5	+ 1	315 42	150	14 25	80	72 12	153	13 05	85	188 45	156	11 40	87	54.1
20	179 38.2	3	23 26.2	0	305 21	157	10 13	89	61 58	160	8 44	92	178 38	161	7 12	93	54.1
21	179 34.9	− 3	N23 26.4	0	295 19	161	S 5 39	+ 95	52 00	162	S 4 04	+ 96	168 42	162	S 2 28	+ 97	54.3
22	179 31.7	3	23 26.3	− 1	285 24	162	S 0 51	97	42 06	160	N 0 46	98	158 46	158	N 2 24	98	54.6
23	179 28.4	3	23 25.7	1	275 24	157	N 4 02	97	32 01	153	5 39	96	148 34	151	7 15	96	55.1
24	179 25.2	3	23 24.7	1	265 05	146	8 51	93	21 31	142	10 24	92	137 53	137	11 56	89	55.8
25	179 22.0	3	23 23.4	2	254 10	132	13 25	86	10 22	127	14 51	82	126 29	120	16 13	78	56.6
26	179 18.8	− 3	N23 21.6	− 2	242 29	113	N17 31	+ 73	358 22	107	N18 44	+ 67	114 09	100	N19 51	+ 61	57.4
27	179 15.7	3	23 19.3	3	229 49	93	20 52	54	345 22	87	21 46	46	100 49	81	22 32	37	58.3
28	179 12.5	3	23 16.7	3	216 10	75	23 09	+ 29	331 25	70	23 38	+ 18	86 35	67	23 56	+ 8	59.2
29	179 09.5	3	23 13.7	4	201 42	63	24 04	− 3	316 45	61	24 01	− 14	71 46	61	23 47	− 24	59.9
30	179 06.5	− 3	N23 10.2	− 4	186 47	61	N23 23	− 36	301 48	63	N22 47	− 46	56 51	65	N22 01	− 57	60.5

1992 JULY, AUGUST — ARIES AND PLANETS

0ʰ UT	ARIES GHA	VENUS GHA	v	VENUS Dec	d	MARS GHA	v	MARS Dec	d	JUPITER GHA	v	JUPITER Dec	d	SATURN GHA	v	SATURN Dec	d
Jul								JULY									
	° ′	° ′		° ′		° ′		° ′		° ′		° ′		° ′		° ′	
1	279 17.9	173 49.6	−21	N23 28.8	− 6	239 28.3	+17	N14 20.7	+14	117 35.1	+51	N 8 57.8	− 4	318 56.2	+62	S16 27.2	− 1
2	280 17.0	173 28.6	21	23 22.6	7	239 45.2	17	14 34.3	13	118 25.7	51	8 54.2	4	319 58.3	62	16 28.3	1
3	281 16.2	173 07.7	21	23 15.7	8	240 02.0	17	14 47.7	13	119 16.2	50	8 50.6	4	321 00.5	62	16 29.3	1
4	282 15.3	172 47.0	21	23 08.2	8	240 18.9	17	15 01.0	13	120 06.6	50	8 47.0	4	322 02.8	62	16 30.5	1
5	283 14.5	172 26.5	21	22 59.9	9	240 35.8	17	15 14.2	13	120 56.9	50	8 43.3	4	323 05.0	62	16 31.6	1
6	284 13.6	172 06.0	−20	N22 51.0	−10	240 52.6	+17	N15 27.1	+13	121 47.2	+50	N 8 39.5	− 4	324 07.4	+63	S16 32.8	− 1
7	285 12.7	171 45.8	20	22 41.4	10	241 09.4	17	15 40.0	13	122 37.3	50	8 35.8	4	325 09.9	63	16 33.9	1
8	286 11.9	171 25.8	20	22 31.2	11	241 26.3	17	15 52.6	13	123 27.4	50	8 32.0	4	326 12.4	63	16 35.1	1
9	287 11.0	171 06.0	20	22 20.3	12	241 43.1	17	16 05.1	12	124 17.4	50	8 28.1	4	327 15.0	63	16 36.3	1
10	288 10.1	170 46.5	19	22 08.7	12	241 59.9	17	16 17.4	12	125 07.3	50	8 24.3	4	328 17.6	63	16 37.5	1
11	289 09.3	170 27.1	−19	N21 56.5	−13	242 16.7	+17	N16 29.6	+12	125 57.1	+50	N 8 20.3	− 4	329 20.3	+63	S16 38.7	− 1
12	290 08.4	170 08.0	19	21 43.7	14	242 33.5	17	16 41.6	12	126 46.9	50	8 16.4	4	330 23.1	63	16 40.0	1
13	291 07.6	169 49.1	19	21 30.2	14	242 50.3	17	16 53.5	12	127 36.5	50	8 12.4	4	331 25.9	63	16 41.2	1
14	292 06.7	169 30.5	18	21 16.1	15	243 07.1	17	17 05.1	12	128 26.1	50	8 08.5	4	332 28.8	63	16 42.5	1
15	293 05.8	169 12.1	18	21 01.4	15	243 24.0	17	17 16.6	11	129 15.6	49	8 04.4	4	333 31.7	63	16 43.8	1
16	294 05.0	168 54.0	−18	N20 46.1	−16	243 40.8	+17	N17 28.0	+11	130 05.0	+49	N 8 00.3	− 4	334 34.7	+63	S16 45.1	− 1
17	295 04.1	168 36.2	18	20 30.2	17	243 57.6	17	17 39.1	11	130 54.4	49	7 56.2	4	335 37.7	63	16 46.4	1
18	296 03.2	168 18.6	17	20 13.7	17	244 14.4	17	17 50.2	11	131 43.7	49	7 52.1	4	336 40.8	63	16 47.8	1
19	297 02.4	168 01.3	17	19 56.7	18	244 31.2	17	18 01.0	11	132 32.9	49	7 47.9	4	337 44.0	63	16 49.1	1
20	298 01.6	167 44.3	17	19 39.0	18	244 48.0	17	18 11.7	10	133 22.1	49	7 43.7	4	338 47.1	63	16 50.4	1
21	299 00.7	167 27.5	−16	N19 20.9	−19	245 04.9	+17	N18 22.1	+10	134 11.2	+49	N 7 39.4	− 4	339 50.3	+63	S16 51.8	− 1
22	299 59.8	167 11.1	16	19 02.2	19	245 21.7	17	18 32.4	10	135 00.2	49	7 35.2	4	340 53.6	63	16 53.2	1
23	300 59.0	166 54.9	16	18 42.9	20	245 38.5	17	18 42.5	10	135 49.1	49	7 30.9	4	341 56.9	63	16 54.5	1
24	301 58.1	166 39.1	16	18 23.2	20	245 55.4	17	18 52.5	10	136 38.0	49	7 26.6	4	343 00.2	63	16 55.9	1
25	302 57.2	166 23.6	15	18 02.9	21	246 12.3	17	19 02.2	10	137 26.9	49	7 22.2	4	344 03.6	63	16 57.3	1
26	303 56.4	166 08.3	−15	N17 42.1	−21	246 29.2	+17	N19 11.8	+ 9	138 15.6	+49	N 7 17.8	− 4	345 07.0	+63	S16 58.7	− 1
27	304 55.5	165 53.3	15	17 20.9	22	246 46.1	17	19 21.2	9	139 04.3	49	7 13.4	4	346 10.4	63	17 00.1	1
28	305 54.7	165 38.6	14	16 59.1	22	247 03.1	17	19 30.4	9	139 53.0	49	7 09.0	4	347 13.9	63	17 01.5	1
29	306 53.8	165 24.2	14	16 36.9	23	247 20.0	17	19 39.5	9	140 41.6	49	7 04.6	5	348 17.3	64	17 02.9	1
30	307 52.9	165 10.2	14	16 14.2	23	247 37.1	17	19 48.3	9	141 30.1	49	7 00.1	5	349 20.8	64	17 04.3	1
31	308 52.1	164 56.4	−14	N15 51.1	−24	247 54.2	+17	N19 57.0	+ 9	142 18.6	+48	N 6 55.6	− 5	350 24.4	+64	S17 05.7	− 1
Aug								AUGUST									
1	309 51.2	164 42.8	−13	N15 27.6	−24	248 11.3	+17	N20 05.5	+ 8	143 07.0	+48	N 6 51.0	− 5	351 27.9	+64	S17 07.1	− 1
2	310 50.3	164 29.6	13	15 03.7	24	248 28.4	17	20 13.8	8	143 55.4	48	6 46.4	5	352 31.4	64	17 08.5	1
3	311 49.5	164 16.7	13	14 39.4	25	248 45.6	17	20 21.9	8	144 43.7	48	6 41.9	5	353 35.0	64	17 10.0	1
4	312 48.6	164 04.0	12	14 14.7	25	249 02.8	17	20 29.8	8	145 32.0	48	6 37.3	5	354 38.6	64	17 11.3	1
5	313 47.8	163 51.6	12	13 49.5	25	249 20.1	17	20 37.6	8	146 20.2	48	6 32.6	5	355 42.2	64	17 12.8	1
6	314 46.9	163 39.5	−12	N13 24.1	−26	249 37.4	+17	N20 45.2	+ 7	147 08.4	+48	N 6 28.0	− 5	356 45.8	+64	S17 14.2	− 1
7	315 46.0	163 27.7	12	12 58.2	26	249 54.8	17	20 52.6	7	147 56.6	48	6 23.3	5	357 49.4	64	17 15.6	1
8	316 45.2	163 16.1	11	12 32.1	27	250 12.2	18	20 59.8	7	148 44.6	48	6 18.7	5	358 53.0	64	17 17.0	1
9	317 44.3	163 04.8	11	12 05.5	27	250 29.8	18	21 06.8	7	149 32.7	48	6 13.9	5	359 56.6	64	17 18.4	1
10	318 43.4	162 53.7	11	11 38.7	27	250 47.3	18	21 13.6	7	150 20.7	48	6 09.2	5	1 00.2	64	17 19.8	1
11	319 42.6	162 42.9	−11	N11 11.5	−27	251 04.9	+18	N21 20.3	+ 7	151 08.7	+48	N 6 04.4	− 5	2 03.8	+64	S17 21.2	− 1
12	320 41.7	162 32.3	10	10 44.1	28	251 22.6	18	21 26.8	6	151 56.6	48	5 59.6	5	3 07.4	64	17 22.6	1
13	321 40.9	162 21.9	10	10 16.4	28	251 40.4	18	21 33.1	6	152 44.5	48	5 54.8	5	4 11.0	64	17 23.9	1
14	322 40.0	162 11.7	10	9 48.4	28	251 58.2	18	21 39.1	6	153 32.3	48	5 50.0	5	5 14.5	64	17 25.3	1
15	323 39.1	162 01.7	10	9 20.2	29	252 16.1	18	21 45.1	6	154 20.2	48	5 45.2	5	6 18.1	64	17 26.6	1
16	324 38.3	161 52.0	−10	N 8 51.7	−29	252 34.1	+18	N21 50.8	+ 6	155 07.9	+48	N 5 40.4	− 5	7 21.7	+64	S17 28.0	− 1
17	325 37.4	161 42.4	9	8 22.9	29	252 52.1	18	21 56.4	5	155 55.6	48	5 35.5	5	8 25.2	64	17 29.3	1
18	326 36.5	161 33.1	9	7 54.0	29	253 10.3	18	22 01.7	5	156 43.3	48	5 30.6	5	9 28.7	64	17 30.7	1
19	327 35.7	161 23.9	9	7 24.9	30	253 28.6	18	22 07.0	5	157 31.0	48	5 25.7	5	10 32.2	63	17 32.0	1
20	328 34.9	161 14.8	9	6 55.4	30	253 46.9	18	22 12.0	5	158 18.7	48	5 20.8	5	11 35.6	63	17 33.4	1
21	329 34.0	161 05.9	− 9	N 6 25.9	−30	254 05.3	+19	N22 16.9	+ 5	159 06.3	+48	N 5 15.9	− 5	12 39.1	+63	S17 34.6	− 1
22	330 33.1	160 57.2	9	5 56.2	30	254 23.8	19	22 21.6	5	159 53.9	48	5 11.0	5	13 42.5	63	17 35.9	1
23	331 32.3	160 48.6	9	5 26.3	30	254 42.5	19	22 26.1	4	160 41.4	48	5 06.0	5	14 45.8	63	17 37.2	1
24	332 31.4	160 40.1	8	4 56.3	30	255 01.3	19	22 30.4	4	161 28.9	48	5 01.0	5	15 49.2	63	17 38.5	1
25	333 30.5	160 31.7	8	4 26.1	30	255 20.1	19	22 34.5	4	162 16.4	48	4 56.0	5	16 52.5	63	17 39.7	1
26	334 29.7	160 23.5	− 8	N 3 55.8	−30	255 39.1	+19	N22 38.5	+ 4	163 03.9	+48	N 4 51.1	− 5	17 55.7	+63	S17 41.0	− 1
27	335 28.8	160 15.4	8	3 25.4	31	255 58.2	19	22 42.3	4	163 51.4	47	4 46.1	5	18 59.0	63	17 42.2	1
28	336 28.0	160 07.3	8	2 54.8	31	256 17.5	19	22 46.0	4	164 38.8	47	4 41.0	5	20 02.2	63	17 43.4	1
29	337 27.1	159 59.3	8	2 24.2	31	256 36.8	20	22 49.5	3	165 26.2	47	4 36.0	5	21 05.3	63	17 44.6	1
30	338 26.2	159 51.4	8	1 53.6	31	256 56.3	20	22 52.8	3	166 13.6	47	4 31.0	5	22 08.4	63	17 45.7	1
31	339 25.4	159 43.5	− 8	N 1 22.8	−31	257 16.0	+20	N22 55.9	+ 3	167 01.0	+47	N 4 25.9	− 5	23 11.4	+63	S17 46.9	− 1

1992 JULY, AUGUST — SUN AND MOON

0^h UT	SUN GHA	v	SUN Dec	d	MOON 0^h–8^h GHA	v	Dec	d	MOON 8^h–16^h GHA	v	Dec	d	MOON 16^h–24^h GHA	v	Dec	d	HP
Jul	(SD 15′.8)				JULY												
	° ′		° ′		° ′		° ′		° ′		° ′		° ′		° ′		′
1	179 03.5	− 3	N23 06.4	− 4	171 56	69	N21 04	− 66	287 05	72	N19 58	− 76	42 17	78	N18 42	− 83	60.8
2	179 00.6	3	23 02.1	5	157 35	82	17 19	91	272 57	87	15 48	98	28 24	92	14 10	103	60.8
3	178 57.8	3	22 57.5	5	143 56	96	12 27	108	259 32	102	10 39	111	15 14	105	8 48	115	60.5
4	178 55.1	3	22 52.5	6	130 59	110	6 53	116	246 49	112	N 4 57	117	2 41	116	N 3 00	117	60.0
5	178 52.4	3	22 47.0	6	118 37	117	N 1 03	117	234 34	120	S 0 54	116	350 34	120	S 2 50	114	59.4
6	178 49.9	− 3	N22 41.1	− 6	106 34	122	S 4 44	−111	222 36	121	S 6 35	−108	338 37	122	S 8 23	−105	58.7
7	178 47.3	2	22 34.9	7	94 39	121	10 08	100	210 40	120	11 48	96	326 40	118	13 24	90	58.0
8	178 45.0	2	22 28.3	7	82 38	118	14 54	85	198 36	115	16 19	79	314 31	114	17 38	72	57.3
9	178 42.7	2	22 21.3	8	70 25	112	18 50	65	186 17	110	19 55	58	302 07	109	20 53	51	56.6
10	178 40.6	2	22 13.8	8	57 56	108	21 44	43	173 44	107	22 27	36	289 31	106	23 03	27	56.1
11	178 38.5	− 2	N22 06.1	− 8	45 17	106	S23 30	− 19	161 03	107	S23 49	− 12	276 50	107	S24 01	− 3	55.5
12	178 36.5	2	21 57.9	9	32 37	109	24 04	+ 5	148 26	111	23 59	+ 13	264 17	113	23 46	+ 20	55.1
13	178 34.7	2	21 49.4	9	20 10	115	23 26	28	136 05	119	22 58	35	252 04	122	22 23	41	54.7
14	178 33.1	2	21 40.5	9	8 06	125	21 42	48	124 11	130	20 54	54	240 21	133	20 00	60	54.4
15	178 31.5	1	21 31.2	10	356 34	136	19 00	64	112 50	141	17 56	70	229 11	144	16 46	74	54.2
16	178 30.1	− 1	N21 21.6	−10	345 35	147	S15 32	+ 77	102 02	150	S14 15	+ 82	218 32	153	S12 53	+ 84	54.1
17	178 28.7	1	21 11.5	10	335 05	156	11 29	87	91 41	158	10 02	90	208 19	160	8 32	91	54.0
18	178 27.5	1	21 01.2	11	324 59	161	7 01	94	81 40	162	5 27	95	198 22	163	S 3 52	95	54.1
19	178 26.5	1	20 50.5	11	315 05	163	S 2 17	97	71 48	162	S 0 40	96	188 30	162	N 0 56	97	54.3
20	178 25.6	1	20 39.4	11	305 12	160	N 2 33	97	61 52	159	N 4 10	96	178 31	156	5 46	95	54.6
21	178 24.8	− 1	N20 28.0	−12	295 07	154	N 7 21	+ 93	51 41	150	N 8 54	+ 92	168 11	146	N10 26	+ 90	55.1
22	178 24.1	− 1	20 16.2	12	284 37	142	11 56	87	40 59	138	13 23	84	157 17	132	14 47	80	55.7
23	178 23.6	0	20 04.1	13	273 29	127	16 07	76	29 36	120	17 23	71	145 36	115	18 34	67	56.5
24	178 23.2	0	19 51.6	13	261 31	108	19 41	60	17 19	102	20 41	53	133 01	95	21 34	47	57.3
25	178 23.0	0	19 38.8	13	248 36	89	22 21	38	4 05	84	22 59	+ 29	119 29	78	23 28	+ 21	58.3
26	178 22.9	0	N19 25.8	−14	234 47	73	N23 49	+ 11	350 00	70	N24 00	0	105 10	66	N24 00	− 10	59.2
27	178 22.9	0	19 12.3	14	220 16	65	23 50	− 21	335 21	63	23 29	− 31	90 24	64	22 58	43	60.1
28	178 23.2	0	18 58.6	14	205 28	65	22 15	52	320 33	67	21 23	63	75 40	69	20 20	73	60.8
29	178 23.5	+ 1	18 44.5	14	190 49	73	19 07	82	306 02	76	17 45	89	61 18	81	16 16	97	61.2
30	178 24.0	1	18 30.1	15	176 39	84	14 39	103	292 03	89	12 56	109	47 32	93	11 07	113	61.3
31	178 24.6	+ 1	N18 15.5	−15	163 05	97	N 9 14	−117	278 42	100	N 7 17	−119	34 22	104	N 5 18	−120	61.1
Aug	(SD 15′.8)				AUGUST												
1	178 25.4	+ 1	N18 00.5	−15	150 06	106	N 3 18	−121	265 52	109	N 1 17	−121	21 41	110	S 0 44	−119	60.6
2	178 26.5	1	17 45.3	16	137 31	112	S 2 43	118	253 23	113	S 4 41	114	9 16	113	6 35	111	59.9
3	178 27.5	1	17 29.7	16	125 09	114	8 26	107	241 03	113	10 13	103	356 56	113	11 56	97	59.0
4	178 28.9	1	17 13.9	16	112 49	112	13 33	91	228 41	111	15 04	85	344 32	111	16 29	79	58.1
5	178 30.2	2	16 57.8	16	100 23	109	17 48	72	216 12	108	19 00	64	332 00	107	20 04	57	57.3
6	178 31.9	+ 2	N16 41.4	−17	87 47	107	S21 01	− 49	203 34	106	S21 50	− 42	319 20	105	S22 32	− 33	56.5
7	178 33.6	2	16 24.7	17	75 05	106	23 05	25	190 51	107	23 30	− 17	306 38	107	23 47	− 9	55.8
8	178 35.4	2	16 07.9	17	62 25	109	23 56	− 2	178 14	110	23 58	+ 7	294 04	113	23 51	+ 15	55.2
9	178 37.5	2	15 50.7	17	49 57	115	23 36	+ 22	165 52	118	23 14	29	281 50	121	22 45	36	54.8
10	178 39.7	2	15 33.3	18	37 51	125	22 09	42	153 56	128	21 27	49	270 04	131	20 38	54	54.4
11	178 42.1	+ 2	N15 15.6	−18	26 15	135	S19 44	+ 60	142 30	139	S18 44	+ 65	258 49	141	S17 39	+ 70	54.2
12	178 44.5	3	14 57.7	18	15 10	146	16 29	74	131 36	148	15 15	78	248 04	151	13 57	81	54.0
13	178 47.2	3	14 39.5	18	4 35	154	12 36	85	121 09	156	11 11	87	237 45	157	9 44	90	54.0
14	178 49.9	3	14 21.1	19	354 22	160	8 14	91	111 02	161	6 43	94	227 43	162	5 09	94	54.0
15	178 52.8	3	14 02.5	19	344 25	162	S 3 35	96	101 07	162	S 1 59	96	217 49	162	S 0 23	97	54.1
16	178 55.8	+ 3	N13 43.6	−19	334 31	161	N 1 14	+ 96	91 12	160	N 2 50	+ 96	207 52	159	N 4 26	+ 95	54.3
17	178 59.0	3	13 24.6	19	324 31	156	6 01	94	81 07	154	7 35	92	197 41	151	9 07	90	54.7
18	179 02.2	3	13 05.4	20	314 12	148	10 37	88	70 40	144	12 05	85	187 04	139	13 30	82	55.1
19	179 05.6	4	12 45.9	20	303 23	135	14 52	78	59 38	131	16 10	74	175 49	125	17 24	69	55.7
20	179 09.1	4	12 26.2	20	291 54	120	18 33	64	47 54	114	19 37	58	163 48	109	20 35	51	56.4
21	179 12.8	+ 4	N12 06.3	−20	279 37	103	N21 26	+ 45	35 20	98	N22 11	+ 37	150 58	93	N22 48	+ 29	57.2
22	179 16.5	4	11 46.2	20	266 31	87	23 17	+ 21	21 58	84	23 38	+ 11	137 22	80	23 49	+ 2	58.1
23	179 20.3	4	11 25.9	20	252 42	77	23 51	− 8	7 59	74	23 43	− 18	123 13	73	23 25	− 28	59.0
24	179 24.3	4	11 05.5	21	238 26	73	22 57	38	353 39	72	22 19	49	108 51	74	21 30	58	59.8
25	179 28.4	4	10 44.9	21	224 05	75	20 32	67	339 20	77	19 25	77	94 37	79	18 08	85	60.6
26	179 32.5	+ 4	N10 24.1	−21	209 56	82	N16 43	− 93	325 18	85	N15 10	− 99	80 43	88	N13 31	−106	61.1
27	179 36.8	4	10 03.1	21	196 11	91	11 45	111	311 42	94	9 54	115	67 16	96	7 59	118	61.3
28	179 41.1	4	9 42.0	21	182 52	99	N 6 01	121	298 31	100	N 4 00	121	54 11	103	N 1 59	123	61.3
29	179 45.5	5	9 20.8	22	169 54	103	S 0 04	121	285 37	105	S 2 05	120	41 22	105	S 4 05	118	60.9
30	179 50.0	5	8 59.3	22	157 07	105	6 03	114	272 52	105	7 57	111	28 37	105	9 48	105	60.2
31	179 54.7	+ 5	N 8 37.7	−22	144 22	104	S11 33	−101	260 06	104	S13 14	− 94	15 50	102	S14 48	− 88	59.3

1992 SEPTEMBER, OCTOBER — ARIES AND PLANETS

0h UT	ARIES GHA	VENUS GHA	v	VENUS Dec	d	MARS GHA	v	MARS Dec	d	JUPITER GHA	v	JUPITER Dec	d	SATURN GHA	v	SATURN Dec	d
Sep								**SEPTEMBER**									
	° ′	° ′		° ′		° ′		° ′		° ′		° ′		° ′		° ′	
1	340 24.5	159 35.7	−8	N 0 52.0	−31	257 35.8	+20	N22 58.9	+3	167 48.3	+47	N 4 20.9	−5	24 14.4	+63	S17 48.0	−1
2	341 23.6	159 27.9	8	N 0 21.1	31	257 55.8	20	23 01.7	3	168 35.6	47	4 15.8	5	25 17.3	63	17 49.1	1
3	342 22.8	159 20.2	8	S 0 09.7	31	258 15.9	20	23 04.5	3	169 22.9	47	4 10.7	5	26 20.2	63	17 50.2	1
4	343 21.9	159 12.4	8	0 40.7	31	258 36.2	20	23 07.0	2	170 10.3	47	4 05.6	5	27 23.1	63	17 51.3	1
5	344 21.1	159 04.7	8	1 11.6	31	258 56.6	21	23 09.3	2	170 57.5	47	4 00.6	5	28 25.9	63	17 52.4	1
6	345 20.2	158 56.9	−8	S 1 42.5	−31	259 17.2	+21	N23 11.5	+2	171 44.8	+47	N 3 55.5	−5	29 28.6	+63	S17 53.4	−1
7	346 19.3	158 49.2	8	2 13.4	31	259 38.0	21	23 13.6	2	172 32.0	47	3 50.4	5	30 31.2	63	17 54.4	1
8	347 18.5	158 41.4	8	2 44.2	31	259 58.9	21	23 15.5	2	173 19.3	47	3 45.3	5	31 33.8	63	17 55.4	1
9	348 17.6	158 33.6	8	3 15.1	31	260 20.0	21	23 17.3	2	174 06.5	47	3 40.1	5	32 36.3	63	17 56.4	1
10	349 16.7	158 25.7	8	3 45.8	31	260 41.3	22	23 18.9	1	174 53.8	47	3 35.0	5	33 38.8	62	17 57.4	1
11	350 15.9	158 17.8	−8	S 4 16.6	−31	261 02.8	+22	N23 20.3	+1	175 41.0	+47	N 3 29.9	−5	34 41.2	+62	S17 58.3	−1
12	351 15.1	158 09.8	8	4 47.2	31	261 24.5	22	23 21.7	1	176 28.2	47	3 24.8	5	35 43.4	62	17 59.2	1
13	352 14.2	158 01.8	8	5 17.8	30	261 46.4	22	23 22.9	1	177 15.4	47	3 19.7	5	36 45.7	62	18 00.1	1
14	353 13.3	157 53.6	8	5 48.2	30	262 08.4	22	23 24.0	1	178 02.6	47	3 14.6	5	37 47.9	62	18 01.0	1
15	354 12.4	157 45.4	8	6 18.5	30	262 30.7	22	23 25.0	1	178 49.8	47	3 09.4	5	38 50.0	62	18 01.8	1
16	355 11.6	157 37.0	−8	S 6 48.7	−30	262 53.1	+23	N23 25.7	+1	179 37.0	+47	N 3 04.3	−5	39 52.0	+62	S18 02.6	−1
17	356 10.7	157 28.6	9	7 18.8	30	263 15.8	23	23 26.5	1	180 24.2	47	2 59.2	5	40 53.9	62	18 03.4	1
18	357 09.8	157 19.9	9	7 48.7	30	263 38.7	23	23 27.0	+1	181 11.4	47	2 54.1	5	41 55.7	62	18 04.1	1
19	358 09.0	157 11.2	9	8 18.5	30	264 01.9	23	23 27.5	0	181 58.6	47	2 48.9	5	42 57.5	62	18 04.9	1
20	359 08.2	157 02.3	9	8 48.1	29	264 25.2	24	23 27.8	0	182 45.8	47	2 43.8	5	43 59.2	62	18 05.6	1
21	0 07.3	156 53.2	−9	S 9 17.5	−29	264 48.8	+24	N23 28.0	0	183 33.0	+47	N 2 38.6	−5	45 00.8	+62	S18 06.3	−1
22	1 06.4	156 44.0	9	9 46.8	29	265 12.6	24	23 28.1	0	184 20.2	47	2 33.5	5	46 02.3	62	18 07.0	1
23	2 05.6	156 34.6	10	10 15.7	29	265 36.7	24	23 28.1	0	185 07.4	47	2 28.4	5	47 03.8	61	18 07.6	1
24	3 04.7	156 24.9	10	10 44.5	29	266 01.1	25	23 28.0	0	185 54.6	47	2 23.3	5	48 05.1	61	18 08.2	1
25	4 03.8	156 15.1	10	11 13.0	28	266 25.7	25	23 27.8	0	186 41.8	47	2 18.2	5	49 06.4	61	18 08.8	1
26	5 03.0	156 05.1	−10	S11 41.4	−28	266 50.5	+25	N23 27.5	0	187 29.0	+47	N 2 13.1	−5	50 07.6	+61	S18 09.3	−1
27	6 02.1	155 54.9	11	12 09.4	28	267 15.6	25	23 27.1	−1	188 16.3	47	2 08.0	5	51 08.6	61	18 09.8	1
28	7 01.3	155 44.4	11	12 37.2	27	267 41.0	26	23 26.6	1	189 03.5	47	2 02.9	5	52 09.6	61	18 10.3	1
29	8 00.4	155 33.7	11	13 04.6	27	268 06.7	26	23 26.0	1	189 50.8	47	1 57.8	5	53 10.5	61	18 10.8	−1
30	8 59.5	155 22.8	−11	S13 31.8	−27	268 32.7	+26	N23 25.4	−1	190 38.0	+47	N 1 52.7	−5	54 11.3	+61	S18 11.3	0
Oct								**OCTOBER**									
1	9 58.7	155 11.6	−11	S13 58.6	−27	268 59.0	+27	N23 24.7	−1	191 25.3	+47	N 1 47.6	−5	55 11.9	+61	S18 11.7	0
2	10 57.8	155 00.2	12	14 25.2	26	269 25.5	27	23 23.8	1	192 12.6	47	1 42.5	5	56 12.6	61	18 12.1	0
3	11 56.9	154 48.5	12	14 51.4	26	269 52.4	27	23 23.0	1	192 59.9	47	1 37.5	5	57 13.1	60	18 12.4	0
4	12 56.1	154 36.6	12	15 17.3	25	270 19.6	28	23 22.0	1	193 47.3	47	1 32.4	5	58 13.5	60	18 12.8	0
5	13 55.2	154 24.4	13	15 42.7	25	270 47.1	28	23 21.0	1	194 34.6	47	1 27.4	5	59 13.8	60	18 13.1	0
6	14 54.4	154 11.9	−13	S16 07.9	−25	271 14.9	+28	N23 19.9	−1	195 22.0	+47	N 1 22.3	−5	60 14.0	+60	S18 13.3	0
7	15 53.5	153 59.2	13	16 32.6	24	271 43.1	29	23 18.8	1	196 09.4	47	1 17.3	5	61 14.1	60	18 13.6	0
8	16 52.6	153 46.2	13	16 57.0	24	272 11.6	29	23 17.6	1	196 56.8	47	1 12.3	5	62 14.2	60	18 13.8	0
9	17 51.8	153 32.8	14	17 20.8	24	272 40.4	29	23 16.4	1	197 44.2	47	1 07.3	5	63 14.0	60	18 14.0	0
10	18 50.9	153 19.3	14	17 44.4	23	273 09.5	29	23 15.1	1	198 31.6	48	1 02.3	5	64 13.9	60	18 14.2	0
11	19 50.0	153 05.4	−14	S18 07.4	−23	273 38.9	+30	N23 13.8	−1	199 19.1	+48	N 0 57.3	−5	65 13.6	+60	S18 14.3	0
12	20 49.2	152 51.3	15	18 30.0	22	274 08.8	30	23 12.5	1	200 06.6	48	0 52.4	5	66 13.2	60	18 14.4	0
13	21 48.4	152 36.8	15	18 52.1	22	274 39.0	31	23 11.1	1	200 54.2	48	0 47.4	5	67 12.7	60	18 14.5	0
14	22 47.5	152 22.0	15	19 13.8	21	275 09.6	31	23 09.7	1	201 41.7	48	0 42.5	5	68 12.2	59	18 14.5	0
15	23 46.6	152 07.0	15	19 35.0	21	275 40.5	31	23 08.3	1	202 29.3	48	0 37.6	5	69 11.5	59	18 14.6	0
16	24 45.8	151 51.6	−16	S19 55.6	−20	276 11.9	+32	N23 06.8	−1	203 16.9	+48	N 0 32.6	−5	70 10.7	+59	S18 14.5	0
17	25 44.9	151 36.0	16	20 15.8	20	276 43.5	32	23 05.4	1	204 04.6	48	0 27.7	5	71 09.8	59	18 14.5	0
18	26 44.0	151 20.1	16	20 35.4	19	277 15.6	33	23 03.9	1	204 52.3	48	0 22.9	5	72 08.8	59	18 14.5	0
19	27 43.1	151 03.9	17	20 54.5	19	277 48.2	33	23 02.5	1	205 40.0	48	0 18.0	5	73 07.7	59	18 14.3	0
20	28 42.3	150 47.4	17	21 13.0	18	278 21.2	33	23 01.0	1	206 27.7	48	0 13.2	5	74 06.5	59	18 14.2	0
21	29 41.5	150 30.5	−17	S21 30.9	−17	278 54.5	+34	N22 59.5	−1	207 15.5	+48	N 0 08.3	−5	75 05.2	+59	S18 14.1	0
22	30 40.6	150 13.5	17	21 48.3	17	279 28.3	34	22 58.1	1	208 03.3	48	N 0 03.5	5	76 03.8	59	18 13.9	0
23	31 39.7	149 56.1	18	22 05.1	16	280 02.6	35	22 56.7	1	208 51.2	48	S 0 01.2	5	77 02.3	58	18 13.7	0
24	32 38.9	149 38.4	18	22 21.4	16	280 37.3	35	22 55.3	1	209 39.1	48	0 06.0	5	78 00.7	58	18 13.4	0
25	33 38.0	149 20.5	18	22 37.0	15	281 12.5	36	22 53.9	1	210 27.0	48	0 10.7	5	78 58.9	58	18 13.2	0
26	34 37.1	149 02.4	−19	S22 52.0	−14	281 48.1	+36	N22 52.6	−1	211 15.0	+48	S 0 15.4	−5	79 57.1	+58	S18 12.9	0
27	35 36.3	148 43.9	19	23 06.3	14	282 24.2	37	22 51.3	1	212 03.0	48	0 20.1	5	80 55.2	58	18 12.5	0
28	36 35.4	148 25.3	19	23 20.1	13	283 00.9	37	22 50.0	1	212 51.1	48	0 24.8	5	81 53.2	58	18 12.2	0
29	37 34.6	148 06.4	19	23 33.2	12	283 37.9	38	22 48.8	1	213 39.2	48	0 29.4	5	82 51.0	58	18 11.8	0
30	38 33.7	147 47.2	19	23 45.6	12	284 15.6	38	22 47.7	1	214 27.4	48	0 34.0	5	83 48.8	58	18 11.4	0
31	39 32.8	147 27.9	−20	S23 57.4	−11	284 53.8	+39	N22 46.6	−1	215 15.6	+48	S 0 38.6	−5	84 46.4	+58	S18 11.0	+1

1992 SEPTEMBER, OCTOBER — SUN AND MOON

0^h UT	SUN GHA	v	Dec	d	MOON 0^h–8^h GHA	v	Dec	d	MOON 8^h–16^h GHA	v	Dec	d	MOON 16^h–24^h GHA	v	Dec	d	HP
Sep	(SD 15′.9)				**SEPTEMBER**												
	° ′		° ′		° ′		° ′		° ′		° ′		° ′		° ′		′
1	179 59.3	+ 5	N 8 16.1	−22	131 32	102	S16 16	− 81	247 14	101	S17 37	− 73	2 55	101	S18 50	− 66	58.4
2	180 04.1	5	7 54.2	22	118 36	99	19 56	57	234 15	100	20 53	50	349 55	100	21 43	41	57.4
3	180 09.0	5	7 32.3	22	105 35	101	22 24	33	221 16	101	22 57	− 24	336 57	102	23 21	− 16	56.5
4	180 13.9	5	7 10.2	22	92 39	105	23 37	− 8	208 24	106	23 45	+ 1	324 10	109	23 44	+ 8	55.8
5	180 18.8	5	6 48.0	22	79 59	111	23 36	+ 16	195 50	115	23 20	23	311 45	118	22 57	31	55.1
6	180 23.9	+ 5	N 6 25.7	−22	67 43	122	S22 26	+ 37	183 45	125	S21 49	+ 43	299 50	129	S21 06	+ 50	54.6
7	180 29.0	5	6 03.3	23	55 59	133	20 16	55	172 12	136	19 21	61	288 28	140	18 20	65	54.3
8	180 34.1	5	5 40.8	23	44 48	143	17 15	70	161 11	146	16 05	74	277 37	150	14 51	78	54.1
9	180 39.3	5	5 18.2	23	34 07	151	13 33	81	150 38	154	12 12	84	267 12	157	10 48	87	54.0
10	180 44.5	5	4 55.5	23	23 49	158	9 21	90	140 27	159	7 51	91	257 06	160	6 20	93	54.0
11	180 49.8	+ 5	N 4 32.7	−23	13 46	161	S 4 47	+ 94	130 27	161	S 3 13	+ 96	247 08	161	S 1 37	+ 96	54.1
12	180 55.1	5	4 09.9	23	3 49	160	S 0 01	96	120 29	160	N 1 35	96	237 09	158	N 3 11	95	54.3
13	181 00.4	5	3 47.0	23	353 47	156	N 4 46	94	110 23	154	6 20	94	226 57	152	7 54	91	54.6
14	181 05.8	5	3 23.9	23	343 29	149	9 25	89	99 58	145	10 54	87	216 23	142	12 21	84	55.0
15	181 11.1	5	3 00.9	23	332 45	138	13 45	80	89 03	134	15 05	76	205 17	130	16 21	72	55.4
16	181 16.4	+ 5	N 2 37.8	−23	321 27	124	N17 33	+ 67	77 31	120	N18 40	+ 61	193 31	116	N19 41	+ 55	55.9
17	181 21.8	5	2 14.6	23	309 27	111	20 36	49	65 18	106	21 25	42	181 04	101	22 07	34	56.5
18	181 27.2	5	1 51.4	23	296 45	98	22 41	+ 26	52 23	94	23 07	+ 18	167 57	90	23 25	+ 10	57.2
19	181 32.5	5	1 28.1	23	283 27	88	23 35	0	38 55	85	23 35	− 9	154 20	84	23 26	− 18	57.9
20	181 37.9	5	1 04.9	23	269 44	84	23 08	− 27	25 08	83	22 41	37	140 31	83	22 04	46	58.6
21	181 43.1	+ 5	N 0 41.6	−23	255 54	84	N21 18	− 56	11 18	85	N20 22	− 64	126 43	87	N19 18	− 72	59.4
22	181 48.4	5	N 0 18.2	23	242 10	89	18 06	80	357 39	91	16 46	88	113 10	93	15 18	94	60.0
23	181 53.7	5	S 0 05.2	23	228 43	95	13 44	101	344 18	97	12 03	106	99 55	99	10 17	110	60.6
24	181 58.9	5	0 28.5	23	215 34	101	8 27	114	331 15	102	6 33	117	86 57	103	N 4 36	119	60.9
25	182 04.1	5	0 51.9	23	202 40	104	N 2 37	120	318 24	104	N 0 37	120	74 08	104	S 1 23	119	60.9
26	182 09.2	+ 5	S 1 15.3	−23	189 52	104	S 3 22	−118	305 36	103	S 5 20	−115	61 19	102	S 7 15	−112	60.6
27	182 14.3	5	1 38.6	23	177 01	101	9 07	107	292 42	99	10 54	103	48 21	98	12 37	97	60.1
28	182 19.3	5	2 02.0	23	163 59	97	14 14	90	279 36	95	15 44	84	35 11	94	17 08	76	59.4
29	182 24.3	5	2 25.4	23	150 45	93	18 24	68	266 18	93	19 32	60	21 51	92	20 32	52	58.5
30	182 29.2	+ 5	2 48.7	−23	137 23	92	21 24	− 42	252 55	93	22 06	− 34	8 28	94	22 40	− 25	57.6
Oct	(SD 16′.1)				**OCTOBER**												
1	182 34.1	+ 5	S 3 12.0	−23	124 02	96	S23 05	− 16	239 38	98	S23 21	− 8	355 16	100	S23 29	+ 1	56.7
2	182 38.9	5	3 35.3	23	110 56	104	23 28	+ 9	226 40	107	23 19	+ 16	342 27	111	23 03	25	55.9
3	182 43.6	5	3 58.5	23	98 18	115	22 38	31	214 13	119	22 07	38	330 12	123	21 29	45	55.2
4	182 48.2	5	4 21.7	23	86 15	128	20 44	50	202 23	131	19 54	56	318 34	136	18 58	61	54.7
5	182 52.8	4	4 44.8	23	74 50	140	17 57	66	191 10	143	16 51	70	307 33	146	15 41	74	54.3
6	182 57.2	+ 4	S 5 07.9	−23	63 59	150	S14 27	+ 78	180 29	152	S13 09	+ 81	297 01	154	S11 48	+ 84	54.1
7	183 01.6	4	5 30.8	23	53 35	157	10 24	86	170 12	158	8 58	89	286 50	159	7 29	91	54.1
8	183 05.9	4	5 53.8	23	43 29	160	5 58	93	160 09	161	S 4 25	93	276 50	160	S 2 52	95	54.2
9	183 10.1	4	6 16.6	23	33 30	160	S 1 17	95	150 10	159	N 0 18	96	266 49	158	N 1 54	95	54.4
10	183 14.2	4	6 39.4	23	23 27	156	N 3 29	95	140 03	154	5 04	94	256 37	152	6 38	93	54.7
11	183 18.1	+ 4	S 7 02.0	−23	13 09	148	N 8 11	+ 90	129 37	146	N 9 41	+ 89	246 03	142	N11 10	+ 86	55.1
12	183 21.9	4	7 24.5	23	2 25	138	12 36	83	118 43	134	13 59	79	234 57	130	15 18	75	55.5
13	183 25.6	4	7 47.0	22	351 07	125	16 33	71	107 12	120	17 44	65	223 12	116	18 49	59	56.0
14	183 29.2	4	8 09.4	22	339 08	112	19 48	53	95 00	107	20 41	47	210 47	103	21 28	39	56.5
15	183 32.7	3	8 31.7	22	326 30	99	22 07	31	82 09	96	22 38	+ 23	197 45	93	23 01	+ 15	57.0
16	183 35.9	+ 3	S 8 53.8	−22	313 18	91	N23 16	+ 6	68 49	89	N23 22	− 3	184 18	88	N23 19	− 12	57.5
17	183 39.0	3	9 15.8	22	299 46	87	23 07	− 21	55 13	88	22 46	30	170 41	88	22 16	39	58.0
18	183 42.0	3	9 37.7	22	286 09	90	21 37	47	41 39	91	20 50	56	157 10	94	19 54	64	58.5
19	183 44.8	3	9 59.5	22	272 44	95	18 50	72	28 19	98	17 38	78	143 57	100	16 20	86	59.0
20	183 47.5	3	10 21.1	21	259 37	103	14 54	91	15 20	105	13 23	97	131 05	106	11 46	101	59.5
21	183 50.1	+ 2	S10 42.5	−21	246 51	109	N10 05	−106	2 40	109	N 8 19	−110	118 29	111	N 6 29	−112	59.8
22	183 52.4	2	11 03.8	21	234 20	112	N 4 37	114	350 12	111	N 2 43	115	106 03	111	N 0 48	116	60.1
23	183 54.6	2	11 24.9	21	221 54	111	S 1 08	115	337 45	110	S 3 03	115	93 35	108	S 4 58	112	60.1
24	183 56.5	2	11 45.9	21	209 23	107	6 50	110	325 10	104	8 40	106	80 54	103	10 26	102	59.9
25	183 58.3	2	12 06.6	21	196 37	100	12 08	97	312 17	97	13 45	91	67 54	96	15 16	85	59.5
26	183 59.9	+ 1	S12 27.2	−20	183 30	93	S16 41	− 77	299 03	91	S17 58	− 70	54 34	90	S19 08	− 62	59.0
27	184 01.3	1	12 47.6	20	170 04	88	20 10	53	285 32	88	21 03	45	41 00	88	21 48	36	58.2
28	184 02.6	1	13 07.8	20	156 28	89	22 24	− 26	271 57	90	22 50	− 18	27 27	92	23 08	− 9	57.4
29	184 03.7	1	13 27.8	20	142 59	95	23 17	0	258 34	97	23 17	+ 9	14 11	102	23 08	+ 16	56.6
30	184 04.5	1	13 47.5	20	129 53	105	22 52	+ 25	245 38	110	22 27	31	1 28	114	21 56	39	55.9
31	184 05.2	+ 1	S14 07.1	−19	117 22	119	S21 17	+ 45	233 21	124	S20 32	+ 51	349 25	128	S19 41	+ 57	55.2

1992 NOVEMBER, DECEMBER — ARIES AND PLANETS

0ʰ UT	ARIES GHA	VENUS GHA	v	Dec	d	MARS GHA	v	Dec	d	JUPITER GHA	v	Dec	d	SATURN GHA	v	Dec	d
Nov	° ′	° ′		° ′		° ′		° ′		° ′		° ′		° ′		° ′	
						NOVEMBER											
1	40 32.0	147 08.4	−20	S24 08.5	−10	285 32.4	+39	N22 45.5	− 1	216 03.9	+48	S 0 43.2	− 5	85 44.0	+58	S18 10.5	+ 1
2	41 31.1	146 48.7	20	24 18.9	10	286 11.7	40	22 44.6	1	216 52.2	48	0 47.8	5	86 41.5	57	18 10.0	1
3	42 30.2	146 28.9	20	24 28.7	9	286 51.4	40	22 43.7	1	217 40.6	48	0 52.3	5	87 38.8	57	18 09.5	1
4	43 29.4	146 08.8	20	24 37.7	8	287 31.8	41	22 42.9	1	218 29.0	49	0 56.8	4	88 36.1	57	18 08.9	1
5	44 28.6	145 48.7	20	24 46.0	8	288 12.6	42	22 42.2	1	219 17.5	49	1 01.2	4	89 33.3	57	18 08.3	1
6	45 27.7	145 28.4	−20	S24 53.6	− 7	288 54.1	+42	N22 41.5	− 1	220 06.1	+49	S 1 05.6	− 4	90 30.4	+57	S18 07.7	+ 1
7	46 26.8	145 08.0	20	25 00.6	6	289 36.1	43	22 41.0	0	220 54.7	49	1 10.0	4	91 27.3	57	18 07.1	1
8	47 25.9	144 47.6	21	25 06.8	5	290 18.7	43	22 40.6	0	221 43.3	49	1 14.4	4	92 24.2	57	18 06.4	1
9	48 25.1	144 27.0	21	25 12.2	5	291 02.0	44	22 40.2	0	222 32.0	49	1 18.7	4	93 20.9	57	18 05.7	1
10	49 24.2	144 06.4	21	25 17.0	4	291 45.9	45	22 40.0	0	223 20.9	49	1 23.0	4	94 17.6	57	18 05.0	1
11	50 23.3	143 45.7	−21	S25 21.0	− 3	292 30.4	+45	N22 39.9	0	224 09.7	+49	S 1 27.3	− 4	95 14.2	+57	S18 04.3	+ 1
12	51 22.5	143 25.0	21	25 24.3	3	293 15.5	46	22 39.9	0	224 58.6	49	1 31.6	4	96 10.7	56	18 03.5	1
13	52 21.7	143 04.3	21	25 26.8	2	294 01.3	47	22 40.0	0	225 47.6	49	1 35.8	4	97 07.1	56	18 02.7	1
14	53 20.8	142 43.6	21	25 28.6	− 1	294 47.8	47	22 40.3	0	226 36.7	49	1 40.0	4	98 03.4	56	18 01.9	1
15	54 19.9	142 22.9	21	25 29.7	0	295 34.9	48	22 40.7	+ 1	227 25.8	49	1 44.1	4	98 59.6	56	18 01.0	1
16	55 19.1	142 02.2	−21	S25 30.0	0	296 22.8	+49	N22 41.2	+ 1	228 15.0	+49	S 1 48.2	− 4	99 55.7	+56	S18 00.1	+ 1
17	56 18.2	141 41.6	21	25 29.6	+ 1	297 11.3	49	22 41.9	1	229 04.3	49	1 52.3	4	100 51.7	56	17 59.2	1
18	57 17.3	141 21.1	20	25 28.5	2	298 00.6	50	22 42.7	1	229 53.6	50	1 56.3	4	101 47.6	56	17 58.3	1
19	58 16.5	141 00.7	20	25 26.6	3	298 50.6	51	22 43.7	1	230 43.1	50	2 00.3	4	102 43.4	56	17 57.3	1
20	59 15.6	140 40.3	20	25 24.0	3	299 41.4	52	22 44.8	1	231 32.6	50	2 04.3	4	103 39.2	56	17 56.3	1
21	60 14.8	140 20.1	−20	S25 20.6	+ 4	300 33.0	+52	N22 46.1	+ 2	232 22.2	+50	S 2 08.2	− 4	104 34.9	+56	S17 55.3	+ 1
22	61 13.9	140 00.0	20	25 16.5	5	301 25.3	53	22 47.6	2	233 11.9	50	2 12.1	4	105 30.4	56	17 54.3	1
23	62 13.0	139 40.1	20	25 11.7	6	302 18.4	54	22 49.2	2	234 01.6	50	2 15.9	4	106 25.9	55	17 53.2	1
24	63 12.2	139 20.4	20	25 06.2	6	303 12.3	55	22 51.1	2	234 51.4	50	2 19.7	4	107 21.3	55	17 52.1	1
25	64 11.3	139 00.9	19	24 59.9	7	304 07.0	56	22 53.0	2	235 41.3	50	2 23.5	4	108 16.6	55	17 51.0	1
26	65 10.4	138 41.6	−19	S24 53.0	+ 8	305 02.6	+56	N22 55.1	+ 2	236 31.4	+50	S 2 27.1	− 4	109 11.8	+55	S17 49.9	+ 1
27	66 09.6	138 22.5	19	24 45.3	8	305 59.0	57	22 57.5	3	237 21.5	50	2 30.8	4	110 07.0	55	17 48.7	1
28	67 08.7	138 03.8	19	24 36.9	9	306 56.3	58	23 00.0	3	238 11.6	50	2 34.4	4	111 02.0	55	17 47.5	1
29	68 07.9	137 45.2	18	24 27.9	10	307 54.4	59	23 02.6	3	239 02.0	50	2 38.0	4	111 57.0	55	17 46.3	1
30	69 07.0	137 26.9	−18	S24 18.1	+10	308 53.3	+60	N23 05.5	+ 3	239 52.3	+51	S 2 41.6	− 4	112 51.9	+55	S17 45.1	+ 1
Dec						**DECEMBER**											
1	70 06.1	137 09.0	−18	S24 07.7	+11	309 53.2	+61	N23 08.5	+ 3	240 42.8	+51	S 2 45.1	− 3	113 46.7	+55	S17 43.8	+ 1
2	71 05.3	136 51.3	17	23 56.6	12	310 53.9	62	23 11.8	3	241 33.4	51	2 48.5	3	114 41.5	55	17 42.5	1
3	72 04.4	136 33.9	17	23 44.8	12	311 55.5	63	23 15.1	4	242 24.1	51	2 51.9	3	115 36.1	55	17 41.2	1
4	73 03.5	136 17.0	17	23 32.4	13	312 58.0	63	23 18.6	4	243 14.8	51	2 55.3	3	116 30.7	55	17 39.9	1
5	74 02.7	136 00.3	16	23 19.3	14	314 01.4	64	23 22.4	4	244 05.7	51	2 58.6	3	117 25.2	54	17 38.6	1
6	75 01.9	135 44.0	−16	S23 05.6	+14	315 05.8	+65	N23 26.3	+ 4	244 56.7	+51	S 3 01.8	− 3	118 19.6	+54	S17 37.2	+ 1
7	76 01.0	135 28.1	16	22 51.3	15	316 11.0	66	23 30.4	4	245 47.8	51	3 05.0	3	119 14.0	54	17 35.8	1
8	77 00.1	135 12.6	15	22 36.3	16	317 17.1	67	23 34.5	4	246 39.0	51	3 08.2	3	120 08.2	54	17 34.4	1
9	77 59.3	134 57.5	15	22 20.8	16	318 24.1	68	23 38.9	5	247 30.3	51	3 11.3	3	121 02.5	54	17 32.9	1
10	78 58.4	134 42.8	14	22 04.7	17	319 32.1	69	23 43.5	5	248 21.7	52	3 14.3	3	121 56.6	54	17 31.4	1
11	79 57.5	134 28.5	−14	S21 47.9	+17	320 40.9	+70	N23 48.2	+ 5	249 13.2	+52	S 3 17.3	− 3	122 50.6	+54	S17 30.0	+ 2
12	80 56.7	134 14.6	14	21 30.6	18	321 50.7	71	23 53.0	5	250 04.9	52	3 20.3	3	123 44.6	54	17 28.5	2
13	81 55.8	134 01.1	13	21 12.8	18	323 01.4	72	23 58.0	5	250 56.6	52	3 23.2	3	124 38.6	54	17 26.9	2
14	82 55.0	133 48.1	13	20 54.4	19	324 13.0	72	24 03.1	5	251 48.5	52	3 26.0	3	125 32.5	54	17 25.4	2
15	83 54.1	133 35.5	12	20 35.5	19	325 25.4	73	24 08.2	5	252 40.5	52	3 28.8	3	126 26.2	54	17 23.8	2
16	84 53.2	133 23.4	−12	S20 16.1	+20	326 38.8	+74	N24 13.5	+ 5	253 32.6	+52	S 3 31.6	− 3	127 20.0	+54	S17 22.3	+ 2
17	85 52.4	133 11.7	11	19 56.1	21	327 53.1	75	24 18.9	6	254 24.9	52	3 34.3	3	128 13.7	54	17 20.6	2
18	86 51.5	133 00.5	11	19 35.6	21	329 08.2	76	24 24.4	6	255 17.2	53	3 36.8	3	129 07.3	54	17 19.0	2
19	87 50.6	132 49.7	10	19 14.7	21	330 24.1	77	24 29.9	6	256 09.7	53	3 39.4	3	130 00.8	54	17 17.3	2
20	88 49.8	132 39.4	10	18 53.3	22	331 40.9	78	24 35.6	6	257 02.4	53	3 41.9	2	130 54.3	54	17 15.7	2
21	89 48.9	132 29.6	− 9	S18 31.4	+22	332 58.5	+78	N24 41.3	+ 6	257 55.1	+53	S 3 44.3	− 2	131 47.8	+53	S17 14.0	+ 2
22	90 48.1	132 20.1	9	18 09.1	23	334 16.9	79	24 47.0	6	258 48.0	53	3 46.7	2	132 41.1	53	17 12.3	2
23	91 47.2	132 11.3	8	17 46.3	23	335 36.0	80	24 52.7	6	259 41.0	53	3 49.1	2	133 34.4	53	17 10.6	2
24	92 46.3	132 02.8	8	17 23.2	23	336 55.8	81	24 58.4	6	260 34.2	53	3 51.4	2	134 27.7	53	17 08.8	2
25	93 45.5	131 54.9	8	16 59.7	24	338 16.3	81	25 04.2	6	261 27.5	53	3 53.6	2	135 20.9	53	17 07.1	2
26	94 44.6	131 47.4	− 7	S16 35.7	+24	339 37.5	+82	N25 09.9	+ 6	262 20.9	+54	S 3 55.7	− 2	136 14.0	+53	S17 05.3	+ 2
27	95 43.7	131 40.3	7	16 11.4	25	340 59.2	82	25 15.6	6	263 14.5	54	3 57.8	2	137 07.1	53	17 03.5	2
28	96 42.9	131 33.8	6	15 46.7	25	342 21.6	83	25 21.2	6	264 08.2	54	3 59.8	2	138 00.2	53	17 01.7	2
29	97 42.1	131 27.8	6	15 21.7	25	343 44.5	83	25 26.8	6	265 02.0	54	4 01.7	2	138 53.2	53	16 59.8	2
30	98 41.2	131 22.2	5	14 56.3	26	345 07.8	84	25 32.3	5	265 56.0	54	4 03.7	2	139 46.2	53	16 58.0	2
31	99 40.3	131 17.1	− 5	S14 30.6	+26	346 31.7	+84	N25 37.7	+ 5	266 50.2	+54	S 4 05.5	− 2	140 39.1	+53	S16 56.1	+ 2

1992 NOVEMBER, DECEMBER — SUN AND MOON

0^h UT	SUN GHA	v	SUN Dec	d	MOON 0^h–8^h GHA	v	Dec	d	MOON 8^h–16^h GHA	v	Dec	d	MOON 16^h–24^h GHA	v	Dec	d	HP
Nov	(SD 16′.2)				NOVEMBER												
	° ′		° ′		° ′		° ′		° ′		° ′		° ′		° ′		′
1	184 05.7	0	S14 26.4	−19	105 33	133	S18 44	+ 61	221 46	137	S17 43	+ 67	338 03	142	S16 36	+ 71	54.7
2	184 06.0	0	14 45.6	19	94 25	145	15 25	74	210 50	148	14 11	78	327 18	152	12 53	81	54.4
3	184 06.1	0	15 04.4	19	83 50	154	11 32	84	200 24	157	10 08	87	317 01	158	8 41	88	54.2
4	184 06.1	0	15 23.0	18	73 39	159	7 13	90	190 18	161	5 43	92	306 59	161	S 4 11	93	54.2
5	184 05.8	− 1	15 41.4	18	63 40	161	S 2 38	94	180 21	160	S 1 04	94	297 01	160	N 0 30	95	54.4
6	184 05.3	− 1	S15 59.5	−18	53 41	157	N 2 05	+ 94	170 18	157	N 3 39	+ 94	286 55	153	N 5 13	+ 94	54.7
7	184 04.6	1	16 17.3	18	43 28	151	6 47	91	159 59	148	8 18	91	276 27	144	9 49	88	55.1
8	184 03.7	1	16 34.8	17	32 51	140	11 17	86	149 11	136	12 43	82	265 27	131	14 05	79	55.6
9	184 02.5	1	16 52.1	17	21 38	127	15 24	75	137 45	121	16 39	70	253 46	116	17 49	65	56.2
10	184 01.2	2	17 09.1	17	9 42	112	18 54	58	125 34	106	19 52	53	241 20	102	20 45	45	56.7
11	183 59.7	− 2	S17 25.8	−16	357 02	97	N21 30	+ 38	112 39	93	N22 08	+ 29	228 12	90	N22 37	+ 22	57.3
12	183 57.9	2	17 42.2	16	343 42	87	22 59	+ 12	99 09	85	23 11	+ 3	214 34	84	23 14	− 5	57.8
13	183 55.9	2	17 58.3	16	329 58	83	23 09	− 15	85 21	84	22 54	− 25	200 45	84	22 29	33	58.2
14	183 53.7	2	18 14.1	15	316 09	86	21 56	43	71 35	88	21 13	50	187 03	91	20 23	60	58.5
15	183 51.3	3	18 29.5	15	302 34	94	19 23	66	58 08	97	18 17	74	173 45	100	17 03	81	58.8
16	183 48.7	− 3	S18 44.7	−15	289 25	103	N15 42	− 86	45 08	107	N14 16	− 93	160 55	109	N12 43	− 96	59.1
17	183 45.9	3	18 59.5	14	276 44	112	11 07	101	32 36	114	9 26	105	148 30	116	7 41	107	59.2
18	183 42.8	3	19 13.9	14	264 26	117	5 54	110	20 23	119	N 4 04	111	136 22	119	N 2 13	111	59.3
19	183 39.6	4	19 28.1	14	252 21	118	N 0 22	112	8 19	119	S 1 30	112	124 18	117	S 3 22	110	59.3
20	183 36.1	4	19 41.8	14	240 15	116	S 5 12	108	356 11	115	7 00	106	112 06	112	8 46	103	59.2
21	183 32.4	− 4	S19 55.3	−13	227 58	110	S10 29	− 98	343 48	107	S12 07	− 94	99 35	104	S13 41	− 89	59.0
22	188 28.5	4	20 08.3	13	215 19	102	15 10	83	331 01	98	16 33	76	86 39	96	17 49	69	58.6
23	183 24.4	4	20 21.0	12	202 15	94	18 58	62	317 49	92	20 00	54	73 21	90	20 54	45	58.2
24	183 20.2	5	20 33.3	12	188 51	90	21 39	36	304 21	89	22 15	28	59 50	90	22 43	− 19	57.6
25	183 15.7	5	20 45.2	12	175 20	90	23 02	− 10	290 50	93	23 12	− 1	46 23	95	23 13	+ 7	57.0
26	183 11.0	− 5	S20 56.8	−11	161 58	99	S23 06	+ 16	277 37	102	S22 50	+ 24	33 19	106	S22 26	+ 31	56.3
27	183 06.2	5	21 07.9	11	149 05	110	21 55	39	264 55	115	21 16	45	20 50	120	20 31	51	55.7
28	183 01.2	5	21 18.6	10	136 50	125	19 40	57	252 55	129	18 43	63	9 04	134	17 40	67	55.1
29	182 56.0	5	21 29.0	10	125 18	139	16 33	71	241 37	143	15 22	75	358 00	146	14 07	78	54.7
30	182 50.6	− 6	S21 39.0	− 9	114 26	150	S12 49	+ 82	230 56	153	S11 27	+ 84	347 29	156	S10 03	+ 87	54.4
Dec	(SD 16′.3)				DECEMBER												
1	182 45.1	− 6	S21 48.4	− 9	104 05	158	S 8 36	+ 88	220 43	160	S 7 08	+ 90	337 23	160	S 5 38	+ 92	54.2
2	182 39.5	6	21 57.6	9	94 03	162	S 4 06	92	210 45	162	S 2 34	93	327 27	162	S 1 01	94	54.3
3	182 33.6	6	22 06.3	8	84 09	161	N 0 33	93	200 50	160	N 2 06	94	317 30	158	N 3 40	93	54.5
4	182 27.7	6	22 14.5	8	74 08	156	5 13	92	190 44	153	6 45	91	307 17	150	8 16	89	54.8
5	182 21.5	6	22 22.3	7	63 47	146	9 45	88	180 13	143	11 13	85	296 36	137	12 38	82	55.4
6	182 15.3	− 6	S22 29.7	− 7	52 53	133	N14 00	+ 78	169 06	128	N15 18	+ 75	285 14	122	N16 33	+ 70	56.0
7	182 08.9	7	22 36.7	7	41 16	117	17 43	65	157 13	111	18 48	59	273 04	105	19 47	53	56.7
8	182 02.4	7	22 43.2	6	28 49	100	20 40	47	144 29	94	21 27	38	260 03	90	22 05	31	57.4
9	181 55.8	7	22 49.3	6	15 33	86	22 36	+ 21	130 59	81	22 57	+ 13	246 20	80	23 10	+ 4	58.1
10	181 49.0	7	22 54.9	5	1 40	77	23 14	− 6	116 57	76	23 08	− 16	232 13	76	22 52	− 26	58.7
11	181 42.2	− 7	S23 00.1	− 5	347 29	77	N22 26	− 35	102 46	78	N21 51	− 44	218 04	81	N21 07	− 54	59.1
12	181 35.3	7	23 04.8	4	333 25	83	20 13	62	88 48	86	19 11	70	204 14	91	18 01	77	59.4
13	181 28.3	7	23 09.0	4	319 45	94	16 44	84	75 19	98	15 20	90	190 57	101	13 50	96	59.6
14	181 21.2	7	23 12.8	3	306 38	106	12 14	99	62 24	108	10 35	104	178 12	112	8 51	107	59.6
15	181 14.0	7	23 16.2	3	294 04	114	7 04	109	49 58	117	N 5 15	110	165 55	118	N 3 25	112	59.4
16	181 06.7	− 7	S23 19.0	− 2	281 53	119	N 1 33	−111	37 52	120	S 0 18	−111	153 52	121	S 2 09	−111	59.2
17	180 59.5	7	23 21.4	2	269 53	120	S 4 00	108	25 53	119	5 48	106	141 52	118	7 34	103	58.9
18	180 52.1	7	23 23.4	1	257 50	117	9 17	100	13 47	114	10 57	95	129 41	113	12 32	91	58.5
19	180 44.7	7	23 24.8	1	245 34	110	14 03	85	1 24	107	15 28	80	117 11	105	16 48	73	58.1
20	180 37.3	8	23 25.8	− 1	232 56	103	18 01	66	348 39	100	19 07	60	104 19	98	20 07	51	57.7
21	180 29.8	− 8	S23 26.3	0	219 57	96	S20 58	− 44	335 33	96	S21 42	− 35	91 09	94	S22 17	− 27	57.3
22	180 22.3	8	23 26.4	+ 1	206 43	95	22 44	− 18	322 18	95	23 02	− 10	77 53	96	23 12	− 1	56.8
23	180 14.8	8	23 25.9	1	193 29	98	23 13	+ 7	309 07	100	23 06	+ 15	64 47	104	22 51	+ 23	56.3
24	180 07.3	7	23 25.1	1	180 31	107	22 28	31	296 18	110	21 57	38	52 08	115	21 19	45	55.8
25	179 59.9	8	23 23.7	2	168 03	119	20 34	51	284 02	124	19 43	57	40 06	128	18 46	62	55.3
26	179 52.4	− 7	S23 21.9	+ 2	156 14	133	S17 44	+ 67	272 27	137	S16 37	+ 71	28 44	141	S15 26	+ 76	54.8
27	179 45.0	7	23 19.6	3	145 05	145	14 10	79	261 30	148	12 51	82	17 58	152	11 29	84	54.5
28	179 37.6	7	23 16.8	3	134 30	154	10 05	87	251 04	157	8 38	89	7 41	159	7 09	90	54.2
29	179 30.2	7	23 13.6	4	124 20	161	5 39	91	241 01	162	S 4 08	92	357 43	162	S 2 36	93	54.1
30	179 23.0	7	23 09.9	4	114 25	163	S 1 03	93	231 08	163	N 0 30	93	347 51	161	N 2 03	93	54.2
31	179 15.8	− 7	S23 05.7	+ 5	104 32	161	N 3 36	+ 92	221 13	158	N 5 08	+ 91	337 51	157	N 6 39	+ 90	54.4

5

5.3.9 INTERPOLATION TABLES — ARIES, SUN, PLANETS 0^h–12^h

Correction to GHA Aries

UT	0^m	1^m	2^m	3^m
s	° ′	° ′	° ′	° ′
00	0 00.0	0 15.0	0 30.1	0 45.1
04	01.0	16.0	31.1	46.1
08	02.0	17.0	32.1	47.1
12	03.0	18.0	33.1	48.1
16	04.0	19.1	34.1	49.1
20	0 05.0	0 20.1	0 35.1	0 50.1
24	06.0	21.1	36.1	51.1
28	07.0	22.1	37.1	52.1
32	08.0	23.1	38.1	53.1
36	09.0	24.1	39.1	54.1
40	0 10.0	0 25.1	0 40.1	0 55.2
44	11.0	26.1	41.1	56.2
48	12.0	27.1	42.1	57.2
52	13.0	28.1	43.1	58.2
56	14.0	29.1	44.1	0 59.2
60	0 15.0	0 30.1	0 45.1	1 00.2

Correction to GHA Aries

UT	4^m	5^m	6^m	7^m
s	° ′	° ′	° ′	° ′
00	1 00.2	1 15.2	1 30.2	1 45.3
04	01.2	16.2	31.2	46.3
08	02.2	17.2	32.3	47.3
12	03.2	18.2	33.3	48.3
16	04.2	19.2	34.3	49.3
20	1 05.2	1 20.2	1 35.3	1 50.3
24	06.2	21.2	36.3	51.3
28	07.2	22.2	37.3	52.3
32	08.2	23.2	38.3	53.3
36	09.2	24.2	39.3	54.3
40	1 10.2	1 25.2	1 40.3	1 55.3
44	11.2	26.2	41.3	56.3
48	12.2	27.2	42.3	57.3
52	13.2	28.2	43.3	58.3
56	14.2	29.2	44.3	1 59.3
60	1 15.2	1 30.2	1 45.3	2 00.3

Correction to GHA Aries

UT	8^m	9^m	10^m	11^m
s	° ′	° ′	° ′	° ′
00	2 00.3	2 15.4	2 30.4	2 45.5
04	01.3	16.4	31.4	46.5
08	02.3	17.4	32.4	47.5
12	03.3	18.4	33.4	48.5
16	04.3	19.4	34.4	49.5
20	2 05.3	2 20.4	2 35.4	2 50.5
24	06.3	21.4	36.4	51.5
28	07.3	22.4	37.4	52.5
32	08.4	23.4	38.4	53.5
36	09.4	24.4	39.4	54.5
40	2 10.4	2 25.4	2 40.4	2 55.5
44	11.4	26.4	41.4	56.5
48	12.4	27.4	42.4	57.5
52	13.4	28.4	43.4	58.5
56	14.4	29.4	44.4	2 59.5
60	2 15.4	2 30.4	2 45.5	3 00.5

UT	Corr. to GHA Aries	Corr. to GHA Sun Planet	Correction to GHA or Declination for *v* or *d* 1	2	3	4	5	6	7	8	9	10	11	12	13	14	15	16
h m	° ′	°	Units of 0′.1															
0 00	0 00.0	0	0	0	0	0	0	0	0	0	0	0	0	0	0	0	0	0
12	3 00.5	3	0	0	0	0	0	1	1	1	1	1	1	1	1	1	1	1
24	6 01.0	6	0	0	1	1	1	1	1	1	2	2	2	2	2	2	3	3
36	9 01.5	9	0	1	1	1	1	2	2	2	2	3	3	3	3	4	4	4
0 48	12 02.0	12	0	1	1	1	2	2	2	3	3	3	4	4	4	5	5	5
1 00	15 02.5	15	0	1	1	2	2	3	3	3	4	4	5	5	5	6	6	7
12	18 03.0	18	1	1	2	2	3	3	4	4	5	5	6	6	7	7	8	8
24	21 03.4	21	1	1	2	2	3	4	4	5	5	6	6	7	8	8	9	9
36	24 03.9	24	1	1	2	3	3	4	5	5	6	7	7	8	9	9	10	11
1 48	27 04.4	27	1	2	2	3	4	5	5	6	7	8	8	9	10	11	11	12
2 00	30 04.9	30	1	2	3	3	4	5	6	7	8	8	9	10	11	12	13	13
12	33 05.4	33	1	2	3	4	5	6	6	7	8	9	10	11	12	13	14	15
24	36 05.9	36	1	2	3	4	5	6	7	8	9	10	11	12	13	14	15	16
36	39 06.4	39	1	2	3	4	5	7	8	9	10	11	12	13	14	15	16	17
2 48	42 06.9	42	1	2	4	5	6	7	8	9	11	12	13	14	15	16	18	19
3 00	45 07.4	45	1	3	4	5	6	8	9	10	11	13	14	15	16	18	19	20
12	48 07.9	48	1	3	4	5	7	8	9	11	12	13	15	16	17	19	20	21
24	51 08.4	51	1	3	4	6	7	9	10	11	13	14	16	17	18	20	21	23
36	54 08.9	54	2	3	5	6	8	9	11	12	14	15	17	18	20	21	23	24
3 48	57 09.4	57	2	3	5	6	8	10	11	13	14	16	17	19	21	22	24	25
4 00	60 09.9	60	2	3	5	7	8	10	12	13	15	17	18	20	22	23	25	27
12	63 10.3	63	2	4	5	7	9	11	12	14	16	18	19	21	23	25	26	28
24	66 10.8	66	2	4	6	7	9	11	13	15	17	18	20	22	24	26	28	29
36	69 11.3	69	2	4	6	8	10	12	13	15	17	19	21	23	25	27	29	31
4 48	72 11.8	72	2	4	6	8	10	12	14	16	18	20	22	24	26	28	30	32
5 00	75 12.3	75	2	4	6	8	10	13	15	17	19	21	23	25	27	29	31	33
12	78 12.8	78	2	4	7	9	11	13	15	17	20	22	24	26	28	30	33	35
24	81 13.3	81	2	5	7	9	11	14	16	18	20	23	25	27	29	32	34	36
36	84 13.8	84	2	5	7	9	12	14	16	19	21	23	26	28	30	33	35	37
5 48	87 14.3	87	2	5	7	10	12	15	17	19	22	24	27	29	31	34	36	39
6 00	90 14.8	90	3	5	8	10	13	15	18	20	23	25	28	30	33	35	38	40
12	93 15.3	93	3	5	8	10	13	16	18	21	23	26	28	31	34	36	39	41
24	96 15.8	96	3	5	8	11	13	16	19	21	24	27	29	32	35	37	40	43
36	99 16.3	99	3	6	8	11	14	17	19	22	25	28	30	33	36	39	41	44
6 48	102 16.8	102	3	6	9	11	14	17	20	23	26	28	31	34	37	40	43	45
7 00	105 17.2	105	3	6	9	12	15	18	20	23	26	29	32	35	38	41	44	47
12	108 17.7	108	3	6	9	12	15	18	21	24	27	30	33	36	39	42	45	48
24	111 18.2	111	3	6	9	12	15	19	22	25	28	31	34	37	40	43	46	49
36	114 18.7	114	3	6	10	13	16	19	22	25	29	32	35	38	41	44	48	51
7 48	117 19.2	117	3	7	10	13	16	20	23	26	29	33	36	39	42	46	49	52
8 00	120 19.7	120	3	7	10	13	17	20	23	27	30	33	37	40	43	47	50	53
12	123 20.2	123	3	7	10	14	17	21	24	27	31	34	38	41	44	48	51	55
24	126 20.7	126	4	7	11	14	18	21	25	28	32	35	39	42	46	49	53	56
36	129 21.2	129	4	7	11	14	18	22	25	29	32	36	39	43	47	50	54	57
8 48	132 21.7	132	4	7	11	15	18	22	26	29	33	37	40	44	48	51	55	59
9 00	135 22.2	135	4	8	11	15	19	23	26	30	34	38	41	45	49	53	56	60
12	138 22.7	138	4	8	12	15	19	23	27	31	35	38	42	46	50	54	58	61
24	141 23.2	141	4	8	12	16	20	24	27	31	35	39	43	47	51	55	59	63
36	144 23.7	144	4	8	12	16	20	24	28	32	36	40	44	48	52	56	60	64
9 48	147 24.1	147	4	8	12	16	20	25	29	33	37	41	45	49	53	57	61	65
10 00	150 24.6	150	4	8	13	17	21	25	29	33	38	42	46	50	54	58	63	67
12	153 25.1	153	4	9	13	17	21	26	30	34	38	43	47	51	55	60	64	68
24	156 25.6	156	4	9	13	17	22	26	30	35	39	43	48	52	56	61	65	69
36	159 26.1	159	4	9	13	18	22	27	31	35	40	44	49	53	57	62	66	71
10 48	162 26.6	162	5	9	14	18	23	27	32	36	41	45	50	54	59	63	68	72
11 00	165 27.1	165	5	9	14	18	23	28	32	37	41	46	50	55	60	64	69	73
12	168 27.6	168	5	9	14	19	23	28	33	37	42	47	51	56	61	65	70	75
24	171 28.1	171	5	10	14	19	24	29	33	38	43	48	52	57	62	67	71	76
36	174 28.6	174	5	10	15	19	24	29	34	39	44	48	53	58	63	68	73	77
48	177 29.1	177	5	10	15	20	25	30	34	39	44	49	54	59	64	69	74	79
12 00	180 29.6	180	5	10	15	20	25	30	35	40	45	50	55	60	65	70	75	80

INTERPOLATION TABLES — ARIES, SUN, PLANETS 12ʰ–24ʰ

UT	Corr. to GHA Aries	Corr. to GHA Sun Planet	Correction to GHA or Declination for v or d: 1	2	3	4	5	6	7	8	9	10	11	12	13	14	15	16
h m	° ′	°	Units of 0′.1															
12 00	180 29.6	180	5	10	15	20	25	30	35	40	45	50	55	60	65	70	75	80
12	183 30.1	183	5	10	15	20	25	31	36	41	46	51	56	61	66	71	76	81
24	186 30.6	186	5	10	16	21	26	31	36	41	47	52	57	62	67	72	78	83
36	189 31.0	189	5	11	16	21	26	32	37	42	47	53	58	63	68	74	79	84
12 48	192 31.5	192	5	11	16	21	27	32	37	43	48	53	59	64	69	75	80	85
13 00	195 32.0	195	5	11	16	22	27	33	38	43	49	54	60	65	70	76	81	87
12	198 32.5	198	6	11	17	22	28	33	39	44	50	55	61	66	72	77	83	88
24	201 33.0	201	6	11	17	22	28	34	39	45	50	56	61	67	73	78	84	89
36	204 33.5	204	6	11	17	23	28	34	40	45	51	57	62	68	74	79	85	91
13 48	207 34.0	207	6	12	17	23	29	35	40	46	52	58	63	69	75	81	86	92
14 00	210 34.5	210	6	12	18	23	29	35	41	47	53	58	64	70	76	82	88	93
12	213 35.0	213	6	12	18	24	30	36	41	47	53	59	65	71	77	83	89	95
24	216 35.5	216	6	12	18	24	30	36	42	48	54	60	66	72	78	84	90	96
36	219 36.0	219	6	12	18	24	30	37	43	49	55	61	67	73	79	85	91	97
14 48	222 36.5	222	6	12	19	25	31	37	43	49	56	62	68	74	80	86	93	99
15 00	225 37.0	225	6	13	19	25	31	38	44	50	56	63	69	75	81	88	94	100
12	228 37.5	228	6	13	19	25	32	38	44	51	57	63	70	76	82	89	95	101
24	231 37.9	231	6	13	19	26	32	39	45	51	58	64	71	77	83	90	96	103
36	234 38.4	234	7	13	20	26	33	39	46	52	59	65	72	78	85	91	98	104
15 48	237 38.9	237	7	13	20	26	33	40	46	53	59	66	72	79	86	92	99	105
16 00	240 39.4	240	7	13	20	27	33	40	47	53	60	67	73	80	87	93	100	107
12	243 39.9	243	7	14	20	27	34	41	47	54	61	68	74	81	88	95	101	108
24	246 40.4	246	7	14	21	27	34	41	48	55	62	68	75	82	89	96	103	109
36	249 40.9	249	7	14	21	28	35	42	48	55	62	69	76	83	90	97	104	111
16 48	252 41.4	252	7	14	21	28	35	42	49	56	63	70	77	84	91	98	105	112
17 00	255 41.9	255	7	14	21	28	35	43	50	57	64	71	78	85	92	99	106	113
12	258 42.4	258	7	14	22	29	36	43	50	57	65	72	79	86	93	100	108	115
24	261 42.9	261	7	15	22	29	36	44	51	58	65	73	80	87	94	102	109	116
36	264 43.4	264	7	15	22	29	37	44	51	59	66	73	81	88	95	103	110	117
17 48	267 43.9	267	7	15	22	30	37	45	52	59	67	74	82	89	96	104	111	119
18 00	270 44.4	270	8	15	23	30	38	45	53	60	68	75	83	90	98	105	113	120
12	273 44.8	273	8	15	23	30	38	46	53	61	68	76	83	91	99	106	114	121
24	276 45.3	276	8	15	23	31	38	46	54	61	69	77	84	92	100	107	115	123
36	279 45.8	279	8	16	23	31	39	47	54	62	70	78	85	93	101	109	116	124
18 48	282 46.3	282	8	16	24	31	39	47	55	63	71	78	86	94	102	110	118	125
19 00	285 46.8	285	8	16	24	32	40	48	55	63	71	79	87	95	103	111	119	127
12	288 47.3	288	8	16	24	32	40	48	56	64	72	80	88	96	104	112	120	128
24	291 47.8	291	8	16	24	32	40	49	57	65	73	81	89	97	105	113	121	129
36	294 48.3	294	8	16	25	33	41	49	57	65	74	82	90	98	106	114	123	131
19 48	297 48.8	297	8	17	25	33	41	50	58	66	74	83	91	99	107	116	124	132
20 00	300 49.3	300	8	17	25	33	42	50	58	67	75	83	92	100	108	117	125	133
12	303 49.8	303	8	17	25	34	42	51	59	67	76	84	93	101	109	118	126	135
24	306 50.3	306	9	17	26	34	43	51	60	68	77	85	94	102	111	119	128	136
36	309 50.8	309	9	17	26	34	43	52	60	69	77	86	94	103	112	120	129	137
20 48	312 51.3	312	9	17	26	35	43	52	61	69	78	87	95	104	113	121	130	139
21 00	315 51.7	315	9	18	26	35	44	53	61	70	79	88	96	105	114	123	131	140
12	318 52.2	318	9	18	27	35	44	53	62	71	80	88	97	106	115	124	133	141
24	321 52.7	321	9	18	27	36	45	54	62	71	80	89	98	107	116	125	134	143
36	324 53.2	324	9	18	27	36	45	54	63	72	81	90	99	108	117	126	135	144
21 48	327 53.7	327	9	18	27	36	45	55	64	73	82	91	100	109	118	127	136	145
22 00	330 54.2	330	9	18	28	37	46	55	64	73	83	92	101	110	119	128	138	147
12	333 54.7	333	9	19	28	37	46	56	65	74	83	93	102	111	120	130	139	148
24	336 55.2	336	9	19	28	37	47	56	65	75	84	93	103	112	121	131	140	149
36	339 55.7	339	9	19	28	38	47	57	66	75	85	94	104	113	122	132	141	151
22 48	342 56.2	342	10	19	29	38	48	57	67	76	86	95	105	114	124	133	143	152
23 00	345 56.7	345	10	19	29	38	48	58	67	77	86	96	105	115	125	134	144	153
12	348 57.2	348	10	19	29	39	48	58	68	77	87	97	106	116	126	135	145	155
24	351 57.7	351	10	20	29	39	49	59	68	78	88	98	107	117	127	137	146	156
36	354 58.2	354	10	20	30	39	49	59	69	79	89	98	108	118	128	138	148	157
23 48	357 58.6	357	10	20	30	40	50	60	69	79	89	99	109	119	129	139	149	159
24 00	360 59.1	360	10	20	30	40	50	60	70	80	90	100	110	120	130	140	150	160

Correction to GHA Sun and Planets

UT	0ᵐ	1ᵐ	2ᵐ	3ᵐ
s	° ′	° ′	° ′	° ′
00	0 00	0 15	0 30	0 45
04	01	16	31	46
08	02	17	32	47
12	03	18	33	48
16	04	19	34	49
20	0 05	0 20	0 35	0 50
24	06	21	36	51
28	07	22	37	52
32	08	23	38	53
36	09	24	39	54
40	0 10	0 25	0 40	0 55
44	11	26	41	56
48	12	27	42	57
52	13	28	43	58
56	14	29	44	0 59
60	0 15	0 30	0 45	1 00

Correction to GHA Sun and Planets

UT	4ᵐ	5ᵐ	6ᵐ	7ᵐ
s	° ′	° ′	° ′	° ′
00	1 00	1 15	1 30	1 45
04	01	16	31	46
08	02	17	32	47
12	03	18	33	48
16	04	19	34	49
20	1 05	1 20	1 35	1 50
24	06	21	36	51
28	07	22	37	52
32	08	23	38	53
36	09	24	39	54
40	1 10	1 25	1 40	1 55
44	11	26	41	56
48	12	27	42	57
52	13	28	43	58
56	14	29	44	1 59
60	1 15	1 30	1 45	2 00

Correction to GHA Sun and Planets

UT	8ᵐ	9ᵐ	10ᵐ	11ᵐ
s	° ′	° ′	° ′	° ′
00	2 00	2 15	2 30	2 45
04	01	16	31	46
08	02	17	32	47
12	03	18	33	48
16	04	19	34	49
20	2 05	2 20	2 35	2 50
24	06	21	36	51
28	07	22	37	52
32	08	23	38	53
36	09	24	39	54
40	2 10	2 25	2 40	2 55
44	11	26	41	56
48	12	27	42	57
52	13	28	43	58
56	14	29	44	2 59
60	2 15	2 30	2 45	3 00

INTERPOLATION TABLES — SUN, PLANETS 0^h–12^h

Correction to GHA or Declination for *v* or *d* (Units of 0′.1)

UT	Corr. to GHA Sun Planet	10	12	14	16	18	20	22	24	26	28	30	32	34	36	38	40	42	44	46	48	50	52	54	56	58	60
h m	°																										
0 00	0	0	0	0	0	0	0	0	0	0	0	0	0	0	0	0	0	0	0	0	0	0	0	0	0	0	0
12	3	1	1	1	1	2	2	2	2	2	2	3	3	3	3	3	3	4	4	4	4	4	4	5	5	5	5
24	6	2	2	2	3	3	3	4	4	4	5	5	5	6	6	6	7	7	7	8	8	8	9	9	9	10	10
36	9	3	3	4	4	5	5	6	6	7	7	8	8	9	9	10	10	11	11	12	12	13	13	14	14	15	15
0 48	12	3	4	5	5	6	7	7	8	9	9	10	11	11	12	13	13	14	15	15	16	17	17	18	19	19	20
1 00	15	4	5	6	7	8	8	9	10	11	12	13	13	14	15	16	17	18	18	19	20	21	22	23	23	24	25
12	18	5	6	7	8	9	10	11	12	13	14	15	16	17	18	19	20	21	22	23	24	25	26	27	28	29	30
24	21	6	7	8	9	11	12	13	14	15	16	18	19	20	21	22	23	25	26	27	28	29	30	32	33	34	35
36	24	7	8	9	11	12	13	15	16	17	19	20	21	23	24	25	27	28	29	31	32	33	35	36	37	39	40
1 48	27	8	9	11	12	14	15	17	18	20	21	23	24	26	27	29	30	32	33	35	36	38	39	41	42	44	45
2 00	30	8	10	12	13	15	17	18	20	22	23	25	27	28	30	32	33	35	37	38	40	42	43	45	47	48	50
12	33	9	11	13	15	17	18	20	22	24	26	28	29	31	33	35	37	39	40	42	44	46	48	50	51	53	55
24	36	10	12	14	16	18	20	22	24	26	28	30	32	34	36	38	40	42	44	46	48	50	52	54	56	58	60
36	39	11	13	15	17	20	22	24	26	28	30	33	35	37	39	41	43	46	48	50	52	54	56	59	61	63	65
2 48	42	12	14	16	19	21	23	26	28	30	33	35	37	40	42	44	47	49	51	54	56	58	61	63	65	68	70
3 00	45	13	15	18	20	23	25	28	30	33	35	38	40	43	45	48	50	53	55	58	60	63	65	68	70	73	75
12	48	13	16	19	21	24	27	29	32	35	37	40	43	45	48	51	53	56	59	61	64	67	69	72	75	77	80
24	51	14	17	20	23	26	28	31	34	37	40	43	45	48	51	54	57	60	62	65	68	71	74	77	79	82	85
36	54	15	18	21	24	27	30	33	36	39	42	45	48	51	54	57	60	63	66	69	72	75	78	81	84	87	90
3 48	57	16	19	22	25	29	32	35	38	41	44	48	51	54	57	60	63	67	70	73	76	79	82	86	89	92	95
4 00	60	17	20	23	27	30	33	37	40	43	47	50	53	57	60	63	67	70	73	77	80	83	87	90	93	97	100
12	63	18	21	25	28	32	35	39	42	46	49	53	56	60	63	67	70	74	77	81	84	88	91	95	98	102	105
24	66	18	22	26	29	33	37	40	44	48	51	55	59	62	66	70	73	77	81	84	88	92	95	99	103	106	110
36	69	19	23	27	31	35	38	42	46	50	54	58	61	65	69	73	77	81	84	88	92	96	100	104	107	111	115
4 48	72	20	24	28	32	36	40	44	48	52	56	60	64	68	72	76	80	84	88	92	96	100	104	108	112	116	120
5 00	75	21	25	29	33	38	42	46	50	54	58	63	67	71	75	79	83	88	92	96	100	104	108	113	117	121	125
12	78	22	26	30	35	39	43	48	52	56	61	65	69	74	78	82	87	91	95	100	104	108	113	117	121	126	130
24	81	23	27	32	36	41	45	50	54	59	63	68	72	77	81	86	90	95	99	104	108	113	117	122	126	131	135
36	84	23	28	33	37	42	47	51	56	61	65	70	75	79	84	89	93	98	103	107	112	117	121	126	131	135	140
5 48	87	24	29	34	39	44	48	53	58	63	68	73	77	82	87	92	97	102	106	111	116	121	126	131	135	140	145
6 00	90	25	30	35	40	45	50	55	60	65	70	75	80	85	90	95	100	105	110	115	120	125	130	135	140	145	150
12	93	26	31	36	41	47	52	57	62	67	72	78	83	88	93	98	103	109	114	119	124	129	134	140	145	150	155
24	96	27	32	37	43	48	53	59	64	69	75	80	85	91	96	101	107	112	117	123	128	133	139	144	149	155	160
36	99	28	33	39	44	50	55	61	66	72	77	83	88	94	99	105	110	116	121	127	132	138	143	149	154	160	165
6 48	102	28	34	40	45	51	57	62	68	74	79	85	91	96	102	108	113	119	125	130	136	142	147	153	159	164	170
7 00	105	29	35	41	47	53	58	64	70	76	82	88	93	99	105	111	117	123	128	134	140	146	152	158	163	169	175
12	108	30	36	42	48	54	60	66	72	78	84	90	96	102	108	114	120	126	132	138	144	150	156	162	168	174	180
24	111	31	37	43	49	56	62	68	74	80	86	93	99	105	111	117	123	130	136	142	148	154	160	167	173	179	185
36	114	32	38	44	51	57	63	70	76	82	89	95	101	108	114	120	127	133	139	146	152	158	165	171	177	184	190
7 48	117	33	39	46	52	59	65	72	78	85	91	98	104	111	117	124	130	137	143	150	156	163	169	176	182	189	195
8 00	120	33	40	47	53	60	67	73	80	87	93	100	107	113	120	127	133	140	147	153	160	167	173	180	187	193	200
12	123	34	41	48	55	62	68	75	82	89	96	103	109	116	123	130	137	144	150	157	164	171	178	185	191	198	205
24	126	35	42	49	56	63	70	77	84	91	98	105	112	119	126	133	140	147	154	161	168	175	182	189	196	203	210
36	129	36	43	50	57	65	72	79	86	93	100	108	115	122	129	136	143	151	158	165	172	179	186	194	201	208	215
8 48	132	37	44	51	59	66	73	81	88	95	103	110	117	125	132	139	147	154	161	169	176	183	191	198	205	213	220
9 00	135	38	45	53	60	68	75	83	90	98	105	113	120	128	135	143	150	158	165	173	180	188	195	203	210	218	225
12	138	38	46	54	61	69	77	84	92	100	107	115	123	130	138	146	153	161	169	176	184	192	199	207	215	222	230
24	141	39	47	55	63	71	78	86	94	102	110	118	125	133	141	149	157	165	172	180	188	196	204	212	219	227	235
36	144	40	48	56	64	72	80	88	96	104	112	120	128	136	144	152	160	168	176	184	192	200	208	216	224	232	240
9 48	147	41	49	57	65	74	82	90	98	106	114	123	131	139	147	155	163	172	180	188	196	204	212	221	229	237	245
10 00	150	42	50	58	67	75	83	92	100	108	117	125	133	142	150	158	167	175	183	192	200	208	217	225	233	242	250
12	153	43	51	60	68	77	85	94	102	111	119	128	136	145	153	162	170	179	187	196	204	213	221	230	238	247	255
24	156	43	52	61	69	78	87	95	104	113	121	130	139	147	156	165	173	182	191	199	208	217	225	234	243	251	260
36	159	44	53	62	71	80	88	97	106	115	124	133	141	150	159	168	177	186	194	203	212	221	230	239	247	256	265
10 48	162	45	54	63	72	81	90	99	108	117	126	135	144	153	162	171	180	189	198	207	216	225	234	243	252	261	270
11 00	165	46	55	64	73	83	92	101	110	119	128	138	147	156	165	174	183	193	202	211	220	229	238	248	257	266	275
12	168	47	56	65	75	84	93	103	112	121	131	140	149	159	168	177	187	196	205	215	224	233	243	252	261	271	280
24	171	48	57	67	76	86	95	105	114	124	133	143	152	162	171	181	190	200	209	219	228	238	247	257	266	276	285
36	174	48	58	68	77	87	97	106	116	126	135	145	155	164	174	184	193	203	213	222	232	242	251	261	271	280	290
11 48	177	49	59	69	79	89	98	108	118	128	138	148	157	167	177	187	197	207	216	226	236	246	256	266	275	285	295
12 00	180	50	60	70	80	90	100	110	120	130	140	150	160	170	180	190	200	210	220	230	240	250	260	270	280	290	300

INTERPOLATION TABLES — SUN, PLANETS 0^h–12^h

UT	Corr. to GHA Sun Planet	Correction to GHA or Declination for v or d: 60	62	64	66	68	70	72	74	76	78	80	82	84	86	88	90
h m	°	Units of 0′.1															
0 00	0	0	0	0	0	0	0	0	0	0	0	0	0	0	0	0	0
12	3	5	5	5	6	6	6	6	6	6	7	7	7	7	7	7	8
24	6	10	10	11	11	11	12	12	12	13	13	13	14	14	14	15	15
36	9	15	16	16	17	17	18	18	19	19	20	20	21	21	22	22	23
0 48	12	20	21	21	22	23	23	24	25	25	26	27	27	28	29	29	30
1 00	15	25	26	27	28	28	29	30	31	32	33	33	34	35	36	37	38
12	18	30	31	32	33	34	35	36	37	38	39	40	41	42	43	44	45
24	21	35	36	37	39	40	41	42	43	44	46	47	48	49	50	51	53
36	24	40	41	43	44	45	47	48	49	51	52	53	55	56	57	59	60
1 48	27	45	47	48	50	51	53	54	56	57	59	60	62	63	65	66	68
2 00	30	50	52	53	55	57	58	60	62	63	65	67	68	70	72	73	75
12	33	55	57	59	61	62	64	66	68	70	72	73	75	77	79	81	83
24	36	60	62	64	66	68	70	72	74	76	78	80	82	84	86	88	90
36	39	65	67	69	72	74	76	78	80	82	85	87	89	91	93	95	98
2 48	42	70	72	75	77	79	82	84	86	89	91	93	96	98	100	103	105
3 00	45	75	78	80	83	85	88	90	93	95	98	100	103	105	108	110	113
12	48	80	83	85	88	91	93	96	99	101	104	107	109	112	115	117	120
24	51	85	88	91	94	96	99	102	105	108	111	113	116	119	122	125	128
36	54	90	93	96	99	102	105	108	111	114	117	120	123	126	129	132	135
3 48	57	95	98	101	105	108	111	114	117	120	124	127	130	133	136	139	143
4 00	60	100	103	107	110	113	117	120	123	127	130	133	137	140	143	147	150
12	63	105	109	112	116	119	123	126	130	133	137	140	144	147	151	154	158
24	66	110	114	117	121	125	128	132	136	139	143	147	150	154	158	161	165
36	69	115	119	123	127	130	134	138	142	146	150	153	157	161	165	169	173
4 48	72	120	124	128	132	136	140	144	148	152	156	160	164	168	172	176	180
5 00	75	125	129	133	138	142	146	150	154	158	163	167	171	175	179	183	188
12	78	130	134	139	143	147	152	156	160	165	169	173	178	182	186	191	195
24	81	135	140	144	149	153	158	162	167	171	176	180	185	189	194	198	203
36	84	140	145	149	154	159	163	168	173	177	182	187	191	196	201	205	210
5 48	87	145	150	155	160	164	169	174	179	184	189	193	198	203	208	213	218
6 00	90	150	155	160	165	170	175	180	185	190	195	200	205	210	215	220	225
12	93	155	160	165	171	176	181	186	191	196	202	207	212	217	222	227	233
24	96	160	165	171	176	181	187	192	197	203	208	213	219	224	229	235	240
36	99	165	171	176	182	187	193	198	204	209	215	220	226	231	237	242	248
6 48	102	170	176	181	187	193	198	204	210	215	221	227	232	238	244	249	255
7 00	105	175	181	187	193	198	204	210	216	222	228	233	239	245	251	257	263
12	108	180	186	192	198	204	210	216	222	228	234	240	246	252	258	264	270
24	111	185	191	197	204	210	216	222	228	234	241	247	253	259	265	271	278
36	114	190	196	203	209	215	222	228	234	241	247	253	260	266	272	279	285
7 48	117	195	202	208	215	221	228	234	241	247	254	260	267	273	280	286	293
8 00	120	200	207	213	220	227	233	240	247	253	260	267	273	280	287	293	300
12	123	205	212	219	226	232	239	246	253	260	267	273	280	287	294	301	308
24	126	210	217	224	231	238	245	252	259	266	273	280	287	294	301	308	315
36	129	215	222	229	237	244	251	258	265	272	280	287	294	301	308	315	323
8 48	132	220	227	235	242	249	257	264	271	279	286	293	301	308	315	323	330
9 00	135	225	233	240	248	255	263	270	278	285	293	300	308	315	323	330	338
12	138	230	238	245	253	261	268	276	284	291	299	307	314	322	330	337	345
24	141	235	243	251	259	266	274	282	290	298	306	313	321	329	337	345	353
36	144	240	248	256	264	272	280	288	296	304	312	320	328	336	344	352	360
9 48	147	245	253	261	270	278	286	294	302	310	319	327	335	343	351	359	368
10 00	150	250	258	267	275	283	292	300	308	317	325	333	342	350	358	367	375
12	153	255	264	272	281	289	298	306	315	323	332	340	349	357	366	374	383
24	156	260	269	277	286	295	303	312	321	329	338	347	355	364	373	381	390
36	159	265	274	283	292	300	309	318	327	336	345	353	362	371	380	389	398
10 48	162	270	279	288	297	306	315	324	333	342	351	360	369	378	387	396	405
11 00	165	275	284	293	303	312	321	330	339	348	358	367	376	385	394	403	413
12	168	280	289	299	308	317	327	336	345	355	364	373	383	392	401	411	420
24	171	285	295	304	314	323	333	342	352	361	371	380	390	399	409	418	428
36	174	290	300	309	319	329	338	348	358	367	377	387	396	406	416	425	435
11 48	177	295	305	315	325	334	344	354	364	374	384	393	403	413	423	433	443
12 00	180	300	310	320	330	340	350	360	370	380	390	400	410	420	430	440	450

Correction to GHA Sun and Planets

UT	0^m	1^m	2^m	3^m
s	° ′	° ′	° ′	° ′
00	0 00	0 15	0 30	0 45
04	01	16	31	46
08	02	17	32	47
12	03	18	33	48
16	04	19	34	49
20	0 05	0 20	0 35	0 50
24	06	21	36	51
28	07	22	37	52
32	08	23	38	53
36	09	24	39	54
40	0 10	0 25	0 40	0 55
44	11	26	41	56
48	12	27	42	57
52	13	28	43	58
56	14	29	44	0 59
60	0 15	0 30	0 45	1 00

Correction to GHA Sun and Planets

UT	4^m	5^m	6^m	7^m
s	° ′	° ′	° ′	° ′
00	1 00	1 15	1 30	1 45
04	01	16	31	46
08	02	17	32	47
12	03	18	33	48
16	04	19	34	49
20	1 05	1 20	1 35	1 50
24	06	21	36	51
28	07	22	37	52
32	08	23	38	53
36	09	24	39	54
40	1 10	1 25	1 40	1 55
44	11	26	41	56
48	12	27	42	57
52	13	28	43	58
56	14	29	44	1 59
60	1 15	1 30	1 45	2 00

Correction to GHA Sun and Planets

UT	8^m	9^m	10^m	11^m
s	° ′	° ′	° ′	° ′
00	2 00	2 15	2 30	2 45
04	01	16	31	46
08	02	17	32	47
12	03	18	33	48
16	04	19	34	49
20	2 05	2 20	2 35	2 50
24	06	21	36	51
28	07	22	37	52
32	08	23	38	53
36	09	24	39	54
40	2 10	2 25	2 40	2 55
44	11	26	41	56
48	12	27	42	57
52	13	28	43	58
56	14	29	44	2 59
60	2 15	2 30	2 45	3 00

5

INTERPOLATION TABLES — SUN, PLANETS 12^h–24^h

UT	Corr. to GHA Sun Planet	Correction to GHA or Declination for *v* or *d* 10	12	14	16	18	20	22	24	26	28	30	32	34	36	38	40	42	44	46	48	50	52	54	56	58	60
h m	°	Units of 0′.1																									
12 00	180	50	60	70	80	90	100	110	120	130	140	150	160	170	180	190	200	210	220	230	240	250	260	270	280	290	300
12	183	51	61	71	81	92	102	112	122	132	142	153	163	173	183	193	203	214	224	234	244	254	264	275	285	295	305
24	186	52	62	72	83	93	103	114	124	134	145	155	165	176	186	196	207	217	227	238	248	258	269	279	289	300	310
36	189	53	63	74	84	95	105	116	126	137	147	158	168	179	189	200	210	221	231	242	252	263	273	284	294	305	315
12 48	192	53	64	75	85	96	107	117	128	139	149	160	171	181	192	203	213	224	235	245	256	267	277	288	299	309	320
13 00	195	54	65	76	87	98	108	119	130	141	152	163	173	184	195	206	217	228	238	249	260	271	282	293	303	314	325
12	198	55	66	77	88	99	110	121	132	143	154	165	176	187	198	209	220	231	242	253	264	275	286	297	308	319	330
24	201	56	67	78	89	101	112	123	134	145	156	168	179	190	201	212	223	235	246	257	268	279	290	302	313	324	335
36	204	57	68	79	91	102	113	125	136	147	159	170	181	193	204	215	227	238	249	261	272	283	295	306	317	329	340
13 48	207	58	69	81	92	104	115	127	138	150	161	173	184	196	207	219	230	242	253	265	276	288	299	311	322	334	345
14 00	210	58	70	82	93	105	117	128	140	152	163	175	187	198	210	222	233	245	257	268	280	292	303	315	327	338	350
12	213	59	71	83	95	107	118	130	142	154	166	178	189	201	213	225	237	249	260	272	284	296	308	320	331	343	355
24	216	60	72	84	96	108	120	132	144	156	168	180	192	204	216	228	240	252	264	276	288	300	312	324	336	348	360
36	219	61	73	85	97	110	122	134	146	158	170	183	195	207	219	231	243	256	268	280	292	304	316	329	341	353	365
14 48	222	62	74	86	99	111	123	136	148	160	173	185	197	210	222	234	247	259	271	284	296	308	321	333	345	358	370
15 00	225	63	75	88	100	113	125	138	150	163	175	188	200	213	225	238	250	263	275	288	300	313	325	338	350	363	375
12	228	63	76	89	101	114	127	139	152	165	177	190	203	215	228	241	253	266	279	291	304	317	329	342	355	367	380
24	231	64	77	90	103	116	128	141	154	167	180	193	205	218	231	244	257	270	282	295	308	321	334	347	359	372	385
36	234	65	78	91	104	117	130	143	156	169	182	195	208	221	234	247	260	273	286	299	312	325	338	351	364	377	390
15 48	237	66	79	92	105	119	132	145	158	171	184	198	211	224	237	250	263	277	290	303	316	329	342	356	369	382	395
16 00	240	67	80	93	107	120	133	147	160	173	187	200	213	227	240	253	267	280	293	307	320	333	347	360	373	387	400
12	243	68	81	95	108	122	135	149	162	176	189	203	216	230	243	257	270	284	297	311	324	338	351	365	378	392	405
24	246	68	82	96	109	123	137	150	164	178	191	205	219	232	246	260	273	287	301	314	328	342	355	369	383	396	410
36	249	69	83	97	111	125	138	152	166	180	194	208	221	235	249	263	277	291	304	318	332	346	360	374	387	401	415
16 48	252	70	84	98	112	126	140	154	168	182	196	210	224	238	252	266	280	294	308	322	336	350	364	378	392	406	420
17 00	255	71	85	99	113	128	142	156	170	184	198	213	227	241	255	269	283	298	312	326	340	354	368	383	397	411	425
12	258	72	86	100	115	129	143	158	172	186	201	215	229	244	258	272	287	301	315	330	344	358	373	387	401	416	430
24	261	73	87	102	116	131	145	160	174	189	203	218	232	247	261	276	290	305	319	334	348	363	377	392	406	421	435
36	264	73	88	103	117	132	147	161	176	191	205	220	235	249	264	279	293	308	323	337	352	367	381	396	411	425	440
17 48	267	74	89	104	119	134	148	163	178	193	208	223	237	252	267	282	297	312	326	341	356	371	386	401	415	430	445
18 00	270	75	90	105	120	135	150	165	180	195	210	225	240	255	270	285	300	315	330	345	360	375	390	405	420	435	450
12	273	76	91	106	121	137	152	167	182	197	212	228	243	258	273	288	303	319	334	349	364	379	394	410	425	440	455
24	276	77	92	107	123	138	153	169	184	199	215	230	245	261	276	291	307	322	337	353	368	383	399	414	429	445	460
36	279	78	93	109	124	140	155	171	186	202	217	233	248	264	279	295	310	326	341	357	372	388	403	419	434	450	465
18 48	282	78	94	110	125	141	157	172	188	204	219	235	251	266	282	298	313	329	345	360	376	392	407	423	439	454	470
19 00	285	79	95	111	127	143	158	174	190	206	222	238	253	269	285	301	317	333	348	364	380	396	412	428	443	459	475
12	288	80	96	112	128	144	160	176	192	208	224	240	256	272	288	304	320	336	352	368	384	400	416	432	448	464	480
24	291	81	97	113	129	146	162	178	194	210	226	243	259	275	291	307	323	340	356	372	388	404	420	437	453	469	485
36	294	82	98	114	131	147	163	180	196	212	229	245	261	278	294	310	327	343	359	376	392	408	425	441	457	474	490
19 48	297	83	99	116	132	149	165	182	198	215	231	248	264	281	297	314	330	347	363	380	396	413	429	446	462	479	495
20 00	300	83	100	117	133	150	167	183	200	217	233	250	267	283	300	317	333	350	367	383	400	417	433	450	467	483	500
12	303	84	101	118	135	152	168	185	202	219	236	253	269	286	303	320	337	354	370	387	404	421	438	455	471	488	505
24	306	85	102	119	136	153	170	187	204	221	238	255	272	289	306	323	340	357	374	391	408	425	442	459	476	493	510
36	309	86	103	120	137	155	172	189	206	223	240	258	275	292	309	326	343	361	378	395	412	429	446	464	481	498	515
20 48	312	87	104	121	139	156	173	191	208	225	243	260	277	295	312	329	347	364	381	399	416	433	451	468	485	503	520
21 00	315	88	105	123	140	158	175	193	210	228	245	263	280	298	315	333	350	368	385	403	420	438	455	473	490	508	525
12	318	88	106	124	141	159	177	194	212	230	247	265	283	300	318	336	353	371	389	406	424	442	459	477	495	512	530
24	321	89	107	125	143	161	178	196	214	232	250	268	285	303	321	339	357	375	392	410	428	446	464	482	499	517	535
36	324	90	108	126	144	162	180	198	216	234	252	270	288	306	324	342	360	378	396	414	432	450	468	486	504	522	540
21 48	327	91	109	127	145	164	182	200	218	236	254	273	291	309	327	345	363	382	400	418	436	454	472	491	509	527	545
22 00	330	92	110	128	147	165	183	202	220	238	257	275	293	312	330	348	367	385	403	422	440	458	477	495	513	532	550
12	333	93	111	130	148	167	185	204	222	241	259	278	296	315	333	352	370	389	407	426	444	463	481	500	518	537	555
24	336	93	112	131	149	168	187	205	224	243	261	280	299	317	336	355	373	392	411	429	448	467	485	504	523	541	560
36	339	94	113	132	151	170	188	207	226	245	264	283	301	320	339	358	377	396	414	433	452	471	490	509	527	546	565
22 48	342	95	114	133	152	171	190	209	228	247	266	285	304	323	342	361	380	399	418	437	456	475	494	513	532	551	570
23 00	345	96	115	134	153	173	192	211	230	249	268	288	307	326	345	364	383	403	422	441	460	479	498	518	537	556	575
12	348	97	116	135	155	174	193	213	232	251	271	290	309	329	348	367	387	406	425	445	464	483	503	522	541	561	580
24	351	98	117	137	156	176	195	215	234	254	273	293	312	332	351	371	390	410	429	449	468	488	507	527	546	566	585
36	354	98	118	138	157	177	197	216	236	256	275	295	315	334	354	374	393	413	433	452	472	492	511	531	551	570	590
23 48	357	99	119	139	159	179	198	218	238	258	278	298	317	337	357	377	397	417	436	456	476	496	516	536	555	575	595
24 00	360	100	120	140	160	180	200	220	240	260	280	300	320	340	360	380	400	420	440	460	480	500	520	540	560	580	600

INTERPOLATION TABLES — SUN, PLANETS 12^h–24^h

Correction to GHA or Declination for *v* or *d* (Units of 0′.1)

UT h m	Corr. to GHA Sun Planet °	60	62	64	66	68	70	72	74	76	78	80	82	84	86	88	90
12 00	180	300	310	320	330	340	350	360	370	380	390	400	410	420	430	440	450
12	183	305	315	325	336	346	356	366	376	386	397	407	417	427	437	447	458
24	186	310	320	331	341	351	362	372	382	393	403	413	424	434	444	455	465
36	189	315	326	336	347	357	368	378	389	399	410	420	431	441	452	462	473
12 48	192	320	331	341	352	363	373	384	395	405	416	427	437	448	459	469	480
13 00	195	325	336	347	358	368	379	390	401	412	423	433	444	455	466	477	488
12	198	330	341	352	363	374	385	396	407	418	429	440	451	462	473	484	495
24	201	335	346	357	369	380	391	402	413	424	436	447	458	469	480	491	503
36	204	340	351	363	374	385	397	408	419	431	442	453	465	476	487	499	510
13 48	207	345	357	368	380	391	403	414	426	437	449	460	472	483	495	506	518
14 00	210	350	362	373	385	397	408	420	432	443	455	467	478	490	502	513	525
12	213	355	367	379	391	402	414	426	438	450	462	473	485	497	509	521	533
24	216	360	372	384	396	408	420	432	444	456	468	480	492	504	516	528	540
36	219	365	377	389	402	414	426	438	450	462	475	487	499	511	523	535	548
14 48	222	370	382	395	407	419	432	444	456	469	481	493	506	518	530	543	555
15 00	225	375	388	400	413	425	438	450	463	475	488	500	513	525	538	550	563
12	228	380	393	405	418	431	443	456	469	481	494	507	519	532	545	557	570
24	231	385	398	411	424	436	449	462	475	488	501	513	526	539	552	565	578
36	234	390	403	416	429	442	455	468	481	494	507	520	533	546	559	572	585
15 48	237	395	408	421	435	448	461	474	487	500	514	527	540	553	566	579	593
16 00	240	400	413	427	440	453	467	480	493	507	520	533	547	560	573	587	600
12	243	405	419	432	446	459	473	486	500	513	527	540	554	567	581	594	608
24	246	410	424	437	451	465	478	492	506	519	533	547	560	574	588	601	615
36	249	415	429	443	457	470	484	498	512	526	540	553	567	581	595	609	623
16 48	252	420	434	448	462	476	490	504	518	532	546	560	574	588	602	616	630
17 00	255	425	439	453	468	482	496	510	524	538	553	567	581	595	609	623	638
12	258	430	444	459	473	487	502	516	530	545	559	573	588	602	616	631	645
24	261	435	450	464	479	493	508	522	537	551	566	580	595	609	624	638	653
36	264	440	455	469	484	499	513	528	543	557	572	587	601	616	631	645	660
17 48	267	445	460	475	490	504	519	534	549	564	579	593	608	623	638	653	668
18 00	270	450	465	480	495	510	525	540	555	570	585	600	615	630	645	660	675
12	273	455	470	485	501	516	531	546	561	576	592	607	622	637	652	667	683
24	276	460	475	491	506	521	537	552	567	583	598	613	629	644	659	675	690
36	279	465	481	496	512	527	543	558	574	589	605	620	636	651	667	682	698
18 48	282	470	486	501	517	533	548	564	580	595	611	627	642	658	674	689	705
19 00	285	475	491	507	523	538	554	570	586	602	618	633	649	665	681	697	713
12	288	480	496	512	528	544	560	576	592	608	624	640	656	672	688	704	720
24	291	485	501	517	534	550	566	582	598	614	631	647	663	679	695	711	728
36	294	490	506	523	539	555	572	588	604	621	637	653	670	686	702	719	735
19 48	297	495	512	528	545	561	578	594	611	627	644	660	677	693	710	726	743
20 00	300	500	517	533	550	567	583	600	617	633	650	667	683	700	717	733	750
12	303	505	522	539	556	572	589	606	623	640	657	673	690	707	724	741	758
24	306	510	527	544	561	578	595	612	629	646	663	680	697	714	731	748	765
36	309	515	532	549	567	584	601	618	635	652	670	687	704	721	738	755	773
20 48	312	520	537	555	572	589	607	624	641	659	676	693	711	728	745	763	780
21 00	315	525	543	560	578	595	613	630	648	665	683	700	718	735	753	770	788
12	318	530	548	565	583	601	618	636	654	671	689	707	724	742	760	777	795
24	321	535	553	571	589	606	624	642	660	678	696	713	731	749	767	785	803
36	324	540	558	576	594	612	630	648	666	684	702	720	738	756	774	792	810
21 48	327	545	563	581	600	618	636	654	672	690	709	727	745	763	781	799	818
22 00	330	550	568	587	605	623	642	660	678	697	715	733	752	770	788	807	825
12	333	555	574	592	611	629	648	666	685	703	722	740	759	777	796	814	833
24	336	560	579	597	616	635	653	672	691	709	728	747	765	784	803	821	840
36	339	565	584	603	622	640	659	678	697	716	735	753	772	791	810	829	848
22 48	342	570	589	608	627	646	665	684	703	722	741	760	779	798	817	836	855
23 00	345	575	594	613	633	652	671	690	709	728	748	767	786	805	824	843	863
12	348	580	599	619	638	657	677	696	715	735	754	773	793	812	831	851	870
24	351	585	605	624	644	663	683	702	722	741	761	780	800	819	839	858	878
36	354	590	610	629	649	669	688	708	728	747	767	787	806	826	846	865	885
23 48	357	595	615	635	655	674	694	714	734	754	774	793	813	833	853	873	893
24 00	360	600	620	640	660	680	700	720	740	760	780	800	820	840	860	880	900

Correction to GHA Sun and Planets

UT s	0^m ° ′	1^m ° ′	2^m ° ′	3^m ° ′
00	0 00	0 15	0 30	0 45
04	01	16	31	46
08	02	17	32	47
12	03	18	33	48
16	04	19	34	49
20	0 05	0 20	0 35	0 50
24	06	21	36	51
28	07	22	37	52
32	08	23	38	53
36	09	24	39	54
40	0 10	0 25	0 40	0 55
44	11	26	41	56
48	12	27	42	57
52	13	28	43	58
56	14	29	44	0 59
60	0 15	0 30	0 45	1 00

Correction to GHA Sun and Planets

UT s	4^m ° ′	5^m ° ′	6^m ° ′	7^m ° ′
00	1 00	1 15	1 30	1 45
04	01	16	31	46
08	02	17	32	47
12	03	18	33	48
16	04	19	34	49
20	1 05	1 20	1 35	1 50
24	06	21	36	51
28	07	22	37	52
32	08	23	38	53
36	09	24	39	54
40	1 10	1 25	1 40	1 55
44	11	26	41	56
48	12	27	42	57
52	13	28	43	58
56	14	29	44	1 59
60	1 15	1 30	1 45	2 00

Correction to GHA Sun and Planets

UT s	8^m ° ′	9^m ° ′	10^m ° ′	11^m ° ′
00	2 00	2 15	2 30	2 45
04	01	16	31	46
08	02	17	32	47
12	03	18	33	48
16	04	19	34	49
20	2 05	2 20	2 35	2 50
24	06	21	36	51
28	07	22	37	52
32	08	23	38	53
36	09	24	39	54
40	2 10	2 25	2 40	2 55
44	11	26	41	56
48	12	27	42	57
52	13	28	43	58
56	14	29	44	2 59
60	2 15	2 30	2 45	3 00

INTERPOLATION TABLES — MOON 0^h–4^h, 8^h–12^h, 16^h–20^h

UT	Corr. to GHA	Correction to GHA or Declination for v or d																				UT	Corr. to GHA
		5	10	15	20	25	30	35	40	45	50	55	60	65	70	75	80	85	90	95	100		
h m	° ′	Units of 1′																				m s	′
0 00	0 00	0	0	0	0	0	0	0	0	0	0	0	0	0	0	0	0	0	0	0	0	0 00	00
04	0 57	0	0	0	0	0	0	0	0	0	0	0	1	1	1	1	1	1	1	1	1	04	01
(8 or 16) 08	1 54	0	0	0	0	0	1	1	1	1	1	1	1	1	1	1	1	1	2	2	2	08	02
12	2 51	0	0	0	1	1	1	1	1	1	1	1	2	2	2	2	2	2	2	2	3	12	03
16	3 48	0	0	1	1	1	1	1	1	2	2	2	2	2	2	3	3	3	3	3	3	16	04
0 20	4 45	0	0	1	1	1	1	1	2	2	2	2	3	3	3	3	3	4	4	4	4	0 20	05
24	5 42	0	1	1	1	1	2	2	2	2	3	3	3	3	4	4	4	4	5	5	5	24	06
28	6 39	0	1	1	1	1	2	2	2	3	3	3	4	4	4	4	5	5	5	6	6	28	07
32	7 36	0	1	1	1	2	2	2	3	3	3	4	4	4	5	5	5	6	6	6	7	32	08
36	8 33	0	1	1	2	2	2	3	3	3	4	4	5	5	5	6	6	6	7	7	8	36	09
0 40	9 30	0	1	1	2	2	3	3	3	4	4	5	5	5	6	6	7	7	8	8	8	0 40	10
44	10 27	0	1	1	2	2	3	3	4	4	5	5	6	6	6	7	7	8	8	9	9	44	10
48	11 24	1	1	2	2	3	3	4	4	5	5	6	6	7	7	8	8	9	9	10	10	48	11
52	12 21	1	1	2	2	3	3	4	4	5	5	6	7	7	8	8	9	9	10	10	11	52	12
0 56	13 18	1	1	2	2	3	4	4	5	5	6	6	7	8	8	9	9	10	11	11	12	0 56	13
1 00	14 15	1	1	2	3	3	4	4	5	6	6	7	8	8	9	9	10	11	11	12	13	1 00	14
04	15 12	1	1	2	3	3	4	5	5	6	7	7	8	9	9	10	11	11	12	13	13	04	15
(9 or 17) 08	16 09	1	1	2	3	4	4	5	6	6	7	8	9	9	10	11	11	12	13	13	14	08	16
12	17 06	1	2	2	3	4	5	5	6	7	8	8	9	10	11	11	12	13	14	14	15	12	17
16	18 03	1	2	2	3	4	5	6	6	7	8	9	10	10	11	12	13	13	14	15	16	16	18
1 20	19 00	1	2	3	3	4	5	6	7	8	8	9	10	11	12	13	13	14	15	16	17	1 20	19
24	19 57	1	2	3	4	4	5	6	7	8	9	10	11	11	12	13	14	15	16	17	18	24	20
28	20 54	1	2	3	4	5	6	6	7	8	9	10	11	12	13	14	15	16	17	17	18	28	21
32	21 51	1	2	3	4	5	6	7	8	9	10	11	12	12	13	14	15	16	17	18	19	32	22
36	22 48	1	2	3	4	5	6	7	8	9	10	11	12	13	14	15	16	17	18	19	20	36	23
1 40	23 45	1	2	3	4	5	6	7	8	9	10	11	13	14	15	16	17	18	19	20	21	1 40	24
44	24 42	1	2	3	4	5	7	8	9	10	11	12	13	14	15	16	17	18	20	21	22	44	25
48	25 39	1	2	3	5	6	7	8	9	10	11	12	14	15	16	17	18	19	20	21	23	48	26
52	26 36	1	2	4	5	6	7	8	9	11	12	13	14	15	16	18	19	20	21	22	23	52	27
1 56	27 33	1	2	4	5	6	7	8	10	11	12	13	15	16	17	18	19	21	22	23	24	1 56	28
2 00	28 30	1	3	4	5	6	8	9	10	11	13	14	15	16	18	19	20	21	23	24	25	2 00	29
04	29 27	1	3	4	5	6	8	9	10	12	13	14	16	17	18	19	21	22	23	25	26	04	29
(10 or 18) 08	30 24	1	3	4	5	7	8	9	11	12	13	15	16	17	19	20	21	23	24	25	27	08	30
12	31 21	1	3	4	6	7	8	10	11	12	14	15	17	18	19	21	22	23	25	26	28	12	31
16	32 18	1	3	4	6	7	9	10	11	13	14	16	17	18	20	21	23	24	26	27	28	16	32
2 20	33 15	1	3	4	6	7	9	10	12	13	15	16	18	19	20	22	23	25	26	28	29	2 20	33
24	34 12	2	3	5	6	8	9	11	12	14	15	17	18	20	21	23	24	26	27	29	30	24	34
28	35 09	2	3	5	6	8	9	11	12	14	15	17	19	20	22	23	25	26	28	29	31	28	35
32	36 06	2	3	5	6	8	10	11	13	14	16	17	19	21	22	24	25	27	29	30	32	32	36
36	37 03	2	3	5	7	8	10	11	13	15	16	18	20	21	23	24	26	28	29	31	33	36	37
2 40	38 00	2	3	5	7	8	10	12	13	15	17	18	20	22	23	25	27	28	30	32	33	2 40	38
44	38 57	2	3	5	7	9	10	12	14	15	17	19	21	22	24	26	27	29	31	32	34	44	39
48	39 54	2	4	5	7	9	11	12	14	16	18	19	21	23	25	26	28	30	32	33	35	48	40
52	40 51	2	4	5	7	9	11	13	14	16	18	20	22	23	25	27	29	30	32	34	36	52	41
2 56	41 48	2	4	6	7	9	11	13	15	17	18	20	22	24	26	28	29	31	33	35	37	2 56	42
3 00	42 45	2	4	6	8	9	11	13	15	17	19	21	23	24	26	28	30	32	34	36	38	3 00	43
04	43 42	2	4	6	8	10	12	13	15	17	19	21	23	25	27	29	31	33	35	36	38	04	44
(11 or 19) 08	44 39	2	4	6	8	10	12	14	16	18	20	22	24	25	27	29	31	33	35	37	39	08	45
12	45 36	2	4	6	8	10	12	14	16	18	20	22	24	26	28	30	32	34	36	38	40	12	46
16	46 33	2	4	6	8	10	12	14	16	18	20	22	25	27	29	31	33	35	37	39	41	16	47
3 20	47 30	2	4	6	8	10	13	15	17	19	21	23	25	27	29	31	33	35	38	40	42	3 20	48
24	48 27	2	4	6	9	11	13	15	17	19	21	23	26	28	30	32	34	36	38	40	43	24	48
28	49 24	2	4	7	9	11	13	15	17	20	22	24	26	28	30	33	35	37	39	41	43	28	49
32	50 21	2	4	7	9	11	13	15	18	20	22	24	27	29	31	33	35	38	40	42	44	32	50
36	51 18	2	5	7	9	11	14	16	18	20	23	25	27	29	32	34	36	38	41	43	45	36	51
3 40	52 15	2	5	7	9	11	14	16	18	21	23	25	28	30	32	34	37	39	41	44	46	3 40	52
44	53 12	2	5	7	9	12	14	16	19	21	23	26	28	30	33	35	37	40	42	44	47	44	53
48	54 09	2	5	7	10	12	14	17	19	21	24	26	29	31	33	36	38	40	43	45	48	48	54
52	55 06	2	5	7	10	12	15	17	19	22	24	27	29	31	34	36	39	41	44	46	48	52	55
3 56	56 03	2	5	7	10	12	15	17	20	22	25	27	30	32	34	37	39	42	44	47	49	3 56	56
4 00	57 00	3	5	8	10	13	15	18	20	23	25	28	30	33	35	38	40	43	45	48	50	4 00	57

INTERPOLATION TABLES — MOON 0^h–4^h, 8^h–12^h, 16^h–20^h

UT	Corr. to GHA	Correction to GHA or Declination for *v* or *d* 100	105	110	115	120	125	130	135	140	145	150	155	160	165	170	175	UT	Corr. to GHA
h m	° ′	Units of 1′																m s	′
0 00	0 00	0	0	0	0	0	0	0	0	0	0	0	0	0	0	0	0	0 00	00
(8 or 16) 04	0 57	1	1	1	1	1	1	1	1	1	1	1	1	1	1	1	1	04	01
08	1 54	2	2	2	2	2	2	2	2	2	2	3	3	3	3	3	3	08	02
12	2 51	3	3	3	3	3	3	3	3	4	4	4	4	4	4	4	4	12	03
16	3 48	3	4	4	4	4	4	4	5	5	5	5	5	5	6	6	6	16	04
0 20	4 45	4	4	5	5	5	5	5	6	6	6	6	6	7	7	7	7	0 20	05
24	5 42	5	5	6	6	6	6	7	7	7	7	8	8	8	8	9	9	24	06
28	6 39	6	6	6	7	7	7	8	8	8	8	9	9	9	10	10	10	28	07
32	7 36	7	7	7	8	8	8	9	9	9	10	10	10	11	11	11	12	32	08
36	8 33	8	8	8	9	9	9	10	10	11	11	11	12	12	12	13	13	36	09
0 40	9 30	8	9	9	10	10	10	11	11	12	12	13	13	13	14	14	15	0 40	10
44	10 27	9	10	10	11	11	11	12	12	13	13	14	14	15	15	16	16	44	10
48	11 24	10	11	11	12	12	13	13	14	14	15	15	16	16	17	17	18	48	11
52	12 21	11	11	12	12	13	14	14	15	15	16	16	17	17	18	18	19	52	12
0 56	13 18	12	12	13	13	14	15	15	16	16	17	18	18	19	19	20	20	0 56	13
1 00	14 15	13	13	14	14	15	16	16	17	18	18	19	19	20	21	21	22	1 00	14
(9 or 17) 04	15 12	13	14	15	15	16	17	17	18	19	19	20	21	21	22	23	23	04	15
08	16 09	14	15	16	16	17	18	18	19	20	21	21	22	23	23	24	25	08	16
12	17 06	15	16	17	17	18	19	20	20	21	22	23	23	24	25	26	26	12	17
16	18 03	16	17	17	18	19	20	21	21	22	23	24	25	25	26	27	28	16	18
1 20	19 00	17	18	18	19	20	21	22	23	23	24	25	26	27	28	28	29	1 20	19
24	19 57	18	18	19	20	21	22	23	24	25	25	26	27	28	29	30	31	24	20
28	20 54	18	19	20	21	22	23	24	25	26	27	28	28	29	30	31	32	28	21
32	21 51	19	20	21	22	23	24	25	26	27	28	29	30	31	32	33	34	32	22
36	22 48	20	21	22	23	24	25	26	27	28	29	30	31	32	33	34	35	36	23
1 40	23 45	21	22	23	24	25	26	27	28	29	30	31	32	33	34	35	36	1 40	24
44	24 42	22	23	24	25	26	27	28	29	30	31	33	34	35	36	37	38	44	25
48	25 39	23	24	25	26	27	28	29	30	32	33	34	35	36	37	38	39	48	26
52	26 36	23	25	26	27	28	29	30	32	33	34	35	36	37	39	40	41	52	27
1 56	27 33	24	25	27	28	29	30	31	33	34	35	36	37	39	40	41	42	1 56	28
2 00	28 30	25	26	28	29	30	31	33	34	35	36	38	39	40	41	43	44	2 00	29
(10 or 18) 04	29 27	26	27	28	30	31	32	34	35	36	37	39	40	41	43	44	45	04	29
08	30 24	27	28	29	31	32	33	35	36	37	39	40	41	43	44	45	47	08	30
12	31 21	28	29	30	32	33	34	36	37	39	40	41	43	44	45	47	48	12	31
16	32 18	28	30	31	33	34	35	37	38	40	41	43	44	45	47	48	50	16	32
2 20	33 15	29	31	32	34	35	36	38	39	41	42	44	45	47	48	50	51	2 20	33
24	34 12	30	32	33	35	36	38	39	41	42	44	45	47	48	50	51	53	24	34
28	35 09	31	32	34	35	37	39	40	42	43	45	46	48	49	51	52	54	28	35
32	36 06	32	33	35	36	38	40	41	43	44	46	48	49	51	52	54	55	32	36
36	37 03	33	34	36	37	39	41	42	44	46	47	49	50	52	54	55	57	36	37
2 40	38 00	33	35	37	38	40	42	43	45	47	48	50	52	53	55	57	58	2 40	38
44	38 57	34	36	38	39	41	43	44	46	48	50	51	53	55	56	58	60	44	39
48	39 54	35	37	39	40	42	44	46	47	49	51	53	54	56	58	60	61	48	40
52	40 51	36	38	39	41	43	45	47	48	50	52	54	56	57	59	61	63	52	41
2 56	41 48	37	39	40	42	44	46	48	50	51	53	55	57	59	61	62	64	2 56	42
3 00	42 45	38	39	41	43	45	47	49	51	53	54	56	58	60	62	64	66	3 00	43
(11 or 19) 04	43 42	38	40	42	44	46	48	50	52	54	56	58	59	61	63	65	67	04	44
08	44 39	39	41	43	45	47	49	51	53	55	57	59	61	63	65	67	69	08	45
12	45 36	40	42	44	46	48	50	52	54	56	58	60	62	64	66	68	70	12	46
16	46 33	41	43	45	47	49	51	53	55	57	59	61	63	65	67	69	71	16	47
3 20	47 30	42	44	46	48	50	52	54	56	58	60	63	65	67	69	71	73	3 20	48
24	48 27	43	45	47	49	51	53	55	57	60	62	64	66	68	70	72	74	24	48
28	49 24	43	46	48	50	52	54	56	59	61	63	65	67	69	72	74	76	28	49
32	50 21	44	46	49	51	53	55	57	60	62	64	66	68	71	73	75	77	32	50
36	51 18	45	47	50	52	54	56	59	61	63	65	68	70	72	74	77	79	36	51
3 40	52 15	46	48	50	53	55	57	60	62	64	66	69	71	73	76	78	80	3 40	52
44	53 12	47	49	51	54	56	58	61	63	65	68	70	72	75	77	79	82	44	53
48	54 09	48	50	52	55	57	59	62	64	67	69	71	74	76	78	81	83	48	54
52	55 06	48	51	53	56	58	60	63	65	68	70	73	75	77	80	82	85	52	55
3 56	56 03	49	52	54	57	59	61	64	66	69	71	74	76	79	81	84	86	3 56	56
4 00	57 00	50	53	55	58	60	63	65	68	70	73	75	78	80	83	85	88	4 00	57

INTERPOLATION TABLES — MOON 4^h–8^h, 12^h–16^h, 20^h–24^h

Correction to GHA or Declination for *v* or *d* — Units of 1′

UT h m	Corr. to GHA ° ′	5	10	15	20	25	30	35	40	45	50	55	60	65	70	75	80	85	90	95	100	UT m s	Corr. to GHA ′
4 00	57 00	3	5	8	10	13	15	18	20	23	25	28	30	33	35	38	40	43	45	48	50	0 00	00
04	57 57	3	5	8	10	13	15	18	20	23	25	28	31	33	36	38	41	43	46	48	51	04	01
(12 or 20) 08	58 54	3	5	8	10	13	16	18	21	23	26	28	31	34	36	39	41	44	47	49	52	08	02
12	59 51	3	5	8	11	13	16	18	21	24	26	29	32	34	37	39	42	45	47	50	53	12	03
16	60 48	3	5	8	11	13	16	19	21	24	27	29	32	35	37	40	43	45	48	51	53	16	04
4 20	61 45	3	5	8	11	14	16	19	22	24	27	30	33	35	38	41	43	46	49	51	54	0 20	05
24	62 42	3	6	8	11	14	17	19	22	25	28	30	33	36	39	41	44	47	50	52	55	24	06
28	63 39	3	6	8	11	14	17	20	22	25	28	31	34	36	39	42	45	47	50	53	56	28	07
32	64 36	3	6	9	11	14	17	20	23	26	28	31	34	37	40	43	45	48	51	54	57	32	08
36	65 33	3	6	9	12	14	17	20	23	26	29	32	35	37	40	43	46	49	52	55	58	36	09
4 40	66 30	3	6	9	12	15	18	20	23	26	29	32	35	38	41	44	47	50	53	55	58	0 40	10
44	67 27	3	6	9	12	15	18	21	24	27	30	33	36	38	41	44	47	50	53	56	59	44	10
48	68 24	3	6	9	12	15	18	21	24	27	30	33	36	39	42	45	48	51	54	57	60	48	11
52	69 21	3	6	9	12	15	18	21	24	27	30	33	37	40	43	46	49	52	55	58	61	52	12
4 56	70 18	3	6	9	12	15	19	22	25	28	31	34	37	40	43	46	49	52	56	59	62	0 56	13
5 00	71 15	3	6	9	13	16	19	22	25	28	31	34	38	41	44	47	50	53	56	59	63	1 00	14
04	72 12	3	6	10	13	16	19	22	25	29	32	35	38	41	44	48	51	54	57	60	63	04	15
(13 or 21) 08	73 09	3	6	10	13	16	19	22	26	29	32	35	39	42	45	48	51	55	58	61	64	08	16
12	74 06	3	7	10	13	16	20	23	26	29	33	36	39	42	46	49	52	55	59	62	65	12	17
16	75 03	3	7	10	13	16	20	23	26	30	33	36	40	43	46	49	53	56	59	63	66	16	18
5 20	76 00	3	7	10	13	17	20	23	27	30	33	37	40	43	47	50	53	57	60	63	67	1 20	19
24	76 57	3	7	10	14	17	20	24	27	30	34	37	41	44	47	51	54	57	61	64	68	24	20
28	77 54	3	7	10	14	17	21	24	27	31	34	38	41	44	48	51	55	58	62	65	68	28	21
32	78 51	3	7	10	14	17	21	24	28	31	35	38	42	45	48	52	55	59	62	66	69	32	22
36	79 48	4	7	11	14	18	21	25	28	32	35	39	42	46	49	53	56	60	63	67	70	36	23
5 40	80 45	4	7	11	14	18	21	25	28	32	35	39	43	46	50	53	57	60	64	67	71	1 40	24
44	81 42	4	7	11	14	18	22	25	29	32	36	39	43	47	50	54	57	61	65	68	72	44	25
48	82 39	4	7	11	15	18	22	25	29	33	36	40	44	47	51	54	58	62	65	69	73	48	26
52	83 36	4	7	11	15	18	22	26	29	33	37	40	44	48	51	55	59	62	66	70	73	52	27
5 56	84 33	4	7	11	15	19	22	26	30	33	37	41	45	48	52	56	59	63	67	70	74	1 56	28
6 00	85 30	4	8	11	15	19	23	26	30	34	38	41	45	49	53	56	60	64	68	71	75	2 00	29
04	86 27	4	8	11	15	19	23	27	30	34	38	42	46	49	53	57	61	64	68	72	76	04	29
(14 or 22) 08	87 24	4	8	12	15	19	23	27	31	35	38	42	46	50	54	58	61	65	69	73	77	08	30
12	88 21	4	8	12	16	19	23	27	31	35	39	43	47	50	54	58	62	66	70	74	78	12	31
16	89 18	4	8	12	16	20	24	27	31	35	39	43	47	51	55	59	63	67	71	74	78	16	32
6 20	90 15	4	8	12	16	20	24	28	32	36	40	44	48	51	55	59	63	67	71	75	79	2 20	33
24	91 12	4	8	12	16	20	24	28	32	36	40	44	48	52	56	60	64	68	72	76	80	24	34
28	92 09	4	8	12	16	20	24	28	32	36	40	44	49	53	57	61	65	69	73	77	81	28	35
32	93 06	4	8	12	16	20	25	29	33	37	41	45	49	53	57	61	65	69	74	78	82	32	36
36	94 03	4	8	12	17	21	25	29	33	37	41	45	50	54	58	62	66	70	74	78	83	36	37
6 40	95 00	4	8	13	17	21	25	29	33	38	42	46	50	54	58	63	67	71	75	79	83	2 40	38
44	95 57	4	8	13	17	21	25	29	34	38	42	46	51	55	59	63	67	72	76	80	84	44	39
48	96 54	4	9	13	17	21	26	30	34	38	43	47	51	55	60	64	68	72	77	81	85	48	40
52	97 51	4	9	13	17	21	26	30	34	39	43	47	52	56	60	64	69	73	77	82	86	52	41
6 56	98 48	4	9	13	17	22	26	30	35	39	43	48	52	56	61	65	69	74	78	82	87	2 56	42
7 00	99 45	4	9	13	18	22	26	31	35	39	44	48	53	57	61	66	70	74	79	83	88	3 00	43
04	100 42	4	9	13	18	22	27	31	35	40	44	49	53	57	62	66	71	75	80	84	88	04	44
(15 or 23) 08	101 39	4	9	13	18	22	27	31	36	40	45	49	54	58	62	67	71	76	80	85	89	08	45
12	102 36	5	9	14	18	23	27	32	36	41	45	50	54	59	63	68	72	77	81	86	90	12	46
16	103 33	5	9	14	18	23	27	32	36	41	45	50	55	59	64	68	73	77	82	86	91	16	47
7 20	104 30	5	9	14	18	23	28	32	37	41	46	50	55	60	64	69	73	78	83	87	92	3 20	48
24	105 27	5	9	14	19	23	28	32	37	42	46	51	56	60	65	69	74	79	83	88	93	24	48
28	106 24	5	9	14	19	23	28	33	37	42	47	51	56	61	65	70	75	79	84	89	93	28	49
32	107 21	5	9	14	19	24	28	33	38	42	47	52	57	61	66	71	75	80	85	89	94	32	50
36	108 18	5	10	14	19	24	29	33	38	43	48	52	57	62	67	71	76	81	86	90	95	36	51
7 40	109 15	5	10	14	19	24	29	34	38	43	48	53	58	62	67	72	77	81	86	91	96	3 40	52
44	110 12	5	10	15	19	24	29	34	39	44	48	53	58	63	68	73	77	82	87	92	97	44	53
48	111 09	5	10	15	20	24	29	34	39	44	49	54	59	63	68	73	78	83	88	93	98	48	54
52	112 06	5	10	15	20	25	30	34	39	44	49	54	59	64	69	74	79	84	89	93	98	52	55
7 56	113 03	5	10	15	20	25	30	35	40	45	50	55	60	64	69	74	79	84	89	94	99	3 56	56
8 00	114 00	5	10	15	20	25	30	35	40	45	50	55	60	65	70	75	80	85	90	95	100	4 00	57

INTERPOLATION TABLES — MOON 4^h–8^h, 12^h–16^h, 20^h–24^h

UT	Corr. to GHA	Correction to GHA or Declination for *v* or *d*																UT	Corr. to GHA
		100	105	110	115	120	125	130	135	140	145	150	155	160	165	170	175		
h m	° ′	Units of 1′																m s	′
4 00	57 00	50	53	55	58	60	63	65	68	70	73	75	78	80	83	85	88	0 00	00
04	57 57	51	53	56	58	61	64	66	69	71	74	76	79	81	84	86	89	04	01
(12 or 20) 08	58 54	52	54	57	59	62	65	67	70	72	75	78	80	83	85	88	90	08	02
12	59 51	53	55	58	60	63	66	68	71	74	76	79	81	84	87	89	92	12	03
16	60 48	53	56	59	61	64	67	69	72	75	77	80	83	85	88	91	93	16	04
4 20	61 45	54	57	60	62	65	68	70	73	76	79	81	84	87	89	92	95	0 20	05
24	62 42	55	58	61	63	66	69	72	74	77	80	83	85	88	91	94	96	24	06
28	63 39	56	59	61	64	67	70	73	75	78	81	84	87	89	92	95	98	28	07
32	64 36	57	60	62	65	68	71	74	77	79	82	85	88	91	94	96	99	32	08
36	65 33	58	60	63	66	69	72	75	78	81	83	86	89	92	95	98	101	36	09
4 40	66 30	58	61	64	67	70	73	76	79	82	85	88	90	93	96	99	102	0 40	10
44	67 27	59	62	65	68	71	74	77	80	83	86	89	92	95	98	101	104	44	10
48	68 24	60	63	66	69	72	75	78	81	84	87	90	93	96	99	102	105	48	11
52	69 21	61	64	67	70	73	76	79	82	85	88	91	94	97	100	103	106	52	12
4 56	70 18	62	65	68	71	74	77	80	83	86	89	93	96	99	102	105	108	0 56	13
5 00	71 15	63	66	69	72	75	78	81	84	88	91	94	97	100	103	106	109	1 00	14
04	72 12	63	67	70	73	76	79	82	86	89	92	95	98	101	105	108	111	04	15
(13 or 21) 08	73 09	64	67	71	74	77	80	83	87	90	93	96	99	103	106	109	112	08	16
12	74 06	65	68	72	75	78	81	85	88	91	94	98	101	104	107	111	114	12	17
16	75 03	66	69	72	76	79	82	86	89	92	95	99	102	105	109	112	115	16	18
5 20	76 00	67	70	73	77	80	83	87	90	93	97	100	103	107	110	113	117	1 20	19
24	76 57	68	71	74	78	81	84	88	91	95	98	101	105	108	111	115	118	24	20
28	77 54	68	72	75	79	82	85	89	92	96	99	103	106	109	113	116	120	28	21
32	78 51	69	73	76	80	83	86	90	93	97	100	104	107	111	114	118	121	32	22
36	79 48	70	74	77	81	84	88	91	95	98	102	105	109	112	116	119	123	36	23
5 40	80 45	71	74	78	81	85	89	92	96	99	103	106	110	113	117	120	124	1 40	24
44	81 42	72	75	79	82	86	90	93	97	100	104	108	111	115	118	122	125	44	25
48	82 39	73	76	80	83	87	91	94	98	102	105	109	112	116	120	123	127	48	26
52	83 36	73	77	81	84	88	92	95	99	103	106	110	114	117	121	125	128	52	27
5 56	84 33	74	78	82	85	89	93	96	100	104	108	111	115	119	122	126	130	1 56	28
6 00	85 30	75	79	83	86	90	94	98	101	105	109	113	116	120	124	128	131	2 00	29
04	86 27	76	80	83	87	91	95	99	102	106	110	114	118	121	125	129	133	04	29
(14 or 22) 08	87 24	77	81	84	88	92	96	100	104	107	111	115	119	123	127	130	134	08	30
12	88 21	78	81	85	89	93	97	101	105	109	112	116	120	124	128	132	136	12	31
16	89 18	78	82	86	90	94	98	102	106	110	114	118	121	125	129	133	137	16	32
6 20	90 15	79	83	87	91	95	99	103	107	111	115	119	123	127	131	135	139	2 20	33
24	91 12	80	84	88	92	96	100	104	108	112	116	120	124	128	132	136	140	24	34
28	92 09	81	85	89	93	97	101	105	109	113	117	121	125	129	133	137	141	28	35
32	93 06	82	86	90	94	98	102	106	110	114	118	123	127	131	135	139	143	32	36
36	94 03	83	87	91	95	99	103	107	111	116	120	124	128	132	136	140	144	36	37
6 40	95 00	83	88	92	96	100	104	108	113	117	121	125	129	133	138	142	146	2 40	38
44	95 57	84	88	93	97	101	105	109	114	118	122	126	130	135	139	143	147	44	39
48	96 54	85	89	94	98	102	106	111	115	119	123	128	132	136	140	145	149	48	40
52	97 51	86	90	94	99	103	107	112	116	120	124	129	133	137	142	146	150	52	41
6 56	98 48	87	91	95	100	104	108	113	117	121	126	130	134	139	143	147	152	2 56	42
7 00	99 45	88	92	96	101	105	109	114	118	123	127	131	136	140	144	149	153	3 00	43
04	100 42	88	93	97	102	106	110	115	119	124	128	133	137	141	146	150	155	04	44
(15 or 23) 08	101 39	89	94	98	103	107	111	116	120	125	129	134	138	143	147	152	156	08	45
12	102 36	90	95	99	104	108	113	117	122	126	131	135	140	144	149	153	158	12	46
16	103 33	91	95	100	104	109	114	118	123	127	132	136	141	145	150	154	159	16	47
7 20	104 30	92	96	101	105	110	115	119	124	128	133	138	142	147	151	156	160	3 20	48
24	105 27	93	97	102	106	111	116	120	125	130	134	139	143	148	153	157	162	24	48
28	106 24	93	98	103	107	112	117	121	126	131	135	140	145	149	154	159	163	28	49
32	107 21	94	99	104	108	113	118	122	127	132	137	141	146	151	155	160	165	32	50
36	108 18	95	100	105	109	114	119	124	128	133	138	143	147	152	157	162	166	36	51
7 40	109 15	96	101	105	110	115	120	125	129	134	139	144	149	153	158	163	168	3 40	52
44	110 12	97	102	106	111	116	121	126	131	135	140	145	150	155	160	164	169	44	53
48	111 09	98	102	107	112	117	122	127	132	137	141	146	151	156	161	166	171	48	54
52	112 06	98	103	108	113	118	123	128	133	138	143	148	152	157	162	167	172	52	55
7 56	113 03	99	104	109	114	119	124	129	134	139	144	149	154	159	164	169	174	3 56	56
8 00	114 00	100	105	110	115	120	125	130	135	140	145	150	155	160	165	170	175	4 00	57

5

5.3.10 STAR DIAGRAM (LHA ARIES 0°-120°)

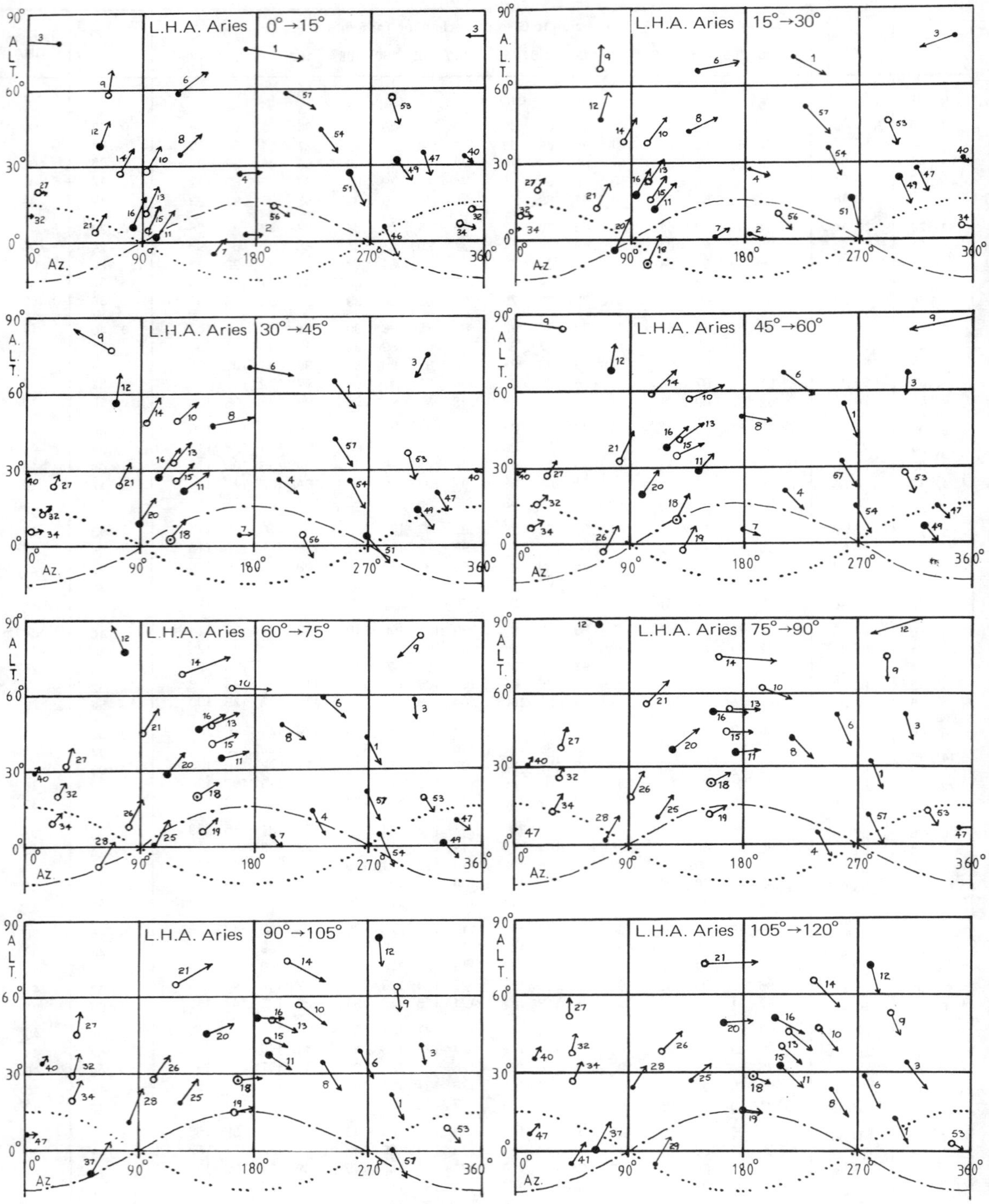
L.H.A. Aries 0°→15°
L.H.A. Aries 15°→30°
L.H.A. Aries 30°→45°
L.H.A. Aries 45°→60°
L.H.A. Aries 60°→75°
L.H.A. Aries 75°→90°
L.H.A. Aries 90°→105°
L.H.A. Aries 105°→120°
ALT.
Az.
0°
30°
60°
90°
180°
270°
360°

The diagrams are explained in 5.2.6 on page 74. Note that when a star is near the zenith its azimuth is liable to a considerable change for a small change in latitude. The magnitude corresponding to the star symbols is shown alongside.

Mag 2.1 to 3.1
○ Mag 1.1 to 2.0
• Mag 0.0 to 1.0
⊙ Mag −1.6 to 0.0

STAR DIAGRAM (LHA ARIES 120°-240°)

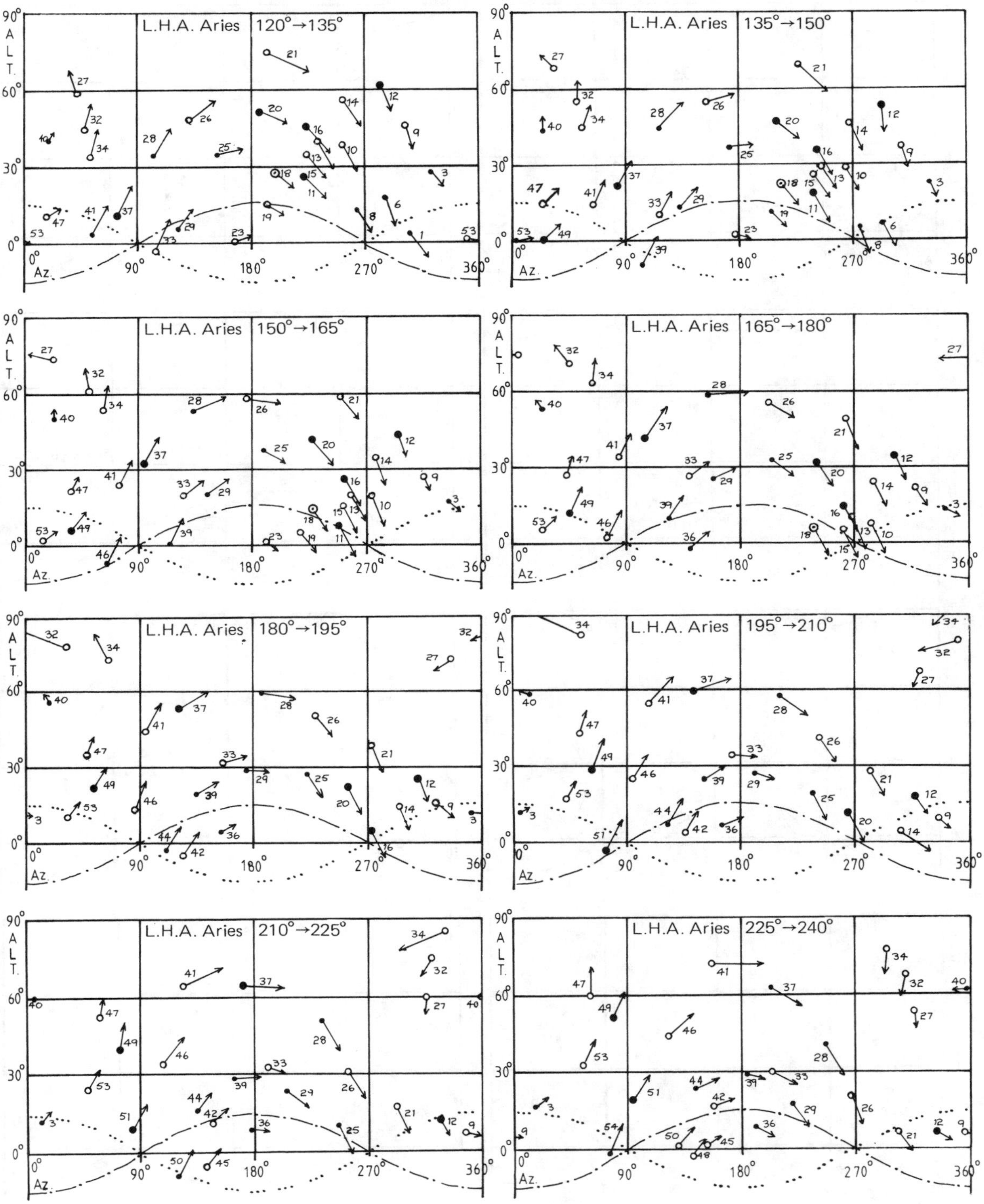
L.H.A. Aries 120°→135°
L.H.A. Aries 135°→150°
L.H.A. Aries 150°→165°
L.H.A. Aries 165°→180°
L.H.A. Aries 180°→195°
L.H.A. Aries 195°→210°
L.H.A. Aries 210°→225°
L.H.A. Aries 225°→240°
ALT.
Az.
0° 90° 180° 270° 360°
0° 30° 60° 90°

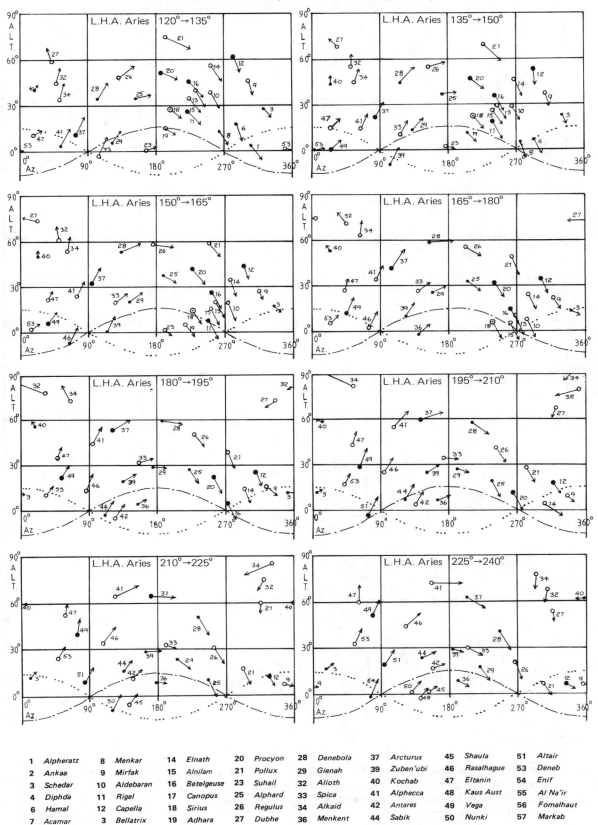

1	*Alpheratz*	8	*Menkar*	14	*Elnath*	20	*Procyon*	28	*Denebola*	37	*Arcturus*	45	*Shaula*	51	*Altair*
2	*Ankaa*	9	*Mirfak*	15	*Alnilam*	21	*Pollux*	29	*Gienah*	39	*Zuben'ubi*	46	*Rasalhague*	53	*Deneb*
3	*Schedar*	10	*Aldebaran*	16	*Betelgeuse*	23	*Suhail*	32	*Alioth*	40	*Kochab*	47	*Eltanin*	54	*Enif*
4	*Diphda*	11	*Rigel*	17	*Canopus*	25	*Alphard*	33	*Spica*	41	*Alphecca*	48	*Kaus Aust*	55	*Al Na'ir*
6	*Hamal*	12	*Capella*	18	*Sirius*	26	*Regulus*	34	*Alkaid*	42	*Antares*	49	*Vega*	56	*Fomalhaut*
7	*Acamar*	3	*Bellatrix*	19	*Adhara*	27	*Dubhe*	36	*Menkent*	44	*Sabik*	50	*Nunki*	57	*Markab*

STAR DIAGRAM (LHA ARIES 240°-360°)

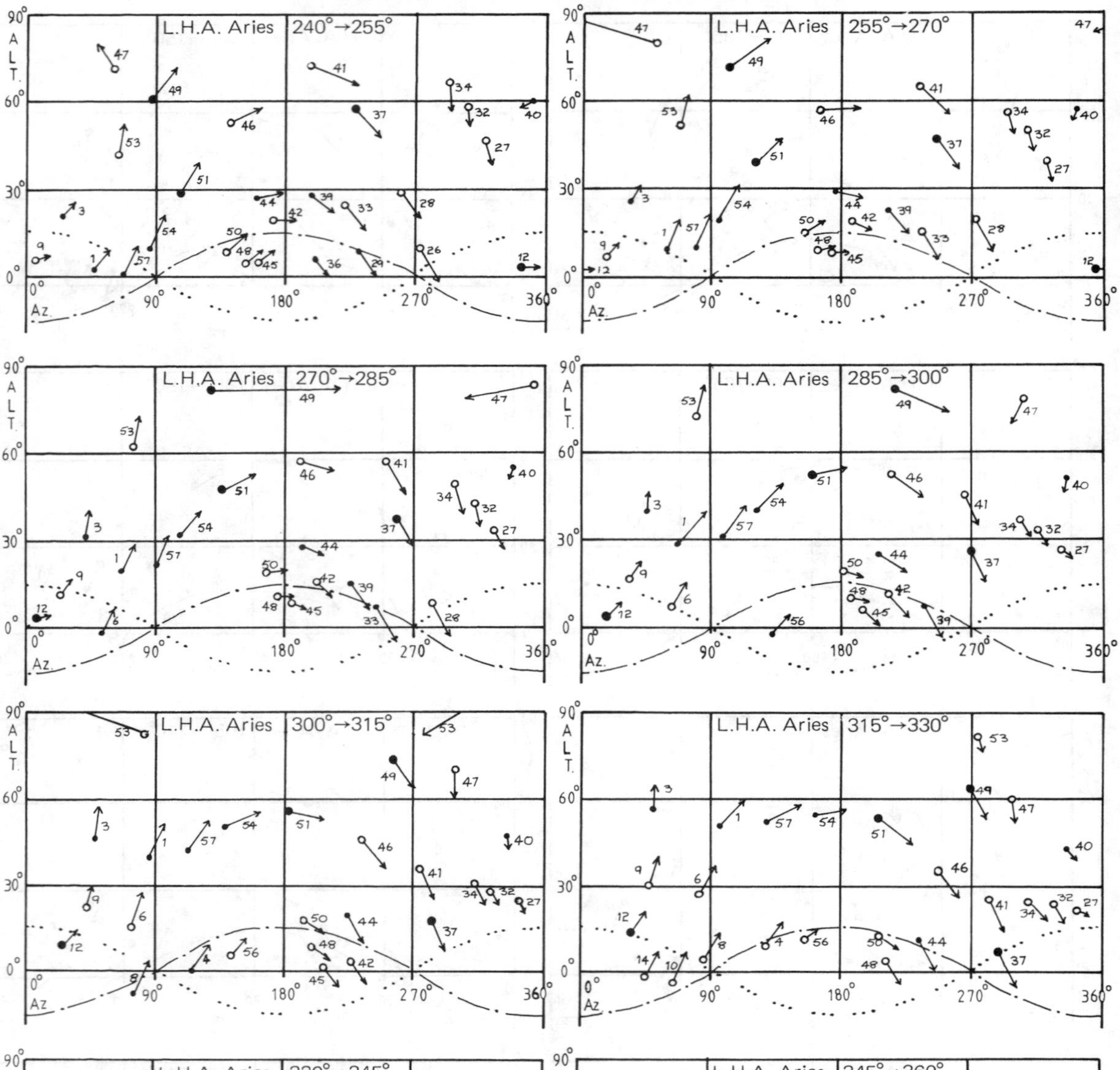
L.H.A. Aries 240°→255°
L.H.A. Aries 255°→270°
L.H.A. Aries 270°→285°
L.H.A. Aries 285°→300°
L.H.A. Aries 300°→315°
L.H.A. Aries 315°→330°
L.H.A. Aries 330°→345°
L.H.A. Aries 345°→360°
ALT.
Az.
0° 90° 180° 270° 360°
0° 30° 60° 90°

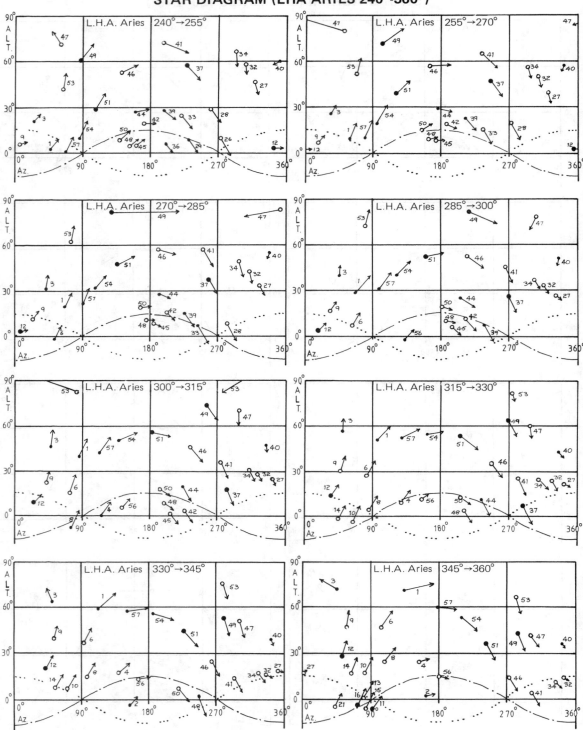

The diagrams are explained in 5.2.6 on page 74. Note that when a star is near the zenith its azimuth is liable to a considerable change for a small change in latitude. The magnitude corresponding to the star symbols is shown alongside.

·	Mag 2.1 to 3.1
○	Mag 1.1 to 2.0
●	Mag 0.0 to 1.0
⊙	Mag −1.6 to 0.0

5.3.11 AZIMUTH DIAGRAM A

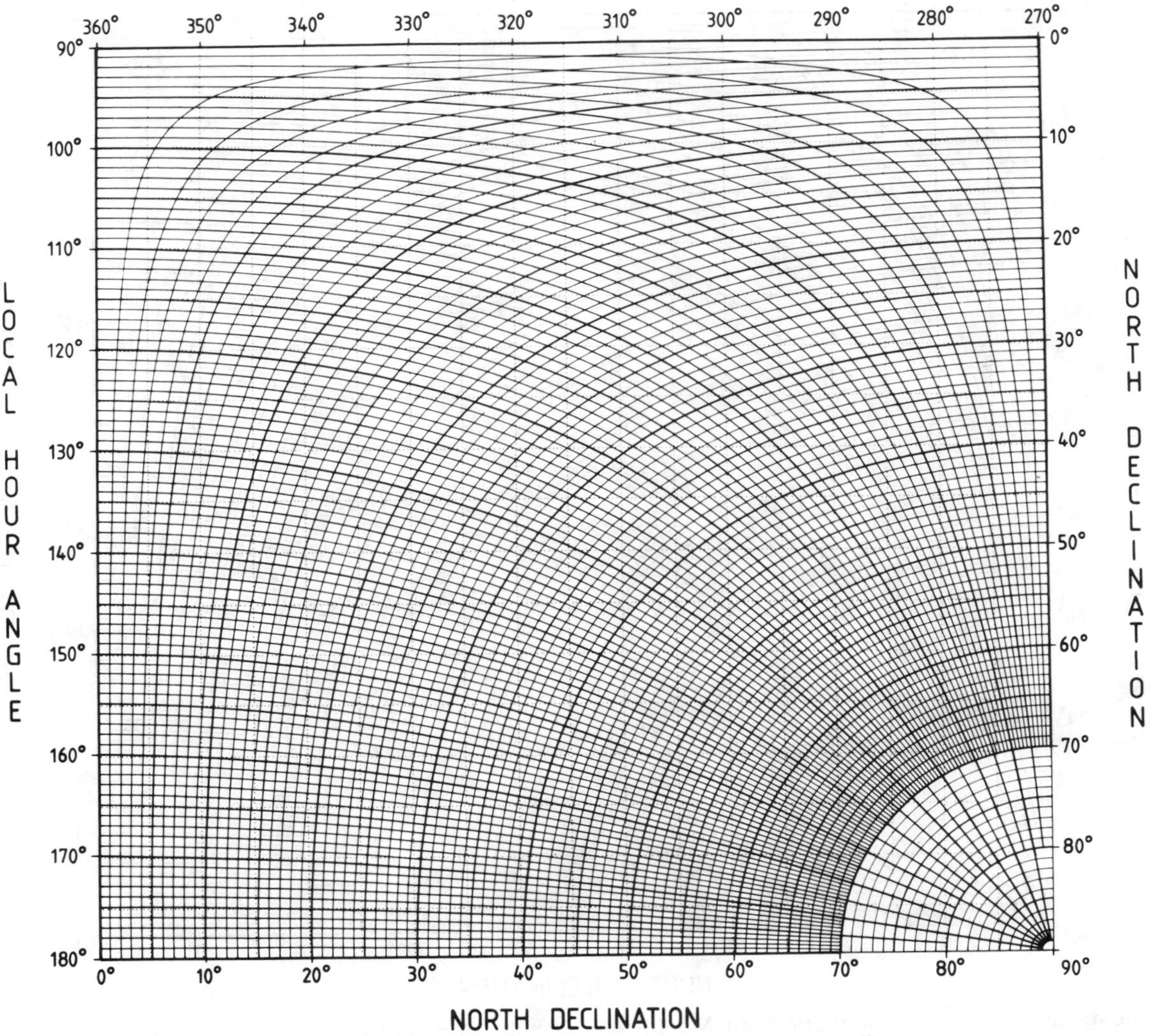
360° 350° 340° 330° 320° 310° 300° 290° 280° 270°
90° 100° 110° 120° 130° 140° 150° 160° 170° 180°
LOCAL HOUR ANGLE
0° 10° 20° 30° 40° 50° 60° 70° 80° 90°
NORTH DECLINATION
0° 10° 20° 30° 40° 50° 60° 70° 80° 90°
NORTH DECLINATION

Instructions — To determine the Azimuth of an observed body given the latitude of the observer (Lat) and the LHA and Dec of the body.

(1) Plot on the diagrams a position corresponding to the LHA and Dec; if the LHA is greater than 180° use 360° — LHA when plotting.
(2) Read the position of the plotted point on the rectangular graticule, using the scale at the top for the horizontal reading, and the declination scale for the vertical reading.
(3) To the horizontal reading in (2) add the co-latitude (i.e. add 90° and subtract Lat). The vertical co-ordinate is unchanged.
(4) At the point corresponding to the co-ordinates in (3) read the corresponding LHA (= Z).
(5) Z is converted to Azimuth as follows:

LHA (body)	*Azimuth*
0° to 180°	180° + Z
180° to 360°	180° — Z

Note that in step (4) a reading of the Dec at the same point gives an approximate value of the altitude, and so gives a check on the plotting.

The diagrams A, B and C are portions of a continuous diagram (see p. 115), so that if the movement for co-latitude goes off the diagram on which step (2) is plotted, then the overlap can be found on the previous diagram.

AZIMUTH DIAGRAM B

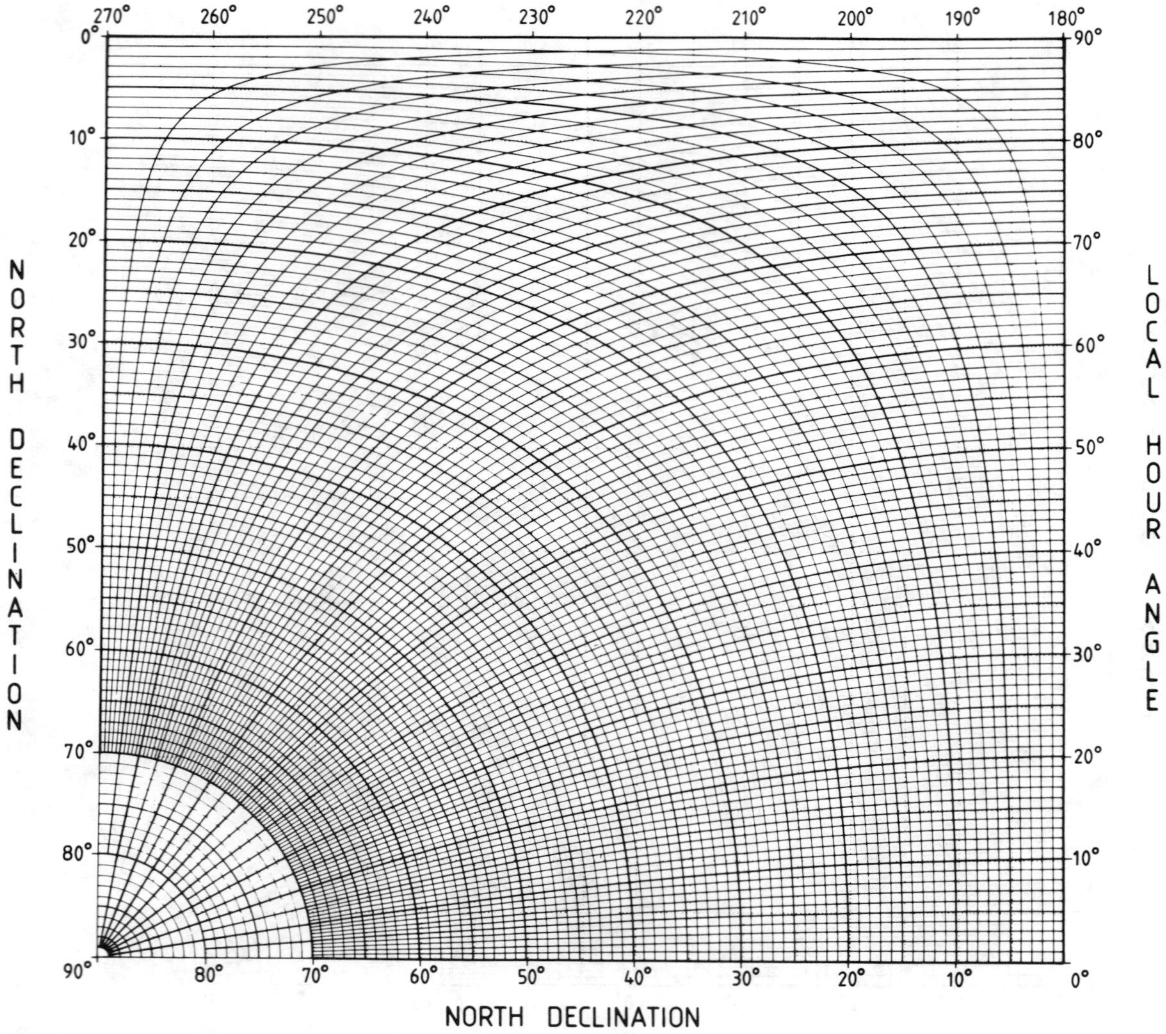
270°
260°
250°
240°
230°
220°
210°
200°
190°
180°
0°
10°
20°
30°
40°
50°
60°
70°
80°
90°
90°
80°
70°
60°
50°
40°
30°
20°
10°
0°
NORTH DECLINATION
LOCAL HOUR ANGLE
90°
80°
70°
60°
50°
40°
30°
20°
10°
0°
NORTH DECLINATION

Illustration — On 1992 January 5 at GMT 14^h 40^m 18^s, the Sun is observed from a position N 44° 36′ W2° 40′ and it is required to determine the azimuth.

				v	Dec	*d*
			° ′	′	° ′	′
Page 89	Jan 5, 00^h	GHA	178 46·1	−6·7	S22 43·0	+6·6
Interpolation	UT 14^h 36^m		219			
Tables	UT 04^m 18^s		1 04·5			
Page 101	*v, d* correction		−04·1		+4·1	
	UT 14^h 40^m 18^s	GHA	398 46·5			
	Longitude W2°40′		−2 40·0			
		LHA	396 06·5			
	Remove 360°		−360			
		LHA	36 06·5		Dec. S22 38·9	

On diagram C plot the point P with LHA = 36°.1 and Dec = S22°.6. The corresponding rectangular coordinates are found to be 153° (across) and 57° (down). To the horizontal coordinate (153°) add 90° and subtract the latitude 44°.6, which equals 198°.4. On diagram B plot the point Q with rectangular coordinates 198°.4 (across) and 57° (down). The corresponding coordinates are LHA (= Z) and Dec which are found to be 34° and 15°. Hence the Azimuth is 180° + 34° = 214°, and the approximate altitude is 15° which can be compared with the observed altitude as a check on the plotting.

AZIMUTH DIAGRAM C

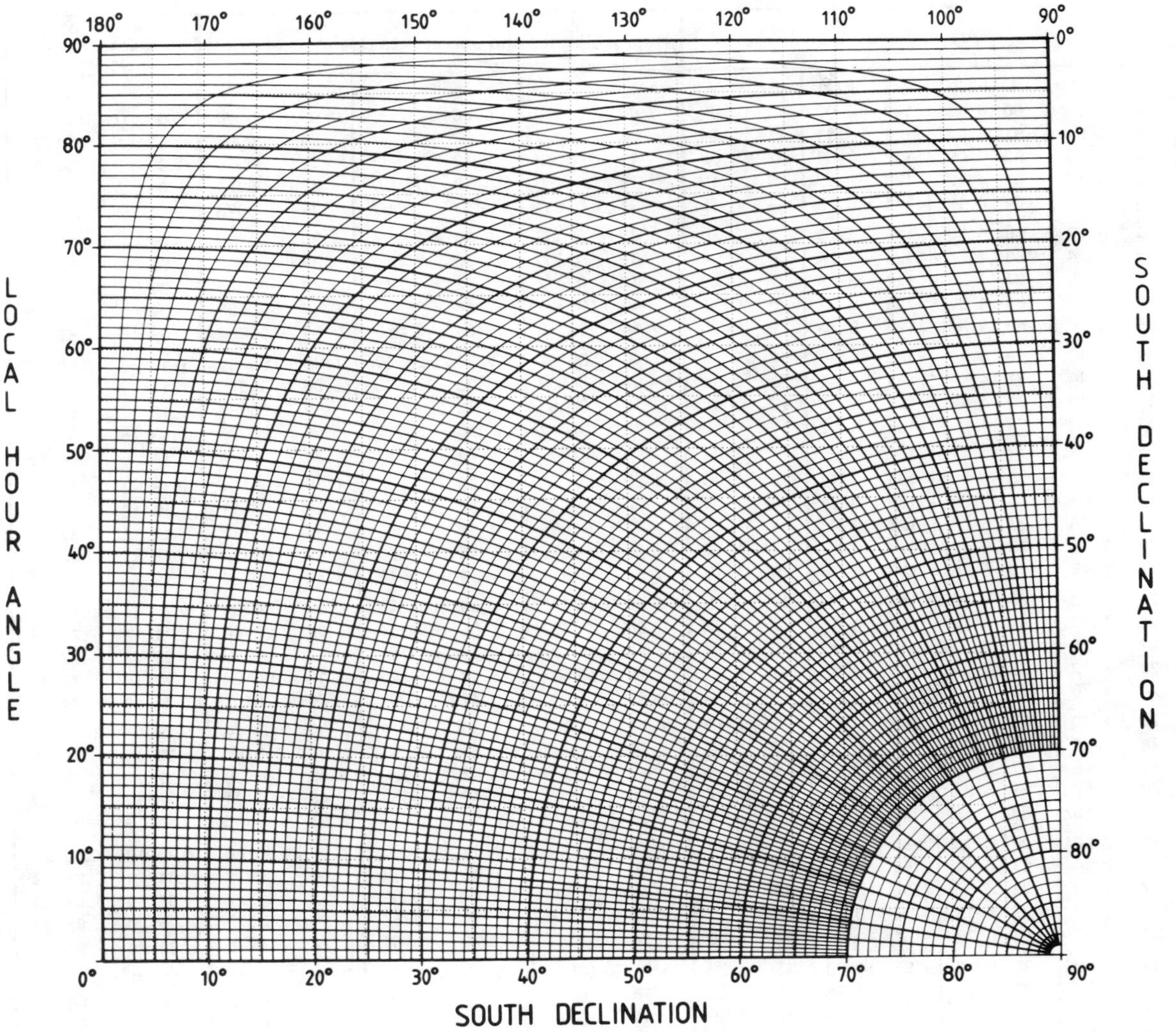
180°
170°
160°
150°
140°
130°
120°
110°
100°
90°
0°
10°
20°
30°
40°
50°
60°
70°
80°
90°
LOCAL HOUR ANGLE
80°
70°
60°
50°
40°
30°
20°
10°
0°
SOUTH DECLINATION
SOUTH DECLINATION

The illustration below shows how A, B and C are portions of a continuous diagram. The points P and Q show the plotting of the example opposite.

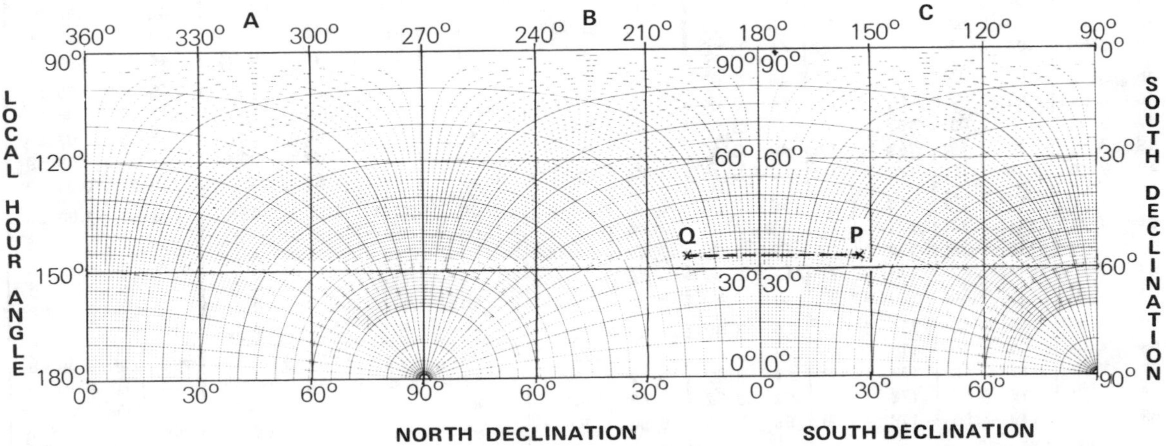
A
B
C
360°
330°
300°
270°
240°
210°
180°
150°
120°
90°
0°
90° 90°
60° 60°
30° 30°
0° 0°
Q
P
30°
60°
90°
LOCAL HOUR ANGLE
120°
150°
180°
SOUTH DECLINATION
NORTH DECLINATION
SOUTH DECLINATION

5.3.12 CONVERSION TABLES

Arc to Time

°	h m	°	h m	°	h m	′	m s
0	0 00	**60**	4 00	**120**	8 00	**0**	0 00
1	0 04	**61**	4 04	**121**	8 04	**1**	0 04
2	0 08	**62**	4 08	**122**	8 08	**2**	0 08
3	0 12	**63**	4 12	**123**	8 12	**3**	0 12
4	0 16	**64**	4 16	**124**	8 16	**4**	0 16
5	0 20	**65**	4 20	**125**	8 20	**5**	0 20
6	0 24	**66**	4 24	**126**	8 24	**6**	0 24
7	0 28	**67**	4 28	**127**	8 28	**7**	0 28
8	0 32	**68**	4 32	**128**	8 32	**8**	0 32
9	0 36	**69**	4 36	**129**	8 36	**9**	0 36
10	0 40	**70**	4 40	**130**	8 40	**10**	0 40
11	0 44	**71**	4 44	**131**	8 44	**11**	0 44
12	0 48	**72**	4 48	**132**	8 48	**12**	0 48
13	0 52	**73**	4 52	**133**	8 52	**13**	0 52
14	0 56	**74**	4 56	**134**	8 56	**14**	0 56
15	1 00	**75**	5 00	**135**	9 00	**15**	1 00
16	1 04	**76**	5 04	**136**	9 04	**16**	1 04
17	1 08	**77**	5 08	**137**	9 08	**17**	1 08
18	1 12	**78**	5 12	**138**	9 12	**18**	1 12
19	1 16	**79**	5 16	**139**	9 16	**19**	1 16
20	1 20	**80**	5 20	**140**	9 20	**20**	1 20
21	1 24	**81**	5 24	**141**	9 24	**21**	1 24
22	1 28	**82**	5 28	**142**	9 28	**22**	1 28
23	1 32	**83**	5 32	**143**	9 32	**23**	1 32
24	1 36	**84**	5 36	**144**	9 36	**24**	1 36
25	1 40	**85**	5 40	**145**	9 40	**25**	1 40
26	1 44	**86**	5 44	**146**	9 44	**26**	1 44
27	1 48	**87**	5 48	**147**	9 48	**27**	1 48
28	1 52	**88**	5 52	**148**	9 52	**28**	1 52
29	1 56	**89**	5 56	**149**	9 56	**29**	1 56
30	2 00	**90**	6 00	**150**	10 00	**30**	2 00
31	2 04	**91**	6 04	**151**	10 04	**31**	2 04
32	2 08	**92**	6 08	**152**	10 08	**32**	2 08
33	2 12	**93**	6 12	**153**	10 12	**33**	2 12
34	2 16	**94**	6 16	**154**	10 16	**34**	2 16
35	2 20	**95**	6 20	**155**	10 20	**35**	2 20
36	2 24	**96**	6 24	**156**	10 24	**36**	2 24
37	2 28	**97**	6 28	**157**	10 28	**37**	2 28
38	2 32	**98**	6 32	**158**	10 32	**38**	2 32
39	2 36	**99**	6 36	**159**	10 36	**39**	2 36
40	2 40	**100**	6 40	**160**	10 40	**40**	2 40
41	2 44	**101**	6 44	**161**	10 44	**41**	2 44
42	2 48	**102**	6 48	**162**	10 48	**42**	2 48
43	2 52	**103**	6 52	**163**	10 52	**43**	2 52
44	2 56	**104**	6 56	**164**	10 56	**44**	2 56
45	3 00	**105**	7 00	**165**	11 00	**45**	3 00
46	3 04	**106**	7 04	**166**	11 04	**46**	3 04
47	3 08	**107**	7 08	**167**	11 08	**47**	3 08
48	3 12	**108**	7 12	**168**	11 12	**48**	3 12
49	3 16	**109**	7 16	**169**	11 16	**49**	3 16
50	3 20	**110**	7 20	**170**	11 20	**50**	3 20
51	3 24	**111**	7 24	**171**	11 24	**51**	3 24
52	3 28	**112**	7 28	**172**	11 28	**52**	3 28
53	3 32	**113**	7 32	**173**	11 32	**53**	3 32
54	3 36	**114**	7 36	**174**	11 36	**54**	3 36
55	3 40	**115**	7 40	**175**	11 40	**55**	3 40
56	3 44	**116**	7 44	**176**	11 44	**56**	3 44
57	3 48	**117**	7 48	**177**	11 48	**57**	3 48
58	3 52	**118**	7 52	**178**	11 52	**58**	3 52
59	3 56	**119**	7 56	**179**	11 56	**59**	3 56

180° = $12^h\ 00^m$

Hours, Minutes and Seconds to Decimals of a Day

h m	d	h m	d	m s	d
0 00	0.00000	**6 00**	0.25000	**0 00**	0.00000
06	.00417	**06**	.25417	**06**	.00007
12	.00833	**12**	.25833	**12**	.00014
18	.01250	**18**	.26250	**18**	.00021
24	.01667	**24**	.26667	**24**	.00028
0 30	0.02083	**6 30**	0.27083	**0 30**	0.00035
36	.02500	**36**	.27500	**36**	.00042
42	.02917	**42**	.27917	**42**	.00049
48	.03333	**48**	.28333	**48**	.00056
0 54	.03750	**6 54**	.28750	**0 54**	.00062
1 00	0.04167	**7 00**	0.29167	**1 00**	0.00069
06	.04583	**06**	.29583	**06**	.00076
12	.05000	**12**	.30000	**12**	.00083
18	.05417	**18**	.30417	**18**	.00090
24	.05833	**24**	.30833	**24**	.00097
1 30	0.06250	**7 30**	0.31250	**1 30**	0.00104
36	.06667	**36**	.31667	**36**	.00111
42	.07083	**42**	.32083	**42**	.00118
48	.07500	**48**	.32500	**48**	.00125
1 54	.07917	**7 54**	.32917	**1 54**	.00132
2 00	0.08333	**8 00**	0.33333	**2 00**	0.00139
06	.08750	**06**	.33750	**06**	.00146
12	.09167	**12**	.34167	**12**	.00153
18	.09583	**18**	.34583	**18**	.00160
24	.10000	**24**	.35000	**24**	.00167
2 30	0.10417	**8 30**	0.35417	**2 30**	0.00174
36	.10833	**36**	.35833	**36**	.00181
42	.11250	**42**	.36250	**42**	.00188
48	.11667	**48**	.36667	**48**	.00194
2 54	.12083	**8 54**	.37083	**2 54**	.00201
3 00	0.12500	**9 00**	0.37500	**3 00**	0.00208
06	.12917	**06**	.37917	**06**	.00215
12	.13333	**12**	.38333	**12**	.00222
18	.13750	**18**	.38750	**18**	.00229
24	.14167	**24**	.39167	**24**	.00236
3 30	0.14583	**9 30**	0.39583	**3 30**	0.00243
36	.15000	**36**	.40000	**36**	.00250
42	.15417	**42**	.40417	**42**	.00257
48	.15833	**48**	.40833	**48**	.00264
3 54	.16250	**9 54**	.41250	**3 54**	.00271
4 00	0.16667	**10 00**	0.41667	**4 00**	0.00278
06	.17083	**06**	.42083	**06**	.00285
12	.17500	**12**	.42500	**12**	.00292
18	.17917	**18**	.42917	**18**	.00299
24	.18333	**24**	.43333	**24**	.00306
4 30	0.18750	**10 30**	0.43750	**4 30**	0.00312
36	.19167	**36**	.44167	**36**	.00319
42	.19583	**42**	.44583	**42**	.00326
48	.20000	**48**	.45000	**48**	.00333
4 54	.20417	**10 54**	.45417	**4 54**	.00340
5 00	0.20833	**11 00**	0.45833	**5 00**	0.00347
06	.21250	**06**	.46250	**06**	.00354
12	.21667	**12**	.46667	**12**	.00361
18	.22083	**18**	.47083	**18**	.00368
24	.22500	**24**	.47500	**24**	.00375
5 30	0.22917	**11 30**	0.47917	**5 30**	0.00382
36	.23333	**36**	.48333	**36**	.00389
42	.23750	**42**	.48750	**42**	.00396
48	.24167	**48**	.49167	**48**	.00403
5 54	.24583	**11 54**	.49583	**5 54**	.00410
6 00	0.25000	**12 00**	0.50000	**6 00**	0.00417

Decimals of a Degree to Minutes of Arc

°	′	°	′
0.00	0	**0.50**	30
.01	1	**.51**	31
.02	1	**.52**	31
.03	2	**.53**	32
.04	2	**.54**	32
0.05	3	**0.55**	33
.06	4	**.56**	34
.07	4	**.57**	34
.08	5	**.58**	35
.09	5	**.59**	35
0.10	6	**0.60**	36
.11	7	**.61**	37
.12	7	**.62**	37
.13	8	**.63**	38
.14	8	**.64**	38
0.15	9	**0.65**	39
.16	10	**.66**	40
.17	10	**.67**	40
.18	11	**.68**	41
.19	11	**.69**	41
0.20	12	**0.70**	42
.21	13	**.71**	43
.22	13	**.72**	43
.23	14	**.73**	44
.24	14	**.74**	44
0.25	15	**0.75**	45
.26	16	**.76**	46
.27	16	**.77**	46
.28	17	**.78**	47
.29	17	**.79**	47
0.30	18	**0.80**	48
.31	19	**.81**	49
.32	19	**.82**	49
.33	20	**.83**	50
.34	20	**.84**	50
0.35	21	**0.85**	51
.36	22	**.86**	52
.37	22	**.87**	52
.38	23	**.88**	53
.39	23	**.89**	53
0.40	24	**0.90**	54
.41	25	**.91**	55
.42	25	**.92**	55
.43	26	**.93**	56
.44	26	**.94**	56
0.45	27	**0.95**	57
.46	28	**.96**	58
.47	28	**.97**	58
.48	29	**.98**	59
.49	29	**0.99**	59
0.50	30	**1.00**	60

This table can also be used for the conversion of decimals of a minute to seconds of arc and vice versa.

PLATE 1 – NAVIGATION LIGHTS (SEE ALSO PLATE 4)

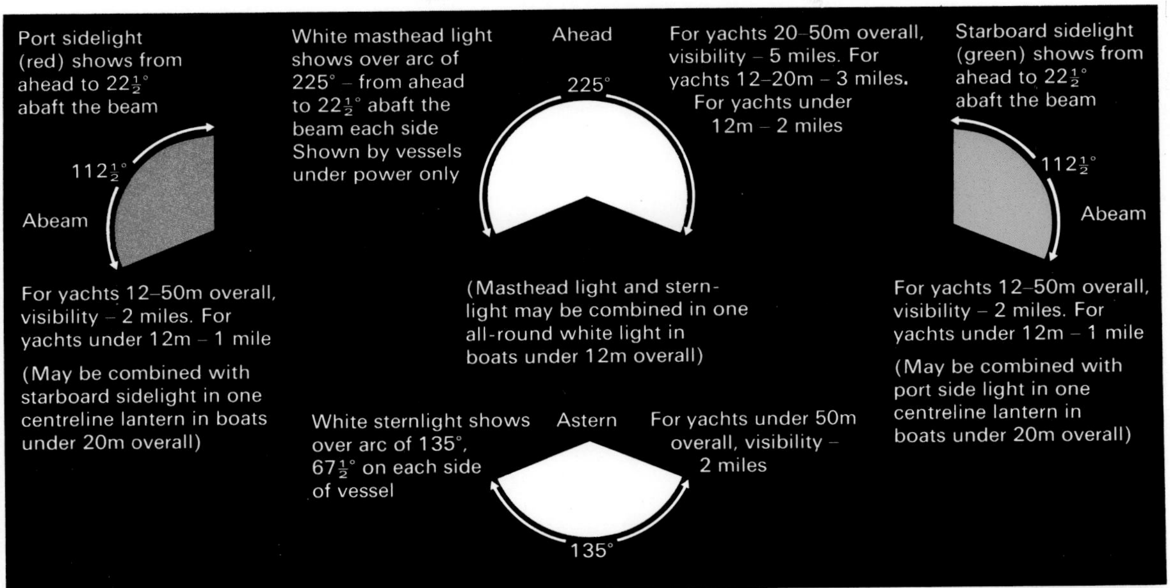
Port sidelight (red) shows from ahead to 22½° abaft the beam
112½°
Abeam
For yachts 12–50m overall, visibility – 2 miles. For yachts under 12m – 1 mile
(May be combined with starboard sidelight in one centreline lantern in boats under 20m overall)
White masthead light shows over arc of 225° – from ahead to 22½° abaft the beam each side Shown by vessels under power only
Ahead
225°
For yachts 20–50m overall, visibility – 5 miles. For yachts 12–20m – 3 miles. For yachts under 12m – 2 miles
(Masthead light and stern-light may be combined in one all-round white light in boats under 12m overall)
Starboard sidelight (green) shows from ahead to 22½° abaft the beam
112½°
Abeam
For yachts 12–50m overall, visibility – 2 miles. For yachts under 12m – 1 mile
(May be combined with port side light in one centreline lantern in boats under 20m overall)
White sternlight shows over arc of 135°, 67½° on each side of vessel
Astern
For yachts under 50m overall, visibility – 2 miles
135°

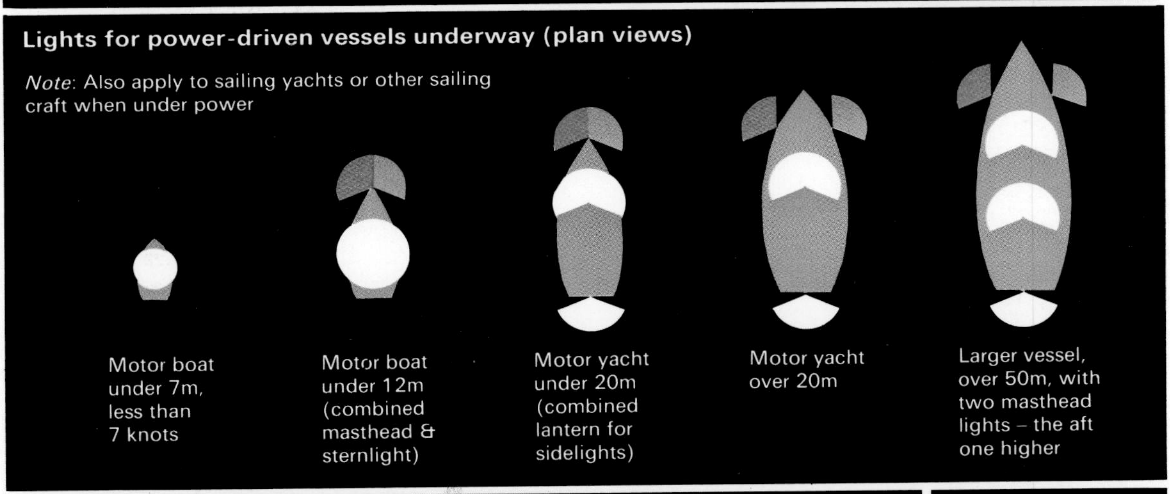
Lights for power-driven vessels underway (plan views)
Note: Also apply to sailing yachts or other sailing craft when under power
Motor boat under 7m, less than 7 knots
Motor boat under 12m (combined masthead & sternlight)
Motor yacht under 20m (combined lantern for sidelights)
Motor yacht over 20m
Larger vessel, over 50m, with two masthead lights – the aft one higher

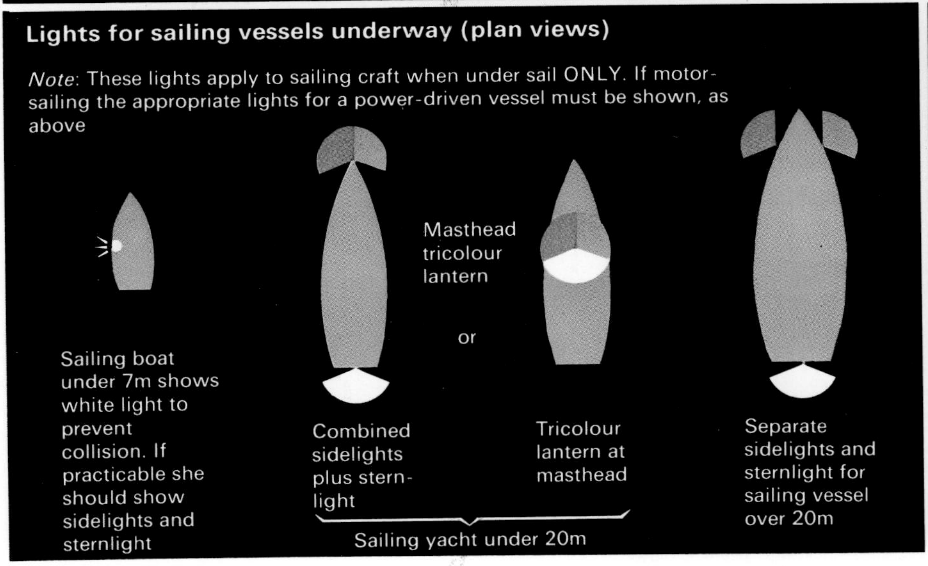
Lights for sailing vessels underway (plan views)
Note: These lights apply to sailing craft when under sail ONLY. If motor-sailing the appropriate lights for a power-driven vessel must be shown, as above
Sailing boat under 7m shows white light to prevent collision. If practicable she should show sidelights and sternlight
Masthead tricolour lantern
or
Combined sidelights plus stern-light
Tricolour lantern at masthead
Sailing yacht under 20m
Separate sidelights and sternlight for sailing vessel over 20m

Bow view
If not using tri-colour masthead lantern, a sailing yacht may show (in addition to other lights) two all-round lights near masthead, the upper red and the lower green

PLATE 2 – ADMIRALTY METRIC CHART SYMBOLS

A selection of the more common symbols from Admiralty Publication 5011

Reproduced by kind permission of H.M. Stationery Office and the Hydrographer of the Navy.

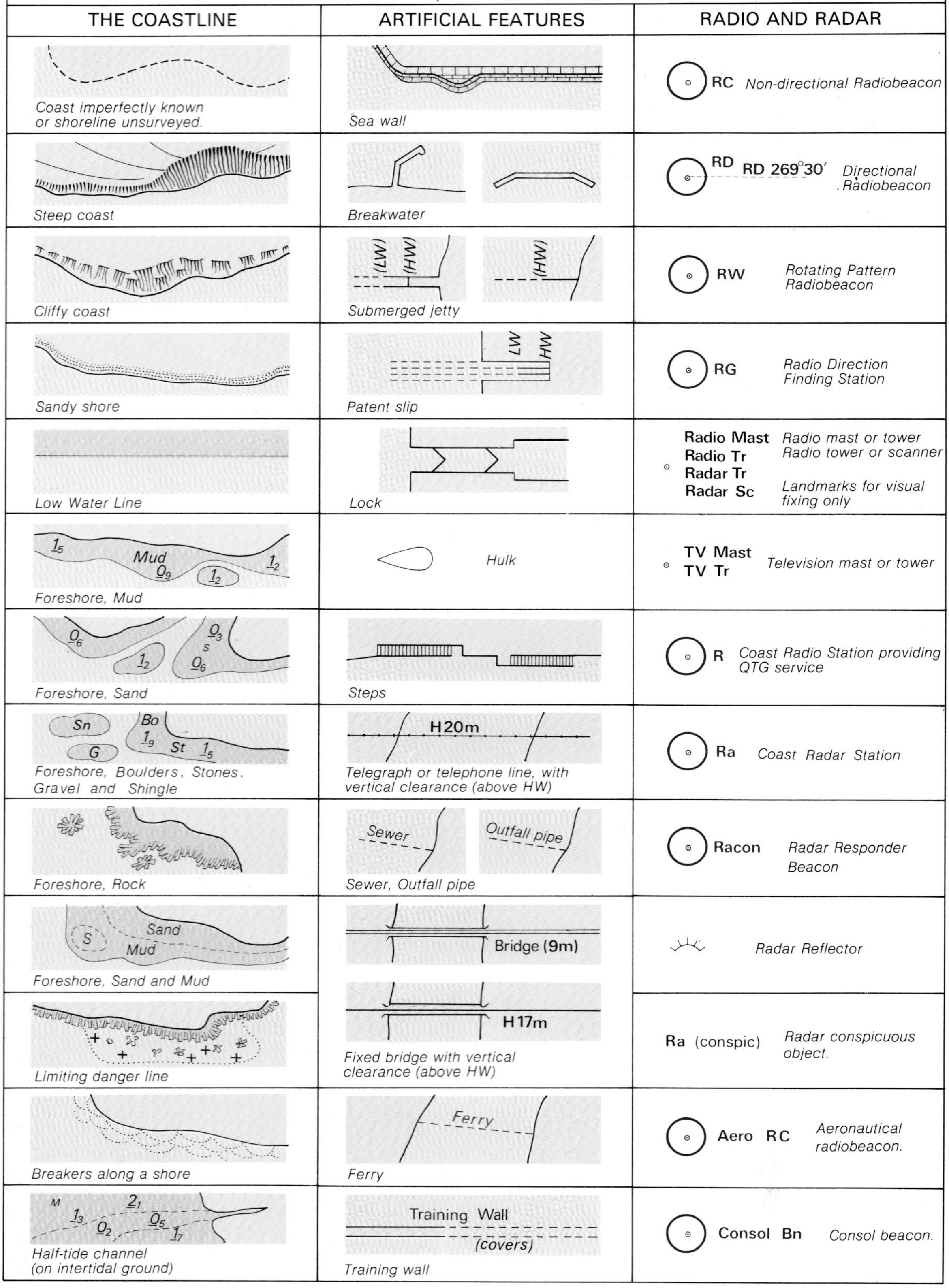
THE COASTLINE
Coast imperfectly known or shoreline unsurveyed.
Steep coast
Cliffy coast
Sandy shore
Low Water Line
Foreshore, Mud
Mud
Foreshore, Sand
Foreshore, Boulders, Stones, Gravel and Shingle
Sn
G
Bo
St
Foreshore, Rock
Foreshore, Sand and Mud
Sand
Mud
S
Limiting danger line
Breakers along a shore
Half-tide channel (on intertidal ground)
M
ARTIFICIAL FEATURES
Sea wall
Breakwater
Submerged jetty
(LW)
(HW)
Patent slip
LW
HW
Lock
Hulk
Steps
Telegraph or telephone line, with vertical clearance (above HW)
H20m
Sewer, Outfall pipe
Sewer
Outfall pipe
Bridge (9m)
H 17m
Fixed bridge with vertical clearance (above HW)
Ferry
Ferry
Training Wall
(covers)
Training wall
RADIO AND RADAR
RC Non-directional Radiobeacon
RD
RD 269°30′ Directional Radiobeacon
RW Rotating Pattern Radiobeacon
RG Radio Direction Finding Station
Radio Mast Radio mast or tower
Radio Tr Radio tower or scanner
Radar Tr
Radar Sc Landmarks for visual fixing only
TV Mast
TV Tr Television mast or tower
R Coast Radio Station providing QTG service
Ra Coast Radar Station
Racon Radar Responder Beacon
Radar Reflector
Ra (conspic) Radar conspicuous object.
Aero RC Aeronautical radiobeacon.
Consol Bn Consol beacon.

PLATE 3 – ADMIRALTY METRIC CHART SYMBOLS

A selection of the more common symbols from Admiralty Publication 5011

Reproduced by kind permission of H.M. Stationery Office and the Hydrographer of the Navy.

DANGERS

4
(4)
(4)

Rock which does not cover (with elevation above MHWS or MHHW, or where there is no tide, above MSL).

Dries 1·2m
Dr1·2m

Rock which covers and uncovers (with elevation above chart datum).

Rock awash at the level of chart datum.

R

Submerged rock with 2 metres or less water over it at chart datum, or rock ledge on which depths are known to be 2 metres or less, or a rock or rock ledge over which the exact depth is unknown but which is considered to be dangerous to surface navigation.

R
R

Shoal sounding on isolated rock.

35
R

Submerged rock not dangerous to surface navigation.

Submerged danger with depth cleared by wire drag.

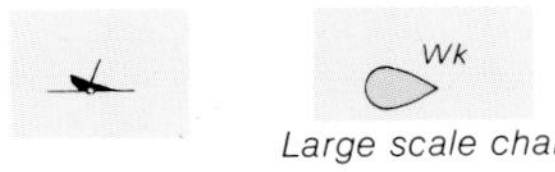
Wk

Large scale charts

Wreck showing any portion of hull or superstructure at the level of chart datum.

(Masts)
(Mast 3 m)
(Funnel)
(Mast dries 2.1 m)

Large scale charts

Wreck of which the masts only are visible.

Wreck over which the exact depth of water is unknown but is thought to be 28 metres or less, and which is considered dangerous to surface navigation.

DANGERS

Wk

Wreck over which the depth has been obtained by sounding, but not by wire sweep.

Wreck over which the exact depth is unknown but thought to be more than 28 metres, or a wreck over which the depth is thought to be 28 metres or less, but which is not considered dangerous to surface vessels capable of navigating in the vicinity.

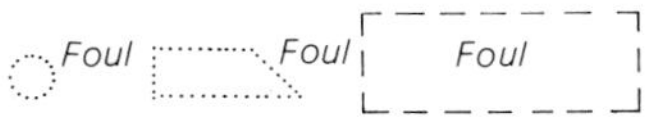
Foul
Foul
Foul

The remains of a wreck, or other foul area no longer dangerous to surface navigation, but to be avoided by vessels anchoring, trawling, etc.

Overfalls and tide-rips

Eddies

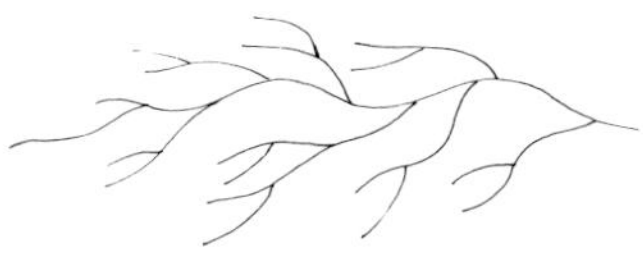

Kelp

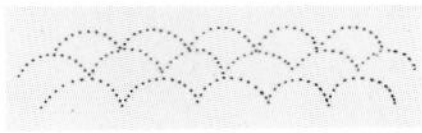

Breakers

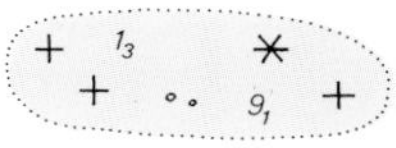

Limiting danger line

LIMITS

Leading Bns 089°53′
Bn
Bn

Leading Line

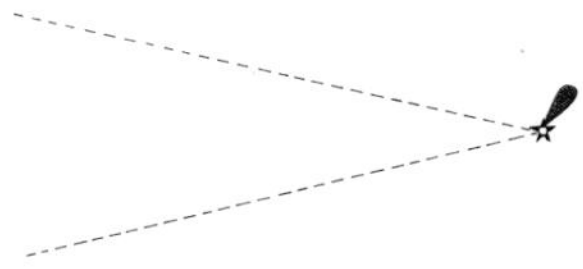

Limit of sector

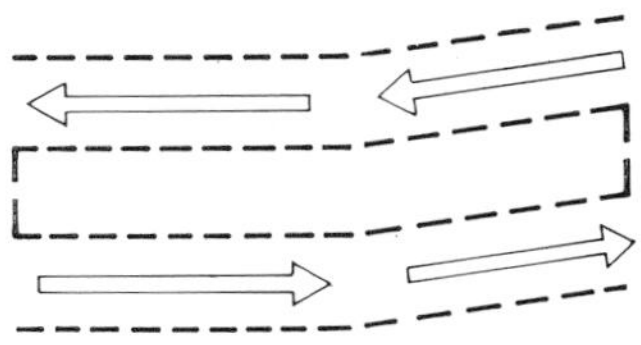

Traffic separation scheme: one-way traffic lanes (separated by zone).

Submarine cable (telegraph & telephone).

Power

Submarine cable (power).

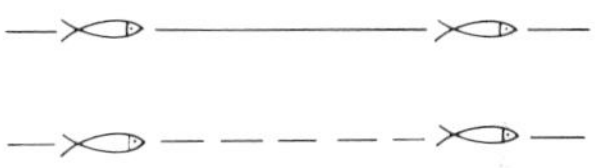

Limits of national fishing zones.

Small Craft Anchorage.

Anchorage Area.

Type of anchorage is usually indicated by legend, e.g. Small Craft Anchorage, Naval Anchorage, Quarantine Anchorage, etc.

Recommended track for deep draught vessels (track not defined by fixed mark(s)).

Where the minimum safe depth along the recommended track (or section thereof) is guaranteed by the competent harbour regional or national authority, the depth is indicated thus:

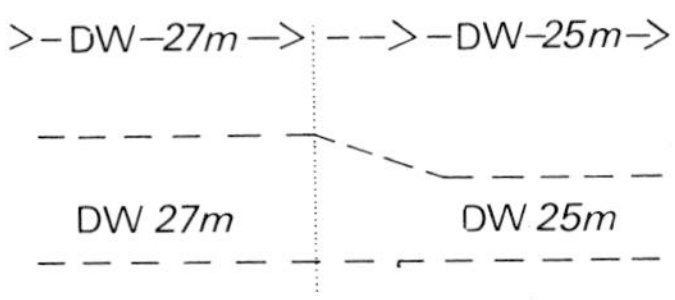
DW–27m
DW–25m
DW 27m
DW 25m

PLATE 4 – PRINCIPAL NAVIGATION LIGHTS AND SHAPES

(*Note*: All vessels seen from starboard beam)

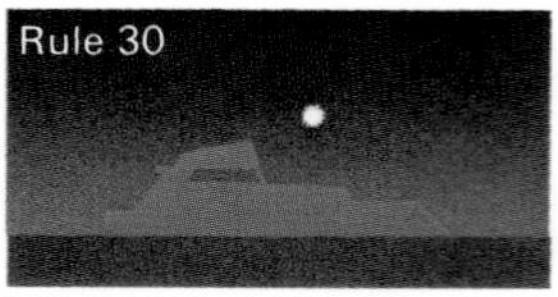
Rule 30

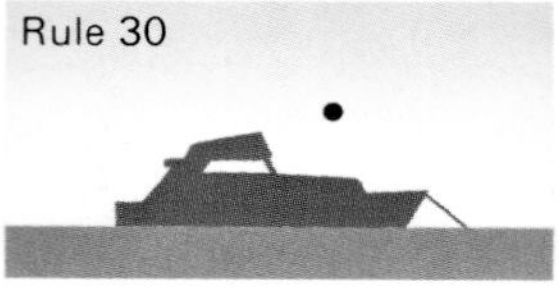
Rule 30

Vessel at anchor

All-round white light: if over 50m, a second light aft and lower

Black ball forward

Rule 27

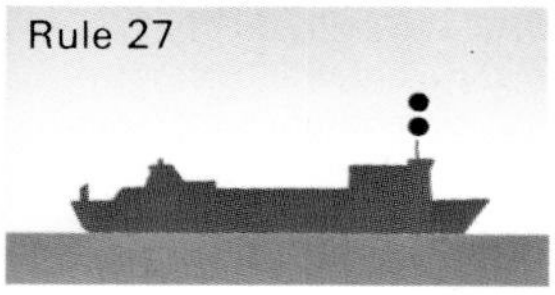
Rule 27

Not under command

Two all-round red lights, plus sidelights and sternlight when making way

Two black balls vertically

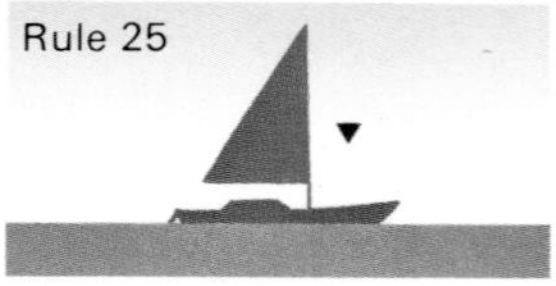
Rule 25

Motor sailing

Cone point down, forward

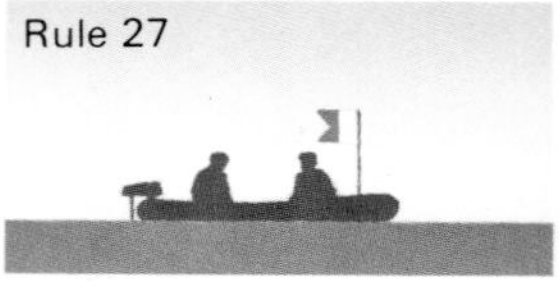
Rule 27

Divers down

Letter 'A' International Code

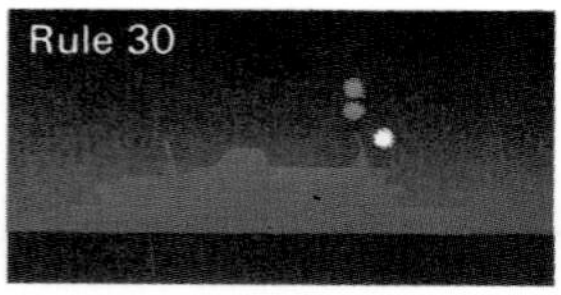
Rule 30

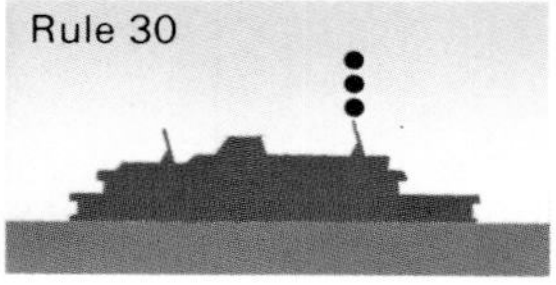
Rule 30

Vessel aground

Anchor light(s), plus two all-round red lights in a vertical line

Three black balls in a vertical line

Rule 24

Vessels being towed and towing

Vessel towed shows sidelights (forward) and sternlight

Tug shows two masthead lights, sidelights, sternlight, yellow towing light

Rule 24

Towing by day – Length of tow more than 200m

Towing vessel and tow display diamond shapes. By night, the towing vessel shows three masthead lights instead of two as for shorter tows

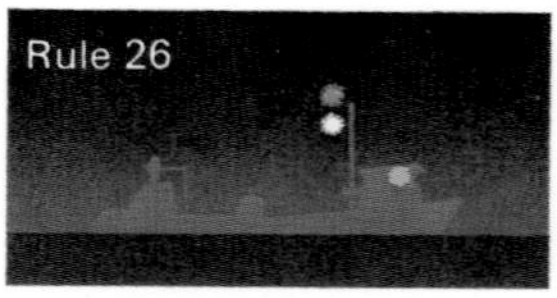
Rule 26

Vessel fishing

All-round red light over all-round white, plus sidelights and sternlight when underway

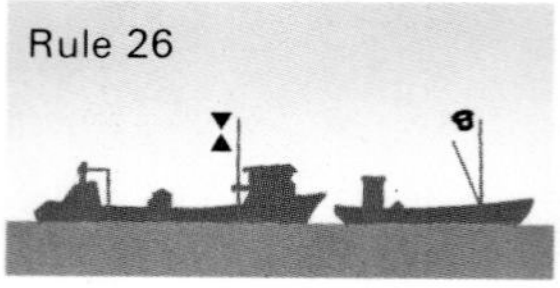
Rule 26

Fishing/trawling

Two cones point to point, or a basket if fishing vessel is less than 20m

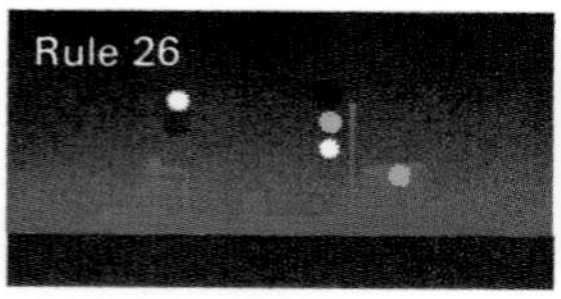
Rule 26

Vessel trawling

All-round green light over all-round white, plus sidelights and sternlight when underway

Rule 29

Pilot boat

All-round white light over all-round red; plus sidelights and sternlight when underway, or anchor light

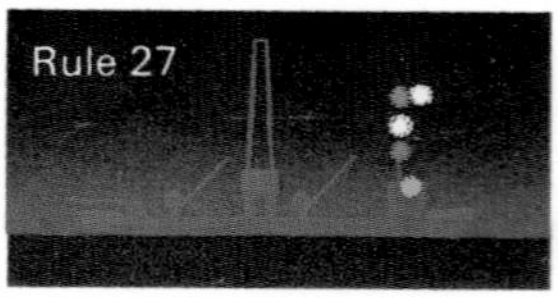
Rule 27

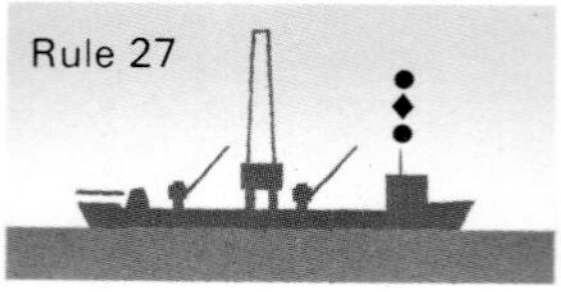
Rule 27

Vessel restricted in her ability to manoeuvre

All-round red, white, red lights vertically; plus normal steaming lights when under way

Three shapes in a vertical line – ball, diamond, ball

Rule 27

Dredger

As left, plus two all-round red lights (or two balls) on foul side, and two all-round green (or two diamonds) on clear side

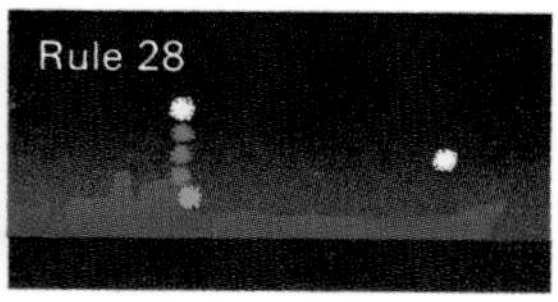
Rule 28

Constrained by draught

Three all-round red lights in a vertical line, plus normal steaming lights. By day – a cylinder

PLATE 5 – IALA BUOYAGE

Lateral marks

Used generally to mark the sides of well defined navigable channels.

Port Hand marks

Light:
Colour – red
Rhythm – any

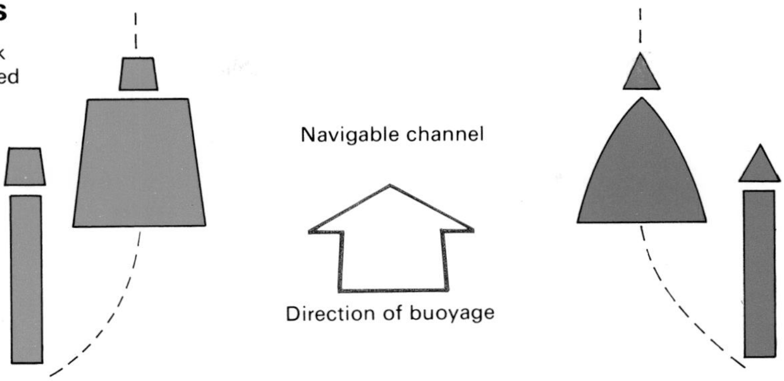
Navigable channel
Direction of buoyage

Starboard Hand marks

Light:
Colour – green
Rhythm – any

Cardinal marks

Used to indicate the direction from the mark in which the best navigable water lies, or to draw attention to a bend, junction or fork in a channel, or to mark the end of a shoal.

Lights: Always white

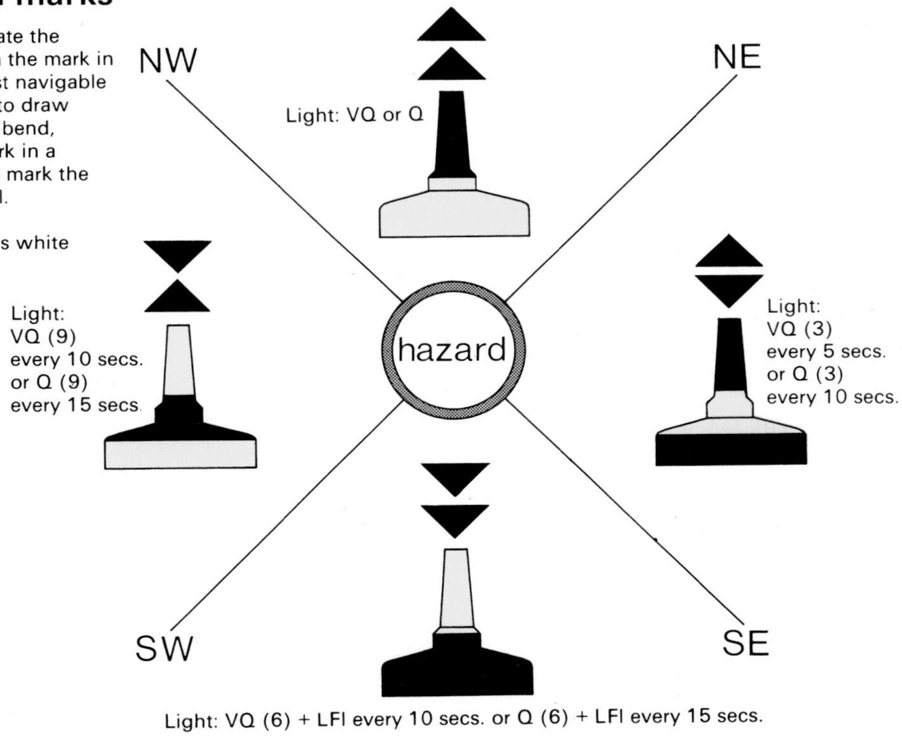
NW
NE
Light: VQ or Q
Light:
VQ (9)
every 10 secs.
or Q (9)
every 15 secs.
hazard
Light:
VQ (3)
every 5 secs.
or Q (3)
every 10 secs.
SW
SE
Light: VQ (6) + LFl every 10 secs. or Q (6) + LFl every 15 secs.

Other marks

Isolated danger marks

Use: To mark a small isolated danger with navigable water all round.
Light: Colour – white
Rhythm – group flashing (2)

Safe water marks

Use: Mid-channel or landfall.
Light: Colour – white
Rhythm – Isophase, occulting or 1 long flash every 10 seconds.

Special marks

Any shape not conflicting with lateral or safe water marks.
Light: Colour – yellow
Rhythm – different from other white lights used on buoys.

PLATES 6-7 – INTERNATIONAL CODE OF SIGNALS
CODE FLAGS, PHONETIC ALPHABET, MORSE SYMBOLS AND SINGLE-LETTER SIGNALS

Notes:
1. Single letter signals may be made by any method of signalling. Those marked * when made by sound must comply with the *International Regulations for Preventing Collisions at Sea*, Rules 34 and 35.
2. Signals 'K' and 'S' have special meanings as landing signals for small boats with persons in distress.
3. In the phonetic alphabet, the syllables to be emphasised are in italics.

A Alfa (*AL* FAH)

● ▬

I have a diver down; keep well clear at slow speed

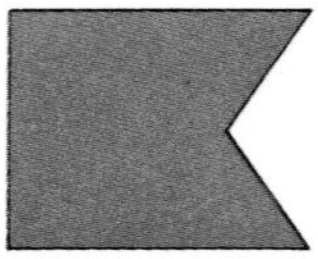

***B Bravo** (*BRAH* VOH)

▬ ● ● ●

I am taking in, or discharging, or carrying dangerous goods

***C Charlie** (*CHAR* LEE)

▬ ● ▬ ●

Yes (affirmative or 'The significance of the previous group should be read in the affirmative)

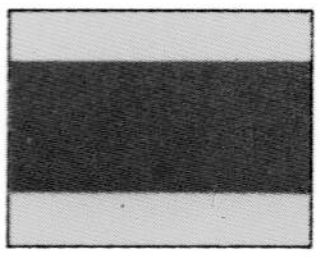

***D Delta** (*DELL* TAH)

▬ ● ●

Keep clear of me; I am manoeuvring with difficulty

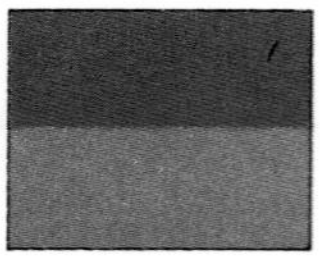

***E Echo** (*ECK* OH)

●

I am altering my course to starboard

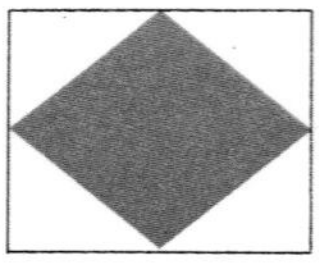

F Foxtrot (*FOKS* TROT)

● ● ▬ ●

I am disabled; communicate with me

***G Golf** (*GOLF*)

▬ ▬ ●

I require a pilot. When made by fishing vessels operating in close proximity on the fishing grounds it means: I am hauling nets

***H Hotel** (HOH *TELL*)

● ● ● ●

I have a pilot on board

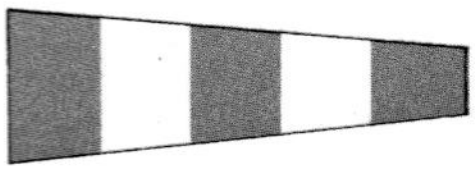

Code and Answering Pendant

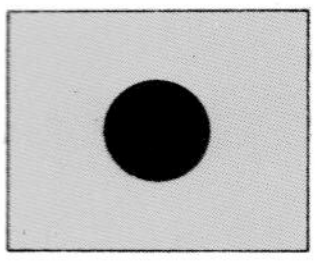

***I India** (*IN* DEE AH)

● ●

I am altering my course to port

J Juliett (*JEW* LEE *ETT*)

● ▬ ▬ ▬

I am on fire and have dangerous cargo on board: keep well clear of me

K Kilo (*KEY* LOH)

▬ ● ▬

I wish to communicate with you

L Lima (*LEE* MAH)

● ▬ ● ●

You should stop your vessel instantly

***M Mike** (MIKE)

▬ ▬

My vessel is stopped and making no way through the water

N November (NO *VEM* BER)

▬ ●

No (negative or 'The significance of the previous group should be read in the negative'). This signal may be given only visually or by sound

O Oscar (*OSS* CAH)

▬ ▬ ▬

Man overboard

P Papa (PAH *PAH*)

● ▬ ▬ ●

In harbour: all persons should report on board as the vessel is about to proceed to sea. **At sea**: it may be used by fishing vessels to mean 'My nets have come fast upon an obstruction'

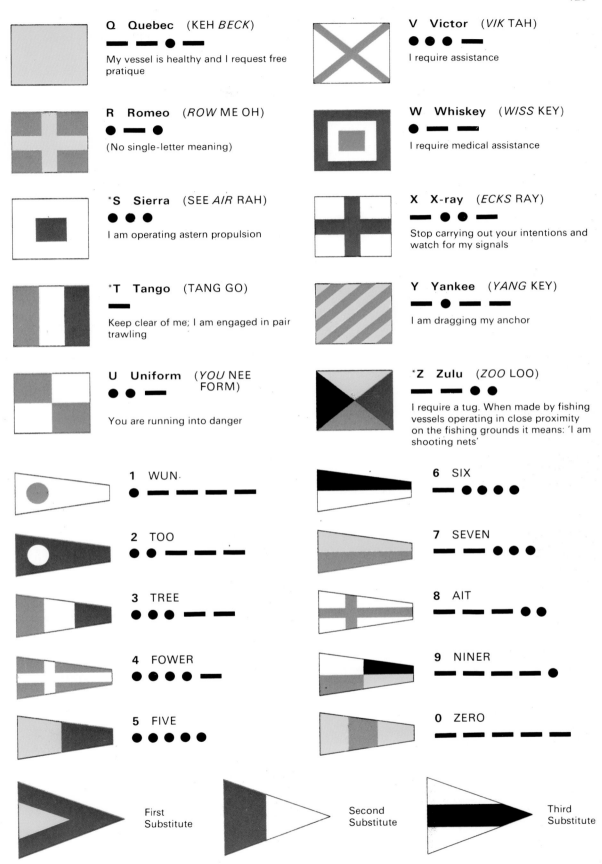

Q Quebec (KEH *BECK*)

— — • —

My vessel is healthy and I request free pratique

R Romeo (*ROW* ME OH)

• — •

(No single-letter meaning)

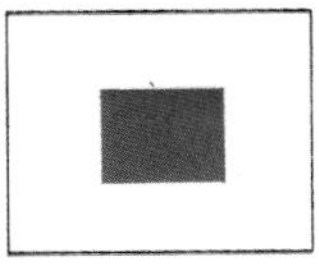

***S Sierra** (SEE *AIR* RAH)

• • •

I am operating astern propulsion

***T Tango** (TANG GO)

—

Keep clear of me; I am engaged in pair trawling

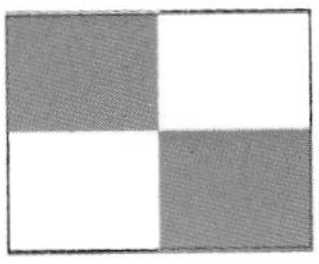

U Uniform (*YOU* NEE FORM)

• • —

You are running into danger

V Victor (*VIK* TAH)

• • • —

I require assistance

W Whiskey (*WISS* KEY)

• — —

I require medical assistance

X X-ray (*ECKS* RAY)

— • • —

Stop carrying out your intentions and watch for my signals

Y Yankee (*YANG* KEY)

— • — —

I am dragging my anchor

***Z Zulu** (*ZOO* LOO)

— — • •

I require a tug. When made by fishing vessels operating in close proximity on the fishing grounds it means: 'I am shooting nets'

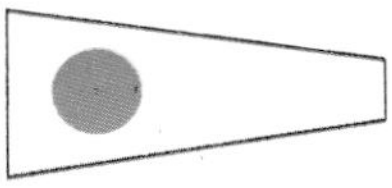

1 WUN

• — — — —

2 TOO

• • — — —

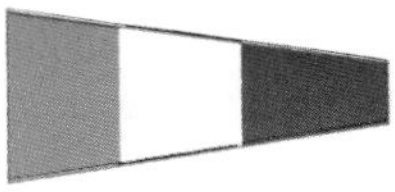

3 TREE

• • • — —

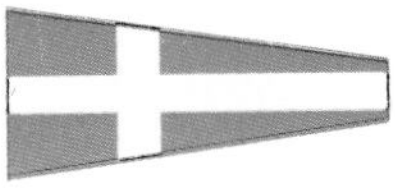

4 FOWER

• • • • —

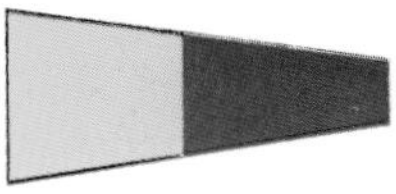

5 FIVE

• • • • •

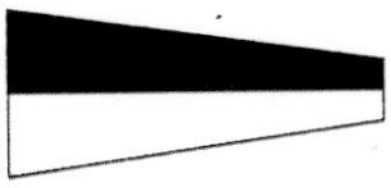

6 SIX

— • • • •

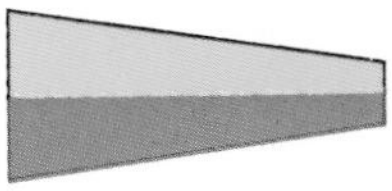

7 SEVEN

— — • • •

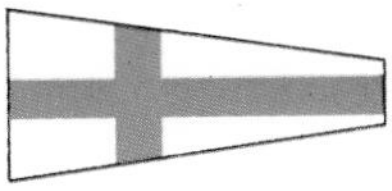

8 AIT

— — — • •

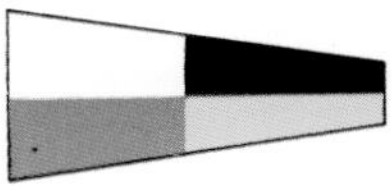

9 NINER

— — — — •

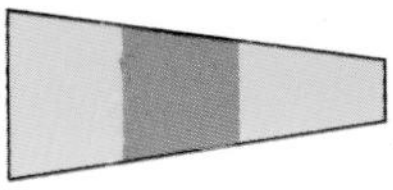

0 ZERO

— — — — —

First Substitute

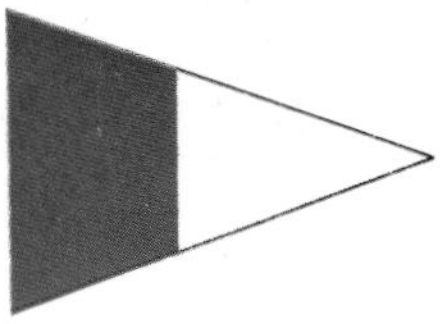

Second Substitute

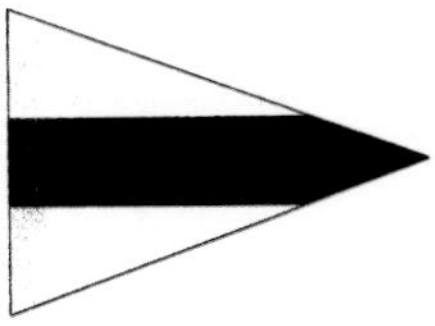

Third Substitute

PLATE 8 – INTERNATIONAL PORT TRAFFIC SIGNALS

No	Lights		Main message
1		Flashing	Serious emergency – all vessels to stop or divert according to instructions
2		Fixed or Slow Occulting	Vessels shall not proceed (*Note*: Some ports may use an exemption signal, as in 2a below)
3			Vessels may proceed. One way traffic
4			Vessels may proceed. Two way traffic
5			A vessel may proceed only when she has received specific orders to do so (*Note*: Some ports may use an exemption signal, as in 5a below)
			Exemption signals and messages
2a	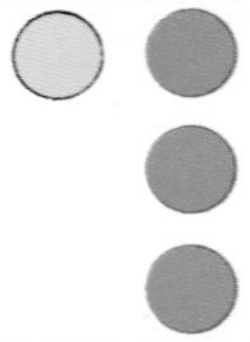	Fixed or Slow Occulting	Vessels shall not proceed, except that vessels which navigate outside the main channel need not comply with the main message
5a	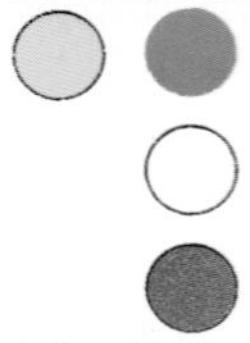		A vessel may proceed only when she has received specific orders to do so, except that vessels which navigate outside the main channel need not comply with the main message
			Auxiliary signals and messages
	White and/or yellow lights, displayed to the right of the main lights		Local meanings, as promulgated in local port orders

This new system is gradually being introduced, but its general adoption is likely to take many years.

Notes on use:

(1) The main movement message given by a port traffic signal shall always comprise three lights, disposed vertically. No additional light shall be added to the column carrying the main message. (The fact that the main message always consists of three vertical lights allows the mariner to recognise it as a traffic signal, and not lights of navigational significance). The signals may also be used to control traffic at locks and bridges.

(2) Red lights indicate 'Do not proceed'.

(3) Green lights indicate 'Proceed, subject to the conditions stipulated'.

(For examples, see opposite).

Note that, to avoid confusion, red and green lights are never displayed together.

(4) A single yellow light, displayed to the left of the column carrying main messages Nos 2 or 5, at the level of the upper light, may be used to indicate that 'Vessels which can safely navigate outside the main channel need not comply with the main message'. This signal is of obvious significance to yachtsmen.

(5) Signals which are auxiliary to the main message may be devised by local authorities. Such auxiliary signals should employ only white and/or yellow lights, and should be displayed to the right of the column carrying the main message. Ports with complex entrances and much traffic may need many auxiliary signals, which will have to be documented; but smaller harbours with less traffic may only need one or two of the basic signals, such as 'Vessels shall not proceed' and 'Vessels may proceed, two way traffic'.

Some signals may be omni-directional – exhibited to all vessels simultaneously: others must be directional, and be shown either to vessels entering or to vessels leaving harbour.

Signal No 5 is based on the assumption that some other means of communication such as VHF radio, signal lamp, loud hailer, or auxiliary signal will be used to inform a vessel that she may specifically proceed.

The 'Serious Emergency' signal must be flashing, at least 60 flashes per minute. All other signals must be either fixed or slow occulting (the latter useful when background glare is a problem). A mixture of fixed and occulting lights must not be used.

Chapter 6

Communications

Contents

Communications — introduction

It is useful — and sometimes essential — for yachts to be able to communicate with other vessels and with shore stations. A full description of the various methods and procedures is given in Chapter 6 of *The Macmillan & Silk Cut Yachtsman's Handbook*, including:

> *The International Code; Morse code; phonetic tables; procedure signals; complements; single-letter signals; flag signalling; Morse code by light; sound signals; radio time signals; pratique messages; port signals; tide signals; radiotelephony; flag etiquette. There are also included colour plates showing national maritime flags, flag etiquette, and burgees of selected yacht clubs.*

Here in this Almanac explanations are kept to a minimum, and only sufficient information is given to allow limited use of the International Code in cases of emergency, and to permit yachtsmen to pass simple messages. Particular emphasis is placed on the use of VHF radiotelephones. For further information on all aspects of signalling, including the subjects listed above, reference should be made to Chapter 6 of *The Macmillan & Silk Cut Yachtsman's Handbook.*

6.1 INTERNATIONAL CODE

6.1.1 International Code of Signals

Most communication afloat is based on the *International Code of Signals* (HMSO), which provides particularly where there are language problems.

The Code can be used by flags, flashing light, sound signalling, voice (e.g. loud hailer), radiotelegraphy, radiotelephony, or by hand flags.

Signals consist of: single-letter signals which are very urgent or very common; two-letter signals in the General Section; and three-letter signals starting with 'M' in the Medical Section.

Complements

In principle each signal has a complete meaning, but complements (which are numerals from 0 to 9, added to the letters of a signal) are used to supplement the available groups — expressing variations in the meaning of a basic signal, asking or answering questions on the same subject, or giving more detailed information. For example:

YD What is the wind expected to do?
YD1 The wind is expected to back.
YD2 The wind is expected to veer.
YD3 The wind is expected to increase.
etc.

Complements should only be used as and when specified in the Code.

6.1.2 Using the International Code

To make full and proper use of the International Code, whereby seamen of nine nations can communicate with each other on matters concerning navigation and safety without knowing any foreign language, it is necessary to hold a copy of the *International Code of Signals*, published by HMSO. It is however possible for yachtsmen to make limited use of the Code so as to pass and receive simple messages, using the information contained in this chapter.

In Plates 6 and 7 on pages 122–123 are shown the International Code flags for the alphabet and for numerals, the phonetic alphabet, the phonetic figure-spelling table, the Morse symbols for letters and numerals, and the single-letter signals of the letters of the alphabet.

6.1.3 General instructions

(1) *Numbers* are signalled: by flags — by numeral pendants; by light — by Morse numerals, but spelt if important; by voice — by phonetic code words, see Plate 7.

(2) *Decimal point* is indicated: by flags — by Answering Pendant; by Light — by $\overline{\text{AAA}}$; by voice — by the word 'Decimal'.

(3) *Depths* are signalled in figures followed by 'F' for feet, or 'M' for metres.

(4) *Bearings* are signalled in three figures, denoting degrees (True) from 000 to 359.

(5) *Courses* are signalled as for bearings, with figures prefixed by the letter 'C'.

(6) *Dates* are signalled by two, four or six figures preceded by 'D'. The first two figures show day of month, the next two the month of the year, and the final two (when six are signalled) the year.

(7) *Latitude* is signalled by four figures preceded by 'L', and followed where necessary by 'N' or 'S'. The first two figures indicate degrees, and the second two indicate minutes.

(8) *Longitude* is signalled by four (or five) figures preceded by 'G', and followed by 'E' or 'W'. The last two figures show minutes, and the first two (or three) show degrees.

(9) *Distance* is signalled by figures (in nautical miles) preceded by 'R'.

(10) *Speed* is signalled by figures preceded by 'S' (for knots) or by 'V' (kilometres per hour).

(11) *Time* is signalled by 24 hour clock, preceded by 'T' for local time or by 'Z' for GMT (or UT).

6.1.4 Procedure signals

Note: A bar over the letters of a signal means that the letters are joined together and made as one symbol.

(1) Signals for voice transmissions (R/T or loud hailer)

Signal	*Pronunciation*	*Meaning*
INTERCO	IN-TER-CO	International Code group(s) follow(s).
CORRECTION	KOR-REK-SHUN	Cancel my last word or group. The correct word or group follows.
DECIMAL	DAY-SEE-MAL	Decimal point
STOP	STOP	Full stop

(2) Signals for Morse transmissions by light

$\overline{\text{AA}}$ $\overline{\text{AA}}$ $\overline{\text{AA}}$ etc	Call for unknown station or general call
$\overline{\text{EEEEEE}}$ etc	Erase signal.
$\overline{\text{AAA}}$	Full stop or decimal point.
TTTT etc	Answering signal.
T	Word or group received.

(3) Signals for flags, radiotelephony and radio-telegraphy transmissions

CQ Call for unknown station(s) or general call to all stations.

Note: When this signal is used in voice transmission, it should be pronounced in accordance with the letter-spelling table (i.e. Charlie Quebec).

(4) Signals for use where appropriate in all forms of transmission

AA 'all after ...' (used after the 'Repeat' signal (RPT) — see below — means 'Repeat all after ...').

AB 'All before ...' (used after the 'Repeat' signal (RPT) — see below — means 'Repeat all before ...').

$\overline{\text{AR}}$ Ending signal, or End of transmission or signal.

$\overline{\text{AS}}$ Waiting signal or period.

BN 'All between ... and ...' (used after the 'Repeat' signal (RPT) — means 'Repeat all between ... and ...').

C Affirmative — YES or 'The significance of the previous group should be read in the affirmative'.

CS 'What is the name or identity signal of your vessel (or station)?'

DE 'From ...' (used to precede the name or identity signal of the calling station).

K 'I wish to communicate with you' or 'Invitation to transmit'.

NO Negative — NO or 'The significance of the previous group should be read in the negative'. When used in voice transmission the pronunciation should be 'NO'.

OK Acknowledging a correct repetition or 'It is correct'.

RQ Interrogative or 'The significance of the previous group should be read as a question'.

R 'Received' or 'I have received your last signal'.

RPT Repeat signal 'I repeat' or 'Repeat what you have sent' or 'Repeat what you have received'.

WA 'Word or group after ...' (used after the 'Repeat' signal (RPT) means 'Repeat word or group after ...').

WB 'Word or group before ...' (used after the 'Repeat' signal (RPT) means 'Repeat word or group before ...').

Notes:

1. The procedure signals 'C', 'NO' and 'RQ' cannot be used in conjunction with single-letter signals.
2. When these signals are used by voice transmission the letters should be pronounced in accordance with the letter-spelling table, except that 'NO' is pronounced 'NO'.

6.1.5 Selected groups from the International Code

AC I am abandoning my vessel
AE I must abandon my vessel
AF I do not intend to abandon my vessel
AN I need a doctor
CB I require immediate assistance
CB4 I require immediate assistance; I am aground
CB5 I require immediate assistance; I am drifting
CB6 I require immediate assistance; I am on fire
CB7 I require immediate assistance; I have sprung a leak
CJ Do you require assistance?
CK Assistance is not (or is no longer) required by me (or vessel indicated).
CV I am unable to give assistance.
DX I am sinking.
ED Your distress signals are understood.
EF SOS/MAYDAY has been cancelled.
FA Will you give me my position?
IL I can only proceed at slow speed.
IM I request to be escorted until further notice.
IT I am on fire.
IW Fire is under control.
IX Fire is gaining.
IZ Fire has been extinguished.
JG I am aground. I am in a dangerous situation.
JH I am aground. I am not in danger.
JI Are you aground?
JL You are running the risk of going aground.
JO I am afloat.
JW I have sprung a leak.
JX Leak is gaining rapidly.
KM I can take you in tow.
KN I cannot take you in tow.
MG You should steer course ...
NC I am in distress and require immediate assistance.
NG You are in a dangerous position.
NH You are clear of all dangers.
OQ I am calibrating radio direction finder or adjusting compasses.
PD Your navigation light(s) is (are) not visible.
PH You should steer as indicated.
PI You should maintain your present course.
PP Keep well clear of me.
QO You should not come alongside.
QP I will come alongside.
QR I cannot come alongside.
QT You should not anchor. You are going to foul my anchor.
RA My anchor is foul.
RB I am dragging my anchor.
RN My engines are out of action.
RY You should proceed at slow speed when passing me (or vessels making signal).
SC I am under way.
SD I am not ready to get under way.
SQ You should stop or heave to.

UM The harbour or port is closed to traffic.
UN You may enter harbour immediately.
UO You must not enter harbour.
UW I wish you a pleasant voyage.
YU I am going to communicate with your station by International Code.
YV The groups which follow are from the International Code of Signals.
ZD2 Please report me to Lloyd's London.
ZL Your signal has been received but not understood.
ZM You should send (or speak) more slowly.

6.1.6 Morse code

When making Morse, it is most important to get the right rhythm and spacing. If a dot is taken as the unit of time, the correct spacing is as follows:

Dot	1 unit
Dash	3 units
Space between each dot/dash in a letter	1 unit
Space between each letter or symbol	3 units
Space between each word or group	7 units

The most likely method whereby a yachtsman will use the Morse code is by light. It helps to have a good light, with a proper flashing key, or trigger.

6.1.7 Flag signalling

The International Code flags (see Plates 6 and 7) consist of 26 alphabetical flags, 11 pendants (numerals 0–9 plus the Answering Pendant or Code Flag), and three triangular flags — the First, Second and Third Substitutes.

Some definitions are important. *Group* — one or more continuous letters and/or numerals comprising a signal. *Hoist* — one or more groups on one halyard. *At the dip* — a signal half-hoisted. *Close up* — a signal fully hoisted. *Tackline* — a line separating two groups. *Superior* — a flag or group above another. *Inferior* — a flag or group below another. *Class* — whether a flag is alphabetical or numeral.

The Answering Pendant is used to answer or acknowledge signals from another vessel. It may also be used as a decimal point.

Substitutes allow for the repetition of one or more letters (or numerals) within a group. The First Sub. repeats the first flag of the group in the class immediately superior to it. The Second Sub. repeats the second flag of that class, and the Third Sub. repeats the third.

A substitute can only repeat a flag of the same class as that immediately preceding it. The Answering Pendant used as a decimal point is disregarded in deciding which substitute to use.

Procedure

The sending ship hoists the identity signal of the ship she is calling: or she hoists the group 'VF' ('You should hoist your identity signal') or 'CS' ('What is the name or identity signal of your vessel/station') — at the same time hoisting her own identity signal.

The sending ship then hoists her message, and when sighted the receiving ship hoists her Answering Pendant at the dip — and close up when the signal has been understood. The procedure is repeated for subsequent hoists.

6.1.8 Radiotelephony (RT)

Plain language is normally used for RT (see 6.3.3), but in the event of language difficulties use the International Code and the following procedure. Letters and figures are spelt in accordance with the spelling tables, see Plates 6 and 7.

(1) *Method of calling.* Call sign or name of station called, not more than three times; the group 'DELTA ECHO'; and the call sign or name of the calling station, not more than three times. After contact is made, the call sign or name need not be sent more than once.

(2) *Reply to call.* Call sign or name of calling station; the group 'DELTA ECHO'; and the call sign or name of the station called.

(3) *Code groups.* The word 'INTERCO' indicates that International Code groups follow. Plain language may be used for names. 'YANKEE ZULU' means 'The words which follow are in plain language'.

(4) For other procedure signals see 6.1.4 (1), (3) and (4).

6.1.9 Morse Code by hand flags, or arms

Exceptionally, it may be useful to signal Morse by hand flags or arms. A dot is made by extending both flags (arms) above the head, and a dash by extending them horizontally at shoulder level. Between dots and dashes the flags (arms) are brought in front of the chest. To separate letters, groups or words the flags (arms) are extended downwards 45° away from the body. Circular motion of the flags (arms) indicates the erase signal if made by the transmitting station, or a request for repetition if made by the receiving station.

A station wishing to communicate by this method sends 'K2' or makes the general Morse call 'AA AA AA'. The station called should make the answering signal (TTTTTT etc) or, if unable to communicate by this method the signal 'YS2' by any means. Other procedure signals as in 6.1.4(4).

6.1.10 Sound signals

The International Code may be sent by sound signal (e.g. whistle, siren, foghorn) but the method is slow, and if misused can cause confusion. In poor visibility it should be reduced to a minimum. Signals other than the single-letter ones should only be used in emergency, and never where there is other traffic around. The signals should be made slowly and distinctly. They may be repeated, if necessary, but at sufficiently long intervals to ensure that no confusion can arise. The single-letter signals of the Code marked by an asterisk, when made by sound, must conform with the *International Regulations for Preventing Collisions at Sea* (Rules 34 and 35), for which see 2.1.7.

6.2 MISCELLANEOUS SIGNALS

6.2.1 Radio time signals

The BBC broadcast time signals at the local times and on the frequencies indicated in the table below. The start of the final, longer pulse marks the minute.

BBC Radio 1 1053 1089 kHz, 97·6–99·8 MHz
BBC Radio 2 88–90·2 MHz
BBC Radio 3 1215 kHz, 90·2–94·4 MHz
BBC Radio 4 198 603 (Tyneside) 720 (N Ireland & London) 1449 (Aberdeen) 1485 (Carlisle) 756 (Redruth) 774 (Plymouth) kHz, 92·5–94·6 MHz
BBC Radio 5 693 909 kHz

Local time	Mon–Fri Radio	Sat Radio	Sun Radio
0000	2	2	2
0500	1	1	1
0530	1		
0600	1,4	1,4	1,4
0700	1,2,3,4	2,3,4	4
0800	1,2,4	2,4	2,4
0900	4	4	2,4
1000	4	4	
1100	4	4	
1200	4		
1300	2,4	1,2,4	4
1400	4	4	
1500	4	4	
1600	4 (not Mon)		4
1700	2,4		1,2,4
1800		2	
1900	2,3,4		4
1930		1,2	
2100			4
2200	2		

6.2.2 Pratique messages

All yachts, whether carrying dutiable stores or not, arriving in the United Kingdom from abroad (including the Channel Islands) are subject to Customs, Health and Immigration requirements — see Customs Notice No 8, summarised in Chapter 2 (2.4). The following Health Clearance Messages (International Code) apply:

Q or ZS My vessel is 'healthy' and I request free pratique. (Note: Flag 'Q' to be flown on entering UK waters, illuminated at night).
QQ (Flag 'Q' over First Substitute, or by night a red light over a white light). I require health clearance.
ZT My Maritime Declaration of Health has negative answers to the six health questions.
ZU My Maritime Declaration of Health has a positive answer to question(s) ... indicated.
ZW I require Port Medical Officer.
ZY You have health clearance.
ZZ You should proceed to anchorage for health clearance.
AM Have you a doctor?

6.2.3 Distress signals

A complete list of distress signals, as in Annex IV of the *International Regulations for Preventing Collisions at Sea*, is given in Chapter 2 (2.1.6). Those which are more appropriate for yachts to use are described in 8.1.4. Full details of RT distress messages and procedures, control of distress traffic on RT, the Urgency Signal and the Safety Signal are given in 6.3.10.

Distress signals must only be used when the boat is in serious and immediate danger, and help is urgently required. For lesser emergencies use 'V' (Victor) International Code — 'I require assistance', or one of the groups shown in 6.1.5.

6.2.4 Signals between shore and ships in distress

The following are used if a vessel is in distress or stranded off the coast of the United Kingdom:

(1) Acknowledgment of distress signal

By day: Orange smoke signal, or combined light and sound signal consisting of three single signals fired at about one minute intervals.

By night: White star rocket consisting of three single signals at about one minute intervals.

(2) Landing signals for small boats

'This is the best place to land' — Vertical motion of a white flag or arms (or white light or flare by night), or signalling 'K' (— • —) by light or sound. An indication of direction may be given by placing a steady white light or flare at a lower level.

'Landing here is highly dangerous' — Horizontal motion of a white flag or arms extended horizontally (or white light or flare by night), or signalling 'S' (• • •). In addition, a better landing place may be signalled by carrying a white flag (or flare, or light), or by firing a white star signal in the direction indicated; or by signalling 'R' (· — ·) if the better landing is to the right in the direction of approach, or 'L' (· — · ·) if it is to the left.

(3) Signals for shore life-saving apparatus
'Affirmative' or specifically 'Rocket line is held', 'Tail block is made fast', 'Hawser is made fast', 'Man is in breeches buoy' or 'Haul away' — Vertical motion of a white flag or the arms (or of a white light or flare).

'Negative' or specifically 'Slack away' or 'Avast hauling' — Horizontal motion of a white flag or the arms (or of a white light or flare).

(4) Warning signal
'You are running into danger' — International Code signal 'U' (· · —) or 'NF'.

Note: Attention may be called to the above signals by a white flare, a white star rocket, or an explosive signal.

6.2.5 Signals used by SAR aircraft

A searching aircraft normally flies at about 3000–5000ft (900–1500m), or below cloud, firing a green Very light every five or ten minutes and at each turning point. On seeing a green flare, a yacht in distress should take the following action:
(1) Wait for the green flare to die out.
(2) Fire one red flare.
(3) Fire another red flare after about 20 seconds (this enables the aircraft to line up on the bearing).
(4) Fire a third red flare when the aircraft is overhead, or appears to be going badly off course.

6.2.6 Directing signals by aircraft

(1) To direct a yacht towards a ship or aircraft in distress — The aircraft circles the yacht at least once; it then crosses low ahead of the yacht, opening and closing the throttle or changing the propeller pitch. Finally it heads in the direction of the casualty.
(2) To indicate that assistance of the yacht is no longer required — The aircraft passes low, astern of the yacht, opening and closing the throttle or changing the propeller pitch.

6.2.7 Port signals

For signals for individual harbours, see Chapter 10. On the Continent traffic signals are to some extent standardised — see 10.14.7 for France, 10.20.7 for the Netherlands, and 10.21.7 for Germany.

A new system of International Port Traffic Signals was introduced in 1983, and is illustrated in Plate 8 on page 124. Although this new system has been adopted in a few ports, it is likely to be some time before it is used widely.

VHF channels for port operations are shown for harbours in Chapter 10. Call on the indicated working channel. The following International Code groups refer to port operations.

UH	Can you lead me into port?
UL	All vessels should proceed to sea as soon as possible owing to danger in port.
UM	The harbour (or port indicated) is closed to traffic.
UN	You may enter harbour immediately (or at time indicated).
UO	You must not enter harbour.
UP	Permission to enter harbour is urgently requested. I have an emergency case.
UQ	You should wait outside the harbour (or river mouth). UQ 1 You should wait outside the harbour until daylight.
UR	My estimated time of arrival (at place indicated) is (time indicated). UR 1 What is your estimated time of arrival (at place indicated)?
RZ 1	You should not proceed out of harbour/anchorage.
RV 2	You should proceed into port.

The following notes apply to individual countries:

British Isles
In an emergency, an Examination Service might be instituted for certain ports, when the following signals would apply:

By day	By night	Meaning
Three red balls shown vertically	Three flashing red lights vertically	Entry to port prohibited
	Three green lights shown vertically	Entry to port permitted
A blue flag	Red, green, red lights shown vertically	Movement of shipping within port or anchorage prohibited

Vessels of the Examination Service wear a special flag, with a blue border and a square in the centre — the top half white and the bottom half red.

France
See 10.14.7 for simplified and full codes of traffic signals. The simplified code is used in some ports where there is less traffic.

Netherlands
In the event of government control of entry to Dutch harbours, the following signals indicate that

entry is prohibited, and that a yacht should proceed towards the vessel flying the same signal.

By day	**By night**
Three red balls, disposed vertically, or	Three red lights, disposed vertically, or
Two cones points together over a ball	Three lights, disposed vertically, green over red over white

For other signals see 10.20.7.

Germany
See 10.21.7.

6.2.8 Visual storm signals

Official storm signals, as previously displayed by Coastguard stations etc, are now discontinued in the British Isles, but signals may be shown in a few places by private arrangement. These should be treated with caution, in case they are not up to date. Signals are shown when a gale is expected within 12 hours, or is already blowing, in the adjacent sea area. The signal is lowered when the wind is below gale force, if a renewal is not expected within six hours. The signals consist of black cones. The North cone, point upwards, indicates gales from a point north of the east–west line. The South cone, point downwards, indicates gales from a point south of the east–west line. A few stations display night signals consisting of a triangle of lights.

International System
An International System of visual storm signals is used in France, the Netherlands, and Germany. This is illustrated in 10.14.7.

6.2.9 Tidal signals

Tidal signals are shown for individual harbours in Chapter 10. There is no standard system for British ports, nor for the Netherlands and Germany. France uses a system for indicating whether the tide is rising or falling, and to show the height of the tide above chart datum by a combination of cones, cylinders and balls by day, and by green, red and white lights at night. See 10.14.7.

6.3 RADIO COMMUNICATIONS

6.3.1 Radiotelephones — general

Many yachts are fitted with radiotelephones, mostly Very High Frequency (VHF) sets with ranges of about 20 miles. Medium Frequency (MF) sets give much greater ranges, but must be Single Sideband (SSB). Double Sideband (DSB) transmissions are prohibited except for emergency transmissions on 2182 kHz, the international MF distress frequency. Full details of the various licences and operating procedures are given in Chapter 6 of *The Macmillan & Silk Cut Yachtsman's Handbook.* The brief notes which follow cover only the most important points.

For a yacht which requires to maintain radio contact with shore on ocean passages it is necessary to use High Frequency (HF) radio, which is more powerful and gives a much bigger range than MF, as is described briefly below.

A Ship Licence for the set is required from the DTI, Marine Licensing Section, Room 613(c), Waterloo Bridge House, Waterloo Road, London, SE1 8UA — who will also give approval for the use of VHF Ch M and Ch M2 for communication between yachts, yacht harbours and yacht clubs, and for race control (see 6.3.2).

A Certificate of Competence and an Authority to Operate are required by the person in charge of a set. For yachtsmen this is likely to be the Certificate of Competence, Restricted VHF Only. The Royal Yachting Association (RYA) is responsible for the conduct of this examination. Details of the syllabus and examination are in RYA booklet G26, available (with application form for the examination) from the RYA.

6.3.2 Radiotelephones — general provisions

For details see the *Handbook for Radio Operators* (Lloyds of London Press). Briefly: operators must not divulge the contents of messages heard; stations must identify themselves when transmitting; except in cases of distress, coast radio stations control communications in their areas; at sea a yacht may call other vessels or shore stations, but messages must not be sent to an address ashore except through a coast radio station; in harbour a yacht may not use inter-ship channels except for safety, and may only communicate with the local Port Operations Service, British Telecom coast stations, or with stations on Ch M or M2; do not interfere with the working of other stations — before transmitting, listen to see that the channel is free; it is forbidden to transmit unnecessary or superfluous signals; priority must be given to distress calls; the transmission of bad language is forbidden; a log must be kept, recording all transmissions, etc.

VHF radio
Very High Frequency (VHF) radio has a range slightly better than the line of sight between the aerials. It pays to fit a good aerial, as high as possible. Maximum power output is 25 watts, and a lower power (usually one watt) is used for short ranges. Most UK coast stations and many harbours now have VHF. So do the principal Coastguard stations and other rescue services.

Marine VHF frequencies are in the band 156·00–174·00 MHz. Ch 16 (156·80 MHz) is for distress and safety purposes, and for calling and answering. Once contact has been made the stations concerned must switch to a working channel, except for safety matters. Yachts at sea are encouraged to listen on Ch 16.

Basic VHF sets are 'simplex', transmitting and receiving on the same frequency, so that it is not possible to speak and listen simultaneously. 'Semi-duplex' sets transmit and receive on different frequencies, while fully 'duplex' sets can do this simultaneously so that conversation is normal.

There are three main groups of frequencies, but certain channels can be used for more than one purpose. They are shown in order of preference.
(1) *Public correspondence* (through coast radio stations). All can be used for duplex. Ch 26, 27, 25, 24 23, 28, 04, 01, 03, 02, 07, 05, 84, 87, 86, 83, 85, 88, 61, 64, 65, 62, 66, 63, 60, 82.
(2) *Inter-ship.* These are all simplex. Ch 06, 08, 10, 13, 09, 72, 73, 69, 67, 77, 15, 17.
(3) *Port operations.* Simplex: Ch 12, 14, 11, 13, 09, 68, 71, 74, 10, 67, 69, 73, 17, 15. Duplex: Ch 20, 22, 18, 19, 21, 05, 07, 02, 03, 01, 04, 78, 82, 79, 81, 80, 60, 63, 66, 62, 65, 64, 61, 84.

Ch 80 (Tx 161·625 MHz Rx 157·025 MHz) is the primary working channel for yachts with yacht harbours, plus Ch M (157·85 MHz) as a stand-by. Yacht clubs may use Ch M2 (161·425 MHz) for race control with Ch M as stand-by (see 6.3.1). Ch 67 (156·375 MHz) is operated in the UK by principal Coastguard stations as the Small Craft Safety Channel, accessed via Ch 16 (see 8.2.2).

Ch 70 is reserved exclusively for digital selective calling for distress and safety purposes.

MF radio
MF radiotelephones operate in the 1605–4200 kHz wavebands. Unlike VHF and HF, MF transmissions tend to follow the curve of the Earth, which makes them suitable for direction finding equipment. For this reason, and because of their good range, the marine distress radiotelephone frequency is in the MF band (2182 kHz). Silence periods are observed on this frequency for three minutes commencing every hour and half hour.

During these silence periods only Distress and Urgency messages may be transmitted (see 6.3.10 below). MF radio equipment must be single sideband (SSB). Double sideband (DSB) transmissions are prohibited except for emergency-only sets operating on 2182 kHz. As for VHF, both the operator and the set must be licenced. MF sets are more complex and more expensive than VHF, and are subject to more regulations.

HF radio
HF radiotelephones use wave bands that are chosen, according to prevailing propagation conditions, from 4, 8, 12, 16 and 22 MHz bands (short wave). HF is more expensive than MF and absorbs more power, but it can provide worldwide coverage—although good installation and correct operation are essential for satisfactory results.

Whereas MF transmissions follow the curve of the earth, HF waves travel upwards and bounce off the ionosphere back to earth. Reception is better at night when the ionosphere is more dense. The directional properties of HF transmissions are poor, and there is no radiotelephone HF distress frequency.

The long-range service in the United Kingdom is provided by Portishead Radio, operated by British Telecom International. Watch is kept on the higher bands during daylight, and on the lower bands at night. A 24-hour watch is kept on the 8 MHz band.

6.3.3 RT procedures

Except for distress, urgency or safety messages, communications between a ship and a coast station are controlled by the latter. Between two ship stations, the station called controls the working. A calling station must use a frequency on which the station called is keeping watch. After making contact, comunication can continue on an agreed working channel. For VHF the name of the station called need normally only be given once, and that of the calling station twice. Once contact is made, each name need only be transmitted once. If a station does not reply, check the settings on the transmitter and repeat the call at three-minute intervals (if the channel is clear).

Prowords
It is important to understand the following:

ACKNOWLEDGE	'Have you received and understood?'
CONFIRM	'My version is . . . is that correct?'
CORRECTION	'An error has been made; the correct version is . . .'
I SAY AGAIN	'I repeat . . . (e.g. important words)'
I SPELL	'What follows is spelt phonetically'
OUT	End of work
OVER	'I have completed this part of my message, and am inviting you to reply'
RECEIVED	'Receipt acknowledged'
SAY AGAIN	'Repeat your message (or part indicated)'
STATION CALLING	Used when a station is uncertain of the identity of a station which is calling

Attention is also called to other procedure signals which can be used for RT, as shown in 6.1.4.

Before making a call, decide exactly what needs to be said. It may help to write the message down. Speak clearly and distinctly. Names or important words can be repeated or spelt phonetically.

For a position, give latitude and longitude, or the yacht's bearing and distance from a charted object. For bearings use 360° True notation. For times use 24 hour notation, and specify GMT, BST etc.

6.3.4 Coast Radio Stations

In the United Kingdom these are operated by British Telecom International, and details are shown in 6.3.15. Coast Stations control communications, and link ship stations with the telephone network ashore. Through them you can call any telephone subscriber in the United Kingdom and in about 200 foreign countries, as described in 6.3.5. At fixed times Coast Stations transmit traffic lists, navigation warnings and weather bulletins. They play an important role in Distress, Urgency and Safety Messages—see 6.3.10.

The major UK Coast Stations operate on both MF and VHF, and they have remotely controlled VHF stations to extend their VHF coverage. The MF stations (and the VHF stations controlled by each) are divided for operational procedures into two regions. The Southern Region comprises Land's End, Niton, North Foreland and Humber Radios. The Northern Region comprises Cullercoats, Stonehaven, Wick/Shetland and Portpatrick Radios.

An incoming call through any station in each region is answered from the first free operating position—not necessarily the nearest manned station. Watch is kept on 2182 kHz by Stonehaven Radio (Northern Region) and Land's End Radio (Southern Region). These stations can engage and speak over all frequencies and channels. Watch may be kept on VHF Ch 16, but distress cover for this primarily rests with HM Coastguard.

Broadcasts are on dedicated MF frequencies and on selected VHF channels (also used for link calls). The Officer in each region making the broadcast can engage and speak over the frequencies and channels of all other stations.

VHF calls to UK Coast Stations

When within range (about 40 miles) you are likely to be able to call a Coast Station. This allows you to make ordinary telephone calls, reverse charge calls, YTD calls (see 6.3.5), or send telegrams. There is also free access to navigational warnings, weather bulletins and gale warnings.

Except in emergency vessels should call a UK Coast Station on one of the working frequencies shown in 6.3.15. For a Distress or Urgency Call (only) use Ch 16. Avoid using the station's designated broadcast channel at about the time of a scheduled broadcast. Proceed as follows:

(1) Listen for a 'clear' channel, with no transmission at all. A busy channel will have either carrier noise, speech or the engaged signal (a series of pips).

(2) Having located a free channel, the initial call must last at least six seconds in order to activate the Coast Station's ship-call latch equipment. For example: "Land's End Radio, Land's End Radio, this is Yacht Seabird, Seabird—Golf Oscar Romeo India—Channel 85, Over".

(3) When the call is accepted by the Coast Station you will hear engaged pips, indicating that you have activated and engaged the channel. Wait for the operator to speak. If you do not hear the pips and have not activated the station's transmitter you may be out of range. Try another station or call again when you get closer.

(4) When you are answered by the Radio Officer be ready to give the following: Vessel's name, callsign, type of call and billing details (see 6.3.5), the telephone number required (and the name of the person in the case of a personal call).

Telephone calls are normally timed automatically. The timing clock stops when the shore subscriber replaces the handset. Both telephone calls and telegrams can be made or sent to another vessel via a Coast Station.

For receiving calls, you are called on Ch 16 when a message or phone call is ready for you, but it is recommended to listen to the regular traffic lists broadcast from the nearest Coast Station. If your vessel is equipped with a selective call device, you can be alerted by a Coast Station transmitting your Selcal number on Ch 16.

VHF calls to foreign coast stations

French, German and Irish stations are called on a working channel, similarly Belgian and Dutch stations but depending on the position of the yacht. VHF calls to Scheveningen Radio should last several seconds and state the calling channel. A four-tone signal indicates temporary delay but you will be answered when an operator is free.

MF calls to UK Coast Stations

(1) Call the Coast Station concerned on the chosen paired frequency channel, as shown for each station in 6.3.15, in the same way as for VHF calls. Stations have speech detection equipment which recognises and responds to voice patterns, but not to other sounds such as whistling or telex tones.

(2) The speech detector will operate, causing channel engaged pips to be transmitted so that you know that your call has been received.

(3) Wait until the Radio Officer answers—your call will have been queued within the system and will be presented to the first available free position. If you are not answered at once do not change channel, or you may lose your original turn.
(4) If the channel engaged pips are not heard within a few seconds, try again making the call last a little longer—up to 10 seconds.
(5) If the pips are still not heard, or if you think the system has not reacted correctly, call on 2182 kHz. The Coast Station will then answer on 2182 kHz, allocate you a channel, and queue you into the system.
(6) The Radio Officer will request the following information: Vessel's name, callsign, Accounting Code (AAIC—see 6.3.6), and category of traffic (e.g. telegram, telephone call).
Note: Distress and Urgency calls should always be made on 2182 kHz, and will be answered on the same channel. This includes urgent medical calls, which should be preceded by the Urgency Signal "PAN PAN MEDICO"—see 6.3.7. Non-urgent medical calls should be made on working channels.

6.3.5 Link calls

A yacht can be connected, via a coast radio station, into the telephone network. It is possible to make personal calls to certain countries and collect (transferred charge) calls to the UK. World-wide accounting for calls is arranged by quoting the 'Accounting Authority Indicator Code' (AAIC). For British yachts this is 'GB 14', followed by the yacht's callsign. Your AAIC is printed with your callsign on your VHF radio licence. Yacht owners making VHF link calls to the UK through a British coast station can transfer the charge to their home telephone bill by quoting the AAIC 'YTD', followed by their UK telephone number. Or payment may be by British Telecom credit card or transferred charge.

The operator makes the connection. When channels are congested calls may be limited to six minutes. Timing is automatic.

Data may be exchanged on VHF over the telephone network by yachts suitably equipped with V22bis specification modem units. Procedures and charges are as for an ordinary VHF call except that data modems are switched into circuit.

Autolink RT allows direct-dial calls from ship to shore into the national or international telephone network without going through a coast station operator. This service on VHF and MF gives quicker access, call scrambling when required, and simplified accounting. It operates through an on-board unit costing £300–£500 which is easily connected to the radio, and which has last number redial and a 10 number memory store.

Link call to a yacht
Telephone calls to vessels via BTI Coast Stations are handled by Portishead Radio. By dialling 0800 378389 you will be connected free of charge to the ships radiotelephone service. This number should be used to book calls on VHF, Short Range; the MF, Medium Range; or the HF, Long Range services. You will be asked for the name of the vessel, station through which vessel normally communicates, voyage details, caller's telephone number (or number to be charged if different), person to whom you wish to speak, and caller's name. Portishead Radio will route the call to the appropriate Coast Station.

6.3.6 Weather information by RT

See Chapter 7 (7.2) — for example 7.2.4 (ships at sea), 7.2.14 (broadcasts by coast stations), 7.2.15 (present weather), 7.2.16 (broadcasts by HM Coastguard).

6.3.7 Medical help by RT

Medical advice can be obtained through any UK coast radio station. If medical assistance is required (a doctor, or a casualty to be off-lifted) the request will be passed to the Coastguard. In either case the messages are passed free of charge. Where appropriate, the Urgency Signal PAN PAN MEDICO (see 6.3.10) may be used. For France call: PAN PAN Radiomédical (name of station) in French. For Belgium call: Radiomédical Oostende, in French, Dutch, English or German. For Netherlands call: Radiomédical Scheveningen, in Dutch, English, French or German. For Germany call: Funkarzt (name of station) in German or English.

6.3.8 Flotilla reporting schemes

Where numbers of yachts are required to report on a regular basis to a control centre, BTI offer two schemes. (a) Where vessels are given a window during which to report, and (b) Where vessels report at fixed times. Details from BTI Maritime Radio, 43 Bartholomew Close, London, EC1A 7HP.

6.3.9 Port operations

Many harbours now have VHF RT facilities, while a few also operate on MF (mostly for pilotage). The nominated channels must only be used for messages concerning port operations or (in emergency) the safety of persons, and not for public correspondence. For details of harbour RT information in Chapter 10, see 10.0.1. In a busy port a yacht can learn a great deal by merely listening on the right channel.

6.3.10 Distress messages and procedures

Anybody in the crew should be able to pass a distress message, should this be necessary. But this must only be done if the yacht or a person is in serious danger and requires immediate assistance. The procedure is:

Check main battery switch ON
Switch set ON, and turn power selector to HIGH
Tune to VHF Ch 16 (or 2182 kHz for MF)
If alarm signal generator fitted, operate for at least 30 seconds
Press 'transmit' button, and say slowly and distinctly:

MAYDAY MAYDAY MAYDAY
THIS IS (name of boat, spoken three times)
MAYDAY (name of boat, spoken once)
MY POSITION IS (latitude and longitude, or true bearing and distance from a known point)
Nature of distress (whether sinking, on fire etc)
Aid required
Number of persons on board
Any other important, helpful information (e.g. if the yacht is drifting, whether distress rockets are being fired)
OVER

The yacht's position is of vital importance, and should be repeated if time allows. On completion of the distress message, release the 'transmit' button and listen. In coastal waters an immediate acknowledgment should be expected, in the following form:

MAYDAY (name of station sending the distress message, spoken three times)
THIS IS ... (name of the station acknowledging, spoken three times)
RECEIVED MAYDAY

If an acknowledgment is not received, check the set and repeat the distress call. For 2182 kHz the call should be repeated during the three-minute silence periods which commence every hour and half-hour.

A yacht which hears a distress message from a vessel in her immediate vicinity and which is able to give assistance should acknowledge accordingly, but only after giving an opportunity for the nearest shore station or some larger vessel to do so.

If a yacht hears a distress message from a vessel further away, and it is not acknowledged, she must try to pass on the message in this form:

MAYDAY RELAY, MAYDAY RELAY, MAYDAY RELAY.
This is (name of vessel re-transmitting the distress message, spoken three times)
Followed by the intercepted message.

Control of distress traffic

A distress (MAYDAY) call imposes general radio silence, until the vessel concerned or some other authority (e.g. the nearest MRCC, MRSC or coast station) cancels the distress.

If necessary the station controlling distress traffic may impose radio silence in this form:

SEELONCE MAYDAY, followed by its name or other identification, on the distress frequency.

If some other station nearby believes it necessary to do likewise, it may transmit:

SEELONCE DISTRESS, followed by its name or other identification.

When appropriate the station controlling distress traffic may relax radio silence as follows:

MAYDAY
HELLO ALL STATIONS (spoken three times)
THIS IS (name or identification)
The time
The name of the station in distress
PRU-DONCE

When all distress traffic has ceased, normal working is authorised as follows:

MAYDAY
HELLO ALL STATIONS (spoken three times)
THIS IS (name or identification)
The time
The name of station which was in distress
SEELONCE FEENEE

Urgency Signal

This consists of the words PAN PAN, spoken three times, and indicates that the station has a very urgent message concerning the safety of a ship or person. Messages prefixed by PAN PAN take priority over all traffic except distress, and are sent on VHF Ch 16 or on 2182 kHz. The Urgency Signal is appropriate when urgent medical advice or attention is needed, or when someone is lost overboard. It should be cancelled when the urgency is over.

Safety Signal

This consists of the word SÉCURITÉ (pronounced SAY-CURE-E-TAY) spoken three times, and indicates that the station is about to transmit an important navigational or meteorological warning. Such messages usually originate from a coast station, and are transmitted on a working frequency after an announcement on the distress frequency.

6.3.11 INMARSAT

World-wide satellite communication (Satcom) is provided by the International Maritime Satellite Organisation (INMARSAT), through satellites in geostationary orbits above the equator over the Atlantic, Pacific and Indian Oceans. These satellites are the links between the Land Earth Stations (LESs), operated by organisations such as British Telecom, and the on-board terminals called Ship Earth Stations (SESs). Satcom is more reliable and gives better reception than HF SSB radio.

A LES connects the satellite system with the landbased communication network. A message to a ship originating on land is transmitted by the LES to one of the satellites, and thence to the ship. A call from a ship is received via the satellite by the LES, which then transmits it to its destination over landbased networks.

Standard 'A' terminals have a large antenna about 4ft (1.2m) in diameter inside a radome, and are only suitable for larger vessels. They provide direct dialling facilities, Telex, data and facsimile transmission, and speedy connection to HM Coastguard's MRCC at Falmouth.

New, Standard 'C' terminals are very much smaller and provide Satcom facilities for transmitting and receiving data or text (but not voice) in even a small yacht.

6.3.12 Navigational Warnings — general

The world-wide Navigational Warning Service covers 16 sea areas (NAVAREAS) numbered I–XVI, each with a country nominated as Area Co-ordinator responsible for issuing long range warnings. These are numbered consecutively through the year and are transmitted in English and in one or more other languages at scheduled times by WT. Other forms of transmission (RT, radiotelex and facsimile) may also be used. Warnings cover items such as failures or changes to navigational aids, wrecks and navigational dangers of all kinds, SAR operations, cable or pipe laying, naval exercises etc.

Within each NAVAREA, Coastal Warnings and Local Warnings may also be issued. Coastal Warnings, up to 100 or 200 n miles offshore, are broadcast in English and in the national language by coast radio stations. Local Warnings are issued by harbour authorities in the national language.

6.3.13 Navigational Warnings — Europe

United Kingdom

The United Kingdom (together with Northern Europe and Scandinavia) come within NAVAREA I, with Britain as the Area Co-ordinator for long range navigational warnings which are broadcast by Portishead Radio (GKA). Messages are numbered in sequence, and the text is published in the weekly *Notices to Mariners* together with a list of warnings still in force.

NAVTEX warnings (see 6.3.14) are broadcast by Niton, Cullercoats and Portpatrick Radio for the areas shown in Fig.6(1).

Coastal Warnings are broadcast by RT at scheduled times from coast radio stations, for the Sea Regions lettered A–N, in Fig.6(2). Important warnings are broadcast at any time on the distress frequencies of 500kHz, 2182kH and VHF Ch 16.

Local warnings from harbour authorities are broadcast by nearby coast radio stations. HM Coastguard broadcasts local warnings for inshore waters outside of harbour limits, on VHF Ch 67 after an announcement on Ch 16.

Vessels which encounter dangers to navigation should notify other craft and the nearest coast radio station, prefacing the message by the safety signal (see 6.3.10).

France

Long range warnings are broadcast in English and French for NAVAREA II, which includes the west coast of France, by St Lys Radio. The north coast comes within NAVAREA I.

AVURNAVS (AVis URgents aux NAVigateurs) are coastal and local warnings issued by regional authorities:

(1) Avurnavs Brest for the west coast of France and the western Channel (Spanish frontier to Mont St Michel).

(2) Avurnavs Cherbourg for the eastern Channel and the North Sea (Mont St Michel to the Belgian frontier).

Avurnavs are broadcast by the appropriate coast radio station, urgent ones on receipt and at the end of the next silence period as well as at scheduled times. RT warnings are prefixed by 'Śecurité Avurnav', followed by the name of the station.

Belgium

Navigational warnings are broadcast by Oostende Radio at scheduled times (see 6.3.16) on 2761kHz MF, 518kHz (NAVTEX) and on Ch 27.

Netherlands

Navigational warnings are broadcast by Scheveningen Radio at scheduled times (see 6.3.16) on 1862kHz (Nes), 1890kHz and 2824kHz MF, and on 518kHz (NAVTEX).

Germany

Navigational warnings are broadcast by Norddeich Radio on 2614kHz on receipt, after the next silence period, and at scheduled times. Broadcasts commence with the safety signal, the words *Nautische Warnnachricht*, and the serial number; they are in English and German. Decca Warnings for the German and Frisian Islands chains (*Decca Warnnachricht*) are included. Dangers to navigation should be reported to Seewarn Cuxhaven.

6.3.14 NAVTEX

NAVTEX provides navigational and meteorological warnings and other safety information by automatic print-outs from a dedicated receiver, and is a component of the International Maritime Organization (IMO) Global Maritime Distress and Safety System (GMDSS) due for world-wide implementation by August 1991.

At present broadcasts are all in English on a single frequency of 518kHz, with excellent coverage of coastal waters in areas such as NW Europe where the scheme originated. Interference between stations is avoided by time sharing and by limiting the range of transmitters to about 300 n miles, so that three stations cover the United Kingdom. IMO is expected to make a second NAVTEX channel available for broadcasts in the local national language.

The use of a single frequency allows a simple receiver with a printer using cash-roll paper, although some yacht receivers have a video screen. The user programmes the receiver for the vessel's area and for the types of messages required. For example, if Decca is not carried Decca Warnings can be rejected. The receiver automatically rejects messages which are corrupt or ones that have already been printed.

Each message is pre-fixed by a four character group. The first character is the code letter of the transmitting station (in the United Kingdom S for Niton, G for Cullercoats and O for Portpatrick). The second character indicates the category of the message as in the code opposite. The third and fourth are message serial numbers, from 01 to 99. The serial number 00 denotes urgent traffic such as gale warnings and SAR alerts, and messages with this prefix are always printed.

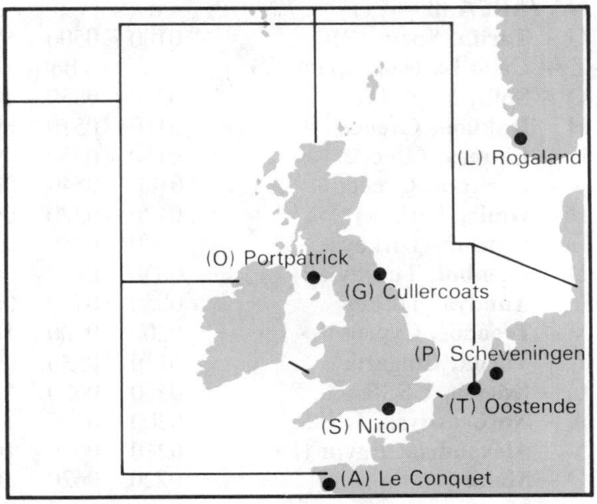
(L) Rogaland
(O) Portpatrick
(G) Cullercoats
(P) Scheveningen
(T) Oostende
(S) Niton
(A) Le Conquet

Fig.6(1) *NAVTEX areas around British Isles.*

Message categories

A Coastal navigation and hazard warnings
B Gale warnings
C Ice reports (unlikely to apply in UK)
D Search and Rescue information
E Weather forecasts
F Pilot Service messages
G Decca messages
H Loran-C messages
I Omega messages
J Satnav messages
L Oil and gas rig information (UK trial)
Z No messages on hand at scheduled time

Information in a NAVTEX broadcast applies only to the area for which the broadcast station is responsible, as shown in Fig.6(1). A user may accept messages from one or more stations.

NAVTEX stations

The table opposite shows the NAVTEX stations in NAVAREAS I, II and III with their station identity codes and transmission times (GMT). The times of weather bulletins for the British stations are shown in bold.

(P) indicates that the station is provisional or projected.

The diagram above shows the stations and their areas around the British Isles.

NAVAREA I						
R – **Reykjavik,** Iceland	0318	0718	1118	1518	1918	2318
B – **Bodø,** Norway	0018	0418	0818	1218	1618	2100
J – **Stockholm,** Sweden	0330	0730	1130	1530	1930	2330
H – **Härnösand,** Sweden	0000	0400	0800	1200	1600	2000
U – **Tallin,** USSR	0030	0430	0830	1230	1630	2030
P – **Netherlands Coast Guard**	0348	0748	1148	1548	1948	2348
T – **Oostende,** Belgium	0248	0648	1048	1448	1848	2248
G – **Cullercoats,** UK	0048	0448	**0848**	1248	1648	**2048**
S – **Niton,** UK	0018	0418	**0818**	1218	1618	**2018**
O – **Portpatrick,** UK	0130	0530	**0930**	1330	1730	**2130**
V – **Vardø,** Norway	0300	0700	1100	1500	1900	2300
L – **Rogaland,** Norway	0148	0548	0948	1348	1748	2148
NAVAREA II						
A – **Le Conquet,** France (P)	0000	0400	0800	1200	1600	2000
F – **Brest,** France*	0118	0518	0918	1318	1718	2118
R – **Lisboa,** Portugal	0250	0650	1050	1450	1850	2250
F – **Horta,** Azores	0050	0450	0850	1250	1650	2050
D – **Finisterre,** Spain (P)	0030	0430	0830	1230	1630	2030
I – **Islas Canarias,** Spain (P)	0100	0500	0900	1300	1700	2100

NAVAREA III

G – **Tarifa,** Spain (P)	0100	0500	0900	1300	1700	2100
Z – **Cabo La Nao,** Spain (P)	to be notified (planned)					
Q – **Split,** Yugoslavia	0250	0650	1050	1450	1850	2250
H – **Iraklion,** Greece	0110	0510	0910	1310	1710	2110
L – **Limnos,** Greece	0150	0550	0950	1350	1750	2150
K – **Kerkyra,** Greece	0140	0540	0940	1340	1740	2140
I – **Izmir,** Turkey	0120	0520	0920	1320	1720	2120
E – **Samsun,** Turkey	0040	0440	0840	1240	1640	2040
D – **Istanbul,** Turkey (P)	0030	0430	0830	1230	1630	2030
F – **Antalya,** Turkey	0050	0450	0850	1250	1650	2050
M – **Troodos,** Cyprus	0200	0600	1000	1400	1800	2200
J – **Varna,** Bulgaria	0130	0530	0930	1330	1730	2130
C – **Odessa,** USSR	0230	0630	1030	1430	1830	2230
A – **Novorossiysk,** USSR	0300	0700	1100	1500	1900	2300
N – **Alexandria,** Egypt (P)	0210	0610	1010	1410	1810	2210
O – **Malta**	0220	0620	1020	1420	1820	2220

* Transmitter on Trial

– **Toulon,** France (P)	to be notified (planned 1992)
– **Ancona,** Italy (P)	to be notified (planned 1990)
– **Cagliari,** Italy (P)	to be notified (planned 1990)
– **Rome,** Italy (P)	to be notified (planned 1990)
– **Haifa,** Israel (P)	to be notified (planned 1990)

6.3.15 UK Coast Radio Stations

Note: Normal primary working frequencies are printed in bold type.

Coast Station: Name Position	MF (Medium Range) RT: Distress, Urgency, Safety (kHz)	MF: Calling and Working Paired Frequencies (kHz): Channel	Coast Station: Transmit	Coast Station: Receive	VHF Ch	Traffic List Times (GMT)	Navigation Warning Times (GMT)	Weather Bulletin Times (GMT)	Gale Warning Times (GMT) *	Decca Warning Times (GMT) for Chains
Land's End Radio 50°07′N 05°40′W *Tel: 0736 87 1364*	2182 Note: VHF Ch 64 directed to Scillies. Selcal (3204): 2170.5 kHz Ch 16	W X	2782 3610	2002 2120	16 27 88 85 64	Broadcasts on 2670 kHz and Ch 27 and Ch 64 at: Follow Navigation Warnings, Weather Bulletins and Gale Warnings at times shown opposite	0233 0633 1033 1433 1833 2233	0733 1933	0303 0903 1503 2103	As for Navigation Warnings 1B 7D
Pendennis Radio 50°09′N 05°03′W	VHF station remotely controlled from Land's End Radio Selcal (3238): Ch 16				16 62 66	Traffic Lists, Weather Bulletins and Warnings broadcast on Ch 62 at same times as for Land's End Radio above				
Start Point Radio 50°21′N 03°43′W	VHF station remotely controlled from Land's End Radio Selcal (3224): Ch 16				16 26 65 60	Traffic Lists, Weather Bulletins and Warnings broadcast on Ch 26 at same times as for Land's End Radio above				

*** Gale warnings — see note at foot of page 139**

6.3.15 UK Coast Radio Stations *continued*

Coast Station: Name Position	MF (Medium Range) RT: Distress, Urgency, Safety (kHz)	Calling and Working Paired Frequencies (kHz): Channel	Coast Station: Transmit	Coast Station: Receive	VHF Ch	Traffic List Times (GMT)	Navigation Warning Times (GMT)	Weather Bulletin Times (GMT)	Gale Warning Times (GMT) *	Decca Warning Times (GMT) for chains
Niton Radio 50°35′N 01°18′W (For Navtex see 6.3.14 p. 137) *Tel: 0983 730496*	2182 Note: VHF Ch 04 directed to Brighton. Selcal (3203): 2170.5 kHz Ch 16	U	2628	2009	16 04 28 81 85 64 87	Broadcasts on 1834 kHz and Ch 28 at: Follow Navigation Warnings, Weather Bulletins and Gale Warnings at times shown opposite	0233 0633 1033 1433 1833 2233	0733 1933	0303 0903 1503 2103	As for Navigation Warnings 1B 5B
Weymouth Bay Radio 50°33′N 02°26′W	VHF station remotely controlled from Niton Radio Selcal (3242): Ch 16				16 05	Traffic Lists, Weather Bulletins and Warnings broadcast on Ch 05 at same times as for Niton Radio above				
St Peter Port Radio 49°27′N 02°32′W Note: Commercial calls only. Link calls available on VHF Ch 62 only. *Tel: 0481 20085*	Ship calls on 2182. Station replies on 1810		1662.5[1] 2182 **1810**	1662.5[1] 2182[2] 2381[3] 2049 2056	16 62[4] 67[5] 78[6]	Broadcasts on 1810 kHz and Ch 62 and 78 at: After navigational warnings. (Ships also called individually on 2182 kHz and Ch 16)	Every 4h from 0133 (GMT) for local waters	No services		
	Notes: (1) Trinity House and SAR only (2) H24. (3) When 2182 is distress working. (4) Link calls available on Ch 62 only. (5) Ch 67 available for yacht safety messages. (6) For VHF services direct calling on Ch 78.									
Jersey Radio 49°11′N 02°14′W Note: Link calls available on VHF Ch 25 (or 82) only. *Tel: 0534 41121*	Ship calls on 2182. Station replies on 1726 (British ships) or 2182 (foreign ships).		2182 **1726**	2182[1] 2049[2] 2104[3] 2534[3]	16 82[4] 25 67[5]	Broadcasts on 1726 kHz and Ch 25 and 82 at: After weather messages. (Ships also called individually on 2182 kHz and Ch 16)	0433 0645 0745 0833 1245 1633 1845 2033 2245	0645 0745 1245 1845 2245	On receipt and at 0307 0907 1507 2107	(1) on receipt (2) at three minutes past the next two hours 1B
	(1) H24. (2) Foreign vessels (3) UK reg. vessels (4) Direct calling for UK reg. vessels (5) Small craft distress/ safety. Call on Ch 16.									
North Foreland Radio 51°22′N 01°25′E *Tel: 0843 291984*	2182 Selcal (3201): 2170.5 kHz Ch 16	T	2698	2016	16 05 26 66 65	Broadcasts on 1848 kHz and Ch 26 at: Follow Navigation Warnings, Weather Bulletins and Gale Warnings at times shown opposite	0133 0533 0933 1333 1733 2133	0733 1933	0303 0903 1503 2103	As for Navigation Warnings 1B 5B 2E
Hastings Radio 50°53′N 00°37′E	VHF station remotely controlled from North Foreland Radio Selcal (3225): Ch 16				16 07 63	Traffic Lists, Weather Bulletins and Warnings broadcast on Ch 07 at same times as for Northforeland Radio above				
Thames Radio 51°20′N 00°20′E	VHF station remotely controlled from North Foreland Radio Selcal (3202): Ch 16				16 02 83	Traffic Lists, Weather Bulletins and Warnings broadcast on Ch 02 at same times as for Northforeland Radio above				
Orfordness Radio 52°00′N 01°25′E	VHF station remotely controlled from North Foreland Radio Selcal (3235): Ch 16				16 62 82	Traffic Lists, Weather Bulletins and Warnings broadcast on Ch 62 at same times as for Northforeland Radio above				
Humber Radio 53°20′N 00°17′E *Tel: 0507 473 448*	2182 Note: VHF Ch 85 directed to The Wash. Selcal (3212): 2170.5 kHz Ch 16	Q R S	1925 2684 2810	2569 2111 2562	16 24 26 85	Broadcasts on 1869 kHz and Ch 26 at: Follow Navigation Warnings, Weather Bulletins and Gale Warnings at times shown opposite	0133 0533 0933 1333 1733 2133	0733 1933	0303 0903 1503 2103	As for Navigation Warnings 5B 2A 2E 9B

For Bacton Radio and Grimsby Radio see page 141.

*GALE WARNINGS are broadcast after the first silence period after receipt and at the next of the times shown or if first broadcast at a scheduled time the warning is repeated at the end of the next silence period.

continued

6

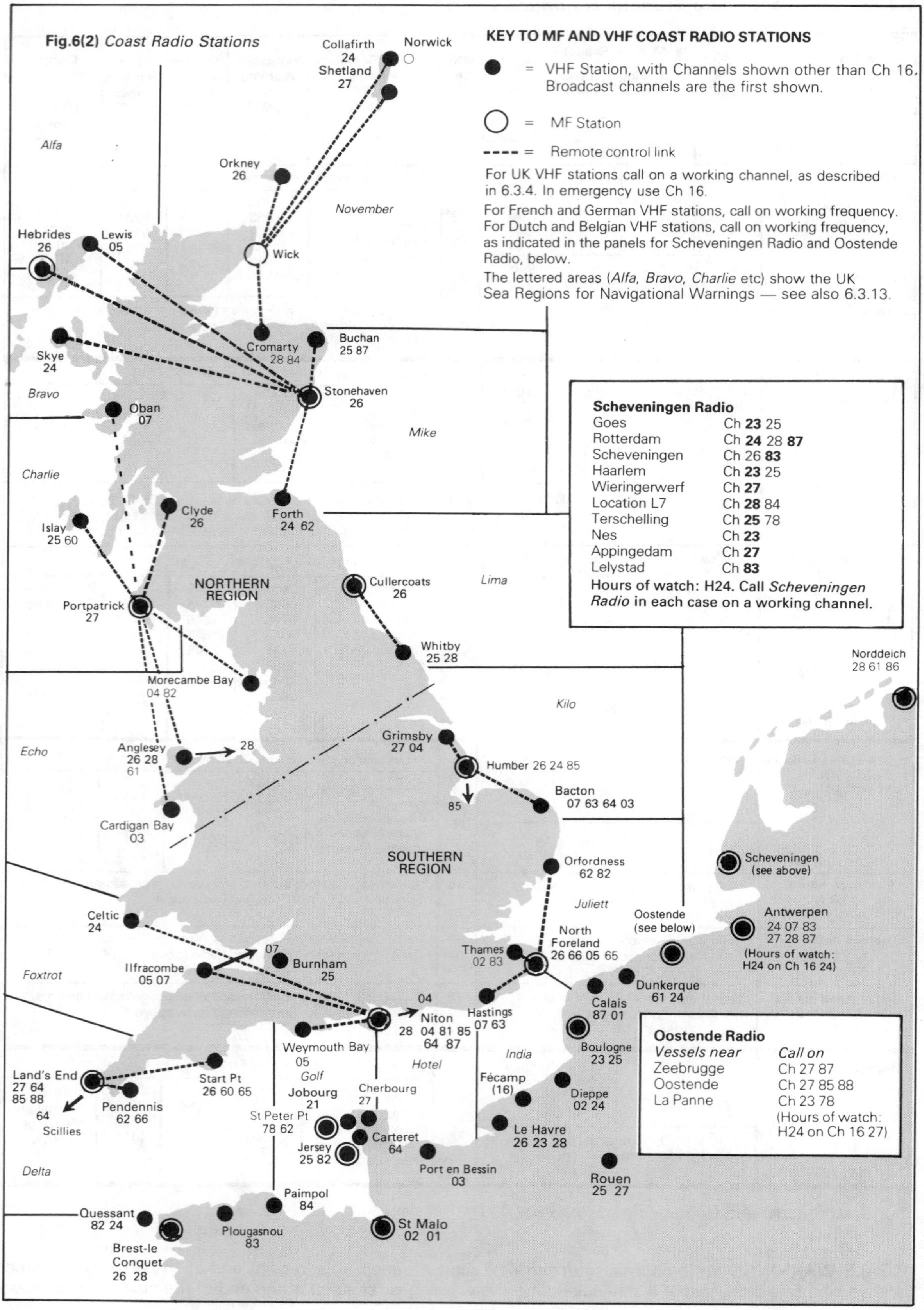
KEY TO MF AND VHF COAST RADIO STATIONS
= VHF Station, with Channels shown other than Ch 16. Broadcast channels are the first shown.
= MF Station
= Remote control link
For UK VHF stations call on a working channel, as described in 6.3.4. In emergency use Ch 16.
For French and German VHF stations, call on working frequency. For Dutch and Belgian VHF stations, call on working frequency, as indicated in the panels for Scheveningen Radio and Oostende Radio, below.
The lettered areas (Alfa, Bravo, Charlie etc) show the UK Sea Regions for Navigational Warnings — see also 6.3.13.
Scheveningen Radio
Goes Ch 23 25
Rotterdam Ch 24 28 87
Scheveningen Ch 26 83
Haarlem Ch 23 25
Wieringerwerf Ch 27
Location L7 Ch 28 84
Terschelling Ch 25 78
Nes Ch 23
Appingedam Ch 27
Lelystad Ch 83
Hours of watch: H24. Call Scheveningen Radio in each case on a working channel.
Oostende Radio
Vessels near / Call on
Zeebrugge Ch 27 87
Oostende Ch 27 85 88
La Panne Ch 23 78
(Hours of watch: H24 on Ch 16 27)
Collafirth 24
Norwick
Shetland 27
Alfa
Orkney 26
November
Hebrides 26
Lewis 05
Wick
Skye 24
Cromarty 28 84
Buchan 25 87
Stonehaven 26
Bravo
Oban 07
Mike
Charlie
Islay 25 60
Clyde 26
Forth 24 62
NORTHERN REGION
Cullercoats 26
Lima
Portpatrick 27
Whitby 25 28
Morecambe Bay 04 82
Norddeich 28 61 86
Kilo
Echo
Anglesey 26 28 61
28
Grimsby 27 04
Humber 26 24 85
85
Bacton 07 63 64 03
Cardigan Bay 03
SOUTHERN REGION
Orfordness 62 82
Scheveningen (see above)
Juliett
Celtic 24
Oostende (see below)
Antwerpen 24 07 83 27 28 87 (Hours of watch: H24 on Ch 16 24)
North Foreland 26 66 05 65
Thames 02 83
07
Burnham 25
Ilfracombe 05 07
Foxtrot
Dunkerque 61 24
Calais 87 01
04
Niton 28 04 81 85 64 87
Hastings 07 63
Boulogne 23 25
Weymouth Bay 05
India
Hotel
Golf
Land's End 27 64 85 88
Start Pt 26 60 65
Fécamp (16)
Dieppe 02 24
64
Scillies
Pendennis 62 66
Jobourg 21
Cherbourg 27
St Peter Pt 78 62
Le Havre 26 23 28
Carteret 64
Jersey 25 82
Delta
Port en Bessin 03
Rouen 25 27
Paimpol 84
Quessant 82 24
Plougasnou 83
St Malo 02 01
Brest-le Conquet 26 28
Fig.6(2) *Coast Radio Stations*

6.3.15 UK Coast Radio Stations *continued*

Coast Station: Name Position	MF (Medium Range) RT				VHF Ch	Traffic List Times (GMT)	Navigation Warning Times (GMT)	Weather Bulletin Times (GMT)	Gale Warning Times (GMT) *	Decca Warning Times (GMT) for Chains
	Distress, Urgency, Safety (kHz)	Calling and Working Paired Frequencies (kHz)								
		Channel	Coast Station							
			Transmit	Receive						
Bacton Radio 52°51′N 01°28′E	VHF station remotely controlled from Humber Radio Selcal (3214): Ch 16				16 07 63 64 03	Traffic Lists, Weather Bulletins and Warnings broadcast on Ch 07 same times as for Humber Radio above (page 139)				
Grimsby Radio 53°34′N 00°05′W	VHF station remotely controlled from Humber Radio Selcal (3239): Ch 16				16 04 27	Traffic Lists, Weather Bulletins and Warnings broadcast on Ch 27 at sames times as for Humber Radio above (page 139)				
Cullercoats Radio 55°04′N 01°28′W (For Navtex see 6.3.14 p. 137) *Tel: 091 297 0301*	2182	N O P	1838 2828 3750	2527 1953 2559	16 26	Broadcasts on 2719 kHz and Ch 26 at:				
	Selcal (3211): 2170.5 kHz Ch 16					Follow Navigation Warnings, Weather Bulletins and Gale Warnings at times shown opposite	0233 0633 1033 1433 1833 2233	0703 1903	0303 0903 1503 2103	As for Navigation Warnings 2A
Whitby Radio 54°29′N 00°36′W	VHF station remotely controlled from Cullercoats Radio Selcal (3231): Ch 16				16 25 28	Traffic Lists, Weather Bulletins and Warnings broadcast on Ch 25 at same times as for Cullercoats Radio above				
Stonehaven Radio 56°57′N 02°13′W *Tel: 0569 62918*	2182	I J K L M	1856 1715 1946 2779 3617	2555 2552 2566 2146 3249	16 26	Broadcast on 2691 kHz and Ch 26 at:				
	Selcal (3222): 2170.5 kHz Ch 16					Follow Navigation Warnings, Weather Bulletins and Gale Warnings at times shown opposite	0233 0633 1033 1433 1833 2233	0703 1903	0303 0903 1503 2103	As for Navigation Warnings 2A 6C 0E
Forth Radio 55°56′N 02°27′W	VHF station remotely controlled from Stonehaven Radio Selcal (3228): Ch 16				16 24 62	Traffic Lists, Weather Bulletins and Warnings broadcast on Ch 24 at same times as for Stonehaven Radio above				
Buchan Radio 57°36′N 02°02′W	VHF station remotely controlled from Stonehaven Radio Selcal (3237): Ch 16				16 25 87	Traffic Lists, Weather Bulletins and Warnings broadcast on Ch 25 at same times as for Stonehaven Radio above				
Hebrides Radio 58°14′N 07°02′W Controlled from (Stonehaven Radio) *Tel: 0569 62918*	2182	Z	1866	2534	**16** **26**	Broadcasts on 1866 kHz and Ch 26 at:				
	Selcal (3234): 2170.5 kHz Ch 16					Follow Navigation Warnings, Weather Bulletins and Gale Warnings at times shown opposite	0203 0603 1003 1403 1803 2203	0703 1903	**0303** **0903** **1503** **2103**	As for Navigation Warnings 6C 8E
Lewis Radio 58°28′N 06°14′W	VHF station remotely controlled from Stonehaven Radio Selcal (3216): Ch 16				**16** **05**	Traffic Lists, Weather Bulletins and Warnings broadcast on Ch 05 at same times as for Hebrides Radio above				
Skye Radio 57°28′N 06°41′W	VHF station remotely controlled from Stonehaven Radio Selcal (3232): Ch 16				**16** **24**	Traffic Lists, Weather Bulletins and Warnings broadcast on Ch 24 at same times as for Hebrides Radio above				
Wick Radio 58°26′N 03°06′W	2182	E F G H	2705 1827 2604 2625	2524 2548 2013 2381		Broadcasts on 1792 kHz (Wick) and 1824 kHz (Shetland) at:				
Shetland Radio (controlled by Wick Radio) 60°49′N 0°49′W *Tel: 0955 2272*	2182	A B C D	2751 2840.6 3538 —	2006 2277 3335 3328		Follow Navigation Warnings, Weather Bulletins and Gale Warnings at times shown opposite	0233 0633 1033 1433 1833 2233	0703 1903	0303 0903 1503 2103	As for Navigation Warnings 6C 0E
	Selcal (3221): 2170.5 kHz									

For Cromarty Radio, Orkney Radio, Shetland Radio and Collafirth Radio see page 142.

*** Gale warnings – see note at foot of page 139**

6

6.3.15 UK Coast Radio Stations *continued*

Coast Station: Name Position	MF (Medium Range) RT: Distress, Urgency, Safety (kHz)	Calling and Working Paired Frequencies (kHz): Channel	Coast Station: Transmit	Coast Station: Receive	VHF Ch	Traffic List Times (GMT)	Navigation Warning Times (GMT)	Weather Bulletin Times (GMT)	Gale Warning Times (GMT) *	Decca Warning Times (GMT) for chains
Cromarty Radio 57°36′N 02°58′W	VHF station remotely controlled from Wick Radio Selcal (3227): Ch 16				16 28 84	Traffic Lists, Weather Bulletins and Warnings broadcast on Ch 28 at same times as for Wick Radio above (page 141)				
Orkney Radio 58°47′N 02°57′W	VHF station remotely controlled from Wick Radio Selcal (3226): Ch 16				16 26	Traffic Lists, Weather Bulletins and Warnings broadcast on Ch 26 at same times as for Wick Radio above (page 141)				
Shetland Radio 60°09′N 01°12′W	VHF station remotely controlled from Wick Radio Selcal (3215): Ch 16				16 27	Traffic Lists, Weather Bulletins and Warnings broadcast on Ch 27 at same times as for Wick Radio above (page 141)				
Collafirth Radio 60°32′N 01°23′W	VHF station remotely controlled from Wick Radio Selcal (3230): Ch 16				16 24	Traffic Lists, Weather Bulletins and Warnings broadcast on Ch 24 at same times as for Wick Radio above (page 141)				
Portpatrick Radio 54°51′N 05°07′W (For Navtex see 6.3.14 p. 137) *Tel: 077 681 312*	2182 Selcal (3207): 2170.5 kHz Ch 16	Y	1883	2104	16 27	Broadcasts on 1883 kHz and Ch 27 at: Follow Navigation Warnings, Weather Bulletins and Gale Warnings at times shown opposite	0203 0603 1003 1403 1803 2203	0703 1903	0303 0903 1503 2103	As for Navigation Warnings 3B 7D 8E
Oban Radio 56°27′N 05°44′W	VHF station remotely controlled from Portpatrick Radio				16 07	Traffic Lists, Weather Bulletins and Warnings broadcast on Ch 07 at same times as for Portpatrick Radio above.				
Clyde Radio 55°38′N 04°47′W	VHF station remotely controlled from Portpatrick Radio Selcal (3213): Ch 16				16 26	Traffic Lists, Weather Bulletins and Warnings broadcast on Ch 26 at same times as for Portpatrick Radio above				
Islay Radio 55°46′N 06°27′W	VHF station remotely controlled from Portpatrick Radio Selcal (3233): Ch 16				16 25 60	Traffic Lists, Weather Bulletins and Warnings broadcast on Ch 25 at same times as for Portpatrick Radio above				
Anglesey Radio 53°20′N 04°18′W	VHF station remotely controlled from Portpatrick Radio Note: VHF Ch 28 directed to R Mersey. Selcal (3206): Ch 16				16 26 28 61	Traffic Lists, Weather Bulletins and Warning broadcast on Ch 26 at same times as for Portpatrick Radio above.				
Morecambe Bay Radio 54°10′N 03°12′W	VHF station remotely controlled from Portpatrick Radio Selcal (3240): Ch 16				16 04 82	Traffic Lists, Weather Bulletins and Warnings broadcast on Ch 04 at same times as for Portpatrick Radio above				
Cardigan Bay Radio 52°50′N 04°37′W	VHF station remotely controlled from Portpatrick Radio Selcal (3241): Ch 16				16 03	Traffic Lists, Weather Bulletins and Warnings broadcast on Ch 03 at same times as for Portpatrick Radio above				
Ilfracombe Radio 51°11′N 04°07′W	VHF station remotely controlled from Niton Radio Note: Ch 07 directed to Severn Bridge Selcal (3205): Ch 16				16 05 07	Broadcasts on Ch 05 at: Follow Navigation Warnings, Weather Bulletins and Gale Warnings at times shown opposite	0233 0633 1033 1433 1833 2233	0733 1933	0303 0903 1503 2103	As for Navigation Warnings 1B 7D
Celtic Radio 51°41′N 05°11′W	VHF station remotely controlled from Niton Radio Selcal (3218): Ch 16				16 24	Traffic Lists, Weather Bulletins and Warnings broadcast on Ch 24 at same times as for Ilfracombe Radio				
Burnham Radio 51°13′N 02°59′W	VHF station for Bristol Channel area				25	No Traffic Lists or broadcasts				

*GALE WARNINGS are broadcast after the first silence period after receipt and at the next of the times shown or if first broadcast at a scheduled time the warning is repeated at the end of the next silence period.

6.3.16 Irish and Continental Coast Radio Stations

IRELAND

Note: Normal primary working frequencies are printed in bold type.

Coast Station Name Position	Medium Frequency RT Service (kHz) Transmits	Receives	VHF Ch Tx Rx	Traffic List Times (GMT)	Navigation Warnings Times (GMT)	Weather Bulletin Times (LT)	Gale Warning Times (LT)	Decca Warning Times (GMT)
Malin Head Radio 55°22′N See 7°21′W Note 2 *Tel: (077) 70103*	**1841**[1] 2182 2593 (1) When 2182 distress working	2049[1] 2182	16 16 23 23 67[3] 67[3] 85 85	1841 kHz and Ch 23 every odd H+03 (not 0303 0703)	1841 kHz and Ch 23 every 4h from 0033	Ch 23 every 3h from 0103	Ch 23 O/R and next of 0033 0633 1233 1833	1841 kHz and Ch 23 O/R & H+03 for next 2h 6C 3B 7D 8E
Glen Head Radio 54°44′N/8°43′W	VHF station remotely controlled from Malin Head Radio		16 16 24 24 67[3] 67[3]	Ch 24	Ch 24	Ch 24	Ch 24	Ch 24
				Broadcast times as for Malin Head Radio VHF above				
Belmullet Radio 54°16′N/10°03′W	VHF station remotely controlled from Malin Head Radio		16 16 67[3] 67[3] 83 83	Ch 83	Ch 83	Ch 83	Ch 83	Ch 83
				Broadcast times as for Malin Head Radio VHF above				
Dublin Radio 53°23′N/6°04′W	VHF station remotely controlled from Malin Head Radio		16 16 67[3] 67[3] 83 83	Ch 83	Ch 83	Ch 83	Ch 83	Ch 83
				Broadcast times as for Malin Head Radio VHF above				
Valentia Radio 51°56′N See 10°21′W Note 4 *Tel: (0667) 6109*	**1827**[1] 2182 2590 2614 (1) When 2182 distress working.	2049[1] 2182	16 16 24 24 28 28 67[3] 67[3]	1827 kHz and Ch 24 every odd H+33 (not 0133 0533)	1827 kHz and Ch 24 every 4h from 0233	1827 kHz 0833 2033 (GMT). Ch 24 every 3h from 0103	1827 kHz S/P1 and next of 0303 0903 1503 2103 (GMT) Ch 24 O/R and next of 0033 0633 1233 1833 (LT)	1827 kHz and Ch 24 O/R & H+03 for next 2h 1B 7D
Clifden Radio 53°29′N/10°06′W	VHF station remotely controlled from Valentia Radio		16 16 26 26 67[3] 67[3]	Ch 26	Ch 26	Ch 26	Ch 26	Ch 26
				Broadcast times as for Valentia Radio VHF above				
Shannon Radio 52°31′N/9°36′W	VHF station remotely controlled from Valentia Radio		16 16 24 24 28 28 67[3] 67[3]	Ch 28	Ch 28	Ch 28	Ch 28	Ch 28
				Broadcast times as for Valentia Radio VHF above				
Bantry Radio 51°38′N/10°00′W	VHF station remotely controlled from Valentia Radio		16 16 23 23 67[3] 67[3] 85 85	Ch 23	Ch 23	Ch 23	Ch 23	Ch 23
				Broadcast times as for Valentia Radio VHF above				
Cork Radio 51°51′N/8°29′W	VHF station remotely controlled from Valentia Radio		16 16 26 26 67[3] 67[3]	Ch 26	Ch 26	Ch 26	Ch 26	Ch 26
				Broadcast times as for Valentia Radio VHF above				
Mine Head Radio 52°00′N/7°35′W	VHF station remotely controlled from Valentia Radio		16 16 67[3] 67[3] 83 83	Ch 83	Ch 83	Ch 83	Ch 83	Ch 83
				Broadcast times as for Valentia Radio VHF above				
Rosslare Radio 52°15′N/6°20′W	VHF station remotely controlled from Valentia Radio		16 16 23 23 67[3] 67[3]	Ch 23	Ch 23	Ch 23	Ch 23	Ch 23
				Broadcast times as for Valentia Radio VHF above				

NOTES FOR IRISH COAST STATIONS

1. When 2182 kHz is distress working.
2. VHF service at Crockalough (55°21′N 7°16′W).
3. Safety information for small craft.
4. VHF service at Kilkeaveragh (51°52′N 10° 20′W).
5. H+ . . means commencing at . . . minutes past hour.
6. LT means Local Time (ie GMT in winter, BST in summer).
7. O/R means on receipt.
8. S/P1 means after first silence period after receipt.
9. Except in emergency call on VHF working channel.

6.3.16 Continental Coast Radio Stations

FRANCE

Coast Station Name Position	Medium Frequency RT Service (kHz) Transmits	Receives	VHF Ch Tx	Rx	Traffic List Times (GMT)	Navigation Warnings Times (GMT)	Weather Bulletin Times (GMT)	Gale Warning Times (GMT)	Decca Warning Times (GMT)
Bayonne Radio 43°16′N 1°24′W	VHF station remotely controlled from Bordeaux-Arcachon See Note (a) below		16 **24**	16 24			Ch24 0733 1233 LT (Fr)	Ch 24 O/R & S/P2 (Fr)	
Bordeaux-Arcachon Radio 44°39′N 1°10′W (MF remotely controlled from Brest-Le Conquet 2200–0700 local time. VHF operates 0700–2200 local time) *Tel: 56.83.40.50*	1820 **1862** 2182 2775 3722	At Royan and Cap Ferret: 2182 2049 2056 2069 2153 2167 2506 2541 At Royan: 2449 3161 At Cap Ferret: 2037 2321 2421 2527 3168	16 **28** **82**	16 28 82	1862 kHz every even H + 07	1820 and 2775 kHz 0703 1703 (in French and English)	1820 kHz 0703 1703 (in French for Areas 23, 24) Ch 82 0733 1233 LT (Fr)	1820 kHz O/R and S/P2 and every even H + 07 (in French for Areas 23, 24) Ch 82 O/R & S/P2 (Fr)	1820 kHz 0703 1703 (in French and English) 1B 8B
Bordeaux Radio 44°53′N 0°30′W	VHF station remotely controlled from Bordeaux-Arcachon (0700–2200 local time)		16 **27**	16 27					
Royan Radio 45°34′N 0°58′W	VHF station remotely controlled from Bordeaux-Arcachon See Note (a) below		16 **23** **25**	16 23 25			Ch 23 0733 1233 LT (Fr)	Ch 23 O/R & S/P2 (Fr)	
La Rochelle Radio 46°20′N 1°05′W	VHF station remotely controlled from Bordeaux-Arcachon See Note (a) below		16 21 26	16 21 26			Ch 21 0733 1233 LT (Fr)	Ch 21 O/R & S/P2 (Fr)	
Ile de Ré Radio 46°12′N 01°22′W	VHF station remotely controlled from Bordeaux-Arcachon. See Note (a) below		16 21 26	16 21 26					
St Hilaire-de-Riez Radio 46°43′N 1°57′W	VHF station remotely controlled from Saint Nazaire See Note (a) below		16 **27**	16 27			Ch 27 0733 1233 LT (Fr)	Ch 27 O/R & S/P2 (Fr)	
St Herblain Radio 47°13′N 1°37′W	VHF station remotely controlled from Saint Nazaire See Note (a) below		16 **28**	16 28			Ch 28 0733 1233 LT (Fr)	Ch 28 O/R & S/P2 (Fr)	
Saint Nazaire Radio 47°21′N 2°06′W 47°17′N } VHF 2°14′W } (MF service remotely controlled from Brest-Le Conquet 2200–0700 local time) *Tel: 40.22.39.04*	**1687** 2182 2740 3795 1722	2182[1] Also at Batz-sur Mer: 1995 2049 2056 2153 2167 2321 2491 2506 3168 Note: (1) 2182 kHz: H24.	16 **23** **24** See Note (a) below	16 23 24	1687kHz every odd H + 07	1687 kHz O/R 1722 kHz 0803 1803 (in French)	1722 and 2740 kHz 0803 1803 (Fr) (Areas 14–24) Ch 23 0733 1233 LT (Fr) (Seine to Vendée coast)	1687 kHz O/R & S/P2 & every odd H+07 (Fr) (Areas 14–16) Ch 23 O/R & S/P2 (Fr) (Seine to Vendée coast)	1722kHz O/R 0803 1803 (in French) Chains 1B 8B

NOTES FOR FRENCH COAST STATIONS

(a) Transmits/receives on Ch 16 H24 for distress and safety traffic only Working channels operate 0700–2200 local time.
(b) H+ . . . means commencing at . . . minutes past hour.
(c) O/R means on receipt.
(d) Ch 16 reserved for distress and safety traffic only. Vessels should normally call on working frequency.
(e) For MF, call on 2182 or (if 2182 is busy) on 2321 kHz.
(f) LT means local (French) time.
(g) (Fr) means in French.
(h) S/P2 means after 1st and 2nd silence periods after receipt.
(i) VHF weather bulletins/gale warnings refer to coastal waters.
(j) For French Fcst Areas (MF Bcsts) see Fig. 7(3), p. 167.

6.3.16 Continental Coast Radio Stations *continued*

Coast Station Name Position	Medium Frequency RT Service (kHz) Transmits	Medium Frequency RT Service (kHz) Receives	VHF Ch Tx	VHF Ch Rx	Traffic List Times (GMT)	Navigation Warning Times (GMT)	Weather Bulletin Times (GMT)	Gale Warning Times (GMT)	Decca Warning Times (GMT)
Belle Ile Radio 47°21′N 3°09′W	VHF station remotely controlled from Saint Nazaire See Note (a) below		16 **25** **05**	16 25 05			Ch 25 0733 1233 LT (Fr)	Ch 25 O/R & S/P2 (Fr)	
Pont-l'Abbé Radio 47°53′N 4°13′W	VHF station remotely controlled from Brest-Le Conquet		**16** **27**	16 27			Ch 27 0733 1233 LT (Fr)	Ch 27 O/R & S/P2 (Fr)	
Brest-Le Conquet Radio 48°20′N 4°44′W Located at St Malo 48°38′N 2°02′W Located at Quimperlé 47°53′N 3°30′W (For Navtex see 6.3.14) *Tel: 98.80.40.26*	1673 **1806** 2182 2726 3722 1673 2182 **2691** 1673 1806 **1876** 2182 Notes: 1) Also receives on 2049 2056 2097 2153 2160 2167 2463 2506 3168 kHz 2) Located at Treffiagat 47°49′N 4°16′W	2182 (H24) 2182[1] (H24) 2182[1,2] (H24)	16 **26** **28**	16 26 28	1806 kHz (Le Conquet) 2691 kHz (St Malo) every even H + 03	1673 kHz (Le Conquet) 2691 kHz (St Malo) 0333 0733 1133 1533 1933 2333 1876 kHz (Quimperlé) 0733 1633 (in English and French)	1673 kHz (Le Conquet) 2691 kHz (St Malo) 1876 kHz (Quimperlé) 0733 1633 2153 and on request (in French for Areas 14–22) Ch 26 0733 1233 LT (Fr)	1673 kHz 1876 kHz 2691 kHz O/R & S/P2 1806 kHz 2691 kHz every even H + 03 (in French for Areas 14–22 Ch 26 O/R & S/P2 (Fr)	
Ouessant Radio 48°27′N 5°05′W	VHF station remotely controlled from Brest-Le Conquet		16 **24** **82**	16 24 82		Ch 82 0733 1233 LT (Fr)	Ch 82 O/R & S/P2 (Fr)		
Plougasnou Radio 48°42′N 3°48′W	VHF station remotely controlled from Brest-Le Conquet		**16** **83**	16 83		Ch 83 0733 1233 LT (Fr)	Ch 83 O/R & S/P2 (Fr)		
Paimpol Radio 48°45′N 2°59′W	VHF station remotely controlled from Brest-Le Conquet		**16** **84**	16 84		Ch 84 0733 1233 LT (Fr)	Ch 84 O/R & S/P2 (Fr)		
St Malo Radio 48°38′N 2°02′W	VHF station remotely controlled from Saint Nazaire		01 02 16	01 02 16		Ch 02 0733 1233 LT (Fr)	Ch 02 O/R & S/P2 (Fr)		
Carteret Radio 49°22′N 1°48′W	VHF station — day service only		16 **64**	16 64					
Jobourg Radio 49°41′N 01°54′W	VHF station remotely controlled from Boulogne See Note (a) below		16 21	16 21					
Cherbourg Radio 49°38′N 1°36′W	VHF station remotely controlled from Boulogne		**16** **27**	16 27			Ch 27 0733 1233 LT (Fr)	Ch 27 O/R & S/P2 (Fr)	
Port en Bessin Radio 49°20′N 0°42′W	VHF station remotely controlled from Boulogne		**03** 16	03 16			Ch 03 0733 1233 LT (Fr)	Ch 03 O/R & S/P2 (Fr)	
Rouen Radio 49°27′N 1°02′E	VHF station remotely controlled from Boulogne See Note (a) below		16 **25** 27	16 25 27					
Le Havre Radio 49°31′N 0°05′E *Tel: 35.70.90.04*	VHF station remotely controlled from Boulogne See Note (a) below		16 23 **26** **28**	16 23 26 28			Ch 26 0733 1233 LT (Fr)	Ch 26 O/R & S/P2 (Fr)	

NOTES FOR FRENCH COAST STATIONS

(a) Transmits/receives on Ch 16 H24 for distress and safety traffic only Working channels operate 0700–2200 local time.
(b) H+ . . . means commencing at . . . minutes past hour.
(c) O/R means on receipt.
(d) Ch 16 reserved for distress and safety traffic only. Vessels should normally call on working frequency.
(e) For MF, call on 2182 or (if 2182 is busy) on 2321 kHz.
(f) LT means local (French) time.
(g) (Fr) means in French.
(h) S/P2 means after 1st and 2nd silence periods after receipt.
(i) VHF weather bulletins/gale warnings refer to coastal waters.
(j) For French Fcst Areas (MF Bcsts) see Fig. 7(3), p. 167.

6.3.16 Continental Coast Radio Stations *continued*

Coast Station Name Position	Medium Frequency RT Service (kHz) Transmits	Receives	VHF Ch Tx	Rx	Traffic List Times (GMT)	Navigation Warning Times (GMT)	Weather Bulletin Times (GMT)	Gale Warning Times (GMT)	Decca Warning Times (GMT)
Fécamp Radio 49°46′N 00°22′E	VHF station (H24). Distress and safety traffic		16	16					
Dieppe Radio 49°55′N 1°04′E	VHF station remotely controlled from Boulogne		16 **02** **24**	16 02 24			Ch 02 0733 1233 LT (Fr)	Ch 02 O/R & S/P2 (Fr)	
Boulogne Radio 50°43′N 1°37′E Escalles: 50°55′N 1°43′E *Tel: 21.31.44.00*	1694 **1771** 2182 2747 3795 Notes: (1) At Boulogne and Escalles. (2) 2182 kHz: H24.	2182[1,2] Also receives on following frequencies at Escalles: 2049 2056 2097 2153 2167 2321 2506 2576 3161 3168	16 **23** **25** See Note (a) below	16 23 25	1771 kHz every odd H + 03	1694 kHz 0133 0533 0933 1333 1733 2133 (in French and English)	1694 kHz 0703 1733 (in French for Areas 1–14) Ch 23 0733 1233 LT (Fr)	1694 kHz O/R & S/P2 1694 and 1771 kHz every odd H + 03 (Fr) (Areas 1–14) Ch 23 O/R & S/P2 (Fr)	1694 kHz (as Navigation Warning times, in French and English) Chain 5B
Calais Radio 50°55′N 1°43′E	VHF station remotely controlled from Boulogne See Note (a) below		**01** 16 **87**	01 16 87			Ch 87 0733 1233 LT (Fr)	Ch 87 O/R & S/P2 (Fr)	
Dunkerque Radio 51°02′N 2°24′E	VHF station remotely controlled from Boulogne		16 **24** **61**	16 24 61			Ch 61 0733 1233 LT (Fr)	Ch 61 O/R & S/P2 (Fr)	

NOTES FOR FRENCH COAST STATIONS

(a) Transmits/receives on Ch 16 H24 for distress and safety traffic only. Working channels operate 0700–2200 local time.
(b) H+ . . . means commencing at . . . minutes past hour.
(c) O/R means on receipt.
(d) Ch 16 reserved for distress and safety traffic only. Vessels should normally call on working frequency.
(e) For MF, call on 2182 or (if 2182 is busy) on 2321 kHz.
(f) LT means local (French) time.
(g) (Fr) means in French.
(h) S/P2 means after 1st and 2nd silence periods after receipt.
(i) VHF weather bulletins/gale warnings refer to coastal waters.
(j) For French Fcst Areas (MF Bcsts) see Fig. 7(3), p. 167.

BELGIUM (for Oostende Radio see next page)

Station	Traffic List Times	Navigation Warning Times	Weather Bulletin Times	Gale Warning Times	Decca Warning Times
Antwerpen Radio **VHF facilities at following positions. The call in each case is Antwerpen Radio** Antwerpen Ch 07 16 **24** 27 **28** 83 87 51°17′N 4°20′E Kortrijk Ch 10 **24** 83 50°50′N 3°17′E Gent Ch 16 **24** 26 81 51°02′N 3°44′E Vilvoorde Ch 16 **24** 28 50°56′N 4°25′E Ronquières Ch 10 **24** 25 50°37′N 4°13′E Mol Ch 16 **24** 87 51°11′N 5°07′E Liège Ch 16 **24** 27 50°34′N 5°33′E	Ch 24 every H+05	Ch 24 O/R and every H+03 H+48 (in English and Dutch for the Schelde)	Ch 24 Fog warnings O/R and every H+03 H+48 (in English and Dutch)	Ch 24 O/R and every H+03 H+48 (strong breeze warnings in English)	

continued

NOTES FOR BELGIAN AND NETHERLANDS COAST STATIONS

(a) H+ . . . means commencing at . . . minutes past hour.
(b) LT means Local Time.
(c) O/R means on receipt.
(d) S/P1 means after first silence period after receipt.
(e) S/P2 means after first and second silence periods after receipt.
(f) Normal primary working frequencies are printed in bold type.

6.3.16 Continental Coast Radio Stations *continued*

Coast Station Name Position	Medium Frequency RT Service (kHz) Transmits	Medium Frequency RT Service (kHz) Receives	VHF Ch Tx Rx	Traffic List Times (GMT)	Navigation Warning Times (GMT)	Weather Bulletin Times (GMT)	Gale Warning Times (GMT)	Decca Warning Times (GMT)
Oostende Radio 51°11′N 2°48′E (See note below VHF column for channels to be used in different areas) (For Navtex see 6.3.14.)	1649.5 1652.5 1705 1708 **1817** **1820**[1] 1901 1904 1905 1908 2087 2090 2170.5 2182 2253 2256 2373 2376 2481 2484 2758 **2761**[1] 2814 **2817**[2] 3629 **3632**[2] 3652 3655 3681 **3684**[1]	2182[3] {2484[4] {3178[4] 2191[5]	16 (H24) **23**[6] **27**[7,8] (H24) 63 78[6] 85[8] 87[7] 88[8] Used for calls in vicinity of: 6) La Panne 7) Zeebrugge 8) Oostende Hours of watch Ch 16 27: H24	2761 kHz every even H+20 Ch 27 every H+20	2761 kHz and Ch 27 O/R S/P2 0233 0633 1033 1433 1833 2233 (in Dutch and English)	2761 kHz and Ch 27 0820 1720 (in Dutch and English for Dover and Thames) Ice reports on Ch 27 every 4h from 0103. Fog warnings on 2761 kHz O/R and S/P2 in English and Dutch for the Schelde	2761 kHz and Ch 27 O/R and S/P2 (in Dutch and English for Dover and Thames)	2761 kHz and Ch 27 S/P2 (in English) Chains 5B 2A 6C 8E 2E 9B

Notes: 1) Working frequencies — Belgian vessels
2) Working frequencies — foreign vessels
3) 2182 kHz: H24
4) 2484 3178 kHz: H24 for Belgian vessels
5) When 2182 kHz is distress working

NETHERLANDS

Coast Station Name Position	Medium Frequency RT Service (kHz)	VHF Ch	Traffic List Times (GMT)	Navigation Warning Times (GMT)	Weather Bulletin Times (GMT)	Gale Warning Times (GMT)	Decca Warning Times (GMT)
Scheveningen Radio 52°06′N 4°16′E Note: Netherlands Coast Guard keeps watch (H24) on 2182 kHz and VHF Ch 16 for safety and distress traffic only. Do not call Scheveningen Radio on these frequencies. (For Navtex see 6.3.14.) *Tel: 2550 62333*	Ch A 2824[1] 2520[1] (H24) B **1764** 2030 C **2600** 1995 D **1939** 2513 E **3673** 3191 F **1862**[2] 2160[2] I **1890** 2048 2057 2045 2051 2054 Notes: (1) Calling and answering (H24). (2) Located at Nes 53°24′N 6°04′E. Hours of service (local time): 1764 2824 kHz: H24 1862 1939 kHz: Mon–Sat: 0800–2300 (LT) Sun: 0900–2300 (LT) 1890 kHz: 0800–2400 (LT) 2600 kHz: Mon–Sat: 0800–2300 (LT) 3673 kHz: Occas	VHF stations remotely controlled (all H24) Call Scheveningen Radio on working channel of nearest station shown below:	1862 kHz 1890 kHz every odd H + 05 VHF on primary channels every H + 05 2824 kHz 0105 0305 0505 2305	1862 kHz 1890 kHz O/R S/P1 and every 4h from 0333 2824 kHz 0333 2333 (all in Dutch and English) For VHF see Note (g) below	1862 kHz 1890 kHz every 6h from 0340 (in Dutch and English) VHF on bracketed channels every 6h from 0005 (LT) (in Dutch)	1862 kHz 1890 kHz O/R S/P1 (in Dutch and English) VHF on bracketed channels O/R and every H + 05 (in Dutch)	As for Navigation Warnings (in Dutch and English) Decca Chains 2E 9B

Goes	Ch (**23**) 25	51°31′N 3°54′E
Rotterdam	Ch **24** 28 (**87**)	51°56′N 4°28′E
Scheveningen	Ch 26 (**83**)	52°06′N 4°16′E
Haarlem	Ch **23** (25)	52°23′N 4°38′E
Wieringermeer	Ch (**27**)	52°55′N 5°04′E
Location L7	Ch (**28**) 84	53°32′N 4°13′E
Terschelling	Ch (**25**) 78	53°22′N 5°13′E
Nes	Ch (**23**)	53°24′N 6°04′E
Appingedam	Ch (**27**)	53°18′N 6°52′E
Lelystad	Ch (**83**)	52°32′N 5°26′E

Note: Bracketed channels are those on which Weather Bulletins and Gale Warnings are broadcast.

NOTES FOR BELGIAN AND NETHERLANDS COAST STATIONS

See Notes (a)–(f) at foot of page 146 opposite.

(g) Navigational Warnings are announced by Scheveningen Radio on VHF Ch 16, and broadcast on the bracketed channels indicated above.

continued

6

6.3.16 Continental Coast Radio Stations *continued*

Coast Station Name Position	Medium Frequency RT Service (kHz) Transmits	Medium Frequency RT Service (kHz) Receives	VHF Ch	Traffic List Times (GMT)	Navigation Warning Times (GMT)	Weather Bulletin Times (GMT)	Gale Warning Times (GMT)	Decca Warning Times (GMT)
GERMANY								
Norddeich Radio 53°38′N 7°12′E	1799 1911 2182 **2614**[2] 2799 2848 Notes: 1) 2182 kHz: H24. 2) During Bcsts station replies on 2848 kHz. 3) 2023 kHz 0700–2300 LT 4) 2045 kHz when 2182 is distress working. Only available 2300–0700 LT to German vessels	2491 2541 2182[1] 2023[3] 2045[4] 2128 3161	16 **28** 61 86	2614 kHz and Ch 28 every H + 45 Also on 2614 kHz at 0810 2010 after weather report	2614 kHz O/R S/P1 0133 0533 0933 1333 1733 2133 and on request (In English and German)	2614 kHz 0910 2110 (local times) (in German for North Sea areas and Skagerrak)	2614 kHz O/R S/P1 and every 4h from 0133 (in German for North Sea areas and Skagerrak. In English for German Bight)	2614 kHz O/R S/P1 0133 0533 0933 1333 1733 2133 and on request (in English and German) 9B
Bremen Radio 53°05′N 8°48′E	VHF station remotely controlled from Elbe-Weser		16 25 **28**	Ch 28 every H + 40				
Helgoland Radio 54°11′N 7°53′E	VHF station remotely controlled from Elbe-Weser		03 16 **27** 88	Ch 27 every H + 20				
Elbe-Weser Radio 53°50′N 8°39′E	**Note**: Ch 23 28 and 62 are for communication with vessels on the Nord-Ostsee Canal		01 16 **23** 24 **26** 28 62	Ch 23 every H + 20 Ch 26 every H + 50				
Hamburg Radio 53°33′N 9°58′E	VHF station remotely controlled from Elbe-Weser		16 25 **27** 82 83	Ch 27 every H + 40				
Eiderstedt Radio 54°20′N 8°47′E	VHF station remotely controlled from Elbe-Weser		16 **25** 64	Ch 25 every H + 40				
Nordfriesland Radio 54°55′N 8°18′E	VHF station remotely controlled from Elbe-Weser		05 16 **26**	Ch 26 every H + 50				

NOTES FOR GERMAN COAST STATIONS

(a) H+ . . . means commencing at . . . minutes past hour.
(b) LT means Local Time.
(c) O/R means on receipt.
(d) S/P1 means after first silence period after receipt.
(e) S/P2 means after first and second silence periods after receipt.

6.4 SHORT NOTES ON FLAG ETIQUETTE

6.4.1 Ensign

A yacht's ensign is the national maritime flag corresponding to the nationality of her owner. Thus a British yacht should wear the Red Ensign, unless she qualifies for a special ensign (see 6.4.2). At sea the ensign must be worn when meeting other vessels, when entering or leaving foreign ports, or when approaching forts, signal and coastguard stations etc. In British harbours the ensign should be hoisted at 0800 (0900 between 1 November and 14 February) and lowered at sunset (or 2100 local time if earlier). The ensign should normally be worn at the stern, but if this is not possible the nearest position should be used, e.g. at the peak in a gaff-rigged boat, at the mizzen masthead in a ketch or yawl, or about two-thirds up the leech of the mainsail.

6.4.2 Special ensigns

Members of certain clubs may apply for permission to wear a special ensign (e.g. Blue Ensign, defaced Blue Ensign, or defaced Red Ensign). For this purpose the yacht must either be a registered ship under Part I of the Merchant Shipping Act 1894 and of at least 2 tons gross tonnage, or be registered under the Merchant Shipping Act 1983 (Small Ships Register) and of at least 7 metres overall length. The owner or owners must be British subjects, and the yacht must not be used for any professional, business or commercial purpose. Full details can be obtained from Secretaries of Clubs concerned.

A special ensign must only be worn when the owner is on board or ashore in the vicinity, and only when the yacht is flying the burgee (or a Flag Officer's flag) of the club concerned. The permit must be carried on board. When the yacht is sold, or the owner ceases to be a member of the Club, the permit must be returned to the Secretary of the Club.

6.4.3 Burgee

A burgee shows that a yacht is in the charge of a member of the club indicated, and does not necessarily indicate ownership. It should be flown at the masthead. If the yacht is on loan, or is chartered, it is correct to use the burgee of the skipper or charterer — not that of the absent owner. Normal practice has been to lower the burgee at night, at the same time as the ensign, but nowadays many owners leave the burgee flying if they are on board or ashore in the vicinity.

6.4.4 Flag officer's flag

Clubs authorise their flag officers to fly special swallow-tailed flags, with the same design as the club burgee and in place of it. The flags of a vice-commodore and a rear-commodore carry one and two balls respectively. A flag officer's flag is flown day and night while he is on board, or ashore nearby. A flag officer should fly his flag with the Red Ensign (or special ensign, where authorised) in preference to the burgee of some other club.

6.4.5 Choice of burgee

An owner who is not a flag officer, and who belongs to more than one club, should normally fly the burgee (and if authorised the special ensign) of the senior club in the harbour where the yacht is lying. An exception may be if another club is staging a regatta or similar function.

6.4.6 Courtesy ensign

It is customary when abroad to fly a small maritime ensign of the country concerned at the starboard crosstrees. The correct courtesy flag for a foreign yacht in British waters is the Red Ensign (not the Union Flag). British yachts do not fly a courtesy flag in the Channel Islands since these are part of the British Isles.

6.4.7 House flag

An owner may fly his personal flag when he is on board in harbour, provided it does not conflict with the design of some existing flag. A house flag is normally rectangular, and is flown at the crosstrees in a sloop or cutter, at the mizzen masthead in a ketch or yawl, or at the foremast head in a schooner.

6.4.8 Salutes

Yachts should salute all Royal Yachts, and all warships of whatever nationality. A salute is made by dipping the ensign (only). The vessel saluted responds by dipping her ensign, and then re-hoisting it, whereupon the vessel saluting re-hoists hers.

Chapter 7

Weather

Contents

7

Weather — introduction

The following subjects are described in detail in Chapter 7 of *The Macmillan & Silk Cut Yachtsman's Handbook*:

> *Transfer of heat; world weather; air masses; atmospheric pressure; wind; humidity; clouds; depressions and fronts; the passage of a depression; anticyclones; fog; sea and land breezes; thunderstorms; tropical storms; glossary of meteorological terms; forecasting your own weather; bibliography.*

Here in the *Almanac*, emphasis is given to obtaining and interpreting forecasts. For more general information on the weather, including the subjects listed above, reference should be made to Chapter 7 of *The Macmillan & Silk Cut Yachtsman's Handbook.*

7.1 GENERAL WEATHER INFORMATION

7.1.1 Beaufort scale

Force	Wind speed (knots)	Description	State of sea	Probable wave height (m)	Probable max. wave height (m)
0	0–1	Calm	Like a mirror	0	0
1	1–3	Light air	Ripples like scales are formed	0	0
2	4–6	Light breeze	Small wavelets, still short but more pronounced, not breaking	0·1	0·3
3	7–10	Gentle breeze	Large wavelets, crests begin to break; a few white horses	0·4	1
4	11–16	Moderate breeze	Small waves growing longer; fairly frequent white horses	1	1·5
5	17–21	Fresh breeze	Moderate waves, taking more pronounced form; many white horses, perhaps some spray	2	2·5
6	22–27	Strong breeze	Large waves forming; white foam crests more extensive; probably some spray	3	4
7	28–33	Near gale	Sea heaps up; white foam from breaking waves begins to blow in streaks	4	5·5
8	34–40	Gale	Moderately high waves of greater length; edges of crests break into spindrift; foam blown in well marked streaks	5·5	7·5
9	41–47	Severe gale	High waves with tumbling crests; dense streaks of foam; spray may affect visibility	7	10
10	48–55	Storm	Very high waves with long overhanging crests; dense streams of foam make surface of sea white. Heavy tumbling sea; visibility affected	9	12·5
11	56–63	Violent storm	Exceptionally high waves; sea completely covered with long white patches of foam; edges of wave crests blown into froth. Visibility affected	11	16
12	64 plus	Hurricane	Air filled with foam and spray; sea completely white with driving spray; visibility very seriously affected	14	—

Notes: (1) The state of sea and probable wave heights are a guide to what may be expected in the open sea, away from land. In enclosed waters, or near land with an off-shore wind, wave heights will be less but possibly steeper — particularly with wind against tide.

(2) It should be remembered that the height of sea for a given wind strength depends upon the fetch and the duration for which the wind has been blowing. For further information on sea state, see Chapter 9 of *The Macmillan & Silk Cut Yachtsman's Handbook*.

7.1.2 Barometer and thermometer conversion scales

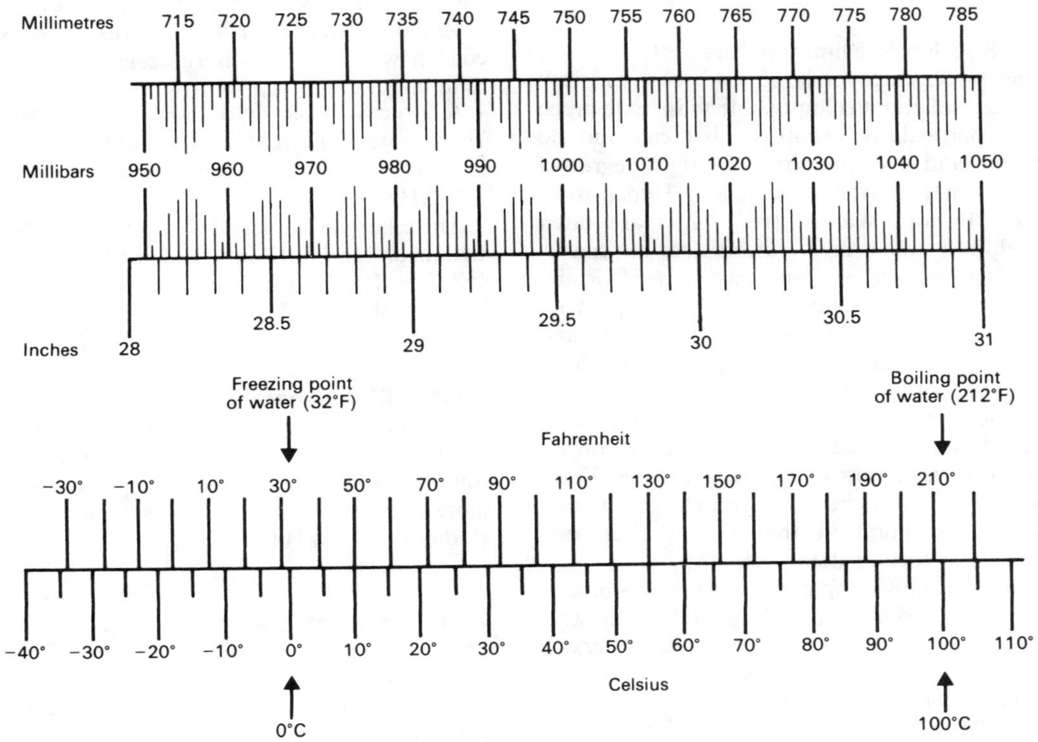
Millimetres
715 720 725 730 735 740 745 750 755 760 765 770 775 780 785
Millibars
950 960 970 980 990 1000 1010 1020 1030 1040 1050
Inches
28 28.5 29 29.5 30 30.5 31
Freezing point of water (32°F)
Boiling point of water (212°F)
Fahrenheit
−30° −10° 10° 30° 50° 70° 90° 110° 130° 150° 170° 190° 210°
−40° −30° −20° −10° 0° 10° 20° 30° 40° 50° 60° 70° 80° 90° 100° 110°
Celsius
0°C
100°C

7.1.3 Meaning of terms used in weather bulletins

Visibility

Good	More than 5 miles
Moderate	5–2 miles
Poor	2 miles — 1000 metres
Fog	Less than 1000 metres

Timing (of gale warnings)

Imminent	Within 6 hours of time of issue
Soon	6–12 hours
Later	12–24 hours

Speeds (of weather systems)

Slowly	0–15 knots
Steadily	15–25 knots
Rather quickly	25–35 knots
Rapidly	35–45 knots
Very rapidly	Over 45 knots

Barometric pressure changes (tendency)

Now falling) pressure
Rising more slowly (or now steady)) higher than
Rising) 3 hours ago
Steady
Now rising (pressure lower or same as 3 hours ago)
Falling more slowly) Pressure lower than
Falling) 3 hours ago

'Rising' and 'Falling' may be qualified by:

Slowly	Change less than 1·6mb in 3 hours
Quickly	3·5–6mb in 3 hours
Very rapidly	More than 6mb in 3 hours

Gale warnings

Indicate that winds of at least force 8 or gusts reaching 43 knots are expected somewhere in the area. 'Severe gale' implies winds of at least force 9 or gusts of 52 knots. 'Storm' implies winds of force 10 or above, or gusts of 61 knots. Gale warnings remain in force until amended or cancelled ('gales now ceased'). If a gale persists for more than 24 hours the warning is re-issued.

Land area forecasts — wind strength

In land area forecasts winds are given in the following terms, which relate to Beaufort forces as indicated:

Calm	0	Fresh	5
Light	1–3	Strong	6–7
Moderate	4	Gale	8

Land area forecasts — visibility

The following definitions are used in land area forecasts:

Mist	200–1100 yards (183–1000m)
Fog	Less than 1000m
Dense fog	Less than 50 yards (46m)

7.2 SOURCES OF WEATHER INFORMATION

7.2.1 BBC Radio Shipping Forecasts

Shipping forecasts cover large sea areas, and in a five minute bulletin it is impossible to include much detail — particularly variations that can and do occur near land — or to convey the right degree of confidence in the weather situation. Hence forecasts for 'Inshore Waters' (see 7.2.2) are often more helpful to yachtsmen cruising near the coast.

Shipping forecasts are broadcast on BBC Radio 4 on 198kHz (1515m) and on local MF frequencies daily at 0033–0038, 0555–0600, 1355–1400 and 1750–1755 (clock times). The 0033–0038 broadcast includes area Trafalgar.

The 0033–0038 and 1355–1400 broadcasts Monday–Friday include a 24-hour forecast for the Minches (between Butt of Lewis and Cape Wrath in the north, and between Barra Head and Ardnamurchan Point in the south), after area Hebrides. For further details see Table 7(2).

The 0033–0038 shipping forecast is also broadcast by Radio Scotland (810kHz), and is followed by a forecast, valid until 1800, for coastal waters of Great Britain up to 12 M offshore, and reports from selected stations — see 7.2.2.

The bulletins include a summary of gale warnings in force; a general synopsis of the weather for the next 24 hours and expected changes within that period; forecasts for each sea area for the next 24 hours, giving wind direction and speed, weather and visibility; and the latest reports from selected stations from those shown at the foot of page 161. For each station are given wind direction and Beaufort force, present weather, visibility, and (if available) sea-level pressure and tendency. These stations are marked by their initial letters on the chart for forecast areas on page 160.

Apart from being included in shipping forecasts, gale warnings are broadcast at the earliest juncture in the BBC Radio 4 programme after receipt, and also after the next news bulletin.

Instructions on recording and interpreting the shipping forecasts are given in 7.6.4 of *The Macmillan & Silk Cut Yachtsman's Handbook*.

7.2.2 BBC Inshore Waters Forecasts

Forecasts are given for inshore waters (up to 12 miles offshore) of Great Britain until 1800 next day at the end of English, Welsh and Scottish Radio 4 programmes, and on Radio Scotland, at about 0038 local (or clock) time. The forecast of wind, weather and visibility is followed by the 2200 reports from the following stations: Boulmer, Bridlington, Walton-on-the-Naze, St Catherine's Point, Land's End, Mumbles, Valley, Blackpool, Ronaldsway, Killough, Orlock Head, Larne, Corsewall Point, Prestwick, Benbecula, Stornoway, Lerwick, Wick, Aberdeen and Leuchars.

Radio Ulster (1341kHz) gives forecasts for coastal waters of Northern Ireland at 0010 local time daily.

A forecast, valid until 1800, is broadcast for inshore waters of Great Britain and Northern Ireland on BBC Radio 3, at 0655 local time daily, on 1215kHz.

The schedule of coastal waters forecasts for Great Britain and Ireland is included in Table 7(2) on page 162. For details of local radio station forecasts see 7.2.17 and Table 7(4) on pages 164–165.

7.2.3 BBC General Forecasts

Land area forecasts may include the outlook period (up to 48 hours beyond the shipping forecast) and some reference to weather along the coasts. The more detailed land area forecasts are broadcast on Radio 4 on 198kHz (1515m).

7.2.4 Special forecasts for ships at sea

Forecasts for areas within the region 65°N to 35°N, and 40°W and the coast of Europe (including the Mediterranean) may be obtained by yachtsmen by contacting the Central Meteorological Office Forecast Office. This may be done by telephone (0344) 854913, which may be by link call. No charge is made by the Met Office.

Alternatively, the request may be addressed to the nearest UK Coast Radio Station. Such a call might be in the form: 'North Foreland Radio. Request weather forecast next 24 hours for sea areas Dover and Wight on passage Ramsgate to Cherbourg.'

When telephoning the forecast office it must be realised that during busy periods, such as occasions of bad weather, the staff may be fully occupied and there is likely to be a delay.

If a forecast is required for some future occasion or period, or if the forecast is to be kept under review and up-dated, the request should be addressed to The Meteorological Office, Met.02a, London Road, Bracknell, Berks RG12 2SZ, or sent by telex 849801 WEABKA G, Fax: (0344) 854412 giving full details of the service required and the address to which the account is to be forwarded. Cheques should be crossed and made payable to 'Met Office HQ. Public a/c'.

Weather Centres

Weather Centres provide a range of services at a charge. To arrange a forecast service ring:

Plymouth	(0752) 402534
Southampton	(0703) 228844
London	071-836 4311

Norwich	(0603) 660779
Nottingham	(0602) 384092
Leeds	(0532) 451990
Newcastle	091-232 6453
Aberdeen Airport	(0224) 210574
Kirkwall Airport	(0856) 3802
Sella Ness, Scotland	(0806) 242069
Glasgow	041-248 3451
Manchester	061-477 1060
Cardiff	(0222) 397020
Bristol	(0272) 279298
Belfast Airport, Crumlin	(08494) 22339
Jersey	(0534) 23660

Irish Republic

Central Forecast Office, Dublin (H24)	(01) 424655
Cork Airport Met. (0900–2000)	(021) 965974
Shannon Airport Met. (H24)	(061) 61333

The numbers of overseas forecast offices and recorded weather messages are shown under 'Telephone' for individual harbours in Areas 14–21 of Chapter 10.

7.2.5 Automatic Telephone Weather Service – Marinecall

Recorded Met Office forecasts are updated twice daily (three times in summer) and cover up to 12 miles offshore including Channel and Irish Sea crossings, Isles of Scilly, Channel Islands, Orkney and the Isle of Man. There are 15 areas, as below. In each case dial 0898 500, and then the three figure number of the area required. The charge is 38p per minute (peak and standard rates) and 25p per minute (evenings and weekends), including VAT. Calls can be made through British Telecom coast stations when the VHF per minute tariff is 95p.

458 South West (Hartland Point to Lyme Regis)
457 Mid-Channel (Lyme Regis to Selsey Bill)
456 Channel East (Selsey Bill to North Foreland)
455 Anglia (North Foreland to The Wash)
454 East (The Wash to Whitby)
453 North East (Whitby to Berwick)
452 Scotland East (Berwick to Rattray Head)
451 Scotland North (Rattray Head to Cape Wrath)
464 Minch (Cape Wrath to Ardnamurchan Point)
463 Caledonia (Ardnamurchan Point to Mull of Kintyre)
462 Clyde (Mull of Kintyre to Mull of Galloway)
461 North West (Mull of Galloway to Colwyn Bay)
460 Wales (Colwyn Bay to St David's Head)
459 Bristol Channel (St David's Head to Hartland Point)
465 Ulster (Carlingford Lough to Lough Foyle)

7.2.6 Facsimile broadcasts

Facsimile recorders that receive pictorial images such as weather maps are now available of a type that makes them suitable for use in yachts and at port locations such as marinas.

The information available is of a general meteorological nature and not all of it is relevant to the average yachtsman, but there are many items that are of direct use such as:

- Isobaric charts (actual and forecast)
- Sea and swell charts
- Representation of cloud satellite images
- Sea temperature charts
- Wind field charts.

Internationally exchanged data is processed at various centres. The main centres in northwest Europe that do this work and make facsimile broadcasts are:

Bracknell (GFA)
(England) 3289·5 4610 8040 11086·5 14582·5 kHz
Bracknell (GFE) 2618·5 4782 9203 14436 18261
(England)
Northwood (GYA) (GYZ) (GZZ) (England)
2813·85 3436·85 4247·85 6436·35 8494·85 12741·85 16938·85
Offenbach (DCF 54) (Germany) 134·2kHz

The quality of reception depends on the frequency used and the terrain between transmitter and receiver.

Additional frequencies to those above are also available for limited periods during the 24 hours. Transmission frequencies and schedules are published in the *Admiralty List of Radio Signals, Vol 3* (NP. 283). See also 7.6.12 of *The Macmillan & Silk Cut Yachtsman's Handbook*.

7

7.2.7 NAVTEX

Gale warnings are broadcast on receipt and are repeated at scheduled times. Weather messages are broadcast at scheduled times. Details of NAVTEX stations, identity codes, message categories and transmission times for NAVAREAS I, II and III are given in Chapter 6 (6.3.14).

7.2.8 Volmet

Volmet broadcasts of weather reports for aircraft in flight can be useful with respect to airfields close to the UK and European coasts. The most useful is the HF SSB (H3E) broadcast by Shannon which operates H24 as follows:

3413 kHz	Sunset to sunrise
5505 kHz	H24
8957 kHz	H24
13264 kHz	Sunrise to sunset

The schedule starts at H+00 at five minute intervals until all airfields are covered. UK and Eire airfield broadcasts are at H+05 and H+35.

Royal Air Force SSB VOLMET continuously broadcasts actual weather (H24) for a number of military and civil airfields, mostly in the UK, on 4722 kHz and 11200 kHz.

7.2.9 W/T transmissions

W/T transmissions of weather information in considerable detail are intended for ocean going vessels. The average yachtsman has neither the equipment nor the ability to receive the coded signals at the speed at which they are transmitted by W/T. However, equipment is available which will decode (or encode) Morse signals, and print out the message in English.

Portishead Radio broadcasts Morse transmissions for the Atlantic Weather Bulletin Areas, see *Admiralty List of Radio Signals Vol 3* (NP 283).

7.2.10 Press forecasts

The delay between the time of issue and the time at which they are available next day make press forecasts of limited value to yachtsmen. However, the better papers publish forecasts which include a synoptic chart which, in the absence of any other chart, can be helpful when interpreting the shipping forecast on first putting to sea.

7.2.11 Television forecasts and Prestel

Some TV forecasts show a synoptic chart which, with the satellite pictures, can be a useful guide to the weather situation at the start of a passage.

Weather information is given on teletext by Ceefax (BBC) and Oracle (ITV). BBC 1 Ceefax gives up to date weather maps on page 581 and standard land area weather forecasts on page 582. Weather statistics for UK and Europe are given on page 584. ITN Oracle shows a marine forecast, updated three times daily, on page 302, Antiope is the French system.

Prestel (operated over a telephone link by British Telecom) has a great deal of weather data supplied by the Met. Office, including shipping forecasts and synopsis for all British sea areas. Main index page, key 209: shipping and sailing 2093: actual weather in UK 20940: actual weather world-wide 2094: aviation Fcsts 20971: European Fcsts 20915: UK weather index 20904: What's New 209091.

Shipping Fcst, 4 times/day 20930 (20p). Gale warnings since last Shipping Fcst 20931 (4p).

Sea crossings. 3 times/day (4p). Southern North Sea 209330. Dover Strait 209331. English Channel (East) 209332. St Georges Channel 209333. Irish Sea 209334.

UK land Fcsts. Caption chart. 3 times/day 20911 (5p). Text, 4 times/day 20910 (5p). 3 day outlook, once a day 20913 (as shown). 7 day outlook, issued Sun 20914 (as shown).

7.2.12 Visual storm signals

Visual storm signals used on the Continent are summarised in 10.14.7, 10.19.7 and 10.20.7.

7.2.13 Radiobeacon wind information

Wind information at La Corbière Lt (49°10′·85N 02°14′·90W is transmitted in Sequence 6 by the Radiobeacon on frequency 305·7 kHz modulated as follows: Callsign CB 4 times at 500 Hz; 1 to 8 dots at 1000 Hz indicates Wind Direction by eight cardinal points (one dot = NE, two dots = E, clockwise to 8 dots = N). Up to 8 dots at 500 Hz indicates average speed on the Beaufort Scale (one dot = Force 1, two dots = Force 2, up to 8 dots = Force 8 or more. One or more dots at 1000 Hz indicates maximum gust above average Beaufort scale.

Similarly, wind information at Chichester Bar (50°45′·88N 00°56′·35W) is transmitted in Sequences 1 and 4 by the Radiobeacon on frequency 303·4 kHz modulated as follows: Callsign CH 4 times; 4s dash; up to eight dashes indicate Wind Direction by eight cardinal points (one dash = NE, two dashes = E, clockwise to eight dashes = N). Up to eight dots indicate average speed on the Beaufort scale (one dot = Force 1, two dots = Force 2, up to eight dots = Force 8 or above).

7.2.14 British and Irish Coast Radio Stations — Weather Bulletins by R/T

Forecasts originating from the Meteorological Office are broadcast by British Telecom Coast Radio Stations, as indicated in Table 7(1) below, by radiotelephone on Medium Frequency, and simultaneously on VHF (where available) after an initial announcement on VHF Ch 16. These stations also give weather information on request — see 7.2.4. Weather messages comprise gale warnings, synopsis and 24-hour forecast for the areas stated.

TABLE 7(1)

Weather Broadcasts R/T.

Weather broadcasts are made by British Telecom Coast Radio Stations twice daily. There is one central Officer in each region who engages broadcast frequencies at each station from his central position, and reads the forecast for the whole of that region.

SOUTHERN REGION — at 0733 and 1933 UT.

The synopsis and forecast for ALL of the following areas are broadcast on the Channels listed:

Tyne, Dogger, German Bight, Humber, Thames, Dover, Wight, Portland, Plymouth, Biscay, Finisterre, Sole, Lundy, Fastnet, Irish Sea, and Shannon.

MF	Land's End	2670 kHz
	Niton	1834 kHz
	North Foreland	1848 kHz
	Humber	1869 kHz

VHF	Celtic	24
	Ilfracombe	05
	Land's End	27 64*
	Pendennis	62
	Start Point	26
	Weymouth Bay	05
	Niton	28
	Hastings	07
	North Foreland	26
	Thames	02
	Orfordness	62
	Bacton	07
	Humber	26
	Grimsby	27

* Directional to Scillies.

NORTHERN REGION — at 0703 and 1903 UT.

The synopsis and forecast for ALL the following areas are broadcast on the Channels listed:

Viking, North Utsire, South Utsire, Forties, Cromarty, Forth, Tyne, Dogger, German Bight, Humber, Thames, Lundy, Irish Sea, Rockall, Malin, Hebrides, Bailey, Fair Isle, Faeroes, Southeast Iceland.

MF	Portpatrick	1883 kHz
	Hebrides	1866 kHz
	Wick	1793 kHz
	Stonehaven	2691 kHz

VHF	Cardigan Bay	03
	Anglesea	26
	Morecambe Bay	04
	Portpatrick	27
	Clyde	26
	Islay	25
	Oban	07
	Skye	24
	Hebrides	26
	Lewis	05
	Collafirth	24
	Shetland	27
	Orkney	26
	Cromarty	28
	Buchan	25
	Stonehaven	26
	Forth	24
	Cullercoats	26
	Whitby	25

JERSEY at 0645 0745 1245 1845 and 2245 UT

The synopsis and forecast for Channel Islands waters, South of 50°N and East of 3°W. Strong wind warnings for Channel Islands waters are broadcast on receipt, and repeated at the next silence period and at 0307, 0907, 1507, and 2107.

MF	Jersey	1726
VHF	Jersey	25 82

EIRE — at 0833 and 2033 UT.

The synopsis and forecast for Irish Coastal waters up to 30M offshore and the Irish Sea are broadcast by all Eire VHF stations, and for Shannon and Fastnet by Valentia on MF.

MF	Valentia	1827

EIRE at 0103 0403 0703 1003 1303 1603 1903 and 2203 UT.

VHF	Malin Head	23
	Glen Head	24
	Belmullet	83
	Dublin	83
	Valentia	24
	Clifden	26
	Shannon	28
	Bantry	23
	Cork	26
	Mine Head	83
	Rosslare	23

Gale Warnings

British Telecom Coast Radio Stations transmit gale warnings on receipt. The R/T MF silence periods are from 00 to 03 and from 30 to 33 minutes past each hour. Gale warnings are repeated at the next of the following times: 0303, 0903, 1503, 2103 UT. Gale warnings are preceded by the R/T Safety Signal SÉCURITÉ (pronounced 'SAY-CURE-E-TAY').

Gale warnings remain in force unless amended or cancelled. If the gale persists for more than 24 hours from the time of origin, the gale warning is re-issued from the local (clock) times shown below. They will also respond to telephone enquiries (for the number see each harbour in Chap 10).

7.2.15 Reports of present weather

Reports of actual local weather conditions prevailing at places around the coast of the British Isles can be obtained by telephone from the following Meteorological Office observation stations, Coastguard stations or from specified lighthouses. The locations are shown in 7(2)):

7

From Meteorological Offices

Station Name	*Telephone No*
Blackpool	0253 43061 (night 43063)
Ronaldsway (Isle of Man)	0624 3311 (night 3313)
Carlisle	0228 23422, ext 440
Prestwick (Firth of Clyde)	0292 79800, ext 2617
Tiree	0879 2456
Benbecula (Hebrides)	0870 351
Stornoway	0851 2256 (night) 2282
Wick	0955 2216
Kirkwall (Orkneys)	0856 3802
Sella Ness (Shetlands)	0806 242069
Kinloss (Moray Firth)	0309 72161, ext 674
Shoeburyness	0370 82271, ext 476
(0700–1700 *Mon–Fri*, except Public Holidays)	

From Coastguard stations

The following Coastguard Maritime Rescue Co-ordination Centres (MRCC's) and Sub-Centres (MRSC's), may provide information on actual weather conditions in their immediate locality.

Station Name	*Telephone No*
MRSC Shetland	0595 2976
MRSC Pentland	0856 3268
MRCC Aberdeen	0224 592334
MRSC Forth	0333 50666
MRSC Tyne/Tees	0912 572691
MRSC Humber	0262 672317
MRCC Yarmouth	0493 851338
MRSC Thames	0255 675518
MRCC Dover	0304 210008
MRSC Solent	0705 552100
MRSC Portland	0305 760439
MRSC Brixham	0803 882704
MRCC Falmouth	0326 317575
MRCC Swansea	0792 366534
MRSC Milford Haven	0646 636218
MRSC Holyhead	0407 762051
MRSC Liverpool	0519 313343
MRSC Belfast	0247 883184
MRCC Clyde	0475 29988
MRSC Oban	0631 63720
MRSC Stornoway	0851 2013

Small craft which require information urgently and are unable to make contact with a Coast Radio Station, may call Coastguard stations listed above on VHF Ch 16 to request the current local forecast.

From Lighthouses

The following lighthouses (LH) and other stations may be able to give information on actual weather locally. Those shown in *italics* are not manned continuously.

Station Name	*Telephone No*
Lizard	0326 290444
Lizard LH	0326 290431
Portland Bill	0305 820400
Portland Bill LH	0305 820495
St Catherine's LH	0983 730284
Eastbourne	0323 20634
Fairlight (Hastings)	0424 813171
Cromer	0263 512507
Whitby	0947 602107
Strathy Point LH	0641 4210
Cape Wrath LH	0971 81230
Butt of Lewis LH	0851 81201
Hyskeir LH	0688 2423
Rhinns of Islay LH	0496 86223
Pladda LH	0655 31657
Corsewall Point LH	0776 853220
Pointe of Ayre LH	0624 880238
Calf of Man LH	0624 822820
Rhyl	0745 39749
Porth Dinllaën (Caernarfon Bay)	0758 720204
Aberdovey	0654 72327
Lundy South LH	0237 3455
Ballycastle	0265 763519
Portrush	0265 823356

7.2.16 HM Coastguard VHF Ch 67

Each MRCC and MRSC keeps watch on VHF Ch 16 and operates Ch 67 — see 8.2.2. They broadcast strong wind warnings for their local area (only) on receipt on Ch 67 after an announcement on Ch 16; also forecasts for their local area on Ch 67 after an announcement on Ch 16 normally every four hours (every two hours if strong wind or gale warning in force) commencing from the local (clock) times shown below. They will also respond to telephone enquiries (for the number see each harbour in Chap 10).

Forecasts every four (or two) hours from: Swansea 0005, Clyde 0020, Yarmouth 0040, Solent 0040, Brixham 0050, Shetland 0105, Dover 0105, Stornoway 0110, Pentland 0135, Falmouth 0140, Tyne/Tees 0150, Forth 0205, Liverpool 0210, Portland 0220, Holyhead 0235, Oban 0240, Thames 0010, Belfast 0305, Aberdeen 0320, Milford Haven 0335, Humber 0340.

Fig. 7(1) — Reports of present weather

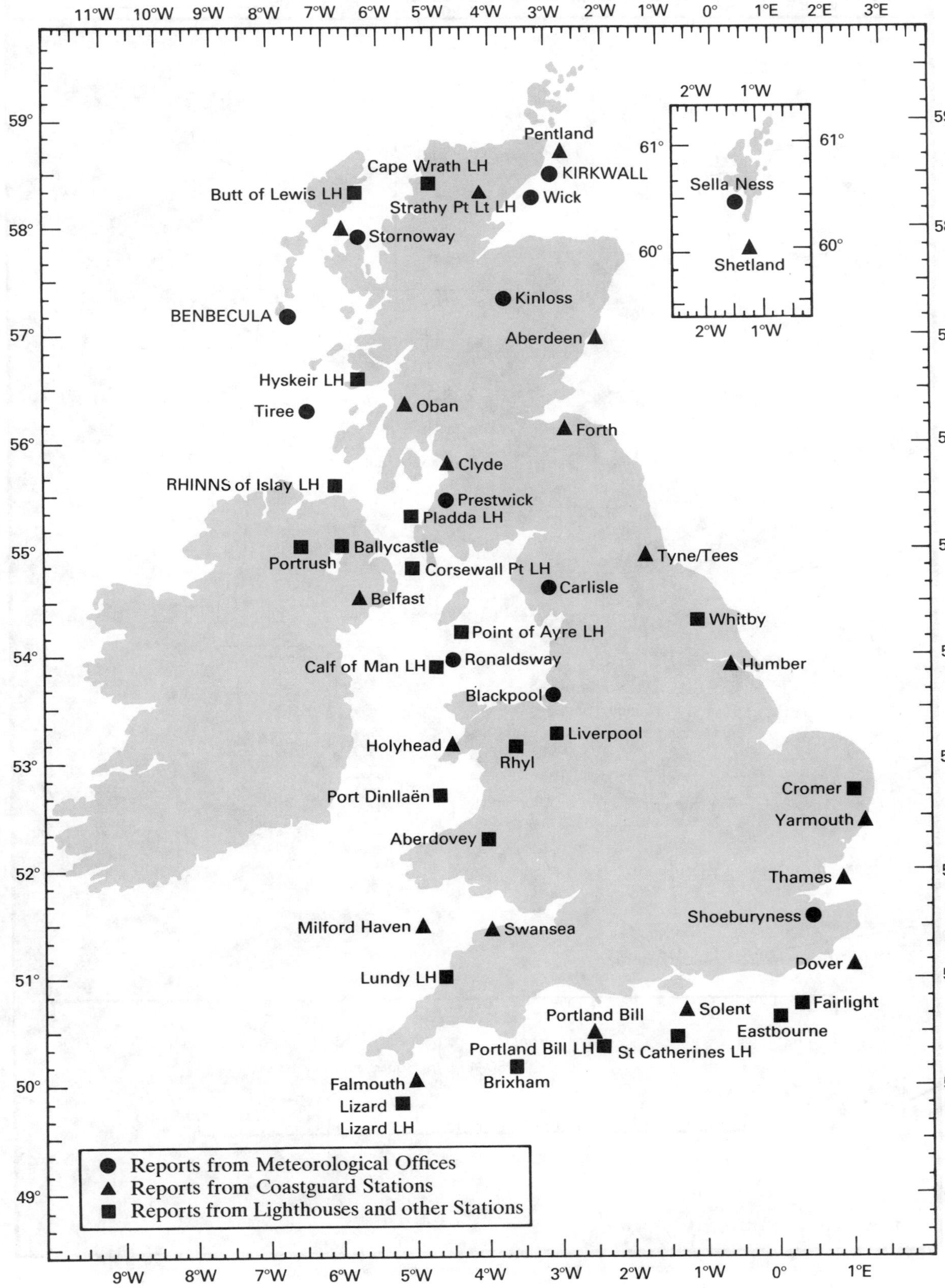

11°W 10°W 9°W 8°W 7°W 6°W 5°W 4°W 3°W 2°W 1°W 0° 1°E 2°E 3°E
59° 58° 57° 56° 55° 54° 53° 52° 51° 50° 49°
9°W 8°W 7°W 6°W 5°W 4°W 3°W 2°W 1°W 0° 1°E
2°W 1°W
61° 60°
Sella Ness
Shetland
Pentland
Cape Wrath LH
KIRKWALL
Butt of Lewis LH
Strathy Pt Lt LH
Wick
Stornoway
Kinloss
BENBECULA
Aberdeen
Hyskeir LH
Oban
Tiree
Forth
Clyde
RHINNS of Islay LH
Prestwick
Pladda LH
Portrush
Ballycastle
Tyne/Tees
Corsewall Pt LH
Carlisle
Belfast
Whitby
Point of Ayre LH
Calf of Man LH
Ronaldsway
Humber
Blackpool
Liverpool
Holyhead
Rhyl
Cromer
Port Dinllaën
Yarmouth
Aberdovey
Thames
Shoeburyness
Milford Haven
Swansea
Dover
Lundy LH
Solent
Fairlight
Portland Bill
Eastbourne
Portland Bill LH
St Catherines LH
Falmouth
Brixham
Lizard
Lizard LH
Reports from Meteorological Offices
Reports from Coastguard Stations
Reports from Lighthouses and other Stations

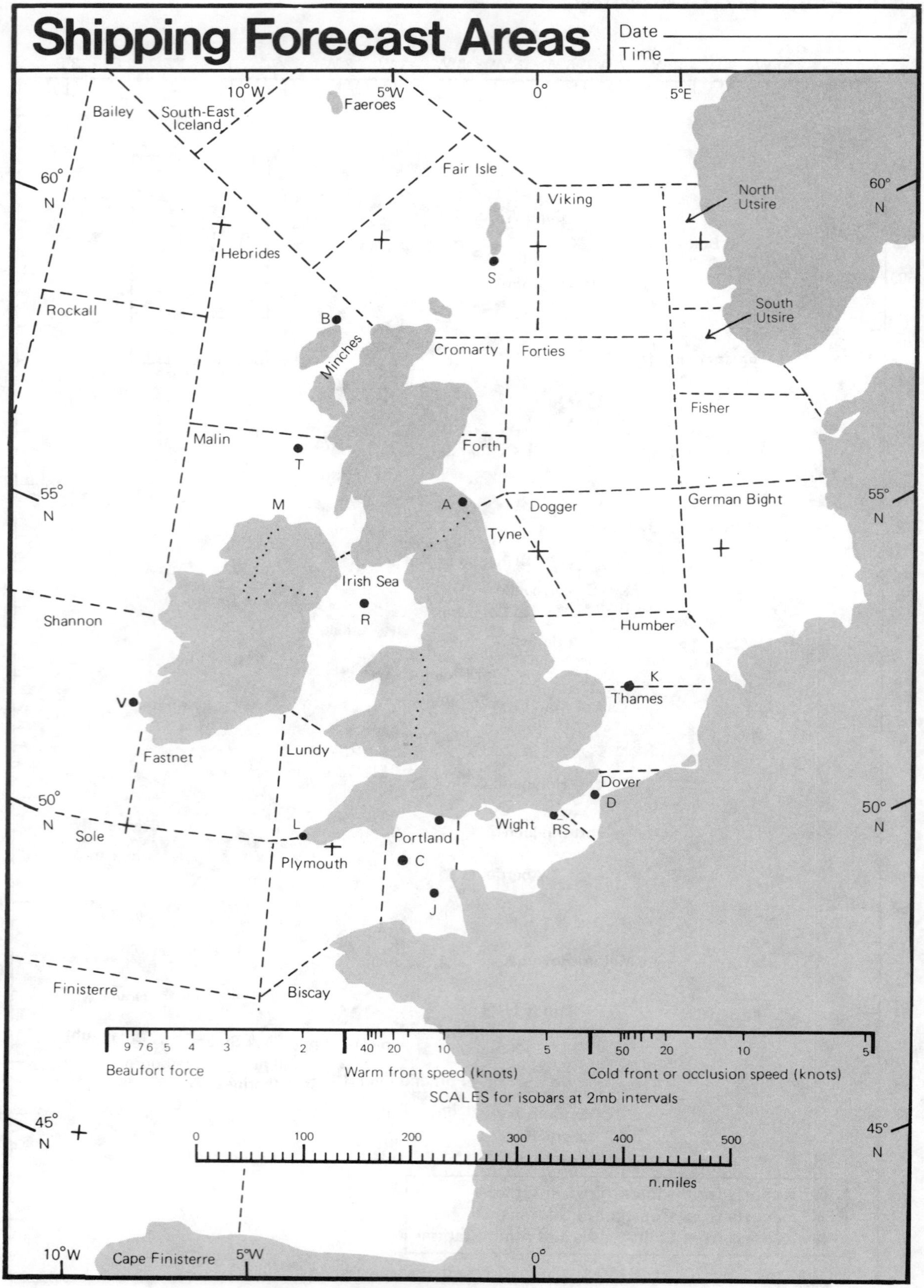
Shipping Forecast Areas
Date
Time
10°W
5°W
0°
5°E
60° N
55° N
50° N
45° N
Bailey
South-East Iceland
Faeroes
Fair Isle
Viking
North Utsire
South Utsire
Hebrides
Rockall
Minches
Cromarty
Forties
Fisher
Malin
Forth
Dogger
German Bight
Tyne
Irish Sea
Shannon
Humber
Thames
Fastnet
Lundy
Dover
Wight
Portland
Sole
Plymouth
Finisterre
Biscay
S
B
T
M
A
R
K
V
L
C
J
D
RS
9 7 6 5 4 3 2
Beaufort force
40 20 10 5
Warm front speed (knots)
50 20 10 5
Cold front or occlusion speed (knots)
SCALES for isobars at 2mb intervals
0 100 200 300 400 500
n.miles
Cape Finisterre

Note: Capital letters refer to coastal reports; see opposite.

Shipping Forecast Record

GENERAL SYNOPSIS at ________ UT/BST

System	Present position	Movement	Forecast position	at

Gales	SEA AREA FORECAST		Wind (At first)	Wind (Later)	Weather	Visibility
	VIKING					
	NORTH UTSIRE					
	SOUTH UTSIRE					
	FORTIES					
	CROMARTY					
	FORTH					
	TYNE					
	DOGGER					
	FISHER					
	GERMAN BIGHT					
	HUMBER					
	THAMES					
	DOVER					
	WIGHT					
	PORTLAND					
	PLYMOUTH					
	BISCAY					
	FINISTERRE					
	SOLE					
	LUNDY					
	FASTNET					
	IRISH SEA					
	SHANNON					
	ROCKALL					
	MALIN					
	HEBRIDES					
	BAILEY					
	FAIR ISLE					
	FAEROES					
	SE ICELAND					

COASTAL REPORTS at ________ BST/UT	Wind Direction	Wind Force	Weather	Visibility	Pressure	Change
Tiree (T)						
Butt of Lewis (B)						
Sumburgh (S)						
St Abb's Head (A)						
Smith's Knoll (K)						
Dover (D)						

COASTAL REPORTS	Wind Direction	Wind Force	Weather	Visibility	Pressure	Change
Royal Sovereign (RS)						
Jersey (J)						
Channel Lt V (C)						
Land's End (L)						
Valentia (V)						
Ronaldsway (R)						
Malin Head (M)						

7

TABLE 7(2) British Isles — Daily Shipping Forecasts and Forecasts for Coastal Waters
as broadcast by British Broadcasting Corporation (BBC) and Radio Telefis Eireann (RTE)

Note: All times are local or 'clock' times, unless otherwise stated

Time	Forecast	Contents	Stations and Frequencies
0010	Coastal Waters (Northern Ireland)	Fcst, valid until 1800 for coastal waters of N Ireland up to 12 M offshore.	*BBC Radio Ulster:* 1341kHz.
0033	Shipping Forecast – Home Waters Fcst Areas	Gale warnings in force, synopsis, 24h Fcst for Home Waters Fcst Areas (including Trafalgar, and Mon-Fri a 24h Fcst for area Minch); reports from selected stations.	*BBC Radio 4:* 198kHz Tyneside 603kHz, London 720kHz, N Ireland 720kHz, Aberdeen 1449kHz, Carlisle 1485kHz, Plymouth 774kHz, Redruth 756kHz. *BBC Radio Scotland:* 810kHz.
0038	Coastal Waters (Great Britain)	Fcst, valid until 1800, for coastal waters of Great Britain up to 12 M offshore; reports from selected stations.	*BBC Radio 4 and Radio Scotland:* as for 0033 Shipping Forecast.
0555	Shipping Forecast – Home Waters Fcst Areas	Gale warnings in force, synopsis, 24h Fcst for Home Waters Fcst Areas; reports from selected stations.	*BBC Radio 4:* as for 0033 Shipping Forecast. Not London on 720kHz
0633	Coastal Waters (Great Britain)	Fcst, valid until 1800, for coastal waters of Great Britain up to 12 M offshore.	*BBC Radio 3*: 1215kHz.
0633	Coastal Waters (Ireland)	Gale warnings in force; 24h Fcst for Irish coastal waters up 30 M offshore and the Irish Sea.	*RTE – Radio 1:* Tullamore 567kHz, Cork 729kHz.
0655	Coastal Waters (Great Britain)	Fcst, valid until 2400, for coastal waters of Great Britain up to 12 M offshore	*BBC Radio 3:* 1215kHz.
1253	Coastal Waters (Ireland)	Gale warnings in force; 24h Fcst for Irish coastal waters up to 30 M offshore and the Irish Sea.	*RTE – Radio 1:* Tullamore 567kHz, Cork 729kHz.
1355	Shipping Forecast – Home Waters Fcst Areas	Gale warnings in force, synopsis, 24h Fcst for Home Waters Fcst Areas; 24h Fcst for area Minch (Mon–Fri); reports from selected stations.	*BBC Radio 4:* as for 0033 Shipping Forecast. (Not London 720 kHz.)
1750	Shipping Forecast – Home Waters Fcst Areas	Gale warnings in force, synopsis, 24h Fcst for Home Waters Fcst Areas; reports from selected stations.	*BBC Radio 4:* as for 0033 Shipping Forecast. (Not London 720 kHz.)
1823	Coastal Waters (Ireland)	Gale warnings in force; 24h Fcst for Irish coastal waters up to 30 M offshore and the Irish Sea.	*RTE – Radio 1:* Tullamore 567kHz, Cork 729kHz.
2355	Coastal Waters (Ireland)	Gale warnings in force; 24h Fcst for Irish coastal waters up to 30 M offshore and the Irish Sea.	*RTE – Radio 1:* Tullamore 567kHz, Cork 729kHz.

* 1823 Sat-Sun (Subject to change).

TABLE 7(3) Gale Warnings

Stations	Areas covered	Times
BBC Radio 4: 198kHz, Tyneside 603 kHz, London 720kHz, N Ireland 720kHz, Aberdeen 1449kHz, Carlisle 1485kHz, Plymouth 774kHz, Redruth 756kHz.	Broadcast gale warnings for all Home Waters Fcst Areas, including Trafalgar	At the first available programme junction after receipt and after the first news bulletin after receipt
RTE – Radio 1: Tullamore 567kHz, Cork 729kHz.	Broadcast gale warnings for Irish coastal waters up to 30 nm offshore and the Irish Sea	At first programme junction after receipt and with news bulletins (0630–2352)
RTE – Radio (2 FM): Athlone 612 kHz, Dublin and Cork 1278kHz.		At first programme junction after receipt and with news bulletins (0630–0150).

British Coast Radio Stations broadcast gale warnings for adjacent areas at the end of the first silence period after receipt (i.e. at H + 03 or H + 33) and subsequently at the next of the following times: 0303, 0903, 1503, 2103 GMT. For further details see 7.2.14. For Irish coast stations see 6.3.16 on pages 138–139.

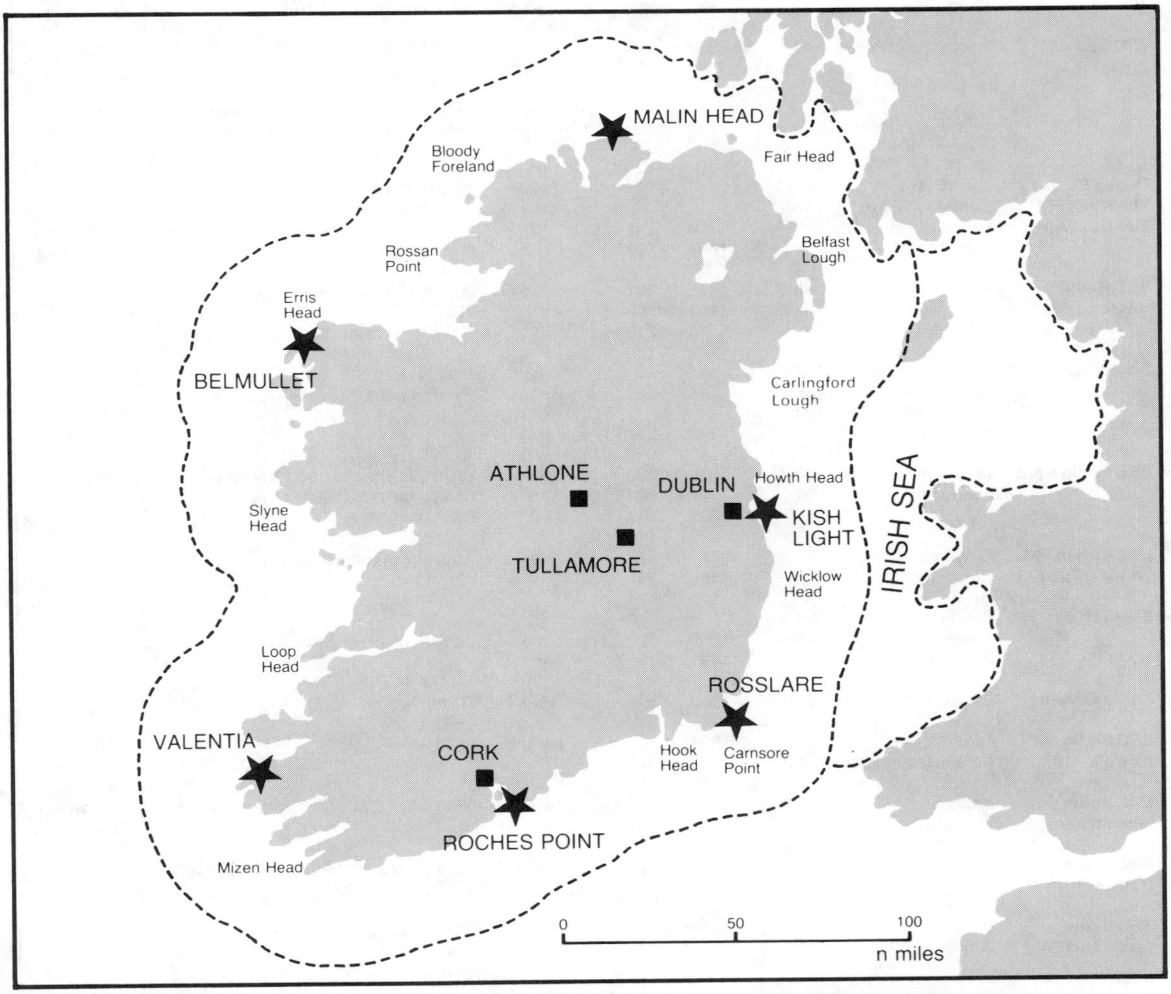

MALIN HEAD
Bloody Foreland
Fair Head
Rossan Point
Belfast Lough
Erris Head
BELMULLET
Carlingford Lough
ATHLONE
DUBLIN
Howth Head
IRISH SEA
Slyne Head
KISH LIGHT
TULLAMORE
Wicklow Head
Loop Head
ROSSLARE
VALENTIA
CORK
Hook Head
Carnsore Point
ROCHES POINT
Mizen Head
0
50
100
n miles

Fig. 7(2) Irish Meterological Service. Sea area forecasts within 25 M of the coast, plus the Irish Sea. Also shown are the stations (starred) from which reports are included in the first and last broadcasts each day and the headlands used to divide up the coastline into smaller areas, depending on the expected weather situation. RTE broadcast stations are also indicated.

Table 7(4) Local Radio Stations — Coastal Weather Forecasts

Station	VHF Transmitter(s)	Frequencies VHF (MHz)	MF (kHz)	(m)		Coastal Waters Forecasts (local times) (*summer months only)	Small Craft Warnings
BBC Radio Cornwall							
Redruth	Redruth	103·9	630	476	*Mon-Fri:*	0715 0745 0815 0845 1715 1740	Yes
Bodmin	Caradon Hill	95·2	657	457	*Sat:*	0715 0745 0815 0845	
Scilly	Scilly	96·0			*Sun:*	0745 0815 0845 0915	
Plymouth Sound	Plympton	97·0			*Daily:*	Approx 0603 0615	Yes
	Tavistock	96·6					
DevonAir Radio	St Thomas	97·0	660	450	*Daily:*	Every H+00 after the news	Yes
(Exeter/Torquay)	Beacon Hill	96·4	954	314		Brixham Coastguard 0830	
BBC Radio Devon							
Exeter	Exeter	95·8	990	303	*Mon-Fri:*	0633 0733 0833 1310 1735	Yes*
Plymouth	N Hessary Tor	103·4	855	351	*Sat:*	0633 0833 1310	
North Devon	Huntshaw Cross	94·8	801	375	*Sun:*	0833 1310	
Torbay	N Hessary Tor	103·4	1458	206			
Okehampton	Okehampton	96·0					
South West 103	Stockland Hill	103·0			*Daily:*	Every H+00 after news	Yes
						Portland Coastguard 0806	
2CR Bournemouth	Poole	102·3	828	362	*Daily:*	0710 0810 0906 1310 1710	Yes
BBC Radio Solent	Rowridge IOW	96·1	999	300	*Mon-Fri:*	0604 0633 0709 0733 0745 0809 0833 0904 1004 1104 1204 1309 1404 1504 1604 1709 1733 1804 2204 2300	Yes
			1359	221	*Sat-Sun:*	0633 1709 0733 0745 0809 0833 0904 1000 1104 1204 1304 1404 1533 1757 1804 1925	
Ocean Sound	Fort Widley	97·5			*Daily:*	0630 0730 0830	Yes
The Light FM	Crabwood Farm	96·7			*Mon-Fri:*	1630 1730	
The Gold AM	Farlington Marshes		1170	257			
	Veals Farm		1557	193			
BBC Radio Sussex	Whitehawk Hill	95·3	1485	202	*Mon-Fri:*	0659 0759 0844 1515 1615 1715 1745	Yes
	Heathfield	104·5	1161	258	*Fri:*	2025	
	N Sussex	104·0	1368	219	*Sat:*	0705 1015 *Sun:* 0905	
Southern Sound	Brighton	103·5			*Daily:*	Every H+00	Yes
	Newhaven	96·9			*Sat-Sun:*	Every H+00 0730 0830	
	Heathfield	102·4					
	Shoreham		1323	227			
BBC Radio Kent	Wrotham	96·7	1035	290	*Mon-Fri:*	0645 0745 0845 1305 1708 1808	Yes
	Swingate	104·2	774	388	*Sat:*	0645 0745 0845 0945 1305	
			1602	187	*Sun:*	0745 0845 1305	
LBC Crown FM	Croydon	97·3			*Daily:*	After the news, every H+00	
London Talkback	Croydon		1152	261			
Essex Radio	Benfleet	96·3					
	Bakers Wood	102·6	1359	220	*Sat-Sun:*	0600 0700 0800 0900	Yes
	Rayleigh		1431	210			
Radio Orwell	Foxhall Heath	97·1	1170	257	*Mon–Fri:*	Coast Reports 0800 1800	Yes*
					Sat–Sun:	0800 1600	
BBC Radio Norfolk	Tacolneston	95·1	855	351	*Daily:*	0850	Yes
	Great Massingham	104·4	873	344			
BBC Radio Lincolnshire	Belmont	94·9	1368	219	*Mon-Fri:*	0645 0715 0745 0815 0845 1145	0715 0815
BBC Radio Humberside	High Hunsley	95·9	1485	202	*Mon-Fri:*	0604 0632 0732 0832 1259 1432 1632 1732	Yes
					Sat-Sun:	0730 0830 0930	
BBC Radio Cleveland	Bilsdale	95·0	1548	194	*Mon-Fri:*	0645 0745 0845 1312 1645	Yes
	Whitby	95.8			*Sat:*	0745 0845	
					Sun:	0745 0845 0945	

Table 7(4) Local Radio Stations — Coastal Weather Forecasts Continued

Station	VHF Transmitter(s)	Frequencies VHF (MHz)	MF (kHz)	(m)	Coastal Waters Forecasts (local times) (*summer months only)	Small Craft Warnings
BBC Radio Newcastle	Pontop Pike Chatton Fenham	95·4 96·0 104·4	1458 in North	206	*Mon-Fri:* 0655 0755 0855 1155 1655 1755 *Sat-Sun:* 0755 0855 0955	Yes
Radio Forth	Craigkelly	97·3	1548	194	*Mon-Sat:* 0600–1800 (every hour) *Sat-Sun*:* 0600 0800 0900 1200 1500 1900	Yes
Radio Tay	Dundee Perth	102·8 96·4	1161 1584	258 189	*Sat-Sun:* 0600 0700 0900 1200 1500 1800 2100 (April-October)	Yes
Radio Clyde	Black Hill	102·5	1152	261	*Daily:* At regular intervals (0600–1800)	Yes
West Sound, Ayr	Symington Girvan Dumfries	96·7 97·5 97·2	1035	290	*Daily* Every H+00 and H+30 after news	Yes
BBC Radio Cumbria	Sandale Morecambe Bay Whitehaven	95·6 96·1 104·2	756 837 837	397 358 358	*Mon-Fri:* 0645 0740 0833 1710 1755* *Sat–Sun:* 0820 0855* 0935 1115 * = (June to September only)	Yes
BBC Radio Furness	Marton	96·1	837	358	*Mon-Fri:* 0735 0845	Yes
Manx Radio	Snaefell Richmond Hill Jurby	89·0 97.2 103·7	1368	219	*Mon-Fri:* 0700 0800 0900 1310 1740 *Sat:* 0700 0800 0900 1200 1700 *Sun:* 0800 0859 1300	
BBC Radio Merseyside	Allerton	95·8	1485	202	*Mon-Fri:* 0633 0733 1145 1309 1804 *Sat:* 0725 1304 1804 *Sun:* 0904 1404 1804	
Swansea Sound	Kilvey Hill	96·4	1170	257	*Mon-Fri:* 0725 0825 0925 1725 *Sat-Sun:* 0825 1003	Yes
Red Dragon Radio	Wenallt Christchurch	103·2 97·4	1359 1305	221 230	*Daily:* 0630 0730 0830 1630 1730 H+00 (0600-2400)	Yes
BBC Radio Bristol	Bristol Bath Avon/Somerset	94.9 104.6 95.5	1548	194	*Mon-Fri:* 0605 0632 0659 0733 0759 0833 0859 1259 1633 1755 *Sat:* 0758 0858 *Sun:* 0758 0858	Yes
Brunel Radio	Tor Marton		1260	238	*Daily:* 0645	Yes
Downtown Radio	Limavady Knockbrecken Sheriff's Mountain Brougher Mountain	96·4 102·4 96·6	 1026		*Mon-Fri:* 0705 0805 0905 1005 1312 1403 1503 1710 2315 *Sat:* 0705 0805 1215 *Sun:* 1105 2303 (0003 Mon)	Yes
BBC Radio Guernsey		93·2	1116	269	*Mon-Fri:* 0732* 0832* 1232* 1715 *Sat:* 0810 0910 1005 *Sun:* 1005 1205	Yes
BBC Radio Jersey		88·8	1026	292	*Mon-Fri:* 0700 0735 0815 0829 0900 1310 1740 2205 *Sat:* 0800 0815 0830 0903 1305 1805 *Sun:* 0805 0815 0912 1259	

7.2.17 Local Radio Stations — coastal forecasts

The details and usefulness of forecasts broadcast by local radio stations vary considerably. Some give no more than an indication of the present weather conditions, while others provide more responsible forecasts in conjunction with the local Weather Centre. The timings of weather information from local radio stations most likely to be of interest to yachtsmen in local coastal waters are shown in Table 7(4). Note that many stations are due to change their VHF frequencies shortly.

Many local radio stations in coastal areas participate in a scheme for broadcasting 'Small Craft Warnings' when winds of Force 6 or more are expected within the next 12 hours on the coast or up to five miles offshore. These warnings are handled in much the same way as gale warnings on Radio 4, being broadcast at the first programme junction or at the end of the first news bulletin after receipt. The stations which participate in this scheme are indicated in Table 7(4). In most cases the services operate from Good Friday until 31 October.

Table 7(5) Western Europe — Shipping Forecasts, Coastal Waters Forecasts, Gale Warnings

Notes:
1. All times local or 'clock' times unless otherwise stated.
2. Unless otherwise described, forecasts include gale or near gale warnings, synopsis, 12h Fcst and outlook for further 12h.
3. Forecasts read in English are printed in **bold type** in columns 2 and 3.
4. On receipt and at end of next two silence periods.

Time	Forecast areas	Contents	Stations and Frequencies	Gale Warnings
FRANCE 0555 UT 1905 UT	French Fcst areas 1-25	See note 2; in French	***France Inter Allouis*** 164kHz; ***Bayonne, Brest & Lille*** 1071kHz	
0733 1233	Spanish border to Sables d'Olonne	See note 2; in French	***Bayonne*** Ch 24, ***Bordeaux-Arcachon*** Ch 82, ***Royan*** Ch 23, ***La Rochelle*** Ch 21	See note 4 (0700-2200); in French for coastal waters, Spanish border to Sables d'Olonne
0800 1200 1500 2000	Spanish border to Sables d'Olonne	See note 2; in French	***Soulac***, CROSS: Ch 13	See note 4.
0703 UT 1703 UT	French Fcst areas 23-24	See note 2; in French	***Bordeaux-Arcachon*** 1820kHz (and on request 0700-2200)	See note 4 (0700-2200); in French for areas 23-24. Also 1862kHz every even H+07 (0607-1807) GMT.
0803 UT 1803 UT	French Fcst areas 14-24	See note 2; in French	***St Nazaire*** 1722kHz	See note 4; in French for areas 14-16. Also 1687 kHz every odd H+07 GMT
0400 1410 0830 1910	Sables d'Olonne to Penmarc'h	See note 2; in French	***Etel***, CROSS: Ch 13	
0733 1233	Sables d'Olonne to Cap de la Hague	See note 2; in French	***St Gilles Croix de Vie*** Ch 27, ***Nantes St Herblain*** Ch 28, ***St Nazaire*** Ch 23, ***Belle Ile*** Ch 87, ***Pont-l'Abbé*** Ch 27, ***Brest-Le Conquet*** Ch 26, ***Ouessant*** Ch 82, ***Plougasnou*** Ch 83, ***Paimpol*** Ch 84, ***St Malo*** Ch 02	See note 4; in French for coastal waters, Sables d'Olonne to Cap de la Hague
0733 UT 1633 UT 2153 UT	French Fcst areas 14-22	See note 2; in French	***Brest-Le Conquet***: 1673kHz, ***Quimperlé***: 1876kHz, ***St Malo***: 2691kHz	See note 4; in French for areas 14-22. 1806 & 2691kHz every even H+03 GMT
Every 3 hours from 0150 UT	French Fcst areas 14–16	See note 2; **in English** (or French)	***Ouessant Traffic*** (Ushant Control Centre, at Corsen): Ch 11 after announcement on Ch 16. General bulletin Ch 11, H+10, H+40	
0900 1900 1600	Penmarc'h to Granville	See note 2; in French	***CROSS***, Ile de Sein Ch 13	
0930 1930 1630	Penmarc'h to Granville	See note 2; in French	***CROSS,*** Ile de Batz Ch 13	
0733 1233	Cap de la Hague to Belgian border	See note 2; in French	***Cherbourg*** Ch 27, ***Port en Bessin*** Ch 03, ***Le Havre*** Ch 26, ***Dieppe*** Ch 02, ***Boulogne*** Ch 23, ***Calais*** Ch 87, ***Dunkerque*** Ch 61	See note 4; in French for coastal waters Cap de la Hague to Belgian border
0703 UT 1733 UT	French Fcst areas 1–14	See note 2; in French	***Boulogne*** 1694kHz	See note 4; in French for areas 1-14. 1771kHz every odd H+03 GMT

continued on page 168

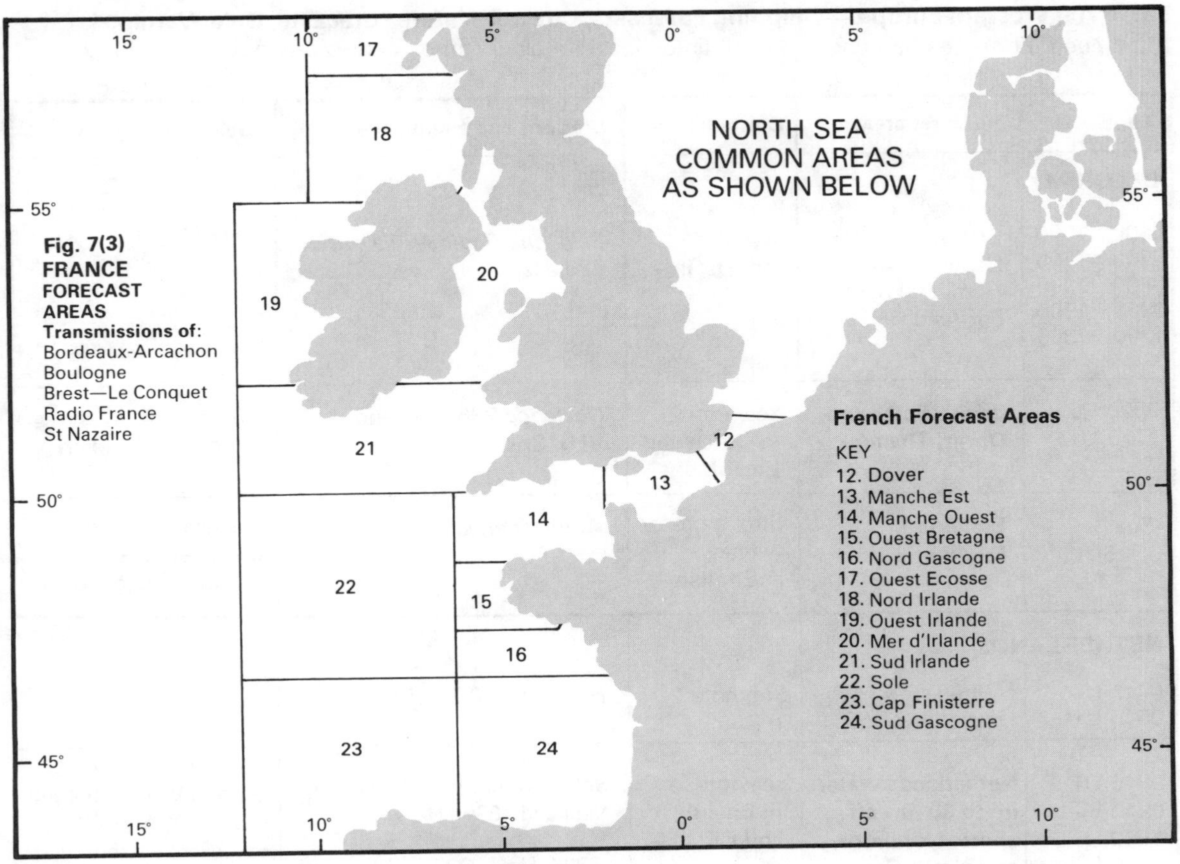
15°
10°
5°
0°
5°
10°
55°
50°
45°
17
18
19
20
21
22
23
24
12
13
14
15
16
NORTH SEA
COMMON AREAS
AS SHOWN BELOW
French Forecast Areas
KEY
12. Dover
13. Manche Est
14. Manche Ouest
15. Ouest Bretagne
16. Nord Gascogne
17. Ouest Ecosse
18. Nord Irlande
19. Ouest Irlande
20. Mer d'Irlande
21. Sud Irlande
22. Sole
23. Cap Finisterre
24. Sud Gascogne

Fig. 7(3)
FRANCE FORECAST AREAS
Transmissions of:
Bordeaux-Arcachon
Boulogne
Brest—Le Conquet
Radio France
St Nazaire

7

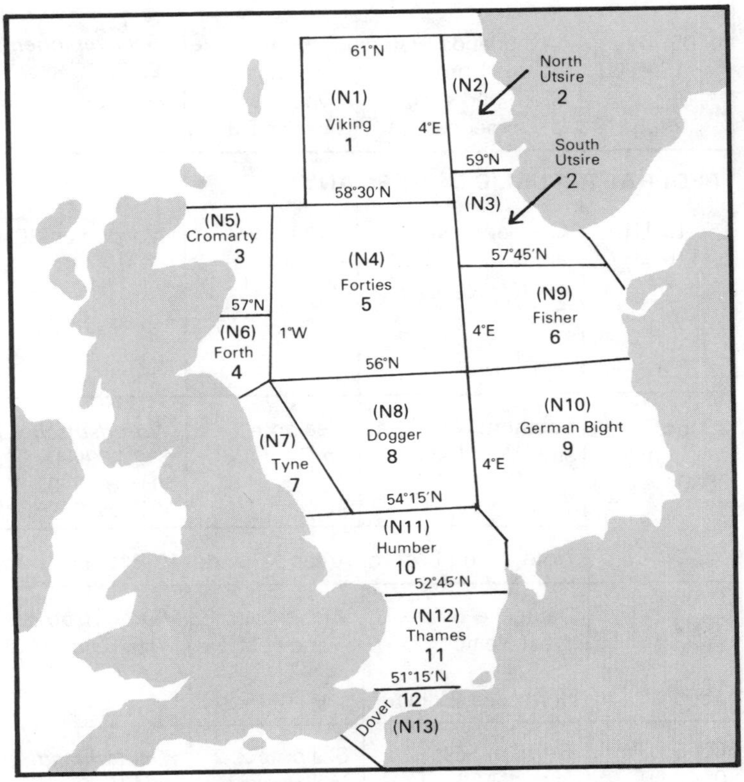
61°N
(N1)
Viking
1
4°E
(N2)
North
Utsire
2
59°N
South
Utsire
2
58°30'N
(N3)
(N5)
Cromarty
3
(N4)
Forties
5
57°45'N
(N9)
Fisher
6
57°N
(N6)
Forth
4
1°W
4°E
56°N
(N8)
Dogger
8
(N10)
German Bight
9
(N7)
Tyne
7
4°E
54°15'N
(N11)
Humber
10
52°45'N
(N12)
Thames
11
51°15'N
12
Dover
(N13)

Fig. 7(4)
NORTH SEA COMMON SHIPPING FORECAST AREAS
As used for forecasts from:
- Belgium
- Netherlands
- West Germany
- Denmark
- Norway
- United Kingdom

Notes:
(1) Numbers are as for French Forecast Areas.
(2) Numbers in brackets with prefix N are as for German Forecast Areas.

Table 7(5) Western Europe — Shipping Forecasts, Coastal Waters Forecasts, Gale Warnings
(Continued. For notes see page 166. All times local or 'clock' times unless otherwise stated.)

Time	Forecast areas	Contents	Stations and Frequencies	Gale Warnings
BELGIUM				
0600 1300 0700 1700 0800 1800 0900 1900 1200 2300	British Fcst areas Dover, Thames, Humber, Wight, Portland	Weather reports; in Dutch	*Belgische Radio en Televisie* 926kHz	
0820 UT 1720 UT	**British Fcst areas Dover, Thames**	See note 2; in Dutch and **English**	*Oostende* 2761kHz and VHF Ch 27	See note 4; in Dutch and **English**
(See col. 5)	**Schelde in English**	Strong breeze warnings in **English**	*Antwerpen* Ch 24	Warnings on receipt and every H+03, H+48; in **English**
NETHERLANDS				
0445 UT 0545 UT	Netherlands coastal waters	See note 2; in Dutch	*Hilversum 2* 747 kHz 1008	Every H+00
0340 UT 0940 UT 1540 UT 2140 UT	**Netherlands waters up to 30 nm off-shore, IJsselmeer and North Sea**	see note 2; **in English** and Dutch	*Scheveningen* 1862 kHz (from Nes) and 1890 kHz. 2824kHz at 0340 GMT only	1862 1890 1939 2600 kHz and VHF on receipt. 1862 1890 kHz after next silence period; in Dutch and **English**
0605 1805 UT 1205 2305 UT	Netherlands waters up to 30 nm off-shore and IJsselmeer	Strong breeze warnings, synopsis, Fcst (in Dutch)	*Scheveningen* VHF Ch 23 25 27 28 83 87 depending on area (see 6.3.16)	Strong breeze warnings on receipt and every H+05 on VHF; in Dutch
FEDERAL REPUBLIC OF GERMANY				
0910 UT 2110 UT	German Fcst areas N1-N4, N8-N12 B14	See note 2; in German	*Norddeich* 2614kHz	In English for N10. In German for N1-N4, N8-N12. On receipt, after next silence period, and every 4h from 0133 GMT
2305 (972kHz only) 0830	Southern North Sea and West Baltic	See note 2; in German	*Norddeutscher Rundfunk:* 612 702kHz, 828kHz, 972kHz VHF 88·9–97·8MHz VHF 87·6–98·7MHz	
	Note: Wind Fcst for Areas N9 and N10 B11 (in German) in weather reports after news			
0700 1300 1900 2305	Deutsche Bucht, West Baltic North Sea, Baltic	In German, wind Fcst see note 2;	*Radio Bremen* 936kHz and VHF 89·3, 93·8MHz	In German for areas N9–N12, B10–B14
0005 UT 0540 UT	German Fcst areas N9–N12	See note 2; in German	*Deutschlandfunk* 1269kHz (and 1539kHz at 0005 UT only)	Every H+00 (except 2100) in German

Chapter 8
Safety

Contents

Safety — introduction

The following subjects are described in detail in Chapter 8 of *The Macmillan & Silk Cut Yachtsman's Handbook*:

Safety equipment — legal requirements and recommended outfits; radar reflectors; bilge pumps; guardrails; fire prevention and fire fighting; lifejackets; safety harnesses; man overboard gear and drill; liferafts; distress signals; SAR organisation; response to distress calls; abandoning ship; liferafts; helicopter rescues; first aid afloat.

Here in the Almanac is given basic information about safety equipment, distress signals and SAR operations. For further information on these subjects, together with those listed above, reference should be made to Chapter 8 of *The Macmillan & Silk Cut Yachtsman's Handbook*.

8.1 SAFETY EQUIPMENT

8.1.1 Safety equipment — general

The skipper is responsible for the safety of the boat and all on board. He must ensure that:

(1) The boat is suitable in design and in construction for her intended purpose.
(2) The boat is maintained in good condition.
(3) The crew is competent and sufficiently strong.
(4) The necessary safety and emergency equipment is carried, is in good condition, and the crew know how to use it.

Individual crew members are responsible for their personal gear. Non-slip shoes or boots are essential. So is foul-weather clothing with close fastenings at neck, wrists and ankles. At least two changes of sailing clothing should be carried, including warm sweaters and towelling strips as neck scarves. Other personal items include a sailor's knife and spike on a lanyard, a waterproof torch, and a supply of anti-seasick pills. Lifejackets and safety harnesses are usually supplied on board, but if individuals bring their own the skipper should make certain they are up to standard.

8.1.2 Safety equipment — legal requirements

Yachts more than 45ft (13·7m) in length are required to carry safety equipment as in the *Merchant Shipping (Life Saving Appliances)* and *Merchant Shipping (Fire Appliances) Rules* (HMSO).

All yachts must carry navigation lights and sound signals which comply with the *International Regulations for Preventing Collisions at Sea.*

Racing yachts are required to carry the safety equipment specified for the class/event concerned.

8.1.3 Safety equipment — recommendations for sea-going yachts 18–45ft (5·5–13·7m) overall length

Full details of recommended safety equipment are given in *The Macmillan & Silk Cut Yachtsman's Handbook.* Below are brief reminders of the minimum equipment which should be carried for (a) coastal and (b) offshore cruising.

But prevention is better than cure, and simple precautions can eliminate accidents. Be particularly careful with bottled gas and petrol. Fit a gas detector. Turn off the gas at the bottle after use. If gas or petrol is smelt — no naked lights, and do not run electrical equipment. Test systems regularly. Insist that crew wear lifejackets and harnesses when necessary, and that they do clip on. Make sure a good look-out is maintained at all times. Listen to every forecast. Double-check all navigational calculations. Take nothing for granted.

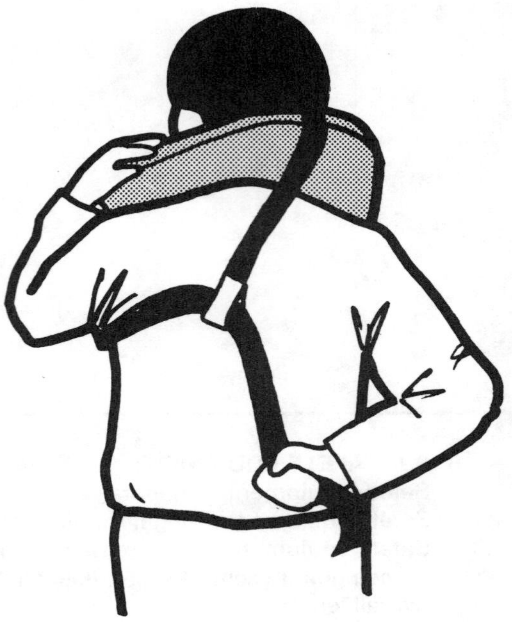

Fig. 8(1) *Putting on a lifejacket — first read the instructions. Hold the jacket up in front of you, put your head through the hole, and secure the waistband at the side or front as appropriate.*

Safety equipment list

	(a) Coastal	(b) Offshore
Safety		
Lifejackets, BS3595, per person	1	1
Harnesses, BS4224, per person	1	1
Navigation		
Charts, almanac, pilot	Yes	Yes
Compass with deviation card	1	1
Hand bearing compass	1	1
Chart table instruments	Yes	Yes
Watch/clock	1	2
Echo sounder	1	1
Leadline	1	1
Radio direction finding set	1	1
Radio receiver (forecasts)	1	1
Barometer	1	1
Navigation lights	Yes	Yes
Radar reflector	1	1
Foghorn	1	1
Powerful waterproof torch	1	1
Anchor with warp or chain	2	2
Towline	1	1
Man overboard		
Lifebuoy, with drogue and light	2	2
Buoyant heaving line	1	1
Dan buoy	–	1
Rope (or boarding) ladder	1	1

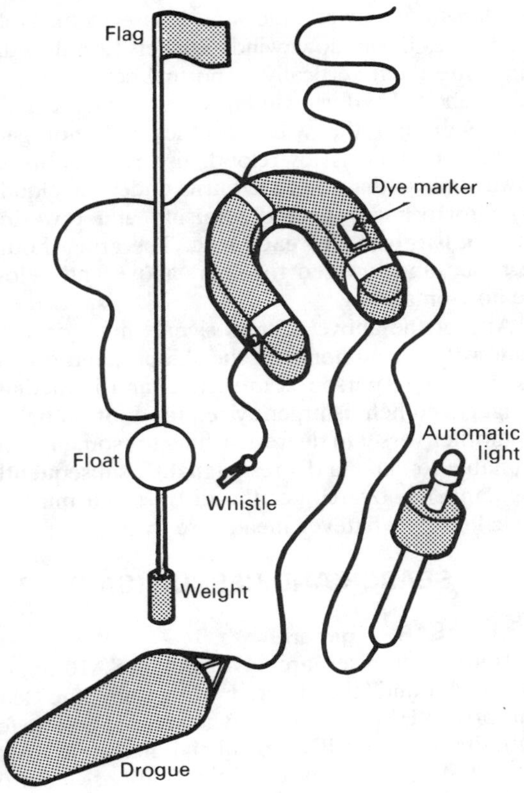
Flag
Dye marker
Automatic light
Float
Whistle
Weight
Drogue

Fig. 8(2) *Lifebuoy with dan buoy and flag, automatic light, whistle, dye marker, and drogue.*

	(a) Coastal	(b) Offshore
Fire		
Fire extinguishers	2	3
Fire blanket	1	1
Sinking		
Bilge pumps	2	2
Buckets with lanyards	2	2
Leak stopping gear	Yes	Yes
Distress signals		
Hand flares, red	2	4
Hand flares, white (warning)	4	4
Red parachute rockets	2	4
Hand smoke signals	2	–
Buoyant orange smoke signals	–	2
Emergency radio transmitter	–	1
Abandon ship		
Liferaft for whole crew	1	1
	or	
Dinghy with buoyancy, or inflated inflatable	1	–
Panic bag, extra water etc	–	1

	(a) Coastal	(b) Offshore
Miscellaneous		
First aid kit	1	1
Engine tool kit	1	1
Name/number prominently displayed	Yes	Yes
Storm canvas	Yes	Yes
Emergency steering arrangements	Yes	Yes

8.1.4 Distress signals

A distress signal must only be made if the yacht or a person is in serious and immediate danger, and help is urgently required.

For a lesser emergency, an urgency signal (PAN PAN) as described in 6.3.10 may be appropriate. If help is needed, but the boat is not in immediate danger, the proper signal is 'V' (Victor) International Code, meaning 'I require assistance'. This can be sent as a flag signal (a white flag with a red St Andrew's cross), or by light or sound in Morse code (· · · —). Other signals of an emergency nature in the International Code are given in 6.1.5.

If medical help is required, the proper signal is 'W' (Whiskey) International Code, meaning 'I require medical assistance'.

A full list of the recognised distress signals is given in Annex IV of the *International Regulations for Preventing Collisions at Sea*, and is reproduced in Chapter 2 (2.1.6). The following are those most appropriate for yachts and small craft, together with notes on their use.

(1) **Continuous sounding with any fog signalling apparatus.** In order to avoid confusion, this is best done by a succession of letters SOS in Morse (· · · — — — · · ·).

(2) **A signal made by radiotelegraphy or by any other signalling method consisting of the group** · · · — — — · · · (SOS) in the Morse Code. For a yacht the most likely methods are by sound signal as in (1) above, or by flashing light.

(3) **A signal sent by radiotelephony consisting of the spoken word MAYDAY.** This procedure is fully described in 6.3.10, but for ease of reference the basic rules are repeated briefly below.

Check the battery switch is ON. Switch the set ON, and select HIGH power. Tune to VHF Ch 16 (or 2182 kHz for MF). If an alarm signal generator is fitted, operate it for at least 30 seconds. Press the 'transmit' button, and say slowly and distinctly:

'MAYDAY MAYDAY MAYDAY — THIS IS (name of boat spoken three times) — MAYDAY — (name of boat spoken once) — MY POSITION IS (latitude and longitude, or true bearing and distance from a known object) — (nature of distress) — (aid required) — (number of persons on board) — (any other important information) — OVER'

8

Release the transmit button, and listen. If no acknowledgment is heard, repeat the message. If transmitting on 2182 kHz, repeat the call during the silence periods commencing each hour and half-hour.

The Urgency Signal (PAN PAN, spoken three times) indicates a lesser emergency than a distress signal, and should be used when there is a very urgent message concerning the safety of a ship or person. For further detail see 6.3.10.

Portable emergency radiotelephones, on 2182 kHz or Ch 16, can be used from the yacht or the liferaft. Also available are Personal Locator Beacons (PLBs) and Emergency Position Indicating Radio Beacons (EPIRBs) operating on 121·5 and 243 MHz. These are primarily for aeronautical purposes and since maritime SAR authorities do not keep watch on these frequencies they are of limited use in coastal waters. More useful is an EPIRB transmitting on 406 MHz, the dedicated COSPAS/SARSAT satellite frequency with full global coverage. Like other radio transmitters, all such equipment must be licensed.

(4) **The International Code signal of distress 'NC'.** This can be made by flag hoist, N being a blue and white chequered flag and C one which is horizontally striped blue, white, red, white, blue.

(5) **A signal consisting of a square flag having above or below it a ball or anything resembling a ball.** This is not too difficult to contrive from any square flag, and a round fender or anchor ball.

(6) **A rocket parachute flare or a hand flare showing a red light.** A red flare is the most effective distress signal at night. Flares serve two purposes — first to raise the alarm, and then to pinpoint the boat's position. Within about three miles from land a hand flare will do both. At greater distances a red parachute rocket (which projects a suspended flare to a height of more than 1000ft, or 300m, and which burns for more than 40 seconds) is needed to raise the alarm, but hand flares are useful to indicate the boat's position. See further comments under (7) below.

(7) **A smoke signal giving off orange-coloured smoke.** By day orange smoke signals (hand held for short distances, or the larger buoyant type for greater ranges) are more effective than flares, although the smoke disperses quickly in a strong wind.

White flares are not distress signals, but are used to indicate the presence of a boat — to another vessel on a collision course for example. An outfit of four is suggested for boats which make night passages. Shield your eyes when using them, to protect night vision.

Pyrotechnics must be stowed where they are accessible, but protected from damp. In good storage conditions they should have a life of three years. Examine them regularly, and replace them by the expiry date. All the crew should know where the flares are stowed, and how to use them. Hold hand flares firmly downwind. Rockets turn into the wind: fire them vertically in normal conditions, or aimed about 15° downwind in strong winds. Do not aim them into the wind, or they will not gain altitude. If there is low cloud, fire rockets at 45° downwind, so that the flare burns under the cloud.

(8) **Slowly and repeatedly raising and lowering arms outstretched to each side.** The arms should be raised and lowered together, above and below the horizontal.

Any of the above distress signals must only be made with the authority of the skipper, and only if the boat or a person is in serious and immediate danger, and help is urgently required: or on behalf of another vessel in distress, which for some reason is unable to make a distress signal. If subsequently the danger is overcome, the distress call must be cancelled by whatever means are available.

8.2 SEARCH AND RESCUE (SAR)

8.2.1 SAR — general

Various authorities are involved in SAR operations. Around the United Kingdom, the lead authority is HM Coastguard who are responsible for initiating and coordinating all civil maritime SAR. To assist them, Coast Radio Stations monitor distress frequencies and control ship/shore communications (see 6.3.15); the RNLI supplies and mans lifeboats; the Royal Navy assists with ships; and, the Royal Air Force, through two Military Rescue Coordination Centres (RCC) at Edinburgh and Plymouth controls all military helicopters and fixed wing aircraft involved in SAR. Air Traffic Control Centres (ATCC) listen out on air distress frequencies and report to the military RCCs. The military RCC at Plymouth also mans the United Kingdom Cospas-Sarsat Mission Control Centre (MCC) which receives satellite data on emergency distress beacons on 121·5 MHz, 243 MHz and 406 MHz. Similar organisations to the above exist in other countries in Western Europe — see 10.12.7 (Republic of Ireland), 10.14.7 (France), 10.20.7 (Belgium, Netherlands), 10.21.7 (Germany).

8.2.2 HM Coastguard

HM Coastguard initiates and coordinates SAR around the United Kingdom and over a large part of the eastern Atlantic. The area is divided into six Maritime Search and Rescue Regions (SRRs), supervised by Maritime Rescue Coordination Centres (MRCCs) at Falmouth, Dover, Great Yarmouth, Aberdeen, the Clyde and Swansea. It also includes 'Shannon' area which is the responsibility of the Republic of Ireland. Each SRR is divided into Districts, each with a Maritime Rescue Sub-Centre (MRSC). Their boundaries are shown in the maps at the start of Areas 1–11 in Chapter 10. The telephone number of the nearest MRCC or

MRSC (or the equivalent in other countries) is shown for each harbour.

Within each of the 21 districts thus formed there is an organisation of Auxiliary Coastguard watch and rescue stations, grouped within Sectors under the management of Regular Coastguard Officers.

All MRCCs and MRSCs keep watch on VHF Ch 16, and are connected to telex and telephone. A visual look-out is maintained when necessary. The Channel Navigation Information Service (CNIS) keeps a constant radar watch on the Dover Strait, with broadcast of navigational and traffic information on Ch 10 at 10 and 40 minutes past each hour. There are about 500 Regular Coastguard Officers, backed up by more than 4200 Auxiliaries on call for emergencies. HM Coastguard also have a cliff and beach rescue role.

A VHF emergency direction finding service, controlled by HM Coastguard, is operated from various stations round Britain. See 4.3.2.

The radio telephony callsign of an MRCC or MRSC is the geographical name, followed by 'Coastguard' — for example 'SOLENT COASTGUARD'.

HM Coastguard operates a Local Warning Service relating to hazards which may affect craft in inshore waters, but outside Port and Harbour Authority limits. These local warnings are broadcast on Ch 67, after an announcement on Ch 16. There is no numerical sequence, and no specific broadcast schedule; any repetition of the broadcast is at the discretion of the originating Coastguard station. Strong wind warnings are broadcast on receipt, and forecasts for local sea areas about every four hours or on request. See also Chapter 7 para 7.2.16.

Yacht and Boat Safety Scheme

This free scheme provides useful information for the Coastguard to mount a successful SAR operation. Owners can obtain a Form CG66 from their local Coastguard station, harbour master or marina. This should be completed with details of the boat and her equipment, and then posted to the local Coastguard Rescue Centre. There is a tear-off section which can be given to a friend or relative so that they know the Coastguard station to contact if they are concerned for the boat's safety.

It is not the function of HM Coastguard to maintain watch for boats on passage, but they will record information by phone before departure or from intermediate ports, or while on passage by visual signals or VHF Ch 67 (the Small Craft Safety Channel). When using Ch 67 for safety messages it is requested that yachts give the name of the Coastguard Rescue Centre holding the boat's Safety Scheme card. In these circumstances the Coastguard must be told of any change to the planned movements of the boat, and it is important that they are informed of the boat's safe arrival at her ultimate destination.

Raising the alarm

If an accident afloat is seen from shore, dial 999 and ask for the Coastguard. You will be asked to report on the incident, and possibly to stay near the telephone for further communications.

If at sea you receive a distress signal and you are in a position to give assistance, you are obliged to do so with all speed, unless or until you are specifically released.

When alerted the Coastguard summon the most appropriate help, they may direct vessels in the vicinity of the distress position; request the launch of an RNLI lifeboat; scramble a military or Coastguard SAR helicopter; other vessels may be alerted through Coast Radio Stations or by Satellite communications.

8.2.3 Royal National Lifeboat Institution (RNLI)

The RNLI, which is supported entirely by voluntary contributions, has about 200 stations around the United Kingdom, the Republic of Ireland, the Isle of Man, and the Channel Islands. From them are deployed about 130 lifeboats over 10m in length and a similar number of smaller lifeboats. Some of the latter only operate in summer.

When launched on service lifeboats over 10m keep watch on 2182 kHz and Ch 16. They can also use other frequencies (including VHF Ch 0, which is reserved exclusively for SAR) to contact HM Coastguard or Coast Radio Stations. Smaller lifeboats are fitted with VHF. All lifeboats show a quick-flashing blue light.

Similar organisations to the RNLI exist in other countries in Western Europe. The positions of lifeboat stations are indicated on the maps at the start of each Area in Chapter 10.

Yachtsmen can help support the RNLI by joining Shoreline. Details from RNLI, West Quay Road, Poole, Dorset BH15 1HZ.

8.2.4 SAR — communications

For details of signals between shore and ships in distress, signals used by SAR aircraft, and directing signals used by aircraft — see 6.2.4, 6.2.5 and 6.2.6 respectively.

8.2.5 Helicopter rescue

SAR helicopters in the UK are based at Chivenor, Culdrose, Portland, Lee-on-Solent, Manston, Woodbridge, Coltishall, Leconfield, Boulmer, Leuchars, Lossiemouth, Sumburgh, Stornoway, Prestwick, Valley and Brawdy.

Wessex helicopters can carry up to ten survivors, but do not usually operate at night, or when the wind exceeds 45 knots. Sea King helicopters can operate to a distance of 300 miles, and at night, and can rescue up to 18 survivors. All can communicate with lifeboats etc on VHF, and some on MF.

When the helicopter is sighted by a boat in distress, a flare, smoke signal, dye marker or a well trained Aldis lamp will assist recognition (very important if there are other vessels in the vicinity). Dodgers with the boat's name or sail number are useful aids to identification.

While hovering the pilot has limited vision beneath him, and relies on instructions from the winch operator. Survivors from a yacht with a mast may need to be picked up from a dinghy or liferaft streamed at least 100ft (30m) away. In a small yacht with no dinghy, survivors (wearing life-jackets) may need to be picked up from the water, at the end of a long warp. It is very important that no survivor boards a liferaft or jumps into the sea until instructed to do so by the helicopter (either by VHF Ch 16 or 67) or by the winchman (by word of mouth). Sails should be lowered and lashed and it is helpful if the drift of the boat is reduced by a sea anchor.

If a crewman descends from the helicopter, he will take charge. Obey his instructions quickly. Never secure the winch wire to the yacht, and beware that it may carry a lethal static charge if it is not dipped (earthed) in the sea before handling.

Survivors may be lifted by double lift in a strop, accompanied by the crewman in a canvas seat. Or it may be necessary, with no crewman, for a survivor to position himself in the strop. Put your head and shoulders through the strop so that the padded part is in the small of the back and the toggle is in front of the face. Pull the toggle down, as close to the chest as possible. When ready, give a thumbs up sign with an extended arm, and place both arms close down by the side of the body (resist the temptation to hang onto the strop). On reaching the helicopter, do exactly as instructed by the crew.

In some circumstances a 'Hi-line' may be used. This is a rope tail, attached to the winch wire by a weak link, and weighted at its lower end. When it is lowered to the yacht do not make it fast, but coil it down carefully. The helicopter pays out the winch wire and descends, while the yacht takes in the slack (keeping it outboard and clear of all obstructions) until the winch hook and strop are on board. When ready to lift, the helicopter ascends and takes in the wire. Pay out the tail, and cast it off well clear of the yacht. But if a further lift is to be made the tail should be retained on board (not made fast) to facilitate recovery of the strop for the next lift.

Injured persons can be lifted, strapped into a special stretcher carried in the helicopter.

When alighting from a helicopter, beware of the tail rotor.

8.2.6 Abandon ship

Although preparations must be made, do not abandon a yacht until she is doomed. She is a better target for rescue craft than a liferaft, and while she is still afloat it is possible to use her resources (such as RT, for distress calls) and to select what extra equipment is put in the liferaft or lashed into the dinghy (which should be taken too, if possible).

Before entering the raft, and cutting it adrift:

(1) Send a distress message (Mayday call), saying that yacht is being abandoned, and position.
(2) Dress warmly with sweaters etc under oilskins, and lifejackets on top. Take extra clothes.
(3) Fill any available containers with tops about $^3/_4$ full with fresh water, so that they will float.
(4) Collect additional food — tins and tin opener.
(5) Collect navigational gear, torch, extra flares, bucket, length of line, first aid kit, knife etc.

Once in the liferaft, plan for the worst. If there has not been time to collect items listed above, collect whatever flotsam is available.

(1) Keep the inside of the raft as dry as possible. Huddle together for warmth. Close the opening as necessary, but keep a good lookout for shipping and aircraft.
(2) Stream the drogue if necessary for stability, or if it is required to stay near the position.
(3) Ration fresh water to $^3/_4$ pint ($^1/_2$ litre) per person per day. Do not drink sea water or urine. Collect rain water.
(4) Use flares sparingly, on the skipper's orders.
(5) Issue and commence anti-seasick pills.

8.2.7 Submarine hazard

There have been a number of incidents in which fishing vessels and occasionally yachts have been snagged or hit by submarines operating just below the surface. The risk is greatest in the Irish Sea, North Channel and approaches to the Clyde, and at night.

The best advice available to yachts is:

a. Where possible avoid charted Submarine Exercise Areas.
b. Keep clear of any surface vessel flying the International Flag Code Group 'NE2' which denotes that submarines are in the vicinity.
c. Run your engine or generator even when under sail.
d. Operate your echo sounder.
e. At night show deck level navigation lights i.e. pulpit and stern.

Information relating to dived submarine activity in the Clyde area east of a line joining Davaar Island Lt (55°26′N 05°35′W) to Killantringan Lt (54°52′N 05°09′W) is broadcast by HM Coastguard Clyde on Ch 67 at 0220 0620 1020 1420 1820 and 2220 (after weather forecasts).

Chapter 9

Tides

Contents

9

Tides — introduction
The following subjects are described in detail in Chapter 9 of *The Macmillan & Silk Cut Yachtsman's Handbook*:

The theory of tides; definitions of terms; calculations of times and heights of HW and LW; calculations of depths of water at specific times; calculations of times at which tide reaches certain heights; Twelfths Rule; tidal calculations by pocket calculator; French tidal coefficients; co-tidal and co-range charts; harmonic constituents; establishment of a port; tidal stream diamonds; tidal stream information on charts and in Sailing Directions ... plus *general information on the sea — how waves are formed; freak waves; wind against tide; bars; overfalls and tide races; refraction of waves; reflected waves; ocean currents etc.*

Here in the Almanac sufficient information is given for the use of the tidal data provided in Chapter 10, but for fuller details of matters concerning tides and the sea reference should be made to Chapter 9 of *The Macmillan & Silk Cut Yachtsman's Handbook.*

9.1 GENERAL

9.1.1 Explanation
This chapter explains how to use the tidal information contained in Chapter 10, where the daily times and heights of High Water (HW) and Low Water (LW) for Standard Ports are given, together with time and height differences for many other places. Tidal predictions are for average meteorological conditions. In abnormal weather the times and heights of HW and LW may vary considerably.

9.1.2 Times
The times tabulated for the Standard Ports in Chapter 10—whether inside or outside the tinted areas—are in the Zone Time shown at the top left-hand corner of each page. Thus all the times printed for Standard Ports in the UK, Channel Islands and Ireland are in Universal Time (UT), which for practical purposes corresponds to GMT. All the times printed for Standard Ports in France, Netherlands and Germany are in Zone −0100 time. To convert these Zone −0100 times to UT, you must subtract one hour.

The tinted areas indicate when clock (or local) time is the same as Zone Time. Outside the tinted areas it is necessary to add one hour to the printed times to obtain local Summer Time, often referred to as Daylight Saving Time (DST) on the Continent.

Under each Secondary Port listed in Chapter 10 are its Time Zone, its Standard Port and the data required to calculate time differences, which when applied to the printed times of HW and LW at the Standard Port give the times of HW and LW at the Secondary Port in the Zone Time of the Port. If Summer Time is required, then one hour is added after the Secondary Port time difference has been applied but not before.

9.1.3 Predicted heights
Predicted heights are given in metres and tenths of metres above Chart Datum (CD) (see 9.2.1). Care must be taken when using charts which show depths in fathoms/feet. See Conversion Paragraph 9(8).

9.2 DEFINITIONS

Certain definitions are given below and in Fig. 9(1). For further details see Chapter 9 of *The Macmillan & Silk Cut Yachtsman's Handbook.*

9.2.1 Chart Datum
Chart Datum (CD) is the reference level above which heights of tide are predicted, and below which charted depths are measured. Hence the actual depth of water is the charted depth (at that place) plus the height of tide (at that time).

Tidal predictions for British ports use as their datum Lowest Astronomical Tide (LAT), which is the lowest sea level predicted under average meteorological conditions. All Admiralty charts of the British Isles use LAT as chart datum, but others, particularly fathom charts, do not. Where tidal predications and charted depths are not referenced to the same datum (e.g. LAT), errors resulting in an over estimation of depth by as much as 0·5m can occur.

9.2.2 Charted depth
Charted depth is the distance of the sea bed below chart datum, and is shown in metres and tenths of metres on metric charts, or in fathoms and/or feet on older charts. Make sure which units are used.

9.2.3 Drying height
Drying height is the height above chart datum of the top of any feature occasionally covered by water. The figures are underlined on the chart, in metres and tenths of metres on metric charts, and in feet on older charts. The depth is the height of tide (at the time) minus the drying height. If the result is negative, then that place is above sea level.

9.2.4 Duration
Duration is the time between LW and the next HW, normally slightly more than six hours, and can be used to calculate the time of LW when only the time of HW is known.

9.2.5 Height of tide
The height of the tide is the vertical distance of sea level above (or very occasionally below) chart datum, as defined in 9.2.1.

9.2.6 Interval
The interval is the period of time between a given time and the time of HW, expressed in hours and minutes before (−) or after (+) HW. Intervals are printed in increments of one hour (−1hr and +1hr) along the bottom of each tidal curve in Chapter 10. For examples, see Figs. 9(3) and 9(4).

9.2.7 Mean Level
Mean Level (ML) is the average of the heights of Mean High Water Springs (MHWS), Mean High Water Neaps (MHWN), Mean Low Water Springs (MLWS) and Mean Low Water Neaps (MLWN).

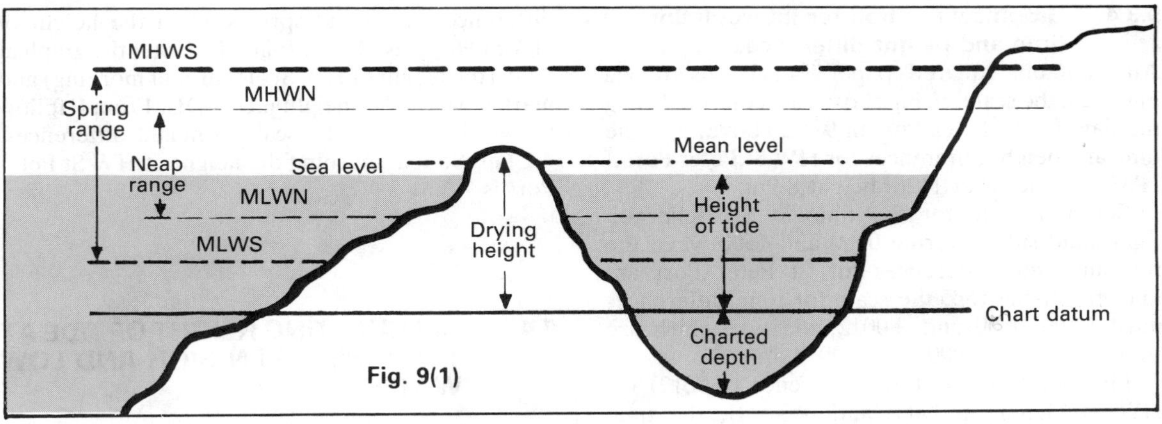
MHWS
Spring range
MHWN
Neap range
Sea level
Mean level
MLWN
MLWS
Drying height
Height of tide
Chart datum
Charted depth

Fig. 9(1)

9.2.8 Range

The range of a tide is the difference between the heights of successive High and Low Waters. Spring range is MHWS–MLWS. Neap range is MHWN–MLWN.

9.3 CALCULATIONS OF TIMES AND HEIGHTS OF HIGH AND LOW WATER

9.3.1 Standard Ports

The times and heights of HW and LW are tabulated for each Standard Port in Chapter 10. The conversion of Zone −0100 time to UT and of either Zone UT or Zone −0100 time to Local Summer or Daylight Saving Time (DST) is dealt with in 9.1.2. See also 9.7 for the effect of wind and barometric pressure.

9.3.2 Secondary Ports — times of HW and LW

Each Secondary Port listed in Chapter 10 has a data block for the calculation of times of HW and LW as explained in 9.1.2. The following example is for St Peter Port:

TIDES

−0450 Dover; ML 4·99; Duration 0550; Zone 0 (UT)

Standard Port ST HELIER

Times				**Height (metres)**			
HW		LW		MHWS	MHWN	MLWN	MLWS
0300	0900	0200	0900	11·1	8·1	4·1	1·3
1500	2100	1400	2100				
Differences ST PETER PORT							
0000	+0012	−0008	+0002	−2·1	−1·4	−0·6	−0·3

Thus −0450 Dover indicates that, on average, HW St Peter Port occurs 4 hours and 50 minutes before HW Dover (the times of HW Dover, in UT, can be found on the bookmark). Duration 0550 indicates that LW St Peter Port occurs 5 hours 50 minutes before its HW. This is a very rough and ready method.

A more accurate and reliable method uses the Standard Port and Time Differences. Thus when HW at St Helier occurs at 0900 and 2100, the difference is +0012, and HW at St Peter Port occurs at 0912 and 2112. When HW at St Helier occurs at 0300 and 1500, the difference is 0000, and HW St Peter Port occurs also at 0300 and 1500. If, as is likely, HW St Helier occurs at some other time, then the Difference for St Peter Port must be found by interpolation – by eye, by calculator or, when calculating a number of tides, by the graphical method in 9.3.4. Thus when HW St Helier occurs at 1030, the Difference is +0009, and HW St Peter Port occurs at 1039. The same method is used for calculating the times of LW.

The times thus obtained are in the Zone Time indicated in the Secondary Port data block. Care must be taken when the Zone Time at the Secondary Port differs from that at the Standard Port. See 9.1.2 for this and for converting time from one Zone to another and for changing to Summer Time.

These calculations are best done by completing boxes 1, 2, 5, 6, 9 and 10 of the tidal prediction form shown in Fig. 9 (5).

9.3.3 Secondary Ports — heights of HW and LW

The Secondary Port data block also contains height Differences which are applied to the heights of HW and LW at the Standard Port. Thus when the height of HW at St Helier is 11·1m (MHWS), the Difference is −2·1m, and the height of HW at St Peter Port is 9·0m (MHWS). When the height of HW at St Helier is 8·1m (MHWN), the Difference is −1·4m, and the height of HW at St Peter Port is 6·7m (MHWN). If, as is likely, the height of tide at the Standard Port does not exactly equal the Mean Spring or Neap level, then the height Difference is found by interpolation as in 9.3.2. Thus if the height of HW at St Helier is 9·2m, the Difference is −1·7m, and the height of HW at St Peter Port is 7·5m. These calculations are best done by completing boxes 3, 4, 7, 8, 11 and 12 of Fig. 9(5).

9.3.4 Graphical method for interpolating time and height differences

Any suitable squared paper can be used, see Fig. 9(2), the scales being chosen as required. Using the data for St Peter Port in 9.3.2 above, find the time and height differences for HW St Peter Port if HW St Helier is at 1126, height 8·9m.

Select a scale for the time at St Helier on right-hand side covering 0900 and 1500 when the relevant time differences for St Peter Port are known. At the top, the scale for time differences must cover 0000 and +0012, the two which are shown for times 0900 and 1500.

Plot point A, the time difference (+0012) for HW St Helier at 0900; and point B, the time difference (0000) for HW St Helier at 1500. Join AB. Enter the graph on the right at time 1126 (HW St Helier) and mark C where that time meets AB. From C proceed vertically to the time difference scale at the top, +0007. So that morning HW St Peter Port is 7 minutes after HW St Helier, i.e. 1133.

In the bottom of the diagram, select scales which cover the height of HW at St Helier vertically (i.e. 8·1 to 11·1m and the relevant height differences (−1·4 to −2·1m) horizontally. Plot point D, the height difference (−1·4m) at neaps when the height of HW St Helier is 8·1m; and E, the height difference −2·1m) at springs when the height of HW St Helier is 11·1m. Join DE. Enter the graph at 8·9m (the height of HW St Helier that morning) and mark F where that height meets DE. From F follow the vertical line to the scale of height differences, −1·6m. So that morning the height of HW St Peter Port is 7·3m.

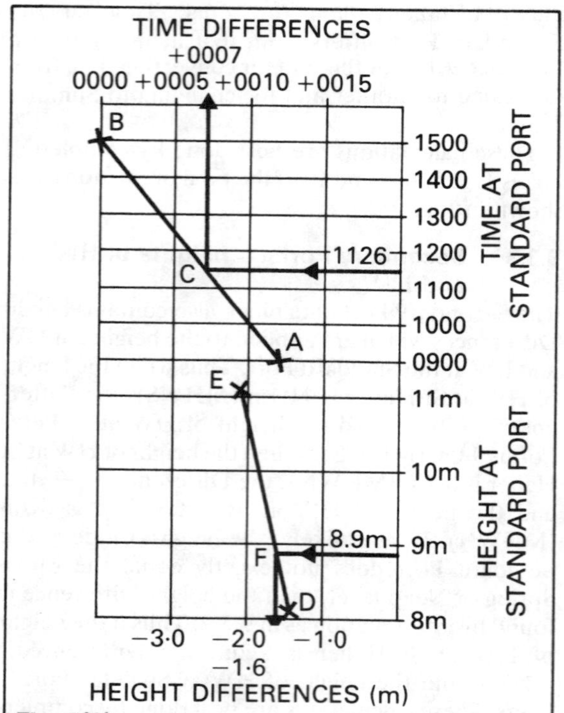
TIME DIFFERENCES
+0007
0000 +0005 +0010 +0015
B
A
C
E
F
D
1500
1400
1300
1126
1200
1100
1000
0900
11m
10m
8.9m
9m
8m
TIME AT STANDARD PORT
HEIGHT AT STANDARD PORT
−3·0 −2·0 −1·0
−1·6
HEIGHT DIFFERENCES (m)

Fig. 9(2)

9.4 CALCULATING HEIGHT OF TIDE AT TIMES BETWEEN HIGH AND LOW WATER

9.4.1 Standard Ports

Intermediate times and heights are best predicted from the Mean Spring and Neap Curves for Standard Ports in Chapter 10. Examples below are for Leith, on a day when the predictions are:

	UT	Ht(m)
22	0202	5·3
	0752	1·0
	1417	5·4
TU	2025	0·5

Example: Find the height at Leith at 1200.
(1) On the Leith tidal diagram plot the heights of HW and LW each side of the required time, and join them by a sloping line, Fig. 9(3).
(2) Enter the HW time and other times as necessary in the boxes below the curves.
(3) From the required time, proceed vertically to the curves. The Spring curve is a solid line, and the Neap curve (where it differs) is pecked. Interpolate between the curves by comparing the actual range −4·4m in this example — with the Mean Ranges printed beside the curves. Never extrapolate. Here the Spring curve applies.
(4) Proceed horizontally to the sloping line plotted in (1), and thence vertically to the height scale, to give 4·2m.

Example: To find the time at which the afternoon height of tide falls to 3·7m.
(1) On the Leith tidal diagram, plot the heights of HW and LW each side of the required event, and join them by a sloping line, Fig. 9(4).
(2) Enter the HW time and others to cover the required event, in the boxes below.
(3) From the required height, proceed vertically to the sloping line and thence horizontally to the curves. Interpolate between them as in the previous example and do not extrapolate. Here the actual range is 4·9m, and the Spring curve applies.
(4) Proceed vertically to the time scale, and read off the time required, 1637.

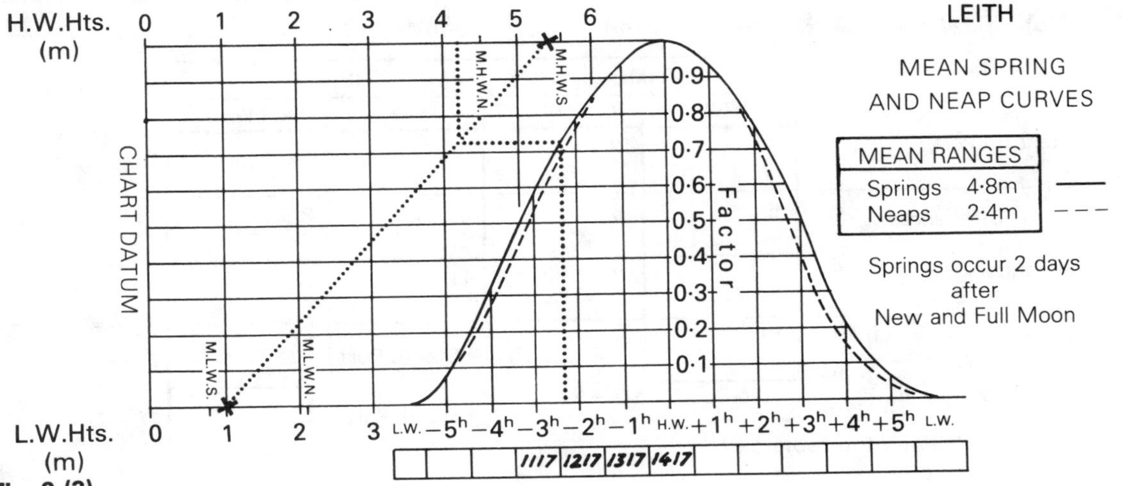

H.W.Hts. (m)
0 1 2 3 4 5 6
LEITH
MEAN SPRING AND NEAP CURVES
MEAN RANGES
Springs 4·8m
Neaps 2·4m
Springs occur 2 days after New and Full Moon
CHART DATUM
M.H.W.N.
M.H.W.S.
M.L.W.S.
M.L.W.N.
Factor
0·9 0·8 0·7 0·6 0·5 0·4 0·3 0·2 0·1
L.W.Hts. (m)
0 1 2 3
L.W. −5h −4h −3h −2h −1h H.W. +1h +2h +3h +4h +5h L.W.
1117 1217 1317 1417

Fig. 9 (3)

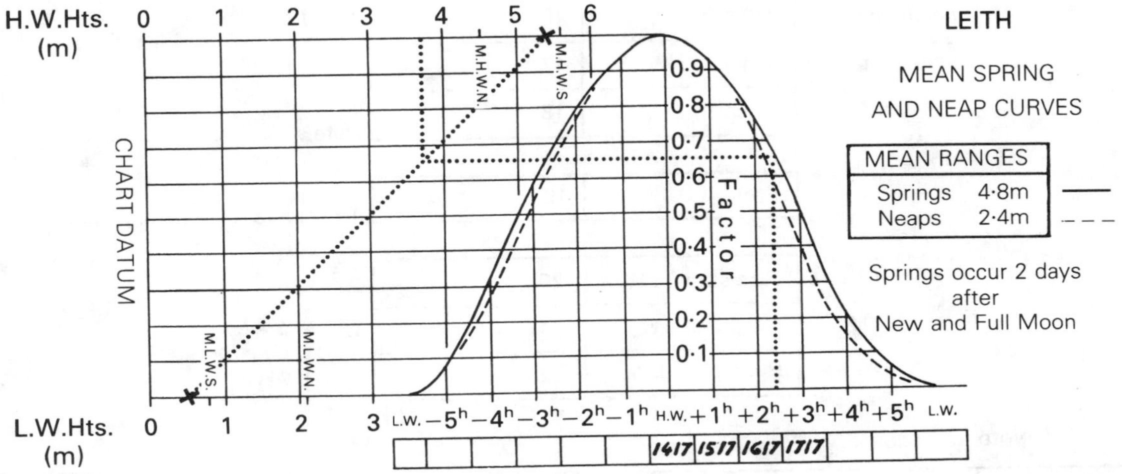

H.W.Hts. (m)
0 1 2 3 4 5 6
LEITH
MEAN SPRING AND NEAP CURVES
MEAN RANGES
Springs 4·8m
Neaps 2·4m
Springs occur 2 days after New and Full Moon
CHART DATUM
M.H.W.N.
M.H.W.S.
M.L.W.S.
M.L.W.N.
Factor
0·9 0·8 0·7 0·6 0·5 0·4 0·3 0·2 0·1
L.W.Hts. (m)
0 1 2 3
L.W. −5h −4h −3h −2h −1h H.W. +1h +2h +3h +4h +5h L.W.
1417 1517 1617 1717

Fig. 9 (4)

9.4.2 Secondary Ports

On coasts where there is little change of shape between tidal curves for adjacent Standard Ports, and where the duration of rise or fall at the Secondary Port is like that of the appropriate Standard Port (where the time differences for HW and LW are nearly the same), intermediate times and heights may be predicted from the tidal curves for the Standard Port in a similar manner to 9.4.1 above. The curves are entered with the times and heights of HW and LW at the Secondary Port, calculated as in 9.3.2 and 9.3.3.

Interpolation between the curves can be made by eye, using the range at the Standard Port as argument. Do not extrapolate, use the spring curve for spring ranges or greater, and the neap curve for neap ranges or less. With a large change in duration between springs and neaps the results may have a slight error, greater near LW.

Special curves for places between Swanage and Selsey (where the tide is very complex) are given in 10.2.8.

9.4.3 The use of factors

Tidal curves show the factor of the range attained at times before and after HW. By definition a factor of 1 = HW, and 0 = LW. So the factor represents the proportion of the range (for the day in question) by which the height of tide is above the height of LW (that day) at the interval (time) concerned.

$$\text{Range} \times \text{factor} = \text{Rise above LW}$$

and

$$\text{Factor} = \text{Rise above LW} \div \text{range}$$

In determining or using the factor it may be necessary to interpolate between the spring and neap curves as described in 9.4.2.

The procedure is shown on the following page, using the tidal prediction form as in Fig. 9(5). Table 9(1) may be used for factor and range calculations.

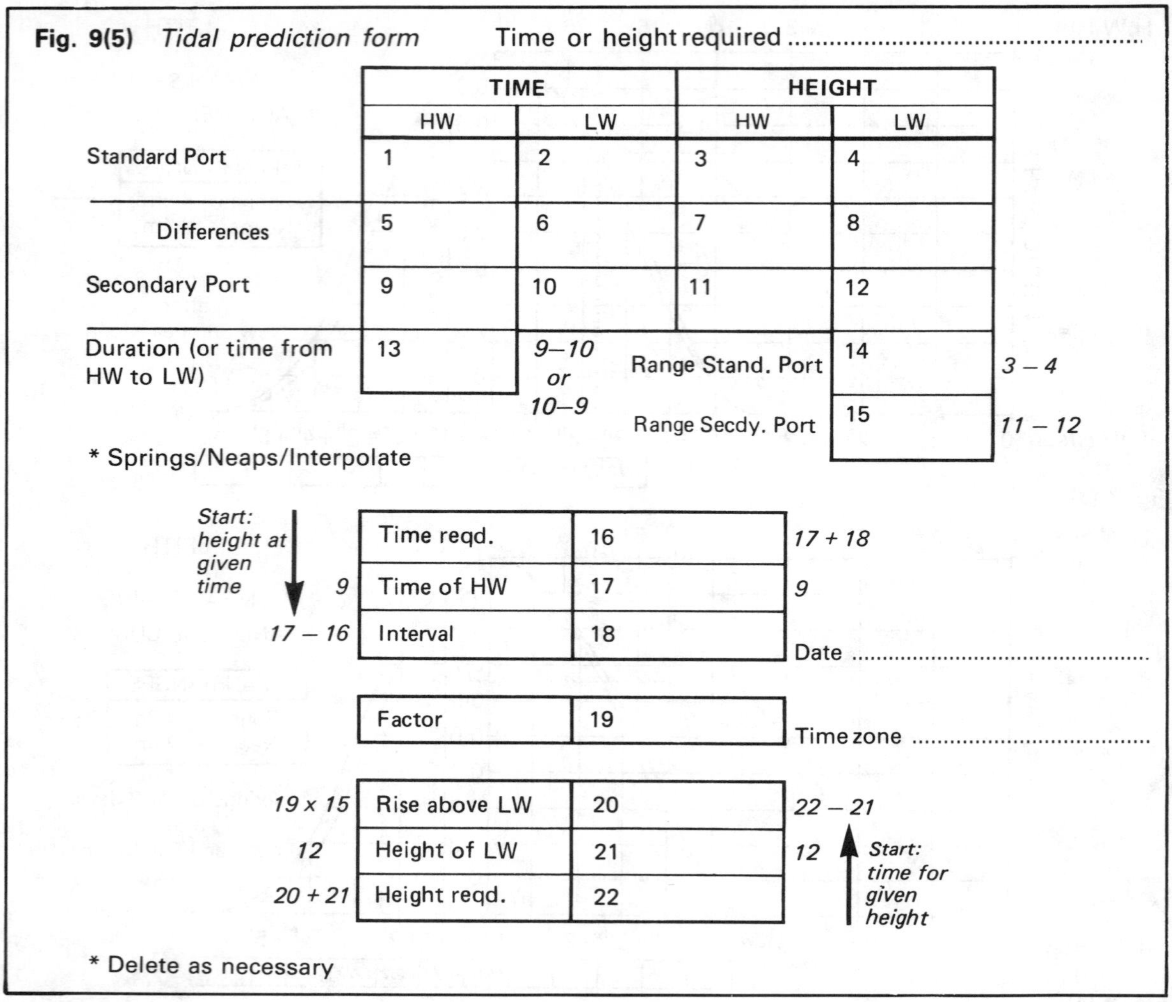
Time or height required ....
TIME
HEIGHT
HW
LW
HW
LW
Standard Port
1
2
3
4
Differences
5
6
7
8
Secondary Port
9
10
11
12
Duration (or time from HW to LW)
13
9–10 or 10–9
Range Stand. Port
14
3 – 4
Range Secdy. Port
15
11 – 12
* Springs/Neaps/Interpolate
Start: height at given time
Time reqd.
16
17 + 18
9
Time of HW
17
9
17 – 16
Interval
18
Date ....
Factor
19
Time zone ....
19 x 15
Rise above LW
20
22 – 21
12
Height of LW
21
12
20 + 21
Height reqd.
22
Start: time for given height
* Delete as necessary

Fig. 9(5) *Tidal prediction form*

Procedure for diagram in Fig. 9(5). First complete the headings on the left. Then enter in boxes indicated:

1 to 4 Predictions for Standard Port
5 to 8 Differences for Secondary Port (interpolated if necessary). Not required for Standard Port.
9 Sum of 1 and 5 (for Standard Port enter 1)
10 Sum of 2 and 6 (for Standard Port enter 2)
11 Sum of 3 and 7 (for Standard Port enter 3)
12 Sum of 4 and 8 (for Standard Port enter 4)
13 Duration (difference of 9 and 10)
14 Range at Standard Port (difference of 3 and 4)
15 Range at Secondary Port (difference of 11 and 12)

TO FIND HEIGHT AT GIVEN TIME

16 Required time
17 HW time from 9
18 Interval (difference of 16 and 17)
19 Factor, from appropriate tidal curve, entered with Interval (18)
20 Rise above LW = Factor (19) × Range (15), or for Standard Port use Range (14)
21 Height of LW from 12
22 Sum of Rise above LW (20) and Height of LW (21)

TO FIND TIME FOR A GIVEN HEIGHT
(start at bottom of diagram)

22 Required height
21 LW Height from 12
20 Rise = Height (22) − LW Height (21)
19 Factor = Rise (20) ÷ Range (15). (For Standard Port use 14)
18 Interval, from interpolation of appropriate tidal curve, entered with Factor (19)
17 HW time from 9
16 Interval (18) applied to HW time (17)

TABLE 9(1) **MULTIPLICATION TABLE for use with Fig. 9(5)**

FACTOR	RANGE																													FACTOR
1.00	1.2	1.6	2.0	2.4	2.8	3.2	3.6	4.0	4.4	4.8	5.2	5.6	6.0	6.4	6.8	7.2	7.6	8.0	8.4	8.8	9.2	9.6	10.0	10.4	10.8	11.2	11.6	12.0	12.4	1.00
.98	1.2	1.6	2.0	2.4	2.7	3.1	3.5	3.9	4.3	4.7	5.1	5.5	5.9	6.3	6.7	7.1	7.4	7.8	8.2	8.6	9.0	9.4	9.8	10.2	10.6	11.0	11.4	11.8	12.1	.98
.96	1.2	1.5	1.9	2.3	2.7	3.1	3.5	3.8	4.2	4.6	5.0	5.4	5.8	6.1	6.5	6.9	7.3	7.7	8.1	8.4	8.8	9.2	9.6	10.0	10.4	10.8	11.1	11.5	11.9	.96
.94	1.1	1.5	1.9	2.3	2.6	3.0	3.4	3.8	4.1	4.5	4.9	5.3	5.6	6.0	6.4	6.8	7.1	7.5	7.9	8.3	8.6	9.0	9.4	9.8	10.2	10.5	10.9	11.3	11.7	.94
.92	1.1	1.5	1.8	2.2	2.6	2.9	3.3	3.7	4.0	4.4	4.8	5.2	5.5	5.9	6.3	6.6	7.0	7.4	7.7	8.1	8.5	8.8	9.2	9.6	9.9	10.3	10.7	11.0	11.4	.92
.90	1.1	1.4	1.8	2.2	2.5	2.9	3.2	3.6	4.0	4.3	4.7	5.0	5.4	5.8	6.1	6.5	6.8	7.2	7.6	7.9	8.3	8.6	9.0	9.4	9.7	10.1	10.4	10.8	11.1	.90
.88	1.1	1.4	1.8	2.1	2.5	2.8	3.2	3.5	3.9	4.2	4.6	4.9	5.3	5.6	6.0	6.3	6.7	7.0	7.4	7.7	8.1	8.4	8.8	9.2	9.5	9.9	10.2	10.6	10.9	.88
.86	1.0	1.4	1.7	2.1	2.4	2.8	3.1	3.4	3.8	4.1	4.5	4.8	5.2	5.5	5.8	6.2	6.5	6.9	7.2	7.6	7.9	8.3	8.6	8.9	9.3	9.6	10.0	10.3	10.7	.86
.84	1.0	1.3	1.7	2.0	2.4	2.7	3.0	3.4	3.7	4.0	4.4	4.7	5.0	5.4	5.7	6.0	6.4	6.7	7.1	7.4	7.7	8.1	8.4	8.7	9.1	9.4	9.7	10.1	10.4	.84
.82	1.0	1.3	1.6	2.0	2.3	2.6	3.0	3.3	3.6	3.9	4.3	4.6	4.9	5.2	5.6	5.9	6.2	6.6	6.9	7.2	7.5	7.9	8.2	8.5	8.9	9.2	9.5	9.8	10.2	.82
.80	1.0	1.3	1.6	1.9	2.2	2.6	2.9	3.2	3.5	3.8	4.2	4.5	4.8	5.1	5.4	5.8	6.1	6.4	6.7	7.0	7.4	7.7	8.0	8.3	8.6	9.0	9.3	9.6	9.9	.80
.78	0.9	1.2	1.6	1.9	2.2	2.5	2.8	3.1	3.4	3.7	4.1	4.4	4.7	5.0	5.3	5.6	5.9	6.2	6.6	6.9	7.2	7.5	7.8	8.1	8.4	8.7	9.0	9.4	9.7	.78
.76	0.9	1.2	1.5	1.8	2.1	2.4	2.7	3.0	3.3	3.6	4.0	4.3	4.6	4.9	5.2	5.5	5.8	6.1	6.4	6.7	7.0	7.3	7.6	7.9	8.2	8.5	8.8	9.1	9.4	.76
.74	0.9	1.2	1.5	1.8	2.1	2.4	2.7	3.0	3.3	3.6	3.8	4.1	4.4	4.7	5.0	5.3	5.6	5.9	6.2	6.5	6.8	7.1	7.4	7.7	8.0	8.3	8.7	8.9	9.2	.74
.72	0.9	1.2	1.4	1.7	2.0	2.3	2.6	2.9	3.2	3.5	3.7	4.0	4.3	4.6	4.9	5.2	5.5	5.8	6.0	6.3	6.6	6.9	7.2	7.5	7.8	8.1	8.4	8.6	8.9	.72
.70	0.8	1.1	1.4	1.7	2.0	2.2	2.5	2.8	3.1	3.4	3.6	3.9	4.2	4.5	4.8	5.0	5.3	5.6	5.9	6.2	6.4	6.7	7.0	7.3	7.6	7.8	8.1	8.4	8.7	.70
.68	0.8	1.1	1.4	1.6	1.9	2.2	2.4	2.7	3.0	3.3	3.5	3.8	4.1	4.4	4.6	4.9	5.2	5.4	5.7	6.0	6.3	6.5	6.8	7.1	7.3	7.6	7.9	8.2	8.4	.68
.66	0.8	1.1	1.3	1.6	1.8	2.1	2.4	2.6	2.9	3.2	3.4	3.7	4.0	4.2	4.5	4.8	5.0	5.3	5.5	5.8	6.1	6.3	6.6	6.9	7.1	7.4	7.7	7.9	8.2	.66
.64	0.8	1.0	1.3	1.5	1.8	2.0	2.3	2.6	2.8	3.1	3.3	3.6	3.8	4.1	4.4	4.6	4.9	5.1	5.4	5.6	5.9	6.1	6.4	6.7	6.9	7.2	7.4	7.7	7.9	.64
.62	0.7	1.0	1.2	1.5	1.7	2.0	2.2	2.5	2.7	3.0	3.2	3.5	3.7	4.0	4.2	4.5	4.7	5.0	5.2	5.5	5.7	6.0	6.2	6.4	6.7	6.9	7.2	7.4	7.7	.62
.60	0.7	1.0	1.2	1.4	1.7	1.9	2.2	2.4	2.6	2.9	3.1	3.4	3.6	3.8	4.1	4.3	4.6	4.8	5.0	5.3	5.5	5.8	6.0	6.2	6.5	6.7	7.0	7.2	7.4	.60
.58	0.7	0.9	1.2	1.4	1.6	1.9	2.1	2.3	2.6	2.8	3.0	3.2	3.5	3.7	3.9	4.2	4.4	4.6	4.9	5.1	5.3	5.6	5.8	6.0	6.3	6.5	6.7	7.0	7.2	.58
.56	0.7	0.9	1.1	1.3	1.6	1.8	2.0	2.2	2.5	2.7	2.9	3.1	3.4	3.6	3.8	4.0	4.3	4.5	4.7	4.9	5.2	5.4	5.6	5.8	6.0	6.3	6.5	6.7	6.9	.56
.54	0.6	0.9	1.1	1.3	1.5	1.7	1.9	2.2	2.4	2.6	2.8	3.0	3.2	3.5	3.7	3.9	4.1	4.3	4.5	4.8	5.0	5.2	5.4	5.6	5.8	6.0	6.3	6.5	6.7	.54
.52	0.6	0.8	1.0	1.2	1.5	1.7	1.9	2.1	2.3	2.5	2.7	2.9	3.1	3.3	3.5	3.7	4.0	4.2	4.4	4.6	4.8	5.0	5.2	5.4	5.6	5.8	6.0	6.2	6.4	.52
.50	0.6	0.8	1.0	1.2	1.4	1.6	1.8	2.0	2.2	2.4	2.6	2.8	3.0	3.2	3.4	3.6	3.8	4.0	4.2	4.4	4.6	4.8	5.0	5.2	5.4	5.6	5.8	6.0	6.2	.50
.48	0.6	0.8	1.0	1.2	1.3	1.5	1.7	1.9	2.1	2.3	2.5	2.7	2.9	3.1	3.3	3.5	3.6	3.8	4.0	4.2	4.4	4.6	4.8	5.0	5.2	5.4	5.6	5.8	5.9	.48
.46	0.6	0.7	0.9	1.1	1.3	1.5	1.7	1.8	2.0	2.2	2.4	2.6	2.8	2.9	3.1	3.3	3.5	3.7	3.9	4.0	4.2	4.4	4.6	4.8	5.0	5.2	5.3	5.5	5.7	.46
.44	0.5	0.7	0.9	1.1	1.2	1.4	1.6	1.8	1.9	2.1	2.3	2.5	2.6	2.8	3.0	3.2	3.3	3.5	3.7	3.9	4.0	4.2	4.4	4.6	4.8	4.9	5.1	5.3	5.5	.44
.42	0.5	0.7	0.8	1.0	1.2	1.3	1.5	1.7	1.8	2.0	2.2	2.4	2.5	2.7	2.9	3.0	3.2	3.4	3.5	3.7	3.9	4.0	4.2	4.4	4.5	4.7	4.9	5.0	5.2	.42
.40	0.5	0.6	0.8	1.0	1.1	1.3	1.4	1.6	1.8	1.9	2.1	2.2	2.4	2.6	2.7	2.9	3.0	3.2	3.4	3.5	3.7	3.8	4.0	4.2	4.3	4.5	4.6	4.8	5.0	.40
.38	0.5	0.6	0.8	0.9	1.1	1.2	1.4	1.5	1.7	1.8	2.0	2.1	2.3	2.4	2.6	2.7	2.9	3.0	3.2	3.3	3.5	3.6	3.8	4.0	4.1	4.3	4.4	4.6	4.7	.38
.36	0.4	0.6	0.7	0.9	1.0	1.2	1.3	1.4	1.6	1.7	1.9	2.0	2.2	2.3	2.4	2.6	2.7	2.9	3.0	3.2	3.3	3.5	3.6	3.7	3.9	4.0	4.2	4.3	4.5	.36
.34	0.4	0.5	0.7	0.8	1.0	1.1	1.3	1.4	1.5	1.6	1.8	1.9	2.0	2.2	2.3	2.4	2.6	2.7	2.9	3.0	3.1	3.3	3.4	3.5	3.7	3.8	3.9	4.1	4.2	.34
.32	0.4	0.5	0.6	0.8	0.9	1.0	1.2	1.3	1.4	1.5	1.7	1.8	1.9	2.0	2.2	2.3	2.4	2.6	2.7	2.8	2.9	3.1	3.2	3.3	3.5	3.6	3.7	3.8	4.0	.32
.30	0.4	0.5	0.6	0.7	0.8	1.0	1.1	1.2	1.3	1.4	1.6	1.7	1.8	1.9	2.0	2.2	2.3	2.4	2.5	2.6	2.8	2.9	3.0	3.1	3.2	3.4	3.5	3.6	3.7	.30
.28	0.3	0.4	0.6	0.7	0.8	0.9	1.0	1.1	1.2	1.3	1.5	1.6	1.7	1.8	1.9	2.0	2.1	2.2	2.4	2.5	2.6	2.7	2.8	2.9	3.0	3.1	3.2	3.4	3.5	.28
.26	0.3	0.4	0.5	0.6	0.7	0.8	0.9	1.0	1.1	1.2	1.4	1.5	1.6	1.7	1.8	1.9	2.0	2.1	2.2	2.3	2.4	2.5	2.6	2.7	2.8	2.9	3.0	3.1	3.2	.26
.24	0.3	0.4	0.5	0.6	0.7	0.8	0.9	1.0	1.1	1.2	1.2	1.3	1.4	1.5	1.6	1.7	1.8	2.1	2.0	2.1	2.2	2.3	2.4	2.5	2.6	2.7	2.8	2.9	3.0	.24
.22	0.3	0.4	0.4	0.5	0.6	0.7	0.8	0.9	1.0	1.1	1.1	1.2	1.3	1.4	1.5	1.6	1.7	1.8	1.8	1.9	2.0	2.1	2.2	2.3	2.4	2.5	2.6	2.6	2.7	.22
.20	0.2	0.3	0.4	0.5	0.6	0.6	0.7	0.8	0.9	1.0	1.0	1.1	1.2	1.3	1.4	1.4	1.5	1.6	1.7	1.8	1.8	1.9	2.0	2.1	2.2	2.2	2.3	2.4	2.5	.20
.18	0.2	0.3	0.4	0.4	0.5	0.6	0.6	0.7	0.8	0.9	0.9	1.0	1.1	1.2	1.2	1.3	1.4	1.4	1.5	1.6	1.7	1.7	1.8	1.9	1.9	2.0	2.1	2.2	2.2	.18
.16	0.2	0.3	0.3	0.4	0.4	0.5	0.6	0.6	0.7	0.8	0.8	0.9	1.0	1.0	1.1	1.2	1.2	1.3	1.3	1.4	1.5	1.5	1.6	1.7	1.7	1.8	1.9	1.9	2.0	.16
.14	0.2	0.2	0.3	0.3	0.4	0.4	0.5	0.6	0.6	0.7	0.7	0.8	0.8	0.9	1.0	1.0	1.1	1.1	1.2	1.2	1.3	1.3	1.4	1.5	1.5	1.6	1.6	1.8	1.7	.14
.12	0.1	0.2	0.2	0.3	0.3	0.4	0.4	0.5	0.5	0.6	0.6	0.7	0.7	0.8	0.8	0.9	0.9	1.0	1.0	1.1	1.1	1.2	1.2	1.2	1.3	1.3	1.4	1.4	1.5	.12
.10	0.1	0.2	0.2	0.2	0.3	0.3	0.4	0.4	0.4	0.5	0.5	0.6	0.6	0,6	0.7	0.7	0.8	0.8	0.8	0.9	0.9	1.0	1.0	1.0	1.1	1.1	1.2	1.2	1.2	.10
.08	0.1	0.1	0.2	0.2	0.2	0.3	0.3	0.3	0.4	0.4	0.4	0.4	0.5	0.5	0.5	0.6	0.6	0.6	0.7	0.7	0.7	0.8	0.8	0.8	0.9	0.9	0.9	1.0	1.0	.08
.06	0.1	0.1	0.1	0.1	0.2	0.2	0.2	0.2	0.3	0.3	0.3	0.3	0.4	0.4	0.4	0.4	0.5	0.5	0.5	0.5	0.6	0.6	0.6	0.6	0.6	0.7	0.7	0.7	0.7	.06
.04	0.0	0.1	0.1	0.1	0.1	0.1	0.1	0.2	0.2	0.2	0.2	0.2	0.2	0.3	0.3	0.3	0.3	0.3	0.3	0.4	0.4	0.4	0.4	0.4	0.4	0.4	0.5	0.5	0.5	.04
.02	0.0	0.0	0.0	0.0	0.1	0.1	0.1	0.1	0.1	0.1	0.1	0.1	0.1	0.1	0.1	0.1	0.2	0.2	0.2	0.2	0.2	0.2	0.2	0.2	0.2	0.2	0.2	0.2	0.2	.02

9.5 CALCULATIONS OF CLEARANCES UNDER BRIDGES ETC.

It is sometimes necessary to calculate whether a boat can pass underneath such objects as bridges or power cables. The heights of such objects are shown on the chart above MHWS, so the clearance will nearly always be greater than the figure shown. The height is shown in metres on metric charts, but in feet on older charts. It is sometimes useful to draw a diagram, as shown in Fig. 9(6), which shows how the measurements are related to chart datum.

Clearance = (Elevation of object + height of MHWS) minus (height of tide at the time + height of mast above above water)

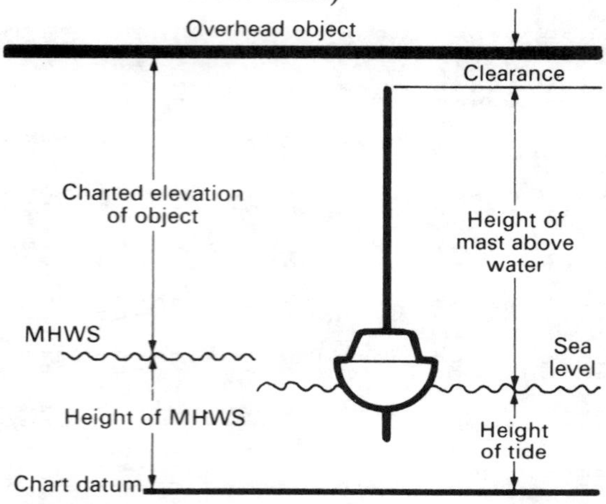

Overhead object
Clearance
Charted elevation of object
Height of mast above water
MHWS
Sea level
Height of MHWS
Height of tide
Chart datum

Fig. 9(6)

9.6 TIDAL STREAMS

9.6.1 General

Tidal streams are the horizontal movement of water caused by the vertical rise and fall of the tide. They normally change direction about every six hours and are quite different from ocean currents, such as the Gulf Stream, which run for long periods in the same direction.

Tidal streams are important to yachtsmen around the British Isles because they often run at about two knots, and much more strongly in a few areas, and at spring tides. There are a few places where they can attain rates of six to eight knots.

The strength and direction of the tidal stream in the more important areas is shown in *Admiralty Tidal Stream Atlases*, as follows:

NP 209 Edition 4 Orkney and Shetland Islands, 1986
218 Edition 4 North Coast of Ireland, West Coast of Scotland, 1983
219 Edition 1 Portsmouth Harbour and Approaches, 1979
220 Edition 1 Rosyth Harbour and Approaches, 1979
221 Edition 1 Plymouth Harbour and Approaches, 1984
233 Edition 2 Dover Strait, 1975
249 Edition 2 Thames Estuary, 1985
250 Edition 3 English and Bristol Channels, 1973
251 Edition 3 North Sea, Southern Part, 1976
252 Edition 3 North Sea, North-Western Part, 1975
253 Edition 1 North Sea, Eastern Part, 1978
256 Edition 3 Irish Sea and Bristol Channel, 1974
257 Edition 3 Approaches to Portland, 1973
264 Edition 4 Channel Islands & Adjacent Coasts of France, 1984
265 Edition 1 France, West Coast, 1978
337 Edition 3 Solent and Adjacent Waters, 1974

Extracts from the above (by permission of the Hydrographer and HMSO) are given in Chapter 10.

The directions of the streams are shown by arrows which are graded in weight and, where possible, in length to indicate the strength of the tidal stream. Thus → indicates a weak stream and ➞ indicates a strong stream. The figures against the arrows give the mean neap and spring rates in tenths of a knot, thus 19,34 indicates a mean neap rate of 1·9 knots and a mean spring rate of 3·4 knots. The comma indicates the approximate position at which the observations were taken.

9.6.2 Computation of tidal stream rates

Using Table 9(2) it is possible to predict the rate of a tidal stream at intermediate times, assuming that it varies with the range of tide at Dover.

Example

It is required to predict the rate of the tidal stream off the northerly point of the Isle of Skye at 0420 UT on a day when the heights of tide at Dover are:

UT	Ht(m)
LW 0328	1·4
HW 0819	6·3
LW 1602	1·1
HW 2054	6·4

The range of the tide is therefore 6·3 − 1·4 = 4·9m. When using either the Tidal Stream Atlas NP 218, or the Tidal Stream charts for Area 8 in Chapter 10, the appropriate chart to use is that for '4 hours before HW Dover' and this gives a mean neap and spring rate of 09 and 17 respectively (0·9 and 1·7 kn). On Table 9(2), Computation of Rates, on the horizontal line marked Neaps, mark the dot above 09 on the horizontal scale; likewise on the

Table 9(2)

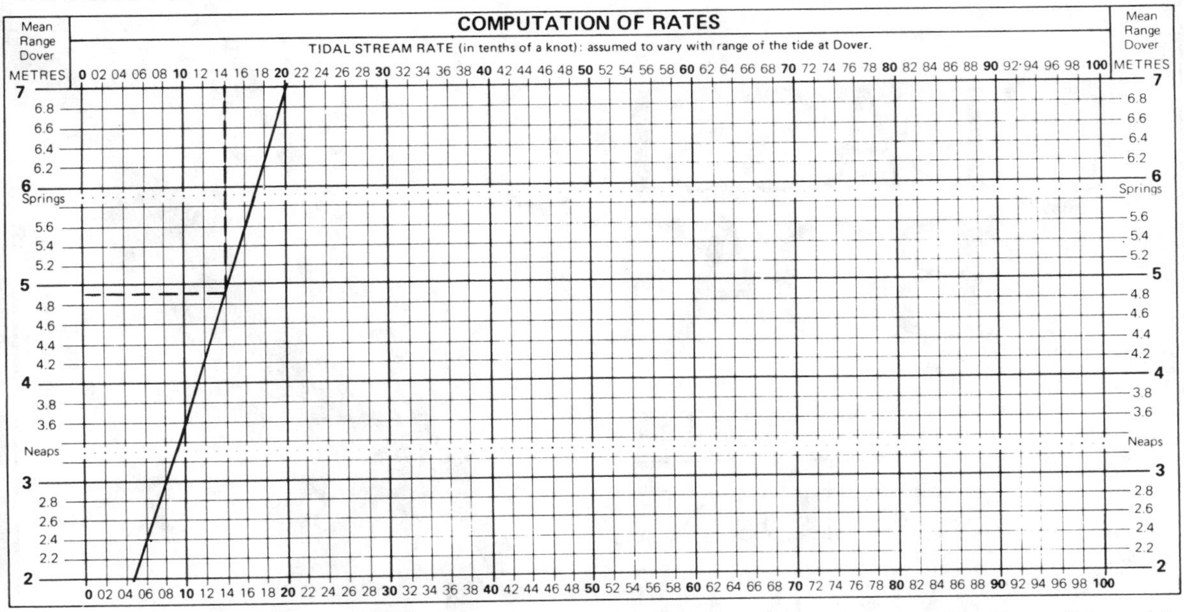
Mean Range Dover
COMPUTATION OF RATES
TIDAL STREAM RATE (in tenths of a knot): assumed to vary with range of the tide at Dover.
METRES
0 02 04 06 08 10 12 14 16 18 20 22 24 26 28 30 32 34 36 38 40 42 44 46 48 50 52 54 56 58 60 62 64 66 68 70 72 74 76 78 80 82 84 86 88 90 92 94 96 98 100
7
6.8
6.6
6.4
6.2
6
Springs
5.6
5.4
5.2
5
4.8
4.6
4.4
4.2
4
3.8
3.6
Neaps
3
2.8
2.6
2.4
2.2
2

line marked Springs, mark the dot below the figure 17 on the horizontal scale. Join these two dots with a straight line. On the vertical scale, 'Mean Range Dover', find the range 4·9. From this point follow across horizontally until the pencil line just drawn is cut; from this intersection follow the vertical line to the scale of Tidal Stream Rates, either top or bottom, and read off the predicted rate. In this example it is 14 or 1·4 knots.

A perspex sheet or a sheet of tracing paper can be used on top of Table 9(2), so as to preserve it for future use.

It should be remembered that tidal atlases cannot show the details of inshore eddies and the tide often sets towards the coast in bays. Along open coasts the turn of the tidal stream does not necessarily occur at HW and LW. It often occurs at about half tide. The tidal stream usually turns earlier inshore than offshore. On modern charts lettered diamonds give information on the tidal streams by reference to a table showing Set, Spring Rate and Neap Rate at hourly intervals before and after HW at a Standard Port. Where appropriate, normal river currents are included. Information on tidal streams and current streams is also included in *Admiralty Sailing Directions*.

9.7 METEOROLOGICAL CONDITIONS

Meteorological conditions can have a significant effect on tides and tidal streams. Sea level tends to rise in the direction towards which a wind is blowing and be lowered in the other direction. The stronger the wind and the longer it blows, the greater the effect. Also the sudden onset of a gale can set up a wave or 'storm surge' which travels along the coast. Under exceptional conditions this can raise the height of the tide by two or three metres, or a 'negative surge' can lower the height of LW by one or two metres which may be more serious for the yachtsman.

Tidal heights are predicted for average barometric pressure. When the barometer is high, tidal heights are likely to be lower, and vice versa. A change of 34 millibars (one inch of mercury) can cause a change of 0·3 metres in the height of sea level, although it may not be felt immediately. Severe conditions giving rise to a storm surge as described above are likely to be caused by a big depression, and the low barometric pressure tends to raise the sea level still more.

Intense minor depressions can have local effects on the height of water, setting up what is known as a 'seiche' which can raise or lower the sea level a metre or more in the space of a few minutes.

9

9.8 CONVERSION — FEET TO METRES, AND METRES TO FEET

In the table below the figures in italics are metres.

Feet		6	12	18	24	30	36	42
Fathoms		1	2	3	4	5	6	7
Feet		*1·8*	*3·6*	*5·5*	*7·3*	*9·1*	*10·9*	*12·8*
1	*0·3*	*2·1*	*3·9*	*5·8*	*7·6*	*9·4*	*11·3*	*13·1*
2	*0·6*	*2·4*	*4·2*	*6·1*	*7·9*	*9·7*	*11·6*	*13·4*
3	*0·9*	*2·7*	*4·5*	*6·4*	*8·2*	*10·0*	*11·9*	*13·7*
4	*1·2*	*3·0*	*4·9*	*6·7*	*8·5*	*10·3*	*12·2*	*14·0*
5	*1·5*	*3·3*	*5·2*	*7·0*	*8·8*	*10·6*	*12·5*	*14·3*

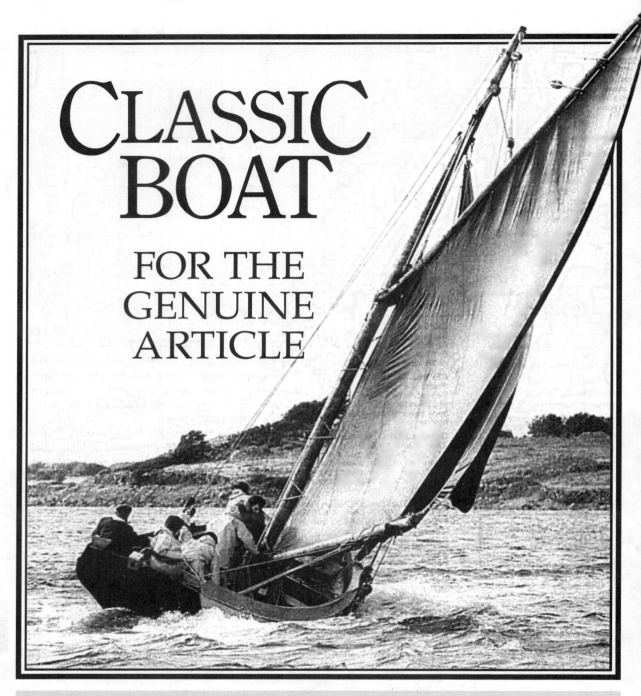

Chapter 10

Harbour, Coastal and Tidal Information

Contents

10.0.1. General information

Harbour, coastal and tidal information is given for the area indicated by the map in 10.0.2, with details of 318 harbours and notes on a further 263 minor harbours and anchorages. The information provided enables a skipper to assess whether he can get into a harbour (tidal height, depth, wind direction etc.), and whether he wants to enter the harbour (shelter, facilities available, early closing days etc.). Each area is arranged as follows:

Index, of the harbours covered in that area.

A sketch of the area showing diagrammatically the positions and characteristics of the harbours covered, principal radiobeacons, coast radio stations, weather information offices, RNLI stations etc.

Tidal stream charts for the area, based on Admiralty tidal stream atlases (by kind permission of the Hydrographer of the Navy and the Controller, HM Stationery Office), showing the strengths and directions of tidal streams for each hour referred to HW Dover and to HW at the nearest Standard Port. For details of the use of tidal stream diagrams see 9.6.2.

A list of principal coastal lights, fog signals and useful waypoints in the area. More powerful lights (ranges 15 miles or more) are in **bold** type; light-vessels and Lanbys are in *CAPITAL ITALICS;* fog signals are in *italics.* Latitude and longitude are shown for more isolated lights and for selected waypoints (underlined). Unless otherwise stated, lights are white. Elevations are in metres (m), and nominal ranges in nautical miles (M). Where appropriate, a brief description is given of the lighthouse or tower. Arcs of visibility, sector limits, and alignment of leading lights etc are true bearings as seen from seward measured in a clockwise direction. Where the latitude and longitude of a light are given (e.g. Bull Point 51 12.ON/4 12.OW) W stands for West. Elsewhere W means white, and except with longitude the word west is written in full to avoid any possible ambiguity. Abbreviations used in the list of lights, fog signals and waypoints are given in 1.4.1.

Passage information, briefly calling attention in note form to some of the principal features of the coast, offlying dangers, tide races, better anhcorages etc.

Table of distances in nautical miles by the most direct route, avoiding dangers, between selected places in that area and in adjacent areas.

In foreign areas (Ireland, France, Belgium, Netherlands and Germany) there follows a section giving **special peculiarities** regarding the area.

Harbour information includes the following:

a. Chartlets. These are based upon Admiralty charts (with the kind permission of Hydrographer of the Navy and the Controller, HM Stationery Office), upon information from Service Hydrographique et Oceanographique de la Marine, France, Deutsches Hydrographisches Institut, Germany, or the Directie Waterhuishouding en Waterbeweging, Netherlands. All depths on the chartlets are in metres. It must be emphasised that these chartlets are not designed or intended for pilotage or navigation, although every effort has been made to ensure that they give an accurate portrayal of the harbour concerned. The publishers and editors disclaim any responsibility for resultant accidents or damage if they are so used. Chartlets do not always cover the whole area referred to in the text (e.g. in E. Anglian rivers). The light tint on the chartlets shows drying area, the dark tint indicates land.

b. After the harbour name, the county (or equivalent abroad) is given, followed by the Admiralty, Stanford, Imray Laurie Norie and Wilson (referred to as Imray) chart numbers for the area, and the Ordnance Survey Map numbers in the new 1:50,000 series.

c. The tidal information in these sections is also kindly provided with the permission of the Hydrographer of the Navy, and the Proudman Oceanographic Laboratory (see 1.1.4). Each Standard Port (see 9.3.1) has the times and heights of High and Low Water for every day of the year. In UK and Eire times are given in GMT; this is also known as UT (Universal Time). The Secondary Ports (see 9.3.2) have the differences quoted on the most suitable (not necessarily the nearest) Standard Port. Time and height differences from the nominated Standard Port are given for each Secondary Port. Explanations of tidal calculations are given in Chapter 9.

At the top of each port's tidal information, the average time difference on Dover is given, whereby the GMT for High Water can be quickly obtained to an accuracy of 15 minutes or so. The times of High Water Dover are under Dover (10.3.15) and also on the bookmark for quick reference, both being shown in GMT. By subtracting the Duration, quoted for most ports, the time of the previous Low Water can be approximately obtained.

Mean Level is also quoted. Zone times are given for each port, but no account is taken of BST or other daylight saving times (DST).

d. Tidal curves are given for all Standard Ports and for Portland and Dunkerque. For calculations with tidal data (finding the height of tide at a given time, for example, or the time for a given height), use the tidal curves provided for the appropriate Standard Port.
e. Shelter. Times of lock openings etc are local times (LT), unless stated.
f. Navigation, starting with the lat/long of a waypoint for the approach or entrance.
g. Principal lights, marks and leading lines.
h. Radio telephone. Details of Port Operations and Traffic Management radio services are shown as appropriate for each harbour covered. Other Port Radio stations which may be useful are shown under the nearest harbour covered.

   Where significant, the call name of a station is shown in *italics*. Frequencies are indicated by their International Maritime Services Channel (Ch) designator. UK Marina Channel is **80** and/or M. MF frequencies are shown in kHz.

   Frequencies used for calling and working may be separated by a semi-colon. For example: Ch16; 12 14 indicated that Ch 16 is used for calling, and that Ch 12 and Ch 14 are working frequencies. Where known, primary frequencies are shown in bold type, thus **14.**

   Where there is a choice of calling frequency, always indicate the channel that you are using when calling another station. This avoids confusion when the station being called is listening on more than one channel. As example, 'Dover Port Control. This is NONSUCH, NONSUCH on Channel 74'.

   Where local times are stated, the letters 'LT' are added. H24 means continuous watch. Time of scheduled broadcasts are shown (for example) as H +20, meaning 20 mins past the hour. HW -3 means 3 hours before local HW; HW +2 means 2 hours after local HW.
i. Telephone numbers are either on the exchange whose dialling code is given after 'Telephone', or on the exchange quoted. E.g. Portsmouth and Gosport numbers are on 0705, so no exchange is shown. But Fareham numbers are on another exchange, as quoted.

   Although the numbers of the appropriate MRCC or MRSC (see 8.2.2) are given, in emergency dial 999 and ask for the Coastguard. Equivalent numbers are given in 10.14.7 (France), 10.20.7 (Belgium and The Netherlands, and 10.21.7 (Germany).
j. At the end of facilities is indicated whether there is a Post Office (✉) Bank (Ⓑ), Railway Station (⇄) or Commercial Airport (✈) in or near the port. Where there is not, the nearest one is indicated in brackets. For continental ports, the nearest UK ferry link is shown.

Facilities at Yacht Clubs are normally available to crews who arrive by sea (as opposed to trailing a dinghy by car) and are members of a recognised yacht club.

Minor harbours and anchorages. Notes on selected places are given at the end of each area.

10.0.2 Map of areas

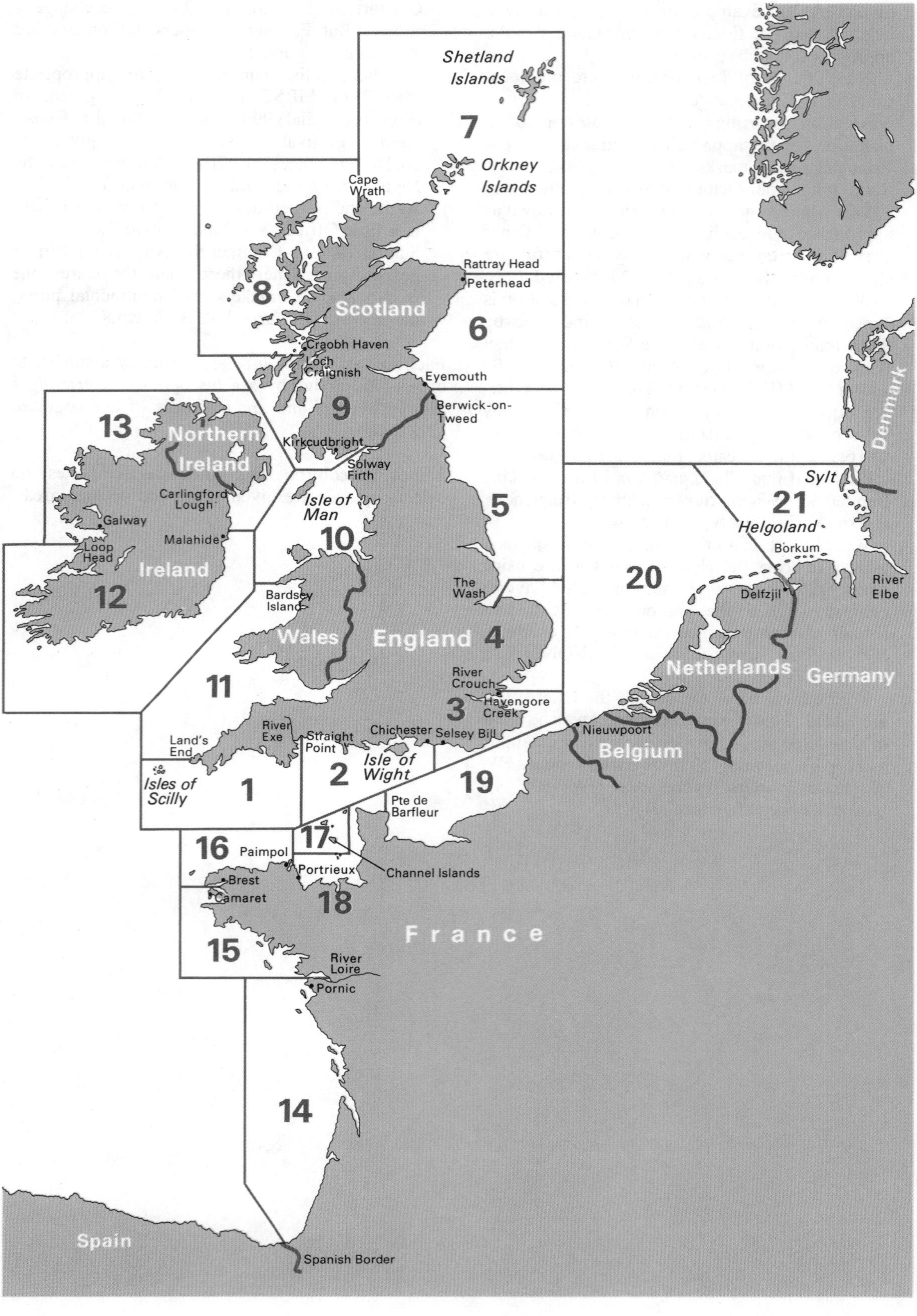
Shetland Islands
7
Orkney Islands
Cape Wrath
Rattray Head
Peterhead
8
Scotland
6
Craobh Haven
Loch Craignish
Eyemouth
Berwick-on-Tweed
13
Northern Ireland
9
Kirkcudbright
Solway Firth
Denmark
Sylt
Carlingford Lough
Isle of Man
5
21
Helgoland
Galway
Malahide
10
Borkum
Loop Head
Ireland
20
Delfzijl
River Elbe
Bardsey Island
The Wash
12
Wales
England
4
Netherlands
Germany
11
River Crouch
3
Havengore Creek
Nieuwpoort
Land's End
River Exe
Straight Point
Chichester
Selsey Bill
Belgium
Isle of Wight
Isles of Scilly
2
19
1
Pte de Barfleur
16
Paimpol
17
Channel Islands
Portrieux
Brest
Camaret
18
France
15
River Loire
Pornic
14
Spain
Spanish Border

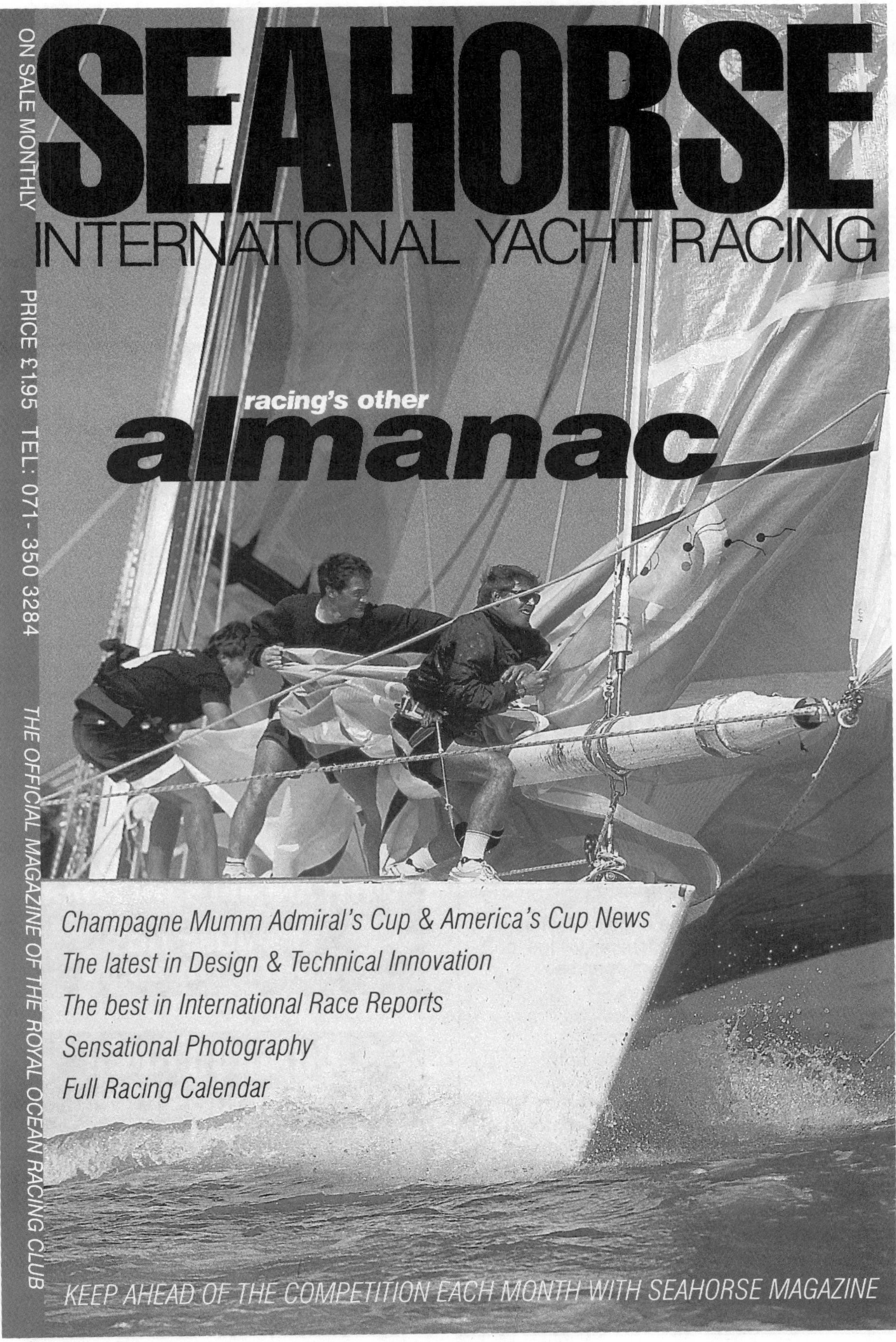
SEAHORSE
INTERNATIONAL YACHT RACING
ON SALE MONTHLY
PRICE £1.95 TEL: 071 - 350 3284
THE OFFICIAL MAGAZINE OF THE ROYAL OCEAN RACING CLUB
racing's other
almanac
Champagne Mumm Admiral's Cup & America's Cup News
The latest in Design & Technical Innovation
The best in International Race Reports
Sensational Photography
Full Racing Calendar
KEEP AHEAD OF THE COMPETITION EACH MONTH WITH SEAHORSE MAGAZINE

Area 1

South-West England
Isles of Scilly to River Exe

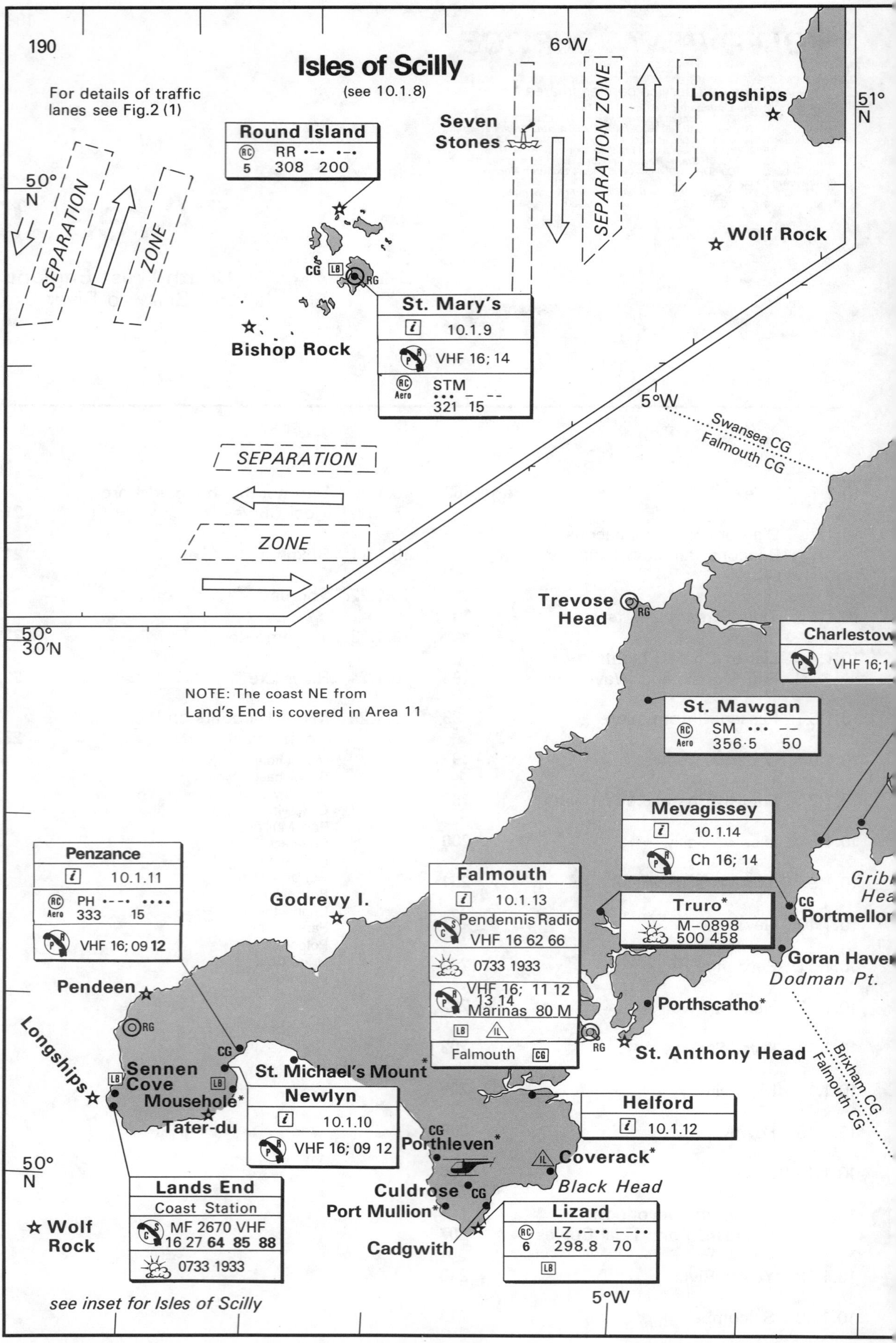

Isles of Scilly
(see 10.1.8)
For details of traffic lanes see Fig.2 (1)
Round Island
RC 5 RR 308 200
SEPARATION
ZONE
Seven Stones
SEPARATION ZONE
Longships
Wolf Rock
6°W
51° N
50° N
CG LB RG
St. Mary's
10.1.9
VHF 16; 14
RC Aero STM 321 15
Bishop Rock
5°W
Swansea CG
Falmouth CG
SEPARATION
ZONE
Trevose Head
RG
Charlestow
VHF 16;1
50° 30'N
NOTE: The coast NE from Land's End is covered in Area 11
St. Mawgan
RC Aero SM 356·5 50
Mevagissey
10.1.14
Ch 16; 14
Penzance
10.1.11
RC Aero PH 333 15
VHF 16; 09 12
Godrevy I.
Falmouth
10.1.13
Pendennis Radio VHF 16 62 66
0733 1933
VHF 16; 11 12 13 14 Marinas 80 M
LB IL
Falmouth CG
Truro*
M–0898 500 458
CG Portmellor
Gribb Hea
Goran Haver
Dodman Pt.
Porthscatho*
St. Anthony Head
RG
Brixham CG
Falmouth CG
Pendeen
RG
Longships
Sennen Cove
LB
CG
LB
Mousehole*
Tater-du
St. Michael's Mount*
Newlyn
10.1.10
VHF 16; 09 12
Helford
10.1.12
CG
Porthleven*
Coverack*
Black Head
Culdrose
CG
Port Mullion*
Cadgwith
Lizard
RC 6 LZ 298.8 70
LB
50° N
Wolf Rock
Lands End
Coast Station
MF 2670 VHF 16 27 64 85 88
0733 1933
see inset for Isles of Scilly
5°W

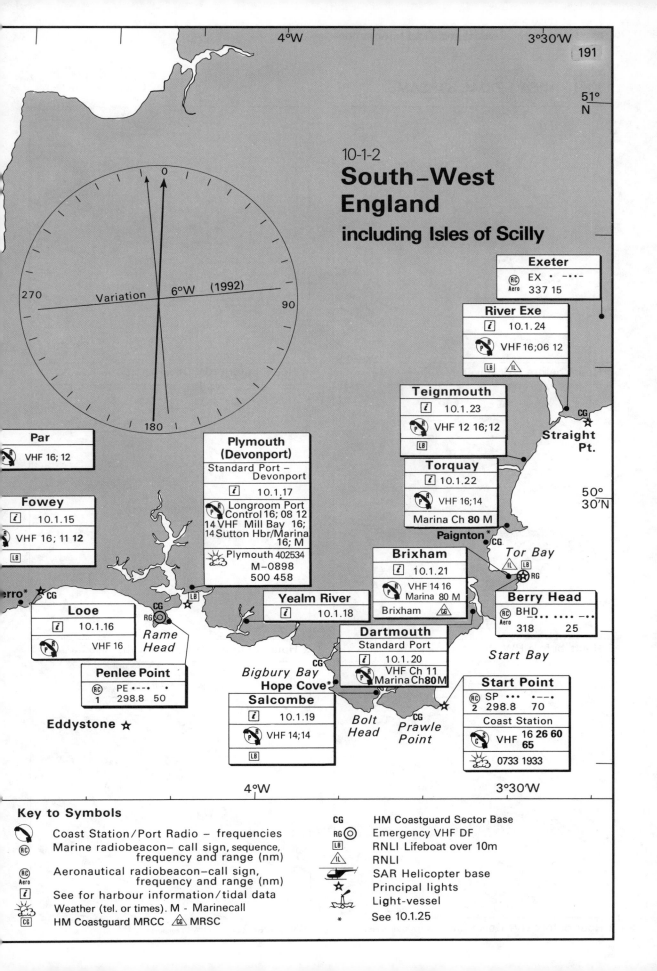

10-1-2
South-West England
including Isles of Scilly

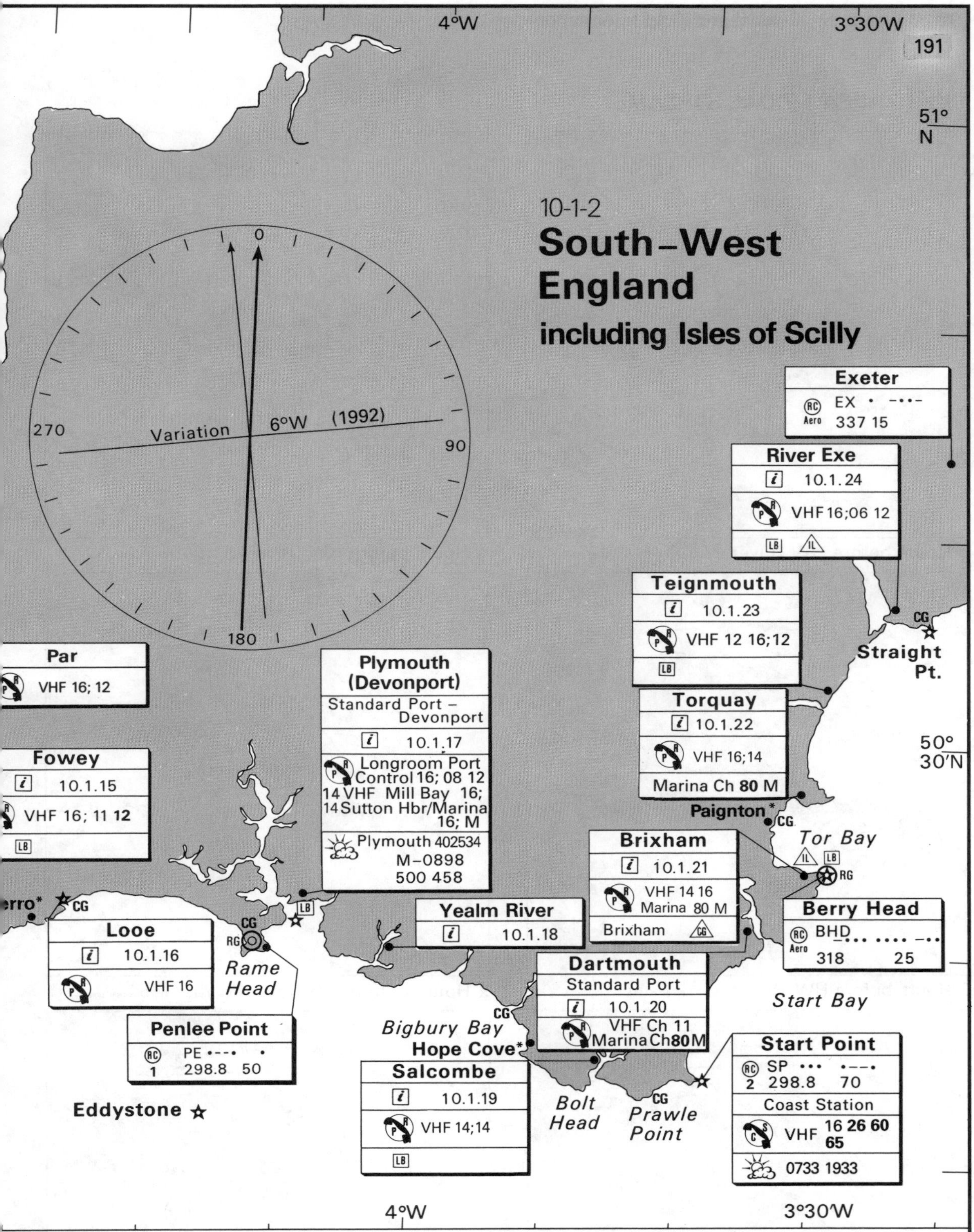
4°W
3°30'W
51° N
50° 30'N
0
90
180
270
Variation 6°W (1992)
Exeter
EX • –••–
Aero 337 15
River Exe
10.1.24
VHF 16;06 12
Teignmouth
10.1.23
VHF 12 16;12
Straight Pt.
Torquay
10.1.22
VHF 16;14
Marina Ch 80 M
Paignton*
Tor Bay
Brixham
10.1.21
VHF 14 16
Marina 80 M
Brixham
Berry Head
BHD –••• •••• –••
Aero 318 25
Start Bay
Dartmouth
Standard Port
10.1.20
VHF Ch 11
Marina Ch80M
Start Point
SP ••• •––•
2 298.8 70
Coast Station
VHF 16 26 60 65
0733 1933
Prawle Point
Bolt Head
Salcombe
10.1.19
VHF 14;14
Hope Cove*
Bigbury Bay
Yealm River
10.1.18
Plymouth (Devonport)
Standard Port – Devonport
10.1.17
Longroom Port Control 16; 08 12 14 VHF Mill Bay 16; 14 Sutton Hbr/Marina 16; M
Plymouth 402534
M–0898 500 458
Rame Head
Penlee Point
PE •–––• •
1 298.8 50
Eddystone
Looe
10.1.16
VHF 16
Fowey
10.1.15
VHF 16; 11 12
Par
VHF 16; 12
erro*
4°W
3°30'W

Key to Symbols

Coast Station/Port Radio – frequencies	CG HM Coastguard Sector Base
RC Marine radiobeacon– call sign, sequence, frequency and range (nm)	RG Emergency VHF DF
RC Aero Aeronautical radiobeacon–call sign, frequency and range (nm)	LB RNLI Lifeboat over 10m
i See for harbour information/tidal data	IL RNLI
Weather (tel. or times). M - Marinecall	SAR Helicopter base
CG HM Coastguard MRCC, CG MRSC	Principal lights
	Light-vessel
	* See 10.1.25

10.1.3 AREA 1 TIDAL STREAMS

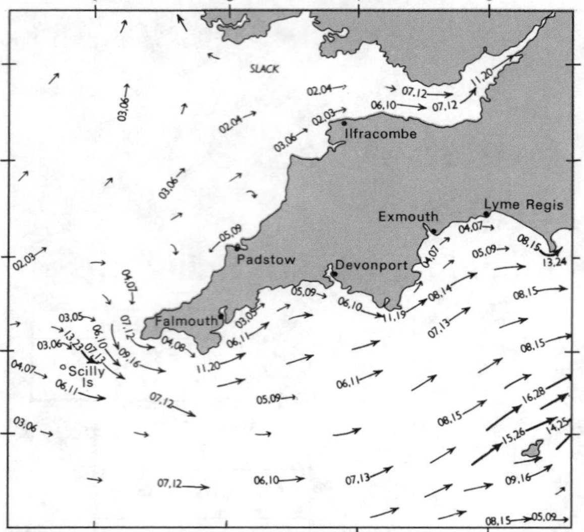
6°
5°
4°
3°
51°
50°
SLACK
Ilfracombe
Exmouth
Lyme Regis
Padstow
Devonport
Falmouth
Scilly Is

5 Hours before HW Dover (0040 after HW Devonport)

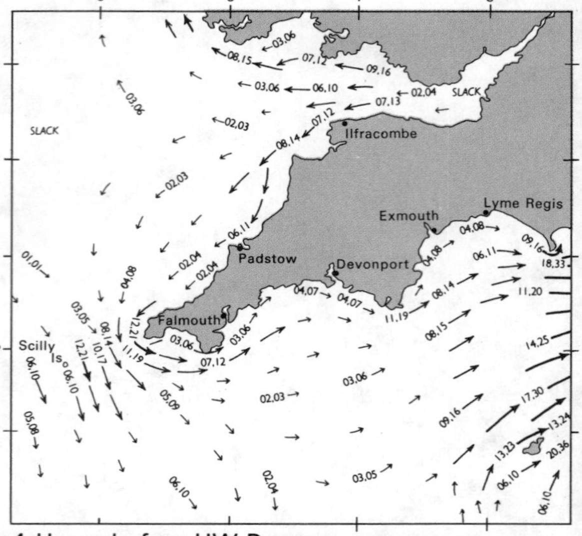
6°
5°
4°
3°
51°
50°
SLACK
Ilfracombe
Exmouth
Lyme Regis
Padstow
Devonport
Falmouth
Scilly Is

4 Hours before HW Dover (0140 after HW Devonport)

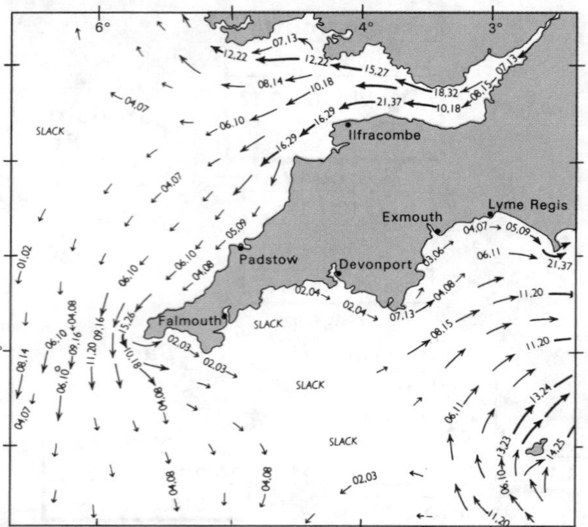
6°
4°
3°
50°
SLACK
Ilfracombe
Exmouth
Lyme Regis
Padstow
Devonport
Falmouth

3 Hours before HW Dover (0240 after HW Devonport)

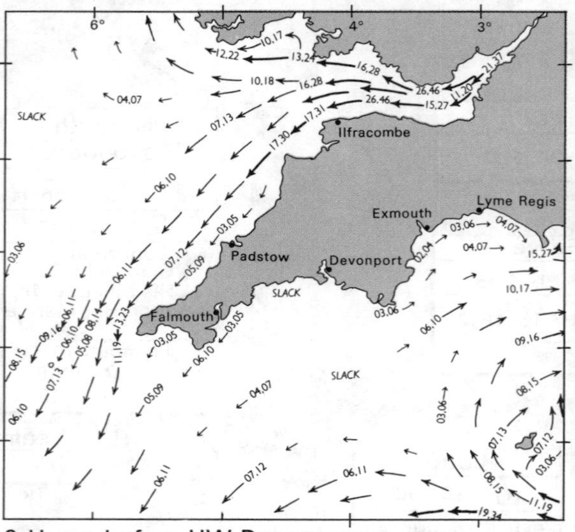
6°
5°
4°
3°
51°
50°
SLACK
Ilfracombe
Exmouth
Lyme Regis
Padstow
Devonport
Falmouth

2 Hours before HW Dover (0340 after HW Devonport)

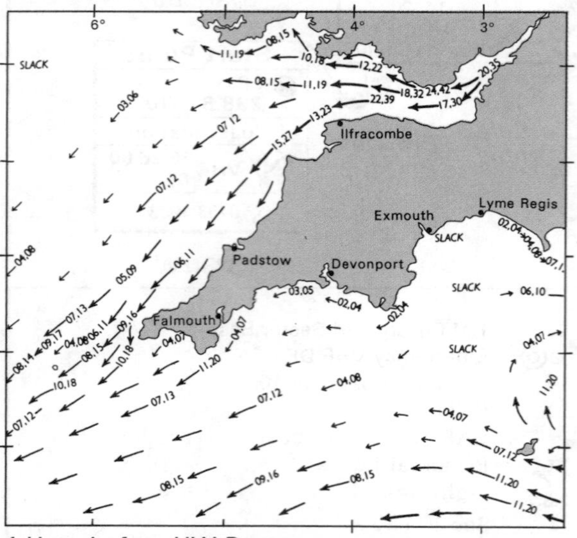
6°
4°
3°
51°
50°
SLACK
Ilfracombe
Exmouth
Lyme Regis
Padstow
Devonport
Falmouth

1 Hour before HW Dover (0440 after HW Devonport)

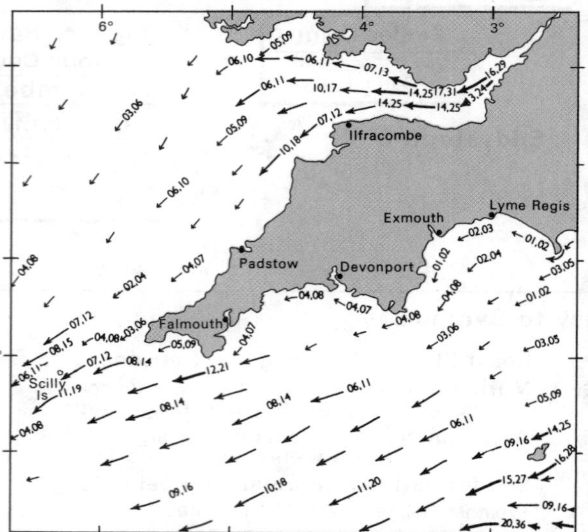
6°
4°
3°
51°
50°
Ilfracombe
Exmouth
Lyme Regis
Padstow
Devonport
Falmouth
Scilly Is

HW Dover (0540 after HW Devonport)

Portland 10.2.10. Isle of Wight 10.2.29. Channel Island 10.17.3. Northward 10.11.3. Eastwood 10.2.3. Southward 10.16.3.

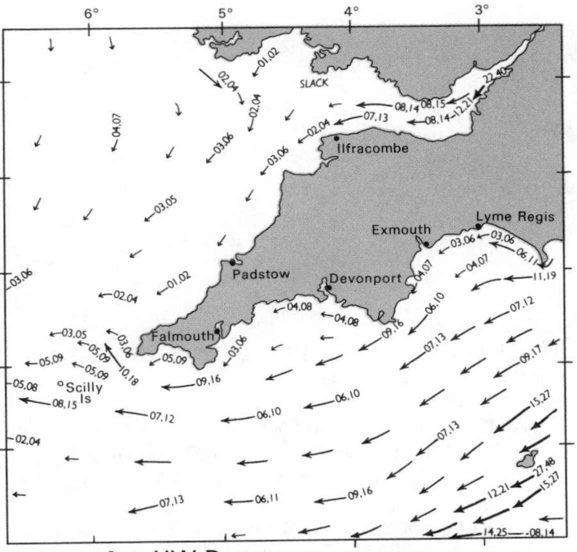
6°
5°
4°
3°
51°
50°
SLACK
Ilfracombe
Lyme Regis
Exmouth
Padstow
Devonport
Falmouth
Scilly Is

1 Hour after HW Dover (0545 before HW Devonport)

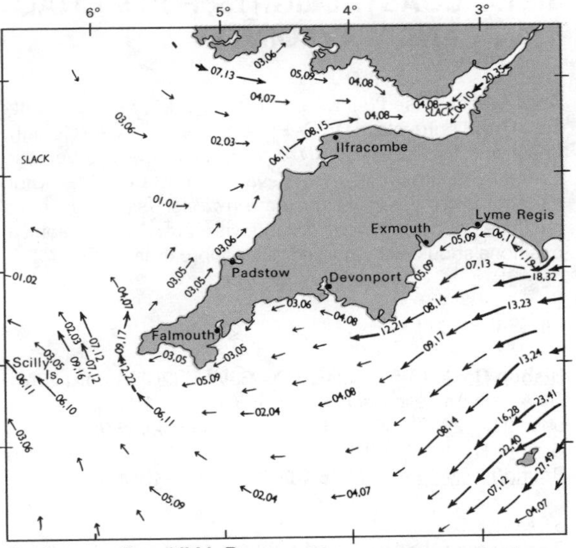
6°
5°
4°
3°
51°
50°
SLACK
Ilfracombe
Lyme Regis
Exmouth
Padstow
Devonport
Falmouth
Scilly Is

2 Hours after HW Dover (0445 before HW Devonport)

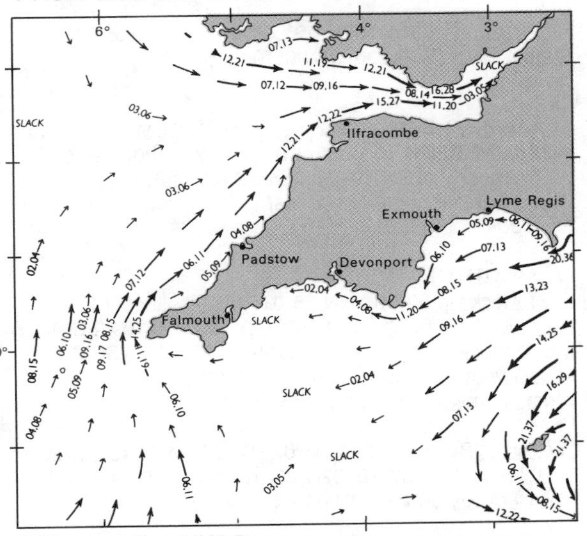
6°
4°
3°
50°
SLACK
Ilfracombe
Lyme Regis
Exmouth
Padstow
Devonport
Falmouth

3 Hours after HW Dover (0345 before HW Devonport)

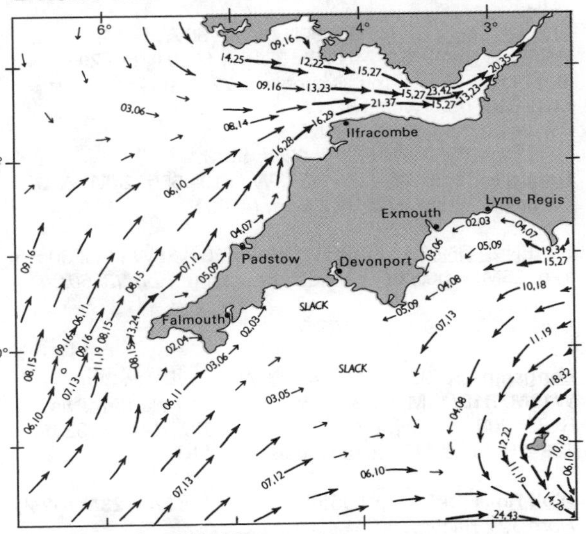
6°
4°
3°
51°
50°
SLACK
Ilfracombe
Lyme Regis
Exmouth
Padstow
Devonport
Falmouth

4 Hours after HW Dover (0245 before HW Devonport)

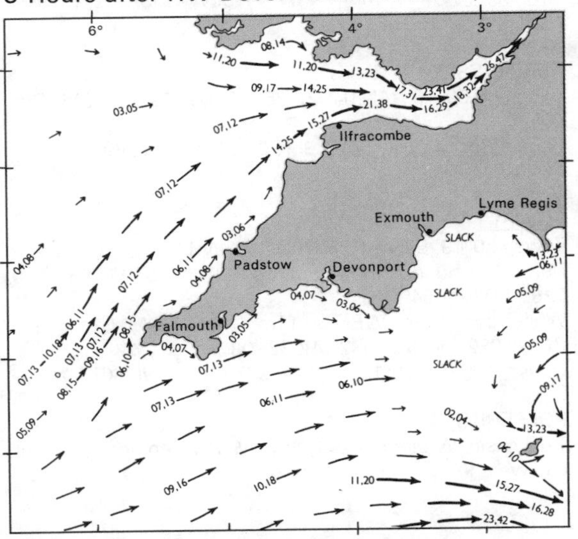
6°
4°
3°
51°
50°
SLACK
Ilfracombe
Lyme Regis
Exmouth
Padstow
Devonport
Falmouth

5 Hours after HW Dover (0145 before HW Devonport)

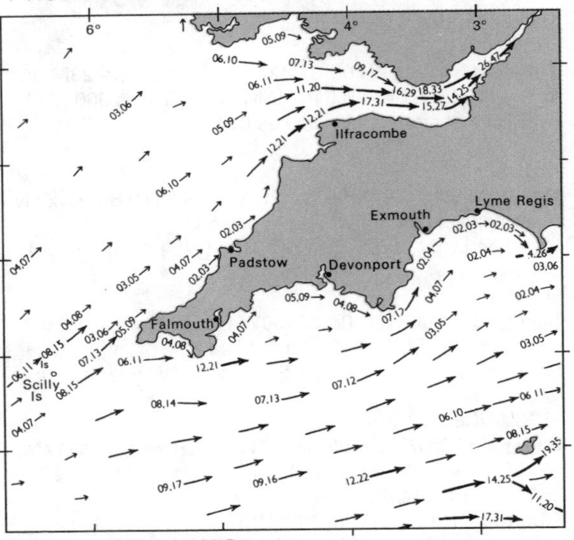
6°
4°
3°
51°
50°
Ilfracombe
Lyme Regis
Exmouth
Padstow
Devonport
Falmouth
Scilly Is

6 Hours after HW Dover (0045 before HW Devonport)

10.1.4 COASTAL LIGHTS, FOG SIGNALS AND WAYPOINTS

Abbreviations used below are given in 1.4.1. Principal lights are in **bold** print, places in CAPITALS, and light-vessels, light floats and Lanbys in *CAPITAL ITALICS*. Unless otherwise stated lights are white. m—elevation in metres; M—nominal range in n. miles. Fog signals are in *italics*. Useful waypoints are underlined – use those on land with care. All geographical positions should be assumed to be approximate. See 4.2.2.

ISLES OF SCILLY

Bishop Rock 49°52'·33N 06°26'·68W Fl (2) 15s 44m **29M**; Gy ● Tr with helicopter platform; part obsc 204°-211°, obsc 211°-233°, 236°-259°; Racon; *Horn Mo(N) 90s.*
Gunner By 49°53'·60N 06°25'·02W; SCM.
Round Rock By 49°53'·06N 06°25'·13W; NCM.

ST MARY'S.
Bartholomew Ledge By 49°54'·38N 06°19'·80W; (unlit); PHM.
Spanish Ledge By 49°53'·90N 06°18'·80W; ECM; *Bell.*
Peninnis Hd 49°54'·24N 06°18'·15W Fl 20s 36m **20M**; W ● metal Tr on B frame, B cupola; vis 231°-117° but part obsc 048°-083° within 5M.
FR Lts on masts to N and NE.
Hats By 49°56'·17N 06°17'·08W; SCM.
Round Is 49°58'·70N 06°19'·33W Fl 10s 55m **24M**; W ● Tr; vis 021°-288°; H24; RC; *Horn (4) 60s.*

SEVEN STONES Lt F 50°03'·58N 06°04'·28W Fl (3) 30s 12m **25M**; R hull, Lt Tr amidships; Racon; *Horn (3) 60s.*

ENGLAND—SOUTH COAST

Longships 50°03'·97N 05°44'·85W Iso WR 10s 35m **W19M**, **R18/15M**; Gy ● Tr with helicopter platform; vis R189°-208°, R (unintens) 208°-307°, R307°-327°, W327°-189°; *Horn 10s.* FR on radio mast 4·9M NE.

Wolf Rock 49°56'·70N 05°48'·50W Fl 15s 34m **23M** (H24); *Horn 30s*; Racon.
Runnel Stone Lt By 50°01'·15N 05°40'·30W Q (6) + L Fl 15s; SCM; *Bell, Whis.*

Tater-du 50°03'·10N 05°34'·60W Fl (3) 15s 34m **23M**; W ● Tr; vis 241°-074°. FR 31m 13M (same Tr) vis 060°-074° over Runnel stone and in places 074°-077° within 3M.

MOUSEHOLE.
N Pier Hd 50°04'·94N 05°32'·21W 2 FG (vert) 8m 4M; Gy mast; replaced by FR when hbr closed.
Low Lee Lt By 50°05'·52N 05°31'·32W Q (3) 10s; ECM.

NEWLYN.
S Pier Hd 50°06'·15N 05°32'·50W Fl 5s 10m 9M; W ● Tr, R base & cupola; vis 253°-336°; *Siren 60s.*
N Pier Hd F WG 4m 2M; vis G238°-248°, W over hbr.

PENZANCE.
S Pier Hd 50°07'·03N 05°31'·63W Fl WR 5s 11m **W17M**, R12M; W ● Tr, B base; vis R (unintens) 159°-224°, R224°-268°, W268°-344·5°, R344·5°-shore.
Albert Pier Hd 2 FG (vert) 11m 2M.
Mountamopus By 50°04'·60N 05°26'·20W; SCM.

PORTHLEVEN.
S Pier 50°04'·87N 05°19'·03W FG 10m 4M; G metal col, shown when inner hbr is open.

Lizard 49°57'·58N 05°12'·07W Fl 3s 70m **29M**; W 8-sided Tr; vis 250°-120°, part vis 235°-250°; reflection may be seen inshore of these bearings; RC; *Siren Mo (N) 60s.*

Culdrose Lt By 50°00'·08N 04°59'·60W Fl Y 10s; SPM.
Manacles Lt By 50°02'·77N 05°01'·85W Q (3) 10s; ECM; *Bell.*
Helston Lt By 50°04'·92N 05°00'·77W Fl Y 2.5s; SPM.
August Rock By 50°06'·07N 05°04'·88W (PA); SHM (seasonal).

St Anthony Hd 50°08'·43N 05°00'·90W Oc WR 15s 22m **W22/20M**, **R20M**; W 8-sided Tr; vis W295°-004°, R004°-022° over Manacles, W (unintens) 022°-100°, W100°-172°; (H24); Fog Det Lt L Fl 5 18m **16M** min vis 148·2°-151·3°; *Horn 30s.*

FALMOUTH.
Black Rock Bn 50°08'·68N 05°01'·95W (unlit); IDM.
Black Rock By 50°08'·65N 05°01'·68W Q (3) 10s; ECM.
Castle Lt By 50°08'·95N 05°01'·58W Fl G 10s; SHM.
The Governor 50°09'·12N 05°02'·32W; ECM.
West Narrows Lt By 50°09'·35N 05°02'·03W Fl (2) R 10s; PHM.
The Vilt Lt By 50°09'·97N 05°02'·17W Fl (4) G 15s; SHM.
Northbank Lt By 50°10'·32N 05°02'·12W Fl R 4s; PHM
No. 1 Port By 50°09'·72N 05°04'·37W Qk Fl R; PHM.

Gwineas Lt By 50°14'·47N 04°45'·30W Q (3) 10s; ECM; *Bell.*

MEVAGISSEY.
S Pier Hd 50°16'·11N 04°46'·85W Fl (2) 10s 9m 12M; *Dia 30.*
Cannis Rock Lt By 50°18'·35N 04°39'·88W Q (6) + L Fl 15s; SCM; *Bell.*

FOWEY.
Fowey 50°19'·59N 04°38'·77W L Fl WR 5s 28m W11M, R9M; W 8-sided Tr, R lantern; vis R284°-295°, W295°-028°, R028°-054°.
Whitehouse Pt Iso WRG 3s 11m W11M, R8M, G8M; vis G017°-022°, W022°-032°, R032°-037°.
Udder Rock By 50°18'·90N 04°33'·78W; *Bell*; SCM.

POLPERRO.
Tidal basin, W Pier FW or R 4m 4M; R when hbr closed in bad weather.

LOOE.
Banjo Pier Hd 50°21'·02N 04°27'·00W Oc WR 3s 8m **W15M** R12M; vis W013°-207°, R207°-267°, W267°-313°, R313°-332°; Nailzee Pt *Siren (2) 30s (occas).*

Eddystone 50°10'·81N 04°15'·87W Fl (2) 10s 41m **24M**; Gy Tr, R lantern. FR 28m 13M (same Tr) vis 112°-129° over Hand deeps; helicopter platform, Racon; *Horn (3) 60s.*

PLYMOUTH SOUND.
Rame Hd, S end 50°18'·63N 04°13'·31W (unlit).
Draystone Lt By 50°18'·82N 04°11'·01W Fl (2) R 5s; PHM.
Knap Lt By 50°19'·52N 04°09'·94W Fl G 5s; SHM.
West Tinker Lt By 50°19'·14N 04°08'·62W Q (9) 15s; WCM.
Shag Stone 50°19'·03N 02°07'·52W Fl (2) 15s.
Detached Breakwater- W Hd 50°20'·04N 04°09'·45W Fl WR 10s 19m **W15M**, R12M; Gy Tr; vis W262°-208°, R208°-262°. Iso W 4s (same Tr) 12m 12M; vis 031°-039°; *Bell (1) 15s.*
Detached Breakwater E Hd Iso WR 5s; vis R190°-353°, W353°-001°, R001°-018°, W018°-190°.
Whidbey 50°19'·5N 04°07'·2W Oc (2) G 10s 29m 3M; Or and W col; vis 000°-160°.
Bovisand Pier Oc (2) G 15s 17m 3M.

E Rutts DZ Lt By 50°12'·60N 03°59'·10W Fl Y 2·5s; SPM. Withdrawn (T).

SALCOMBE.
Sandhill Pt Dir Lt 000° Dir Fl WRG 2s 27m W10M, R7M, G7M; R&W ◆ on W mast; vis R002·5°-182·5°, G182·5°-357·5°, W357·5°-002·5°.
Blackstone Rk 50°13'·57N 03°46'·43W Q WR 4m 2M; G & W Bn; vis R218°-048°, W048°-218°.
Starhole By 50°12'·50N 03°46'·80W; SPM (Racing); (Apr-Sep).
Gara By 50°12'·80N 03°45'·20W; SPM (Racing);); (Apr-Sep).
Gammon By 50°12'·00N 03°45'·50W; SPM (Racing); (Apr-Sep).
Prawle By 50°12'·10N 03°43'·80W; SPM (Racing); (Apr-Sep).

Start Pt 50°13'·32N 03°38'·47W Fl (3) 10s 62m **25M**; W ● Tr; vis 184°-068°; RC. FR 55m 12M (same Tr) vis 210°-255° over Skerries bank; *Horn 60s.* FR Lts on radio mast 0·9M WNW.
Skerries Bank By 50°16'·28N 03°33'·70W; PHM; *Bell.*

DARTMOUTH.
Homestone By 50°19'·56N 03°33'·48W; PHM.
Castle Ledge Lt By 50°19'·96N 03°33'·05W Fl G 5s; SHM.
Checkstone Lt By 50°20'·42N 03°33'·73W Fl (2) R 5s; PHM.
Kingswear 50°20'·78N 03°34'·02W Iso WRG 3s 9m 8M; W I Tr; vis G318°-325°, W325°-331°, R331°-340°, TE.
RDYC 1 By 50°18'·80N 03°35'·25W; SPM (Racing); (Apr-Oct).
RDYC 2 By 50°18'·68N 03°33'·29W; SPM (Racing); (Apr-Oct).
RDYC 3 By 50°20'·07N 03°31'·42W; SPM (Racing); (Apr-Oct).

Berry Hd 50°23'·95N 03°28'·94W Fl (2) 15s 58m **18M**; W Tr; vis 100°-023°. R Lts on radio mast 5·7M NW.

BRIXHAM.
Victoria Breakwater Hd 50°24'·29N 03°30'·70W Oc R 15s 9m 6M; W Tr.

PAIGNTON.
E quay Fl R 7m 3M.

TORQUAY.
Princess Pier Hd QR 9m 6M.
Haldon Pier Hd 50°27'·40N 03°31'·67W QG 9m 6M.

TEIGNMOUTH.
The Den, Lts in line 334°. Front FR 10m 6M; Gy ● Tr; vis 225°-135°. Rear FR 11m 3M.
The Point 50°32'·38N 03°29'·98W Oc G 5s FG (vert); s on G Bn.

EXMOUTH.
Exe Fairway Lt By 50°36'·00N 03°21'·97W Fl 10s; SWM; *Bell.*
Straight Pt 50°36'·45N 03°21'·67W Fl R 10s 34m 7M; vis 246°-071°.
Ldg Lts 305°. Front FY 6m 7M. Rear 57m from front, FY 12m 7M.
DZS Lt By 50°36'·10N 03°19'·30W Fl Y 3s; SPM.
DZN Lt By 50°36'·80N 03°19'·20W Fl Y 3s; SPM.

Note. For English Channel Waypoints see 10.1.7

10.1.5 PASSAGE INFORMATION

NORTH CORNWALL (charts 1149, 1156)

The coast of North Cornwall is covered in Area 11, to which reference should be made. For Padstow see 10.11.23. For Bude, Newquay, Hayle and St Ives see 10.11.24. For ease of reference, certain general information is repeated below.

Approach to Bristol chan along N coast of Cornwall is very exposed, with little shelter in bad weather. St Ives (dries) is sheltered from E and S, but exposed to N. Padstow is a refuge, but in strong NW winds the sea breaks on bar and prevents entry. Shelter is available under lee of Lundy Is; but there are bad races to NE (White Horses), the NW (Hen and Chickens), and to SE; also overfalls over NW Bank. So in this area yachts need to be sturdy and well equipped, since if bad weather develops no shelter may be at hand. Streams are moderate W of Lundy, but strong round the Is. They get much stronger towards Bristol chan proper.

ISLES OF SCILLY (10.1.8 and charts 34, 883)

The Scillies comprise 48 islands, extending 21-31M WSW of Land's End. There are many rky outcrops and offlying dangers, and although they are all well charted care is needed particularly in poor visibility. For pilotage details see *Channel Pilot* or *South England Pilot*, Vol 5 (Brandon). There is a useful local publication – *A Yachtsman's Guide to Scilly*.

Several transits are shown on chart 34, and these should be followed, because the tidal streams in and between the Is are difficult to predict with any accuracy. They run harder off points and over rks, where overfalls may occur.

Conspic landmarks are Bishop Rk Lt Ho, Round Is Lt Ho, the disused Lt Ho on St Agnes, the daymark at the E end of St Martin's, Penninis Lt Ho at the S end of St Mary's, and the TV mast and CG sig stn (at the old telegraph tower) both in the NW corner of St Mary's. Yachts must expect to lie to their anchors. There is no one anch giving shelter in all wind directions, so it may be necessary to move at short notice. All anchs may be penetrated by swell. The most popular and useful ones are shown in 10.1.8.

LAND'S END/SCILLIES (chart 1148)

From St Ives to Land's End coast is rugged and exposed. There are overfalls SW of Pendeen Pt (Lt, fog sig). Vyneck Rks lie awash about 0·3M NW of C Cornwall. The Brisons are two rky Is 0·5M SW of C Cornwall, and rky ledges extend inshore and to the S and SW. The Longships (Lt, fog sig) are a group of rks about 1M W of Land's End, with ledges 0·2M further seaward. The inshore pass is not recommended.

Between Land's End and the Scillies (chart 1148) streams are rotatory, clockwise. They run ENE from HW Devonport –0100 (1 kn at sp), SSE from HW Devonport +0200 (2 kn at sp), WNW from HW Devonport +0600 (1 kn at sp), and N from HW Devonport –0400 (1·75 kn at sp). The Seven Stones (rks) lie 14M W of the Longships and 7M NE of the Scillies; many of them dry, with ledges in between. They are marked by Lt V (Lt, fog sig) on E side. Wolf Rk (Lt, fog sig) is 8M SW of Land's End, and is steep-to. For traffic schemes see Fig. 2(1).

LAND'S END TO LIZARD HEAD (chart 777)

From Land's End to Gwennap Hd, 2M SE, rks extend up to 0·15M offshore, and depths are irregular to seaward causing a bad sea in strong W winds with W-going tide. The Runnel Stone (dries) lies 0·7M S of Gwennap Hd, with rks between it and shore. These dangers are in R sectors of Longships and Tater-du Lts. Do not anch off Porth Curno, due to cables.

Entering Mount's B, the Bucks (dry) are 0·2M SE and E of Tater-du Lt Ho. Gull Rk (24m) is 0·9M NE of Tater-du, close off the E point of Lamorna Cove. Little Heaver (dries) is 0·05M SW of Gull Rk, and Kemyel Rk (dries) is 0·17 ENE. Mousehole is a small drying hbr, sheltered from W and N, but exposed to winds in E or S, when ent may be closed: approach from S side of St Clement's Is. In W winds there is good anch off the hbr. See 10.1.25.

Low Lee, a dangerous steep-to rk, is 0·4M NE of Penlee Pt, marked by By. Carn Base Rk lies 0·3M NNW of Low Lee. Newlyn (10.1.10) is only hbr in Mount's B safe to appr in strong onshore winds, but only near HW. From here to Penzance (10.1.11) beware Dog Rk and Gear Rk.

From Penzance to St Michael's Mount the head of the B is flat, and dries for 0·4M in places. Dangers include Cressar Rks, Long Rk, Hogus Rks, and Outer Penzeath Rk. Venton chy on with pierheads of St Michael's Mount hbr at 084° leads S of these dangers. This tiny hbr dries, but is well sheltered, with anch about 0·1M W of ent, see 10.1.25.

Two dangerous rks, Guthen Rk and Maltman Rk, lie within 0·2M of St Michael's Mount. 1M SE is The Greeb (7m), with rks between it and shore. The Bears (dry) lie 0·17M E of The Greeb. The Stone (dries) is 0·5M S of Cudden Pt, while offshore is Mountamopus shoal marked by By which should be passed to seaward. Welloe Rk (dries) lies 0·5M SW of Trewavas Hd.

Porthleven is small tidal hbr, entered between pier on S side and Deazle Rks (dry) on N. Dry out alongside in inner hbr, closed in bad weather when appr is dangerous. In fair weather there is good anch off Porth Mellin, about 0·15M NE of Mullion Is; the hbr is not recommended. See 10.1.25.

2·5 M W of Lizard Hd is The Boa, a rky shoal on which sea breaks in SW gales. The Lizard (Lt, fog sig, RC) is a significant headland (chart 2345) with tidal streams up to 3 kn at sp. The outer rks, all of which dry, from W to E are Mulvin, (0·25M SW of Lizard Pt), Taylor's Rk (0·2M SSW of Lizard Pt), Clidgas Rks (0·5M SW of Lt Ho), Men Hyr Rk and the Dales or Stags (0·5M SSW of Lt Ho), and Enoch Rk (0·3M S of Lt Ho). S of the rks the stream turns E at HW Devonport –0500, and W at HW Devonport +0155. Offshore it turns an hour earlier. A dangerous race extends 2-3M S when stream is strong in either direction, worst in W winds against W-going tide. Then keep at least 3M to seaward. There may be a race SE of the hd.

LIZARD HEAD TO START POINT (chart 442)

Vrogue, a dangerous sunken rk, is 0·4M ESE of Bass Pt, NE of Lizard Hd. Craggan Rks are 0·5M offshore, and 1M N of Vrogue Rk. From Black Hd to beyond Chynnalls Pt, rks extend at least 0·1M offshore. Coverack gives good anch in W winds, see 10.1.25. From Dolor Pt to E of Lowland Pt are drying rks 0·25M offshore.

The Manacles (dry), 0·75M E and SE of Manacle Pt, are marked by By to seaward and are in R sector of St Anthony Hd Lt. Off the Manacles the stream runs NE from HW Devonport –0345, and SW from HW Devonport +0200, sp rates 1·25 kn. From E of the Manacles there are no offshore dangers on courses NNW to Helford ent (10.1.12) or N to Falmouth (10.1.13).

Sailing NE from St Anthony Hd, Gull Rk lies 0·6M E of Nare Hd, at W side of Veryan B. The Whelps (dry) are 0·5M SW of Gull Rk. There is a pass between Gull Rk and the shore. In Veryan B beware Lath Rk 1M SE of Portloe.

On E side of Veryan B, Dodman Pt is a 110m cliff, with a stone cross near SW end. Depths are irregular for 1M S, with heavy overfalls in strong winds, when it is best to pass 2M off. Gorran Haven, a sandy cove with L-shaped pier which dries at sp, is a good anch in offshore winds. See 10.1.25.

2·1M NE of Dodman Pt cross, and 1M ENE of Gorran Haven, is Gwineas Rk (8m). 0·1M E of Gwineas Rk is Yaw Rk (dries 0·9m), marked by By on E side. Passage inside Gwineas Rk is possible, but not recommended in strong onshore winds or poor vis. Portmellon and Mevagissey B (see 10.1.25 and 10.1.14) are good anchs in offshore winds. For Charlestown and Par see 10.1.25.

Gribbin Hd has a conspic daymark — a ■ Tr 25m high with R & W stripes. In bad weather the sea breaks on rks round Hd. Cannis Rk (dries) is 0·25M SE, and marked by By to seaward. 3M E of Fowey (10.1.15) is Udder Rk (dries), 0·5M offshore in E part of Lantivet B. Larrick Rk (dries) is 0·15M off Nealand Pt.

Polperro hbr dries, but the inlet gives good anch in offshore winds. See 10.1.25. Beware E Polca Rk roughly in mid-chan. There are shoals extending 0·25M seaward from Downend Pt, E of Polperro. The chan between Hannafore Pt and St George's (or Looe) Is nearly dries. The Rennies (dry) are rks extending 0·25M E and SE of the Is. (See 10.1.16). There are overfalls S of Looe Is in bad weather.

Eddystone rks (chart 1613) lie 8M S of Rame Hd. Shoals extend 0·3M E. Close NW of the Lt Ho (Lt, fog sig) is the stump of old one. The sea can break on Hand Deeps — sunken rks 3·5M NW of Eddystone.

Rame Hd is on W side of ent to Plymouth Sound (10.1.17). It is conspic cone shaped, with small chapel on top. Rks extend about 0·1M off. On the E side of Plymouth Sound, the Mewstone (59m) is a conspic rky Is 0·4M off Wembury Pt. Drying rks extend 0·15M SW of Little Mewstone, and the Slimers, which dry, (see 10.1.18) lie 0·2M E of Mewstone. E and W Ebb Rks (awash) lie 0·25M off Gara Pt (chart 30).

Between Gara Pt and Stoke Pt, 2·5M to E, offlying dangers extend about 0·4M offshore in places. In Bigbury B beware Wells Rk and other dangers 0·5M S of Erme Hd. From Bolt Tail to Bolt Hd keep 0·5M offshore to clear Greystone Ledge, sunken rks near Ham Stone (11m), and Gregory Rks 0·5M SE of Ham Stone. The Great and Little Mewstones lie just off Bolt Hd, where coast turns N to Salcombe ent (10.1.19).

START POINT TO STRAIGHT POINT (charts 1613, 3315)

Start Pt (Lt, fog sig, RC) is 3M NE of Prawle Pt, and is a long headland with W Lt Ho near end and conspic radio masts in rear. Rks extend 0·25M offshore, and the stream runs 4 kn at sp, causing a race extending 1M to seaward. 3M S of Start the stream turns ENE at HW Devonport –0150, and WSW at HW Devonport +0420. Inshore it turns 0·5 hr earlier. In reasonable weather the overfalls can be avoided by passing close to rks, but in bad weather keep at least 2M off.

Start Pt is W end of Lyme B (chart 3315), stretching 50M NE to Portland Bill, and with no secure hbr in its E part. NE of Start Pt is Skerries Bank, on which sea breaks in bad weather (chart 1634). Good anch off Hallsands in offshore winds.

Between Dartmouth (10.1.20) and Brixham (10.1.21) rks extend 0·5M offshore. Berry Hd (Lt) is steep, flat-topped headland (55m). Here the stream turns N at HW Devonport –0105, and S at HW Devonport +0440, sp rates 1·5 kn. In Torbay (chart 26) the more obvious dangers are steep-to, but beware the Sunker 0·05M SW of Ore Stone, and Morris Rogue 0·5M W of Thatcher Rk.

There are good anchs in Babbacombe B and in Anstey's cove in W winds: beware the Three Brothers (drying rks), S side of Anstey's cove. From Long Quarry Pt for 4M N to Teignmouth (10.1.23) there are no offlying dangers. Off Teignmouth the NNE-going stream begins at HW Devonport –0135, and the SSW-going at HW Devonport +0510. In the ent the flood begins at HW Devonport –0535, and the ebb at HW Devonport +0040. The stream runs hard off Ferry Pt.

Between Teignmouth and Dawlish Rks extend 0·1M offshore. Beware Dawlish Rk (depth 2·1m) about 0·5M off N end of town. Warren Sands and Pole Sands lie W of ent to Exmouth (10.1.24), and are liable to shift. Along the NE (Exmouth) side of the chan, towards Orcomb Pt and Straight Pt (Lt), drying rks and shoals extend up to 0·25M from shore.

10.1.6 DISTANCE TABLE

Approximate distances in nautical miles are by the most direct route while avoiding dangers and allowing for traffic separation schemes etc. Places in *italics* are in adjoining areas.

1 *Fastnet Rock*	**1**																			
2 *Tuskar Rock*	138	**2**																		
3 *South Bishop*	162	36	**3**																	
4 *Lundy Island*	187	85	50	**4**																
5 *Appledore*	207	103	70	20	**5**															
6 *Padstow*	186	112	82	40	48	**6**														
7 Longships	167	130	109	82	89	49	**7**													
8 Bishop Rock	152	141	132	110	120	76	30	**8**												
9 Wolf Rock	169	135	117	90	97	57	8	26	**9**											
10 Lizard Point	190	153	132	105	112	72	23	50	24	**10**										
11 Falmouth	206	169	148	121	128	88	39	66	40	16	**11**									
12 Fowey	224	187	166	139	146	106	57	84	58	34	22	**12**								
13 Plymouth	239	202	181	154	161	121	72	99	73	49	39	22	**13**							
14 Eddystone	229	192	171	144	151	111	62	89	63	39	31	17	12	**14**						
15 Start Point	253	216	195	168	175	135	86	113	87	63	55	40	24	24	**15**					
16 Berry Head	266	229	208	181	188	148	99	126	100	76	68	53	37	37	13	**16**				
17 Straight Point	280	243	222	195	202	162	113	140	114	90	82	67	51	51	27	14	**17**			
18 *Portland Bill*	302	265	244	217	224	184	135	162	136	112	104	89	73	73	49	41	36	**18**		
19 *Le Four*	250	229	208	181	188	148	99	103	95	87	99	109	115	103	113	125	139	153	**19**	
20 *Casquets*	300	263	142	215	222	182	133	160	134	110	107	96	80	79	57	61	66	48	120	**20**

ENGLISH CHANNEL WAYPOINTS 10-1-7

Selected waypoints for use in Channel crossings, listed from West to East in each Area nominated below. Waypoints marked with an asterisk (*) are special (yellow) racing marks, which may be removed in winter. Further waypoints in coastal waters are given in section 4 of each relevant area (i.e. to 10.2.4 and 10.3.4 on the English Coast, and 10.17.4 and 10.18.4 for the French coast and the Channel Islands).

ENGLISH COAST

AREA 1

Bishop Rock Lt	49°52'·33N 06°26'·68W
Seven Stones Lt V	50°03'·58N 06°04'·28W
Wolfe Rock Lt	49°56'·70N 05°48'·50W
Runnel Stone Lt By	50°01'·15N 05°40'·30W
Tater Du Lt	50°03'·10N 05°34'·60W
Low Lee Lt By	50°05'·52N 05°31'·32W
Lizard Point Lt	49°57'·58N 05°12'·07W
Culdrose Lt By	50°00'·08N 05°59'·60W
Manacles Lt By	50°02'·77N 05°01'·85W
Helston Lt By	50°04'·92N 05°00'·77W
August Rk	50°06'·07N 05°04'·88W
Black Rk By	50°08'·65N 05°01'·68W
Castle Lt By	50°08'·95N 05°01'·58W
St Anthony Hd Lt	50°08'·43N 05°00'·90W
Gwineas Lt By	50°14'·47N 04°45'·30W
Cannis Rk Lt By	50°18'·35N 04°39'·88W
Udder Rk By	50°18'·90N 04°33'·78W
Eddystone Lt	50°10'·80N 04°15'·87W
Start Point Lt	50°13'·32N 03°38'·47W
Castle Ledge Lt By	50°19'·96N 03°33'·05W
***RDYC No. 1 By**	50°18'·80N 03°35'·25W
***RDYC No. 2 By**	50°18'·68N 03°33'·29W
***RDYC No. 3 By**	50°20'·07N 03°31'·42W
Berry Head Lt	50°23'·95N 03°28'·94W

AREA 2

Straight Point Lt	50°36'·46N 03°21'·68W
Portland Bill Lt	50°30'·82N 02°27'·32W
W Shambles Lt By	50°29'·75N 02°24'·33W
E Shambles Lt By	50°30'·75N 02°20'·00W
Anvil Point Lt	50°35'·48N 01°57'·52W
Poole Fairway Lt By	50°38'·95N 01°54'·78W
Needles Fairway Lt By	50°38'·20N 01°38'·90W
Bembridge Ledge Lt By	50°41'·12N 01°02'·74W
Needles Lt	50°39'·70N 01°35'·43W
St Catherine's Pt Lt	50°34'·52N 01°17'·80W
Nab Tower Lt	50°40'·05N 00°57'·07W

AREA 3

Owers Lanby	50°37'·30N 00°40'·60W
Brighton Marina Lt	50°48'·46N 00°06'·29W
Royal Sovereign Lt	50°43'·38N 00°26'·13E
Dungeness Lt	50°54'·77N 00°58'·67E
S Goodwin Lt F	51°07'·95N 01°28'·60E

OFFSHORE AIDS

AREAS 3, 17, AND 18

Channel Lt V	49°54'·42N 02°53'·67W
E Channel Lt F	49°58'·67N 02°28'·87W
EC1 Lt By	50°05'·90N 01°48'·35W
EC2 Lt By	50°12'·10N 01°12'·40W
EC3 Lt By	50°18'·30N 00°36'·10W
CS1 Lt By	50°33'·67N 00°03'·83W
Greenwich Lanby	50°24'·50N 00°00'·00
CS2 Lt By	50°39'·08N 00°32'·70E
CS3 Lt By	50°52'·00N 01°02'·30E
CS4 Lt By	51°08'·58N 01°34'·03E
Bullock Bank Lt By	50°46'·90N 01°07'·70E
S Varne Lt By	50°55'·60N 01°17'·40E
Varne Lanby	51°01'·25N 01°24'·00E
MPC Lt By	51°06'·17N 01°38'·33E
Sandettie Lt V/ By	51°09'·40N 01°47'·20E

FRENCH COAST

AREA 16

Ouessant SW Lanby	48°31'·68N 05°49'·10W
Créach Lt	48°27'·62N 05°07'·72W
Ouessant NE Lt By	48°45'·90N 05°11'·60W
Basse Paotr Bihan By	48°35'·38N 04°46'·16W
Basse de Portsall Lt By	48°36'·78N 04°46'·05W
Le Relec Lt By	48°36'·05N 04°40'·77W
Ruzven Lt By	48°36'·15N 04°39'·30W
Libenter Lt By	48°37'·57N 04°38'·21W
Trépied By	48°37'·37N 04°37'·45W
Ile Vierge Lt	48°38'·38N 04°34'·00W

Ile de Batz Lt	48°44'·78N 04°01'·55W
Astan Lt By	48°44'·95N 03°57'·55W
Méloine By	48°45'·62N 03°50'·54W
Les Triagoz Lt	48°52'·35N 03°38'·73W
Les Sept Iles Lt	48°52'·78N 03°29'·33W
Basse Crubient Lt By	48°54'·35N 03°11'·09W
La Jument des Héaux By	48°55'·41N 03°07'·96W
Les Heaux Lt	48°54'·53N 03°05'·20W
Rosédo (Bréhat) Lt	48°51'·50N 03°00'·32W
Les Echaudés By	48°53'·44N 02°57'·27W
Roche Gautier Lt By	49°00'·05N 02°52'·92W
Barnouic Lt	49°01'·70N 02°48'·40W
Roches Douvres Lt	49°06'·47N 02°48'·82W

CHANNEL ISLANDS

AREA 17

Les Hanois Lt	49°26'·16N 02°42'·02W
St Martin's Point Lt	49°25'·37N 02°31'·61W
Reffée Lt By	49°27'·80N 02°31'·18W
Platte Fougère Lt	49°30'·88N 02°29'·05W
Casquets Lt	49°43'·38N 02°22'·55W
Corbière Lt	49°10'·85N 02°14'·90W
Desormes Lt By	49°19'·00N 02°17'·90W
Alderney Main Lt	49°43'·81N 02°09'·77W
Canger Rk Lt By	49°07'·41N 02°00'·30W
Frouquier Aubert Lt By	49°06'·15N 01°58'·70W
NW Minquiers Lt By	48°59'·70N 02°20'·50W
SW Minquiers Lt By	48°54'·40N 02°19'·30W
S Minquiers Lt By	48°53'·15N 02°10'·00W
SE Minquiers Lt By	48°53'.50N 02°00'.00W
N Minquiers Lt By	49°01'·70N 02°00'·50W
NE Minquiers Lt By	49°00'·90N 01°55'·20W

FRENCH COAST

AREA 18

Le Légué Lt By	48°34'·39N 02°41'·09W
Cap Fréhel Lt	48°41'·10N 02°19'·07W
Banchenou Lt By	48°40'·51N 02°11'·41W
Basse de Vieux Banc By	48°42'·50N 02°09'·36W
Le Guildo Lt By	48°41'·42N 02°07'·22W
St Malo Fairway Lt By	48°41'·42N 02°07'·21W
Chausey, Grand Ile Lt	48°52'·23N 01°49'·26W
Le Videcoq Lt By	48°49'·70N 01°42'·00W
Anvers Lt By	48°53'·90N 01°40'·84W
La Catheue Lt By	48°57'·83N 01°42'·00W
Basse Jourdan Lt By	49°06'·90N 01°44'·07W
Écrévière Lt By	49°15'·33N 01°52'·08W
Cap de Carteret Lt	49°22'·46N 01°48'·35W
Les Trois-Grunes Lt By	49°21'·83N01°54'·80W
Cap de la Hague Lt	49°43'·37N 01°57'·19W
Basse Bréfort Lt By	49°43'·70N 01°51'·05W
CH1 Lt By	49°43'·30N 01°42'·10W
Anvers Lt By	48°53'·90N 01°40'·84W
Cherbourg Fort Ouest Lt	49°40'·50N 01°38'·87W
Le Pierre Noire Lt By	49°43'·57N 01°28'·98W
Cap Lévi Lt	49°41'·80N 01°28'·30W
Basse du Rénier Lt By	49°44'·90N 01°22'·00W
Les Equets Lt By	49°43'·68N 01°18'·28W

AREA 19

Pointe de Barfleur Lt	49°41'·87N 01°15'·87W
Iles St Marcouf Lt	49°29'·90N 01°08'·90W
Ver-sur-Mer Lt	49°20'·47N 00°31'·15W
LHA Lanby	49°31'·67N 00°09'·80W
Cap de la Hève Lt	49°30'·80N 00°04'·24E
Cap d'Antifer Lt	49°41'·07N 00°10'·00E
Pointe d'Ailly Lt	49°55'·13N 00°57'·56E
Bassurelle Lt By	50°32'·70N 00°57'·80E
Ecovouge Lt By	50°33'·62N 00°59'·00E
Vergoyer SW Lt By	50°26'·90N 01°00'·00E
Vergoyer N Lt By	50°39'·70N 01°22'·30E
ZC1 Lt By	50°44'·85N 01°27'·10E
Ault Lt	50°06'·35N 01°27'·24E
ZC2 Lt By	50°53'·50N 01°31'·00E
Pointe de Haut Blanc Lt	50°23'·90N 01°33'·75E
Cap d'Alprech Lt	50°41'·95N 01°33'·83E
Cap Gris Nez Lt	50°52'·17N 01°35'·07E
CA4 Lt By	50°58'·94N 01°45'·18E
Sangatte Lt	50°57'·23N 01°46'·57E
Dunkerque Lanby	51°03'·00N 01°51'·83E
Walde Lt	50°59'·57N 01°55'·00E

ISLES OF SCILLY 10-1-8

The Isles of Scilly are made up of 48 islands and numerous rocky outcrops, extending approx 10M by 5M and lying 21-31M WSW of Land's End. Only six islands are inhabited, St Mary's, Gugh, St Agnes, St Martin's, Tresco and Bryher. The islands belong to the Duchy of Cornwall and details of arrangements for visiting uninhabited islands are given in the booklet *Duchy of Cornwall – Information for visiting craft* obtainable from the Harbour Master, Hugh Town Harbour, St Mary's. There is a lifeboat and a HM Coastguard Sector Base at St Mary's.

CHARTS

Admiralty 883, 34; passage from Lands End 1148; Stamford 2; Imray C7.

TIDES

Standard Port is Devonport. Tidal differences for St Mary's are given in 10.1.9 below. The tidal heights, times, speeds and directions round islands are irregular.

SHELTER

There are numerous anchorages, the following being but a selection:

HUGH TOWN HARBOUR (St Mary's). See 10.1.9 below.

PORTH CRESSA (St Mary's S of Hugh Town). Beware of dangers on each side of entrance and the submarine cable. Exposed to swell from SE to SW. Anchor in approx 2m. Facilities: all facilities in Hugh Town to N.

NEW GRIMSBY (between Tresco and Bryher). Approach through New Grimsby Sound, or with sufficient rise of tide across Tresco Flats. Good shelter except in NW winds. Anchor between Hangman Is and the quay in 1·5 to 4·5m. Facilities: Bar, R, FW, V, ✉, Ferry to St Mary's.

WATERMILL COVE (NE corner of St Mary's). Excellent shelter in winds NW to S. Anchor in approx 5m.

THE COVE (St Agnes/Gugh). Well sheltered from W and N winds, except when the sand bar between the islands covers near HW sp with a strong NW wind.

PORTH CONGER (St Agnes/Gugh). On the N side of the sand bar, sheltered in winds from E through S to W. May be uncomfortable when the bar is covered. Facilities; L (two quays), ferry to St Mary's; in Middle Town (¼M), St Agnes, V, ✉, R, Bar

OLD GRIMSBY (between Tresco and St Helen's). Green Porth and Raven's Porth, divided by a quay, form the W side of Old Grimsby and both dry. Anchor 2 ca NE of quay in 2·5m. Access more difficult than New Grimsby. Well sheltered in SW winds but open to swell if wind veers N of W. Facilities; L(quay), hotel, slip (hotel).

TEAN SOUND (St Martin's, W side). Requires careful pilotage, but attractive anchorage in better weather. (See St. Martins Hotel below). More suitable for shoal draught boats which can anchor out of main tidal stream in channel. There are several other anchorages which can be used in settled weather, or by shoal draught boats which can take the ground.

NAVIGATION

See chart 34 (essential), 10.1.5 and *A Yachtsman's Guide to Scilly*. For traffic separation schemes, see Chapter 2 Fig. 2(8).

The many offlying dangers need care if the leading lines (lettered on chartlet) cannot be identified, when it is best to lie off. Tidal streams are irregular and run hard off points and over shoals, where overfalls may occur. Many of the channels between the islands have dangerous shallows, often rocky ledges. Beware lobster pots and the ferry entering or leaving. Also beware the grave possibility of normal yacht anchors dragging through the fine sand, even with plenty of scope.

St Mary's Sound (line B) is the normal access to St Mary's Road. From the NE beware the Gilstone (dries) 3ca E of Peninnis Head. An E cardinal bell buoy marks Spanish Ledges which extend from the Gugh shore, and a port-hand buoy marks Bartholomew Ledges (least depth 0·6m). The Woolpack Bn (S cardinal) marks SW end of St Mary's. In the approach to Hugh Town, transit E1 clears Woodcock Ledge, which breaks in bad weather.

Crow Sound (line A) is not difficult with sufficient rise of tide, but is rough in strong winds from E or S. From the NE a yacht can pass close to Menawethan and Biggal Rock. Avoid Trinity Rock and the Ridge, which break in bad weather. Hats buoy (S cardinal) marks a drying shoal with an old boiler on it. The bar (dries) lies off Bar Point, but there is slightly deeper water nearer Bar Point. Leave Crow Rock Bn either side before altering course to SW.

North Channel (line D) is about ¾M wide and provides easy access if the leading marks can be seen. Beware cross tide and Steeple Rock (awash) ¾M SW of Mincarlo. In bad weather the sea breaks on Jeffrey Rock and Spencer's Ledge either side of channel.

Broad Sound (line C) is about ¼M wide at narrowest point, and is entered between Bishop Rock and Fleming's Ledge about ¾M to the N. Leading marks are not conspic, but the channel is shown by Round Rock, Gunner and Old Wreck buoys which mark the main dangers other than Jeffrey Rock.

LIGHTS AND MARKS

See 10.1.4 for lights. It is wise to study the various marks on the chart before arrival.

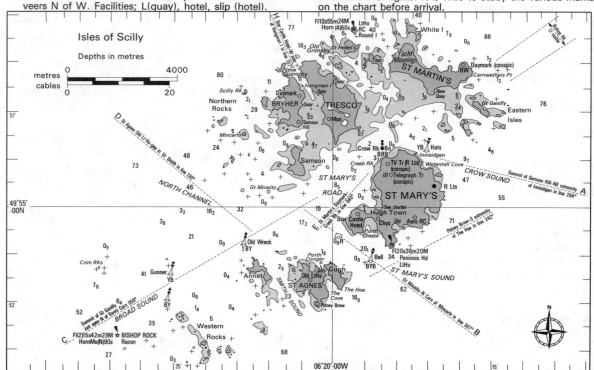

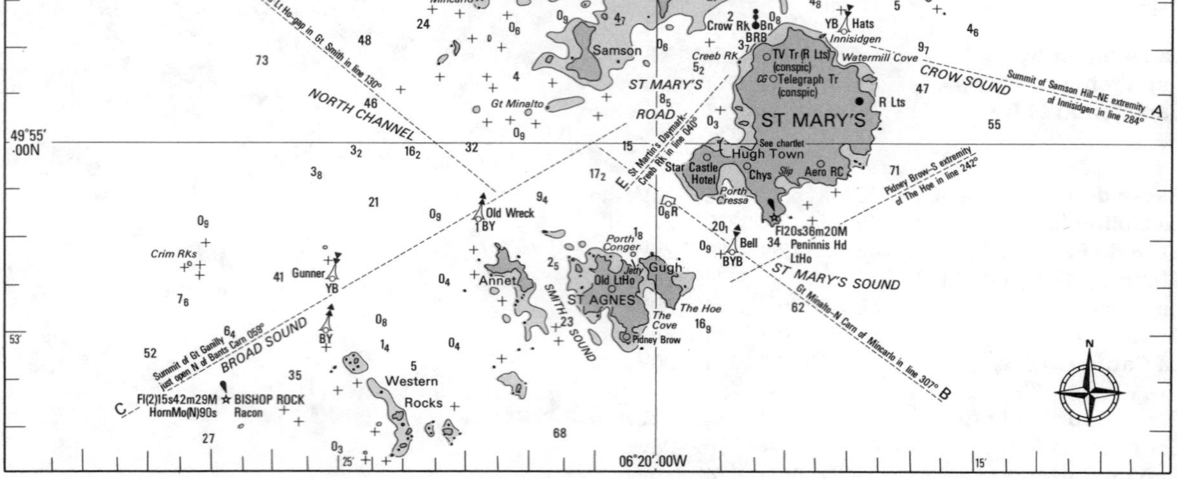
Isles of Scilly
Depths in metres
metres 0 4000
cables 0 20
BRYHER
TRESCO
ST MARTIN'S
ST MARY'S
ST AGNES
Samson
Gugh
Annet
Hugh Town
Star Castle Hotel
Porth Cressa
Old Grimsby
New Grimsby
St Helen's
Tean
Yacht Moorings
Round I
White I
Daymark (conspic)
Carnwethers Pt
Gt Ganilly
Eastern Isles
Hats
Innisidgen
Watermill Cove
CROW SOUND
NORTH CHANNEL
BROAD SOUND
SMITH SOUND
ST MARY'S SOUND
ST MARY'S ROAD
Northern Rocks
Scilly Rk
Mincarlo
Gt Minalto
Old Wreck
Gunner
Crim Rks
Western Rocks
Fl(2)15s42m29M BISHOP ROCK
HornMo(N)90s Racon
Fl10s55m24M LtHo
Horn (4)60s RC
Fl20s36m20M Peninnis Hd LtHo
Bell
Porth Conger
Old LtHo
The Cove
The Hoe
Pidney Brow
Crow Rk Bn
Creeb Rk
TV Tr (R Lts) (conspic)
Telegraph Tr (conspic)
R Lts
Aero RC
Chys
49°55'·00N
06°20'·00W

ISLES OF SCILLY *continued*

RADIO TELEPHONE

For port operations see 10.1.9. Scillies area is served by directional aerial from Land's End Radio on Ch 64. St Mary's Coastguard Ch 16; 67 (manned in bad weather only). Pilot Ch 16; 14.

TELEPHONE (0720)

Hr Mr Hugh Town Harbour 22768; Pilot 22066 # 22571; Info Office 22537; MRCC Falmouth (0326) 317575; Airport Reservations 22646; Marinecall 0898 500 458; Ⓗ 22508.

FACILITIES

St Martins Hotel ☎ (0720) 22092 M (6), V, R, Bar, D, FW.

ST MARY'S 10-1-9

Isles of Scilly

CHARTS

Admiralty 883, 34; Stanford 2; Imray C7; OS 203

NOTE: The old Admiralty fathom chart 34 shows more inshore dangers.

TIDES

+0607 Dover; ML 3·1; Duration 0600; Zone 0 (GMT)

Standard Port DEVONPORT (⟶)

Times				Height (metres)			
HW		LW		MHWS	MHWN	MLWN	MLWS
0000	0600	0000	0600	5·5	4·4	2·2	0·8
1200	1800	1200	1800				
Differences ST MARY'S ROADS							
−0030	−0110	−0100	−0020	+0·2	−0·1	−0·2	−0·1

SHELTER

St Mary's Pool gives good shelter in most winds but is exposed to W and NW, when Porth Cressa (see 10.1.8) is better. Anchoring is not permitted S of a line from the pierhead to the lifeboat slip, off the pierhead where the ferry turns, or in the harbour approaches. Speed limit 3kn.

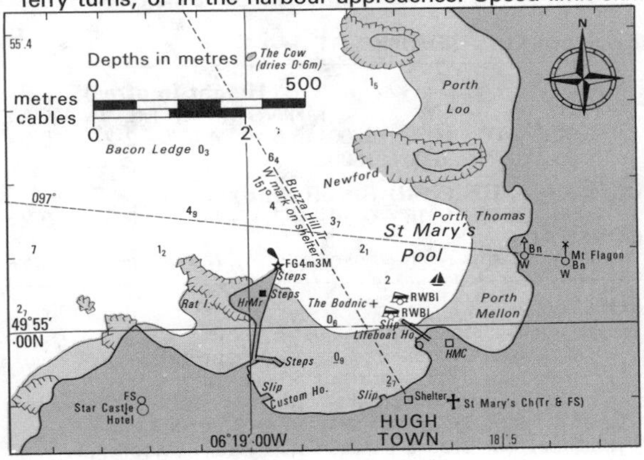
Depths in metres
metres
cables
0
500
2
The Cow (dries 0·6m)
Porth Loo
Bacon Ledge
Newford I
Porth Thomas
St Mary's Pool
Mt Flagon
Bn
Porth Mellon
FG4m3M
Steps
Rat I.
HrMr
The Bodnic
RWBI
Slip
Lifeboat Ho
HMC
Custom Ho.
Shelter
St Mary's Ch(Tr & FS)
Star Castle Hotel
HUGH TOWN
097°
49°55'·00N
06°19'·00W

NAVIGATION

Waypoint St Mary's Sound. Spanish Ledge E cardinal buoy, Bell, 49°53'·90N 06°18'·80W, 128°/308° from/to Great Minalto, 2·4M. See also 10.1.4 and 10.1.8. Other channels into St Mary's Road include Smith Sound between St Agnes and Annet, and with sufficient rise of tide through New Grimsby across Tresco Flats. In the approaches to St Mary's Pool beware Woodcock Ledge (see 10.1.8). Bacon Ledge (depth 0·3m) lies 2½ca W of Newford Island, while further N are The Cow and The Calf (both dry). The 097° transit on the chartlet leads S of Bacon Ledge. If coming from the N, the 151° transit shown leads W of The Cow and E of Bacon Ledge.

LIGHTS AND MARKS

There are two leading marks, rather distant W beacons, bearing 097° for entry into the harbour. Nearest mark is a triangle, the distant mark an X. There are no navigational lights in the harbour except Lt on pier showing FG 4m 3M; vis 072°-192°.

RADIO TELEPHONE

Call: *St Mary's Harbour* VHF Ch 16; 14. (0800-1700 LT).

TELEPHONE (0720)

Hr Mr 22768; MRCC Falmouth 317575; # 22571; Marinecall 0898 500 458; Police 22444; Ⓗ 22392; Dr 22628.

FACILITIES

EC Wednesday (or Thursday according to boat sailings); Harbour Office will hold mail for visiting yachts if addressed c/o the Harbour Master. **Harbour** Slip, M, Gas, Gaz, P (cans), D, L, FW*, C (6 ton); **T. H. Chudleigh** ☎ 22505, Sh, CH; **Chris Jenkins** ☎ 22321, ME; **H.J. Thomas** ☎ 22710, L, ME, CH; **Scillonian Marine** ☎ 22124, CH, El, ACA; **Isles of Scilly YC** ☎ 22352, Bar, ◙, R; **Island Supply Stores** ☎ 22388, Gas; **Hugh Town** has limited shopping facilities. ✉; Ⓑ; ⇶ (ferry to Penzance); ✈ (Helicopter service to Penzance and fixed wing to London and mainland). There are ✉, R, V, Bar etc. at Tresco, Bryher, St Martins and St Agnes.

*0830-1130 except Sat. – see Hr Mr.

NEWLYN 10-1-10

Cornwall

CHARTS

Admiralty 2345, 777; Stanford 13; Imray C7; OS 203

TIDES

+0600 Dover; ML 3·1; Duration 0555; Zone 0 (GMT)

Standard Port DEVONPORT (⟶)

Times				Height (metres)			
HW		LW		MHWS	MHWN	MLWN	MLWS
0000	0600	0000	0600	5·5	4·4	2·2	0·8
1200	1800	1200	1800				
Differences NEWLYN							
−0040	−0105	−0045	−0020	+0·1	0·0	−0·2	0·0

SHELTER

Good except in SE winds when heavy swell occurs in the harbour. In off-shore winds there are good anchorages outside the harbour in Gwavas Lake. Anchoring inside breakwaters is prohibited. No visitors' moorings; overnight stay only.

NAVIGATION

Waypoint Low Lee E cardinal buoy, Q(3) 10s, 50°05'·52N 05°31'·32W, 130°/310° from/to Newlyn pierhead, 1·0M. Approaching from E beware Mountamopus, from S beware Low Lee and Carn Base. Also beware Dog Rk, 3½ ca NE of harbour entrance. Harbour is available at all states of the tide but entrance is narrow, i.e. 45m between pierheads. Leave Lt Ho to port and keep close to New Pier. Newlyn is a commercial fishing port and fishing boats must take priority.

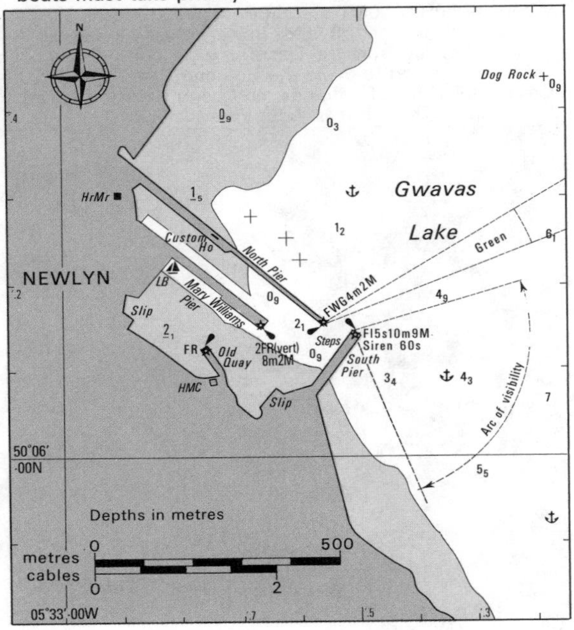
Dog Rock
Gwavas Lake
HrMr
Custom Ho
North Pier
NEWLYN
LB
Mary Williams Pier
Slip
FWG4m2M
Green
Steps
Fl5s10m9M Siren 60s
South Pier
FR
Old Quay
2FR(vert) 8m2M
HMC
Slip
Arc of visibility
50°06'·00N
Depths in metres
metres
cables
0
500
2
05°33'·00W

NEWLYN *continued*

LIGHTS AND MARKS
S Pier, head Fl 5s 10m 9M; vis 253°-336°, W Tr, R base and cupola; Siren 60s. N Pier, head F WG 4m 2M; vis G238°-248°, W over harbour. Old Quay, head FR 3m 1M.
RADIO TELEPHONE
Call: *Newlyn Harbour* VHF Ch 16; 09 **12** (Mon-Fri 0800-1700, Sat 0800-1200 LT).
TELEPHONE (0736)
Hr Mr 62523; MRCC Falmouth 317575; ⌗ (0752) 220661; Marinecall 0898 500 458; Police 62395; Ⓗ 62382; Dr 63866.
FACILITIES
EC Wednesday; **North Pier** Slip, D, L, FW, ME, El, C (6 ton); **South Pier** L; **C. K. Jones** ☎ 63095, ME, Sh; **J. H. Bennetts** ☎ 69988, Gas; **Kernow Marine** ☎ 68606, El, Ⓔ; **Sea-Com Electronic** ☎ 69695, Ⓔ; **Cosalt** ☎ 63094, CH.
There is a BY with all repair facilities but it is usually booked up with work on fishing boats.
Town CH, ⊡, V, R, Bar; ✉ Ⓑ (AM only); ⇌ (bus to Penzance); ✈ (Penzance).

PENZANCE 10-1-11

Cornwall

CHARTS
Admiralty 2345, 777; Stanford 13; Imray C7; OS 203
TIDES
−0635 Dover; ML 3·1; Duration 0550; Zone 0 (GMT)

Standard Port DEVONPORT (⟶)

Times				Height (metres)			
HW		LW		MHWS	MHWN	MLWN	MLWS
0000	0600	0000	0600	5·5	4·4	2·2	0·8
1200	1800	1200	1800				
Differences PENZANCE							
−0040	−0105	−0045	−0020	+0·1	0·0	−0·2	0·0
PORTHLEVEN							
−0045	−0105	−0035	−0025	0·0	−0·1	−0·2	0·0
LIZARD POINT							
−0045	−0055	−0040	−0030	−0·2	−0·2	−0·3	−0·2

SHELTER
Perfectly protected within the wet dock. Dock is open HW−2 to HW+1. Mounts Bay is unsafe anchorage in S or SE winds. Strong S or SE winds make the harbour entrance dangerous.
NAVIGATION
Waypoint 50°06′·70N 05°31′·10W, 135°/315° from/to Penzance S pierhead, 0·48M. Beware Gear Rk coming from S. Coming from the Lizard in wind or swell approach on NNW heading to avoid the Boa and Iron Gates. Cressar (5 ca NE of entrance) and Long Rks are marked by beacons. There is a harbour speed limit of 5 kn.

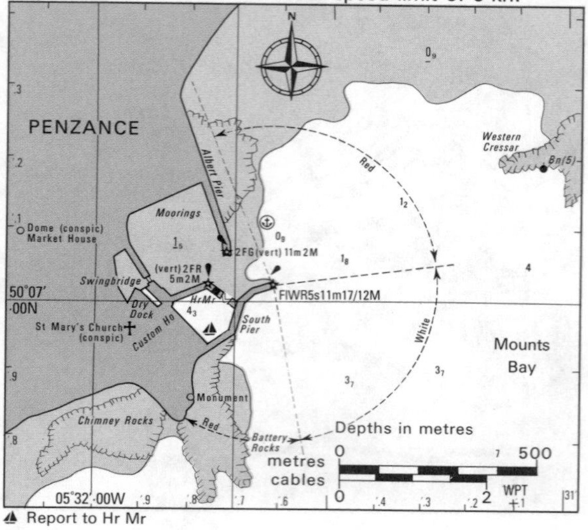

PENZANCE
N
Western Cressar
Bn(5)
Albert Pier
Red
Moorings
Dome (conspic) Market House
2FG(vert) 11m 2M
(vert) 2FR 5m2M
Swingbridge
Dry Dock
HrMr
FlWR5s11m17/12M
50°07′·00N
St Mary's Church (conspic)
Custom Ho
South Pier
White
Mounts Bay
Monument
Chimney Rocks
Red
Battery Rocks
Depths in metres
metres
cables
500
WPT
05°32′·00W

▲ Report to Hr Mr

LIGHTS AND MARKS
There are no Ldg Lts or marks. South pierhead Lt Fl WR 5s 11m 17/12M; vis R159°-224° (unintens), R224°-268°, W268°-344·5°, R344·5°-shore.
Dock entry signals, shown from FS at N side of Dock gate (may not be given for yachts).
2B balls (hor) (2FR (vert) by night) — Dock gates open.
2B balls (vert) (FR over FG by night) — Dock gates shut.
RADIO TELEPHONE
VHF Ch 16; 09 **12** (HW−2 to HW+1, and office hours).
TELEPHONE (0736)
Hr Mr 07415; Hr Office 66113; MRCC Falmouth 317575; ⌗ (0752) 220661; Marinecall 0898 500 458; Police 62395; Dr 63866, Ⓗ 62382
FACILITIES
EC Wednesday (except in summer); **Wet Dock** (50 visitors) ☎ 66113, Access HW−1½ to HW+1, Slip, M, D (cans), L, FW, AC, C (3 ton); **Holman Marine** ☎ 63838, Slip (dry dock), ME, El, C, CH, AB; **Matthews Sail Loft** ☎ 64004, CH, SM; **Cosalt Newlyn** ☎ 63094, CH; **R. Curnow** ☎ 762025, CH, Sh; **South Pier** ☎ 66113, D, FW, V, R, Bar; **Penzance YC** ☎ 64989, Bar, L, FW, R; **J. H. Bennetts** ☎ 69988, Gas, Gaz; **Town** ⊡, CH, V, R, Bar. ✉; Ⓑ; ⇌; ✈.

HELFORD RIVER 10-1-12

Cornwall

CHARTS
Admiralty 147, 154; Stanford 13; Imray C6, Y57; OS 204
TIDES
−0613 Dover; ML 3·0; Duration 0550; Zone 0 (GMT).

Standard Port DEVONPORT (⟶)

Times				Height (metres)			
HW		LW		MHWS	MHWN	MLWN	MLWS
0000	0600	0000	0600	5·5	4·4	2·2	0·8
1200	1800	1200	1800				
Differences HELFORD RIVER (Ent)							
−0030	−0035	−0015	−0010	−0·2	−0·2	−0·3	−0·2
COVERACK							
−0030	−0040	−0020	−0010	−0·2	−0·2	−0·3	−0·2

SHELTER
Excellent shelter except against E winds.
Anchorages:- Durgan Bay, good except in E winds.
Off Helford but tides strong.
Navas Creek — good shelter — little room.
Gillan Creek is good but beware rock in middle of entrance, Car Croc E cardinal spar buoy. (Moorings administered by Hr Mr). Visitors buoys marked 'Visitors' on green pick up buoys.
NAVIGATION
Waypoint 50°05′·70N 05°04′·50W, 093°/273° from/to The Voose N cardinal Bn, 1·5M. If coming from N beware August Rock (or the Gedges). August Rock buoy G conical (seasonal). If from SE keep well clear of Nare Point and Dennis Head. Keep Helford Pt open of Bosahan Pt to clear rocky reef E end of Bosahan Point (The Voose) marked by N Cardinal buoy (seasonal). Avoid mud bank marked by G conical buoy (Bar buoy-seasonal) on N side of river opposite Helford Creek. Port and Stbd markers mark channel from Mawgan Creek to Gweek. Speed limit 6 kn.
LIGHTS AND MARKS
There is a Lt on August Rk Buoy FlG 5s. A useful natural transit exists as a line from Bosahan Point to Mawnan Shear (259°) keeps one clear of the dangerous rocks, The Gedges. Note: There is a local bye-law stating that there are oyster beds in the river and creeks W of buoy, mid channel SW of Navas Creek, and yachts must not anchor or take the ground in that area.

HELFORD RIVER *continued*

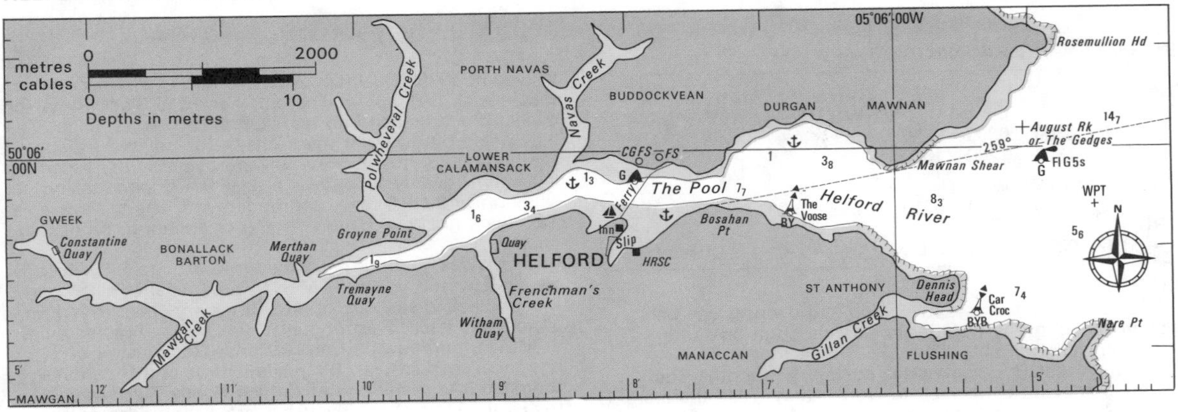
05°06'·00W
metres
cables
0
2000
0
10
Depths in metres
PORTH NAVAS
Navas Creek
Polwheveral Creek
BUDDOCKVEAN
DURGAN
MAWNAN
Rosemullion Hd
August Rk or The Gedges
Fl G 5s
259°
50°06'·00N
LOWER CALAMANSACK
CGFS
FS
The Pool
Mawnan Shear
WPT
N
GWEEK
Constantine Quay
BONALLACK BARTON
Merthan Quay
Groyne Point
Ferry
Inn
Slip
The Voose
BY
Helford River
Bosahan Pt
Quay
HELFORD
HRSC
Tremayne Quay
Frenchman's Creek
Witham Quay
ST ANTHONY
Dennis Head
Car Croc
BYB
Nare Pt
Mawgan Creek
Gillan Creek
MANACCAN
FLUSHING
MAWGAN

RADIO TELEPHONE
Helford River SC and Gweek Quay VHF Ch **80**, M.

TELEPHONE (0326)
Moorings Officer 280422; MRCC 317575; ⌗ (0752) 220661; Marinecall 0898 500 458; Police 72231; Ⓗ Helston 572151.

FACILITIES
EC Wednesday; **Cove Boats** ☎ 250116, M; **Port Navas YC** ☎ 40419, C (1½ ton), Gas, C (3 ton), M, AC, V, L, Bar, R, FW, P, D; **Gweek Quay** ☎ Mawgan 657, C (30 ton), M, CH, R, El, Sh, ME, FW, Ⓔ; **Star Hire Boats** ☎ 260675, M; **Helford Passage** Slip, L, FW; **Helford River SC** ☎ Manaccan 460, Slip, M, L, FW, Bar; **Ferry Boat Inn** ☎ 250278, M, Gas, Gaz, ◎, FW, R, Bar; **J. Badger** (Durgan), Slip, L, FW; **Sailaway** ☎ Manaccan 357, M, FW, Sh, CH, L. ✉ (Helford, Gweek, Mawnan-Smith, Mawgan); Ⓑ Mawnan-Smith (Jan-Sept Mon, Wed, Fri AM only. Oct-May Tues, Fri AM only); ⇄ (bus to Falmouth); ✈ (Penzance or Newquay).
Note: Ferry will collect yachtsmen from boats, requested during normal ferry operating hours.

RIVER FAL 10-1-13
Cornwall

CHARTS
Admiralty 32, 18, 154; Stanford 13; Imray C6, Y58; OS 204

TIDES
−0558 Dover; ML 3·0; Duration 0550; Zone 0 (GMT).

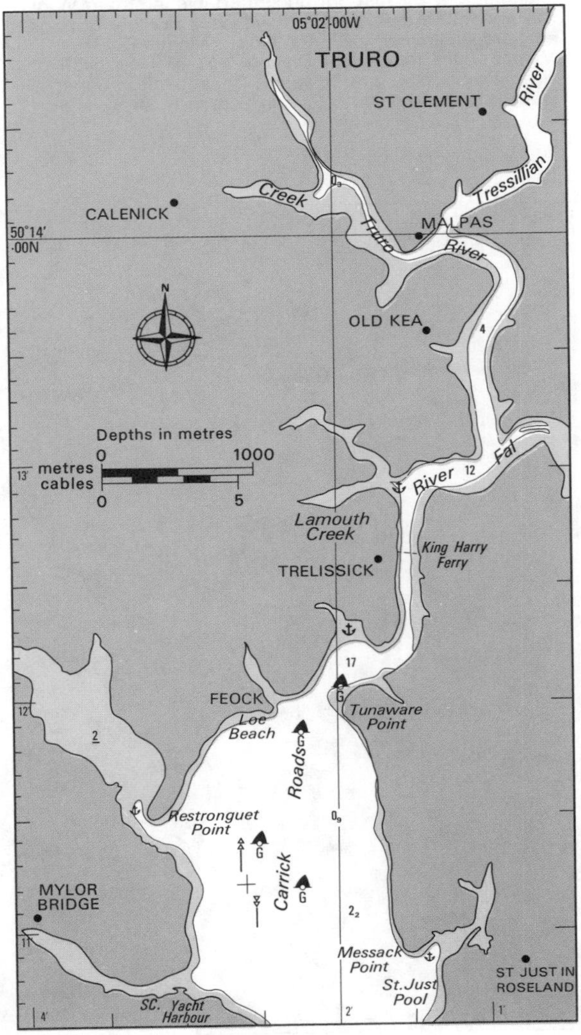
05°02'·00W
TRURO
ST CLEMENT
Tressillian River
Creek
Truro River
CALENICK
MALPAS
50°14'·00N
N
OLD KEA
Depths in metres
0
1000
metres
cables
0
5
River Fal
Lamouth Creek
King Harry Ferry
TRELISSICK
FEOCK
Loe Beach
Tunaware Point
Roads
Restronguet Point
Carrick
MYLOR BRIDGE
Messack Point
St.Just Pool
ST JUST IN ROSELAND
SC. Yacht Harbour

RIVER FAL *continued*

Standard Port DEVONPORT (⟶)

Times				Height (metres)			
HW		LW		MHWS	MHWN	MLWN	MLWS
0000	0600	0000	0600	5·5	4·4	2·2	0·8
1200	1800	1200	1800				
Differences FALMOUTH							
−0030	−0030	−0010	−0010	−0·2	−0·2	−0·3	−0·2
TRURO							
−0020	−0025	Dries out		−2·0	−2·0	Dries out	

SHELTER

Excellent. Entrance is a mile wide and deep. It can be approached in any weather or tide although on-shore winds against an ebb tide make it a bit rough. The Visitors Yacht Haven operates in summer months, the pontoons being connected to North Quay. Also there are visitors moorings on the port side of the main channel, clearly marked, operated by the Harbour Commissioner or the Royal Cornwall YC. Port Pendennis is a marina (at present for residents only) to the SW of the commercial port and Falmouth Marina, about ½M beyond Greenbank up the Penryn River, available at all tides. On E side is St Mawes Harbour, with excellent shelter except in SW winds. In these circumstances proceed beyond Amsterdam Pt to anchor. Further up-stream on the W bank is Mylor Yacht Harbour, sheltered from prevailing winds but uncomfortable in strong easterlies. Further up on the W bank is Restronguet Creek, a good anchorage but most of the creek dries. On the E side there is a good anchorage at St Just but uncomfortable in strong W or SW winds. Further up river there are a number of good anchorages including Church Creek, Mopus Reach, Malpas (Bar Creek Yacht Station ¼M up Tresillian R has visitors moorings) and Tolverne. Speed limit in upper reaches and in creeks is 5kn; in Penryn R. 8kns.

NAVIGATION

Waypoint 50°08′·00N 05°02′·00W, 183°/003° from/to Black Rock Bn, 0·68M. The only hazard is Black Rk which divides the entrance into two. Entrance can be made either side but at night the E channel is advised leaving the buoy Q (3) 10s to port. Beware oyster beds, especially in Penryn River. Falmouth is a deep water port, taking ships up to 90,000 tons; appropriate facilities are available. Take care not to impede shipping or anchor in prohibited areas.

In St Mawes Harbour entrance beware Lugo Rk, which is always covered; leave St Mawes S cardinal buoy to port. Mylor Creek is shallow, approx 1m everywhere except in Mylor Pool itself. Restronguet Creek has as little as 0·6m at MLWS and beware Carrick Carlys Rock just N of entrance, marked with BY posts with N and S cardinal topmarks. At the N end of Carrick Roads Turnaway Pt marks the start of the river; beware strong tides and rips. 'On final approach to Falmouth Yacht Marina leave E cardinal mark to starboard and pass within 20m of outside pontoons to ensure narrow channel is adhered to'.

LIGHTS AND MARKS

St Anthony Head light, R sector covers the Manacles Rocks.

RADIO TELEPHONE

Call: *Falmouth Harbour Radio*, VHF Ch 16; 11 12 13 14 (Mon-Fri 0900-1700, Sat and Sun 0900-1700 in summer. LT). Coastguard – Ch 16 67. Customs launch Ch 16 12 09 06 10 14. Port Health Ch 16 12 06. Mylor Yacht Harbour, Falmouth Yacht Marina, Port Pendennis Marina and Royal Cornwall YC Ch **80**. M (H24) Visitors Yacht Haven Ch 16, 12;

TELEPHONE (0326)

Hr Mrs Falmouth 312285; Truro/Penryn Truro 72130; St Mawes 270553; MRCC 317575; ⌗ (0752) 220661; Weather Plymouth 42534; Marinecall 0898 500 458; Police 72231; Dr 312033; Ⓗ Truro 74242.

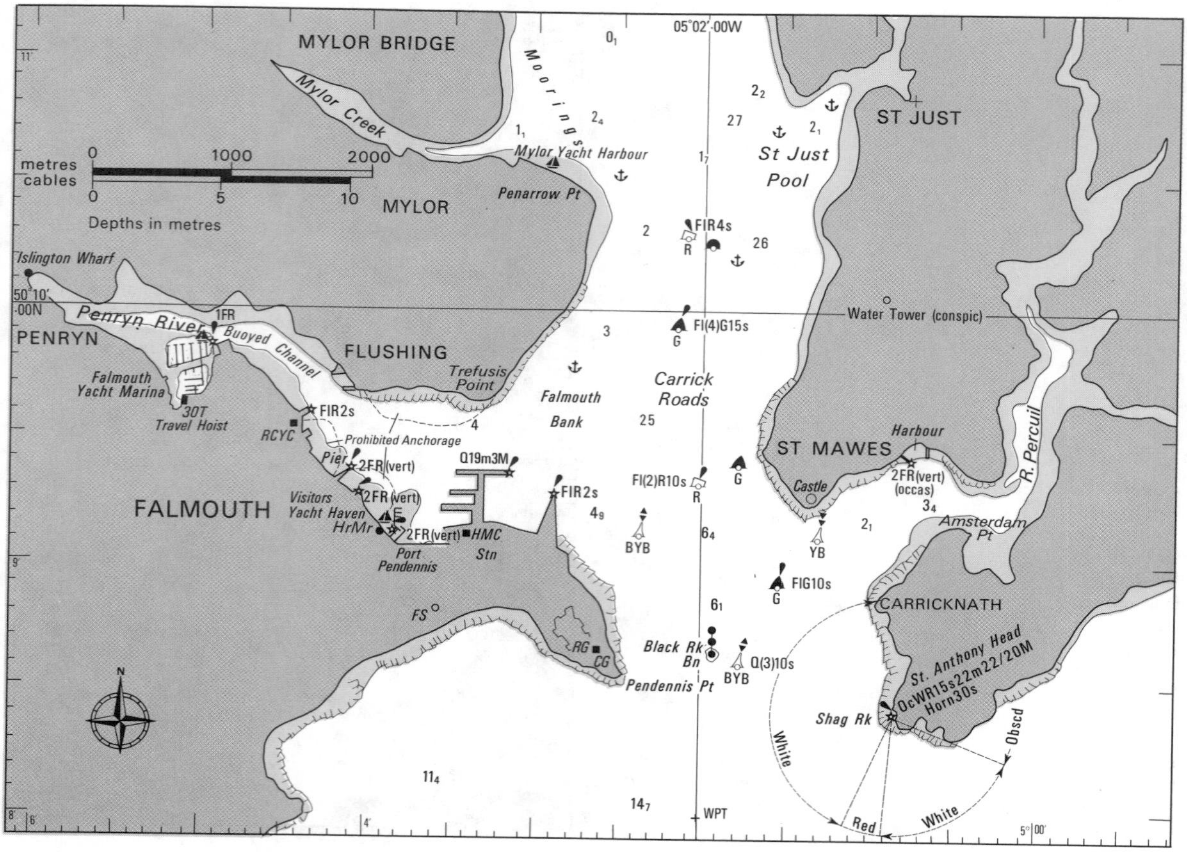
MYLOR BRIDGE
Mylor Creek
Moorings
Mylor Yacht Harbour
Penarrow Pt
MYLOR
metres 0 1000 2000
cables 0 5 10
Depths in metres
Islington Wharf
50°10′·00N
PENRYN
Penryn River
Buoyed Channel
1FR
Falmouth Yacht Marina
30T Travel Hoist
FLUSHING
Trefusis Point
RCYC
FlR2s
Prohibited Anchorage
Pier
2FR(vert)
Q19m3M
FALMOUTH
Visitors Yacht Haven
HrMr
Port Pendennis
HMC Stn
FS
RG
CG
Pendennis Pt
05°02′·00W
St Just Pool
ST JUST
FlR4s
Water Tower (conspic)
Fl(4)G15s
Carrick Roads
Falmouth Bank
Fl(2)R10s
ST MAWES
Harbour
Castle
2FR(vert) (occas)
R. Percuil
Amsterdam Pt
BYB
YB
FlG10s
CARRICKNATH
Black Rk Bn
Q(3)10s
St. Anthony Head OcWR15s22m22/20M Horn30s
Shag Rk
White
Red
Obscd
WPT

RIVER FAL *continued*

FACILITIES

FALMOUTH EC Wednesday (winter only). **Falmouth Yacht Marina** (280+80 visitors), ☎ 316620, AC, FW, CH, V, P (cans), D, Bar, R, ME, El, Sh, ▣, BH (30 ton), C (2 ton), Gas, Gaz, SM, Access H24; **Falmouth Harbour Commissioners Visitors Yacht Haven** (40) ☎ 312285 (Apr-Sept inclusive), P, D, FW, Access H24; **Port Pendennis Marina** (Residents only at present) Visitors harbour planned to N of Marina, plus YC (R, Bar, ▣, Ch etc). **Port Falmouth BY** ☎ 313248, ME, El, Sh, M, Slip; **Western Electronic Services** ☎ 317728, Ⓔ; **Penrose** ☎ 312402, SM; **West Country Chandlers** ☎ 312611, CH, Gas, Gaz; **Bosuns Locker** ☎ 312414, CH, ACA; **Nautibits Used Boat Gear** ☎ 317474, CH; **Mainbrace Chandlers** ☎ 318314, CH; **Falmouth Ship Repairers** ☎ 311400, Slip, P, D, FW, ME, El, Sh, C, CH; **Town** V, R, Bar; ✉; Ⓑ; ≹; ✈ (Plymouth or Newquay).

PENRYN/FLUSHING **Falmouth Boat Construction** ☎ 74309, M, Slip, El, FW, ME, C (12 ton), Sh; **Williams BY** ☎ 73819, Sh, ME, C; **Penryn Bridge BY** ☎ 73322, BY, ME, El, Sh; **South West Sails** ☎ 752291, SM; **The Boathouse** ☎ 74177, CH, SM, ACA; **Falmouth Chandlers** ☎ 73988, CH, Gas, Gaz; **Falmouth Bass Boat Co.** ☎ 74685, BY, ME, El, Sh; **SKB** ☎ 72107, SM.

MYLOR/RESTRONGUET **Mylor Yacht Harbour** (250+20 visitors) ☎ 72121, BH (25 ton), CH, Gas, Gaz, AC, FW, Slip, C (4 ton), Sh, ME, El, Ⓔ, CH, V, D, Bar, ▣, Access HW∓1; **Mylor Marine Electronics** ☎ 74001, Ⓔ; **Mylor Chandlery** ☎ 75482, CH, Gas, Gaz; **Restronguet Yacht Basin** ☎ 73613, Slip, M, Sh; **Pandora Inn** ☎ 72678, V, R, Bar.

ST MAWES **Freshwater BY** ☎ 270443, M, ME, Sh, El; **Percuil BY** ☎ Portscatho 564, BY, CH; **St Mawes Inner Harbour** FW, Slip; **Pascoes BY** ☎ 270269, ME, El, Sh, M, SM, Gas.

TRURO/MALPAS **Bar Creek Yacht Station** ☎ Truro 73919, BY, M, Slip, ME, Sh, El; **Malpas Marine** ☎ Truro 71260, M, CH, ME, El, Sh; **Reg Langdon** ☎ Truro 72668, CH; **Quay Chandlers** ☎ Truro 72116, CH, Gas;

YACHT CLUBS etc.
- Port of Falmouth Sailing Association ☎ 77061.
- Royal Cornwall Yacht Club ☎ 311105, M, Slip, FW, R, Bar.
- Mylor Yacht Club ☎ 74391, Bar.
- St Mawes SC. ☎ 270686.
- Flushing SC. ☎ 74043.
- Restronguet SC. ☎ 74536.
- Falmouth Town SC. ☎ 315284.

Note 1 Fuel Barge June to early Sept

MEVAGISSEY 10-1-14

Cornwall

CHARTS

Admiralty 147, 148, 1267; Stanford 13; Imray C6; OS 204

TIDES

−0600 Dover; ML 3·1; Duration 0600; Zone 0 (GMT).

Standard Port DEVONPORT (⟶)

Times				Height (metres)			
HW		LW		MHWS	MHWN	MLWN	MLWS
0000	0600	0000	0600	5·5	4·4	2·2	0·8
1200	1800	1200	1800				
Differences MEVAGISSEY							
−0010	−0015	−0005	+0005	−0·1	−0·1	−0·2	−0·1

SHELTER

Harbour is available at all states of the tide but entrance faces NE and is exposed to E winds. Dangerous to approach when there are strong SE winds. Anchorage off is unsuitable when wind is E of S. Inner harbour is reserved for fishing boats except when taking on fuel or water. Visitors berth S Pier.

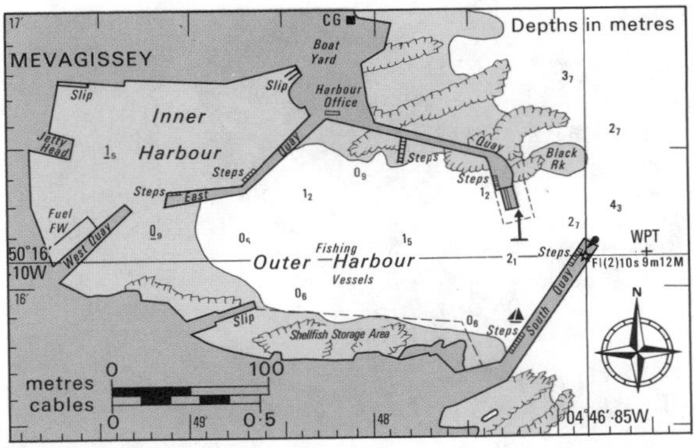
MEVAGISSEY
Depths in metres
CG
Boat Yard
Slip
Harbour Office
Inner Harbour
Jetty Head
Quay
Steps
East
Fuel FW
West Quay
Black Rk
Fishing
Outer Harbour
Vessels
WPT
Fl(2)10s 9m12M
Shellfish Storage Area
South Quay
Steps
50°16'·10W
metres
cables
0
100
0·5
04°46'·85W

NAVIGATION

Waypoint 50°16'·11N 04°46'·54W, 090°/270° from/to pierhead Lt, 0·20M. Beware rock ledges off the N Quay. Harbour entrance between breakwaters is 46m wide. Speed limit in the harbour is 3 kn. Harbour is crowded and is used by large number of fishing boats.

LIGHTS AND MARKS

S Quay Fl (2) 10s 9m 12M; Dia (1) 30s (occas).

RADIO TELEPHONE

Hr Mr VHF Ch 16; 14 (Summer 0900–2100 LT. Winter 0900–1700 LT).

TELEPHONE (0726)

Hr Mr 842496; MRSC Brixham 882704; # (0752) 220661; Marinecall 0898 500 458; Police 842262; Dr 843701.

FACILITIES

EC Thursday; **N Quay** L, FW; **S Quay** L, FW, AB; **W Quay** P, D, L, FW; **J. Moores BY** ☎ 842962, Slip, Sh (wood), CH; **Jetty Head** L, FW; **Inner Harbour** Slip, M, L; **Village** V, R, ▣, Gas, Bar. ✉; Ⓑ (June-Sept 1000-1430, Oct-June 1000-1300); ≹ (bus to St. Austell); ✈ (Newquay).

FOWEY 10-1-15

Cornwall

CHARTS

Admiralty 31, 148, 1267; Stanford 13; Imray C6, Y52; OS 204

TIDES

−0540 Dover; ML 3·1; Duration 0605; Zone 0 (GMT).

Standard Port DEVONPORT (⟶)

Times				Height (metres)			
HW		LW		MHWS	MHWN	MLWN	MLWS
0000	0600	0000	0600	5·5	4·4	2·2	0·8
1200	1800	1200	1800				
Differences FOWEY							
−0010	−0015	−0010	−0005	−0·1	−0·1	−0·2	−0·2
PAR							
−0005	−0015	0000	−0010	−0·4	−0·4	−0·4	−0·2

SHELTER

Good sheltered harbour but partly exposed to winds from S to SW. Gales from these directions can cause heavy swells in the lower harbour and confused seas, especially on the ebb. Entry at any tide in any conditions. Visitors buoys are white and marked 'FHC – visitors'. Visitors moorings situated in Pont Pill, in the main stream opposite Albert Quay and at Mixtow Pill (1M upstream). Pont Pill offers double berth fore and aft moorings and 60' of moorings on a floating pontoon. In the stream there is a line of single swinging moorings and another 60' of mooring pontoon. Mixtow offers 60' of pontoon mooring in quieter conditions. Pontoons are in situ May to October. Albert Quay – there is a 'T' shaped pontoon offering a deep water mooring for a short stay (2 hours), FW available.

FOWEY *continued*

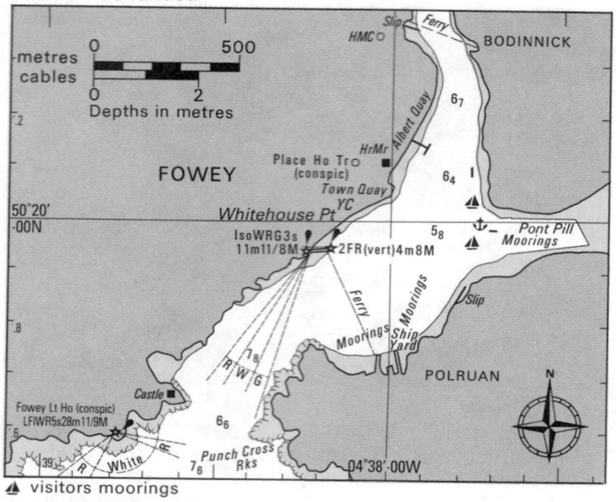

metres
cables
0 500
0 2
Depths in metres
BODINNICK
HMC
Slip
Ferry
Albert Quay
Place Ho Tr
(conspic)
HrMr
FOWEY
Town Quay
YC
Whitehouse Pt
50°20'·00N
IsoWRG3s
11m11/8M
2FR(vert)4m8M
Pont Pill
Moorings
Ferry
Moorings
Slip
Ship Yard
POLRUAN
Castle
Fowey Lt Ho (conspic)
LFlWR5s28m11/9M
Punch Cross Rks
White
04°38'·00W

▲ visitors moorings

NAVIGATION
Waypoint 50°19'·30N 04°38'·70W, 205°/025° from/to Whitehouse Pt Lt, Iso WRG, 0·72M. From E beware Udder Rk (3 M E of entrance); from SW beware Cannis Rk (4 ca SE of Gribbin Head). Entering, keep well clear of Punch Cross Ledge. Fowey is a busy commercial port, so take necessary precautions. Speed limit 6 kn. Navigable up to Lostwithiel at HW for boats with shallow draught. Channel is unmarked.

LIGHTS AND MARKS
A daymark on Gribbin Head, RW Tower on headland, 76m, can be seen from all sea directions. Fowey Lt Ho, L Fl WR 5s 28m 11/9M R 284°-295°, W 295°-028°, R 028°-054°.

RADIO TELEPHONE
Call *Fowey Harbour Radio* VHF Ch 16; 11 **12** (office hours). Boat Marshall Patrol (0900-2000 LT) Ch 16 12. Other stations: Charlestown Ch 16; 14 (HW−1 to HW+1 and when vessel expected). Par (call: *Par Port Radio*) Ch 16; 12 (Office hours and HW−2 to HW+1). Call *Fowey Refueller* Ch 16; 1 Water taxi VHF Ch 06.

TELEPHONE (0726)
Hr Mr 832471; MRSC Brixham 882704; # (0752) 220661; Marinecall 0898 500 458; Police (St Austell) (0726) 72313; Ⓗ 832241; Dr 832451.

FACILITIES
EC Wednesday and Saturday; **Royal Fowey YC** ☎ 832245, FW, R, Bar; **Upper Deck Marine** ☎ 832287, M, Gas, Gaz, CH; **Troy Chandlery** ☎ 833265, CH, Gas, Gaz, ACA, Ⓔ; **Albert Quay Pontoon** L, FW; **Polruan Quay** Slip, P, D, L, FW, C (3 ton); **C. Toms BY** ☎ Polruan 232, Slip (up to 21m by arrangement), FW, ME, El, Sh, C (7 ton), CH; **Fowey Gallants SC** ☎ 832335, Bar; **Winklepicker** ☎ Polruan 296, CH; **Fowey Refueller** (0900–1800 LT daily – winter Mon–Fri) or ☎ 87697 P, D; Emergencies ☎ Polruan 697 **Town** ⊡, ✉; Ⓑ; ≷ (bus to Par); ✈ (Newquay).
A port guide is available from harbour office.

LOOE 10-1-16
Cornwall

CHARTS
Admiralty 147, 148, 1267; Stanford 13; Imray C6; OS 201

TIDES
−0538 Dover; ML 3·0; Duration 0610; Zone 0 (GMT).

Standard Port DEVONPORT (→)

Times				Height (metres)			
HW		LW		MHWS	MHWN	MLWN	MLWS
0000	0600	0000	0600	5·5	4·4	2·2	0·8
1200	1800	1200	1800				
Differences LOOE							
−0010	−0010	−0005	−0005	−0·1	−0·2	−0·2	−0·2
WHITSAND BAY							
0000	0000	0000	0000	0·0	+0·1	−0·1	+0·2

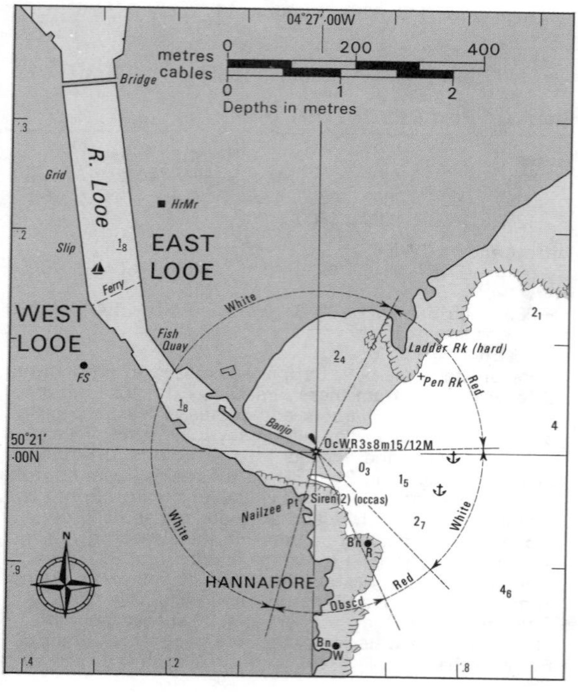

04°27'·00W
metres
cables
0 200 400
0 1 2
Depths in metres
Bridge
R. Looe
Grid
HrMr
Slip
EAST LOOE
Ferry
WEST LOOE
FS
Fish Quay
White
Ladder Rk (hard)
Pen Rk
Red
Banjo
50°21'·00N
OcWR3s8m15/12M
Nailzee Pt
Siren(2) (occas)
White
Bn
R
HANNAFORE
Red
Obscd
Bn
W

SHELTER
Good except in strong SE winds when the harbour becomes uncomfortable. The whole harbour dries. Visitors berth on W side of Hr marked in Y.

NAVIGATION
Waypoint 50°19'·73N 04°24'·60W, 130°/310° from/to pierhead Lt, 2·0M. Entrance dangerous in strong SE winds, when seas break over the bar heavily. Coming from W, beware Ranneys Rks extending SE and E from Looe Is. From E, beware Longstone Rks extending 1½ ca from shore NE of harbour entrance. At springs, tide runs up to 5 kn. Do not secure to W bank anywhere to S of shops due to rocky outcrops.

LIGHTS AND MARKS
Mid Main Beacon (off Hannafore Pt, halfway between pierhead and Looe Island) Q(3) 10s 2M; E cardinal mark. From West at night keep in W sector (267°-313°) of pierhead Lt Oc WR 3s 8m 15/12M; vis W013°-207°, R207°-267°, W267°-313°, R313°-332°. Nailzee Pt Siren (2) 30s.
R flag is displayed from FS on quay when it is too rough for small craft to put to sea.

RADIO TELEPHONE
VHF Ch 16 (no constant watch).

TELEPHONE (050 36)
Hr Mr 2839; CG 2138; MRSC Brixham 882704; # (0752) 220661; Marinecall 0898 500 458; Police 2233; Dr 3195.

FACILITIES
EC Thursday (winter only); **East Looe Quay** Access HW ∓3, Slip, P and D (cans), L, FW, ME, El, C (2½ ton), CH; **Looe SC** ☎ 2559, L, R, Bar; **West Looe Quay** Slip, M, P and D (cans), L, FW, ME, El, CH, AB; **Curtis Frank & Pope** ☎ 2332, Slip, M, Sh (Wood); **Marine Engineering Looe** ☎ 2887, ME, El, Ⓔ; **Pearn Norman & Co** ☎ 2244, Slip, M, ME, El, Sh, CH; **Jack Bray & Son** ☎ 2504, CH; **Millendreath Marine** ☎ 3003, CH; **Looe Harbour Chandlers** ☎ 4760, CH, El, Ⓔ, Gas; **Town** P, FW, V, R, Bar, ⊡, ✉; Ⓑ; ≷; ✈ (Plymouth).

PLYMOUTH 10-1-17 (DEVONPORT)

Devon

CHARTS
Admiralty 871, 1902, 1901, 30, 1967, 1613; Stanford 13; Imray C14, OS 201

TIDES
−0540 Dover; ML 3·3; Duration 0610; Zone 0 (GMT).

Standard Port DEVONPORT (⟶)

Times				Height (metres)			
HW		LW		MHWS	MHWN	MLWN	MLWS
0000	0600	0000	0600	5·5	4·4	2·2	0·8
1200	1800	1200	1800				
Differences JUPITER POINT							
+0010	+0005	0000	−0005	0·0	0·0	+0·1	0·0
SALTASH							
0000	+0010	0000	−0005	+0·1	+0·1	+0·1	+0·1
CARGREEN							
0000	+0010	+0020	+0020	0·0	0·0	−0·1	0·0
COTEHELE QUAY							
0000	+0020	+0045	+0045	−0·9	−0·9	−0·8	−0·4
ST GERMANS							
0000	0000	+0020	+0020	−0·3	−0·1	0·0	+0·2
BOVISAND PIER							
0000	−0020	0000	−0010	−0·2	−0·1	0·0	+0·1

NOTE: Devonport is a Standard Port and times and heights of tides are given below.

SHELTER
Excellent shelter. The entrance to the Sound can be made through either the west or east channel in both of which there is deep water. The Sound itself has no shallow patches with less than 3·7m at MLWS. Winds from SE to W increase the flood and retard the ebb, while winds from the NW to E have the opposite effect. The R Tamar which is joined by the R Tavy about 1¼ M above Saltash offers good shelter, as does the R Lynher. R Tamar is navigable to Cotehele, and beyond by shallow draught boats.

BYE LAWS
Plymouth is a Naval Base. The whole harbour comes under the jurisdiction of the Queen's Harbour Master although specific parts are allowed local control; Cattewater Harbour Commissioners; Sutton Harbour Improvements Co; Associated British Ports run Mill Bay Docks. There is frequent movement of naval vessels. These vessels have right of way in the channels. Signals are hoisted on HM Ships and at the Long Room and Flag Staff Steps and apply to the waters off the dockyard port and 125m either side of the deep water channel out to the western entrance of the breakwater. The Cattewater, Mill Bay Docks and Sutton Harbour are excluded. Plymouth is also a busy commercial port principally using Mill Bay Docks, and a busy fishing port based mainly on the Barbican area.

NAVIGATION
Waypoint 50°19'·70N 04°09'·80W, 213°/033° from/to West breakwater Lt, 0·40M. There are no real hazards entering the harbour as it is very well lit and buoyed. It is not advised to go between Drake's Island and Mount Edgcumbe although this is a short cut to the Hamoaze (known as the Bridge) and has about 1·7m at LWS and is buoyed. As will be seen from the chart, yachts need not keep to the deep water channels.

HMS Cambridge at Wembury has a firing range out to sea. Firing usually occurs between 0830 and 1700 (LT) Tuesday to Friday inclusive and when in progress 3 large red flags are flown at Wembury Point and from Penlee. HMS Cambridge can be called up on VHF Ch 16 (working 10, 11) if you are worried about being near the closed area. To enter the Sound during firings, keep to the W of Eddystone. HMS Cambridge Range Officer ☎ 553740, ext 412 (office hours) or Quartermaster on ext 406 (other times).

LIGHTS AND MARKS
Wembury Pt Oc Y 10s (occas). W end of breakwater Fl WR 10s 19m 15/12M (vis W 262°-208°, R 208°-262°) and Iso 4s 12m 12M (vis 031°-039°). E end of breakwater Iso WR 5s 9m 8M vis R190°-353°, W353°-001°, R001°-018°, W018°-190°. Mallard Shoal Ldg Lts 349°. Front Q WRG 10/3M (vis G 233°-043°, R 043°-067°, G 067°-087°, W 087°-099°, R 099°-108°). Rear 396m from front (on Hoe) Oc G 1·3s (vis 310°-040°).
Dir Lts, with W sectors showing the leading lines, are established at Withyhedge (070°), West Hoe Bn (315°), Mill Bay (048°30'), Western Kings (271°), Ravenness (225°), Mount Wise (343°). In each case above a G sector indicates that the yacht is to stbd of the leading line, and a R sector that she is to port of it.
In fog the following Dir Lts show white lights as indicated: Mallard (front) Fl 5s (vis 232°-110°); Royal Western YC F (vis 313°-317°); Ravenness Dir WRG 11m 13/5M. Fog Fl (2) 15s vis 160°-305°; Mount Wise F (vis 341°-345°).
Note: Principal lights in Plymouth Sound may show QY in the event of a mains power failure.

TRAFFIC SIGNALS
See below.

RADIO TELEPHONE
Call: *Long Room Port Control* VHF Ch 16; 08 12 14 (H24).
Call: *Mill Bay Docks* Ch 16; 14 (During ferry operations only).
Call: *Sutton Harbour Radio* Ch 16; **80** M (1 Apr- 15 Oct: 0830-2000. 16 Oct-31 Mar: 0900-1800 LT). Mayflower Marina, Queen Anne's Battery Marina, Sutton Harbour Marina, Ballast Pound Yacht Harbour and Royal Western YC Ch **80** M Call: *Cattewater Harbour Office* Ch 16; 12 (Mon-Fri, 0900-1700 LT).

TELEPHONE (0752)
Hr Mr QHM 663225; Cattewater Hr Mr 665934; Associated British Docks at Mill Bay 662191; MRSC Brixham 882704; Control Centre 53777 Ex 12 or 62; # (0752) 220661; Marinecall 0898 500 458; Weather Centre 402534; Police 701188; Dr 53533; Ⓗ 668080.

FACILITIES
EC Wednesday
Mayflower International Marina (220+60 visitors) ☎ 556633, Slip, P, D, FW, ME, El, Sh, AC, C (2 ton), BH (25 ton), CH, V, R, Gas, Gaz, Divers, SM, Bar, BY, YC, ⊡; **Sutton Harbour Marina** (310) ☎ 664186, P, D, FW, AC, C (3 ton), Slip, ME, El, Sh, SM; **Queen Anne's Battery Marina** (240+60 visitors) ☎ 671142, Slip, ME, El, Sh, FW, BH (20 ton), C (50 ton), P, D, CH, Gas, ⊡, SM, V, R, AC, Bar; **Mill Bay Docks** ☎ 662191; facilities here are limited and yachtsmen should contact the Royal Western YC on arrival. **Mill Bay Village Marina** No visitors; **Ballast Pound Yacht Harbour** (50+10 visitors) ☎ 813658, FW, ME, El, Sh, AC, Diver, SM, Access HW∓2; **Boathaven** (10) ☎ Tavistock 832502, ME, El, SH, C (10 ton); **Royal Dockyard** has unlimited facilities but is expensive; **Seachest Nautical Bookshop** ☎ 222012 ACA; **A S Blagdon** ☎ 28155, ME, El, Sh, C (7 ton), P, D; **Eddystone Marine Repairs** ☎ 509974, El, ME, Sh; **Mashford Bros** ☎ 822232, ME, El, Sh, D, C (10 ton), Slip, Gas; **Sutton Marine Services** ☎ 662129, C (7 ton), CH, P, D; **Ocean Marine Services** ☎ 223922, El, CH; **Saltash Marine** ☎ Saltash 3885, CH, ACA; **A E Monsen** ☎ 664384, CH, ACA; **Fox Haggart** ☎ 662587, ME, Sh; **The Quarterdeck** ☎ 24567, ME, C (12 ton); **Royal Western YC of England** ☎ 660077; Bar, R, M, C (20 ton), D, P, CH, FW, L, ⊡, Slip; **Royal Plymouth Corinthian** ☎ 664327, M, R, Bar; **RNSA** c/o QHM ☎ 663225; **Weir Quay YC** ☎ Tavistock 840474; **Retreat BY** ☎ 228855, M, BY; **Greenham Marine** ☎ 228114, Ⓔ; **Tolley Marine Electronics** ☎ 222530, Ⓔ; **City** P, D, V, R, CH, ✉; Ⓑ; ⇌; ✈.

PLYMOUTH *continued*

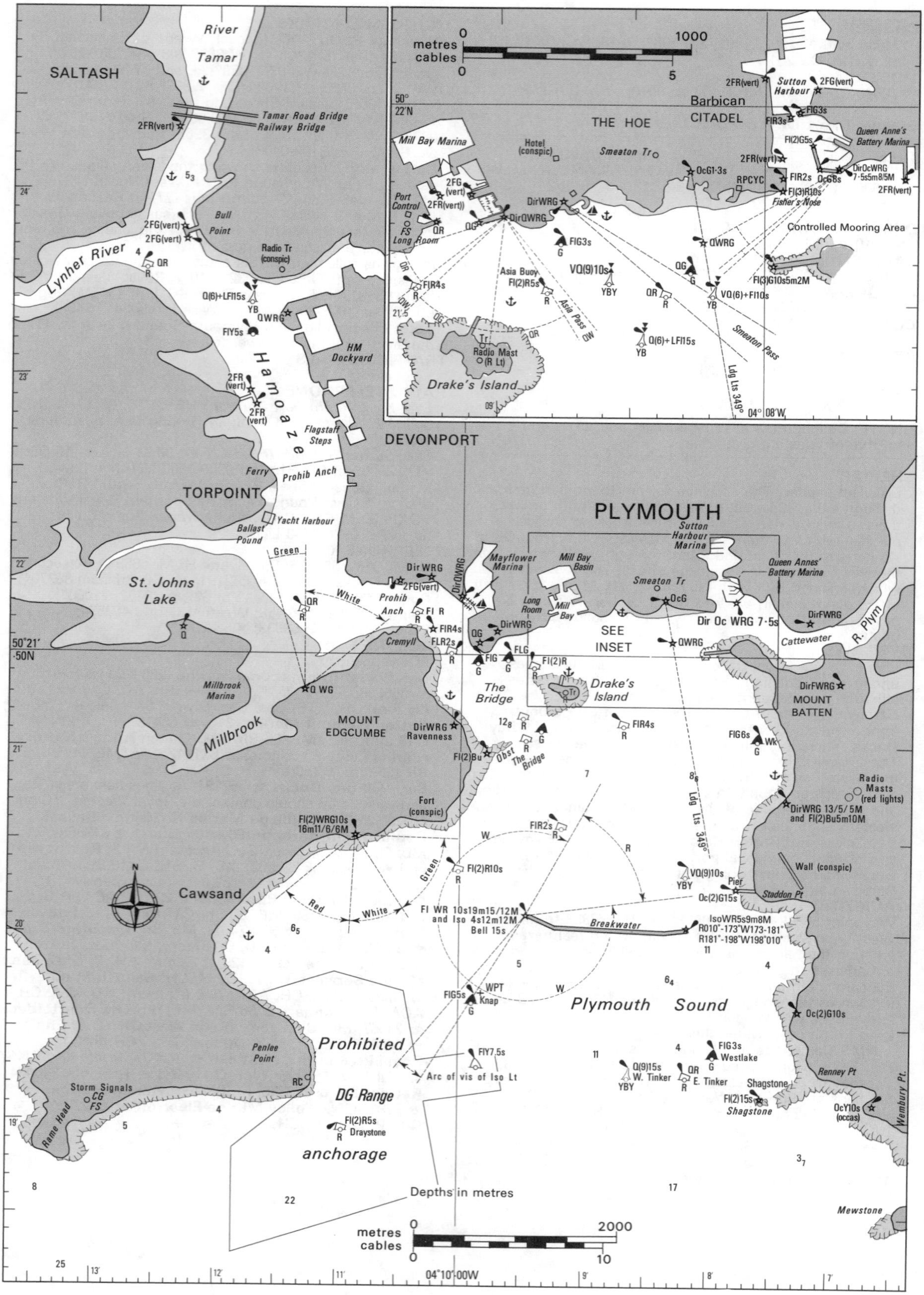
River Tamar
SALTASH
Tamar Road Bridge
Railway Bridge
Bull Point
Lynher River
Radio Tr (conspic)
Hamoaze
HM Dockyard
Flagstaff Steps
DEVONPORT
Ferry
Prohib Anch
TORPOINT
Yacht Harbour
Ballast Pound
St. Johns Lake
Millbrook Marina
Millbrook
MOUNT EDGCUMBE
Mayflower Marina
Cremyll
The Bridge
Drake's Island
SEE INSET
PLYMOUTH
Sutton Harbour Marina
Mill Bay Basin
Queen Annes' Battery Marina
Smeaton Tr
Cattewater
R. Plym
MOUNT BATTEN
Radio Masts (red lights)
Fort (conspic)
Cawsand
Breakwater
Wall (conspic)
Staddon Pt
Plymouth Sound
Prohibited
DG Range
anchorage
Penlee Point
Storm Signals
Rame Head
Arc of vis of Iso Lt
W. Tinker
E. Tinker
Westlake
Shagstone
Renney Pt
Wembury Pt.
Draystone
Mewstone
Depths in metres
metres 0 2000
cables 0 10
04°10'·00W
50°21'·50N
THE HOE
Barbican
CITADEL
Sutton Harbour
Queen Anne's Battery Marina
Mill Bay Marina
Hotel (conspic)
Port Control
Long Room
RPCYC
Fisher's Nose
Controlled Mooring Area
Asia Buoy
Asia Pass
Smeaton Pass
Radio Mast (R Lt)
Ldg Lts 349°
metres 0 1000
cables 0 5

PLYMOUTH *continued*

Traffic signals

Shown from Long Room and Morice Yard controlling the Main Ship Channel between the Breakwater and No1 Jetty

Day	Night	Meaning	Day	Meaning
	Red Green Green	No movement in Main Channel Small craft keep clear		Ship traffic between Sound and Hamoaze stopped
	White Green	Exit only in Main Channel Small craft keep clear		Caution necessary between Sound and Hamoaze
	Green White	Entry only in Main Channel Small craft keep clear		Caution necessary in Sound
	– Code – Pt9	Vessels may enter and leave but must give a wide berth to ships displaying Answering Pendant over Numeral Zero		Caution necessary in Hamoaze

Flown from HM ships and tugs — Code / Zero — Give wide berth to these vessels

Dock signals-Mill Bay

Shown from the head of Mill Bay Pier

Day	Night	Meaning	Day	Night	Meaning
	Green Green	Entry permitted to Outer Mill Bay		Red Red	Exit permitted from Outer Mill Bay

Shown from the head of Mill Bay Pier and W side of Lock

Day	Night	Meaning	Day	Night	Meaning
	Green Green Green	Entry permitted to the Inner Basin		Red Red Red	Exit permitted from the Inner Basin

Note. Coloured flags and lights are waved on occasions but these are only berthing instructions to large vessels and do not concern yachts.

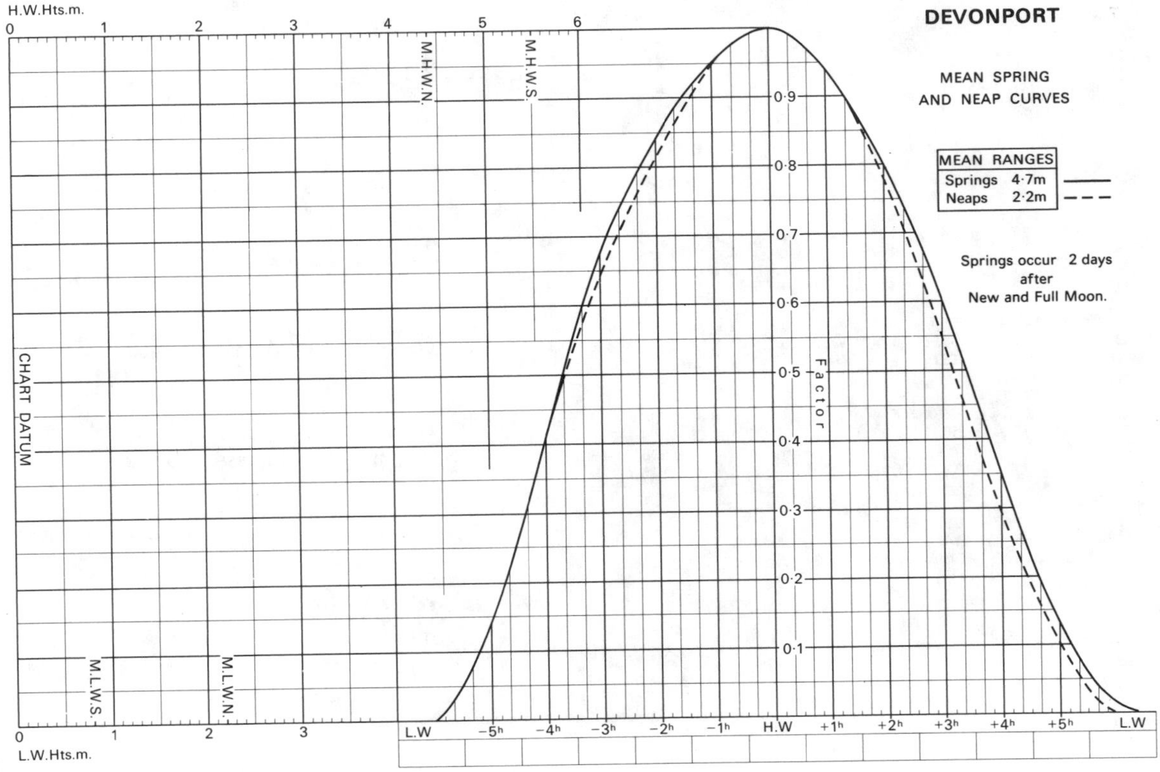

DEVONPORT
MEAN SPRING AND NEAP CURVES
MEAN RANGES
Springs 4·7m
Neaps 2·2m
Springs occur 2 days after New and Full Moon.
H.W.Hts.m.
M.H.W.N.
M.H.W.S.
CHART DATUM
M.L.W.S.
M.L.W.N.
L.W.Hts.m.
Factor
L.W -5h -4h -3h -2h -1h H.W +1h +2h +3h +4h +5h L.W

ENGLAND, SOUTH COAST - PLYMOUTH (DEVONPORT)

TIME ZONE UT(GMT)

For Summer Time add ONE hour in non-shaded areas

LAT 50°22'N LONG 4°11'W

TIMES AND HEIGHTS OF HIGH AND LOW WATERS

YEAR **1992**

JANUARY

Day	Time	m	Day	Time	m
1 W	0234 0852 1501 2120	4.7 2.0 4.6 1.8	**16** TH	0135 0803 1413 2044	4.5 2.1 4.5 1.9
2 TH	0333 0952 1600 2215	4.8 1.8 4.7 1.7	**17** F	0258 0924 1536 2155	4.7 1.7 4.7 1.5
3 F	0425 1043 1651 2301	5.0 1.6 4.9 1.5	**18** SA	0409 1028 1645 2252	5.1 1.3 5.0 1.1
4 SA	0511 1128 1735 ● 2343	5.2 1.4 5.0 1.4	**19** SU	0509 1122 1741 ○ 2343	5.4 0.9 5.3 0.8
5 SU	0552 1208 1814	5.3 1.3 5.0	**20** M	0601 1210 1832	5.7 0.5 5.5
6 M	0021 0628 1244 1849	1.3 5.3 1.2 5.0	**21** TU	0029 0648 1256 1917	0.5 5.8 0.3 5.6
7 TU	0056 0701 1317 1920	1.3 5.3 1.2 5.0	**22** W	0114 0732 1340 2000	0.4 5.9 0.3 5.5
8 W	0129 0731 1349 1949	1.3 5.3 1.3 4.9	**23** TH	0157 0814 1422 2041	0.5 5.8 0.4 5.4
9 TH	0200 0758 1420 2015	1.4 5.2 1.3 4.8	**24** F	0239 0854 1504 2120	0.6 5.6 0.7 5.2
10 F	0231 0824 1452 2042	1.5 5.0 1.4 4.8	**25** SA	0321 0933 1546 2200	0.9 5.3 1.0 4.9
11 SA	0304 0852 1527 2114	1.6 4.9 1.5 4.7	**26** SU	0403 1013 1629 ☾ 2243	1.3 5.0 1.4 4.7
12 SU	0342 0927 1607 2156	1.7 4.8 1.7 4.6	**27** M	0449 1059 1716 2333	1.7 4.7 1.8 4.5
13 M	0426 1016 1656 ☽ 2256	1.9 4.7 1.8 4.5	**28** TU	0542 1156 1813	2.0 4.4 2.1
14 TU	0521 1123 1758	2.0 4.5 2.0	**29** W	0034 0651 1305 1931	4.4 2.3 4.3 2.3
15 W	0011 0633 1245 1918	4.4 2.1 4.5 2.0	**30** TH	0146 0821 1423 2054	4.4 2.3 4.3 2.2
			31 F	0259 0935 1535 2157	4.6 2.0 4.4 1.9

FEBRUARY

Day	Time	m	Day	Time	m
1 SA	0401 1028 1633 2245	4.8 1.7 4.7 1.6	**16** SU	0357 1017 1636 2240	5.0 1.2 5.0 1.1
2 SU	0452 1112 1720 2326	5.0 1.4 4.9 1.4	**17** M	0457 1109 1730 2328	5.4 0.7 5.3 0.6
3 M ●	0535 1150 1759	5.2 1.2 5.0	**18** TU ○	0548 1155 1817	5.7 0.3 5.6
4 TU	0003 0612 1225 1834	1.2 5.3 1.0 5.1	**19** W	0013 0633 1238 1859	0.3 5.9 0.1 5.7
5 W	0037 0645 1257 1905	1.1 5.4 1.0 5.1	**20** TH	0056 0714 1319 1939	0.2 5.9 0.1 5.6
6 TH	0109 0715 1327 1933	1.0 5.3 1.0 5.1	**21** F	0136 0753 1359 2016	0.3 5.8 0.3 5.5
7 F	0139 0741 1357 1956	1.1 5.2 1.0 5.0	**22** SA	0215 0829 1437 2050	0.5 5.5 0.6 5.2
8 SA	0209 0802 1428 2016	1.1 5.1 1.1 4.9	**23** SU	0254 0903 1514 2122	0.8 5.2 1.0 5.0
9 SU	0241 0823 1500 2038	1.3 5.0 1.3 4.8	**24** M	0332 0936 1552 2158	1.2 4.9 1.5 4.7
10 M	0315 0850 1537 2113	1.4 4.9 1.5 4.7	**25** TU	0411 1016 1632 ☾ 2244	1.7 4.6 1.9 4.5
11 TU	0355 0932 1621 ☽ 2209	1.6 4.7 1.7 4.5	**26** W	0457 1109 1721 2344	2.1 4.3 2.2 4.3
12 W	0446 1040 1718 2331	1.9 4.4 2.0 4.4	**27** TH	0601 1219 1839	2.4 4.1 2.5
13 TH	0556 1213 1841	2.1 4.3 2.2	**28** F	0058 0748 1344 2028	4.3 2.4 4.1 2.4
14 F	0104 0737 1356 2025	4.4 2.2 4.3 2.0	**29** SA	0220 0914 1508 2135	4.4 2.1 4.3 2.0
15 SA	0239 0913 1528 2143	4.6 1.8 4.6 1.6			

MARCH

Day	Time	m	Day	Time	m
1 SU	0331 1006 1610 2223	4.6 1.8 4.6 1.7	**16** M	0340 0959 1620 2221	5.0 1.1 5.0 1.0
2 M	0426 1048 1657 2302	4.9 1.4 4.8 1.3	**17** TU	0439 1049 1711 2308	5.4 0.6 5.3 0.6
3 TU	0510 1124 1736 2338	5.2 1.1 5.1 1.1	**18** W	0528 1133 1756 ○ 2351	5.7 0.3 5.6 0.3
4 W ●	0549 1157 1812	5.3 0.9 5.2	**19** TH	0612 1215 1837	5.8 0.1 5.7
5 TH	0011 0623 1230 1843	0.9 5.4 0.8 5.2	**20** F	0033 0652 1255 1913	0.2 5.8 0.2 5.6
6 F	0043 0654 1301 1911	0.8 5.4 0.8 5.2	**21** SA	0113 0728 1333 1947	0.3 5.7 0.4 5.5
7 SA	0115 0721 1332 1936	0.8 5.3 0.8 5.1	**22** SU	0150 0802 1409 2018	0.5 5.4 0.7 5.3
8 SU	0146 0744 1404 1955	0.9 5.1 1.0 5.0	**23** M	0227 0832 1444 2047	0.9 5.1 1.1 5.0
9 M	0219 0803 1437 2016	1.1 5.0 1.2 4.9	**24** TU	0302 0903 1518 2120	1.3 4.8 1.6 4.8
10 TU	0254 0828 1514 2049	1.3 4.8 1.4 4.7	**25** W	0339 0940 1554 2203	1.7 4.5 1.9 4.5
11 W	0335 0911 1558 2147	1.5 4.6 1.7 4.5	**26** TH	0420 1032 1639 ☾ 2301	2.1 4.2 2.3 4.3
12 TH	0426 1026 1656 ☽ 2312	1.8 4.3 2.0 4.4	**27** F	0518 1139 1749	2.3 4.0 2.5
13 F	0538 1205 1823	2.1 4.2 2.2	**28** SA	0012 0658 1301 1943	4.2 2.4 4.0 2.5
14 SA	0048 0725 1349 2012	4.4 2.1 4.2 2.0	**29** SU	0132 0834 1425 2059	4.3 2.2 4.2 2.1
15 SU	0224 0859 1517 2126	4.6 1.7 4.6 1.5	**30** M	0247 0929 1531 2148	4.5 1.8 4.5 1.7
			31 TU	0347 1012 1621 2229	4.8 1.4 4.8 1.4

APRIL

Day	Time	m	Day	Time	m
1 W	0435 1049 1703 2306	5.1 1.1 5.1 1.1	**16** TH	0502 1107 1729 2327	5.5 0.5 5.5 0.5
2 TH	0517 1125 1741 2341	5.2 0.9 5.2 0.9	**17** F ○	0546 1149 1810	5.6 0.4 5.6
3 F ●	0555 1159 1816	5.3 0.7 5.3	**18** SA	0009 0626 1230 1846	0.4 5.6 0.5 5.5
4 SA	0016 0629 1234 1847	0.8 5.3 0.7 5.3	**19** SU	0049 0703 1307 1919	0.5 5.4 0.7 5.4
5 SU	0050 0701 1308 1916	0.8 5.3 0.8 5.2	**20** M	0127 0736 1343 1949	0.8 5.2 1.0 5.2
6 M	0125 0730 1343 1943	0.8 5.1 0.9 5.1	**21** TU	0203 0806 1417 2018	1.1 4.9 1.3 5.0
7 TU	0202 0758 1420 2011	1.0 4.9 1.1 5.0	**22** W	0238 0837 1451 2051	1.4 4.7 1.6 4.8
8 W	0241 0831 1500 2050	1.2 4.7 1.4 4.8	**23** TH	0313 0913 1526 2132	1.7 4.4 1.9 4.6
9 TH	0325 0923 1548 2151	1.5 4.5 1.7 4.6	**24** F	0353 1001 1608 ☾ 2225	2.0 4.2 2.2 4.4
10 F	0420 1037 1649 ☽ 2308	1.8 4.3 2.0 4.5	**25** SA	0445 1102 1708 2328	2.2 4.1 2.4 4.3
11 SA	0534 1204 1814	2.0 4.2 2.1	**26** SU	0558 1212 1834	2.3 4.1 2.4
12 SU	0034 0710 1336 1949	4.5 1.9 4.3 1.9	**27** M	0038 0727 1327 1959	4.3 2.2 4.2 2.2
13 M	0201 0832 1454 2100	4.6 1.6 4.6 1.5	**28** TU	0149 0834 1436 2059	4.5 1.9 4.4 1.9
14 TU	0314 0932 1555 2155	4.9 1.1 5.0 1.1	**29** W	0255 0925 1533 2146	4.7 1.6 4.7 1.5
15 W	0413 1022 1645 2243	5.3 0.7 5.3 0.7	**30** TH	0350 1008 1622 2229	4.9 1.3 5.0 1.2

Chart Datum: 3.22 metres below Ordnance Datum (Newlyn)

ENGLAND, SOUTH COAST - PLYMOUTH (DEVONPORT)

TIME ZONE UT(GMT)

For Summer Time add ONE hour in non-shaded areas

LAT 50°22'N LONG 4°11'W

TIMES AND HEIGHTS OF HIGH AND LOW WATERS

YEAR **1992**

MAY

Date	Day	Time	m	Time	m	Time	m	Time	m
1	F	0439	5.1	1049	1.0	1706	5.2	2309	1.0
2	SA ●	0523	5.2	1129	0.8	1746	5.3	2349	0.8
3	SU	0605	5.2	1208	0.8	1824	5.3		
4	M	0028	0.8	0644	5.2	1247	0.8	1901	5.3
5	TU	0109	0.8	0722	5.1	1327	0.9	1937	5.2
6	W	0150	0.9	0802	4.9	1409	1.1	2016	5.1
7	TH	0234	1.1	0846	4.8	1454	1.3	2102	4.9
8	F	0323	1.3	0939	4.6	1545	1.6	2157	4.8
9	SA ☽	0418	1.5	1042	4.4	1644	1.8	2302	4.7
10	SU	0525	1.7	1153	4.4	1756	1.9		
11	M	0014	4.6	0641	1.7	1308	4.5	1915	1.8
12	TU	0129	4.7	0756	1.5	1419	4.6	2025	1.6
13	W	0239	4.9	0859	1.3	1520	4.9	2124	1.3
14	TH	0340	5.0	0952	1.0	1613	5.1	2216	1.0
15	F	0433	5.2	1040	0.9	1700	5.3	2303	0.8
16	SA ○	0520	5.3	1124	0.8	1742	5.4	2346	0.8
17	SU	0602	5.2	1206	0.8	1821	5.4		
18	M	0028	0.8	0640	5.2	1245	1.0	1855	5.3
19	TU	0107	1.0	0715	5.0	1322	1.2	1927	5.2
20	W	0144	1.2	0747	4.8	1357	1.4	1958	5.0
21	TH	0219	1.4	0818	4.7	1431	1.6	2030	4.9
22	F	0254	1.6	0853	4.5	1506	1.8	2107	4.7
23	SA	0331	1.8	0934	4.4	1545	2.0	2152	4.6
24	SU ☾	0414	1.9	1024	4.3	1632	2.1	2244	4.5
25	M	0507	2.0	1122	4.2	1732	2.2	2343	4.4
26	TU	0612	2.0	1225	4.3	1843	2.2		
27	W	0047	4.5	0722	1.9	1332	4.4	1954	2.0
28	TH	0154	4.5	0828	1.7	1437	4.6	2057	1.8
29	F	0259	4.7	0924	1.5	1536	4.8	2151	1.5
30	SA	0359	4.9	1015	1.2	1629	5.0	2240	1.2
31	SU	0453	5.0	1102	1.0	1719	5.2	2326	0.9

JUNE

Date	Day	Time	m	Time	m	Time	m	Time	m
1	M ●	0543	5.1	1147	0.9	1805	5.3		
2	TU	0012	0.8	0630	5.2	1232	0.8	1849	5.4
3	W	0057	0.7	0717	5.1	1317	0.8	1933	5.4
4	TH	0143	0.7	0802	5.1	1402	0.9	2017	5.3
5	F	0229	0.8	0849	4.9	1448	1.0	2103	5.2
6	SA	0317	1.0	0938	4.8	1537	1.2	2152	5.0
7	SU ☽	0408	1.2	1031	4.7	1630	1.4	2247	4.9
8	M	0504	1.4	1128	4.6	1729	1.6	2346	4.8
9	TU	0606	1.5	1230	4.5	1835	1.7		
10	W	0051	4.7	0713	1.6	1336	4.6	1945	1.7
11	TH	0159	4.7	0820	1.5	1440	4.7	2051	1.6
12	F	0304	4.7	0921	1.4	1539	4.9	2149	1.4
13	SA	0404	4.8	1014	1.3	1631	5.0	2241	1.2
14	SU	0456	4.9	1103	1.2	1718	5.1	2328	1.1
15	M ○	0542	5.0	1147	1.1	1800	5.2		
16	TU	0012	1.1	0623	5.0	1228	1.2	1837	5.2
17	W	0052	1.1	0659	4.9	1306	1.2	1911	5.2
18	TH	0128	1.2	0732	4.8	1341	1.3	1942	5.1
19	F	0202	1.3	0803	4.7	1414	1.4	2013	5.0
20	SA	0235	1.4	0833	4.7	1446	1.6	2044	4.9
21	SU	0308	1.5	0906	4.6	1520	1.7	2119	4.8
22	M	0344	1.6	0945	4.5	1559	1.8	2200	4.7
23	TU ☾	0425	1.7	1031	4.4	1644	1.9	2249	4.6
24	W	0515	1.8	1126	4.4	1740	2.0	2348	4.5
25	TH	0615	1.9	1230	4.4	1847	2.0		
26	F	0055	4.4	0726	1.9	1340	4.5	2003	1.9
27	SA	0209	4.5	0840	1.7	1451	4.6	2115	1.7
28	SU	0322	4.6	0945	1.5	1558	4.9	2217	1.4
29	M	0429	4.8	1042	1.2	1657	5.1	2310	1.0
30	TU ●	0528	5.0	1133	0.9	1750	5.3		

JULY

Date	Day	Time	m	Time	m	Time	m	Time	m
1	W	0000	0.7	0620	5.2	1221	0.7	1839	5.5
2	TH	0047	0.5	0709	5.3	1307	0.6	1925	5.6
3	F	0133	0.4	0755	5.3	1352	0.6	2010	5.5
4	SA	0218	0.5	0839	5.2	1436	0.7	2053	5.4
5	SU	0303	0.6	0923	5.1	1521	0.8	2137	5.3
6	M	0348	0.9	1008	4.9	1608	1.1	2223	5.0
7	TU ☽	0436	1.2	1056	4.7	1658	1.4	2314	4.8
8	W	0528	1.5	1149	4.6	1754	1.7		
9	TH	0011	4.6	0628	1.7	1250	4.5	1901	1.9
10	F	0117	4.5	0739	1.9	1357	4.5	2017	1.9
11	SA	0229	4.4	0852	1.8	1505	4.6	2128	1.8
12	SU	0338	4.5	0955	1.7	1606	4.8	2226	1.6
13	M	0437	4.6	1047	1.5	1658	5.0	2315	1.3
14	TU ○	0526	4.8	1132	1.3	1743	5.1	2357	1.2
15	W	0608	4.9	1212	1.2	1822	5.2		
16	TH	0035	1.1	0644	4.9	1249	1.1	1856	5.2
17	F	0110	1.1	0716	4.9	1322	1.1	1927	5.2
18	SA	0142	1.1	0745	4.9	1353	1.2	1955	5.1
19	SU	0212	1.2	0812	4.8	1423	1.3	2021	5.0
20	M	0242	1.2	0838	4.8	1453	1.4	2047	4.9
21	TU	0313	1.3	0906	4.7	1527	1.5	2118	4.8
22	W ☾	0349	1.5	0941	4.6	1605	1.7	2158	4.6
23	TH	0430	1.7	1029	4.5	1652	1.8	2253	4.5
24	F	0523	1.9	1134	4.4	1753	2.0		
25	SA	0005	4.4	0632	2.0	1252	4.4	1915	2.1
26	SU	0129	4.3	0802	2.0	1415	4.5	2049	1.9
27	M	0258	4.5	0925	1.7	1535	4.8	2201	1.5
28	TU	0415	4.7	1027	1.3	1642	5.1	2258	1.0
29	W ●	0516	5.1	1120	0.8	1737	5.4	2347	0.6
30	TH	0609	5.3	1207	0.5	1827	5.7		
31	F	0033	0.3	0655	5.5	1252	0.3	1912	5.8

AUGUST

Date	Day	Time	m	Time	m	Time	m	Time	m
1	SA	0117	0.2	0739	5.5	1335	0.2	1954	5.8
2	SU	0200	0.2	0820	5.4	1417	0.4	2035	5.6
3	M	0242	0.4	0900	5.3	1459	0.6	2115	5.4
4	TU	0323	0.7	0939	5.0	1541	0.9	2155	5.1
5	W ☽	0406	1.1	1021	4.8	1626	1.3	2239	4.8
6	TH	0451	1.5	1108	4.6	1715	1.7	2332	4.5
7	F	0545	1.9	1206	4.4	1819	2.1		
8	SA	0037	4.3	0657	2.2	1316	4.3	1947	2.2
9	SU	0157	4.2	0828	2.2	1434	4.4	2112	2.0
10	M	0317	4.3	0939	1.9	1544	4.6	2212	1.7
11	TU	0420	4.5	1031	1.6	1639	4.9	2258	1.4
12	W	0509	4.8	1114	1.3	1724	5.1	2338	1.2
13	TH ○	0549	5.0	1152	1.1	1802	5.3		
14	F	0013	1.0	0624	5.1	1226	1.0	1836	5.3
15	SA	0046	0.9	0655	5.1	1258	0.9	1906	5.3
16	SU	0116	0.9	0723	5.1	1328	1.0	1933	5.2
17	M	0145	1.0	0748	5.0	1357	1.1	1957	5.1
18	TU	0214	1.1	0810	4.9	1426	1.2	2017	5.0
19	W	0244	1.2	0830	4.8	1458	1.3	2040	4.9
20	TH	0317	1.4	0857	4.7	1534	1.5	2113	4.7
21	F ☾	0356	1.6	0941	4.6	1618	1.8	2207	4.5
22	SA	0445	1.9	1050	4.4	1716	2.0	2329	4.3
23	SU	0555	2.1	1218	4.3	1844	2.2		
24	M	0106	4.2	0737	2.2	1352	4.4	2033	2.0
25	TU	0245	4.4	0910	1.8	1519	4.8	2148	1.5
26	W	0403	4.8	1013	1.3	1627	5.2	2243	0.9
27	TH	0502	5.2	1103	0.8	1721	5.6	2330	0.5
28	F ●	0551	5.5	1149	0.4	1809	5.8		
29	SA	0014	0.2	0636	5.7	1233	0.1	1852	5.9
30	SU	0057	0.1	0717	5.7	1314	0.1	1933	5.9
31	M	0137	0.2	0756	5.6	1355	0.3	2012	5.7

Chart Datum: 3.22 metres below Ordnance Datum (Newlyn)

ENGLAND, SOUTH COAST - PLYMOUTH (DEVONPORT)

TIME ZONE UT(GMT)

For Summer Time add ONE hour in non-shaded areas

LAT 50°22'N LONG 4°11'W

TIMES AND HEIGHTS OF HIGH AND LOW WATERS

YEAR **1992**

SEPTEMBER

Day	Time	m	Day	Time	m
1	0217	0.4	16	0147	1.0
	0832	5.4		0745	5.1
TU	1434	0.6	W	1402	1.1
	2048	5.4		1954	5.0
2	0256	0.8	17	0219	1.2
	0908	5.1		0804	5.0
W	1514	1.0	TH	1435	1.3
	2124	5.0		2013	4.9
3	0335	1.3	18	0253	1.4
	0944	4.9		0829	4.8
TH	1555	1.5	F	1512	1.5
☽	2204	4.7		2046	4.7
4	0416	1.7	19	0333	1.7
	1028	4.6		0914	4.6
F	1640	1.9	SA	1557	1.8
	2254	4.4	☾	2145	4.4
5	0504	2.1	20	0423	2.0
	1124	4.4		1028	4.5
SA	1740	2.3	SU	1658	2.1
				2315	4.2
6	0000	4.1	21	0535	2.2
	0616	2.4		1159	4.4
SU	1236	4.3	M	1830	2.2
	1918	2.4			
7	0124	4.1	22	0055	4.2
	0802	2.4		0721	2.2
M	1359	4.4	TU	1335	4.5
	2052	2.2		2017	2.0
8	0250	4.2	23	0232	4.5
	0917	2.1		0851	1.8
TU	1514	4.6	W	1501	4.8
	2149	1.8		2128	1.4
9	0354	4.5	24	0345	4.9
	1007	1.7		0951	1.3
W	1611	4.9	TH	1606	5.3
	2232	1.5		2221	0.9
10	0442	4.8	25	0441	5.3
	1048	1.4		1041	0.8
TH	1656	5.1	F	1700	5.6
	2309	1.2		2307	0.5
11	0521	5.1	26	0529	5.6
	1124	1.1		1127	0.4
F	1735	5.3	SA	1747	5.8
	2343	0.9	●	2351	0.2
12	0557	5.2	27	0612	5.7
	1157	0.9		1209	0.2
SA	1810	5.4	SU	1830	5.9
○					
13	0015	0.8	28	0032	0.2
	0629	5.3		0652	5.8
SU	1230	0.9	M	1251	0.2
	1841	5.4		1909	5.8
14	0047	0.8	29	0113	0.3
	0658	5.3		0729	5.7
M	1300	0.9	TU	1331	0.4
	1909	5.3		1946	5.6
15	0117	0.9	30	0151	0.6
	0724	5.2		0804	5.5
TU	1331	1.0	W	1410	0.8
	1934	5.2		2021	5.3

OCTOBER

Day	Time	m	Day	Time	m
1	0229	1.0	16	0159	1.2
	0836	5.2		0752	5.1
TH	1448	1.2	F	1419	1.3
	2054	5.0		2007	4.9
2	0306	1.5	17	0237	1.5
	0910	4.9		0823	4.9
F	1527	1.6	SA	1500	1.5
	2131	4.6		2046	4.7
3	0344	1.9	18	0321	1.7
	0951	4.7		0911	4.8
SA	1610	2.0	SU	1549	1.8
☽	2218	4.3		2148	4.5
4	0429	2.3	19	0414	2.0
	1045	4.5		1022	4.6
SU	1706	2.3	M	1652	2.0
	2322	4.1	☾	2312	4.3
5	0535	2.5	20	0527	2.2
	1153	4.3		1145	4.5
M	1835	2.5	TU	1818	2.1
6	0041	4.1	21	0043	4.4
	0718	2.5		0659	2.1
TU	1312	4.4	W	1314	4.7
	2011	2.3		1950	1.9
7	0205	4.2	22	0210	4.6
	0838	2.3		0822	1.8
W	1429	4.6	TH	1435	4.9
	2111	2.0		2059	1.4
8	0312	4.5	23	0319	4.9
	0930	1.9		0924	1.4
TH	1530	4.8	F	1540	5.2
	2155	1.6		2154	1.0
9	0403	4.8	24	0415	5.3
	1012	1.5		1016	0.9
F	1618	5.1	SA	1634	5.5
	2234	1.3		2242	0.7
10	0446	5.1	25	0503	5.5
	1050	1.2		1103	0.6
SA	1700	5.3	SU	1722	5.7
	2309	1.0	●	2326	0.5
11	0524	5.3	26	0547	5.7
	1125	1.0		1146	0.5
SU	1739	5.4	M	1805	5.7
○	2343	0.9			
12	0559	5.4	27	0008	0.5
	1159	0.9		0626	5.7
M	1814	5.4	TU	1229	0.5
				1845	5.7
13	0017	0.9	28	0049	0.6
	0631	5.4		0703	5.6
TU	1234	0.9	W	1309	0.7
	1845	5.4		1922	5.5
14	0051	0.9	29	0128	0.9
	0701	5.3		0738	5.5
W	1307	1.0	TH	1348	1.0
	1915	5.2		1956	5.2
15	0124	1.0	30	0205	1.3
	0727	5.2		0809	5.2
TH	1342	1.1	F	1426	1.3
	1941	5.1		2028	4.9
			31	0241	1.6
				0841	5.0
			SA	1504	1.7
				2103	4.6

NOVEMBER

Day	Time	m	Day	Time	m
1	0318	1.9	16	0315	1.6
	0919	4.8		0917	5.0
SU	1545	2.0	M	1546	1.6
	2146	4.4		2156	4.6
2	0400	2.2	17	0409	1.8
	1008	4.6		1017	4.8
M	1634	2.2	TU	1645	1.7
☽	2242	4.3	☾	2304	4.5
3	0455	2.4	18	0513	2.0
	1108	4.5		1128	4.8
TU	1740	2.4	W	1756	1.8
	2350	4.2			
4	0611	2.5	19	0020	4.5
	1216	4.5		0629	2.0
W	1903	2.3	TH	1245	4.8
				1913	1.8
5	0104	4.3	20	0138	4.7
	0735	2.4		0746	1.8
TH	1328	4.6	F	1401	4.9
	2013	2.1		2024	1.6
6	0215	4.5	21	0246	4.9
	0838	2.1		0852	1.5
F	1435	4.7	SA	1509	5.1
	2106	1.8		2124	1.3
7	0314	4.8	22	0345	5.2
	0928	1.8		0949	1.2
SA	1532	5.0	SU	1607	5.3
	2151	1.5		2216	1.0
8	0403	5.0	23	0437	5.4
	1012	1.5		1040	1.0
SU	1621	5.2	M	1658	5.4
	2232	1.3		2303	0.9
9	0448	5.3	24	0522	5.5
	1052	1.2		1126	0.9
M	1705	5.3	TU	1744	5.5
	2312	1.1	●	2347	0.9
10	0528	5.4	25	0604	5.6
	1131	1.1		1210	0.9
TU	1746	5.4	W	1825	5.4
○	2350	1.0			
11	0606	5.5	26	0029	1.0
	1210	1.0		0642	5.6
W	1825	5.3	TH	1252	1.0
				1903	5.3
12	0028	1.0	27	0109	1.1
	0642	5.4		0716	5.4
TH	1249	1.0	F	1331	1.2
	1901	5.3		1937	5.1
13	0107	1.0	28	0146	1.3
	0716	5.4		0748	5.3
F	1329	1.1	SA	1409	1.4
	1937	5.1		2008	4.9
14	0147	1.2	29	0222	1.6
	0751	5.3		0819	5.1
SA	1410	1.2	SU	1445	1.6
	2015	5.0		2040	4.7
15	0229	1.4	30	0257	1.8
	0829	5.1		0853	5.0
SU	1455	1.4	M	1521	1.8
	2059	4.8		2117	4.6

DECEMBER

Day	Time	m	Day	Time	m
1	0334	2.0	16	0357	1.4
	0933	4.8		1006	5.1
TU	1602	2.0	W	1629	1.4
	2203	4.5	☾	2246	4.7
2	0417	2.2	17	0452	1.6
	1022	4.7		1105	4.9
W	1649	2.1	TH	1727	1.6
☽	2258	4.4		2350	4.6
3	0510	2.3	18	0555	1.8
	1120	4.6		1212	4.8
TH	1748	2.2	F	1834	1.7
4	0002	4.4	19	0059	4.6
	0616	2.3		0706	1.9
F	1225	4.6	SA	1325	4.8
	1856	2.2		1945	1.7
5	0110	4.5	20	0210	4.7
	0729	2.3		0819	1.8
SA	1333	4.6	SU	1437	4.8
	2005	2.0		2053	1.6
6	0217	4.6	21	0315	4.9
	0835	2.0		0925	1.6
SU	1439	4.7	M	1542	4.9
	2104	1.8		2153	1.5
7	0317	4.9	22	0413	5.1
	0932	1.8		1021	1.4
M	1540	4.9	TU	1639	5.1
	2156	1.5		2244	1.3
8	0411	5.1	23	0502	5.3
	1022	1.5		1111	1.2
TU	1634	5.1	W	1727	5.1
	2243	1.3		2331	1.2
9	0500	5.3	24	0547	5.4
	1108	1.2		1156	1.1
W	1723	5.2	TH	1810	5.2
○	2328	1.1	●		
10	0545	5.4	25	0013	1.1
	1152	1.0		0625	5.5
TH	1809	5.3	F	1238	1.1
				1848	5.2
11	0012	1.0	26	0053	1.2
	0627	5.5		0700	5.4
F	1236	1.0	SA	1316	1.1
	1852	5.3		1921	5.1
12	0055	0.9	27	0129	1.3
	0708	5.5		0731	5.3
SA	1320	0.9	SU	1351	1.2
	1935	5.2		1951	5.0
13	0138	1.0	28	0203	1.4
	0749	5.5		0800	5.2
SU	1404	0.9	M	1424	1.4
	2017	5.1		2019	4.9
14	0222	1.1	29	0235	1.5
	0831	5.4		0829	5.1
M	1449	1.0	TU	1456	1.5
	2101	5.0		2049	4.8
15	0308	1.2	30	0307	1.7
	0915	5.2		0901	5.0
TU	1537	1.2	W	1529	1.7
	2150	4.8		2124	4.7
			31	0342	1.8
				0939	4.8
			TH	1606	1.8
				2208	4.6

Chart Datum: 3.22 metres below Ordnance Datum (Newlyn)

YEALM RIVER 10-1-18

Devon

TELEPHONE (0752)
Hr Mr 872533; MRSC Brixham 882704; # (0752) 220661; Marinecall 0898 500 458; Police 701188; Dr 880392.

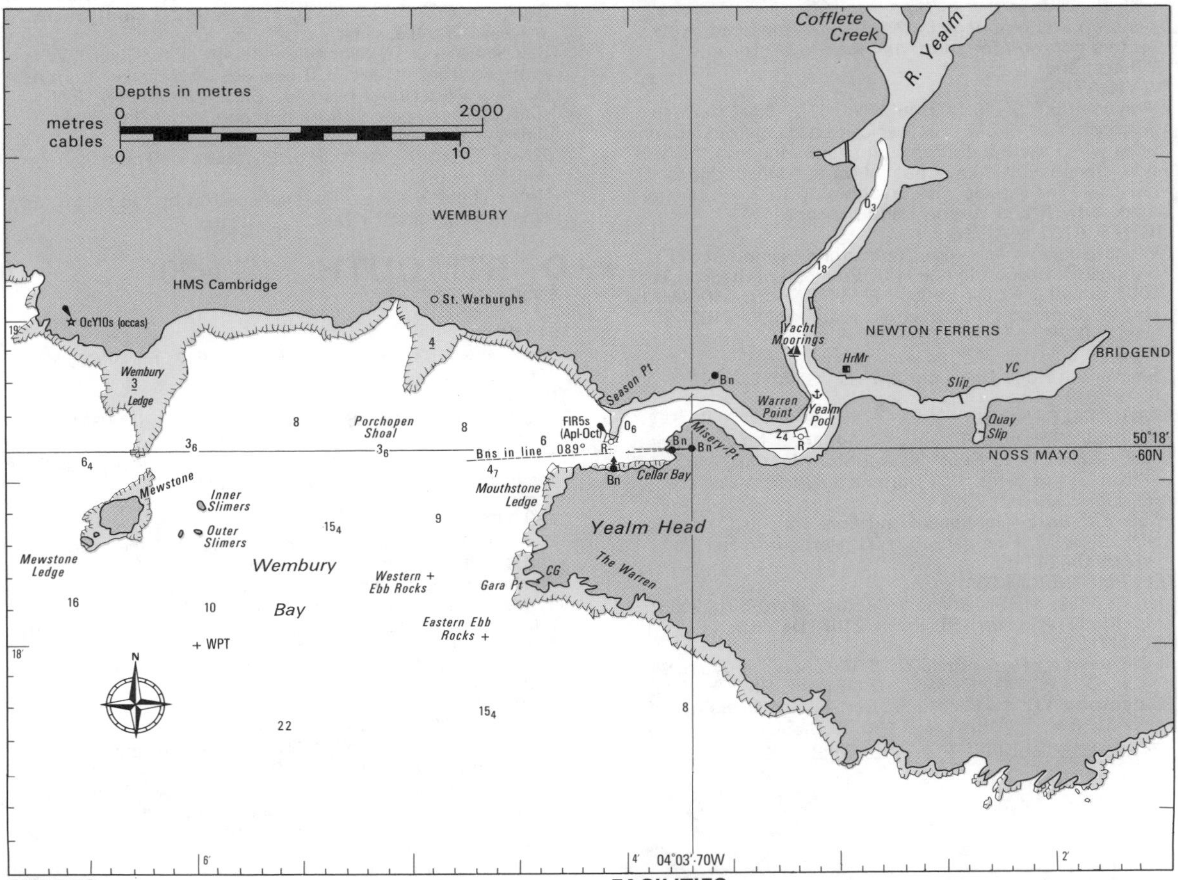

Depths in metres
metres
cables
0
2000
0
10
WEMBURY
HMS Cambridge
St. Werburghs
OcY10s (occas)
Wembury Ledge
Porchopen Shoal
Season Pt
FIR5s (Apl-Oct)
Bns in line 089°
Bn
Cellar Bay
Misery Pt
Mewstone
Inner Slimers
Outer Slimers
Mewstone Ledge
Mouthstone Ledge
Wembury Bay
Western Ebb Rocks
Eastern Ebb Rocks
Gara Pt
CG
Yealm Head
The Warren
WPT
Cofflete Creek
R. Yealm
Yacht Moorings
NEWTON FERRERS
HrMr
Warren Point
Yealm Pool
Slip
YC
BRIDGEND
Quay Slip
NOSS MAYO
50°18'·60N
04°03'·70W

CHARTS
Admiralty 28, 30, 1613; Stanford 13; Imray C6, C14; OS 201

TIDES
−0522 Dover; ML 3·2; Duration 0615; Zone 0 (GMT).

Standard Port DEVONPORT (←)

Times				Height (metres)			
HW		LW		MHWS	MHWN	MLWN	MLWS
0000	0600	0000	0600	5·5	4·4	2·2	0·8
1200	1800	1200	1800				
Differences YEALM RIVER ENTRANCE							
+0006	+0006	+0002	+0002	−0·1	−0·1	−0·1	−0·1

SHELTER
Very good shelter and easy entrance except in strong onshore winds. Anchorage in Cellar Bay open to NW winds.

NAVIGATION
Waypoint 50°18'·00N 04°06'·00W, 240°/060° from/to Season Pt, 1·4M. The W and E Ebb rocks and the Inner and Outer Slimers are dangerous, lying awash on either side of Wembury Bay. Ldg Bns at 089° clear Mouthstone Ledge on S side of ent. Beware sand bar running S from Season Pt, marked by port hand buoy Fl R 5s (April-Oct), leaving narrow channel on S side. Also sand spit running S from Warren Pt. You cannot beat in on an ebb tide. Strong SW winds hold up the ebb and increase levels, as does the river when in spate. Speed limit 6 kn.
For information about Wembury firing range, see 10.1.17.

LIGHTS AND MARKS
Leave 'spit' R can buoy off Warren Pt to port. From Sand Bar to Misery Pt is only 1·2 m at LWS. R can buoy, Fl R5s, marks end of sand bar (Apr-Oct); Ldg Bns at 089°. When abeam of Bn (G triangle on W back) on S shore, turn NE towards Bn on N shore.

RADIO TELEPHONE
None.

FACILITIES
EC Thursday; **Yealm Pool** M, L, FW; **Newton Ferrers Village** L, Slip, FW, V, Gas, Gaz, R, Bar; **Yealm Boat Co** ☎ 872564, ME, El, Ⓔ, Sh, Gas, Gaz, CH; **Yealm YC** ☎ 872291, FW, R, Bar; **Bridgend** L, Slip (HW∓2½), FW; **Bridgend Boat Co** ☎ 872162, ME, El, Sh; **Noss Mayo** L, Slip, FW, V, R, Bar; **J. Hockaday** ☎ 872369, El, ME; **A. Hooper** ☎ (075530) 411, SM. Nearest fuel 3M at Yealmpton.
✉ (Newton Ferrers, Noss Mayo); Ⓑ (Newton Ferrers, Tues and Thurs mornings only); ⇌ (Plymouth); ✈ (Plymouth).

SALCOMBE 10-1-19

Devon

CHARTS
Admiralty 28, 1634, 1613; Stanford 13; Imray C6, Y48; OS 202

TIDES
−0523 Dover; ML 3·1; Duration 0615; Zone 0 (GMT).

Standard Port DEVONPORT (←)

Times				Height (metres)			
HW		LW		MHWS	MHWN	MLWN	MLWS
0100	0600	0100	0600	5·5	4·4	2·2	0·8
1300	1800	1300	1800				
Differences SALCOMBE							
0000	+0010	+0005	−0005	−0·2	−0·3	−0·1	−0·1
START POINT							
+0005	+0030	−0005	+0005	−0·2	−0·4	−0·1	−0·1

SHELTER
Perfectly protected harbour but entrance is affected by S winds. The estuary is 4 M long and has 8 creeks off it, called lakes, which dry. Limited anchorage between ferry and prohibited area. Plenty of visitors deep water moorings. (Hr Mr's launch will contact — on duty

SALCOMBE *continued*
0700-2000 (LT) in season (0600-2200 (LT) in peak season) all have VHF Ch 14). There can be an uncomfortable swell with S winds in the anchorage off the town. Visitors' pontoon and moorings in the Bag are sheltered. New visitors pontoon for short stay by Hr Mr office, Whitestrand.

NAVIGATION
Waypoint 50°12'·40N 03°46'·60W, 180°/000° from/to Sandhill Pt Lt, 1·3M. The bar can be dangerous at spring tides when there are strong on-shore winds on the ebb tide. Speed limit 8 kn. Channel up to Kingsbridge is navigable for vessels with draughts up to 2m. Channel marked by R and W port hand beacons.

LIGHTS AND MARKS
White House in line with Poundstone beacon at 327°. Sandhill Pt beacon in line with Poundstone beacon at 000°. Sandhill Pt Dir Lt 000° Fl WRG 2s 27m 10/7M. R and W diamond on W mast — R002°-182°, G182°-357°, W357°-002°.
Harbour Ldg Lts 042° as shown.
Blackstone Rock QWR 4m 2M vis W048°-218°, R218°-048°.

RADIO TELEPHONE
VHF call *Salcombe Harbour* Ch 14; 14 (1 May–14 Sept 0830–2030 LT; 15 Sept–30 Apl Mon–Fri 0830–1630 LT – Not Sat or Sun). Call Harbour Launch: *Salcombe Harbour Launch,* , Ch 14.
Call: *ICC Base* (clubhouse) and *Egremont* (ICC floating HQ) Ch **80** M. Fuel barge Ch 06. Harbour Water taxi service Ch 14.

TELEPHONE (054 884)
Hr Mr 3791; MRSC Brixham 882704; # (0752) 220661; Marinecall 0898 500 458; Police 2107; Dr 2284.

FACILITIES
EC Thursday; **Harbour** (300 + 150 visitors) ☎ 3791, Slip, Ⓔ, P, D, FW, ME, El, M, L, C (15 ton), Sh, CH, SM; **Salcombe YC** ☎ 2872, L, R, Bar; **Island Cruising Club** ☎ 3481, Bar, ⊡; **Winters BY** ☎ 3838, Slip, M, P, D, FW, ME; **Devon Rigging** ☎ 3195 Rigging, ME, CH;

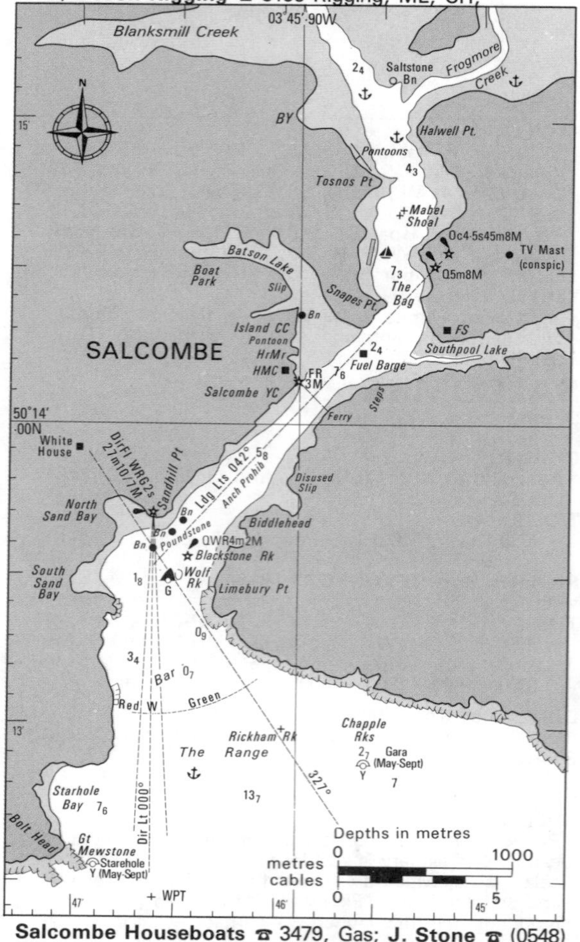

03°45'·90W
Blanksmill Creek
Saltstone Bn
Frogmore Creek
BY
Halwell Pt.
Pontoons
Tosnos Pt
Mabel Shoal
Oc4·5s45m8M
TV Mast (conspic)
Q5m8M
Batson Lake
Boat Park
Slip
Snapes Pt.
The Bag
Island CC Pontoon HrMr HMC
FS
Southpool Lake
SALCOMBE
Fuel Barge
FR 3M
Salcombe YC
Ferry
Steps
50°14'·00N
White House
DirFl WRG2s 27m10/7M
Sandhill Pt
Ldg Lts 042°
Anch Prohib
Disused Slip
North Sand Bay
Poundstone
Biddlehead
QWR4m2M
Blackstone Rk
Wolf Rk
South Sand Bay
Limebury Pt
Bar
Red W Green
Chapple Rks
Rickham Rk
The Range
Gara (May-Sept)
327°
Starhole Bay
Dir Lt 000°
Bolt Head
Gt Mewstone
Starehole (May-Sept)
Depths in metres
metres 0 1000
cables 0 5
WPT

Salcombe Houseboats ☎ 3479, Gas; **J. Stone** ☎ (0548) 51242, M, FW, ME, El, Sh, CH; **Salcombe Chandlers** ☎ 2620, CH, ACA; **Tideway Boat Construction** ☎ 2987, Slip, CH; **J. Alsop** ☎ 3702, SM; **J. McKillop** ☎ Kingsbridge 2343, SM; **Burwin Marine Electronics** ☎ 3321, Ⓔ; **Sailing** ☎ 2094, ME; **Hudson Thomas Fuel Barge** ☎ (0836) 715644, D, P; **Salcombe Boat Store** ☎ 3708, CH, Ice, Gas:
Salcombe is very well equipped with all facilities. FW is available from a boat – if needed, fly a bucket from a halyard. Water boat has Gas, Gaz. Alternatively, FW available from new visitors pontoon by Hr Mr. Public slipways at Batson Creek and at Kingsbridge.
Town ⊡; ✉; Ⓑ; ≠ (bus to Plymouth or Totnes); ✈ (Plymouth).
Note: There is a water taxi service run by the Hr Mr. For timetable contact Hr Mr.

DARTMOUTH 10-1-20

Devon

CHARTS
Admiralty 2253, 1634, 1613; Stanford 12; Imray C5, Y47, Y43; OS 202

TIDES
–0501 Dover; ML 2·8; Duration 0630; Zone 0 (GMT).

NOTE: Dartmouth is a Standard Port and tidal predictions for each day of the year are given below.

SHELTER
Excellent protection inside the harbour but the entrance can be difficult with strong winds from the SE to SW. Anchorages E of fairway opposite Nos 3a to 5 buoys. There are three marinas, as shown on the chartlet, and four sets of pontoons for visiting yachts as follows: – by The Dartmouth YC; near the Hr Mr's office and on N embankment; for short stays only, by the ferry pontoon on the East side.

NAVIGATION
Waypoint 50°19'·50N 03°32'·80W, 148°/328° from/to Kingswear Lt, Iso WRG, 1·5M. To the E of entrance erected on Inner Froward Pt (153m high) is a stone pyramid (24·5m high) which is very conspic. There is no bar and the harbour is always available. The river is navigable on the tide to Totnes. Information from Hr Mr. Speed limit 6 kn.

LIGHTS AND MARKS
Kingswear Main Lt Iso WRG 3s 9m 8M W sector 325°-331°. Bayard's Cove Lt Fl WRG 2s W sector 289°-297°.
Entry buoys as on chartlet.

RADIO TELEPHONE
Hr Mr VHF Ch 11 (Mon–Fri 0900–1700; Sat 0900–1200 LT). Darthaven Marina (Kingswear), Dart Marina, Dart Sailing Centre VHF Ch **80** M; Kingswear Marina Noss Works, Call *Dart Marina Four* Ch **80** M; Fuel barge Ch 16. Water taxi, Ch 16 or **80**.

TELEPHONE (0803)
Hr Mr 832337; MRSC Brixham 882704; # 835060; Marinecall 0898 500 458; Police 832288; Dr 832212; [H] 832255.

FACILITIES
EC Wednesday/Saturday; **Darthaven Marina** (230 + 12 visitors) ☎ Kingswear 22545, FW, ME, El, Gas, Gaz, ⊡, Sh, CH, Bar, R, BH (30 ton), AC; **Kingswear Marina** (110) ☎ 833351, Slip, FW, ME, El, Sh, C (14 ton), CH, BH (16 ton), Gas, Gaz, AC; **Dart Marina** (80 + 40 visitors) ☎ 833351, Slip, D, FW, AC, ME, El, Sh, C (4 ton), BH (4 ton), Bar, R, ⊡, Gas, Gaz, CH; **Dartside Quay Yard** (Galmpton) (40) ☎ 845445 Slip, AC, BH (53, 16), CH, El, Ⓔ, FW, ME, Sh; **Dart Harbour and Navigation Authority** (450 + 90 visitors), ☎ 832337, Slip, D, FW, ME, El, Sh, CH, V, R; **Royal Dart YC** ☎ Kingswear 272, M, L, FW, Bar; **The Dartmouth YC** ☎ 832305, L, FW, Bar, R; **Creekside BY**(Mill Creek) ☎ 832649, Slip, dry dock, M, ME, Sh, El, C (1 ton), CH, AB; **Philip and Son** ☎ 833351, M, ME, El, Sh, BH, CH; **Bosuns Locker** ☎ 832595, CH, ACA; **Dart Sails** ☎ 832185, SM; **Peter Lucas** ☎ 833094, SM, rigging, masts; **J. W. Upham** ☎ Kingswear 545, El, ME, CH, Sh, Ⓔ; **Burwin Electronics** ☎ 835417, El, Ⓔ; **Torbay Boat Construction** (Dolphin Haven at Galmpton) ☎ Churston 842424, CH, D, FW, L, M, C (27 ton), ME, Sh, Slip, SM, V; **River Taxi** ☎ 833727 (or VHF Ch 16); **Dart Sailing Centre** ☎ 834716, AB, AC, Bar, R; **Misc** Fuel Barge P, D, Slip at Higher Ferry; **Town** V, P (cans), ⊡, R, Bar, ✉; Ⓑ; ≠ (steam train, in season, or bus to Paignton); ✈ (Plymouth or Exeter).

DARTMOUTH *continued*

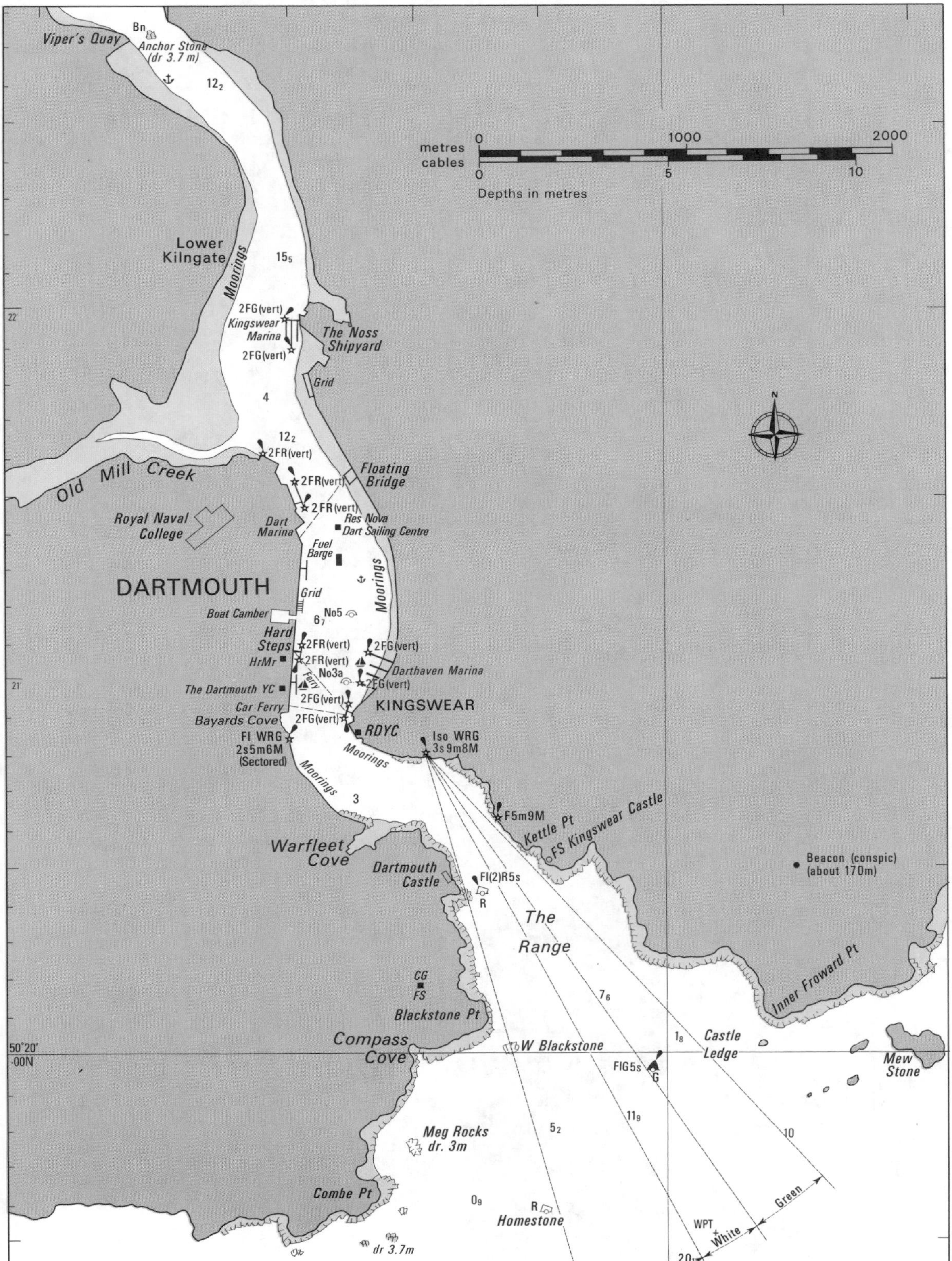
Viper's Quay
Bn
Anchor Stone (dr 3.7 m)
12₂
metres
cables
0
1000
2000
0
5
10
Depths in metres
Lower Kilngate
Moorings
15₅
2FG(vert)
Kingswear Marina
2FG(vert)
The Noss Shipyard
Grid
4
12₂
2FR(vert)
Old Mill Creek
2FR(vert)
Floating Bridge
2FR(vert)
Royal Naval College
Dart Marina
Res Nova
Dart Sailing Centre
Fuel Barge
DARTMOUTH
Grid
Moorings
Boat Camber
No5
6₇
Hard Steps
2FR(vert)
2FG(vert)
HrMr
2FR(vert)
No3a
Darthaven Marina
The Dartmouth YC
Ferry
2FG(vert)
2FG(vert)
KINGSWEAR
Car Ferry
Bayards Cove
2FG(vert)
RDYC
Fl WRG 2s5m6M (Sectored)
Iso WRG 3s9m8M
Moorings
Moorings
3
F5m9M
Kettle Pt
FS Kingswear Castle
Warfleet Cove
Dartmouth Castle
Fl(2)R5s
R
The Range
Beacon (conspic) (about 170m)
CG
FS
Blackstone Pt
7₆
Inner Froward Pt
Compass Cove
W Blackstone
1₈
Castle Ledge
Mew Stone
50°20'·00N
Fl G5s
G
11₉
5₂
10
Meg Rocks dr. 3m
Combe Pt
0₉
R
Homestone
WPT
White
Green
Red
20₁
dr 3.7m
35'
34'
03°33'·00W
32'
22'
21'

ENGLAND, SOUTH COAST - DARTMOUTH

TIME ZONE UT(GMT)

For Summer Time add ONE hour in non-shaded areas

LAT 50°21'N LONG 3°34'W

TIMES AND HEIGHTS OF HIGH AND LOW WATERS

YEAR 1992

JANUARY

Day	Time	m	Day	Time	m
1 W	0252 0849 1520 2117	4.1 1.8 4.0 1.6	16 TH	0151 0759 1430 2041	3.9 1.9 3.9 1.7
2 TH	0353 0950 1621 2213	4.2 1.6 4.1 1.5	17 F	0317 0921 1556 2153	4.1 1.5 4.1 1.3
3 F	0447 1042 1714 2300	4.4 1.4 4.3 1.3	18 SA	0430 1026 1708 2251	4.5 1.1 4.4 0.9
4 SA ●	0534 1127 1759 2342	4.6 1.2 4.4 1.2	19 SU ○	0532 1121 1805 2342	4.8 0.7 4.7 0.6
5 SU	0617 1207 1839	4.7 1.1 4.4	20 M	0626 1209 1856	5.1 0.3 4.9
6 M	0020 0653 1244 1913	1.1 4.7 1.0 4.4	21 TU	0028 0712 1256 1940	0.3 5.2 0.1 5.0
7 TU	0056 0725 1317 1943	1.1 4.7 1.0 4.4	22 W	0114 0755 1339 2022	0.2 5.3 0.1 4.9
8 W	0129 0754 1348 2011	1.1 4.7 1.1 4.3	23 TH	0156 0836 1421 2102	0.3 5.2 0.2 4.8
9 TH	0159 0820 1419 2037	1.2 4.6 1.1 4.2	24 F	0237 0915 1502 2140	0.4 5.0 0.5 4.6
10 F	0229 0846 1450 2103	1.3 4.4 1.2 4.2	25 SA	0319 0953 1543 2219	0.7 4.7 0.8 4.3
11 SA	0302 0913 1525 2135	1.4 4.3 1.3 4.1	26 SU ☾	0400 1032 1626 2301	1.1 4.4 1.2 4.1
12 SU	0339 0947 1604 2215	1.5 4.2 1.5 4.0	27 M	0445 1117 1712 2350	1.5 4.1 1.6 3.9
13 M ☽	0423 1035 1652 2314	1.7 4.1 1.6 3.9	28 TU	0537 1212 1808	1.8 3.8 1.9
14 TU	0517 1140 1753	1.8 3.9 1.8	29 W	0049 0647 1320 1927	3.8 2.1 3.7 2.1
15 W	0027 0629 1300 1914	3.8 1.9 3.9 1.8	30 TH	0203 0817 1441 2051	3.8 2.1 3.7 2.0
			31 F	0318 0933 1555 2155	4.0 1.8 3.8 1.7

FEBRUARY

Day	Time	m	Day	Time	m
1 SA	0422 1026 1655 2244	4.2 1.5 4.1 1.4	16 SU	0418 1015 1658 2239	4.4 1.0 4.4 0.9
2 SU	0515 1111 1744 2325	4.4 1.2 4.3 1.2	17 M	0520 1108 1754 2327	4.8 0.5 4.7 0.4
3 M ●	0559 1149 1824	4.6 1.0 4.4	18 TU ○	0613 1154 1842	5.1 0.1 5.0
4 TU	0002 0637 1224 1858	1.0 4.7 0.8 4.5	19 W	0012 0657 1238 1923	0.1 5.3 -0.1 5.1
5 W	0037 0709 1257 1929	0.9 4.8 0.8 4.5	20 TH	0056 0738 1319 2002	0.0 5.3 -0.1 5.0
6 TH	0109 0739 1327 1956	0.8 4.7 0.8 4.5	21 F	0135 0815 1358 2038	0.1 5.2 0.1 4.9
7 F	0138 0804 1356 2018	0.9 4.6 0.8 4.4	22 SA	0214 0851 1435 2111	0.3 4.9 0.4 4.6
8 SA	0208 0824 1427 2038	0.9 4.5 0.9 4.3	23 SU	0252 0924 1512 2142	0.6 4.6 0.8 4.4
9 SU	0239 0845 1458 2059	1.1 4.4 1.1 4.2	24 M	0329 0956 1549 2217	1.0 4.3 1.3 4.1
10 M	0313 0911 1534 2134	1.2 4.3 1.3 4.1	25 TU ☾	0408 1035 1628 2302	1.5 4.0 1.7 3.9
11 TU ☽	0352 0952 1618 2228	1.4 4.1 1.5 3.9	26 W	0453 1127 1717	1.9 3.7 2.0
12 W	0442 1058 1714 2348	1.7 3.8 1.8 3.8	27 TH	0001 0556 1235 1835	3.7 2.2 3.5 2.3
13 TH	0551 1229 1837	1.9 3.7 2.0	28 F	0113 0744 1400 2024	3.7 2.2 3.5 2.2
14 F	0119 0733 1413 2021	3.8 2.0 3.7 1.8	29 SA	0238 0911 1527 2133	3.8 1.9 3.7 1.8
15 SA	0257 0910 1548 2141	4.0 1.6 4.0 1.4			

MARCH

Day	Time	m	Day	Time	m
1 SU	0351 1004 1631 2221	4.0 1.6 4.0 1.5	16 M	0400 0957 1642 2219	4.4 0.9 4.4 0.8
2 M	0448 1047 1720 2301	4.3 1.2 4.2 1.1	17 TU	0501 1048 1734 2307	4.8 0.4 4.7 0.4
3 TU	0533 1123 1800 2337	4.6 0.9 4.5 0.9	18 W ○	0552 1132 1821 2350	5.1 0.1 5.0 0.1
4 W ●	0614 1156 1837	4.7 0.7 4.6	19 TH	0637 1214 1901	5.2 -0.1 5.1
5 TH	0010 0648 1230 1907	0.7 4.8 0.6 4.6	20 F	0033 0716 1255 1937	0.0 5.2 0.0 5.0
6 F	0043 0718 1301 1935	0.6 4.8 0.6 4.6	21 SA	0113 0751 1332 2009	0.1 5.1 0.2 4.9
7 SA	0115 0744 1331 1959	0.6 4.7 0.6 4.5	22 SU	0149 0824 1408 2040	0.3 4.8 0.5 4.7
8 SU	0145 0807 1403 2017	0.7 4.5 0.8 4.4	23 M	0226 0853 1442 2108	0.7 4.5 0.9 4.4
9 M	0218 0825 1435 2038	0.9 4.4 1.0 4.3	24 TU	0300 0924 1516 2140	1.1 4.2 1.4 4.2
10 TU	0252 0850 1512 2110	1.1 4.2 1.2 4.1	25 W	0336 1000 1551 2222	1.5 3.9 1.7 3.9
11 W	0332 0932 1555 2206	1.3 4.0 1.5 3.9	26 TH ☾	0417 1050 1635 2319	1.9 3.6 2.1 3.7
12 TH ☽	0423 1045 1652 2330	1.6 3.7 1.8 3.8	27 F	0514 1156 1744	2.1 3.4 2.3
13 F	0533 1221 1818	1.9 3.6 2.0	28 SA	0028 0654 1316 1939	3.6 2.2 3.4 2.3
14 SA	0103 0721 1406 2008	3.8 1.9 3.6 1.8	29 SU	0148 0831 1443 2056	3.7 2.0 3.6 1.9
15 SU	0242 0856 1537 2123	4.0 1.5 4.0 1.3	30 M	0306 0926 1551 2146	3.9 1.6 3.9 1.5
			31 TU	0408 1010 1643 2227	4.2 1.2 4.2 1.2

APRIL

Day	Time	m	Day	Time	m
1 W	0457 1048 1726 2305	4.5 0.9 4.5 0.9	16 TH	0525 1106 1753 2326	4.9 0.3 4.9 0.3
2 TH	0541 1124 1805 2340	4.6 0.7 4.6 0.7	17 F ○	0611 1148 1835	5.0 0.2 5.0
3 F ●	0620 1158 1841	4.7 0.5 4.7	18 SA	0008 0651 1230 1910	0.2 5.0 0.3 4.9
4 SA	0015 0654 1234 1911	0.6 4.7 0.5 4.7	19 SU	0049 0727 1307 1942	0.3 4.8 0.5 4.8
5 SU	0050 0725 1308 1939	0.6 4.7 0.6 4.6	20 M	0127 0759 1342 2011	0.6 4.6 0.8 4.6
6 M	0125 0753 1342 2006	0.6 4.5 0.7 4.5	21 TU	0202 0828 1416 2040	0.9 4.3 1.1 4.4
7 TU	0201 0820 1419 2033	0.8 4.3 0.9 4.4	22 W	0236 0858 1449 2112	1.2 4.1 1.4 4.2
8 W	0239 0852 1458 2111	1.0 4.1 1.2 4.2	23 TH	0311 0934 1524 2152	1.5 3.8 1.7 4.0
9 TH	0323 0943 1545 2210	1.3 3.9 1.5 4.0	24 F ☾	0350 1020 1605 2244	1.8 3.6 2.0 3.8
10 F ☽	0417 1055 1645 2326	1.6 3.7 1.8 3.9	25 SA	0441 1120 1704 2345	2.0 3.5 2.2 3.7
11 SA	0529 1220 1809	1.8 3.6 1.9	26 SU	0553 1228 1830	2.1 3.5 2.2
12 SU	0049 0706 1352 1945	3.9 1.7 3.7 1.7	27 M	0053 0723 1343 1955	3.7 2.0 3.6 2.0
13 M	0218 0829 1513 2057	4.0 1.4 4.0 1.3	28 TU	0206 0831 1454 2056	3.9 1.7 3.8 1.7
14 TU	0333 0930 1616 2153	4.3 0.9 4.4 0.9	29 W	0314 0922 1553 2144	4.1 1.4 4.1 1.3
15 W	0434 1020 1708 2242	4.7 0.5 4.7 0.5	30 TH	0411 1006 1644 2227	4.3 1.1 4.4 1.0

Chart Datum: 2.62 metres below Ordnance Datum (Newlyn)

ENGLAND, SOUTH COAST - DARTMOUTH

TIME ZONE UT(GMT)

For Summer Time add ONE hour in non-shaded areas

LAT 50°21'N LONG 3°34'W

TIMES AND HEIGHTS OF HIGH AND LOW WATERS

YEAR **1992**

MAY

Day	Time	m	Day	Time	m
1 F	0501 1048 1729 2308	4.5 0.8 4.6 0.8	16 SA ○	0544 1123 1806 2345	4.7 0.6 4.8 0.6
2 SA ●	0547 1128 1811 2348	4.6 0.6 4.7 0.6	17 SU	0627 1205 1846	4.6 0.6 4.8
3 SU	0630 1207 1849	4.6 0.6 4.7	18 M	0027 0704 1245 1919	0.6 4.6 0.8 4.7
4 M	0027 0708 1247 1925	0.6 4.6 0.6 4.7	19 TU	0107 0739 1322 1950	0.8 4.4 1.0 4.6
5 TU	0109 0745 1327 2000	0.6 4.5 0.7 4.6	20 W	0143 0809 1356 2020	1.0 4.2 1.2 4.4
6 W	0149 0824 1408 2038	0.7 4.3 0.9 4.5	21 TH	0218 0840 1429 2052	1.2 4.1 1.4 4.3
7 TH	0232 0907 1452 2123	0.9 4.2 1.1 4.3	22 F	0252 0914 1504 2128	1.4 3.9 1.6 4.1
8 F	0321 0959 1542 2216	1.1 4.0 1.4 4.2	23 SA	0328 0954 1542 2211	1.6 3.8 1.8 4.0
9 SA ☽	0415 1100 1640 2320	1.3 3.8 1.6 4.1	24 SU ☾	0411 1043 1628 2302	1.7 3.7 1.9 3.9
10 SU	0521 1209 1751	1.5 3.8 1.7	25 M	0503 1139 1727	1.8 3.6 2.0
11 M	0030 0637 1323 1911	4.0 1.5 3.9 1.6	26 TU	0000 0607 1241 1839	3.8 1.8 3.7 2.0
12 TU	0145 0752 1437 2021	4.1 1.3 4.0 1.4	27 W	0102 0718 1348 1950	3.9 1.7 3.8 1.8
13 W	0257 0856 1540 2121	4.3 1.1 4.3 1.1	28 TH	0211 0824 1455 2054	3.9 1.5 4.0 1.6
14 TH	0400 0950 1634 2214	4.4 0.8 4.5 0.8	29 F	0318 0921 1556 2149	4.1 1.3 4.2 1.3
15 F	0455 1039 1723 2302	4.6 0.7 4.7 0.6	30 SA	0420 1013 1651 2239	4.3 1.0 4.4 1.0
			31 SU	0516 1101 1743 2325	4.4 0.8 4.6 0.7

JUNE

Day	Time	m	Day	Time	m
1 M ●	0607 1146 1830	4.5 0.7 4.7	16 TU	0011 0648 1227 1901	0.9 4.4 1.0 4.6
2 TU	0011 0655 1232 1913	0.6 4.6 0.6 4.8	17 W	0052 0723 1306 1935	0.9 4.3 1.0 4.6
3 W	0057 0740 1317 1956	0.5 4.5 0.6 4.8	18 TH	0128 0755 1340 2005	1.0 4.2 1.1 4.5
4 TH	0142 0824 1401 2039	0.5 4.5 0.7 4.7	19 F	0201 0825 1413 2035	1.1 4.1 1.2 4.4
5 F	0228 0910 1446 2124	0.6 4.3 0.8 4.6	20 SA	0233 0854 1444 2105	1.2 4.1 1.4 4.3
6 SA	0315 0958 1534 2211	0.8 4.2 1.0 4.4	21 SU	0306 0927 1518 2139	1.3 4.0 1.5 4.2
7 SU ☽	0405 1049 1627 2305	1.0 4.1 1.2 4.3	22 M	0341 1005 1556 2219	1.4 3.9 1.6 4.1
8 M	0500 1145 1725	1.2 4.0 1.4	23 TU ☾	0422 1049 1640 2307	1.5 3.8 1.7 4.0
9 TU	0002 0601 1246 1831	4.2 1.3 3.9 1.5	24 W	0511 1143 1735	1.6 3.8 1.8
10 W	0106 0709 1352 1941	4.1 1.4 4.0 1.5	25 TH	0004 0610 1246 1843	3.9 1.7 3.8 1.8
11 TH	0216 0816 1458 2048	4.1 1.3 4.1 1.4	26 F	0110 0722 1356 1959	3.8 1.7 3.9 1.7
12 F	0323 0918 1559 2147	4.1 1.2 4.3 1.2	27 SA	0226 0837 1510 2112	3.9 1.5 4.0 1.5
13 SA	0425 1012 1653 2240	4.2 1.1 4.4 1.0	28 SU	0342 0943 1619 2215	4.0 1.3 4.3 1.2
14 SU	0519 1102 1742 2327	4.3 1.0 4.5 0.9	29 M	0451 1041 1720 2309	4.2 1.0 4.5 0.8
15 M ○	0606 1146 1825	4.4 0.9 4.6	30 TU ●	0552 1132 1815 2359	4.4 0.7 4.7 0.5

JULY

Day	Time	m	Day	Time	m
1 W	0645 1220 1903	4.6 0.5 4.9	16 TH	0035 0708 1249 1920	0.9 4.3 0.9 4.6
2 TH	0047 0733 1307 1948	0.3 4.7 0.4 5.0	17 F	0110 0739 1322 1950	0.9 4.3 0.9 4.6
3 F	0132 0817 1351 2032	0.2 4.7 0.4 4.9	18 SA	0141 0808 1352 2017	0.9 4.3 1.0 4.5
4 SA	0217 0900 1434 2114	0.3 4.6 0.5 4.8	19 SU	0211 0834 1422 2043	1.0 4.2 1.1 4.4
5 SU	0301 0943 1519 2157	0.4 4.5 0.6 4.7	20 M	0240 0859 1451 2108	1.0 4.2 1.2 4.3
6 M	0345 1027 1605 2242	0.7 4.3 0.9 4.4	21 TU	0311 0927 1525 2138	1.1 4.1 1.3 4.2
7 TU ☽	0432 1114 1654 2332	1.0 4.1 1.2 4.2	22 W ☾	0346 1001 1602 2217	1.3 4.0 1.5 4.0
8 W	0524 1205 1749	1.3 4.0 1.5	23 TH	0427 1048 1648 2311	1.5 3.9 1.6 3.9
9 TH	0027 0623 1305 1857	4.0 1.5 3.9 1.7	24 F	0519 1151 1748	1.7 3.8 1.8
10 F	0133 0735 1414 2013	3.9 1.7 3.9 1.7	25 SA	0021 0628 1307 1911	3.8 1.8 3.8 1.9
11 SA	0247 0849 1524 2125	3.8 1.6 4.0 1.6	26 SU	0145 0758 1433 2046	3.7 1.8 3.9 1.7
12 SU	0358 0953 1627 2224	3.9 1.5 4.2 1.4	27 M	0317 0922 1555 2159	3.9 1.5 4.2 1.3
13 M	0459 1046 1721 2314	4.0 1.3 4.4 1.1	28 TU	0437 1025 1704 2257	4.1 1.1 4.5 0.8
14 TU ○	0550 1131 1807 2356	4.2 1.1 4.5 1.0	29 W ●	0540 1119 1801 2346	4.5 0.6 4.8 0.4
15 W	0633 1211 1847	4.3 1.0 4.6	30 TH	0634 1206 1852	4.7 0.3 5.1
			31 F	0033 0719 1252 1936	0.1 4.9 0.1 5.2

AUGUST

Day	Time	m	Day	Time	m
1 SA	0117 0802 1334 2016	0.0 4.9 0.0 5.2	16 SU	0116 0746 1328 1956	0.7 4.5 0.8 4.6
2 SU	0159 0842 1416 2056	0.0 4.8 0.2 5.0	17 M	0144 0810 1356 2019	0.8 4.4 0.9 4.5
3 M	0240 0921 1457 2136	0.2 4.7 0.4 4.8	18 TU	0213 0832 1425 2039	0.9 4.3 1.0 4.4
4 TU	0321 0959 1538 2214	0.5 4.4 0.7 4.5	19 W	0242 0852 1456 2101	1.0 4.2 1.1 4.3
5 W ☽	0403 1040 1623 2257	0.9 4.2 1.1 4.2	20 TH	0315 0918 1531 2134	1.2 4.1 1.3 4.1
6 TH	0447 1126 1711 2349	1.3 4.0 1.5 3.9	21 F ☾	0353 1001 1615 2226	1.4 4.0 1.6 3.9
7 F	0540 1222 1814	1.7 3.8 1.9	22 SA	0441 1108 1712 2346	1.7 3.8 1.8 3.7
8 SA	0052 0653 1332 1943	3.7 2.0 3.7 2.0	23 SU	0550 1234 1840	1.9 3.7 2.0
9 SU	0214 0824 1452 2109	3.6 2.0 3.8 1.8	24 M	0121 0733 1409 2030	3.6 2.0 3.8 1.8
10 M	0337 0937 1604 2210	3.7 1.7 4.0 1.5	25 TU	0304 0907 1539 2146	3.8 1.6 4.2 1.3
11 TU	0442 1030 1701 2257	3.9 1.4 4.3 1.2	26 W	0424 1011 1649 2242	4.2 1.1 4.6 0.7
12 W	0532 1113 1748 2337	4.2 1.1 4.5 1.0	27 TH	0525 1102 1745 2329	4.6 0.6 5.0 0.3
13 TH ○	0614 1151 1827	4.4 0.9 4.7	28 F ●	0616 1148 1834	4.9 0.2 5.2
14 F	0012 0649 1225 1900	0.8 4.5 0.8 4.7	29 SA	0013 0700 1233 1916	0.0 5.1 -0.1 5.3
15 SA	0046 0719 1258 1930	0.7 4.5 0.7 4.7	30 SU	0057 0740 1314 1956	-0.1 5.1 -0.1 5.3
			31 M	0136 0818 1354 2034	0.0 5.0 0.1 5.1

Chart Datum: 2.62 metres below Ordnance Datum (Newlyn)

ENGLAND, SOUTH COAST - DARTMOUTH

TIME ZONE UT(GMT)

For Summer Time add ONE hour in non-shaded areas

LAT 50°21'N LONG 3°34'W

TIMES AND HEIGHTS OF HIGH AND LOW WATERS

YEAR 1992

SEPTEMBER

	Time	m		Time	m
1	0216	0.2	16	0146	0.8
	0853	4.8		0808	4.5
TU	1432	0.4	W	1401	0.9
	2109	4.8		2016	4.4
2	0254	0.6	17	0218	1.0
	0929	4.5		0826	4.4
W	1512	0.8	TH	1433	1.1
	2144	4.4		2035	4.3
3	0332	1.1	18	0251	1.2
	1004	4.3		0851	4.2
TH	1552	1.3	F	1510	1.3
☽	2223	4.1		2107	4.1
4	0413	1.5	19	0330	1.5
	1047	4.0		0935	4.0
F	1636	1.7	SA	1554	1.6
	2312	3.8	☾	2205	3.8
5	0500	1.9	20	0420	1.8
	1141	3.8		1047	3.9
SA	1735	2.1	SU	1654	1.9
				2333	3.6
6	0016	3.5	21	0530	2.0
	0611	2.2		1215	3.8
SU	1251	3.7	M	1826	2.0
	1914	2.2			
7	0140	3.5	22	0110	3.6
	0758	2.2		0717	2.0
M	1416	3.8	TU	1351	3.9
	2049	2.0		2013	1.8
8	0309	3.6	23	0250	3.9
	0914	1.9		0848	1.6
TU	1533	4.0	W	1520	4.2
	2147	1.6		2125	1.2
9	0415	3.9	24	0406	4.3
	1005	1.5		0949	1.1
W	1632	4.3	TH	1627	4.7
	2231	1.3		2219	0.7
10	0504	4.2	25	0503	4.7
	1047	1.2		1040	0.6
TH	1719	4.5	F	1723	5.0
	2308	1.0		2306	0.3
11	0545	4.5	26	0553	5.0
	1123	0.9		1126	0.2
F	1759	4.7	SA	1812	5.2
	2342	0.7	●	2350	0.0
12	0622	4.6	27	0637	5.1
	1156	0.7		1208	0.0
SA	1835	4.8	SU	1855	5.3
○					
13	0014	0.6	28	0032	0.0
	0654	4.7		0716	5.2
SU	1230	0.7	M	1251	0.0
	1905	4.8		1933	5.2
14	0047	0.6	29	0113	0.1
	0722	4.7		0752	5.1
M	1300	0.7	TU	1330	0.2
	1933	4.7		2008	5.0
15	0117	0.7	30	0150	0.4
	0747	4.6		0826	4.9
TU	1330	0.8	W	1409	0.6
	1957	4.6		2043	4.7

OCTOBER

	Time	m		Time	m
1	0228	0.8	16	0158	1.0
	0857	4.6		0814	4.5
TH	1446	1.0	F	1418	1.1
	2115	4.4		2029	4.3
2	0304	1.3	17	0235	1.3
	0931	4.3		0845	4.3
F	1525	1.4	SA	1458	1.3
	2151	4.0		2107	4.1
3	0341	1.7	18	0319	1.5
	1010	4.1		0932	4.2
SA	1607	1.8	SU	1546	1.6
☽	2237	3.7		2207	3.9
4	0426	2.1	19	0411	1.8
	1103	3.9		1041	4.0
SU	1702	2.1	M	1648	1.8
	2339	3.5	☾	2330	3.7
5	0530	2.3	20	0523	2.0
	1209	3.7		1202	3.9
M	1831	2.3	TU	1813	1.9
6	0056	3.5	21	0058	3.8
	0714	2.3		0655	1.9
TU	1327	3.8	W	1329	4.1
	2007	2.1		1946	1.7
7	0222	3.6	22	0227	4.0
	0835	2.1		0818	1.6
W	1447	4.0	TH	1453	4.3
	2108	1.8		2056	1.2
8	0331	3.9	23	0339	4.3
	0928	1.7		0921	1.2
TH	1550	4.2	F	1600	4.6
	2153	1.4		2152	0.8
9	0424	4.2	24	0437	4.7
	1010	1.3		1014	0.7
F	1640	4.5	SA	1656	4.9
	2233	1.1		2241	0.5
10	0509	4.5	25	0526	4.9
	1049	1.0		1102	0.4
SA	1723	4.7	SU	1746	5.1
	2308	0.8	●	2325	0.3
11	0548	4.7	26	0612	5.1
	1124	0.8		1145	0.3
SU	1803	4.8	M	1830	5.1
○	2342	0.7			
12	0624	4.8	27	0007	0.3
	1158	0.7		0651	5.1
M	1839	4.8	TU	1228	0.3
				1909	5.1
13	0016	0.7	28	0049	0.4
	0655	4.8		0727	5.0
TU	1234	0.7	W	1309	0.5
	1909	4.8		1945	4.9
14	0051	0.7	29	0128	0.7
	0725	4.7		0801	4.9
W	1307	0.8	TH	1347	0.8
	1939	4.6		2018	4.6
15	0124	0.8	30	0204	1.1
	0750	4.6		0831	4.6
TH	1341	0.9	F	1425	1.1
	2004	4.5		2050	4.3
			31	0239	1.4
				0902	4.4
			SA	1502	1.5
				2124	4.0

NOVEMBER

	Time	m		Time	m
1	0316	1.7	16	0313	1.4
	0939	4.2		0937	4.4
SU	1542	1.8	M	1543	1.4
	2205	3.8		2215	4.0
2	0357	2.0	17	0406	1.6
	1027	4.0		1036	4.2
M	1630	2.0	TU	1641	1.5
☽	2300	3.7	☾	2322	3.9
3	0451	2.2	18	0509	1.8
	1126	3.9		1145	4.2
TU	1735	2.2	W	1751	1.6
4	0006	3.6	19	0036	3.9
	0606	2.3		0624	1.8
W	1232	3.9	TH	1300	4.2
	1859	2.1		1909	1.6
5	0119	3.7	20	0154	4.1
	0731	2.2		0742	1.6
TH	1344	4.0	F	1418	4.3
	2009	1.9		2020	1.4
6	0233	3.9	21	0305	4.3
	0835	1.9		0849	1.3
F	1453	4.1	SA	1528	4.5
	2103	1.6		2121	1.1
7	0333	4.2	22	0406	4.6
	0925	1.6		0947	1.0
SA	1552	4.4	SU	1628	4.7
	2149	1.3		2214	0.8
8	0424	4.4	23	0459	4.8
	1010	1.3		1039	0.8
SU	1643	4.6	M	1721	4.8
	2231	1.1		2302	0.7
9	0511	4.7	24	0546	4.9
	1051	1.0		1125	0.7
M	1728	4.7	TU	1808	4.9
	2311	0.9	●	2346	0.7
10	0552	4.8	25	0629	5.0
	1130	0.9		1209	0.7
TU	1811	4.8	W	1850	4.8
○	2349	0.8			
11	0631	4.9	26	0028	0.8
	1209	0.8		0706	5.0
W	1850	4.7	TH	1252	0.8
				1927	4.7
12	0027	0.8	27	0109	0.9
	0706	4.8		0739	4.8
TH	1249	0.8	F	1330	1.0
	1925	4.7		2000	4.5
13	0107	0.8	28	0145	1.1
	0739	4.8		0810	4.7
F	1329	0.9	SA	1408	1.2
	2000	4.5		2030	4.3
14	0146	1.0	29	0221	1.4
	0813	4.7		0841	4.5
SA	1409	1.0	SU	1443	1.4
	2037	4.4		2101	4.1
15	0228	1.2	30	0255	1.6
	0851	4.5		0914	4.4
SU	1453	1.2	M	1519	1.6
	2120	4.2		2137	4.0

DECEMBER

	Time	m		Time	m
1	0331	1.8	16	0354	1.2
	0953	4.2		1025	4.5
TU	1559	1.8	W	1626	1.2
	2222	3.9	☾	2304	4.1
2	0414	2.0	17	0448	1.4
	1041	4.1		1123	4.3
W	1645	1.9	TH	1723	1.4
☽	2316	3.8			
3	0506	2.1	18	0006	4.0
	1137	4.0		0550	1.6
TH	1743	2.0	F	1228	4.2
				1830	1.5
4	0018	3.8	19	0114	4.0
	0611	2.1		0702	1.7
F	1241	4.0	SA	1341	4.2
	1852	2.0		1941	1.5
5	0125	3.9	20	0227	4.1
	0725	2.1		0815	1.6
SA	1349	4.0	SU	1455	4.2
	2001	1.8		2050	1.4
6	0235	4.0	21	0335	4.3
	0832	1.8		0922	1.4
SU	1457	4.1	M	1602	4.3
	2101	1.6		2151	1.3
7	0337	4.3	22	0434	4.5
	0930	1.6		1019	1.2
M	1600	4.3	TU	1701	4.5
	2154	1.3		2243	1.1
8	0432	4.5	23	0525	4.7
	1020	1.3		1110	1.0
TU	1656	4.5	W	1751	4.5
	2242	1.1		2330	1.0
9	0523	4.7	24	0612	4.8
	1107	1.0		1155	0.9
W	1747	4.6	TH	1835	4.6
○	2327	0.9	●		
10	0610	4.8	25	0012	0.9
	1151	0.8		0650	4.9
TH	1834	4.7	F	1238	0.9
				1912	4.6
11	0011	0.8	26	0053	1.0
	0652	4.9		0724	4.8
F	1236	0.7	SA	1316	0.9
	1916	4.7		1944	4.5
12	0055	0.7	27	0129	1.1
	0732	4.9		0754	4.7
SA	1320	0.7	SU	1350	1.0
	1958	4.6		2013	4.4
13	0137	0.8	28	0202	1.2
	0811	4.9		0822	4.6
SU	1403	0.7	M	1423	1.2
	2039	4.5		2041	4.3
14	0221	0.9	29	0233	1.3
	0852	4.8		0851	4.5
M	1447	0.8	TU	1454	1.3
	2122	4.4		2110	4.2
15	0306	1.0	30	0305	1.5
	0936	4.6		0922	4.4
TU	1534	1.0	W	1527	1.5
	2209	4.2		2144	4.1
			31	0339	1.6
				0959	4.2
			TH	1603	1.6
				2227	4.0

Chart Datum: 2.62 metres below Ordnance Datum (Newlyn)

DARTMOUTH *continued*

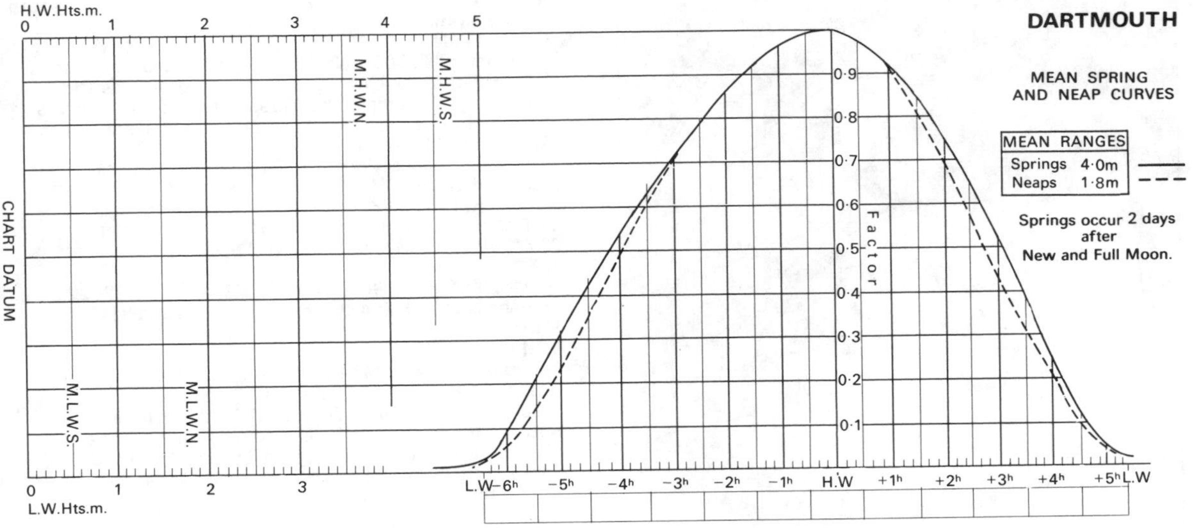
DARTMOUTH
MEAN SPRING AND NEAP CURVES
MEAN RANGES
Springs 4·0m
Neaps 1·8m
Springs occur 2 days after New and Full Moon.
H.W.Hts.m.
L.W.Hts.m.
CHART DATUM
M.H.W.N.
M.H.W.S.
M.L.W.S.
M.L.W.N.
Factor
L.W −6h −5h −4h −3h −2h −1h H.W +1h +2h +3h +4h +5h L.W

BRIXHAM 10-1-21

Devon

CHARTS
Admiralty 26, 1613, 3315; Stanford 12; Imray C5, Y43; OS 202

TIDES
−0505 Dover; ML 2·9; Duration 0635; Zone 0 (GMT).

Standard Port DEVONPORT (⟵)

Times				Height (metres)			
HW		LW		MHWS	MHWN	MLWN	MLWS
0100	0600	0100	0600	5·5	4·4	2·2	0·8
1300	1800	1300	1800				
Differences BRIXHAM							
+0025	+0045	+0010	0000	−0·6	−0·7	−0·2	−0·1

SHELTER
Good, but outer harbour is dangerous in NW winds. Visitors buoys (white) to E of main channel.

NAVIGATION
Waypoint 50°24′·70N 03°30′·00W, 050°/230° from/to Victoria breakwater Lt, 0·60M. No dangers — Little run in tide. Easy access — Inner harbour dries.

LIGHTS AND MARKS
There are no leading marks or leading lights coming into Brixham. Breakwater head — Oc R 15s. Three R balls or three R Lts (vert) at entrance indicate 'harbour closed'.

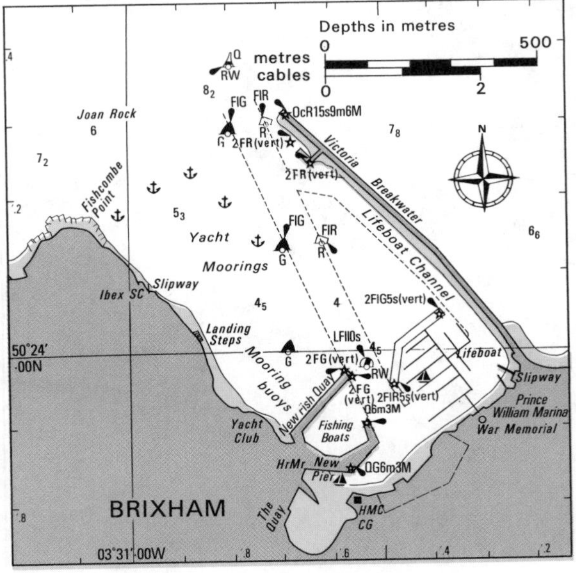
Depths in metres
metres 0 500
cables 0 2
Joan Rock
Fishcombe Point
Yacht Moorings
Ibex SC
Slipway
Landing Steps
Mooring buoys
New Fish Quay
Yacht Club
Fishing Boats
HrMr New Pier
The Quay
HMC CG
BRIXHAM
Victoria Breakwater
Lifeboat Channel
Lifeboat
Slipway
Prince William Marina
War Memorial
OcR15s9m6M
2FR(vert)
2FIG5s(vert)
LFlI0s
2FG(vert)
2FIR5s(vert)
QG6m3M
50°24′·00N
03°31′·00W

RADIO TELEPHONE
VHF Ch 14 16 (May-Sep: 0900-1300, 1400-1700, 1800-2000. Oct-Apr: Mon-Fri 0900-1300, 1400-1700 LT). Brixham Coastguard: Ch 16 10 67 73; Yacht Club and Marina Club Ch 80 M.

TELEPHONE (0803)
Hr Mr 883321; MRSC 882704; Pilot 882214; Brixham Marina 882929 (Dockmaster 882711); # (0752) 220661; Marinecall 0898 500 458; Police 882231; Dr 882731; H 882153.

FACILITIES
EC Wednesday; **Brixham Marina** (535+30 visitors) ☎ 882929, AC, FW, D (H 24), ◻, Access H24; **Harbour Office** (New Fish Quay) Slip, M, L, FW, C (2 ton), AB; **Brixham YC** ☎ 883332, M, L, Slip, FW, R, Bar; **Fish Quay** Bunker Berth D, **Brixham Yacht Supplies** ☎ 882290, CH, ACA; **Portbury** ☎ 882809 ACA, Gas, Gaz CH; **Cosalt** ☎ 857448 CH; **TM Engineering** ☎ 846012 ME; **Queen Anne Marine** ☎ 294509 P, D; **Brixham Net Co** ☎ 886115, CH, ME; **B J R Electrical** ☎ 858158, El, Ⓔ; **Inner Harbour** C; **Quay Electrics** Tel. 883030, El, Ⓔ; **Water Taxi:** call sign *'Shuttle'* on Ch 37. **Town** ◻, ✉; Ⓑ; ⇌ (bus to Paignton); ✈ (Exeter).

TORQUAY 10-1-22

Devon

CHARTS
Admiralty 26, 1613, 3315; Stanford 12; Imray C5, Y43; OS 202

TIDES
−0500 Dover; ML 2·9; Duration 0640; Zone 0 (GMT).

Standard Port DEVONPORT (⟵)

Times				Height (metres)			
HW		LW		MHWS	MHWN	MLWN	MLWS
0100	0600	0100	0600	5·5	4·4	2·2	0·8
1300	1800	1300	1800				
Differences TORQUAY							
+0025	+0045	+0010	0000	−0·6	−0·7	−0·2	−0·1

TORQUAY *continued*

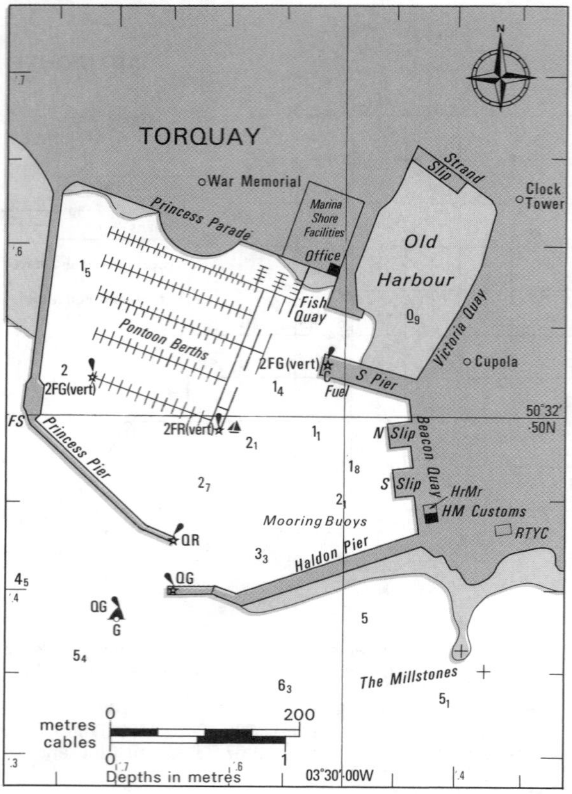
TORQUAY
War Memorial
Princess Parade
Marina Shore Facilities
Office
Strand Slip
Old Harbour
Clock Tower
Fish Quay
Pontoon Berths
Victoria Quay
Cupola
2FG(vert)
S Pier
Fuel
2FR(vert)
Princess Pier
N Slip
S Slip
Beacon Quay
HrMr
HM Customs
RTYC
Mooring Buoys
Haldon Pier
QR
QG
The Millstones
50°32'·50N
metres
cables
Depths in metres
03°30'·00W

SHELTER

Good shelter but some swell in harbour with strong south easterly winds.

NAVIGATION

Waypoint 50°27'·00N 03°31'·50W, 165°/345° from/to Haldon Pier Lt, 0·40M. Inner harbour (known as Old Harbour) dries completely. Three R balls or three R Lts show harbour closed due to navigational hazard.

LIGHTS AND MARKS

No leading marks. Princess Pier head QR 9m 6M. Haldon Pier head QG 9m 6M. South Pier head 2FG (vert) 5M.

RADIO TELEPHONE

VHF Ch 14 16 (Oct-Mar 0900-1700 Mon-Fri) (Apl-Sept 0900-2000 LT). Marina Ch **80** (H24), M.

TELEPHONE (0803)

Hr Mr 292429; MRSC Brixham 882704; # (0752) 220661; Marinecall 0898 500 458; Police 214491; Dr 298441; Ⓗ 614567.

FACILITIES

Torquay Marina (440+60 visitors) ☎ 214624, FW, ME, Gas, Gaz, P, D, ◙, AC, SM, El, Ⓔ, Sh, CH, V, R, Bar (Access H24); **Haldon Pier** L, FW, AB; **Princess Pier** L; **South Pier** P, D, L, FW, C (6 ton); **Queen Anne Marine** ☎ 294509, P, D; **Royal Torbay YC** ☎ 292006, R, Bar; **Town** All normal facilities, V, R, ◙, Bar, ✉; Ⓑ; ≷; ✈ (Exeter or Plymouth).

TEIGNMOUTH 10-1-23

Devon

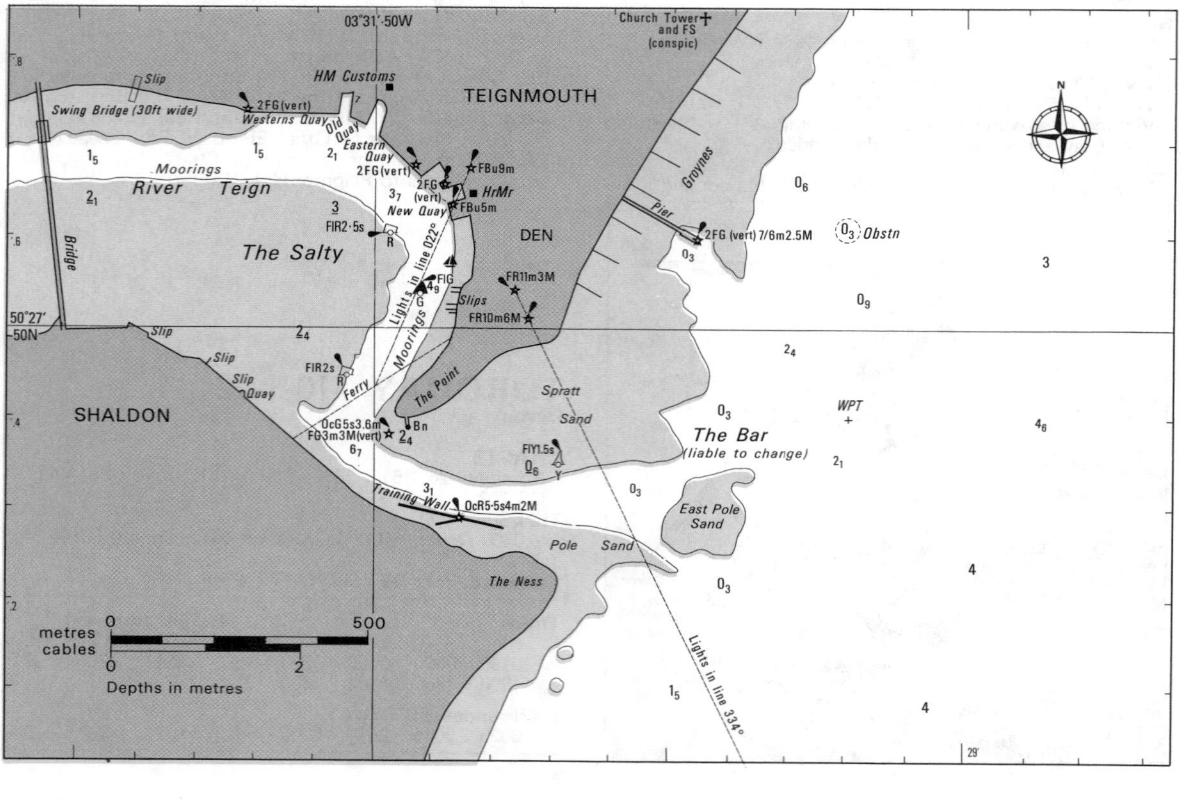
03°31'·50W
Church Tower and FS (conspic)
HM Customs
TEIGNMOUTH
Slip
Swing Bridge (30ft wide)
2FG(vert)
Westerns Quay
Old Quay
Eastern Quay
2FG(vert)
FBu9m
HrMr
New Quay
FBu5m
Moorings
River Teign
The Salty
FIR2·5s
Lights in line 022°
FlG
Slips
FR11m3M
FR10m6M
DEN
Groynes
Pier
2FG (vert) 7/6m2.5M
Obstn
Bridge
50°27'·50N
Slip
Slip Quay
FIR2s
Ferry
Moorings
The Point
SHALDON
OcG5s3.6m
FG3m3M(vert)
Bn
Spratt Sand
The Bar (liable to change)
WPT
FlY1.5s
Training Wall
OcR5·5s4m2M
East Pole Sand
Pole Sand
The Ness
Lights in line 334°
metres
cables
Depths in metres

TEIGNMOUTH *continued*

CHARTS
Admiralty 26, 3315; Stanford 12; Imray C5, Y43; OS 192

TIDES
−0450 Dover; ML 2·7; Duration 0625; Zone 0 (GMT).

Standard Port DEVONPORT (⟵)

Times				Height (metres)			
HW		LW		MHWS	MHWN	MLWN	MLWS
0100	0600	0100	0600	5·5	4·4	2·2	0·8
1300	1800	1300	1800				
Differences TEIGNMOUTH (Approaches)							
+0025	+0040	0000	0000	−0·7	−0·8	−0·3	−0·2

SHELTER
Harbour completely sheltered but difficult to enter especially with strong winds between NE & S when surf forms on the bar. Access HW∓3. Channel is not buoyed so local advice is recommended.

NAVIGATION
Waypoint 50°32′·40N 03°29′·20W, 076°/256° from/to Training Wall Lt, 0·43M. Bar shifts very frequently.
Beware — rocks off the Ness
— variable extent of Salty flats.
Clearance under Shaldon bridge is 3·5m at MHWS.

LIGHTS AND MARKS
Oc G, 5s FG (vert) on The Point.
Two sets of leading lights:- Approaching from SE, lights at 334°. This line keeps clear of the Ness Rocks but does not normally lead through channel through the bar. Once round The Point, lights on the quays at 022°.

RADIO TELEPHONE
VHF Ch 12 16; 12 (Mon-Fri: 0800-1700 LT; Sat 0900-1200 LT).

TELEPHONE (0626)
Hr Mr 773165; MRSC Brixham 882704; # (0752) 220661; Marinecall 0898 500 458; Police 772433; Dr 774355; Ⓗ 772161.

FACILITIES
EC Thursday; **E Quay Polly Steps** Slip (up to 10m); **DCS Electrics** ☎ 775960, ME, El; **Teign Corinthian YC** ☎ 772734, M, FW; **Mariners Weigh** ☎ 773698, ME, CH; **Chris Humphrey** ☎ 772324, Slip, BY, ME, Sh, D, C (8 ton); **Bobbets Garage** ☎ 774220, P and D (cans); **Sleeman and Hawken** ☎ 872750, ME; **Brigantine** ☎ 772400, Gas, Gaz, FW, CH; **Bartletts** ☎ 773812, D; **J & C Engineering** ☎ 778633, ME, Sh; **PFB Electronics** ☎ 776845, Ⓔ. **Town** P, D, L, FW, V, R, ⊡, Bar; ✉; Ⓑ; ⇌; ✈ (Exeter).

RIVER EXE 10-1-24
Devon

CHARTS
Admiralty 2290, 3315; Stanford 12; Imray C5, Y43; OS 192

TIDES
−0445 Dover; ML 2·1; Duration 0625; Zone 0 (GMT).

Standard Port DEVONPORT (⟵)

Times				Height (metres)			
HW		LW		MHWS	MHWN	MLWN	MLWS
0100	0600	0100	0600	5·5	4·4	2·2	0·8
1300	1800	1300	1800				
Differences EXMOUTH (Approaches)							
+0030	+0050	+0015	+0005	−0·9	−1·0	−0·5	−0·3
STARCROSS							
+0040	+0110	No data		−1·4	−1·5	−0·8	−0·1
TOPSHAM							
+0045	+0105	No data		−1·5	−1·6	No data	

SHELTER
Entrance difficult when wind between S and E. Shelter good in Exe River. Access to Exeter is through the Exeter Canal and passage through locks, S of Topsham, by arrangement with Exeter City Council ☎ Exeter 74306.

NAVIGATION
Waypoint Exe Fairway (safe water) buoy, Fl 10s, Bell, 50°36′·01N 03°21′·97W, 102°/282° from/to channel entrance, 0·60M. Long shallow bar extends SE with rocks to the N of channel. Channel is difficult but well marked. Pole sands are liable to change. There is a Royal Marine firing range at Straight Pt, just E of Exe fairway buoy. R flags are flown when range in use and safety launch on station (callsign '*Straight Point Range*' VHF Ch 16 08.

LIGHTS AND MARKS
Ldg Lts FY 6m 7M by The Point in line at 305°; not safe seaward of No 3 Buoy.

RADIO TELEPHONE
Exeter VHF Ch 16; 06 12 (Mon-Fri: 0730-1630 LT, and when vessel expected).

TELEPHONE (0395)
Dockmaster 272009; # (0752) 220661; MRSC Brixham 882704; Pilot 264036; Marinecall 0898 500 458; Police 264651, Dr 273001; Ⓗ 279684.

FACILITIES
EXMOUTH EC Wednesday; **Dixon & Son** ☎ 263063, ME, Sh, CH; **Exe Sailing Club** ☎ 264607, M, L, AB; **Lavis & Son** ☎ 263095, El, Sh, CH; **Tidal Docks** ☎ 272009, L, FW, ME, C; **Victoria Marine Services** ☎ 265044, ME, Gaz, CH; **Peter Dixon** ☎ 273248, CH, ACA; **M. McNamara** ☎ 264907, SM; **Exmouth Dock Co.** ☎ 272009, C; **Rowsell and Morrison** ☎ 263911, CH, El, SM, Ⓔ, Sh; **Pierhead** V, R, Bar, CH; **Town** P, V, R, ⊡, Bar, ✉; Ⓑ; ⇌; ✈ (Exeter).

STARCROSS (0626) **Starcross Fishing and Cruising Club** ☎ 890582; **Wills Starcross Garage** ☎ 890225, P and D (cans), ME, M, Gas; **Starcross YC** ☎ 890470; **Village** P, V, Bar, ✉; Ⓑ; ⇌; ✈ (Exeter).

TOPSHAM (0392) **Topsham SC** Slip, L, FW, Bar; **Retreat BY** ☎ 874720, Access HW ∓2, M, D, ME, El, C, Gas, CH; **Scanes** ☎ 877527, SM; **Foc'sle** ☎ 874105, ACA, CH; **Grimshaw Engineering** ☎ 873539, ME, El; **Trouts BY** ☎ 3044, CH, BY; **Village** P, R, V, ⊡, Bar, ✉; Ⓑ; ⇌; ✈ (Exeter).

EXETER (0392) For moorings and anchorages apply Hr Mr Exeter City, ☎ Exeter 74306. No moorings in Exmouth, but some in estuary. **Leisure Warehouse** ☎ 50970, (Exeter Canal Basin) CH, ME.

RIVER EXE *continued*

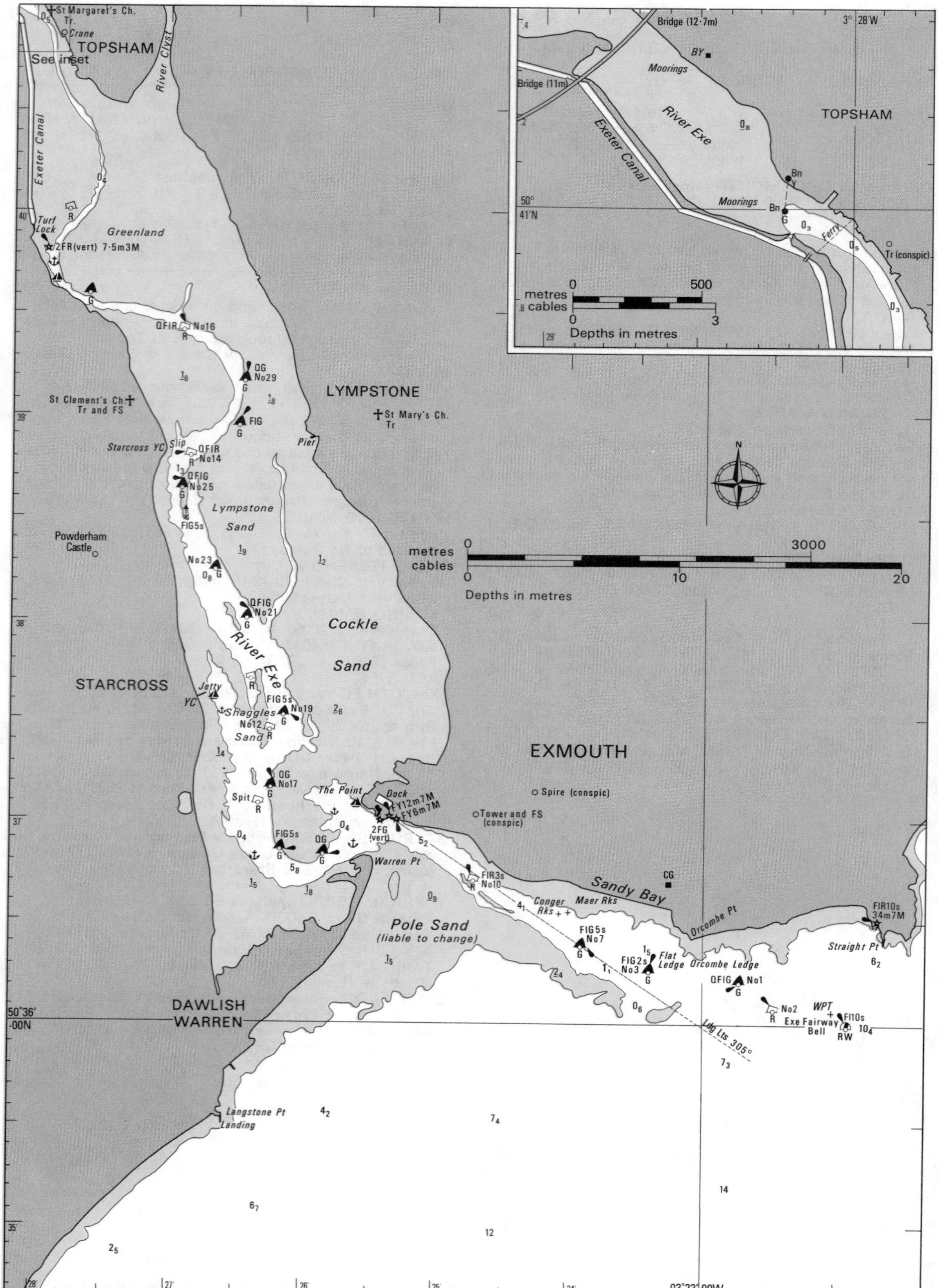
St Margaret's Ch. Tr.
Crane
TOPSHAM
See inset
River Clyst
Exeter Canal
Turf Lock
2FR(vert) 7·5m3M
Greenland
QFIR No16
QG No29
St Clement's Ch. Tr and FS
LYMPSTONE
St Mary's Ch. Tr
FIG
Pier
Starcross YC
Slip
QFIR No14
QFIG No25
FIG5s
Lympstone Sand
Powderham Castle
No23
QFIG No21
Cockle Sand
River Exe
STARCROSS
Jetty
YC
FIG5s No19
Shaggles Sand
No12
QG No17
Spit
The Point
Dock
FY12m7M
FY6m7M
2FG (vert)
FIG5s
QG
Warren Pt
EXMOUTH
Spire (conspic)
Tower and FS (conspic)
CG
FIR3s No10
Sandy Bay
Conger Rks
Maer Rks
Pole Sand (liable to change)
FIG5s No7
FIG2s No3
Flat Ledge
Orcombe Ledge
Orcombe Pt
QFIG No1
No2
WPT
Exe Fairway Bell
FI10s
RW
FIR10s 34m7M
Straight Pt
Ldg Lts 305°
DAWLISH WARREN
50°36'·00N
Langstone Pt Landing
03°23'·00W
metres
cables
Depths in metres
Bridge (12·7m)
3° 28'W
BY
Moorings
Bridge (11m)
River Exe
TOPSHAM
Exeter Canal
Bn
50° 41'N
Ferry
Tr (conspic)

⛵ At Starcross Apply Starcross Garage Tel. Starcross 890225

MINOR HARBOURS AND ANCHORAGES 10.1.25

MOUSEHOLE, Cornwall, 50°05′·00N, 05°32′·00W, Zone 0 (GMT), Admty chart 2345. HW +0550 on Dover, −0024 on Devonport; HW height 0·0 on Devonport; ML 3·2m; Duration 0600. Shelter good except from NE and SE winds; protected by St Clements I. from E winds. Entrance 11m wide; harbour dries at LW. It has depths of 3·8m at MHWS and 2·6m at MHWN. It is closed with timber baulks from Nov–Apl. Lights N Pier 2 FG (vert) 5/6m 4M. 2 FR (vert) shown when harbour closed. Hr Mr ☎ Penzance 731511. Facilities limited: FW, V, Slip. Buses to Penzance.

ST MICHAEL'S MOUNT, Cornwall, 50°07′·00N, 05°29′·00W, Zone 0 (GMT), Admty charts 2345, 777. HW +0550 on Dover, −0024 on Devonport; HW height +0·1m on Devonport; ML 3·2m; Duration 0550. Shelter good from N through E to SE. Harbour dries, it has approx 3·3m at MHWS and 1·4m at MHWN. Beware Hogus Rocks to NW of harbour and Outer Penzeath Rock about 3 ca WSW of Hogus Rocks. Also beware Maltman Rock 1 ca SSW of the Mount. There are no lights. Entrance between piers is 30m wide. No facilities on the island except FW. Marazion, ½ M across the causeway to N has some. EC Wed.

PORTHLEVEN, Cornwall, 50°05′·00N, 05°19′·00W, Zone 0 (GMT), Admty charts 2345, 777. HW +0551 on Dover, −0055 on Devonport; HW height 0·0 on Devonport; ML 3·1m; Duration 0545. See 10.1.11. Harbour dries above the old LB house but has approx 2·3m in centre of entrance. It is open to W and SW. Beware rocks round pierhead and Deazle Rocks to W. Light on S pier FG 10m 4M shown when inner harbour open. Inside harbour FG vis 033°-067° when required for vessels entering. Visitors go alongside the Quay on E side. Facilities: EC Wed; Hr Mr ☎ Helston 563042; **J. T. Cowls** ME, P and D (in cans); **Inner Harbour** C, FW, L, V, Bar; **Village** ✉, ◙, R, Ⓑ.

CADGWITH, Cornwall, 49°59′·20N, 05°10′·70W, Zone 0 (GMT), Admty charts 2345, 154 and 777; HW +0555 on Dover; −0030 on Devonport; −0·2m on Devonport; ML 3·0m. Harbour dries; it is divided into two by a rocky outcrop called The Todden. Beware the extension of this, rocks called The Mare; also beware the rocks to ENE called The Boa which cover at quarter tide. Anchor off The Mare in about 2-3m. Not recommended in on-shore winds. There are no lights. Many local fishing boats operate from here and are hauled up the shingle beach. Facilities: ✉, Bar, R.

PORT MULLION, Cornwall, 50°02′·00N, 05°15′·00W, Zone 0 (GMT), Admty charts 2345, 777. Lizard HW +0552 on Dover, −0050 on Devonport; HW height −0·2m on Devonport; ML 3·0m; Duration 0545. Harbour dries but has 5·3m at MHWS and 4·2m at MHWN. It is open to all W winds. Anchorage in Mullion Cove is safer especially in lee of Mullion Island where there is approx 3·5m. National Trust owns the island and the harbour. Fin keel boats not allowed in harbour. Visitors not allowed overnight. There are no lights. There is a slip on E side of harbour. Hr Mr ☎ (0326) 240510 Only facilities at Mullion village (1M) EC Wed; Bar, V.

COVERACK, Cornwall, 50°01′·00N, 05°05′·00W, Zone 0 (GMT), Admty chart 154, 777. HW +0605 on Dover, −0035 on Devonport; HW height −0·2m on Devonport; ML 3·0m; Duration 0550. See 10.1.12. Harbour dries but has 3·3m at MHWS and 2·2m at MHWN. Given good weather and off-shore winds it is better to anchor outside. Harbour is very small and full of fishing boats so berths are unlikely to be available. Beware the Guthens, off Chynhalls Pt, coming from the S, the Dava and other rocks off Lowland Pt coming from the N, and Manacle Rocks to the NE (BYB E cardinal, Q(3) 10s bell). There are no lights. Facilities: Hr Mr ☎ St Keverne 280593; EC Tues; FW (hotel) D, P from garage (in cans), shop, ✉.

PORTSCATHO, Cornwall, 50°11′·00N, 04°58′·00W, Zone 0 (GMT), Admty chart 154. HW −0600 on Dover, −0025 on Devonport; HW height −0·2m on Devonport; ML 3·0m; Duration 0550. Shelter – small drying harbour but in good weather and off-shore winds there is a good anchorage outside. There are no lights and very few facilities. Hr Mr ☎ 616.

GORRAN HAVEN, Cornwall, 50°14′·00N, 04°47′·00W, Zone 0 (GMT), Admty charts 148, 1267. HW −0600 on Dover, −0010 on Devonport; HW height −0·1m on Devonport. Shelter good with good flat sand beach for drying out in off-shore wind; good anchorage 100 to 500m E of Hr. Beware Gwineas Rk and Yaw Rk marked by E cardinal buoy. Beware pot markers on approach. Not suitable anchorage when wind is in E. Fin keels without legs should not anchor closer than 300m from Hr wall where depth is 1·8m at MLWS. Facilities: ✉, V, Bar, P (cans), R, L.

PORTMELLON, Cornwall, 50°15′·00N, 04°47′·00W, Zone 0 (GMT), Admty charts 148, 1267. HW −0600 on Dover, −0010 on Devonport; HW height −0·1m on Devonport; ML 3·1m; Duration 0600. Shelter good but only suitable as a temporary anchorage in settled weather and off-shore winds. There are no lights and few facilities. **G.P. Mitchell** ☎ 842407, BY.

CHARLESTOWN, Cornwall, 50°20′·00N, 04°45′·00W, Zone 0 (GMT), Admty charts 31, 148, 1267. HW −0555 on Dover, −0010 on Devonport; HW height −0·1m on Devonport; ML 3·1m; Duration 0605. It is a china clay port but has some yacht berths in the inner harbour. Entrance is safe but should only be attempted by day and in off-shore winds with calm weather. N breakwater FG 5m 1M, S breakwater FR 5m 1M. Entry signals – G Lt (night) or R ensign (day) = harbour open. R Lt (night) or B shape (day) = harbour shut. VHF Ch 16; 14 (HW−1 to HW+1 when vessel expected). Yachts should make arrangements before entering on VHF or by telephone, St Austell 3331. Facilities: EC Thurs; Bar, FW, P and D (cans or pre-arranged tanker), R, V.

PAR, Cornwall, 50°21′·00N, 04°42′·00W, Zone 0 (GMT), Admty charts 31, 148, 1267. HW −0555 on Dover, −0010 on Devonport; HW height −0·1m on Devonport; ML 3·1m; Duration 0605. See 10.1.15. A china clay port which is only suitable as a temporary stop for yachts. Harbour dries. Beware Killyvarder Rocks to SE of entrance marked by a R Bn. Entrance should not be tried except by day, in calm weather with off-shore winds. Entry signals R shape (day) or R Lt (night) = port closed or vessel leaving. VHF Ch 16; 12 (by day and HW−2 to HW+1). Yachts should make arrangements before entering on VHF or by ☎ Par 2282. Facilities: EC Thurs; Bar, D, FW, P, R, V.

POLPERRO, Cornwall, 50°20′·00N, 04°31′·00W, Zone 0 (GMT), Admty charts 148, 1267. HW −0554 on Dover, −0007 on Devonport; HW height −0·2m on Devonport; ML 3·1m; Duration 0610. Shelter good but harbour dries. There is 3·3m at MHWS and 2·5m at MHWN. The entrance is only 9·8m wide. Entrance closed by hydraulically operated gate in bad weather. Beware The Ranneys to W of entrance, and the rocks to E. Lights: Dir FW (occas) shown from measured distance beacons 1 and 2·2M to ENE. Tidal Basin, W pierhead FW 4m 4M on post, replaced by FR when harbour closed. Facilities: EC Sat; Hr Mr on Fish Quay, FW on quays.

HOPE COVE, Devon, 50°15′·00N, 03°49′·00W, Zone 0 (GMT), Admty chart 1613. HW −0525 on Dover, River Avon +0015 on Devonport; HW height −0·6m on Devonport; ML 2·6m; Duration 0615. Popular day anchorage but poor holding ground and only safe in off shore winds. Beware rock, which dries 2·7m, ½ ca off shore, 3 ca E off Bolt Tail. There are no lights. Facilities: EC Thurs; very limited facilities at Hope Cove but good at Kingsbridge,
(9M bus) or Salcombe, (4M bus).

PAIGNTON, Devon, 50°26′·00N, 03°33′·00W, Zone 0 (GMT), Admty charts 26, 1613; HW −0500 on Dover, +0035 on Devonport; HW height −0·6m on Devonport; ML 2·9m; Duration 0640. Harbour dries and is only suitable for small boats. E winds cause heavy swell in harbour. Rocks extend 180m E from E wall. Fl R 7m 3M Lt on E arm of entrance. Facilities: Hr Mr (summer only) ☎ 557812. Other telephone numbers and facilities as for Torquay (see 10.1.22). EC Wed. **Paignton SC** ☎ 525817; **Torbay Boating Centre** ☎ 558760, M, ME, Sh, Gas, CH.

Area 2

Central Southern England
Straight Point to Chichester

10-2-2

Central Southern England

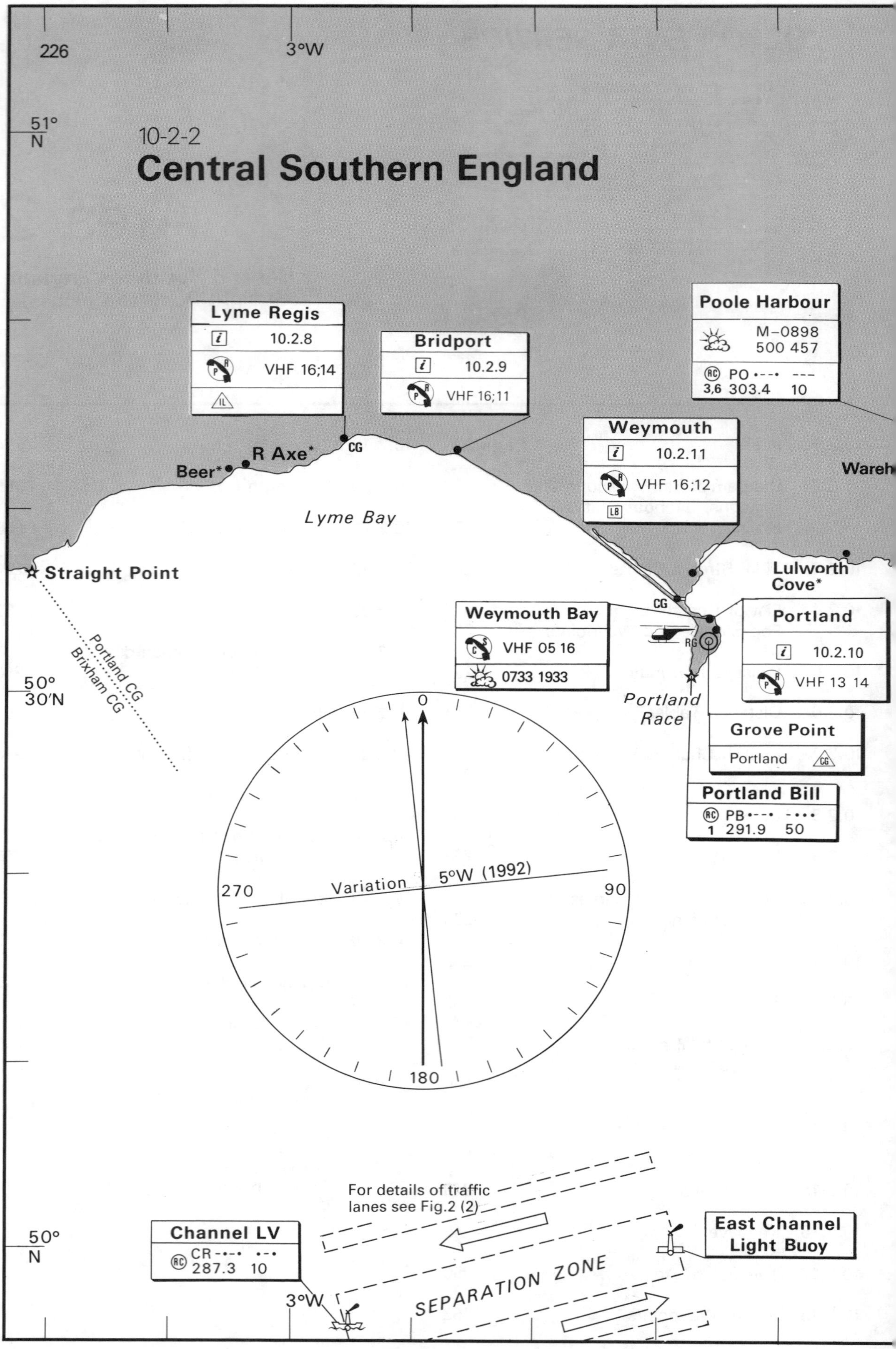
3°W
51° N
Lyme Regis
10.2.8
VHF 16;14
IL
Bridport
10.2.9
VHF 16;11
Poole Harbour
M–0898
500 457
PO
3,6 303.4 10
Weymouth
10.2.11
VHF 16;12
LB
Wareh
R Axe*
CG
Beer*
Lyme Bay
Straight Point
Lulworth
Cove*
CG
Weymouth Bay
VHF 05 16
0733 1933
RG
Portland
10.2.10
VHF 13 14
Portland CG
Brixham CG
50° 30'N
Portland
Race
Grove Point
Portland
CG
Portland Bill
PB
1 291.9 50
0
270
90
180
Variation 5°W (1992)
For details of traffic
lanes see Fig.2 (2)
East Channel
Light Buoy
Channel LV
CR
287.3 10
50° N
3°W
SEPARATION ZONE

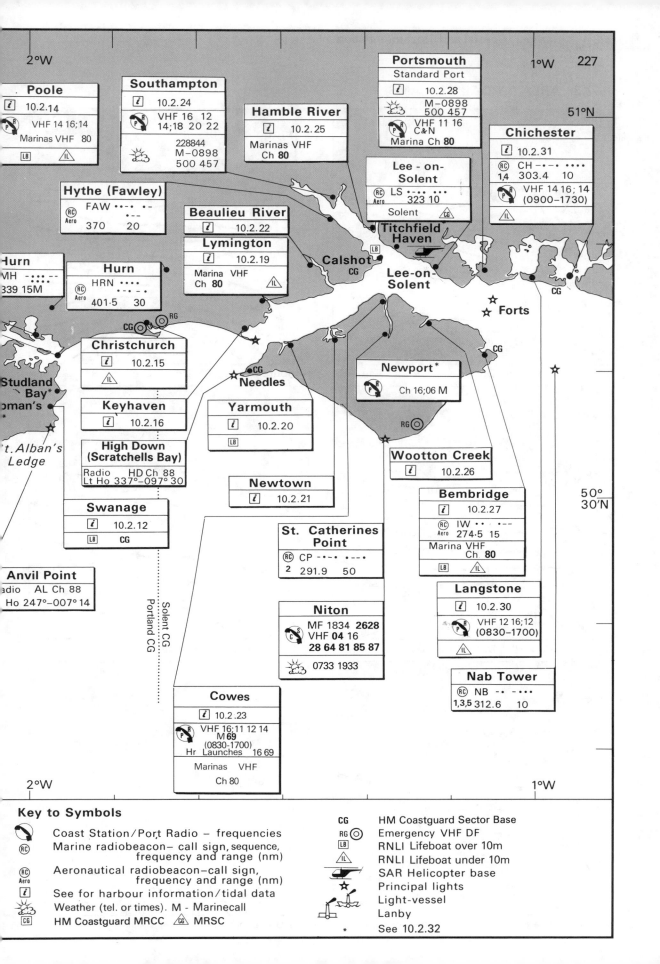

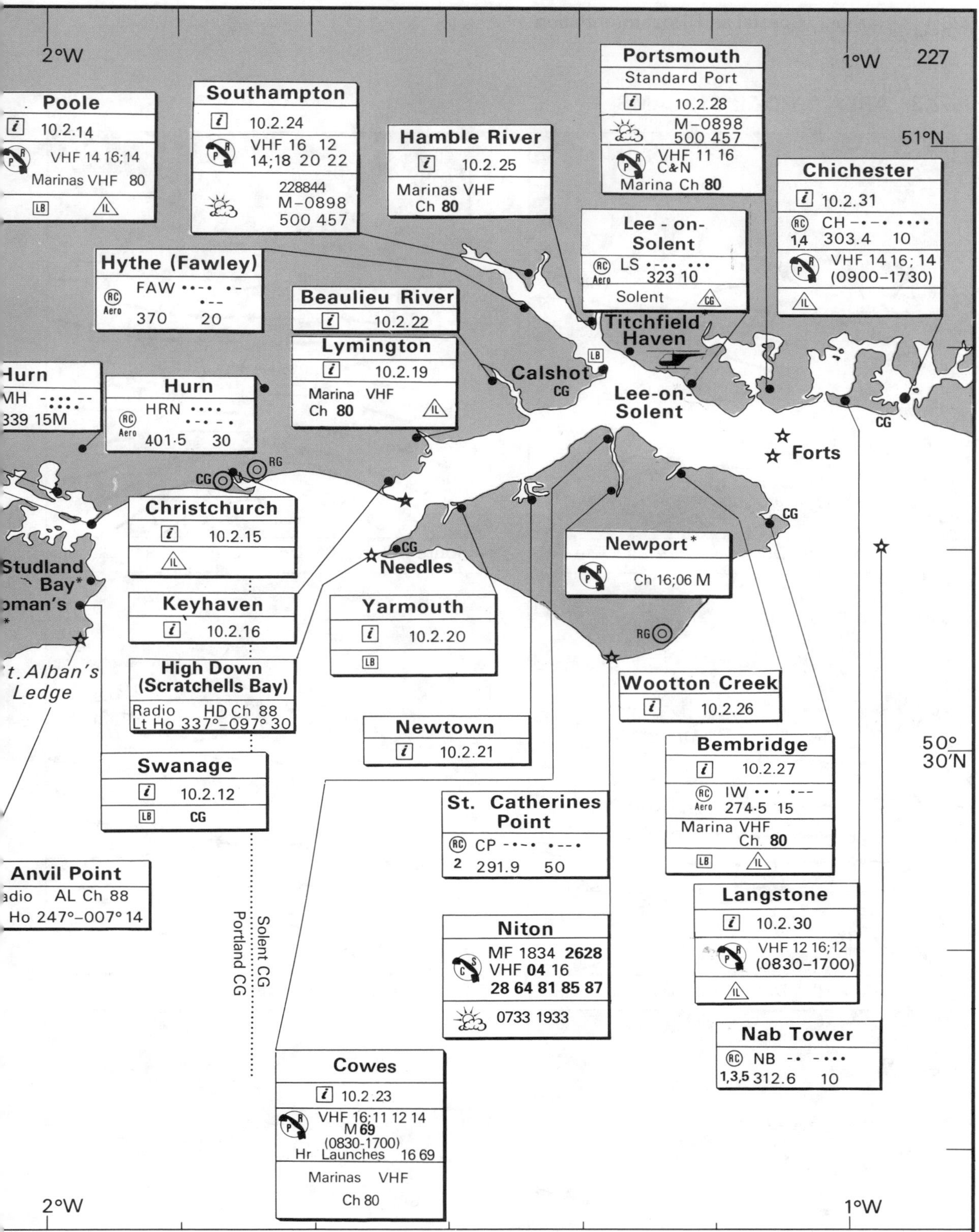
2°W
1°W
51°N
50° 30′N
Poole
10.2.14
VHF 14 16;14
Marinas VHF 80
Southampton
10.2.24
VHF 16 12 14;18 20 22
228844
M–0898 500 457
Hamble River
10.2.25
Marinas VHF Ch 80
Portsmouth
Standard Port
10.2.28
M–0898 500 457
VHF 11 16 C&N
Marina Ch 80
Chichester
10.2.31
CH –•–• ••••
1,4 303.4 10
VHF 14 16; 14 (0900–1730)
Lee - on- Solent
LS •–•• •••
323 10
Solent
Hythe (Fawley)
FAW ••–• •– •––
370 20
Beaulieu River
10.2.22
Lymington
10.2.19
Marina VHF Ch 80
Titchfield Haven
Calshot
CG
Lee-on-Solent
Hurn
MH
339 15M
Hurn
HRN ••••
401·5 30
Forts
CG
RG
Christchurch
10.2.15
Needles
Newport*
Ch 16;06 M
Studland Bay*
St. Alban's Ledge
Keyhaven
10.2.16
Yarmouth
10.2.20
High Down (Scratchells Bay)
Radio HD Ch 88
Lt Ho 337°–097° 30
Wootton Creek
10.2.26
Newtown
10.2.21
Bembridge
10.2.27
IW •• •––
274·5 15
Marina VHF Ch 80
Swanage
10.2.12
CG
St. Catherines Point
CP –•–• •––•
2 291.9 50
Anvil Point
Radio AL Ch 88
Ho 247°–007° 14
Solent CG
Portland CG
Niton
MF 1834 2628
VHF 04 16
28 64 81 85 87
0733 1933
Langstone
10.2.30
VHF 12 16;12 (0830–1700)
Nab Tower
NB –• –•••
1,3,5 312.6 10
Cowes
10.2.23
VHF 16;11 12 14
M 69
(0830-1700)
Hr Launches 16 69
Marinas VHF
Ch 80

Key to Symbols

(Coast Station symbol)	Coast Station/Port Radio – frequencies	CG	HM Coastguard Sector Base
RC	Marine radiobeacon– call sign, sequence, frequency and range (nm)	RG	Emergency VHF DF
RC Aero	Aeronautical radiobeacon–call sign, frequency and range (nm)	LB	RNLI Lifeboat over 10m
i	See for harbour information/tidal data	IL	RNLI Lifeboat under 10m
(Weather symbol)	Weather (tel. or times). M - Marinecall	(Helicopter symbol)	SAR Helicopter base
CG	HM Coastguard MRCC; CG MRSC	☆	Principal lights
		(Light-vessel symbol)	Light-vessel
		(Lanby symbol)	Lanby
		*	See 10.2.32

10.2.3 AREA 2 TIDAL STREAMS

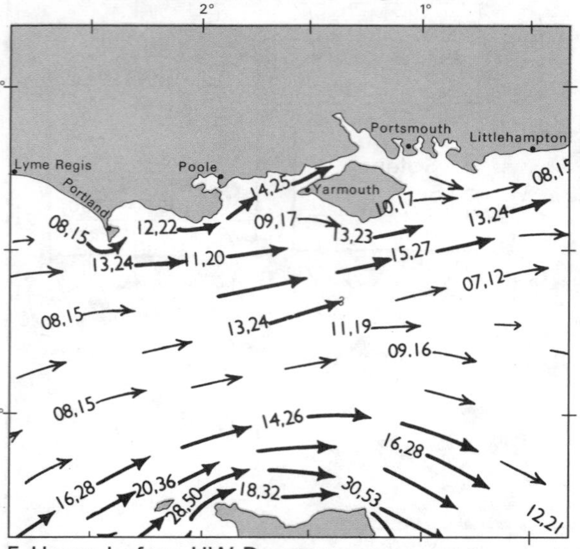
2°
1°
51°
50°
Portsmouth
Littlehampton
Lyme Regis
Poole
Portland
Yarmouth
14,25
08,15
10,17
12,22
09,17
13,23
13,24
13,24
11,20
15,27
07,12
08,15
13,24
11,19
09,16
08,15
14,26
16,28
16,28
20,36
28,50
18,32
30,53
12,21

5 Hours before HW Dover (0530 before HW Portsmouth)

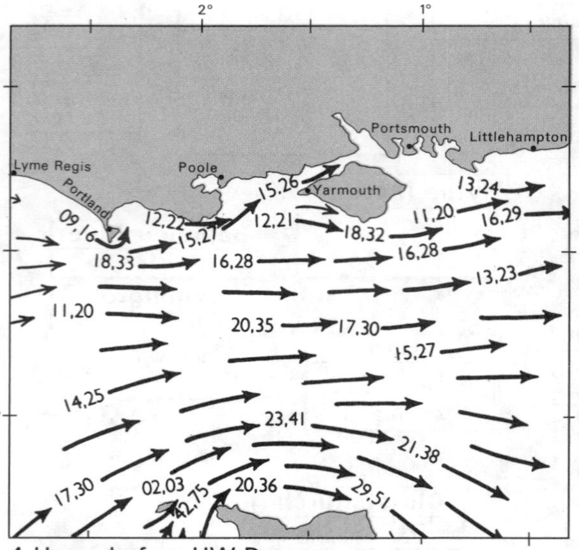
2°
1°
51°
50°
Portsmouth
Littlehampton
Lyme Regis
Poole
Portland
Yarmouth
15,26
13,24
09,16
12,22
15,27
12,21
18,32
11,20
16,29
18,33
16,28
16,28
13,23
11,20
20,35
17,30
15,27
14,25
23,41
21,38
17,30
02,03
42,75
20,36
29,51

4 Hours before HW Dover (0430 before HW Portsmouth)

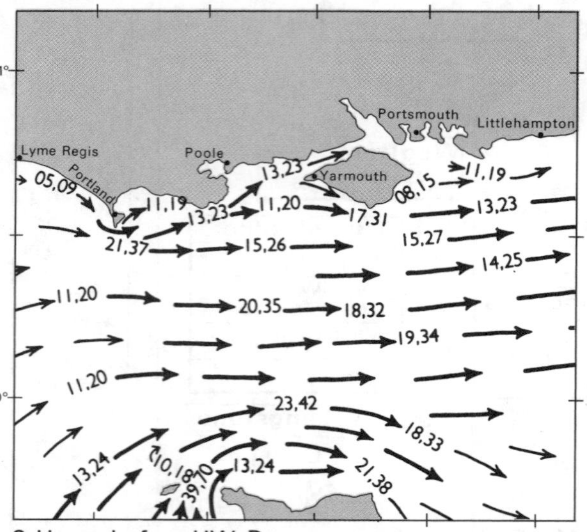
51°
50°
Portsmouth
Littlehampton
Lyme Regis
Poole
Portland
Yarmouth
13,23
11,19
05,09
08,15
11,19
13,23
11,20
17,31
13,23
21,37
15,26
15,27
14,25
11,20
20,35
18,32
19,34
11,20
23,42
18,33
13,24
10,18
13,24
39,70
21,38

3 Hours before HW Dover (0330 before HW Portsmouth)

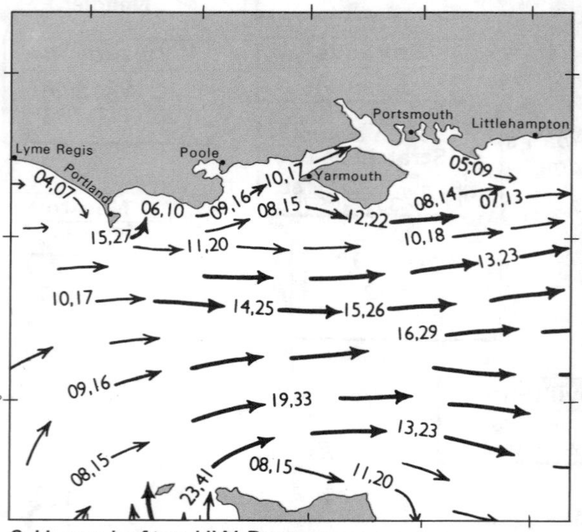
51°
50°
Portsmouth
Littlehampton
Lyme Regis
Poole
Portland
Yarmouth
05,09
04,07
10,17
06,10
09,16
08,15
08,14
07,13
15,27
12,22
11,20
10,18
13,23
10,17
14,25
15,26
16,29
09,16
19,33
13,23
08,15
08,15
23,41
11,20

2 Hours before HW Dover (0230 before HW Portsmouth)

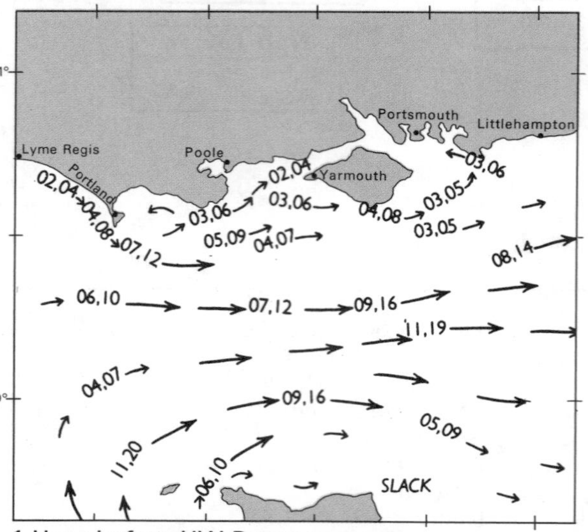
51°
50°
Portsmouth
Littlehampton
Lyme Regis
Poole
Portland
Yarmouth
03,06
02,04
02,04
03,06
03,06
03,05
04,08
04,08
05,09
04,07
03,05
07,12
08,14
06,10
07,12
09,16
11,19
04,07
09,16
05,09
11,20
06,10
SLACK

1 Hour before HW Dover (0130 before HW Portsmouth)

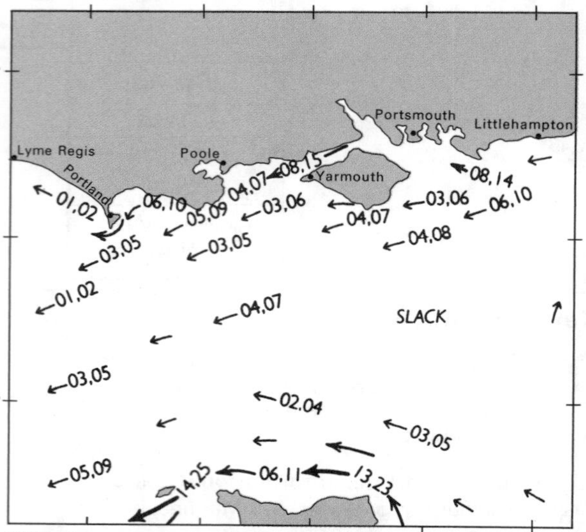
51°
50°
Portsmouth
Littlehampton
Lyme Regis
Poole
Portland
Yarmouth
08,15
08,14
04,07
01,02
06,10
05,09
03,06
03,06
06,10
04,07
03,05
03,05
04,08
01,02
04,07
SLACK
03,05
02,04
03,05
05,09
14,25
06,11
13,23

HW Dover (0030 before HW Portsmouth)

Portland 10.2.10. Isle of Wight 10.2.29. Eastward 10.3.3. Southward 10.18.3. Westward 10.1.3

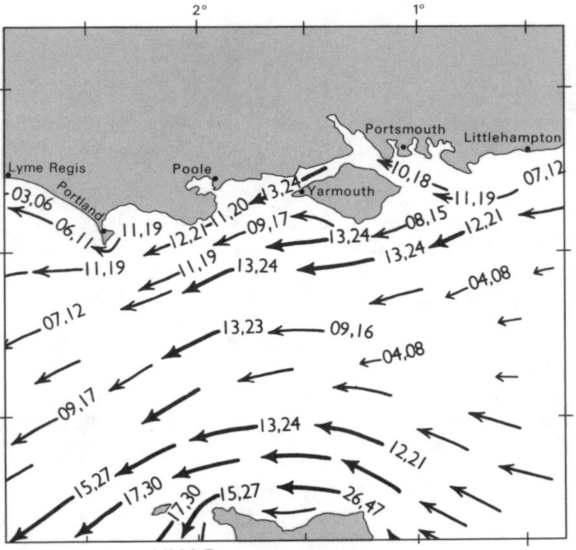
2°
1°
51°
50°
Lyme Regis
Portland
Poole
Portsmouth
Yarmouth
Littlehampton

1 Hour after HW Dover (0030 after HW Portsmouth)

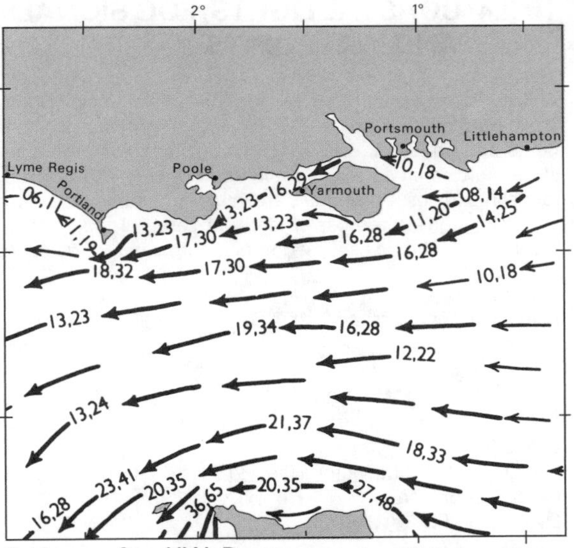
2°
1°
51°
50°
Lyme Regis
Portland
Poole
Portsmouth
Yarmouth
Littlehampton

2 Hours after HW Dover (0130 after HW Portsmouth)

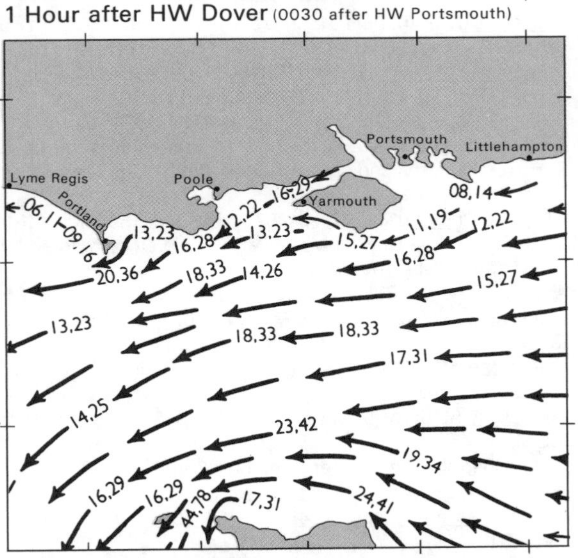
51°
50°
Lyme Regis
Portland
Poole
Portsmouth
Yarmouth
Littlehampton

3 Hours after HW Dover (0230 after HW Portsmouth)

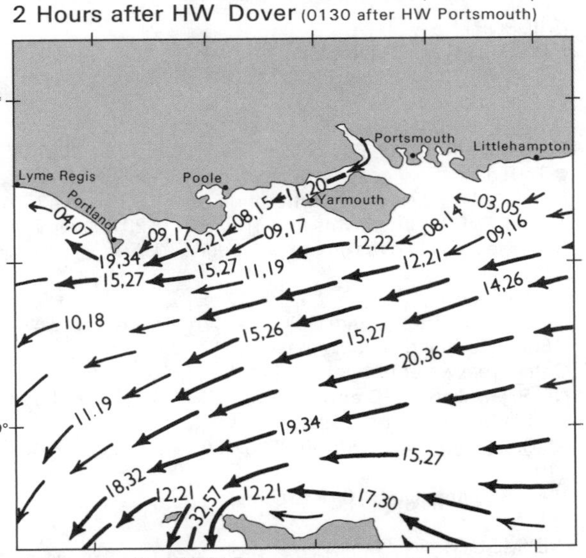
51°
50°
Lyme Regis
Portland
Poole
Portsmouth
Yarmouth
Littlehampton

4 Hours after HW Dover (0330 after HW Portsmouth)

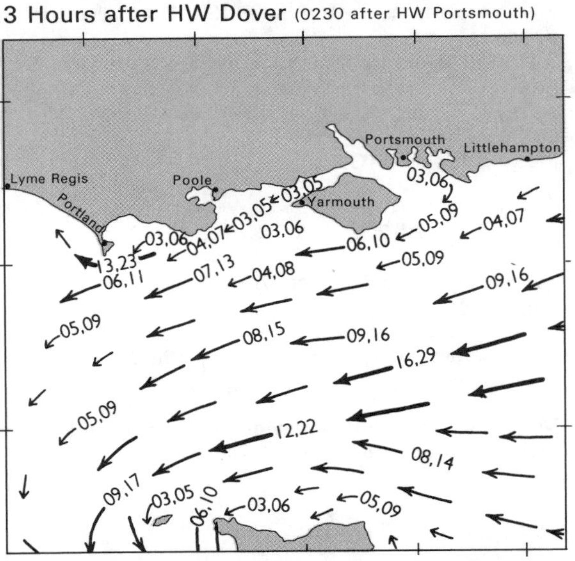
51°
50°
Lyme Regis
Portland
Poole
Portsmouth
Yarmouth
Littlehampton

5 Hours after HW Dover (0430 after HW Portsmouth)

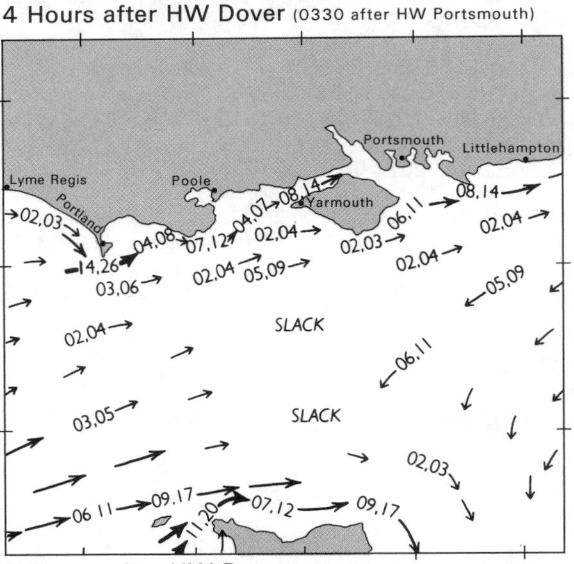
51°
50°
Lyme Regis
Portland
Poole
Portsmouth
Yarmouth
Littlehampton
SLACK
SLACK

6 Hours after HW Dover (0530 after HW Portsmouth)

10.2.4 COASTAL LIGHTS, FOG SIGNALS AND WAYPOINTS

Abbreviations used below are given in 1.4.1. Principal lights are in **bold** print, places in CAPITALS, and light-vessels, light floats and Lanbys in *CAPITAL ITALICS*. Unless otherwise stated lights are white. m—elevation in metres; M—nominal range in n. miles. Fog signals are in *italics*. Useful waypoints are underlined – use those on land with care. All geographical positions should be assumed to be approximate. See 4.2.2

ENGLAND—SOUTH COAST

AXMOUTH.
Pier Hd 50°42'·10N 03°03'·21W Fl 5s 7m 2M.

LYME REGIS.
Ldg Lts 296°. Front, Victoria Pier Hd 50°43'·14N 02°56'·09W Oc WR 8s 6m W9M. R7M; Bu col; vis R296°-116°, W116°.-296°. Rear, FG 8m 9M.

BRIDPORT.
E Pier Hd FG 3m 2M; (occas).
W Pier Hd 50°42'·52N 02°45'·77W FR 3m 2M; occas.
W Pier Root Iso R 2s 9m 5M.
DZ Lt By 50°36'·50N 02°42'·00W Fl Y 3s; SPM.
Portland Bill 50°30'·82N 02°27'·32W Fl (4) 20s 43m **29M**; W ● Tr, R band. Changes from 1 flash to 4 flashes 221°-244°, 4 flashes 244°-117°, changes from 4 flashes to 1 flash 117°-141°; RC. FR 19m 13M (same Tr) vis 271°-291° over The Shambles; *Dia 30s maximum power 005°-085°*.

PORTLAND.
Outer Breakwater (S end) Oc R 30s 12m 5M. FR on radar Tr 0·68M WSW and on radio mast 2·8M NW.
Outer breakwater (N end) QR 14m 5M; vis 013°-268°.
NE Breakwater (SE end) 50°35'·11N 02°24'·99W Fl 10s 22m **20M**; W Tr; *Horn 10s*.
NE Breakwater (NW end) 50°35'·62N 02°25'·80W Oc R 15s 11m 5M.
N arm (SE end) Oc G 10s 11m 5M.

WEYMOUTH.
S Pier Hd 50°36'·54N 02°26'·41W Q 10m 9M; tfc sigs 190m SW; *Reed 15s* (when vessels docking).
Ldg Lts 237·5° both FR 5/4m 4M; R ◆ on W post.
N Pier Hd 2 FG (vert) 9m 6M. *Bell* (when vessels expected).
W Shambles Lt By 50°29'·75N 02°24'·33W Q (9) 15s; WCM; *Bell*.
E Shambles Lt By 50°30'·75N 02°20'·00W Q (3) 10s; ECM; *Whis*,
Lulworth Cove ent, E Pt 50°36'·97N 02°14'·69W (unlit).
Bindon Hill 50 37 3N 02°13'·6W and St Alban's Hd 50°34'·8N 02°03 4W Iso R 2s when firing taking place.
Anvil Pt 50 35 48N 01°57'·52W Fl 10s 45m **24M**; W ● Tr; vis 237°-076 , (H24), RW.

SWANAGE.
Pier Hd 50°36'·52N 01°56'·88W 2 FR (vert) 6m 3M.
Peveril Ledge By 50°36'·38N 01°56'·02W (unlit); PHM.

POOLE.
Poole Fairway Lt By 50°38'·95N 01°54'·78W L Fl 10s; SWM.
Poole Bar (No. 1) Lt By 50°39·31N 01°55'·10W QG; SHM; *Bell*.
(Historic wreck) 50°39'·67N 01°54'·79W Fl Y 5s; SPM.
No. 2 Lt By 50°39'·18N 01°55'·17W Fl R 2s; PHM.
No. 9 Lt By 50°40'·19N 01°55'·74W Fl G 5s; SHM.
No. 10 Lt By 50°40'·11N 01°55'·84W Fl R 4s; PHM.
No. 11 (Hook Sands) Lt By 50°40'·46N 01°56'·05W Fl G 3s; SHM.
Training bank, outer end 50°39'·75N 01°55'·76W QR 7m 2M; R framework Tr. (TE)
Training Bank Lt By 50°39'·77N 01°55'·72W QR (T).
Swash Chan marked by PHM and SHM, unlit except for No. 12 (Channel) Lt By 50°40'·41N 01°56'·19W Fl R R 2s; PHM.
No. 13 Lt By 50°40'·85N 01°56'·62W Fl G 5s; SHM, and No. 14 Lt By 50°40'·76N 01°56'·73W Fl R 4s; PHM.

Sandbanks 50°40'·95N 01°56'·79W FY 10m 4M (RC 80m E).
RMYC Pier Hds 50°41'·31N 01°56'·73W 2 FG (vert).
E Looe No. 16A Lt By 50°41'·02N 01°56'·03W QR; PHM.
E Looe Dir Lt 50°41'·16N 01°56'·38W Oc WRG 6s 9m W10M, R6M, G6M; vis R234°-294°, W294°-304°, G304°-024°.
Ferry landing, E side 2 FG (vert) 3m, either side of ramp.
S Haven Pt, ferry landing 2 QR (hor) 3m 3M. Fl R on either side of ramp.
N Haven Pt Bn 50°41'·12N 01°57'·10W Q (9) 15s 5m; WCM.
N chan to Poole Hbr YC Marina and Poole Quay marked by PHM and SHM's, mostly lit.
Bullpit Bn 50°41'·69N 01°56'·62W Q (9) 15s 7m 4M; WCM.
Salterns Bn 50°42'·18N 01°57'·12W Q (6) + L Fl 15s 5m 5M; SCM.
Parkstone YC platform 50°42'·33N 01°58'·00W Q 8m 1M; hut on dolphin.
Stakes No 55 Lt By 50°42'·41N 01°58'·92W Q (6) + LFl 15s; SCM.
Little Chan, E side, Oyster Bank 50°42'·59N 01°59'·02W Fl (3) G 5s; SHM.
PYC Haven ent E side 50°42'·41N 01°59'·70W Fl G 5s. W side Fl (3) 10s.
Wareham Chan marked by PHM and SHM's initially, and then by stakes.
S Deep. Marked by Lt Bns and unlit Bns from ent S of Brownsea Castle to Furzey Is.
Furzey Is, SE corner, slipway 50°40'·88N 01°58'·86W Ldg Lts 305° Fl Y 2s.
Mooring dolphins Fl G 5s.

BOURNEMOUTH.
Pier Hd 2 FR (vert) 9m 1M; W Col. *Reed (2) 120s* when vessel expected.
Boscombe Pier Hd 2 FR (vert) 7m 1M; R Col.
Hengistbury Hd, groyne, Bn 50°42'·63N 01°44'·85W (unlit).
Needles Fairway Lt By 50°38'·20N 01°38'·90W L Fl 10s; SWM; *Whis*.

NOTE: For waypoints of navigational buoys and racing marks in Solent area, see 10.2.18.

Needles Lt 50°39'·70N 01°35'·43W Oc (2) WRG 20s 24m **W17M**, **R17M**, R14M G14M; ●Tr, R band and lantern; vis R291°-300°, W300°-083°, R (unintens) 083°-212°, W212°-217°, G217°-224°; *Horn (2) 30s.*

NEEDLES CHANNEL.
SW Shingles Lt By 50°39'·52N 01°37'·20W Fl R 2·5s; PHM.
Bridge Lt By 50°39'·59N 01°36'·80W VQ (9) 10s; WCM.
Shingles Elbow Lt By 50°40'·31N 01°35'·92W Fl (2) R 5s; PHM.
Mid Shingles Lt By 50°41'·19N 01°34'·59W; Fl (3) R 10s; PHM.
Totland Bay Pier Hd 2 FR (vert) 6m 2M.
Warden Lt By 50°41'·46N 01°33'·48W Fl G 2.5s; SHM; Bell.

NORTH CHANNEL.
N Hd Lt By 50°42'·65N 01°35'·42W Fl (3) G 10s; SHM.
NE Shingles Lt By 50°41'·93N 01°33'·32W Q (3) 10s; ECM.

Hurst Pt Ldg Lts 042°. Front 50°42'·36N 01°33'·05W Iso 4s 15m 14M; R ■ Tr; vis 029°-053°. Rear 215m from front Iso WR 6s 23m W14/13M, R11M; W ● Tr; vis W(unintens) 080°-104°, W234°-244°, R244°-250°, W250°-053°.

LYMINGTON.
Jack in the Basket 50°44'·25N 01°30'·50W Fl R 2s 9m; Ra refl.
Ldg Lts 319·5°. Front 50°45'·2N 01°31'·6W FR 12m 8M; vis 309·5°-329·5°. Rear 363m from front FR 17m 8M; vis as front.
Cross Boom No. 2 Fl R 2s 4m 3M; R can on pile.
No. 1 Fl G 2s 2m 3M; G ▲ on pile.

Durn's Pt obstn, S end, 50°45'·37N 01°26'·95W QR; Dolphin.

BEAULIEU RIVER.
Beaulieu Spit, E end 50°46'·83N 01°21'·67W Fl R 5s 3M; R dolphin; vis 277°-037°.
Ent chan Bn Nos. 5, 9, 19, 21 Fl G 4s; Bn Nos 12, 20 Fl R 4s.

Stansore Pt. 50°46'·7N 01°20'·8W, 50°46'·8N 01°20'·5W, 50°46'·9N 01°20'·4W. In each of these positions is a QR Lt 4m 1M; R ◆, W band, on R pile, marking cables.

Fort Victoria Pier Hd 2 FG (vert) 4M.

YARMOUTH.
Pier Hd, centre, 2 FR (vert) 2M; G col. High intensity FW (occas).

W Bramble Lt By 50°47'·17N 01°18'·57W VQ (9) 10s; WCM; *Bell*; Racon.
Outfall 50°48'·25N 01°18'·73W Iso R 10s 6m 5M; col on n structure; Ra refl; FR Lt on each corner; *Horn 20s.*

CALSHOT SPIT Lt F 50°48'·32N 01°17'·55W Fl 5s 12m 11M; R hull, Lt Tr amidships; *Horn (2) 60s.*
Obstn Lts, QR on chy 0·9M W.

Fawley Chan No. 2 50°49'·45N 01°18'·75W Fl R 3s.
Ldg Lts 218·7°. Front QR 6m (occas). Rear Q 11m (occas).
Hamble Pt Lt By 50°50'·12N 01°18'·58W Q (6) + LFl 15s; SCM.

RIVER HAMBLE.
Ldg Lts 345·5°. Front No. 6 pile 50°50'·58N 01°18'·74W Oc (2) R 12s 4m 2M. Rear 820m from front QR 12m; W mast; vis 341·5°-349·5°.
No. 1 pile 50°50'·31N 01°18'·57W Fl G 3s 3M; SHM.
No. 2 pile 50°50'·36N 01°18'·68W Q (3) 10s 3M; ECM.
No. 3 pile Fl (2) G 5s.
No. 5 pile Fl (3) G 10s.
No. 7 pile Fl G 3s.
No. 8 pile Fl R 3s.
No. 9 pile Fl (2) G 5s.
No. 10 pile Fl (2) R 5s.
Ldg Lts 026°, Warsash shore. Front 50°51'°0N 01°18'·3W QG; B & W chequered pile Bn. Rear, Sailing Club, Iso G 6s; vis 022°-030°.

SOUTHAMPTON WATER.
Esso Marine terminal, SE end 50°50'·05N 01°19'·33W 2 FR (vert) 9m 10M; *Whis (2) 20s.*
BP Hamble Jetty 50°50'·8N 01°19'·4W 2 FG (vert) 5/3m 2M (on each side of the 4 dolphins).
Hythe Pier Hd 50°52'·45N 01°23'·52W 2 FR (vert) 12/5m 5M.
Hythe Marina Village 50°52'·6N 01°23'·8W Q (3) 10s; ECM.
Lock ent 2 FG (vert); G s, and 2 FR (vert); R ■.
Queen Elizabeth II terminal, S end 50°52'·97N 01°23'·64W 4 FG (vert) 16m 3M.

RIVER ITCHEN.
E side. No. 1 dolphin 50°53'·12N 01°23'·32W QG; G s; SHM.
No. 2 dolphin 50°53'·27N 01°23'·28W Fl G 5s 2M; SHM.
No. 3 dolphin 50°53'·45N 01°23'·18W Fl G 7s; SHM.
No. 4 pile 50°53'·58N 01°23'·07W QG 4m 2M; SHM.
Itchen Bridge. FW on bridge span each side marks main chan. 2 FG (vert) 2M each side on E pier. 2 FR (vert) 2M each side on W pier.
Crosshouse Bn 50°54'·01N 01°23'·10W Oc R 5s 5m 2M; PHM, power cable.
Chapel Bn 50°54'12N 01°23'·13W Fl G 3s 5m 3M; SHM.
Shamrock Quay pontoon, SW end 50°54'·45N 01°22'·83W 2 FR (vert) 4m and NE ends 2 FR (vert) 4m.
No. 5 Bn Fl G 3s.
No. 6 Bn 50°54'·57N 01°22'·55W Fl R 3s.
No. 7 Bn Fl (2) G 5s.
No. 9 Bn 50°54'·72N 01°22'·38W Fl (4) G 10s.
Kemps Marina Jetty Hd 50°54'·80N 01°22'·57W 2 FG (vert) 5m 1M

RIVER TEST.
Lower Foul Ground Lt Bn 50°53'·23N 01°24'·47W Fl (2) R 10s; PHM Bn.
Upper Foul Ground Lt Bn 50°53'·50N 01°24'·80W Fl (2) R 10s; PHM Bn.
Town Quay Ldg Lts 329°, both FY 12/22m 3/2M (occas).
Middle Swinging Ground, Lts in line 336°, both Oc G 6s 26m.

COWES.
No. 4 Lt By 50°46'·04N 01°17'·78W QR; PHM.
Ldg Lts 164°. Front 50°45'·9N 01°17'·8W Iso 2s 3m 6M. Rear 290m from front Iso R 2s 5m 3M; vis 120°-240°.
E Breakwater Hd Fl R 3s 3M.
W Cowes Marina N end 2 FG (vert) 6m.

WOOTTON.
Bn 50°44'·46N 01°12'·08W Q 1M; NCM.

RYDE.
Pier, NW corner, N corner and E corner each marked by 2 FR (vert). In fog FY from N corner, vis 045°-165°, 200°-320°.
Fort Gilkicker 50°46'·40N 01°08'·38W Oc G 10s 7M.
Spit Sand Fort, N side 50°46'·20N 01°05'·85W Fl R 5s 18m 7M; large ● stone structure.
Horse Sand Fort 50°44'·97N 01°04'·25W Fl 10s 21m **15M**; large ● stone structure.
No Man's Land Fort 50°44'·37N 01°05'·61W Fl 5s 21m **15M**; large ● stone structure.
St Helen's Fort (IOW) 50°42'·27N 01°04'·95W Fl (3) 10s 16m 8M; large ● stone structure.
Bembridge Tide Gauge 50°42'·43N 01°04'·93W Fl Y 2s 1M; SPM.
Bembridge Ledge Lt By 50°41'·12N 01°02'·74W Q (3) 10s; ECM.
West Princessa Lt By 50°40'·12N 01°03'·58W Q (9) 15s; WCM.
Sandown Pier Hd 2 FR (vert) 7/5m 2M.
Shanklin Pier Hd 2 FR (vert) 6m 4M; TE; *Bell*.
Ventnor Pier 2 FR (vert) 10m 3M.
St Catherine's Pt (IOW) 50°34'·52N 01°17'·80W Fl 5s 41m **30M**; W 8-sided Tr; vis 257°-117°; RC. FR 35m 17M (same Tr) vis 099°-116°.
Nab Tr. 50°40'·05N 00°57'·07W Fl (2) 10s 27m **19M**; *Horn(2)30s*; RC; Racon. Fog Det Lt, vis 300°-120°.

PORTSMOUTH.
Outer Spit Lt By 50°45'·55N 01°05'·41W Q (6) + LFl 15s; SCM.
Southsea Castle N corner 50°46'·66N 01°05'·25W Iso 2s 16m 11M, W stone Tr, B band; vis 339°-066°.
Dir Lt 001·5° Dir WRG 11m W13M, R5M, G5M; same structure FG 351·5°-357·5°, Al WG 357·5°-000° (W phase incr with brg), FW 000°-003°, Al WR 003°-005·5° (R phase incr with brg), FR 005·5°-011·5°.
Fort Blockhouse 50°47'·34N 01°06'·65W Dir Lt 320°; Dir WRG 6m W13M, R5M, G5M; Oc G 310°-316°, Al WG 316°-318·5° (W phase incr with brg), Oc 318·5°-321·5°, Al WR 321·5°-324° (R phase incr with brg), OcR 324°-330°. 2 FR (vert) 20m E.
Dolphin, close E of C&N Marina, 50°47'·8N 01°06'·9W, Dir WRG 2m 1M; vis Iso G 2s 322·5°-330°, Al WG 330°-332·5°, Iso 2s 332·5°-335° (main chan), Al WR 335°-337·5°, Iso R 2s 337.5°-345° (Small Boat Chan).
Victoria Pile 50°47'·31N 01°06'·40W Oc G 15s 1M; SHM. ● Tr 2FG(vert).
The Point 50°47'·54N 01°06'·48W QG 2M; pile, SHM.

LANGSTONE.
Roway Wreck Bn 50°46'·08N 01°02'·20W Fl (2) 5s; IDM.
Langstone Fairway Lt By 50°46'·28N 01°01'·27W L Fl 10s; SWM.
Eastney Pt, drain Bn 50°47'·20N 01°01'·58W QR 2m 2M. FR Lts combined with Y Lts shown when firing taking place.
Water intake 50°47'·7N 01°01'·7W Fl R 10s; pile.
Hayling Is ferry landing 2 FG (vert).

Langstone Channel
S Lake 50°49'·45N 00°59'·80W Fl G 3s 3m 2M; pile, SHM.
Binness 50°49'·60N 00°59'·85W Fl R 3s 3m 2M; pile, PHM.

CHICHESTER.
Bar Bn 50°45'·88N 00°56'·37W Fl WR 5s 14m W7M, R5M; vis W322°-080°, R080°-322°; Fl (2) R 10s 7m 2M; same structure; vis 020°-080°; RC.
Eastoke Bn 50°46'·62N 00°56'·08W QR 2m.
W Winner 50°46'·83N 00°55'·89W QG.

EMSWORTH CHANNEL
Verner 50°48'·33N 00°56'·62W Fl R 10s; pile, PHM.
Marker Pt 50°48'·87N 00°56'·62W Fl (2) G 10s 8m; pile, SHM.
NE Hayling 50°49'·60N 00°56'·75W Fl (2) R 10s 8m; pile, PHM.
Emsworth 50°49'·63N 00°56'·67W Q (6) + LFl 15s; pile, SCM, tide gauge.

CHICHESTER CHANNEL.
E Hd 50°47'·32N 00°54'·70W Fl (4) G 10s; pile, SHM, tide gauge.
Camber Bn 50°47'·84N 00°53'·98W Q (6) + LFl 15s; SCM.
Chalkdock Bn 50°48'·46N 00°53'·20W Fl (2) G 10s; pile, SHM.
Itchenor, jetty 50°48'·44N 00°51'·89W 2 FG (vert); tide gauge.
Birdham 50°48'·30N 00°50'·17W Fl (4) G 10s; pile, SHM, depth gauge.

Note. For English Channel Waypoints see 10.1.7

(For Channel Lt V, E Channel Lt F, Channel Is and adjacent coast of France see 10.17.4).

10.2.5 PASSAGE INFORMATION

LYME BAY (chart 3315)

Between Torbay and Portland there is no hbr accessible in onshore winds, and yachtsmen must take care not to be caught on a lee shore. Tides are weak, seldom reaching more than 0·75 kn. There are no dangers offshore. In offshore winds there is a good anch off Beer, NE of Beer Hd, the most W chalk cliff in England, see 10.2.32. 3·5M E of Lyme Regis (10.2.8) is Golden Cap (186m and conspic). High Ground and Pollock are rks 0·7M offshore, 2M and 3M ESE of Golden Cape.

E of Bridport (10.2.9) is the start of the Chesil Beach, which runs almost straight to N end of Portland peninsula, with its conspic wedge-shaped appearance. In E winds there is anch in Chesil Cove on NW side of Portland, but beware any shift of wind to the W.

PORTLAND (chart 2255)

Portland (10.2.10) is mostly steep-to, but rks extend 0·25M beyond the extremity of the Bill, where there is a stone Bn (18m). Depths S of Bill are irregular. On E side there is rk awash at HW 0·05M off Grove Pt, the E extremity of Portland. From a distance Portland looks like an Is, with the highest land (144m) in N, sloping to the Bill where the Lt Ho is conspic.

Tidal streams run very strongly, with eddies either side of Portland. Stream runs S down each side for about 10 hrs out of 12, causing great turbulence where they meet off the Bill. The direction and strength of stream is shown hour by hour, relative to HW Devonport, in 10.2.10. Note that the sp rate reaches 7 kn, but even stronger streams can occur in vicinity of the race. The diagrams show that the race varies in position and extent — usually SE of the Bill on E-going stream, and SW of the Bill on W-going stream.

There is usually a stretch of relatively smooth water 0·25 – 0·5M offshore, between the Bill and the race, but yachts using this must take care not to be swept S into the race by the strong stream usually running down either side of Portland. Also beware lobster pots – this is no place for a fouled propeller.

On passage E, unless bound for Weymouth (10.2.11) it is safest to pass 5M S of the Bill, to seaward of the race and of the Shambles bank. If bound for Weymouth, and conditions are suitable for the inshore passage, aim for a point well N of the Bill itself, to allow for tide. It is ideal to round the Bill about HW Devonport –0130 (HW Portland –0230) when there will be a favourable tide up the E side of Portland, taking the boat away from the race.

On passage W it is best to round the Bill with the first of the ebb, leaving Weymouth about HW Devonport +0400 (HW Portland +0300), so that a yacht will carry the tide well W of Portland.

PORTLAND TO ISLE OF WIGHT (chart 2615)

The Shambles bank is about 3M E of Portland Bill, and should be avoided at all times. In bad weather the sea breaks heavily on it. It is marked by Bys on its E side and at SW end. E of Weymouth are rky ledges extending 0·3M offshore as far as Lulworth Cove, which provide a reasonable anch in fine, settled weather and offshore winds. Rky ledges extend each side of ent, more so on the W. See 10.2.32.

A firing range extends 5M offshore between Lulworth and St Alban's Hd. Yachts must pass through this area as quickly as possible, when the range is in use. See 10.2.32. Beware Kimmeridge Ledges, which run over 0·5M seaward. Warbarrow B and Chapman's Pool provide anchs in calm weather and offshore winds. See 10.2.32.

St Alban's Hd (107m and conspic) is steep-to and has a dangerous race off it which may extend 3M seaward. The race lies to the E on the flood and to the W on the ebb; the latter is the more dangerous. An inshore passage about 0·5M wide avoids the worst of the overfalls. There is an eddy on W side of St Alban's, where the stream runs almost continuously SE. 1M S of St Alban's the ESE stream begins at HW Portsmouth +0520, and the WNW stream at HW Portsmouth –0030, with sp rates of 4·75 kn.

There is deep water quite close inshore between St Alban's Hd and Anvil Pt (Lt). 1M NE of Durlston Hd is Peveril Ledge running 0·25M seaward, and causing quite a bad race which extends nearly 1M eastwards, particularly on W-going stream against a SW wind. Proceeding towards Poole (10.2.14), overfalls may be met off Ballard Pt and Old Harry on the W-going stream. Studland B (chart 2172) is a good anch except in winds between NE and SE. Anch about 0·4M WNW of Handfast Pt. Avoid foul areas on chart. See 10.2.32.

Poole B offers good sailing in waters sheltered from W and N winds, and with no dangers to worry the average yacht. Tidal streams are weak N of a line between Handfast Pt and Hengistbury Hd. The latter is a dark headland, S of Christchurch hbr (10.2.15), with a groyne extending 0·1M S and Beerpan Rks a further 0·05M offshore. Christchurch Ledge extends 2·75M SE from Hengistbury Hd. There are often lobster pots in this area. The tide runs hard over the ledge at sp, and there may be overfalls. Within Christchurch B the streams are weak.

APPROACHES TO SOLENT (charts 2219, 2050)

The Needles with their Lt Ho are conspic landmark for W end of Isle of Wight. There are rks 0·25M (dries) and 0·05M WNW of Lt Ho, with remains of wreck close SW of inner one. In bad weather broken water and overfalls extend along The Bridge — a reef which runs 0·8M of W of the Lt Ho with extremity marked by By.

The NW side of Needles chan is defined by the Shingles bank, parts of which dry and on which the sea breaks very heavily. The SE side of the bank is fairly steep, the NW side much more gradual in slope. On the ebb the stream sets very strongly in a WSW direction across the Shingles. Gale force winds between S and W against the ebb tide cause a very dangerous sea in Needles chan. In such conditions the eastern approach to the Solent, via the Forts and Spithead, should be used. In strong winds the North chan, N of the Shingles, is to be preferred to the Needles chan. The two join S of Hurst Pt, where overfalls may be met. Beware The Trap, a bank close S of Hurst Fort.

The E approach to the Solent, via Spithead, presents few problems. The main chan is well buoyed and easy to follow, but there is plenty of water for the normal yacht to the S of it when approaching No Man's Land Fort and Horse Sand Fort, which must be passed between. Ryde Sand dries extensively and is a trap for the unwary; so too is Hamilton Bank on the W side of the chan to Portsmouth (10.2.28).

THE SOLENT (charts 2040, 394)

Within the Solent there are few dangers in mid-chan. The most significant is Bramble bank (dries) between Cowes and Calshot. The main chan (buoyed) passes S and W of the Brambles, but yachts can use the North Ch running N of the

Brambles at any state of tide. Tidal streams are strong at sp, but principally follow the direction of the main chan. For details see 10.2.17. For waypoints of navigational Bys and racing marks see 10.2.18.

There are several spits, banks, rks and ledges which a yachtsman should know. From the W they include: Pennington and Lymington Spits on the N shore; Black Rk 0·4M W of entrance to Yarmouth (10.2.20); Hamstead Ledge 0·8M W of entrance to Newtown R (10.2.21) and Saltmead Ledge 1·5M to E; Gurnard Ledge 1·5M W of Cowes; Lepe Middle and Beaulieu Spit, S and W of the ent to Beaulieu R (10.2.22); the shoals off Stone Pt, where three Bns mark cable area; Shrape Mud, which extends N from the breakwater of Cowes hbr (10.2.23) and along to Old Castle Pt; the shoals and occasional rks which fringe the Is shore from Old Castle Pt to Ryde, including either side of the ent to Wootton Creek (10.2.26); and Calshot Spit which extends almost to the Lt F which marks the turn of chan into Southampton Water.

Depending on the direction of wind, there are many good anchs in Solent for yachts which are on passage up or down the coast. For example, in E winds Alum B, close NE of the Needles, is an attractive daytime anch with its coloured cliffs — but beware Long Rk (dries) in middle of B, and Five Fingers Rk 0·15M SW of Hatherwood Pt on N side. Totland B is good anch in settled weather, but avoid Warden Ledge.

In W winds there is anch on E side of Hurst, as close inshore as depth permits, NE of High Lt. In S winds, or in good weather, anch W of Yarmouth hbr ent, as near shore as possible; reasonably close to town (see 10.2.20).

In winds between W and N there is good anch in Stanswood B, about 1M NE of Stansore Pt. Just N of Calshot Spit there is shelter from SW and W. Osborne B, 2M E of Cowes, is sheltered from winds between S and W. In E winds Gurnard B, the other side of Cowes is preferable. In N winds anch in Stokes B. At E end of IOW there is good anch off Bembridge in winds from S, SW or W; but clear out if wind goes into E. Within the Solent there are many places which a shoal-draught boat can explore at the top of the tide — such as Ashlett Creek between Fawley and Calshot, Eling up the R. Test, and the upper reaches of the Medina.

ISLE OF WIGHT – SOUTH COAST (chart 2045)

From the Needles into Freshwater B the cliffs can be approached to within 0·1M, but beyond the E end of chalk cliffs there are ledges off Brook and again off Atherfield which demand keeping at least 0·5M offshore. The E-going stream sets towards these dangers. 4M SSW of the Needles the stream turns E x N at HW Portsmouth +0530, and W at HW Portsmouth –0030, sp rate 2 kn. The E-going stream starts running NE, but soon changes to E x N, towards Atherfield ledges. In Freshwater B, 3M E of Needles, the stream turns ESE at HW Portsmouth +0445, and WNW at HW Portsmouth –0130, sp rate 1 kn.

St Catherine's Lt Ho (Lt, RC) is conspic. It is safe to pass 0·2M off, but a race occurs off the Pt and can be very dangerous at or near sp with a strong opposing wind, particularly SE of the Pt on a W-going stream in a W gale – when St Catherine's should be given a berth of at least 2M. 1·25M SE of the Pt the stream turns E x N at HW Portsmouth +0520, and W x S at HW Portsmouth –0055, sp rate 3·75 kn.

From St Catherine's Pt to Dunnose, rks extend about 0·25M in places. A race occurs at Dunnose. In Sandown B, between Dunnose and Culver Cliff, the streams are weak inshore. Off the centre of the B they turn NE x E at HW Portsmouth +0500, and SW x W at HW Portsmouth –0100, sp rates 2 kn. Whitecliff B provides an anch in winds between W and N. From here to Foreland (Bembridge Pt) the coast is fronted by a ledge of rks (dry) extending up to 0·3M offshore, and it is advisable to keep to seaward (E) of Bembridge Ledge By.

4·5M E of Foreland is Nab Tr (Lt, fog sig, RC), a conspic steel and concrete structure (28m), marking Nab Shoal for larger vessels and of no direct significance to yachtsmen. It is however a most useful landmark when approaching the E end of Isle of Wight, or when making for the hbrs of Langstone (10.2.30) or Chichester (10.2.31).

For notes on cross-Channel passages see 10.3.5.

10.2.6 DISTANCE TABLE

Approximate distances in nautical miles are by the most direct route while avoiding dangers and allowing for traffic separation schemes etc. Places in *italics* are in adjoining areas.

1 *Le Four*	**1**																			
2 *Start Point*	113	**2**																		
3 *Berry Head*	126	13	**3**																	
4 *Casquets*	120	57	61	**4**																
5 *Cherbourg*	151	85	86	31	**5**															
6 Portland Bill	153	49	41	48	62	**6**														
7 Anvil Point	172	69	61	56	58	20	**7**													
8 Poole Bar	177	74	66	61	63	25	5	**8**												
9 Needles	180	84	76	64	61	35	15	12	**9**											
10 St Catherines	188	95	86	67	58	45	25	25	12	**10**										
11 Nab Tower	206	110	101	81	66	60	40	30	27	15	**11**									
12 Lymington	187	91	83	71	68	42	22	19	7	19	25	**12**								
13 Cowes	194	98	90	78	75	49	29	26	14	25	15	10	**13**							
14 Hamble	198	102	94	82	79	53	33	30	18	29	19	14	6	**14**						
15 Portsmouth	203	107	99	87	84	58	38	35	23	20	10	19	10	13	**15**					
16 Chichester Bar	207	112	104	92	89	63	43	40	28	19	6	23	15	18	8	**16**				
17 *Owers Lanby*	208	119	110	87	70	69	49	49	36	24	11	34	25	29	20	14	**17**			
18 *Le Havre*	223	156	151	101	70	118	104	107	98	86	85	105	112	116	95	91	77	**18**		
19 *Royal Sovereign*	248	163	153	124	102	114	92	92	82	67	54	77	68	72	63	57	43	82	**19**	
20 *North Foreland*	310	225	215	186	162	176	154	154	144	129	116	139	130	134	125	119	105	137	62	**20**

LYME REGIS 10-2-8

Dorset

CHARTS
Admiralty 3315; Stanford 12; Imray C5; OS 193

TIDES
−0455 Dover; ML 2·4; Duration 0700; Zone 0 (GMT).

Standard Port DEVONPORT (←)

Times				Height (metres)			
HW		LW		MHWS	MHWN	MLWN	MLWS
0100	0600	0100	0600	5·5	4·4	2·2	0·8
1300	1800	1300	1800				
Differences LYME REGIS							
+0040	+0100	+0005	−0005	−1·2	−1·3	−0·5	−0·2

NOTE: Rise is relatively fast for the first hour after LW, then a slackening for the next 1½ hours after which the rapid rate is resumed — there is usually a stand of up to 1½ hours at HW.

SHELTER
The harbour, known as The Cobb, offers excellent shelter except in strong winds from E or SE. Harbour dries at LW. Max length allowed in harbour 9m. Keel boats can dry out alongside Victoria Pier or anchor as shown. Five spherical R visitors buoys available. Access about HW∓2½.

NAVIGATION
Waypoint 50°43′·00N 02°55′·60W, 116°/296° from/to front Ldg Lt 0·35M. Rock breakwater south of entrance marked by R can beacon. Beware numerous fishing floats in all directions. Red flag on flagpole on Victoria Pier indicates 'Gale warning in force'.

LIGHTS AND MARKS
Ldg Lts 296°.

RADIO TELEPHONE
Call: *Lyme Regis Harbour Radio* Ch 16; 14. (May-Sept: 0900-1200, 1600-1800 LT).

TELEPHONE (0297)
Hr Mr 442137; MRSC Portland 760439; # (0305) 774747; Marinecall 0898 500 457; Police 442603; Dr 445777; Ⓗ 442254.

FACILITIES
EC Thursday; **Harbour (The Cobb)** ☎ 442137, Slip, M, P and D (cans), L, FW, ME, El, Ⓔ, Sh, AB, V, R, Bar; **Rob Perry Marine** ☎ 445816 ME, El, Ⓔ; **Lyme Regis Sailing Club** ☎ 443573, FW, R, Bar; **Lyme Regis Power Boat Club** ☎ 443788, R, Bar; **Axminster Chandlery** ☎ Axminster 33980, CH, ACA; **Town** V, R, Bar; Gas, Gaz, ✉; Ⓑ; ⇌ (bus to Axminster); ✈ (Exeter).

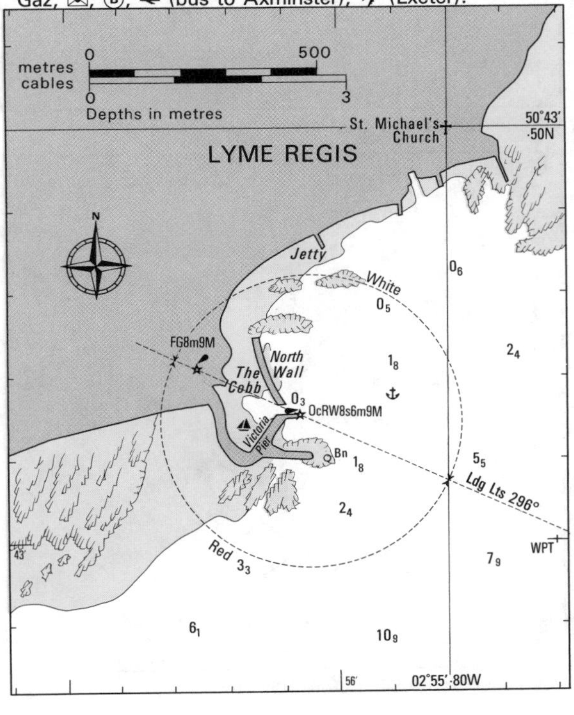
metres
cables
0
500
0
3
Depths in metres
St. Michael's Church
50°43′·50N
LYME REGIS
N
Jetty
White
North Wall
The Cobb
Victoria Pier
FG8m9M
OcRW8s6m9M
Bn
Ldg Lts 296°
WPT
Red
02°55′·80W
56′
43

BRIDPORT 10-2-9

Dorset

CHARTS
Admiralty 3315; Stanford 12; Imray C5; OS 193

TIDES
−0500 Dover; ML 2·4; Duration 0650; Zone 0 (GMT).

Standard Port DEVONPORT (←)

Times				Height (metres)			
HW		LW		MHWS	MHWN	MLWN	MLWS
0100	0600	0100	0600	5·5	4·4	2·2	0·8
1300	1800	1300	1800				
Differences BRIDPORT (West Bay)							
+0025	+0040	0000	0000	−1·4	−1·4	−0·6	−0·2

NOTE: Rise is relatively fast for first hour after LW thence a slackening for the next 1½ hours after which the rapid rise is resumed. There is usually a stand of up to 1½ hours at HW.

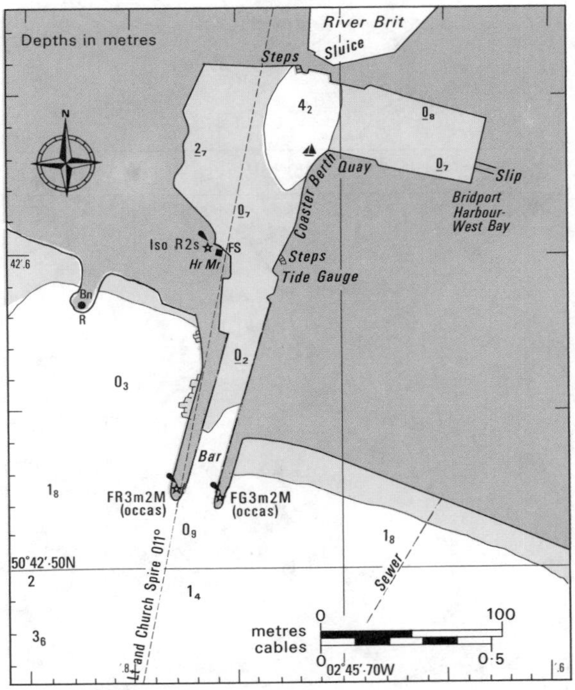
Depths in metres
River Brit
Sluice
Steps
Quay
Coaster Berth
Slip
Bridport Harbour-West Bay
Iso R2s
FS
Hr Mr
Steps
Tide Gauge
42′.6
Bn
R
Bar
FR3m2M (occas)
FG3m2M (occas)
50°42′·50N
Sewer
L'and Church Spire 011°
metres
cables
0
100
0·5
02°45′·70W

SHELTER
Good once inside the 12m wide, 180m long entrance, but entrance becomes dangerous in even moderate on-shore winds.
NOTE: Bridport town is 1½ M inland of the harbour.

NAVIGATION
Waypoint 50°42′·20N 02°46′·07W, 210°/030° from/to entrance, 0·37M. Concrete block and unlit BY buoy about ¾M S of entrance indicates end of sewer line. Pier lights are only switched on for commercial vessels. It is safe to enter HW∓3, in favourable weather.

LIGHTS AND MARKS
Harbour can be identified at night by Iso R Lt 2s 9m 5M on roof of Hr Mr office at the shore end of W pier.
Entry signals: Night — No lights on pier — unfit to enter.
Day — B ball if port closed.

RADIO TELEPHONE
Call: *Bridport Radio* VHF Ch 16; 11.

TELEPHONE (0308)
Hr Mr 23222; MRSC (0305) 760439; # (0305) 774747; Marinecall 0898 500 457; Police 22266; Dr 23771.

FACILITIES
Quay ☎ 23222, Access HW ∓3, Slip, P, ⊡, Sh, M, FW, ME, CH, AB, V; **D. Ackerman** ☎ 56815, ME. **Town** P, D, V, R, Bar; ✉; Ⓑ; ⇌ (bus to Axminster); ✈ (Exeter).

PORTLAND 10-2-10 TIDAL STREAMS
Dorset

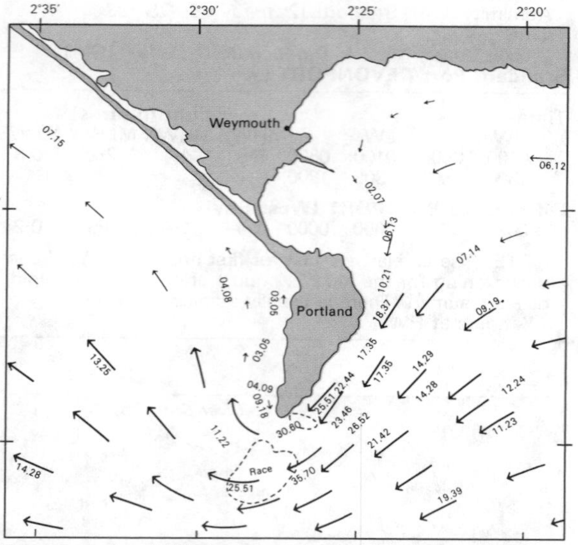
2°35′
2°30′
2°25′
2°20′
50° 35′
50° 30′
Weymouth
Portland
Race
5 Hours before HW Devonport (0145 after HW Dover)

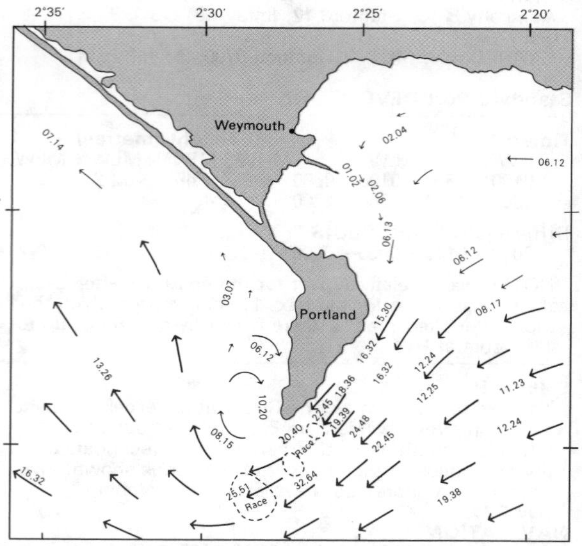
2°35′
2°30′
2°25′
2°20′
50° 35′
50° 30′
Weymouth
Portland
Race
4 Hours before HW Devonport (0245 after HW Dover)

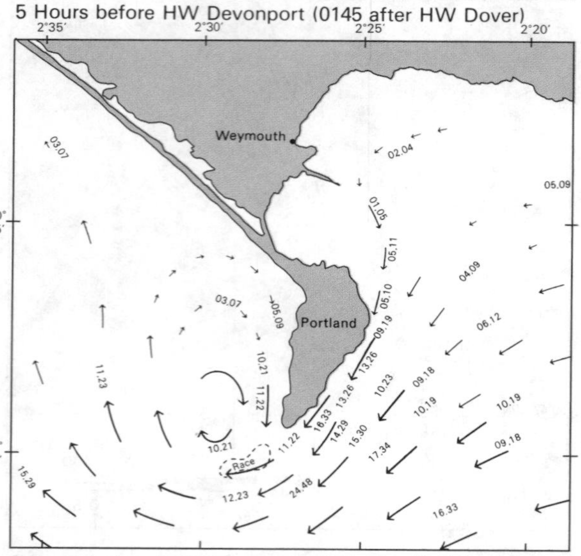
2°35′
2°30′
2°25′
2°20′
50° 35′
50° 30′
Weymouth
Portland
Race
3 Hours before HW Devonport (0345 after HW Dover)

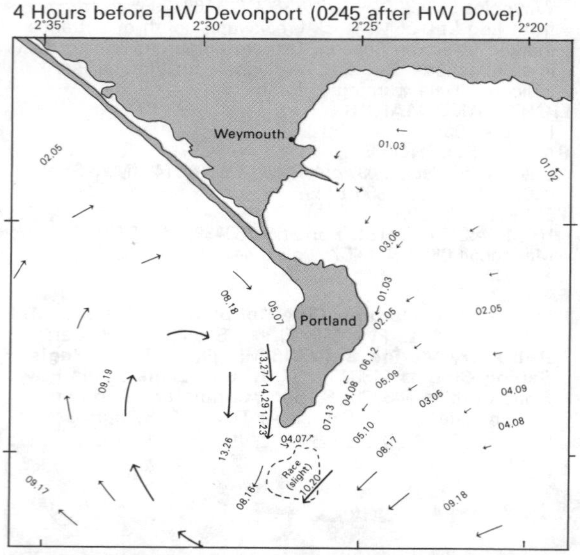
2°35′
2°30′
2°25′
2°20′
50° 35′
50° 30′
Weymouth
Portland
Race (slight)
2 Hours before HW Devonport (0445 after HW Dover)

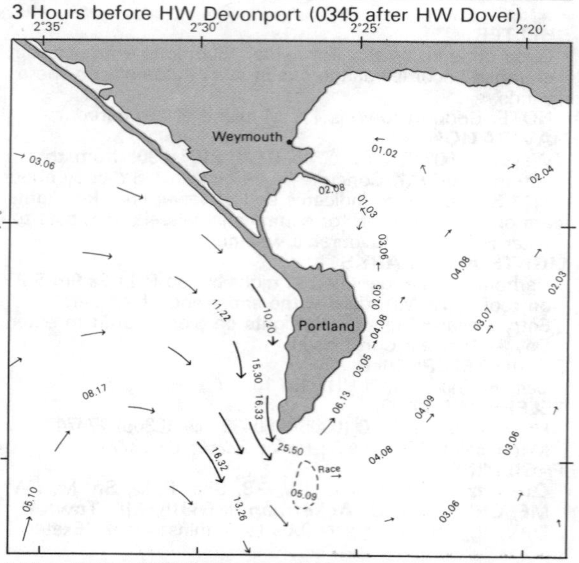
2°35′
2°30′
2°25′
2°20′
50° 35′
50° 30′
Weymouth
Portland
Race
1 Hour before HW Devonport (0545 after HW Dover)

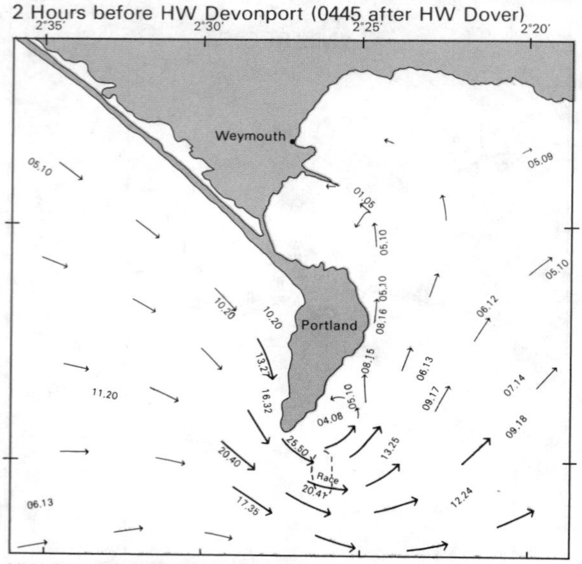
2°35′
2°30′
2°25′
2°20′
50° 35′
50° 30′
Weymouth
Portland
Race
HW Devonport (0545 before HW Dover)

General Area 2 10.2.3

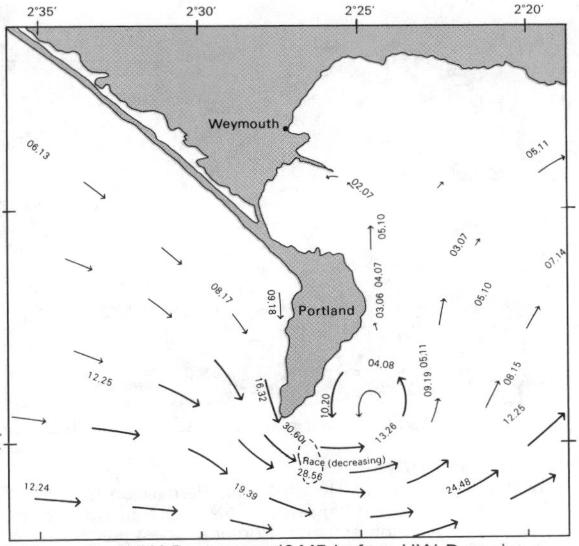
2°35′
2°30′
2°25′
2°20′
50° 35′
50° 30′
Weymouth
Portland
Race (decreasing)

1 Hour after HW Devonport (0445 before HW Dover)

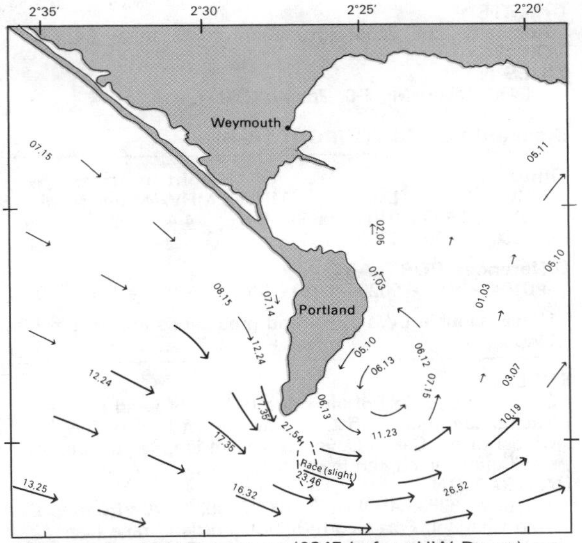
2°35′
2°30′
2°25′
2°20′
50° 35′
50° 30′
Weymouth
Portland
Race (slight)

2 Hours after HW Devonport (0345 before HW Dover)

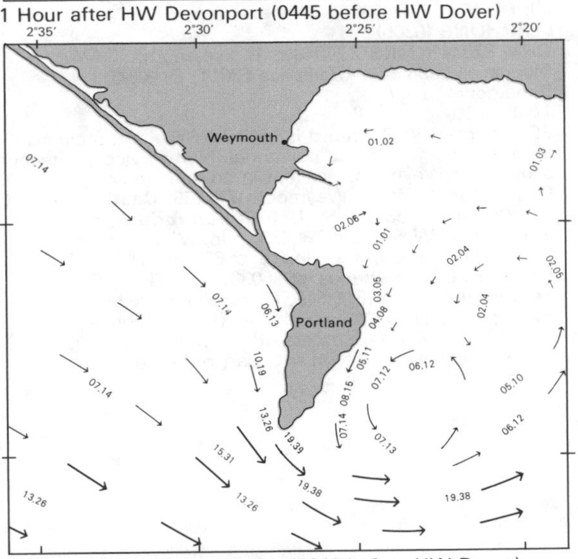
2°35′
2°30′
2°25′
2°20′
50° 35′
50° 30′
Weymouth
Portland

3 Hours after HW Devonport (0245 before HW Dover)

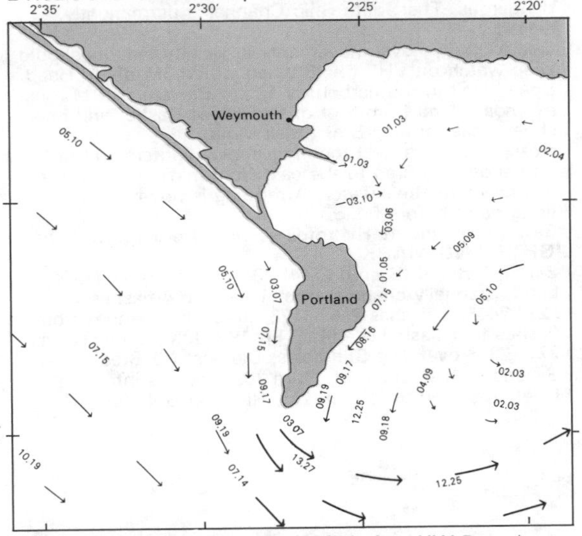
2°35′
2°30′
2°25′
2°20′
50° 35′
50° 30′
Weymouth
Portland

4 Hours after HW Devonport (0145 before HW Dover)

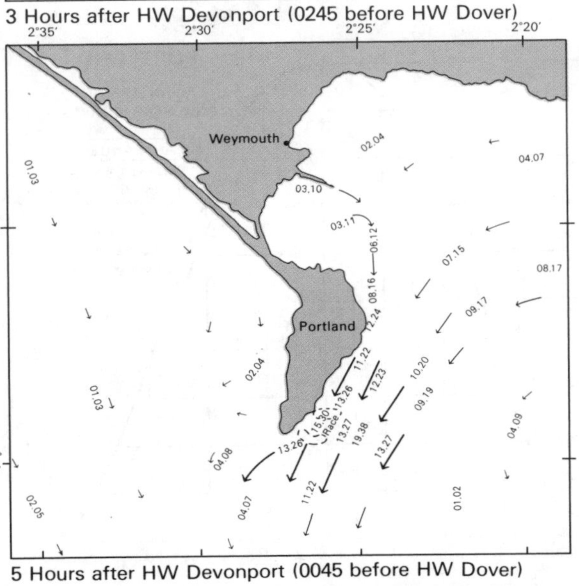
2°35′
2°30′
2°25′
2°20′
50° 35′
50° 30′
Weymouth
Portland
Race

5 Hours after HW Devonport (0045 before HW Dover)

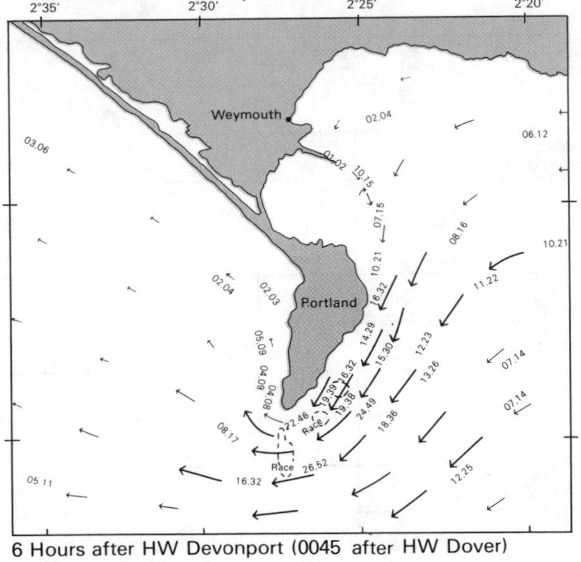
2°35′
2°30′
2°25′
2°20′
50° 35′
50° 30′
Weymouth
Portland
Race
Race

6 Hours after HW Devonport (0045 after HW Dover)

PORTLAND *continued*

CHARTS
Admiralty 2268, 2255, 2610; Stanford 12; Imray C4, C5; OS 194

TIDES
–0430 Dover; ML 1·0; Zone 0 (GMT).

Standard Port DEVONPORT (⟵)

Times				Height (metres)			
HW		LW		MHWS	MHWN	MLWN	MLWS
0100	0600	0100	0600	5·5	4·4	2·2	0·8
1300	1800	1300	1800				
Differences PORTLAND							
+0104	+0112	–0029	–0030	–3·4	–3·0	–1·5	–0·6

NOTE: Double LWs occur and predictions are for the first LW.

SHELTER
Shelter is poor in Portland due to lack of wind breaks. Yachts can anchor off Castletown (best in S or SW winds) or off Castle Cove. East Fleet is only suitable for small craft which can lower their masts.

NAVIGATION
Waypoint 50°35'·07N 02°24'·00W, 090°/270° from/to East Ship Channel, Fort Head, 0·50M. Portland race (see diagram of Portland Tidal Streams) is extremely dangerous. The South Ship Channel is permanently closed.
Due to many naval movements in vicinity, yachts should keep watch on VHF Ch 13 when within 3M of 'A' Head. Speed limit in the harbour is 12 kn. Beware reef of rocks extending 1 ca from foot of Sandsfoot Castle, and new shoal areas forming E of Small Mouth.
At night beware unlit mooring buoys, lighters and rafts. Torpedoes are fired to the east from midway along the Northeastern Breakwater. A red flag is flown from the firing point before firing.
Beware Hovercraft/Hydrofoil services from Weymouth.

LIGHTS AND MARKS
Bill of Portland (S end) Fl (4) 20s 43m 29M; W Tr, R band; gradually changes from 1 flash to 4 flashes 221°-244°, 4 flashes 244°-117°, gradually changes from 4 flashes to 1 flash 117°-141°. FR 19m 13M; same Tr; vis 271°-291° over The Shambles; Dia 30s. NE Breakwater, SE end Fl 10s 22m 20M; Horn 10s. Ldg Lts into East Fleet, 288°, Front QG 3m 2M, Rear Iso G 4s 5m 2M.

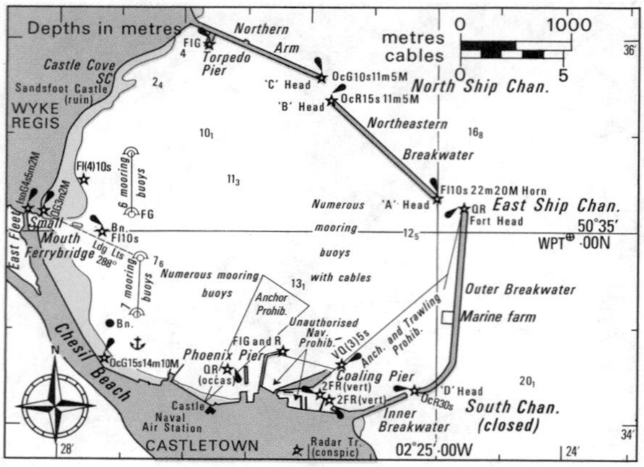

Depths in metres
metres
cables
0
1000
5
Northern
Arm
Torpedo
Pier
Castle Cove
SC
Sandsfoot Castle
(ruin)
WYKE
REGIS
'C' Head
OcG10s11m5M
'B' Head
OcR15s11m5M
North Ship Chan.
Northeastern
Breakwater
Fl10s 22m20M Horn
'A' Head
QR East Ship Chan.
Fort Head
50°35'
WPT ·00N
Numerous
mooring
buoys
with cables
East Fleet
Small
Mouth
Ferrybridge
Ldg Lts 288°
Numerous mooring
buoys
Anchor
Prohib.
Unauthorised
Nav.
Prohib.
Anch. and Trawling
Prohib.
Outer Breakwater
Marine farm
Chesil Beach
Phoenix Pier
QR
(occas)
FlG and R
VQ(3)5s
Coaling Pier
2FR(vert)
2FR(vert)
OcR30s
'D' Head
South Chan.
(closed)
Inner
Breakwater
Castle
Naval
Air Station
CASTLETOWN
Radar Tr.
(conspic)
02°25'·00W
28'
24'
36'
34'

RADIO TELEPHONE
Portland Naval Base VHF Ch 13 14. Permission to enter, Ch 13 to QHM in working hours, otherwise to Ops Room. Casquets separation scheme, Portland Coastguard: Ch 16 69; 69. 67.

TELEPHONE (0305)
QHM 820311; MRSC 760439; # Weymouth 774747; Marinecall 0898 500 457; Police 63011; Dr 820311 (Emergency only).

FACILITIES
EC Wednesday; **Portland** is a Naval Base and provides facilities only for service personnel. Non-service yachtsmen should use Weymouth, except in an emergency.
Royal Dorset YC ☎ Weymouth 771155; **Castle Cove SC** ☎ Weymouth 783708, M, L, FW; **Ferrybridge Marine Services** ☎ Weymouth 786463, Slip, M, L, FW, ME, El, Sh, C; **Marine Engine Centre** ☎ 821175, ME, El, CH. **Barret Marine Services** ☎ 860337 ME, El, D, Gas, Sh; **PB Services** ☎ 781815 ME, El (mobile workshop); **Town** ✉; Ⓑ; ⇌ (bus to Weymouth); ✈ (Bournemouth).
Note: Low flying helicopters often operate for long periods, day and night, over S part of harbour.

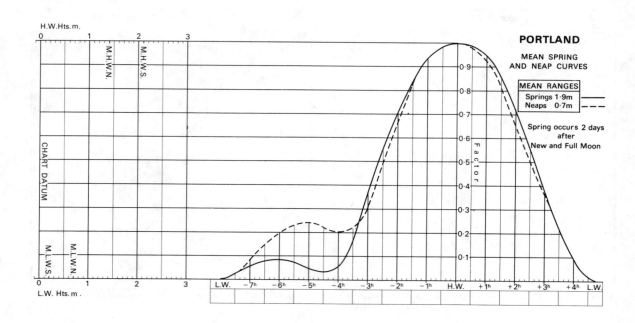

H.W.Hts. m.
M.H.W.N.
M.H.W.S.
CHART DATUM
M.L.W.S.
M.L.W.N.
L.W. Hts. m .
PORTLAND
MEAN SPRING AND NEAP CURVES
MEAN RANGES
Springs 1·9m
Neaps 0·7m
Spring occurs 2 days after New and Full Moon
Factor
L.W. -7h -6h -5h -4h -3h -2h -1h H.W. +1h +2h +3h +4h L.W.

2

WEYMOUTH 10-2-11

Dorset

CHARTS
Admiralty 2172, 2255, 2268, 2610; Stanford 12; Imray C4, C5; OS 194

TIDES
−0438 Dover; ML 1·1; Zone 0 (GMT).

Standard Port PORTSMOUTH (⟶)

Times				Height (metres)			
HW		LW		MHWS	MHWN	MLWN	MLWS
0000	0600	0500	1100	4·7	3·8	1·8	0·6
1200	1800	1700	2300				
Differences WEYMOUTH							
−0421	−0525	−0520	−0515	−2·6	−2·4	−1·1	−0·4

NOTE: Double LWs occur. Predictions are for first LW.

SHELTER
Swell runs up the harbour if strong wind from E, otherwise shelter is good. Visitors' berth in Cove area or as directed.

NAVIGATION
Waypoint 50°36'·70N, 02°26'·10E, 057·5°/237·5° from/to front Ldg Lt, 0·50M. Town Bridge will open on request (2 hours notice) 0900-1300, 1400-1700, 1800-2000 (LT). Clearance under is 2·7m to 3·8m at HW, 4·6 to 5·2m at LW.
NOTE: Due to the eddy effect, tide in Weymouth Roads is westerly at all times except HW −0510 to HW −0310. Speed limit in the harbour is 'Dead Slow'.

LIGHTS AND MARKS
Ldg Lts 237°. Traffic signals are shown from position near root of S pier.

3 Fl R	Port closed (emergency)
2 R over 1 G	Entry & departure forbidden
G W G (vert)	Vessels may only proceed with specific orders
3 G	Departure forbidden
3 R	Entry forbidden
No signals	All clear to enter or leave

RADIO TELEPHONE
VHF Ch 16; 12 (when vessel expected). (See Portland).

TELEPHONE (0305)
Hr Mr 206421; MRSC 760439; Berthing Master 206423; # 774747; Marinecall 0898 500 457; Police 251212; Ⓗ 772211.

FACILITIES
EC Wednesday; **Outer Harbour** M; **Weymouth SC** ☎ 785481, M, Bar; **Custom House Quay** D, FW, AB; **W. L. Bussells** ☎ 785633, CH, Sh, ACA, Gaz, Rigging; **Ladyline** ☎ 771603, CH; **Royal Dorset YC** ☎ 786258, M, Bar; **Small Boat** ☎ 782109, ME, CH, Ⓔ, Sh; **R. J. Davis** ☎ 834415, ME, El, CH; **Moto-sails** ☎ 786710, CH; **Weymouth Chandlers** ☎ 771603, CH. **Town** P, D, FW, V, R, Bar. ✉; Ⓑ; ⇌; ✈ (Bournemouth).

NOTE: If proceeding eastwards, check Lulworth firing programme – see 10.2.31.

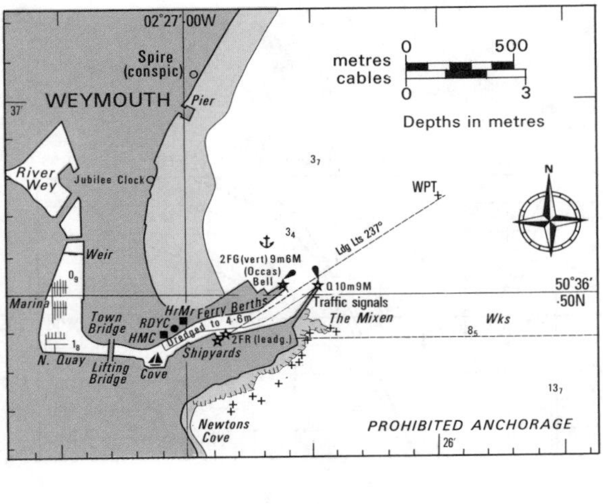
02°27'·00W
Spire (conspic)
Pier
WEYMOUTH
37'
metres 0 500
cables 0 3
Depths in metres
River Wey
Jubilee Clock
Weir
WPT
Ldg Lts 237°
2FG(vert) 9m6M (Occas) Bell
Q 10m9M
Traffic signals
HrMr Ferry Berths
Marina
Town Bridge
RDYC
HMC
Dredged to 4·6m
2FR (leadg.)
Shipyards
The Mixen
Wks
N. Quay
Lifting Bridge
Cove
50°36' ·50N
Newtons Cove
PROHIBITED ANCHORAGE
26'

SWANAGE 10-2-12

Dorset

CHARTS
Admiralty 2172, 2610, 2175; Stanford 12; Imray C4; OS 195

TIDES
HW Spring −0235, Neap −0515 Dover; ML 1·5
+0125 +0120 Zone 0 (GMT)

Standard Port PORTSMOUTH (⟶)

Times				Height (metres)			
HW		LW		MHWS	MHWN	MLWN	MLWS
0000	0600	0500	1100	4·7	3·8	1·8	0·6
1200	1800	1700	2300				
Differences SWANAGE							
−0250	+0105	−0105	−0105	−2·7	−2·2	−0·7	−0·3

NOTE: Double HWs occur except at neaps and predictions are for the higher HW. Near neaps there is a stand, and the predictions shown are for the middle of the stand. See 10.2.13

SHELTER
Shelter is good in winds between SW and N. It is bad in E or SE when winds over Force 4 cause swell. Over Force 6 holding becomes very difficult. Nearest haven Poole. Pier is now completely closed.

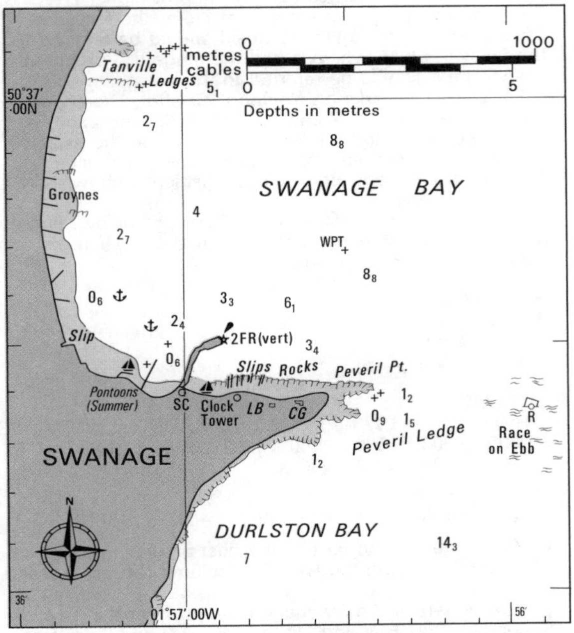
Tanville Ledges
metres 0 1000
cables 0 5
50°37' ·00N
Depths in metres
SWANAGE BAY
Groynes
WPT
Slip
2FR(vert)
Slips
Rocks
Peveril Pt.
Pontoons (Summer)
SC
Clock Tower
LB
CG
Race on Ebb
Peveril Ledge
SWANAGE
DURLSTON BAY
36'
01°57'·00W
56'

NAVIGATION
Waypoint 50°36'·70N 01°56'·50W, 054°/234° from/to Swanage Pier head, 0·30M. Beware Peveril Ledge coming from S and Tanville Ledges coming from N. On the S side of the pier there are the ruins of an old pier. It is difficult to pick up pierhead Lts at night due to confusing street lights behind.

LIGHTS AND MARKS
The only lights are 2 FR (vert) on the end of the pier. Peveril Ledge buoy, R can unlit (pass to E).

RADIO TELEPHONE
None

TELEPHONE (0929)
MRSC Portland 760439; # (0703) 827350; Marinecall 0898 500 457; Police 422004; Dr 422676; Ⓗ 422282.

FACILITIES
EC Monday; **Boat Park** (Peveril Point), Slip, FW, L; **Town Jetty**, L, AB (HW only); **Swanage SC** ☎ 422987, Slip, L, FW, Bar; **Diving facilities on Pier** ☎ 423565. **Maritime Services** ☎ 424786 Diving, Salvage, Towing; **Town** P and D (cans), FW, V, R, Bar. ✉; Ⓑ; ⇌ (bus to Wareham); ✈ (Bournemouth).

SPECIAL TIDAL PROBLEMS BETWEEN SWANAGE AND SELSEY 10-2-13

Owing to the distorted tidal regime in this area, special curves, as shown on the two following pages, are given for certain ports. Since their low water (LW) points are better defined than high water (HW), the times on these curves are referred to LW, but otherwise they are used as described in 9·4. Box 17 of the tidal prediction form shown in Fig.9(5) should be amended to read 'Time of LW'.

Height differences for places between Swanage and Yarmouth always refer to the higher HW (that which reaches a factor of 1·0 on the curves). The time differences, which are not needed for this calculation, also refer to the higher HW.

Since the tides at these places cannot be adequately defined by two curves, a third is shown for the range at Portsmouth (indicated on the right of the graph) at which the two high waters are equal at the port concerned. Interpolation should be between this critical curve and either the spring or neap curve, as appropriate. The higher HW should be used to obtain the range at the Secondary Port.

While the critical curve extends throughout the tidal cycle, the spring and neap curves stop at higher HW. Thus for a range at Portsmouth of 3·5m, the factor for 7 hrs after LW Poole (Town Quay) should be referred to the following LW, whereas had the range at Portsmouth been 2·5m it should be referred to the preceding LW.

For special remarks on Newport, Calshot, Wareham and Tuckton see notes 1, 2 and 3 on the following page.

The procedure to be followed is shown in the example below, referring to the special tidal curve for Swanage, Poole (Entrance) and Bournemouth which is shown at the foot of the page.

Example: Using the tidal data for Swanage below, find the height of tide at Swanage at 0200 on a day when the tidal predictions for Portsmouth are:

19 0100 4·6
0613 1·1
M 1314 4·5
1833 0·8

PORTSMOUTH

HW		LW		MHWS	MHWN	MLWN	MLWS
0000	0600	0500	1100	4·7	3·8	1·8	0·6
1200	1800	1700	2300				

Differences **SWANAGE**

−0250	+0105	−0105	−0105	−2·7	−2·2	−0·7	−0·3

(1) Complete the top part of the tidal prediction form, as in Fig.9(5), omitting the HW time column (boxes 1, 5 and 9).
(2) On the left of the Swanage diagram, plot the Secondary Port HW and LW heights (1·9 and 0·6m from (1) above), and join the points by a sloping line.
(3) The time required (0200) is 3h 8m before the time of LW at the Secondary Port, so from this point draw a vertical line to the curve. It is necessary to interpolate from the range at Portsmouth (3·5m), which is midway between the spring range (4·1m) and the critical curve (2·9m). This should give a point level with a factor of 0·84.

Fig. 9(5) *Tidal prediction form* Time or ~~height~~ required 0200

	TIME HW	TIME LW	HEIGHT HW	HEIGHT LW	
Standard Port Portsmouth	1	2 0613	3 4·6	4 1·1	
Differences	5	6 −0105	7 −2·7	8 −0·5	
Secondary Port Swanage	9	10 0508	11 1·9	12 0·6	
Duration (or time from HW to LW)	13	9–10 or 10–9	Range Stand. Port	14 3·5	3 – 4
			Range Secdy. Port	15 1·3	11 – 12

*Springs/Neaps/Interpolate

Start height at given time ↓

	Time reqd.	16 0200	17 + 18
9	Time of ~~HW~~ LW	17 0508	9
17 – 16	Interval	18 −0308	
	Factor	19 0·84	
19 x 15	Rise above LW	20 1·1	22 – 21
12	Height of LW	21 0·6	12
20 + 21	Height reqd.	22 1·7	

↑ Start: time for given height

Date 19th Nov

Time zone 0 (GMT)

*Delete as necessary

(4) From this point draw a horizontal line to meet the sloping line constructed in (2) above.
(5) From the point where the horizontal line meets the sloping line, proceed vertically to the height scale at the top, and read off the height required, 1·7m.

The completed lower part of the tidal prediction form above shows how the calculation is done using the factor method instead of the graphical method just described. The procedure follows that given in 9.4.3. Note that box 9 is amended to read 'Time of LW'.

A less accurate but quick method of finding intermediate heights for certain places is by use of Fig 10A shown later in this section. It is useful to note that the area enclosed by the dotted lines represents the period during which the tide stands and in which a second high tide may occur.

To use this table, note that the first of the three figures given is for mean spring tides, the second for average and the third for mean neap tides. Work out whether the time required is nearer the HW or LW at Portsmouth and find the interval (between time required and the nearest HW or LW at Portsmouth). Extract the height of the corresponding predicted HW (left hand column) or LW (right hand column). By interpolation between the heights of HW or LW, read off the height of tide under the appropriate column (hrs before or after HW or hrs before or after LW).

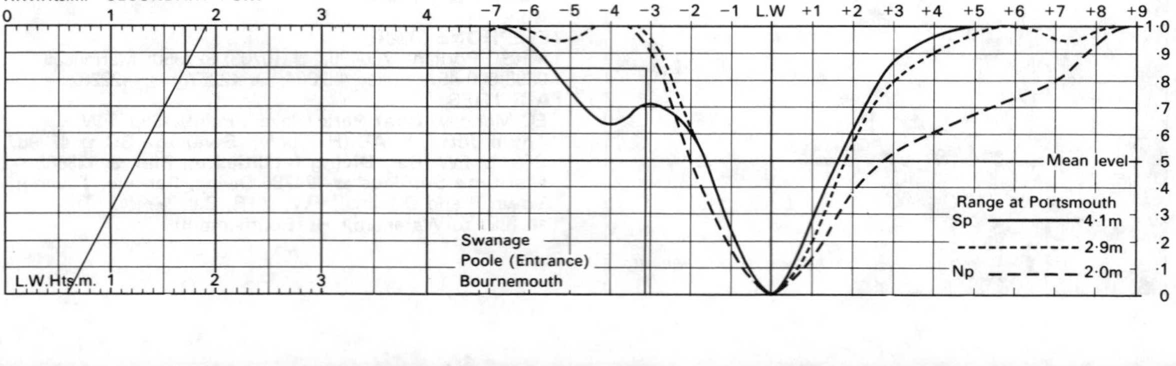
H.W.Hts.m. SECONDARY PORT
0 1 2 3 4
−7 −6 −5 −4 −3 −2 −1 L.W +1 +2 +3 +4 +5 +6 +7 +8 +9
1·0 ·9 ·8 ·7 ·6 ·5 ·4 ·3 ·2 ·1 0
Mean level
Range at Portsmouth
Sp 4·1m
2·9m
Np 2·0m
Swanage
Poole (Entrance)
Bournemouth
L.W.Hts.m. 1 2 3

2

TIDAL CURVES — SWANAGE TO SELSEY

Tidal curves for places between Swanage and Selsey are given below, and their use is explained above. In this area the times of Low Water are defined more sharply than the times of High Water, and the curves are therefore drawn with their times relative to Low Water instead of High Water.

Apart from referring the times to Low Water, the procedure for obtaining intermediate heights with these curves is the same as that used for normal Secondary Ports (see 9.4.2). For most places a third curve is shown, for the range at Portsmouth at which the two High Waters are equal at the port concerned: for interpolation between the curves see the previous page.

Note 1. Owing to constrictions in the River Medina, Newport requires special treatment. The calculation should be made using the time and Low Water height differences for Cowes, and the High Water height differences for Newport. Any height which falls below 1·9m can be disregarded since the tide never falls below this level.
Note 2. Calshot is referred to Southampton as Standard Port. The curves shown below for Calshot should be taken as referring to the Spring and Neap ranges at Southampton (4·0 and 1·9m respectively).
Note 3. Wareham and Tuckton LWs do not fall below 0·7m except under very low river flow conditions.

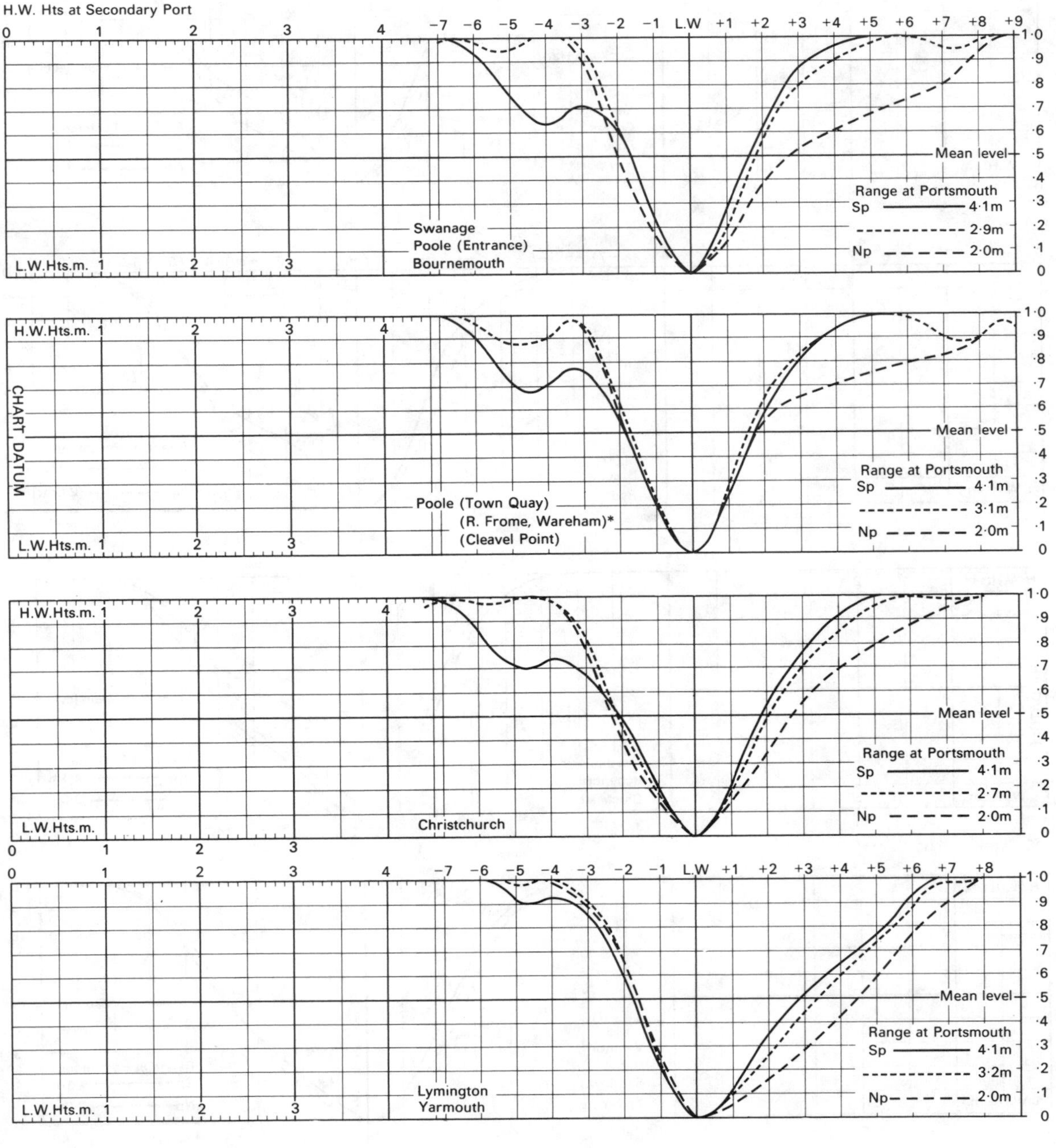
H.W. Hts at Secondary Port
L.W.Hts.m.
Swanage
Poole (Entrance)
Bournemouth
Mean level
Range at Portsmouth
Sp 4·1m
2·9m
Np 2·0m
H.W.Hts.m.
CHART DATUM
Poole (Town Quay)
(R. Frome, Wareham)*
(Cleavel Point)
Range at Portsmouth
Sp 4·1m
3·1m
Np 2·0m
Christchurch
Range at Portsmouth
Sp 4·1m
2·7m
Np 2·0m
Lymington
Yarmouth
Range at Portsmouth
Sp 4·1m
3·2m
Np 2·0m

TIDAL CURVES *continued*

H.W. Hts at Secondary Port

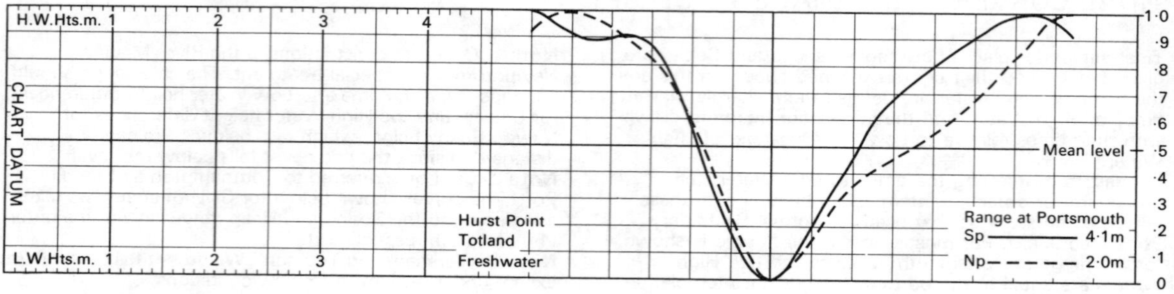
H.W.Hts.m. 1 2 3 4
CHART DATUM
L.W.Hts.m. 1 2 3
Hurst Point
Totland
Freshwater
Mean level
Range at Portsmouth
Sp 4·1m
Np 2·0m
1·0 ·9 ·8 ·7 ·6 ·5 ·4 ·3 ·2 ·1 0

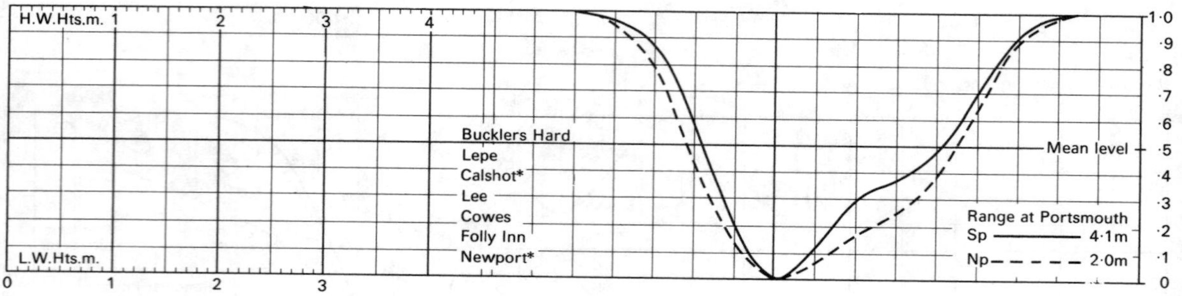
H.W.Hts.m. 1 2 3 4
L.W.Hts.m.
0 1 2 3
Bucklers Hard
Lepe
Calshot*
Lee
Cowes
Folly Inn
Newport*
Mean level
Range at Portsmouth
Sp 4·1m
Np 2·0m
1·0 ·9 ·8 ·7 ·6 ·5 ·4 ·3 ·2 ·1 0

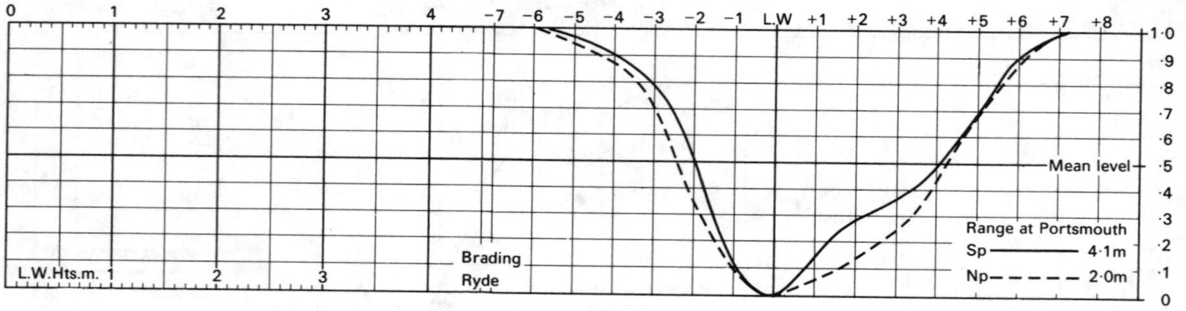
0 1 2 3 4 −7 −6 −5 −4 −3 −2 −1 L.W +1 +2 +3 +4 +5 +6 +7 +8
L.W.Hts.m. 1 2 3
Brading
Ryde
Mean level
Range at Portsmouth
Sp 4·1m
Np 2·0m
1·0 ·9 ·8 ·7 ·6 ·5 ·4 ·3 ·2 ·1 0

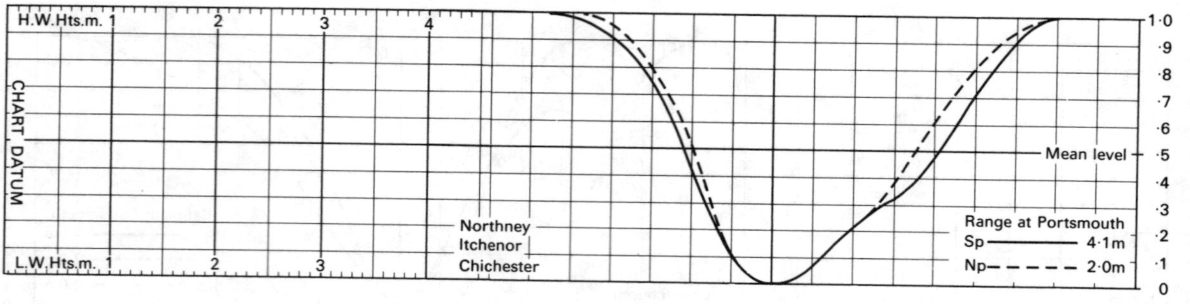
H.W.Hts.m. 1 2 3 4
CHART DATUM
L.W.Hts.m. 1 2 3
Northney
Itchenor
Chichester
Mean level
Range at Portsmouth
Sp 4·1m
Np 2·0m
1·0 ·9 ·8 ·7 ·6 ·5 ·4 ·3 ·2 ·1 0

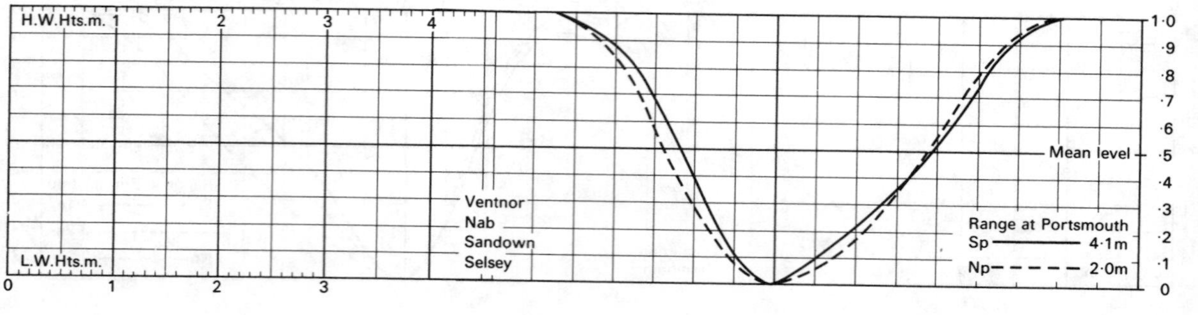
H.W.Hts.m. 1 2 3 4
L.W.Hts.m.
0 1 2 3
Ventnor
Nab
Sandown
Selsey
Mean level
Range at Portsmouth
Sp 4·1m
Np 2·0m
1·0 ·9 ·8 ·7 ·6 ·5 ·4 ·3 ·2 ·1 0

SWANAGE TO NAB TOWER

FIG 10A (To be used for finding intermediate heights in metres for places named)

Place	Height of H.W. at Portsmouth	HOURLY HEIGHTS ABOVE CHART DATUM AT THE PLACE — Hours before or after HIGH WATER AT PORTSMOUTH: 3b.	2b.	1b.	H.W.	1a.	2a.	3a.	Hours before or after LOW WATER AT PORTSMOUTH: 2b.	1b.	L.W.	1a.	2a.	3a.	Height of L.W. at Portsmouth
	m.	m.	m.	m.	m.	m.	m.	m.	m.	m.	m.	m.	m.	m.	m.
SWANAGE	4·7	1·9	1·8	1·5	1·3	1·4	1·2	0·8	0·6	0·3	0·8	1·3	1·7	1·8	0·6
	4·3	1·6	1·6	1·5	1·5	1·2	1·4	1·1	0·9	0·8	1·0	1·3	1·5	1·6	1·2
	3·8	1·5	1·5	1·5	1·5	1·6	1·5	1·3	1·2	1·1	1·2	1·3	1·4	1·4	1·8
POOLE ENTRANCE	4·7	2·0	1·9	1·6	1·4	1·5	1·4	0·9	0·7	0·3	0·8	1·3	1·6	1·9	0·6
	4·3	1·6	1·6	1·5	1·5	1·5	1·5	1·1	1·0	0·8	0·9	1·2	1·5	1·6	1·2
	3·8	1·4	1·5	1·5	1·5	1·6	1·5	1·3	1·2	1·1	1·1	1·2	1·3	1·4	1·8
POOLE BRIDGE	4·7	2·2	2·2	1·9	1·6	1·6	1·7	1·3	1·1	0·6	0·5	1·0	1·6	1·9	0·6
	4·3	1·8	1·7	1·6	1·7	1·8	1·8	1·5	1·4	1·0	0·8	1·1	1·5	1·7	1·2
	3·8	1·5	1·5	1·6	1·7	1·8	1·8	1·5	1·5	1·3	1·2	1·3	1·5	1·5	1·8
BOURNE-MOUTH	4·7	2·1	2·0	1·7	1·5	1·5	1·5	0·9	0·7	0·3	0·6	1·2	1·7	1·9	0·6
	4·3	1·6	1·7	1·6	1·6	1·6	1·5	1·2	1·0	0·8	0·8	1·2	1·4	1·5	1·2
	3·8	1·5	1·5	1·5	1·5	1·6	1·5	1·4	1·3	1·1	1·1	1·2	1·3	1·4	1·8
CHRIST- † CHURCH HARBOUR	4·7	1·8	1·8	1·5	1·3	1·5	1·1	0·7	0·7	0·5	0·4	0·9	1·3	1·6	0·6
	4·3	1·5	1·5	1·4	1·5	1·5	1·2	0·9	0·8	0·6	0·6	1·0	1·2	1·4	1·2
	3·8	1·2	1·2	1·3	1·4	1·4	1·1	0·9	0·8	0·6	0·7	0·9	1·0	1·1	1·8
FRESHWATER BAY	4·7	2·4	2·5	2·4	2·2	2·2	1·9	1·1	0·9	0·5	0·8	1·5	2·0	2·2	0·6
	4·3	2·2	2·3	2·2	2·2	2·2	1·9	1·4	1·2	0·9	1·1	1·5	1·8	2·0	1·2
	3·8	1·9	2·0	2·2	2·2	2·2	2·0	1·6	1·6	1·3	1·3	1·6	1·7	1·8	1·8
TOTLAND BAY	4·7	2·3	2·5	2·4	2·3	2·3	2·1	1·4	1·1	0·5	0·8	1·4	1·8	2·1	0·6
	4·3	2·1	2·3	2·3	2·3	2·2	2·1	1·6	1·4	0·9	1·1	1·4	1·7	1·9	1·2
	3·8	2·0	2·1	2·3	2·3	2·2	2·1	1·8	1·7	1·4	1·4	1·6	1·8	1·8	1·8
HURST-POINT	4·7	2·3	2·6	2·7	2·5	2·5	2·3	1·6	1·2	0·5	0·7	1·3	1·7	2·0	0·6
	4·3	2·0	2·3	2·5	2·5	2·4	2·3	1·7	1·5	1·1	1·0	1·4	1·7	1·9	1·2
	3·8	1·9	2·1	2·3	2·3	2·3	2·2	1·8	1·7	1·4	1·3	1·5	1·7	1·9	1·8
YARMOUTH I.O.W.	4·7	2·4	2·8	3·0	2·8	2·8	2·7	1·8	1·5	0·7	0·8	1·4	1·8	1·8	0·6
	4·3	2·2	2·5	2·7	2·7	2·7	2·6	1·9	1·6	1·1	1·2	1·6	1·8	2·0	1·2
	3·8	2·0	2·3	2·5	2·5	2·5	2·3	1·9	1·7	1·5	1·5	1·6	1·7	1·8	1·8
LYMINGTON	4·7	2·2	2·6	3·0	2·8	2·9	2·8	2·1	1·7	0·7	0·5	1·1	1·6	1·9	0·6
	4·3	2·0	2·3	2·7	2·7	2·7	2·6	2·1	1·8	1·1	1·0	1·3	1·6	1·7	1·2
	3·8	1·9	2·2	2·4	2·5	2·5	2·4	2·0	1·8	1·5	1·4	1·5	1·6	1·7	1·8
SOLENT BANKS	4·7	2·4	2·9	3·4	3·3	3·2	3·0	2·2	1·8	0·7	0·6	1·2	1·8	2·0	0·6
	4·3	2·2	2·6	3·0	3·1	3·0	2·9	2·2	1·9	1·2	1·1	1·4	1·6	1·9	1·2
	3·8	2·1	2·3	2·6	2·7	2·7	2·6	2·2	2·0	1·6	1·5	1·7	1·9	2·0	1·8
COWES ROAD	4·7	2·5	3·4	4·1	4·2	4·1	3·8	3·0	2·5	1·1	0·6	1·2	1·8	2·1	0·6
	4·3	2·4	3·1	3·7	3·8	3·7	3·5	2·8	2·6	1·5	1·2	1·5	1·8	2·1	1·2
	3·8	2·5	3·0	3·3	3·4	3·4	3·2	2·7	2·5	2·0	1·7	1·9	2·0	2·2	1·8
CALSHOT CASTLE	4·7	2·6	3·6	4·3	4·4	4·3	4·1	3·2	2·6	1·2	0·7	1·3	1·9	2·2	0·6
	4·3	2·6	3·3	3·8	4·0	4·0	3·7	3·0	2·6	1·6	1·2	1·6	2·0	2·2	1·2
	3·8	2·7	3·2	3·5	3·6	3·6	3·4	2·8	2·6	2·0	1·9	2·0	2·2	2·3	1·8
LEE-ON-SOLENT	4·7	2·7	3·6	4·4	4·5	4·4	4·2	3·1	2·5	1·1	0·6	1·2	1·8	2·1	0·6
	4·3	2·7	3·4	3·9	4·1	4·0	3·7	2·9	2·5	1·4	1·2	1·6	2·0	2·2	1·2
	3·8	2·7	3·2	3·6	3·7	3·6	3·3	2·8	2·6	2·1	1·9	2·0	2·2	2·4	1·8
RYDE	4·7	2·7	3·7	4·3	4·5	4·3	4·0	2·9	2·4	1·1	0·7	1·2	1·8	2·1	0·6
	4·3	2·7	3·4	4·0	4·1	4·0	3·7	2·9	2·6	1·6	1·3	1·6	1·9	2·2	1·2
	3·8	2·7	3·2	3·6	3·7	3·6	3·4	2·9	2·7	2·1	1·9	2·0	2·2	2·4	1·8
NAB TOWER	4·7	2·9	3·8	4·4	4·5	4·3	3·6	2·4	2·0	0·9	0·6	1·0	1·5	2·1	0·6
	4·3	2·9	3·6	4·1	4·2	4·0	3·4	2·5	2·2	1·4	1·2	1·4	1·8	2·2	1·2
	3·8	2·9	3·3	3·7	3·7	3·6	3·1	2·6	2·3	1·9	1·7	1·8	2·1	2·4	1·8
SANDOWN	4·7	2·6	3·3	3·8	4·0	3·8	3·3	2·1	1·7	0·8	0·6	1·0	1·5	1·9	0·6
	4·3	2·6	3·0	3·5	3·6	3·5	3·1	2·2	1·9	1·3	1·1	1·4	1·7	2·0	1·2
	3·8	2·6	2·9	3·2	3·3	3·1	2·8	2·3	2·1	1·8	1·6	1·7	1·9	2·2	1·8
VENTNOR	4·7	2·8	3·3	3·7	3·8	3·5	2·9	2·0	1·7	1·0	0·9	1·3	1·7	2·1	0·6
	4·3	2·6	3·1	3·4	3·4	3·2	2·8	2·1	1·9	1·4	1·3	1·6	1·9	2·2	1·2
	3·8	2·5	2·8	3·1	3·1	3·0	2·8	2·3	2·2	1·8	1·7	1·9	2·1	2·3	1·8

Note.—Area enclosed by pecked lines represents the period during which the tide stands, or during which a second high water may occur.
† Heights at Christchurch are for inside the bar; outside the bar, L.W. falls about 0·6 metres lower at Springs.

POOLE 10-2-14

Dorset

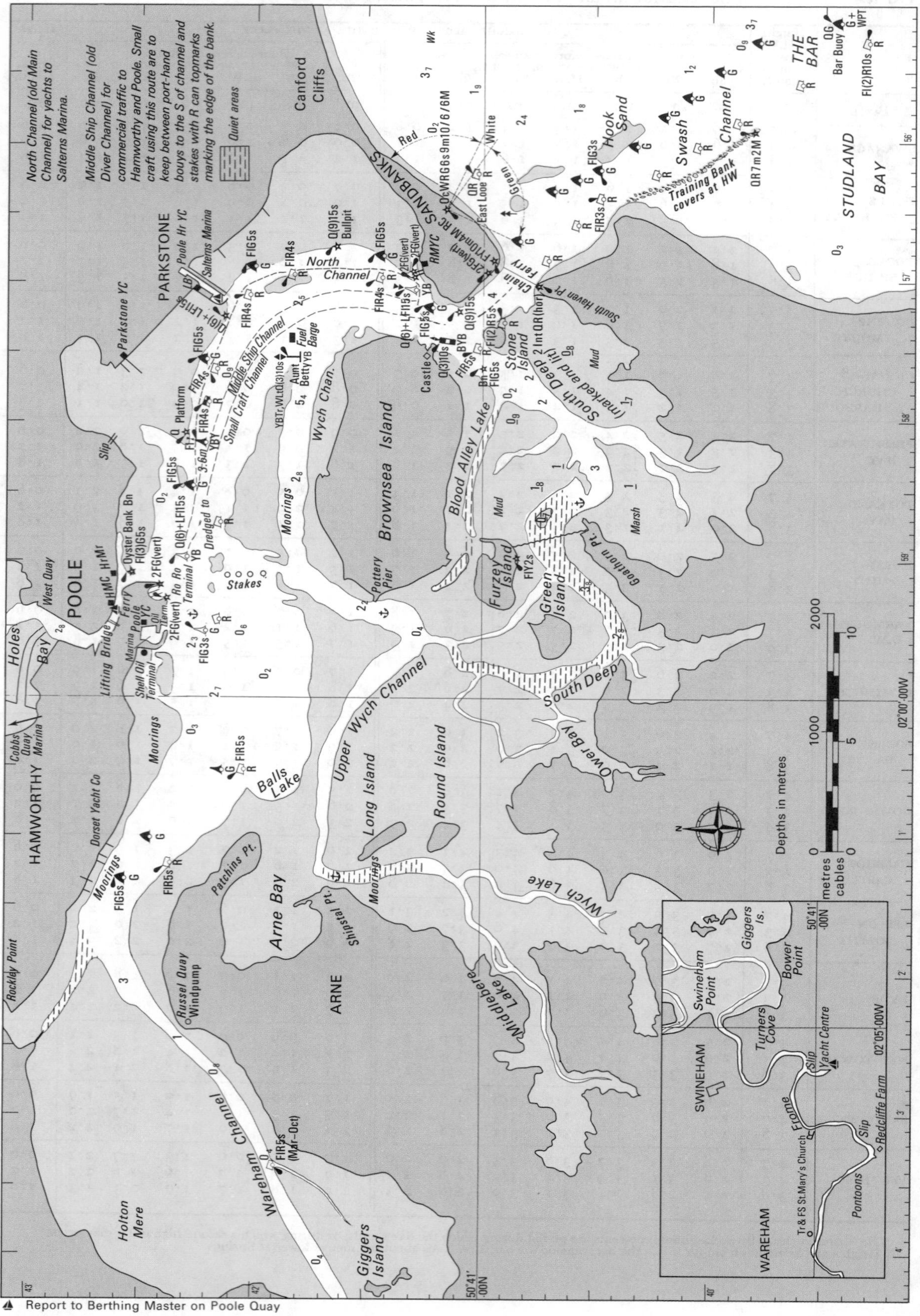
North Channel (old Main Channel) for yachts to Salterns Marina.
Middle Ship Channel (old Diver Channel) for commercial traffic to Hamworthy and Poole. Small craft using this route are to keep between port-hand bouys to the S of channel and stakes with R can topmarks marking the edge of the bank.
Quiet areas
Canford Cliffs
PARKSTONE
Poole Hr YC
Salterns Marina
Parkstone YC
SANDBANKS
RMYC
North Channel
Middle Ship Channel
Small Craft Channel
Wych Chan.
Brownsea Island
Bullpit
Castle
Aunt Betty
Fuel Barge
Platform
Stakes
Pottery Pier
Blood Alley Lake
Furzey Island
Green Island
Goathorn Pt.
South Deep (marked and lit)
Stone Island
Mud
Marsh
Chain Ferry
South Haven Pt
East Looe
Hook Sand
Swash Channel
Training Bank covers at HW
THE BAR
Bar Buoy
STUDLAND BAY
POOLE
West Quay
HMC
Hr Mr
Oyster Bank Bn
Ferry
Poole YC
Marina
Shell Oil Terminal
Ro Ro Terminal
Lifting Bridge
Holes Bay
Slip
Cobbs Quay Marina
HAMWORTHY
Dorset Yacht Co
Moorings
Balls Lake
Upper Wych Channel
Long Island
Round Island
South Deep
Ower Bay
Wych Lake
Patchins Pt.
Arne Bay
Shipstal Pt.
ARNE
Middlebere Lake
Rockley Point
Russel Quay
Windpump
Wareham Channel
Holton Mere
Giggers Island
Depths in metres
metres
cables
SWINEHAM
Swineham Point
Giggers Is.
Bower Point
Turners Cove
Yacht Centre
Frome
Redcliffe Farm
Tr & FS St.Mary's Church
Pontoons
WAREHAM
02°00'·00W
02°05'·00W
50°41'·00N

⛵ Report to Berthing Master on Poole Quay

ENGLAND, SOUTH COAST - POOLE (TOWN QUAY)

TIME ZONE UT(GMT)

For Summer Time add ONE hour in non-shaded areas

LAT 50°43'N LONG 1°59'W

TIMES AND HEIGHTS OF HIGH AND LOW WATERS

YEAR 1992

JANUARY

Date	Day	Time	m	Time	m	Time	m	Time	m
1	W	0129	1.1		1.9	1405	1.0		1.8
2	TH	0224	1.0		1.9	1454	0.9		1.9
3	F	0313	1.0		1.9	1537	0.9		1.9
4	SA ●	0355	0.9		2.0	1615	0.8		2.0
5	SU	0432	0.9		2.0	1650	0.7		2.0
6	M	0508	0.8		2.0	1724	0.7		
7	TU		2.0	0542	0.8		2.0	1755	0.7
8	W		2.0	0614	0.8		1.9	1827	0.7
9	TH		2.0	0647	0.8		1.9	1858	0.7
10	F		2.0	0721	0.9		1.9	1932	0.8
11	SA		1.9	0758	0.9		1.8	2011	0.9
12	SU		1.9	0842	1.0		1.8	2057	0.9
13	M ☽		1.8	0935	1.1		1.7	2153	1.0
14	TU		1.8	1042	1.2		1.7	2306	1.1
15	W		1.8	1159	1.2		1.7		
16	TH	0026	1.1		1.8	1316	1.0		1.7
17	F	0139	1.0		1.9	1420	0.9		1.9
18	SA	0241	0.9		2.0	1515	0.7		2.0
19	SU ○	0335	0.7		2.1	1603	0.5		2.2
20	M	0423	0.5		2.2	1648	0.3		2.3
21	TU	0509	0.4		2.3	1734	0.2		
22	W		2.3	0555	0.4		2.3	1816	0.2
23	TH		2.3	0640	0.4		2.2	1900	0.3
24	F		2.2	0726	0.5		2.1	1946	0.5
25	SA		2.2	0814	0.6		1.9	2034	0.6
26	SU ☾		2.0	0907	0.8		1.8	2129	0.9
27	M		1.9	1007	1.0		1.7	2234	1.0
28	TU		1.8	1121	1.1		1.6	2350	1.2
29	W		1.7	1238	1.2		1.6		
30	TH	0106	1.2		1.7	1345	1.1		1.7
31	F	0208	1.2		1.8	1439	1.0		1.8

FEBRUARY

Date	Day	Time	m	Time	m	Time	m	Time	m
1	SA	0259	1.1		1.8	1522	0.9		1.9
2	SU	0340	1.0		1.9	1600	0.8		1.9
3	M ●	0416	0.9		1.9	1632	0.6		2.0
4	TU	0448	0.8		1.9	1703	0.6		
5	W		2.0	0519	0.7		2.0	1732	0.5
6	TH		2.0	0549	0.6		2.0	1800	0.5
7	F		2.0	0619	0.6		1.9	1830	0.6
8	SA		2.0	0649	0.7		1.9	1901	0.6
9	SU		1.9	0724	0.8		1.9	1938	0.8
10	M		1.9	0803	0.8		1.8	2021	0.9
11	TU ☽		1.8	0852	1.0		1.7	2114	1.0
12	W		1.8	0957	1.1		1.6	2230	1.2
13	TH		1.7	1127	1.2		1.6		
14	F	0006	1.2		1.7	1259	1.0		1.7
15	SA	0129	1.0		1.8	1407	0.9		1.8
16	SU	0232	0.9		1.9	1503	0.6		2.0
17	M	0323	0.6		2.1	1550	0.4		2.2
18	TU ○	0409	0.5		2.2	1632	0.2		2.3
19	W	0452	0.3		2.3	1715	0.2		
20	TH		2.3	0535	0.2		2.3	1755	0.2
21	F		2.3	0616	0.3		2.2	1836	0.2
22	SA		2.2	0658	0.4		2.1	1918	0.4
23	SU		2.1	0742	0.6		1.9	2001	0.6
24	M		1.9	0829	0.8		1.8	2051	0.9
25	TU ☾		1.8	0925	1.0		1.7	2154	1.2
26	W		1.7	1038	1.2		1.5	2319	1.3
27	TH		1.5	1206	1.2		1.5		
28	F	0044	1.3		1.5	1322	1.2		1.6
29	SA	0150	1.2		1.6	1417	1.0		1.7

MARCH

Date	Day	Time	m	Time	m	Time	m	Time	m
1	SU	0240	1.1		1.7	1501	0.9		1.8
2	M	0319	0.9		1.8	1536	0.8		1.9
3	TU	0354	0.8		1.9	1607	0.6		2.0
4	W ●	0424	0.6		1.9	1636	0.5		2.0
5	TH	0452	0.6		2.0	1705	0.5		
6	F		2.0	0521	0.5		2.0	1733	0.5
7	SA		2.0	0550	0.5		2.0	1802	0.5
8	SU		2.0	0621	0.5		2.0	1835	0.6
9	M		1.9	0655	0.6		1.9	1912	0.7
10	TU		1.9	0735	0.8		1.8	1956	0.9
11	W		1.8	0824	0.9		1.7	2053	1.0
12	TH ☽		1.7	0930	1.0		1.6	2215	1.2
13	F		1.6	1109	1.1		1.6	2358	1.2
14	SA		1.6	1244	1.0		1.7		
15	SU	0119	1.0		1.8	1352	0.8		1.9
16	M	0218	0.8		1.9	1445	0.6		2.0
17	TU	0308	0.6		2.0	1531	0.3		2.2
18	W ○	0352	0.4		2.2	1613	0.2		2.3
19	TH	0431	0.3		2.3	1652	0.2		2.3
20	F	0512	0.2		2.2	1733	0.2		
21	SA		2.3	0551	0.3		2.2	1811	0.3
22	SU		2.2	0631	0.4		2.0	1850	0.5
23	M		2.0	0711	0.6		1.9	1932	0.8
24	TU		1.9	0754	0.8		1.8	2019	1.0
25	W		1.7	0845	1.0		1.7	2118	1.2
26	TH ☾		1.6	0952	1.2		1.5	2243	1.3
27	F		1.5	1122	1.3		1.5		
28	SA	0010	1.3		1.4	1242	1.2		1.5
29	SU	0118	1.3		1.5	1340	1.1		1.7
30	M	0208	1.1		1.6	1425	0.9		1.8
31	TU	0248	0.9		1.8	1502	0.8		1.9

APRIL

Date	Day	Time	m	Time	m	Time	m	Time	m
1	W	0322	0.8		1.9	1535	0.6		2.0
2	TH	0354	0.6		1.9	1605	0.6		2.0
3	F ●	0423	0.5		2.0	1635	0.5		2.1
4	SA	0452	0.5		2.0	1706	0.5		
5	SU		2.0	0523	0.5		2.0	1739	0.5
6	M		2.0	0557	0.5		2.0	1815	0.6
7	TU		2.0	0634	0.6		1.9	1855	0.7
8	W		1.9	0717	0.7		1.9	1944	0.9
9	TH		1.8	0810	0.9		1.8	2047	1.0
10	F ☽		1.7	0920	1.0		1.7	2212	1.2
11	SA		1.6	1055	1.0		1.7	2345	1.1
12	SU		1.7	1222	1.0		1.8		
13	M	0100	1.0		1.8	1329	0.8		1.9
14	TU	0158	0.8		1.9	1422	0.6		2.0
15	W	0246	0.6		2.0	1509	0.5		2.2
16	TH	0329	0.5		2.2	1550	0.3		2.2
17	F ○	0409	0.3		2.2	1630	0.3		2.2
18	SA	0448	0.3		2.2	1709	0.3		
19	SU		2.2	0526	0.4		2.2	1747	0.5
20	M		2.1	0605	0.5		2.0	1827	0.6
21	TU		2.0	0644	0.6		1.9	1907	0.8
22	W		1.9	0726	0.8		1.8	1952	1.0
23	TH		1.7	0812	1.0		1.7	2046	1.2
24	F ☾		1.6	0909	1.2		1.6	2155	1.3
25	SA		1.5	1024	1.2		1.5	2315	1.3
26	SU		1.5	1141	1.2		1.6		
27	M	0024	1.3		1.5	1245	1.2		1.7
28	TU	0120	1.2		1.6	1336	1.0		1.8
29	W	0205	1.0		1.7	1418	0.9		1.9
30	TH	0243	0.9		1.8	1456	0.8		2.0

SEA LEVEL IS ABOVE MEAN TIDE LEVEL FROM 2.0 HOURS AFTER L.W. TO 2.0 HOURS BEFORE THE NEXT L.W. AND H.W. WILL OCCUR BETWEEN 5.0 HOURS AFTER L.W. AND 3.0 HOURS BEFORE THE NEXT L.W.

Chart Datum: 1.40 metres below Ordnance Datum (Newlyn)

ENGLAND, SOUTH COAST - POOLE (TOWN QUAY)

TIME ZONE UT(GMT)

For Summer Time add ONE hour in non-shaded areas

LAT 50°43'N LONG 1°59'W

TIMES AND HEIGHTS OF HIGH AND LOW WATERS

YEAR **1992**

MAY

Day	Time m	Time m	Time m	Time m
1 F	0318 0.7	1.9	1532 0.6	2.0
2 SA ●	0353 0.6	2.0	1607 0.6	2.1
3 SU	0427 0.5	2.0	1642 0.6	2.1
4 M	0503 0.5	2.1	1721 0.6	
5 TU	2.0	0541 0.5	2.0	1802 0.6
6 W	2.0	0623 0.6	2.0	1848 0.8
7 TH	1.9	0711 0.7	1.9	1941 0.9
8 F	1.8	0807 0.8	1.9	2044 1.0
9 SA ☽	1.8	0914 0.9	1.8	2159 1.0
10 SU	1.7	1034 0.9	1.8	2319 1.0
11 M	1.7	1151 0.9	1.9	
12 TU	0030 1.0	1.8	1258 0.8	1.9
13 W	0130 0.8	1.9	1354 0.7	2.0
14 TH	0221 0.7	2.0	1442 0.6	2.1
15 F	0307 0.6	2.0	1527 0.6	2.2
16 SA ○	0349 0.5	2.1	1608 0.5	2.2
17 SU	0429 0.5	2.1	1647 0.6	2.1
18 M	0508 0.5	2.0	1727 0.6	
19 TU	2.0	0546 0.6	2.0	1806 0.8
20 W	2.0	0625 0.7	1.9	1846 0.9
21 TH	1.9	0704 0.8	1.8	1928 1.0
22 F	1.8	0745 0.9	1.8	2014 1.1
23 SA	1.7	0831 1.0	1.7	2107 1.2
24 SU ☾	1.7	0926 1.1	1.7	2209 1.3
25 M	1.6	1029 1.2	1.7	2315 1.3
26 TU	1.5	1134 1.2	1.7	
27 W	0017 1.2	1.6	1234 1.1	1.8
28 TH	0112 1.1	1.7	1328 1.0	1.8
29 F	0200 1.0	1.8	1415 0.9	1.9
30 SA	0244 0.8	1.9	1500 0.8	2.0
31 SU	0326 0.7	2.0	1543 0.7	2.1

JUNE

Day	Time m	Time m	Time m	Time m
1 M ●	0407 0.6	2.0	1625 0.6	2.1
2 TU	0448 0.5	2.1	1709 0.6	
3 W	2.1	0532 0.5	2.1	1755 0.6
4 TH	2.1	0618 0.5	2.1	1843 0.6
5 F	2.0	0707 0.6	2.0	1936 0.7
6 SA	2.0	0800 0.6	2.0	2032 0.8
7 SU ☽	1.9	0859 0.8	1.9	2136 0.9
8 M	1.8	1005 0.8	1.9	2246 1.0
9 TU	1.8	1115 0.9	1.9	2354 1.0
10 W	1.8	1223 0.9	1.9	
11 TH	0059 0.9	1.8	1325 0.9	1.9
12 F	0156 0.9	1.9	1419 0.8	2.0
13 SA	0246 0.8	1.9	1508 0.8	2.0
14 SU	0332 0.8	2.0	1552 0.8	2.0
15 M ○	0414 0.7	2.0	1632 0.8	2.0
16 TU	0453 0.7	2.0	1712 0.8	
17 W	2.0	0530 0.7	2.0	1750 0.8
18 TH	1.9	0607 0.7	1.9	1827 0.8
19 F	1.9	0643 0.8	1.9	1904 0.9
20 SA	1.9	0719 0.8	1.9	1942 1.0
21 SU	1.8	0756 0.9	1.8	2023 1.0
22 M	1.8	0838 0.9	1.8	2109 1.1
23 TU ☾	1.7	0925 1.0	1.8	2204 1.2
24 W	1.7	1023 1.1	1.8	2308 1.2
25 TH	1.7	1128 1.1	1.8	
26 F	0014 1.2	1.7	1235 1.1	1.8
27 SA	0117 1.0	1.7	1337 1.0	1.9
28 SU	0214 0.9	1.8	1434 0.9	2.0
29 M	0306 0.8	1.9	1524 0.8	2.0
30 TU ●	0353 0.6	2.0	1612 0.6	2.1

JULY

Day	Time m	Time m	Time m	Time m
1 W	0438 0.5	2.2	1658 0.5	
2 TH	2.2	0523 0.4	2.2	1746 0.5
3 F	2.2	0609 0.3	2.2	1833 0.5
4 SA	2.2	0655 0.4	2.2	1921 0.5
5 SU	2.1	0745 0.5	2.2	2013 0.6
6 M	2.0	0837 0.6	2.0	2108 0.8
7 TU ☽	1.9	0933 0.8	2.0	2210 0.9
8 W	1.8	1038 0.9	1.9	2318 1.0
9 TH	1.8	1147 1.0	1.8	
10 F	0028 1.0	1.7	1258 1.0	1.8
11 SA	0135 1.0	1.8	1400 1.0	1.8
12 SU	0232 0.9	1.8	1453 1.0	1.9
13 M	0320 0.9	1.9	1540 0.9	1.9
14 TU ○	0402 0.8	1.9	1620 0.8	1.9
15 W	0439 0.7	2.0	1657 0.8	2.0
16 TH	0515 0.6	2.0	1733 0.8	
17 F	2.0	0548 0.6	2.0	1805 0.8
18 SA	1.9	0620 0.6	2.0	1838 0.8
19 SU	1.9	0650 0.7	1.9	1910 0.8
20 M	1.9	0722 0.8	1.9	1945 0.9
21 TU	1.9	0757 0.8	1.9	2023 0.9
22 W ☾	1.8	0838 0.9	1.8	2108 1.0
23 TH	1.7	0927 1.0	1.8	2206 1.1
24 F	1.7	1031 1.1	1.8	2320 1.2
25 SA	1.7	1150 1.2	1.7	
26 SU	0040 1.1	1.7	1309 1.1	1.8
27 M	0151 1.0	1.8	1415 1.0	1.9
28 TU	0249 0.8	1.9	1512 0.8	2.0
29 W ●	0340 0.6	2.0	1601 0.6	2.1
30 TH	0426 0.4	2.2	1646 0.5	2.2
31 F	0511 0.3	2.3	1733 0.3	

AUGUST

Day	Time m	Time m	Time m	Time m
1 SA	2.3	0554 0.2	2.3	1816 0.3
2 SU	2.2	0638 0.2	2.3	1901 0.4
3 M	2.2	0722 0.3	2.2	1948 0.5
4 TU	2.0	0810 0.5	2.1	2038 0.7
5 W ☽	1.9	0901 0.8	1.9	2134 0.9
6 TH	1.8	1002 1.0	1.8	2242 1.0
7 F	1.7	1116 1.1	1.7	2359 1.2
8 SA	1.7	1235 1.2	1.7	
9 SU	0114 1.1	1.7	1345 1.2	1.7
10 M	0216 1.0	1.8	1441 1.1	1.8
11 TU	0306 0.9	1.9	1527 1.0	1.8
12 W	0347 0.8	1.9	1605 0.9	1.9
13 TH ○	0422 0.7	2.0	1638 0.8	1.9
14 F	0453 0.6	2.0	1711 0.7	
15 SA	2.0	0523 0.6	2.0	1741 0.6
16 SU	2.0	0552 0.6	2.0	1809 0.6
17 M	2.0	0621 0.6	2.0	1839 0.6
18 TU	1.9	0650 0.6	2.0	1910 0.7
19 W	1.9	0723 0.8	1.9	1946 0.8
20 TH	1.9	0801 0.9	1.9	2028 0.9
21 F ☾	1.8	0849 1.0	1.8	2123 1.0
22 SA	1.7	0952 1.2	1.7	2240 1.2
23 SU	1.6	1121 1.2	1.7	
24 M	0013 1.2	1.7	1251 1.2	1.7
25 TU	0132 1.0	1.8	1401 1.0	1.8
26 W	0233 0.8	1.9	1457 0.8	2.0
27 TH	0323 0.5	2.1	1545 0.5	2.2
28 F ●	0409 0.3	2.3	1630 0.3	2.3
29 SA	0451 0.2	2.3	1713 0.3	
30 SU	2.3	0534 0.2	2.3	1755 0.3
31 M	2.3	0615 0.2	2.3	1838 0.3

SEA LEVEL IS ABOVE MEAN TIDE LEVEL FROM 2.0 HOURS AFTER L.W. TO 2.0 HOURS BEFORE THE NEXT L.W. AND H.W. WILL OCCUR BETWEEN 5.0 HOURS AFTER L.W. AND 3.0 HOURS BEFORE THE NEXT L.W.

Chart Datum: 1.40 metres below Ordnance Datum (Newlyn)

ENGLAND, SOUTH COAST - POOLE (TOWN QUAY)

TIME ZONE UT(GMT)

For Summer Time add ONE hour in non-shaded areas

LAT 50°43'N LONG 1°59'W

TIMES AND HEIGHTS OF HIGH AND LOW WATERS

YEAR 1992

SEPTEMBER

Date	Time	m	Date	Time	m
1 TU	 0658 1921	2.2 0.3 2.2 0.5	16 W	 0623 1841	2.0 0.6 2.0 0.7
2 W	 0743 2008	2.1 0.6 2.1 0.7	17 TH	 0657 1917	2.0 0.8 2.0 0.8
3 TH ☽	 0832 2101	1.9 0.8 1.9 0.9	18 F	 0737 2001	1.9 0.9 1.9 0.9
4 F	 0931 2206	1.8 1.0 1.8 1.1	19 SA ☾	 0826 2057	1.8 1.0 1.8 1.0
5 SA	 1048 2329	1.7 1.2 1.7 1.2	20 SU	 0933 2216	1.7 1.2 1.7 1.1
6 SU	 1212	1.6 1.3 1.6	21 M	 1106 2352	1.7 1.2 1.7 1.1
7 M	0049 1325	1.2 1.7 1.3 1.6	22 TU	 1233	1.7 1.2 1.7
8 TU	0154 1421	1.1 1.7 1.2 1.7	23 W	0111 1342	1.0 1.8 1.0 1.9
9 W	0242 1505	1.0 1.8 1.0 1.8	24 TH	0212 1437	0.8 2.0 0.8 2.0
10 TH	0322 1542	0.9 1.9 0.9 1.9	25 F	0303 1525	0.5 2.2 0.5 2.2
11 F	0357 1613	0.8 2.0 0.8 1.9	26 SA ●	0348 1608	0.3 2.3 0.4 2.3
12 SA ○	0427 1642	0.6 2.0 0.6 2.0	27 SU	0430 1650	0.3 2.3 0.3 2.3
13 SU	0455 1712	0.6 2.1 0.6	28 M	0511 1733	0.2 2.3 0.3
14 M	 0523 1740	2.0 0.6 2.1 0.6	29 TU	 0553 1813	2.3 0.3 2.3 0.4
15 TU	 0552 1809	2.0 0.6 2.0 0.6	30 W	 0635 1855	2.2 0.5 2.2 0.5

OCTOBER

Date	Time	m	Date	Time	m
1 TH	 0718 1941	2.1 0.7 2.0 0.8	16 F	 0639 1858	2.0 0.8 2.0 0.8
2 F	 0806 2030	1.9 0.9 1.9 0.9	17 SA	 0723 1946	2.0 0.9 1.9 0.9
3 SA ☽	 0902 2132	1.8 1.2 1.8 1.2	18 SU	 0816 2045	1.9 1.0 1.8 1.0
4 SU	 1015 2251	1.7 1.3 1.6 1.3	19 M ☾	 0925 2201	1.8 1.2 1.8 1.0
5 M	 1137	1.6 1.4 1.5	20 TU	 1051 2329	1.8 1.2 1.7 1.0
6 TU	0009 1250	1.3 1.7 1.3 1.5	21 W	 1211	1.8 1.1 1.8
7 W	0114 1346	1.2 1.7 1.2 1.7	22 TH	0044 1318	0.9 1.9 0.9 1.9
8 TH	0205 1431	1.0 1.8 1.1 1.8	23 F	0146 1413	0.8 2.0 0.8 2.0
9 F	0246 1508	0.9 1.9 0.9 1.9	24 SA	0237 1502	0.6 2.2 0.6 2.2
10 SA	0321 1542	0.8 2.0 0.8 1.9	25 SU ●	0324 1547	0.5 2.3 0.5 2.2
11 SU ○	0355 1612	0.7 2.0 0.7 2.0	26 M	0407 1629	0.4 2.3 0.4 2.3
12 M	0425 1641	0.6 2.1 0.6 2.0	27 TU	0449 1710	0.4 2.3 0.5
13 TU	0455 1712	0.6 2.1 0.6	28 W	 0532 1752	2.3 0.5 2.2 0.5
14 W	 0526 1744	2.1 0.6 2.1 0.6	29 TH	 0613 1833	2.2 0.6 2.2 0.6
15 TH	 0601 1820	2.1 0.7 2.0 0.7	30 F	 0656 1916	2.1 0.8 2.0 0.8
			31 SA	 0742 2003	2.0 1.0 1.9 1.0

NOVEMBER

Date	Time	m	Date	Time	m
1 SU	 0833 2056	1.9 1.2 1.8 1.1	16 M	 0811 2037	2.0 0.9 1.9 0.9
2 M ☽	 0935 2200	1.8 1.3 1.7 1.2	17 TU ☾	 0914 2144	1.9 1.0 1.8 0.9
3 TU	 1047 2311	1.7 1.4 1.6 1.3	18 W	 1028 2301	1.9 1.1 1.8 1.0
4 W	 1155	1.7 1.3 1.5	19 TH	 1141	1.9 1.0 1.8
5 TH	0017 1256	1.2 1.7 1.3 1.6	20 F	0012 1250	0.9 1.9 1.0 1.9
6 F	0113 1345	1.2 1.8 1.2 1.7	21 SA	0117 1348	0.9 2.0 0.9 2.0
7 SA	0200 1428	1.0 1.9 1.0 1.8	22 SU	0212 1440	0.8 2.1 0.8 2.1
8 SU	0241 1506	0.9 2.0 0.9 1.9	23 M	0302 1527	0.7 2.2 0.6 2.2
9 M	0319 1541	0.8 2.0 0.8 2.0	24 TU ●	0348 1611	0.6 2.2 0.6 2.2
10 TU ○	0355 1615	0.8 2.1 0.7 2.1	25 W	0431 1652	0.6 2.2 0.6 2.2
11 W	0430 1649	0.7 2.2 0.6 2.1	26 TH	0513 1735	0.6 2.2 0.6
12 TH	0507 1726	0.7 2.2 0.6	27 F	 0555 1814	2.2 0.8 2.1 0.7
13 F	 0546 1805	2.1 0.7 2.1 0.6	28 SA	 0636 1854	2.0 0.8 2.0 0.8
14 SA	 0629 1849	2.1 0.8 2.0 0.7	29 SU	 0718 1936	2.0 0.9 1.9 0.9
15 SU	 0716 1939	2.0 0.9 2.0 0.8	30 M	 0802 2019	1.9 1.1 1.8 1.0

DECEMBER

Date	Time	m	Date	Time	m
1 TU	 0851 2107	1.8 1.2 1.7 1.1	16 W ☾	 0855 2120	2.0 0.9 1.9 0.8
2 W ☽	 0947 2203	1.8 1.3 1.7 1.2	17 TH	 0959 2227	2.0 1.0 1.8 0.9
3 TH	 1050 2307	1.8 1.3 1.6 1.2	18 F	 1110 2339	1.9 1.0 1.8 1.0
4 F	 1152	1.8 1.3 1.6	19 SA	 1221	1.9 1.0 1.8
5 SA	0008 1252	1.2 1.8 1.2 1.7	20 SU	0048 1326	1.0 2.0 0.9 1.9
6 SU	0107 1344	1.2 1.9 1.1 1.8	21 M	0151 1424	0.9 2.0 0.9 2.0
7 M	0159 1431	1.0 1.9 1.0 1.9	22 TU	0245 1514	0.9 2.0 0.8 2.0
8 TU	0245 1514	0.9 2.0 0.9 2.0	23 W	0334 1559	0.8 2.1 0.7 2.1
9 W ○	0328 1554	0.9 2.1 0.8 2.0	24 TH ●	0418 1639	0.8 2.1 0.6 2.1
10 TH	0410 1633	0.8 2.2 0.6 2.1	25 F	0458 1719	0.8 2.1 0.6
11 F	0451 1714	0.7 2.2 0.6	26 SA	 0538 1756	2.1 0.8 2.0 0.6
12 SA	 0535 1756	2.2 0.6 2.2 0.5	27 SU	 0615 1831	2.0 0.8 2.0 0.7
13 SU	 0620 1841	2.2 0.6 2.1 0.5	28 M	 0652 1906	2.0 0.9 1.9 0.8
14 M	 0707 1928	2.2 0.7 2.0 0.6	29 TU	 0729 1942	2.0 0.9 1.9 0.8
15 TU	 0758 2021	2.1 0.8 2.0 0.7	30 W	 0809 2020	1.9 1.0 1.8 0.9
			31 TH	 0851 2102	1.9 1.1 1.7 1.0

SEA LEVEL IS ABOVE MEAN TIDE LEVEL FROM 2.0 HOURS AFTER L.W. TO 2.0 HOURS BEFORE THE NEXT L.W. AND H.W. WILL OCCUR BETWEEN 5.0 HOURS AFTER L.W. AND 3.0 HOURS BEFORE THE NEXT L.W.

Chart Datum: 1.40 metres below Ordnance Datum (Newlyn)

POOLE *continued*

CHARTS
Admiralty 2611, 2175, 2615; Stanford 15, 12, 7; Imray C4, Y23; OS 195

TIDES
Town Quay −0141, +0114 Dover; ML 1·5; Zone 0 (GMT).

Standard Port PORTSMOUTH (⟶)

Times				Height (metres)			
HW		LW		MHWS	MHWN	MLWN	MLWS
0000	0600	0500	1100	4·7	3·8	1·8	0·6
1200	1800	1700	2300				
Differences POOLE ENTRANCE							
−0240	+0105	−0100	−0030	−2·7	−2·2	−0·7	−0·3
TOWN QUAY							
−0210	+0140	−0015	−0005	−2·6	−2·2	−0·7	−0·2
WAREHAM (River Frome)							
−0140	+0205	+0110	+0035	−2·5	−2·1	−0·7	+0·1

NOTE: Times and heights of LW for each day of the year are given above. Double HWs occur except at neaps and predictions are for the higher HW. Near neaps there is a stand and the predictions shown are for the middle of the stand. See 10.2.13.

SHELTER
An excellent harbour with narrow entrance from sea, accessible in all conditions except very strong E and SE winds. Anchorages may be found in most parts of the harbour, anywhere sheltered from the wind and free from moorings. Speed limit throughout harbour 8 kn; in quiet areas 6 kn.

NAVIGATION
Waypoint Poole Bar (stbd-hand) buoy, QG, 50°39′·42N 01°55′·15W, 148°/328° from/to Haven Hotel, 1·95M. The Bar is dangerous in strong SE-S winds especially on the ebb. Beware number of lobster pots round Studland Bay and close to training bank. A recreational boat channel has been established in the Swash Way on the western side of the channel, from Poole Bar to Shell Bay. Suitable for craft up to 3m draught. There are two channels up to Poole; the Middle Ship Channel (formerly the Diver Channel) and the North Channel (formerly the Main Channel). The former is dredged to 5m for traffic to the ferry terminal at Hamworthy, and is mostly only 60m wide. Recreational traffic must keep out of the Middle Ship Channel but may use the small vessel channel running to the S of the dredged channel between port hand buoys to the S and stakes having R can topmarks marking the edge of the bank. Depth in this channel is 2·0m above CD except close to the stakes where it drops to 1·5m. Alternatively yachts can use the North Channel (formerly the main channel). Both channels are clearly marked by lateral buoys, mostly lit, with divisions marked by cardinal buoys. The Harbour is changing to adapt to the needs of the Oil Industry and cross channel traffic. Changes to buoyage and channels are now frequent.
Yachts departing westwards should note regulations regarding Lulworth gunnery range (see 10.2.31).
Information is shown in Hr Mr's mooring office on Poole Quay and broadcast on Radio Solent at times given in 10.2.17.

LIGHTS AND MARKS
Radio beacon 303·4 kHz PO 10 M located on Haven Hotel at harbour entrance.
Chain Ferry Sandbanks
Moving: Day—B Ball For'd; Night—WGR Lts For'd;
Fog—1 long, 2 short blasts every 2 mins.
Stationary: Night—W Lt.; Fog—5 sec bell every min.
Poole Bridge (Lights shown from tower)
FR — Do not approach bridge;
Fl Or — Bridge opening, proceed with caution;
FG — Proceed;
Bridge opened on request (large vessels) and at routine times for small — Mon-Fri 0930, 1130, 1430, 1630, 1830, 2130, 2330. Sat, Sun & Bank holidays 0730, 0930, 1130, 1330, 1530, 1730, 1930, 2130, 2330. (LT)
Salterns Marina
Lts 2FG (vert) to stbd, 2FR (vert) to port.
Poole YC Haven
Entrance E side FlG 5s. W side Fl (3) 10s.

RADIO TELEPHONE
Call: *Poole Harbour Control* VHF Ch 14 16; 14. (H24).
Salterns Marina (call: *Gulliver Base*) and Cobbs Quay Marina, Ch **80** M.

TELEPHONE (0202)
Hr Mr 685261; MRSC Portland 760439; Pilots 673320; Bridge 674115; Harbour Control 666464; Hamworthy Bridge 674115; # (0703) 827350; Weather Southampton 228844; Marinecall 0898 500 457; Police 22099; Ⓗ 675100.

FACILITIES
EC Wednesday. The facilities in Poole Harbour are very extensive and the following is not an exhaustive list.
Salterns Marina (340, some visitors) ☎ 709971, ME, El, Ⓔ, Sh, C (5 ton), BH (40 ton), AC, FW, CH, Bar, Gas, Gaz, P, D, R, ⊡; **Cobbs Quay Marina** (600, some visitors) ☎ 674299, Slip, P, D, Gas, ⊡, SM, FW, AC, ME, El, Ⓔ, Sh, C (10 ton), CH, R, Bar; **Sunseekers International Marina** (50) ☎ 685335, Slip, BH (2 ton), C (40 ton), AC, Sh, D, FW, ME, El, CH, V, R, Bar; **Dorset Yacht Co** (120+12 visitors) ☎ 674531, Slip, P, D, Gas, Gaz, FW, ME, El, Sh, C (5 ton), Bar, AC;
Harbour Office ☎ 685261 is opposite the quay. There is an office on the quay for Berthing Officer open 0900-2300.
Landing Places: Public landing places on Poole Quay, at Holes Bay and by ferry hards at Sandbanks.
Fresh water is available at Town Quay, at all marinas and boatyards.
Fuel (P and D) and FW is available from Esso barge when on station near Aunt Betty buoy (No 50) and all major yards.
Yacht Clubs
Poole YC ☎ 672687; **Poole Quay YC** ☎ 680746; **Poole Harbour YC** ☎ 707321; **Parkstone YC** ☎ 743610; **Royal Motor YC** ☎ 707227, Bar, R, M; **Cobb's Quay YC** ☎ 673690.
Note: **Poole Quay** (AB, C (24 ton) FW) is close to town centre and many facilities listed below.
Arthur Bray ☎ 676469, M, L, FW, C (2 ton), AB; **J. Harvey** ☎ 666226, M; **Marine Engine Centre** ☎ 672082, FW, ME, El, Sh, CH, AB, C (4 ton); **Rockley Boating Centre** ☎ 665001, Slip, M, C (5 ton), FW, CH, AB; **Quay Sails** ☎ 681128, SM; **Tab Sails** ☎ 684638, SM; **Crusader Sails** ☎ 670580, SM; **Sandbanks Yacht Co.** ☎ 707500, Slip, M, D, P, L, FW, ME, El, CH, V, Sh; **Mitchell BY** ☎ 747857, Slip, M, FW, ME, El, L, C (18 ton), Sh, CH; **Lilliput Yacht Station** ☎ 707176, Slip, L, M, FW, Sh; **Latham and Sons** ☎ 748029, Slip, L, FW, C (4 ton), CH, ME, El, Sh; **H. Pipler** ☎ 673056, L, CH, ACA; **Marine Power** ☎ 676469, Spares; **Greenham Marine** ☎ 676363, El, Ⓔ; **Melmarine** ☎ 680462, CH; **Danlea** ☎ 590468, Ⓔ; **Poole Inflatables** ☎ 677777, Safety Equipment and Inflatables; **Town** ✉; Ⓑ; ⇌; ✈ (Bournemouth).

CHRISTCHURCH 10-2-15

Dorset

CHARTS
Admiralty 2172, 2175, 2219, 2615; Stanford 7, 12; Imray C4; OS 195

TIDES
HW Spring −0210 Neap −0140 Dover; ML 1·2
+0120 +0105 Zone 0 (GMT)

Standard Port PORTSMOUTH (⟶)

Times				Height (metres)			
HW		LW		MHWS	MHWN	MLWN	MLWS
0000	0600	0500	1100	4·7	3·8	1·8	0·6
1200	1800	1700	2300				
Differences CHRISTCHURCH (Ent)							
−0230	+0030	−0035	−0035	−2·9	−2·4	−1·2	−0·2
CHRISTCHURCH (Tuckton)							
−0205	+0110	+0110	+0105	−3·0	−2·5	−1·0	+0·1
BOURNEMOUTH							
−0240	+0055	−0050	−0030	−2·7	−2·2	−0·8	−0·3

NOTE: Double HWs occur except near neaps and predictions are for the higher HW. Near neaps there is a stand and the predictions shown are for the middle of the stand. Tidal levels are for inside the bar. Outside the bar the tide falls about 0·6m lower at springs. Floods (or drought) in the 2 rivers cause considerable variations from predicted heights. See 10.2.13

CHRISTCHURCH *continued*

SHELTER
Good shelter in lee of Hengistbury Head but otherwise very exposed to prevailing SW winds. The Stour is navigable at HW up to Tuckton Bridge and the Avon up to the first bridge across to the island, and both give good shelter from all winds. Recommend entry or departure on the stand. Most anchorage areas in the harbour dry. Anchoring forbidden in main channel. It is also forbidden to secure alongside ferry terminal on Mudeford sandbank. Christchurch SC offers limited moorings to monohulls up to 7·9m.

NAVIGATION
Waypoint 50°43'·50N 01°43'·50W, 090°/270° from/to NE end of Mudeford Quay 0·5M. The position of the bar is liable to change after storms. The entrance is difficult on the ebb tide due to very strong streams, 4 to 5 kn in 'The Run'. Beware groynes S of Hengistbury Head and also Beerpan Rks and Yarranton (or Clarendon) Rks.
There is a speed limit in the harbour of 4 kn.

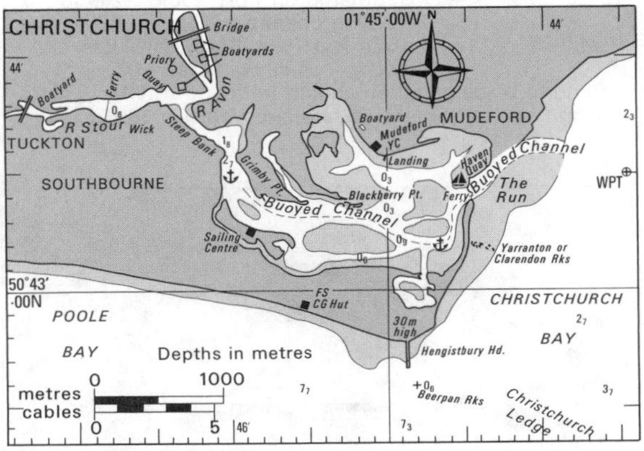
CHRISTCHURCH
Bridge
Boatyards
Priory
Quay
Boatyard
Ferry
R Avon
R Stour
Wick
TUCKTON
Steep Bank
SOUTHBOURNE
Grimby Pt
Buoyed Channel
Blackberry Pt.
Ferry
Boatyard
Mudeford YC
MUDEFORD
Landing
Haven Quay
Buoyed Channel
The Run
WPT
Sailing Centre
Yarranton or Clarendon Rks
FS CG Hut
POOLE
BAY
CHRISTCHURCH
BAY
30m high
Hengistbury Hd.
Depths in metres
Beerpan Rks
Christchurch Ledge
metres
cables
0
1000
5
01°45'·00W
50°43'·00N

LIGHTS AND MARKS
Buoyage in harbour and entrance is carried out privately by the Christchurch Harbour Association and buoys are often withdrawn in winter. Information can be obtained from Christchurch Marine ☎ 483250. Outer port hand buoy Fl (2) R 10s (May–Sept incl). E end of Mudeford Quay 2 FG (vert).

RADIO TELEPHONE
None.

TELEPHONE (0202)
Quay & Moorings Supt. Highcliffe 274933; MRSC Portland 760439; # (0703) 827350; Marinecall 0898 500 457; Police 486333; Ⓗ 486361.

FACILITIES
Mudeford Quay (Apl-Sept), Slip, M, P (cans, ½M), L, FW, C (mobile), AB, V; **Christchurch Marine** ☎ 483250, Slip, M, FW, ME, El, Sh, CH, ACA; **John Lack** ☎ 483191, FW, ME, El; **RIBS Marine** ☎ 477327, M, FW, ME, El, Sh; **Leak Hayes** ☎ 483141, C (8 ton); **Bob Hoare** ☎ 485708, Sh, CH; **Slaters Marine** ☎ 482751, CH; **R. A. Stride** ☎ 485949, CH.
Town ✉; Ⓑ; ⇌; ✈ (Bournemouth).

KEYHAVEN 10-2-16

Hampshire

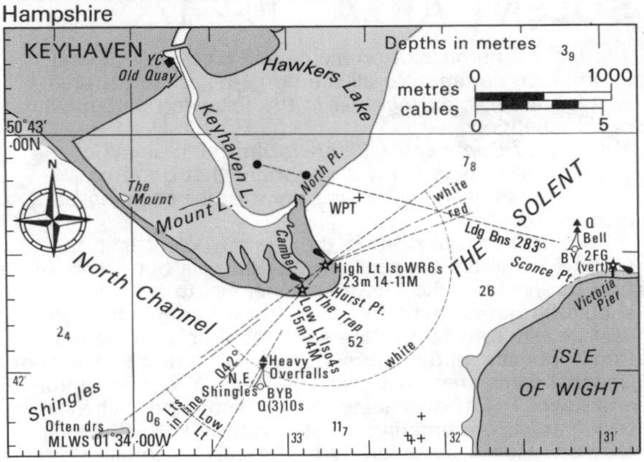
KEYHAVEN
YC
Old Quay
Hawkers Lake
Keyhaven L.
Depths in metres
metres
cables
0
1000
5
50°43'·00N
The Mount
Mount L.
North Pt.
WPT
white
red
THE SOLENT
Ldg Bns 283°
Bell
BY 2FG (vert)
Sconce Pt.
Victoria Pier
Camber
High Lt IsoWR6s 23m 14-11M
Hurst Pt.
The Trap
North Channel
Low Lt IsoWR4s 15m 14M
042°
Heavy Overfalls
N.E. Shingles BYB Q(3)10s
white
ISLE OF WIGHT
Shingles
Often drs
Lts in line
Low Lt
MLWS 01°34'·00W

CHARTS
Admiralty 2021, 2219, 2040; Stanford 11, 7; Imray C4, C3, Y20; OS 196

TIDES
−0020, +0105 Dover; ML 2·0; Zone 0 (GMT).

Standard Port PORTSMOUTH (⟶)

Times				Height (metres)			
HW		LW		MHWS	MHWN	MLWN	MLWS
0000	0600	0500	1100	4·7	3·8	1·8	0·6
1200	1800	1700	2300				
Differences HURST POINT							
−0115	−0005	−0030	−0025	−2·0	−1·5	−0·5	−0·1

NOTE: Double tides occur at or near springs and on other occasions there is a stand which lasts about 2 hours. Predictions refer to the first HW when there are two. At other times they refer to the middle of the stand. See 10.2.13.
River is administered by New Forest District Council aided by the Keyhaven Consultative Committee.

SHELTER
Good, but the river gets extremely congested. All moorings and anchorages are exposed to winds across the marshland. Access HW ∓4½.

NAVIGATION
Waypoint 50°42'·70N 01°32'·50W, 115°/295° from/to channel entrance, 0·40M. Bar is constantly changing. Entrance should not be attempted in strong E winds. Approaching from W, beware Shingles over which seas break and which very occasionally dry. Give 'The Trap' a wide berth. Leave channel marker buoys well to Stbd. Beware lobster pots.

LIGHTS AND MARKS
When E of the High Lt, two leading beacons in line ('X' topmarks) at 283° lead to entrance of buoyed channel.
NOTE: Ldg Lts 042° do *not* lead into the harbour but keep clear of the Shingles.

RADIO TELEPHONE
None.

TELEPHONE (0590)
River Warden 645695; MRSC Lee-on-Solent 552100; # (0703) 827350; Marinecall 0898 500 457; Police 675411; Dr 672212; Ⓗ 677011.

FACILITIES
EC (Milford-on-Sea) Wednesday; **Keyhaven YC** ☎ 642165, Bar, C, M, L (on beach), FW; **West Solent Boat Builders** ☎ 642080, Slip, ME, El, Sh, C (9 ton), CH; **New Forest District Council** ☎ (0703) 285000, Slip, M; **Milford-on-Sea** P, D, FW, CH, V, R, Bar; **Hurst Castle SC** M, L, FW; **Quay** Slip, L.
Village R, Bar, CH, V, ✉ (Milford-on-Sea); Ⓑ(Milford-on-Sea); ⇌ (bus to New Milton); ✈ (Bournemouth).

SOLENT AREA 10-2-17

There are a number of problems and pieces of general information common to all the ports in the Solent area which are collected together in the following paragraphs to avoid repetition.

Yachts and Commercial Shipping. In the interests of the safety of all concerned it is important that good co-operation between yachts and commercial shipping be maintained.

The most crucial point in the central Solent is in the vicinity of the NE Gurnard and W Bramble buoys where the turn to and from the Thorn Channel has to be made. It should be noted that large ships inward bound from the east usually turn first to the southward on passing the Prince Consort buoy before starting the turn into the Thorn Channel somewhere between the Royal Yacht Squadron and Egypt Point, depending on tide and wind. When very large vessels are entering or leaving the Thorn Channel, they are usually preceded by an Associated British Ports Harbour Master's launch (see also 'Local Signals' below).

Other areas in the Solent requiring special co-operation are:—

(a) at the Needles between the Bridge and the SW Shingles buoys; there is plenty of sea-room for yachts to the south of the main channel.

(b) at the turn round Calshot Lt Float. The area bounded by Bourne Gap buoy, Calshot Lt Float, Castle Point buoy, Reach buoy, Calshot buoy and North Thorn buoy is prohibited to yachts and small craft when vessels over 100m (329ft) are navigating the channel between West Bramble buoy and Hook buoy. Southampton Port Radio (SPR) broadcasts traffic information on Ch 12 every two hours on the hour from 0600-2200, Fri-Sun inclusive and Bank Holiday Mondays, from Easter to end September.

(c) Portsmouth Harbour entrance.

VHF Radio Telephone. The proliferation of VHF radio telephones in yachts is causing problems in port communication networks. Yachtsmen are reminded that CHANNEL 16 is a DISTRESS, SAFETY AND CALLING Channel. Other than for distress, it must only be used to establish contact before going onto a recognised working channel. If another calling channel is available, it should be used in preference to Channel 16. Port Operation channels must not be used for ship to ship communication. The recognised ship to ship channels are 06, 08, 72 and 77. Port Operations channels are as follows:—

12 and 14	—	Southampton Port Radio general calling and working channels
11 and 13	—	Queen's Harbour Master Portsmouth general working channels
11	—	Commercial Harbourmaster Portsmouth general working channel
09	—	Pilot working channel
18, 20, 22	—	Southampton Port Radio, selected working channels
71 and 74	—	Ship/Tug/Pilot/Berthing Master working channels (keep off)

Reports of oil pollution should be made to HM Coastguard (call *Solent Coastguard* VHF Ch 16 67).

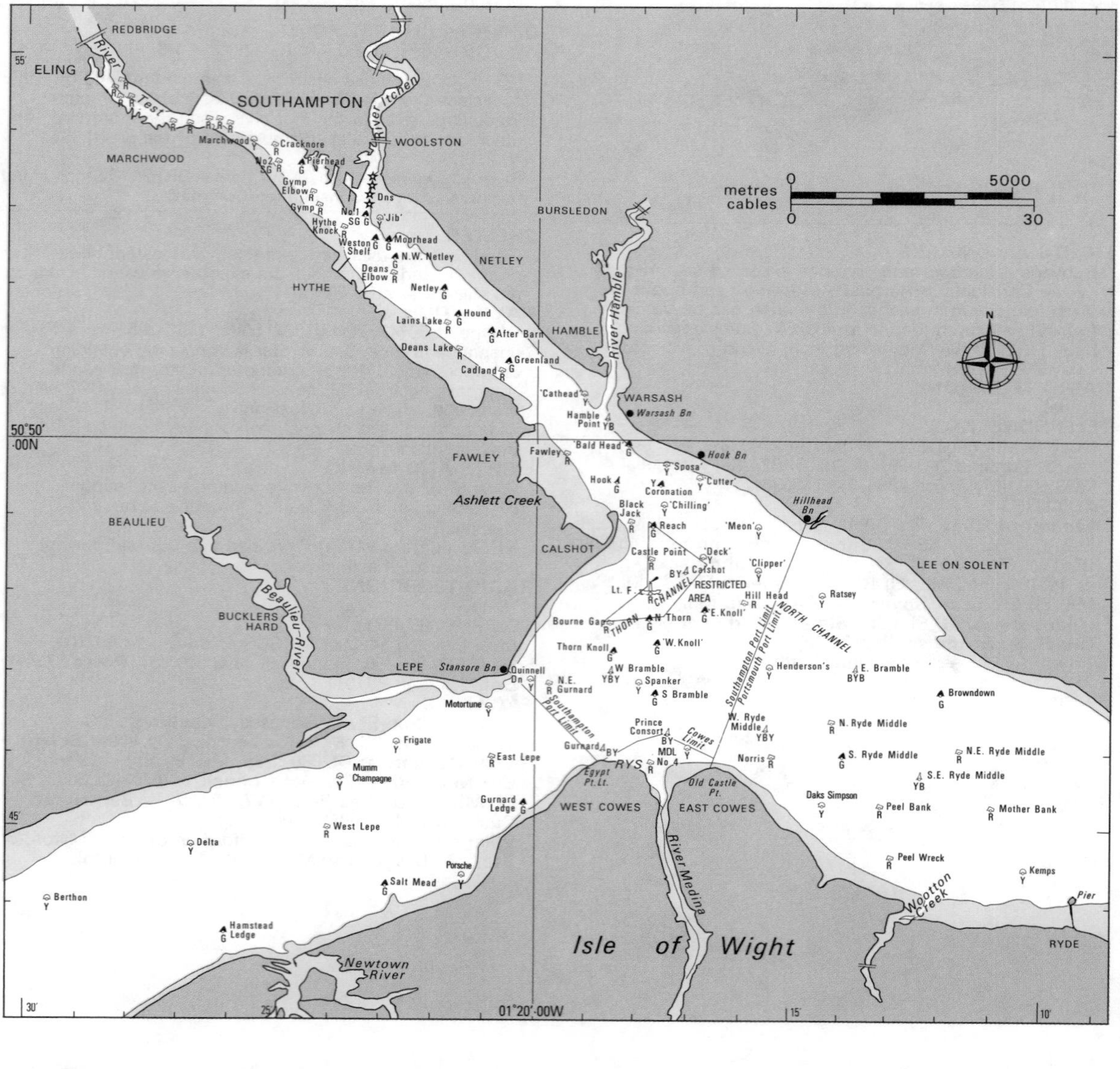

REDBRIDGE
ELING
River Test
SOUTHAMPTON
River Itchen
WOOLSTON
MARCHWOOD
BURSLEDON
NETLEY
HYTHE
HAMBLE
River Hamble
WARSASH
Warsash Bn
FAWLEY
Hook Bn
Ashlett Creek
Hillhead Bn
BEAULIEU
CALSHOT
LEE ON SOLENT
RESTRICTED AREA
THORN CHANNEL
NORTH CHANNEL
Beaulieu River
BUCKLERS HARD
LEPE
Stansore Bn
Southampton Port Limit
Portsmouth Port Limit
Cowes Limit
RYS
Egypt Pt.Lt.
Old Castle Pt.
WEST COWES
EAST COWES
River Medina
Wootton Creek
Pier
RYDE
Isle of Wight
Newtown River
metres
cables
0
5000
0
30
N
50°50′·00N
01°20′·00W
55′
45′
30′
25′
15′
10′

SOLENT AREA *continued*

Sailing Information from BBC Radio Solent
999 kHz (300m) and 96·1 MHz VHF.
1359 kHz (221m) in Bournemouth area.

A. Local weather forecasts.
B. Shipping forecasts for Channel sea areas, with general synopsis and Coastal Station reports.
C. Coastguard Station reports.
D. Tidal details.
E. Shipping movements.
F. Gunnery range firing times.

MONDAY TO FRIDAY

0604 — A
0633 — A B C D E F
0709 — A
0733 — A*
0745 — B C D E F
0809 — A
0833 — A*
0904 — A
1004 — A
1104 — A
1204 — A
1309 — A
1404 — A
1504 — A
1604 — A
1709 — A
1733 — A* D F
1804 — A
2204 — A
2300 — A*

*Live forecast from Southampton Weather Centre.

SATURDAY

0633 — A B C D E F
0709 — A
0733 — A*
0745 — B C D E F
0809 — A
0833 — A*
0904 — A
1000 — A
1104 — A
1204 — A
1304 — A
1404 — A
1533 — A
1804 — A
1925 — A*

SUNDAY

0633 — A*
0709 — A
0733 — A*
0745 — B C D E F
0809 — A
0904 — A*
1000 — A
1104 — A
1204 — A
1304 — A
1504 — A*

Recorded weather forecasts can be obtained for this area on 0898 500403. Southampton Weather Centre is Southampton 228844.

Local Signals
Outward bound vessels normally hoist the following flag signals during daylight hours.

Signal	*Meaning*
International 'E' Flag over Answering Pendant	I am bound East (Nab Tower)
Answering Pendant over International 'W' Flag	I am bound West (The Needles)

Southampton Patrol launch by day has Harbour Master painted on after cabin in Black lettering on Yellow background. By night it has a blue all round light above the white masthead light.

HM Coastguard – Solent District. The Maritime Rescue Sub Centre (MRSC) at Lee-on-Solent (☎ Lee-on-Solent 552100) controls all Search and Rescue (SAR) activities in HM Coastguard Solent District.

Anyone wishing to obtain the services of any rescue authority should contact the Coastguard and not the rescue authority itself. The Coastguard is able to call on lifeboats and also on the fast inshore boats stationed at Hamble, Lepe, Gosport, Ryde, Cowes, Freshwater Bay and Shanklin; he can also call on the police launch *Ashburton*, helicopters, ships at sea, naval vessels and RAF long range aircraft.

There is an auxiliary Coastguard yacht section made up of yachtsmen willing to assist the Coastguards by making their vessels available for lifesaving purposes; they supplement the lifeboat service. Many of these boats have the Coastguard VHF frequency fitted and so are in touch with all the rescue services. They are all registered and are attached to the MRSC. MRCCs and MRSCs broadcast strong wind warnings and local forecasts.

The area of responsibility for MRSC Solent is bounded on the West by a line from Hengistbury Head South to the Anglo/French median line, and on the East by a line from Beachy Head to the Greenwich buoy.

Radio sets under the control of MRSC Solent (call: *Solent Coastguard*) are:

VHF (Ch 0 06 10 16 67 73)	*VHF DF*	*MF* (2182 3023 5680 kHz)
Needles	Boniface	Lee-on-Solent
Boniface	Selsey	
Lee-on-Solent	Newhaven	
Selsey	NB. Call Portland Coastguard for fix from Highdown, IOW	
Newhaven		

To contact Solent Coastguard call on Ch 16; yachtsmen will be transferred to Ch 67 or 73 for traffic.

Sector Stations manned by regular Coastguards and Auxiliaries are sited at Totland (☎ Isle of Wight 753451), Bembridge (☎ Isle of Wight 873943), Calshot (☎ Fawley 893574), Hayling (☎ Portsmouth 464095), Shoreham (☎ Shoreham 2226), Newhaven (☎ Newhaven 514008) and Littlehampton (☎ Littlehampton 715512).

Auxiliary Stations are sited at Needles, Atherfield, Ventnor, Eastney and Selsey.

All Sector and Auxiliary Lookouts are manned for Casualty Risk or heavy traffic periods.

Note: Much useful information is given in the *Solent Year Book* published by the Solent Cruising and Racing Association (SCRA). Also a free booklet *"The Yachtsman's Guide to Southampton Water"*.

SOLENT AREA WAYPOINTS 10.2.18

Waypoints marked with an asterisk (*) are special (yellow) racing marks, which may be removed in winter. Racing buoys marked with a bullet (•) against the longitude are only laid during Cowes week. Other waypoints are navigational buoys, unless otherwise stated.

***Alpha**	50°46'·40N 01°07'·80W•
***AFN London**	50°46'·55N 01°21'·37W
After Barn	50°51'·50N 01°20'·73W
***Ashlett**	50°49'·95N 01°19'·67W
Bald Head	50°49'·88N 01°18'·15W
Bank Lt Bn	50°53'·58N 01°23'·24W
Bay	50°46'·16N 00°57'·53W
***Beken**	50°45'·75N 01°19'·65W
Bembridge Ledge	50°41'·12N 01°02'·74W
Bembridge Tide Gauge	50°42'·43N 01°04·93W
***Berthon**	50°44'·18N 01°29'·13W
***Beta**	50°46'·80N 01°07'·25W•
Black Jack	50°49'·10N 01°17'·98W
Black Rock	50°42'·55N 01°30'·55W
***Bob Kemp**	50°45'·15N 01°09'·55W
Boulder (Looe Channel)	50°41'·53N 00°49'·00W
Bourne Gap	50°47'·80N 01°18'·25W
***Bowring Rose**	50°47'·28N 01°12'·00W
Boyne	50°46'·11N 01°05'·18W
Bramble Bn	50°47'·38N 01°17'·05W
Browndown	50°46'·54N 01°10'·87W
Bridge	50°39'·59N 01°36'·80W
Bury	50°54'·10N 01°27'·03W
Cadland	50°50'·98N 01°20'·45W
Calshot	50°48'·40N 01°16'·95W
Calshot Spit Lt F	50°48'·32N 01°17'·55W
Castle Point	50°48'·67N 01°17'·60W
Castle (NB)	50°46'·43N 01°05'·29W
***Cathead**	50°50'·58N 01°19'·15W
***Champagne Mumm**	50°45'·60N 01°23'·03W
Chichester Bar Bn	50°45'·88N 00°56'·37W
***Chilling**	50°49'·23N 01°17'·42W
Chi Spit	50°45'·68N 00°56'·48W
***Clipper**	50°48'·43N 01°15'·38W
Coronation	50°49'·52N 01°17'·53W
Cowes Breakwater Lt	50°45'·84N 01°17'·43W
Cowes No.3	50°46'·04N 01°17'·95W
Cowes No.4	50°46'·04N 01°17'·78W
Cracknore	50°53'·92N 01°25'·12W
Crosshouse Lt Bn	50°54'·01N 01°23'·11W
***Cutter**	50°49'·47N 01°16'·82W
***Daks-Simpson**	50°45'·50N 01°14'·30W
Dean Elbow	50°43'·55N 01°01'·83W
Deans Elbow	50°52'·13N 01°22'·68W
Deans Lake	50°51'·35N 01°21'·52W
Dean Tail	50°43'·02N 00°59'·03W
***Deck**	50°48'·60N 01°16'·70W
Dibden Bay	50°53'·67N 01°24'·82W
Durns Pt obstn (S end)	50°45'·37N 01°26'·95W
East Bramble	50°47'·20N 01°13'·55W
East Knoll	50°47'·93N 01°16'·75W
East Lepe	50°46'·09N 01°20'·81W
East Winner	50°45'·07N 01°00'·01W
***Echo**	50°46'·50N 01°05'·66W
Eling	50°54'·45N 01°27'·75W
***Frigate**	50°46'·10N 01°22'·10W
Fairway	50°38'·20N 01°38'·90W
Fawley	50°49'·97N 01°19'·38W
***Gamma**	50°46'·48N 01°05'·87W
Greenland	50°51'·08N 01°20'·33W
Gurnard	50°46'·18N 01°18'·76W
Gurnard Ledge	50°45'.48N 01°20'·50W
Gymp	50°53'·15N 01°24'·22W
Gymp Elbow	50°53'·48N 01°24'·53W
Hamble Point	50°50'·12N 01°18'·57W
Hamstead Ledge	50°43'·83N 01°26'·10W
Hard	50°45'·01N 00°57'·47W
***Hendersons**	50°47'·38N 01°15'·82W
Hill Head	50°48'·12N 01°15'·91W
Hook	50°49'·48N 01°18'·22W
Horse Elbow	50°44'·23N 01°03'·80W
Horse Sand	50°45'·49N 01°05'·18W
Horse Sand Fort Lt	50°44'·97N 01°04'·25W
Hound	50°51'·65N 01°21'·43W
Hythe Knock	50°52'·80N 01°23'·73W
Jack in Basket	50°44'·24N 01°30'·48W
***Jib**	50°52'·93N 01°22'·97W
Lains Lake	50°51'·55N 01°21'·57W
***Lambeth**	50°41'·50N 01°41'·60W
***Land Rover**	50°48'·10N 01°14'·55W
Langstone Fairway	50°46'·28N 01°01'·27W
Lee Pt Bn	50°47'·40N 01°11'·85W
***Lucas**	50°46'·23N 01°08'·67W

Main Passage	50°45'·98N 01°04'·02W
Marchwood	50°53'·95N 01°25'·50W
***Mark**	50°49'·53N 01°18'·87W
***MDL**	50°46'·12N 01°16'·55W
***Meon**	50°49'·15N 01°15'·62W
Mid Shingles	50°41'·18N 01°34'·58W
Milbrook	50°54'·08N 01°26'·73W
Mixon Bn	50°42'·35N 00°46'·21W
***Mobell**	50°46'·13N 01°13'·00W
Moorhead	50°52'·52N 01°22'·82W
Mother Bank	50°45'·45N 01°11'·13W
Nab 1	50°41'·23N 00°56'·43W
Nab 2	50°41'·70N 00°56'·71W
Nab 3	50°42'·17N 00°57'·05W
Nab East	50°42'·82N 01°00'·72W
Nab End	50°42'·82N 01°00'·72W
Nab Tower	50°40'·05N 00°57'·07W
Needles Fairway	50°38'·20N 01°38'·90W
Netley	50°52'·03N 01°21'·72W
New Grounds	50°41'·97N 00°58'·53W
Newtown G By	50°43'·57N 01°24'·70W
No Mans Land Fort Lt	50°44'·37N 01°05'·61W
Norris	50°45'·94N 01°15'·42W
North East Gurnard	50°47'·03N 01°19'·34W
N. E. Mining Ground	50°44'·71N 01°06'·30W
North East Ryde Middle	50°46'·18N 01°11'·80W
North East Shingles	50°41'·93N 01°33'·32W
North Head	50°42'·65N 01°35'·42W
North Ryde Middle	50°46'·58N 01°14'·30W
North Sturbridge	50°45'·31N 01°08'·15W
North Thorn	50°47'·88N 01°17'·75W
North West Netley	50°52'·28N 01°22'·65W
No. 2 Yarmouth	50°42'·73N 01°29'·54W
***Ossory**	50°47'·30N 01°16'·72W
Outer Nab	50°41'·00N 00°56'·56W
Outer Spit	50°45'·55N 01°05'·41W
Peel Bank	50°45'·47N 01°13'·25W
Peel Wreck	50°44'·88N 01°13'·34W
Pier Head	50°53'·63N 01°24'·57W
Poole Fairway	50°38'·95N 01°54'·78W
***Porsche**	50°44'·60N 01°21'·80W
Portsmouth No. 4	50°46'·98N 01°06'·27W
Prince Consort	50°46'·38N 01°17'·47W
***Quinnell**	50°47'·02N 01°19'·48W
***Ratsey**	50°47'·63N 01°13'·56W
Reach	50°49'·02N 01°17'·57W
Ridge	50°46'·42N 01°05'·56W
Roway Wk	50°46'·08N 01°02'·18W
***Royal Thames**	50°47'·47N 01°19'·10W
Ryde Pier Hd	50°44'·35N 01°09'·51W
RYS flagstaff	50°45'·97N 01°17'·97W
Saddle	50°45'·18N 01°04'·79W
Salt Mead	50°44'·48N 01°22'·95W
Sconce	50°42'·50N 01°31'·35W
Shingles Elbow	50°40'·31N 01°35'·92W
***Short**	50°49'·73N 01°19'·32W
South Bramble	50°46'·95N 01°17'·65W
South East Ryde Middle	50°45'·90N 01°12'·00W
South Ryde Middle	50°46'·10N 01°14'·08W
S. W. Mining Ground	50°44'·63N 01°07'·95W
South West Shingles	50°39'·52N 01°37'·20W
***Spanker**	50°47'·05N 01°17'·57W
***Sposa**	50°49'·70N 01°17'·50W
Spit Refuge	50°46'·22N 01°05'·37W
Spit Sand Fort Lt	50°46'·20N 01°05'·85W
No. 1 Swinging Ground	50°53'·97N 01°23'·35W
No. 2 Swinging Ground	50°53'·78N 01°25'·03W
***Start**	50°47'·05N 01°06'·66W
Stokes Bay	50°46'·64N 01°10'·52W
Street	50°41'·65N 00°48'·80W
***Tesco**	50°45'·08N 01°27'·25W
Thorn Knoll	50°47'·47N 01°18'·35W
***Trap**	50°46'·17N 01°17'·51W
Trinity House (Cowes)	50°46'·10N 01°17'·15W
Warden	50°41'·45N 01°33'·47W
Warner	50°43'·83N 01°03'·92W
West Bramble	50°47'·17N 01°18'·57W
West Knoll	50°47'·52N 01°17'·68W
West Lepe	50°45'·20N 01°24'·00W

LYMINGTON 10-2-19

Hampshire

CHARTS

Admiralty 2021, 2040, 2045; Stanford 7, 11; Imray C3, Y20, Y30; OS 196

TIDES

Spring −0040, Neap +0020 Dover; ML 2·0; Zone 0 (GMT) +0100

Standard Port PORTSMOUTH (⟶)

Times				Height (metres)			
HW		LW		MHWS	MHWN	MLWN	MLWS
0000	0600	0500	1100	4·7	3·8	1·8	0·6
1200	1800	1700	2300				
Differences LYMINGTON							
−0110	+0005	−0020	−0020	−1·7	−1·2	−0·5	−0·1

NOTE: Double high waters occur at or near springs and on other occasions there is a stand which lasts about 2 hrs. Predictions refer to the first HW when there are two. At other times they refer to the middle of the stand. See 10.2.13

SHELTER

There are two large marinas and river is accessible at all states of the tide. Anchoring in the river is prohibited, but in off-shore winds yachts can anchor off the mud flats outside. Yachts may use Town Quay or Customs House Quay (see Hr Mr) and there are up to 100 visitors moorings in the river opposite Town Quay (W moorings).

NAVIGATION

Waypoint 50°44′·00N 01°30′·00W, 319·5°/139·5° from/to front Ldg Lt, 1·52M. Min. depth in mid-channel from entrance to Railway Pier/Lymington Marina 1·8m; from there to Town Quay min depth 1·1m. There are extensive mud banks round the entrance but they are well marked. Two sewer outlets to the W are dangerous. Entering, leave Jack-in-the-Basket about 45m to port to clear Cross Boom.

LIGHTS AND MARKS

Ldg Lts 319°, both FR 12/17m 8M. Entrance marked by Jack-in-the-Basket, Fl R 2s. Channel marked by R piles with can topmarks, with radar reflectors, to port, G piles with G triangular topmarks to starboard. Port side has four lights Fl R 2s and Harper Post Q (3) 10s 5m 1M and to starboard seven lights Fl G 2s. Ldg Lts into Lymington Yacht Haven 244° both FY. There are two sets of Ldg marks on the central section; two RW posts on flats to SSE of Seymore's Post in line at 187°30′ for outgoing craft; two BW posts on flats to SE of Cage Boom in line at 007°30′ for incoming craft.

RADIO TELEPHONE

Marinas VHF Ch **80** M (office hours).

TELEPHONE (0590)

Hr Mr 672014; MRSC Lee-on-Solent 552100; ⌗ (0703) 827350; Marinecall 0898 500 457; Police 675411; Dr 677011.

FACILITIES

EC Wednesday; **Lymington Marina** (300 + 100 visitors) ☎ 673312, Slip, P, AC, D, FW, ME, El, Sh, CH, BH (100 ton), C, (37, 80 ton), Gas, Gaz; **Lymington Yacht Haven** (450 + 100 visitors) ☎ 677071, P, D, FW, ME, AC, El, Sh, C (10 ton), BH (45 ton), CH, Gas, Gaz, ⊡; **Berthon Boat Co.** ☎ 673312, M, P, FW, ME, El, Sh, C, CH, AB; **Royal Lymington YC** ☎ 672677, R, Bar; **Lymington Town SC** ☎ 674514, AB, R, Bar; **Town Quay** Slip, M, FW, AB (see Hr Mr); **Aquaboats** ☎ 674266, ME, Sh, CH; **J.G. Claridge** ☎ 674821, CH; **Shipmates** ☎ 672765, CH; **Greenham Marine** ☎ 671144, Ⓔ; **Brookes and Gatehouse** ☎ 675200, Ⓔ; **Hood** ☎ 673797, SM; **Lymington Sail and Tent** ☎ 673139, SM, CH; **Haven BY** ☎ 673489, ACA; **Sanders** ☎ 673981, SM; **Yachtmail** ☎ 672784, CH; **S.A.L. Marine** ☎ 679588, ME, El; **Quayside Marine** ☎ 679582, Sh (Wood and GRP); **Datayacht** ☎ 671252, Ⓔ; **Bath Road** public pontoon, FW; **Town Quay** FW, AB (see Hr Mr); **Regis Marine Electronics** ☎ 679251, Ⓔ; **Town** has every facility including ✉; Ⓑ; ⇌; ✈ (Bournemouth or Southampton).

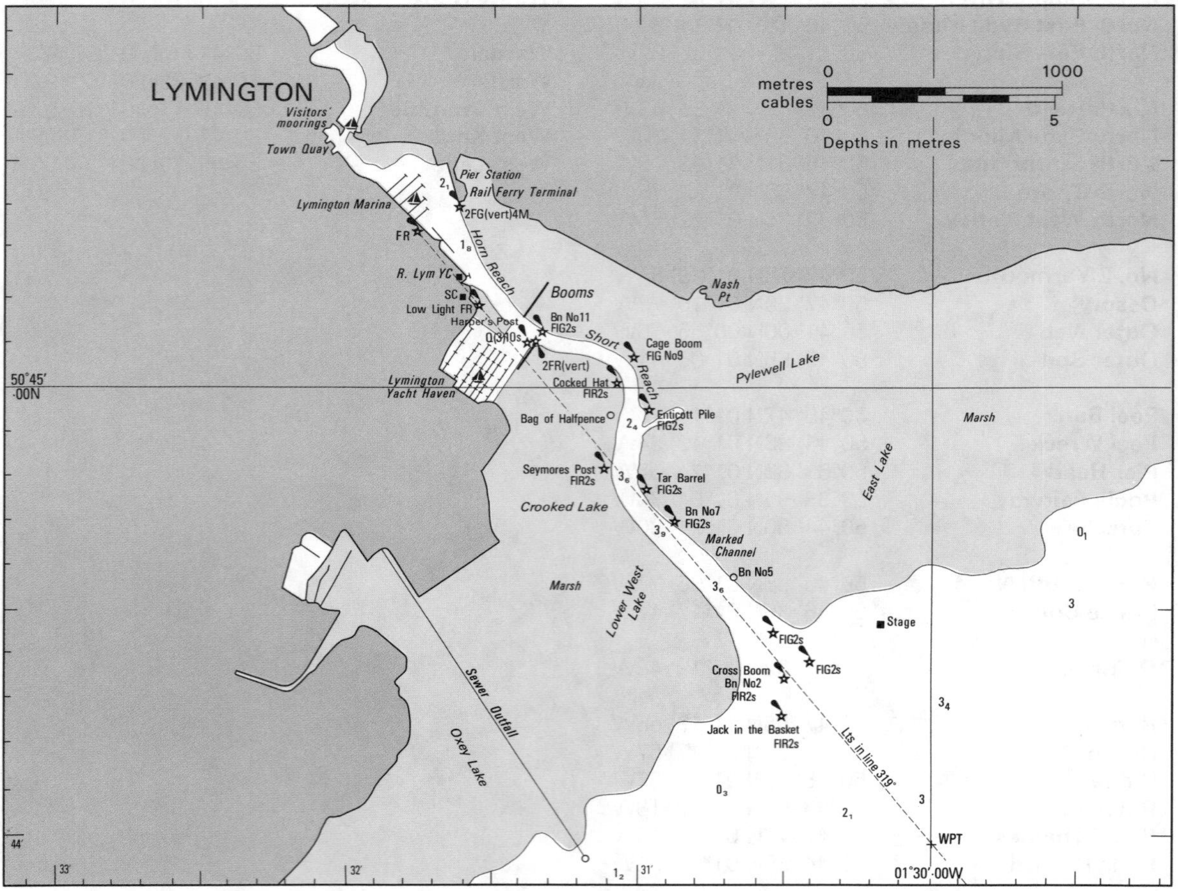
LYMINGTON
metres
cables
0
1000
0
5
Depths in metres
Visitors' moorings
Town Quay
Pier Station
Rail Ferry Terminal
Lymington Marina
2FG(vert)4M
FR
Horn Reach
R. Lym YC
SC
Low Light FR
Booms
Harper's Post
Q(3)10s
Bn No11
FlG2s
Short Reach
Cage Boom
FlG No9
2FR(vert)
Cocked Hat
FlR2s
Lymington Yacht Haven
Pylewell Lake
Nash Pt
50°45′·00N
Bag of Halfpence
Enticott Pile
FlG2s
Marsh
Seymores Post
FlR2s
Tar Barrel
FlG2s
Crooked Lake
Bn No7
FlG2s
Marked Channel
East Lake
Bn No5
Marsh
Lower West Lake
Stage
FlG2s
FlG2s
Cross Boom
Bn No2
FlR2s
Jack in the Basket
FlR2s
Sewer Outfall
Oxey Lake
Lts in line 319°
WPT
44′
33′
32′
31′
01°30′·00W

YARMOUTH 10-2-20
Isle of Wight

CHARTS
Admiralty 2021, 2040 2045; Stanford 11; Imray C3, Y20; OS 196

TIDES
Spring −0050, Neap +0020 Dover; ML 2·0; Zone 0 (GMT) +0150

Standard Port PORTSMOUTH (⟶)

Times				Height (metres)			
HW		LW		MHWS	MHWN	MLWN	MLWS
0000	0600	0500	1100	4·7	3·8	1·8	0·6
1200	1800	1700	2300				
Differences YARMOUTH							
−0105	+0005	−0025	−0030	−1·6	−1·3	−0·4	0·0
FRESHWATER							
−0210	+0025	−0040	−0020	−2·1	−1·5	−0·4	0·0
TOTLAND BAY							
−0130	−0045	−0040	−0040	−2·0	−1·5	−0·5	−0·1

NOTE: Double HWs occur at or near springs; at other times there is a stand which lasts about 2hrs. Predictions refer to the first HW when there are two. At other times they refer to the middle of the stand. See 10.2.13

SHELTER
Harbour affords complete shelter from all directions of wind and sea. Harbour gets very full, and on occasions, closed. Boats over 15m length, 4m beam or 2·4m draft should give notice of arrival by telephone or VHF.

NAVIGATION
Waypoint 50°42′·60N 01°29′·93W, 008°/188° from/to front Ldg Lt, 0·28M. Dangers on approach are Black Rock and shallow water to the N of the breakwater. There are four large Admiralty buoys (two unlit), three E of pier, one W of pier. The most E and the most W are lit. Beware ferries entering and leaving. The road bridge across the R Yar opens on request (Oct–Apr) for boats proceeding up the river to their moorings or the boatyard above the bridge. Bridge opening times (May–Sept) 0805, 0900, 1000, 1200, 1400, 1600, 1730, 1830, 2000 (LT). Speed limit in harbour 4 kn as far as the pierhead.

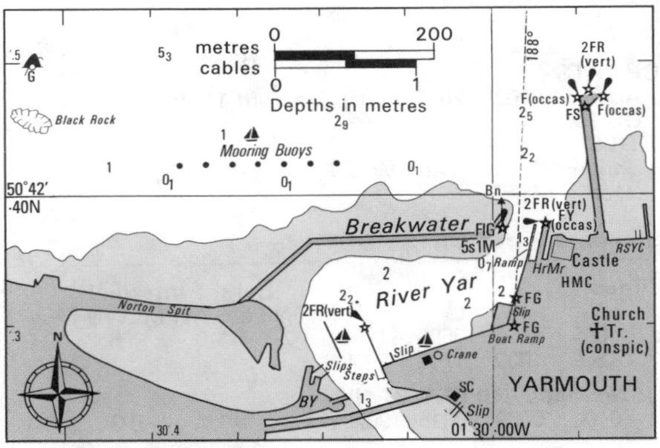
metres
cables
0
200
1
Depths in metres
Black Rock
Mooring Buoys
50°42′·40N
Breakwater
FlG
5s1M
River Yar
Norton Spit
2FR(vert)
Slips
Steps
Slip
Crane
BY
SC
Slip
01°30′·00W
30′·4
188°
2FR (vert)
F(occas)
FS
F(occas)
Bn
2FR(vert)
FY (occas)
RSYC
HrMr
Castle
HMC
Ramp
FG
FG
Boat Ramp
Church Tr. (conspic)
YARMOUTH

LIGHTS AND MARKS
Leading beacons (two W diamonds) or Ldg Lts (FG), on quay, 188°. When harbour is closed (eg when full in summer at week-ends) a R flag is hoisted at seaward end of Ferry jetty by day and an illuminated board displayed saying 'Harbour Full', by night.

RADIO TELEPHONE
None.

TELEPHONE (0983)
Hr Mr 760321; Berthing Master 760300 MRSC Lee-on-Solent 552100; # (0703) 827350; Marinecall 0898 500 457; Police 528000; Dr 760434.

FACILITIES
EC Wednesday, **South Quay** ☎ 760300, Slip, P, D, L, M, FW, C; **Harold Hayles Yacht Yard** ☎ 760373, Slip, M, ME, El, Sh, CH, Gas, Gaz; **Richardson Yacht Repairs** ☎ 761091 Sh; **Royal Solent YC** ☎ 760256, Bar, R, L, M, Slip; **Yarmouth Outboards** ☎ 760436, ME, Sh, CH; **Buzzard International** ☎ 760707, M, ME, El, Sh, CH; **Salterns Sail Loft** ☎ 760120 SM; **Harwoods Chanlery** ☎ 760258 CH, Gas, Gaz; **Yarmouth Marine Services** ☎ 760309, ME, El, Sh, Divers; **Yarmouth SC** ☎ 760270 Bar.
Town V, R, Bar, ✉; Ⓑ (Sept-May AM only, May-Sept 1000-1445); ⇌ (Ferry to Lymington); ✈ (Bournemouth, IoW airport or Southampton).

NEWTOWN 10-2-21
Isle of Wight

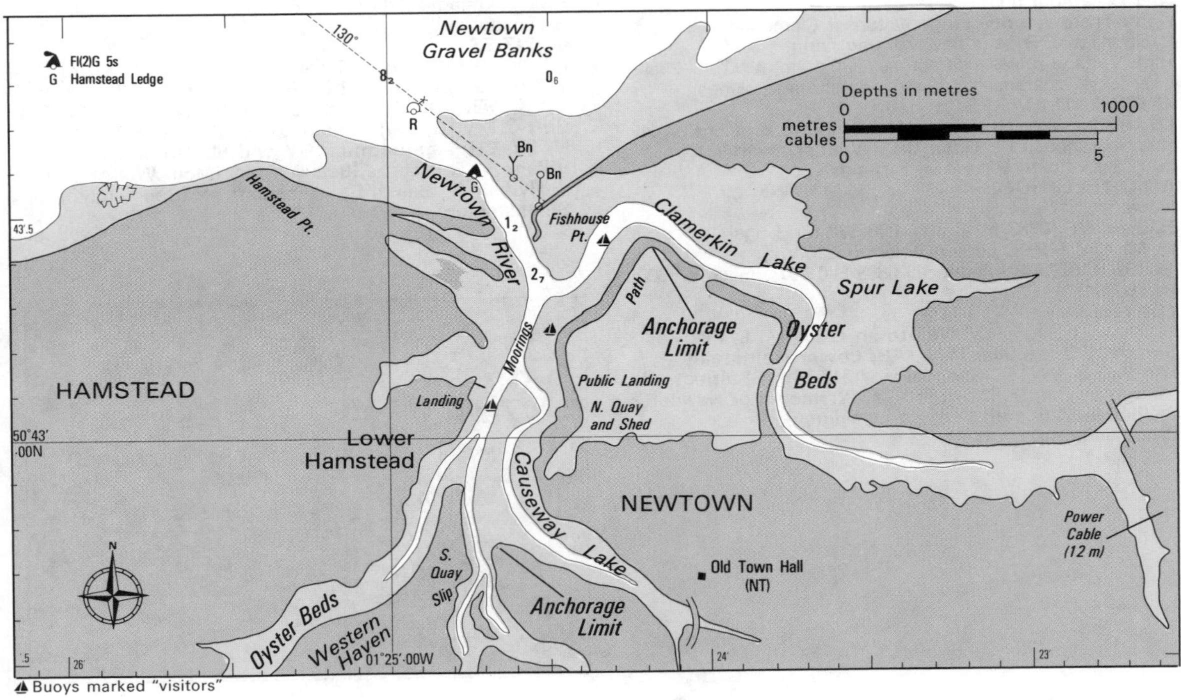
Fl(2)G 5s
G Hamstead Ledge
130°
Newtown Gravel Banks
Depths in metres
0
1000
metres
cables
0
5
Hamstead Pt.
Newtown River
Bn
Bn
Fishhouse Pt.
Clamerkin Lake
Spur Lake
Path
Anchorage Limit
Oyster Beds
Moorings
Public Landing
N. Quay and Shed
Landing
HAMSTEAD
Lower Hamstead
Causeway Lake
NEWTOWN
Power Cable (12 m)
Old Town Hall (NT)
S. Quay
Slip
Anchorage Limit
Oyster Beds
Western Haven
50°43′·00N
01°25′·00W
43′·5

▲ Buoys marked "visitors"

NEWTOWN *continued*

CHARTS
Admiralty 2021, 2040, 1905; Stanford 11; Imray C3, Y20; OS 196

TIDES
Spring −0108 Dover; ML 2·3; Zone 0 (GMT)
Neap +0058

Standard Port PORTSMOUTH (→)

Times				Height (metres)			
HW		LW		MHWS	MHWN	MLWN	MLWS
0000	0600	0500	1100	4·7	3·8	1·8	0·6
1200	1800	1700	2300				
Differences SOLENT BANK							
−0100	0000	−0015	−0020	−1·3	−1·0	−0·3	−0·1

NOTE: Double HWs occur at or near springs; at other times there is a stand which lasts about 2 hrs. Predictions refer to the first HW when there are two. At other times they refer to the middle of the stand. See 10.2.13

SHELTER
3½M E of Yarmouth, Newtown gives good shelter although exposed to winds from the N. Best entrance is on the flood before the mud flats cover. Ent between two shingle spits and can be rough in N winds especially near HW. There are six visitors buoys (conspic W) in Clamerkin Lake and sixteen (conspic W) in the main arm leading to Shalfleet, all are numbered – check with Hr Mr. Do not anchor above boards showing "Anchorage Limit" on account of oyster beds. Fin keel boats can stay afloat from entrance to Hamstead landing or to Clamerkin Limit Boards. Public landing on E side of river N of quay. The whole peninsular ending in Fishouse Pt is a nature reserve. Yachtsmen are asked not to land there between April and June inclusive.

NAVIGATION
Waypoint 50°44′·00N 01°25′·00W, 335°/155° from/to Fishouse Pt 0·67M. From W, make Hamstead Ledge G Conical Buoy; from E beware Newtown gravel banks; leave bar buoy to port. There is only about 0·9m over the bar. After entry there are so many perches that confusion may result. Perches mark the mud banks. Near junction to Causeway Lake depth is down to 0·9m and beyond this water quickly shoals. Clamerkin Lake is deep (1·2m); channel is marked by occasional perches and one small G buoy. Keep to E to avoid gravel spit off W shore, marked by three perches. Beware numerous oyster beds. Speed limit in harbour 5 kn.
Note: There is a rifle range at top of Clamerkin Lake and in Spur Lake. R flags flown during firing.
High Voltage power line across Clamerkin at 50°42′·79N 1°22′·52W clearance of 12m – no shore markings.

LIGHTS AND MARKS
Ldg marks. Two Bns on posts on mud to E of Ent on NE side of Fishouse Pt. Outer Bn RW stripes with Y topmark; inner Bn W with W disc with B circle.

RADIO TELEPHONE
None.

TELEPHONE (0983 for 6 figs; 098 378 for 3 figs)
Hr Mr 424; MRSC Lee-on-Solent 552100; # (0703) 827350; Marinecall 0898 500 457; Police 528000; Dr 760434.

FACILITIES
EC Newport Thursday; **Newtown Quay** M, L, FW; **Shalfleet Quay** Slip, M, L, AB; **Lower Hamstead Landing** L, FW; **R. Seabroke** ☎ 213, Sh; **Shalfleet Village** V, Bar; ✉ (Newport); Ⓑ (Yarmouth or Newport); ⇌ (bus to Yarmouth, ferry to Lymington); ✈ (Southampton).

BEAULIEU RIVER 10-2-22

Hampshire

CHARTS
Admiralty 2021, 2040, 1905; Stanford 11; Imray C3, Y20; OS 196

TIDES
−0100 and +0140 Dover; ML 2·4; Zone 0 (GMT)

Standard Port PORTSMOUTH (→)

Times				Height (metres)			
HW		LW		MHWS	MHWN	MLWN	MLWS
0000	0600	0500	1100	4·7	3·8	1·8	0·6
1200	1800	1700	2300				
BUCKLERS HARD							
−0040	−0010	+0010	−0010	−1·0	−0·8	−0·2	−0·3
STANSORE POINT							
−0050	−0010	−0005	−0010	−0·9	−0·6	−0·2	0·0

NOTE: Double HWs occur at or near springs; on other occasions there is stand which lasts about 2 hours. The predictions refer to the first HW when there are two, or to the middle of the stand.

SHELTER
Very good shelter from all winds. Anchorage possible in reach between Lepe and Needs Oar Point but preferable to proceed up to Bucklers Hard.

NAVIGATION
Waypoint 50°46′·50N 01°21′·47W, 159°/339° from/to Beaulieu Spit Bn, Fl R 5s, 0·3M. The swatchway at W end of Beaulieu Spit is closed.
There are shoal depths of 0·5m to 0·8m below CD from 100 to 300m out from Beaulieu spit dolphin on line of Ldg marks from pilr No 2 and shore. Entrance dangerous LW∓2. Leave Ldg marks open to E for best water.
A speed limit of 5 knots applies to the whole river.

LIGHTS AND MARKS
Entrance beacons in line at 341°, N beacon is triangle over a square fluorescent topmark, S beacon is R and carries a fluorescent topmark. Beaulieu Spit, E end, R dolphin with Fl R 5s 3M vis 277°-037°; ra refl. Lt. River is clearly marked by R and G beacons and perches. Stbd 5, 9, 19 and 21, Fl G 4s; Port 12 and 20, Fl R 4s. There is a Lt Bn, No 21, Fl G 4s, 75m E of marina.

RADIO TELEPHONE
None.

TELEPHONE (0590)
Hr Mr 616200; MRSC Lee-on-Solent 552100; # (0703) 827350; Marinecall 0898 500 457; Police Lymington 75411; Dr 612451 or Hythe 845955; Ⓗ Lymington 77011.

FACILITIES
EC Village Shop opens 7 days a week; **Bucklers Hard Yacht Harbour** (110+20 visitors) ☎ 616234, Slip, M, P, D, AC, FW, ME, El, Sh, C (2 ton), BH (26 ton), SM, Gas, Gaz, CH, V, R, Bar; **Palace Quay BY** ☎ 612338, M, ME, El, Sh, CH; **Agamemnon BY** ☎ 616214/5, ME, El, Sh; **Village** V, R, Bar. ✉ (Beaulieu); Ⓑ (Mon, Wed, Fri AM or Hythe); ⇌ (bus to Brockenhurst); ✈ (Bournemouth or Southampton).

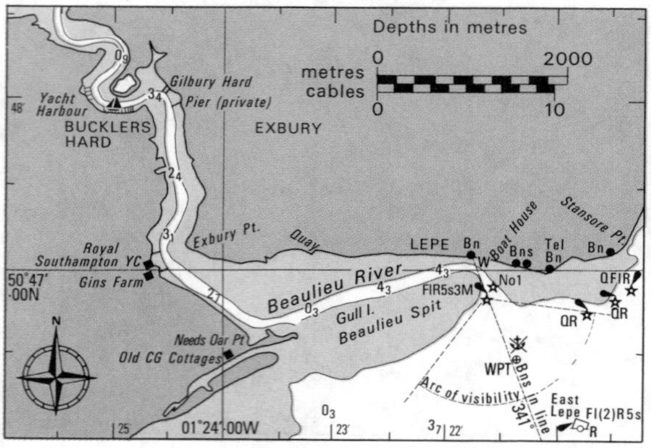

Depths in metres
0
2000
metres
cables
0
10
Yacht Harbour
Gilbury Hard
Pier (private)
BUCKLERS HARD
EXBURY
Exbury Pt.
Quay
LEPE
Bn
Boat House
Bns
Tel Bn
Stansore Pt
Royal Southampton YC
Gins Farm
50°47′·00N
Beaulieu River
No1
FlR5s3M
QFlR
QR
Gull I.
Beaulieu Spit
Needs Oar Pt
Old CG Cottages
WPT
Bns in line 341°
Arc of visibility
East Lepe Fl(2)R5s
R
01°24′·00W

COWES 10-2-23

Isle of Wight

CHARTS
Admiralty 2793, 2040, 394, 2045; Stanford 7, 11; Imray C3, Y20; OS 196

TIDES
+0029 Dover; ML 2·7; Zone 0 (GMT)

Standard Port PORTSMOUTH (⟶)

Times				Height (metres)			
HW		LW		MHWS	MHWN	MLWN	MLWS
0000	0600	0500	1100	4·7	3·8	1·8	0·6
1200	1800	1700	2300				
Differences COWES							
−0015	+0015	0000	−0020	−0·5	−0·3	−0·1	0·0
FOLLY INN							
−0015	+0015	0000	−0020	−0·6	−0·4	−0·1	+0·2
NEWPORT							
No data		No data		−0·6	−0·4	+0·1	+0·8

NOTE: Double high tides occur at or near springs; on other occasions a stand occurs which lasts up to 2 hrs. Times given represent the middle of the stand. See 10.2.13

SHELTER
Good, but outer harbour is exposed to N and NE winds. R Medina is navigable to Newport but the upper reaches dry. Visitors may pick up any mooring so labelled: buoys off the Parade; piles S of West Cowes Marina, opposite Lallows; Thetis Pontoon Landing, between Shepards Wharf and Spencer Thetis Wharf (for short stay and overnight only, dredged to 2m); piles S of the chain ferry, Whitegates area; and considerable berthing alongside pontoon opposite the Folly Inn. Marina berths at West Cowes Marina, Cowes Marina (E Cowes, above chain ferry), and Island Harbour on E shore beyond Folly Inn, see 10.2.32.

NAVIGATION
Waypoint 50°46′·20N 01°17′·90W, 344°/164° from/to front Ldg Lt, 0·35M. On the E side of the entrance, the Shrape (mud flats) extend to Old Castle Point. Yachts are required to use the main channel near W shore. It is forbidden to sail through or anchor in the mooring area. Beware of the floating bridge, ferries and commercial shipping. Speed limit 6 kn in harbour. Chain ferry exhibits all round W Fl LT at fore-end. Floating bridge (chain ferry) normally operates Mon-Sat: 0530-2315, then 2400. Sunday 0700-2315, then 2400 (all LT).

LIGHTS AND MARKS
Entrance is marked by No 3 buoy Fl (G) 3s and No 4 buoy (QR). Ldg Lts 164°. Front Iso 2s 3m 6M; post by Customs House. Rear, 290m from front, Iso R 2s 5m 3M; dolphin by Jubilee Pontoon; vis 120°-240°; No 8 buoy Fl (2) R5s. E breakwater head FlR 3s 3M. The ends of jetties and certain dolphins are marked by 2FR (vert) on E side of harbour, and by 2FG (vert) on W side.

RADIO TELEPHONE
VHF Ch 16; 11 12 14 69 M. (0830-1730, LT) Island Harbour and Cowes Marina Ch 80 M; West Cowes Marina Ch 80 M (office hours). Harbourmaster's launches Ch 16 69. Chain Ferry Ch 69 (when ferry operating). Vessels are required to advise ferry of their intention to pass, ferry will acknowledge. Water Bus Service, call: *Yachting World Ferry* Ch 08. HM Coastguard liaison Ch. 67.

TELEPHONE (0983)
Hr Mr 293952; MRSC Lee-on-Solent 552100; # (0703) 827350; Waterguard 293132; Folly Reach Harbour Office 295722; Weather Centre Southampton 228844; Marinecall 0898 500 457; Police 528000; Ⓗ 524081; Ⓗ (Frank James) 296504; Dr 295251.

FACILITIES
EC Wednesday; **Cowes Marina** (E. Cowes) (120 + 130 visitors) ☎ 293983, FW, BH (10 ton), D, ME, El, Sh, AC, Gas, V; **West Cowes Marina** (80 + 120 visitors) ☎ 299976, D, FW, AC, Gas, Gaz, Kos, R, SM, CH, C (6 ton), Ⓔ; **Pascall Atkey** ☎ 292381, ME, CH, ACA, Gas, Gaz; **Cowes Marine Services** ☎ 294861 ME, El, Sh, Ⓔ, AC, Gas, Gaz, L, BH (30 ton), C (6 ton); **Saltern Sail Loft** ☎ 280014 SM **Clare Lallow** ☎ 292112, Gas, Slip, P, D, L, FW, CH, ME, El, Sh; **Souters Shipyard** ☎ 294711, Slip, P, D, FW, AB, ME, El, Sh, C (40 ton); **FBM Marine** ☎ 292561, ME, El, Sh; **Spencer Rigging** ☎ 292022, CH, M, Rigging; **Marine Bazaar** ☎ 298869, CH; **The Book Cabin** ☎ 295409, Books and charts;

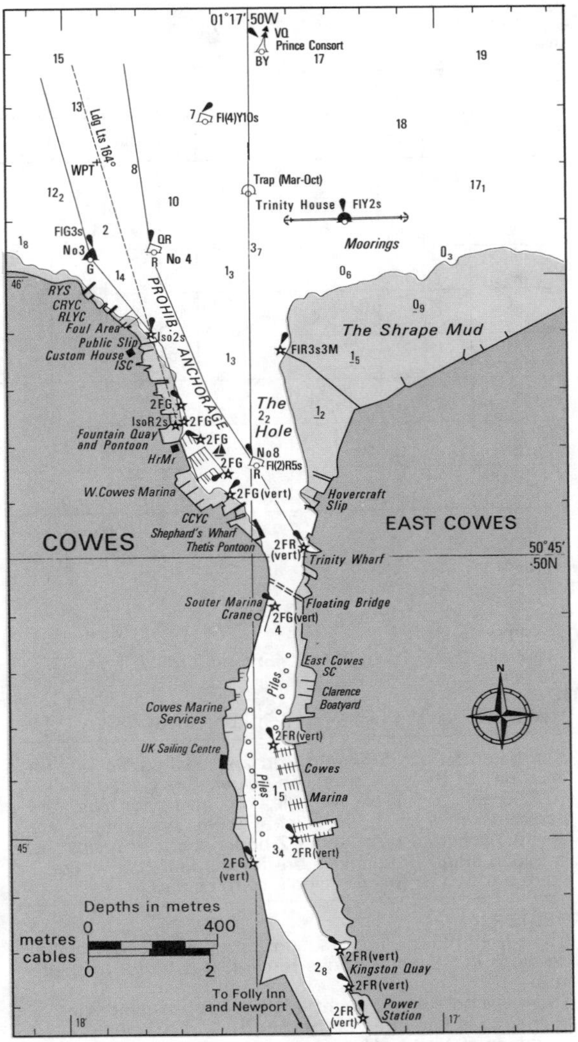
01°17′·50W
VQ
Prince Consort
BY
Fl(4)Y10s
Ldg Lts 164°
WPT
Trap (Mar-Oct)
Trinity House
FlY2s
Moorings
FlG3s
No 3
G
QR
No 4
R
RYS
CRYC
RLYC
Foul Area
Public Slip
Custom House
ISC
Iso2s
PROHIB ANCHORAGE
The Shrape Mud
FlR3s3M
The Hole
IsoR2s
Fountain Quay and Pontoon
HrMr
No8
Fl(2)R5s
W.Cowes Marina
Hovercraft Slip
CCYC
Shephard's Wharf
Thetis Pontoon
COWES
EAST COWES
Trinity Wharf
50°45′·50N
Souter Marina
Crane
Floating Bridge
East Cowes SC
Clarence Boatyard
Piles
Cowes Marine Services
UK Sailing Centre
Cowes Marina
Depths in metres
metres
cables
Kingston Quay
Power Station
To Folly Inn and Newport

McWilliam ☎ 298855, SM; **Ratsey and Lapthorn** ☎ 294051, SM; **RHP Marine** ☎ 290421, ME, El; **Eddie Richards** ☎ 298949, Sh; **Adrian Stone** ☎ 297898, Sh; **Island Boat Repairs** ☎ 298015, Sh; **Martin Marine** ☎ 292892, ME; **Regis Marine Electronics** ☎ 293996, El, Ⓔ; **Martec** ☎ 296913, El, Ⓔ; **Powerplus Marine** ☎ 200036, ME; (H24 – ☎ (0860) 435476) **Britannia Wharf** ☎ 292724, Slip, Sh, ME; **D. Floyd** ☎ 295408, Divers; **Aquatogs** ☎ 295071, CH; **UK Sailing Centre** ☎ 294941, AB, Slip, Bar, FW;

Yacht Clubs: **Royal Yacht Squadron** ☎ 292743; **Royal London YC** ☎ 299727; **Cowes Corinthian YC** ☎ 296333; **Cowes Combined Clubs** ☎ 295744; **Island SC** ☎ 293061. **Castle Rock YC** ☎ 293581;
Casualties – (Ch 67) land at W Cowes Fountain Pier for ambulance.

FW is available at Town Quay, Whitegates Public Pontoon, Watch House slipway (by Customs), in marinas and Folly Pier. **Do-It-Yourself** at Shepard's Wharf ☎ 297821, CH, C (6 ton), AB, BH (20 ton), Gas, AC, Tools etc; Thetis Public Pontoon Landing.
Town P, D, Bar, R, V, Slip, ✉; Ⓑ; ≠ (Ferry to Southampton); ✈ (Southampton).
Ferry Services: Red Funnel ferries ☎ 292101; Hydrofoil ☎ 292101.
WHIPPINGHAM: **Folly Inn** ☎ 297171, L, Bar, R, M, Slip, ◙.

SOUTHAMPTON 10-2-24

Hampshire

SOUTHAMPTON

MEAN SPRING AND NEAP CURVES

Springs occur 2 days after New and Full Moon

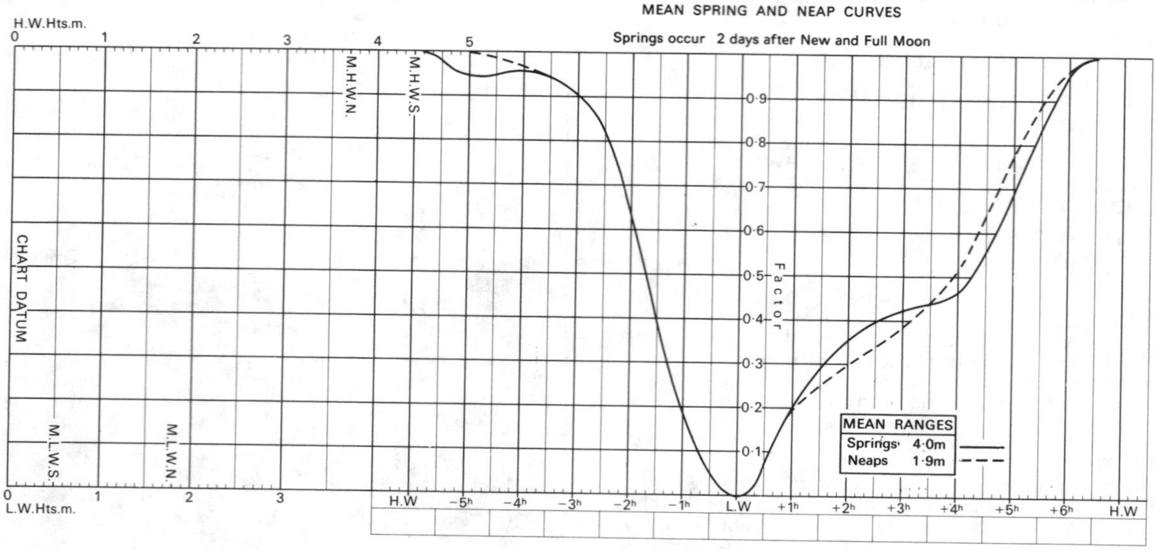
H.W.Hts.m.
0 1 2 3 4 5
M.H.W.N.
M.H.W.S.
CHART DATUM
M.L.W.S.
M.L.W.N.
0 1 2 3
L.W.Hts.m.
Factor
0·9
0·8
0·7
0·6
0·5
0·4
0·3
0·2
0·1
MEAN RANGES
Springs 4·0m
Neaps 1·9m
H.W −5h −4h −3h −2h −1h L.W +1h +2h +3h +4h +5h +6h H.W

CHARTS

Admiralty 2041, 1905, 394, 2045; Stanford 11; Imray C3; OS 196

TIDES

HW (1st) −0001 Dover; ML 2·9; Zone 0 (GMT)

Southampton is a Standard Port and tidal predictions for each day of the year are given below. See Sections 10.2.13 and 10.2.17. A NE gale combined with high barometer may lower sea level by 0·6m. At springs there are two separate HWs about 2 hours apart; at neaps there is a long stand. Predictions are for the first HW where there are two or for the middle of the stand.

SHELTER

Good from most wind directions although a heavy chop develops in SE winds above force 4. It is better to shelter in marinas.

There are no specific yacht anchorages but temporary anchoring is permitted (subject to Hr Mr) off club moorings at Netley, Hythe, Weston & Marchwood in about 2m. Keep clear of main or secondary channels and Hythe Pier. Public moorings for large yachts opposite Royal Pier near Gymp Shoal in 4m by arrangement with the Hr Mr. The nearest landing is a slipway at Town Quay Marina. Visitors berths available in Hythe Marina (with lock entrance), at Shamrock Quay Marina (R Itchen), at Kemp's Quay Marina (R Itchen) and at Ocean Village Marina.

NAVIGATION

Waypoint Weston Shelf (stbd-hand) buoy, Fl(3)G 15s, 50°52′·68N 01°23′·16W, 138°/318° from/to Port Sig Stn, 0·40M. There are no hidden dangers or navigational hazards. Main channels are well marked. There are several unlit large mooring buoys at Hythe both to E and W of the main channel. Other isolated buoys exist and yachtsmen entering the port during darkness should keep just outside the lighted buoyed fairway. Very large tankers operate from Fawley and very large passenger and container ships from Southampton. It is essential to keep clear of ocean-going shipping; see 10.2.17.

R Test — Eling Creek dries. There is foul ground at Marchwood and Royal Pier.

R Itchen — Care is necessary, particularly at night, above Itchen Bridge; the channel bends sharply to port and favours the W side. There are unlit moorings in the centre of the river. Navigation above Northam Bridge (14′ 6″, 4·4m) is not advisable.

There is a speed limit of 6 kn. in both rivers above the line Hythe Pier to Weston Shelf.

LIGHTS AND MARKS

These are too numerous to elaborate and reference should be made to the charts.

The following should be noted:

(1) Southampton Water bifurcates at Dock Head which is clearly marked by a high lattice mast showing traffic signals which are mandatory for commercial vessels but may be disregarded by yachts navigating outside the main channels. The signals are shown on the side of Test or Itchen as appropriate thus:

(a)	A green shape or light	A vessel may enter or leave the docks
(b)	A red shape or light	Entry or departure forbidden
(c)	A red shape or light over a green shape or light	Departure forbidden to facilitate entry of large vessel.
(d)	A green shape or light over a red shape or light	Entry forbidden to facilitate entry of large vessel.

(2) Hythe Marina Village, close NW of Hythe Pier, marked by Q (3) 10s; E cardinal Bn. Lock entrance, N side 2 FG (vert); S side 2 FR (vert).

(3) Dock Head, West side (Queen Elizabeth II Terminal, S end) 4 FG (vert) 3M; framework Tr; mark entrance to R Test.

(4) Entrance to R Itchen marked by Lt Buoy Oc G 4s, beyond which piles with G Lts mark E side of channel leading under road bridge.

(5) Above Itchen Bridge, which is marked by 2 FR (vert) and 2 FG (vert), the principal marks are Crosshouse Bn Oc R 5s, Chapel Bn FlG 3s, Shamrock Quay pontoons 2 FR (vert) at SW and NE ends, No 5 Bn FlG 3s, No 7 Bn Fl (2) G 5s, Millstone Pt jetty 2 FR (vert), No 9 Bn Fl (4) G 10s and Kemps Quay Marina 2 FG (vert).

RADIO TELEPHONE

Vessel Traffic Services (VTS) Centre Southampton. Call: *Southampton VTS* VHF Ch 12 14 16 (H24). Traffic information for small craft on Ch every even H+00 0600-2200 Fri-Sun and Bank Holiday Mondays from Easter – 30 Sept.

Southampton Harbour Patrol Call: *Southampton Patrol* VHF Ch 12 16; 01-28, 60-88 (H24) both have Ch 10, 12, 14, 16, 18, 22, 71 & 74.

Marinas VHF Ch **80** M.

TELEPHONE (0703)

Dock and Harbour Master 339733; MRSC Lee-on-Solent 552100; # (0703) 827350; Southampton Weather Centre 228844; Marinecall 0898 500 457; Police 581111; Dr 226631 (Port Health); H 777222.

TIME ZONE UT(GMT)

For Summer Time add ONE hour in non-shaded areas

ENGLAND, SOUTH COAST – SOUTHAMPTON

Lat 50°54′ N Long 1°24′ W

TIMES AND HEIGHTS OF HIGH AND LOW WATERS

YEAR **1992**

JANUARY

Day	Time	m	Day	Time	m
1	0125	1·6	**16**	0017	1·8
	0820	4·0		0716	3·9
W	1358	1·4	Th	1303	1·5
	2057	4·0		1957	3·9
2	0226	1·5	**17**	0134	1·5
	0910	4·1		0821	4·1
Th	1453	1·3	F	1412	1·2
	2146	4·1		2100	4·1
3	0316	1·4	**18**	0240	1·2
	0951	4·1		0916	4·3
F	1538	1·1	Sa	1511	0·9
	2227	4·2		2154	4·3
4	0357	1·2	**19**	0339	0·9
	1029	4·2		1006	4·4
Sa	1616	0·9	Su	1605	0·5
●	2303	4·2	○	2241	4·5
5	0435	1·1	**20**	0431	0·6
	1103	4·3		1054	4·6
Su	1651	0·8	M	1655	0·3
	2337	4·3		2328	4·7
6	0507	1·0	**21**	0521	0·4
	1136	4·3		1139	4·7
M	1721	0·8	Tu	1744	0·1
7	0009	4·3	**22**	0013	4·8
	0538	1·0		0608	0·3
Tu	1208	4·3	W	1225	4·7
	1753	0·8		1829	0·1
8	0039	4·3	**23**	0058	4·8
	0610	1·0		0652	0·3
W	1239	4·3	Th	1311	4·6
	1822	0·8		1912	0·2
9	0111	4·3	**24**	0144	4·7
	0642	1·0		0733	0·5
Th	1312	4·2	F	1358	4·5
	1852	0·9		1950	0·4
10	0144	4·2	**25**	0231	4·6
	0714	1·1		0812	0·7
F	1349	4·2	Sa	1447	4·3
	1925	1·0		2030	0·7
11	0221	4·2	**26**	0322	4·3
	0749	1·2		0854	1·0
Sa	1428	4·1	Su	1544	4·1
	2001	1·2	☾	2116	1·1
12	0303	4·1	**27**	0419	4·1
	0830	1·4		0944	1·4
Su	1515	3·9	M	1647	3·8
	2044	1·4		2213	1·6
13	0353	4·0	**28**	0523	3·8
	0921	1·6		1049	1·7
M	1612	3·8	Tu	1805	3·7
☽	2142	1·7		2328	1·9
14	0454	3·9	**29**	0638	3·7
	1027	1·8		1210	1·8
Tu	1722	3·7	W	1931	3·6
	2253	1·8			
15	0605	3·8	**30**	0052	1·9
	1144	1·7		0752	3·7
W	1842	3·7	Th	1330	1·8
				2043	3·8
			31	0204	1·8
				0852	3·8
			F	1435	1·6
				2136	3·9

FEBRUARY

Day	Time	m	Day	Time	m
1	0259	1·6	**16**	0228	1·2
	0939	4·0		0902	4·2
Sa	1524	1·3	Su	1457	0·8
	2216	4·1		2139	4·4
2	0343	1·3	**17**	0326	0·8
	1016	4·1		0951	4·4
Su	1601	1·0	M	1550	0·4
	2249	4·2		2226	4·6
3	0417	1·1	**18**	0416	0·5
	1049	4·2		1037	4·6
M	1634	0·8	Tu	1639	0·2
●	2320	4·3	○	2308	4·8
4	0449	0·9	**19**	0504	0·3
	1119	4·3		1122	4·7
Tu	1703	0·7	W	1725	0·0
	2349	4·4		2352	4·9
5	0519	0·8	**20**	0548	0·2
	1149	4·4		1205	4·7
W	1734	0·6	Th	1808	0·0
6	0017	4·4	**21**	0033	4·9
	0550	0·7		0630	0·2
Th	1218	4·4	F	1249	4·7
	1804	0·6		1848	0·1
7	0045	4·4	**22**	0115	4·7
	0621	0·7		0707	0·3
F	1248	4·4	Sa	1332	4·5
	1833	0·6		1924	0·3
8	0113	4·4	**23**	0159	4·5
	0651	0·8		0742	0·6
Sa	1320	4·3	Su	1418	4·3
	1901	0·7		1958	0·7
9	0146	4·3	**24**	0243	4·3
	0721	0·9		0816	0·9
Su	1356	4·2	M	1508	4·0
	1932	1·0		2037	1·2
10	0223	4·2	**25**	0334	4·0
	0756	1·1		0858	1·4
M	1439	4·1	Tu	1607	3·8
	2008	1·3	☾	2127	1·7
11	0309	4·1	**26**	0433	3·7
	0840	1·4		0956	1·8
Tu	1533	3·9	W	1722	3·5
☽	2058	1·6		2239	2·0
12	0407	3·9	**27**	0547	3·5
	0940	1·7		1122	2·0
W	1642	3·7	Th	1857	3·5
	2212	1·8			
13	0520	3·8	**28**	0012	2·2
	1103	1·8		0715	3·5
Th	1813	3·7	F	1256	2·0
	2346	1·9		2018	3·6
14	0646	3·8	**29**	0135	2·0
	1237	1·6		0826	3·6
F	1941	3·8	Sa	1410	1·7
				2115	3·8
15	0117	1·6			
	0802	4·0			
Sa	1356	1·3			
	2047	4·1			

MARCH

Day	Time	m	Day	Time	m
1	0236	1·7	**16**	0212	1·2
	0916	3·8		0846	4·2
Su	1500	1·4	M	1439	0·8
	2153	4·0		2120	4·4
2	0318	1·4	**17**	0306	0·7
	0954	4·0		0934	4·4
M	1537	1·1	Tu	1530	0·4
	2226	4·2		2204	4·6
3	0352	1·0	**18**	0355	0·4
	1026	4·2		1018	4·6
Tu	1609	0·8	W	1616	0·2
	2253	4·3	○	2245	4·8
4	0424	0·8	**19**	0439	0·2
	1055	4·3		1101	4·7
W	1639	0·6	Th	1700	0·1
●	2321	4·4		2326	4·8
5	0455	0·6	**20**	0522	0·1
	1125	4·4		1142	4·7
Th	1710	0·5	F	1743	0·1
	2349	4·5			
6	0528	0·5	**21**	0006	4·8
	1154	4·5		0602	0·2
F	1741	0·5	Sa	1225	4·6
				1822	0·2
7	0016	4·5	**22**	0047	4·6
	0559	0·5		0639	0·3
Sa	1223	4·5	Su	1306	4·5
	1811	0·5		1857	0·5
8	0044	4·5	**23**	0126	4·4
	0629	0·6		0711	0·6
Su	1255	4·4	M	1351	4·3
	1841	0·6		1929	0·8
9	0116	4·4	**24**	0209	4·2
	0659	0·7		0744	0·9
M	1332	4·3	Tu	1438	4·0
	1911	0·8		2003	1·3
10	0154	4·3	**25**	0256	3·9
	0732	1·0		0820	1·4
Tu	1416	4·1	W	1534	3·7
	1947	1·2		2049	1·7
11	0241	4·1	**26**	0349	3·7
	0814	1·3		0913	1·8
W	1511	4·0	Th	1642	3·5
	2039	1·5	☾	2155	2·1
12	0339	4·0	**27**	0458	3·5
	0915	1·6		1030	2·0
Th	1624	3·8	F	1811	3·4
☽	2153	1·8		2324	2·2
13	0456	3·8	**28**	0624	3·4
	1041	1·7		1207	2·0
F	1758	3·8	Sa	1935	3·5
	2332	1·9			
14	0627	3·8	**29**	0052	2·1
	1219	1·6		0743	3·5
Sa	1927	3·9	Su	1325	1·8
				2034	3·7
15	0104	1·6	**30**	0154	1·7
	0747	4·0		0839	3·7
Su	1338	1·2	M	1420	1·5
	2032	4·2		2115	3·9
			31	0241	1·4
				0919	3·9
			Tu	1500	1·1
				2149	4·1

APRIL

Day	Time	m	Day	Time	m
1	0319	1·0	**16**	0328	0·4
	0954	4·1		0958	4·5
W	1534	0·8	Th	1549	0·3
	2219	4·3		2220	4·7
2	0351	0·8	**17**	0412	0·3
	1025	4·3		1041	4·5
Th	1607	0·6	F	1634	0·3
	2249	4·4	○	2301	4·7
3	0426	0·6	**18**	0455	0·2
	1057	4·4		1122	4·5
F	1641	0·5	Sa	1716	0·3
●	2318	4·5		2340	4·6
4	0501	0·5	**19**	0535	0·3
	1130	4·4		1204	4·5
Sa	1715	0·5	Su	1755	0·5
	2347	4·5			
5	0536	0·4	**20**	0019	4·5
	1202	4·4		0611	0·4
Su	1751	0·5	M	1245	4·3
				1831	0·7
6	0019	4·5	**21**	0059	4·3
	0610	0·5		0644	0·7
M	1237	4·4	Tu	1328	4·2
	1824	0·6		1903	1·0
7	0054	4·4	**22**	0139	4·1
	0644	0·6		0716	1·0
Tu	1317	4·3	W	1414	4·0
	1859	0·8		1937	1·3
8	0135	4·3	**23**	0223	3·9
	0719	0·8		0752	1·3
W	1404	4·2	Th	1506	3·8
	1940	1·1		2021	1·7
9	0225	4·1	**24**	0314	3·7
	0804	1·1		0839	1·6
Th	1505	4·0	F	1607	3·6
	2034	1·5	☾	2119	2·0
10	0327	4·0	**25**	0415	3·5
	0907	1·4		0945	1·9
F	1619	3·9	Sa	1720	3·5
☽	2150	1·7		2234	2·1
11	0445	3·8	**26**	0529	3·5
	1029	1·6		1106	1·9
Sa	1747	3·9	Su	1836	3·6
	2320	1·7		2353	2·0
12	0612	3·8	**27**	0645	3·5
	1159	1·5		1223	1·8
Su	1908	4·1	M	1938	3·7
13	0043	1·5	**28**	0101	1·7
	0727	4·0		0747	3·7
M	1314	1·1	Tu	1325	1·5
	2009	4·3		2025	3·9
14	0149	1·1	**29**	0153	1·4
	0826	4·2		0836	3·8
Tu	1415	0·8	W	1411	1·2
	2057	4·5		2104	4·1
15	0242	0·7	**30**	0236	1·1
	0914	4·4		0915	4·0
W	1504	0·5	Th	1452	1·0
	2140	4·6		2139	4·2

Chart Datum: 2.74 metres below Ordnance Datum (Newlyn)

ENGLAND, SOUTH COAST – SOUTHAMPTON

Lat 50°54′ N Long 1°24′ W

TIMES AND HEIGHTS OF HIGH AND LOW WATERS

YEAR **1992**

TIME ZONE UT(GMT)
For Summer Time add ONE hour in non-shaded areas

MAY

Day	Time	m	Day	Time	m
1 F	0314 0953 1530 2213	0·8 4·2 0·8 4·4	**16** Sa ○	0347 1023 1610 2239	0·5 4·4 0·6 4·5
2 Sa ●	0352 1029 1609 2247	0·6 4·3 0·6 4·5	**17** Su	0430 1107 1652 2318	0·5 4·4 0·7 4·4
3 Su	0434 1106 1651 2322	0·5 4·4 0·6 4·5	**18** M	0510 1149 1732 2357	0·5 4·3 0·8 4·3
4 M	0513 1144 1731 2359	0·4 4·4 0·6 4·5	**19** Tu	0547 1230 1808	0·6 4·2 0·9
5 Tu	0554 1225 1813	0·5 4·4 0·7	**20** W	0035 0621 1311 1841	4·2 0·8 4·1 1·1
6 W	0040 0633 1311 1855	4·4 0·5 4·3 0·8	**21** Th	0114 0653 1353 1915	4·0 1·0 4·0 1·3
7 Th	0126 0716 1403 1941	4·3 0·7 4·2 1·1	**22** F	0155 0728 1439 1955	3·9 1·2 3·8 1·5
8 F	0218 0804 1503 2036	4·2 0·9 4·1 1·3	**23** Sa	0242 0809 1530 2045	3·8 1·4 3·7 1·7
9 Sa ☽	0321 0904 1613 2144	4·0 1·2 4·1 1·5	**24** Su ☾	0335 0902 1628 2144	3·6 1·6 3·7 1·8
10 Su	0433 1015 1730 2300	3·9 1·3 4·1 1·5	**25** M	0437 1005 1731 2252	3·6 1·7 3·7 1·8
11 M	0552 1132 1840	3·9 1·3 4·2	**26** Tu	0544 1115 1834 2358	3·6 1·7 3·7 1·7
12 Tu	0013 0703 1242 1941	1·3 4·0 1·1 4·3	**27** W	0649 1221 1929	3·6 1·6 3·9
13 W	0118 0803 1343 2032	1·1 4·1 0·9 4·4	**28** Th	0058 0746 1318 2015	1·5 3·8 1·4 4·0
14 Th	0213 0854 1436 2116	0·8 4·3 0·7 4·5	**29** F	0150 0836 1408 2058	1·2 3·9 1·2 4·2
15 F	0302 0940 1525 2159	0·6 4·3 0·6 4·5	**30** Sa	0236 0920 1455 2139	1·0 4·1 1·0 4·3
			31 Su	0323 1004 1542 2220	0·7 4·2 0·8 4·4

JUNE

Day	Time	m	Day	Time	m
1 M ●	0409 1047 1630 2300	0·6 4·3 0·7 4·4	**16** Tu	0452 1137 1713 2340	0·7 4·2 0·9 4·2
2 Tu	0455 1131 1718 2343	0·5 4·4 0·7 4·5	**17** W	0528 1216 1748	0·7 4·2 1·0
3 W	0542 1217 1806	0·4 4·4 0·7	**18** Th	0016 0602 1253 1821	4·2 0·8 4·2 1·1
4 Th	0029 0628 1306 1853	4·4 0·4 4·4 0·7	**19** F	0052 0632 1329 1854	4·1 0·9 4·1 1·2
5 F	0117 0713 1357 1939	4·4 0·5 4·4 0·8	**20** Sa	0129 0706 1407 1929	4·0 1·0 4·0 1·3
6 Sa	0210 0800 1454 2030	4·3 0·7 4·4 1·0	**21** Su	0209 0741 1449 2010	3·9 1·2 3·9 1·4
7 Su ☽	0308 0852 1555 2127	4·2 0·9 4·3 1·2	**22** M	0255 0823 1536 2056	3·8 1·4 3·9 1·6
8 M	0414 0953 1702 2231	4·1 1·1 4·2 1·3	**23** Tu ☾	0347 0912 1629 2152	3·7 1·5 3·8 1·7
9 Tu	0525 1059 1809 2339	4·0 1·2 4·2 1·3	**24** W	0445 1011 1730 2256	3·7 1·7 3·8 1·7
10 W	0636 1208 1912	4·0 1·2 4·2	**25** Th	0551 1119 1831	3·6 1·7 3·8
11 Th	0045 0742 1313 2008	1·2 4·0 1·2 4·2	**26** F	0003 0658 1227 1930	1·6 3·7 1·6 3·9
12 F	0145 0837 1412 2057	1·1 4·1 1·1 4·3	**27** Sa	0106 0800 1330 2023	1·4 3·8 1·4 4·1
13 Sa	0240 0928 1503 2141	0·9 4·2 1·0 4·3	**28** Su	0205 0854 1428 2112	1·2 4·0 1·2 4·2
14 Su	0328 1013 1551 2222	0·8 4·2 0·9 4·3	**29** M	0259 0945 1522 2159	0·9 4·2 1·0 4·3
15 M ○	0412 1056 1634 2301	0·7 4·3 0·9 4·3	**30** Tu ●	0351 1032 1615 2244	0·6 4·3 0·8 4·4

JULY

Day	Time	m	Day	Time	m
1 W	0441 1119 1707 2330	0·4 4·5 0·6 4·5	**16** Th	0510 1158 1728 2357	0·7 4·3 1·0 4·2
2 Th	0531 1206 1757	0·3 4·6 0·5	**17** F	0541 1230 1800	0·7 4·3 1·0
3 F	0016 0619 1254 1844	4·5 0·3 4·6 0·5	**18** Sa	0028 0611 1301 1830	4·2 0·8 4·2 1·0
4 Sa	0104 0705 1342 1930	4·5 0·3 4·6 0·6	**19** Su	0101 0642 1334 1902	4·2 0·8 4·2 1·1
5 Su	0154 0748 1434 2015	4·4 0·4 4·5 0·7	**20** M	0136 0712 1408 1935	4·1 1·0 4·1 1·2
6 M	0248 0834 1528 2103	4·3 0·7 4·4 0·9	**21** Tu	0215 0746 1448 2013	4·0 1·1 4·0 1·3
7 Tu ☽	0347 0925 1628 2158	4·1 0·9 4·3 1·2	**22** W ☾	0300 0826 1536 2101	3·9 1·4 3·9 1·6
8 W	0454 1024 1734 2301	4·0 1·2 4·1 1·4	**23** Th	0353 0917 1632 2159	3·8 1·6 3·9 1·7
9 Th	0608 1133 1842	3·9 1·4 4·0	**24** F	0500 1024 1739 2314	3·7 1·8 3·8 1·8
10 F	0014 0722 1245 1947	1·5 3·9 1·5 4·0	**25** Sa	0615 1144 1849	3·7 1·8 3·9
11 Sa	0123 0828 1353 2044	1·4 4·0 1·5 4·1	**26** Su	0032 0732 1302 1956	1·6 3·8 1·7 4·0
12 Su	0224 0922 1451 2130	1·3 4·1 1·4 4·1	**27** M	0142 0836 1410 2051	1·3 4·0 1·4 4·2
13 M	0316 1008 1539 2213	1·1 4·1 1·2 4·2	**28** Tu	0244 0930 1510 2142	1·0 4·2 1·0 4·3
14 Tu ○	0400 1048 1619 2249	0·9 4·2 1·1 4·2	**29** W ●	0337 1018 1603 2228	0·6 4·4 0·7 4·5
15 W	0438 1125 1655 2324	0·8 4·2 1·0 4·2	**30** Th	0428 1103 1654 2313	0·4 4·6 0·5 4·6
			31 F	0517 1149 1741 2359	0·2 4·7 0·4 4·6

AUGUST

Day	Time	m	Day	Time	m
1 Sa	0604 1233 1828	0·1 4·8 0·3	**16** Su	0003 0548 1230 1805	4·3 0·7 4·4 0·8
2 Su	0045 0648 1318 1911	4·6 0·1 4·8 0·4	**17** M	0033 0617 1258 1836	4·3 0·7 4·4 0·8
3 M	0131 0729 1405 1952	4·6 0·3 4·6 0·6	**18** Tu	0105 0645 1330 1906	4·3 0·8 4·3 1·0
4 Tu	0222 0809 1455 2034	4·4 0·6 4·4 0·8	**19** W	0139 0715 1406 1939	4·2 1·0 4·2 1·2
5 W ☽	0318 0853 1551 2121	4·2 1·0 4·2 1·2	**20** Th	0222 0750 1450 2020	4·0 1·3 4·1 1·5
6 Th	0421 0948 1656 2224	3·9 1·4 4·0 1·5	**21** F ☾	0313 0837 1545 2116	3·9 1·6 3·9 1·7
7 F	0538 1100 1811 2343	3·8 1·7 3·8 1·7	**22** Sa	0419 0946 1654 2235	3·7 1·9 3·8 1·9
8 Sa	0705 1222 1927	3·7 1·9 3·8	**23** Su	0546 1116 1818	3·7 2·0 3·8
9 Su	0105 0821 1340 2032	1·7 3·8 1·8 3·9	**24** M	0006 0714 1247 1935	1·8 3·8 1·8 4·0
10 M	0214 0917 1441 2122	1·5 4·0 1·6 4·0	**25** Tu	0127 0822 1358 2035	1·4 4·1 1·4 4·2
11 Tu	0306 1001 1527 2200	1·3 4·1 1·4 4·1	**26** W	0231 0915 1457 2126	1·0 4·3 1·0 4·4
12 W	0348 1035 1603 2235	1·0 4·2 1·1 4·2	**27** Th	0322 1000 1548 2211	0·6 4·6 0·6 4·6
13 Th ○	0420 1105 1636 2305	0·8 4·3 1·0 4·3	**28** F ●	0411 1043 1635 2254	0·3 4·7 0·4 4·7
14 F	0450 1134 1705 2334	0·7 4·4 0·9 4·3	**29** Sa	0457 1124 1722 2338	0·1 4·9 0·2 4·7
15 Sa	0520 1202 1736	0·7 4·4 0·8	**30** Su	0542 1207 1806	0·0 4·9 0·2
			31 M	0022 0626 1249 1847	4·7 0·1 4·8 0·3

Chart Datum: 2.74 metres below Ordnance Datum (Newlyn)

2

TIME ZONE UT(GMT)

For Summer Time add ONE hour in non-shaded areas

ENGLAND, SOUTH COAST – SOUTHAMPTON

Lat 50°54′ N Long 1°24′ W

TIMES AND HEIGHTS OF HIGH AND LOW WATERS

YEAR **1992**

SEPTEMBER

Day	Time	m	Day	Time	m
1 Tu	0107 0706 1335 1925	4·6 0·3 4·6 0·5	**16** W	0038 0623 1257 1842	4·4 0·7 4·4 0·8
2 W	0155 0744 1421 2003	4·4 0·6 4·4 0·8	**17** Th	0113 0652 1334 1913	4·3 1·0 4·3 1·1
3 Th	0248 0823 1514 ☽ 2045	4·1 1·1 4·1 1·3	**18** F	0155 0728 1417 1954	4·1 1·3 4·1 1·4
4 F	0350 0915 1617 2145	3·9 1·6 3·8 1·7	**19** Sa	0246 0814 1512 ☾ 2048	3·9 1·6 4·0 1·7
5 Sa	0508 1026 1735 2309	3·7 2·0 3·6 2·0	**20** Su	0355 0925 1625 2211	3·8 1·9 3·8 1·9
6 Su	0642 1158 1903	3·6 2·1 3·6	**21** M	0526 1100 1756 2347	3·7 2·0 3·8 1·8
7 M	0043 0805 1321 2014	2·0 3·7 2·0 3·7	**22** Tu	0657 1232 1917	3·9 1·8 3·9
8 Tu	0156 0901 1421 2104	1·7 3·9 1·8 3·9	**23** W	0109 0804 1344 2019	1·4 4·2 1·4 4·2
9 W	0247 0940 1507 2141	1·4 4·1 1·4 4·1	**24** Th	0212 0854 1439 2107	1·0 4·4 0·9 4·4
10 Th	0326 1011 1541 2212	1·1 4·2 1·1 4·2	**25** F	0303 0937 1527 2151	0·6 4·7 0·5 4·6
11 F	0356 1039 1610 2241	0·9 4·3 0·9 4·3	**26** Sa	0349 1019 1613 ● 2233	0·3 4·8 0·3 4·7
12 Sa	0425 1106 1639 ○ 2310	0·7 4·4 0·7 4·4	**27** Su	0435 1059 1658 2317	0·1 4·9 0·2 4·8
13 Su	0454 1133 1710 2338	0·6 4·5 0·7 4·5	**28** M	0520 1140 1741	0·1 4·9 0·2
14 M	0524 1200 1742	0·6 4·5 0·6	**29** Tu	0000 0602 1223 1822	4·7 0·2 4·8 0·3
15 Tu	0007 0554 1226 1812	4·4 0·6 4·5 0·7	**30** W	0045 0641 1306 1858	4·6 0·5 4·6 0·5

OCTOBER

Day	Time	m	Day	Time	m
1 Th	0130 0717 1351 1933	4·4 0·8 4·3 0·9	**16** F	0057 0640 1313 1859	4·3 0·9 4·3 0·9
2 F	0222 0755 1439 2014	4·1 1·2 4·0 1·3	**17** Sa	0140 0718 1357 1941	4·2 1·2 4·2 1·2
3 Sa	0320 0843 1537 ☽ 2107	3·8 1·7 3·7 1·7	**18** Su	0235 0807 1455 2037	4·0 1·5 4·0 1·5
4 Su	0433 0949 1651 2227	3·6 2·1 3·5 2·0	**19** M	0344 0916 1606 ☾ 2154	3·9 1·8 3·9 1·7
5 M	0604 1118 1819	3·5 2·2 3·5	**20** Tu	0509 1043 1733 2324	3·9 1·9 3·8 1·7
6 Tu	0001 0728 1243 1937	2·1 3·6 2·1 3·6	**21** W	0633 1209 1855	4·0 1·7 4·0
7 W	0118 0826 1346 2031	1·9 3·8 1·9 3·8	**22** Th	0043 0740 1319 1957	1·4 4·2 1·3 4·2
8 Th	0212 0906 1432 2111	1·6 4·0 1·5 4·0	**23** F	0147 0830 1415 2047	1·0 4·5 0·9 4·4
9 F	0251 0938 1507 2143	1·2 4·2 1·2 4·2	**24** Sa	0238 0915 1503 2132	0·7 4·6 0·6 4·5
10 Sa	0323 1006 1540 2214	1·0 4·3 0·9 4·3	**25** Su	0326 0956 1549 ● 2215	0·4 4·7 0·4 4·6
11 Su	0354 1034 1611 ○ 2243	0·8 4·5 0·7 4·4	**26** M	0411 1036 1634 2258	0·3 4·8 0·3 4·7
12 M	0425 1102 1644 2314	0·7 4·5 0·6 4·5	**27** Tu	0456 1118 1717 2342	0·3 4·7 0·3 4·6
13 Tu	0458 1132 1717 2345	0·6 4·6 0·6 4·5	**28** W	0539 1159 1758	0·5 4·6 0·4
14 W	0532 1201 1751	0·7 4·6 0·6	**29** Th	0026 0619 1240 1833	4·5 0·7 4·4 0·6
15 Th	0018 0605 1234 1824	4·4 0·8 4·5 0·7	**30** F	0111 0654 1323 1908	4·3 1·0 4·2 0·9
			31 Sa	0159 0731 1409 1946	4·1 1·3 4·0 1·3

NOVEMBER

Day	Time	m	Day	Time	m
1 Su	0252 0814 1500 2032	3·9 1·7 3·8 1·6	**16** M	0229 0807 1443 2031	4·2 1·3 4·1 1·2
2 M	0353 0908 1601 ☽ 2134	3·7 2·0 3·6 1·9	**17** Tu	0331 0907 1550 ☾ 2136	4·1 1·5 4·0 1·4
3 Tu	0506 1021 1716 2254	3·6 2·2 3·5 2·0	**18** W	0444 1019 1706 2252	4·1 1·6 3·9 1·5
4 W	0622 1140 1833	3·6 2·1 3·5	**19** Th	0601 1136 1824	4·1 1·5 4·0
5 Th	0014 0727 1249 1938	2·0 3·7 1·9 3·7	**20** F	0008 0708 1246 1932	1·3 4·2 1·3 4·1
6 F	0117 0816 1343 2027	1·7 3·9 1·6 3·8	**21** Sa	0115 0804 1347 2028	1·1 4·4 1·0 4·3
7 Sa	0204 0855 1426 2107	1·4 4·1 1·3 4·0	**22** Su	0211 0852 1440 2117	0·9 4·5 0·8 4·4
8 Su	0244 0929 1504 2143	1·2 4·2 1·0 4·2	**23** M	0303 0937 1528 2203	0·7 4·6 0·6 4·5
9 M	0320 1002 1541 2218	1·0 4·4 0·8 4·4	**24** Tu	0351 1018 1614 ● 2247	0·6 4·6 0·5 4·5
10 Tu	0357 1034 1618 ○ 2253	0·8 4·5 0·7 4·4	**25** W	0437 1101 1658 2330	0·6 4·6 0·5 4·5
11 W	0435 1108 1658 2328	0·7 4·6 0·6 4·5	**26** Th	0520 1142 1737	0·7 4·5 0·6
12 Th	0514 1142 1736	0·7 4·6 0·6	**27** F	0014 0558 1222 1813	4·4 0·8 4·4 0·7
13 F	0007 0554 1219 1815	4·5 0·8 4·5 0·6	**28** Sa	0057 0634 1301 1847	4·3 1·0 4·2 0·9
14 Sa	0047 0634 1300 1853	4·4 0·9 4·4 0·8	**29** Su	0138 0709 1341 1921	4·2 1·2 4·0 1·2
15 Su	0134 0717 1348 1937	4·3 1·1 4·3 1·0	**30** M	0223 0746 1426 1958	4·0 1·5 3·9 1·4

DECEMBER

Day	Time	m	Day	Time	m
1 Tu	0310 0828 1515 2045	3·8 1·7 3·7 1·7	**16** W	0312 0849 1529 ☾ 2113	4·4 1·1 4·2 1·1
2 W	0404 0922 1612 ☽ 2143	3·7 1·9 3·6 1·8	**17** Th	0415 0948 1636 2216	4·3 1·3 4·0 1·3
3 Th	0506 1027 1719 2253	3·6 2·0 3·5 1·9	**18** F	0523 1057 1750 2329	4·2 1·4 4·0 1·4
4 F	0612 1136 1829	3·7 1·9 3·6	**19** Sa	0634 1209 1906	4·2 1·4 4·0
5 Sa	0004 0713 1242 1933	1·8 3·8 1·7 3·7	**20** Su	0041 0739 1317 2011	1·4 4·2 1·3 4·1
6 Su	0105 0805 1339 2026	1·7 3·9 1·5 3·9	**21** M	0148 0834 1419 2108	1·2 4·3 1·1 4·2
7 M	0159 0849 1427 2113	1·4 4·1 1·2 4·1	**22** Tu	0246 0923 1512 2157	1·1 4·4 0·9 4·3
8 Tu	0246 0931 1512 2154	1·2 4·3 1·0 4·2	**23** W	0339 1009 1602 2241	1·0 4·4 0·7 4·4
9 W	0332 1009 1556 ○ 2235	1·0 4·4 0·8 4·4	**24** Th	0424 1050 1644 ● 2324	0·9 4·4 0·7 4·4
10 Th	0416 1048 1641 2316	0·8 4·5 0·6 4·5	**25** F	0505 1129 1723	0·9 4·4 0·6
11 F	0502 1127 1724 2357	0·7 4·5 0·5 4·5	**26** Sa	0004 0541 1205 1756	4·4 0·9 4·3 0·7
12 Sa	0547 1207 1807	0·7 4·5 0·5	**27** Su	0040 0614 1241 1827	4·3 1·0 4·3 0·8
13 Su	0040 0630 1251 1850	4·5 0·7 4·5 0·5	**28** M	0115 0645 1316 1857	4·3 1·1 4·2 0·9
14 M	0126 0713 1338 1933	4·5 0·8 4·4 0·6	**29** Tu	0150 0717 1353 1929	4·2 1·2 4·1 1·1
15 Tu	0217 0759 1429 2019	4·5 1·0 4·3 0·8	**30** W	0227 0751 1433 2003	4·0 1·4 3·9 1·3
			31 Th	0310 0830 1518 2045	3·9 1·5 3·8 1·5

Chart Datum: 2.74 metres below Ordnance Datum (Newlyn)

SOUTHAMPTON *continued*

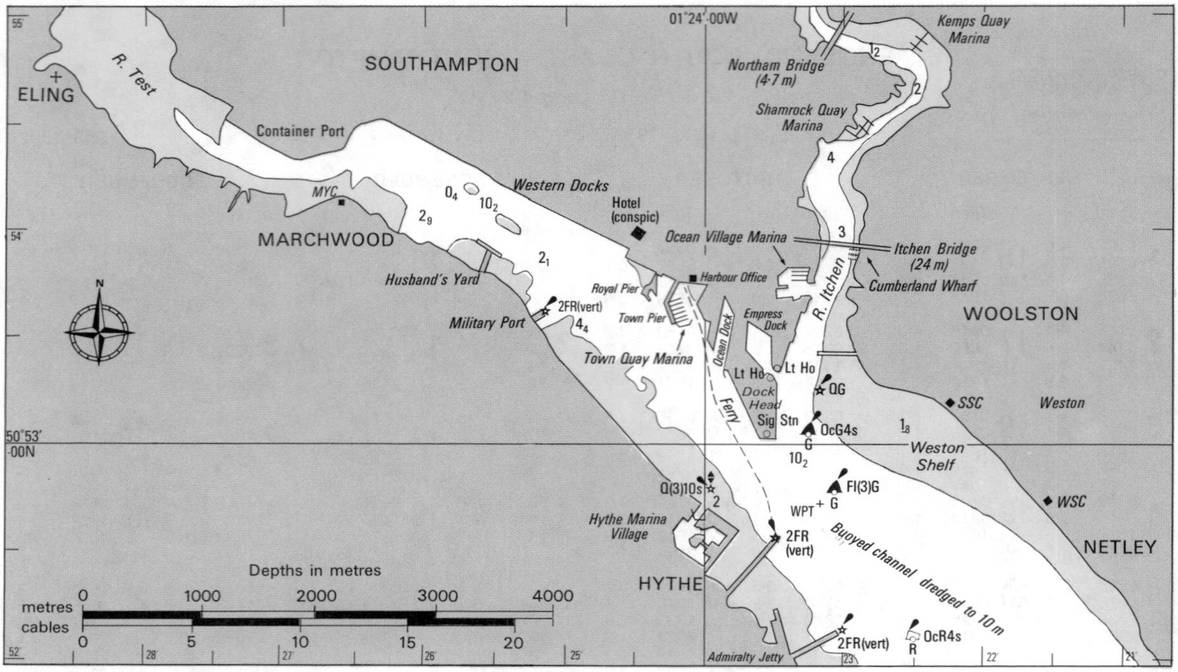

SOUTHAMPTON
R. Test
ELING
Container Port
MYC
MARCHWOOD
Western Docks
Husband's Yard
Military Port
2FR(vert)
Royal Pier
Town Pier
Town Quay Marina
Hotel (conspic)
Ocean Village Marina
Harbour Office
Empress Dock
Ocean Dock
Lt Ho
Dock Head
Sig Stn
Ferry
R. Itchen
Itchen Bridge (24 m)
Cumberland Wharf
Northam Bridge (4·7 m)
Kemps Quay Marina
Shamrock Quay Marina
WOOLSTON
QG
OcG4s
SSC
Weston
Weston Shelf
WSC
NETLEY
Fl(3)G
WPT
Q(3)10s
Hythe Marina Village
2FR (vert)
Buoyed channel dredged to 10 m
HYTHE
2FR(vert)
OcR4s
Admiralty Jetty
01°24'·00W
50°53'·00N
Depths in metres
metres
cables
0
1000
2000
3000
4000
5
10
15
20

FACILITIES

Ocean Village Marina (450 + 50 visitors) ☎ 229385, FW, V, R, Bar, CH, Slip, Gas, Gaz, Kos, ME, Sh, ⊡, P, D, AC, (Access H24); **Shamrock Quay Marina** (220 + 40 visitors) ☎ 229461, BH (62 ton), C (12 ton), ME, El, Sh, SM, ⊡, R, Bar, AC, CH, FW, Gas, Gaz, Kos, V, (Access H24); **Hythe Marina** (180 + 50 visitors) ☎ 207073, BH (30 ton), C (12 ton), AC, P, D, El, ME, Sh, CH, FW, V, R, Bar, SM, (Access H24); **Kemp's Quay Marina** (180 + 5 visitors) ☎ 632323, AC, C (5 ton), D, FW, Gas, ME, (Access HW ∓ 3½); **Town Quay Marina** (400) ☎ 234397, R, Bar; **Itchen Marina** ☎ 631500, D, BY, C (12 ton); **Royal Southampton YC** ☎ 223352, Bar, R, M, FW, L, ⊡; **Hythe SC** ☎ 846563; **Marchwood YC** ☎ 864641, Bar, M, C (10 ton), FW, L; **Netley SC** ☎ 454272; **Southampton SC** ☎ 446575; **Weston SC** ☎ 452527; **Hythe Marina Yacht Services** ☎ 840460, ME, El, Sh; **Kelvin Hughes** ☎ 634911, CH, ACA; **Stephen Ratsey** ☎ 221683, SM; **Pumpkin Marine** ☎ 229713, CH; **Southampton Yacht Services** ☎ 335266, Sh; **Solent Rigging** ☎ 639976, Rigging; **Southern Spar Services** ☎ 331714, Spars; **Alpha Sails** ☎ 553623, SM; **G Sailmakers** ☎ 221453, SM; **Ullman Sails** ☎ 454254, SM; **B. D. Marine** ☎ 220178, ME, El; **Waters Yacht Engineers** ☎ 220144, ME, El; **Hythe Marine Services** ☎ 848782 ME, El, Sh; **Boat Shop** ☎ 449338, CH; **Belsize BY** ☎ 671555, CH; **Larry Marks** ☎ 447037, CH; **Shamrock Chandlery** ☎ 632725, CH (and at the Hythe marina); ☎ 848102; **Captain Pumpkin** ☎ 229713, CH; **Bowdeck** ☎ 331841, Ⓔ; **Hards** at Hythe, Crackmore, Eling, Mayflower Park (Test), Northam (Itchen). Public landings at Cross House hand, Cross House slip, Block House hard (Itchen), Carnation public hard & Cowporters public hard. **City** V, R, Bar, Ⓑ; ✉; ⇌; ✈; Ferries/Hydrofoil to IoW ☎ 333042.

NOTE

Associated British Ports publish a Yachtsman's Guide to the area. Apply to *Vessel Traffic Services Centre*, Berth 37, Eastern Docks.

HAMBLE 10-2-25

Hampshire

CHARTS

Admiralty 2022, 1905; Stanford 11; Imray C3; OS 196

TIDES

+0130, −0010 Dover; ML 2·9; Zone 0 (GMT)

Standard Port SOUTHAMPTON (←)

Times				Height (metres)			
HW		LW		MHWS	MHWN	MLWN	MLWS
0400	1100	0000	0600	4·5	3·7	1·8	0·5
1600	2300	1200	1800				
Differences WARSASH							
+0020	+0010	+0010	0000	0·0	+0·1	+0·1	+0·3
BURSLEDON							
+0020	+0020	+0010	+0010	+0·1	+0·1	+0·2	+0·2
CALSHOT CASTLE							
+0015	+0030	+0015	+0005	0·0	0·0	+0·2	+0·3

NOTE: Double high waters occur at or near springs — on other occasions there is a stand which lasts about 2 hours. Predictions are for the first HW where there are two or for the middle of the stand. See 10.2.13.

SHELTER

Excellent with many marinas and boat yards. Anchoring prohibited.

NAVIGATION

Waypoint Hamble Point S cardinal buoy, Q(6) + LFl 15s, 50°50'·12N 01°18'·57W, 168°/348° from/to front Ldg Lt, 0·48M. Unlit piles and buoys are a danger at night. NE gales can lower depths up to 0·6m. River is extremely crowded. Bridge clearances; Road 4·0m; Rly 6·0m; M27 4·3m.

LIGHTS AND MARKS

Ldg Lts 345°. Front Oc(2) R 12s 4m 2M; No 6 pile Bn. Rear, 820m from front, QR 12m; W mast on shore; vis 341°-349°. No 1 pile FlG 3s 3M; stbd-hand mark. No 2 pile Q(3) 10s 3M; E cardinal mark. No 3 pile Fl(2) G 5s; stbd-hand mark. No 5 pile Fl(3) G 10s; stbd-hand mark. Ldg Lts 026° on Warsash shore. Front QG; B&W chequered pile Bn; Rear Iso G 6s. No 7 pile FlG 3s; stbd-hand mark. No 8 pile FlR 3s; port-hand mark. No 9 pile Fl(2) G 5s; stbd-hand mark. No 10 pile Fl(2) R 5s; port-hand mark. Above Warsash, jetties and pontoons etc on the E side are marked by G Lts, and those on the W side by R Lts.

HAMBLE *continued*

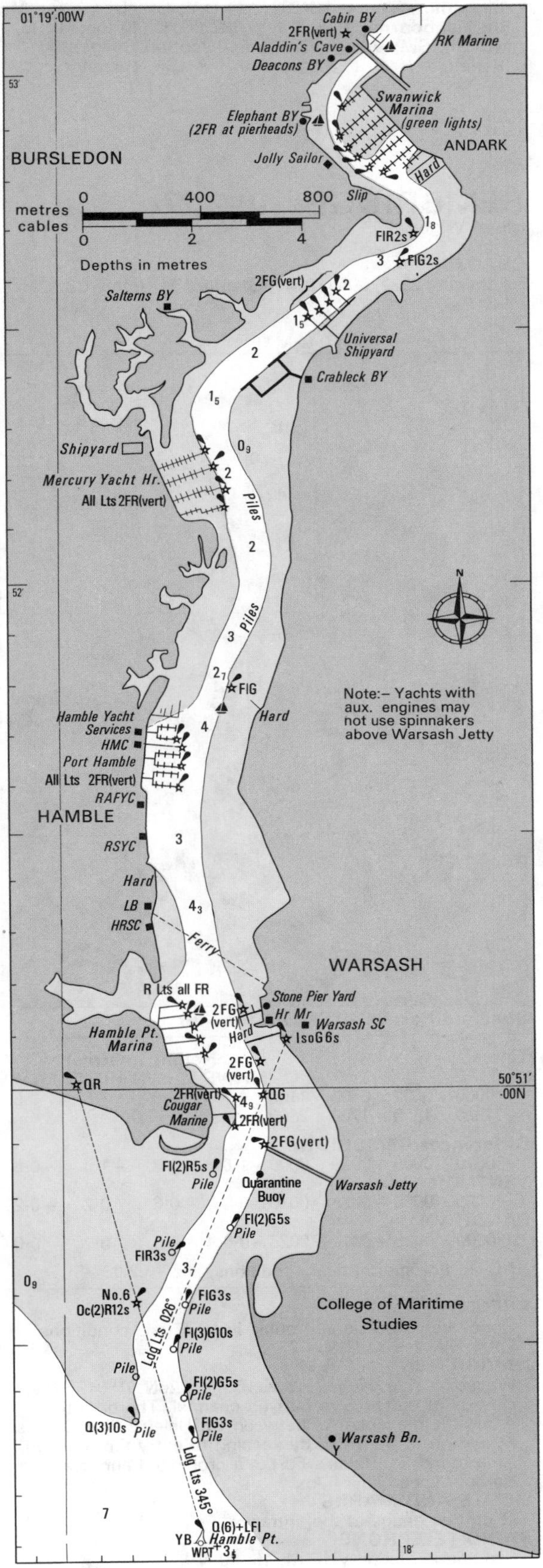

01°19'.00W
Cabin BY
2FR(vert)
Aladdin's Cave
Deacons BY
RK Marine
53'
Swanwick Marina (green lights)
Elephant BY (2FR at pierheads)
BURSLEDON
ANDARK
Jolly Sailor
Hard
metres
cables
0 400 800
0 2 4
Slip
FIR2s
FIG2s
Depths in metres
2FG(vert)
Salterns BY
Universal Shipyard
Crableck BY
Shipyard
Mercury Yacht Hr.
All Lts 2FR(vert)
Piles
52'
Piles
N
FIG
Hard
Note:– Yachts with aux. engines may not use spinnakers above Warsash Jetty
Hamble Yacht Services
HMC
Port Hamble
All Lts 2FR(vert)
RAFYC
HAMBLE
RSYC
Hard
LB
HRSC
Ferry
WARSASH
R Lts all FR
Stone Pier Yard
2FG (vert)
Hr Mr
Warsash SC
Hamble Pt. Marina
Hard
IsoG6s
2FG (vert)
QR
50°51'.00N
2FR(vert)
QG
Cougar Marine
2FR(vert)
2FG(vert)
FI(2)R5s Pile
Quarantine Buoy
Warsash Jetty
FI(2)G5s Pile
Pile FIR3s
No.6 Oc(2)R12s
FIG3s Pile
Ldg Lts 026°
FI(3)G10s Pile
College of Maritime Studies
Pile
FI(2)G5s Pile
Q(3)10s Pile
FIG3s Pile
Warsash Bn.
Ldg Lts 345°
Q(6)+LFI
YB Hamble Pt.
WPT
18'

RADIO TELEPHONE
Call: *Hamble Harbour Radio* Ch 16 68 (Mon–Fri 0830-1700; Sat & Sun April–Oct 0900-1830 Nov–Mar 0900-1300). Marinas Ch **80** M. See also Southampton 10.2.24.

TELEPHONE (0703)
Hr Mr Locks Heath 576387; MRSC Lee-on-Solent 552100; # (0703) 827350; Southampton Weather Centre 228844; Marinecall 0898 500 457; Police 581111; Dr Locks Heath 573110.

FACILITIES
EC Wednesday; **Hamble Point Marina** (220 + 10 visitors) ☎ 452464, AC, Bar, BH (40 ton), C (8 ton), CH, D, Ⓔ, El, FW, Gas, Gaz, ME, Sh, V, YC, (Access H24); **Mercury Yacht Harbour** (346) ☎ 452741, AC, Bar, BH (20 ton), El, Slip, CH, D, Ⓔ, FW, Gas, Gaz, ME, P, Sh, SM, V, (Access H24); **Port Hamble Marina** (340) ☎ 452741, AC, Bar, BH (100 ton), C (7 ton), CH, D, Ⓔ, FW, Gas, Gaz, ME, P, Sh, El, SM, Slip, V, (Access H24); **Swanwick Marina** (350 + 50 visitors) ☎ Locks Heath 885000 (After 1700, Locks Heath 885262), AC, ACA, BH (60 ton), C (12 ton), CH, D, Ⓔ, FW, Gas, Gaz, #, ⊡, ME, P, ✉, Sh, SM, V, (Access H24); **Aladdin's Cave** ☎ Bursledon 2182, CH; **BK Electro-Marine** ☎ Locks Heath 455112, Ⓔ; **Bursledon Riggers** ☎ Bursledon 4263 **Cabin BY** ☎ Bursledon 2516, AB, C (3 ton), Ⓔ, FW, Gas, M, ME, R, Sh, Slip; **Compass Point Chandlery** ☎ 452388, CH; **Crableck BY** ☎ Locks Heath 572570, Sh; **Deacons BY** ☎ Bursledon 2253, C (10 ton), Ⓔ, ME, Sh, Slip (16 ton), SM; **Ditty Box** ☎ Locks Heath 583436, CH; **Eastlands BY** ☎ Bursledon 3556, BY; **Elephant BY** ☎ Bursledon 3268, Ⓔ, ME, Sh, Slip; **Foulkes & Son** ☎ Bursledon 6349, C (10 ton), CH; **Greenham Marine** ☎ 455044, Ⓔ, El; **Hamble River BY** ☎ Locks Heath 572318, ME, Sh, Slip; **Hamble River SC** ☎ 452070; **Hamble Yacht Services** ☎ 454111, BY, BH (60 ton), C (5 ton), Ⓔ, ME, Sh, Slip (150 ton), SM; **Hudson Marine Electronics** ☎ 455129, Ⓔ; **Marine Power** ☎ Bursledon 3918, ME; **Marine Technology** ☎ 455743, El; **Piper Marine Services** ☎ 454563, (or call *Piper Fuel* Ch 37), D, P; **RAF YC** ☎ 452208, Bar, R, L; **R K Marine** ☎ Locks Heath 583572, ME; **Royal Southern YC** ☎ 453271; **Salterns BY** ☎ Bursledon 3911, BY; **Sea Fever** ☎ Locks Heath 582804, CH, Gaz; **Seasure** ☎ Locks Heath 885330 CH; **The Solent Trading Co.** ☎ 454849, CH; **Stone Pier Yard** ☎ Locks Heath 885400, BY, C, D, FW, Sh, Slip; **Universal Shipyards** (110) ☎ Locks Heath 574272, ACA, BH (50 ton), BY, C, CH, Ⓔ, FW, M, ME, Sh; **Victoria Rampart** ☎ Locks Heath 885400, BH (25 ton), BY, C (12 ton), CH, D, Ⓔ, FW, ME, P, SM; **Warsash SC** ☎ Locks Heath 583575; **Warsash Nautical Bookshop** ☎ Locks Heath 572384, ACA; **Yachtmail** ☎ 455058, CH.

Divers
Andark ☎ Locks Heath 581755 (emergency/after hours ☎ Botley 786006); **Warsash Divers** ☎ 0860-627800.

Sailmakers
Alpha Sails ☎ 553623; **Bruce Banks** ☎ Locks Heath 582444; **Hamble Sailing Services** ☎ 455868; **Lucas** ☎ 452247; **Relling** ☎ Titchfield 46816; **Richardson Sails** ☎ Bursledon 3914; **Shore Sails** ☎ Locks Heath 589450; **Sobstad** ☎ 456205; **Ullman Sails** ☎ 454254; **W L Sails** ☎ 453109.

Hards at Warsash, Hamble and Swanwick. **Slips** at Warsash, Hamble, Bursledon and Lower Swanwick.
✉ (Hamble, Bursledon, Warsash and Lower Swanwick); Ⓑ (Hamble, Bursledon, Sarisbury Green, Swanwick, Warsash); ⇌ (Hamble and Bursledon); ✈ (Southampton).
'Hamble River Guide' available from Hr Mr.

WOOTTON CREEK 10-2-26

Isle of Wight

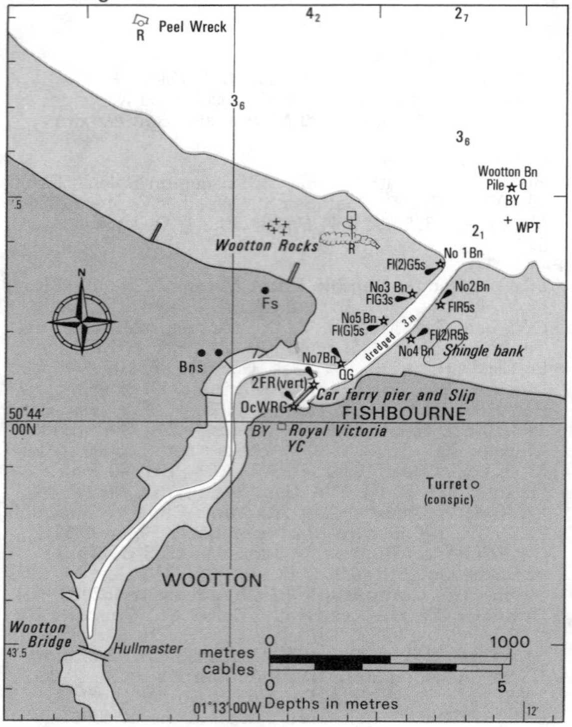

Peel Wreck
Wootton Bn Pile Q BY
WPT
Wootton Rocks
No 1 Bn
Fl(2)G5s
No3 Bn
FlG3s
No2 Bn
FlR5s
No5 Bn
Fl(G)5s
Fl(2)R5s
No4 Bn
Shingle bank
dredged 3m
Fs
Bns
No7 Bn
QG
2FR(vert)
Car ferry pier and Slip
OcWRG
FISHBOURNE
BY
Royal Victoria YC
Turret (conspic)
WOOTTON
Wootton Bridge
Hullmaster
metres
cables
0
1000
5
Depths in metres
50°44'·00N
01°13'·00W

CHARTS

Admiralty 2022, 394; Stanford 11; Imray C3, Y20; OS 196

TIDES

+0023 Dover; ML 2·8; Zone 0 (GMT)

Standard Port PORTSMOUTH (⟶)

Times				Height (metres)			
HW		LW		MHWS	MHWN	MLWN	MLWS
0000	0600	0500	1100	4·7	3·8	1·8	0·6
1200	1800	1700	2300				
Differences RYDE							
−0010	+0010	−0005	−0010	−0·2	−0·1	0·0	+0·1

NOTE: Wootton Creek comes under the authority of the Queen's Harbour Master, Portsmouth but it is exercised through a private association, Wootton Creek Fairways Association. Sec. R. Perraton Tel. 882763. For special tidal information see 10.2.13

SHELTER

Good except when stormy winds in N or E. The creek dries at MLWS above ferry terminal. Anchoring in the fairway prohibited.

NAVIGATION

Waypoint Wootton N cardinal Bn, Q, 50°44'·47N 01°12'·08W, 043°/223° from/to ferry slip, 0·59M. Beware large Sealink ferries; ferries leave astern and turn at Wootton Bn. It is difficult to beat in on the ebb. Speed limit 5 kn.

LIGHTS AND MARKS

Entrance to creek due S of SE Ryde Middle buoy and 1¾ M W of Ryde Pier. Once in channel follow four beacons on stbd side. Keep in W sector of Lt at root of ferry pier Oc WRG 10s G221°-224°, W224°-225½°, R225½°-230½°. By ferry terminal, turn on leading marks on W shore (two marks, an upright and an inverted triangle, which together form a diamond when in line).

RADIO TELEPHONE

None.

TELEPHONE (0983)

Royal Victoria YC 882325; MRSC Lee-on-Solent 552100; Fairways Association 882763; ⊞ (0703) 827350; Marinecall 0898 500 457; Police 528000; Dr 882424.

FACILITIES

EC Wootton Bridge — Wednesday, Wootton Village — Thursday; **Royal Victoria YC** ☎ 882325, Slip, M, FW, R, Bar; **Hullmaster** ☎ 884232 C (4 ton), CH, D, ER, Ⓔ, ME, Sh; **Fishbourne Quay BY** ☎ 882200, C (40 ton), D, El, ME, Sh, SM; **Village** ✉ (Ryde, Wootton Bridge); Ⓑ (Ryde); ⇌ (ferry to Portsmouth); ✈ (Southampton).

BEMBRIDGE 10-2-27

Isle of Wight

CHARTS

Admiralty 2022, 2050, 2045; Stanford 11; Imray C3, C9; OS 196

TIDES

+0020 Dover; Zone 0 (GMT)

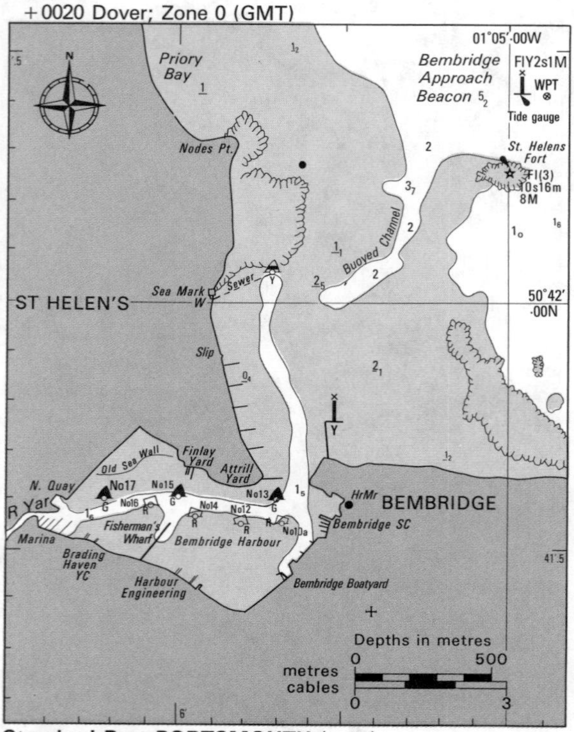

Priory Bay
01°05'·00W
Bembridge Approach Beacon
FlY2s1M
WPT
Tide gauge
Nodes Pt.
St. Helens Fort
Fl(3)10s16m 8M
Buoyed Channel
Sea Mark W
Sewer
ST HELEN'S
50°42'·00N
Slip
Old Sea Wall
Finlay Yard
Attrill Yard
N. Quay
R Yard
No17
No15
No13
No16
No14
No12
No10a
Marina
Fisherman's Wharf
Bembridge Harbour
HrMr
BEMBRIDGE
Bembridge SC
Brading Haven YC
Harbour Engineering
Bembridge Boatyard
Depths in metres
metres
cables
0
500
3

Standard Port PORTSMOUTH (⟶)

Times				Height (metres)			
HW		LW		MHWS	MHWN	MLWN	MLWS
0000	0600	0500	1100	4·7	3·8	1·8	0·6
1200	1800	1700	2300				
Differences BEMBRIDGE							
−0010	+0005	+0020	0000	−1·6	−1·5	−1·4	−0·6
VENTNOR							
−0025	−0030	−0025	−0030	−0·8	−0·6	−0·2	+0·2
SANDOWN							
0000	+0005	+0010	+0025	−0·6	−0·5	−0·2	0·0

NOTE: For special tidal conditions, see 10.2.13

SHELTER

Good. Very occasional trouble in NNE gale conditions. Entry HW −3 to HW +2.

NAVIGATION

Waypoint Tide gauge, FlY 2s, 50°42'·26N 01°04'·57W, close N of entrance to buoyed channel. The bar dries. Avoid the gravel banks between St. Helen's Fort, Nodes Pt and on to Seaview, by keeping to entry times above. Area round St. Helen's Fort is a prohibited anchorage. Harbour speed limit 6 kn.

LIGHTS AND MARKS

Lt on tide gauge at the entrance, Fl Y 2s 1M.

RADIO TELEPHONE

Bembridge Marina VHF Ch 16; **80** M.

BEMBRIDGE *continued*

TELEPHONE (0983)
Hr Mr 872828; Berthing Master 874436; MRSC Lee-on-Solent 552100; ⌗ (0703) 827350; Marinecall 0898 500 457; Police 528000; Dr 872614

FACILITIES
EC Thursday; **Bembridge Marina** (40 + 100 visitors) ☎ 874436, FW, ME, El, D, AC, ⊡, V, R, Bar; Access HW−3 to HW+2; **F. Attrill & Sons** ☎ 872319, Slip, M, ME, El, Sh, CH; **Spinnaker Yacht Chandlery** ☎ 874324, CH, Gas; **Alan Coombes** ☎ 872296, Slip, M, FW, ME, D, El, Sh, CH; **St. Helen's Quay** P, D, FW, CH; **Harbour Engineering** ☎ 872306, D, FW, ME; **Bembridge Outboards** ☎ 872817, ME, Sh; **Bembridge BY** ☎ 872423, Slip, M, ME, Sh; **Stratton BY** ☎ 873185, D; **Bembridge SC** ☎ 872683; **Brading Haven YC** ☎ 872289, Bar, R, FW; Various other boatyards with limited facilities. **Town** P, D, CH, V, R, Bar. ✉ (Bembridge, St. Helens); Ⓑ (Bembridge); ⇌ (Brading); ✈ (Southampton).

PORTSMOUTH 10-2-28

Hampshire

CHARTS
Admiralty 2628, 2629, 2625, 2631, 394, 2050, 2045; Stanford 11; Imray C3, C9; OS 197

TIDES
+0029 Dover; ML 2·8; Zone 0 (GMT)
Standard Port PORTSMOUTH (→)

Times				Height (metres)			
HW		LW		MHWS	MHWN	MLWN	MLWS
0500	1000	0000	0600	4·7	3·8	1·8	0·6
1700	2200	1200	1800				
Differences LEE-ON-SOLENT							
−0005	+0005	−0015	−0010	−0·2	−0·1	+0·1	+0·2

Portsmouth is a Standard Port and tidal predictions for each day of the year are given below. See sections 10.2.13 and 10.2.17.

SHELTER
Excellent. This very large harbour affords shelter in some area for any wind. Navigational and shipping information available from Duty Harbour Controller (VHF Ch 11 13). Call *QHM*.

Good shelter in Camber, but this is a busy little commercial dock and often full. Also beware the Isle of Wight car ferry docking near the entrance.

Anchor in Portchester Lake near the Castle, clear of moorings. Otherwise pick up a vacant mooring in the area desired, land and consult local SC.
Old Hard and steps near NE corner of castle are public but piers are private Portchester SC landings.
Yachts fitted with engines must use them between Southsea War Memorial and the Ballast Buoy (2 ca N of Fort Blockhouse). Fishing or anchoring in fairways is forbidden. Yachts must keep 100m clear of submarines berthed in Haslar Creek. If over 20m in length, ask QHM's permission (VHF R/T Ch 11) or telephone for permission to enter, leave or move in harbour, especially in fog.

NAVIGATION
Waypoint Outer Spit S cardinal buoy, Q(6) + LFl 15s, 50°45′·55N 01°05′·41W, 185°/005° from/to Southsea Castle, 1·1M. Portsmouth is a major naval port and all comes under the authority of the Queen's Harbour Master. On approaching from E inshore, yachts may go through the gap in the submerged barrier. The gap is 1 M S of Lumps Fort and is marked by a pile on the N side and a dolphin (QR) on the S side.
Beware: very strong tides in Harbour mouth; Commercial shipping and ferries; Gosport ferry; HM Ships and submarines entering and leaving. (HM Ships hoist a Code pendant, ship's pendants and a pendant Zero).
A Small Boat Channel for craft under 20m in length exists at the entrance to Portsmouth Harbour. It lies to the West of (and parallel to) the main dredged channel, and runs from No 4 Bar Buoy (QR, off Clarence Pier) to the north end of Fort Blockhouse, extending about 50m off the latter. Yachts entering harbour by the Small Boat Channel must keep to the West of the line to the Ballast Buoy until North of same. Yachts entering on the Portsmouth side of the main dredged channel must keep well to starboard, clear of the main channel. All yachts leaving harbour must use the Small Boat Channel, as described above.
Yachts crossing the entrance may only do so to the N of Ballast Buoy or to the S of No 4 Bar Buoy. Dir Lt on dolphin S of Cold Harbour jetty, Dir WRG 2m 1M, Iso G 2s 322·5°-330°, Al WG 330°-332·5°, Iso W 2s 332·5°-335° (covering the main channel), Al WR 335°-337·5°, Iso R 2s 337·5°-345° (covering the small boat channel).
Haslar Creek; a reserved area, prohibited to yachts, exists in Haslar Creek near all submarines berthed at HMS Dolphin. Speed limit within the harbour 10 kn.

FIRING AREAS
Fraser Gunnery Range, Eastney, in use Monday to Friday, 0900-1600.
Details from Portsmouth 822351 ext 6420 or from Radio Solent (see 10.2.9).
Areas and sectors of circles centred on 50°47′ N, 01°02′ W
Area 1 200 yds 120°-200°
Area 2 6,000 yds 120°-155°
Area 3 18,000 yds 120°-155°
From 30 mins before firing, R Flag with International Numeral (1 for area 1, 2 for area 2, etc) displayed from:
Range Building
Hayling Island YC

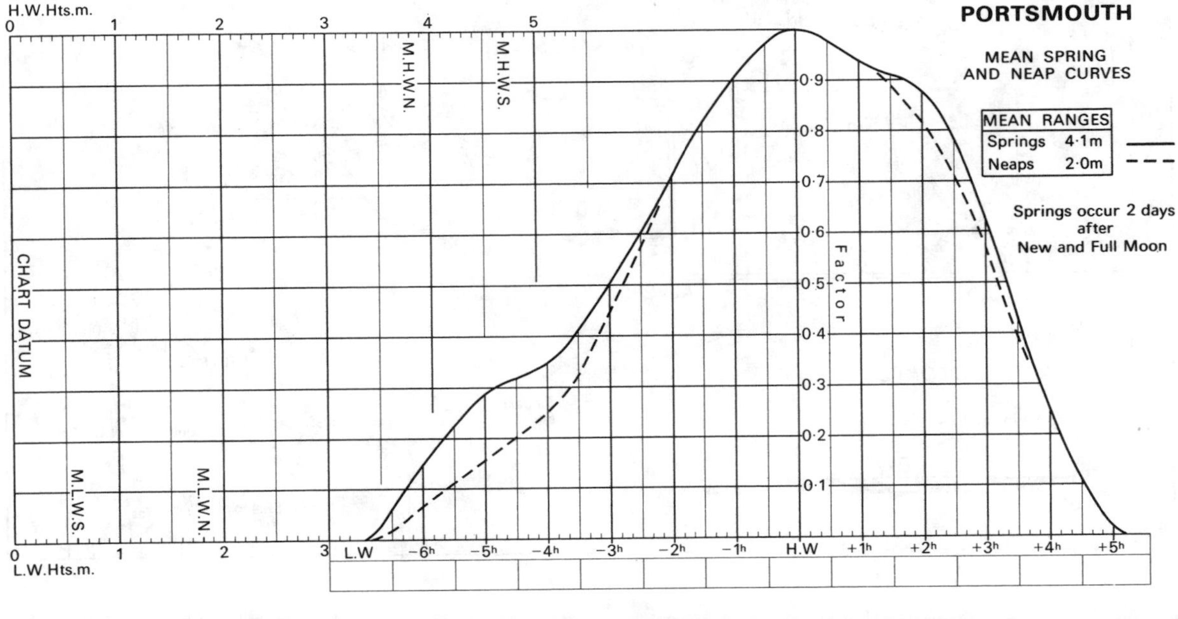
PORTSMOUTH
MEAN SPRING AND NEAP CURVES
MEAN RANGES
Springs 4·1m
Neaps 2·0m
Springs occur 2 days after New and Full Moon
H.W.Hts.m.
L.W.Hts.m.
CHART DATUM
M.H.W.N.
M.H.W.S.
M.L.W.S.
M.L.W.N.
Factor
L.W
−6h
−5h
−4h
−3h
−2h
−1h
H.W
+1h
+2h
+3h
+4h
+5h

PORTSMOUTH *continued*

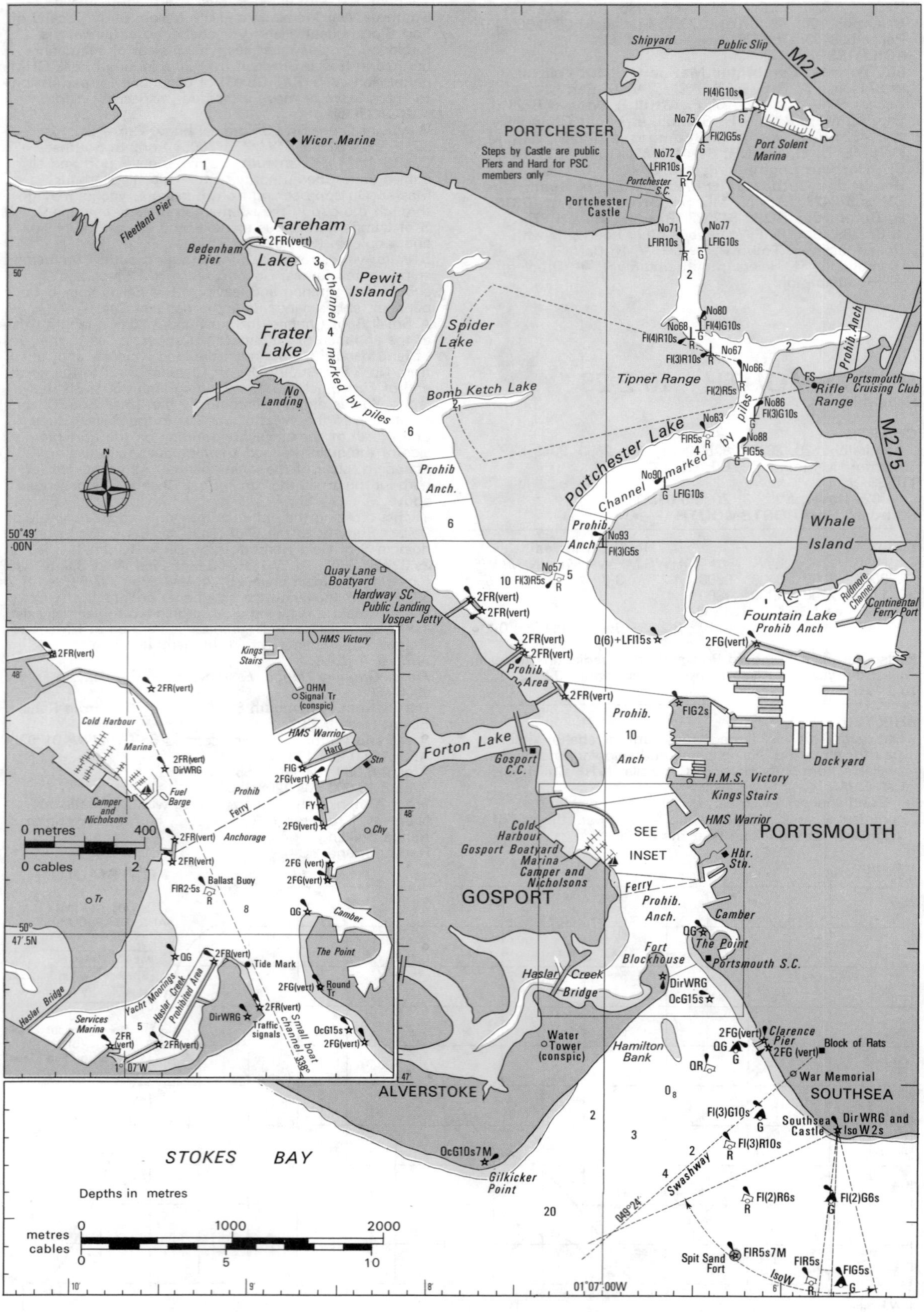

Shipyard
Public Slip
M27
Port Solent Marina
PORTCHESTER
Wicor Marine
Steps by Castle are public Piers and Hard for PSC members only
Portchester S.C.
Portchester Castle
Fleetland Pier
Bedenham Pier
Fareham Lake
Pewit Island
Channel marked by piles
Frater Lake
Spider Lake
No Landing
Bomb Ketch Lake
Tipner Range
Prohib. Anch
Portsmouth Cruising Club
Rifle Range
M275
Portchester Lake
Channel marked by piles
Prohib Anch.
Whale Island
Quay Lane Boatyard
Hardway SC Public Landing
Vosper Jetty
Rudmore Channel
Continental Ferry Port
Fountain Lake Prohib Anch
Prohib. Area
Forton Lake
Gosport C.C.
Prohib. Anch
Dockyard
H.M.S. Victory
Kings Stairs
HMS Warrior
PORTSMOUTH
SEE INSET
Cold Harbour
Gosport Boatyard
Marina
Camper and Nicholsons
GOSPORT
Ferry
Camber
The Point
Fort Blockhouse
Portsmouth S.C.
Haslar Creek Bridge
Water Tower (conspic)
Hamilton Bank
Clarence Pier
Block of Rats
War Memorial
SOUTHSEA
Southsea Castle
DirWRG and IsoW2s
ALVERSTOKE
STOKES BAY
Gilkicker Point
Swashway
Spit Sand Fort
Depths in metres
metres 0 1000 2000
cables 0 5 10
50°49′ ·00N
01°07′·00W
Inset:
HMS Victory
Kings Stairs
QHM Signal Tr (conspic)
HMS Warrior
Cold Harbour Marina
Camper and Nicholsons
Fuel Barge
Prohib Ferry Anchorage
Ballast Buoy
Camber
The Point
Tide Mark
Round Tr
Traffic signals
Small boat channel 338°
Yacht Moorings
Haslar Creek Prohibited Area
Haslar Bridge
Services Marina
0 metres 400
0 cables 2
50° 47′.5N
1° 07′W

PORTSMOUTH *continued*

Admiralty Trial Station, W of Langstone Harbour
FS by Hr Mr's Office, Langstone
FS by Hr Mr's Office, Itchenor
FS on South Parade Pier
Tipner Firing Range as shown on chartlet; danger area extends 2,500 metres from firing range.
When firing in progress R flags by day or R Lt by night shown on Tipner Range FS. When firing is in progress, yachts should keep clear of the range or pass through the area as quickly as possible.

LIGHTS AND MARKS

St Jude's church spire and Southsea Castle Lt Ho in line at 003° lead between Outer Spit buoy and Horse Sand buoy. At night keep in the W sector (000°-003°) between the Al WG and Al WR sectors of the Dir Lt on Southsea Castle, which also shows an Iso W 2s Lt, vis 339°-066°.
Swashway Channel at the NW of Elbow Spit and No 2 buoy, keep War Memorial and RH edge of block of flats in line at 049°24'.
At night the Oc W sector of the Dir Lt on Fort Blockhouse (west side of harbour entrance) shows 318.5°-321.5° between the Al WG and Al WR sectors.
The following signals displayed at Central Signal Station, Fort Blockhouse, Gilkicker Point and sometimes in the HM Ship concerned, must be obeyed.

		SIGNAL	MEANING AND APPLICATION	HOISTED/ DISPLAYED BY
1.	DAY	Red Flag with white diagonal bar.	Large vessel underway in Main Channel or Harbour. Other vessels may be required by QHM to wait alongside or hold in a waiting position.	Central Signal Station, Blockhouse Signal Station, Gilkicker Signal Station.
	NIGHT	R G G		
2.	DAY	Red Flag with white diagonal bar over one black ball.	Large vessel leaving Harbour. Vessels entering Harbour will be kept clear by QHM. Vessels leaving harbour will be allowed to proceed clear of the large vessel.	Central Signal Station, Blockhouse Signal Station, Gilkicker Signal Station.
	NIGHT	WW GG		
3.	DAY	One Black Ball over Red Flag and white diagonal bar.	Large vessel entering habour. Vessels leaving harbour will be kept clear of QHM. Vessels entering harbour will be allowed to proceed clear of the large vessel.	Central Signal Station Blockhouse Signal Station
	NIGHT	GG WW		
4.	DAY	Large Black Pennant.	No merchant or private vessel to anchor in Man-of-War Anchorage at Spithead.	Gilkicker Signal Station.
	NIGHT	W G G		
5.	DAY	International Code Pennant. Superior to Pennant Zero.	Warship or RFA underway in Main Channel or Harbour warning signal to other ships. Specific instructions will be given by QHM.	Warship or RFA.
6.	DAY	International Code Pennant Superior to Pennant NINE.	Warship or RFA underway in Main Channel or Harbour warning signal to other ships. Specific instruction will be given by QHM.	Central Signal Station, Blockhouse Signal Station, Gilkicker Signal Station.
	NIGHT	G G G		
7.	DAY	Flag E	Submarine entering or leaving Haslar Creek. Warning signal to other ships. Specific instructions will be given by QHM but all vessels are less than 20m in length are to keep clear	Blockhouse Signal Station, Blockhouse Pierhead (NOTE: The Amber Light at Blockhouse Pierhead will flash when submarines are actually underway).
	NIGHT	R Y		
8.	DAY	International Code Pennant Superior to Flag A.	Have divers down.	Ships or boats employing Divers.
	NIGHT	RR		

Fog Routine. When fog routine comes into force it is broadcast on Ch 11 13 73. Flags will be hoisted as in 1. above. Yacht traffic may continue at the skipper's discretion but must proceed with great caution.

RADIO TELEPHONE

Queens Harbour Master (call: *QHM*) VHF Ch 11 (commercial vessels & yachts), Ch 13 (RN vessels) (H24).
Fort Gilkicker (call *Gilkicker*) Ch 16 (H24).
Call: *Portsmouth Harbour Radio* (Commercial Port Manager) Ch **11** 14 (H24).
Camper and Nicholson Marina Call: *Camper Base* Ch **80** M (office hours), Fareham Yacht Harbour Ch **80** M (summer 0900-1800, winter Sun 0900-1300 LT).

TELEPHONE (0705)

QHM 822351 Ex 23694; Commercial Port Manager 820436; Camber Berthing Offices ☎ 834764 ⌗ (0703) 827350; MRSC Lee-on-Solent 552100; Marinecall 0898 500 457; Weather Centre (0703) 228844; Police 321111; Dr Gosport 80922; Fareham Health Centre Fareham 282911; ⊞ 822331

FACILITIES

PORTSMOUTH EC Wednesday (Southsea Saturday)
Port Solent (900) ☎ 210765, P, D, FW, ME, El, Ⓔ, Sh, BH (40 ton), CH, V, AC, R, Bar, Gas, Gaz, ◎ Access H24 via lock (43m × 12.5m); **Vosper Thornycroft** ☎ 379481, FW, ME, El, Ⓔ, Sh; **W G Lucas** ☎ 826629, SM; **Tudor S C** ☎ 662002, Slip, M, FW, Bar; **Royal Albert YC** ☎ 825924, M, Bar; **Ron Hale** ☎ 732985, ME, CH; **Nautech** ☎ 693611, El, Ⓔ; **Chris Hornsey** ☎ 734728, CH; **Gieves & Hawkes** ☎ 821351, ACA; Harbour Moorings ☎ 832484 **Town** ✉, Ⓑ, ⇌, ✈ (Southampton). Ferries to Continent and IoW.

GOSPORT EC Wednesday **Camper & Nicholson Marina** (350, some visitors) ☎ 524811, P, D, FW, ME, El, Sh, BH (150, 40 ton), CH, V, R, AC, Bar, Gas, Gaz, SM, ◎; **W G Lucas** ☎ 504434, CH; **Hardway SC** ☎ 581875, Slip, M, L, FW, C (mast stepping only), AB; **Hardway Marine** ☎ 580420, P, D, ACA, CH; **Solent Marine Services** ☎ 584622, El, Ⓔ, CH; **B & H Sails** ☎ 510204, CH; **Crewsaver** ☎ 528621, CH; **Blake** ☎ 523411, CH; **Camper & Nicholson Yard** ☎ 580221, BY, ME, El, Sh, Ⓔ; **Clarence Marina** ☎ 511555 ME, El, Ⓔ, Sh (also at Port Solent); **R. Arthur** ☎ 526522 CH; **Upper Deck Chandley** ☎ 504434 CH; **Allday Aluminium** ☎ 587741, Sh; **Barter & Hugget** ☎ 589431, Ⓔ, CH, SM; **Gosport BY** ☎ 586216, Slip, ME, El, Sh, C; **Town** ✉; Ⓑ; ⇌ (Portsmouth); ✈ (Southampton)
Note:– Approval has been given to build a marina at the entrance to Haslar Creek.

FAREHAM EC Wednesday **Fareham Yacht Harbour** ☎ Fareham 232854, Slip, D, FW, ME, El, Ⓔ, Sh, V, Bar, CH; (Access HW∓3); **Ladyline** ☎ Fareham 234297, M, Sh, CH; **Hamper Marine** ☎ Fareham 280203, Sh; **M B Marine Sales** ☎ Fareham 234277, ME, CH; **Wicor Marine** (200) ☎ Fareham 237112, Slip, M, D, ME, Sh, CH, AC, BH (10 ton), C (7 ton), FW, El, Ⓔ, Gas, Gaz; **Portsmouth Marine Engineering** ☎ Fareham 232854, Slip, ME, El, Ⓔ, Sh, D, FW, Gas, AC, C (10 ton), CH; **North Sails (UK)** ☎ Fareham 231525, SM; **Sobstad Sailmakers (UK)** ☎ Fareham 233242, SM; **Portchester SC** ☎ 376375 **Town** ✉; Ⓑ; ⇌; ✈ (Southampton).

ENGLAND, SOUTH COAST - PORTSMOUTH

TIME ZONE UT(GMT)

For Summer Time add ONE hour in non-shaded areas

LAT 50°48'N LONG 1°07'W

TIMES AND HEIGHTS OF HIGH AND LOW WATERS

YEAR **1992**

JANUARY

Day		Time	m
1	W	0138 0819 1415 2057	1.8 4.3 1.7 4.2
2	TH	0235 0914 1506 2150	1.7 4.4 1.5 4.3
3	F	0325 1002 1550 2236	1.6 4.4 1.4 4.4
4	SA	0408 1043 1629 ● 2315	1.5 4.5 1.3 4.5
5	SU	0447 1120 1705 2351	1.4 4.5 1.1 4.5
6	M	0522 1154 1738	1.3 4.5 1.1
7	TU	0024 0555 1226 1808	4.6 1.3 4.5 1.1
8	W	0057 0627 1258 1839	4.5 1.3 4.4 1.1
9	TH	0129 0659 1330 1910	4.5 1.3 4.4 1.1
10	F	0202 0732 1404 1943	4.5 1.4 4.3 1.2
11	SA	0237 0808 1442 2020	4.4 1.5 4.2 1.4
12	SU	0317 0850 1525 2105	4.3 1.6 4.1 1.5
13	M	0403 0942 1619 ☽ 2200	4.2 1.8 4.0 1.7
14	TU	0500 1047 1726 2311	4.2 1.9 3.9 1.8
15	W	0607 1206 1845	4.1 1.9 3.9
16	TH	0034 0721 1325 2005	1.8 4.2 1.7 4.0
17	F	0149 0833 1431 2116	1.7 4.3 1.4 4.3
18	SA	0253 0937 1527 2216	1.4 4.5 1.1 4.5
19	SU	0348 1032 1617 ○ 2308	1.1 4.7 0.7 4.8
20	M	0437 1122 1703 2356	0.8 4.9 0.5 5.0
21	TU	0523 1209 1747	0.6 5.0 0.3
22	W	0042 0608 1255 1829	5.1 0.6 5.0 0.3
23	TH	0126 0652 1339 1912	5.1 0.6 4.8 0.4
24	F	0210 0737 1424 1956	4.9 0.8 4.7 0.7
25	SA	0255 0823 1511 2043	4.8 1.0 4.4 1.0
26	SU	0342 0915 1601 ☾ 2136	4.6 1.3 4.2 1.4
27	M	0432 1014 1659 2240	4.3 1.6 4.0 1.7
28	TU	0529 1127 1807 2357	4.1 1.8 3.8 2.0
29	W	0635 1246 1926	4.0 1.9 3.8
30	TH	0114 0747 1355 2039	2.0 4.0 1.8 3.9
31	F	0219 0853 1451 2136	1.9 4.1 1.6 4.1

FEBRUARY

Day		Time	m
1	SA	0311 0945 1535 2221	1.8 4.2 1.4 4.3
2	SU	0353 1027 1613 2259	1.6 4.3 1.2 4.4
3	M	0430 1103 1647 ● 2332	1.4 4.4 1.0 4.5
4	TU	0503 1136 1717	1.2 4.4 0.9
5	W	0004 0533 1208 1745	4.6 1.1 4.5 0.8
6	TH	0035 0602 1239 1813	4.6 1.0 4.5 0.8
7	F	0105 0631 1310 1842	4.6 1.0 4.4 0.9
8	SA	0135 0701 1342 1913	4.5 1.1 4.4 1.0
9	SU	0208 0735 1417 1948	4.4 1.2 4.3 1.2
10	M	0243 0813 1457 2030	4.3 1.3 4.1 1.4
11	TU	0326 0900 1549 ☽ 2122	4.2 1.6 4.0 1.7
12	W	0421 1004 1657 2236	4.1 1.8 3.8 1.9
13	TH	0532 1133 1823	4.0 1.9 3.8
14	F	0013 0656 1307 1952	1.9 4.0 1.7 3.9
15	SA	0138 0818 1418 2106	1.7 4.1 1.4 4.2
16	SU	0243 0925 1515 2205	1.4 4.4 1.0 4.5
17	M	0336 1021 1603 2254	1.0 4.7 0.6 4.8
18	TU	0423 1109 1647 ○ 2339	0.7 4.9 0.3 5.0
19	W	0507 1153 1729	0.4 5.0 0.2
20	TH	0022 0548 1236 1808	5.1 0.3 5.0 0.2
21	F	0103 0629 1318 1848	5.1 0.4 4.9 0.3
22	SA	0143 0710 1359 1929	4.9 0.6 4.7 0.6
23	SU	0223 0752 1441 2011	4.7 0.9 4.4 1.0
24	M	0305 0838 1527 2059	4.4 1.3 4.1 1.5
25	TU	0350 0932 1620 ☾ 2201	4.2 1.6 3.9 1.9
26	W	0442 1044 1727 2325	3.9 1.9 3.7 2.1
27	TH	0550 1213 1853	3.7 2.0 3.7
28	F	0052 0713 1331 2017	2.2 3.7 1.9 3.8
29	SA	0200 0830 1428 2116	2.0 3.8 1.7 4.0

MARCH

Day		Time	m
1	SU	0252 0924 1513 2158	1.8 4.0 1.5 4.2
2	M	0332 1005 1549 2233	1.5 4.2 1.2 4.4
3	TU	0407 1040 1621 2306	1.3 4.3 1.0 4.5
4	W	0438 1113 1651 ● 2337	1.0 4.4 0.8 4.6
5	TH	0507 1145 1719	0.9 4.5 0.7
6	F	0007 0535 1217 1746	4.6 0.8 4.5 0.7
7	SA	0038 0603 1249 1815	4.6 0.8 4.5 0.8
8	SU	0109 0633 1321 1847	4.5 0.8 4.5 0.9
9	M	0141 0707 1357 1923	4.4 1.0 4.3 1.1
10	TU	0217 0745 1439 2006	4.3 1.2 4.2 1.4
11	W	0300 0833 1533 2101	4.1 1.4 4.0 1.7
12	TH	0357 0937 1644 ☽ 2221	4.0 1.7 3.8 1.9
13	F	0513 1114 1813	3.8 1.8 3.8
14	SA	0005 0643 1252 1941	1.9 3.8 1.7 4.0
15	SU	0128 0807 1402 2052	1.7 4.1 1.3 4.3
16	M	0229 0912 1457 2147	1.3 4.4 0.9 4.6
17	TU	0320 1005 1544 2234	0.9 4.6 0.5 4.9
18	W	0405 1051 1627 ○ 2317	0.6 4.9 0.3 5.0
19	TH	0446 1134 1707 2358	0.4 5.0 0.2 5.0
20	F	0526 1214 1746	0.3 4.9 0.3
21	SA	0036 0604 1254 1824	5.0 0.4 4.8 0.5
22	SU	0114 0643 1333 1902	4.8 0.6 4.6 0.8
23	M	0151 0722 1413 1943	4.6 0.9 4.4 1.2
24	TU	0229 0804 1455 2028	4.3 1.3 4.1 1.6
25	W	0309 0853 1544 2126	4.0 1.7 3.9 2.0
26	TH	0357 0959 1646 ☾ 2248	3.8 2.0 3.7 2.2
27	F	0500 1128 1809	3.6 2.1 3.6
28	SA	0017 0624 1250 1935	2.2 3.5 2.0 3.7
29	SU	0127 0750 1350 2037	2.1 3.6 1.8 3.9
30	M	0219 0848 1436 2121	1.8 3.8 1.5 4.2
31	TU	0300 0931 1514 2158	1.5 4.1 1.3 4.4

APRIL

Day		Time	m
1	W	0335 1009 1548 2232	1.3 4.3 1.0 4.5
2	TH	0407 1044 1619 2305	1.0 4.4 0.9 4.6
3	F	0437 1118 1650 ● 2338	0.8 4.5 0.8 4.7
4	SA	0507 1153 1720	0.8 4.6 0.7
5	SU	0011 0537 1228 1752	4.6 0.7 4.6 0.8
6	M	0045 0610 1304 1828	4.6 0.8 4.5 0.9
7	TU	0120 0646 1344 1907	4.5 0.9 4.4 1.1
8	W	0200 0728 1431 1954	4.3 1.1 4.3 1.4
9	TH	0247 0819 1528 2055	4.1 1.4 4.1 1.7
10	F	0347 0928 1639 ☽ 2218	3.9 1.6 3.9 1.9
11	SA	0504 1100 1802 2352	3.8 1.7 3.9 1.8
12	SU	0630 1229 1922	3.9 1.6 4.1
13	M	0108 0748 1338 2028	1.6 4.1 1.3 4.4
14	TU	0208 0851 1433 2122	1.2 4.4 0.9 4.6
15	W	0258 0943 1521 2209	0.9 4.6 0.7 4.8
16	TH	0342 1029 1603 2252	0.7 4.8 0.5 4.9
17	F	0423 1111 1644 ○ 2332	0.5 4.9 0.5 4.9
18	SA	0503 1152 1723	0.5 4.9 0.5
19	SU	0010 0540 1231 1800	4.9 0.6 4.8 0.7
20	M	0046 0618 1309 1839	4.7 0.8 4.6 1.0
21	TU	0122 0656 1347 1918	4.5 1.0 4.4 1.3
22	W	0157 0737 1427 2002	4.3 1.3 4.2 1.7
23	TH	0234 0821 1512 2054	4.0 1.6 4.0 2.0
24	F	0318 0917 1606 ☾ 2202	3.8 1.9 3.8 2.2
25	SA	0413 1030 1713 2321	3.7 2.0 3.7 2.2
26	SU	0523 1148 1828	3.6 2.0 3.8
27	M	0032 0641 1253 1935	2.1 3.6 1.9 3.9
28	TU	0129 0749 1345 2029	1.9 3.8 1.7 4.1
29	W	0215 0843 1429 2113	1.6 4.0 1.4 4.3
30	TH	0255 0928 1508 2153	1.4 4.2 1.2 4.5

Chart Datum: 2.73 metres below Ordnance Datum (Newlyn)

ENGLAND, SOUTH COAST - PORTSMOUTH

TIME ZONE UT(GMT)

For Summer Time add ONE hour in non-shaded areas

LAT 50°48′N LONG 1°07′W

TIMES AND HEIGHTS OF HIGH AND LOW WATERS

YEAR **1992**

MAY

Day	Time	m	Day	Time	m
1	0331	1.1	**16**	0402	0.8
	1010	4.4		1050	4.7
F	1545	1.0	SA	1622	0.8
	2232	4.6		○ 2308	4.8
2	0406	1.0	**17**	0443	0.8
	1050	4.5		1131	4.7
SA	1621	0.9	**SU**	1702	0.9
	● 2309	4.7		2346	4.7
3	0441	0.8	**18**	0522	0.8
	1129	4.6		1210	4.6
SU	1657	0.9	M	1741	1.0
	2347	4.7			
4	0517	0.8	**19**	0022	4.6
	1209	4.7		0559	1.0
M	1735	0.9	TU	1249	4.5
				1819	1.2
5	0026	4.6	**20**	0057	4.5
	0554	0.8		0637	1.1
TU	1252	4.6	W	1326	4.4
	1815	1.0		1858	1.4
6	0107	4.5	**21**	0131	4.3
	0635	0.9		0715	1.3
W	1337	4.5	TH	1404	4.2
	1900	1.2		1939	1.6
7	0151	4.4	**22**	0207	4.1
	0722	1.1		0755	1.5
TH	1427	4.4	F	1444	4.1
	1951	1.4		2023	1.8
8	0242	4.2	**23**	0247	4.0
	0816	1.3		0840	1.7
F	1524	4.3	SA	1530	4.0
	2052	1.6		2115	2.0
9	0341	4.1	**24**	0333	3.9
	0922	1.4		0933	1.8
SA	1630	4.2	**SU**	1622	3.9
	☽ 2206	1.7		☾ 2215	2.1
10	0450	4.0	**25**	0428	3.8
	1040	1.5		1035	1.9
SU	1741	4.2	M	1721	3.9
	2325	1.7		2321	2.1
11	0606	4.0	**26**	0531	3.7
	1158	1.5		1140	1.9
M	1853	4.3	TU	1824	4.0
12	0038	1.6	**27**	0024	2.0
	0718	4.1		0639	3.8
TU	1306	1.3	W	1242	1.8
	1957	4.4		1925	4.1
13	0139	1.3	**28**	0121	1.8
	0822	4.3		0744	3.9
W	1404	1.1	TH	1337	1.6
	2053	4.6		2021	4.2
14	0232	1.1	**29**	0210	1.6
	0917	4.5		0843	4.1
TH	1454	1.0	F	1426	1.4
	2142	4.7		2111	4.4
15	0319	0.9	**30**	0256	1.3
	1005	4.6		0935	4.3
F	1540	0.9	SA	1512	1.2
	2226	4.8		2159	4.6
			31	0339	1.1
				1023	4.5
			SU	1556	1.1
				2244	4.7

JUNE

Day	Time	m	Day	Time	m
1	0421	0.9	**16**	0508	1.1
	1110	4.6		1155	4.5
M	1639	1.0	TU	1726	1.2
	● 2328	4.7			
2	0503	0.8	**17**	0004	4.5
	1156	4.7		0544	1.1
TU	1723	0.9	W	1233	4.5
				1803	1.3
3	0012	4.7	**18**	0038	4.4
	0545	0.8		0620	1.1
W	1243	4.7	TH	1308	4.4
	1808	0.9		1839	1.3
4	0058	4.7	**19**	0112	4.4
	0630	0.8		0655	1.2
TH	1331	4.7	F	1343	4.4
	1855	1.0		1915	1.4
5	0145	4.6	**20**	0145	4.3
	0718	0.9		0730	1.3
F	1421	4.6	SA	1418	4.3
	1946	1.1		1952	1.6
6	0235	4.5	**21**	0220	4.2
	0810	1.0		0806	1.4
SA	1514	4.5	**SU**	1456	4.2
	2041	1.3		2032	1.7
7	0329	4.3	**22**	0259	4.1
	0907	1.2		0846	1.5
SU	1611	4.4	M	1538	4.2
	☽ 2143	1.5		2117	1.8
8	0429	4.2	**23**	0344	4.0
	1012	1.3		0932	1.7
M	1712	4.4	TU	1625	4.1
	2251	1.6		☾ 2211	1.9
9	0535	4.1	**24**	0436	3.9
	1121	1.4		1029	1.8
TU	1817	4.3	W	1720	4.1
				2313	1.9
10	0001	1.6	**25**	0538	3.9
	0643	4.1		1134	1.8
W	1231	1.4	TH	1822	4.1
	1920	4.4			
11	0107	1.5	**26**	0021	1.9
	0749	4.2		0648	3.9
TH	1334	1.4	F	1243	1.8
	2020	4.4		1927	4.2
12	0206	1.4	**27**	0126	1.7
	0850	4.3		0759	4.0
F	1430	1.3	SA	1347	1.6
	2115	4.5		2031	4.3
13	0258	1.3	**28**	0225	1.5
	0944	4.4		0905	4.2
SA	1520	1.3	**SU**	1445	1.4
	2204	4.6		2130	4.5
14	0345	1.2	**29**	0318	1.2
	1032	4.5		1003	4.4
SU	1605	1.2	M	1537	1.2
	2248	4.6		2224	4.6
15	0428	1.1	**30**	0406	1.0
	1116	4.5		1056	4.6
M	1647	1.2	TU	1626	1.0
	○ 2327	4.6		● 2313	4.7

JULY

Day	Time	m	Day	Time	m
1	0453	0.7	**16**	0529	1.0
	1146	4.8		1216	4.5
W	1713	0.8	TH	1746	1.2
2	0001	4.8	**17**	0021	4.5
	0537	0.6		0601	1.0
TH	1234	4.9	F	1249	4.5
	1759	0.7		1818	1.2
3	0048	4.8	**18**	0053	4.4
	0622	0.5		0632	1.0
F	1321	4.9	SA	1320	4.5
	1845	0.7		1850	1.2
4	0134	4.8	**19**	0124	4.4
	0707	0.6		0702	1.1
SA	1407	4.9	**SU**	1351	4.4
	1932	0.8		1921	1.3
5	0222	4.7	**20**	0156	4.3
	0755	0.7		0733	1.2
SU	1455	4.8	M	1424	4.4
	2022	1.0		1955	1.4
6	0311	4.5	**21**	0230	4.3
	0845	0.9		0807	1.3
M	1546	4.6	TU	1459	4.3
	2116	1.2		2032	1.5
7	0404	4.4	**22**	0309	4.2
	0940	1.2		0846	1.5
TU	1639	4.5	W	1540	4.2
	☽ 2216	1.4		☾ 2116	1.7
8	0502	4.2	**23**	0355	4.0
	1044	1.4		0934	1.7
W	1738	4.3	TH	1629	4.1
	2324	1.6		2213	1.8
9	0607	4.1	**24**	0453	3.9
	1154	1.6		1037	1.8
TH	1842	4.2	F	1730	4.1
				2326	1.9
10	0036	1.7	**25**	0604	3.9
	0718	4.0		1157	1.9
F	1306	1.7	SA	1841	4.0
	1948	4.2			
11	0144	1.6	**26**	0048	1.8
	0828	4.1		0726	3.9
SA	1410	1.7	**SU**	1318	1.8
	2051	4.2		1958	4.1
12	0243	1.5	**27**	0201	1.6
	0929	4.2		0844	4.1
SU	1505	1.6	M	1426	1.6
	2146	4.3		2109	4.3
13	0333	1.4	**28**	0301	1.3
	1020	4.3		0950	4.3
M	1553	1.5	TU	1524	1.2
	2233	4.4		2209	4.5
14	0416	1.2	**29**	0353	0.9
	1104	4.4		1045	4.6
TU	1634	1.3	W	1614	0.9
	○ 2313	4.4		● 2301	4.7
15	0454	1.1	**30**	0440	0.6
	1142	4.5		1133	4.9
W	1712	1.2	TH	1701	0.7
	2348	4.5		2349	4.9
			31	0525	0.4
				1219	5.0
			F	1746	0.5

AUGUST

Day	Time	m	Day	Time	m
1	0034	5.0	**16**	0032	4.5
	0607	0.3		0605	0.9
SA	1304	5.1	**SU**	1255	4.6
	1829	0.5		1822	1.0
2	0119	4.9	**17**	0102	4.5
	0650	0.3		0633	0.9
SU	1347	5.0	M	1324	4.5
	1913	0.6		1851	1.0
3	0203	4.8	**18**	0133	4.4
	0733	0.5		0702	1.0
M	1431	4.9	TU	1354	4.5
	1958	0.8		1921	1.1
4	0248	4.6	**19**	0205	4.4
	0819	0.8		0734	1.2
TU	1516	4.7	W	1427	4.4
	2046	1.1		1956	1.3
5	0337	4.4	**20**	0242	4.3
	0909	1.2		0811	1.4
W	1604	4.4	TH	1504	4.3
	☽ 2141	1.4		2037	1.5
6	0430	4.2	**21**	0326	4.1
	1009	1.6		0857	1.6
TH	1658	4.2	F	1551	4.2
	2247	1.7		☾ 2130	1.7
7	0534	4.0	**22**	0422	4.0
	1122	1.8		0959	1.9
F	1802	4.0	SA	1651	4.0
				2245	1.9
8	0006	1.9	**23**	0537	3.8
	0649	3.9		1127	2.0
SA	1243	2.0	**SU**	1809	3.9
	1916	3.9			
9	0123	1.8	**24**	0020	1.9
	0810	3.9		0706	3.9
SU	1355	1.9	M	1259	1.9
	2031	4.0		1935	4.0
10	0227	1.7	**25**	0141	1.6
	0917	4.1		0830	4.1
M	1453	1.8	TU	1411	1.6
	2131	4.1		2053	4.2
11	0318	1.5	**26**	0244	1.2
	1007	4.3		0936	4.4
TU	1540	1.6	W	1509	1.2
	2218	4.2		2154	4.5
12	0400	1.3	**27**	0336	0.8
	1048	4.4		1029	4.7
W	1619	1.4	TH	1558	0.8
	2256	4.3		2245	4.8
13	0436	1.1	**28**	0423	0.5
	1123	4.5		1116	5.0
TH	1653	1.2	F	1644	0.5
	○ 2330	4.4		● 2332	5.0
14	0508	1.0	**29**	0506	0.3
	1155	4.6		1200	5.1
F	1725	1.1	SA	1727	0.4
15	0001	4.5	**30**	0016	5.0
	0537	0.9		0547	0.2
SA	1225	4.6	**SU**	1242	5.1
	1754	1.0		1808	0.4
			31	0059	5.0
				0628	0.3
			M	1323	5.1
				1850	0.5

Chart Datum: 2.73 metres below Ordnance Datum (Newlyn)

ENGLAND, SOUTH COAST - PORTSMOUTH

TIME ZONE UT(GMT)

For Summer Time add ONE hour in non-shaded areas

LAT 50°48'N LONG 1°07'W

TIMES AND HEIGHTS OF HIGH AND LOW WATERS

YEAR **1992**

SEPTEMBER

Day	Time	m	Day	Time	m
1	0141	4.9	16	0110	4.6
	0710	0.5		0635	1.0
TU	1404	4.9	W	1328	4.6
	1932	0.7		1853	1.1
2	0224	4.7	17	0144	4.5
	0753	0.9		0709	1.2
W	1446	4.7	TH	1401	4.5
	2017	1.1		1928	1.2
3	0309	4.4	18	0222	4.4
	0841	1.3		0747	1.4
TH	1530	4.4	F	1439	4.3
	☽ 2109	1.4		2011	1.4
4	0400	4.2	19	0308	4.2
	0938	1.7		0835	1.7
F	1620	4.1	SA	1526	4.2
	2213	1.8		☾ 2105	1.7
5	0502	3.9	20	0406	4.0
	1053	2.0		0940	1.9
SA	1722	3.9	SU	1629	4.0
	2335	2.0		2222	1.8
6	0620	3.8	21	0523	3.9
	1219	2.2		1111	2.0
SU	1842	3.8	M	1750	3.9
				2359	1.8
7	0057	2.0	22	0651	4.0
	0748	3.9		1241	1.9
M	1334	2.1	TU	1918	4.0
	2006	3.8			
8	0204	1.8	23	0120	1.6
	0856	4.0		0812	4.2
TU	1432	1.9	W	1352	1.6
	2109	4.0		2035	4.3
9	0254	1.6	24	0223	1.2
	0944	4.2		0915	4.5
W	1517	1.7	TH	1449	1.2
	2154	4.1		2135	4.5
10	0335	1.4	25	0315	0.8
	1022	4.4		1007	4.8
TH	1555	1.4	F	1538	0.8
	2231	4.3		2225	4.8
11	0410	1.2	26	0401	0.5
	1055	4.5		1053	5.0
F	1627	1.2	SA	1622	0.6
	2304	4.4		● 2311	5.0
12	0441	1.0	27	0444	0.4
	1127	4.6		1136	5.1
SA	1657	1.0	SU	1705	0.4
	○ 2336	4.5		2354	5.1
13	0510	0.9	28	0525	0.3
	1157	4.7		1217	5.1
SU	1726	1.0	M	1746	0.4
14	0007	4.6	29	0036	5.0
	0537	0.9		0606	0.5
M	1227	4.7	TU	1258	5.0
	1753	0.9		1826	0.6
15	0039	4.6	30	0118	4.9
	0605	0.9		0647	0.7
TU	1257	4.6	W	1337	4.9
	1822	1.0		1907	0.8

OCTOBER

Day	Time	m	Day	Time	m
1	0200	4.7	16	0128	4.6
	0729	1.1		0651	1.2
TH	1417	4.6	F	1342	4.5
	1951	1.2		1910	1.2
2	0243	4.4	17	0210	4.5
	0815	1.5		0734	1.4
F	1458	4.3	SA	1424	4.4
	2039	1.5		1956	1.4
3	0331	4.2	18	0259	4.3
	0910	1.9		0825	1.7
SA	1544	4.1	SU	1514	4.2
	☽ 2139	1.9		2053	1.6
4	0429	4.0	19	0359	4.2
	1021	2.2		0932	1.9
SU	1641	3.8	M	1618	4.1
	2256	2.1		☾ 2208	1.7
5	0541	3.8	20	0512	4.1
	1143	2.3		1056	1.9
M	1755	3.7	TU	1735	4.0
				2335	1.7
6	0016	2.1	21	0632	4.1
	0705	3.9		1218	1.8
TU	1258	2.2	W	1858	4.1
	1921	3.7			
7	0123	2.0	22	0052	1.5
	0814	4.0		0746	4.3
W	1356	2.0	TH	1327	1.5
	2028	3.9		2010	4.3
8	0215	1.7	23	0156	1.2
	0904	4.2		0848	4.6
TH	1442	1.8	F	1424	1.2
	2116	4.1		2110	4.6
9	0258	1.5	24	0249	1.0
	0944	4.4		0941	4.8
F	1520	1.5	SA	1514	1.0
	2156	4.3		2202	4.8
10	0334	1.3	25	0337	0.7
	1019	4.5		1028	5.0
SA	1555	1.3	SU	1600	0.7
	2232	4.4		● 2249	4.9
11	0408	1.1	26	0421	0.6
	1048	4.6		1111	5.1
SU	1626	1.1	M	1643	0.6
	○ 2306	4.6		2333	5.0
12	0439	1.0	27	0504	0.6
	1126	4.7		1153	5.1
M	1656	1.0	TU	1724	0.7
	2340	4.6			
13	0510	1.0	28	0015	5.0
	1158	4.7		0545	0.8
TU	1726	1.0	W	1233	4.9
				1805	0.8
14	0015	4.7	29	0057	4.8
	0540	1.0		0626	1.0
W	1232	4.7	TH	1311	4.8
	1757	1.0		1845	1.0
15	0051	4.7	30	0137	4.7
	0614	1.1		0708	1.3
TH	1306	4.6	F	1349	4.6
	1832	1.1		1927	1.3
			31	0219	4.5
				0752	1.6
			SA	1428	4.3
				2013	1.6

NOVEMBER

Day	Time	m	Day	Time	m
1	0304	4.3	16	0254	4.5
	0842	1.9		0820	1.5
SU	1510	4.1	M	1507	4.3
	2104	1.8		2045	1.4
2	0354	4.1	17	0351	4.4
	0942	2.1		0922	1.7
M	1559	3.9	TU	1607	4.2
	☽ 2207	2.0		☾ 2151	1.5
3	0453	4.0	18	0456	4.3
	1052	2.3		1034	1.8
TU	1700	3.8	W	1716	4.1
	2317	2.1		2306	1.6
4	0601	3.9	19	0605	4.3
	1202	2.2		1148	1.7
W	1812	3.7	TH	1831	4.2
5	0024	2.0	20	0019	1.5
	0708	4.0		0714	4.4
TH	1304	2.1	F	1258	1.6
	1923	3.8		1941	4.3
6	0122	1.9	21	0126	1.4
	0806	4.2		0817	4.6
F	1355	1.9	SA	1358	1.4
	2022	4.0		2044	4.5
7	0210	1.7	22	0223	1.2
	0854	4.3		0913	4.7
SA	1439	1.7	SU	1452	1.2
	2111	4.2		2139	4.7
8	0253	1.5	23	0314	1.1
	0937	4.5		1003	4.9
SU	1518	1.5	M	1540	1.0
	2154	4.4		2229	4.8
9	0332	1.3	24	0401	1.0
	1016	4.6		1048	4.9
M	1554	1.3	TU	1625	0.9
	2235	4.5		● 2314	4.8
10	0408	1.2	25	0445	1.0
	1054	4.7		1131	4.9
TU	1629	1.1	W	1707	0.9
	○ 2315	4.7		2357	4.8
11	0444	1.1	26	0527	1.0
	1132	4.8		1210	4.8
W	1704	1.0	TH	1748	0.9
	2355	4.7			
12	0521	1.1	27	0038	4.8
	1210	4.8		0608	1.2
TH	1740	1.0	F	1248	4.7
				1827	1.1
13	0035	4.7	28	0118	4.6
	0559	1.1		0648	1.3
F	1249	4.7	SA	1324	4.5
	1818	1.0		1906	1.2
14	0118	4.7	29	0156	4.5
	0641	1.2		0729	1.5
SA	1330	4.6	SU	1400	4.4
	1901	1.1		1946	1.4
15	0203	4.6	30	0236	4.4
	0727	1.4		0812	1.8
SU	1415	4.5	M	1438	4.2
	1949	1.2		2028	1.6

DECEMBER

Day	Time	m	Day	Time	m
1	0317	4.2	16	0335	4.6
	0859	1.9		0903	1.4
TU	1520	4.0	W	1551	4.4
	2115	1.8		☾ 2128	1.3
2	0404	4.1	17	0432	4.5
	0954	2.1		1006	1.6
W	1608	3.9	TH	1653	4.2
	☽ 2210	1.9		2233	1.4
3	0457	4.1	18	0535	4.4
	1055	2.2		1116	1.6
TH	1706	3.8	F	1801	4.2
	2312	2.0		2345	1.6
4	0556	4.1	19	0641	4.4
	1159	2.1		1228	1.6
F	1812	3.8	SA	1913	4.2
5	0015	2.0	20	0056	1.6
	0658	4.1		0746	4.5
SA	1300	2.0	SU	1335	1.5
	1920	3.9		2021	4.3
6	0115	1.9	21	0201	1.5
	0757	4.3		0847	4.5
SU	1354	1.8	M	1435	1.4
	2022	4.1		2121	4.5
7	0209	1.7	22	0257	1.4
	0851	4.4		0941	4.6
M	1442	1.6	TU	1526	1.2
	2118	4.3		2214	4.6
8	0257	1.5	23	0347	1.3
	0940	4.5		1030	4.7
TU	1526	1.4	W	1612	1.1
	2207	4.5		2301	4.7
9	0341	1.4	24	0432	1.2
	1026	4.7		1113	4.7
W	1607	1.2	TH	1654	1.0
	○ 2254	4.6		● 2344	4.7
10	0424	1.2	25	0513	1.2
	1109	4.8		1152	4.7
TH	1648	1.0	F	1733	1.0
	2339	4.7			
11	0506	1.1	26	0023	4.7
	1152	4.8		0551	1.2
F	1728	0.9	SA	1229	4.6
				1809	1.0
12	0023	4.8	27	0059	4.6
	0548	1.0		0628	1.3
SA	1236	4.8	SU	1302	4.5
	1809	0.8		1843	1.1
13	0108	4.8	28	0133	4.5
	0632	1.0		0704	1.4
SU	1320	4.7	M	1335	4.4
	1853	0.8		1917	1.2
14	0155	4.8	29	0207	4.5
	0718	1.1		0740	1.5
M	1406	4.6	TU	1408	4.3
	1939	0.9		1952	1.3
15	0243	4.7	30	0242	4.4
	0808	1.2		0818	1.7
TU	1456	4.5	W	1444	4.2
	2030	1.1		2029	1.5
			31	0320	4.3
				0859	1.8
			TH	1525	4.0
				2110	1.7

Chart Datum: 2.73 metres below Ordnance Datum (Newlyn)

10.2.29 ISLE OF WIGHT TIDAL STREAMS

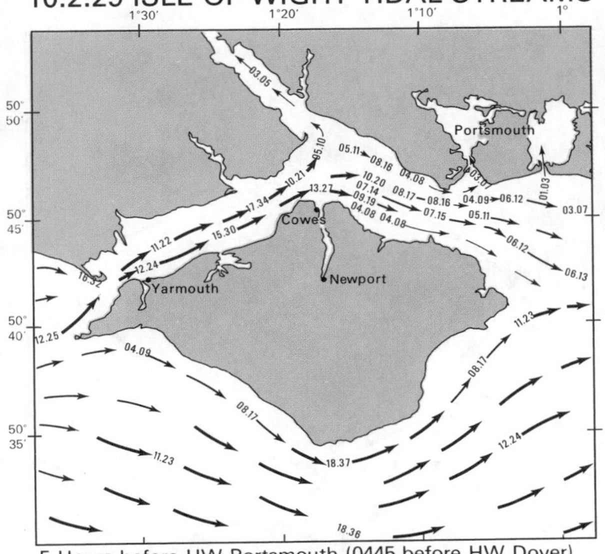
1°30′
1°20′
1°10′
1°
50° 50′
50° 45′
50° 40′
50° 35′
Portsmouth
Cowes
Newport
Yarmouth

5 Hours before HW Portsmouth (0445 before HW Dover)

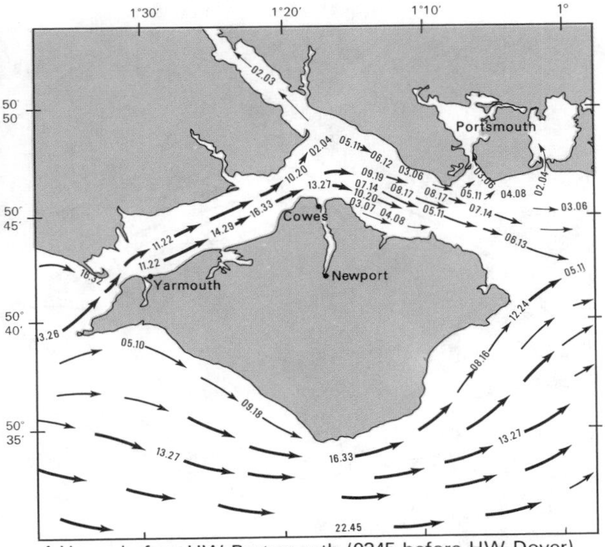
1°30′
1°20′
1°10′
1°
50° 50′
50° 45′
50° 40′
50° 35′
Portsmouth
Cowes
Newport
Yarmouth

4 Hours before HW Portsmouth (0345 before HW Dover)

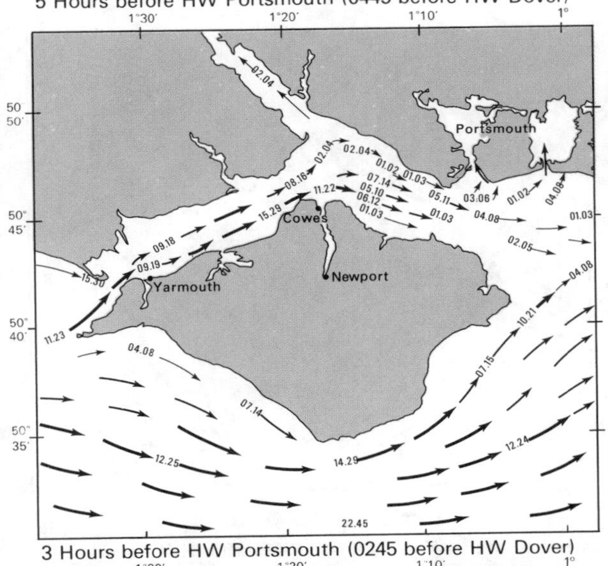
1°30′
1°20′
1°10′
1°
50° 50′
50° 45′
50° 40′
50° 35′
Portsmouth
Cowes
Newport
Yarmouth

3 Hours before HW Portsmouth (0245 before HW Dover)

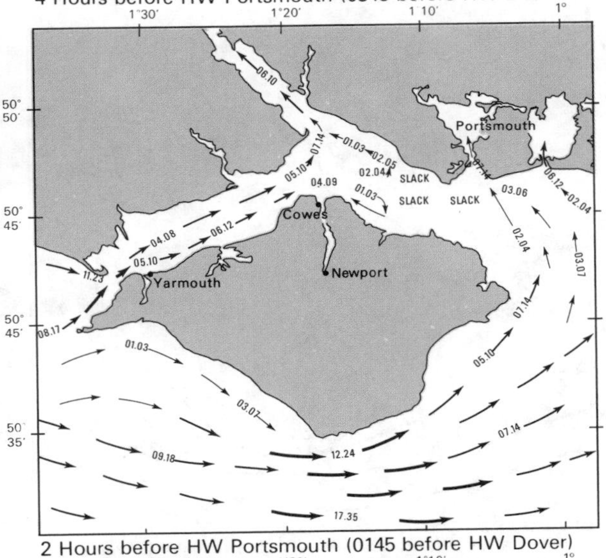
1°30′
1°20′
1°10′
1°
50° 50′
50° 45′
50° 45′
50° 35′
Portsmouth
Cowes
Newport
Yarmouth
SLACK
SLACK
SLACK
SLACK

2 Hours before HW Portsmouth (0145 before HW Dover)

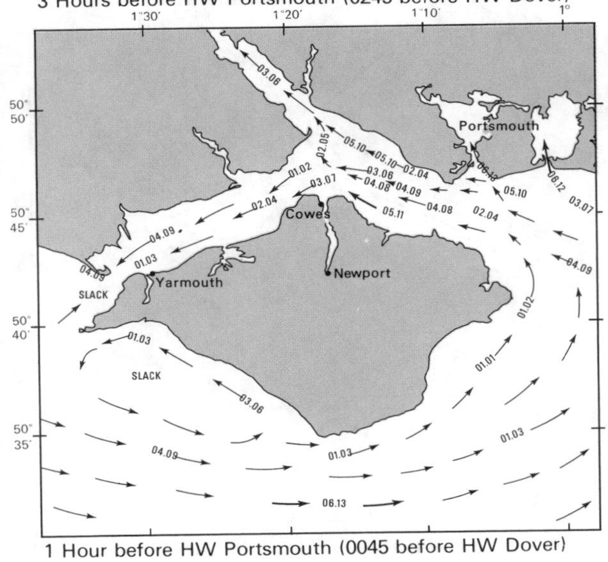
1°30′
1°20′
1°10′
1°
50° 50′
50° 45′
50° 40′
50° 35′
Portsmouth
Cowes
Newport
Yarmouth
SLACK
SLACK

1 Hour before HW Portsmouth (0045 before HW Dover)

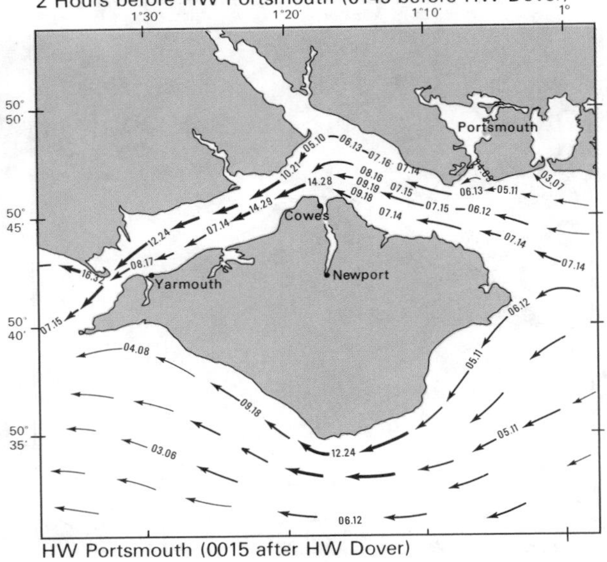
1°30′
1°20′
1°10′
1°
50° 50′
50° 45′
50° 40′
50° 35′
Portsmouth
Cowes
Newport
Yarmouth

HW Portsmouth (0015 after HW Dover)

General Area 2 10.2.3

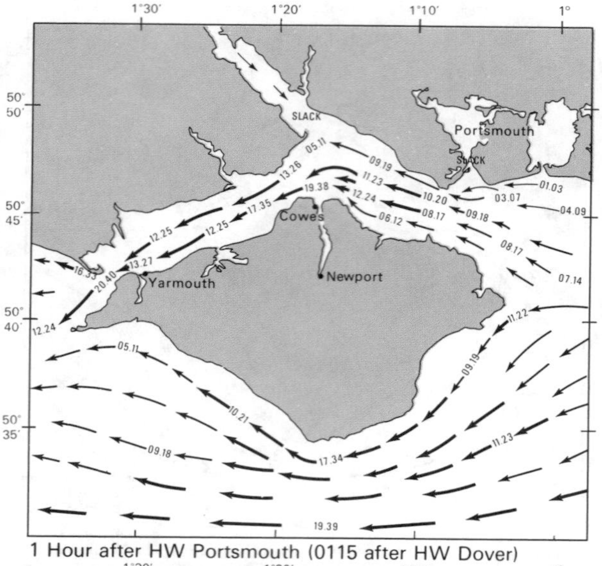

1°30′
1°20′
1°10′
1°
50° 50′
50° 45′
50° 40′
50° 35′
SLACK
Portsmouth
Cowes
Yarmouth
Newport

1 Hour after HW Portsmouth (0115 after HW Dover)

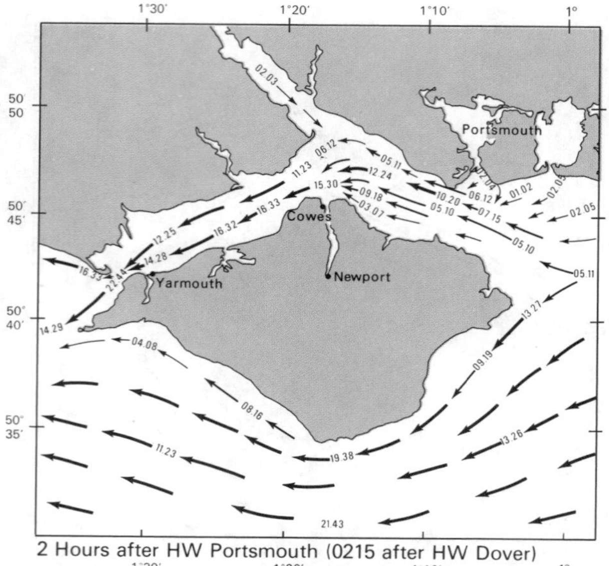

1°30′
1°20′
1°10′
1°
50 50
50° 45′
50° 40′
50° 35′
Portsmouth
Cowes
Yarmouth
Newport

2 Hours after HW Portsmouth (0215 after HW Dover)

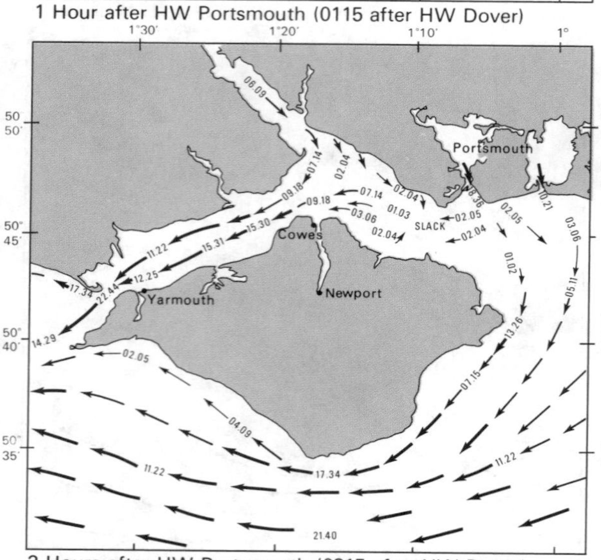

1°30′
1°20′
1°10′
1°
50° 50′
50° 45′
50° 40′
50° 35′
Portsmouth
SLACK
Cowes
Yarmouth
Newport

3 Hours after HW Portsmouth (0315 after HW Dover)

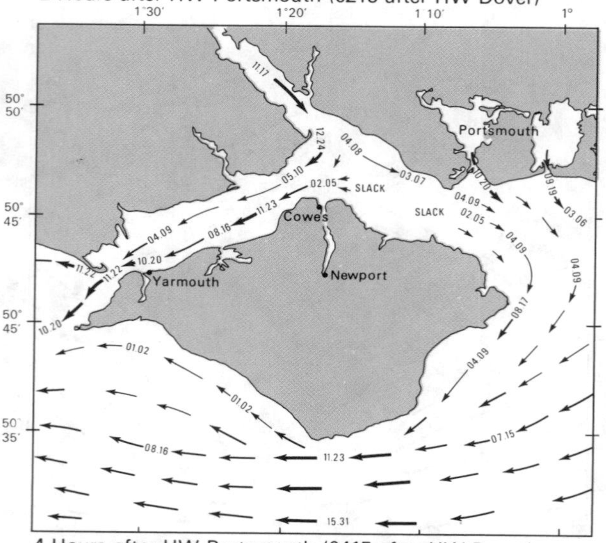

1°30′
1°20′
1°10′
1°
50° 50′
50° 45′
50° 45′
50° 35′
Portsmouth
SLACK
SLACK
Cowes
Yarmouth
Newport

4 Hours after HW Portsmouth (0415 after HW Dover)

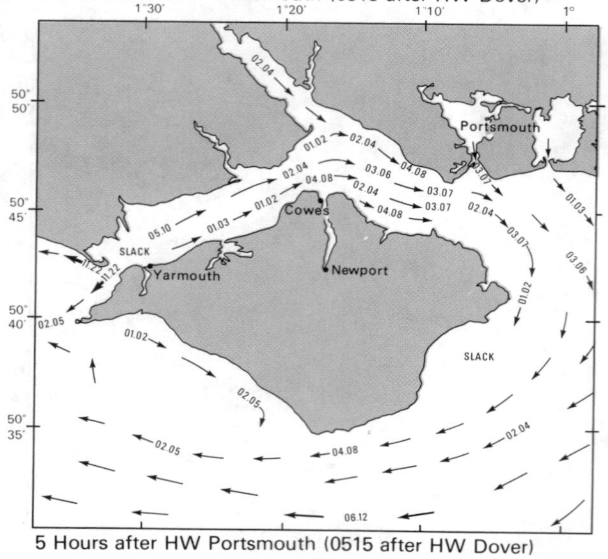

1°30′
1°20′
1°10′
1°
50° 50′
50° 45′
50° 40′
50° 35′
Portsmouth
Cowes
SLACK
Yarmouth
Newport
SLACK

5 Hours after HW Portsmouth (0515 after HW Dover)

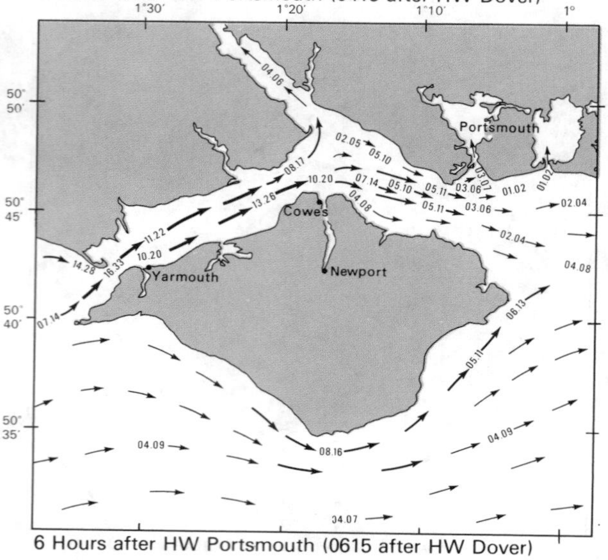

1°30′
1°20′
1°10′
1°
50° 50′
50° 45′
50° 40′
50° 35′
Portsmouth
Cowes
Yarmouth
Newport

6 Hours after HW Portsmouth (0615 after HW Dover)

LANGSTONE 10-2-30

Hampshire

CHARTS
Admiralty 3418, 2045; Stanford 10, 11; Imray C3, Y33; OS 196, 197

TIDES
+0022 Dover; Zone 0 (GMT)

Standard Port PORTSMOUTH (⟵)

Times				Height (metres)			
HW		LW		MHWS	MHWN	MLWN	MLWS
0500	1000	0000	0600	4·7	3·8	1·8	0·6
1700	2200	1200	1800				
Differences LANGSTONE							
0000	0000	+0010	+0010	+0·1	+0·1	0·0	0·0
NAB TOWER							
+0015	0000	+0015	+0015	−0·2	0·0	+0·2	0·0

SHELTER
Very good shelter but it must be entered with caution when a heavy sea is running. Shelter in marina to W inside entrance. Anchorage in Russell's Lake. For overnight stay apply Hr Mr at the ferry on Hayling Island. Also anchorage in Langstone Channel out of fairway.

NAVIGATION
Waypoint Langstone Fairway (safe water) buoy, LFl 10s, 50°46′·28N 01°01′·27W, 167°/347° from/to QR Lt at entrance, 0·94M. Entrance between E Winner bank and W Winner bank but apart from these the entrance is straightforward. Tides are strong in the entrance. Harbour speed limit 10 kn.

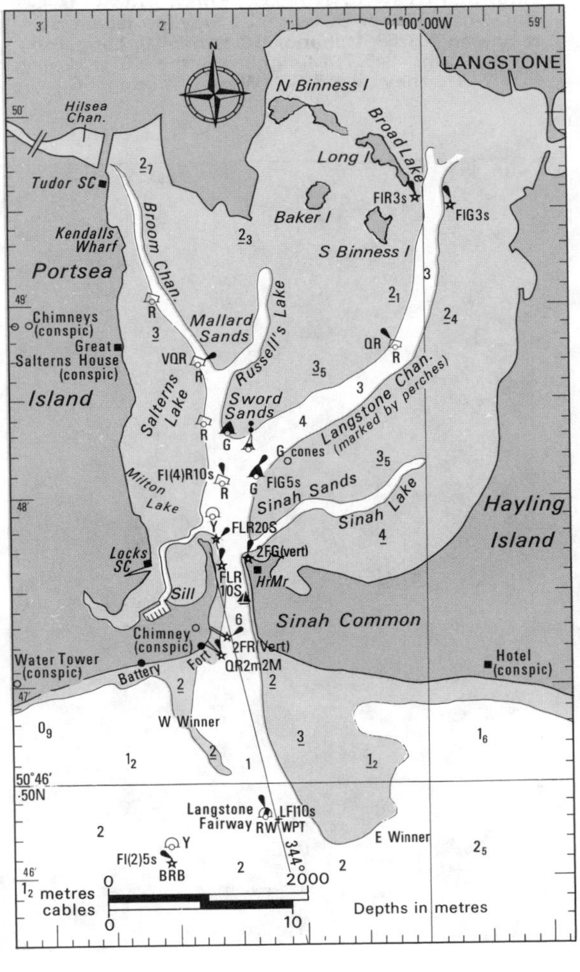
01°00'·00W
LANGSTONE
N Binness I
Broad Lake
Long I
Hilsea Chan.
Tudor SC
Broom Chan.
Baker I
S Binness I
FlR3s
FlG3s
Kendalls Wharf
Portsea
Chimneys (conspic)
Great Salterns House (conspic)
Island
Mallard Sands
Russell's Lake
Salterns Lake
VQR
QR
Sword Sands
Langstone Chan. (marked by perches)
G cones
Fl(4)R10s
FlG5s
Milton Lake
Sinah Sands
Sinah Lake
Hayling Island
FLR20S
Locks SC
2FG(vert)
HrMr
Sill
FLR 10S
Sinah Common
Chimney (conspic)
2FR(Vert)
QR2m2M
Water Tower (conspic)
Battery
Fort
Hotel (conspic)
W Winner
50°46'·50N
Langstone Fairway RW WPT
LFl10s
E Winner
Fl(2)5s BRB
344°
metres
cables
Depths in metres

LIGHTS AND MARKS
Leading marks (concrete dolphins) 344°. Red flag, with numeral pendant below, flown at the Fort, Battery and Hr Mr's flag staff indicates firing from range to W of harbour entrance (frequently across harbour approach). See 10.2.28.

RADIO TELEPHONE
VHF Ch 12 16; 12 (Summer 0830-1700. Winter: Mon-Fri 0830-1700; Sat-Sun 0830-1300 LT). Marina Ch **80** M (H24).

TELEPHONE (0705)
Hr Mr 463419; MRSC Lee-on-Solent 552100; # (0703) 827350; Marinecall 0898 500 457; Police 321111; Dr 465721.

FACILITIES
EC Havant - Wednesday; **Langstone Marina** (300) ☎ 822719 CH, BH (20 ton), D, Gaz, C, AC, FW, Access HW∓3; **Hayling Pontoons** (Entrance to Sinah Lake), Slip, D, FW, L, P, AB; **Langstone SC** ☎ Havant 484577, Slip, M, L, FW, Bar; **Eastney Cruising Ass.** ☎ 734103; **Solartron SC; Locks SC** ☎ 829833; **Tudor SC** (Eastney) ☎ 662002.
✉ (Eastney, Hayling); Ⓑ (Havant, Hayling, Emsworth); ⇄ (bus to Havant); ✈ (Southampton).

CHICHESTER 10-2-31

W. Sussex

CHARTS
Admiralty 3418, 2045; Stanford 10, 11; Imray C3, C9, Y33; OS 197

TIDES
+0027 Dover; ML 2·8; Zone 0 (GMT)

Standard Port PORTSMOUTH (⟵)

Times				Height (metres)			
HW		LW		MHWS	MHWN	MLWN	MLWS
0500	1000	0000	0600	4·7	3·8	1·8	0·6
1700	2200	1200	1800				
Differences HARBOUR ENTRANCE							
−0010	+0005	+0015	+0020	+0·2	+0·2	0·0	+0·1
BOSHAM							
0000	+0010	No data		+0·2	+0·1	No data	
ITCHENOR							
−0005	+0005	+0005	+0025	+0·1	0·0	−0·2	−0·2
DELL QUAY							
+0005	+0015	No data		+0·2	+0·1	No data	
SELSEY BILL							
−0005	−0005	+0035	+0035	+0·6	+0·6	0·0	0·0

SHELTER
Chichester harbour has excellent shelter in all four main arms of the harbour, Emsworth, Thorney, Bosham and Chichester. Beware shallow patches W and S of Bar Bn. There are a large number of yacht harbours, marinas etc. Good anchorages at East Head; in Thorney Channel off Pilsey Is; W of Fairway buoy on S side of channel. No anchoring E of Cobnor Pt. Advisable to make prior arrangement for mooring.

NAVIGATION
Waypoint 50°45′·50N 00°56′·50W, 193°/013° from/to Bar Bn, 0·47M. The entrance is about ½ M wide at HW but this dries exposing a sandbank known as the Winner from the East Head side leaving a deep channel close to Hayling Island. There is a bar 1 M S of the entrance with a channel giving depths of 0·4m close E of the Bar Bn. There is a patch drying 0·3m about 2 ca ESE of the Bn. A port-hand buoy lies 194° 2·2 ca from Bar Bn (Apl-Nov). In winds above force 5 from S quarter and particularly during spring ebbs, seas over the bar are confused. It is advised to cross the bar from HW−3 to HW+1. There is a speed limit throughout the harbour of 8 kn.

LIGHTS AND MARKS
Bar Bn Fl WR 5s 14m 7/5 M vis W 322°-080°, R080°-322°. On same structures Fl(2) R 10s 7m 2M vis 020°-080°; both on W pylon with tide gauge; RC.
All channels well marked.

RADIO TELEPHONE
Harbour Office, Itchenor VHF Ch **14** 16 (Call *Chichester* on Ch 14). (Apl-Sept 0900-1730. Oct-Mar: Mon-Sat 0900-1300, Mon-Fri 1400-1730 LT). Emsworth and Northney Marinas Ch **80** M.

CHICHESTER *continued*

TELEPHONE (0243)
Harbour Office Itchenor 512301; # (0703) 827350; MRSC Lee-on-Solent 552100; Weather information Portsmouth 8091; Marinecall 0898 500 457; Police 784433; Ⓗ 787970.

FACILITIES

EMSWORTH CHANNEL: channel is straight, broad and deep. Good anchorages especially N of Sandy Pt near entrance to channel. Visitors moorings on 5 outer piles. EC Wednesday; **Slips** at South St, Kings St, and Slipper Mill. Contact the Warden ☎ 376422; **Emsworth Yacht Harbour** (200 + 4 visitors) ☎ 375211, Slip, Gas, ME, El, AC, Sh, P, D, FW, C (20 ton); (Access HW∓2); **David Still Marine** ☎ 374242, ME, Sh, CH; **Ostar Marine** ☎ 376414; **Greenham Marine Ltd** ☎ 378314, El.

HAYLING ISLAND: EC Wednesday; **Northney Marina** (260 + 27 visitors) ☎ Hayling 466321, D, BH (35 ton), Bar, FW, AC, El, Sh, R, CH, ME; **Chichester Harbour Yacht Services** ☎ Hayling 465051 ME, El, Sh, Slip, C, CH; **Hayling Yacht Co.** ☎ Hayling 463592, ME, El, Slip, BH (8 ton), P, D, FW, AB Sh, CH; **Hayling Is Marine Services** ☎ Hayling 464869; **Sparkes Yacht Harbour** (140) ☎ Hayling 463572, Slip, ME, El, FW, P, D, Gas, Gaz, ◙, Sh, C (20 ton), CH.

THORNEY CHANNEL: Strangers are advised to go up at half flood. Channel is marked by perches. After Thorney village, channel splits, Prinsted Chan to port (full of moorings) and Nutbourne Chan to stbd. There is plenty of room to anchor in Thorney Chan and it is well protected from E and SE winds.
Thornton Marina (77 + 6 visitors) ☎ 375335, Slip, P and D (cans), FW, Sh, ME, C (10 ton), BH (12 ton).
Printsted — **Paynes BY** ☎ 572224, Slip, L, FW, ME;

BOSHAM CHANNEL: There are some Harbour Authority moorings in this channel and there is a hard at Bosham Quay. Most of the channel dries. Anchoring in channel is prohibited.
EC Wednesday; **Bosham Quay** L, FW, AB; **Capt. Charles Currey** ☎ 573174, CH; **Rockall Sails** ☎ 572149, SM; **Bosham SC** ☎ 572341; **Arun Sails** ☎ 573185 SM;

CHICHESTER CHANNEL: this runs up to Itchenor. From Sandhead buoy proceed 034° to Fl (2) G 10s Chaldock Bn; alter course to 039° to Fairway buoy, Fl (3). Anchoring prohibited in Itchenor Reach.
EC Itchenor Thursday. Hard available at all stages of the tide. There are six visitor's buoys off Itchenor jetty and 90ft pontoon. For single moorings apply Hr Mr. **G. Haines** ☎ 512228, Slip, P, D, CH, Sh; **E. M. Coombes** ☎ 573194, FW, CH, Slip, P and D (cans); **Northshore Yacht Yards** ☎ 512611, Slip, M; **Regis Marine** ☎ 511070, El, Ⓔ; **H. C. Darley** ☎ 512243, P and D (cans), CH; **E. Bailey** ☎ 512374, ME, P, D, Sh; **Francis Marine** ☎ 787987, CH; **Penguin Engineering** ☎ 465607, CH, ME.

CHICHESTER LAKE AND FISHBOURNE CHANNEL: Birdham Pool Yacht Basin, Access HW∓3 when lock gates open. At Chichester Yacht Basin, the approach dries at CD but is dredged to about 1m at normal LWS. Secure to pontoons whilst waiting: lock control boards show 'Red' indicating 'wait' or 'Green' for 'enter'. They are floodlit at night. When the gates are open with a free flow in and out, there is a QY Lt on top of the Control Tr.
Birdham — Chichester Yacht Basin (900 + 50 visitors) ☎ 512731, Slip, P, D, FW, ME, El, Sh, AC, Gas, Gaz, CH, V, R, BH (20 ton), Access HW∓4½; **Vernons Shipyard** ☎ 512606; **Greenham Marine** ☎ 512995, El, Ⓔ; **Yacht and Sports Gear** ☎ 784572, CH, ACA; **B. A. Peters** ☎ 512923, CH; **Copp Sails** ☎ 533622, SM.
Birdham Pool — Birdham Pool Marina (230 + 10 visitors) ☎ 512310, Slip, P, D, FW, El, Ⓔ, AC, Sh, CH, Gas, Gaz, ME, SM, C (3 ton), Access HW∓3; **Birdham Shipyard** ☎ 512310; Slip, M, P, Sh, CH; **Sterndrives** ☎ 512831, ME; **Seahorse Sails** ☎ 512195, SM;
Dell Quay — Launching is possible on the hard, depending on the tide, on payment of harbour dues.
Ted Bailey (Dell Quay) ☎ 781110 Sh; **Wyche Marine** ☎ 782768, M, L, Sh.

Clubs: Bosham SC ☎ 572341; **Chichester YC** ☎ 512918, R, Bar, ◙; **Chichester Cruiser and Racing Club; Dell Quay SC** ☎ 785080; **Emsworth SC** ☎ 43065; **Emsworth Slipper SC** ☎ 42523; **Hayling Island SC** ☎ Hayling 463768; **Itchenor SC** ☎ 512400; **Langstone SC** ☎ Havant 484577; **Mengham Rythe SC** ☎ Hayling 463337; **Thorney Island SC; West Wittering SC.**

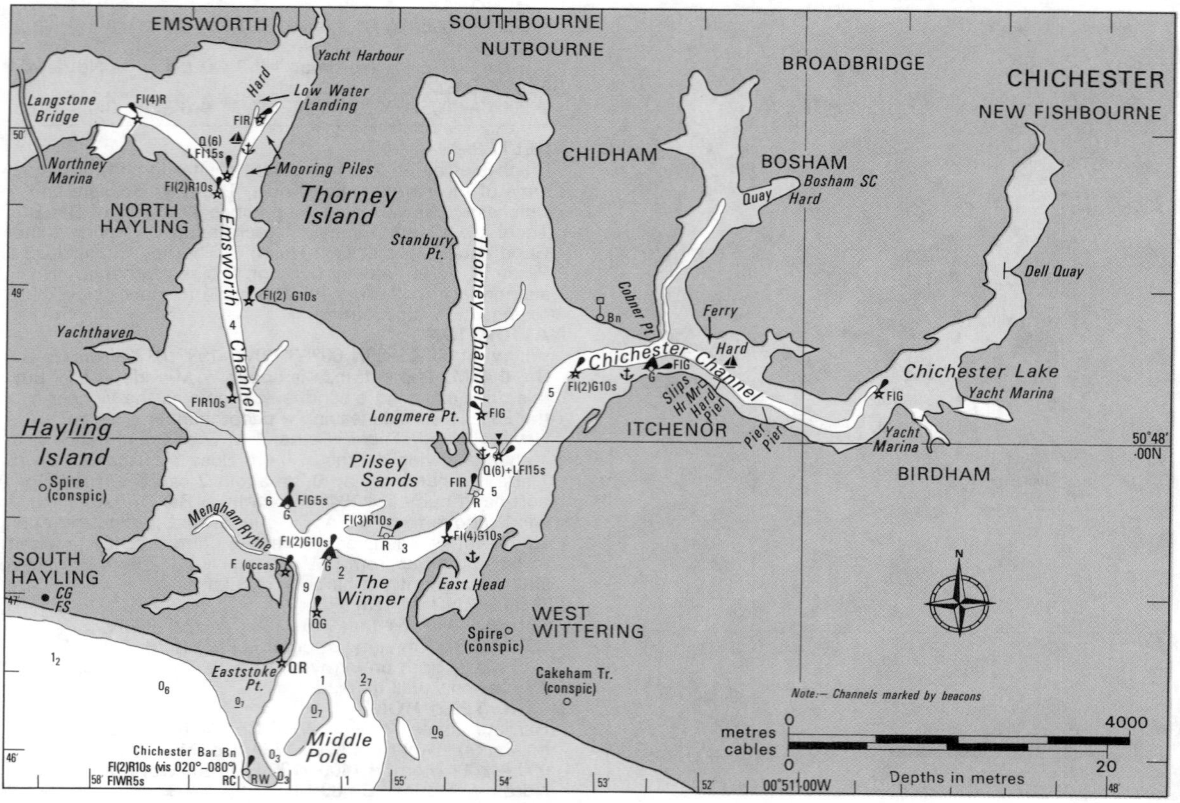
EMSWORTH
SOUTHBOURNE
NUTBOURNE
BROADBRIDGE
CHICHESTER
NEW FISHBOURNE
Yacht Harbour
Langstone Bridge
Low Water Landing
Hard
Mooring Piles
Northney Marina
NORTH HAYLING
Thorney Island
Emsworth Channel
Thorney Channel
Stanbury Pt.
CHIDHAM
BOSHAM
Bosham SC
Quay
Hard
Dell Quay
Cobner Pt
Ferry
Chichester Channel
Chichester Lake
Yacht Marina
Slips
Hr Mr
ITCHENOR
Yachthaven
Hayling Island
Longmere Pt.
Pilsey Sands
Spire (conspic)
Mengham Rythe
SOUTH HAYLING
CG FS
The Winner
East Head
WEST WITTERING
Spire (conspic)
Eaststoke Pt.
Middle Pole
Cakeham Tr. (conspic)
BIRDHAM
Note:– Channels marked by beacons
metres
cables
Depths in metres
Chichester Bar Bn
Fl(2)R10s (vis 020°–080°)
50°48'·00N
00°51'·00W

MINOR HARBOURS AND ANCHORAGES 10.2.32

BEER, Devon, 50°41′00N, 03°06′·00W, Zone 0 (GMT), Admty chart 3315. HW −0440 on Dover, +0045 on Devonport; HW height −1·1m on Devonport; ML 2·3m; Duration 0640. Beer roads afford a sheltered anchorage in winds from W to N. It is open to prevailing winds. Go ashore by boat over open beach. From E beware rocks at the bottom of headland on E side of cove. Facilities: EC Thurs in Beer and Seaton; **Jimmy Green Marine** ☎ 20744, CH; SC, ✉, Bar, BY, R, V.

RIVER AXE, Devon 50°41′00N, 03°06′·00W, Zone 0 (GMT), Admty chart 3315. HW −0440 on Dover, +0045 on Devonport; HW height +1·1m on Devonport; ML 2·3m; Duration 0640. Good shelter for smallish boats; boats up to 1m draught can enter at HW. Cross bar, which dries, then turn sharply to W. Entrance is 7m wide. The channel through the bar is unmarked and shifts constantly. Local knowledge is needed. A road bridge (2m clearance) crosses the river 2 ca within the entrance. Facilities: EC Thurs (Seaton), BY; **Axe YC** ☎ Seaton 20779, Slip, Bar; **Seaton** ✉, R, V, Gas, Gaz, P and D (cans).

LULWORTH COVE, Dorset, 50°37′00N, 02°15′·00W, Zone 0 (GMT), Admty chart 2172. HW −0449 on Dover, −0410 on Portsmouth; HW height −2·4m on Portsmouth; ML 1·2m. Good shelter in offshore winds but S and SW winds cause heavy swell in the cove. The centre of the cove has a depth of about 4m below CD. There is a can buoy in the centre of the cove. Anchor in NE part in 2·5m. Holding ground is poor. Village is on W bank. Facilities: EC Wed and Sat; FW at tap in car park, Bar, ✉, Slip, R.

Note. There are two danger areas to E, one extending 6M seawards, the other 13M. Firing takes place most weekdays from 0930-1700 (1200 on Fridays), often on Tues and Thurs nights and up to 6 weekends per year. There is NO firing during August. When firing is in progress R flags (Red lights at night) are flown from St Albans Head and Bindon Hill. However, further ashore, mariners may notice some red flags which fly whether or not firing is taking place; these mark the range boundary. No visual signals ashore warn of naval firings, but warships using the range will patrol S of Lulworth Banks and fly red flags. Times of firing are published locally, sent to Hr Mrs and YCs and can be obtained from the Range Officer ☎ Bindon Abbey (0929) 462721 ext. 4819 during normal working hours and from guardroom ext. 4824 at other times. Firing details are broadcast by Radio Solent (999 kHz−300 AM or 96·1 MHz VHF) daily (see 10.2.9) and Two Counties Radio and can be obtained from Portland CG (Ch 67), Portland Naval Base (Ch 13 & 14), or Range Safety Boats (Ch 08).

All the Land Area and the Inner Sea Danger Area (DO26(INNER)) are subject to the regulations laid down in "The Lulworth Ranges Byelaws 1978 operative from 10th November 1978 – Statutory Instruments 1978 No 1663". A copy may be obtained from HMSO if required. A key passage in the rules is as follows: "The Byelaws shall not apply to any vessel in the ordinary course of navigation not being used for fishing in the Sea Area and remaining in the Sea Area no longer than is reasonably necessary to pass through the Sea Area."

CHAPMAN'S POOL, Dorset, 50°35′00N, 02°04′·00W, Zone 0 (GMT), Admty chart 2172. Tidal data is approx that for Swanage see 10.2.15. Chapman's Pool, like Worbarrow Bay, Brandy Bay and Kimmeridge Bay is picturesque and is convenient anchorage in depths of about 3m when the wind is off-shore. Anchor centre of bay to avoid tidal swirl. Beware large B buoy unlit in centre. There are no lights and no facilities.

STUDLAND BAY, Dorset, 50°39′00N, 01°56′·00W, Zone 0 (GMT), Admty charts 2172, 2175. Tidal data is approx that for Swanage. See 10.2.12. Shelter is good except from winds from N and E. Beware Redend Rocks off S shore. Best anchorage in depths of about 3m below CD, 3 ca NW of The Yards (3 strange projections on the chalk cliffs near Handfast Pt). Facilities: EC Thurs; shops, hotel etc in Studland village. No marine facilities. P and D (cans).

WAREHAM, Dorset, 50°41′00N, 02°05′·00W, Zone 0 (GMT), Admty chart 2611. HW −0030 (Np), +0320 (Sp) on Dover, −0140 (Np), +0205 (Sp) on Portsmouth (See 10.2.14). Shelter very good, approach narrow and winding up R Frome but well marked by buoys and posts at entrance. Beware prohibited anchorages (salmon holes) marked on the chart and moored boats. Passage is unlit; keep outside at all bends. Facilities: **Ridge Wharf Yacht Centre** (180+6 visitors) (½M upstream of Ent) ☎ 2650, Access HW∓2 approx AB, M, FW, P, D, ME, El, Gas, Gaz, AC, BH (20 ton), Slip, Sh, CH; **Redclyffe YC** ☎ 51227 (½M below bridge); **Wareham Quay** AB, FW, R; **Town** EC Wed, P and D in cans, V, Gas, R, Dr ☎ 3444, Bar, ✉, Ⓑ, ⇌.

NEWPORT, Isle of Wight, 50°42′00N, 01°17′·00W, Zone 0 (GMT), Admty chart 2793. For tidal predictions see 10.2.13 and 10.2.23. For approaches up R Medina see 10.2.23. Southwards from Folly Inn on E shore the Medina Borough Council is the harbour authority.

½M south of Folly Inn is **Island Harbour Marina** (170) ☎ 526733, AC, Bar, BH (16 ton), CH, D, P, El, FW, Gas, ◙, ME, R, Sh, Slip, V. Marina has excellent shelter and is approached through dredged channel (access HW∓3½) and lock. Waiting pontoon outside lock.

Channel S from Island Harbour to Newport dries but there is 2m or more from HW Portsmouth −1½ to HW Portsmouth +2. Speed limit 6 kn up to Seaclose (just past Newport Rowing Club) and 4 kn from there to Newport. In Newport depth at pontoons 1·4m HW∓2. Bilge keel boats lie alongside pontoons, and single keel boats at quay wall – these areas are dredged and kept level. Hr Mr will supply rubbing boards. **Newport Yacht Harbour** (40 visitors) Hr Mr ☎ 525994, VHF Ch 16; 06 (office hours or by arrangement), AC, D, FW. **Town** EC Thursday; Ⓑ, Bar, BY, C (5 ton mobile, 12 ton fixed), CH, D, Dr, El, Gas, Ⓗ; ◙, ME, P, ✉, R, Sh, Slip, SM, V.

TITCHFIELD HAVEN, Hampshire 50°49′00N, 01°14′·00W, Zone 0 (GMT), Admty charts 2022, 1905. HW +0030 on Dover (GMT); 0000 on Portsmouth; HW height −0·2m on Portsmouth. Short term anchorage for small craft at mouth of R. Meon. Bar dries ¼M offshore. Ent. dries 1·2m at LWS. Entrance marked by Hillhead SC house (white conspic), beacons mark channel, spherical topmarks to port, triangular ones to stbd. Small harbour to W inside ent where yachts can lie in soft mud alongside bank. Facilities: **Hillhead village** EC Thurs, ✉, CH, V, P and D (cans).

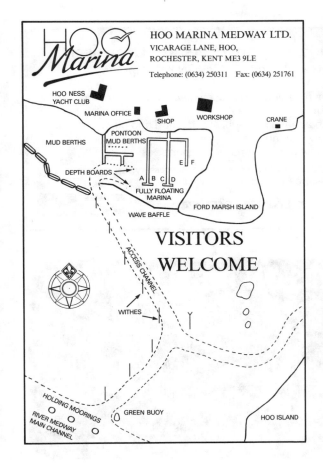

Area 3

South-East England
Selsey Bill to Havengore Creek

10-3-2

South-East England

Key to Symbols

- Coast Station/Port Radio – frequencies
- (RC) Marine radiobeacon– call sign, sequence, frequency and range (nm)
- (RC) Aero Aeronautical radiobeacon–call sign, frequency and range (nm)
- (i) See for harbour information/tidal data
- Weather (tel. or times). M - Marinecall
- CG HM Coastguard MRCC; CG MRSC
- CG HM Coastguard Sector Base
- LB RNLI Lifeboat over 10m
- IL RNLI Lifeboat under 10m
- SAR Helicopter base
- ☆ Principal lights
- Light-vessel
- Lanby
- RG Emergency VHF DF
- * See 10.3.24

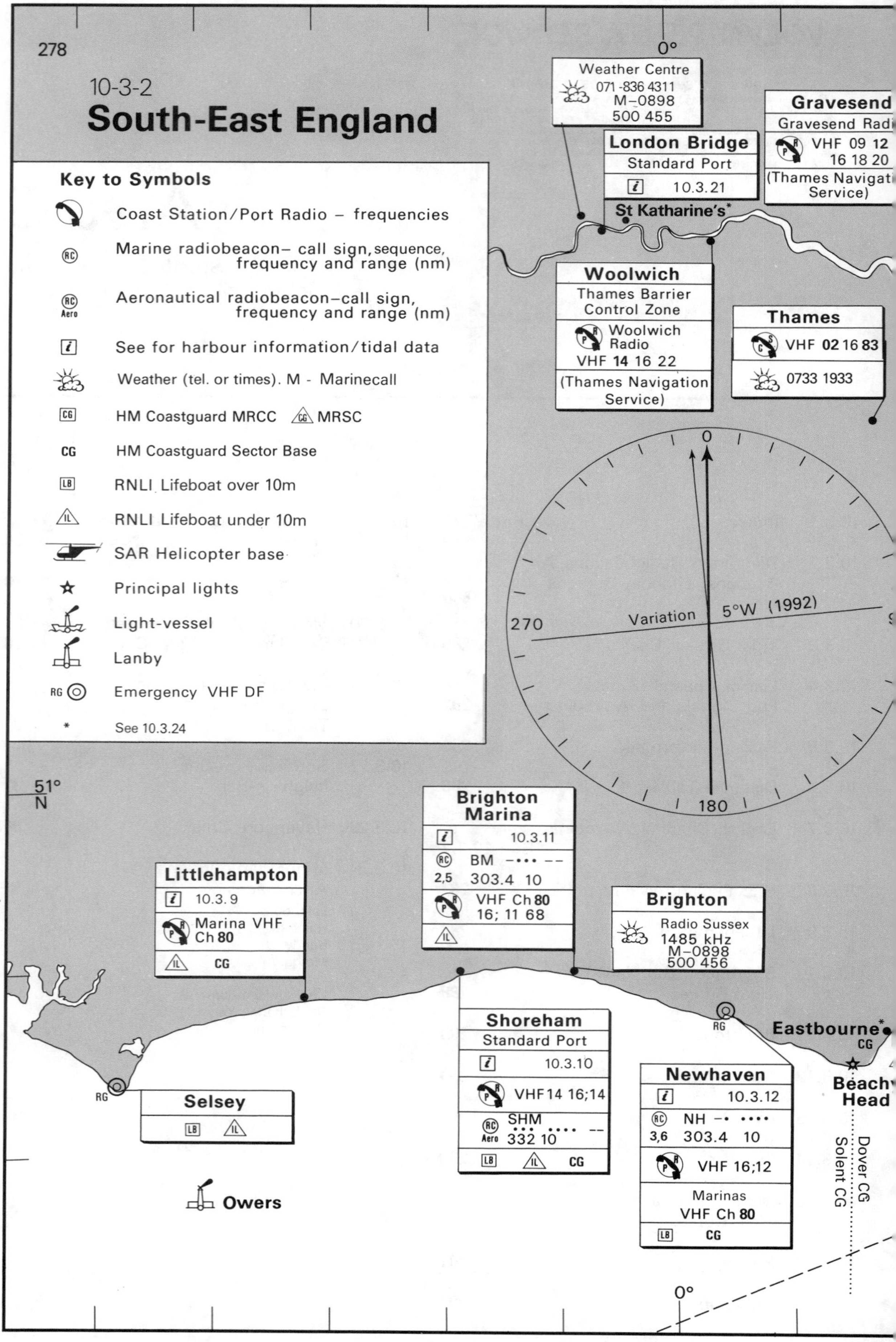
0°
Weather Centre
071-836 4311
M–0898
500 455
London Bridge
Standard Port
10.3.21
St Katharine's*
Gravesend
Gravesend Radi
VHF 09 12
16 18 20
(Thames Navigat
Service)
Woolwich
Thames Barrier
Control Zone
Woolwich
Radio
VHF 14 16 22
(Thames Navigation
Service)
Thames
VHF 02 16 83
0733 1933
0
270
Variation 5°W (1992)
180
51°
N
Brighton
Marina
10.3.11
BM
2,5 303.4 10
VHF Ch 80
16; 11 68
Littlehampton
10.3.9
Marina VHF
Ch 80
CG
Brighton
Radio Sussex
1485 kHz
M–0898
500 456
RG
Eastbourne*
CG
Beachy
Head
Shoreham
Standard Port
10.3.10
VHF14 16;14
SHM
Aero 332 10
CG
Newhaven
10.3.12
NH
3,6 303.4 10
VHF 16;12
Marinas
VHF Ch 80
CG
RG
Selsey
Owers
Dover CG
Solent CG
0°

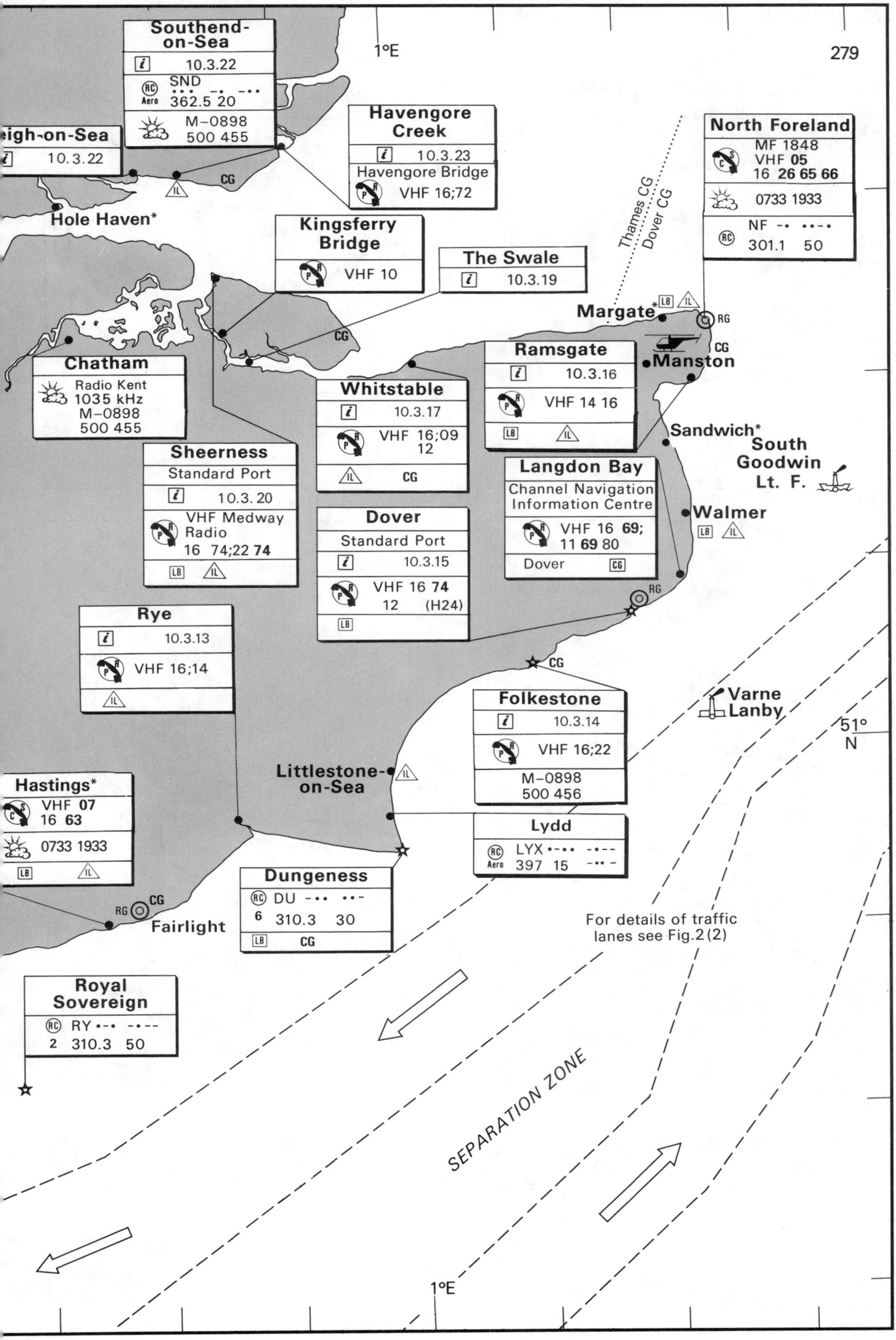
1°E
Southend-on-Sea
10.3.22
SND
362.5 20
M–0898
500 455
Leigh-on-Sea
10.3.22
Havengore Creek
10.3.23
Havengore Bridge
VHF 16;72
CG
Hole Haven*
Kingsferry Bridge
VHF 10
The Swale
10.3.19
North Foreland
MF 1848
VHF 05
16 26 65 66
0733 1933
NF
301.1 50
Thames CG
Dover CG
Margate*
RG
CG
Manston
Ramsgate
10.3.16
VHF 14 16
Chatham
Radio Kent
1035 kHz
M–0898
500 455
Whitstable
10.3.17
VHF 16;09
12
CG
Sandwich*
South Goodwin Lt. F.
Sheerness
Standard Port
10.3. 20
VHF Medway Radio
16 74;22 74
Langdon Bay
Channel Navigation Information Centre
VHF 16 69;
11 69 80
Dover
Walmer
Dover
Standard Port
10.3.15
VHF 16 74
12 (H24)
RG
Rye
10.3.13
VHF 16;14
CG
Folkestone
10.3.14
VHF 16;22
M–0898
500 456
Varne Lanby
51° N
Littlestone-on-Sea
Lydd
LYX
397 15
Hastings*
VHF 07
16 63
0733 1933
Dungeness
DU
6 310.3 30
CG
RG
CG
Fairlight
For details of traffic lanes see Fig.2(2)
Royal Sovereign
RY
2 310.3 50
SEPARATION ZONE
1°E

10.3.3 AREA 3 TIDAL STREAMS

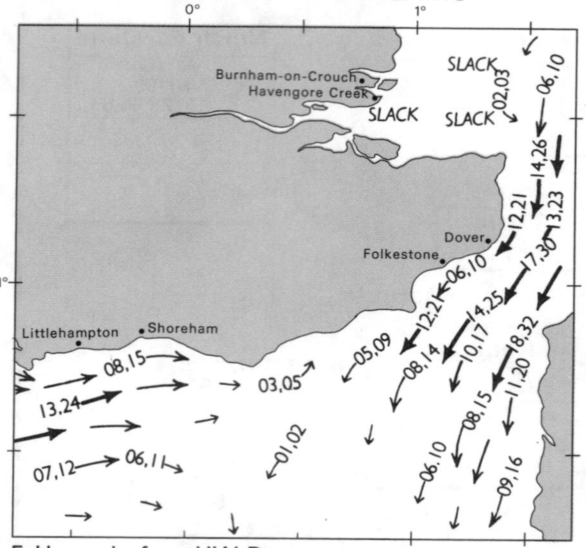
0°
1°
51°
Burnham-on-Crouch
Havengore Creek
SLACK
SLACK
SLACK
Dover
Folkestone
Littlehampton
Shoreham

5 Hours before HW Dover

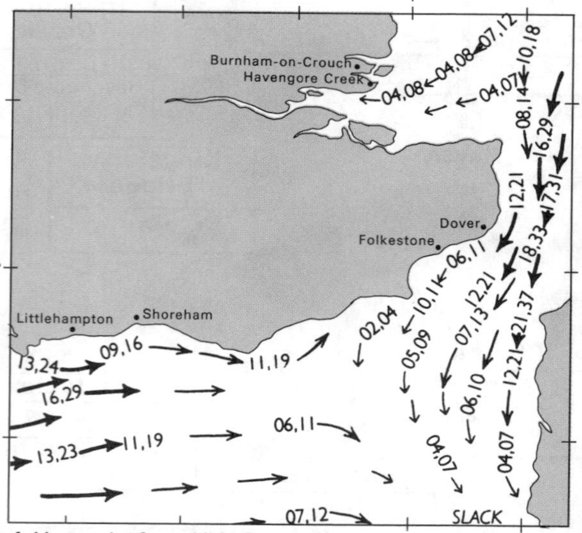
0°
1°
51°
Burnham-on-Crouch
Havengore Creek
Dover
Folkestone
Littlehampton
Shoreham
SLACK

4 Hours before HW Dover

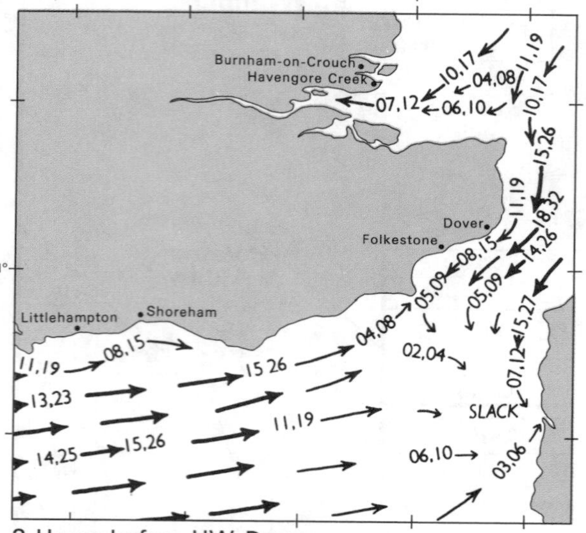
1°
51°
Burnham-on-Crouch
Havengore Creek
Dover
Folkestone
Littlehampton
Shoreham
SLACK

3 Hours before HW Dover

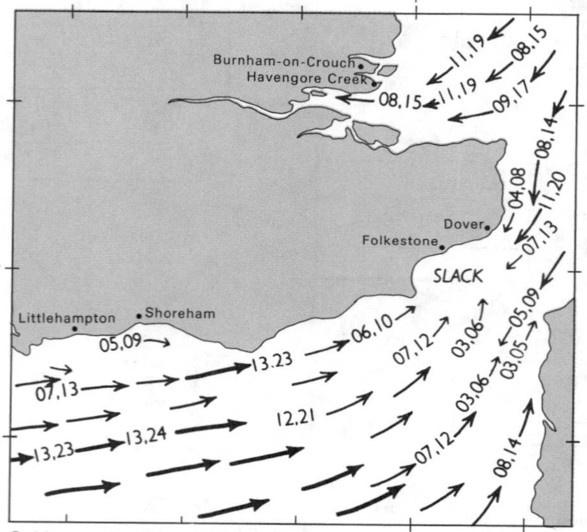
1°
51°
Burnham-on-Crouch
Havengore Creek
Dover
Folkestone
SLACK
Littlehampton
Shoreham

2 Hours before HW Dover

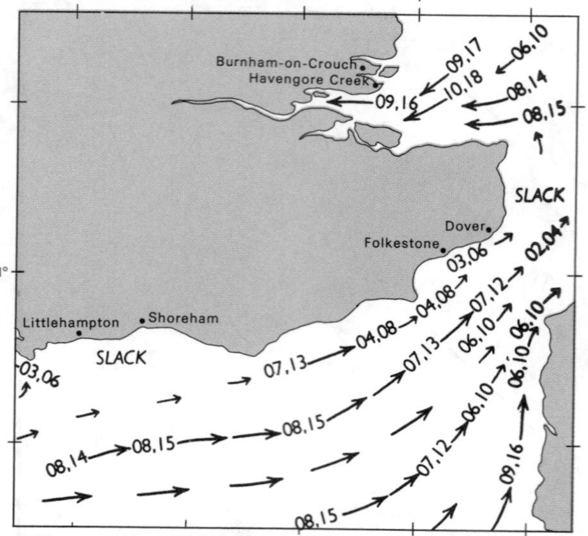
1°
51°
Burnham-on-Crouch
Havengore Creek
SLACK
Dover
Folkestone
Littlehampton
Shoreham
SLACK

1 Hour before HW Dover

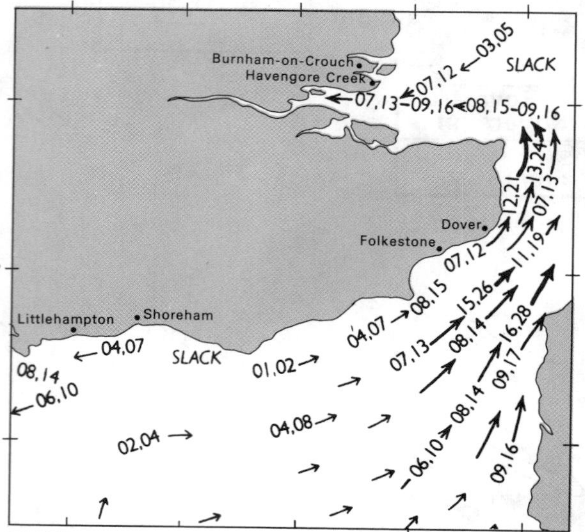
1°
51°
Burnham-on-Crouch
Havengore Creek
SLACK
Dover
Folkestone
Littlehampton
Shoreham
SLACK

HW Dover

Thames Estuary 10.3.18. Westward 10.2.3. Southward 10.19.3. Northward 10.4.3.

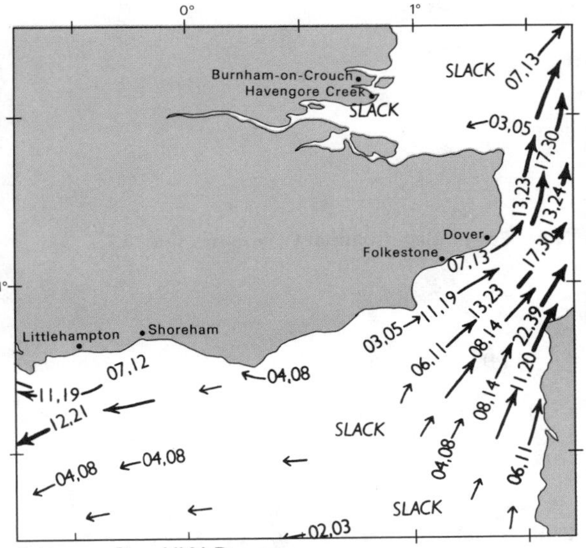
0°
1°
51°
Burnham-on-Crouch
Havengore Creek
Dover
Folkestone
Littlehampton
Shoreham
SLACK
07,13
03,05
17,30
13,23
13,24
07,13
17,30
11,19
13,23
03,05
22,39
06,11
08,14
04,08
11,20
07,12
11,19
12,21
08,14
04,08
04,08
06,11
02,03
1 Hour after HW Dover

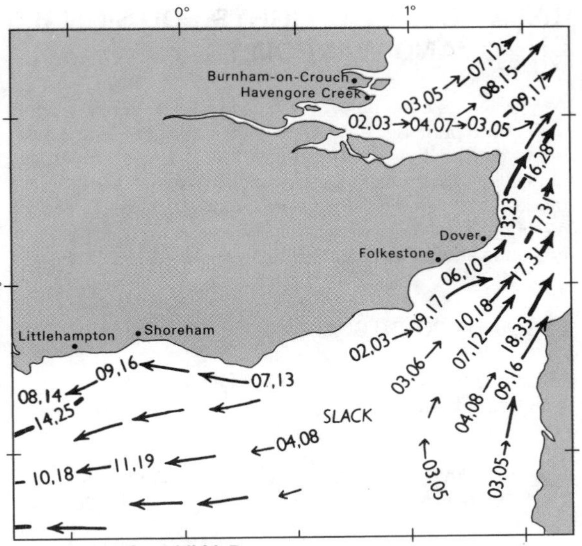
0°
1°
51°
Burnham-on-Crouch
Havengore Creek
Dover
Folkestone
Littlehampton
Shoreham
SLACK
03,05
07,12
08,15
09,17
02,03
04,07
03,05
16,28
13,23
17,31
06,10
17,31
02,03
09,17
10,18
07,12
18,33
09,16
07,13
08,14
14,25
03,06
04,08
09,16
04,08
10,18
11,19
03,05
03,05
2 Hours after HW Dover

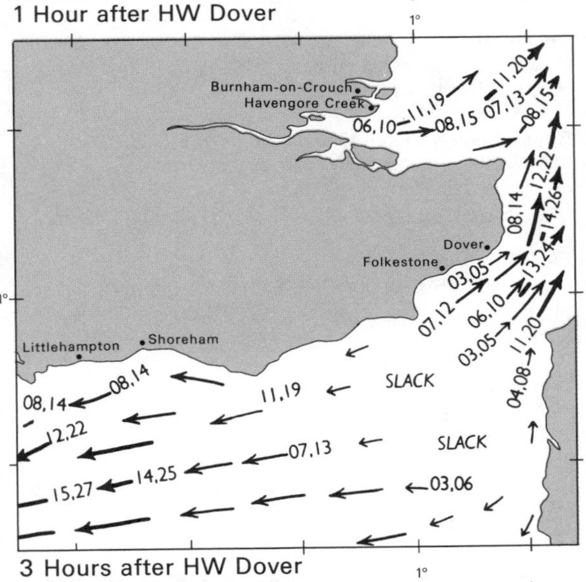
1°
51°
Burnham-on-Crouch
Havengore Creek
Dover
Folkestone
Littlehampton
Shoreham
SLACK
11,20
11,19
07,13
06,10
08,15
08,15
12,22
08,14
14,26
03,05
13,24
07,12
06,10
03,05
11,20
04,08
08,14
08,14
11,19
12,22
07,13
14,25
15,27
03,06
3 Hours after HW Dover

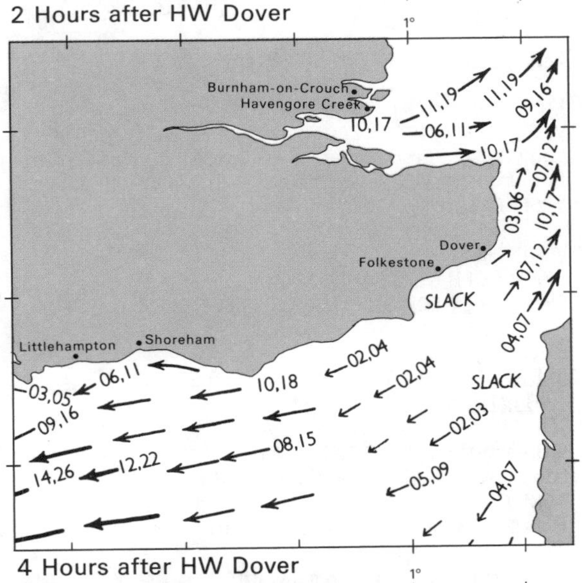
1°
51°
Burnham-on-Crouch
Havengore Creek
Dover
Folkestone
Littlehampton
Shoreham
SLACK
11,19
11,19
09,16
10,17
06,11
10,17
07,12
03,06
10,17
07,12
04,07
02,04
02,04
06,11
03,05
10,18
09,16
02,03
08,15
12,22
14,26
05,09
04,07
4 Hours after HW Dover

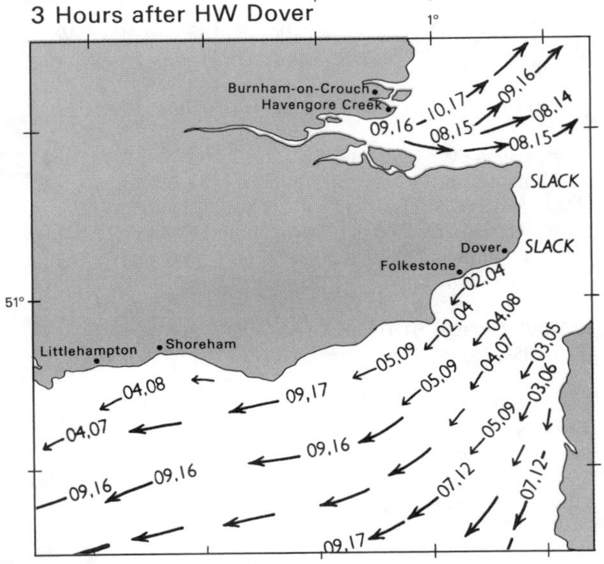
1°
51°
Burnham-on-Crouch
Havengore Creek
Dover
Folkestone
Littlehampton
Shoreham
SLACK
10,17
09,16
09,16
08,14
08,15
08,15
02,04
02,04
04,08
05,09
05,09
04,07
03,05
03,06
04,08
09,17
04,07
05,09
09,16
09,16
09,16
07,12
07,12
09,17
5 Hours after HW Dover

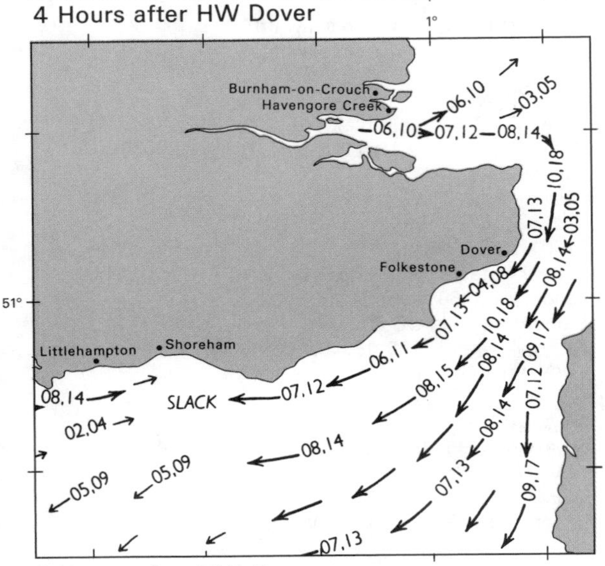
1°
51°
Burnham-on-Crouch
Havengore Creek
Dover
Folkestone
Littlehampton
Shoreham
SLACK
06,10
03,05
06,10
07,12
08,14
10,18
07,13
03,05
04,08
08,14
07,13
10,18
09,17
06,11
08,15
08,14
07,12
08,14
07,12
02,04
08,14
08,14
07,13
05,09
05,09
09,17
07,13
6 Hours after HW Dover

10.3.4 COASTAL LIGHTS, FOG SIGNALS AND WAYPOINTS

Abbreviations used below are given in 1.4.1. Principal lights are in **bold** print, places in CAPITALS, and light-vessels, light floats and Lanbys in *CAPITAL ITALICS*. Unless otherwise stated lights are white. m—elevation in metres; M—nominal range in n. miles. Fog signals are in *italics*. Useful waypoints are underlined – use those on land with care. All geographical positions should be assumed to be approximate. See 4.2.2.

ENGLAND—SOUTH COAST

Mixon Bn 50°42'·35N 00°46'·21W (unlit); PHM.
E Borough Hd Lt By 50°41'·50N 00°39'·00W Q (3) 10s; NCM.

OWERS LANBY 50°37'·27N 00°40'·60W Fl (3) 20s 12m **22M**; R tubular structure on circular By; ; *Horn (3) 60s.*

Bognor Regis Pier Hd 50°46'·70N 00°40'·42W 2 FR (vert).

Outfall Lt By 50°46'·20N 00°30'·45W Fl Y 5s; SPM.

LITTLEHAMPTON.
W Pier Hd 50°47'·85N 00°32'·37W 2 FR (vert) 7m 6M.
Ldg Lts 346°. Front E pier Hd FG 6m 7M; B col. Rear 64m from front Oc WY 7·5s 9m 10M; W Tr; vis W290°-356°, Y356°-042°.

WORTHING.
Pier Hd 2 FR (vert) 6m 1M.
Outfall Lt By 50°48'·45N 00°19'·40W Fl (2) R 10s; PHM.

SHOREHAM.
Lt By 50°47'·00N 00°15'·33W Fl Y 5s; SPM.
W Breakwater Hd 50°49'·45N 00°14'·79W Fl R 5s 7m 7M.
E Breakwater Hd Fl G 5s 7m 8M; *Siren 120s.*
Ldg Lts 355° Middle Pier. Front F WR or G 8m W10M, R9M, G9M; W watchhouse, R base; tidal Lts, tfc sigs; *Horn 20s.* **Rear** 192m from front Fl 10s 13m **15M**; vis 283°-103°.
W Pier Hd F WR 6m; R to seaward.
E Pier Hd F WG 7m; G to seaward.

BRIGHTON.
Lt By 50°46'·00N 00°08'·30W Fl Y 3s; SPM.
W Pier Hd Fl R 10s 13m 2M; *Bell (1) 13s* (when vessel expected).
Palace Pier 2 FR (vert) 10m 2M.

BRIGHTON MARINA.
E breakwater Fl (4) WR 20s 16m W10M, R8M; W pillar, G bands; vis R260°-295°, W295°-100°.
E breakwater Hd QG 8m 7M.
W Breakwater Hd 50°48'·46N 00°06'·29W QR 10m 7M; W ● structure, R bands; *Horn (2) 30s.*

NEWHAVEN.
Breakwater Hd 50°46'·52N 00°03'·60E Oc (2) 10s 17m 12M; *Horn 30s.*
W Pier Hd 2 FR (vert); RC.
E Pier Hd Iso G 5s 12m 6M; W framework Tr.

Note. For English Channel Waypoints see 10.1.7

CS 1 Lt By 50°33'·67N 00°03'·83W Fl Y 2·5s; SPM; *Whis.*
CS 2 Lt By 50°39'·08N 00°32'·70E Fl Y 5s; SPM.
CS 3 Lt By 50°52'·00N 01°02'·30E Fl Y 10s; SPM; *Bell.*
CS 4 Lt By 51°08'·57N 01°34'·02E Fl (4)Y 15s; SPM; *Whis.*

GREENWICH LANBY 50°24'·50N 00°00'·00 Fl 5s 12m **21M**; R structure on ● By; Racon; Ra refl; *Horn 30s.*

Beachy Hd 50°44'·00N 00°14'·60E Fl (2) 20s 31m **25M**; W ● Tr, R band and lantern; vis 248°-101°; (H24); *Horn 30s.* Fog Det Lt vis 085°-265°.

Royal Sovereign 50°43'·38N 00°26'·13E Fl 20s 28m **28M**; W Tr, R band on W cabin on concrete col; Helicopter platform; *Dia (2) 30s.*
Royal Sovereign By 50°44'·20N 00°25'·95E (unlit); PHM.

EASTBOURNE.
Pier Hd 50°45'·88N 00°17'·85E 2 FR (vert) 8m 2M.
St Leonard's outfall Lt By 50°49'·27N 00°32'·00E Fl Y 5s; SPM.

HASTINGS.
Pier Hd 2 FR (vert) 8m 5M; W hut.
W Breakwater Hd 50°51'·13N 00°35'·70E Fl R 2·5s 5m 4M.
Ldg Lts 356·3°. Front FR 14M 4M. Rear 357m from front FR 55m 4M.

RYE.
Rye Fairway Lt By 50°54'·00N 00°48'·13E L Fl 10s;SWM.
W Groyne Hd 50°55'·55N 00°46'·65E Fl R 5s 7m 6M; Ra refl.
E Arm Hd Q (9) 15s 7m 5M; G ▲ on structure; *Horn 7s.*

Dungeness 50°54'·77N 00°58'·67E Fl 10s 40m **27M**; B ● Tr, W bands and lantern, floodlit; Part obsc 078°-shore; RC; (H24). F RG 37m 11M (same Tr); vis R057°-073°, G073°-078°, R196°-216°; FR Lts shown 2·4 and 5·2M WNW when firing taking place. QR and FR on radio mast 1·2M NW; *Horn (3) 60s.*

VARNE LANBY 51°01'·25N 01°24'·00E Fl R 20s 12m**19M**; *Horn 30s*; Racon.

FOLKESTONE.
Breakwater Hd 51°04'·53N 01°11'·79E Fl (2) 10s 14m **22M**; *Dia (4) 60s.* In fog Fl 2s; vis 246°-306°, intens 271·5°-280·5°.
Outer Hbr, E Pier Hd QG.

DOVER.
Admiralty Pier Extension Hd 51°06'·65N 01°19'·77E Fl 7·5s 21m **20M**; W Tr; vis 096°-090°, obsc in The Downs by S Foreland inshore of 226°; *Horn 10s.*
Prince of Wales Pier Hd VQ G 14m 4M; W Tr; Fl Y 1·5s (intens, occas).
S Breakwater, W Hd Oc R 30s 21m **18M**; W Tr.
Knuckle Oc WR 10s 15m **W15M**, R13M; W Tr; vis R059°-239°, W239°-059°.
N Hd 51°07'·17N 01°20'·72E FY 17m 4M.
E Arm Hd, Port Control Sig Stn; *Horn (2) 30s.*

S GOODWIN Lt F 51°07'·95N 01°28'·60E Fl (2) 30s 12m **21M**; R hull with Lt Tr amidships; *Horn (2) 60s.*
SW Goodwin Lt By 51°08'·57N 01°28'·80E Q (6) + LFl 15s; SCM.
S Goodwin Lt By 51°10'·57N 01°32'·37E Fl (4) R 15s; PHM.
SE Goodwin Lt By 51°12'·95N 01°34'·55E Fl (3) R 10s; PHM.

E GOODWIN Lt F 51°13'·05N 01°36'·31E Fl 15s 12m **21M**; R hull with Lt Tr amidships; Racon; *Horn 30s.*
E Goodwin Lt By 51°16'·00N 01°35'·60E Q (3) 10s; ECM.
NE Goodwin Lt By 51°20'·28N 01°34'·27E Q (3) 10s; ECM; Racon.

DEAL.
Pier Hd 51°13'·40N 01°24'·65E 2 FR (vert) 7m 5M.

THE DOWNS.
Deal Bank Lt By 51°12'·90N 01°25'·68; QR; PHM.
Goodwin Fork Lt By 51°13'·25N 01°27'·13E Q (6) + LFl 15s; SCM; *Bell.*
Downs Lt By 51°14'·31N 01°26'·90E Fl (2) R 5s; PHM.

GULL STREAM.
W Goodwin Lt By 51°15'·28N 01°27'·32E Fl G 5s; SHM.
S Brake Lt By 51°15'·40N 01°27'·00E Fl (3) R 10s; PHM.
NW Goodwin Lt By 51°16'·55N 01°28'·55E Q (9) 15s; WCM; *Bell*.
Brake Lt By 51°16'·90N 01°28'·40E Fl(4) R 15s; PHM; *Bell.*
N Goodwin Lt By 51°17'·60N 01°30'·03E Fl G 2·5s; SHM.
Gull Stream Lt By 51°18'·10N 01°30'·02E QR; PHM.
Gull Lt By 51°19'·55N 01°31'·40E VQ (3) 5s; ECM.
Goodwin Knoll Lt By 51°19'·55N 01°32'·30E Fl (2) G 5s; SHM.

RAMSGATE CHANNEL.
B1 By 51°15'·75N 01°25'·70E (unlit); SHM.
B2 By 51°18'·05N 01°24'·20E (unlit); SHM.

RIVER STOUR.
Chan marked by PHM & SHM Bys and Bns.
Pegwell Bay, Sandwich appr 51°18'·72N 01°23'·05E Fl R 10s 3m 4M; framework Tr; moved to meet changes in chan.

RAMSGATE.
E Brake Lt By 51°19'·45N 01°29'·10E Q (3) 10s; ECM.
Dredged appr chan marked by Lt Bys, Fl (4) Y 10s on S side and Q Fl on N side.
Channel Lt By, S side 51°19'·44N 01°26'·00E Q; NCM.
N side 51°15'·51N 01°26'·00E Q (6) + LFl 15s; SCM.
S breakwater Hd VQ R 10m 5M; W pillar, R bands.
N breakwater Hd QG 10m 5M; W pillar, G bands.
W ferry terminal Dir Lt 270°, Dir Oc·WRG 10s 10m 5M; B ▲, Or stripe; vis G259°-269°, W269°-271°, R271°-281°.
Rear 493m from front Oc W 5s 17m 5M; B ▼, Or stripe; vis 263°-278°.
Royal Harbour ent E side Oc 10s 8m 4M.

BROADSTAIRS.
Broadstairs Knoll Lt By 51°20'·85N 01°29'·57E Fl R 2·5s; PHM.
Pier SE end 51°21'·46N°1 26'.83E 2 FR (vert) 7m 4M.

N Foreland 51°22'·47N 01°26'·80E Fl (5) WR 20s 57m **W21M, R18M, R16M**; W 8-sided Tr; vis W shore-150°, R150°-200°, W200°-011°; RC.

ENGLAND—EAST COAST

FALLS Lt F 51°18'·10N 01°48'·50E Fl (2) 10s 12m **24M**; R hull with Lt Tr amidships; RC; Racon; *Horn Mo (N) 60s.*
F3 LANBY 51°23'·82N 02°00'·62E Fl 10s 12m **22M**; Racon; *Horn 10s.*
Falls Hd Lt By 51°28'·20N 01°50'·00E Q; NCM.
NE Spit Lt By 51°27'·92N 01°30'·00E VQ (3) 5s; ECM.
Elbow Lt By 51°23'·20N 01°31'·68E Q; NCM.
Foreness Pt, sewer outfall Lt By 51°24'·60N 01°26'·10E Fl Y 5s; SPM.
Longnose By 51°24'·12N 01°26'·20E (unlit); PHM.
Longnose Spit By 51°23'·90N 01°25'·85E (unlit); NCM.

MARGATE.
Promenade Pier N Hd 51°23'·65N 01°22'·93E Fl (3) R 10s.
Stone Pier Hd FR 18m 4M.

GORE CHANNEL.
SE Margate Lt By 51°24'·10N 01° 20'·50E Q (3) 10s; ECM.
S Margate Lt By 51°23'·90N 01°16'·75E Fl G 2.5s; SHM.
Margate Hook Bn 51°24'·03N 01°12'·68E (unlit); SHM.
Hook Spit By 51°24'·03N 01°12'·68E (unlit); SHM.
E Last Lt By 51°24'·00N 01°12'·27E QR; PHM.

HERNE BAY.
Pier Hd (isolated from shore) 51°22'·88N 01°07'·00E Q 8m 4M.
2 FR (vert) near root.

WHITSTABLE.
Whitstable Street Lt By 51°23'·83N 01°01'·70E Q; NCM.
Whitstable Oyster Lt By 51°22'·03N 01°01'·16E Fl (2) R 10s; PHM.
On E side of Hbr F 15m 8M; W mast; FR 10m 5M (same structure) shown when ent/dep prohib.
W Quay, dolphin 51°21'·82N 01°01'·55E Fl WRG 2m 5s W5M, R3M, G3M; vis W118°-156°, G156°-178°, R178°-201°.
E Quay, N end 2 FR (vert) 4m 1M.

THE SWALE.
Columbine By 51°24'·23N 01°01'·45E (unlit); SHM.
Columbine Spit By 51°23'·83N 01°00'·12E (unlit); SHM.
Pollard Spit Lt By 51°22'·95N 00° 58'·66E QR; PHM.
Ham Gat By 51°23'·05N 00°58'·41E (unlit); SHM.
Sand End Lt By 51°21'·40N 00°56'·00E FlG 5s; SHM.
Faversham Spit By 51°20'·72N 00°54'·28E (unlit); NCM.

QUEENS CHANNEL/FOUR FATHOMS CHANNEL.
E Margate Lt By 51°27'·00N 01°26'·50E Fl R 2·5s; PHM.
Spaniard Lt By 51°26'·20N 01°04'·10E Q (3) 10s; ECM.
Spile Lt By 51°26'·40N 00°55'·85E Fl G 2·5s; SHM.

PRINCES CHANNEL.
Outer Tongue Lt By 51°30'·70N 01°26'·50E L Fl 10s; SWM; *Whis*; Racon.
Tongue Sand Tower 51°29'·55N 01°22'·10E (unlit) NCM & SCM Lt Bys close N and S).
E Tongue Lt By 51°28'·73N 01°18'·70E Fl (2) R 5s; PHM.
N Tongue Lt By 51°28'·80N 01°13'·20E Fl (3) R 10s; PHM.
SE Girdler Lt By 51°29'·47N 01°10'·00E Fl (3) G 10s; SHM.
W Girdler Lt By 51°29'·60N 01°06'·90E Q (9)15s; WCM; *Bell.*
Girdler Lt By 51°29'·15N 01°06'·50E Fl (4) R 15s; PHM.
Shivering Sand Tr 51°29'·90N 01°04'·90E (unlit NCM & SCM Lt Bys close N and S).
E Redsand Lt By 51°29'·38N 01°04'·12E Fl (2) R 5s; PHM.

SOUTH EDINBURGH/KNOB CHANNELS
S Shingles Lt By 51°29'·20N 01°16'·15E Q (6) + LFl 15s; SCM; *Bell.*
Shingles Patch Lt By 51°32'·98N 01°15'·47E Q; NCM.
N Shingles Lt By 51°32'·63N 01°14'·35E Fl R 2·5s; PHM.
Tizard Lt By 51°32'·90N 01°13'·50E Q (6) + L Fl 15s; SCM.
Mid Shingles Lt By 51°31'·93N 01°12'·08E Fl (2) R 5s; PHM.
NE Knob Lt By 51°32'·00N 01°10'·10E QG; SHM.
NW Shingles Lt By 51°31'·23N 01°09'·83E VQ; NCM.

OAZE DEEP.
Red Sand Tr 51°28'·60N 00°59'·50E (unlit PHM & SHM Lt Bys close NW and E).
S Oaze Lt By 51°30'·00N 01°00'·80E Fl (2) G 5s; SHM.
SW Oaze Lt By 51°29'·03N 00°57'·05E Q (6) + LFl 15s; SCM.
W Oaze Lt By 51°29'·03N 00°55'·52E VQ (9) 10s; WCM.
Cant Bn 51°27'·73N 00°55'·45E (unlit).
E Cant Lt By 51°28'·50N 00°55'·70E QR; PHM.
W Cant Lt By 51°27'·19N 00°45'·61E QR; PHM.

Medway Lt By 51°28'·80N 00°52'·92E Iso 2s; SWM.

SHEERNESS.
Garrison Pt 51°26'·80N 00°44'·73E 2 FR (vert); R ◆, W top, on col on fort; *Horn(3) 30s* .
Isle of Grain 51°26'·6N 00°43'·5E Q WRG 20m W13M, R7M, G8M; R & W ◆ on R Tr; vis R220°-234°, G234°-241°, W241°-013°; Ra refl.

SEA REACH.
No. 1 Lt By 51°29'·42N 00°52'·67E Fl Y 2·5s; SPM; Racon.
No. 2 Lt By 51°29'·37N 00°49'·85E Iso 5s; SWM.
No. 3 Lt By 51°29'·30N 00°46'·65E L Fl 10s; SWM.
No. 4 Lt By 51°29'·58N 00°44'·28E Fl Y 2·5s; SPM.
No. 5 Lt By 51°29'·92N 00°41'·54E Iso 5s; SWM.
No. 6 Lt By 51°30'·00N 00°39'·94E Iso 2s; SWM.
No. 7 Lt By 51°30'·07N 00°37'·15E Fl Y 2·5s; SPM; Racon.
Mid Blyth Lt By 51°30'·05N 00°32'·50E Q; NCM.

CANVEY ISLAND.
Jetty Hd, E end 2 FG (vert); *Bell (1) 10s.*
W Hd 2 FG (vert) 13m 8M. Lts 2 FR (vert) to port, and 2 FG (vert) to stbd, are shown from wharves etc above this Pt.

Shornmead 51°27'·0N 00°26'·6E Fl (2) WRG 10s 12m **W17M**, R13M, G13M; vis G shore-080°, R080°-085°, W085°-088°, G088°-141°, W141°-205°, R205°-213°.

Northfleet Lower 51°26'·9N 00°20'·4E Oc WR 5s 15m **W17M**, R14M; vis W164°-271°, R271°-S shore.

Northfleet Upper 51°26'·9N 00°20'·2E Oc WRG 10s 30m **W16M**, R12M, G12M; vis R126°-149°, W149°-159°, G159°-269°, W269°-279°.
Broadness. 51°28'·ON 00°18'·7E Oc R 5s 12m 12M; R metal Tr.

SOUTHEND.
Pie E end 51°30'·84N 00°43'·51E 2 FG (vert) 7/5m. *Horn Mo (N) 30s* (temp inop, 1986).
W Hd 2 FG (vert) 13m 8M.

Shoebury Bn 51°30'·27N 00°49'·40E Fl (3) G 10s.
Inner Bn 51°30'·96N 00°49'·28E Fl Y 2·5s.
Blacktail (W) Bn 51°31'·43N 00°55'·30E Iso G 10s 10m 6M.
Blacktail (E) Bn 51°31'·75N 00°56'·60E Iso G 5s 10m 6M.

IMPORTANT NOTE. Changes to buoyage in the Thames Estuary are regularly made. Check Notices to Mariners for the latest position.

10.3.5 PASSAGE INFORMATION

This area embraces the greatest concentration of commercial shipping in the world, and it must be recognised that in such waters the greatest danger to a small yacht is being run down by a larger vessel, especially in poor visibility. In addition to the many ships plying up and down the traffic lanes, there are fast ferries, hovercraft and hydrofoils passing to and fro between English and Continental harbours; warships and submarines on exercises; fishing vessels operating both inshore and offshore; many other yachts; and static dangers such as lobster pots and fishing nets which are concentrated in certain places.

Even for coastal cruising it is essential to have knowledge of the TSS in force, see Fig. 2(2), observing that the SW-bound lane from the Dover Strait passes only 4M off Dungeness, for example. Radar surveillance of the Dover Strait is maintained continuously by the Channel Navigation Information Service (CNIS).

It should be remembered that in the English Chan wind can have a big effect on tidal streams, and on the range of tides. Also N winds, which give smooth water and pleasant sailing off the shores of England, can cause rough seas on the French coast. The rates of tidal streams vary with the locality, and are greatest in the narrowest parts of the chan and off large headlands: in the Dover Strait sp rates can reach 4 kn, but elsewhere in open water they seldom exceed 2 kn. In strong winds the Dover Strait can become very rough. With strong S winds the English coast between Isle of Wight and Dover is very exposed, and shelter is hard to find.

CROSS-CHANNEL PASSAGES

Various factors need to be considered when planning a passage between, say, England and France in whichever direction. It is an advantage for the average yacht to minimise the length of time out of sight of land, thus reducing not only fatigue (which can soon become apparent in a family crew) but also the risk of navigational error due in part to tidal streams. Thus, when proceeding from Brighton to St Malo for example, it pays to cruise coastwise to Poole or Weymouth before setting off for Cherbourg, Alderney or the Casquets. Such tactics also combine the legal requirement to cross traffic separation schemes at right angles (see 2.1.2). Naturally the coastwise sections of any cruise should be timed to take maximum advantage from favourable tidal streams.

Prevailing winds also need to be considered. If it is accepted (as statistics show) that in the English Channel between Portland and the Channel Is the wind more commonly blows from a direction between S and W, the likelihood of getting a good slant is improved by sailing from Portland rather than Brighton: departure from Brighton might give a long beat to windward. Such decisions may depend of course on forecast wind directions in the immediate future.

It is also helpful to plan that points of departure and arrival have powerful lights and conspic landmarks, and radiobeacons which can be used in the event of visibility closing down. Do not forget the importance of taking back bearings in the early stages of a Channel crossing, in order to assess the correct course and proper allowance for leeway and tidal stream.

On some passages soundings can be a useful aid to navigation: thus in the example quoted above from Portland to the Casquets, the Hurd Deep is a useful guide to progress made.

THE OWERS (chart 1652)

Selsey Bill is a low headland, and off it lie the Owers – groups of rks and shoals extending 3M to the S, and 5M to the SE. Just W and SW of the Bill, The Streets (awash) extend 1·25M seaward. 1·25M SSW of the Bill are The Grounds (or Malt Owers) and The Dries (dry). 1M E of The Dries, and about 1·25M S of the lifeboat house on E side of Selsey Bill is a group of rks called The Mixon, marked by Bn at E end.

Immediately S of dangers above is the Looe chan, which runs E/W about 0·75M S of Mixon Bn, and is marked by Bys at W end, where it is narrowest between Brake (or Cross) Ledge on N side and Boulder Bank to the S. In daylight and in good vis and moderate weather, the Looe chan is an easy and useful short cut. The E-going stream begins at HW Portsmouth +0430, and the W-going at HW Portsmouth –0135, sp rates 2·5 kn. Beware lobster pots in this area.

In poor vis or in bad weather (and always in darkness) keep S of the Owers Lanby, moored 7M SE of Selsey Bill, marking SE end of Owers. Over much of Owers there is less than 3m, and large parts virtually dry: so a combination of tidal stream and strong wind produces heavy breaking seas and overfalls over a large area.

SELSEY BILL TO DUNGENESS (charts 1652, 536)

The coast from Selsey Bill to Brighton is low, faced by a shingle beach, and with few offlying dangers, Bognor Rks (dry in places) extend 1·75M E from a point 1M W of the pier, and Bognor Spit extends E and S from the end of them. Middleton ledge are rks running 0·8M offshore, about 1·5M E of Bognor pier, with depths of less than 1m. Shelley Rks lie 0·5M S of Middleton ledge, with depths of less than 1 m.

Winter Knoll, about 2·5M SSW of Littlehampton (10.3.9) has depths of 2·1m. Kingston rks, with depth of 2·0m lie about 3·25M ESE of Littlehampton. Grass Banks, an extensive shoal with depths of 3·0m at W end, lie about 1M S of Worthing Elbow, with depth of 3·1m, lies 1·75M SE of Worthing pier.

Off Shoreham (10.3.10) Church Rks, with depth of 0·3m, lie 1·5M W of Ent and 0·25M offshore. Jenny Rks, with depth 0·9m, are 1·25M E of the Ent, 0·3M offshore.

At Brighton (10.3.11) the S Downs join the coastline, and high chalk cliffs are conspic from here to Beachy Hd. There are no dangers more than 0·3 from shore, until Birling Gap, where a rky ledge begins, on which is built Beachy Hd Lt Ho (Lt, fog sig). Below the watch house on cliff top, Head Ledge (dries) extends about 0·4M S. 2M S of Beachy Hd the W-going stream begins at HW Dover +0030, and the E-going at HW Dover –0520, sp rates 2·25 kn. In bad weather there are overfalls off the Hd, which should then be given a berth of 2M.

Royal Sovereign Lt Tr (Lt, fog sig) lies about 7M E of Beachy Hd. The extensive Royal Sovereign shoals lie from between 1·5M N of the Tr to 3M NW of it, and have a least depth of 3·5m. There are strong eddies over the shoals at sp, and the sea breaks on them in bad weather.

On the direct course from Royal Sovereign Lt Tr to clear Dungeness there are no dangers. Along the coast in Pevensey B and Rye B there are drying rky ledges or shoals extending 0·5M offshore in places. These include Boulder Bank near Wish Tr, S of Eastbourne; Oyster Reef off Cooden; Bexhill Reef off Bexhill-on-Sea; Bopeep Rks off St Leonards; and the shoals at the mouth of R Rother, at entrance to Rye (10.3.13). There are also shoals 2-3M offshore, on which the sea builds in bad weather.

Dungeness (Lt, fog sig, RC) is at SE extremity of Romney Marsh. The nuclear power station is conspic. The Pt is steep-to on SE side. Good anch close NE of Dungeness.

DUNGENESS TO NORTH FORELAND (charts 1892, 1828)

From Dungeness to Folkestone (10.3.14) the coast forms a Bay. Beware Roar bank, depth 2·7m, E of New Romney: otherwise there are no offlying dangers. Good anch off Sandgate in offshore winds. Off Folkestone hbr the E-going stream begins HW Dover –0155, sp rate 2 kn; the W-going begins HW Dover +0320, sp rate 1·5kn.

Past Dover (10.3.15) and S Foreland keep 0·5M offshore: do not pass too close to Dover Hbr because ferries etc leave at speed, and also there can be considerable backwash off hbr walls. 8M S of Dover is the Varne, a shoal 5M in extent with least depth 3·7m and a heavy sea in bad weather, marked by Lanby. Between S and N Foreland the N-going stream begins at about HW Dover –0150, and the S-going at about HW Dover +0415.

Goodwin Sands are extensive, shifting shoals, running about 10M from N to S, and 5M from E to W at their widest part. Along the E and N sides large areas dry up to 3m. The sands are well marked by Lt Fs and Bys. Kellett Gut is a chan about 0·5M wide, running from SW to NE through the middle of the sands, but it is not regularly surveyed and liable to change. The Gull Stream (buoyed) leads inside Goodwin Sands and outside Brake Sands off Ramsgate (10.3.16). The Ramsgate chan leads inside the Brake Sands and Cross Ledge.

THAMES ESTUARY (chart 1607)

N Foreland (Lt, RC) marks the S Ent to Thames Estuary, an area encumbered by banks many of which dry. N Foreland (chart 1828) is well marked by Lt Ho and Bys offshore. From HW Dover –0120 to HW Dover +0045 the stream runs N and W from the Downs into Thames Estuary. From HW Dover +0045 to HW Dover +0440 the N-going stream from The Downs meets the E-going stream from Thames Estuary, which in strong winds causes a bad sea. From HW Dover –0450 to HW Dover –0120 the streams turn W into Thames Estuary and S towards The Downs.

The sandbanks shift constantly, and it is important to have corrected charts showing recent buoyage changes. With wind against tide a short, steep sea is raised, particularly in E or NE winds. The stream runs 3 kn at sp in places, mostly in the directions of the chans but sometimes across the shoals in between. The main chans carry much commercial shipping and are well buoyed and lit, but this does not apply to lesser chans and swatchways which are convenient for yachtsmen, particularly when crossing the estuary from N to S, or S to N.

The main chans on the S side of the estuary are as follows. S chan, which leads W about 1M off the N Kent coast and into Gore chan, Horse chan and Four Fathoms chan across the Kentish Flats (most of this route is sparsely buoyed, and very sparsely lit); Queens chan; Princes chan, a main E/W route, passing S of Tongue Sand Tr, where the W-going stream begins at HW Sheerness –0610, and the E-going at HW Sheerness +0030, sp rates 2 kn; the Edinburgh chans, which run into Knob chan; and Oaze Deep, a continuation of Knock John chan and Barrow Deep, which join it from a NE direction.

When crossing the estuary it is essential to study the tides carefully, both to ensure sufficient depth in places and also to make the best use of tidal streams. Good vis is needed to pick out the Bys and marks, and to avoid commercial shipping. Proceeding N from N Foreland to Orford Ness or beyond (or coming in opposite direction) it may be preferable to keep to seaward of the main banks, passing Kentish Knock By and thence to Shipwash Lt F 24M further N.

Bound from N Foreland to the Crouch or Blackwater proceed through S Edinburgh chan, through the swatchway about 0·5M NE of Knock John Tr into Barrow Deep, and thence round the end of W Barrow Sand. With sufficient rise of tide it is possible to cut across between Maplin Spit and Barrow Sand, but usually it is better to proceed SW to Maplin Bank By, and thence into E Swin to the Whitaker By. This is just one of many routes which could be followed, depending on wind direction and tidal conditions.

10.3.6 DISTANCE TABLE

Approximate distances in nautical miles are by the most direct route while avoiding dangers and allowing for traffic separation schemes etc. Places in *italics* are in adjoining areas.

1 *Casquets*	**1**																			
2 *Cherbourg*	31	**2**																		
3 *Nab Tower*	81	66	**3**																	
4 Owers Lanby	87	70	11	**4**																
5 Shoreham	106	88	32	21	**5**															
6 Brighton Marina	109	90	35	24	5	**6**														
7 Newhaven	114	94	40	29	12	7	**7**													
8 Royal Sovereign	124	102	54	43	27	22	15	**8**												
9 Folkestone	162	140	92	81	65	60	53	38	**9**											
10 Dover	167	145	97	86	70	65	58	43	5	**10**										
11 Ramsgate	182	160	112	101	85	80	73	58	20	15	**11**									
12 North Foreland	186	164	116	105	89	84	77	62	24	19	4	**12**								
13 Whitstable	203	179	133	122	106	101	94	79	41	36	22	17	**13**							
14 Sheerness	216	194	146	135	119	114	107	92	54	49	34	30	14	**14**						
15 London Bridge	258	236	188	177	161	156	149	134	96	91	76	72	55	45	**15**					
16 Shoeburyness	215	193	145	134	118	113	106	91	53	48	33	29	14	4	43	**16**				
17 *Orford Ness*	231	209	161	150	134	129	122	107	69	64	49	45	50	53	92	49	**17**			
18 *Dieppe*	139	108	92	81	75	70	65	55	71	75	90	94	111	124	166	123	135	**18**		
19 *Cap Gris Nez*	175	147	101	90	74	69	62	47	19	19	28	32	49	62	104	61	74	61	**19**	
20 *Goeree Tower*	278	250	204	193	177	172	165	150	106	101	94	91	104	114	154	111	78	164	103	**20**

S.E. ENGLAND WAYPOINTS 10-3-8

Selected waypoints for use in Area 3 are listed in alphabetical order below. Further waypoints for use in coastal waters are given in sections 10.2.18, 10.4.6 and 10.9.6. Selected waypoints for use in Channel crossings are given in 10.1.7.

Brake Lt By	51°16'·90N 01°28'·40E
Broadstairs Knoll Lt By	51°20'·85N 01°29'·58E
Brighton Marina Hd	50°48'·46N 00°06'·29W
Bullock Bank Lt By	50°46'·90N 01°07'·70E
Colbalt N Lt By	50°57'·44N 01°23'·40E
Colbalt SW Lt By	50°48'·82N 01°16'·40E
Columbine By	51°24'·23N 01°01'·45E
Columbine Spit By	51°23'·83N 01°00'·12E
CS 1 Lt By	50°33'·67N 00°03'·83W
CS 2 Lt By	50°39'·10N 00°32'·70E
CS 3 Lt By	50°52'·00N 01°02'·30E
CS 4 Lt By	51°08'·58N 01°34'·03E
Deal Bank Lt By	51°12'·90N 01°25'·68E
Downs Lt By	51°14'·32N 01°26'·92E
Drill Stone Lt By	51°25'·80N 01°43'·00E
Dungeness Lt	50°54'·77N 00°58'·67E
Dungeness Lt By	50°54'·43N 00°58'·33E
East Brake Lt By	51°19'·45N 01°29'·10E
East Borough Hd Lt By	50°41'·50N 00°39'·00W
East Goodwin Lt F	51°13'·05N 01°36'·31E
East Goodwin Lt By	51°16'·00N 01°35'·60E
East Last Lt By	51°24'·00N 01°12'·27E
East Margate Lt By	51°27'·00N 01°26'·50E
East Redsand Lt By	51°29'·38N 01°04'·15E
East Tongue Lt By	51°28'·73N 01°18'·70E
East Varne Lt By	50°58'·20N 01°21'·00E
Elbow Lt By	51°23'·20N 01°31'·70E
F1 Lt By	51°11'·33N 01°45'·10E
F2 Lt By	51°20'·38N 01°56'·30E
Falls Lt F	51°18'·10N 01°48'·50E
Falls Head Lt By	51°28'·20N 0 1°50'·00E
Falls Mid Lt By	51°20'·50N 01°48'·00E
Goodwin Fork Lt By	51°13'·25N 01°27'·13E
Goodwin Knoll Lt By	51°19'·55N 01°32'·30E
Greenwich Lanby	50°24'·50N 00°00'·00
Gull Lt By	51°19'·55N 01°31'·40E
Gull Stream Lt By	51°18'·10N 01°30'·02E
Hook Spit By	51°24'·05N 01°12'·65E
Margate Hook Bn	51°24'·12N 01°14'·41E
Mid Falls Lt By	51°20'·50N 01°48'·00E
Mid Varne Lt By	50°58'·90N 01°20'·00E
MPC Lt By	51°06'·17N 01°38'·33E

Newhaven Breakwater Hd	50°46'·52N 00°03'·60E
North Goodwin Lt By	51°17'·60N 01°30'·03E
North Goodwin Lt V	51°20'·28N 01°34'·27E
North Redsand Trs Lt By	51°28'·70N 00°59'·42E
North East Goodwin Lt By	51°20'·28N 01°34'·27E
North East Spit Lt By	51°27'·92N 01°30'·00E
N.E. Tongue Sand Tr Lt By	51°29'·65N 01°22'·13E
N. W. Goodwin Lt By	51°16'·55N 01°28'·55E
Outer Owers By	50°38'·75N 00°41'·30W
Outer Tongue Lt By	51°30'·70N 01°26'·50E
Owers Lanby	50°37'·30N 00°40'·60W
Pollard Spit Lt By	51°22'·95N 00°58'·66E
Pullar By	50°40'·45N 00°50'·00W
Quern Lt By	51°19'·39N 01°26'·20E
Ramsgate Chan B.1 By	51°15'·75N 01°25'·70E
Ramsgate Chanl B.2 By	51°18'·05N 01°24'·20E
Royal Sovereign Lt	50°43'·38N 00°26'·13E
Rye Fairway Lt By	50°54'·00N 00°48'·13E
Shoreham Lt By	50°47'·00N 00°15'·33W
South Brake Lt By	51°15'·40N 01°27'·00E
S. E. Goodwin Lt By	51°12'·95N 01°34'·55E
S. E. Margate Lt By	51°24'·10N 01°20'·50E
South Falls Lt By	51°14'·00N 00°44'·00E
South Goodwin Lt By	51°10'·57N 01°32'·37E
South Goodwin Lt F	51°07'·95N 01°28'·60E
S. Inner Gabbard Lt By	51°51'·20N 01°52'·40E
South Margate Lt By	51°23'.90N 01°16'.75E
S. Redsand Towers Lt By	51°28'·57N 00°59'·77E
South East Margate Lt By	51°24'·10N 01°20'·50E
South Varne Lt By	50°55'·60N 01°17'·40E
S. W. Goodwin Lt By	51°08'·57N 01°28'·80E
S. W. Sandettie Lt By	51°09'·80N 01°45'·70E
S. W. Tongue Tr Lt By	51°29'·40N 01°22'·13E
Spaniard Lt By	51°26'·20N 01°04'·10E
Spile Lt By	51°26'·40N 00°55'·85E
Varne Lanby	51°01'·25N 01°24'·00E
West Girdler Lt By	51°29'·58N 01°06'·82E
West Goodwin Lt By	51°15'·28N 01°27'·32E
Whitstable St Lt By	51°23'·83N 01°01'·70E
WSW Sandettie Lt By	51°12'·40N 01°51'·20E

LITTLEHAMPTON 10-3-9

W. Sussex

CHARTS
Admiralty 1991, 1652; Stanford 9; Imray C9; OS 197

TIDES
+0015 Dover; ML 2·8; Zone 0 (GMT).

Standard Port SHOREHAM (⟶)

Times				Height (metres)			
HW		LW		MHWS	MHWN	MLWN	MLWS
0500	1000	0000	0600	6·3	4·9	2·0	0·6
1700	2200	1200	1800				
Differences LITTLEHAMPTON (ENT)							
+0010	0000	−0005	−0010	−0·4	−0·4	−0·2	−0·2
LITTLEHAMPTON (NORFOLK WHARF)							
+0015	+0005	0000	+0045	−0·7	−0·7	−0·3	+0·2
PAGHAM							
+0015	0000	−0015	−0025	−0·7	−0·5	−0·1	−0·1
BOGNOR REGIS							
+0010	−0005	−0005	−0020	−0·6	−0·5	−0·2	−0·1

NOTE: Tidal heights inside harbour are affected by flow down River Arun. Tide seldom falls lower than 0·7m above datum.

SHELTER
Good. SE winds cause a certain swell up the harbour; SW winds cause roughness on the bar. Entrance dangerous with strong SE winds.

NAVIGATION
Waypoint 50°47′·50N 00°32′·20W, 166°/346° from/to front Ldg Lt, 0·60M. Bar ½ M offshore. Harbour available from HW−4 to HW+3 for boats with about 2m draught. The ebb stream runs so fast at springs that yachts may have difficulty entering. When Pilot boat with P at the bow displays a RW flag by day or W over R lights at night, all boats keep clear of entrance. Speed limit 6½ kn. Depth over the bar is 0·6m less than depth shown on tide gauges. On departure check tide gauge at East Pier to calculate depth on bar.

LIGHTS AND MARKS
Leading marks for entrance are lighthouse at inshore end of E breakwater and the black steel column for the light at the outer end of E breakwater; Ldg Lts 346°.
Swing bridge Fl G Lt – Open / Fl R Lt – Closed — from high mast to port.
The central retractable section of the bridge has 2 FR (vert) to port at each end and 2 FG (vert) to stbd at each end. Opening section is 22m wide. Bridge retracted on request provided notice given before 1630 previous day.

RADIO TELEPHONE
Marinas Ch **80** M (office hours).

TELEPHONE (0903)
Hr Mr 721215/6; MRSC Lee-on-Solent 552100; # (0703) 827350; Marinecall 0898 500 456; Police 716161; Dr 714113.

FACILITIES
EC Wednesday **Littlehampton Marina** (120+30 visitors) ☎ 713553, Slip, BH (16 ton), CH, P, D, V, R, Bar, FW, AC, Sh, ME; **Ship and Anchor Marina** (182, some visitors) ☎ Yapton 551262, Slip, FW, C (6 ton), ME, Sh, CH, V, R, Bar (Access HW∓4); **Arun YC** (90+10 visitors) ☎ 714533, Slip, AC, FW, L, M, Bar (Access HW∓3); **E side of Harbour** M, C, FW; **Littlehampton Sailing and Motor Club** ☎ 715859, M, FW, Bar; **Wm Osbornes** ☎ 713996, BY; **Delta Yachts** ☎ 717369, BY; **Arrow Marine** ☎ 721686, FW, ME, El, Sh, P, D; **County Wharf** FW, C (5 ton); **Hillyards** ☎ 713327, M, FW, ME, Sh (Wood), C;
Town P, D, V, R, Bar. ✉; Ⓑ; ⇌; ✈ (Shoreham).

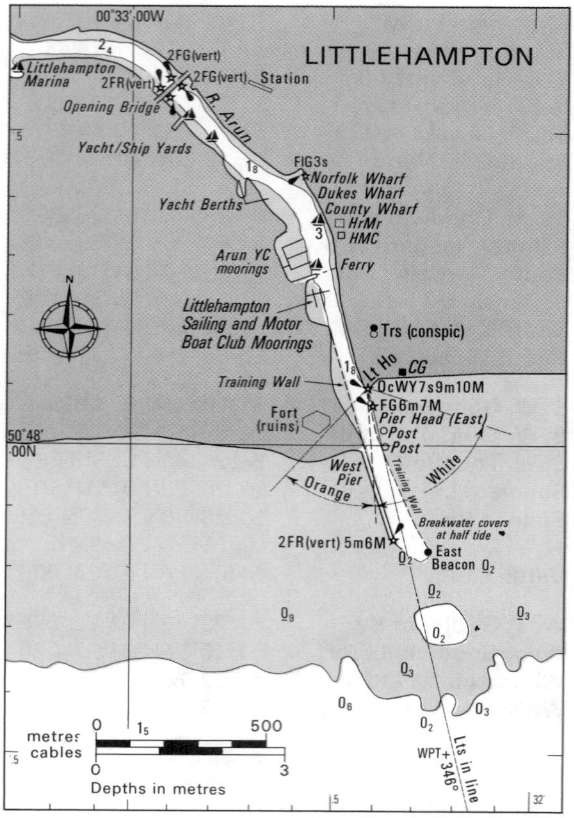

00°33′·00W
LITTLEHAMPTON
Littlehampton Marina
2FR(vert)
2FG(vert)
Station
Opening Bridge
R. Arun
Yacht/Ship Yards
FlG3s
Norfolk Wharf
Dukes Wharf
County Wharf
Yacht Berths
HrMr
HMC
Arun YC moorings
Ferry
Littlehampton Sailing and Motor Boat Club Moorings
Trs (conspic)
Lt Ho
CG
Training Wall
QcWY7s9m10M
FG6m7M
Pier Head (East)
Post
Post
Fort (ruins)
50°48′·00N
West Pier
Orange
White
Training Wall
Breakwater covers at half tide
2FR(vert) 5m6M
East Beacon
metres
cables
0
500
3
Depths in metres
WPT
Lts in line 346°

SHOREHAM 10-3-10

W. Sussex

CHARTS
Admiralty 2044, 1652; Stanford 9; Imray C9; OS 197/8

TIDES
+0009 Dover; ML 3·4; Duration 0605; Zone 0 (GMT)

Standard Port SHOREHAM (⟶)

Times				Height (metres)			
HW		LW		MHWS	MHWN	MLWN	MLWS
0500	1000	0000	0600	6·3	4·9	2·0	0·6
1700	2200	1200	1800				
Differences WORTHING							
+0010	0000	−0005	−0010	−0·1	−0·2	0·0	0·0

NOTE: Shoreham is a Standard Port and tidal predictions for the year are given below.

SHELTER
Excellent. There is complete shelter once through the locks into Southwick Canal. Locks are manned HW∓4. The shallow water at the entrance can be very rough in strong on-shore winds. Berthing space for yachts is very limited and arrangements should be made in advance. Harbour dues are high.

NAVIGATION
Waypoint 50°49′·20N 00°14′·72W, 175°/355° from/to front Ldg Lt, 0·52M. From E, beware Jenny Rks; from W beware Church Rks. Yachtsmen are advised not to use the W arm if possible. Harbour is mainly commercial, so before entering yachtsmen should familiarise themselves with bye-laws, control signals, lock signals, tidal signals etc. Prince George lock usually used for light craft and yachts.
Prince George Lock opens (subject to commercial traffic)
Outward HW−3¾, −1¾, +½, +2¾
Inward HW−3¼, −1¼, +1, +3¼

SHOREHAM *continued*

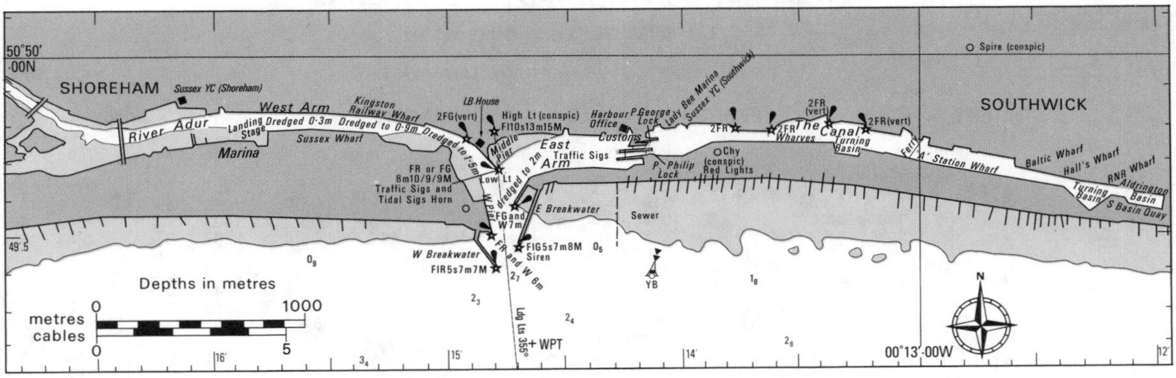

SHOREHAM
Sussex YC (Shoreham)
West Arm
Kingston Railway Wharf
River Adur
Landing Stage
Dredged 0·3m
Dredged to 0·9m
Dredged to 1·5m
Sussex Wharf
Marina
LB House
2FG(vert)
High Lt (conspic)
Fl10s13m15M
Middle Pier
FR or FG 8m10/9/9M
Traffic Sigs and Tidal Sigs Horn
Low Lt
Dredged to 2m
East Arm
Traffic Sigs
Harbour Office
Customs
P George Lock
Lady Bee Marina
Sussex YC (Southwick)
P Philip Lock
Chy (conspic)
Red Lights
2FR
2FR (vert)
The Canal
Wharves
Turning Basin
Ferry
'A' Station Wharf
SOUTHWICK
Spire (conspic)
Baltic Wharf
Hall's Wharf
RNR Wharf
Aldrington Basin
Turning Basin
S Basin Quay
FG and W7m
E Breakwater
W Pier
W Breakwater
FlR5s7m7M
FlG5s7m8M
Siren
FR and W 6m
Sewer
YB
Depths in metres
metres 0 1000
cables 0 5
Ldg Lts 355°
+ WPT
50°50'·00N
49'·5
16'
15'
14'
00°13'·00W
12'
N

Apl to Oct on Sat, Sun and Bank Holidays
Outward HW−3¾, −2½, −1, +¼, +1½, +3
Inward HW−3¼, −2, −½, +½, +1¾, +3¼

LIGHTS AND MARKS
International Port Traffic Signals (see 6.2.7) are displayed from Middle Pier Control Station. In line with High Lighthouse they form leading line for entrance. Additional signals are displayed as follows. From Lifeboat House: focussed over Eastern Arm, and controlling movement therein. From Lifeboat House: focussed over Western Arm, and controlling movement therein. From Prince George Lock: controlling entrance thereto. From Prince Philip Lock: controlling entrance thereto.

RADIO TELEPHONE
VHF Ch 14 16; 14 (H24). Lady Bee Marina Ch **80** M

TELEPHONE (0273)
Hr Mr 592613; Harbour Locks Office 591803; MRSC Lee-on-Solent 552100; # (0703) 827350; Marinecall 0898 500 456; Police 454521; Ⓗ 455622; Dr 461101 (Health Centre).

FACILITIES
EC Wednesday; **Lady Bee Marina** (110+10 visitors) ☎ 593801, Slip, P, D, FW, ME, El, Sh, SM, AC, R, V, CH; Access HW∓3½; **Surry BY** ☎ 461491, Slip, M, FW, AB, Access HW ∓2½; **Sussex Motor YC** ☎ 453078, M, L, Bar; **Shoreham Ship Services** ☎ 454737, CH; **Riverside Marine** ☎ 464831, ME, FW, El, Sh, SM, Slip, M; **A. O. Muggeridge** ☎ 592211, CH, Rigging, ACA; **G. P. Barnes** ☎ 591705, Gas. **Sussex YC** ☎ 494868; **Town** ▣, ✉; Ⓑ; ⇌; ✈.

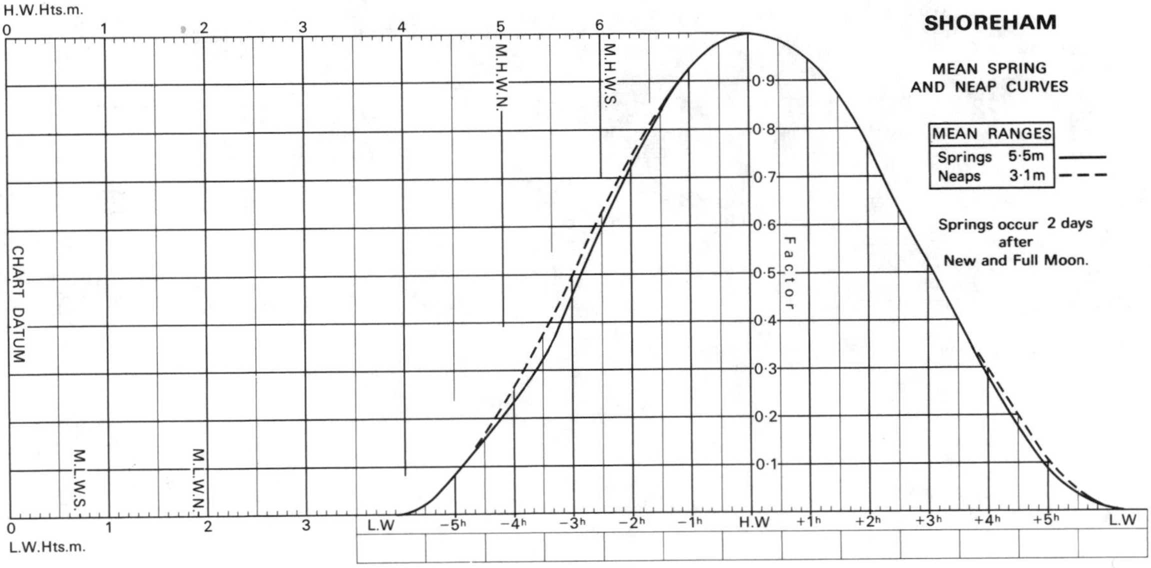

H.W.Hts.m.
0 1 2 3 4 5 6
M.H.W.N.
M.H.W.S.
CHART DATUM
M.L.W.S.
M.L.W.N.
0 1 2 3
L.W.Hts.m.
Factor
0·9 0·8 0·7 0·6 0·5 0·4 0·3 0·2 0·1
L.W −5h −4h −3h −2h −1h H.W +1h +2h +3h +4h +5h L.W
SHOREHAM
MEAN SPRING AND NEAP CURVES
MEAN RANGES
Springs 5·5m
Neaps 3·1m
Springs occur 2 days after New and Full Moon.

TIME ZONE UT(GMT)

For Summer Time add ONE hour in non-shaded areas

ENGLAND, SOUTH COAST – SHOREHAM

Lat 50°50′ N Long 0°15′ W

TIMES AND HEIGHTS OF HIGH AND LOW WATERS

YEAR **1992**

JANUARY

Day	Time	m
1 W	0217 0815 1450 2056	1·6 5·3 1·5 5·2
2 Th	0315 0912 1542 2149	1·5 5·4 1·3 5·4
3 F	0405 1000 1627 2233	1·3 5·6 1·1 5·6
4 Sa	0446 1042 1705 ● 2312	1·2 5·8 1·0 5·8
5 Su	0523 1118 1741 2347	1·2 5·9 1·0 5·9
6 M	0556 1151 1812	1·2 5·9 1·0
7 Tu	0020 0629 1223 1844	5·9 1·2 5·9 1·0
8 W	0050 0701 1255 1917	5·9 1·2 5·8 1·0
9 Th	0120 0734 1329 1949	5·8 1·2 5·7 1·1
10 F	0151 0809 1404 2024	5·7 1·3 5·6 1·1
11 Sa	0224 0844 1441 2059	5·6 1·3 5·4 1·3
12 Su	0259 0924 1522 2141	5·4 1·4 5·2 1·5
13 M	0345 1012 1612 ☽ 2234	5·2 1·6 5·0 1·6
14 Tu	0442 1116 1719 2344	5·0 1·7 4·9 1·7
15 W	0557 1233 1840	5·0 1·7 4·9
16 Th	0105 0715 1350 1958	1·7 5·2 1·5 5·2
17 F	0221 0827 1459 2105	1·4 5·5 1·2 5·6
18 Sa	0326 0928 1559 2205	1·1 5·9 0·9 6·0
19 Su	0422 1023 1653 ○ 2259	0·9 6·2 0·7 6·3
20 M	0514 1115 1743 2350	0·8 6·4 0·6 6·5
21 Tu	0603 1204 1830	0·7 6·5 0·6
22 W	0037 0649 1252 1917	6·6 0·7 6·5 0·6
23 Th	0123 0736 1338 2001	6·6 0·7 6·4 0·6
24 F	0206 0820 1424 2044	6·5 0·7 6·2 0·7
25 Sa	0245 0904 1507 2126	6·3 0·9 5·9 0·9
26 Su	0326 0949 1551 ☾ 2212	6·0 1·1 5·5 1·2
27 M	0411 1042 1645 2310	5·5 1·4 5·1 1·6
28 Tu	0511 1149 1758	5·1 1·7 4·7
29 W	0026 0627 1310 1922	1·9 4·9 1·9 4·7
30 Th	0146 0746 1425 2036	1·9 4·8 1·8 4·9
31 F	0255 0854 1524 2135	1·8 5·0 1·6 5·2

FEBRUARY

Day	Time	m
1 Sa	0349 0947 1611 2222	1·6 5·3 1·3 5·5
2 Su	0432 1030 1651 2259	1·3 5·6 1·1 5·8
3 M	0508 1105 1724 ● 2332	1·2 5·8 0·9 5·9
4 Tu	0539 1136 1754	1·1 5·9 0·9
5 W	0002 0609 1206 1825	6·0 1·0 5·9 0·8
6 Th	0030 0639 1236 1856	6·0 0·9 5·9 0·8
7 F	0058 0710 1308 1926	6·0 0·9 5·9 0·8
8 Sa	0125 0741 1339 1957	5·9 0·9 5·8 0·8
9 Su	0153 0814 1411 2030	5·8 0·9 5·7 1·0
10 M	0225 0849 1446 2106	5·7 1·1 5·4 1·2
11 Tu	0303 0932 1531 ☽ 2155	5·4 1·3 5·1 1·5
12 W	0359 1031 1636 2305	5·1 1·6 4·9 1·7
13 Th	0516 1155 1808	4·9 1·7 4·8
14 F	0038 0649 1328 1943	1·8 5·0 1·6 5·1
15 Sa	0206 0813 1446 2057	1·5 5·3 1·3 5·6
16 Su	0316 0919 1548 2155	1·2 5·8 0·9 6·1
17 M	0412 1013 1640 2247	0·8 6·2 0·6 6·4
18 Tu	0501 1101 1729 ○ 2333	0·6 6·5 0·5 6·6
19 W	0547 1146 1813	0·5 6·6 0·4
20 Th	0017 0631 1232 1856	6·7 0·5 6·6 0·4
21 F	0059 0714 1316 1936	6·7 0·5 6·5 0·4
22 Sa	0138 0754 1356 2015	6·5 0·6 6·3 0·6
23 Su	0212 0833 1433 2052	6·3 0·7 6·0 0·8
24 M	0246 0911 1512 2133	5·9 1·0 5·5 1·2
25 Tu	0324 0957 1559 ☾ 2224	5·5 1·4 5·0 1·7
26 W	0418 1058 1709 2339	4·9 1·9 4·6 2·1
27 Th	0539 1223 1844	4·6 2·1 4·5
28 F	0111 0713 1351 2010	2·2 4·5 2·1 4·7
29 Sa	0229 0831 1457 2113	2·1 4·8 1·8 5·0

MARCH

Day	Time	m
1 Su	0325 0930 1546 2159	1·8 5·1 1·5 5·4
2 M	0407 1011 1624 2236	1·4 5·5 1·1 5·7
3 Tu	0442 1044 1658 2307	1·1 5·8 0·9 5·9
4 W	0513 1113 1728 ● 2335	0·9 5·9 0·8 6·0
5 Th	0543 1142 1759	0·8 6·0 0·7
6 F	0002 0613 1212 1830	6·1 0·7 6·0 0·7
7 Sa	0031 0644 1244 1901	6·1 0·7 6·0 0·7
8 Su	0059 0715 1315 1932	6·1 0·7 6·0 0·7
9 M	0128 0748 1348 2005	6·0 0·7 5·8 0·9
10 Tu	0200 0823 1423 2044	5·8 0·9 5·6 1·1
11 W	0239 0907 1509 2133	5·4 1·2 5·3 1·5
12 Th	0333 1006 1616 ☽ 2247	5·1 1·6 5·0 1·7
13 F	0455 1132 1754	4·8 1·7 4·9
14 Sa	0024 0635 1312 1931	1·8 4·9 1·6 5·2
15 Su	0153 0802 1431 2045	1·5 5·3 1·3 5·7
16 M	0302 0908 1531 2140	1·1 5·7 0·9 6·1
17 Tu	0356 0958 1622 2227	0·8 6·1 0·6 6·4
18 W	0443 1043 1706 ○ 2310	0·5 6·4 0·4 6·6
19 Th	0527 1126 1750 2351	0·4 6·5 0·4 6·6
20 F	0609 1208 1830	0·4 6·5 0·4
21 Sa	0030 0648 1250 1908	6·6 0·5 6·4 0·5
22 Su	0105 0725 1328 1944	6·4 0·6 6·2 0·7
23 M	0138 0800 1403 2020	6·2 0·7 5·9 0·9
24 Tu	0209 0836 1439 2058	5·8 1·1 5·5 1·3
25 W	0246 0916 1522 2146	5·4 1·5 5·1 1·8
26 Th	0336 1013 1627 ☾ 2257	4·9 1·9 4·7 2·2
27 F	0452 1131 1758	4·5 2·2 4·5
28 Sa	0026 0630 1304 1929	2·4 4·4 2·2 4·6
29 Su	0148 0755 1416 2035	2·2 4·6 2·0 5·0
30 M	0247 0856 1508 2123	1·9 5·0 1·6 5·4
31 Tu	0331 0940 1549 2200	1·5 5·4 1·3 5·7

APRIL

Day	Time	m
1 W	0407 1013 1623 2232	1·1 5·7 1·0 5·9
2 Th	0439 1042 1656 2301	0·9 5·9 0·8 6·0
3 F	0511 1112 1729 ● 2332	0·7 6·0 0·7 6·1
4 Sa	0544 1145 1801	0·7 6·0 0·7
5 Su	0002 0617 1220 1836	6·1 0·6 6·1 0·7
6 M	0035 0653 1257 1911	6·1 0·6 6·0 0·8
7 Tu	0109 0729 1334 1949	6·0 0·8 5·9 0·9
8 W	0145 0810 1415 2033	5·8 0·9 5·7 1·2
9 Th	0229 0857 1506 2128	5·5 1·2 5·4 1·5
10 F	0329 0958 1615 ☽ 2241	5·1 1·5 5·1 1·7
11 Sa	0447 1122 1748	4·9 1·7 5·1
12 Su	0013 0623 1253 1916	1·7 4·9 1·5 5·3
13 M	0136 0746 1409 2024	1·4 5·2 1·2 5·7
14 Tu	0241 0848 1508 2117	1·1 5·6 0·9 6·1
15 W	0335 0937 1557 2203	0·8 6·0 0·6 6·3
16 Th	0422 1021 1643 2243	0·6 6·2 0·5 6·4
17 F	0505 1102 1725 ○ 2324	0·5 6·3 0·5 6·4
18 Sa	0544 1143 1804	0·5 6·3 0·6
19 Su	0000 0622 1224 1841	6·3 0·6 6·2 0·7
20 M	0035 0657 1302 1917	6·2 0·7 6·0 0·9
21 Tu	0109 0731 1338 1953	6·0 0·9 5·8 1·1
22 W	0142 0807 1415 2031	5·7 1·1 5·5 1·5
23 Th	0218 0846 1458 2118	5·3 1·5 5·2 1·8
24 F	0307 0937 1554 ☾ 2220	4·9 1·8 4·8 2·2
25 Sa	0412 1043 1709 2335	4·5 2·1 4·6 2·3
26 Su	0535 1203 1830	4·4 2·2 4·7
27 M	0053 0701 1317 1940	2·2 4·5 2·1 4·9
28 Tu	0155 0806 1416 2035	2·0 4·8 1·8 5·2
29 W	0244 0855 1502 2116	1·6 5·2 1·4 5·5
30 Th	0326 0931 1542 2151	1·2 5·5 1·1 5·8

Chart Datum: 3.27 metres below Ordnance Datum (Newlyn)

3

TIME ZONE UT(GMT)

For Summer Time add ONE hour in non-shaded areas

ENGLAND, SOUTH COAST - SHOREHAM

Lat 50°50′ N Long 0°15′ W

TIMES AND HEIGHTS OF HIGH AND LOW WATERS

YEAR **1992**

MAY

Date	Time	m	Time	m	Time	m	Time	m
1 F	0403	1·0	1006	5·7	1620	0·9	2225	5·9
2 Sa ●	0439	0·8	1042	5·9	1657	0·8	2301	6·0
3 Su	0517	0·7	1121	6·0	1736	0·8	2338	6·1
4 M	0556	0·7	1203	6·1	1815	0·9		
5 Tu	0017	6·1	0637	0·8	1246	6·1	1857	0·9
6 W	0058	6·1	0719	0·9	1330	6·0	1942	1·1
7 Th	0141	5·9	0805	1·0	1417	5·9	2032	1·2
8 F	0231	5·6	0856	1·2	1511	5·6	2128	1·4
9 Sa ☽	0330	5·3	0957	1·4	1617	5·4	2236	1·5
10 Su	0442	5·1	1109	1·5	1732	5·4	2354	1·5
11 M	0603	5·1	1228	1·4	1848	5·5		
12 Tu	0110	1·4	0719	5·2	1340	1·3	1955	5·7
13 W	0215	1·1	0822	5·5	1440	1·0	2048	5·9
14 Th	0310	0·9	0913	5·7	1532	0·9	2136	6·0
15 F	0359	0·8	0959	5·9	1620	0·8	2219	6·1
16 Sa ○	0442	0·7	1042	6·0	1702	0·8	2259	6·1
17 Su	0522	0·7	1125	6·0	1743	0·8	2337	6·1
18 M	0601	0·8	1205	5·9	1819	1·0		
19 Tu	0012	6·0	0635	0·9	1244	5·9	1856	1·1
20 W	0046	5·9	0710	1·0	1321	5·7	1932	1·3
21 Th	0121	5·7	0746	1·2	1357	5·6	2010	1·5
22 F	0200	5·4	0825	1·4	1437	5·3	2055	1·7
23 Sa	0243	5·1	0909	1·7	1523	5·1	2145	2·0
24 Su ☾	0336	4·8	1001	1·9	1620	4·9	2243	2·1
25 M	0442	4·6	1102	2·0	1726	4·8	2348	2·1
26 Tu	0552	4·5	1209	2·0	1833	4·9		
27 W	0052	2·0	0700	4·7	1313	1·9	1932	5·1
28 Th	0150	1·7	0758	5·0	1409	1·6	2024	5·3
29 F	0240	1·4	0845	5·3	1459	1·3	2108	5·6
30 Sa	0325	1·1	0930	5·6	1545	1·1	2152	5·8
31 Su	0410	0·9	1015	5·8	1630	1·0	2235	6·0

JUNE

Date	Time	m	Time	m	Time	m	Time	m
1 M ●	0455	0·8	1101	6·0	1716	1·0	2318	6·1
2 Tu	0540	0·8	1151	6·1	1802	1·0		
3 W	0005	6·2	0627	0·9	1240	6·2	1849	1·0
4 Th	0051	6·1	0716	0·9	1329	6·2	1938	1·1
5 F	0140	6·0	0804	1·0	1419	6·1	2030	1·1
6 Sa	0231	5·9	0855	1·0	1510	6·0	2123	1·2
7 Su ☽	0327	5·6	0948	1·1	1605	5·8	2222	1·3
8 M	0426	5·4	1049	1·3	1707	5·6	2328	1·4
9 Tu	0534	5·2	1156	1·4	1813	5·5		
10 W	0039	1·4	0646	5·1	1306	1·4	1920	5·5
11 Th	0147	1·3	0752	5·2	1412	1·3	2019	5·6
12 F	0246	1·2	0849	5·3	1509	1·2	2111	5·7
13 Sa	0339	1·1	0941	5·5	1600	1·1	2158	5·8
14 Su	0425	1·0	1028	5·7	1645	1·1	2243	5·8
15 M ○	0507	1·0	1111	5·8	1727	1·1	2321	5·9
16 Tu	0544	1·0	1153	5·8	1804	1·2	2357	5·9
17 W	0620	1·0	1231	5·8	1839	1·3		
18 Th	0031	5·8	0654	1·1	1305	5·8	1915	1·3
19 F	0106	5·7	0729	1·2	1340	5·7	1950	1·4
20 Sa	0142	5·5	0805	1·3	1415	5·5	2029	1·5
21 Su	0221	5·3	0843	1·4	1452	5·4	2110	1·7
22 M	0303	5·1	0923	1·6	1535	5·2	2155	1·8
23 Tu ☾	0350	4·8	1010	1·8	1624	5·0	2246	1·9
24 W	0446	4·7	1104	1·9	1722	4·9	2348	1·9
25 Th	0550	4·7	1209	1·9	1828	4·9		
26 F	0053	1·8	0657	4·8	1317	1·8	1932	5·1
27 Sa	0157	1·6	0801	5·1	1420	1·6	2031	5·4
28 Su	0255	1·3	0900	5·4	1518	1·3	2126	5·7
29 M	0348	1·1	0955	5·7	1611	1·1	2215	5·9
30 Tu ●	0440	0·9	1047	6·0	1701	1·0	2304	6·1

JULY

Date	Time	m	Time	m	Time	m	Time	m
1 W	0530	0·9	1140	6·2	1752	1·0	2354	6·3
2 Th	0618	0·8	1232	6·3	1841	1·0		
3 F	0044	6·3	0707	0·8	1321	6·4	1931	0·9
4 Sa	0134	6·3	0756	0·8	1410	6·4	2020	0·9
5 Su	0222	6·1	0844	0·8	1457	6·3	2109	1·0
6 M	0310	5·9	0932	0·9	1543	6·0	2200	1·1
7 Tu ☽	0402	5·6	1022	1·1	1632	5·7	2257	1·3
8 W	0458	5·2	1121	1·4	1732	5·4		
9 Th	0002	1·5	0606	5·0	1230	1·6	1840	5·2
10 F	0114	1·6	0720	4·9	1344	1·7	1949	5·2
11 Sa	0223	1·6	0828	5·0	1450	1·6	2051	5·3
12 Su	0322	1·4	0927	5·2	1546	1·5	2146	5·4
13 M	0412	1·3	1018	5·5	1634	1·4	2232	5·6
14 Tu ○	0454	1·1	1101	5·7	1713	1·3	2310	5·8
15 W	0531	1·1	1140	5·8	1749	1·2	2345	5·8
16 Th	0603	1·1	1215	5·8	1822	1·2		
17 F	0016	5·8	0637	1·1	1247	5·8	1854	1·2
18 Sa	0048	5·8	0709	1·1	1318	5·8	1928	1·2
19 Su	0121	5·7	0742	1·1	1348	5·7	2001	1·3
20 M	0153	5·5	0814	1·2	1419	5·6	2035	1·3
21 Tu	0228	5·3	0849	1·3	1452	5·4	2111	1·5
22 W ☾	0305	5·1	0926	1·5	1530	5·2	2154	1·7
23 Th	0349	4·9	1012	1·8	1622	5·0	2249	1·8
24 F	0447	4·7	1114	1·9	1729	4·8	2359	1·9
25 Sa	0604	4·7	1233	1·9	1848	4·9		
26 Su	0119	1·8	0726	4·9	1350	1·7	2002	5·2
27 M	0231	1·5	0839	5·3	1459	1·4	2107	5·6
28 Tu	0332	1·2	0939	5·8	1557	1·2	2201	6·0
29 W ●	0427	0·9	1035	6·1	1650	1·0	2251	6·3
30 Th	0518	0·8	1126	6·4	1739	0·9	2341	6·4
31 F	0606	0·7	1216	6·5	1828	0·8		

AUGUST

Date	Time	m	Time	m	Time	m	Time	m
1 Sa	0030	6·5	0654	0·7	1303	6·6	1916	0·7
2 Su	0117	6·4	0740	0·7	1349	6·6	2001	0·7
3 M	0203	6·3	0824	0·7	1431	6·4	2046	0·8
4 Tu	0246	6·0	0906	0·8	1510	6·1	2131	1·0
5 W ☽	0329	5·7	0951	1·1	1554	5·7	2220	1·3
6 Th	0418	5·2	1044	1·5	1648	5·3	2322	1·7
7 F	0524	4·8	1154	1·9	1800	4·9		
8 Sa	0039	1·9	0648	4·7	1316	2·0	1922	4·8
9 Su	0158	1·9	0808	4·8	1432	2·0	2035	5·0
10 M	0303	1·7	0912	5·1	1531	1·8	2133	5·2
11 Tu	0355	1·5	1004	5·4	1618	1·5	2220	5·5
12 W	0436	1·3	1045	5·7	1655	1·3	2255	5·8
13 Th ○	0511	1·1	1121	5·9	1729	1·2	2326	5·9
14 F	0544	1·0	1151	5·9	1759	1·1	2355	5·9
15 Sa	0614	1·0	1221	5·9	1830	1·1		
16 Su	0025	5·9	0645	1·0	1249	5·9	1900	1·0
17 M	0056	5·8	0715	1·0	1316	5·9	1930	1·0
18 Tu	0124	5·7	0744	1·0	1344	5·8	2002	1·1
19 W	0154	5·6	0815	1·2	1414	5·6	2035	1·2
20 Th	0227	5·4	0849	1·4	1450	5·3	2114	1·5
21 F ☾	0306	5·1	0933	1·7	1537	5·0	2205	1·8
22 Sa	0403	4·8	1036	1·9	1647	4·8	2320	1·9
23 Su	0528	4·7	1201	2·0	1817	4·8		
24 M	0050	1·9	0703	4·9	1331	1·8	1944	5·1
25 Tu	0212	1·6	0823	5·4	1444	1·5	2053	5·6
26 W	0316	1·2	0925	5·9	1542	1·1	2148	6·1
27 Th	0412	0·9	1018	6·3	1633	0·8	2235	6·4
28 F ●	0501	0·7	1107	6·5	1722	0·7	2321	6·6
29 Sa	0547	0·6	1153	6·7	1808	0·6		
30 Su	0008	6·6	0633	0·6	1238	6·7	1853	0·6
31 M	0053	6·5	0715	0·6	1320	6·6	1936	0·6

Chart Datum: 3.27 metres below Ordnance Datum (Newlyn)

ENGLAND, SOUTH COAST – SHOREHAM

TIME ZONE UT(GMT)
For Summer Time add ONE hour in non-shaded areas

Lat 50°50′ N Long 0°15′ W

TIMES AND HEIGHTS OF HIGH AND LOW WATERS

YEAR **1992**

SEPTEMBER

Day	Time	m	Day	Time	m
1 Tu	0136	6·4	16 W	0056	5·9
	0756	0·7		0716	1·0
	1359	6·4		1313	5·9
	2017	0·8		1931	1·0
2 W	0216	6·1	17 Th	0127	5·8
	0836	0·9		0747	1·1
	1435	6·1		1344	5·7
	2057	1·0		2005	1·1
3 Th	0255	5·7	18 F	0200	5·6
	0918	1·3		0824	1·4
	1514	5·7		1421	5·5
	☽ 2142	1·4		2046	1·4
4 F	0341	5·2	19 Sa	0242	5·3
	1007	1·7		0909	1·7
	1605	5·1		1511	5·1
	2240	1·8		☾ 2139	1·7
5 Sa	0444	4·8	20 Su	0342	5·0
	1117	2·1		1013	1·9
	1719	4·7		1623	4·9
				2255	1·9
6 Su	0000	2·1	21 M	0509	4·9
	0613	4·6		1142	2·0
	1246	2·3		1757	4·9
	1850	4·6			
7 M	0127	2·2	22 Tu	0030	1·9
	0741	4·7		0647	5·1
	1407	2·2		1314	1·8
	2012	4·8		1928	5·2
8 Tu	0237	2·0	23 W	0154	1·5
	0848	5·0		0805	5·5
	1507	2·0		1426	1·4
	2113	5·1		2036	5·6
9 W	0329	1·7	24 Th	0258	1·1
	0939	5·4		0905	6·0
	1552	1·6		1525	1·0
	2158	5·5		2129	6·1
10 Th	0409	1·4	25 F	0350	0·8
	1019	5·7		0955	6·4
	1629	1·3		1614	0·7
	2233	5·8		2214	6·4
11 F	0444	1·1	26 Sa	0438	0·6
	1052	5·9		1041	6·6
	1701	1·1		1701	0·6
	2302	5·9		● 2257	6·5
12 Sa	0516	1·0	27 Su	0524	0·5
	1121	6·0		1123	6·7
	1730	1·0		1745	0·5
	○ 2329	6·0		2343	6·6
13 Su	0545	0·9	28 M	0606	0·5
	1149	6·0		1206	6·6
	1800	0·9		1828	0·6
	2357	6·0			
14 M	0615	0·9	29 Tu	0026	6·5
	1216	6·0		0648	0·6
	1830	0·9		1246	6·5
				1907	0·7
15 Tu	0027	5·9	30 W	0107	6·3
	0645	0·9		0727	0·8
	1245	6·0		1324	6·3
	1900	0·9		1947	0·8

OCTOBER

Day	Time	m	Day	Time	m
1 Th	0147	6·1	16 F	0110	5·9
	0805	1·1		0727	1·2
	1359	6·0		1326	5·8
	2025	1·1		1947	1·1
2 F	0223	5·7	17 Sa	0147	5·7
	0846	1·4		0809	1·4
	1438	5·6		1407	5·6
	2106	1·5		2033	1·3
3 Sa	0307	5·3	18 Su	0235	5·5
	0935	1·8		0859	1·6
	1527	5·1		1501	5·3
	☽ 2200	1·9		2128	1·6
4 Su	0408	4·9	19 M	0336	5·3
	1040	2·2		1005	1·8
	1638	4·7		1612	5·0
	2315	2·2		☾ 2242	1·8
5 M	0532	4·6	20 Tu	0459	5·1
	1205	2·4		1129	1·9
	1810	4·5		1741	5·0
6 Tu	0043	2·3	21 W	0009	1·7
	0700	4·7		0628	5·3
	1327	2·4		1254	1·7
	1936	4·6		1907	5·2
7 W	0157	2·1	22 Th	0129	1·5
	0809	5·0		0742	5·7
	1430	2·1		1404	1·3
	2041	5·0		2014	5·6
8 Th	0251	1·8	23 F	0233	1·1
	0901	5·3		0839	6·0
	1517	1·7		1501	0·9
	2126	5·4		2107	6·0
9 F	0334	1·5	24 Sa	0326	0·8
	0942	5·7		0929	6·3
	1554	1·3		1553	0·7
	2200	5·7		2152	6·3
10 Sa	0410	1·2	25 Su	0414	0·6
	1015	5·9		1014	6·5
	1627	1·1		1638	0·6
	2229	5·9		● 2235	6·4
11 Su	0442	1·0	26 M	0500	0·6
	1045	6·0		1056	6·5
	1659	0·9		1723	0·6
	○ 2257	6·0		2318	6·4
12 M	0513	0·9	27 Tu	0542	0·7
	1115	6·0		1137	6·5
	1730	0·8		1803	0·6
	2328	6·0			
13 Tu	0544	0·9	28 W	0002	6·3
	1145	6·0		0622	0·8
	1801	0·8		1217	6·4
				1841	0·8
14 W	0001	6·0	29 Th	0043	6·2
	0618	1·0		0700	1·0
	1216	6·0		1254	6·2
	1835	0·9		1918	0·9
15 Th	0034	6·0	30 F	0121	6·0
	0651	1·0		0739	1·2
	1250	6·0		1330	5·9
	1910	1·0		1955	1·2
			31 Sa	0159	5·7
				0819	1·5
				1409	5·6
				2037	1·5

NOVEMBER

Day	Time	m	Day	Time	m
1 Su	0242	5·4	16 M	0236	5·8
	0906	1·8		0856	1·4
	1456	5·2		1459	5·6
	2127	1·8		2124	1·3
2 M	0335	5·1	17 Tu	0333	5·6
	1004	2·2		0957	1·6
	1558	4·8		1604	5·3
	☽ 2228	2·1		☾ 2229	1·5
3 Tu	0444	4·8	18 W	0443	5·5
	1115	2·4		1110	1·6
	1717	4·6		1719	5·2
	2345	2·2		2343	1·5
4 W	0603	4·8	19 Th	0559	5·5
	1232	2·3		1227	1·5
	1840	4·6		1838	5·3
5 Th	0059	2·2	20 F	0059	1·4
	0715	4·9		0711	5·7
	1338	2·1		1338	1·3
	1950	4·8		1946	5·5
6 F	0200	1·9	21 Sa	0205	1·2
	0812	5·2		0811	5·9
	1430	1·8		1438	1·0
	2041	5·2		2043	5·7
7 Sa	0249	1·6	22 Su	0303	1·0
	0856	5·5		0902	6·1
	1512	1·4		1531	0·8
	2120	5·5		2131	6·0
8 Su	0329	1·3	23 M	0353	0·8
	0935	5·7		0949	6·2
	1551	1·1		1620	0·7
	2153	5·7		2216	6·1
9 M	0406	1·1	24 Tu	0439	0·8
	1008	5·9		1034	6·2
	1626	1·0		1704	0·7
	2226	5·9		● 2301	6·1
10 Tu	0442	1·0	25 W	0522	0·8
	1042	6·0		1115	6·2
	1702	0·9		1743	0·8
	○ 2302	6·0		2345	6·1
11 W	0518	1·0	26 Th	0603	1·0
	1117	6·1		1155	6·2
	1737	0·8		1821	0·9
	2340	6·1			
12 Th	0555	1·0	27 F	0025	6·1
	1155	6·1		0640	1·1
	1817	0·9		1232	6·1
				1857	1·0
13 F	0020	6·1	28 Sa	0103	6·0
	0634	1·1		0717	1·3
	1234	6·1		1309	5·9
	1856	1·0		1934	1·2
14 Sa	0103	6·1	29 Su	0140	5·8
	0717	1·2		0756	1·5
	1318	6·0		1347	5·6
	1940	1·1		2013	1·4
15 Su	0146	6·0	30 M	0219	5·6
	0803	1·3		0839	1·7
	1404	5·8		1432	5·3
	2028	1·2		2056	1·6

DECEMBER

Day	Time	m	Day	Time	m
1 Tu	0302	5·3	16 W	0323	6·0
	0927	1·9		0943	1·2
	1521	5·0		1549	5·6
	2145	1·8		☾ 2211	1·1
2 W	0354	5·1	17 Th	0420	5·8
	1022	2·1		1045	1·3
	1621	4·8		1651	5·4
	☽ 2243	2·0		2313	1·3
3 Th	0457	4·9	18 F	0524	5·6
	1126	2·2		1155	1·4
	1731	4·6		1803	5·2
	2349	2·1			
4 F	0604	4·9	19 Sa	0025	1·4
	1233	2·1		0633	5·5
	1842	4·7		1307	1·4
				1916	5·2
5 Sa	0057	2·0	20 Su	0137	1·3
	0708	5·0		0740	5·6
	1334	1·9		1414	1·2
	1943	4·9		2021	5·4
6 Su	0156	1·8	21 M	0241	1·2
	0803	5·2		0840	5·7
	1427	1·6		1514	1·1
	2033	5·2		2116	5·6
7 M	0246	1·5	22 Tu	0338	1·1
	0851	5·5		0933	5·8
	1513	1·3		1606	1·0
	2118	5·5		2206	5·8
8 Tu	0332	1·3	23 W	0427	1·0
	0935	5·7		1021	5·9
	1557	1·1		1650	0·9
	2159	5·8		2253	5·9
9 W	0414	1·1	24 Th	0510	1·0
	1016	5·9		1102	6·0
	1639	0·9		1731	0·9
	○ 2242	6·0		● 2335	6·0
10 Th	0456	1·0	25 F	0549	1·1
	1057	6·1		1142	6·1
	1721	0·9		1807	0·9
	2327	6·1			
11 F	0540	1·0	26 Sa	0013	6·0
	1141	6·2		0625	1·1
	1805	0·9		1218	6·0
				1841	1·0
12 Sa	0011	6·2	27 Su	0048	6·0
	0624	1·0		0700	1·2
	1226	6·2		1253	5·9
	1850	0·9		1915	1·0
13 Su	0058	6·3	28 M	0121	5·9
	0709	1·1		0735	1·3
	1313	6·2		1329	5·8
	1936	0·9		1951	1·1
14 M	0145	6·2	29 Tu	0154	5·8
	0758	1·1		0813	1·4
	1403	6·1		1406	5·5
	2025	0·9		2028	1·2
15 Tu	0232	6·1	30 W	0229	5·6
	0849	1·1		0851	1·5
	1453	5·9		1446	5·3
	2115	1·0		2106	1·4
			31 Th	0308	5·4
				0933	1·7
				1530	5·0
				2149	1·7

Chart Datum: 3.27 metres below Ordnance Datum (Newlyn)

BRIGHTON 10-3-11

E. Sussex

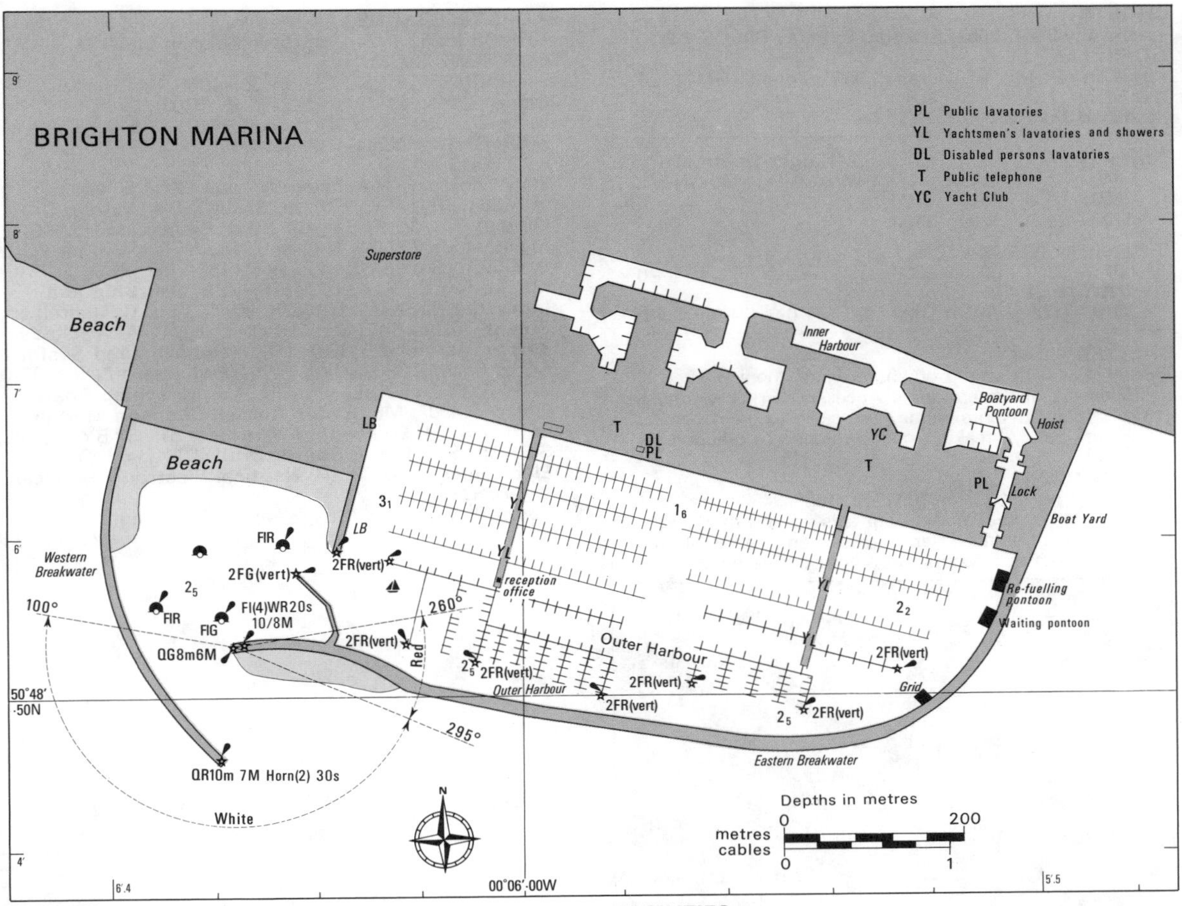

BRIGHTON MARINA
PL Public lavatories
YL Yachtsmen's lavatories and showers
DL Disabled persons lavatories
T Public telephone
YC Yacht Club
Superstore
Beach
Beach
Inner Harbour
Boatyard Pontoon
Hoist
Lock
Boat Yard
Re-fuelling pontoon
Waiting pontoon
Outer Harbour
Outer Harbour
Grid
Eastern Breakwater
Western Breakwater
reception office
LB
LB
FlR
FlR
FlG
2FG(vert)
Fl(4)WR20s 10/8M
QG8m6M
2FR(vert)
QR10m 7M Horn(2) 30s
White
Red
100°
260°
295°
50°48'·50N
00°06'·00W
Depths in metres
metres
cables
0
200
0
1

CHARTS

Admiralty 1991, 1652; Stanford 9; Imray C9; OS 198

TIDES

+0004 Dover; ML 3·5; Duration 0605; Zone 0 (GMT)

Standard Port SHOREHAM (←)

Times				Height (metres)			
HW		LW		MHWS	MHWN	MLWN	MLWS
0500	1000	0000	0600	6·3	4·9	2·0	0·6
1700	2200	1200	1800				
Differences BRIGHTON							
−0010	−0005	−0005	−0005	+0·3	+0·1	0·0	−0·1

BRIGHTON MARINA

SHELTER

The marina gives good shelter under all conditions, but the approach in strong S winds could be very rough.

NAVIGATION

Waypoint 50°48'·20N 00°06'·29W, 180°/000° from/to West breakwater Lt, 0·26M. 180° safe sector of approach except shallow water to E of entrance in main Lt R sector. Shoaling may occur at entrance after gales.

LIGHTS AND MARKS

E breakwater Fl(4) WR 20s 16m 10/8M; vis R260°-295°, W295°-100°. E breakwater head QG 8m 7M.
W breakwater head QR 10m 7M; Horn (2) 30s.
Inner Harbour Lock controlled by normal R and G traffic control.
Times: 0800-2000 LT.

RADIO TELEPHONE

Call: *Brighton Control* VHF Ch 16; **80** 68 11. M. Listening Ch 16 37 (H24).

TELEPHONE (0273)

Hr Mr 693636; MRSC Lee-on-Solent 552100; # 592664; Marinecall 0898 500 456; Police 606744; Ⓗ 696955; Dr 686863.

FACILITIES

Brighton Marina (1600+200 visitors) ☎ 693636, #, FW, P, D, AC, Gas, Gaz, ◙, R, Bar; **Brighton Marina Boatyard** ☎ 609235, BH (60 ton), C (35 ton); **Brighton Marina Yacht Club** ☎ 697049, Bar, R; **Felton Marine Engineering** ☎ 601779, El, ME; **Leonard Marine** ☎ 515987, Me; **Scott Marine** ☎ 671665, ME; **Terry Pachol & Son** ☎ 682724, Sh; **F.A.M. Enterprises** ☎ 684385, Ⓔ; **Nautical Electronics Services** ☎ 693258, Ⓔ; **Wilkinson** ☎ 677758, Sm; **Welch Marine Services** ☎ 675972, SM; **Russell Simpson** ☎ 697161, CH; **Moores Marine Maintenance** ☎ (0860) 525966 Diving; **Superstore** V; **Town** V, R, Bar, ✉, Ⓑ, ⇌, ✈ Shoreham, Harbour Guides available from Harbour Manager

NEWHAVEN 10-3-12

E. Sussex

CHARTS
Admiralty 2154, 1652; Stanford 9; Imray C9; OS 198

TIDES
0004 Dover; ML 3·6; Duration 0550; Zone 0 (GMT).

Standard Port SHOREHAM (⟵)

Times				Height (metres)			
HW		LW		MHWS	MHWN	MLWN	MLWS
0500	1000	0000	0600	6·3	4·9	2·0	0·6
1700	2200	1200	1800				
Differences NEWHAVEN							
−0015	−0010	0000	0000	+0·4	+0·2	0·0	−0·2
EASTBOURNE							
−0010	−0005	+0015	+0020	+1·1	+0·6	+0·2	+0·1

SHELTER
Good, but with strong on-shore winds there is often a difficult sea at the entrance. Accessible in all weathers but with strong on-shore winds pass close to breakwater; there are heavy breaking seas on E side of dredged channel.

NAVIGATION
Waypoint 50°46′·20N 00°03′·70E, 168°/348° from/to West breakwater Lt, 0·32M. Harbour silts up and dredging is in continuous operation. Cargo vessels and ferries often warp off by means of hawsers run across the harbour.

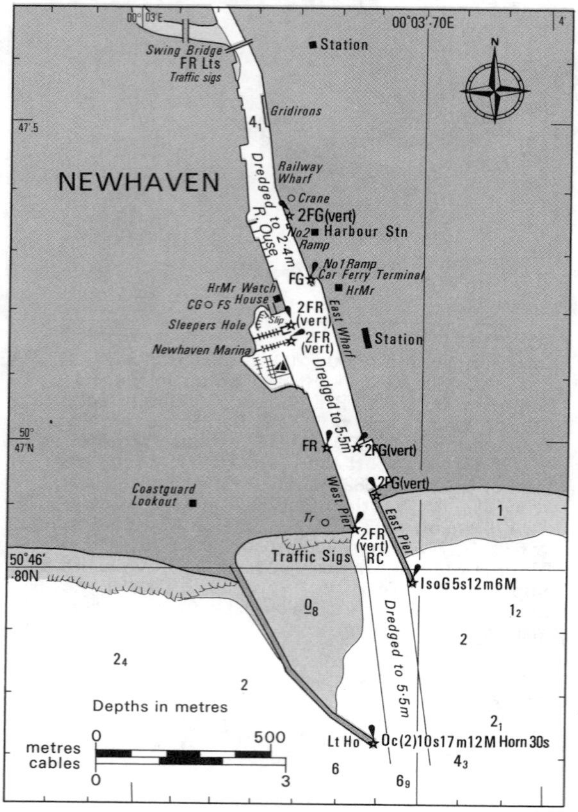
00°03′E
00°03′·70E
Swing Bridge
FR Lts
Traffic sigs
Station
Gridirons
47′5
NEWHAVEN
Railway Wharf
Dredged to 2·4m
R. Ouse
Crane
2FG(vert)
No2 Harbour Stn
Ramp
No1 Ramp
Car Ferry Terminal
FG
HrMr
HrMr Watch House
CG FS
2FR (vert)
Sleepers Hole
Slip
2FR (vert)
Newhaven Marina
East Wharf
Station
Dredged to 5·5m
50° 47′N
FR
2FG(vert)
2FG(vert)
Coastguard Lookout
West Pier
East Pier
Tr
2FR (vert)
RC
Traffic Sigs
50°46′ ·80N
IsoG5s12m6M
Dredged to 5·5m
Depths in metres
metres 0 500
cables 0 3
Lt Ho
Oc(2)10s17m12M Horn 30s

LIGHTS AND MARKS
Traffic signals, displayed from Tr on W side of river.

Triangle over ball, or G Lt	— only entry permitted.
Ball over triangle, or R Lt	— only departure permitted.
Ball, triangle, ball (vert) or RGR Lts (vert)	— No entry or departure
Ball or G R Lts (vert)	— Entry and departure permitted with care for vessels under 15m

Swing bridge signals
FlG — Bridge opening or closing
FR — Vessels may pass N to S
FG — Vessels may pass S to N

RADIO TELEPHONE
VHF Ch 16; 12 (H24). Newhaven Marina Ch **80** M.

TELEPHONE (0273)
Hr Mr 514131; MRSC Lee-on-Solent 552100; Harbour Signal Station 514131 ext. 247; # (0703) 827350; Marinecall 0898 500 456; Police 515801; Dr 515076; Ⓗ 609411 (Accidents (0273) 696955).

FACILITIES
EC Wednesday; **Newhaven Marina** (300+50 visitors) ☎ 513881, Slip, FW, ME, El, Sh, AC, BH (18 ton), C (10 ton), CH, V, R, Bar, Gas, Gaz, ⊡, (Access HW∓5), fuel pontoon 200 yds N of ent; **Newhaven Marina YC** ☎ 513976; **Sealink Quays** ☎ 514131, Slip, P, D, L, FW, ME, El, Sh, C (3 ton), CH, AB, V, R, Bar; **Ship and Industrial Repairs** ☎ 516298, ME, El, Sh, C; **Cantell & Son** ☎ 514118, ME, Sh, CH, SM, Slip, C, ACA; **Golden Arrow Marine** ☎ 513987, ME; **Newhaven and Seaford SC** ☎ Seaford 890077, M, FW; **Newhaven YC** ☎ 513770, Slip, M, P, D, ME, El, Sh, CH, AB; **Meeching Boats** (80) ☎ 514907, ME, El, Sh; **Russell Simpson Marine** ☎ 513458 CH, El; **Leonard Marine** ☎ 515987 BY, El, ME, Sh, Slip, SM; **C & E Sports** ☎ 515450, Gas; **L D Electronics** ☎ 56179, Ⓔ; **Nautical Electronic Services** ☎ 693258, Ⓔ.
Town P, V, R, Bar. ✉; Ⓑ; ≹; ✈ (Shoreham).

RYE 10-3-13

E. Sussex

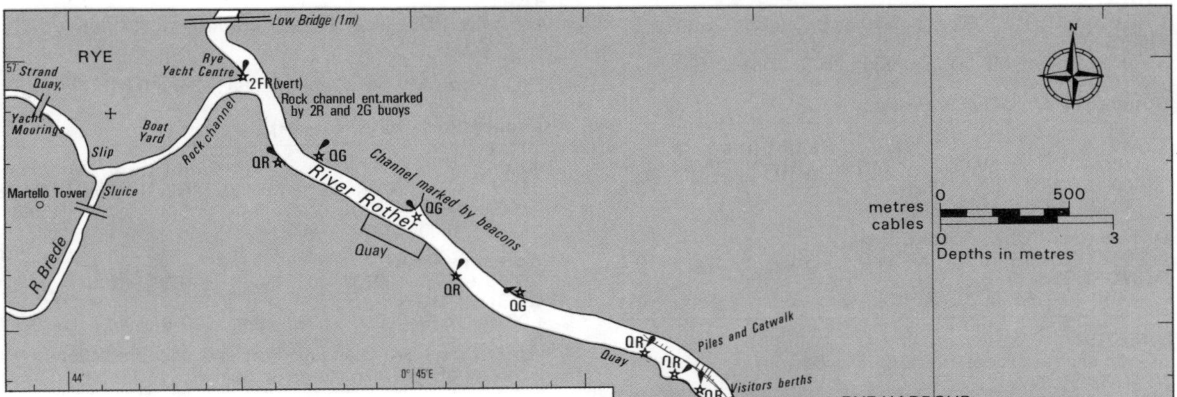
Low Bridge (1m)
RYE
Strand Quay
Rye Yacht Centre
2FR(vert)
Rock channel ent.marked by 2R and 2G buoys
Yacht Moorings
Boat Yard
Slip
Rock channel
QR
QG
Channel marked by beacons
River Rother
Martello Tower
Sluice
QG
R Brede
Quay
QR
QG
Piles and Catwalk
QR
Quay
QR
QR
Visitors berths
Fresh Water
metres
cables
0
500
0
3
Depths in metres
44'
0° 45'E

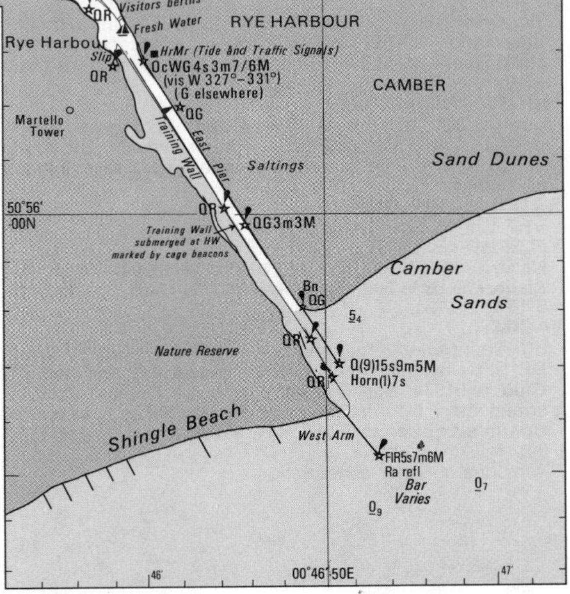
RYE HARBOUR
Rye Harbour
Slip
QR
HrMr (Tide and Traffic Signals)
OcWG4s3m7/6M
(vis W 327°–331°)
(G elsewhere)
QG
CAMBER
Martello Tower
Training Wall
East Pier
Saltings
Sand Dunes
50°56'
·00N
QR
QG3m3M
Training Wall submerged at HW marked by cage beacons
Camber
Bn
QG
Sands
Nature Reserve
QR
Q(9)15s9m5M
Horn(1)7s
QR
Shingle Beach
West Arm
FlR5s7m6M
Ra refl
Bar
Varies
46'
00°46'·50E
47'

CHARTS

Admiralty 1991, 536; Stanford 9; Imray C8; OS 189

TIDES

+0002 Dover; ML 2·0; Zone 0 (GMT).

Standard Port DOVER (⟶)

Times				Height (metres)			
HW		LW		MHWS	MHWN	MLWN	MLWS
0000	0600	0100	0700	6·7	5·3	2·0	0·8
1200	1800	1300	1900				
Differences RYE HARBOUR							
+0005	−0010	No data		−1·4	−1·7	Dries	
RYE (approaches)							
+0005	−0010	No data	No data	+1·0	+0·7	No data	No data
HASTINGS							
0000	−0010	−0030	−0030	+0·8	+0·5	+0·1	−0·1

SHELTER

Very good in river. Entrance requires care when wind strong (force 7 or over) from SE to SW. Enter HW−2 to HW+3. Rye harbour is ¾M inside entrance and is a small village used by commercial shipping. The town of Rye is another 2M up river; it is a Cinque Port.

NAVIGATION

Waypoint Rye Fairway (safe water) buoy, LFl 10s, 50°54'·00N 00°48'·13E, 150°/330° from/to West Arm head Lt, 1·81M. Beware:

(1) Narrow entrance. Limited width of channel (42m).
(2) Bar at entrance.
(3) Strong flood stream in river — up to 4·5 kn (max HW−3 to HW−1).
(4) Shallow water E & W of entrance with ground swell or surf.

Harbour speed limit 6 kn.

LIGHTS AND MARKS

East Arm, head Q(9) 15s 9m 5M; Horn 7s.
Tide Signals on Hr Mr office:—
Night — FG 2·1-3·0m on bar
F Purple Over 3·0m on bar
Day — None, but horizontal timbers on tripod beacon marking W arm indicate depths 5', 10' and 15'.
Traffic signals on Hr Mr office to indicate big ship movements
1 B Ball — Vessel entering
2 B Balls (hor) — Vessel leaving
3 B Balls (triangle) — Vessels entering and leaving.
In addition a Q orange Lt is exhibited at Harbour office.

RADIO TELEPHONE

VHF Ch 16; 14 (0900–1700 LT).

TELEPHONE (0797)

Hr Mr 225225; MRCC Dover 210008; # (0703) 223110; Marinecall 0898 500 456; Police 222112; Dr 222031; Ⓗ 222109.

FACILITIES

EC Tuesday; **Admiralty Jetty** Slip, M*, L, FW, AB*; **Strand Quay** Slip, M*, P and D (50m, cans), L, FW, AB*; **Rye Yacht Centre** ☎ 223336, M, L, FW, ME, El, C (15 ton), AB; **Phillips BY** ☎ 223234, Slip, M, L, FW, ME, El, C (3 ton); **Sandrock Marine** ☎ 222679, Slip, M, D, L, FW, ME, El, CH, AB; **Sea Cruisers** ☎ 222070, ME, Sh, CH, ACA. **Town** ✉; Ⓑ; ⇌; ✈ (Lydd).

* See Hr Mr.

FOLKESTONE 10-3-14

Kent

CHARTS
Admiralty 1991, 1892; Stanford 9; Imray C8; OS 179

TIDES
−0010 Dover; ML 3·7; Duration 0500; Zone 0 (GMT).

Standard Port DOVER (⟶)

Times				Height (metres)			
HW		LW		MHWS	MHWN	MLWN	MLWS
0000	0600	0100	0700	6·7	5·3	2·0	0·8
1200	1800	1300	1900				
Differences FOLKESTONE							
−0020	−0005	−0010	−0010	+0·4	+0·4	0·0	−0·1
DUNGENESS							
−0010	−0015	−0020	−0010	+1·0	+0·6	+0·4	+0·1

SHELTER
Good shelter except in strong E winds.

NAVIGATION
Waypoint 51°04′·30N 01°12′·00E, 150°/330° from/to breakwater head Lt, 0·26M. Beware Copt Rocks and Mole Head Rocks. Also ferries and pulling off wires from the jetty.

LIGHTS AND MARKS
Ldg Lts 295° at ferry terminal, FR and FG (occas). 305° on QG Lt at E pierhead leads to inner harbour. Bu flag or 3FR(vert) at FS on S arm, ¼hr before ferry sails, indicates port closed.

RADIO TELEPHONE
VHF Ch 16; 22 (occas).

TELEPHONE (0303)
Hr Mr 54947; MRCC Dover 210008; ⌗ (0304) 202441; Marinecall 0898 500 456; Police 850055; Port Health Office 57574; Ⓗ 57311.

FACILITIES
EC Wednesday (larger shops open all day); **South Quay BR Slipway** Slip (free), FW; **Folkestone Y and MB Club** ☎ 51574, Bar, D, FW, L, Slip, M; **Sealink** C (by arrangement 5 ton); **Garage** P and D (100 yds, cans); **Bosun's Locker** ☎ 55752, CH. **Town** P, V, R, Bar. ✉; Ⓑ; ⇌; ✈ (Lydd).
A marina is under construction

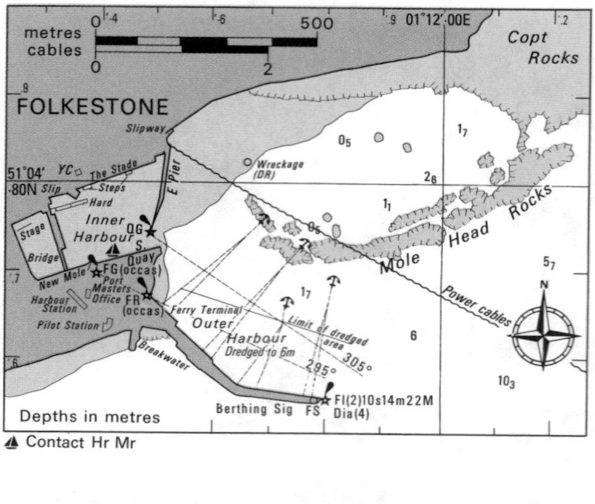

metres
cables
500
0
2
01°12′·00E
Copt Rocks
FOLKESTONE
Slipway
51°04′·80N
YC
Slip
The Stade
Steps
Hard
Inner Harbour
QG
Stage
Bridge
Quay
FG(occas)
New Mole
Port Masters Office
FR (occas)
Harbour Station
Pilot Station
Ferry Terminal
Outer Harbour
Dredged to 6m
Limit of dredged area
295°
305°
E Pier
Wreckage (DR)
Mole Head Rocks
Power cables
Breakwater
Berthing Sig
FS
Fl(2)10s14m22M
Dia(4)
N
Depths in metres

⚠ Contact Hr Mr

DOVER 10-3-15

Kent

CHARTS
Admiralty 1698, 1828, 1892; Stanford 1, 9, 19; Imray C8; OS 179

TIDES
0000 Dover; ML 3·7; Duration 0505; Zone 0 (GMT)

Standard Port DOVER (⟶)

Times				Height (metres)			
HW		LW		MHWS	MHWN	MLWN	MLWS
0000	0600	0100	0700	6·7	5·3	2·0	0·8
1200	1800	1300	1900				
Differences DEAL							
+0010	+0020	+0010	+0005	−0·6	−0·3	0·0	0·0
RICHBOROUGH							
+0015	+0015	+0030	+0030	−3·4	−2·6	−1·7	−0·7

NOTE: Dover is a Standard Port and tidal predictions for each day of the year are given below.

SHELTER
The small craft anchorage is exposed to winds from NE through S to SW and in gales a heavy sea builds up. Visiting yachts are welcome for up to 14 days. For longer periods, apply in advance. Berthing instructions for Wellington Dock given from Dockmaster's Office at entrance to Granville Dock. Dock gates open, a minimum of HW−1½ to HW+1. Waiting pontoon available. Yachtsmen intending to leave the dock should inform the Dockmaster's Office (manned from HW−2). Small craft may not be left unattended in Outer Harbour.

NAVIGATION
Waypoint from SW 51°06′·15N 01°19′·77E, 180°/000° from/to Admiralty Pier Lt Ho, 0·5M. Waypoint from NE 51°07′·27N 01°21′·51E, 090°/270° from/to S end Eastern Arm, 0·5M. Frequent ferry and hovercraft movements through both entrances. Strong tides across entrances and high walls make entry under sail slow and difficult — use of engine very strongly recommended. Observe traffic signals and follow instructions of harbour patrol launch. Do not pass between buoy marking wreck inside W entrance, Q, and southern breakwater.

LIGHTS AND MARKS
Admiralty Pier head Fl 7·5s 21m 20M; W Tr; vis 096°-090°.
International Port Traffic Signals are in operation, (see 6.2.7) shown for the Eastern entrance, day and night, on panels near Port Control; for Western entrance, day and night, on panels near Admiralty Pier Signal Station.
N.B. Specific permission to enter or leave Eastern or Western entrance *must* first be obtained from Port Control on VHF Ch 74, Ch 12 or, if not fitted with VHF/RT, with Aldis Lamp signals:
SV — I wish to enter port
SW — I wish to leave port.
Port Control will reply 'OK' or 'Wait'.
A Q Fl lamp from the Control Tower means keep clear of entrance you are approaching.
Docking signals
International Port Traffic Signals together with small Fl Y light to be shown 5 min before bridge is swung.

RADIO TELEPHONE
Call: *Dover Port Control* VHF Ch 16 **74**; 12 (H24). Channel Navigation Information Service (CNIS) — call: *Dover Coastguard* Ch 16 **69**; 11 **69** (Ch 80 for yachts).
Information broadcasts on Ch 11 at H+40, and also at H+55 when visibility is less than 2M.

TELEPHONE (0304)
Hr Mr 240400; MRCC 210008; ⌗ (0304) 202441; Marinecall 0898 500 456; Police 240055; Ⓗ 201624.

FACILITIES
EC Wednesday; **Wellington Dock** ☎ 240400 ext 4531, Slip, L, FW, C, AB; **Royal Cinque Ports YC** ☎ 206262, L, Bar, M, C, FW, R; **Dover Yacht Co** ☎ 201073, D, FW, ME, El, Sh, C; **Dover Marine Supplies** ☎ 201677, D, FW, ME, El, Sh, Slip, C, SM, ACA, CH; **Smye-Rumsby** ☎ 201187, El, Ⓔ. **Sharp and Enright** ☎ 206295 CH;
Town P and D (cans), V, R, Bar. ✉; Ⓑ; ⇌; ✈ (Lydd).
Note: *A Yachtsman's Guide* is available from Harbour House or Dockmaster.

DOVER *continued*

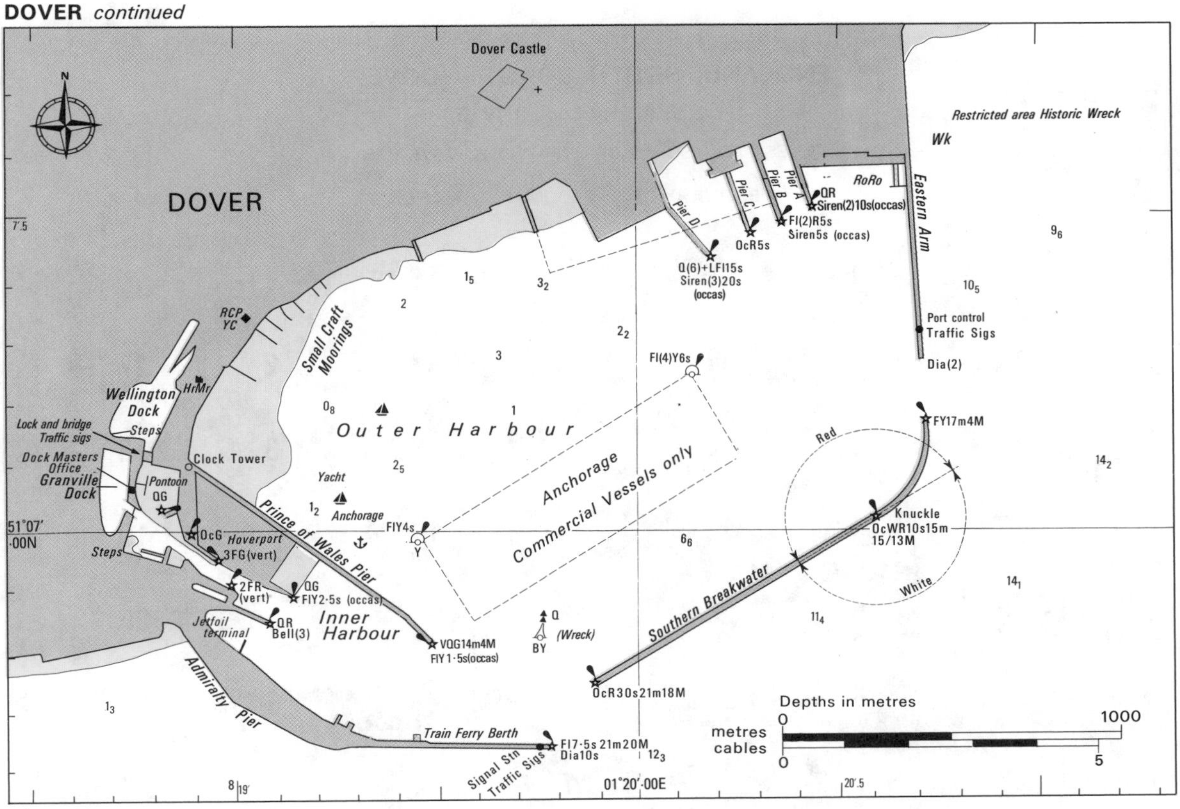

Dover Castle
DOVER
N
Restricted area Historic Wreck
Wk
RoRo
Eastern Arm
Pier A
Pier B
Pier C
Pier D
QR
Siren(2)10s(occas)
Fl(2)R5s
Siren5s (occas)
OcR5s
Q(6)+LFl15s
Siren(3)20s
(occas)
Port control
Traffic Sigs
Dia(2)
Fl(4)Y6s
FY17m4M
RCP
YC
HrMr
Small Craft Moorings
Wellington Dock
Lock and bridge Traffic sigs
Steps
Dock Masters Office
Granville Dock
Pontoon
QG
Clock Tower
Outer Harbour
Yacht
Anchorage
Anchorage
Commercial Vessels only
Red
Knuckle
OcWR10s15m
15/13M
White
51°07'
·00N
OcG
Hoverport
3FG(vert)
Steps
2FR
(vert)
QG
FlY2·5s (occas)
Prince of Wales Pier
FlY4s
Y
QR
Bell(3)
Inner Harbour
Jetfoil terminal
VQG14m4M
FlY 1·5s(occas)
Q
(Wreck)
BY
Southern Breakwater
OcR30s21m18M
Admiralty Pier
Train Ferry Berth
Fl7·5s 21m20M
Dia10s
Signal Stn
Traffic Sigs
Depths in metres
metres
cables
0
1000
0
5
7'5
01°20'·00E
20'5

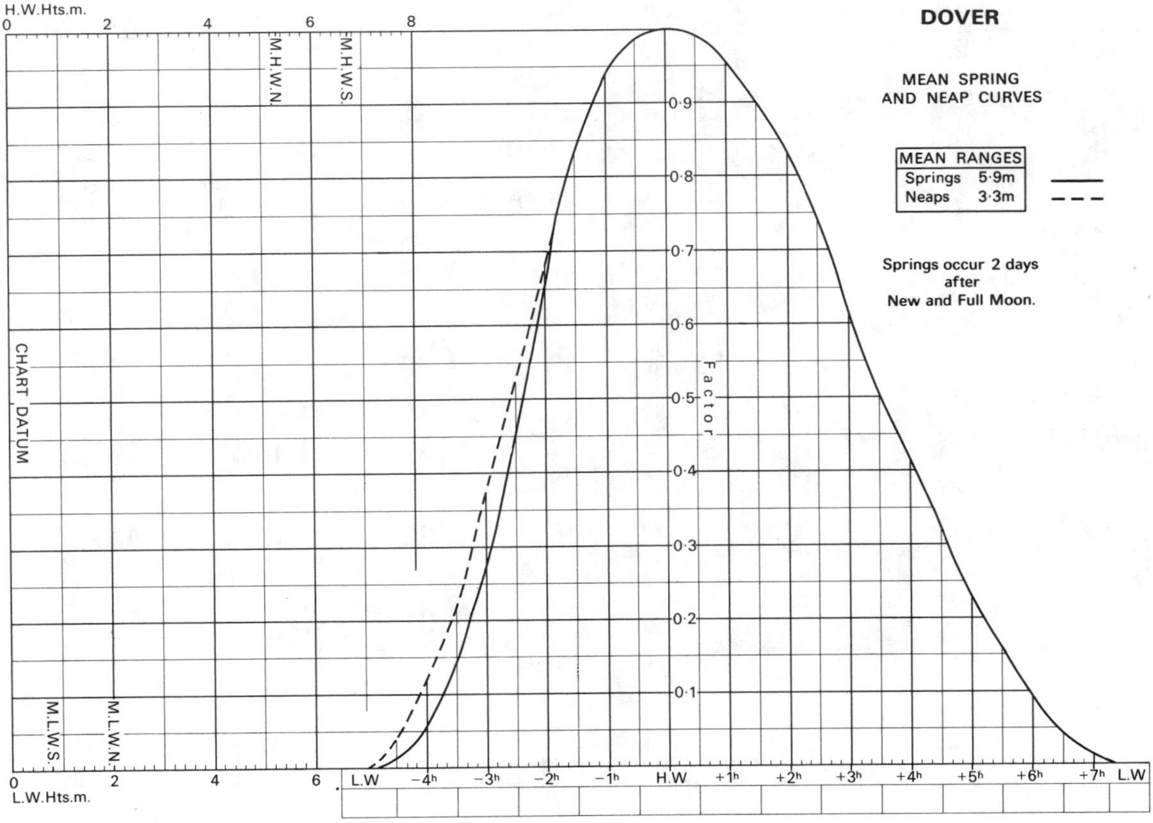

H.W.Hts.m.
0
2
4
6
8
M.H.W.N.
M.H.W.S.
CHART DATUM
M.L.W.S.
M.L.W.N.
0
2
4
6
L.W.Hts.m.
Factor
0·9
0·8
0·7
0·6
0·5
0·4
0·3
0·2
0·1
L.W
-4h
-3h
-2h
-1h
H.W
+1h
+2h
+3h
+4h
+5h
+6h
+7h
L.W
DOVER
MEAN SPRING AND NEAP CURVES
MEAN RANGES
Springs 5·9m
Neaps 3·3m
Springs occur 2 days after New and Full Moon.

TIME ZONE UT(GMT)
For Summer Time add ONE hour in non-shaded areas

ENGLAND, SOUTH COAST – DOVER

Lat 51°07′ N Long 1°19′ E

TIMES AND HEIGHTS OF HIGH AND LOW WATERS

YEAR **1992**

JANUARY

Day	Time	m	Day	Time	m
1 W	0303 0813 1538 2051	1·9 5·7 1·7 5·6	16 Th	0154 0700 1439 1944	2·1 5·6 1·8 5·6
2 Th	0406 0912 1633 2142	1·8 5·8 1·6 5·8	17 F	0317 0809 1555 2050	1·8 5·8 1·5 5·9
3 F	0457 1002 1719 2226	1·6 6·0 1·5 6·1	18 Sa	0426 0911 1658 2149	1·4 6·1 1·2 6·2
4 Sa	0540 1045 1800 ● 2304	1·4 6·1 1·4 6·2	19 Su	0525 1007 1756 ○ 2242	1·1 6·4 1·0 6·5
5 Su	0619 1123 1835 2340	1·2 6·2 1·3 6·3	20 M	0619 1101 1850 2332	0·8 6·6 0·8 6·8
6 M	0655 1157 1907	1·1 6·2 1·2	21 Tu	0710 1151 1940	0·5 6·7 0·6
7 Tu	0012 0728 1228 1938	6·4 1·1 6·2 1·2	22 W	0018 0757 1238 2023	6·9 0·4 6·7 0·6
8 W	0043 0801 1257 2009	6·4 1·1 6·1 1·2	23 Th	0103 0842 1324 2103	6·9 0·4 6·6 0·7
9 Th	0114 0833 1327 2040	6·4 1·2 6·1 1·3	24 F	0145 0922 1408 2139	6·8 0·6 6·5 0·9
10 F	0145 0905 1358 2112	6·3 1·3 6·0 1·4	25 Sa	0229 1003 1453 2216	6·7 0·8 6·2 1·2
11 Sa	0218 0939 1433 2146	6·2 1·4 5·8 1·6	26 Su	0315 1045 1542 ☾ 2257	6·4 1·2 5·9 1·6
12 Su	0253 1013 1515 2224	6·1 1·6 5·7 1·8	27 M	0406 1133 1638 2350	6·0 1·6 5·5 2·0
13 M	0338 1055 1609 ☽ 2315	5·9 1·8 5·5 2·0	28 Tu	0509 1234 1751	5·6 2·0 5·2
14 Tu	0435 1156 1715	5·7 2·0 5·4	29 W	0102 0628 1349 1917	2·2 5·3 2·1 5·1
15 W	0025 0546 1316 1829	2·2 5·6 2·0 5·4	30 Th	0229 0752 1510 2033	2·2 5·3 2·0 5·3
			31 F	0345 0900 1614 2128	1·9 5·5 1·8 5·6

FEBRUARY

Day	Time	m	Day	Time	m
1 Sa	0441 0952 1704 2212	1·6 5·7 1·6 5·9	16 Su	0407 0907 1644 2143	1·4 6·0 1·2 6·2
2 Su	0526 1033 1746 2247	1·4 5·9 1·4 6·1	17 M	0509 1002 1743 2233	0·9 6·3 0·9 6·5
3 M	0605 1106 1821 ● 2319	1·2 6·0 1·2 6·3	18 Tu	0607 1051 1839 ○ 2318	0·6 6·6 0·6 6·8
4 Tu	0641 1137 1852 2350	1·0 6·2 1·1 6·4	19 W	0657 1136 1927	0·4 6·8 0·5
5 W	0712 1204 1920	0·9 6·2 1·1	20 Th	0000 0744 1218 2005	7·0 0·3 6·8 0·5
6 Th	0019 0742 1232 1948	6·5 0·9 6·3 1·0	21 F	0041 0823 1259 2039	7·0 0·3 6·7 0·6
7 F	0048 0812 1259 2018	6·5 0·9 6·3 1·0	22 Sa	0120 0900 1340 2111	6·9 0·5 6·5 0·8
8 Sa	0116 0842 1327 2049	6·5 1·0 6·2 1·1	23 Su	0159 0935 1420 2143	6·7 0·8 6·3 1·1
9 Su	0142 0912 1358 2118	6·4 1·2 6·1 1·3	24 M	0242 1010 1505 2219	6·4 1·2 5·9 1·5
10 M	0215 0942 1434 2150	6·3 1·4 6·0 1·6	25 Tu	0329 1049 1557 ☾ 2304	6·0 1·6 5·5 1·9
11 Tu	0256 1016 1524 ☽ 2234	6·2 1·6 5·8 1·8	26 W	0428 1143 1706	5·5 2·1 5·1
12 W	0350 1108 1628 2339	5·9 1·9 5·5 2·1	27 Th	0010 0553 1300 1845	2·3 5·0 2·4 4·9
13 Th	0504 1229 1751	5·6 2·0 5·3	28 F	0148 0731 1437 2009	2·4 5·0 2·3 5·1
14 F	0113 0632 1408 1927	2·1 5·4 1·9 5·4	29 Sa	0318 0843 1549 2105	2·0 5·3 1·9 5·5
15 Sa	0251 0758 1535 2046	1·8 5·6 1·6 5·7			

MARCH

Day	Time	m	Day	Time	m
1 Su	0419 0934 1641 2148	1·6 5·6 1·6 5·8	16 M	0349 0901 1626 2129	1·2 6·0 1·2 6·2
2 M	0504 1012 1723 2221	1·3 5·8 1·4 6·1	17 Tu	0451 0950 1725 2214	0·9 6·3 0·9 6·6
3 Tu	0543 1041 1800 2252	1·1 6·0 1·2 6·3	18 W	0547 1034 1818 ○ 2257	0·6 6·5 0·7 6·8
4 W	0618 1108 1831 ● 2320	0·9 6·2 1·0 6·4	19 Th	0638 1116 1902 2336	0·4 6·7 0·5 7·0
5 Th	0650 1134 1859 2350	0·8 6·3 0·9 6·5	20 F	0720 1156 1937	0·3 6·7 0·5
6 F	0721 1201 1927	0·8 6·4 0·9	21 Sa	0015 0757 1234 2009	7·0 0·4 6·7 0·6
7 Sa	0017 0751 1229 1957	6·6 0·8 6·4 0·9	22 Su	0053 0832 1312 2043	6·8 0·6 6·5 0·8
8 Su	0043 0819 1259 2027	6·6 0·9 6·4 1·0	23 M	0131 0905 1351 2115	6·6 0·8 6·3 1·1
9 M	0113 0849 1330 2058	6·5 1·0 6·3 1·1	24 Tu	0212 0939 1433 2150	6·3 1·2 5·9 1·4
10 Tu	0147 0919 1408 2134	6·4 1·2 6·1 1·4	25 W	0257 1016 1522 2231	5·8 1·7 5·6 1·8
11 W	0227 0956 1457 2216	6·2 1·5 5·9 1·7	26 Th	0353 1101 1626 ☾ 2326	5·3 2·1 5·1 2·2
12 Th	0324 1048 1604 ☽ 2320	5·8 1·8 5·5 1·9	27 F	0518 1207 1800	4·9 2·4 4·9
13 F	0441 1207 1736	5·4 2·0 5·2	28 Sa	0050 0702 1342 1930	2·4 4·9 2·4 5·1
14 Sa	0053 0624 1351 1921	2·0 5·3 1·9 5·4	29 Su	0234 0812 1507 2029	2·1 5·2 2·1 5·4
15 Su	0233 0758 1518 2036	1·7 5·6 1·5 5·8	30 M	0339 0901 1603 2111	1·7 5·5 1·7 5·7
			31 Tu	0427 0936 1647 2145	1·4 5·7 1·4 6·0

APRIL

Day	Time	m	Day	Time	m
1 W	0509 1004 1725 2216	1·1 5·9 1·2 6·2	16 Th	0520 1012 1747 2231	0·7 6·4 0·8 6·7
2 Th	0547 1031 1801 2247	1·0 6·2 1·0 6·4	17 F	0608 1052 1829 ○ 2312	0·6 6·5 0·7 6·8
3 F	0624 1101 1834 ● 2316	0·8 6·3 0·9 6·5	18 Sa	0650 1133 1906 2353	0·5 6·6 0·7 6·8
4 Sa	0656 1130 1906 2346	0·8 6·4 0·8 6·6	19 Su	0728 1212 1942	0·6 6·5 0·7
5 Su	0728 1203 1937	0·8 6·5 0·8	20 M	0031 0805 1250 2018	6·6 0·7 6·4 0·9
6 M	0017 0758 1235 2011	6·6 0·8 6·4 0·9	21 Tu	0109 0840 1328 2053	6·4 1·0 6·2 1·1
7 Tu	0050 0830 1312 2046	6·5 1·0 6·3 1·0	22 W	0149 0914 1411 2128	6·1 1·3 6·0 1·4
8 W	0128 0905 1355 2125	6·4 1·1 6·2 1·2	23 Th	0233 0948 1456 2206	5·7 1·7 5·7 1·7
9 Th	0216 0948 1450 2213	6·1 1·4 5·9 1·5	24 F	0325 1027 1552 ☾ 2254	5·3 2·0 5·3 2·0
10 F	0318 1042 1602 ☽ 2316	5·7 1·7 5·5 1·7	25 Sa	0437 1120 1705 2357	5·0 2·3 5·1 2·2
11 Sa	0442 1200 1733	5·4 1·9 5·4	26 Su	0607 1232 1829	4·9 2·4 5·1
12 Su	0043 0625 1335 1907	1·8 5·4 1·8 5·5	27 M	0119 0719 1354 1934	2·1 5·1 2·2 5·3
13 M	0215 0747 1456 2015	1·5 5·7 1·5 5·9	28 Tu	0236 0809 1501 2020	1·9 5·4 1·9 5·6
14 Tu	0325 0844 1600 2105	1·1 6·0 1·2 6·2	29 W	0334 0847 1555 2100	1·6 5·6 1·6 5·9
15 W	0426 0929 1657 2149	0·9 6·2 1·0 6·5	30 Th	0423 0919 1642 2135	1·3 5·9 1·3 6·1

Chart Datum: 3.67 metres below Ordnance Datum (Newlyn)

3

TIME ZONE UT(GMT)
For Summer Time add ONE hour in non-shaded areas

ENGLAND, SOUTH COAST – DOVER

Lat 51°07′ N Long 1°19′ E

TIMES AND HEIGHTS OF HIGH AND LOW WATERS

YEAR **1992**

MAY

Day	Time	m	Day	Time	m
1 F	0509 0953 1726 2209	1·1 6·1 1·1 6·3	16 Sa ○	0540 1033 1800 2252	0·9 6·3 1·0 6·5
2 Sa ●	0551 1027 1808 2244	0·9 6·3 1·0 6·5	17 Su	0624 1116 1841 2336	0·9 6·4 0·9 6·5
3 Su	0632 1104 1846 2319	0·9 6·4 0·9 6·6	18 M	0703 1157 1920	0·9 6·4 0·9
4 M	0709 1140 1921 2356	0·8 6·5 0·8 6·6	19 Tu	0017 0740 1236 1957	6·4 1·0 6·3 1·0
5 Tu	0742 1221 1958	0·8 6·5 0·8	20 W	0055 0816 1314 2033	6·2 1·1 6·2 1·1
6 W	0038 0819 1307 2039	6·5 0·9 6·4 0·9	21 Th	0133 0850 1352 2108	6·0 1·3 6·1 1·3
7 Th	0124 0900 1359 2122	6·3 1·1 6·2 1·1	22 F	0213 0922 1433 2145	5·8 1·5 5·9 1·5
8 F	0220 0946 1458 2213	6·0 1·3 6·0 1·3	23 Sa	0258 0959 1519 2226	5·5 1·8 5·7 1·7
9 Sa ☽	0328 1041 1604 2315	5·8 1·5 5·8 1·4	24 Su ☾	0352 1042 1613 2315	5·3 2·0 5·4 1·9
10 Su	0445 1154 1720	5·6 1·7 5·7	25 M	0457 1137 1718	5·1 2·1 5·3
11 M	0032 0608 1316 1838	1·5 5·6 1·7 5·7	26 Tu	0014 0604 1242 1824	2·0 5·1 2·2 5·3
12 Tu	0151 0720 1427 1942	1·3 5·7 1·5 5·9	27 W	0124 0702 1352 1920	1·9 5·3 2·0 5·5
13 W	0258 0816 1529 2036	1·2 5·9 1·3 6·1	28 Th	0232 0751 1458 2009	1·7 5·5 1·8 5·7
14 Th	0357 0904 1626 2124	1·0 6·1 1·2 6·3	29 F	0334 0834 1559 2053	1·5 5·7 1·5 6·0
15 F	0452 0949 1715 2209	1·0 6·2 1·1 6·5	30 Sa	0430 0917 1654 2135	1·3 6·0 1·3 6·2
			31 Su	0522 0959 1743 2216	1·1 6·2 1·1 6·4

JUNE

Day	Time	m	Day	Time	m
1 M ●	0608 1042 1828 2259	1·0 6·4 0·9 6·5	16 Tu	0643 1144 1902	1·1 6·3 1·0
2 Tu	0652 1127 1910 2346	0·9 6·5 0·8 6·5	17 W	0005 0720 1222 1938	6·2 1·1 6·3 1·0
3 W	0733 1217 1952	0·8 6·5 0·8	18 Th	0042 0755 1257 2013	6·1 1·2 6·3 1·1
4 Th	0035 0813 1310 2034	6·5 0·9 6·5 0·8	19 F	0116 0826 1333 2047	6·0 1·3 6·2 1·2
5 F	0130 0857 1404 2121	6·4 0·9 6·4 0·8	20 Sa	0151 0858 1408 2121	5·9 1·4 6·1 1·3
6 Sa	0227 0945 1456 2212	6·2 1·1 6·3 1·0	21 Su	0227 0932 1444 2157	5·8 1·5 6·0 1·5
7 Su ☽	0325 1037 1550 2308	6·0 1·3 6·1 1·1	22 M	0307 1009 1527 2237	5·6 1·7 5·8 1·7
8 M	0427 1139 1652	5·8 1·5 6·0	23 Tu ☾	0355 1052 1616 2325	5·4 1·9 5·6 1·8
9 Tu	0012 0533 1246 1758	1·3 5·7 1·6 5·9	24 W	0451 1146 1713	5·3 2·0 5·5
10 W	0120 0641 1352 1904	1·3 5·7 1·6 5·9	25 Th	0025 0553 1252 1817	1·9 5·3 2·1 5·5
11 Th	0227 0744 1457 2006	1·4 5·7 1·6 5·9	26 F	0134 0655 1406 1919	1·9 5·4 2·0 5·6
12 F	0329 0842 1557 2101	1·3 5·8 1·5 6·0	27 Sa	0247 0752 1519 2015	1·7 5·6 1·8 5·8
13 Sa	0427 0932 1652 2152	1·3 6·0 1·3 6·1	28 Su	0355 0847 1624 2107	1·5 5·9 1·5 6·1
14 Su	0518 1020 1739 2240	1·2 6·1 1·2 6·2	29 M	0455 0939 1722 2157	1·3 6·1 1·2 6·3
15 M ○	0603 1104 1822 2323	1·2 6·2 1·1 6·3	30 Tu ●	0550 1030 1812 2248	1·0 6·4 0·9 6·5

JULY

Day	Time	m	Day	Time	m
1 W	0639 1120 1900 2339	0·9 6·6 0·7 6·6	16 Th	0703 1203 1921	1·2 6·4 1·0
2 Th	0727 1211 1947	0·8 6·7 0·6	17 F	0021 0734 1235 1954	6·2 1·2 6·4 1·0
3 F	0031 0811 1300 2032	6·6 0·7 6·7 0·5	18 Sa	0052 0804 1306 2026	6·2 1·2 6·4 1·1
4 Sa	0123 0856 1349 2117	6·6 0·8 6·7 0·6	19 Su	0121 0833 1337 2057	6·1 1·2 6·3 1·2
5 Su	0213 0939 1437 2203	6·4 0·9 6·6 0·7	20 M	0151 0904 1408 2129	6·0 1·3 6·2 1·3
6 M	0304 1024 1525 2251	6·3 1·1 6·4 1·0	21 Tu	0223 0938 1440 2203	5·9 1·5 6·1 1·5
7 Tu ☽	0355 1112 1619 2344	6·0 1·4 6·2 1·3	22 W ☾	0300 1013 1519 2241	5·7 1·7 5·9 1·7
8 W	0452 1208 1719	5·7 1·6 5·9	23 Th	0346 1057 1612 2332	5·6 1·9 5·7 1·9
9 Th	0045 0600 1314 1828	1·5 5·5 1·8 5·7	24 F	0448 1158 1718	5·4 2·1 5·5
10 F	0154 0713 1426 1941	1·7 5·5 1·9 5·7	25 Sa	0042 0601 1319 1832	2·0 5·3 2·1 5·5
11 Sa	0304 0823 1536 2047	1·7 5·6 1·7 5·7	26 Su	0204 0719 1444 1945	1·9 5·4 1·9 5·7
12 Su	0409 0921 1635 2142	1·6 5·8 1·5 5·9	27 M	0325 0829 1600 2050	1·7 5·7 1·5 6·0
13 M	0502 1009 1726 2230	1·5 6·0 1·3 6·0	28 Tu	0433 0928 1702 2146	1·3 6·1 1·2 6·3
14 Tu ○	0549 1049 1808 2312	1·4 6·2 1·2 6·1	29 W ●	0532 1020 1757 2238	1·1 6·4 0·8 6·5
15 W	0628 1127 1848 2349	1·3 6·3 1·1 6·2	30 Th	0627 1109 1849 2327	0·8 6·7 0·6 6·7
			31 F	0719 1156 1938	0·7 6·9 0·4

AUGUST

Day	Time	m	Day	Time	m
1 Sa	0015 0804 1241 2023	6·8 0·6 6·9 0·4	16 Su	0021 0738 1235 2001	6·3 1·1 6·5 1·0
2 Su	0102 0846 1326 2105	6·7 0·6 6·9 0·5	17 M	0048 0808 1302 2032	6·3 1·1 6·5 1·1
3 M	0147 0922 1409 2146	6·6 0·8 6·8 0·7	18 Tu	0114 0837 1328 2101	6·2 1·2 6·4 1·2
4 Tu	0232 1000 1454 2227	6·4 1·0 6·5 1·0	19 W	0142 0908 1358 2132	6·1 1·4 6·3 1·4
5 W ☽	0319 1040 1543 2312	6·1 1·4 6·2 1·4	20 Th	0216 0941 1433 2204	6·0 1·6 6·1 1·7
6 Th	0414 1129 1641	5·7 1·7 5·8	21 F ☾	0258 1020 1522 2249	5·8 1·9 5·9 1·9
7 F	0008 0520 1234 1756	1·8 5·4 2·1 5·5	22 Sa	0357 1118 1631	5·5 2·1 5·5
8 Sa	0119 0645 1357 1924	2·0 5·2 2·1 5·4	23 Su	0000 0519 1241 1800	2·1 5·3 2·2 5·4
9 Su	0240 0808 1518 2039	2·0 5·4 1·9 5·5	24 M	0131 0657 1418 1933	2·1 5·3 2·0 5·5
10 M	0352 0908 1621 2134	1·8 5·7 1·6 5·8	25 Tu	0301 0819 1538 2043	1·8 5·7 1·5 5·9
11 Tu	0447 0953 1711 2217	1·6 6·0 1·4 5·9	26 W	0412 0918 1641 2136	1·4 6·2 1·1 6·3
12 W	0533 1031 1754 2254	1·4 6·2 1·2 6·1	27 Th	0513 1006 1739 2224	1·0 6·5 0·8 6·6
13 Th ○	0612 1105 1831 2325	1·3 6·4 1·1 6·2	28 F ●	0610 1051 1832 2309	0·8 6·8 0·5 6·8
14 F	0643 1137 1902 2354	1·2 6·5 1·0 6·3	29 Sa	0700 1134 1920 2353	0·6 7·0 0·4 6·9
15 Sa	0712 1207 1931	1·1 6·5 1·0	30 Su	0744 1215 2004	0·6 7·1 0·4
			31 M	0035 0822 1256 2043	6·8 0·6 7·0 0·5

Chart Datum: 3.67 metres below Ordnance Datum (Newlyn)

ENGLAND, SOUTH COAST – DOVER

Lat 51°07′ N Long 1°19′ E

TIMES AND HEIGHTS OF HIGH AND LOW WATERS

YEAR **1992**

TIME ZONE UT(GMT)
For Summer Time add ONE hour in non-shaded areas

SEPTEMBER

	Time	m		Time	m
1 Tu	0117 0856 1338 2121	6·7 0·8 6·8 0·7	16 W	0042 0813 1255 2034	6·4 1·2 6·5 1·2
2 W	0159 0931 1422 2157	6·4 1·1 6·5 1·1	17 Th	0112 0846 1326 2105	6·3 1·3 6·4 1·4
3 Th ☽	0246 1009 1510 2238	6·1 1·4 6·1 1·6	18 F	0145 0919 1402 2141	6·2 1·6 6·2 1·7
4 F	0338 1054 1607 2330	5·7 1·9 5·7 2·0	19 Sa ☾	0229 1000 1451 2227	6·0 1·8 5·9 1·9
5 Sa	0444 1156 1727	5·3 2·2 5·2	20 Su	0329 1058 1604 2336	5·6 2·1 5·5 2·2
6 Su	0042 0617 1324 1909	2·3 5·1 2·3 5·2	21 M	0458 1219 1746	5·3 2·2 5·3
7 M	0212 0747 1456 2025	2·3 5·3 2·1 5·4	22 Tu	0110 0646 1357 1926	2·1 5·4 1·9 5·6
8 Tu	0328 0846 1559 2117	2·0 5·6 1·7 5·7	23 W	0242 0806 1515 2033	1·8 5·8 1·4 6·0
9 W	0424 0931 1648 2156	1·7 5·9 1·4 5·9	24 Th	0350 0901 1619 2122	1·4 6·2 1·0 6·4
10 Th	0508 1006 1729 2227	1·5 6·2 1·2 6·1	25 F	0449 0946 1715 2206	1·1 6·6 0·8 6·6
11 F	0546 1037 1804 2255	1·3 6·4 1·1 6·3	26 Sa ●	0544 1028 1807 2248	0·8 6·9 0·6 6·8
12 Sa ○	0617 1106 1836 2320	1·2 6·5 1·0 6·4	27 Su	0632 1109 1855 2329	0·7 7·1 0·5 6·9
13 Su	0645 1134 1906 2347	1·1 6·6 1·0 6·4	28 M	0713 1150 1935	0·7 7·1 0·5
14 M	0713 1201 1935	1·1 6·6 1·0	29 Tu	0010 0749 1229 2015	6·8 0·7 7·0 0·6
15 Tu	0014 0742 1228 2005	6·4 1·1 6·6 1·1	30 W	0049 0826 1310 2051	6·7 0·9 6·8 0·9

OCTOBER

	Time	m		Time	m
1 Th	0131 0903 1352 2128	6·4 1·2 6·4 1·3	16 F	0050 0827 1304 2046	6·4 1·3 6·4 1·4
2 F	0216 0942 1440 2207	6·1 1·5 6·0 1·7	17 Sa	0130 0905 1347 2125	6·3 1·5 6·2 1·6
3 Sa ☽	0307 1024 1538 2254	5·8 1·9 5·5 2·1	18 Su	0218 0950 1442 2214	6·0 1·7 5·9 1·9
4 Su	0409 1119 1657 2358	5·4 2·2 5·1 2·5	19 M ☾	0324 1048 1559 2323	5·7 1·9 5·5 2·1
5 M	0534 1239 1839	5·1 2·4 5·1	20 Tu	0449 1205 1739	5·5 2·0 5·4
6 Tu	0127 0707 1415 1954	2·5 5·2 2·2 5·3	21 W	0053 0627 1335 1910	2·0 5·6 1·8 5·7
7 W	0249 0811 1522 2046	2·2 5·6 1·8 5·6	22 Th	0218 0741 1451 2012	1·8 5·9 1·4 6·0
8 Th	0345 0856 1612 2124	1·9 5·9 1·5 5·9	23 F	0324 0834 1552 2100	1·4 6·3 1·1 6·3
9 F	0430 0932 1652 2153	1·6 6·1 1·3 6·1	24 Sa	0420 0921 1647 2143	1·2 6·6 0·9 6·5
10 Sa	0508 1003 1730 2219	1·4 6·3 1·2 6·2	25 Su ●	0512 1003 1737 2226	1·0 6·8 0·8 6·7
11 Su ○	0543 1031 1805 2247	1·3 6·5 1·1 6·4	26 M	0558 1045 1824 2308	0·9 7·0 0·7 6·8
12 M	0615 1101 1838 2315	1·1 6·6 1·0 6·5	27 Tu	0641 1127 1906 2349	0·8 7·0 0·7 6·7
13 Tu	0648 1129 1910 2344	1·1 6·7 1·0 6·5	28 W	0721 1208 1947	0·9 6·9 0·9
14 W	0720 1158 1941	1·1 6·6 1·1	29 Th	0029 0801 1249 2025	6·6 1·0 6·6 1·1
15 Th	0017 0754 1229 2012	6·5 1·2 6·6 1·2	30 F	0112 0840 1331 2101	6·4 1·2 6·3 1·4
			31 Sa	0154 0918 1416 2138	6·2 1·5 6·0 1·8

NOVEMBER

	Time	m		Time	m
1 Su	0240 0957 1508 2219	5·9 1·8 5·6 2·1	16 M	0223 0945 1446 2207	6·2 1·4 5·9 1·7
2 M ☽	0334 1045 1614 2309	5·6 2·1 5·2 2·4	17 Tu ☾	0324 1040 1557 2311	6·0 1·6 5·7 1·9
3 Tu	0441 1146 1742	5·3 2·3 5·1	18 W	0434 1150 1718	5·8 1·7 5·6
4 W	0018 0604 1304 1900	2·5 5·2 2·3 5·2	19 Th	0031 0551 1310 1836	1·9 5·8 1·6 5·7
5 Th	0138 0716 1422 1957	2·4 5·4 2·1 5·4	20 F	0148 0703 1422 1941	1·8 5·9 1·4 5·9
6 F	0246 0808 1519 2037	2·1 5·7 1·8 5·7	21 Sa	0254 0804 1524 2034	1·6 6·2 1·2 6·1
7 Sa	0338 0847 1607 2111	1·9 5·9 1·5 5·9	22 Su	0352 0854 1620 2122	1·4 6·4 1·1 6·3
8 Su	0424 0922 1651 2142	1·6 6·2 1·3 6·1	23 M	0445 0942 1712 2209	1·2 6·5 1·0 6·4
9 M	0508 0956 1732 2214	1·4 6·4 1·2 6·3	24 Tu ●	0533 1028 1758 2254	1·1 6·7 1·0 6·6
10 Tu ○	0549 1028 1811 2248	1·2 6·5 1·1 6·5	25 W	0618 1113 1842 2336	1·0 6·7 1·0 6·6
11 W	0627 1102 1848 2323	1·1 6·6 1·1 6·6	26 Th	0700 1156 1923	1·0 6·6 1·0
12 Th	0703 1137 1921	1·1 6·6 1·1	27 F	0017 0741 1236 2001	6·6 1·1 6·4 1·2
13 F	0001 0738 1215 1957	6·6 1·1 6·6 1·2	28 Sa	0056 0819 1316 2037	6·4 1·2 6·2 1·4
14 Sa	0042 0816 1257 2034	6·5 1·2 6·4 1·3	29 Su	0135 0856 1357 2111	6·3 1·4 6·0 1·6
15 Su	0128 0858 1347 2117	6·4 1·3 6·2 1·4	30 M	0216 0932 1440 2145	6·1 1·6 5·7 1·9

DECEMBER

	Time	m		Time	m
1 Tu	0300 1012 1528 2226	5·9 1·8 5·5 2·1	16 W ☾	0312 1030 1541 2254	6·3 1·3 6·0 1·6
2 W ☽	0349 1057 1627 2315	5·6 2·0 5·2 2·3	17 Th	0409 1130 1644 2358	6·1 1·4 5·8 1·7
3 Th	0449 1154 1736	5·4 2·2 5·1	18 F	0512 1239 1753	6·0 1·5 5·7
4 F	0018 0557 1302 1842	2·4 5·4 2·2 5·2	19 Sa	0112 0622 1349 1904	1·8 5·9 1·5 5·7
5 Sa	0128 0700 1411 1937	2·3 5·5 2·0 5·4	20 Su	0220 0730 1457 2011	1·8 5·9 1·5 5·8
6 Su	0237 0754 1515 2023	2·1 5·6 1·8 5·6	21 M	0327 0833 1559 2108	1·6 6·0 1·4 5·9
7 M	0339 0839 1612 2105	1·8 5·9 1·5 5·9	22 Tu	0426 0928 1655 2200	1·5 6·2 1·3 6·2
8 Tu	0434 0921 1702 2146	1·5 6·1 1·3 6·2	23 W	0518 1019 1743 2245	1·3 6·3 1·2 6·3
9 W ○	0523 1002 1749 2227	1·3 6·3 1·2 6·4	24 Th ●	0604 1105 1827 2326	1·1 6·4 1·1 6·5
10 Th	0608 1042 1831 2309	1·1 6·5 1·1 6·5	25 F	0646 1147 1906	1·0 6·4 1·1
11 F	0650 1125 1910 2354	1·0 6·6 1·0 6·6	26 Sa	0005 0724 1225 1941	6·5 1·0 6·3 1·2
12 Sa	0730 1210 1947	1·0 6·6 1·0	27 Su	0041 0801 1300 2013	6·5 1·1 6·2 1·3
13 Su	0041 0809 1257 2027	6·6 0·9 6·5 1·1	28 M	0116 0834 1333 2044	6·4 1·2 6·1 1·4
14 M	0130 0851 1348 2111	6·6 1·0 6·4 1·2	29 Tu	0149 0907 1408 2115	6·3 1·3 5·9 1·6
15 Tu	0220 0938 1443 2159	6·5 1·1 6·2 1·3	30 W	0226 0941 1444 2148	6·2 1·5 5·7 1·7
			31 Th	0304 1016 1527 2227	6·0 1·7 5·5 2·0

Chart Datum: 3.67 metres below Ordnance Datum (Newlyn)

RAMSGATE 10-3-16

Kent

CHARTS
Admiralty 1827, 1828, 323; Stanford 5, 19; Imray C1, C8; OS 179

TIDES
+0020 Dover; ML 2·6; Duration 0530; Zone 0 (GMT).

Standard Port DOVER (⟵)

Times				Height (metres)			
HW		LW		MHWS	MHWN	MLWN	MLWS
0000	0600	0100	0700	6·7	5·3	2·0	0·8
1200	1800	1300	1900				
Differences RAMSGATE							
+0020	+0020	−0007	−0007	−1·8	−1·5	−0·8	−0·4

HW Broadstairs = HW Dover +0027 approx.

SHELTER
Good in inner harbour (marina). Access HW∓2 approx.

NAVIGATION
Waypoint 51°19′·50N 01°26′·00E, 090°/270° from/to new breakwater entrance, 0·25M. Beware Dyke Bank to the N, and Brake and Cross Ledge to the S; all these dry. Access is by main channel from the E. Contact Port Control VHF Ch 14. Reception pontoon in West Gully of Royal Harbour.

LIGHTS AND MARKS
Entrance channel has lateral and cardinal buoys and marks. Breakwater entrance N side QG, S side VQR. Ldg Lts 270°. Front Dir Oc WRG 10s; G259°-269°, W269°-271°, R271°-281°. Rear Oc 5s. International Port Traffic Signals control main channel and entry to Royal Harbour and marina. West Pier Lt refers to depth between piers:— FR over 3m, FG less than 3m.

RADIO TELEPHONE
VHF Ch 16 (H24). Marina Ch 14. (Call *Dock Office*).

TELEPHONE (0843)
Hr Mr 592277; MRSC Frinton-on-Sea 675518; # 593501; Marinecall 0898 500 456; Police 581724; Dr 595051.

FACILITIES
EC Thursday; **Ramsgate Yacht Marina** (400+100 visitors) ☎ 592277, Slip, AC, FW, C (20 ton), ⊡, (Access HW∓2; **Royal Temple YC** ☎ 591766, Bar; **Ramsgate Marine** ☎ 601245, Slip, Ⓔ, ME, El, Sh, BH; **Richards Marine Services** ☎ 852452, ME, El; **Seagear** ☎ 591733, ACA, Gaz, CH; **Foy Boat Marine** ☎ 592662, P, D, L, AB; **Bosun's Locker** ☎ 597158, CH, ACA; **Walkers Marine** ☎ 592176, ME; **Davis Marine** ☎ 586172, ME; **A J C White** ☎ Dover 617800, SM. **Town** P, Gas, Gaz, V, R, Bar. ✉; Ⓑ; ⇌; ✈ (Manston).

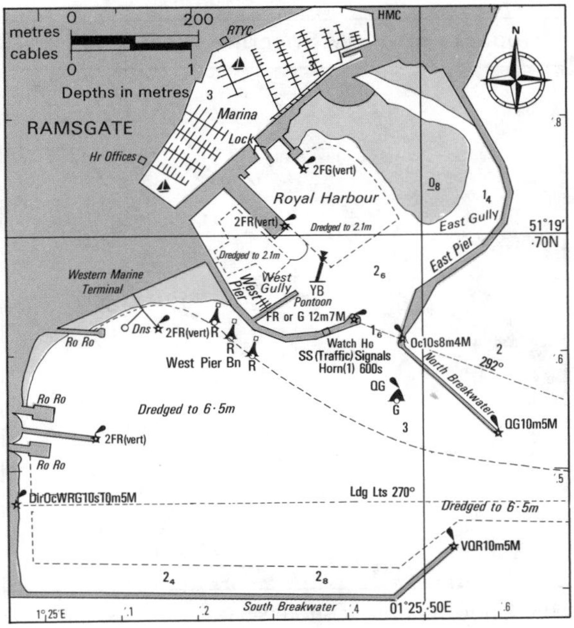
metres 0 200
cables 0 1
Depths in metres
RAMSGATE
RTYC
HMC
Marina
Lock
Hr Offices
2FG(vert)
Royal Harbour
East Gully
East Pier
51°19′·70N
2FR(vert)
Dredged to 2.1m
Western Marine Terminal
West Pier
West Gully
YB Pontoon
FR or G 12m7M
Dns
2FR(vert)
West Pier Bn
Watch Ho
SS (Traffic) Signals
Horn(1) 60s
Oc10s8m4M
North Breakwater
292°
QG
QG10m5M
Ro Ro
Dredged to 6·5m
2FR(vert)
DirOcWRG10s10m5M
Ldg Lts 270°
VQR10m5M
South Breakwater
1°25′E
01°25′·50E

WHITSTABLE 10-3-17

Kent

CHARTS
Admiralty 2571, 1607; Stanford 5; Imray Y14; OS 179

TIDES
+0135 Dover; ML 3·0; Duration 0605; Zone 0 (GMT).

Standard Port SHEERNESS (⟶)

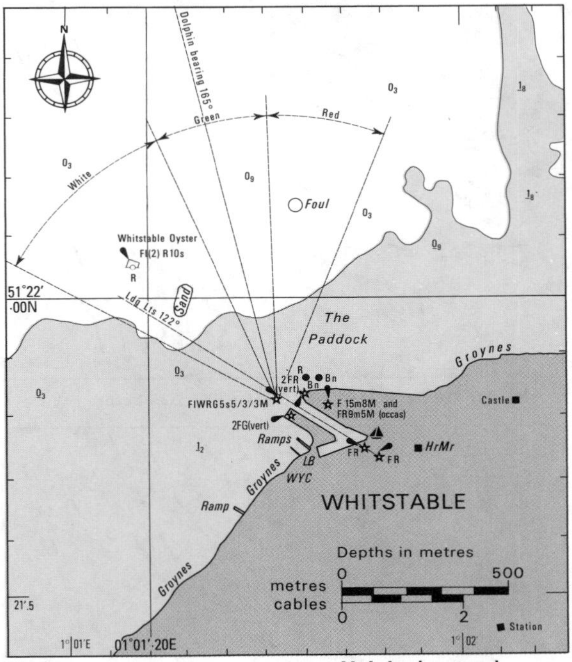
Dolphin bearing 165°
Green
Red
White
Foul
Whitstable Oyster Fl(2) R10s
Sand
Ldg Lts 122°
51°22′·00N
The Paddock
Groynes
2FR (vert)
Bn
FlWRG5s5/3/3M
F 15m8M and FR9m5M (occas)
2FG(vert)
Ramps
Castle
HrMr
FR
LB
WYC
WHITSTABLE
Ramp
Depths in metres
metres 0 500
cables 0 2
Station
1°01′E
01°01′·20E
1°02′

Times				Height (metres)			
HW		LW		MHWS	MHWN	MLWN	MLWS
0200	0800	0200	0700	5·7	4·8	1·5	0·6
1400	2000	1400	1900				
Differences WHITSTABLE							
−0008	−0011	+0005	0000	−0·3	−0·3	0·0	−0·1
MARGATE							
−0050	−0040	−0020	−0050	−0·9	−0·9	−0·1	0·0
HERNE BAY							
−0025	−0015	0000	−0025	−0·5	−0·5	−0·1	−0·1

SHELTER
Good shelter except in strong winds from NNW to NE. Berthing is restricted to genuine refuge seekers since priority is given to commercial shipping. Moorings to NW of harbour controlled by YC, Access HW∓1.

NAVIGATION
Waypoint 51°22′·62N 01°01′·20E, 165°/345° from/to West Quay dolphin, 0·83M. Approach (not before half flood) either direct in the G sector or via Whitstable Oyster port hand lit buoy in W sector. Beware shoals near approaches, which are very shallow. Harbour dries. Oyster beds are numerous.

LIGHTS AND MARKS
Ldg Lts 122°, both FR, West Quay, off head Fl WRG 5s; dolphin; vis W118°-156°, G156°-178°, R178°-201°. NE arm FW 15m 8M; indicates harbour open; FR below this Lt indicates harbour closed.

RADIO TELEPHONE
VHF Ch 16; 09 12 (Mon-Fri: 0800-1700 LT. Other times: HW−3 to HW+1). Tidal information on request.

TELEPHONE (0227)
Hr Mr 274086; MRSC Frinton-on-Sea 675518; # (0304) 202441; Marinecall 0898 500 455; Police 770055; Dr 263811.

FACILITIES
EC Wednesday; **Harbour** ☎ 274086, L, FW, D, C (15 ton), AB; **Whitstable YC** ☎ 272942, M, R, Slip, L, FW, Bar; **The Dinghy Store** ☎ 274168, ME, Sh, CH, ACA; **Whitstable Marine** ☎ 262525, ME, El, Sh, CH, C, V; **H. Goldfinch** ☎ 272295, SM; **Waldens** ☎ 272098, Gas; **Barton Marine** ☎ 273917, CH; **W. Grantham** ☎ 273505, ME, El; **ICOM UK** ☎ 363859, Ⓔ. **Town** ⊡, P, V, R, Bar. ✉; Ⓑ; ⇌, ✈ (Lydd or Manston).

CAUTION:– Due to very strong rates of tidal streams in some areas, eddies may occur. Where possible, some indication of these is shown but in many areas there is insufficient information or eddies are unstable

10.3.19 THAMES ESTUARY TIDAL STREAMS

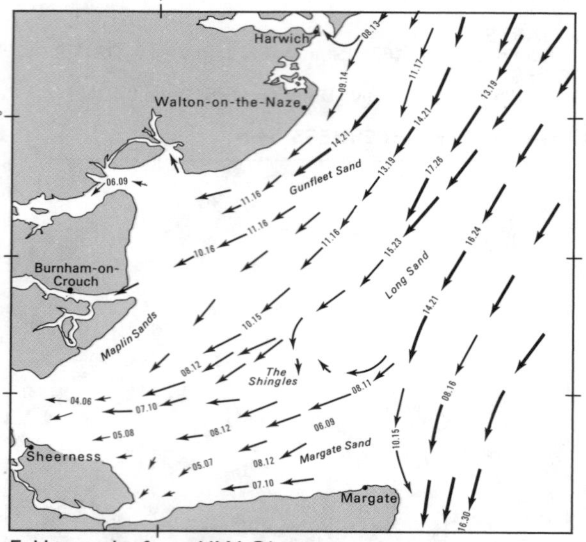
1°
50°
Harwich
Walton-on-the-Naze
Gunfleet Sand
Burnham-on-Crouch
Long Sand
Maplin Sands
The Shingles
Sheerness
Margate Sand
Margate

5 Hours before HW Sheerness (0335 before HW Dover)

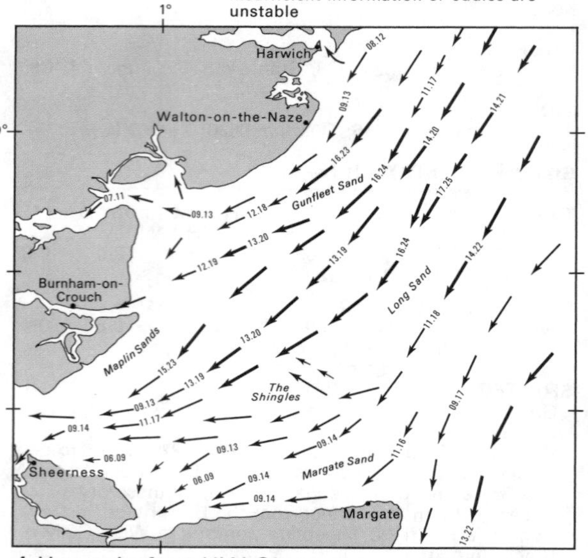
1°
50°
Harwich
Walton-on-the-Naze
Gunfleet Sand
Burnham-on-Crouch
Long Sand
Maplin Sands
The Shingles
Sheerness
Margate Sand
Margate

4 Hours before HW Sheerness (0235 before HW Dover)

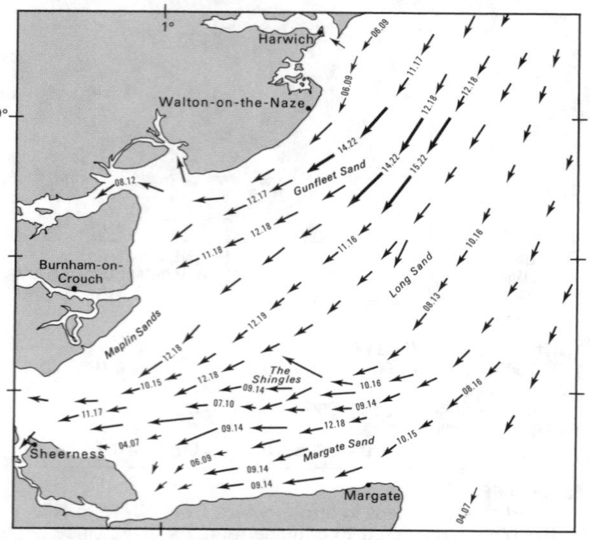
1°
50°
Harwich
Walton-on-the-Naze
Gunfleet Sand
Burnham-on-Crouch
Long Sand
Maplin Sands
The Shingles
Sheerness
Margate Sand
Margate

3 Hours before HW Sheerness (0135 before HW Dover)

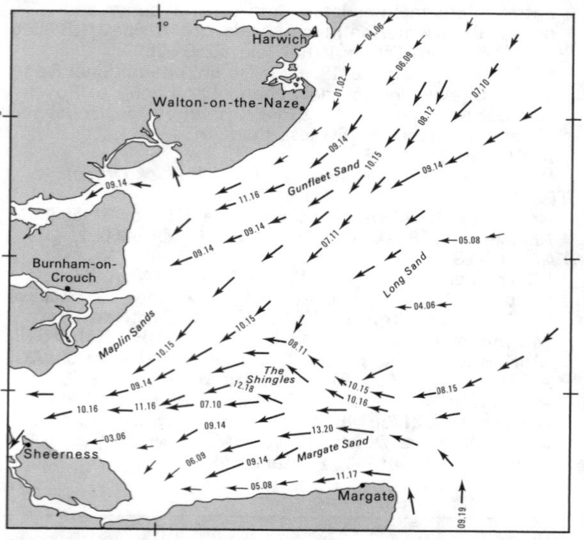
1°
50°
Harwich
Walton-on-the-Naze
Gunfleet Sand
Burnham-on-Crouch
Long Sand
Maplin Sands
The Shingles
Sheerness
Margate Sand
Margate

2 Hours before HW Sheerness (0035 before HW Dover)

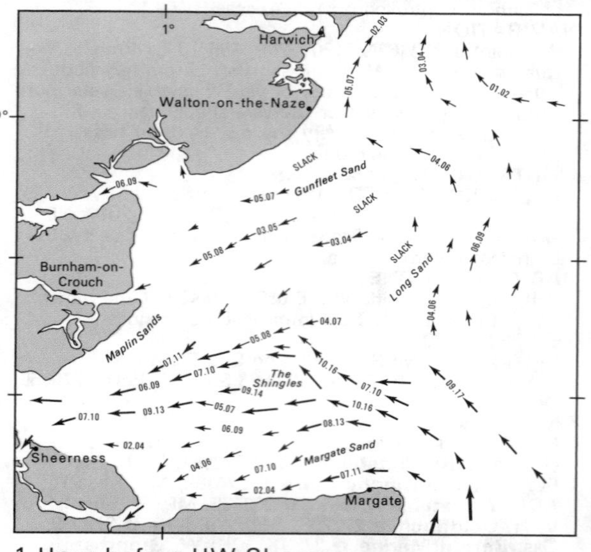
1°
50°
Harwich
Walton-on-the-Naze
SLACK
Gunfleet Sand
SLACK
SLACK
Burnham-on-Crouch
Long Sand
Maplin Sands
The Shingles
Sheerness
Margate Sand
Margate

1 Hour before HW Sheerness (0025 after HW Dover)

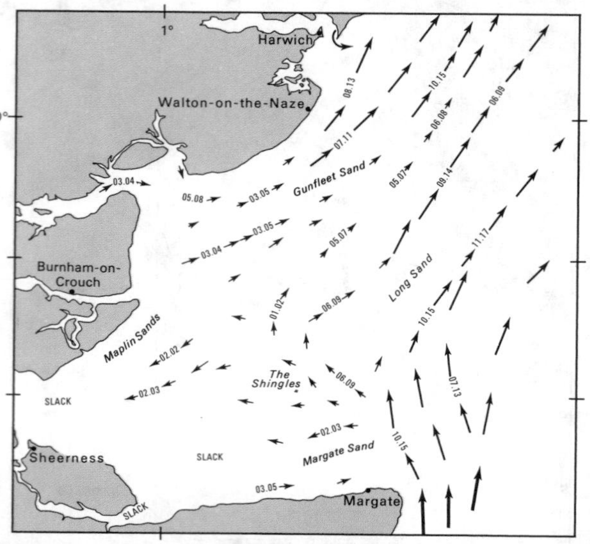
1°
50°
Harwich
Walton-on-the-Naze
Gunfleet Sand
Burnham-on-Crouch
Long Sand
Maplin Sands
The Shingles
SLACK
SLACK
Sheerness
Margate Sand
SLACK
Margate

HW Sheerness (0125 after HW Dover)

General Areas 10.3.3 10.4.3

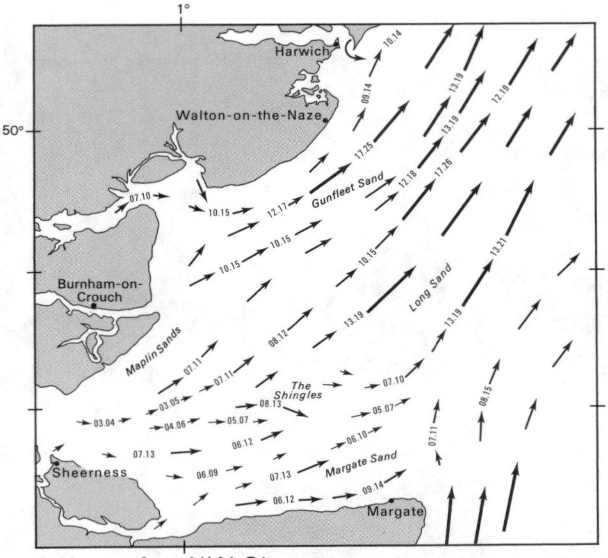
1°
50°
Harwich
Walton-on-the-Naze
Gunfleet Sand
Burnham-on-Crouch
Long Sand
Maplin Sands
The Shingles
Margate Sand
Sheerness
Margate

1 Hour after HW Sheerness (0225 after HW Dover)

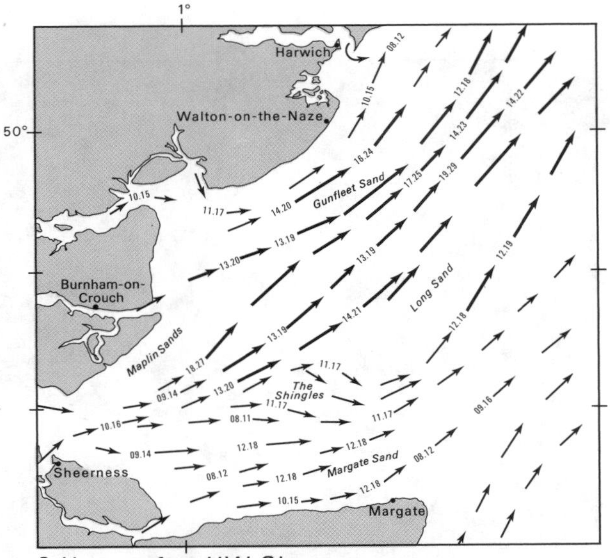
1°
50°
Harwich
Walton-on-the-Naze
Gunfleet Sand
Burnham-on-Crouch
Long Sand
Maplin Sands
The Shingles
Margate Sand
Sheerness
Margate

2 Hours after HW Sheerness (0325 after HW Dover)

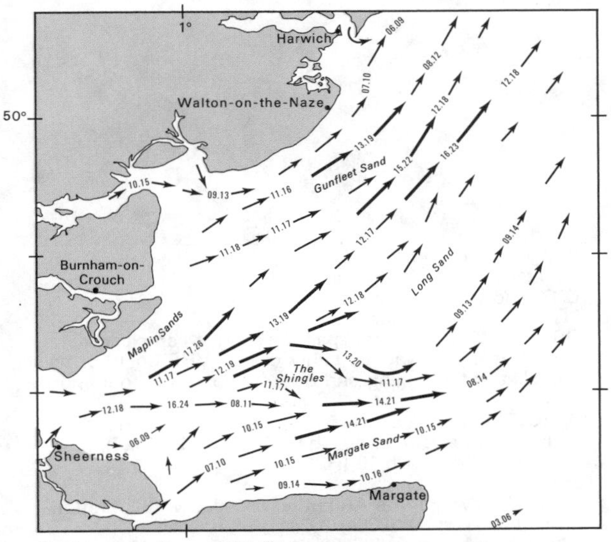
1°
50°
Harwich
Walton-on-the-Naze
Gunfleet Sand
Burnham-on-Crouch
Long Sand
Maplin Sands
The Shingles
Margate Sand
Sheerness
Margate

3 Hours after HW Sheerness (0425 after HW Dover)

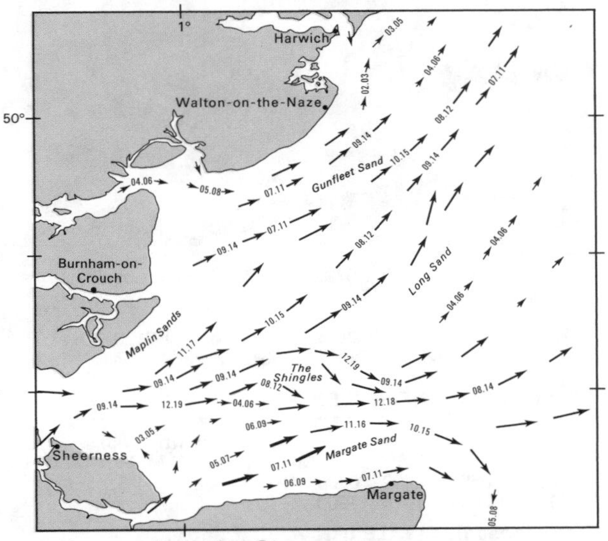
1°
50°
Harwich
Walton-on-the-Naze
Gunfleet Sand
Burnham-on-Crouch
Long Sand
Maplin Sands
The Shingles
Margate Sand
Sheerness
Margate

4 Hours after HW Sheerness (0525 after HW Dover)

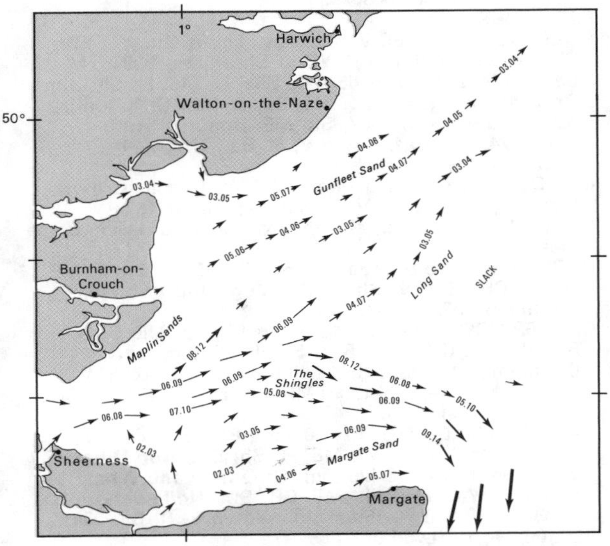
1°
50°
Harwich
Walton-on-the-Naze
Gunfleet Sand
Burnham-on-Crouch
Long Sand
SLACK
Maplin Sands
The Shingles
Margate Sand
Sheerness
Margate

5 Hours after HW Sheerness (0600 before HW Dover)

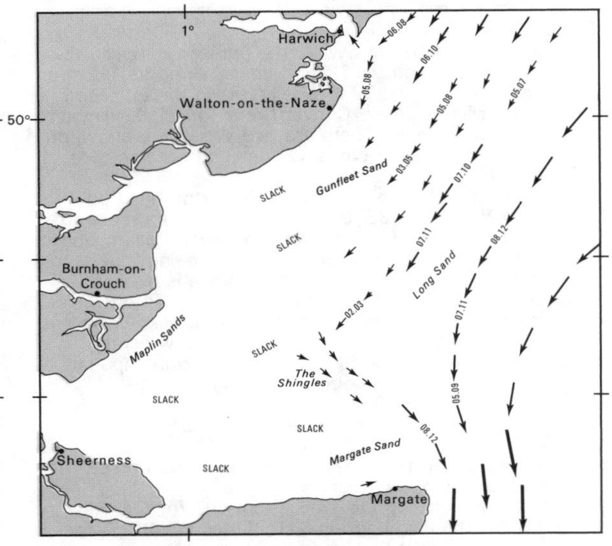
1°
50°
Harwich
Walton-on-the-Naze
Gunfleet Sand
SLACK
Burnham-on-Crouch
Long Sand
Maplin Sands
The Shingles
Margate Sand
Sheerness
Margate

6 Hours after HW Sheerness (0500 before HW Dover)

THE SWALE 10-3-19
Kent

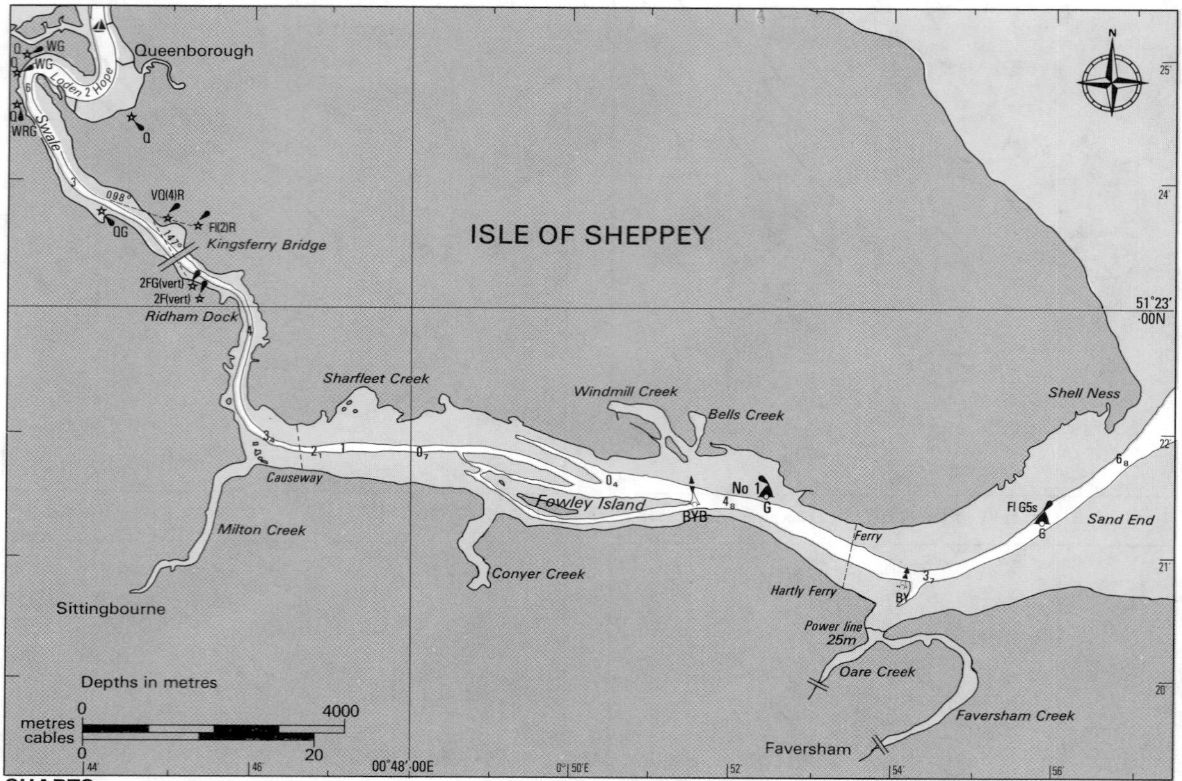

Queenborough
Loden Hope
Swale
WG
WRG
Q
VQ(4)R
Fl(2)R
QG
098°
147°
Kingsferry Bridge
2FG(vert)
2F(vert)
Ridham Dock
ISLE OF SHEPPEY
Sharfleet Creek
Windmill Creek
Bells Creek
Shell Ness
Causeway
Fowley Island
No 1
BYB
Fl G5s
Sand End
Ferry
Milton Creek
Conyer Creek
Hartly Ferry
BY
Power line 25m
Oare Creek
Faversham Creek
Sittingbourne
Faversham
Depths in metres
metres
cables
4000
20
00°48'·00E
0°|50'E
51°23'·00N

CHARTS
Admiralty 2571, 2482, 2572, 1834, 3683; Stanford 5; Imray Y18, Y14; OS 178.

TIDES
Queenborough +0130 Dover; Harty Ferry +0120 Dover; ML (Harty Ferry) 3·0; Duration 0610; Zone 0 (GMT).

Standard Port SHEERNESS (⟶)

Times				Height (metres)			
HW		LW		MHWS	MHWN	MLWN	MLWS
0200	0800	0200	0700	5·7	4·8	1·5	0·6
1400	2000	1400	1900				
Differences R. SWALE (Grovehurst Jetty)							
−0007	0000	0000	+0016	0·0	0·0	0·0	−0·1

SHELTER
Excellent shelter in the Swale, the passage between the Isle of Sheppey and the N Kent coast, along its 14M from Queenborough in the W to Shell Ness in the E. Yachts can enter Milton Creek, Conyer Creek (dries), Faversham Creek or Oare Creek. There are two W visitors buoys off Queenborough, and a concrete lighter to go alongside.

NAVIGATION
Waypoint (E entrance) Columbine Spit stbd-hand buoy, 51°23'·84N, 01°00'·13E, 050°/230° from/to entrance to buoyed channel 1·3M. E entrance between Pollard Spit and Ham Gat is well marked, the buoys being moved to suit the shifting channel. The W entrance is marked by Queenborough Spit buoy 1M from Garrison Pt on S side. Direction of buoyage changes at Milton Creek. There are numerous oyster beds in the area. Beware wreck in Faversham Creek; lock gates by swing bridge impound water at top of the harbour.

LIGHTS AND MARKS
No fixed lights at E entrance. In W Swale:
(1) Entrance Lt Q 16m 5M; vis 163°-168°.
(2) Round Loden Hope bend: two QWG and one QWRG on Bns; keep in G sectors.
(3) Horse Reach Ldg Lts 113°. Front QG 7m 5M. Rear FlG 3s 10m 6M. Ldg Lts 098°. Front VQ(4)R 5s 6m 5M. Rear Fl(2)R 5s 10m 9M.
(4) Kingsferry Bridge Ldg Lts 147°. Front 2FG(vert) 9/7m. Rear 2FW(vert) 11/9m. Lights on bridge 2×2 FG (vert) on SW; 2×2 FR (vert) on NE.

Bridge traffic signals: –

No Lts	=	Bridge down
Q Or and QG	=	Centre span lifting
FG	=	Bridge open
QR	=	Centre span lowering. Keep clear.

Bridge opens for yachts; either call on VHF Ch 10 or hoist a bucket in the rigging and give one long and four short blasts.

RADIO TELEPHONE
Call: *Medway Radio* VHF Ch 09 11 **74** 16 22 (H24); Kingsferry Bridge Ch 10 (H24);

TELEPHONE (0795)
Hr Mr (Medway Ports Authority) 580003; MRSC Frinton-on-Sea 675518; # (0304) 202441; Marinecall 0898 500 455; Police 536639; Dr or Ⓗ contact Medway Navigation Service 663025.

FACILITIES
QUEENBOROUGH: EC Wednesday. **Town Quay** L, FW, Slip, M; **Queenborough YC** ☎ Sheerness 663955, M, Bar; **Calfcastle BY** ☎ 661141, Slip, C, ME, El, Sh; **Jim Brett Marine** ☎ 667121, ME, Sh, El, AB, C (10 ton); **André Hardy** ☎ 873767, Sh, ME; **Bosun's Store** ☎ 662674, CH, Gas; **Town** V, R, Bar. ✉; Ⓑ; ⇌; ✈ (Lydd or Gatwick).

MILTON CREEK (Sittingbourne): EC Wednesday **Crown Quay** M, FW; **Town** V, R, Bar. ✉; Ⓑ; ⇌; ✈ (Lydd or Gatwick); also the Dolphin Yard Sailing Barge Museum.

OARE CREEK: **Youngboats** ☎ 536176, M, C (8 ton), ME, El, Sh, CH; **Hollow Shore Cruising Club** Bar; **Fuller Marine** ☎ 532294, CH, Gas.

CONYER CREEK: **Swale Marina** ☎ 521562, ME, Sh, BH (15 ton), C (3 ton), Slip, **Swale Rigging and Chandlery** ☎ 522872 CH; **Wilkinson** ☎ 521503 SM; **Conyer Marine** ☎ 521285, ME, Sh, El, Ⓔ, Slip, D, SM; **Conyer Cruising Club**.

FAVERSHAM: EC Thursday; **Brents BY** ☎ 537809, M, AB, Ⓔ, C (40 ton), AC, FW, ME, El, Sh, SM; **Iron Wharf BY** ☎ 536296, M, AC, C (25 ton), D; **Quay Lane Wharf** ☎ 531660, AC, FW, Sh, ME, CH, SM; **Hollowshore BY** ☎ 532317, Sh, El, C (5 ton), Ⓔ; **Town** V, R, Bar, Gas. ✉; Ⓑ; ⇌; ✈ (Lydd or Gatwick).

RIVER MEDWAY (SHEERNESS) 10-3-20

Kent

CHARTS
Admiralty 3683, 2482, 1835, 1834, 1183; Stanford 5; Imray Y18; OS 178

TIDES
+0136 Dover; ML 3·1; Duration 0610; Zone 0 (GMT).

Standard Port SHEERNESS (→)

Times				Height (metres)			
HW		LW		MHWS	MHWN	MLWN	MLWS
0200	0800	0200	0700	5·7	4·8	1·5	0·6
1400	2000	1400	1900				
Differences UPNOR							
+0015	+0015	+0015	+0025	+0·2	+0·2	−0·1	−0·1
ROCHESTER (STROOD PIER)							
+0018	+0018	+0018	+0028	+0·2	+0·2	−0·2	−0·3
ALLINGTON LOCK							
+0050	+0035	No data		−2·1	−2·2	−1·3	−0·4

NOTE: Sheerness is a Standard Port and tidal predictions for each day of the year are given below.

SHELTER
The Medway and Swale give shelter from all directions if the correct anchorage is chosen. Lower reaches are bad in strong NE winds; Stangate Creek is good in all weathers. River is tidal up to Allington Lock (21·6M).

NAVIGATION
Waypoint Medway (safe water) buoy, Iso 2s, 51°28′·80N, 00°52′·92E, 069°/249° from/to Garrison Pt Lt, 5·5M. The wreck of the ammunition ship 'Richard Montgomery' lies 2 M from the harbour mouth, her masts showing above the water. Yachtsmen intending to proceed up the Medway or Swale should obtain a copy of *Medway Ports River Byelaws 1979* from Medway Ports Authority Sheerness Docks, Sheerness, Kent. ME 12 IRX.

Bridge Clearances (MHWS):
Rochester – 5·9m
New Hythe (M20) – 11·3m
Aylesford (Stone) – 2·87m
Aylesford (Bailey) – 3·26m
Maidstone Bypass – 9·45m
Kingsferry (Shut) – 3·35m

Speed Limits: –
6 kn – W of Folly Pt Longitude
8 kn – S of Kingsferry Bridge
8 kn – in Queenborough harbour in area between line Swale Ness – Queenborough Pt and line 270° from Long Pt

For ease of reference the area is split up as follows:-
(1) Lower Medway
(2) Upper Medway

LIGHTS AND MARKS
Garrison Pt Sig Stn, Traffic sigs, Horn (3) 30s.
Isle of Grain Lt Q WRG 20m 13/7M.
Traffic Signals: Powerful Lt, Fl 7s shown from Garrison Pt Signal Station indicates movement of large vessels; shown up river, inward bound; shown to seaward, outward bound.

RADIO TELEPHONE
Call: *Medway Radio* (at Garrison Point, Sheerness) VHF Ch 16 74; 22 74 (H24). Yachts should keep watch on Ch 74 underway and Ch 16 at anchor. Kingsferry Bridge, West Swale, Ch 10 (H24). Gillingham Marina, Hoo Marina, Medway Bridge Marina, Ch **80** M (0900-1700 LT).

TELEPHONE (0795)
Hr Mr Sheerness 580003; MRSC Frinton-on-Sea 675518; # (0474) 537115; Marinecall 0898 500 455; Police Chatham 811281 Sheerness (0795) 661451; Dr Contact Medway Navigation Service Sheerness 663025.

FACILITIES
EC Wednesday; The Medway estuary and the Swale provide a huge area to explore, although much of it dries out to mud. The Medway is well buoyed and perched up to Rochester. *Medway Ports River Byelaws* obtainable from Medway Ports Authority.

LOWER MEDWAY Sheerness is a Standard Port and is the headquarters of Medway Ports Authority. It is a commercial harbour with Ro-Ro ferry berths and no accommodation for yachts. Shelter is good except in the entrance reaches in strong NE winds. In Stangate Creek it is good in all conditions. There are also good anchorages in Sharfleet Creek; from about 4 hrs flood it is possible to go right through into Half Acre Creek. Some minor creeks are buoyed.
Sheppey YC ☎ Sheerness 663052; **W. Hurst** ☎ Sheerness 662356, ACA.

UPPER MEDWAY Admiralty Chart 1835 Folly Point to Maidstone. Harbour Master (Medway Ports Authority) ☎ Sheerness 580003. Speed limit above Folly Point is 6 kn. There are landing facilities (only) at Gillingham Pier, Gillingham Dock steps, Sun Pier (Chatham), Ship Pier, Town Quay steps (Rochester) and Strood Pier. Medway Port Authority have two visitors moorings in Tower Reach just upstream of Rochester Bridge. All other moorings are administered by YCs or marinas. There are slips at Commodore Hard, Gillingham and Upnor Causeway opposite Pier public house. Slips also available at Auto Marine Boatyard, Cuxton, Rochester (HW ∓3).

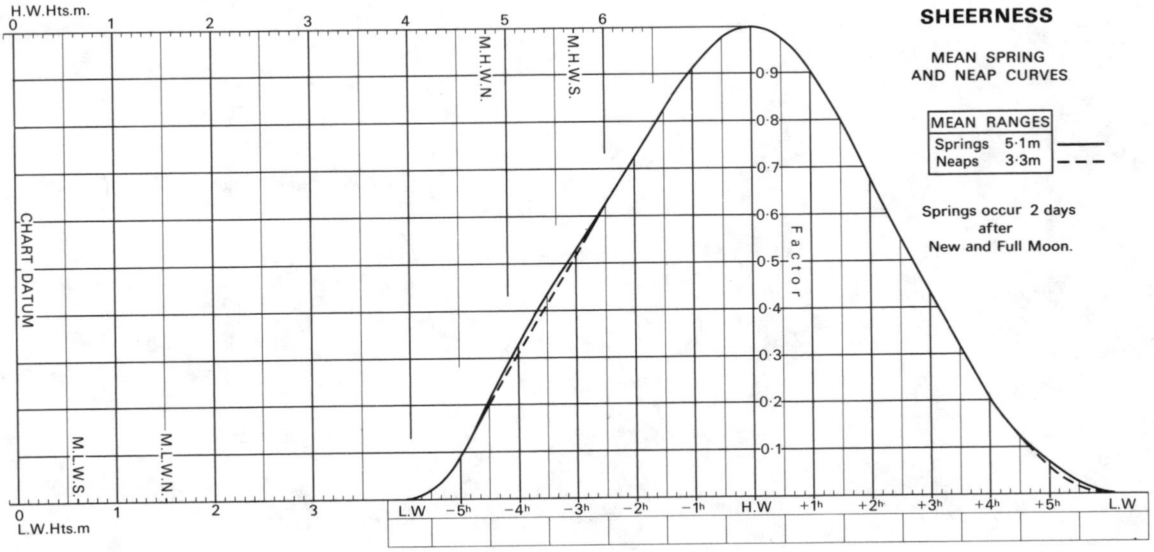
H.W.Hts.m.
0 1 2 3 4 5 6
M.H.W.N.
M.H.W.S.
CHART DATUM
M.L.W.S.
M.L.W.N.
0 1 2 3
L.W.Hts.m
Factor
0·9 0·8 0·7 0·6 0·5 0·4 0·3 0·2 0·1
L.W −5h −4h −3h −2h −1h H.W +1h +2h +3h +4h +5h L.W
SHEERNESS
MEAN SPRING AND NEAP CURVES
MEAN RANGES
Springs 5·1m
Neaps 3·3m
Springs occur 2 days after New and Full Moon.

RIVER MEDWAY *continued*

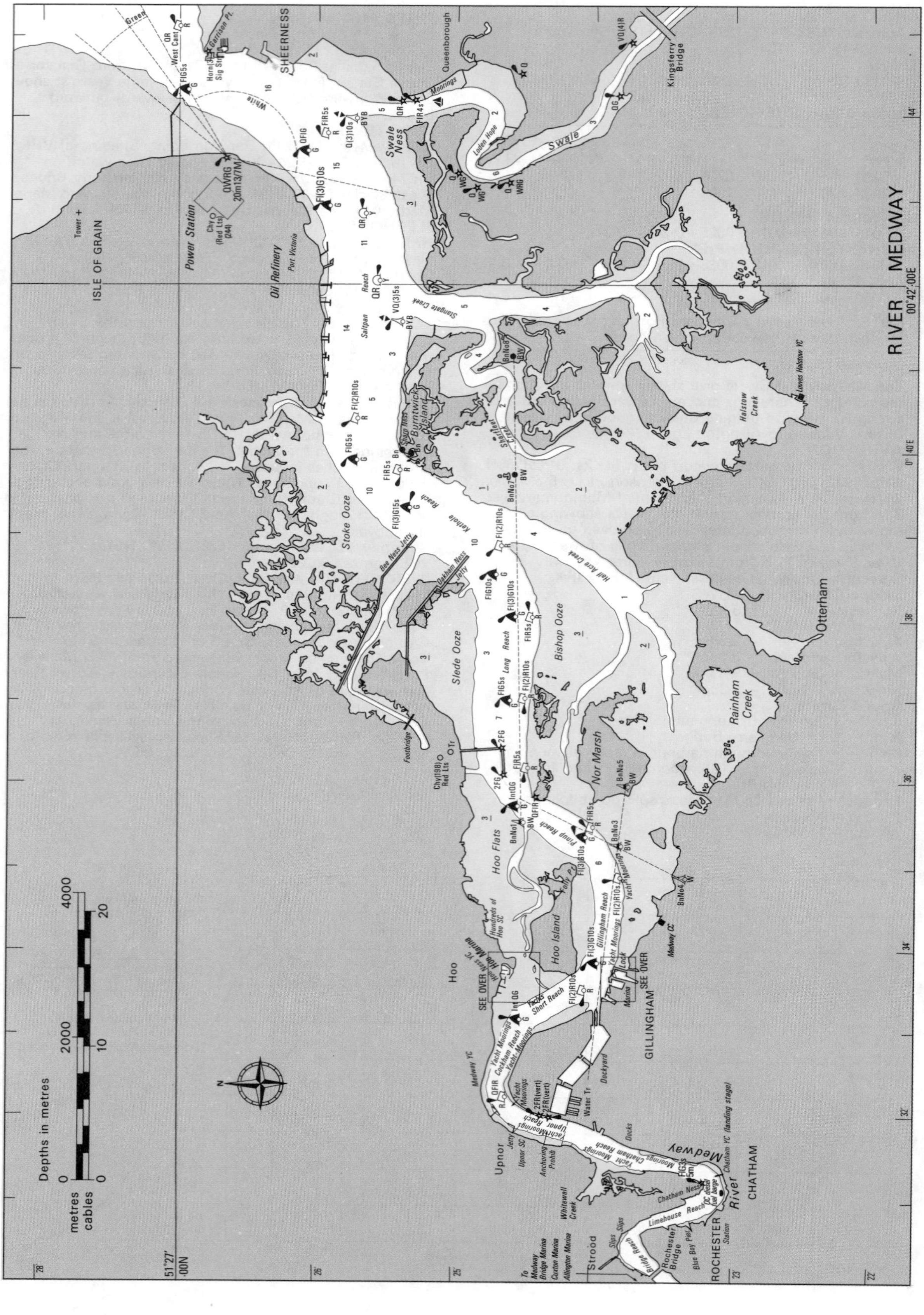

RIVER MEDWAY
00°42'.00E
ISLE OF GRAIN
SHEERNESS
Queenborough
Kingsferry Bridge
Garrison Pt.
Power Station
Oil Refinery
Port Victoria
Swale Ness
Swale
Saltpan Reach
Burntwick Island
Stoke Ooze
Kethole Reach
Bee Ness Jetty
Oakham Ness Jetty
Slede Ooze
Long Reach
Bishop Ooze
Half Acre Creek
Otterham
Rainham Creek
Nor Marsh
Hoo Flats
Pinup Reach
Hoo Island
Gillingham Reach
Hoo
Hoo Marina
SEE OVER
Short Reach
GILLINGHAM
Cockham Reach
Medway YC
Dockyard
Upnor
Upnor Reach
Chatham Reach
Medway
CHATHAM
Chatham Ness
Limehouse Reach
River
Rochester Bridge
ROCHESTER
Strood
Whitewall Creek
Depths in metres
metres
cables
0
2000
4000
0
10
20
51°27'
·00N

3

ENGLAND, EAST COAST – SHEERNESS

Lat 51°27′ N Long 0°45′ E

TIMES AND HEIGHTS OF HIGH AND LOW WATERS

YEAR **1992**

TIME ZONE UT(GMT)
For Summer Time add ONE hour in non-shaded areas

JANUARY

Date	Day	Time	m
1	W	0315 0943 1559 2219	1.5 5.0 1.2 5.1
2	Th	0427 1045 1655 2312	1.3 5.1 1.2 5.2
3	F	0526 1137 1740 2358	1.1 5.2 1.2 5.3
4	Sa ●	0614 1222 1819	1.0 5.3 1.1
5	Su	0038 0655 1300 1853	5.4 0.9 5.4 1.1
6	M	0113 0730 1335 1926	5.4 0.9 5.4 1.0
7	Tu	0144 0802 1408 1957	5.5 0.8 5.5 1.0
8	W	0215 0833 1440 2029	5.5 0.8 5.5 0.9
9	Th	0246 0904 1512 2103	5.5 0.8 5.5 1.0
10	F	0318 0936 1546 2136	5.5 0.8 5.4 1.1
11	Sa	0350 1009 1623 2209	5.4 0.9 5.3 1.2
12	Su	0427 1041 1704 2247	5.3 1.0 5.1 1.3
13	M ☽	0509 1120 1751 2334	5.2 1.1 5.0 1.4
14	Tu	0603 1214 1855	5.0 1.2 4.9
15	W	0042 0713 1330 2008	1.5 4.9 1.3 4.9
16	Th	0206 0832 1456 2119	1.5 5.0 1.3 5.0
17	F	0328 0946 1609 2226	1.3 5.2 1.1 5.2
18	Sa	0438 1054 1712 2326	1.1 5.4 1.0 5.5
19	Su ○	0544 1153 1810	0.8 5.7 0.8
20	M	0019 0646 1245 1900	5.6 0.5 5.9 0.7
21	Tu	0107 0740 1334 1947	5.8 0.3 6.0 0.7
22	W	0152 0827 1419 2030	5.9 0.2 6.1 0.6
23	Th	0236 0911 1504 2110	6.0 0.1 6.0 0.7
24	F	0318 0952 1549 2148	6.0 0.2 5.9 0.8
25	Sa	0402 1030 1634 2226	5.9 0.4 5.6 0.9
26	Su ☾	0447 1108 1722 2306	5.6 0.7 5.3 1.1
27	M	0536 1149 1814 2357	5.3 1.0 5.0 1.4
28	Tu	0636 1245 1919	5.0 1.3 4.7
29	W	0107 0752 1405 2036	1.6 4.7 1.5 4.6
30	Th	0244 0919 1527 2153	1.6 4.7 1.5 4.8
31	F	0412 1031 1633 2254	1.4 4.9 1.4 5.0

FEBRUARY

Date	Day	Time	m
1	Sa	0515 1125 1723 2342	1.2 5.1 1.3 5.2
2	Su	0603 1207 1803	1.0 5.3 1.1
3	M ●	0021 0641 1243 1838	5.3 0.9 5.4 1.0
4	Tu	0055 0713 1316 1909	5.5 0.8 5.5 0.9
5	W	0126 0744 1347 1941	5.6 0.7 5.6 0.8
6	Th	0155 0815 1416 2013	5.6 0.6 5.6 0.7
7	F	0225 0847 1447 2046	5.7 0.6 5.6 0.8
8	Sa	0256 0918 1519 2115	5.7 0.6 5.6 0.9
9	Su	0327 0945 1553 2143	5.6 0.8 5.5 1.0
10	M	0359 1009 1630 2212	5.5 0.9 5.3 1.1
11	Tu ☽	0438 1037 1713 2252	5.4 1.0 5.1 1.2
12	W	0526 1123 1810 2354	5.1 1.2 4.9 1.4
13	Th	0634 1238 1926	4.9 1.4 4.7
14	F	0126 0801 1423 2049	1.5 4.8 1.5 4.8
15	Sa	0303 0927 1546 2206	1.3 5.0 1.3 5.0
16	Su	0423 1041 1655 2311	1.0 5.3 1.1 5.3
17	M	0537 1142 1756	0.7 5.7 0.9
18	Tu ○	0004 0636 1232 1848	5.6 0.4 5.9 0.7
19	W	0050 0727 1319 1933	5.9 0.2 6.0 0.6
20	Th	0134 0811 1401 2013	6.0 0.1 6.1 0.5
21	F	0215 0851 1443 2051	6.1 0.1 6.0 0.5
22	Sa	0256 0928 1524 2127	6.1 0.2 5.8 0.7
23	Su	0336 1000 1604 2200	5.9 0.5 5.6 0.8
24	M	0419 1033 1645 2235	5.7 0.8 5.3 1.1
25	Tu ☾	0504 1106 1730 2318	5.3 1.1 4.9 1.4
26	W	0558 1154 1828	4.9 1.5 4.6
27	Th	0019 0713 1312 1947	1.6 4.5 1.8 4.4
28	F	0209 0850 1453 2121	1.7 4.5 1.8 4.5
29	Sa	0346 1007 1604 2227	1.5 4.8 1.5 4.8

MARCH

Date	Day	Time	m
1	Su	0449 1101 1657 2316	1.2 5.1 1.3 5.1
2	M	0536 1143 1739 2354	1.0 5.3 1.1 5.3
3	Tu	0614 1218 1814	0.8 5.5 0.9
4	W ●	0028 0646 1249 1846	5.5 0.7 5.6 0.8
5	Th	0059 0719 1320 1919	5.6 0.6 5.7 0.7
6	F	0128 0749 1349 1952	5.7 0.5 5.8 0.6
7	Sa	0159 0822 1420 2025	5.8 0.5 5.8 0.6
8	Su	0229 0854 1453 2056	5.8 0.6 5.7 0.8
9	M	0301 0919 1527 2122	5.7 0.7 5.6 0.9
10	Tu	0336 0942 1602 2150	5.6 0.9 5.4 1.0
11	W	0416 1010 1645 2231	5.4 1.0 5.1 1.1
12	Th ☽	0506 1058 1740 2333	5.2 1.3 4.9 1.3
13	F	0615 1214 1856	4.9 1.5 4.7
14	Sa	0106 0744 1359 2025	1.4 4.8 1.6 4.7
15	Su	0249 0914 1527 2148	1.3 5.0 1.4 5.0
16	M	0412 1028 1638 2252	0.9 5.4 1.1 5.3
17	Tu	0523 1126 1737 2344	0.6 5.7 0.9 5.6
18	W ○	0619 1214 1828	0.3 5.9 0.7
19	Th	0029 0706 1257 1912	5.9 0.2 6.0 0.5
20	F	0112 0747 1338 1951	6.0 0.1 6.0 0.4
21	Sa	0151 0825 1418 2029	6.1 0.2 5.9 0.5
22	Su	0232 0858 1456 2105	6.1 0.4 5.8 0.6
23	M	0311 0929 1534 2138	5.9 0.7 5.5 0.8
24	Tu	0352 0959 1612 2209	5.6 1.0 5.2 1.1
25	W	0435 1031 1652 2245	5.2 1.3 4.9 1.3
26	Th ☾	0526 1113 1742 2340	4.8 1.6 4.6 1.6
27	F	0634 1219 1852	4.5 1.9 4.3
28	Sa	0116 0802 1404 2025	1.7 4.4 1.9 4.3
29	Su	0301 0927 1522 2145	1.5 4.6 1.6 4.6
30	M	0404 1024 1617 2237	1.2 5.0 1.3 5.0
31	Tu	0454 1106 1702 2318	1.0 5.3 1.1 5.2

APRIL

Date	Day	Time	m
1	W	0534 1143 1740 2354	0.8 5.5 0.9 5.5
2	Th	0611 1217 1817	0.6 5.6 0.8
3	F ●	0027 0645 1249 1852	5.6 0.6 5.7 0.7
4	Sa	0059 0720 1321 1928	5.7 0.5 5.8 0.6
5	Su	0131 0755 1354 2005	5.8 0.5 5.8 0.6
6	M	0205 0827 1427 2039	5.8 0.6 5.7 0.7
7	Tu	0242 0857 1503 2110	5.8 0.8 5.6 0.8
8	W	0321 0925 1542 2143	5.6 0.9 5.4 0.9
9	Th	0404 1002 1627 2230	5.5 1.1 5.2 1.0
10	F ☽	0459 1054 1725 2334	5.2 1.3 4.9 1.2
11	Sa	0610 1208 1839	5.0 1.5 4.7
12	Su	0103 0733 1341 2004	1.2 4.9 1.6 4.8
13	M	0234 0858 1503 2124	1.1 5.1 1.4 5.0
14	Tu	0353 1007 1613 2227	0.8 5.4 1.1 5.3
15	W	0501 1104 1713 2320	0.6 5.6 0.9 5.6
16	Th	0556 1151 1804	0.4 5.8 0.7
17	F ○	0005 0639 1235 1848	5.8 0.3 5.8 0.6
18	Sa	0049 0719 1314 1930	5.9 0.3 5.9 0.5
19	Su	0130 0755 1354 2009	6.0 0.4 5.8 0.5
20	M	0211 0829 1430 2046	5.9 0.6 5.7 0.7
21	Tu	0250 0901 1507 2118	5.7 0.8 5.4 0.9
22	W	0331 0931 1542 2149	5.4 1.1 5.2 1.1
23	Th	0412 1002 1620 2221	5.1 1.3 5.0 1.3
24	F ☾	0458 1041 1705 2309	4.9 1.6 4.7 1.4
25	Sa	0554 1137 1804	4.6 1.8 4.5
26	Su	0019 0703 1255 1919	1.5 4.5 1.8 4.4
27	M	0155 0822 1423 2037	1.5 4.6 1.7 4.6
28	Tu	0305 0927 1525 2141	1.2 4.9 1.4 4.9
29	W	0400 1017 1616 2230	1.0 5.2 1.2 5.1
30	Th	0447 1101 1659 2312	0.8 5.4 1.0 5.4

Chart Datum: 2.90 metres below Ordnance Datum (Newlyn)

TIME ZONE UT(GMT)

For Summer Time add ONE hour in non-shaded areas

ENGLAND, EAST COAST – SHEERNESS

Lat 51°27′ N Long 0°45′ E

TIMES AND HEIGHTS OF HIGH AND LOW WATERS

YEAR **1992**

MAY

Date	Day	Time	m	Date	Day	Time	m
1	F	0529 1139 1743 2351	0·7 5·6 0·8 5·6	16	Sa ○	0611 1214 1828	0·6 5·7 0·7
2	Sa ●	0610 1217 1824	0·6 5·7 0·7	17	Su	0029 0652 1255 1910	5·7 0·6 5·7 0·6
3	Su	0029 0650 1253 1906	5·7 0·6 5·8 0·6	18	M	0113 0728 1333 1951	5·7 0·7 5·7 0·6
4	M	0107 0728 1331 1947	5·8 0·6 5·8 0·6	19	Tu	0154 0804 1409 2029	5·7 0·8 5·6 0·7
5	Tu	0147 0806 1408 2027	5·8 0·7 5·7 0·6	20	W	0233 0836 1446 2103	5·6 1·0 5·4 0·9
6	W	0227 0842 1449 2107	5·8 0·8 5·6 0·7	21	Th	0312 0907 1519 2134	5·4 1·1 5·2 1·0
7	Th	0312 0919 1531 2150	5·7 1·0 5·4 0·8	22	F	0352 0938 1556 2206	5·2 1·3 5·1 1·1
8	F	0402 1002 1621 2241	5·5 1·1 5·3 0·9	23	Sa	0433 1016 1637 2247	5·0 1·4 5·0 1·2
9	Sa ☽	0459 1055 1718 2343	5·3 1·3 5·1 0·9	24	Su ☾	0518 1102 1725 2339	4·9 1·5 4·8 1·2
10	Su	0604 1201 1825	5·2 1·4 5·0	25	M	0611 1200 1821	4·8 1·6 4·7
11	M	0056 0719 1317 1941	1·0 5·1 1·5 5·0	26	Tu	0043 0714 1309 1928	1·3 4·7 1·6 4·7
12	Tu	0213 0834 1433 2056	0·9 5·2 1·3 5·1	27	W	0155 0820 1420 2036	1·2 4·8 1·5 4·8
13	W	0327 0942 1542 2200	0·8 5·4 1·2 5·3	28	Th	0301 0921 1522 2136	1·1 5·1 1·3 5·1
14	Th	0433 1040 1645 2255	0·7 5·5 1·0 5·5	29	F	0357 1014 1617 2230	0·9 5·3 1·1 5·3
15	F	0526 1129 1740 2344	0·6 5·6 0·8 5·6	30	Sa	0448 1102 1708 2319	0·8 5·5 0·9 5·5
				31	Su	0537 1147 1758	0·8 5·6 0·8

JUNE

Date	Day	Time	m	Date	Day	Time	m
1	M ●	0005 0624 1231 1846	5·6 0·8 5·7 0·7	16	Tu	0102 0706 1319 1938	5·5 0·9 5·5 0·7
2	Tu	0049 0707 1313 1934	5·7 0·7 5·7 0·6	17	W	0141 0741 1354 2016	5·5 0·9 5·5 0·7
3	W	0134 0751 1357 2022	5·8 0·8 5·7 0·5	18	Th	0219 0815 1429 2050	5·5 1·0 5·5 0·8
4	Th	0220 0833 1440 2110	5·9 0·8 5·7 0·5	19	F	0254 0846 1501 2121	5·5 1·0 5·4 0·9
5	F	0308 0917 1527 2157	5·8 0·9 5·6 0·5	20	Sa	0329 0918 1535 2152	5·4 1·1 5·3 0·9
6	Sa	0359 1002 1616 2245	5·7 1·0 5·5 0·6	21	Su	0406 0953 1610 2226	5·3 1·2 5·2 0·9
7	Su ☽	0452 1049 1708 2339	5·6 1·1 5·4 0·6	22	M	0444 1033 1649 2305	5·2 1·2 5·1 1·0
8	M	0551 1144 1807	5·4 1·2 5·3	23	Tu ☾	0527 1116 1734 2353	5·1 1·4 5·0 1·1
9	Tu	0038 0656 1248 1914	0·7 5·3 1·3 5·2	24	W	0618 1210 1829	4·9 1·5 4·9
10	W	0144 0805 1359 2025	0·8 5·2 1·3 5·1	25	Th	0050 0720 1316 1937	1·2 4·9 1·5 4·9
11	Th	0254 0912 1511 2134	0·9 5·2 1·3 5·2	26	F	0201 0826 1429 2047	1·2 5·0 1·4 5·0
12	F	0400 1014 1621 2235	0·9 5·3 1·1 5·3	27	Sa	0310 0929 1536 2152	1·1 5·1 1·3 5·1
13	Sa	0459 1109 1722 2330	0·9 5·4 1·0 5·4	28	Su	0413 1028 1637 2251	1·0 5·3 1·1 5·4
14	Su	0547 1156 1812	0·9 5·5 0·8	29	M	0509 1123 1736 2346	0·9 5·5 0·9 5·6
15	M ○	0018 0628 1239 1857	5·5 0·9 5·5 0·7	30	Tu ●	0603 1214 1834	0·9 5·6 0·7

JULY

Date	Day	Time	m	Date	Day	Time	m
1	W	0036 0653 1300 1927	5·7 0·8 5·7 0·5	16	Th	0127 0721 1337 1959	5·5 1·0 5·5 0·7
2	Th	0126 0741 1347 2018	5·9 0·8 5·8 0·4	17	F	0201 0754 1409 2030	5·6 0·9 5·6 0·7
3	F	0212 0826 1432 2105	6·0 0·7 5·8 0·3	18	Sa	0233 0826 1440 2101	5·6 0·9 5·6 0·7
4	Sa	0300 0910 1517 2152	6·0 0·8 5·8 0·3	19	Su	0304 0858 1511 2132	5·6 0·9 5·6 0·7
5	Su	0348 0953 1602 2235	5·9 0·8 5·8 0·3	20	M	0338 0931 1543 2202	5·5 1·0 5·5 0·8
6	M	0437 1035 1651 2320	5·8 0·9 5·7 0·5	21	Tu	0412 1003 1617 2234	5·4 1·1 5·4 0·9
7	Tu ☽	0529 1122 1743	5·5 1·1 5·5	22	W ☾	0448 1038 1655 2308	5·3 1·2 5·2 1·1
8	W	0008 0627 1215 1843	0·7 5·3 1·3 5·3	23	Th	0532 1119 1742 2354	5·1 1·4 5·1 1·2
9	Th	0106 0730 1323 1955	1·0 5·1 1·4 5·1	24	F	0627 1217 1845	4·9 1·5 4·9
10	F	0218 0840 1443 2111	1·1 5·0 1·4 5·0	25	Sa	0100 0735 1335 2002	1·4 4·8 1·6 4·9
11	Sa	0331 0950 1603 2221	1·2 5·1 1·3 5·1	26	Su	0226 0850 1501 2119	1·4 4·9 1·4 5·0
12	Su	0435 1051 1711 2320	1·2 5·2 1·1 5·3	27	M	0342 1000 1613 2230	1·3 5·1 1·2 5·3
13	M	0527 1143 1804	1·1 5·3 0·9	28	Tu	0447 1102 1719 2330	1·1 5·4 0·9 5·6
14	Tu ○	0008 0611 1225 1848	5·4 1·1 5·4 0·8	29	W ●	0546 1157 1822	0·9 5·6 0·6
15	W	0050 0648 1303 1926	5·5 1·0 5·5 0·7	30	Th	0024 0639 1246 1919	5·8 0·8 5·8 0·4
				31	F	0113 0728 1331 2008	6·0 0·7 5·9 0·2

AUGUST

Date	Day	Time	m	Date	Day	Time	m
1	Sa	0159 0813 1415 2053	6·1 0·6 6·0 0·1	16	Su	0205 0804 1413 2034	5·7 0·8 5·7 0·6
2	Su	0243 0856 1458 2135	6·1 0·6 6·1 0·1	17	M	0236 0836 1443 2105	5·7 0·8 5·7 0·6
3	M	0328 0936 1542 2214	6·0 0·7 6·0 0·3	18	Tu	0307 0907 1514 2135	5·7 0·9 5·6 0·8
4	Tu	0413 1014 1627 2252	5·8 0·9 5·8 0·6	19	W	0339 0935 1546 2200	5·5 1·1 5·5 1·0
5	W ☽	0459 1054 1715 2333	5·5 1·1 5·5 0·9	20	Th	0413 1002 1621 2226	5·4 1·2 5·4 1·1
6	Th	0551 1142 1812	5·2 1·3 5·2	21	F ☾	0452 1037 1705 2304	5·2 1·3 5·2 1·3
7	F	0024 0652 1245 1926	1·2 4·9 1·5 4·9	22	Sa	0543 1130 1805	4·9 1·5 4·9
8	Sa	0137 0806 1418 2050	1·5 4·8 1·6 4·8	23	Su	0007 0652 1252 1927	1·5 4·8 1·6 4·8
9	Su	0303 0927 1550 2207	1·6 4·8 1·4 5·0	24	M	0145 0813 1432 2056	1·6 4·8 1·5 4·9
10	M	0414 1033 1659 2306	1·4 5·1 1·1 5·3	25	Tu	0315 0934 1553 2213	1·4 5·0 1·2 5·3
11	Tu	0509 1125 1749 2353	1·3 5·3 0·9 5·4	26	W	0426 1042 1705 2315	1·2 5·3 0·8 5·6
12	W	0551 1207 1829	1·2 5·4 0·8	27	Th	0527 1139 1810	1·0 5·6 0·5
13	Th ○	0031 0627 1242 1903	5·5 1·0 5·5 0·7	28	F ●	0008 0622 1227 1902	5·9 0·8 5·9 0·3
14	F	0104 0659 1314 1934	5·6 0·9 5·6 0·6	29	Sa	0055 0710 1310 1948	6·1 0·7 6·1 0·1
15	Sa	0135 0731 1344 2005	5·7 0·8 5·7 0·6	30	Su	0138 0754 1352 2030	6·2 0·6 6·2 0·1
				31	M	0222 0834 1434 2110	6·1 0·6 6·2 0·2

Chart Datum: 2.90 metres below Ordnance Datum (Newlyn)

TIME ZONE UT(GMT)

For Summer Time add ONE hour in non-shaded areas

ENGLAND, EAST COAST – SHEERNESS

Lat 51°27′ N Long 0°45′ E

TIMES AND HEIGHTS OF HIGH AND LOW WATERS

YEAR **1992**

SEPTEMBER

Day	Time	m	Day	Time	m
1 Tu	0304 0914 1517 2146	6·0 0·7 6·0 0·5	16 W	0236 0842 1446 2104	5·8 0·9 5·7 0·9
2 W	0345 0950 1600 2220	5·7 0·9 5·8 0·8	17 Th	0308 0908 1518 2127	5·6 1·1 5·6 1·0
3 Th ☽	0428 1027 1647 2255	5·4 1·1 5·5 1·2	18 F	0342 0935 1556 2150	5·4 1·2 5·4 1·2
4 F	0515 1109 1743 2340	5·1 1·4 5·1 1·5	19 Sa ☾	0421 1009 1642 2231	5·2 1·3 5·2 1·4
5 Sa	0611 1208 1853	4·8 1·6 4·7	20 Su	0511 1104 1743 2337	5·0 1·5 5·0 1·6
6 Su	0049 0724 1349 2023	1·8 4·6 1·7 4·7	21 M	0618 1228 1904	4·8 1·6 4·8
7 M	0229 0854 1527 2145	1·8 4·6 1·5 4·9	22 Tu	0117 0744 1412 2036	1·7 4·7 1·4 5·0
8 Tu	0345 1006 1633 2242	1·6 4·9 1·2 5·2	23 W	0250 0910 1535 2155	1·5 5·0 1·1 5·3
9 W	0440 1058 1720 2326	1·4 5·2 0·9 5·5	24 Th	0402 1019 1648 2255	1·3 5·4 0·7 5·7
10 Th	0522 1139 1758	1·2 5·4 0·8	25 F	0505 1115 1749 2347	1·0 5·7 0·5 5·9
11 F	0004 0558 1214 1831	5·6 1·0 5·6 0·7	26 Sa ●	0600 1203 1839	0·8 5·9 0·3
12 Sa ○	0036 0631 1245 1902	5·7 0·9 5·7 0·6	27 Su	0034 0648 1246 1924	6·1 0·7 6·1 0·2
13 Su	0106 0703 1314 1933	5·8 0·8 5·8 0·6	28 M	0116 0731 1328 2004	6·1 0·6 6·2 0·3
14 M	0135 0737 1344 2004	5·8 0·7 5·8 0·6	29 Tu	0157 0812 1411 2042	6·1 0·6 6·2 0·4
15 Tu	0205 0809 1415 2036	5·8 0·8 5·8 0·7	30 W	0237 0850 1453 2115	5·9 0·7 6·0 0·7

OCTOBER

Day	Time	m	Day	Time	m
1 Th	0317 0927 1536 2148	5·7 0·9 5·7 1·0	16 F	0242 0849 1458 2101	5·6 1·0 5·6 1·1
2 F	0357 1002 1621 2220	5·4 1·2 5·4 1·4	17 Sa	0318 0919 1541 2134	5·5 1·1 5·5 1·3
3 Sa ☽	0440 1040 1713 2301	5·1 1·4 5·0 1·7	18 Su	0400 1000 1630 2219	5·3 1·2 5·3 1·4
4 Su	0530 1132 1818	4·8 1·6 4·7	19 M ☾	0452 1058 1733 2326	5·0 1·3 5·0 1·6
5 M	0000 0636 1300 1940	1·9 4·5 1·8 4·6	20 Tu	0558 1221 1850	4·9 1·4 4·9
6 Tu	0134 0801 1443 2104	2·0 4·5 1·6 4·8	21 W	0055 0720 1354 2016	1·7 4·8 1·3 5·1
7 W	0258 0921 1546 2204	1·8 4·8 1·3 5·1	22 Th	0222 0842 1514 2131	1·6 5·0 1·0 5·4
8 Th	0357 1017 1635 2249	1·5 5·1 1·0 5·4	23 F	0334 0952 1624 2231	1·3 5·4 0·7 5·7
9 F	0442 1101 1716 2327	1·2 5·4 0·8 5·5	24 Sa	0438 1048 1723 2323	1·1 5·6 0·5 5·8
10 Sa	0522 1137 1753	1·0 5·5 0·7	25 Su ●	0534 1137 1814	0·9 5·9 0·4
11 Su ○	0001 0558 1211 1825	5·7 0·9 5·7 0·7	26 M	0010 0624 1224 1856	5·9 0·7 6·0 0·4
12 M	0032 0634 1242 1859	5·8 0·8 5·8 0·6	27 Tu	0052 0709 1307 1935	6·0 0·6 6·1 0·5
13 Tu	0104 0709 1314 1933	5·8 0·8 5·8 0·7	28 W	0133 0751 1349 2012	5·9 0·6 6·0 0·7
14 W	0135 0744 1347 2005	5·9 0·8 5·8 0·8	29 Th	0212 0830 1433 2046	5·8 0·7 5·8 0·9
15 Th	0208 0818 1422 2034	5·8 0·9 5·8 0·9	30 F	0251 0907 1515 2117	5·6 0·9 5·6 1·2
			31 Sa	0329 0941 1559 2149	5·3 1·2 5·3 1·4

NOVEMBER

Day	Time	m	Day	Time	m
1 Su	0409 1014 1645 2226	5·1 1·3 5·0 1·6	16 M	0350 1007 1626 2217	5·4 1·0 5·4 1·3
2 M ☽	0454 1058 1739 2316	4·9 1·5 4·8 1·8	17 Tu ☾	0442 1104 1726 2318	5·2 1·1 5·2 1·5
3 Tu	0549 1201 1843	4·7 1·6 4·6	18 W	0544 1212 1835	5·1 1·1 5·1
4 W	0025 0656 1331 1958	1·9 4·6 1·6 4·7	19 Th	0031 0656 1330 1951	1·6 5·0 1·1 5·1
5 Th	0154 0812 1447 2107	1·8 4·7 1·4 4·9	20 F	0149 0812 1446 2103	1·5 5·1 1·0 5·3
6 F	0303 0919 1542 2200	1·6 4·9 1·1 5·1	21 Sa	0303 0922 1555 2206	1·3 5·3 0·8 5·5
7 Sa	0356 1012 1628 2244	1·3 5·2 0·9 5·4	22 Su	0410 1024 1657 2301	1·2 5·5 0·7 5·6
8 Su	0441 1055 1709 2322	1·1 5·4 0·8 5·6	23 M	0511 1118 1747 2349	1·0 5·7 0·7 5·7
9 M	0522 1134 1749	1·0 5·6 0·8	24 Tu ●	0604 1207 1831	0·8 5·8 0·7
10 Tu ○	0000 0603 1212 1827	5·7 0·9 5·7 0·8	25 W	0034 0650 1252 1910	5·7 0·7 5·8 0·7
11 W	0035 0642 1249 1903	5·8 0·8 5·8 0·8	26 Th	0114 0734 1335 1947	5·7 0·7 5·8 0·8
12 Th	0110 0721 1327 1940	5·8 0·8 5·8 0·8	27 F	0154 0815 1418 2020	5·7 0·7 5·7 1·0
13 F	0147 0801 1405 2013	5·7 0·8 5·8 0·9	28 Sa	0232 0851 1458 2053	5·5 0·9 5·5 1·1
14 Sa	0225 0840 1447 2049	5·6 0·9 5·7 1·1	29 Su	0308 0924 1538 2122	5·4 1·0 5·3 1·3
15 Su	0305 0921 1534 2128	5·5 0·9 5·6 1·2	30 M	0343 0955 1617 2157	5·2 1·2 5·2 1·4

DECEMBER

Day	Time	m	Day	Time	m
1 Tu	0423 1028 1701 2238	5·1 1·2 5·0 1·5	16 W ☾	0433 1102 1713 2305	5·5 0·8 5·5 1·2
2 W ☽	0506 1115 1750 2332	4·9 1·3 4·8 1·6	17 Th	0527 1156 1814	5·3 0·9 5·3
3 Th	0558 1214 1848	4·8 1·4 4·7	18 F	0004 0631 1259 1921	1·4 5·2 1·0 5·1
4 F	0035 0702 1326 1954	1·7 4·7 1·4 4·7	19 Sa	0113 0742 1411 2033	1·4 5·1 1·0 5·1
5 Sa	0151 0811 1437 2057	1·7 4·8 1·3 4·9	20 Su	0230 0856 1525 2141	1·4 5·2 1·0 5·2
6 Su	0300 0915 1536 2153	1·5 4·9 1·1 5·1	21 M	0346 1004 1631 2241	1·3 5·3 1·0 5·4
7 M	0356 1010 1628 2242	1·3 5·2 1·0 5·4	22 Tu	0455 1105 1726 2333	1·1 5·4 0·9 5·5
8 Tu	0447 1101 1715 2329	1·1 5·4 1·0 5·5	23 W	0553 1157 1811	0·9 5·5 0·9
9 W ○	0534 1146 1758	1·0 5·5 0·9	24 Th ●	0019 0641 1243 1850	5·5 0·8 5·6 0·9
10 Th	0011 0621 1229 1841	5·6 0·9 5·7 0·9	25 F	0102 0723 1324 1926	5·6 0·7 5·7 0·9
11 F	0052 0707 1313 1921	5·7 0·8 5·8 0·9	26 Sa	0140 0802 1404 1959	5·6 0·7 5·6 0·9
12 Sa	0133 0752 1357 2002	5·7 0·7 5·8 0·9	27 Su	0215 0836 1440 2032	5·6 0·7 5·6 1·0
13 Su	0215 0840 1442 2044	5·7 0·6 5·8 0·9	28 M	0249 0907 1515 2101	5·5 0·8 5·5 1·0
14 M	0258 0927 1528 2128	5·6 0·6 5·7 1·0	29 Tu	0321 0935 1549 2134	5·4 0·9 5·4 1·1
15 Tu	0343 1013 1619 2214	5·6 0·7 5·6 1·1	30 W	0355 1004 1626 2207	5·3 0·9 5·2 1·2
			31 Th	0430 1040 1705 2248	5·2 1·0 5·1 1·3

Chart Datum: 2·90 metres below Ordnance Datum (Newlyn)

MEDWAY RIVER *continued*

MARINAS (from seaward)
Mariners Farm Boatpark ☎ 33179; **Gillingham Marina** (250 + 12 visitors) ☎ 280022, Slip, P, D, FW, ME, El, Ⓔ, Sh, CH, V, AC, Bar, BH (20 ton), C (1 ton), Gas, Gaz; Access W basin HW∓2, E basin (via lock), HW∓4½; **Medway Pier Marina** ☎ 51113, D, FW, BY, Ⓔ, C (6 ton), Slip; **Hoo Marina** (245) ☎ 250311, FW, Sh, C (20 ton), ME, SM, AC, CH, El, Ⓔ, Gas, Gaz; Access W basin HW∓1½, E basin (via lock) HW∓2; **Medway Bridge Marina** (160 + 15 visitors) ☎ 43576, Slip, D, P, FW, ME, El, Ⓔ, Sh, C (3 ton), BH (10 ton), Gas, Gaz, R, SM, AC, CH, V, Bar; **Cuxton Marina** (150 + some visitors) ☎ 721941, Slip, FW, ME, El, Ⓔ, Sh, BH (12 ton), AC, CH; **Elmhaven Marina** (60) ☎ 240489, Slip, FW, ME, El, Sh, C, AC; **Allington Lock Marina** (120) ☎ Maidstone 52864, CH, ME, El, Sh, P, D, Slip, C (10 ton), FW, Gas, Gaz; (non-tidal). Note: Old HM Dockyard basins are being converted to Chatham Maritime Marina, ☎ 815081.
Yacht Clubs
Chatham YC ☎ 723051; **Hoo Ness YC** ☎ 250052, Bar, R, M, L, FW; **Medway Cruising Club** ☎ 54752, Bar, M, L, FW; **Medway Motor Cruising Club** ☎ 827194; **Medway Motor YC** ☎ 389856; **Medway YC** ☎ 718399; **Rochester CC** ☎ 841350, Bar, R, M, FW, L, ⊡; **Strood YC** ☎ 718261, Bar, M, C (1·5 ton), FW, L, Slip.
Other Facilities
Gransden Marine ☎ 826770, CH, ACA; **Letley Moorings** (Sufference Wharf), ☎ 814429, ME, El, Sh, dry dock, AB; **A + B Textiles** ☎ 579686, SM; **Invicta Services** ☎ 574191, Sh; **Cabin Yacht Stores** ☎ 718020, CH; **Dave Elliot** ☎ 408160, SM; **Baker Marine** ☎ 843227 CH **OC Diesel Refuelling Barge** (Ship pier, Rochester) ☎ 813773, D, CH;
Towns – all facilities R, V, ⊡, ✉; ⇌; ✈ (Lydd or Gatwick).

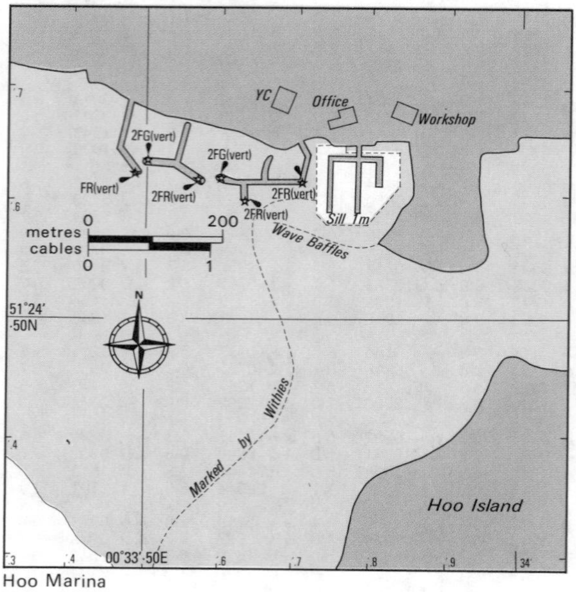
YC
Office
Workshop
2FG(vert)
2FG(vert)
FR(vert)
2FR(vert)
2FR(vert)
2FR(vert)
Sill Tm
Wave Baffles
metres
cables
0
200
0
1
N
51°24'
·50N
Marked by Withies
Hoo Island
00°33'·50E
Hoo Marina

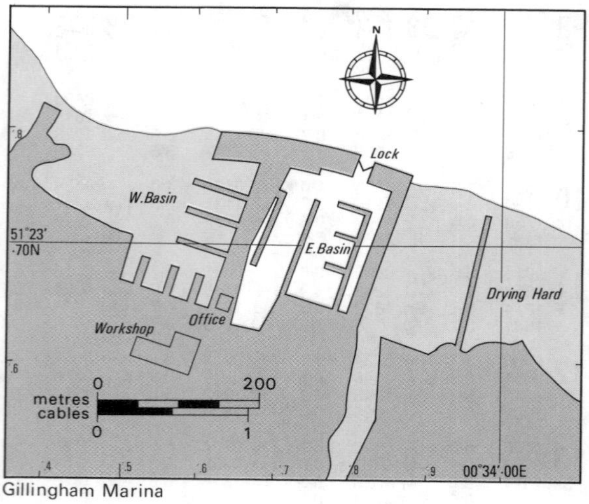
N
Lock
W.Basin
E.Basin
51°23'
·70N
Drying Hard
Office
Workshop
metres
cables
0
200
0
1
00°34'·00E
Gillingham Marina

RIVER THAMES 10-3-21

London

CHARTS

Admiralty 3319, 2484, 3337, 2151, 1186, 1185; Stanford 5; Imray C2, C1; OS 176, 177, 178. More details obtainable from *'Nicholsons Guide to the Thames'*, from PLA publications and *'London Waterways Guide'* (Imray).

TIDES

+0252 Dover; ML 3·7; Duration 0555; Zone 0 (GMT).

Standard Port LONDON BRIDGE (→)

Times				Height (metres)			
HW		LW		MHWS	MHWN	MLWN	MLWS
0300	0900	0400	1100	7·1	5·8	1·6	0·5
1500	2100	1600	2300				
Differences WOOLWICH (GALLIONS POINT)							
−0020	−0020	−0025	−0040	−0·1	−0·1	+0·1	0·0
CHELSEA BRIDGE							
+0020	+0015	+0055	+0100	−0·8	−0·7	−0·6	−0·3
RICHMOND LOCK							
+0100	+0055	+0325	+0305	−2·1	−2·2	−1·4	−0·3

NOTE: London Bridge is a Standard Port and tidal predictions for each day of the year are given below. The river is tidal up to Teddington Lock with half-tide lock at Richmond. When the Thames Barrier is closed, water levels will vary considerably from predictions.

TIDES — TIME DIFFERENCES ON LONDON BRIDGE

Place	MHWS	MHWN	MLWN	MLWS
Teddington Lock	+0106	+0056	—	—
Richmond Lock	+0100	+0055	+0325	+0305
Chiswick Bridge	+0049	+0044	+0235	+0224
Hammersmith Bridge	+0038	+0037	+0200	+0156
Putney Bridge	+0032	+0030	+0138	+0137
Battersea Bridge	+0023	+0020	+0109	+0110
Chelsea Bridge	+0020	+0015	+0055	+0100
Westminster Bridge	+0012	+0011	+0031	+0035
London Bridge	0000	0000	0000	0000
Surrey Comm Dock Greenland Entrance	−0010	−0008	−0013	−0015
Millwall Dock Entrance	−0010	−0008	−0014	−0016
Deptford Creek	−0012	−0011	−0018	−0021
Greenwich Pier	−0014	−0012	−0020	−0023
India and Millwall Dock Entrance	−0018	−0015	−0026	−0029
Royal Victoria Dock Entrance	−0021	−0018	−0031	−0025
Woolwich Ferry	−0028	−0024	−0042	−0047
Royal Albert Dock Entrance	−0029	−0024	−0043	−0050
Southern Outfall (below Crossness)	−0030	−0025	−0048	−0056
Coldharbour Point	−0037	−0030	−0053	−0103
Stoneness Lighthouse	−0048	−0037	−0059	−0114
Broadness Lighthouse	−0052	−0040	−0101	−0119
Tilburyness	−0056	−0042	−0103	−0123
Gravesend Town Pier	−0059	−0044	−0106	−0125

SHELTER

Very good shelter in many places above the Thames Barrier. In Bow Creek (Bugsby's Reach), in Deptford Creek (HW∓2), South Dock Marina, St Katharine's Yacht Haven (see 10.3.24), Lambeth Pier (PLA), Chelsea Harbour Marina, Chelsea Yacht & Boat Co (Cheyne Walk), Cadogan Pier (PLA), Hurlingham YC, Chas Newens (BY, Putney), Alan See (Hammersmith), Hammersmith Pier, Chiswick Quay Marina, Auto Marine Services (Chiswick), Grand Union Canal ent (Brentford), Howlett's BY (Twickenham) and Tough's BY (Teddington) as well as numerous Draw Docks belonging to the PLA.

PIERS WHERE LANDING CAN BE MADE BY ARRANGEMENT

Hampton Court Pier Richmond Landing Stage Kew Pier	(071) 930 2641
Hammersmith Pier	(081) 748 2715
Putney Pier	(071) 930 2641
Chelsea Harbour Pier	(071) 351 4433
Cadogan Pier	(071) 352 4604
Lambeth Pier Westminster Pier Charing Cross Pier London Bridge City Pier	(071) 930 2641
Swan Lane Pier	(071) 987 1185/ (071) 730 4812
Tower Pier	(071) 930 2641
Cherry Garden Pier	(071) 237 3498/5134
West India Dock Pier	(071) 987 1185/ (071) 730 4812
Greenwich Pier	(071) 930 2641
London City Airport Pier	(071) 474 5555
Barrier Gardens Pier	(081) 854 5555

NAVIGATION

River users are advised to read the Port of London River Bye Laws and *Pleasure Users Guide to the Thames*, obtainable from Thames House, St Andrews Road, Tilbury, Essex, RM18 7JH (☎ Tilbury 3444 Ext 584). When proceeding up or down river, unless impracticable, keep to the starboard side of mid-channel. Boats approaching a bridge against the tide give way to those approaching with the tide. However, vessels over 40m always have priority. Below Wandsworth there is no speed limit. Above, limit is 8 kn.

A triangle of three red discs, or lights, hanging below an arch apex down indicates that that arch is closed. The Thames Tidal Barrier is in the centre of Woolwich Reach and consists of 9 piers between which rotating gates can form a barrier. The spans between piers are designated 'A' to 'K' from South to North. Spans A and from H to K inclusive are not navigable. The main navigational spans are C, D, E and F. Green lights forming arrows, point towards the span in use and clear for traffic. Red lights forming a St Andrews Cross each side of a span indicate that it is closed. Lights may be exhibited from: Thamesmead, False Point, Blackwall Point and Brunswick Wharf. These will indicate: Y flashing — Proceed with extreme caution, barrier about to close; R flashing — all vessels stop, barrier being closed. The Thames Barrier Navigation Centre, call sign *Woolwich Radio*, is the communications centre for that part of the river to the W of Crayfordness. The Traffic Controller regulates all traffic through the barrier, controlling it from Margaret Ness to Blackwall Point. Radio VHF Chs 14 and 22. General shipping information is not available from this centre but from the Thames Navigation Service (Woolwich Radio or Gravesend Radio or ☎ Gravesend 67684). All vessels with VHF (vessels without VHF see below) intending to go through the barrier must inform Woolwich Radio on Ch 14 of their ETA when passing Crayfordness inward bound or Tower Bridge outward bound. Then, when passing Margaret Ness Point inward or Blackwall Point outward obtain permission from the Controller to proceed. Yachts without VHF should proceed with caution, normally using span G (N side) if bound up river or span B (S side) if bound down river, and keeping clear of larger vessels. Note however that depths in spans B and G may only be about 1·5m at LW springs. If possible ring Barrier Control 855 0315, before arrival. The barrier is completely closed monthly for test. Individual spans are closed weekly. When barrier is closed, water levels will differ considerably from predictions.

The Half tide weir at Richmond is operated to maintain a min depth of 1·7m between Teddington and Richmond bridges. When the weir gates are down, lock is available. Other times (approx. HW∓2) sail straight through.

HEADWAY OF CENTRE SPAN OF BRIDGES AND HEIGHT OF MHWS.

Name of Bridge	Distance above London Bridge Sea Miles	Headway of Centre Span above Chart Datum (m)	MHWS (m)
Richmond	13·97	7·9	2·6
Richmond Railway	13·67	7·9	2·6
Twickenham	13·64	8·5	2·6
Richmond Footbridge	13·49	9·7	4·8
Kew	11·33	10·6	5·3
Kew Railway	10·98	10·9	5·3
Chiswick	10·22	12·2	5·3
Barnes Railway	9·55	10·9	5·5

RIVER THAMES *continued*

Hammersmith	7·97	9·4	5·7
Putney	6·45	11·4	5·9
Fulham Railway	6·31	12·8	6·1
Wandsworth	5·46	11·9	6·1
Battersea Railway	4·83	12·2	6·1
Battersea	4·27	11·7	6·2
Albert	4·04	11·1	6·2
Chelsea	3·40	12·9	6·3
Victoria Railway	3·31	12·3	6·3
Vauxhall	2·46	12·1	6·5
Lambeth	2·02	13·1	6·6
Westminster	1·64	12·2	6·8
Charing Cross Rly	1·32	13·8	6·8
Waterloo	1·12	15·3	6·8
Blackfriars	0·63	14·0	6·9
Blackfriars Rly	0·62	13·9	6·9
Southwark	0·24	14·3	6·9
Cannon St. Rly	0·16	14·0	6·9
London Bridge	0	16·0	7·1
Tower	below 0·49	15·7	7·1

Note: The tidal Thames is divided by the PLA into two sections
Upper Section – Teddington to Cross Ness
Lower Section – Cross Ness to the Sea

LIGHTS AND MARKS
Margaret Ness or Tripcock Pt Fl(2) W 5s 11m 8M. Tower Bridge sounds horn 20s or gong 30s when bascules open for shipping. When Richmond half-tide barrier is shut, a triangle of red discs (red lights at night) is hung below the centre span of the footbridge.

RADIO TELEPHONE
Call *Woolwich Radio* VHF Ch **14** 16 22 (H24) (for Thames Barrier control)
St Katharines Yacht Haven VHF Ch **80** M (HW−2 to HW+1½; 0600-2030 LT in summer, 0800-1800 LT in winter). Chelsea Harbour Marina VHF Ch 14 16 **80** (HW−2 to HW+1½).
Brentford Dock Marina VHF Ch 14 16
Gravesend Radio VHF Ch **12** 14 16 18 20 (H24)
Information broadcasts every H and H+30 on Ch 12 by Gravesend, and every H+15 and H+45 on Ch 14 by Woolwich. These are repeated by North Foreland Radio Ch 26, Thames Radio Ch 02, Hastings Radio Ch 07 and Orfordness Radio Ch 62 at the end of first silence period after receipt. PLA Patrol Launches (call: *Thames Patrol*) VHF Ch 12 14 16 06. Police Ch 14.

TELEPHONE
Port of London Authority, Chief Hr Mr (0375) 852325; Hr Mr (Upper Section) (071) 481 0720; Hr Mr (Lower Section) (0474) 567684; Duty Officer (Woolwich) (081) 855 0315; Duty Officer (Gravesend) (0474) 560311; MRSC (0255) 675518; Richmond Lock & Hr Office (081) 940 0634; General Enquiries (071) 481 8484; London Port Health Authority (071) 606 3030 Ext 1603; River Police (071) 488 5291; Thames Navigation Service (0474) 560311; London Weather Centre (071) 836 4311; Tower Bridge Master (071) 407 0922; # (071) 865 5861 Ext 570 (or night (071) 626 3524); Marinecall 0898 500 455; Ⓗ (071) 987 7011.

FACILITIES (Letters in brackets refer to chartlets)
TEDDINGTON (081)
Tough Shipyards (A) ☎ 977 4494, BY, CH, AC, ME, M, Gas, C (6 ton), Sh, El, FW; **Swan Island Harbour (B)** ☎ 892 2861, D, M, ME, El, Sh, FW, Gas, Slip; **Eel Pie Marine** ☎ 892 3626 M, ME, El, Sh, CH, FW, Gas.
RICHMOND (081)
J T Howlett (C) ☎ 892 3183, BY, CH, D, Gas, M, FW; **Richmond Slipways** ☎ 892 5062, BY, Gas, ME, El, Sh, M, FW. **Petersham Boat Services** ☎ 940 0173 M, FW.
BRENTFORD (081)
Brentford Dock Marina (D) (80+10 visitors) ☎ 568 0287 (VHF Ch 14, 16), AC, Bar, CH, El, FW, ME, R, V, Sh; Access HW∓2½; **Thames Locks (No 101)** ☎ 560 8942, M, AB, Entrance to Grand Union Canal; **T Norris** ☎ 560 3453, CH, ME.
KEW (081)
Bason and Arnold (F) ☎ 994 2431, CH, D, P, Gas; **Cranfield** ☎ 788 9255, SM. **Red Eye Marine** ☎ 940 8364 M. **Dove Marina** ☎ 748 9474 M, FW.
CHISWICK (081)
Chiswick Quay Marina (50) ☎ 994 8743 M, FW; (Access HW∓2); **Alan See** ☎ 748 7738, BY, M, ME, El, Sh.
WANDSWORTH (081)
Hurlingham YC ☎ 788 5547, M; **Chas Newens Marina** ☎ 788 4587 CH, ME, FW, M, El, Sh.
CHELSEA (071)
Chelsea Harbour (G) see 10.3.24; **Chelsea Yacht & Boat Co (H)** ☎ 352 1427, M, Gas; **Cadogan Pier (I)** ☎ 352 4604, M, L.
KINGS REACH (071)
Threestokes Marine ☎ 247 4595, CH, Gas.
POOL OF LONDON (071)
St Katharines Yacht Haven (J) ☎ 488 2400 (see 10.3.24); **Crawleys (K)** ☎ 481 1774, (Fuel barge), P, D, Gas; **Kelvin Hughes** ☎ 709 9076, CH, ACA; **Pumpkin Marine (J)** ☎ 480 6630, CH, P, D; **Beckwith Marine Services** (Barge Freddy) ☎ 930 0068 Gas, CH, D, L, FW.
LIMEHOUSE REACH (071)
South Dock Marina (372) ☎ 252 2244, AC, ME, Sh, El, M, FW, CH, V, C (20 ton), Bar, R; **Limehouse Lock** ☎ 895 9930, Access HW∓3½; AB, M. Entry to Regents Canal.
GREENWICH (081)
East Greenwich Garage ☎ 858 4881, ME, P, D; **Charlton Marine** ☎ 858 1446, CH, Gas; **W H Donovan** ☎ 858 1143, BY; **Caldergate (L)** P, D; **Greenwich YC** ☎ 858 7339.

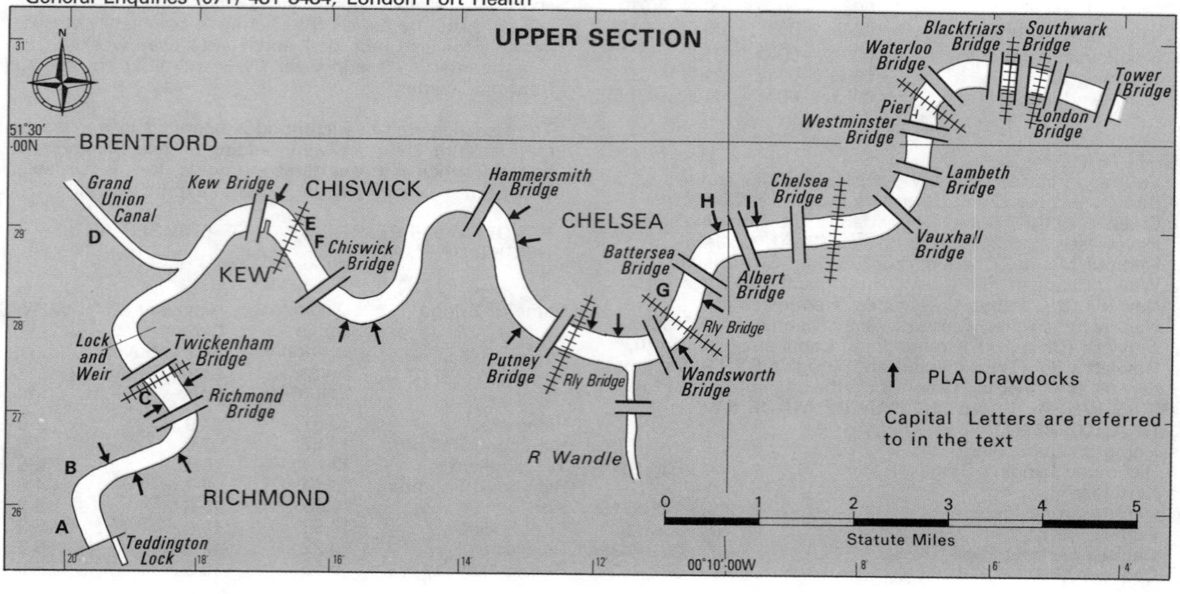
UPPER SECTION
N
51°30'·00N
BRENTFORD
CHISWICK
CHELSEA
KEW
RICHMOND
Grand Union Canal
Kew Bridge
Chiswick Bridge
Hammersmith Bridge
Putney Bridge
Rly Bridge
Battersea Bridge
Albert Bridge
Rly Bridge
Wandsworth Bridge
Chelsea Bridge
Vauxhall Bridge
Lambeth Bridge
Westminster Bridge
Pier
Waterloo Bridge
Blackfriars Bridge
Southwark Bridge
London Bridge
Tower Bridge
Lock and Weir
Twickenham Bridge
Richmond Bridge
Teddington Lock
R Wandle
A
B
C
D
E
F
G
H
I
PLA Drawdocks
Capital Letters are referred to in the text
0 1 2 3 4 5
Statute Miles
00°10'·00W

RIVER THAMES *continued*

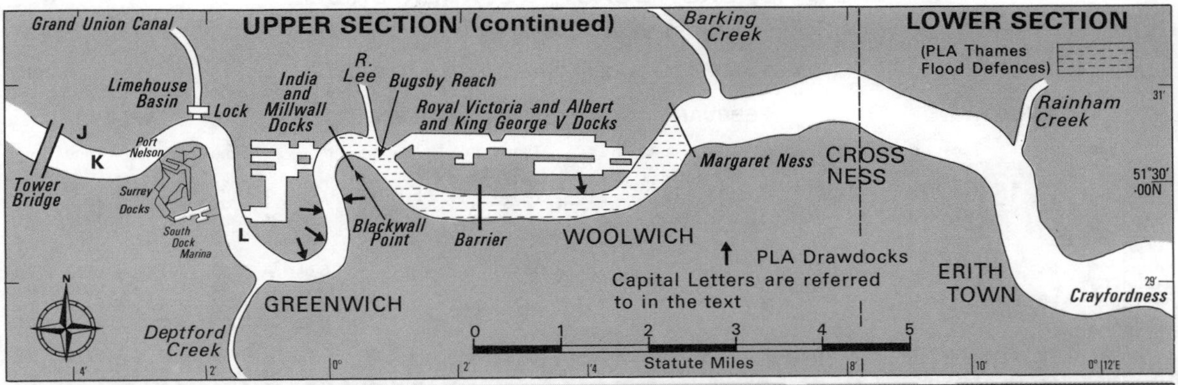
UPPER SECTION (continued)
LOWER SECTION
(PLA Thames Flood Defences)
Grand Union Canal
Limehouse Basin
Lock
India and Millwall Docks
R. Lee
Bugsby Reach
Royal Victoria and Albert and King George V Docks
Barking Creek
Rainham Creek
Tower Bridge
J
K
L
Port Nelson
Surrey Docks
South Dock Marina
Blackwall Point
Barrier
WOOLWICH
Margaret Ness
CROSS NESS
ERITH TOWN
Crayfordness
GREENWICH
Deptford Creek
PLA Drawdocks
Capital Letters are referred to in the text
Statute Miles
51°30′·00N

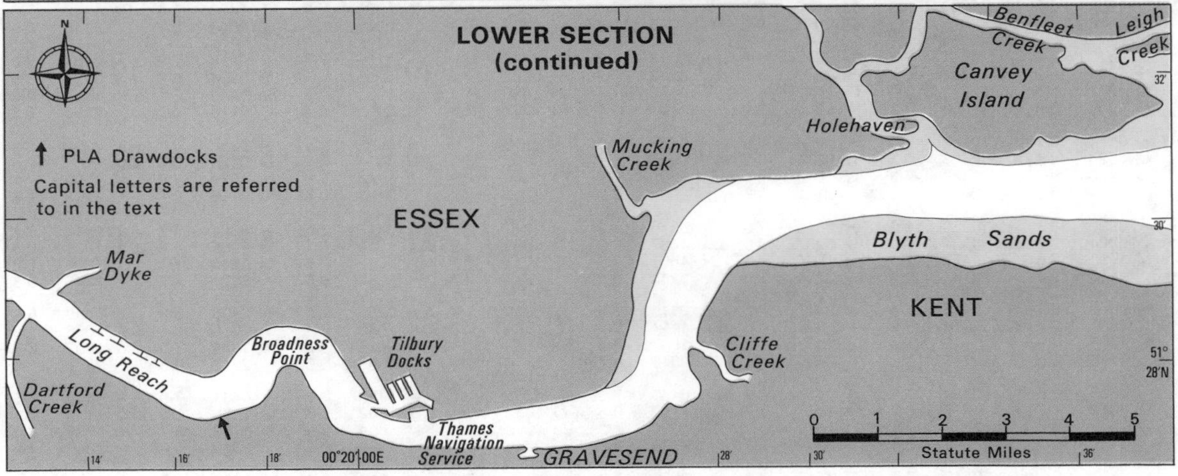
LOWER SECTION (continued)
PLA Drawdocks
Capital letters are referred to in the text
ESSEX
Benfleet Creek
Leigh Creek
Canvey Island
Holehaven
Mucking Creek
Blyth Sands
KENT
Mar Dyke
Long Reach
Broadness Point
Tilbury Docks
Cliffe Creek
Dartford Creek
Thames Navigation Service
GRAVESEND
Statute Miles
51° 28′N
00°20′·00E

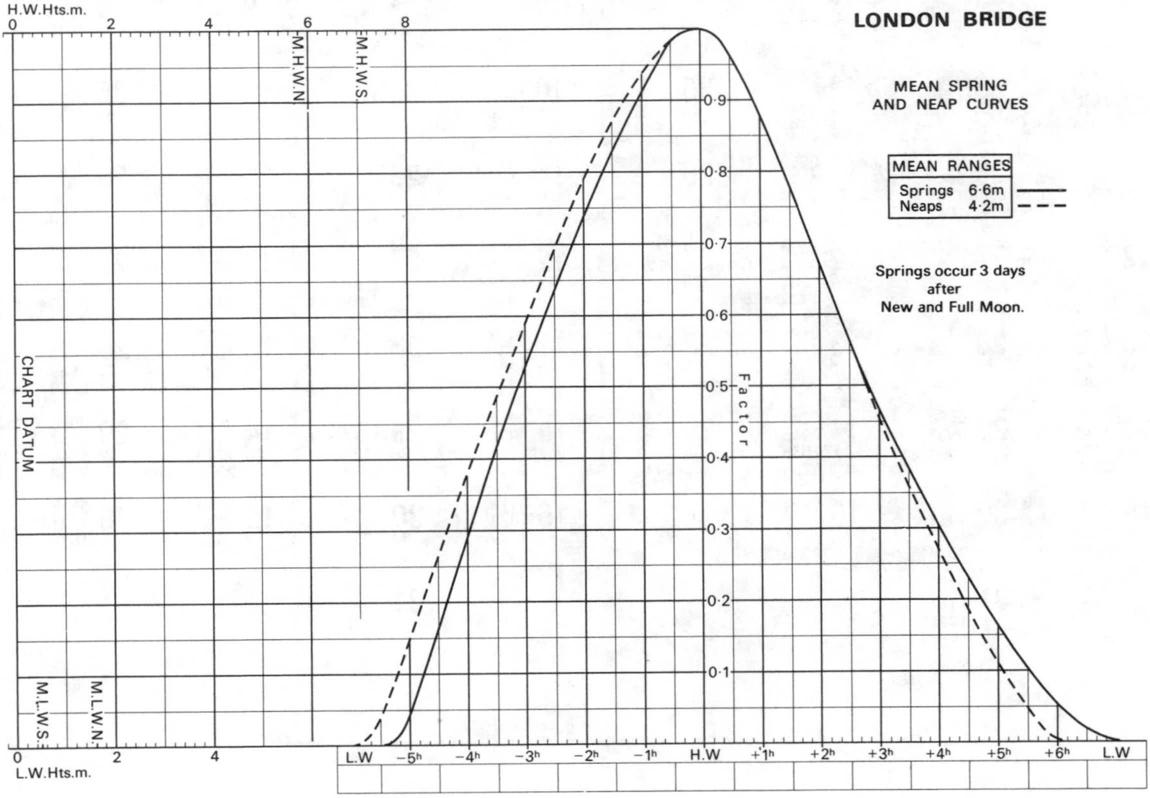
LONDON BRIDGE
MEAN SPRING AND NEAP CURVES
MEAN RANGES
Springs 6·6m
Neaps 4·2m
Springs occur 3 days after New and Full Moon.
H.W.Hts.m.
M.H.W.N.
M.H.W.S.
CHART DATUM
Factor
M.L.W.S.
M.L.W.N.
L.W.Hts.m.
L.W
−5h
−4h
−3h
−2h
−1h
H.W
+1h
+2h
+3h
+4h
+5h
+6h
L.W

ENGLAND, EAST COAST – LONDON BRIDGE

Lat 51°30′ N Long 0°05′ W

TIME ZONE UT(GMT)

For Summer Time add ONE hour in non-shaded areas

TIMES AND HEIGHTS OF HIGH AND LOW WATERS

YEAR **1992**

JANUARY

Day	Time	m	Time	m	Time	m	Time	m
1 W	0441	1·4	1105	6·2	1719	1·1	2339	6·4
2 Th	0554	1·2	1208	6·3	1821	1·0		
3 F	0034	6·5	0656	1·0	1259	6·5	1910	1·0
4 Sa ●	0117	6·6	0744	0·9	1341	6·6	1952	0·9
5 Su	0155	6·7	0826	0·8	1420	6·7	2032	0·9
6 M	0230	6·8	0904	0·7	1456	6·8	2110	0·8
7 Tu	0303	6·8	0939	0·7	1529	6·9	2145	0·9
8 W	0335	6·9	1012	0·7	1603	6·9	2219	0·9
9 Th	0407	6·8	1042	0·8	1637	6·8	2251	1·0
10 F	0440	6·7	1112	0·8	1711	6·7	2320	1·1
11 Sa	0512	6·6	1142	0·9	1744	6·5	2350	1·2
12 Su	0544	6·4	1211	1·0	1821	6·2		
13 M ☽	0024	1·3	0622	6·2	1248	1·1	1906	6·0
14 Tu	0106	1·5	0710	6·0	1334	1·2	2005	5·8
15 W	0202	1·6	0820	5·8	1442	1·4	2122	5·8
16 Th	0327	1·6	0946	5·9	1616	1·4	2238	6·0
17 F	0458	1·4	1105	6·2	1736	1·1	2349	6·4
18 Sa	0615	1·0	1215	6·6	1850	0·9		
19 Su ○	0050	6·7	0731	0·7	1316	7·0	1958	0·7
20 M	0142	7·0	0833	0·3	1408	7·3	2053	0·6
21 Tu	0230	7·2	0927	0·0	1457	7·6	2142	0·5
22 W	0315	7·4	1014	−0·2	1543	7·7	2226	0·4
23 Th	0359	7·5	1057	−0·2	1628	7·6	2305	0·6
24 F	0442	7·4	1136	0·0	1712	7·4	2339	0·8
25 Sa	0525	7·2	1210	0·4	1757	7·0		
26 Su ☾	0010	1·0	0608	6·9	1239	0·7	1842	6·7
27 M	0042	1·2	0655	6·6	1314	1·0	1931	6·3
28 Tu	0124	1·4	0752	6·2	1404	1·2	2030	6·0
29 W	0226	1·6	0901	5·9	1518	1·5	2142	5·9
30 Th	0359	1·6	1031	5·8	1637	1·4	2306	5·9
31 F	0523	1·4	1147	6·1	1744	1·3		

FEBRUARY

Day	Time	m	Time	m	Time	m	Time	m
1 Sa	0010	6·2	0635	1·1	1242	6·3	1843	1·1
2 Su	0057	6·4	0726	0·9	1324	6·6	1931	1·0
3 M ●	0137	6·6	0809	0·7	1402	6·7	2015	0·9
4 Tu	0212	6·8	0847	0·7	1436	6·9	2054	0·8
5 W	0244	6·9	0924	0·6	1508	7·0	2131	0·8
6 Th	0315	7·0	0957	0·6	1539	7·0	2204	0·8
7 F	0346	7·0	1027	0·6	1610	7·0	2235	0·9
8 Sa	0416	6·9	1055	0·7	1642	6·9	2301	1·0
9 Su	0447	6·8	1119	0·8	1713	6·7	2325	1·1
10 M	0518	6·6	1142	0·9	1749	6·5	2351	1·1
11 Tu ☽	0553	6·4	1211	1·0	1828	6·2		
12 W	0029	1·2	0638	6·2	1253	1·1	1920	5·9
13 Th	0121	1·4	0744	5·9	1352	1·4	2039	5·7
14 F	0240	1·6	0915	5·8	1538	1·6	2206	5·9
15 Sa	0430	1·4	1045	6·1	1711	1·3	2329	6·3
16 Su	0600	1·0	1204	6·6	1835	1·0		
17 M	0035	6·7	0721	0·5	1304	7·1	1945	0·7
18 Tu ○	0128	7·1	0822	0·1	1357	7·4	2040	0·5
19 W	0215	7·3	0912	−0·2	1442	7·6	2127	0·4
20 Th	0257	7·5	0957	−0·3	1525	7·7	2207	0·4
21 F	0339	7·6	1037	−0·2	1607	7·6	2244	0·5
22 Sa	0419	7·5	1111	0·1	1647	7·4	2313	0·7
23 Su	0459	7·3	1137	0·5	1726	7·0	2339	0·9
24 M	0539	7·0	1201	0·8	1804	6·6		
25 Tu ☾	0007	1·0	0621	6·6	1229	1·0	1848	6·3
26 W	0042	1·2	0714	6·2	1312	1·3	1940	5·9
27 Th	0131	1·5	0820	5·8	1413	1·7	2047	5·7
28 F	0254	1·8	0948	5·6	1555	1·8	2220	5·6
29 Sa	0451	1·6	1122	5·9	1713	1·5	2342	5·9

MARCH

Day	Time	m	Time	m	Time	m	Time	m
1 Su	0605	1·2	1218	6·3	1815	1·2		
2 M	0032	6·3	0659	0·9	1300	6·6	1906	1·0
3 Tu	0112	6·6	0742	0·7	1337	6·7	1951	0·9
4 W ●	0147	6·8	0822	0·6	1409	6·9	2032	0·8
5 Th	0218	7·0	0858	0·6	1440	7·0	2108	0·7
6 F	0249	7·1	0932	0·5	1511	7·1	2143	0·7
7 Sa	0318	7·1	1004	0·6	1542	7·1	2214	0·8
8 Su	0349	7·1	1033	0·6	1613	7·1	2240	0·9
9 M	0421	7·0	1055	0·8	1647	6·9	2302	0·9
10 Tu	0455	6·8	1115	0·9	1720	6·6	2329	1·0
11 W	0534	6·6	1146	1·0	1801	6·3		
12 Th ☽	0007	1·1	0622	6·2	1228	1·2	1853	5·9
13 F	0059	1·3	0731	5·9	1328	1·5	2012	5·7
14 Sa	0218	1·5	0901	5·9	1514	1·7	2143	5·8
15 Su	0413	1·3	1033	6·2	1649	1·4	2309	6·3
16 M	0546	0·8	1150	6·7	1817	1·0		
17 Tu	0015	6·8	0707	0·4	1249	7·2	1927	0·7
18 W ○	0109	7·1	0805	0·0	1338	7·4	2020	0·5
19 Th	0155	7·3	0853	−0·1	1422	7·5	2105	0·4
20 F	0236	7·5	0934	−0·1	1503	7·6	2145	0·4
21 Sa	0317	7·5	1010	0·1	1542	7·5	2217	0·5
22 Su	0355	7·5	1040	0·4	1619	7·2	2245	0·6
23 M	0433	7·2	1102	0·7	1654	6·9	2309	0·8
24 Tu	0512	6·9	1126	0·9	1729	6·6	2336	0·9
25 W	0553	6·5	1157	1·1	1807	6·3		
26 Th ☾	0010	1·1	0642	6·1	1236	1·3	1855	5·9
27 F	0055	1·3	0744	5·8	1328	1·7	1959	5·6
28 Sa	0155	1·7	0903	5·6	1454	2·0	2121	5·5
29 Su	0407	1·7	1037	5·7	1637	1·7	2257	5·7
30 M	0523	1·3	1142	6·1	1739	1·4	2356	6·1
31 Tu	0619	1·0	1227	6·5	1832	1·1		

APRIL

Day	Time	m	Time	m	Time	m	Time	m
1 W	0038	6·4	0706	0·8	1303	6·7	1919	0·9
2 Th	0113	6·7	0748	0·7	1337	6·8	2001	0·8
3 F ●	0145	6·9	0827	0·6	1409	7·0	2040	0·7
4 Sa	0218	7·0	0904	0·6	1440	7·1	2118	0·7
5 Su	0250	7·1	0938	0·6	1514	7·2	2152	0·7
6 M	0324	7·2	1009	0·6	1548	7·1	2221	0·7
7 Tu	0400	7·2	1035	0·7	1624	7·0	2248	0·8
8 W	0441	7·0	1059	0·9	1702	6·7	2319	0·9
9 Th	0526	6·7	1133	1·1	1747	6·3		
10 F ☽	0000	1·0	0621	6·3	1219	1·3	1843	6·0
11 Sa	0055	1·2	0730	6·1	1323	1·6	1958	5·8
12 Su	0218	1·3	0851	6·1	1500	1·7	2122	6·0
13 M	0357	1·0	1016	6·4	1627	1·4	2245	6·4
14 Tu	0525	0·7	1129	6·8	1749	1·1	2351	6·8
15 W	0643	0·3	1228	7·2	1903	0·8		
16 Th	0046	7·0	0741	0·2	1317	7·3	1957	0·6
17 F ○	0133	7·1	0826	0·2	1401	7·3	2040	0·6
18 Sa	0215	7·2	0905	0·3	1440	7·3	2118	0·5
19 Su	0254	7·3	0939	0·5	1517	7·2	2150	0·5
20 M	0332	7·3	1007	0·6	1552	7·1	2219	0·6
21 Tu	0412	7·1	1031	0·8	1626	6·8	2245	0·8
22 W	0449	6·8	1058	1·0	1659	6·6	2313	0·9
23 Th	0530	6·5	1130	1·1	1736	6·3	2346	1·0
24 F ☾	0615	6·2	1210	1·3	1818	6·0		
25 Sa	0028	1·2	0710	5·9	1256	1·6	1916	5·7
26 Su	0120	1·4	0818	5·7	1358	1·9	2030	5·5
27 M	0232	1·6	0932	5·7	1532	1·9	2150	5·6
28 Tu	0424	1·5	1042	5·9	1649	1·6	2259	5·9
29 W	0526	1·2	1137	6·2	1746	1·3	2350	6·2
30 Th	0618	1·0	1221	6·5	1836	1·1		

Chart Datum: 3.20 metres below Ordnance Datum (Newlyn)

TIME ZONE UT(GMT)

For Summer Time add ONE hour in non-shaded areas

ENGLAND, EAST COAST – LONDON BRIDGE

Lat 51°30′ N Long 0°05′ W

TIMES AND HEIGHTS OF HIGH AND LOW WATERS

YEAR **1992**

MAY

	Time	m		Time	m
1	0032	6·5	16	0112	6·8
	0706	0·8		0757	0·6
F	1259	6·7	Sa	1338	7·0
	1924	0·9	○	2015	0·7
2	0110	6·7	17	0155	6·9
	0751	0·7		0836	0·7
Sa	1335	6·9	Su	1418	6·9
●	2011	0·8		2054	0·7
3	0148	6·9	18	0236	7·0
	0833	0·7		0910	0·8
Su	1413	7·0	M	1454	6·9
	2053	0·7		2128	0·6
4	0226	7·1	19	0315	7·0
	0914	0·6		0939	0·8
M	1450	7·1	Tu	1529	6·9
	2134	0·6		2159	0·7
5	0305	7·2	20	0353	7·0
	0950	0·6		1009	0·9
Tu	1529	7·1	W	1603	6·8
	2212	0·5		2228	0·8
6	0348	7·3	21	0431	6·8
	1026	0·7		1038	1·0
W	1610	7·0	Th	1637	6·6
	2248	0·6		2257	0·9
7	0434	7·1	22	0511	6·6
	1058	0·9		1111	1·1
Th	1654	6·8	F	1712	6·4
	2325	0·7		2329	1·0
8	0525	6·9	23	0551	6·3
	1134	1·1		1147	1·3
F	1743	6·5	Sa	1751	6·2
9	0008	0·9	24	0008	1·0
	0621	6·6		0638	6·1
Sa	1222	1·4	Su	1229	1·4
☽	1839	6·2	☾	1838	5·9
10	0104	1·0	25	0052	1·2
	0726	6·4		0731	5·9
Su	1324	1·5	M	1319	1·6
	1947	6·1		1934	5·7
11	0219	1·0	26	0145	1·3
	0836	6·4		0833	5·8
M	1443	1·5	Tu	1418	1·7
	2100	6·2		2044	5·6
12	0338	0·8	27	0251	1·4
	0950	6·6		0936	5·8
Tu	1559	1·3	W	1531	1·7
	2216	6·4		2152	5·7
13	0452	0·6	28	0409	1·3
	1102	6·8		1035	6·0
W	1713	1·1	Th	1644	1·5
	2325	6·6		2252	5·9
14	0610	0·5	29	0516	1·1
	1203	7·0		1130	6·3
Th	1831	1·0	F	1746	1·3
				2346	6·2
15	0022	6·8	30	0617	0·9
	0710	0·5		1219	6·5
F	1255	7·0	Sa	1845	1·0
	1928	0·8			
			31	0035	6·5
				0713	0·8
			Su	1306	6·7
				1940	0·8

JUNE

	Time	m		Time	m
1	0121	6·7	16	0222	6·7
	0805	0·7		0844	0·9
M	1351	6·9	Tu	1437	6·7
●	2032	0·6		2112	0·7
2	0208	7·0	17	0300	6·8
	0854	0·6		0918	0·9
Tu	1434	7·0	W	1511	6·8
	2121	0·5		2146	0·7
3	0254	7·2	18	0338	6·9
	0939	0·6		0952	0·9
W	1518	7·1	Th	1545	6·7
	2207	0·4		2217	0·8
4	0341	7·3	19	0413	6·8
	1023	0·7		1024	1·0
Th	1602	7·1	F	1619	6·7
	2252	0·3		2247	0·9
5	0430	7·3	20	0449	6·7
	1104	0·8		1057	1·1
F	1648	7·0	Sa	1652	6·6
	2336	0·4		2318	0·9
6	0520	7·1	21	0526	6·5
	1143	1·0		1129	1·1
Sa	1737	6·8	Su	1729	6·4
				2350	0·9
7	0019	0·6	22	0605	6·3
	0614	6·9		1205	1·2
Su	1225	1·2	M	1805	6·2
☽	1829	6·6			
8	0107	0·7	23	0028	1·0
	0710	6·7		0646	6·1
M	1314	1·3	Tu	1245	1·3
	1927	6·5	☾	1846	6·0
9	0204	0·7	24	0109	1·1
	0813	6·6		0734	5·9
Tu	1416	1·4	W	1330	1·5
	2032	6·4		1937	5·8
10	0307	0·7	25	0158	1·2
	0921	6·5		0833	5·8
W	1525	1·3	Th	1426	1·6
	2142	6·4		2044	5·7
11	0414	0·7	26	0301	1·3
	1030	6·6		0938	5·9
Th	1637	1·2	F	1539	1·6
	2257	6·4		2156	5·8
12	0525	0·8	27	0421	1·2
	1136	6·6		1042	6·0
F	1753	1·1	Sa	1658	1·4
				2302	6·0
13	0000	6·5	28	0533	1·1
	0632	0·8		1144	6·3
Sa	1231	6·6	Su	1807	1·1
	1900	1·0			
14	0053	6·5	29	0005	6·3
	0726	0·9		0641	0·9
Su	1319	6·6	M	1242	6·6
	1952	0·9		1914	0·8
15	0140	6·6	30	0103	6·7
	0808	1·0		0744	0·7
M	1359	6·7	Tu	1334	6·8
○	2034	0·8	●	2016	0·6

JULY

	Time	m		Time	m
1	0157	7·0	16	0244	6·8
	0840	0·6		0903	0·9
W	1422	7·0	Th	1454	6·8
	2111	0·3		2134	0·7
2	0246	7·3	17	0319	6·9
	0931	0·5		0938	0·9
Th	1507	7·2	F	1527	6·8
	2202	0·1		2206	0·7
3	0334	7·5	18	0352	6·9
	1017	0·5		1010	0·9
F	1552	7·3	Sa	1557	6·8
	2249	0·0		2234	0·8
4	0420	7·5	19	0426	6·8
	1059	0·6		1041	0·9
Sa	1637	7·3	Su	1630	6·8
	2333	0·1		2302	0·8
5	0508	7·4	20	0458	6·7
	1139	0·8		1111	1·0
Su	1723	7·1	M	1702	6·6
				2330	0·8
6	0012	0·3	21	0532	6·5
	0557	7·1		1140	1·1
M	1215	1·0	Tu	1734	6·4
	1810	6·9			
7	0052	0·5	22	0000	0·9
	0646	6·8		0607	6·3
Tu	1253	1·1	W	1211	1·2
☽	1900	6·7	☾	1810	6·2
8	0133	0·7	23	0034	1·0
	0741	6·6		0645	6·1
W	1340	1·2	Th	1249	1·3
	1958	6·5		1852	6·0
9	0225	0·9	24	0114	1·1
	0843	6·4		0734	5·9
Th	1443	1·3	F	1335	1·4
	2107	6·3		1948	5·8
10	0332	1·0	25	0208	1·3
	0952	6·3		0842	5·7
F	1559	1·4	Sa	1443	1·6
	2224	6·2		2108	5·7
11	0441	1·1	26	0331	1·4
	1105	6·3		1000	5·8
Sa	1718	1·3	Su	1617	1·5
	2339	6·2		2228	5·9
12	0553	1·1	27	0459	1·2
	1208	6·3		1115	6·1
Su	1838	1·1	M	1737	1·1
				2344	6·3
13	0038	6·4	28	0614	1·0
	0655	1·1		1222	6·5
M	1300	6·4	Tu	1856	0·8
	1934	0·9			
14	0126	6·5	29	0049	6·8
	0744	1·0		0726	0·8
Tu	1342	6·5	W	1319	6·8
○	2019	0·8	●	2005	0·4
15	0208	6·6	30	0144	7·2
	0825	1·0		0827	0·6
W	1420	6·7	Th	1406	7·1
	2057	0·7		2101	0·1
			31	0233	7·5
				0918	0·4
			F	1451	7·4
				2150	−0·1

AUGUST

	Time	m		Time	m
1	0319	7·6	16	0325	6·9
	1004	0·4		0950	0·8
Sa	1535	7·5	Su	1532	7·0
	2237	−0·2		2213	0·7
2	0404	7·6	17	0356	6·9
	1045	0·4		1020	0·8
Su	1619	7·5	M	1602	6·9
	2316	−0·1		2240	0·7
3	0448	7·4	18	0427	6·8
	1122	0·6		1047	0·9
M	1701	7·3	Tu	1633	6·8
	2353	0·2		2305	0·8
4	0532	7·1	19	0458	6·7
	1154	0·9		1113	1·0
Tu	1744	7·1	W	1705	6·6
				2330	0·8
5	0022	0·6	20	0532	6·5
	0617	6·8		1140	1·0
W	1224	1·0	Th	1739	6·4
☽	1831	6·7		2358	0·9
6	0055	0·8	21	0608	6·2
	0704	6·4		1214	1·1
Th	1302	1·2	F	1819	6·2
	1924	6·4	☾		
7	0135	1·1	22	0036	1·1
	0801	6·2		0653	5·9
F	1352	1·4	Sa	1259	1·3
	2030	6·1		1916	5·9
8	0240	1·3	23	0127	1·4
	0907	5·9		0758	5·7
Sa	1517	1·5	Su	1401	1·5
	2152	5·9		2034	5·7
9	0403	1·4	24	0249	1·6
	1031	5·9		0925	5·7
Su	1649	1·4	M	1545	1·5
	2319	6·1		2204	5·9
10	0519	1·3	25	0433	1·4
	1146	6·1		1051	6·0
M	1817	1·1	Tu	1716	1·1
				2329	6·4
11	0021	6·4	26	0551	1·0
	0627	1·1		1203	6·5
Tu	1241	6·4	W	1842	0·7
	1914	0·8			
12	0109	6·6	27	0035	6·9
	0720	0·9		0709	0·7
W	1323	6·6	Th	1300	7·0
	1958	0·7		1951	0·2
13	0148	6·8	28	0128	7·3
	0804	0·8		0811	0·5
Th	1359	6·8	F	1348	7·3
○	2037	0·6	●	2046	−0·1
14	0223	6·8	29	0215	7·6
	0842	0·8		0901	0·4
F	1433	6·9	Sa	1432	7·5
	2112	0·6		2134	−0·2
15	0256	6·9	30	0300	7·6
	0918	0·8		0945	0·3
Sa	1503	6·9	Su	1514	7·6
	2143	0·7		2216	−0·2
			31	0342	7·6
				1024	0·4
			M	1556	7·6
				2252	0·0

Chart Datum: 3.20 metres below Ordnance Datum (Newlyn)

ENGLAND, EAST COAST – LONDON BRIDGE

Lat 51°30′ N Long 0°05′ W

TIME ZONE UT(GMT)

For Summer Time add ONE hour in non-shaded areas

TIMES AND HEIGHTS OF HIGH AND LOW WATERS

YEAR **1992**

SEPTEMBER

Date	Day	Time	m
1	Tu	0424 1058 1637 2323	7·4 0·6 7·4 0·4
2	W	0505 1126 1719 2349	7·0 0·8 7·1 0·7
3	Th ☽	0546 1154 1803	6·7 1·0 6·7
4	F	0017 0628 1227 1853	1·0 6·3 1·1 6·3
5	Sa	0055 0719 1312 1957	1·2 6·0 1·4 5·9
6	Su	0149 0822 1422 2115	1·6 5·7 1·7 5·7
7	M	0322 0948 1621 2252	1·7 5·6 1·6 5·9
8	Tu	0449 1118 1747 2357	1·5 6·0 1·1 6·4
9	W	0557 1214 1843	1·1 6·4 0·8
10	Th	0043 0650 1257 1928	6·7 0·9 6·7 0·6
11	F	0123 0735 1334 2008	6·8 0·7 6·9 0·6
12	Sa ○	0157 0815 1405 2043	6·9 0·7 7·0 0·6
13	Su	0226 0851 1434 2115	6·9 0·7 7·0 0·6
14	M	0256 0925 1503 2145	7·0 0·7 7·1 0·7
15	Tu	0325 0955 1534 2213	7·0 0·7 7·1 0·7
16	W	0356 1023 1604 2238	7·0 0·8 7·0 0·8
17	Th	0427 1048 1638 2302	6·8 0·9 6·8 0·8
18	F	0501 1115 1716 2332	6·6 0·9 6·6 1·0
19	Sa ☾	0539 1149 1801	6·3 1·1 6·3
20	Su	0010 0625 1235 1859	1·2 6·0 1·2 6·0
21	M	0102 0731 1338 2019	1·4 5·7 1·5 5·8
22	Tu	0225 0900 1527 2150	1·7 5·7 1·4 6·0
23	W	0410 1030 1659 2313	1·5 6·1 1·0 6·6
24	Th	0529 1142 1827	1·0 6·6 0·5
25	F	0017 0649 1238 1933	7·1 0·7 7·1 0·1
26	Sa ●	0109 0749 1327 2025	7·4 0·5 7·4 0·0
27	Su	0155 0839 1411 2110	7·5 0·4 7·5 0·0
28	M	0237 0922 1451 2149	7·5 0·4 7·6 0·1
29	Tu	0318 0959 1532 2223	7·5 0·4 7·6 0·3
30	W	0357 1031 1614 2251	7·3 0·5 7·4 0·6

OCTOBER

Date	Day	Time	m
1	Th	0437 1059 1655 2316	7·0 0·7 7·1 0·9
2	F	0515 1127 1739 2346	6·6 0·9 6·7 1·1
3	Sa ☽	0554 1200 1827	6·2 1·1 6·2
4	Su	0022 0641 1241 1926	1·4 5·9 1·4 5·9
5	M	0112 0741 1337 2037	1·7 5·6 1·7 5·7
6	Tu	0227 0900 1542 2207	1·9 5·5 1·7 5·8
7	W	0413 1034 1705 2320	1·7 5·8 1·3 6·2
8	Th	0519 1139 1803	1·3 6·2 0·9
9	F	0010 0614 1224 1849	6·6 0·9 6·6 0·7
10	Sa	0049 0700 1300 1930	6·8 0·8 6·8 0·6
11	Su ○	0123 0742 1333 2008	6·9 0·7 6·9 0·6
12	M	0154 0820 1402 2043	6·9 0·7 7·0 0·6
13	Tu	0223 0857 1434 2117	7·0 0·7 7·1 0·6
14	W	0256 0931 1507 2149	7·1 0·7 7·1 0·6
15	Th	0329 1003 1542 2217	7·1 0·7 7·1 0·7
16	F	0403 1033 1620 2244	6·9 0·8 7·0 0·8
17	Sa	0441 1101 1704 2313	6·7 0·9 6·8 1·0
18	Su	0522 1137 1753 2354	6·4 1·0 6·4 1·3
19	M ☾	0611 1225 1853	6·0 1·2 6·1
20	Tu	0049 0719 1334 2011	1·5 5·8 1·4 6·0
21	W	0212 0842 1515 2135	1·7 5·9 1·2 6·3
22	Th	0348 1006 1640 2252	1·4 6·2 0·8 6·7
23	F	0502 1116 1801 2354	1·1 6·7 0·4 7·1
24	Sa	0621 1215 1909	0·8 7·1 0·2
25	Su ●	0048 0724 1304 1959	7·3 0·6 7·2 0·2
26	M	0134 0815 1349 2043	7·3 0·5 7·3 0·3
27	Tu	0216 0857 1432 2121	7·3 0·5 7·4 0·4
28	W	0256 0935 1512 2153	7·2 0·5 7·4 0·5
29	Th	0334 1007 1555 2221	7·1 0·5 7·3 0·7
30	F	0412 1037 1635 2249	6·9 0·7 7·0 0·9
31	Sa	0448 1106 1718 2320	6·6 0·9 6·7 1·1

NOVEMBER

Date	Day	Time	m
1	Su	0526 1137 1803 2357	6·3 1·1 6·3 1·4
2	M ☽	0608 1215 1855	6·0 1·3 6·0
3	Tu	0042 0702 1304 1958	1·6 5·7 1·5 5·7
4	W	0138 0812 1413 2110	1·9 5·5 1·7 5·7
5	Th	0310 0931 1610 2223	1·9 5·6 1·5 5·9
6	F	0433 1044 1711 2322	1·6 5·9 1·1 6·2
7	Sa	0529 1137 1801	1·2 6·3 0·9
8	Su	0007 0618 1219 1846	6·5 1·0 6·5 0·7
9	M	0045 0703 1256 1928	6·7 0·8 6·7 0·6
10	Tu ○	0120 0748 1331 2011	6·9 0·7 6·9 0·6
11	W	0155 0830 1409 2051	7·0 0·6 7·0 0·6
12	Th	0232 0911 1447 2129	7·1 0·6 7·2 0·6
13	F	0310 0950 1528 2206	7·1 0·5 7·2 0·7
14	Sa	0349 1028 1612 2238	7·0 0·6 7·2 0·8
15	Su	0430 1104 1658 2312	6·8 0·8 7·0 1·1
16	M	0515 1143 1749 2351	6·6 0·9 6·7 1·3
17	Tu ☾	0605 1231 1848	6·3 1·1 6·4
18	W	0045 0706 1335 1957	1·5 6·1 1·1 6·3
19	Th	0158 0819 1457 2111	1·6 6·1 1·0 6·4
20	F	0319 0936 1612 2224	1·4 6·3 0·7 6·7
21	Sa	0433 1049 1727 2330	1·1 6·6 0·6 6·9
22	Su	0549 1151 1838	1·0 6·8 0·5
23	M	0027 0659 1245 1933	7·0 0·8 6·9 0·5
24	Tu ●	0114 0752 1333 2016	7·0 0·7 7·0 0·6
25	W	0158 0836 1416 2054	7·0 0·6 7·1 0·7
26	Th	0237 0915 1458 2128	7·0 0·6 7·1 0·7
27	F	0315 0950 1538 2159	7·0 0·6 7·2 0·8
28	Sa	0352 1021 1619 2230	6·9 0·7 7·0 0·9
29	Su	0427 1051 1658 2302	6·7 0·9 6·8 1·1
30	M	0504 1122 1739 2336	6·5 1·0 6·5 1·3

DECEMBER

Date	Day	Time	m
1	Tu	0542 1156 1822	6·2 1·2 6·2
2	W ☽	0015 0625 1238 1914	1·5 6·0 1·3 5·9
3	Th	0100 0720 1327 2013	1·6 5·7 1·4 5·8
4	F	0155 0827 1429 2117	1·8 5·6 1·5 5·8
5	Sa	0307 0935 1553 2219	1·8 5·7 1·4 5·9
6	Su	0427 1035 1702 2313	1·6 5·9 1·2 6·2
7	M	0527 1129 1757	1·3 6·2 0·9
8	Tu	0003 0622 1218 1849	6·4 1·0 6·4 0·8
9	W ○	0048 0716 1306 1941	6·7 0·8 6·7 0·6
10	Th	0133 0808 1351 2030	6·9 0·6 7·0 0·6
11	F	0215 0858 1436 2117	7·0 0·5 7·2 0·5
12	Sa	0258 0945 1519 2200	7·1 0·4 7·4 0·6
13	Su	0341 1030 1606 2241	7·2 0·3 7·4 0·8
14	M	0423 1113 1652 2319	7·1 0·5 7·2 1·0
15	Tu	0508 1154 1742 2357	6·9 0·6 7·0 1·2
16	W ☾	0556 1236 1835	6·7 0·8 6·7
17	Th	0041 0649 1326 1934	1·4 6·5 0·9 6·5
18	F	0135 0751 1427 2042	1·4 6·4 0·9 6·4
19	Sa	0244 0903 1536 2153	1·4 6·4 0·9 6·5
20	Su	0359 1019 1647 2302	1·3 6·4 0·8 6·6
21	M	0515 1129 1801	1·1 6·5 0·8
22	Tu	0004 0635 1229 1904	6·7 1·0 6·6 0·8
23	W	0057 0734 1320 1952	6·7 0·8 6·7 0·9
24	Th ●	0142 0820 1405 2033	6·7 0·7 6·8 0·9
25	F	0223 0903 1446 2110	6·8 0·6 7·0 0·8
26	Sa	0300 0939 1524 2143	6·9 0·6 7·1 0·8
27	Su	0335 1012 1602 2216	6·9 0·7 7·0 0·9
28	M	0407 1040 1637 2245	6·8 0·8 6·9 1·0
29	Tu	0441 1108 1712 2316	6·7 0·9 6·7 1·1
30	W	0515 1137 1750 2350	6·5 1·0 6·4 1·2
31	Th	0553 1211 1829	6·3 1·0 6·2

Chart Datum: 3.20 metres below Ordnance Datum (Newlyn)

SOUTHEND-ON-SEA/ LEIGH-ON-SEA 10-3-22

Essex

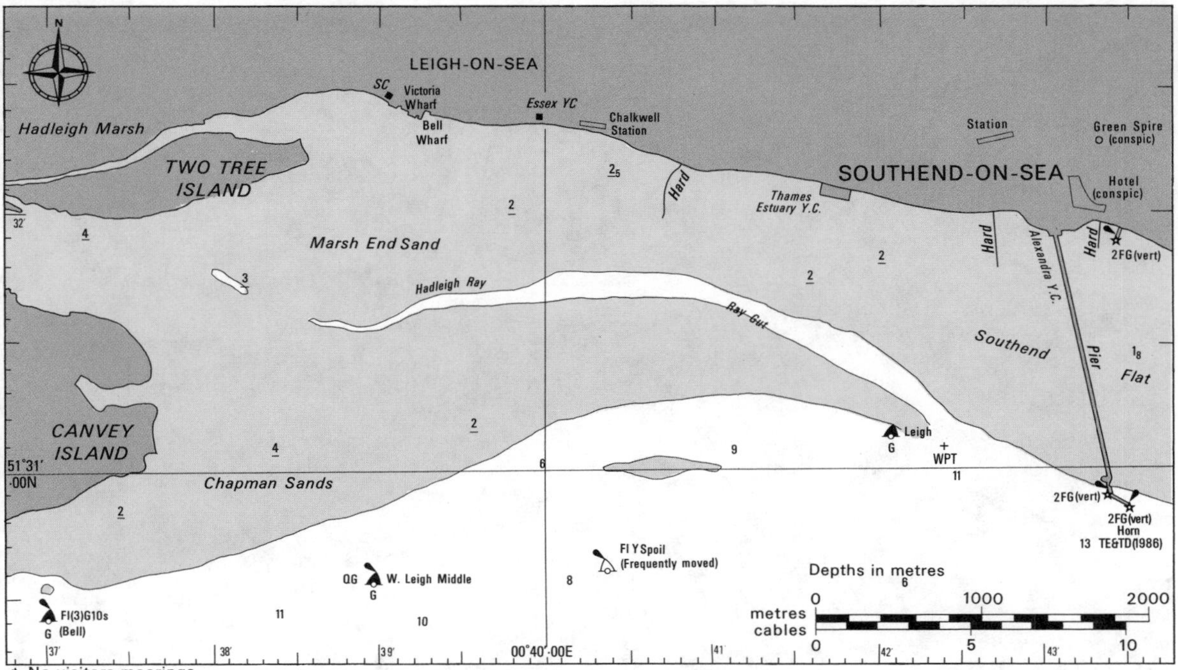
LEIGH-ON-SEA
SC
Victoria Wharf
Bell Wharf
Essex YC
Chalkwell Station
Hadleigh Marsh
TWO TREE ISLAND
Station
Green Spire (conspic)
SOUTHEND-ON-SEA
Hotel (conspic)
Thames Estuary Y.C.
Hard
Alexandria Y.C.
2FG(vert)
Marsh End Sand
Hadleigh Ray
Ray Gut
Southend
Pier
Flat
CANVEY ISLAND
Leigh
G
WPT
51°31'·00N
Chapman Sands
2FG(vert)
2FG(vert)
Horn
13 TE&TD(1986)
Fl Y Spoil (Frequently moved)
QG
W. Leigh Middle
G
Fl(3)G10s
G (Bell)
Depths in metres
metres
cables
00°40'·00E

▲ No visitors moorings

CHARTS

Admiralty 1185, 1183; Stanford 5; Imray C2, Y6; OS 178

TIDES

+0130 Dover; ML 3·0; Duration 0610; Zone 0 (GMT).

Standard Port SHEERNESS (⟵)

Times				Height (metres)			
HW		LW		MHWS	MHWN	MLWN	MLWS
0200	0800	0200	0700	5·7	4·8	1·5	0·6
1400	2000	1400	1900				
Differences SOUTHEND-ON-SEA							
−0005	−0005	−0005	−0005	0·0	0·0	−0·1	−0·1

SHELTER

The whole area dries soon after half ebb, except Ray Gut. Some moorings are available at Leigh-on-Sea. Yachts can take the ground alongside Bell Wharf or Victoria Wharf.

NAVIGATION

Waypoint Leigh (stbd-hand) buoy, 51°31'·10N 00°42'·43E, at entrance to Ray Gut. Approaching from Shoeburyness, keep outside the two buoys Mid Shoebury (Con G) and W Shoebury (Con G Fl G 2·5s). Beware some 3000 small boat moorings a mile either side of Southend pier. Speed limit in Canvey Island/Hadleigh Ray areas is 8kn.

NOTE: Southend-on-Sea and Leigh-on-Sea are both part of the lower Port of London Authority Area. Southend BC launches *'Alec White II'* and *'Sidney Bates II'* patrol area (VHF Ch 16), April-October.

LIGHTS AND MARKS

Pier lights as shown in chartlet.

RADIO TELEPHONE

Police launches, Thames Navigation Service all VHF Ch 12. Southend Borough Council launches 'Alec White II' and 'Sidney Bates', Ch 16 (Apr to Oct inclusive).

TELEPHONE (0702)

Hr Mr 611889; Hr Mr Leigh-on-Sea 710561; MRSC Frinton-on-Sea 675518; Essex Police Marine Section Rayleigh 775533; # (0702) 547141 Ext 26 or (071) 865 5861; Marinecall 0898 500 455; Police 341212; Dr 49451; Ⓗ 348911.

FACILITIES

SOUTHEND-ON-SEA EC Wednesday. **Alexandra YC** ☎ 340363, Bar, FW; **Thames Estuary YC** ☎ 345967; **Halfway YC** ☎ 582025; **Thorpe Bay YC** ☎ 587563, Bar, L, Slip, R, FW; **Southend Pier** ☎ 355620, M, L, FW, Bar; **Cruisermart** ☎ 460055, CH; **IYE (England)** ☎ 511215, Ⓔ; **Town** V, R, Bar, ✉; Ⓑ; ⇌; ✈.

LEIGH-ON-SEA EC Wednesday. **Essex YC** ☎ 78404, FW, Bar; **Leigh on Sea SC** ☎ 76788, FW, Bar; **Bell Wharf**, AB; **Victoria Wharf** AB, SM, Slip; **Mikes BY** ☎ 713151, Slip, D (cans), L, FW, ME, El, Sh, C, CH; **Sea King** ☎ 73612, Slip, L, D, ME, El, Sh, C, CH; **Johnson and Jago** ☎ 76639, ME, El, Sh, D (cans); **W Sails** ☎ 714550, SM; **Two Tree Island** ☎ 711010, Slip, FW (see Hr Mr).

CANVEY ISLAND. (0268) **Halcon Marine** (250) ☎ Canvey Island 511611, Slip, M, D, FW, ME, El, Sh, C, Gas, CH, Access HW∓2. **Island YC** ☎ Canvey Island 683729.

BENFLEET **Benfleet YC** ☎ South Benfleet 792278, Slip, FW, Bar; **Dauntless** ☎ South Benfleet 793782, Slip, D, M, FW, ME, El, Sh, C, Access HW∓2½. **A.J. Long** ☎ South Benfleet 758874 M.

HAVENGORE 10-3-23

Essex

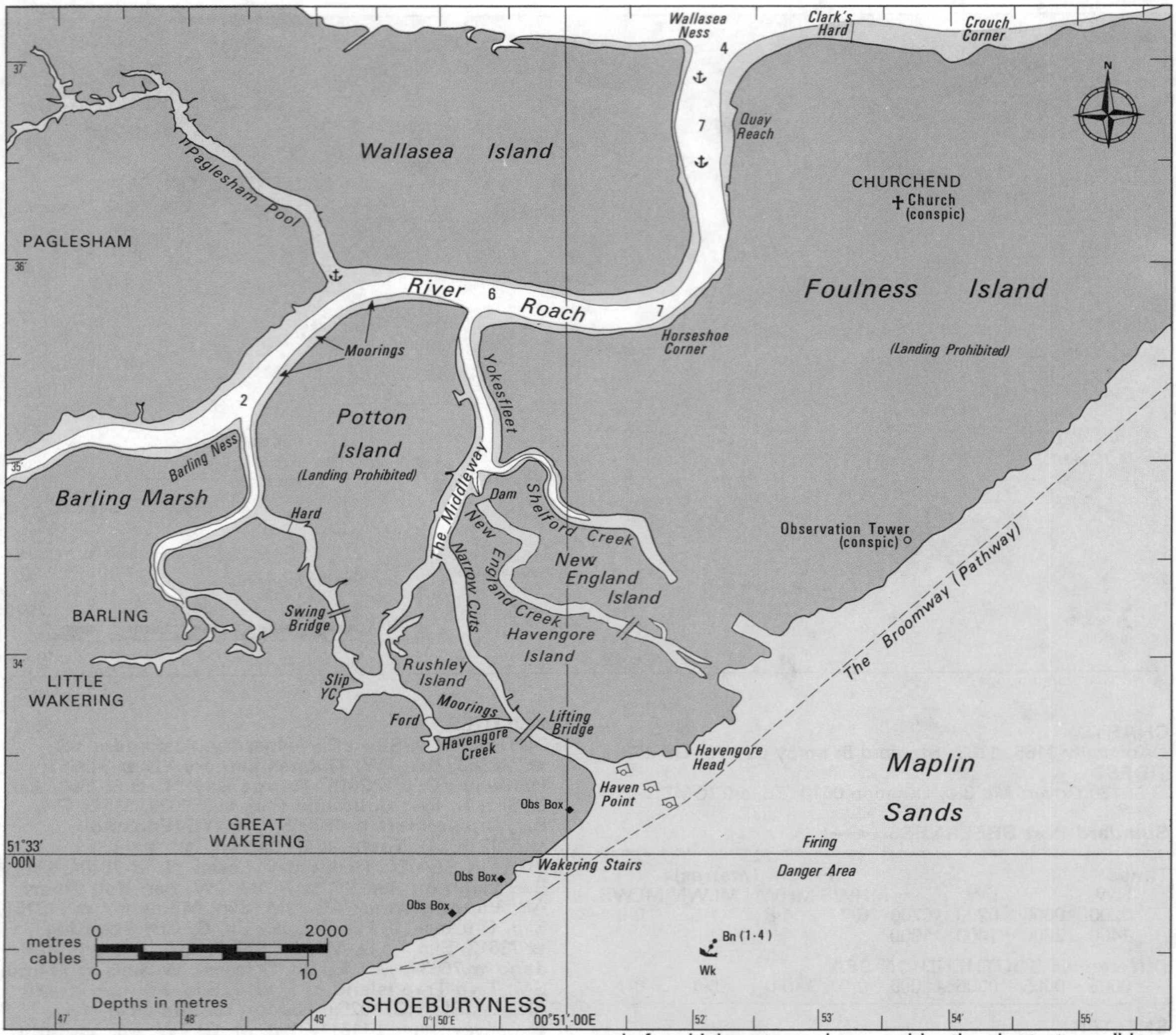
Wallasea Ness
Clark's Hard
Crouch Corner
Quay Reach
Wallasea Island
Paglesham Pool
PAGLESHAM
CHURCHEND
Church (conspic)
River Roach
Foulness Island
Moorings
Horseshoe Corner
(Landing Prohibited)
Yokesfleet
Potton Island
(Landing Prohibited)
Barling Ness
Barling Marsh
Hard
Dam
The Middleway
Shelford Creek
New England Creek
Narrow Cuts
New England Island
Observation Tower (conspic)
The Broomway (Pathway)
BARLING
Swing Bridge
Havengore Island
Rushley Island
LITTLE WAKERING
Slip YC
Moorings
Ford
Havengore Creek
Lifting Bridge
Havengore Head
Maplin Sands
Haven Point
Obs Box
GREAT WAKERING
Firing Danger Area
Wakering Stairs
Bn (1·4)
Wk
metres
cables
Depths in metres
SHOEBURYNESS
51°33'·00N
00°51'·00E

CHARTS

Admiralty 3750, 1185; Stanford 4, 5; Imray C1, Y17; OS 178

TIDES

+0110 Dover; ML 2·7; Duration 0615; Zone 0 (GMT).

Standard Port SHEERNESS (⟵)

Times				Height (metres)			
HW		LW		MHWS	MHWN	MLWN	MLWS
0200	0700	0100	0700	5·7	4·8	1·5	0·6
1400	1900	1300	1900				
Differences SHIVERING SANDS TOWER							
−0025	−0019	−0008	−0026	−0·6	−0·6	−0·1	−0·1

SHELTER

Good shelter and a short cut at spring tides between the Thames and the Crouch for craft drawing less than 1·5m. Recommended to start passage about HW−1 using Yokesfleet, Middleway and Narrow Cuts.

NAVIGATION

Waypoint 51°30'·78N 00°54'·07E, 146°/326° from/to Havengore Creek entrance, 3·0M. Approach crosses Shoeburyness gunnery range which is in use most weekdays. The rules are laid down in *Statutory Rules & Orders No 714 of 1936* obtainable from HMSO. Key paragraph is 'Any vessel wishing to enter Havengore Creek during such time or times as the whole of the target area is not closed in accordance with Bye Law No 3 must enter the target area not later than half an hour before high water and proceed by the shortest possible course to the Creek'. Red flags are hoisted at many points 1 hour before firing starts. Before setting off to Havengore, ring the Range Operations Officer, ☎ Southend-on-Sea 292271 Ext 3211; permission must be obtained preferably 24 hours in advance. Range is clear on bank holidays and at weekends. No passage allowed in dark hours. Lifting bridge across the creek will normally be opened on request. ☎ Southend-on-Sea 292271 Ext 3436 (Bridge manned HW∓2 sunrise to sunset). There is no charge. When tide gauge at Southend pier shows 5m there is 1·5 over the Broomway. Speed limit in creeks 8 kn.

LIGHTS AND MARKS

There are no lights.

RADIO TELEPHONE

Gravesend Radio VHF Ch 12 gives half hourly navigational information. Range Operations Officer listens on Ch 16; 72 during working hours. Call sign '*Shoe Base*'. Bridgekeeper call *Shoebridge* Ch 16; 72 (HW∓2).

TELEPHONE (0702)

(071) 865 5861 Ext 5861; MRSC Frinton-on-Sea 675518; Marinecall 0898 500 455; Police 431212; Dr Southend-on-Sea 218678.

FACILITIES

EC Great Wakering Wednesday; **Sutton's BY** ☎ Southend-on-Sea 219422, Slip, P, D, FW, ME, El, Sh, C, CH, AB; **Wakering YC** (0268) 692786, M, L, Bar; **Great Wakering** V, R, Bar. ✉ (Great Wakering & Barling); Ⓑ (Shoeburyness, Thorpe Bay); ⇌ (Shoeburyness); ✈ (Southend).

MINOR HARBOURS AND ANCHORAGES 10.3.24

EASTBOURNE, E Sussex, 50°46′·00N, 00°17′·00E, Zone 0 (GMT), Admty chart 536. HW −0005 on Dover, −0007 on Shoreham; HW height +0·9m on Shoreham; ML 3·8m; Duration 0540. See 10.3.12. Anchorage in Eastbourne Bay sheltered from W winds through N to NE and good holding ground. Beware Boulder Bank, rocks dry 0·2m, extend ¼M seaward by Wish Tower. There is a beacon on shore 1 ca E of Tower. Landing steps on pier (NE side). Pierhead Lts 2 FR (vert) 8m 2M. R Lt occas is shown W of lifeboat station as a guide to local fishermen. There are all shore facilities but few marine facilities. A marina is under construction.

HASTINGS, E Sussex, 50°51′·00N, 00°35′·00E, Zone 0 (GMT), Admty chart 536. HW −0005 on Dover; HW height +0·7m on Dover; ML 3·8m; Duration 0530. See 10.3.13. Anchorage off Hastings is only recommended in fair weather; beware dangerous wreck 3 ca SW of pier head. Lts: Pierhead 2 FR (vert) 8m 5M from white hut; W breakwater head Fl R 2·5s 5m 4M; No 2 Groyne, E breakwater Fl G 3m 3M; Ldg Lts 356° front FR 14m 4M on W metal column, rear 357m from front, FR 55m 4M on 5-sided W Tr on West Hill. The stone breakwater is in a state of dis-repair and is only for the protection of fishing vessels. Facilities: EC Wed; # (0304) 202441; all shore facilities at Hastings and St Leonards. Few marine facilities – **Hastings and St Leonards YC** ☎ Hastings 420656. Landing places on pier.

SANDWICH, Kent, 51°18′·00N, 01°21′·00E, Zone 0 (GMT), Admty chart 1828. HW +0015 on Dover; HW height −1·0m on Dover; ML 1·4m; Duration 0520. Sandwich is on the S side of the R Stour, Richborough on the N side. Sandwich being 3M above Richborough Wharf. The river is winding but vessels with draught up to 2m can reach Sandwich on spring tides. There are six channel buoys and one fairway buoy marking the entrance, all fitted with rotating reflective beacons. (searchlight needed). There are moorings for visitors at Sandwich Quay (ring Quaymaster ☎ 613283). Facilities: EC Wed, Slip; # (0304) 202441; **Marina** (120+some visitors) ☎ (0304) 613783 (max 18m length, 2·1m draught), BH (15 ton), Sh, Slip, FW; Access HW∓2; **A. J. C. White** ☎ (0304) 617800, SM; **Richborough Port** has D by tanker. **Sandwich Sailing and Motorboat Club** ☎ (0304) 611116 and **Sandwich Bay Sailing and Water Ski Clubs** offer some facilities. Both ports are administered by The Sandwich Port and Haven Commissioners.

MARGATE, Kent, 51°23′·00N, 01°23′·00E, Zone 0 (GMT), Admty charts 1827, 1607, 1828. HW+0050 on Dover; −0040 on Sheerness; HW height −0·9m on Sheerness; ML 2·6m; Duration 0610. See 10.3.17. There is a small harbour open to NW winds inside Stone Pier – Pierhead Lt FR 18m 4M. Beware remains of old pier, known as Margate Iron Jetty, extending 2½ ca N from root of Stone Pier, Fl(3)R 10s. The harbour dries 2m; alternative anchorages W of Margate or N of pier. Facilities: EC Thurs; Bar, LB, D and P in cans from garage, R, V, all stores. # (0304) 202441; **Margate YC** ☎ Thanet (0304) 292602, R, Bar. A marina is proposed.

GRAVESEND, Kent, 51°26′·00N, 00°22′·00E, Zone 0 (GMT), Admty charts 1186, 2151. HW +0150 on Dover, +0020 on Sheerness; HW height +0·7m on Sheerness; ML 3·3m; Duration 0610. See 10.3.21. Anchorage E of the piers just below entrance to Gravesend Canal Basin. There are visitors buoys off the Club. Lock gates open HW −1½ to HW on request to Lockkeeper, Tel. 352392 (24 hrs notice required for night tides). East end of Gravesend Reach marked by Ovens Buoy Fl 1s Bell. Royal Terrace Pierhead FR. Gravesend Radio (Thames Navigation Service) VHF Ch 12 14 16 18 20 (H24). Broadcasts on Ch 12 every H+00, H+30. Facilities: EC Wed; Bar, C (at canal entrance – ask at Club), CH, FW (standpipe near lock), P (from garage), R, V; # 626 1515 Ext 5861; **J&R Starbuck** ☎ (0474) 350671 CH; **Gravesend SC** ☎ 533974; Bar, C, FW, M, P&D (cans). # 363555; **Tame Technology** ☎ 334414 Ⓔ. **Denton Shipyard** ☎ 567881 ME, El, Sh.
Note: Boats can be left unattended in canal basin but not at anchorages.

CHELSEA HARBOUR, Greater London, 51°28′·00N, 00°11′·00W Zone 0 (GMT), Admty chart 3319. HW times London Bridge + 20mins. See 10.3.21. Good shelter under all conditions. Basin entrance (5·9m width × 2·5m sill depth) with bascule bridge; Access HW−2 to HW+1½, H24. Waiting berths on Chelsea Harbour Pier (keep clear of reserved area for Thames Line fast river service). Radio telephone (call *Chelsea Harbour*) VHF Ch 80. Marina (60+10 visitors). ☎ 071 351 4433, AC, FW, Bar, CH, R, D, Gas, V, YC.

ST KATHARINE YACHT HAVEN, Greater London, 51°30′·00N, 00°05′·00W, Zone 0 (GMT), Admty chart 33, 37, 3319. HW +0245 on Dover. HW times and heights as London Bridge. See 10.3.21. Good shelter under all conditions. Lock (42·7m × 9·1m with 2 lifting bridges), access HW−2 to HW+1½, winter 0800-1800, (lock shut Tues and Wed, Nov to Feb), summer 0600-2030. Moor to St Katharine's Pier 183m downstream whilst waiting (no shore access). Radio telephone (call *St Katharines*) VHF Ch **80. Yacht Haven** (100+50 visitors) ☎ (071) 481 8286, CH, M, ME, El, Sh, AC, Bar, YC, FW, Gas, R, V, #; **Robbins Marine** ☎ (071) 987 5884, ME, El, Sh; **Millwall Marine** ☎ (071) 515 9351, ME, El, Sh; **Captain Pumpkin** ☎ (071) 480 6630, CH.

HOLEHAVEN, Essex, 51°30′·00N, 00°33′·00E, Zone 0 (GMT), Admty chart 1185/6, 2484. HW +0140 on Dover, +0010 on Sheerness; height as Leigh-on-Sea; (10.3.22) ML 3·0m; Duration 0610. Shelter is good. Moorings S side of pier – very crowded; see Piermaster for mooring. Beware swell from passing traffic; keep to E (Canvey) side on entrance; once over bar, depths increase to 5m; anchor on W side as E side has long stone groynes running out. Lts Coryton Refinery Jetty No 4 2 FG (vert). ½ M up creek a bridge crosses, 9m at MHWS and opening span of 30m. Facilities: EC Thurs; FW (from 'The Lobster Smack' yard), P and D from village (1M); all other facilities at Canvey Island.

Area 4

East England
River Crouch to The Wash

10-4-2

East England

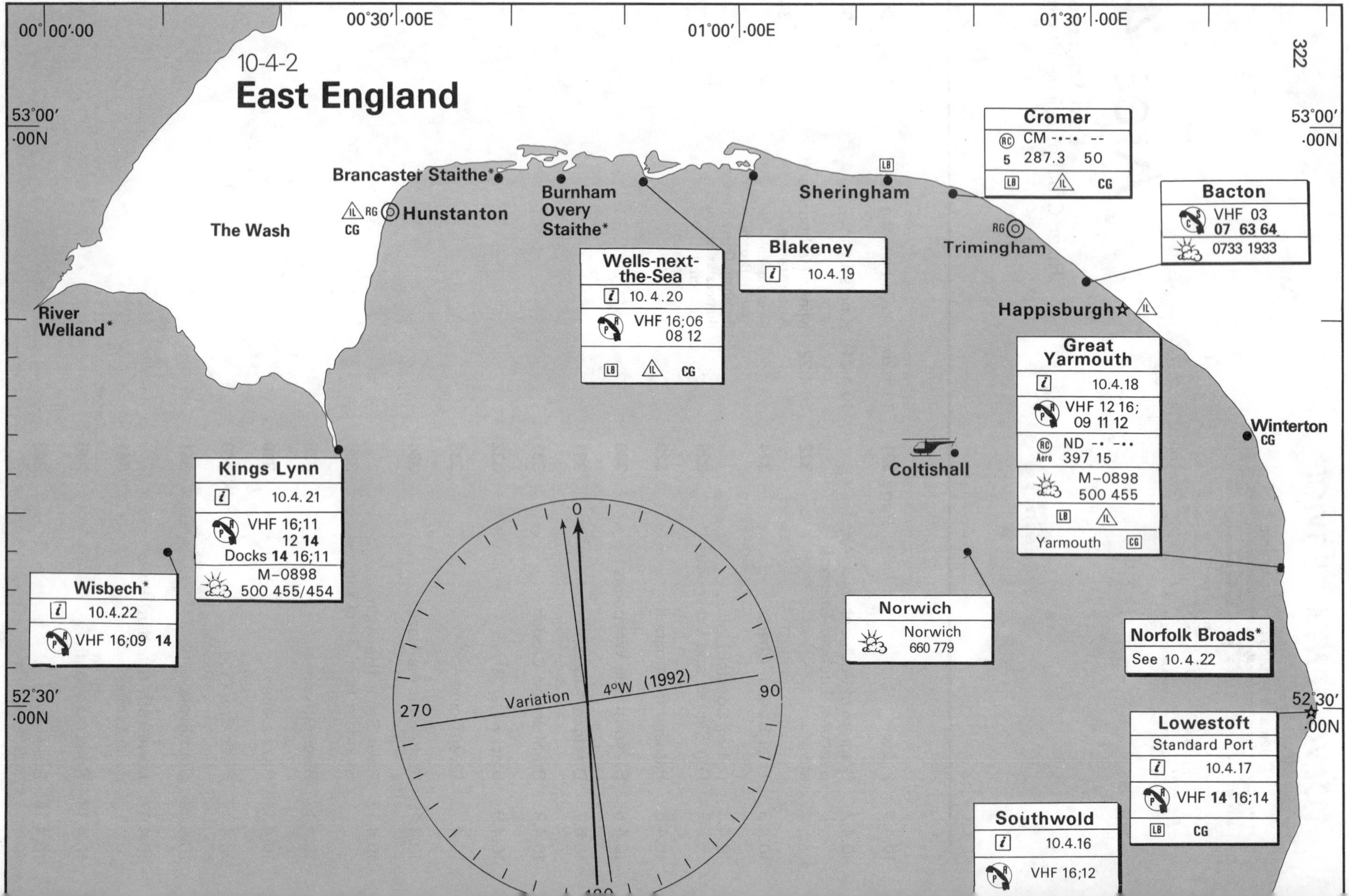
00° 00'·00
00°30' ·00E
01°00' ·00E
01°30' ·00E
53°00' ·00N
52°30' ·00N
The Wash
River Welland*
Brancaster Staithe*
Hunstanton
RG
CG
Burnham Overy Staithe*
Wells-next-the-Sea
10.4.20
VHF 16;06 08 12
LB
CG
Blakeney
10.4.19
Sheringham
LB
Cromer
RC CM -•-• --
5 287.3 50
LB
CG
Trimingham
RG
Bacton
VHF 03 07 63 64
0733 1933
Happisburgh
Great Yarmouth
10.4.18
VHF 12 16; 09 11 12
ND -• -••
Aero 397 15
M-0898 500 455
LB
Yarmouth
CG
Winterton
CG
Coltishall
Norwich
Norwich 660 779
Norfolk Broads*
See 10.4.22
Lowestoft
Standard Port
10.4.17
VHF 14 16;14
LB
CG
Southwold
10.4.16
VHF 16;12
Kings Lynn
10.4.21
VHF 16;11 12 14
Docks 14 16;11
M-0898 500 455/454
Wisbech*
10.4.22
VHF 16;09 14
0
90
270
180
Variation 4°W (1992)

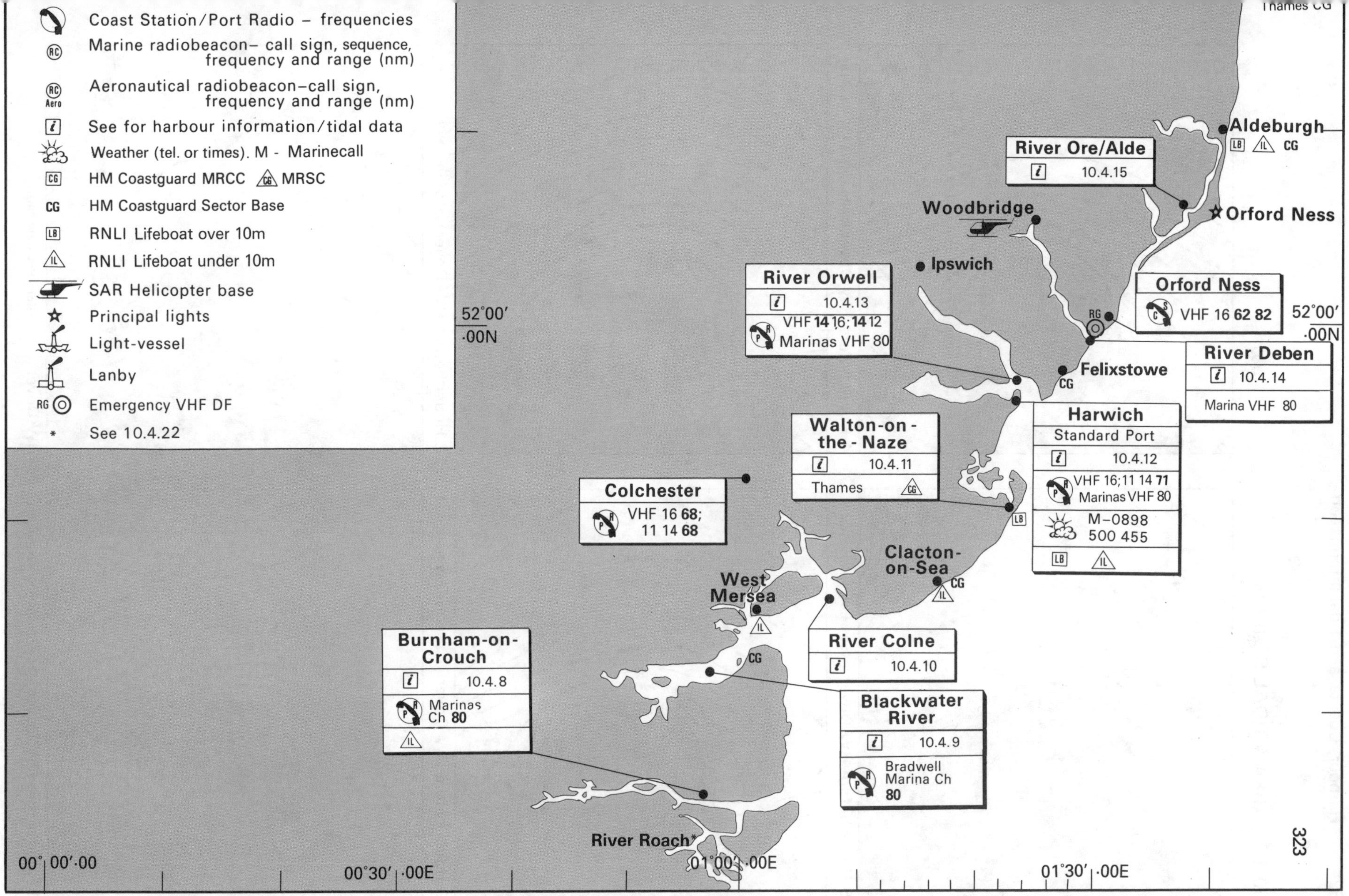
Thames CG
Coast Station/Port Radio – frequencies
Marine radiobeacon– call sign, sequence, frequency and range (nm)
Aeronautical radiobeacon–call sign, frequency and range (nm)
See for harbour information/tidal data
Weather (tel. or times). M - Marinecall
HM Coastguard MRCC
MRSC
HM Coastguard Sector Base
RNLI Lifeboat over 10m
RNLI Lifeboat under 10m
SAR Helicopter base
Principal lights
Light-vessel
Lanby
Emergency VHF DF
* See 10.4.22
Aldeburgh
River Ore/Alde
10.4.15
Woodbridge
Orford Ness
Ipswich
River Orwell
10.4.13
VHF 14 16; 14 12
Marinas VHF 80
Orford Ness
VHF 16 62 82
52°00′ ·00N
River Deben
10.4.14
Marina VHF 80
Felixstowe
Harwich
Standard Port
10.4.12
VHF 16;11 14 71
Marinas VHF 80
M–0898
500 455
Walton-on-the-Naze
10.4.11
Thames
Colchester
VHF 16 68; 11 14 68
Clacton-on-Sea
West Mersea
River Colne
10.4.10
Burnham-on-Crouch
10.4.8
Marinas Ch 80
Blackwater River
10.4.9
Bradwell Marina Ch 80
River Roach*
00° 00′·00
00°30′ ·00E
01°00′ ·00E
01°30′ ·00E

10.4.3 AREA 4 TIDAL STREAMS

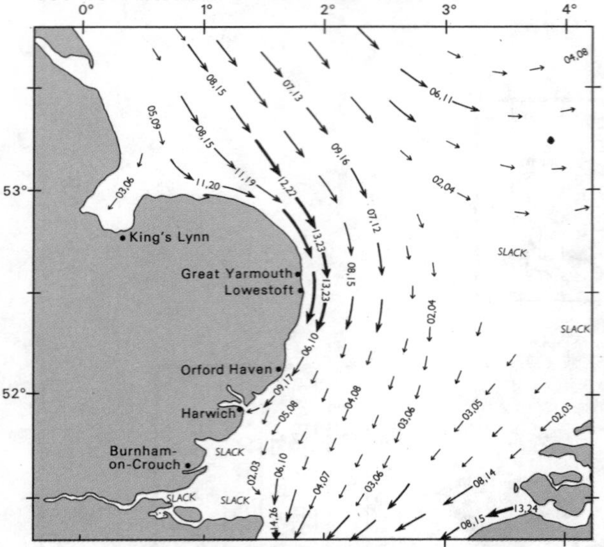
0°
1°
2°
3°
4°
53°
52°
King's Lynn
Great Yarmouth
Lowestoft
Orford Haven
Harwich
Burnham-on-Crouch
SLACK

5 Hours before HW Dover (0530 before HW Harwich)

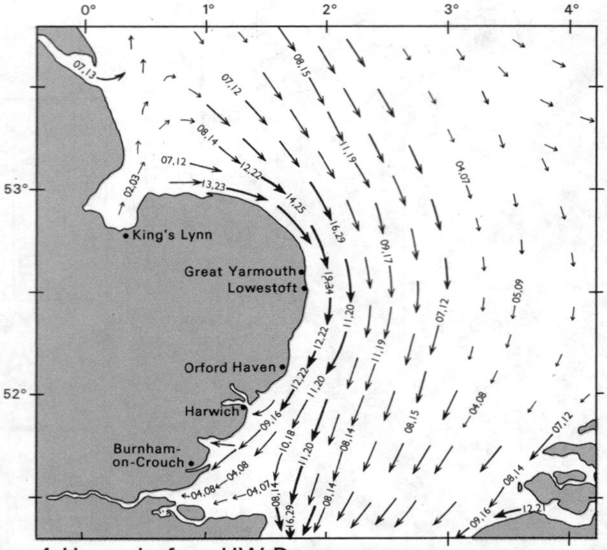
0°
1°
2°
3°
4°
53°
52°
King's Lynn
Great Yarmouth
Lowestoft
Orford Haven
Harwich
Burnham-on-Crouch

4 Hours before HW Dover (0430 before HW Harwich)

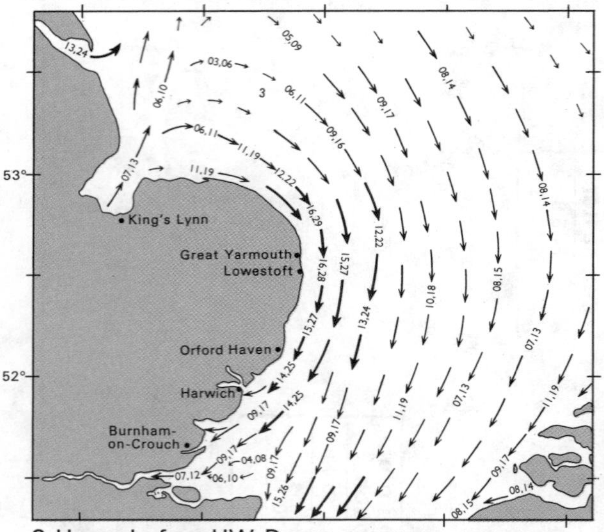
53°
52°
King's Lynn
Great Yarmouth
Lowestoft
Orford Haven
Harwich
Burnham-on-Crouch

3 Hours before HW Dover (0330 before HW Harwich)

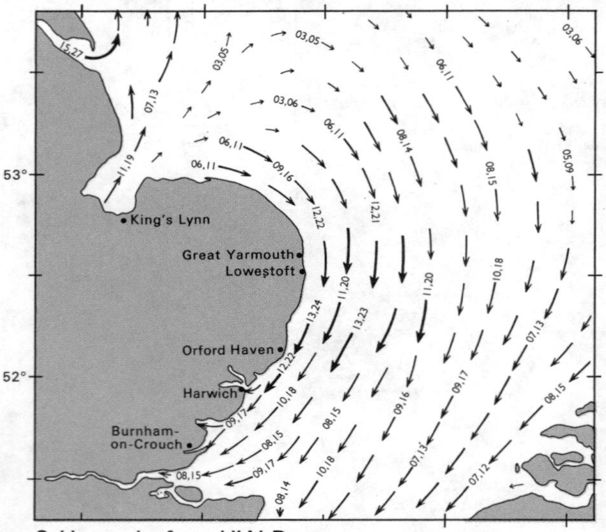
53°
52°
King's Lynn
Great Yarmouth
Lowestoft
Orford Haven
Harwich
Burnham-on-Crouch

2 Hours before HW Dover (0230 before HW Harwich)

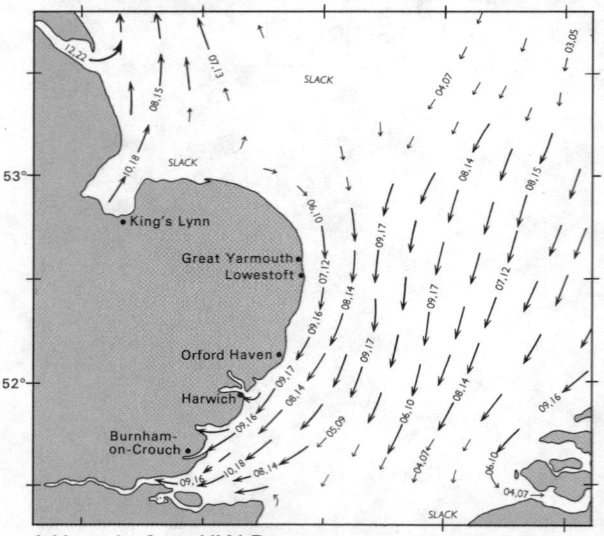
53°
52°
King's Lynn
Great Yarmouth
Lowestoft
Orford Haven
Harwich
Burnham-on-Crouch
SLACK

1 Hour before HW Dover (0130 before HW Harwich)

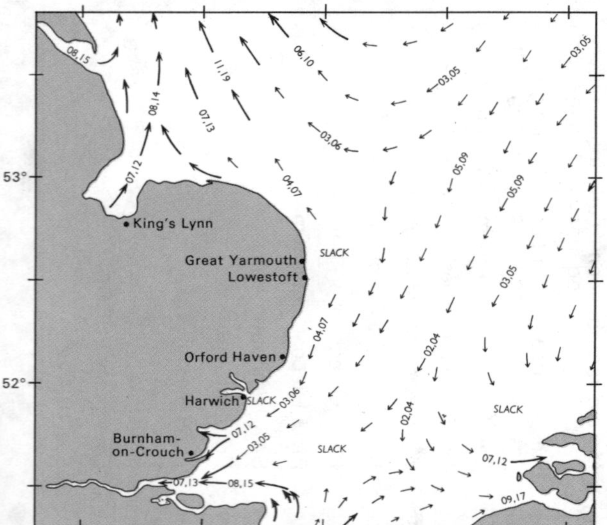
53°
52°
King's Lynn
Great Yarmouth
Lowestoft
Orford Haven
Harwich
Burnham-on-Crouch
SLACK

HW Dover (0030 before HW Harwich)

Southward 10.3.3. Thames Estuary 10.3.18. Northward 10.5.3. Eastward 10.20.3.

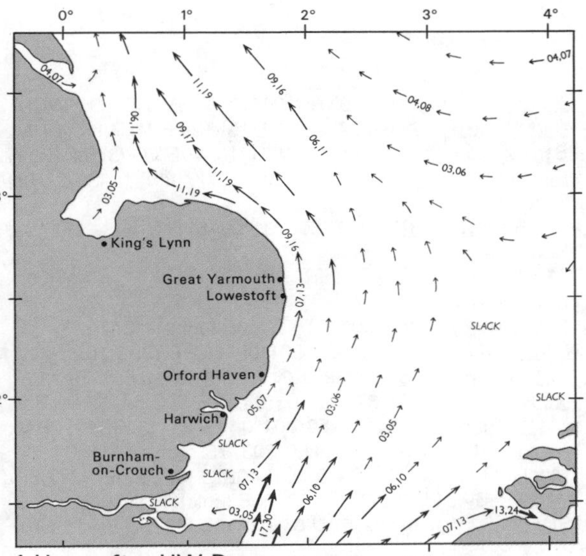
0°
1°
2°
3°
4°
53°
52°
King's Lynn
Great Yarmouth
Lowestoft
Orford Haven
Harwich
Burnham-on-Crouch
SLACK

1 Hour after HW Dover (0030 after HW Harwich)

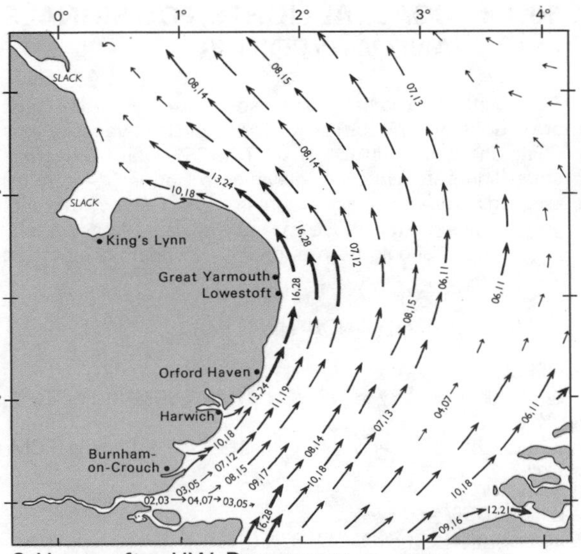
0°
1°
2°
3°
4°
53°
52°
SLACK
King's Lynn
Great Yarmouth
Lowestoft
Orford Haven
Harwich
Burnham-on-Crouch

2 Hours after HW Dover (0130 after HW Harwich)

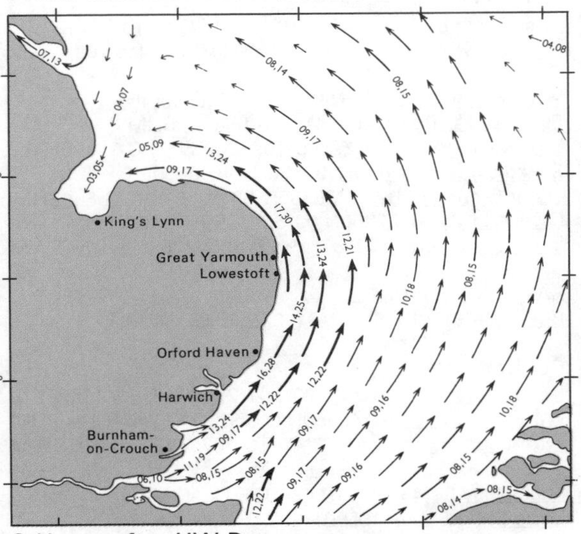
53°
52°
King's Lynn
Great Yarmouth
Lowestoft
Orford Haven
Harwich
Burnham-on-Crouch

3 Hours after HW Dover (0230 after HW Harwich)

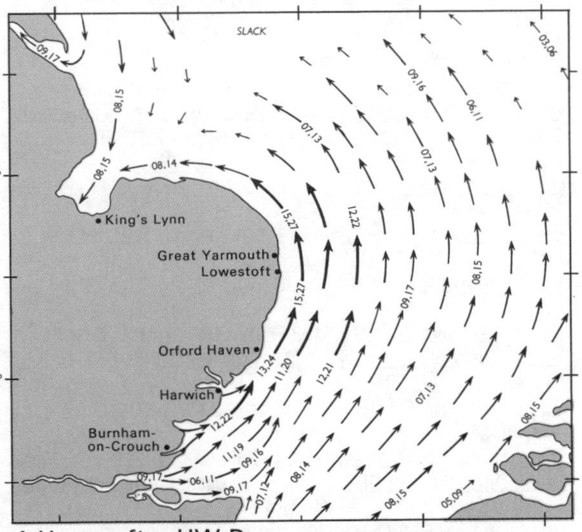
SLACK
53°
52°
King's Lynn
Great Yarmouth
Lowestoft
Orford Haven
Harwich
Burnham-on-Crouch

4 Hours after HW Dover (0330 after HW Harwich)

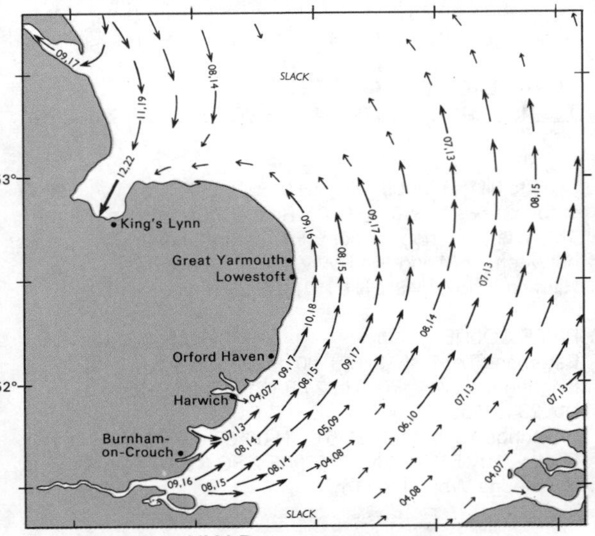
SLACK
53°
52°
King's Lynn
Great Yarmouth
Lowestoft
Orford Haven
Harwich
Burnham-on-Crouch

5 Hours after HW Dover (0430 after HW Harwich)

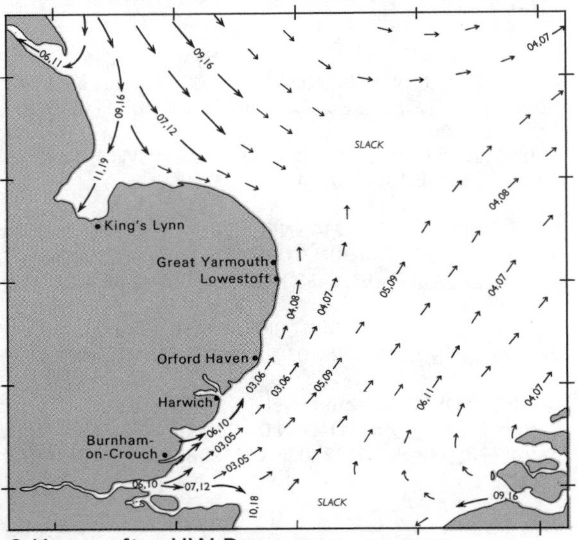
SLACK
53°
52°
King's Lynn
Great Yarmouth
Lowestoft
Orford Haven
Harwich
Burnham-on-Crouch

6 Hours after HW Dover (0530 after HW Harwich)

10.4.4 COASTAL LIGHTS, FOG SIGNALS AND WAYPOINTS

Abbreviations used below are given in 1.4.1. Principal lights are in **bold** print, places in CAPITALS, and light-vessels, light floats and Lanbys in *CAPITAL ITALICS*. Unless otherwise stated lights are white. m—elevation in metres; M—nominal range in n. miles. Fog signals are in *italics*. Useful waypoints are underlined – use those on land with care. All geographical positions should be assumed to be approximate. See 4.2.2.

THAMES ESTUARY—NORTHERN PART

OFFSHORE MARKS.
Kentish Knock Lt By 51°38'·50N 01°40'·50E Q (3) 10s; ECM; *Whis.*
S Knock Lt By 51°34'·73N 01°36'·10E Q (6) + LFl 15s; SCM; *Bell.*

BLACK DEEP
Long Sand Hd Lt By 51°47'·87N 01°39'·51E VQ; NCM; *Bell.*
Trinity Lt By 51°49'·02N 01°36'·50E Q (6) + LFl 15s; SCM; *Whis.*
Black Deep No 2 Lt By 51°46'·00N 01°32'·69E VQ (9) 10s; WCM.
Sunk Head Tr Lt By 51°46'·59N 01°30'·60E Q; NCM.
Black Deep No 1 Lt By 51°44'·00N 01°28'·20E Fl G 5s; SHM.
Black Deep No 3 Lt By 51°41'·75N 01°25'·65E Fl (3) G 15s; SHM; *Bell.*
Black Deep No 4 Lt By 51°41'·60N 01°28'·60E Fl (2) R 5s; PHM.
Black Deep No 5 Lt By 51°39'·50N 01°23'·10E VQ (3) 5s; ECM.
Black Deep No 6 Lt By 51°38'·40N 01°24'·40E Q (9) 15s; WCM.
Black Deep No 7 Lt By 51°37'·05N 01°17'·80E QG; SHM.
Black Deep No 8 Lt By 51°35'·60N 01°18'·50E Fl R 2·5s; PHM.
Black Deep No 9 Lt By 51°35'·10N 01°15'·20E Q (6) + LFl 15s; SCM.
Black Deep No 10 Lt By 51°34'·70N 01°15'·70E QR; PHM.
Black Deep No 11 Lt By 51°34'·30N 01°13'·50E Fl (3) G 10s; SHM.
Black Deep No 12 Lt By 51°33'·80N 01°13'·60E Fl (4) R 15s; PHM.

KNOCK JOHN CHANNEL (selected Bys).
Knock John Lt By 51°33'·46N 01°11'·08E Fl (2) R 5s; PHM.
Knock John No 5 Lt By 51°32'·75N 01°08'·68E Fl (3) G 10s; SHM.
Knob Lt By 51°30'·66N 01°04'·38E Iso 5s; SWM; *Bell.*
(For OAZE DEEP see 10.3.4).

EAST SWIN (KING'S) CHANNEL.
W Sunk Lt By 51°44'·30N 01°25'·90E Q (9) 15s; WCM.
Gunfleet Spit Lt By 51°45'·30N 01°21'·80E Q (6) + LFl 15s; SCM; *Bell.*
Gunfleet Old Lt Ho 51°46'·08N 01°20'·52E (unlit).
W Sunk Lt By 51°44'·30N 01°25'·90E Q (9) 15s; WCM.

BARROW DEEP (selected Bys).
Barrow No 2 Lt By 51°41'·95N 01°23'·00E Fl (2) R 5s; PHM.
Barrow No 3 Lt By 51°42'·00N 01°19'·87E Q (3) 10s ECM; Racon.
Barrow No 4 Lt By 51°39'·75N 01°17'·80E VQ (9) 10s; WCM.
Barrow No 6 Lt By 51°37'·78N 01°15'·18E Fl (4) R 15s; PHM.
Barrow No 9 Lt By 51°35'·50N 01°10'·40E VQ (3) 5s; ECM.
Barrow No 11 Lt By 51°33'·73N 01°05'·85E Fl (3) G 10s; SHM.
SW Barrow Lt By 51°31'·80N 01°00'·53E Q (6) + LFl 15s; SCM; *Bell.*

EAST SWIN.
N Middle By 51°41'·00N 01°12'·00E (unlit); NCM.
S Whitaker Lt By 51°40'·20N 01°09'·15E Fl (2) G 10s; SHM.
W Hook Middle By 51°39'·13N 01°08'·10E (unlit); PHM.
NE Maplin Lt By 51°37'·43N 01°04'·90E Fl G 5s; SHM; *Bell.*
Maplin Bank Lt By 51°35'·47N 01°04'·80E Fl (3) R 10s; PHM.
Maplin Edge By 51°35'·30N 01°03'·75E (unlit); SHM.
Maplin Lt By 51°34'·00N 01°02'·40E Q (3) 10s; ECM; *Bell.*
W Swin By 51°33'·82N 01°03'·80E (unlit); PHM.
SW Swin Lt By 51°32'·74N 01°01'·18E Fl (2) R 5s; PHM.

WHITAKER CHANNEL.
Whitaker Lt By 51°41'·40N 01°10'·61E Q (3) 10s; ECM; *Bell.*
Swin Spitway Lt By 51°41'·92N 01°08'·45E Iso 10s; SWM; *Bell.*
Whitaker Bn 51°39'·62N 01°06'·30E (unlit); IDM.
Swallow Tail By 51°40'·44N 01°40'·81E; SHM.
S Buxey Lt By 51°39'·82N 01°02'·60E Fl (3) G 15s; SHM.
Sunken Buxey Lt By 51°39'·50N 01°00'·60E Q; NCM.
Outer Crouch Lt By 51°38'·35N 00°58'·61E Fl G 5s; SHM.
Crouch Lt By 51°37'·60N 00°56'·49E Fl R 10s; PHM.
Inner Crouch Lt By 51°37'·19N 00°55'·22E L Fl 10s; SWM.

RAY SAND CHANNEL.
Buxey Bn 51°41'·10N 01°01'·38E (unlit); NCM.

GOLDMER GAT/WALLET.
NE Gunfleet Lt By 51°49'·90N 01°27'·90E Q (3) 10s; ECM.
Wallet No 4 Lt By 51°46'·50N 01°17'·33E Fl (4) R 10s;PHM.
Wallet Spitway Lt By 51°42'·83N 01°07'·42E L Fl 10s; SWM; *Bell.*
Knoll Lt By 51°43'·85N 01°05'·17E Q; NCM.
Eagle Lt By 51°44'·10N 01°03'·92E QG; SHM
NW Knoll Lt By 51°44'·19N 01°02'·50E Fl (2) R 5s; PHM.
Colne Bar Lt By 51°44'·58N 01°02'·65E Fl (2) G 5s; NCM.
Bench Head By 51°44'·54N 01°01'·05E; SHM.

RIVER BLACKWATER.
The Nass 51°45'·75N 00°54'·88E VQ (3) 5s 6m 2M; ECM.

BRIGHTLINGSEA.
Ldg Lts 041°. Front 51°48'·4N 01°01'·3E FR 7m 4M; Y ■, W stripe on post; vis 020°-080°. Rear 50m from front FR 10m 4M; Y ■, W stripe on post. FR Lts are shown on 7 masts between 1·5M and 3M NW when firing occurs.
Hardway, Hd 51°48'·2N 01°01'·5E 2 FR (vert) 2m.

RIVER COLNE.
Batemans Tr 51°48'·3N 01°00'·8E FY 12m.
Fingringhoe Wick, Pier Hd 2 FR (vert) 6/4m (occas).
No. 23 51°50'·6N 00°59'·0E Fl G 5s 5m.
Wivenhoe Yacht Club 51°51'·3N 00°57'·6E FY.
Cooks Jetty 51°51'·2N 00°57'·8E 2 FG (vert).
Rowhedge Wharf FY 11m.

CLACTON-ON-SEA.
Berthing arm 51°47'·00N 01°09'·60E 2 FG (vert) 5m 4M; *Reed(2) 120s* (occas).

WALTON-ON-THE-NAZE.
Pier head 51°50'·60N 01°16'·90E 2 FG (vert) 5m 2M.

OFFSHORE MARKS
S Galloper Lt By 51°43'·95N 01°56'·50E Q (6) LFl 15s; SCM; *Whis*; Racon.
OUTER GABBARD Lt V 51°59'·38N 02°04'·63E Fl (4) 20s 12m **23M**; R hull with Lt Tr amidships; RC; *Horn(4) 60s*.
S Inner Gabbard Lt By 51°51'·20N 01°52'·40E Q (6) + LFl 15s; SCM.
N Inner Gabbard Lt By 51°59'·10N 01°56'·10E Q; NCM.

HARWICH APPROACHES

MEDUSA CHANNEL.
Medusa Lt By 51°51'·20N 01°20'·46E Fl G 5s; NCM.
Naze Tr 51°51'·85N 01°17'·40E (unlit).
Stone Banks By 51°53'·18N 01°19'·32E (unlit); PHM.

(Direction of buoyage N to S).

Pye End By 51°55'·00N 01°18'·00E (unlit); SWM.

CORK SAND /ROUGH SHOALS.
S Cork By 51°51'·30N 01°24'·20E (unlit); SCM.
Roughs Tr SE Lt By 51°53'·61N 01°29'·06E Q (3) 10s; ECM; *Bell*.
Roughs Tr NW Lt By 51°53'·78N 01°28'·88E Q (9) 15s; WCM.
Rough Lt By 51°55'·65N 01°31'·30E VQ; NCM.
Cork Lt By 51° 55'·44N 01°27'·30E QR; PHM.
Cork Sand Lt Bn 51°55'·20N 01°25'·31E Q; NCM.
Washington Lt By 51°56'·54N 01°27°·30E QG; SHM.
Felixtowe Ledge Lt By 51°56'·30N 01°24'·56E Fl (3) G10s; SHM.
SUNK Lt F 51°51'·00N 01°35'·00E Fl (2) 20s 12m **24M**; R hull with Lt Tr amidships; RC; Racon; *Horn(2) 60s*.

SHIPWASH.
Shipwash Lt By 51°52'·65N 01°34'·05E Q (6) + LFl 15s; SCM.
Shiphead Lt By 51°53'·75N 01°34'·05E Fl R 5s; PHM.
SW Shipwash Lt By 51°54'·82N 01°34'·10E L Fl R 10s; PHM.
E Shipwash Lt By 51°57'·05N 01°38'·00E VQ (3) 5s; ECM.
N Shipwash Lt By 52°01'·70N 01°38'·38E Q; NCM; *Bell*.
SHIPWASH Lt F 52°02'·03N 01°42'05E Fl (3) 20s 12m **24M**; R hull with Lt Tr amidships; *Horn(3) 60s*.

HARWICH CHANNEL.
HA Lt By 51°56'·40N 01°31'·20E Iso 5s; SWM; *Whis*.
Harwich Channel Lt By No. 1 51°56'·11N 01°27·30E Fl Y 2·5s; SPM; Racon.
Harwich Channel No.3 Lt By 51°55'·96N 01°24'·56E Fl Y 5s; SHM.
Harwich Channel No 5 Lt By 51°55'·94N 01°22'·45E Fl Y 10s; SHM.
Landguard Lt By 51°55'·35N 01°18'·98E Q; NCM.

FELIXSTOWE.
Landguard Pt Jetty Elbow 51°56'·2N 01°19'·2E 2 FG (vert) 8/6m.
Jetty Hd 51°56'·3N 01°19'·2E 2 FG (vert) 8/6m; on Dolphin.
Container berth, S end 2 FG (vert).
Crane quay, S end 2 FG (vert).
Dock ent. S pier Hd FG 3m.
N pier Hd 51°56'·9N 01°19'·1E FR 3m 10M.
Felixstowe Town Pier, Hd 51°57'·4N 01°21'·0E 2 FG (vert) 7m.

HARWICH.
Wharves, jetties and piers show 2 FR (vert).
Shotley Spit 51°57'·26N 01°17'·67E Q (6) + L Fl 15s; SCM.
Shotley Marina Lock 51°57'·4N 01°16'·7E Dir Lt; or structure.
Shotley Marina Ent, E side Fl (4)G 15s; G ▲ on pile.
Shotley Marina, W side VQ (3) W 5s 5s; ECM.
Erwarton Ness 51°57'·08N 01°13'·35E Q (6) + LFl 15s; SCM Bn.
Holbrook 51°57'·19N 01°10'·46E VQ (6) + LFl 10s; SCM Bn.
Shotley Ganges Pier, Hd 2 FG (vert) 4m 1M; G post.
Mistley, Baltic wharf 51°56'·7N 01°05'·3E 2 FR (vert).

RIVER ORWELL
Orwell Lt By 51°58'·14N 01°16'·65E Fl R 2·5s; PHM.
Fagbury Lt By 51°57'.983N 01°16'·910E Fl G 2·5s; NCM.
No. 1 Lt By 51°58'·256N 01°16'·775E Fl G 5s; SHM
Suffolk Yacht Harbour. Ldg Lts. Front Iso Y Rear Oc Y 4s.
Woolverstone Marina 52°00'·4N 01°11'·8E 2 FR (vert).
Orwell Bridge FY 39m 3M at centre; 2 FR (vert) on pier 9 and 2 FG (vert) on pier 10.

WOODBRIDGE HAVEN.
By 51°58'·47N 01°24'·35E (unlit); SWM.
Ldg Lts FIW or FIY moved as required (on request). Front W ▲ on R post. Rear; R line on post.
Ferry landing, E side 2 FG (vert).
W side 2 FR (vert).
Groyne, outer end QR; TE.

BAWDSEY BANK.
S Bawdsey Lt By 51°57'·20N 01°30'·32E Q (6) + LFl 15s; SCM; *Whis*.
Mid Bawdsey Lt By 51°58'·85N 01°33'·70E Fl (3) G 10s; NCM.
NE Bawdsey Lt By 52°01'·70N 01°36'·20E Fl G 10s; NCM.

CUTLER/WHITING BANK.
Cutler By 51°58'·50N 01°27'·60E (unlit); NCM.
SW Whiting By 52°01'·22N 01°30'·90E (unlit); SCM.
Whiting Hook By 52°02'·95N 01°31'·95E (unlit); PHM.
NE Whiting By 52°03'·75N 01°33'·85E (unlit); ECM.

Orford Ness 52°05'·00N 01°34'·55E Fl 5s 28m **30M**; W ● Tr, R bands. F RG 14m R14M, **G15M** (same Tr); vis R shore-210°, R038°-047°, G047°-shore.

SIZEWELL.
Power station, S pipeline 52°12'·5N 01°37'·7E 2 FR (vert) 12/10m.
N pipeline 2 FR (vert) 12/10m.

SOUTHWOLD.
Southwold Lt Ho 52°19'·60N 01°41'·00E Fl (4) WR 20s 37m **W22M, R22M, R20M**; W ● Tr; vis R (intens) 204°-220°, W220°-001°, R001°-032°.
N pier Hd 52°18'·77N 01°40'·63E Fl G 1·5s 4m 4M. S pier Hd QR 4m 2M.
E Barnard Lt By 52°24'·60N 01°46'·20E Q (3) 10s; ECM.
S Newcome Lt By 52°25'·70N 01°45'·20E Fl G 2·5s; NCM.
Pakefield Lt By 52°27'·05N 01°45'·30E Fl (2) G 5s; NCM.
Newcome Lt By 52°28'·48N 01°49'·32E Fl (2) R 5s; PHM.

Lowestoft Roads, Claremont Pier 52°27'·9N 01°45'·0E 2 FR (vert) 5/4m 4M; W col.
3 FR mark firing range 1·5M SSW.

LOWESTOFT
Lowestoft 52°29'·2N 01°45'·5E Lt Ho. Fl 15s 37m **28M**; W Tr; part obscd 347°-shore. FR 30m **18M** (same Tr); vis 184°-211°.
Outer harb S pier Hd Oc R 5s 12m 6M; *Horn (4) 60s*.
N pier Hd 52°28'·29N 01°45'·50E Oc G 5s 12m 8M.
Corton Lt By 52°31'·10N 01°51'·50E Q (3) 10s; ECM; *Whis*.

GREAT YARMOUTH.
Gorleston S pier Hd Fl R 3s 11m 11M; vis 235°-340°; *Horn (3) 60s*.
Ldg Lts 264°. Front Oc 3s 6m 10M. Rear Oc 6s 7m 10M.
N pier Hd 52°34'·36N 01°44'·49E QG; vis 176°-078°.
Brush lighthouse FR 20m 6M; R ● Tr.
Groyne, head 52°34'·3N 01°44'·4E 2 FG (vert) 4m.
52°34'·3N 01°44'·3E 2 FG (vert).
52°34'·3N 01°44'·2E 2 FG (vert).
5F mark pile structure close W.
Haven Bridge 52°36'·4N 01°43'·5E marked by pairs of 2 FR (vert) and 2 FG (vert) showing up and down stream. 1 FR marks centre of chan.

YARMOUTH ROADS.
South Denes, outfall 52°35'·10N 01°44'·50E QR 5m 2M; B and Y ▲.
Wellington Pier Hd 52°35'·9N 01°44'·4E 2 FR (vert) 8m 3M.
Jetty Hd 2FR(vert) 7m 2M.
Britannia Pier Hd 52°36'·5N 01°44'·6E 2 FR (vert) 11m 4M; W col.
North Scroby Lt By 52°42'·20N 01°45'·80E VQ; WCM; *Bell; Whis*.

Cockle Lt By 52°44'·00N 01°43'·70E VQ (3) 5s; ECM.
Cross Sand Lt By 52 37.00N°1 59.25E L Fl 10s 6m 5M; W HFP By, RWVS; Racon.
E Cross Sand Lt By 52 40.00N° 1 53.80E Fl (4) R 15s; PHM.
NE Cross Sand Lt By 52 43.00N°1 53.80E VQ (3) 5s; ECM.

SMITH'S KNOLL Lt F 52°43'·50N 02°18'·00E Fl (3) 20s 12m **23M**; R hull with Lt Tr amidships; RC; Racon; *Horn (3) 60s*.

S Winterton Ridge Lt By 52°47'·20N 02°03'·60E Q (6) + LFl 15s; SCM.
N Winterton Ridge Lt By 52°50'·10N 01°59'·87E Q; NCM.

NEWARP Lt F 52°48'·35N 01°55'·80E Fl 10s 12m 11M (H24); R hull with Lt Tr amidships; *Horn 20s* (H24), Racon.

S Haisbro Lt By 52°50'·80N 01°48.40E Q (6) + LFl 15s; SCM; *Bell*.
Mid Haisbro Lt By 52 54.20N°1 41.70E Fl (2) G 5s; NCM.

N Haisbro Lt By 53°00'·20N 01°32'·40E Q; NCM; *Bell*; Racon.
Happisburgh 52°49'·20N 01°32'·30E Fl (3) 30s 41m 14M; W Tr, 3 R bands.
R Lts on radio mast 1·2M NW.

CROMER
Cromer 52°55'·5N 01°19'·1E Fl 5s 84m **23M**; W 8-sided Tr; RC; vis 102°-307°; Racon.
Lifeboat House 2 FR (vert) 8m 5M.
E Sheringham Lt By 53°02'·20N 01°15'·00E Q (3) 10s; ECM.
W Sheringham Lt By 53°02'·97N 01°07'·70E Q (9) 15s; WCM.
Blakeney Overfalls Lt By 53°03'·00N 01°01'·50E Fl (2) R 5s; PHM; *Bell*.

WELLS.
Channel, W side 52°59'·0N 00°50'·2E Fl 5s 2m 3M; metal tripod.
East side Fl R 3s; ■ on metal tripod.
E Docking Lt By 53°09'·80N 00°50'·50E F IR 2·5s; PHM.
N Docking Lt By 53°14'·80N 00°41'·60E Q; NCM.
S Race Lt By 53°08'·65N 00°55'·80E Q (6) + LFl 15s; SCM; *Bell*.
N Race Lt By 53°14.·97N 00°44'·00E Fl G 5s; NCM; *Bell*.

(For marks further North, see 10.5.4).

Burnham Flats Lt By 53°07'·50N 00°35'·00E VQ (9) 10s; WCM; *Bell*.
North Well Lt By 53°03'·00N 00°28'·00E L Fl 10s; SWM; *Whis*; Racon.
Lynn Knock Lt By 53°04'·40N 00°27'·31E QG; NCM.
Woolpack Lt By 53°02'·65N 00°31'·55E Fl R 10s; PHM.

ROARING MIDDLE Lt F 52°58'·50N 00 21'·00E Q 5m 8M; NCM; *Bell*. Replaced May-June annually by B&Y pillar and bell By Q.

CORK HOLE.
Sunk Lt By 52°56'·50N 00°23'·85E Q (9) 15s; WCM.
No 1 Lt By 52°55'·70N 00°22'·10E VQ; NCM; *Bell*.
No 3 Lt By 52°54'·43N 00°24'·50E Q (3) 10s; ECM.
No 3A Lt By 52°53'·45N 00°24'·10E Fl G 5s; NCM. (Buoyage from Cork Hole to Lynn Cut subject to change).

KING'S LYNN.
Bn B 52°49'·1N 00°21'·2E Fl Y 2s 3m 2M; ▲ on B post.
Bn E 58°48'·2N 00°21'·5E Fl Y 6s 3m 2M; ▲ on B post.
West Bank 52°47'·4N 00°22'·1E Fl Y 2s 3m 4M; R pile structure.
Old Lynn Chan 52°51'·3N 00°15'·7E Fl G 10s 6m 1M; B ▲ on B col.
Trial Bank Bn 52°50'·5N 00°14'·7E Fl (2) 5s 13m 3M.

WISBECH CHANNEL (Note: Bns are moved as required)
Dale 52°50'·8N 00°12'·8E Fl G 2s 3M.
Double Brush 52°50'·1N 00°13'·1E QG 3M; X on Bn.

10.4.5 PASSAGE INFORMATION

THAMES ESTUARY (charts 1183, 1975)
On the N side of Thames Estuary (chart 1975) the main chans run seaward in a NE direction (e.g. West Swin, Barrow Deep, Black Deep, Knock Deep) lined by banks which dry in places. The main chans are well buoyed, but there have been many recent buoyage changes in this area. All the sandbanks in Thames Estuary are liable to change, and particular care is needed when crossing the est in a NW/SE direction. Bad vis and much shipping can add to the hazards. Even with a moderate wind against tide, a short and steep sea is easily raised in these shallow waters. For further notes on Thames Estuary, see 10.3.5. For North Sea crossing see 10.20.5.

FOULNESS TO HARWICH (charts 1975, 2052)

Foulness Sand extends nearly 6M NE from Foulness Pt, the extremity being marked by Whitaker Bn. On N side of Whitaker chan leading to R Crouch (10.4.8 and chart 3750) lies Buxey Sand, inshore of which is the Ray Sand chan (dries), a convenient short cut between R. Crouch and R. Blackwater with sufficient rise of tide. For detailed directions to E Coast hbrs (R Swale to Humber) see E Coast Rivers (Yachting Monthly). To seaward of Buxey Sand is Wallet Spitway (buoyed), and to NE of this is Gunfleet Sand, marked by Bys and drying in places along much of its 10M length. A conspic disused Lt Tr stands on SE side of Gunfleet Sand, about 6M SSE of Naze Tr, and here the SW- going (flood) stream begins about HW Sheerness +0600, and the NE-going stream at about HW Sheerness –0030, sp rates 2 kn.

Goldmer Gat and the Wallet give access to R. Colne (10.4.10) and R. Blackwater (10.4.9 and chart 3741). The chan is well marked and always accessible. The final appr 2M S of Colne Pt leads between Knoll (dries) on S side, and Eagle (depth 0·1m) on N side.

11M E of The Naze, the Sunk Lt F (Lt, fog sig, RC) guards the entrance to Harwich (10.4.12), an extensive and well sheltered hbr accessible at all times (chart 2693). From the S, approach through Medusa chan about 1M E of Naze Tr: at N end of this chan, 1M off Dovercourt, is Pye End By marking chan to Walton Backwaters (10.4.11). Making Harwich from the E beware Cork Sand (dries), S of which there is a minor chan. The main chan (well buoyed) passes N of Cork Sand and carries much commercial shipping. Approaching from NE beware Wadgate Ledge and the Platters about 1·5M ENE of Landguard Pt. S of Landguard Pt the W-going (flood) stream begins at HW Harwich +0600, and the E-going stream at HW Harwich, sp rates about 1·5 kn.

HARWICH TO GREAT YARMOUTH (charts 2052, 1543)
From 9M E of Felixstowe to 4M SSE of Orford Ness is the Shipwash shoal, marked by Bys and with a drying patch near its S end. Inshore of this is Bawdsey Bank, marked by Bys, with depths of 1·4m, on which the sea breaks in E gales. Still further inshore, and slightly S, 2M off the ent to R Deben (10.4.14) is a rky shoal called Cutler, with least depth of 1·8m, marked by By on E side.

Whiting Bank (buoyed) lies close SW of Orford Ness, and has a least depth of 0·9m. Hollesley Chan, about 1M wide, runs inshore W and N of this bank. In the SW part of Hollesley B is the ent to Orford Haven (10.4.15).

There are overfalls S of Orford Ness on both the ebb and flood streams. 2M E of Orford Ness the SW-going stream begins at HW Harwich +0605, sp rate 2·5 kn: the NE-going stream begins at HW Harwich –0010, sp rate 3kn.

Note that the direction of lateral buoyage changes just S of Orfordness near 52°N.

N of Orford Ness the coast is clear of offlying dangers past Aldeburgh and Southwold (10.4.16), as far as Benacre Ness, 5M S of Lowestoft (10.4.17). Sizewell power station is a conspic ■ building 1·5M N of Thorpe Ness.

Lowestoft may be approached from S by buoyed chan to Pakefield Road, Lowestoft South Road (close E of pier heads), W of Lowestoft Bank: beware strong set possibly across hbr ent. From the N, approach through Yarmouth Road and then proceed S through Gorleston, Corton and Lowestoft North Roads (buoyed). From E, approach through Holm chan. 2M E of Hr ent the S-going stream begins at HW Harwich +0530, and the N-going at HW Harwich –0110, sp rates 3 kn.

In the approaches to Great Yarmouth (10.4.18) from seaward there are frequent changes to the chans. The sea often breaks on North Scroby, Middle Scroby and Caister Shoal (all of which dry), and there are heavy tide rips over parts of Corton and South Scroby Sands, Middle and South Cross Sands, and Winterton Overfalls. 1M E of entrance to Gt Yarmouth Haven the S-going stream begins at HW Harwich +0530, and the N-going at HW Harwich –0050, sp rates 2·25 kn. Breydon Water (tidal) affects streams in the Haven: after heavy rain the out-going stream at Brush Quay may attain over 5 kn. For Norfolk Broads see 10.4.22.

About 12 M NE of Great Yarmouth lie Newarp Banks, on which the sea breaks in bad weather.

NORTH NORFOLK COAST (charts 106, 108)

Haisborough Sand (buoyed) lies 8M off the Norfolk coast, with depths of less than 1·8m in many places, and down to 0·4m. The shoal is steep-to, on its NE side in particular, and there are tidal eddies. Even a moderate sea or swell breaks on the shallower parts. There are dangerous wks near the S end. Haisborough Tail and Hammond Knoll (with wk depth 1·2m) lie to the E of S end of Haisborough Sand.

The streams follow the directions of the coast and of chans between the banks NE of the Norfolk coast. But in the outer chans the stream is somewhat rotatory: when changing from SE-going to NW-going it sets SW, and when changing from NW-going to SE-going it sets NE, across the shoals. Close S of Haisborough Sand the SE-going stream begins at HW Harwich +0530, and the NW-going at HW Harwich –0040, sp rates about 2·5 kn.

The coast of N Norfolk is unfriendly in bad weather, with no hbr accessible when there is any N in the wind. The hbrs all dry, and seas soon build up in the entrances or over the bars, some of which are dangerous even in a moderate breeze and an ebb tide. But in settled weather and moderate offshore winds it is a peaceful area to explore, particularly for boats which can take the ground. See 10.4.22.

If proceeding direct from Cromer to the Humber, pass S of Sheringham Shoal (buoyed) where the ESE-going stream begins at HW Immingham –0225, and the WNW-going at +0430. Proceed to NE of Blakeney Overfalls and Docking Shoal, and to SW of Race Bank, so as to fetch Inner Dowsing Lt Tr (Lt, fog sig). Thence pass E of Protector Overfalls, and steer for Rosse Spit By at SE side of Ent to Humber (10.5.8).

THE WASH (charts 108,1200)

The Wash is a shallow area of shifting sands, formed by the estuaries of the rivers Great Ouse, Nene, Welland and Witham. Important factors are the strong tidal streams, the low shore line, and frequent poor vis. Keep a careful watch on the echo sounder, and remember that Bys may have been moved to accommodate changes in the chan. In general terms the in-going stream begins at HW Immingham –0520, and the out-going at HW Immingham –0045, sp rates about 2 kn. The in-going stream is usually stronger than the out-going, but its duration is less. Prolonged NE winds cause an in-going current, which can increase the rate and duration of the in-going stream and also the height of sea level at the head of the estuary. Do not attempt entry to the rivers too early on the flood, which runs hard in the rivers.

4

SOUTHERN NORTH SEA WAYPOINTS 10-4-6

Selected waypoints for use in the Southern North Sea are nominated below. Further waypoints in coastal waters are given in 10.4.4 for the English Coast and 10.20.4 for the Belgium and Dutch coasts.

Aldeburgh Ridge Lt By	51°06'·82N 01°37'·60E
Barrow No.3 Lt By	51°42'·00N 01°19'·87E
Blakeney Overfalls Lt By	53°03'·00N 00°01'·50E
Burnham Flats Lt By	53°07'·50N 00°35'·00E
Buxey No 1 Lt By	51°39'·02N 01°00'·86E
Colne Bar Lt By	51°44'·58N 01°02'·65E
Cockle Lt By	52°44'·00N 01°43'·70E
Corton Lt By	52°31'·10N 01°51'·50E
Cross Sand Lt By	52°37'·00N 01°59'·25E
Crouch Lt By	51°37'·60N 00°56'·49E
Eagle Lt By	51°44'·10N 01°03'·92E
East Barnard Lt By	51°24'·60N 01°46'·20E
East Cross Sand Lt By	52°40'·00N 01°53'·80E
East Newcome Lt By	52°28'·48N 01°49'·32E
East Sheringham Lt By	53°02'·20N 01°15'·00E
East Shipwash Lt By	51°57'·05N 01°38'·00E
Foulness Lt By	51°39'·82N 01°03'·92E
Gunfleet Spit Lt By	51°45'·30N 01°21'·80E
Harwich HA Lt By	51°56'·40N 01°31'·20E
Horse Shoal Lt By	51°37'·07N 00°51'·62E
Inner Crouch Lt By	51°37'·19N 00°55'·22E
Knoll Lt By	51°43'·85N 01°05'·17E
Long Sand Hd Lt By	51°47'·87N 01°39'·53E
Medusa Lt By	51°51'·20N 01°20'·46E
Newarp Lt F	52°48'·35N 01°55'·80E
North Caister Lt By	52°41'·00N 01°45'·00E
North Docking Lt By	53°14'·80N 00°41'·60E
North East Gunfleet	51°49'·90N 01°27'·90E
North Galloper Lt By	51°50'·00N 01°59'·50E
North Haisbro Lt By	53°00'·20N 01°32'·40E
North Inner Gabbard Lt By	51°59'·10N 01°56'·10E
North Scroby Lt By	52°42'·20N 01°45'·80E
North Shipwash Lt By	52°01'·70N 01°38'·38E
North Well Lt By	53°03'·00N 00°28'·00E
North West Scroby Lt By	52°40'·00N 01°46'·20E
Orford Haven By	52°01'·78N 01°27'·98E
Outer Crouch Lt By	51°38'·35N 00°58'·61E
Outer Gabbard Lt V	51°59'·38N 02°04'·63E
Ridge Lt By	51°40'·10N 01°04'·99E
Rough Lt By	51°55'·65N 01°31'·30E
Scott Patch Lt By	51°11'·10N 00°36'·50E
Scroby Elbow Lt By	51°37'·70N 01°46'·50E
Shiphead Lt By	51°53'·75N 01°34'·05E
Shipwash Lt F	52°02'·03N 01°42'·05E
Smiths Knoll Lt F	52°43'·50N 02°18'·00E
South Cork Lt By	51°51'·30N 01°24'·20E
South Inner Gabbard Lt By	51°51'·20N 01°52'·40E
South Galloper Lt By	51°43'·95N 01°56'·50E
South Haisbro Lt By	52°50'·80N 01°48'·40E
South Newcome Lt By	52°25'·70N 01°45'·20E
South Race Lt By	53°08'·65N 00°55'·80E
South West Scroby Lt By	52°35'·81N 01°46'·55E
Sunk Lt F	51°51'·00N 01°35'·00E
Sunk Head Tr Lt By	51°46'·60N 01°30'·60E
Sunken Buxey Lt By	51°39'·50N 01°00'·60E
Swin Spitway Lt By	51°41'·92N 01°08'·45E
Trinity Lt By	51°49'·00N 01°36'·50E
Wallet No.2 Lt By	51°48'·85N 01°23'·10E
Wallet No.4 Lt By	51°46'·50N 01°17'·33E
Wells Fairway Lt By	53°00'·20N 00°51'·15E
West Sheringham Lt By	53°02'·97N 01°07'·70E
Whitaker Lt By	51°41'·40N 01°10'·61E
Whitaker No 1 Lt By	51°41'·15N 01°09'·77E
Woodbridge Haven Lt By	51°58'·47N 01°24'·35E
Woolpack Lt By	53°02'·65N 00°31'·55E

AREAS 19 AND 20

Abbeville Lt By	50°56'·08N 01°37'·42E
Akkaert NE Lt By	51°27'·31N 02°59'·38E
Akkaert Midden Lt By	51°24'·23N 02°53'·50E
Akkaert SW Lt By	51°22'·30N 02°46'·40E
A-Noord Lt By	51°23'·50N 02°37'·00E
A-Zuid Lt By	51°21'·50N 02°37'·00E
Bergues N Lt By	51°19'·90N 02°24'·62E
Bergues Lt By	51°16'·20N 02°18'·70E
Bergues S Lt Buoy	51°15'·16N 02°19'·50E
Binnenstroombank Lt By	51°14'·50N 02°53'·73E
BT Ratel Lt By	51°11'·58N 02°28'·00E
Buitenstroombank Lt By	51°15'·20N 02°51'·80E
Dunkerque Lanby	51°03'·00N 01°51'·83E
Dyck E Lt By	51°05'·70N 02°05'·80E
Fairy S Lt By	51°21'·22N 02°17'·35E
Fairy W Lt By	51°23'·90N 02°09'·44E
F3 Lanby	51°23'·80N 02°00'·60E
Goote Bank Lt By	51°27'·00N 02°52'·70E
Hinder 1	51°20'·90N 02°11'·06E
Kwintebank Lt By	51°21'·75N 02°43'·00E
LST "420" Lt By	51°15'·50N 02°40'·70E
Middelkirkebank N Lt By	51°20'·87N 02°46'·40E
Middelkirkebank S Lt By	51°14'·78N 02°42°·00E
Middelkirkebank Lt By	51°18'·25N 02°42'·80E
Nautica Ena Lt By	51°18'·12N 02°52'·85E
Nieuwpoortbank Lt By	51°10'·21N 02°36'·16E
Oost Dyck W Lt By	51°17'·18N 02°26'·42E
Oostendebank N Lt By	51°21'·25N 02°53'·00E
Oostendebank Oost Lt By	51°17'·36N 02°52'·00E
Oostendebank W Lt By	51°16'·25N 02°44'·85E
Ruytingen SW Lt By	51°05'·00N 01°46'·85E
Ruytingen SE Lt By	51°09'·18N 01°08'·98E
Sandettié Lt V	51°09'·30N 01°47'·20E
Sandettié N Lt By	51°18'·42N 02°04'·80E
Sandettié SW Lt By	51°09'·70N 01°45'·70E
Sandettié WSW Lt By	51°12'·32N 01°51'·10E
SW Wandelaar Lt By	51°22'·00N 03°01'·00E
SCH 3 Lt By	51°24'·35N 03°02'·90E
SCH 4 Lt By	51°25'·05N 03°03'·10E
Scheur-Zand Lt By	51°23'·70N 03°07'·68E
SW Thornton Lt By	51°31'·01N 02°51'·00E
Trapegeer Lt By	51°08'·45N 02°34'·45E
Wenduinebank E Lt By	51°18'·88N 03°01'·71E
Wenduinebank W Lt By	51°17'·30N 02°52'·87E
West Hinder Lt V	51°22·98N 02°26'·40E
Westroombank Lt Buoy	51°11'·39N 02°43'·15E
Wielingen Zand Lt By	51°22'·60N 03°10'·80E
Zand Lt By	51°22'·50N 03°10'·12E
Zuidstroombank Lt Buoy	51°12'·33N 02°47'·50E

4

10.4.7 DISTANCE TABLE

Approximate distances in nautical miles are by the most direct route while avoiding dangers and allowing for traffic separation schemes etc. Places in *italics* are in adjoining areas.

1 *Cap Gris Nez*	**1**																			
2 *North Foreland*	32	**2**																		
3 *Shoeburyness*	61	29	**3**																	
4 Burnham-on-Crouch	68	36	27	**4**																
5 West Mersea	67	35	30	22	**5**															
6 Walton-on-Naze	68	36	31	25	18	**6**														
7 Harwich	74	42	37	31	24	6	**7**													
8 River Deben	75	43	41	35	28	10	8	**8**												
9 Orford Ness	74	44	49	43	36	18	15	8	**9**											
10 Southwold	91	59	64	58	51	33	30	23	15	**10**										
11 Lowestoft	101	69	74	68	61	43	40	33	25	10	**11**									
12 Great Yarmouth	109	77	82	76	69	51	48	41	33	18	7	**12**								
13 Wells	157	125	130	124	117	99	96	89	81	66	56	50	**13**							
14 Kings Lynn	184	152	157	151	144	126	123	116	108	93	83	77	33	**14**						
15 *Grimsby*	201	169	174	168	161	143	140	133	125	110	100	94	54	61	**15**					
16 *Flamborough Head*	224	192	197	191	184	166	163	156	148	133	123	117	77	86	44	**16**				
17 *Oostende*	50	58	80	91	88	74	76	73	72	81	83	93	143	187	194	211	**17**			
18 *Goeree Tower*	103	91	111	108	104	100	99	85	78	79	81	83	125	152	169	186	51	**18**		
19 *IJmuiden*	149	137	155	151	140	125	126	122	110	105	102	102	143	170	182	193	97	46	**19**	
20 *Brunsbüttel*	362	337	348	342	337	320	320	312	306	296	288	287	310	343	332	330	314	263	221	**20**

BURNHAM-ON-CROUCH

Essex

10-4-8

CHARTS

Admiralty 3750, 1975, 1183; Stanford 4, 5; Imray, Y17; OS 168/178

TIDES

+0129 Dover; ML 3·0; Duration 0610; Zone 0 (GMT).

Standard Port SHEERNESS (⟵)

Times				Height (metres)			
HW		LW		MHWS	MHWN	MLWN	MLWS
0000	0600	0100	0700	5·7	4·7	1·5	0·6
1200	1800	1300	1900				
Differences BURNHAM-ON-CROUCH							
−0020	−0020	−0005	−0005	−0·5	−0·5	−0·5	−0·4

NOTE: Rivers Crouch and Roach, out as far as Foulness Point, are controlled by the Crouch River Authority. The Crouch is navigable up to Battlesbridge, 15 M from Foulness.

SHELTER

Rivers are exposed to all winds. Anchoring prohibited in fairway but is possible just above or below the moorings. Cliff Reach is important to yachtsmen as it provides shelter from SW winds. There are many moorings and landing places in the R Roach S of Wallasea Island. See 10.4.22.

NAVIGATION

Waypoint Outer Crouch Lt Buoy Fl G5s 51° 38′·35N, 00° 58′61E. There are few landmarks to assist entering the Crouch. By day, the buoys marking Whitaker Channel are easily found. Channel now lit, Lt Buoys from Outer Crouch to westward. There is a 'Firing Danger Area' just to S of Foulness Point. Speed limit in river is 8kn.

N.B. Landing on Bridgemarsh Is (up river) is strictly forbidden.

LIGHTS AND MARKS

From Sunken Buxey N cardinal Lt Buoy, St Mary's church spire bearing 233° leads to Outer Crouch stbd-hand buoy, Fl G 5s, and from here 240° leads into river. Crouch buoy Fl R 10s, Inner Crouch buoy LFl 10s.

RADIO TELEPHONE

Essex Marina VHF Ch **80** (0900-1700 LT). West Wick Marina Ch **80** M (1000-1700 LT).

TELEPHONE (0621)

Hr Mr 783602; MRSC Frinton-on-Sea 675518; # (0473) 219481; Marinecall 0898 500 455; Police 782121; Dr 782054.

FACILITIES

BURNHAM EC Wednesday; **Burnham Yacht Harbour** (350) ☎ 782150, ME, El, Sh, BH (30 ton), CH, ▣, R, Access H24; **Royal Corinthian YC** ☎ 782105, AB, FW, M, L, R, Bar; **Royal Burnham YC** ☎ 782044, FW, L, R, Bar; **R. J. Prior** ☎ 782160, AB, BY, C (15 ton), D, FW, L, ME, El, Sh, M, Slip; **Kelvin Aqua** ☎ 782659, L, CH, FW, ACA, Gas, Gaz; **W. Yardley** ☎ 782076, BY, D, FW, M, ME, CH, M; **Petticrow** (200) ☎ 782115, BY, C (4 ton), D, El, FW, M, ME, Sh, Slip; **Rice and Cole** ☎ 782063, BY, C (4½ ton), CH, D, M, Sh, L, Gas, Gaz, M, FW; **Crouch YC** ☎ 782252, L, FW, R, Bar; **Hood** ☎ 782821, SM; **Cranfield Sails** ☎ 782108, SM; **Crouch Engineering** ☎ 782130, D, El, L, ME, P, AB; **Duerr Engineering** ☎ 782726, El, ME (H24); **Peter Barker** ☎ 782403, Sh; **Tubby Lee Yachting Services** ☎ 783562, Rigging;

Town V, R, Bar, ✉; Ⓑ; ⇌; ✈ (Southend).

WALLASEA **Essex Marina** (400) ☎ Canewdon 531, AB, BY, Gas, Bar, C (13 ton), BH (40 ton), CH, D, El, FW, L, M, ME, P, R, Sh, Slip, V, YC; **Shuttlewoods BY** ☎ Canewdon 226, ME, El, Sh; **Essex YC.**

FAMBRIDGE **West Wick Marina** (Stow Creek) (180) ☎ 741268, AB, Gas, Gaz, CH, El, Slip, FW, D, C (5 ton), YC, Bar; **North Fambridge Yacht Station** (150) ☎ 740370, CH, Sh, M, ME, BY, C (5 ton), El, FW, L, Slip, Gas, Gaz, Access HW∓5; **Brandy Hole Yacht Station** (120) ☎ Southend-on-Sea 230248, L, M, ME, Sh, Slip, Gas, Gaz, Bar, BY, D, FW, Access HW∓4.

ALTHORNE **Bridge Marsh Marina** (125+6 visitors) ☎ 740414 FW, Sh, ▣, ME, El, C (8 ton), Slip Access HW∓4.

BURNHAM-ON-CROUCH *continued*

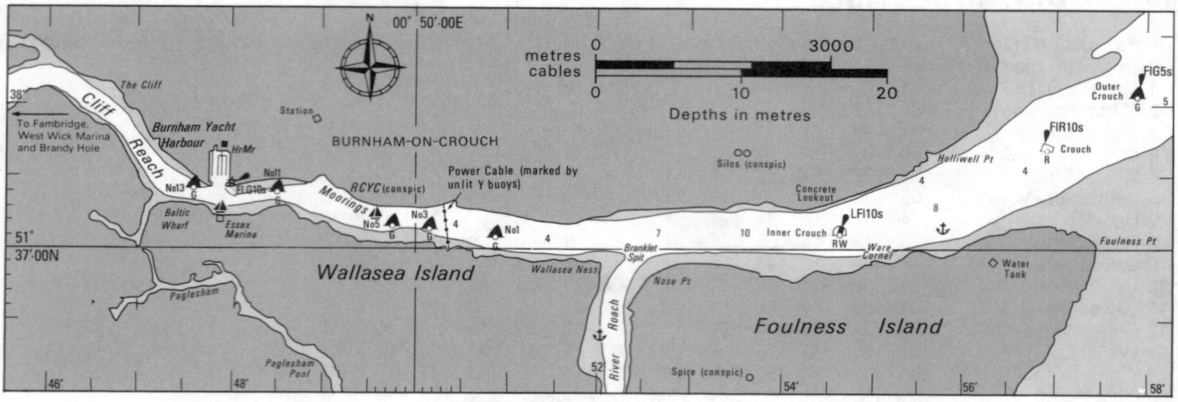
00° 50'·00E
metres
cables
0
3000
0
10
20
Depths in metres
The Cliff
Cliff Reach
To Fambridge, West Wick Marina and Brandy Hole
Burnham Yacht Harbour
HrMr
Station
BURNHAM-ON-CROUCH
No13
No11
FlG10s
RCYC (conspic)
Moorings
Power Cable (marked by unlit Y buoys)
No5
No3
No1
Baltic Wharf
Essex Marina
Silos (conspic)
Concrete Lookout
LFl10s
Inner Crouch
RW
Holliwell Pt
FlR10s
Crouch
Outer Crouch
FlG5s
Ware Corner
Foulness Pt
Water Tank
Branklet Spit
Wallasea Ness
Nase Pt
Wallasea Island
Foulness Island
Paglesham
Paglesham Pool
River Roach
Spire (conspic)
51° 37'·00N
46'
48'
54'
56'
58'

BLACKWATER RIVER 10-4-9

Essex

CHARTS
Admiralty 3741, 1975, 1183; Stanford 4, 5; Imray, Y17; OS 168

TIDES
Maldon +0140 Dover; ML 2·8; Duration 0620; Zone 0 (GMT).

Standard Port SHEERNESS (⟵)

Times				Height (metres)			
HW		LW		MHWS	MHWN	MLWN	MLWS
0000	0600	0100	0700	5·7	4·7	1·5	0·6
1200	1800	1300	1900				
Differences TOLLESBURY (Mill Creek)							
−0027	−0027	−0019	−0019	−0·9	−0·8	−0·6	−0·4
OSEA ISLAND							
−0005	−0005	−0016	−0016	−0·4	−0·4	−0·2	−0·1
MALDON							
+0005	+0005	No data		−2·8	−2·4	No data	

SHELTER
By choosing the appropriate area good shelter can always be found. Entrance to the Chelmer and Blackwater canal by Heybridge basin at Maldon. Lock opens HW−1 to HW. For moorings, ring River Bailiff.

NAVIGATION
Waypoint Knoll N cardinal buoy, Q, 51°43'·85N 01°05'·17E, 107°/287° from/to Nass Bn, 6·7M.
WEST MERSEA Beware oyster beds between Cobmarsh Is and Packing Marsh Is and in Salcott Chan.
BRADWELL No dangers but only suitable for small craft and area gets very crowded.
TOLLESBURY FLEET Proceeding up Woodrolfe Creek, a tide mark shows the depth over the yacht harbour entrance sill (approx 3m at MHWS and 2m at MHWN). Speed limits: Woodrolfe Creek 4 kms upper reaches and at Osea Is, Tollesbury Fleet S.Channel 8 kms.

LIGHTS AND MARKS
Bradwell Yacht Marina entrance W side has two beacons B triangular topmarks; E side has beacon with R square topmark.
MALDON After rounding S of Osea Is, 'The Doctor', Blackwater SC Lt showing Iso G 5s at 300° leads approximately up the channel. Alternatively No 3 and No 8 buoys in line at 305°.

RADIO TELEPHONE
Bradwell Marina VHF Ch **80** M (office hours). Tollesbury Marina Ch **80** M (office hours).

TELEPHONE (0621)
Hr Mr 856726; River Bailiff 854477; Hr Mr (Maldon) 53110; MRSC Frinton-on-Sea 675518; Canal Lockmaster 853506; # (0473) 219481; Marinecall 0898 500 455; Police (0245) 491212 (West Mersea (0206) 762212); Dr 854118, West Mersea 382015.

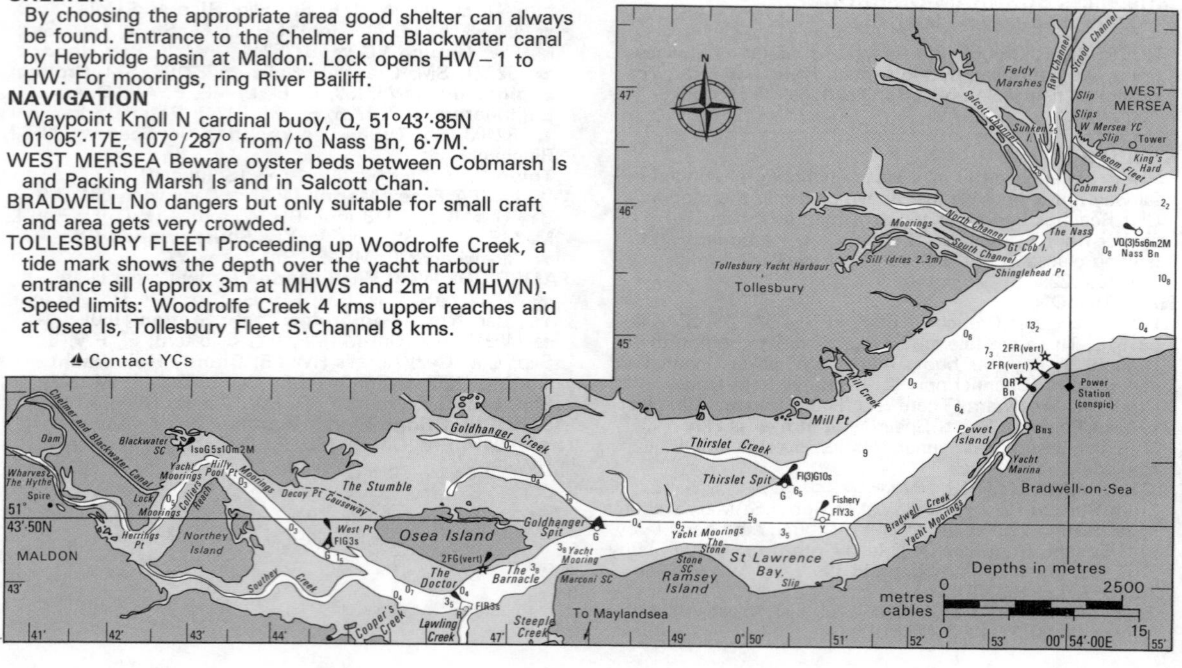
▲ Contact YCs
Feldy Marshes
Ray Channel
Strood Channel
Salcott Channel
Sunken I.
WEST MERSEA
Slip
Slips
W Mersea YC
Tower
King's Hard
Besom Fleet
Cobmarsh I.
Moorings
North Channel
South Channel
The Nass
Gt Cob I.
Sill (dries 2.3m)
Tollesbury Yacht Harbour
Tollesbury
Shinglehead Pt
VQ(3)5s6m2M
Nass Bn
2FR(vert)
2FR(vert)
QR Bn
Power Station (conspic)
Mill Creek
Mill Pt
Pewet Island
Bns
Yacht Marina
Bradwell-on-Sea
Thirslet Creek
Thirslet Spit
Fl(3)G10s
Fishery
FlY3s
Bradwell Creek
Yacht Moorings
Goldhanger Creek
Blackwater SC
IsoG5s10m2M
Chelmer and Blackwater Canal
Dam
Wharves The Hythe
Spire
Lock
Moorings
Hilly Pool Pt
Collier's Reach
Moorings
The Stumble
Decoy Pt
Causeway
Herrings Pt
Northey Island
MALDON
West Pt
FlG3s
Osea Island
Goldhanger Spit
2FG(vert)
The Doctor
The Barnacle
Yacht Mooring
Yacht Moorings
The Stone
Stone SC
St Lawrence Bay
Ramsey Island
Marconi SC
Southey Creek
Cooper's Creek
Lawling Creek
Steeple Creek
Fl R3s
To Maylandsea
Slip
Depths in metres
metres
cables
0
2500
15
51° 43'·50N
00° 54'·00E

BLACKWATER RIVER *continued*

FACILITIES

EC W Mersea, Tollesbury, Maldon — Wednesday.
TOLLESBURY: **Tollesbury Marina** (240+20 visitors) ☎ 868471, Slip, D, AC, BH (10 ton), Gas, Gaz, FW, ME, El, Sh, C (5 ton), CH, V, R, Bar, ◙, Access HW∓1½; **Tollesbury Cruising Club** ☎ 869561, Bar, R, M, C (20 ton), D, CH, FW, L, Slip, AC, ME, El, Sh; **Pier** FW; **Volspec** ☎ 869756, ME; **Tollesbury Saltings** ☎ 868421, Access HW ∓ 2 Slip, FW, ME, El, Sh; **A.P. Marine** ☎ 869589, CH. **Village** P, V, R, Bar. ✉; Ⓑ (Tues, Thurs 1000-1430); ⇌ (bus to Witham); ✈ (Southend or Cambridge).
WEST MERSEA: (0206) **Clarke & Carter BY** ☎ 382244, Slip (+ dock), M, L (at high water), FW, ME, El, C (10 ton), CH; **William Wyatt** ☎ 382856, Slip, M, ME, El, CH; **Causeway** P and D (A. Clark), L, FW, ME, El, V; **Gowen Sails** ☎ 382922, SM; **West Mersea YC** ☎ 382947, M (see boatman), R, Bar; **Mersea Chandlers** ☎ 384433, CH, ACA; **Town** P, D, FW, ME, El, CH, V, R, Bar. ✉; Ⓑ; ⇌ (bus to Colchester); ✈ (Southend or Cambridge).
BRADWELL: **Bradwell Marina** (280, some visitors) ☎ 76235, Slip, AC, Gas, Gaz, D, P, FW, ME, El, Sh, BH (16 ton), CH, R, Bar, Access HW∓4½; **Bradwell Quay** Slip, L; **Bradwell Quay YC** ☎ 76539, M, FW, Bar, L, Slip. **Town** ✉; Ⓑ (Maldon); ⇌ (bus to Southminster); ✈ (Southend).
MALDON: **Maldon Quay** Slip, M, P, D, FW, AB; **Dan Webb & Feesey** ☎ 854280, Slip, D, Sh, CH, M; **Fairways Marine Engineers** ☎ 852866, ME, El; **Heybridge Basin** ☎ 854022, D, ME, El, Sh, CH, Bar; **Blackwater SC** ☎ 853923, L, FW; **Holt and James** ☎ 854022, Slip, D, L, M, FW, CH; **Mantsbrite Marine Electronics** ☎ 853003, Ⓔ, El; **A Taylor** ☎ 853456, SM; **Anglian Yacht Services** ☎ 852290 emergencies. **Town** ✉; Ⓑ; ⇌ (bus to Chelmsford); ✈ (Southend, Cambridge or Stanstead).
MAYLANDSEA: **Marina** Access HW∓2; **Dan Webb and Feesey** (350) ☎ 740264, Slip, D, Sh, CH.

RIVER COLNE 10-4-10

Essex

CHARTS

Admiralty 3741, 1975, 1183; Stanford 5, 4; Imray, Y17; OS 168

TIDES

+0055 Dover; ML 2·5; Duration 0615; Zone 0 (GMT).
Standard Port SHEERNESS (⟵)

Times				Height (metres)			
HW		LW		MHWS	MHWN	MLWN	MLWS
0200	0800	0100	0700	5·7	4·7	1·5	0·6
1400	2000	1300	1900				
Differences BRIGHTLINGSEA							
−0035	−0035	−0025	−0025	−0·7	−0·9	−0·3	−0·2
WIVENHOE							
−0011	−0011	No data			No data		

SHELTER

Suitable shelter can be found for most winds. Anchorages in Brightlingsea Creek; to the W of Mersea Stone Pt; in Pyefleet, E of Pewit Is; R Colne navigable up to Wivenhoe (4·5m draught) or Hythe, Colchester (3m draught). Outer harbour is exposed to westerly winds.

NAVIGATION

Waypoint Colne Bar (stbd-hand) buoy, 51°44′·58N 01°02′·66E, 158°/338° from/to Mersea Stone, 3·6M. See also 10.4.9. Extensive mud and sand banks flank the entrance channel. The entrance to Brightlingsea creek is very narrow at LW. River traffic in the Colne is considerable. Large coasters use the Brightlingsea channels. Speed limits – 8kn; Buoy 13 to Fingringhoe (except Buoy 12 to 16) 5kn; Fingringhoe to Colchester 4kn.

LIGHTS AND MARKS

Up as far as Wivenhoe, where the river dries out, it is extremely well buoyed. Brightlingsea has FR Ldg Lts adjusted according to the channel and channel buoys Fl (3) G 8s and Fl (2) R 8s. A Y Lt is exhibited from The Tower by Westmarsh Pt.

RADIO TELEPHONE

Colchester Harbour Radio VHF Ch 16 **68**; 11 14 **68** (Office hrs & HW−2 to HW+1). Tel. Colchester 575858.

TELEPHONE (0621)

Hr Mr 52110; Harbour Office Brightlingsea 2200; MRSC Frinton-on-Sea 675518; Canal Lockmaster 53506; # (0473) 219481; Marinecall 0898 500 455; Police 52255; Dr 52535, West Mersea 382015.

FACILITIES

BRIGHTLINGSEA: (020 630) **Town Hard** ☎ 3535, L, FW; **Colne YC** ☎ 2594, L, FW, R, Bar; **L.H. Morgan** ☎ 2003, M, Gas, D, L, FW, ME, El, Ⓔ, Sh, CH, ACA; **Cox Marine** ME, El, Sh; **French Marine Motors** ☎ 2133, CH, P, D, ME, El, Ⓔ; **Brightlingsea SC** Slip, Bar; **James Lawrence** ☎ 2863, SM; **The Boatcentre** ☎ 2003, CH; **St Osyth BY** ☎ St Osyth 820005, M, L, FW, ME, C, Sh, El, Slip; **Town** P, D, FW, ME, El, Sh, C (mobile), CH, V, R, Bar; ✉; Ⓑ; ⇌ (bus to Wivenhoe or Colchester); ✈ (Southend or Cambridge).
WIVENHOE: (020 622) **Colne Marine Yacht** ☎ 2417, L, ME, El, Sh, C; **Wivenhoe SC; Village near quay** P, V, Bar; ✉; Ⓑ (AM only); ⇌; ✈ (Southend or Cambridge).
Note: A marina is planned at Brightlingsea shipyard.

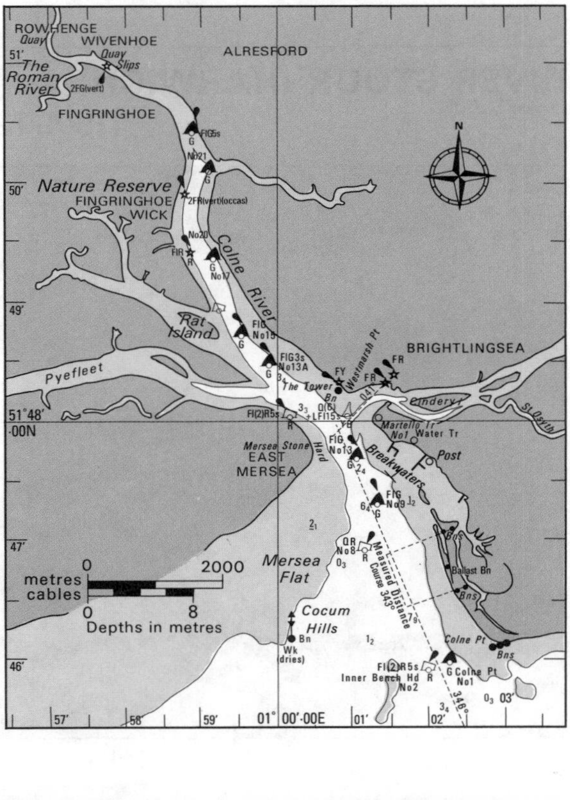
ROWHENGE Quay
WIVENHOE
Quay Slips
ALRESFORD
The Roman River
FINGRINGHOE
Nature Reserve
FINGRINGHOE WICK
Colne River
Rat Island
Pyefleet
BRIGHTLINGSEA
The Tower
Westmarsh Pt
Cindery I
St Osyth
Martello Tr
Water Tr
Mersea Stone
Hard
EAST MERSEA
Breakwaters
Post
Mersea Flat
Measured Distance
Ballast Bn
Cocum Hills
Colne Pt
Inner Bench Hd
metres 0 2000
cables 0 8
Depths in metres
01° 00′·00E
51°48′·00N

WALTON-ON-THE-NAZE

Essex

10-4-11

CHARTS
Admiralty 2695, 2052; Stanford 5, 6; Imray, Y16; OS 169

TIDES
+0040 Dover; ML 2·3; Duration 0615; Zone 0 (GMT).

Standard Port HARWICH (⟶)

Times				Height (metres)			
HW		LW		MHWS	MHWN	MLWN	MLWS
0000	0600	0000	0600	4·0	3·4	1·1	0·4
1200	1800	1200	1800				
Differences WALTON-ON-THE-NAZE							
−0008	−0011	+0008	+0005	+0·2	0·0	0·0	0·0

SHELTER
The 'Walton Backwaters' give good shelter in any weather. Go alongside in marina in The Twizzle or anchor in Hamford Water, or in Walton Channel. W & F Yacht Trust Basin, Tel. Frinton 675873, entry HW−1 to HW. Keel boats can stay afloat in Walton Channel (N end 7m, S end 5m) or in the Twizzle (E end 5m).

NAVIGATION
Waypoint Pye End (safe water) buoy, 51°55'·00N 01°18'·00E, 054°/234° from/to buoyed channel entrance, 1·0M. Beware lobster pots off the Naze, Pye Sands and oyster beds S and W of Horsey I.

LIGHTS AND MARKS
Whether approaching from N or S it is necessary to find Pye End buoy marking the N extremity of Pye sand. The most conspic landmark is the Naze tower just N of Walton- on-the-Naze. There are no lights so the Backwaters cannot be entered at night.

RADIO TELEPHONE
None.

TELEPHONE (0255)
Hr Mr Harwich 243030; MRSC Frinton-on-Sea 675518; # (0473) 219481; Marinecall 0898 500 455; Police 241312; Ⓗ 502446.

FACILITIES
EC Wednesday; **Titchmarsh Marina** (450+10 visitors), ☎ 672185, Slip, D, FW, Gas, Gaz, AC, ME, C (35 ton), BH (10 ton), CH, R, Bar, Sh, Access HW∓4½; **Walton Channel** M; **Walton & Frinton YC** ☎ 675526, L, FW, AB, Bar; **Twizzle Creek** M, L; **Bedwell & Co** ☎ 675873, Slip, M, D, C (½ ton), Sh, CH; **Frank Halls** ☎ 675596, Slip, M, FW, D, Sh, CH, ME, El, Sh; **Bateson** ☎ 671348, El; **Town** P, V, R, Bar. ✉; Ⓑ; ≹; ✈ (Southend or Cambridge).

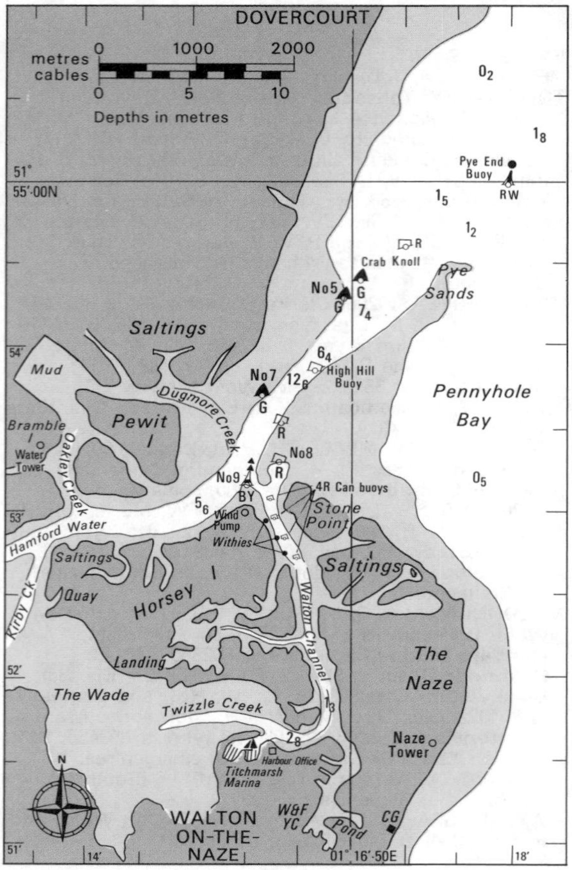
DOVERCOURT
metres 0 1000 2000
cables 0 5 10
Depths in metres
Pye End Buoy
RW
Crab Knoll
Pye Sands
No5
No7
No8
No9
High Hill Buoy
Pennyhole Bay
Saltings
Mud
Pewit I
Dugmore Creek
Bramble I
Water Tower
Oakley Creek
4R Can buoys
Stone Point
Wind Pump
Withies
Hamford Water
Saltings
Horsey I
Quay
Kirby Ck
Walton Channel
The Naze
Landing
The Wade
Twizzle Creek
Naze Tower
Harbour Office
Titchmarsh Marina
WALTON ON-THE-NAZE
W&F YC
Pond
CG
01° 16'·50E
55'·00N

RIVER STOUR (HARWICH)

Essex/Suffolk

10-4-12

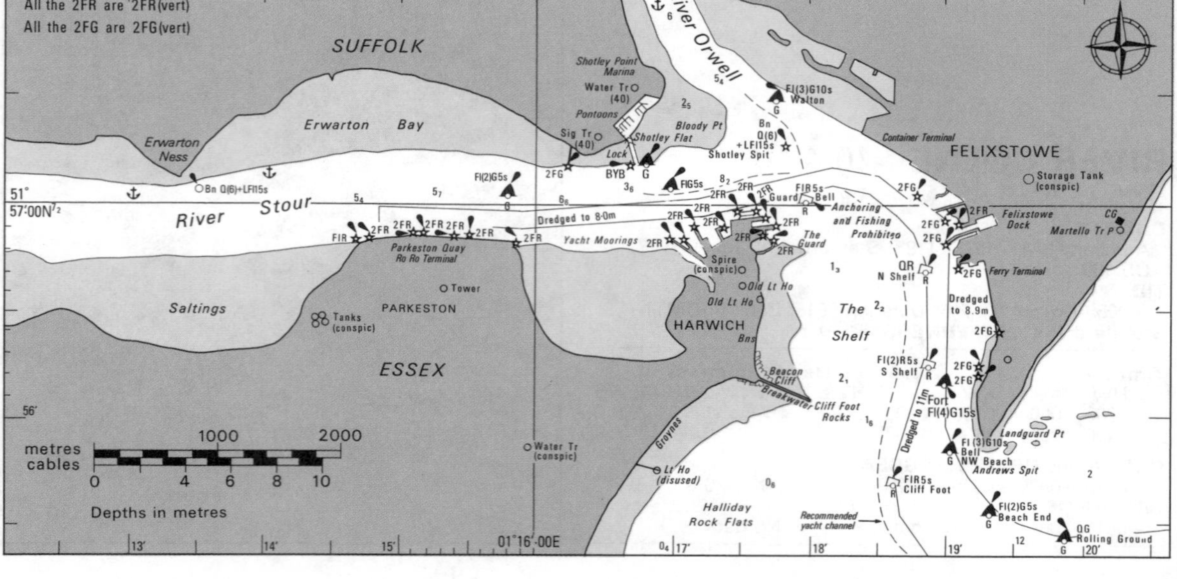
All the 2FR are 2FR(vert)
All the 2FG are 2FG(vert)
SUFFOLK
Erwarton Bay
Erwarton Ness
River Stour
Shotley Point Marina
River Orwell
Fl(3)G10s Walton
Shotley Spit
Container Terminal
FELIXSTOWE
Storage Tank (conspic)
Felixstowe Dock
Martello Tr
Dredged to 8·0m
Yacht Moorings
Parkeston Quay Ro Ro Terminal
Anchoring and Fishing Prohibited
The Guard
Ferry Terminal
Saltings
Tanks (conspic)
PARKESTON
Tower
HARWICH
Spire (conspic)
Old Lt Ho
The Shelf
N Shelf
S Shelf
Dredged to 8·9m
ESSEX
Beacon Cliff
Breakwater
Cliff Foot Rocks
Landguard Pt
NW Beach
Andrews Spit
Beach End
Rolling Ground
Lt Ho (disused)
Halliday Rock Flats
Recommended yacht channel
Water Tr (conspic)
metres 0 1000 2000
cables 0 4 6 8 10
Depths in metres
01°16'·00E

RIVER STOUR (HARWICH) *continued*

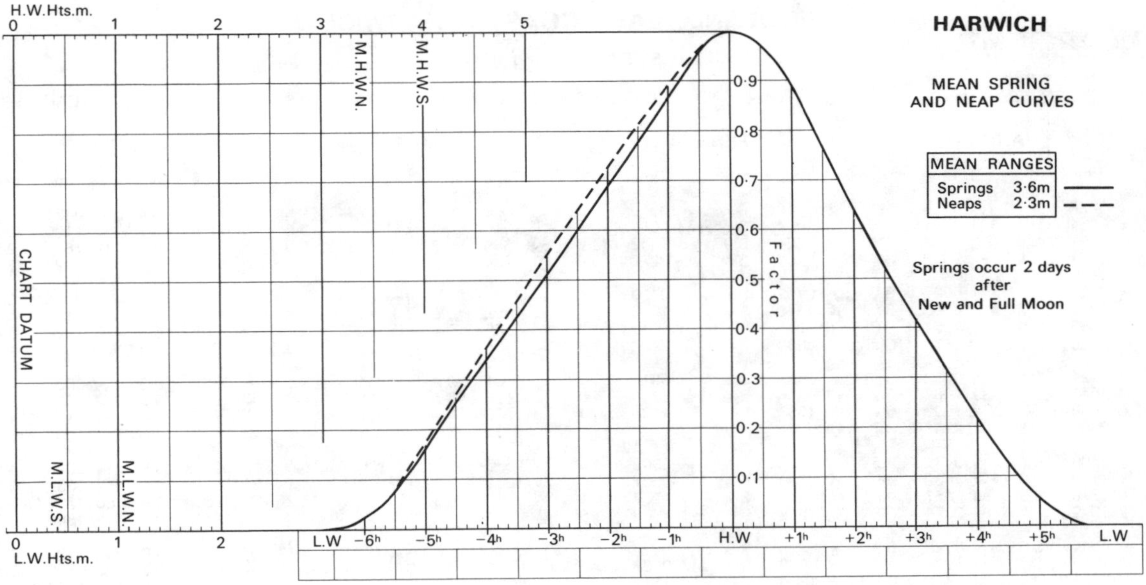
HARWICH
MEAN SPRING AND NEAP CURVES
MEAN RANGES
Springs 3·6m
Neaps 2·3m
Springs occur 2 days after New and Full Moon
H.W.Hts.m.
L.W.Hts.m.
CHART DATUM
M.H.W.N.
M.H.W.S.
M.L.W.S.
M.L.W.N.
Factor
L.W -6h -5h -4h -3h -2h -1h H.W +1h +2h +3h +4h +5h L.W

CHARTS
Admiralty 2693, 1594, 1491, 1593; Stanford 5, 6; Imray, Y16; OS 169

TIDES
+0050 Dover; ML 2·2; Duration 0630; Zone 0 (GMT)

Standard Port HARWICH (⟶)

Times				Height (metres)			
HW		LW		MHWS	MHWN	MLWN	MLWS
0000	0600	0000	0600	4·0	3·4	1·1	0·4
1200	1800	1200	1800				
Differences MISTLEY							
+0025	+0025	0000	+0020	+0·2	0·0	−0·1	−0·1

NOTE: Harwich is a Standard Port and times and heights of tidal predicitions for each day of the year are given below.

SHELTER
Good. Anchor off Erwarton Ness, Wrabness or Holbrook Creek. Alongside berths at Shotley Point Marina, Harwich Quay (dries) for short periods near HW, and at New Mistley and Manningtree (dry; off chartlet). No facilities for yachts at Felixstowe.

NAVIGATION
Waypoint Cork Sand (port-hand) Lt By Fl(3) R10s 51°55′·43N, 01°25′·56E, 086°/266° from/to position 0·7M S of Landguard Point, 3·9M. Beware commercial shipping. Yachts must keep clear of deep water channel: recommended track to S of it from Cork Sand Bn and thence to W of it past Harwich. Entrance to Shotley Point Marina through marked channel, with outer limits lit, to lock gate at all states of tide. The channel up the R Stour is well marked. Beware 'The Horse' 2 ca NW of Stone Pt and also the drying bank 1½ ca NW of Wrabness Point. The channel from Mistley Quay to Manningtree is narrow and tortuous, local knowledge is invaluable.

Special Local Sound Signals
Commercial vessels may use these additional signals:

Four short and rapid blasts followed by one short blast	=	I am turning short around to starboard.
Four short and rapid blasts followed by two short blasts	=	I am turning short around to port.
One prolonged blast	=	I am leaving a dock, quay or anchorage.

LIGHTS AND MARKS
The channel West from Harwich past Parkeston Quay to Harkstead Pt (off chartlet) is marked by G conical stbd-hand buoys, Fl G or QG. There is a conspic factory chimney at Cattawade, straight up the river about 8 M. If kept dead ahead on course 270° it will lead through the best water up to Harkstead Pt. Shotley Pt Marina Dir Lt 339° on E side of lock entrance indicates dredged channel. Entrance to marina assisted by Inogen Visual Guidance Marker Lights which are square, ambered displays on which a vertical black line indicates position on the approach centre line. Off the centre line, arrows indicate the direction to steer to regain the correct approach line.

RADIO TELEPHONE
Call: *Harwich Harbour Control* VHF Ch 16 11 14 **71** (H24). Yachts are requested not to use Ch 71 but it is useful to monitor the channel to obtain information on shipping. Local weather, tidal information etc available on request. The Harwich Harbour Board Patrol launch, *Godwit* keeps regular patrol and listening watch on VHF Ch 11. Shotley Point Marina Ch **80** M (lock master).
See also River Orwell. (10.4.13).

TELEPHONE (0255)
Hr Mr 243030; MRSC Frinton-on-Sea 675518; Harwich Haven Authority 243030; Harbour Operations Room 243111; # (0473) 219481; Marinecall 0898 500 455; Police 241312; Dr 506451; Ⓗ 502446.

FACILITIES
EC Wednesday
HARWICH: **Town Pier** L, FW, AB (tidal); **Royal Harwich YC** ☎ Woolverstone 780319; **Dolphin Sails** ☎ 243366, SM; **F.M. Services** ☎ 506808, Gas; **R & J Marine** ☎ 502849, El; **Town** P, D, ME, El, Sh, V, R, Bar. ✉; Ⓑ; ⇌; ✈ (Cambridge or Norwich).
SHOTLEY: **Shotley Point Marina** (350—visitors welcome) ☎ Shotley 788908, FW, AC, D, P, ⊡, ME, El, Ⓔ, Sh, Slip, BH (30 ton), C, V, CH, SM, Bar, R; Access H24 via lock; entrance controlled by INOGEN lights. **Shotley SC** ☎ Shotley 787500, Slip, L, FW, Bar; **Harwich and Dovercourt SC** ☎ Harwich 240672, M, L, FW, C (5 ton), AB, V, R, Bar. **Shotley BY** ☎ Shotley 787714, Slip, M, ME, El, Sh.
WRABNESS: M, FW, V, Bar.
MISTLEY: AB, M, FW, V, P, D, Bar.
MANNINGTREE: M, AB, FW, V, Bar; **Stour SC** ☎ Colchester 393924, FW, M, Bar; **DN Howells** ☎ 392577, Gas.

RIVER ORWELL 10-4-13
Suffolk

CHARTS
Admiralty 2693, 2052, 1491; Stanford 5, 6; Imray, Y16; OS 169

ENGLAND, EAST COAST – HARWICH

TIME ZONE UT(GMT)
For Summer Time add ONE hour in non-shaded areas

Lat 51°57′ N Long 1°17′ E

TIMES AND HEIGHTS OF HIGH AND LOW WATERS

YEAR **1992**

JANUARY

Day	Time	m	Day	Time	m
1 W	0222 0854 1501 2131	1·1 3·4 0·9 3·4	16 Th	0119 0744 1359 2032	1·1 3·4 0·8 3·4
2 Th	0329 0957 1555 2224	0·9 3·5 0·9 3·6	17 F	0227 0900 1504 2139	0·9 3·5 0·8 3·5
3 F	0421 1049 1638 2309	0·8 3·6 0·9 3·6	18 Sa	0332 1009 1603 2241	0·7 3·7 0·7 3·7
4 Sa ●	0506 1133 1716 2349	0·7 3·7 0·8 3·7	19 Su ○	0431 1109 1657 2334	0·5 3·9 0·6 3·8
5 Su	0544 1212 1751	0·6 3·7 0·8	20 M	0525 1203 1743	0·3 4·1 0·5
6 M	0024 0619 1248 1822	3·7 0·5 3·7 0·8	21 Tu	0024 0612 1250 1827	3·9 0·1 4·2 0·4
7 Tu	0057 0652 1320 1853	3·7 0·5 3·7 0·7	22 W	0109 0657 1335 1909	4·0 0·0 4·2 0·4
8 W	0128 0723 1352 1926	3·8 0·5 3·7 0·7	23 Th	0151 0742 1420 1951	4·1 –0·1 4·1 0·5
9 Th	0158 0755 1425 1959	3·8 0·5 3·7 0·7	24 F	0233 0826 1503 2033	4·1 0·0 4·0 0·6
10 F	0229 0829 1457 2033	3·7 0·5 3·7 0·8	25 Sa	0315 0911 1548 2118	4·0 0·1 3·8 0·7
11 Sa	0304 0904 1534 2110	3·7 0·5 3·6 0·9	26 Su ☾	0359 0957 1633 2206	3·9 0·4 3·6 0·9
12 Su	0341 0942 1616 2152	3·7 0·6 3·5 1·0	27 M	0448 1049 1725 2304	3·7 0·6 3·4 1·0
13 M ☽	0424 1027 1705 2244	3·6 0·7 3·4 1·1	28 Tu	0546 1154 1827	3·4 0·9 3·2
14 Tu	0519 1129 1807 2358	3·5 0·8 3·3 1·1	29 W	0022 0702 1317 1945	1·1 3·2 1·0 3·1
15 W	0627 1246 1919	3·4 0·9 3·3	30 Th	0201 0832 1439 2105	1·1 3·2 1·1 3·2
			31 F	0317 0942 1538 2204	0·9 3·3 1·0 3·4

FEBRUARY

Day	Time	m	Day	Time	m
1 Sa	0410 1034 1624 2251	0·7 3·5 0·9 3·5	16 Su	0318 0957 1549 2226	0·6 3·6 0·7 3·6
2 Su	0452 1116 1701 2330	0·6 3·6 0·8 3·6	17 M	0420 1058 1641 2320	0·4 3·9 0·6 3·8
3 M ●	0527 1154 1733	0·5 3·7 0·7	18 Tu ○	0512 1149 1726	0·1 4·0 0·4
4 Tu	0005 0600 1228 1803	3·7 0·4 3·7 0·6	19 W	0008 0557 1235 1808	4·0 0·0 4·1 0·3
5 W	0038 0629 1300 1832	3·8 0·3 3·8 0·6	20 Th	0050 0639 1319 1849	4·1 –0·1 4·2 0·3
6 Th	0109 0659 1330 1903	3·8 0·3 3·8 0·5	21 F	0131 0721 1358 1930	4·2 –0·1 4·1 0·3
7 F	0138 0731 1401 1935	3·9 0·3 3·8 0·5	22 Sa	0211 0802 1437 2011	4·2 0·0 4·0 0·4
8 Sa	0208 0802 1433 2006	3·9 0·3 3·8 0·6	23 Su	0250 0843 1517 2051	4·1 0·2 3·8 0·6
9 Su	0240 0834 1507 2040	3·8 0·4 3·7 0·7	24 M	0331 0924 1557 2135	3·9 0·5 3·5 0·7
10 M	0314 0907 1543 2117	3·8 0·5 3·6 0·8	25 Tu ☾	0414 1009 1641 2226	3·6 0·8 3·3 0·9
11 Tu ☽	0355 0945 1628 2203	3·7 0·6 3·5 0·9	26 W	0508 1106 1736 2340	3·3 1·0 3·1 1·1
12 W	0444 1037 1725 2309	3·5 0·8 3·3 1·0	27 Th	0624 1229 1856	3·0 1·2 2·9
13 Th	0550 1200 1838	3·3 1·0 3·2	28 F	0133 0806 1408 2033	1·1 3·0 1·2 3·0
14 F	0042 0713 1328 1959	1·0 3·3 1·0 3·2	29 Sa	0253 0919 1512 2138	0·9 3·2 1·1 3·2
15 Sa	0205 0839 1444 2118	0·9 3·4 0·9 3·4			

MARCH

Day	Time	m	Day	Time	m
1 Su	0346 1010 1559 2224	0·7 3·4 0·9 3·4	16 M	0304 0943 1531 2207	0·5 3·6 0·8 3·5
2 M	0427 1052 1635 2304	0·6 3·6 0·8 3·6	17 Tu	0404 1042 1623 2301	0·3 3·8 0·6 3·8
3 Tu	0501 1129 1706 2339	0·4 3·7 0·7 3·7	18 W ○	0454 1132 1706 2347	0·1 4·0 0·4 4·0
4 W ●	0532 1201 1736	0·4 3·8 0·6	19 Th	0537 1215 1747	0·0 4·1 0·3
5 Th	0011 0601 1234 1805	3·8 0·3 3·9 0·4	20 F	0029 0617 1256 1827	4·1 –0·1 4·1 0·3
6 F	0043 0631 1304 1836	3·9 0·2 3·9 0·4	21 Sa	0109 0656 1334 1907	4·2 0·0 4·0 0·3
7 Sa	0113 0703 1335 1909	3·9 0·2 3·9 0·4	22 Su	0147 0735 1411 1948	4·1 0·1 3·9 0·4
8 Su	0145 0734 1408 1942	3·9 0·3 3·8 0·5	23 M	0225 0815 1446 2027	4·0 0·4 3·7 0·5
9 M	0216 0805 1440 2016	3·9 0·4 3·7 0·6	24 Tu	0304 0853 1522 2108	3·8 0·6 3·5 0·7
10 Tu	0251 0839 1517 2054	3·8 0·5 3·6 0·6	25 W	0346 0934 1602 2155	3·5 0·9 3·3 0·9
11 W	0332 0918 1600 2141	3·7 0·7 3·5 0·7	26 Th ☾	0434 1024 1648 2301	3·2 1·2 3·1 1·0
12 Th ☽	0423 1012 1655 2247	3·5 0·9 3·3 0·9	27 F	0542 1139 1756	3·0 1·3 2·9
13 F	0529 1132 1807	3·3 1·0 3·1	28 Sa	0043 0723 1319 1940	1·0 2·9 1·3 2·9
14 Sa	0018 0655 1306 1933	0·9 3·2 1·1 3·1	29 Su	0211 0843 1432 2056	0·9 3·1 1·2 3·1
15 Su	0148 0826 1426 2058	0·7 3·4 0·9 3·3	30 M	0307 0936 1522 2148	0·7 3·4 1·0 3·3
			31 Tu	0349 1019 1600 2228	0·5 3·6 0·8 3·5

APRIL

Day	Time	m	Day	Time	m
1 W	0424 1055 1633 2305	0·4 3·7 0·6 3·7	16 Th	0431 1109 1644 2323	0·1 3·9 0·5 3·9
2 Th	0457 1130 1705 2340	0·3 3·8 0·5 3·8	17 F ○	0513 1151 1726	0·1 4·0 0·4
3 F ●	0527 1204 1737	0·3 3·9 0·4	18 Sa	0005 0553 1231 1807	4·0 0·1 4·0 0·3
4 Sa	0014 0600 1236 1811	3·9 0·2 3·9 0·4	19 Su	0046 0632 1309 1849	4·1 0·2 3·9 0·3
5 Su	0048 0634 1310 1846	4·0 0·3 3·9 0·4	20 M	0124 0712 1344 1930	4·0 0·4 3·8 0·4
6 M	0123 0707 1344 1921	4·0 0·3 3·9 0·4	21 Tu	0204 0748 1418 2009	3·9 0·6 3·7 0·5
7 Tu	0158 0741 1419 1958	3·9 0·5 3·8 0·5	22 W	0242 0826 1453 2049	3·7 0·8 3·5 0·7
8 W	0236 0819 1457 2042	3·8 0·6 3·6 0·5	23 Th	0322 0904 1529 2132	3·5 1·0 3·3 0·8
9 Th	0319 0904 1542 2132	3·7 0·7 3·5 0·6	24 F ☾	0406 0950 1610 2228	3·3 1·2 3·2 0·9
10 F ☽	0413 1002 1637 2241	3·5 0·9 3·3 0·7	25 Sa	0501 1052 1705 2343	3·1 1·3 3·0 0·9
11 Sa	0520 1118 1749	3·4 1·1 3·2	26 Su	0617 1212 1822	3·0 1·3 2·9
12 Su	0007 0643 1245 1910	0·7 3·3 1·1 3·2	27 M	0103 0741 1328 1949	0·9 3·1 1·2 3·0
13 M	0131 0811 1404 2033	0·6 3·4 1·0 3·3	28 Tu	0208 0846 1427 2054	0·7 3·3 1·0 3·2
14 Tu	0244 0924 1507 2142	0·4 3·6 0·8 3·5	29 W	0258 0934 1514 2143	0·6 3·5 0·8 3·5
15 W	0343 1020 1559 2237	0·2 3·8 0·6 3·8	30 Th	0341 1016 1553 2226	0·5 3·7 0·7 3·6

Chart Datum: 2.02 metres below Ordnance Datum (Newlyn)

4

ENGLAND, EAST COAST – HARWICH

Lat 51°57′ N Long 1°17′ E

TIMES AND HEIGHTS OF HIGH AND LOW WATERS

YEAR **1992**

TIME ZONE UT(GMT)
For Summer Time add ONE hour in non-shaded areas

MAY

Day	Time	m	Day	Time	m
1 F	0417 1055 1631 2306	0·4 3·8 0·6 3·8	**16** Sa ○	0452 1129 1709 2346	0·3 3·9 0·5 3·9
2 Sa ●	0455 1132 1709 2346	0·4 3·9 0·5 3·9	**17** Su	0533 1210 1753	0·4 3·9 0·4
3 Su	0532 1210 1749	0·4 4·0 0·4	**18** M	0028 0612 1246 1835	3·9 0·5 3·8 0·4
4 M	0025 0608 1248 1827	4·0 0·4 3·9 0·4	**19** Tu	0107 0650 1323 1916	3·9 0·6 3·8 0·4
5 Tu	0104 0646 1326 1907	4·0 0·4 3·9 0·3	**20** W	0145 0727 1357 1954	3·8 0·7 3·7 0·5
6 W	0145 0726 1405 1949	3·9 0·5 3·8 0·4	**21** Th	0223 0804 1430 2032	3·7 0·8 3·6 0·6
7 Th	0229 0808 1446 2037	3·9 0·6 3·7 0·4	**22** F	0301 0840 1505 2111	3·5 1·0 3·5 0·7
8 F	0315 0857 1534 2132	3·8 0·8 3·5 0·5	**23** Sa	0341 0922 1543 2157	3·4 1·0 3·4 0·7
9 Sa ☽	0410 0955 1628 2237	3·6 0·9 3·4 0·5	**24** Su ☾	0424 1013 1628 2254	3·3 1·1 3·3 0·8
10 Su	0515 1104 1734 2351	3·5 1·0 3·3 0·5	**25** M	0518 1115 1723 2358	3·2 1·2 3·2 0·8
11 M	0629 1219 1848	3·5 1·1 3·3	**26** Tu	0622 1222 1832	3·2 1·2 3·2
12 Tu	0109 0745 1334 2002	0·5 3·5 1·0 3·4	**27** W	0103 0734 1327 1945	0·7 3·3 1·1 3·3
13 W	0220 0856 1440 2112	0·4 3·6 0·9 3·6	**28** Th	0201 0836 1423 2049	0·6 3·4 0·9 3·4
14 Th	0319 0955 1536 2212	0·3 3·7 0·7 3·7	**29** F	0253 0929 1514 2143	0·6 3·6 0·8 3·6
15 F	0409 1045 1624 2301	0·3 3·8 0·6 3·8	**30** Sa	0341 1017 1600 2234	0·5 3·8 0·7 3·7
			31 Su	0426 1104 1645 2322	0·5 3·9 0·5 3·9

JUNE

Day	Time	m	Day	Time	m
1 M ●	0508 1147 1730	0·5 3·9 0·4	**16** Tu	0014 0557 1231 1825	3·8 0·7 3·8 0·4
2 Tu	0007 0550 1231 1814	3·9 0·5 3·9 0·3	**17** W	0053 0634 1306 1903	3·8 0·7 3·8 0·4
3 W	0052 0632 1313 1859	4·0 0·5 3·9 0·3	**18** Th	0130 0709 1340 1938	3·8 0·7 3·7 0·5
4 Th	0137 0716 1357 1945	4·0 0·6 3·8 0·2	**19** F	0205 0742 1412 2013	3·7 0·8 3·7 0·5
5 F	0223 0801 1440 2034	4·0 0·6 3·8 0·2	**20** Sa	0240 0816 1444 2049	3·6 0·8 3·6 0·5
6 Sa	0312 0850 1528 2128	3·9 0·7 3·7 0·2	**21** Su	0315 0854 1518 2127	3·6 0·9 3·6 0·6
7 Su ☽	0404 0942 1619 2226	3·8 0·8 3·7 0·3	**22** M	0352 0935 1557 2212	3·5 1·0 3·5 0·6
8 M	0502 1041 1716 2329	3·7 0·9 3·6 0·4	**23** Tu ☾	0434 1023 1642 2302	3·4 1·1 3·4 0·7
9 Tu	0605 1149 1821	3·6 1·0 3·5	**24** W	0525 1122 1737	3·3 1·1 3·4
10 W	0041 0713 1302 1931	0·5 3·5 1·0 3·5	**25** Th	0004 0628 1229 1845	0·8 3·3 1·1 3·3
11 Th	0151 0823 1413 2044	0·5 3·5 0·9 3·5	**26** F	0109 0737 1335 1957	0·8 3·4 1·0 3·4
12 F	0256 0928 1518 2150	0·5 3·6 0·8 3·6	**27** Sa	0211 0843 1436 2104	0·7 3·5 0·9 3·5
13 Sa	0350 1023 1613 2245	0·6 3·7 0·7 3·7	**28** Su	0308 0943 1532 2206	0·7 3·6 0·7 3·7
14 Su	0435 1109 1701 2332	0·6 3·7 0·6 3·8	**29** M	0400 1038 1627 2302	0·6 3·8 0·6 3·8
15 M ○	0518 1151 1744	0·6 3·8 0·5	**30** Tu ●	0451 1129 1718 2353	0·6 3·8 0·4 4·0

JULY

Day	Time	m	Day	Time	m
1 W	0537 1217 1805	0·5 3·9 0·3	**16** Th	0038 0615 1249 1845	3·8 0·7 3·8 0·4
2 Th	0042 0621 1303 1852	4·1 0·5 4·0 0·1	**17** F	0113 0648 1321 1917	3·8 0·7 3·8 0·4
3 F	0128 0704 1347 1937	4·1 0·5 4·0 0·1	**18** Sa	0145 0719 1351 1948	3·8 0·7 3·8 0·4
4 Sa	0215 0748 1430 2025	4·1 0·5 4·0 0·0	**19** Su	0216 0751 1422 2020	3·8 0·7 3·8 0·4
5 Su	0301 0834 1515 2112	4·0 0·6 4·0 0·1	**20** M	0247 0825 1453 2054	3·7 0·7 3·8 0·5
6 M	0349 0922 1602 2203	3·9 0·7 3·9 0·2	**21** Tu	0321 0900 1528 2131	3·7 0·8 3·7 0·6
7 Tu ☽	0440 1014 1654 2301	3·8 0·9 3·8 0·4	**22** W ☾	0359 0938 1607 2210	3·6 0·9 3·6 0·7
8 W	0536 1115 1751	3·6 1·0 3·6	**23** Th	0442 1024 1655 2304	3·5 1·0 3·5 0·8
9 Th	0007 0638 1229 1902	0·6 3·5 1·1 3·5	**24** F	0537 1129 1757	3·4 1·1 3·4
10 F	0121 0749 1351 2022	0·7 3·4 1·0 3·4	**25** Sa	0017 0646 1250 1913	0·9 3·3 1·1 3·3
11 Sa	0234 0903 1505 2135	0·8 3·4 0·9 3·5	**26** Su	0131 0801 1404 2032	0·9 3·4 1·0 3·4
12 Su	0335 1003 1606 2233	0·8 3·6 0·7 3·6	**27** M	0240 0912 1510 2143	0·9 3·5 0·8 3·6
13 M	0424 1054 1654 2320	0·8 3·7 0·6 3·7	**28** Tu	0341 1017 1612 2247	0·8 3·7 0·6 3·8
14 Tu ○	0505 1136 1734	0·8 3·7 0·5	**29** W ●	0435 1112 1705 2340	0·7 3·8 0·4 4·0
15 W	0001 0542 1214 1811	3·8 0·8 3·8 0·4	**30** Th	0522 1203 1753	0·6 4·0 0·2
			31 F	0029 0607 1248 1838	4·1 0·5 4·1 0·0

AUGUST

Day	Time	m	Day	Time	m
1 Sa	0116 0648 1331 1921	4·2 0·4 4·2 –0·1	**16** Su	0119 0652 1327 1919	3·9 0·6 4·0 0·3
2 Su	0159 0730 1413 2005	4·2 0·5 4·2 0·0	**17** M	0148 0723 1355 1949	3·9 0·6 4·0 0·4
3 M	0243 0813 1456 2049	4·1 0·5 4·2 0·1	**18** Tu	0219 0755 1426 2020	3·9 0·7 3·9 0·5
4 Tu	0327 0857 1538 2135	4·0 0·6 4·1 0·3	**19** W	0250 0826 1500 2053	3·8 0·8 3·8 0·6
5 W ☽	0412 0945 1626 2227	3·8 0·8 3·9 0·6	**20** Th	0325 0901 1536 2128	3·7 0·9 3·7 0·7
6 Th	0501 1041 1720 2327	3·6 1·0 3·6 0·8	**21** F ☾	0406 0942 1621 2213	3·6 1·0 3·6 0·9
7 F	0600 1156 1832	3·4 1·1 3·4	**22** Sa	0457 1040 1720 2323	3·4 1·1 3·4 1·1
8 Sa	0048 0714 1333 2002	1·0 3·2 1·1 3·3	**23** Su	0604 1208 1839	3·3 1·1 3·3
9 Su	0212 0837 1454 2119	1·1 3·3 0·9 3·4	**24** M	0056 0724 1337 2005	1·1 3·3 1·0 3·4
10 M	0318 0945 1553 2217	1·0 3·5 0·7 3·6	**25** Tu	0215 0844 1451 2127	1·0 3·4 0·8 3·6
11 Tu	0407 1034 1638 2302	0·9 3·6 0·6 3·7	**26** W	0322 0956 1555 2231	0·9 3·6 0·5 3·9
12 W	0447 1116 1716 2342	0·9 3·7 0·5 3·8	**27** Th	0417 1054 1648 2325	0·7 3·8 0·3 4·1
13 Th ○	0520 1153 1749	0·8 3·8 0·4	**28** F ●	0504 1143 1734	0·6 4·0 0·1
14 F	0017 0551 1227 1819	3·8 0·7 3·9 0·4	**29** Sa	0012 0546 1228 1818	4·2 0·5 4·2 0·0
15 Sa	0049 0622 1257 1849	3·9 0·6 4·0 0·3	**30** Su	0056 0627 1310 1859	4·3 0·4 4·3 –0·1
			31 M	0138 0709 1351 1941	4·2 0·4 4·3 0·0

Chart Datum: 2.02 metres below Ordnance Datum (Newlyn)

ENGLAND, EAST COAST – HARWICH

Lat 51°57′ N Long 1°17′ E

TIMES AND HEIGHTS OF HIGH AND LOW WATERS

YEAR **1992**

TIME ZONE **UT(GMT)**

For Summer Time add ONE hour in non-shaded areas

SEPTEMBER

Day	Time	m	Day	Time	m
1	0219	4·1	16	0151	4·0
	0751	0·5		0727	0·6
Tu	1432	4·2	W	1401	4·0
	2022	0·2		1948	0·6
2	0258	3·9	17	0222	3·9
	0833	0·6		0759	0·7
W	1512	4·1	Th	1434	3·9
	2105	0·5		2020	0·7
3	0339	3·7	18	0257	3·8
	0918	0·8		0834	0·8
Th	1557	3·8	F	1512	3·8
☽	2152	0·8		2056	0·8
4	0424	3·5	19	0336	3·6
	1012	1·0		0917	0·9
F	1651	3·5	Sa	1557	3·6
	2248	1·1	☾	2142	1·0
5	0518	3·3	20	0426	3·4
	1123	1·1		1014	1·0
Sa	1801	3·3	Su	1657	3·4
				2252	1·2
6	0007	1·3	21	0532	3·3
	0632	3·1		1142	1·1
Su	1307	1·1	M	1815	3·3
	1937	3·2			
7	0141	1·3	22	0027	1·2
	0805	3·2		0653	3·3
M	1432	0·9	Tu	1313	0·9
	2057	3·4		1945	3·4
8	0251	1·2	23	0151	1·1
	0917	3·4		0816	3·4
Tu	1528	0·7	W	1430	0·7
	2152	3·6		2107	3·6
9	0341	1·0	24	0258	0·9
	1007	3·6		0931	3·6
W	1612	0·6	Th	1534	0·4
	2237	3·7		2212	3·9
10	0420	0·9	25	0353	0·8
	1048	3·7		1030	3·9
Th	1648	0·5	F	1627	0·2
	2313	3·8		2304	4·1
11	0454	0·8	26	0440	0·6
	1125	3·9		1120	4·1
F	1719	0·4	Sa	1712	0·1
	2349	3·9	●	2350	4·2
12	0523	0·7	27	0523	0·5
	1157	3·9		1205	4·2
Sa	1747	0·4	Su	1754	0·0
○					
13	0019	4·0	28	0034	4·2
	0553	0·6		0604	0·4
Su	1228	4·0	M	1246	4·3
	1817	0·3		1835	0·1
14	0050	4·0	29	0113	4·2
	0622	0·5		0646	0·4
M	1259	4·1	Tu	1327	4·3
	1846	0·4		1916	0·2
15	0120	4·0	30	0152	4·1
	0655	0·6		0728	0·5
Tu	1328	4·0	W	1408	4·2
	1917	0·4		1955	0·4

OCTOBER

Day	Time	m	Day	Time	m
1	0230	3·9	16	0158	3·9
	0812	0·6		0738	0·7
Th	1449	4·0	F	1416	3·9
	2036	0·7		1957	0·8
2	0308	3·7	17	0234	3·8
	0856	0·8		0818	0·7
F	1532	3·8	Sa	1457	3·8
	2119	1·0		2037	0·9
3	0349	3·5	18	0315	3·6
	0945	1·0		0904	0·8
Sa	1621	3·5	Su	1545	3·7
☽	2210	1·2		2128	1·0
4	0437	3·3	19	0406	3·5
	1049	1·1		1006	0·9
Su	1725	3·2	M	1645	3·5
	2318	1·4	☾	2235	1·2
5	0542	3·1	20	0511	3·3
	1222	1·1		1125	0·9
M	1855	3·1	Tu	1801	3·4
6	0049	1·4	21	0000	1·3
	0713	3·1		0628	3·3
Tu	1348	1·0	W	1250	0·8
	2018	3·3		1924	3·5
7	0208	1·3	22	0121	1·2
	0833	3·3		0747	3·4
W	1449	0·8	Th	1406	0·6
	2117	3·5		2043	3·7
8	0303	1·1	23	0230	1·0
	0928	3·5		0901	3·6
Th	1534	0·7	F	1510	0·4
	2202	3·7		2148	3·9
9	0345	0·9	24	0327	0·8
	1012	3·7		1003	3·9
F	1610	0·6	Sa	1603	0·3
	2240	3·8		2241	4·0
10	0419	0·8	25	0416	0·7
	1049	3·8		1055	4·0
Sa	1642	0·5	Su	1648	0·2
	2315	3·9	●	2327	4·1
11	0449	0·7	26	0501	0·5
	1125	3·9		1142	4·2
Su	1712	0·4	M	1730	0·2
○	2347	4·0			
12	0522	0·6	27	0010	4·1
	1158	4·0		0544	0·5
M	1743	0·4	Tu	1225	4·2
				1811	0·3
13	0019	4·0	28	0049	4·1
	0554	0·6		0628	0·4
Tu	1231	4·1	W	1306	4·2
	1815	0·4		1852	0·4
14	0052	4·0	29	0127	4·0
	0628	0·6		0712	0·5
W	1304	4·1	Th	1347	4·1
	1848	0·5		1931	0·6
15	0124	4·0	30	0205	3·9
	0702	0·6		0754	0·6
Th	1340	4·0	F	1427	3·9
	1921	0·6		2011	0·9
			31	0242	3·7
				0836	0·7
			Sa	1510	3·7
				2051	1·1

NOVEMBER

Day	Time	m	Day	Time	m
1	0319	3·5	16	0305	3·7
	0921	0·9		0901	0·6
Su	1555	3·5	M	1539	3·7
	2136	1·2		2119	1·0
2	0402	3·4	17	0356	3·6
	1014	1·0		0959	0·7
M	1647	3·3	Tu	1638	3·6
☽	2231	1·4	☾	2221	1·1
3	0452	3·2	18	0455	3·5
	1122	1·0		1108	0·7
Tu	1754	3·2	W	1746	3·5
	2343	1·4		2333	1·2
4	0603	3·1	19	0604	3·5
	1239	1·0		1224	0·7
W	1914	3·2	Th	1859	3·5
5	0100	1·4	20	0049	1·2
	0726	3·2		0717	3·5
Th	1349	0·9	F	1338	0·6
	2023	3·4		2013	3·6
6	0206	1·2	21	0159	1·0
	0833	3·4		0830	3·6
F	1443	0·8	Sa	1444	0·5
	2115	3·6		2119	3·8
7	0257	1·0	22	0303	0·9
	0925	3·6		0938	3·8
Sa	1525	0·7	Su	1539	0·5
	2159	3·7		2216	3·9
8	0338	0·9	23	0356	0·7
	1009	3·7		1034	3·9
Su	1602	0·6	M	1628	0·5
	2238	3·9		2305	3·9
9	0414	0·8	24	0445	0·6
	1049	3·9		1123	4·0
M	1638	0·6	Tu	1712	0·5
	2315	4·0	●	2349	4·0
10	0452	0·7	25	0532	0·5
	1127	4·0		1208	4·1
Tu	1713	0·6	W	1753	0·5
○	2351	4·0			
11	0529	0·6	26	0029	4·0
	1207	4·0		0615	0·5
W	1749	0·6	Th	1250	4·1
				1832	0·6
12	0028	4·0	27	0107	3·9
	0607	0·5		0657	0·5
Th	1245	4·0	F	1331	4·0
	1825	0·6		1912	0·7
13	0104	4·0	28	0144	3·8
	0645	0·5		0738	0·5
F	1324	4·0	Sa	1409	3·9
	1902	0·7		1949	0·9
14	0142	3·9	29	0219	3·7
	0726	0·5		0818	0·6
Sa	1405	3·9	Su	1449	3·7
	1941	0·8		2026	1·0
15	0222	3·8	30	0256	3·6
	0811	0·6		0857	0·7
Su	1450	3·9	M	1528	3·6
	2027	0·9		2105	1·1

DECEMBER

Day	Time	m	Day	Time	m
1	0332	3·5	16	0346	3·8
	0941	0·8		0946	0·4
Tu	1610	3·4	W	1626	3·7
	2150	1·2	☾	2200	0·9
2	0413	3·4	17	0440	3·7
	1030	0·9		1045	0·5
W	1658	3·3	Th	1725	3·6
☽	2245	1·3		2302	1·1
3	0502	3·3	18	0540	3·6
	1130	0·9		1154	0·6
Th	1757	3·2	F	1831	3·5
	2351	1·3			
4	0605	3·3	19	0015	1·1
	1235	0·9		0649	3·5
F	1906	3·3	Sa	1309	0·6
				1941	3·5
5	0059	1·2	20	0131	1·1
	0719	3·3		0804	3·5
Sa	1338	0·9	Su	1419	0·7
	2012	3·4		2053	3·6
6	0159	1·1	21	0243	0·9
	0827	3·4		0918	3·6
Su	1433	0·8	M	1522	0·7
	2108	3·5		2155	3·7
7	0253	1·0	22	0346	0·8
	0925	3·6		1020	3·7
M	1522	0·7	Tu	1614	0·7
	2157	3·7		2248	3·8
8	0341	0·8	23	0438	0·6
	1016	3·7		1112	3·8
Tu	1606	0·7	W	1659	0·7
	2244	3·8		2333	3·8
9	0426	0·7	24	0525	0·5
	1102	3·8		1157	3·9
W	1648	0·7	Th	1739	0·7
○	2327	3·9	●		
10	0509	0·6	25	0014	3·8
	1147	3·9		0607	0·4
Th	1729	0·6	F	1238	3·9
				1817	0·7
11	0010	3·9	26	0052	3·8
	0553	0·5		0646	0·4
F	1231	4·0	Sa	1316	3·9
	1810	0·6		1853	0·7
12	0052	3·9	27	0127	3·8
	0635	0·4		0723	0·4
Sa	1314	4·0	Su	1352	3·8
	1850	0·6		1927	0·7
13	0133	3·9	28	0201	3·8
	0720	0·3		0758	0·5
Su	1359	4·0	M	1426	3·8
	1933	0·7		2001	0·8
14	0215	3·9	29	0232	3·7
	0805	0·3		0832	0·5
M	1444	4·0	Tu	1500	3·7
	2018	0·7		2036	0·8
15	0258	3·8	30	0305	3·7
	0854	0·3		0907	0·6
Tu	1534	3·9	W	1535	3·6
	2107	0·8		2112	0·9
			31	0341	3·6
				0946	0·7
			Th	1613	3·5
				2155	1·0

Chart Datum: 2.02 metres below Ordnance Datum (Newlyn)

RIVER ORWELL *continued*

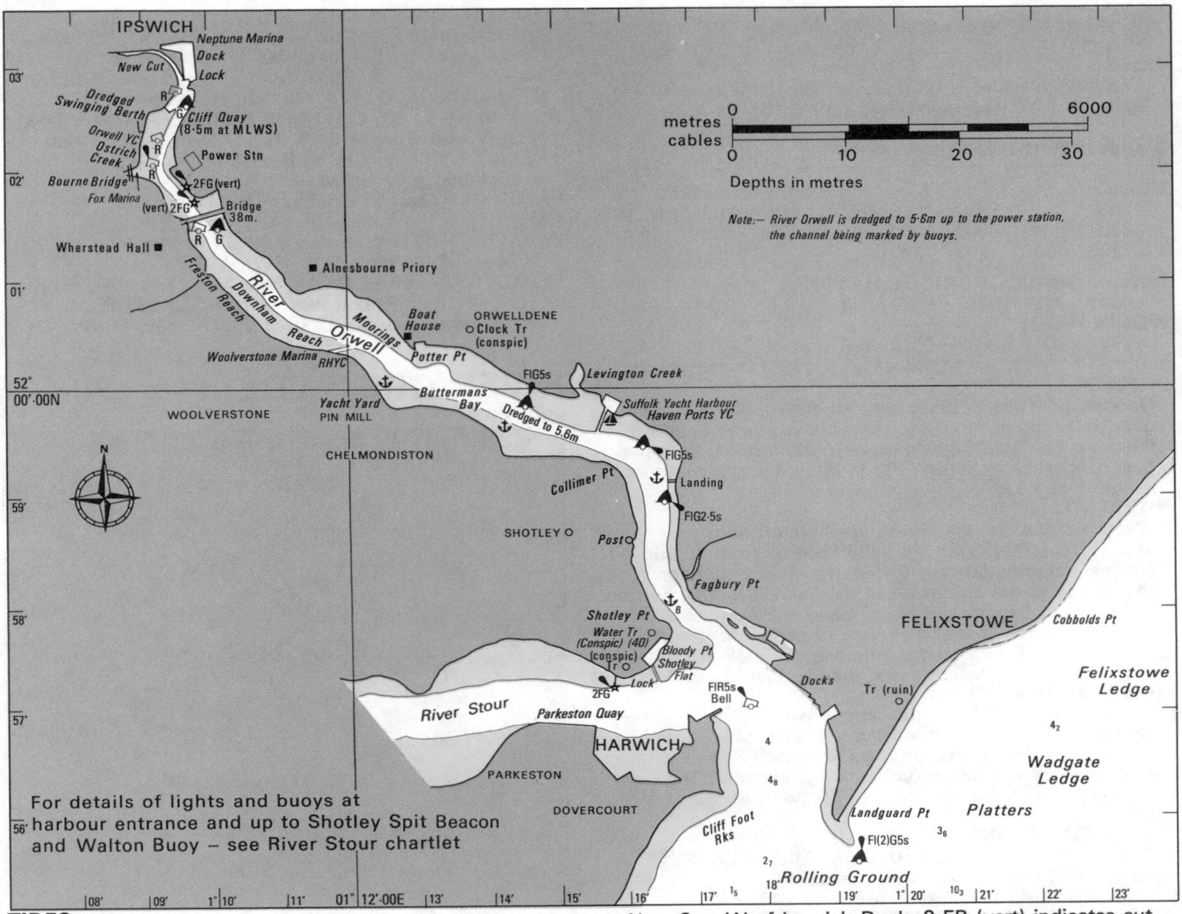
IPSWICH
Neptune Marina
Dock
Lock
New Cut
Dredged Swinging Berth
Cliff Quay (8·5m at MLWS)
Orwell YC
Ostrich Creek
Power Stn
Bourne Bridge
Fox Marina
2FG(vert)
(vert) 2FG
Bridge 38m.
Wherstead Hall
Alnesbourne Priory
Freston Reach
Downham Reach
River Orwell
Moorings
Boat House
ORWELLDENE
Clock Tr (conspic)
Potter Pt
Woolverstone Marina
RHYC
Levington Creek
FlG5s
Buttermans Bay
Suffolk Yacht Harbour
Haven Ports YC
Yacht Yard
PIN MILL
WOOLVERSTONE
CHELMONDISTON
Dredged to 5.6m
FlG5s
Collimer Pt
Landing
FlG2·5s
SHOTLEY
Post
Fagbury Pt
Shotley Pt
Water Tr (Conspic) (40)
(conspic) Tr
Bloody Pt
Shotley Flat
Lock
2FG
FlR5s Bell
Docks
FELIXSTOWE
Cobbolds Pt
Tr (ruin)
Felixstowe Ledge
River Stour
Parkeston Quay
HARWICH
PARKESTON
DOVERCOURT
Wadgate Ledge
Landguard Pt
Platters
Cliff Foot Rks
Fl(2)G5s
Rolling Ground
metres 0 6000
cables 0 10 20 30
Depths in metres
Note:– River Orwell is dredged to 5·6m up to the power station, the channel being marked by buoys.
For details of lights and buoys at harbour entrance and up to Shotley Spit Beacon and Walton Buoy – see River Stour chartlet
52° 00'·00N
01° 12'·00E

TIDES
Pin Mill +0100 Dover; Ipswich +0115 Dover; ML 2·4; Duration 0555; Zone 0 (GMT)

Standard Port HARWICH (⟵)

Times				Height (metres)			
HW		LW		MHWS	MHWN	MLWN	MLWS
0000	0600	0000	0600	4·0	3·4	1·1	0·4
1200	1800	1200	1800				
Differences IPSWICH							
+0015	+0025	0000	+0010	+0·2	0·0	−0·1	−0·1

SHELTER
Good. Entrance and river well marked. Anchorages above Shotley Pt on W side, or in Buttermans Bay. No facilities for yachts at Felixstowe. Berths available by arrangement in Suffolk Yacht Harbour, Woolverstone Marina and Fox Marina (Ipswich). For berths in Ipswich Dock it is essential to contact Ipswich Port Radio before arrival (Tel. 230109) or call *Neptune Marina* ☎ 215204 or Ch 14. Then call Ipswich Port Radio (Ch 14) for lock to open. Keep clear of commercial shipping at all times.

NAVIGATION
Waypoint Shotley Spit S cardinal Bn, Q(6)+LFl 15s, 51°57'·22N 01°17'·70E, at river entrance. Main danger is the large amount of merchant shipping, ferries etc entering and leaving Harwich, Felixstowe and passing up river to Ipswich. Ipswich dock opens from HW−1 to HW but mainly for commercial vessels.
There is a speed limit of 6 knots in the R Orwell.

LIGHTS AND MARKS
Entrance between Shotley Spit Lt Bn Q(6) + L Fl 15s to port and Walton buoy, Fl (3) G 10s to stbd. For detail see R Stour Chartlet. (⟵) 10.4.12.
Suffolk Yacht Harbour approach marked by four Bns. Ldg Lts Front Iso Y, Rear Oc Y 4s. Woolverstone Marina Lts 2 FR (vert). R and G Lts control entry to Ipswich Dock (H24).
New Cut, W of Ipswich Dock, 3 FR (vert) indicates cut closed.
Bridge Lts – Centre FY
No 9 Pier 2 FR (vert) shown up and
No 10 Pier 2 FG (vert) down stream.

RADIO TELEPHONE
Call: *Ipswich Port Radio* VHF Ch **14** 16; 12 **14** (H24). Once above the bridge keep constant listening watch on Ch 14. Fox Marina, Woolverstone Marina, Suffolk Yacht Harbour, Neptune Marina, Ch **80** M.(0800–1730 LT)

TELEPHONE (0473)
Hr Mr Orwell Navigation Service 231010; MRSC Frinton-on-Sea 675518; # (0473) 219481; Marinecall 0898 500 455; Police 233000; Ⓗ 712233.

FACILITIES
EC Chelmondiston - Thursday; Ipswich - Wednesday;
PIN MILL/WOOLVERSTONE: **Woolverstone Marina** (300+22 visitors) ☎ 780206, Slip, P (cans), D, FW, ME, El, Sh, AC, Gas, Gaz, ⊡, C (25 ton mobile), CH, V; **Royal Harwich YC** ☎ 780206, R, Bar; **Pin Mill SC** ☎ 780271; **J. Ward** ☎ 780276, Slip, M, (10 visitors), D, L, FW, ME, El, Sh, CH, AB, V, R, Bar; **F. A. Webb BY** ☎ 780291, ME, El, Sh, Slip.
Town ✉; Ⓑ (Ipswich); ⇌ (Ipswich); ✈ (Cambridge).
LEVINGTON: **Suffolk Yacht Harbour** (390+10 visitors) ☎ Nacton 659240, Slip, P, D, FW, ME, El, Ⓔ, Sh, C (9 ton), BH (10 ton), CH, V, Gas, Gaz, AC, SM, Bar Access H24; **J. Parker** ☎ 659878, SM; **Bob Spalding** ☎ 659674, ME.
Town ✉; Ⓑ (Felixstowe); ⇌ (bus to Ipswich); ✈ (Cambridge or Norwich).
IPSWICH: **Fox's Marina** (100+some visitors) ☎ 689111 FW, AC, D, Gas, Gaz, BH (26 and 44 ton), C (7 ton), ME, El, Ⓔ, Sh, Bar, CH, ACA; **Neptune Marina** (18 visitors) ☎ 780366, Sh, ME, FW; **Wherry Quay Marina** ☎ 230109, AB, M, FW, AC, R, Access via lock (HW−2 to HW+½; **Orwell YC** ☎ 602288, Slip, L, FW, Bar; **Orwell Auto Electrics** ☎ 749624, El, Ⓔ;
Town ✉; Ⓑ; ⇌; ✈ (Cambridge or Norwich).

RIVER DEBEN 10-4-14
Suffolk

CHARTS
Admiralty 2693, 2052; Stanford 3, 6; Imray C28, Y15; OS 169

TIDES
Woodbridge Haven +0025 Dover; Woodbridge +0125 Dover; ML 2·0; Duration 0635; Zone 0 (GMT)

Standard Port HARWICH (⟵)

Times				Height (metres)			
HW		LW		MHWS	MHWN	MLWN	MLWS
0000	0600	0000	0600	4·0	3·4	1·1	0·4
1200	1800	1200	1800				
Differences WOODBRIDGE HAVEN							
−0008	−0016	−0012	−0020	−0·3	−0·5	−0·1	+0·1
WOODBRIDGE							
+0037	+0014	+0033	−0015	0·0	−0·3	−0·2	0·0

SHELTER
Good at all times in yacht harbour at Woodbridge. Also good at anchorages up the river, above Horse Sand, at Ramsholt, at Waldringfield and at Woodbridge. Entrance gets dangerously choppy with strong on-shore winds and is only 1 ca wide.

NAVIGATION
Waypoint Woodbridge Haven (safe water) buoy, 51°58′·47N 01°24′·35E, 126°/306° approx from/to buoyed channel entrance (shifts), 0·40M. There is a shifting shingle bar at the entrance but the channel is well buoyed and marked. Beware the Horse Sand just up river of Felixstowe ferry. It is entirely free of commercial traffic. From Wilford Bridge to the entrance of Creek at lower end of Ramsholt Reach, speed limit is 8 kn.

LIGHTS AND MARKS
If a pilot is required, dip the burgee when passing Martello Tower T. The Woodbridge Haven Buoy is unlit. Leading marks, Front W triangle on R background, Rear R rectangle, are moved according to the channel. There are 2 FR (vert) on Felixstowe side, 2 FG (vert) on Bardsey side.

RADIO TELEPHONE
Tide Mill Yacht Harbour VHF Ch **80** M Pilot Ch 08.

TELEPHONE (0394 – for 4 fig nos 03943)
Hr Mr 5118; MRSC Frinton-on-Sea 675518; Pilot Felixstowe 283469; ⵑ (0473) 219481; Marinecall 0898 500 455; Police 3377; Dr 2046.

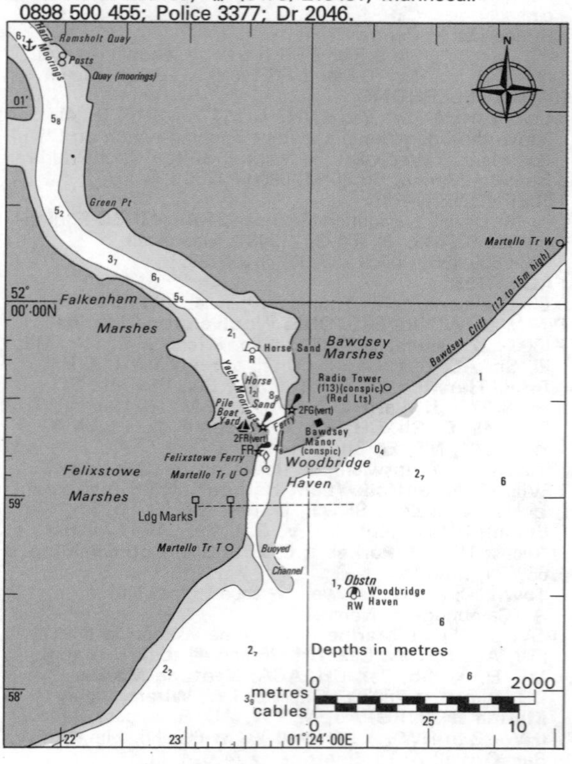

Ramsholt Quay
Posts
Quay (moorings)
Yacht Moorings
Green Pt
Falkenham
Marshes
Horse Sand
Bawdsey Marshes
Radio Tower (113)(conspic) (Red Lts)
Bawdsey Cliff (12 to 15m high)
Martello Tr W
Pile Boat Yard
Ferry
2FG(vert)
2FR(vert)
Bawdsey Manor (conspic)
Felixstowe Ferry
Martello Tr U
Woodbridge Haven
Felixstowe
Marshes
Ldg Marks
Martello Tr T
Buoyed Channel
Obstn
Woodbridge Haven
RW
Depths in metres
metres
cables
2000
10
01°24′·00E
52° 00′·00N

FACILITIES
EC Wednesday.
WOODBRIDGE: **Tide Mill Yacht Harbour** (150 + 50 visitors) ☎ 385745, Slip, D, L, FW, ME, El, Sh, C (10 ton), AC, V, Access HW−3½ to HW+2½; **Granary Yacht Harbour** ☎ 36327, CH, ME, Slip, C, Sh; **Whisstocks BY** ☎ 4222, Slip, MD, FW, ME, El, Sh, C (20 ton), CH, V; **Eversons BY** ☎ 4358, Access HW∓4, Slip, M, D, ME, El, Sh, C (6 ton), CH; **Frank Knights BY** ☎ 2318, M, D, FW, ME, Sh; **Robertsons** ☎ 2305, Slip, M, D, L, Sh, CH; **Small Craft Deliveries** ☎ 2600, ACA; **Webb Bros** ☎ 2183, Gas; **Town** P, D, L (opp Everson BY), FW, CH, V, R, Bar, ✉; Ⓑ; ⇌; ✈ (Cambridge or Norwich).
RAMSHOLT **George Collins** ☎ Shottisham 229, M, FW, ME, Bar;
WALDRINGFIELD **Waldringfield BY** ☎ Waldringfield 260, C, Slip, BH (40 ton), D, L, FW, V, Bar;
FELIXSTOWE FERRY QUAY Slip, M, L, FW, ME, El, Sh, CH, V, R, Bar; **Felixstowe Ferry SC** ☎ 283785; **Felixstowe Ferry BY** (200) ☎ 282173, ME, El, Sh, CH, Gas.

RIVER ORE/ALDE 10-4-15
Suffolk

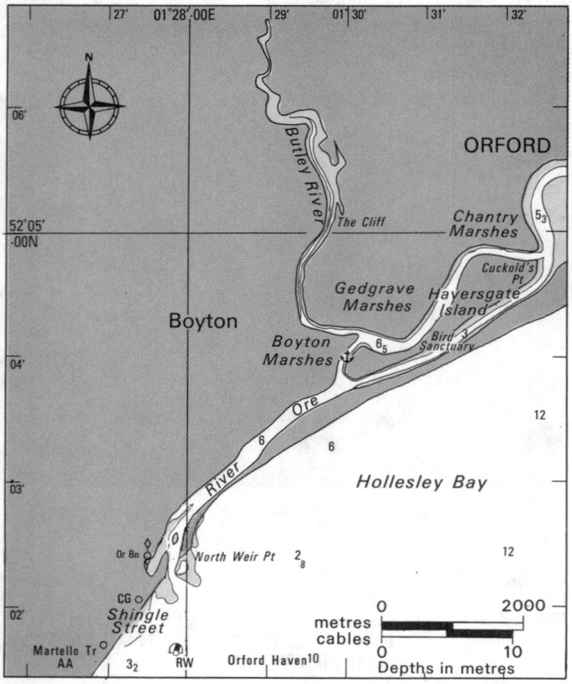

01°28′·00E
ORFORD
Butley River
The Cliff
Chantry Marshes
52°05′·00N
Cuckold's Pt
Gedgrave Marshes
Havergate Island
Boyton
Boyton Marshes
Bird Sanctuary
River Ore
Hollesley Bay
Or Bn
North Weir Pt
CG
Shingle Street
Martello Tr AA
RW
Orford Haven
metres
cables
2000
10
Depths in metres

CHARTS
Admiralty 2695, 2693, 1543, 2052; Stanford 6, 3; Imray Y15, C28; OS 169

TIDES
Ent. +0010 Dover Slaughden Quay +0155 Dover; ML 1·5; Duration 0620; Zone 0 (GMT).

Standard Port LOWESTOFT (⟶)

Times				Height (metres)			
HW		LW		MHWS	MHWN	MLWN	MLWS
0300	0900	0200	0800	2·4	2·1	1·0	0·5
1500	2100	1400	2000				
Differences ALDEBURGH							
+0120	+0120	+0120	+0110	+0·4	+0·6	0·0	0·0
ORFORD NESS							
+0135	+0135	+0135	+0125	+0·4	+0·6	−0·1	0·0

Standard Port HARWICH (⟵)

Times				Height (metres)			
HW		LW		MHWS	MHWN	MLWN	MLWS
0000	0600	0000	0600	4·0	3·4	1·1	0·4
1200	1800	1200	1800				
Differences ORFORD HAVEN BAR							
−0025	−0025	−0040	−0015	−0·8	−0·8	−0·2	−0·1
ORFORD QUAY							
+0021	+0021	+0053	+0053	−1·4	−1·3	+0·2	0·0

RIVER ORE/ALDE *continued*

Differences at Slaughden Quay are +0115 on Harwich: Snape Bridge +0315 on Harwich

SHELTER
R Ore changes name to R Alde between Orford and Aldeburgh, and is navigable up to Snape. Good anchorages where shown, also between Slaughden Quay and Martello Tower and at Iken. Upper reaches of river are shallow and winding, and although marked by withies these may be damaged. Landing prohibited on MoD land and on Havergate Island bird sanctuary.

NAVIGATION
Waypoint Orford Haven (safe water) buoy, 52°01′·78N 01°27′·98E, although this is moved from time to time dependent on changes to the bar. The bar shifts after onshore gales and is dangerous in rough or confused seas. Ebb runs up to 6 kn. Up to date plan of entrance available from Orford Chandlery or Secretary, Aldeburgh YC. In absence of local information do not enter before half flood. Beware shoals off the orange tipped Bn on W shore just inside entrance (keep well to E side), and S to SW of Dove Pt (the most SW point of Havergate Island).

LIGHTS AND MARKS
Shingle Street, about 0·2M S of entrance, is located by a Martello Tower and CG Stn. Buoy and Bn are moved according to channel.

RADIO TELEPHONE
VHF Ch 16; 67 (H24).

TELEPHONE (Aldeburgh, 0728; Orford and Shottisham, 0394)
Hr Mr Aldeburgh 452896 and Orford c/o 450210; MRSC Frinton-on-Sea 675518; and Shingle Street (week ends, bad weather), Shottisham 411558; # (0473) 219481; Marinecall 0898 500 455; Police 452716; Dr Orford 450315, 450369, Shottisham 411214, and Aldeburgh 452027.

FACILITIES
ORFORD. EC Wed; **Orford Quay** Slip, AB (short-stay), M, L, FW, C (5 ton), SC, Bar; **Orford Chandlery** ☎ 450210, CH, D (cans), Gas, Gaz, R, Sh (small craft); **Orford SC** Slip, L, FW. **Village** (¼M). P and D (cans), ✉, V, R, Bar, ⇌ (occ. bus to Woodbridge).
ALDEBURGH. EC Wed; **Slaughden Quay** L, FW; **R. F. Upson** ☎ 452896, Slip, M, D (cans), ME, Sh; **Aldeburgh BY** ☎ 452019, Slip, Gas, Gaz, P, D, ME, Sh, CH; **Aldeburgh YC** ☎ 452562, Slip, L, FW, Bar, R, D, P, CH. **Town** (¾M), V, R, Bar, ✉; Ⓑ; ⇌ (bus to Wickham Market); ✈ (Norwich).

SOUTHWOLD 10-4-16
Suffolk

CHARTS
Admiralty 2695, 1543; Stanford 3; Imray C28; OS 156

TIDES
−0105 Dover; ML 1·3; Duration 0620; Zone 0 (GMT).

Standard Port LOWESTOFT (→)

Times				Height (metres)			
HW		LW		MHWS	MHWN	MLWN	MLWS
0300	0900	0200	0800	2·4	2·1	1·0	0·5
1500	2100	1400	2000				
Differences SOUTHWOLD							
+0035	+0035	+0040	+0030	+0·1	+0·1	−0·1	−0·1

SHELTER
Good shelter and a stage, 100m beyond the LB on N bank opposite the Harbour Inn, is reserved for visiting yachtsmen. In strong winds from S through E to N entrance is dangerous. Work is in progress at N pier, narrowing ent by 10m. Yachts should contact Hr Mr (Ch 12) before entering.

NAVIGATION
Waypoint 52°18′·06N 01°41′·80E, 135°/315° from/to North Pier Lt, 1·0M. Entry should be made on the flood since the ebb runs up to 5 kn. Some shoals are unpredictable. A sand and shingle bar lies off the harbour entrance, whose extent varies. Obtain details of approach channels from Hr Mr before entering or ask for a pilot (Ch 12 or 09 or Tel. 724712). Shoal forms inside N pier. Unlit low bridge ¾ M upstream of entrance.

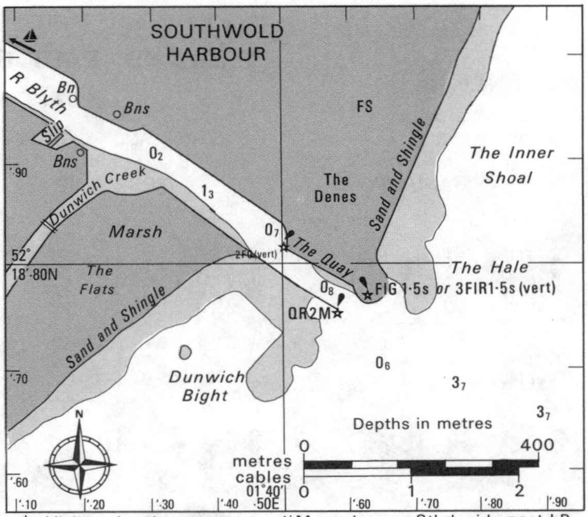
SOUTHWOLD HARBOUR
R Blyth
Bn
Bns
Slip
Bns
Dunwich Creek
Marsh
The Flats
Sand and Shingle
Dunwich Bight
The Denes
FS
Sand and Shingle
The Inner Shoal
The Hale
The Quay
2F(vert)
FIG 1·5s or 3FIR1·5s (vert)
QR2M
52° 18′·80N
01°40′ ·50E
Depths in metres
metres
cables
0
400
1
2
N

▲ Visitors berths at pontoon ¼M up river on Stbd. side past LB house and Hr Mr office

LIGHTS AND MARKS
N Pier Lt & Lt Ho in line - 010°
N Pier Lt & Water Tr (conspic) - 342°
N Pier Lt & Walberswick Church - 268°
Harbour mouth opens on - 300°
Two red flags or 3Fl R 1·5s (vert) at N pier means entry inadvisable or shipping movements in harbour.
NOTE: Lt Ho is in Southwold town, about 1 M N from harbour entrance, Fl (4) WR 20s 37m 22/20M; vis R (intens) 204°-220°, W220°-001°, R001°—032°.

RADIO TELEPHONE
Call: *Southwold Port Radio* VHF Ch 12; 16 (0800-1800 LT). Pilots Ch 12 09.

TELEPHONE (0502)
Hr Mr 724712; MRCC Great Yarmouth 851338; # (0473) 219481; Marinecall 0898 500 455; Weather Norwich 660779; Police 722666; Dr 722326; [H] 723333.

FACILITIES
EC Wednesday (both Southwold and Walberswick); **Hr Mr** Slip, L, FW, Sh, C (10 ton), AB; **Harbour Marine Services** ☎ 724721 D, CH, ME, Sh, Slip, BH (12 ton); **Harbour Inn** (on quay), Bar; **Southwold SC; Jeckells** ☎ 565007, SM; **Town** (¾ M) V, R, Gas, Gaz, Kos, ✉; Ⓑ; ⇌ (bus to Brampton or Darsham); ✈ (Norwich).

LOWESTOFT 10-4-17
Suffolk

CHARTS
Admiralty 1536, 1543; Stanford 3; Imray C28; OS 156/134

TIDES
−0133 Dover; ML 1·6; Duration 0620; Zone 0 (GMT).
Lowestoft is a standard port and tidal predictions for each day of the year are given below.

SHELTER
Harbour is always available. Yacht basin in the SW corner. Yachts lie in 3 tiers on the North side (bad in E winds). Yacht basin is controlled by Royal Norfolk & Suffolk YC. Mooring on inner side of S Pier is dangerous due to bad state of the pier. Bridge to inner harbour (and Lake Lothing) opens (LT)

October to April					
Mon – Sat	0700	0930	1900	2100	
Sunday	0800	0930	1400	1900	2100
May to September					
Mon – Sat	0700	0930	1900	2100	
Sunday	0730	0930	1400	1900	2100

and also when ships pass through. Bridge clearance 2·2m at MHWS. Small craft may pass under the bridge at any time but VHF Ch 14 contact advisable (see 10.4.22).
Note: Mutford Lock will be closed in 1992 mid to end February and all May and June.

ENGLAND, EAST COAST – LOWESTOFT

Lat 52°28′ N Long 1°45′ E

TIME ZONE UT(GMT)

For Summer Time add ONE hour in non-shaded areas

TIMES AND HEIGHTS OF HIGH AND LOW WATERS

YEAR **1992**

JANUARY

Day	Time	m	Day	Time	m
1 W	0018	1·1	16 Th	0531	2·2
	0633	2·2		1158	0·8
	1252	0·9		1822	2·1
	1920	2·2			
2 Th	0130	1·0	17 F	0026	1·0
	0743	2·2		0637	2·2
	1345	0·9		1254	0·8
	2005	2·3		1913	2·2
3 F	0224	0·9	18 Sa	0131	0·8
	0835	2·2		0739	2·3
	1430	0·9		1350	0·7
	2043	2·3		2003	2·3
4 Sa	0309	0·8	19 Su	0237	0·6
	0920	2·2		0839	2·4
	1507	1·0		1446	0·7
●	2116	2·4	○	2050	2·5
5 Su	0348	0·7	20 M	0331	0·3
	1001	2·2		0935	2·4
	1537	0·9		1541	0·6
	2146	2·4		2137	2·6
6 M	0424	0·6	21 Tu	0422	0·1
	1037	2·2		1026	2·5
	1603	0·9		1628	0·6
	2216	2·5		2224	2·7
7 Tu	0458	0·6	22 W	0507	0·0
	1111	2·2		1113	2·4
	1631	0·9		1713	0·6
	2248	2·5		2309	2·7
8 W	0530	0·6	23 Th	0552	0·0
	1145	2·2		1200	2·3
	1703	0·8		1754	0·6
	2320	2·5		2354	2·7
9 Th	0603	0·6	24 F	0635	0·1
	1216	2·1		1246	2·2
	1739	0·9		1835	0·7
	2356	2·4			
10 F	0637	0·6	25 Sa	0041	2·6
	1250	2·1		0718	0·2
	1816	0·9		1333	2·1
				1916	0·8
11 Sa	0033	2·4	26 Su	0130	2·5
	0711	0·6		0805	0·5
	1330	2·1		1426	2·0
	1858	0·9	☾	2001	0·9
12 Su	0113	2·4	27 M	0226	2·4
	0750	0·7		0856	0·7
	1416	2·0		1528	2·0
	1943	1·0		2058	1·0
13 M	0158	2·3	28 Tu	0333	2·2
	0837	0·8		1000	0·9
	1516	2·0		1635	2·0
☽	2037	1·1		2218	1·1
14 Tu	0256	2·2	29 W	0456	2·1
	0937	0·8		1120	1·0
	1624	2·0		1746	2·0
	2146	1·2			
15 W	0416	2·2	30 Th	0009	1·1
	1050	0·9		0630	2·1
	1726	2·1		1235	1·1
	2315	1·1		1854	2·1
			31 F	0124	0·9
				0743	2·1
				1333	1·0
				1946	2·2

FEBRUARY

Day	Time	m	Day	Time	m
1 Sa	0215	0·8	16 Su	0122	0·6
	0833	2·1		0733	2·2
	1416	1·0		1339	0·8
	2026	2·2		1941	2·3
2 Su	0254	0·7	17 M	0226	0·4
	0913	2·2		0833	2·3
	1450	0·9		1435	0·7
	2100	2·3		2033	2·4
3 M	0330	0·6	18 Tu	0316	0·1
	0948	2·2		0924	2·4
	1518	0·9		1524	0·6
●	2130	2·4	○	2120	2·6
4 Tu	0403	0·5	19 W	0403	0·0
	1020	2·2		1011	2·4
	1545	0·8		1609	0·5
	2158	2·4		2207	2·7
5 W	0435	0·4	20 Th	0446	−0·1
	1050	2·2		1052	2·4
	1615	0·7		1652	0·5
	2230	2·5		2250	2·7
6 Th	0505	0·4	21 F	0530	0·0
	1118	2·2		1135	2·3
	1646	0·7		1731	0·5
	2301	2·5		2335	2·7
7 F	0537	0·4	22 Sa	0611	0·1
	1145	2·2		1216	2·2
	1720	0·7		1809	0·5
	2335	2·5			
8 Sa	0607	0·5	23 Su	0018	2·6
	1215	2·1		0650	0·3
	1752	0·7		1258	2·1
				1848	0·7
9 Su	0009	2·4	24 M	0105	2·5
	0637	0·5		0730	0·6
	1248	2·1		1343	2·1
	1828	0·8		1931	0·8
10 M	0045	2·4	25 Tu	0200	2·3
	0713	0·6		0815	0·9
	1330	2·0		1435	2·0
	1909	0·9	☾	2024	0·9
11 Tu	0128	2·3	26 W	0309	2·1
	0754	0·7		0911	1·1
	1420	2·0		1539	2·0
☽	2000	0·9		2143	1·1
12 W	0224	2·2	27 Th	0437	2·0
	0850	0·8		1045	1·2
	1528	2·0		1654	2·0
	2105	1·0		2352	1·0
13 Th	0348	2·1	28 F	0616	2·0
	1007	0·9		1218	1·2
	1643	2·0		1813	2·0
	2241	1·0			
14 F	0513	2·1	29 Sa	0103	0·9
	1130	0·9		0726	2·0
	1748	2·0		1315	1·1
				1916	2·1
15 Sa	0009	0·9			
	0626	2·1			
	1237	0·9			
	1846	2·1			

MARCH

Day	Time	m	Day	Time	m
1 Su	0150	0·7	16 M	0105	0·5
	0815	2·1		0728	2·2
	1354	1·0		1322	0·8
	2001	2·1		1920	2·3
2 M	0228	0·6	17 Tu	0205	0·2
	0852	2·1		0822	2·3
	1424	0·9		1415	0·7
	2033	2·2		2013	2·4
3 Tu	0301	0·5	18 W	0256	0·1
	0926	2·2		0907	2·3
	1450	0·8		1503	0·5
	2103	2·3	○	2101	2·6
4 W	0333	0·4	19 Th	0341	0·0
	0954	2·2		0948	2·4
	1520	0·7		1546	0·4
●	2133	2·4		2146	2·7
5 Th	0405	0·4	20 F	0424	0·0
	1022	2·2		1028	2·4
	1552	0·6		1628	0·4
	2207	2·4		2231	2·7
6 F	0435	0·4	21 Sa	0503	0·1
	1046	2·2		1107	2·3
	1626	0·6		1709	0·4
	2239	2·5		2315	2·6
7 Sa	0507	0·4	22 Su	0543	0·3
	1115	2·2		1145	2·3
	1658	0·6		1748	0·5
	2313	2·4		2358	2·5
8 Su	0535	0·5	23 M	0618	0·5
	1145	2·2		1224	2·2
	1731	0·6		1828	0·6
	2346	2·4			
9 M	0603	0·5	24 Tu	0045	2·3
	1216	2·2		0654	0·8
	1805	0·7		1303	2·1
				1909	0·7
10 Tu	0024	2·3	25 W	0139	2·2
	0637	0·6		0733	1·0
	1254	2·1		1350	2·1
	1846	0·7		2000	0·9
11 W	0109	2·2	26 Th	0245	2·0
	0718	0·8		0820	1·2
	1341	2·0		1445	2·0
	1937	0·8	☾	2107	1·0
12 Th	0211	2·1	27 F	0411	1·9
	0816	0·9		0937	1·3
	1443	2·0		1552	1·9
☽	2048	0·9		2309	0·9
13 F	0337	2·0	28 Sa	0539	1·9
	0937	1·0		1141	1·3
	1601	2·0		1703	1·9
	2224	0·8			
14 Sa	0503	2·0	29 Su	0022	0·8
	1109	1·0		0652	2·0
	1716	2·0		1237	1·2
	2354	0·7		1818	2·0
15 Su	0620	2·1	30 M	0111	0·7
	1222	0·9		0743	2·1
	1820	2·1		1315	1·0
				1915	2·1
			31 Tu	0150	0·6
				0822	2·1
				1345	0·9
				1956	2·2

APRIL

Day	Time	m	Day	Time	m
1 W	0224	0·5	16 Th	0230	0·2
	0854	2·2		0845	2·3
	1416	0·8		1439	0·6
	2030	2·3		2041	2·5
2 Th	0256	0·4	17 F	0315	0·2
	0922	2·2		0924	2·4
	1450	0·7		1524	0·5
	2103	2·4	○	2128	2·6
3 F	0330	0·4	18 Sa	0358	0·2
	0948	2·2		1001	2·4
	1526	0·6		1609	0·5
●	2139	2·4		2213	2·6
4 Sa	0401	0·4	19 Su	0437	0·4
	1015	2·3		1039	2·4
	1603	0·5		1650	0·5
	2215	2·4		2256	2·5
5 Su	0433	0·4	20 M	0515	0·6
	1045	2·3		1116	2·3
	1639	0·5		1731	0·5
	2252	2·4		2341	2·4
6 M	0505	0·5	21 Tu	0548	0·8
	1116	2·3		1150	2·3
	1715	0·6		1811	0·6
	2330	2·4			
7 Tu	0535	0·6	22 W	0028	2·2
	1152	2·3		0618	0·9
	1752	0·6		1228	2·2
				1852	0·7
8 W	0011	2·3	23 Th	0118	2·1
	0611	0·7		0652	1·1
	1231	2·2		1309	2·2
	1839	0·6		1939	0·8
9 Th	0101	2·2	24 F	0222	2·0
	0658	0·8		0735	1·2
	1316	2·1		1358	2·1
	1937	0·7	☾	2035	0·8
10 F	0209	2·1	25 Sa	0333	2·0
	0800	1·0		0835	1·3
	1416	2·1		1458	2·0
☽	2048	0·7		2152	0·9
11 Sa	0335	2·0	26 Su	0446	2·0
	0918	1·1		1003	1·3
	1530	2·0		1601	2·0
	2213	0·7		2318	0·8
12 Su	0458	2·1	27 M	0556	2·0
	1046	1·1		1133	1·2
	1646	2·1		1707	2·0
	2333	0·5			
13 M	0611	2·1	28 Tu	0015	0·7
	1158	1·0		0654	2·0
	1754	2·2		1220	1·1
				1809	2·1
14 Tu	0041	0·4	29 W	0100	0·6
	0713	2·2		0737	2·1
	1258	0·9		1301	1·0
	1856	2·3		1903	2·1
15 W	0139	0·3	30 Th	0137	0·6
	0801	2·2		0813	2·2
	1350	0·7		1339	0·9
	1952	2·4		1950	2·2

Chart Datum: 1.50 metres below Ordnance Datum (Newlyn)

ENGLAND, EAST COAST – LOWESTOFT

TIME ZONE UT(GMT)
For Summer Time add ONE hour in non-shaded areas

Lat 52°28′ N Long 1°45′ E

TIMES AND HEIGHTS OF HIGH AND LOW WATERS

YEAR **1992**

4

MAY

Date	Time	m	Date	Time	m
1 F	0215	0·5	16 Sa	0248	0·4
	0843	2·2		0900	2·4
	1420	0·7		1509	0·6
	2031	2·3		○ 2113	2·4
2 Sa	0250	0·5	17 Su	0331	0·5
	0911	2·3		0939	2·4
	1501	0·6		1556	0·5
	● 2113	2·4		2200	2·4
3 Su	0328	0·5	18 M	0411	0·6
	0943	2·3		1015	2·4
	1543	0·6		1639	0·5
	2154	2·4		2245	2·3
4 M	0403	0·5	19 Tu	0446	0·8
	1018	2·4		1050	2·4
	1626	0·5		1720	0·5
	2235	2·4		2328	2·2
5 Tu	0439	0·6	20 W	0518	0·9
	1054	2·4		1124	2·4
	1709	0·5		1758	0·6
	2318	2·4			
6 W	0518	0·7	21 Th	0013	2·2
	1133	2·4		0546	1·0
	1756	0·5		1158	2·3
				1837	0·6
7 Th	0005	2·3	22 F	0101	2·1
	0601	0·8		0620	1·0
	1215	2·3		1235	2·3
	1848	0·5		1918	0·7
8 F	0101	2·2	23 Sa	0152	2·0
	0652	0·9		0701	1·1
	1301	2·3		1320	2·2
	1945	0·5		2003	0·7
9 Sa	0211	2·1	24 Su	0250	2·0
	0752	1·0		0752	1·2
	1358	2·2		1411	2·1
	☽ 2046	0·5		☾ 2056	0·8
10 Su	0330	2·1	25 M	0350	2·0
	0900	1·1		0852	1·2
	1505	2·2		1509	2·1
	2156	0·5		2200	0·8
11 M	0445	2·1	26 Tu	0452	2·0
	1015	1·1		1005	1·2
	1616	2·2		1613	2·1
	2307	0·4		2309	0·8
12 Tu	0548	2·1	27 W	0548	2·0
	1126	1·0		1120	1·2
	1728	2·2		1716	2·1
13 W	0011	0·4	28 Th	0003	0·7
	0648	2·2		0641	2·1
	1228	0·9		1216	1·1
	1831	2·3		1816	2·1
14 Th	0109	0·4	29 F	0050	0·7
	0737	2·2		0722	2·2
	1326	0·8		1305	1·0
	1931	2·4		1911	2·2
15 F	0201	0·4	30 Sa	0131	0·6
	0820	2·3		0800	2·2
	1418	0·7		1352	0·8
	2024	2·4		2000	2·3
			31 Su	0215	0·6
				0837	2·3
				1439	0·7
				2048	2·3

JUNE

Date	Time	m	Date	Time	m
1 M	0256	0·6	16 Tu	0350	0·8
	0915	2·4		0954	2·4
	1530	0·6		1630	0·5
	● 2135	2·4		2237	2·2
2 Tu	0341	0·6	17 W	0424	0·9
	0954	2·4		1028	2·4
	1620	0·5		1707	0·5
	2224	2·4		2318	2·2
3 W	0426	0·6	18 Th	0454	0·9
	1035	2·5		1101	2·4
	1709	0·4		1743	0·5
	2313	2·4			
4 Th	0513	0·7	19 F	0000	2·2
	1118	2·5		0524	0·9
	1758	0·3		1135	2·4
				1818	0·5
5 F	0003	2·3	20 Sa	0039	2·1
	0601	0·8		0556	0·9
	1203	2·5		1211	2·4
	1846	0·2		1854	0·6
6 Sa	0100	2·2	21 Su	0120	2·1
	0650	0·9		0635	1·0
	1250	2·4		1250	2·3
	1937	0·3		1931	0·6
7 Su	0201	2·2	22 M	0205	2·0
	0741	0·9		0718	1·0
	1343	2·4		1333	2·3
	☽ 2031	0·3		2013	0·7
8 M	0309	2·1	23 Tu	0256	2·0
	0837	1·0		0807	1·1
	1443	2·3		1424	2·2
	2130	0·4		☾ 2101	0·7
9 Tu	0416	2·1	24 W	0352	2·0
	0939	1·1		0903	1·1
	1550	2·3		1522	2·1
	2235	0·5		2201	0·8
10 W	0520	2·1	25 Th	0450	2·0
	1050	1·1		1015	1·2
	1701	2·3		1631	2·1
	2341	0·5		2309	0·8
11 Th	0618	2·1	26 F	0546	2·1
	1200	1·0		1130	1·1
	1811	2·3		1739	2·1
12 F	0041	0·6	27 Sa	0007	0·8
	0713	2·2		0635	2·1
	1307	0·9		1231	1·0
	1916	2·3		1839	2·1
13 Sa	0137	0·6	28 Su	0056	0·7
	0800	2·3		0722	2·2
	1409	0·8		1328	0·9
	2016	2·3		1935	2·2
14 Su	0228	0·7	29 M	0145	0·7
	0841	2·3		0807	2·3
	1501	0·7		1426	0·7
	2107	2·3		2030	2·3
15 M	0311	0·8	30 Tu	0235	0·7
	0918	2·4		0850	2·4
	1546	0·6		1522	0·5
	○ 2154	2·3		● 2124	2·3

JULY

Date	Time	m	Date	Time	m
1 W	0326	0·6	16 Th	0403	0·9
	0935	2·5		1011	2·4
	1613	0·3		1648	0·4
	2215	2·4		2303	2·2
2 Th	0418	0·6	17 F	0433	0·8
	1020	2·6		1043	2·5
	1701	0·2		1722	0·4
	2305	2·4		2337	2·2
3 F	0507	0·6	18 Sa	0501	0·8
	1103	2·6		1115	2·5
	1748	0·1		1754	0·5
	2356	2·4			
4 Sa	0552	0·7	19 Su	0011	2·2
	1150	2·6		0533	0·8
	1833	0·1		1146	2·4
				1826	0·5
5 Su	0046	2·3	20 M	0043	2·1
	0635	0·7		0609	0·8
	1237	2·6		1222	2·4
	1920	0·1		1858	0·6
6 M	0139	2·2	21 Tu	0118	2·1
	0720	0·8		0646	0·9
	1326	2·5		1300	2·3
	2007	0·3		1933	0·6
7 Tu	0235	2·1	22 W	0200	2·0
	0809	0·9		0728	1·0
	1422	2·4		1345	2·3
	☽ 2101	0·4		☾ 2015	0·7
8 W	0339	2·1	23 Th	0252	2·0
	0905	1·0		0818	1·1
	1528	2·3		1439	2·2
	2201	0·6		2107	0·8
9 Th	0445	2·1	24 F	0356	2·0
	1016	1·0		0920	1·1
	1641	2·2		1550	2·1
	2311	0·7		2215	0·9
10 F	0546	2·1	25 Sa	0458	2·0
	1141	1·0		1045	1·1
	1800	2·2		1707	2·1
				2328	0·9
11 Sa	0018	0·8	26 Su	0556	2·1
	0646	2·2		1203	1·0
	1303	0·9		1815	2·1
	1916	2·2			
12 Su	0120	0·9	27 M	0030	0·8
	0739	2·2		0648	2·2
	1405	0·8		1311	0·8
	2018	2·2		1916	2·2
13 M	0213	0·9	28 Tu	0124	0·8
	0824	2·3		0739	2·3
	1454	0·7		1413	0·6
	2107	2·2		2018	2·3
14 Tu	0256	0·9	29 W	0220	0·7
	0901	2·4		0828	2·4
	1535	0·6		1509	0·4
	○ 2150	2·2		● 2115	2·4
15 W	0333	0·9	30 Th	0315	0·6
	0937	2·4		0916	2·5
	1613	0·5		1600	0·1
	2228	2·2		2203	2·4
			31 F	0405	0·6
				1001	2·7
				1645	0·0
				2250	2·4

AUGUST

Date	Time	m	Date	Time	m
1 Sa	0450	0·5	16 Su	0437	0·7
	1048	2·7		1050	2·5
	1730	−0·1		1724	0·4
	2337	2·4		2337	2·2
2 Su	0533	0·6	17 M	0509	0·7
	1133	2·7		1122	2·5
	1813	0·0		1752	0·5
3 M	0022	2·3	18 Tu	0005	2·2
	0615	0·6		0541	0·8
	1218	2·7		1156	2·4
	1856	0·1		1822	0·6
4 Tu	0109	2·2	19 W	0035	2·1
	0658	0·7		0616	0·8
	1307	2·6		1231	2·4
	1941	0·3		1854	0·7
5 W	0158	2·1	20 Th	0113	2·1
	0743	0·8		0656	0·9
	1401	2·4		1313	2·3
	☽ 2030	0·6		1931	0·8
6 Th	0256	2·1	21 F	0200	2·1
	0835	0·9		0743	1·0
	1505	2·3		1405	2·2
	2126	0·8		☾ 2020	0·9
7 F	0401	2·1	22 Sa	0300	2·0
	0946	1·0		0843	1·0
	1626	2·2		1520	2·1
	2241	1·0		2130	1·0
8 Sa	0511	2·1	23 Su	0411	2·0
	1131	1·0		1009	1·0
	1756	2·1		1645	2·1
				2256	1·0
9 Su	0003	1·0	24 M	0518	2·1
	0620	2·1		1141	0·9
	1258	0·9		1758	2·1
	1918	2·1			
10 M	0109	1·0	25 Tu	0007	1·0
	0720	2·2		0618	2·2
	1354	0·7		1252	0·7
	2015	2·2		1905	2·2
11 Tu	0200	1·0	26 W	0107	0·9
	0807	2·3		0713	2·3
	1437	0·6		1356	0·5
	2058	2·2		2007	2·3
12 W	0239	1·0	27 Th	0203	0·7
	0845	2·3		0805	2·5
	1516	0·5		1450	0·2
	2135	2·2		2100	2·4
13 Th	0311	0·9	28 F	0256	0·6
	0918	2·4		0856	2·6
	1550	0·5		1539	0·1
	○ 2209	2·2		● 2146	2·4
14 F	0339	0·8	29 Sa	0345	0·5
	0948	2·5		0943	2·7
	1622	0·4		1624	0·0
	2241	2·2		2230	2·5
15 Sa	0407	0·7	30 Su	0428	0·5
	1020	2·5		1028	2·8
	1654	0·4		1707	0·0
	2309	2·2		2311	2·4
			31 M	0511	0·5
				1113	2·8
				1748	0·1
				2354	2·4

Chart Datum: 1.50 metres below Ordnance Datum (Newlyn)

ENGLAND, EAST COAST – LOWESTOFT

TIME ZONE UT(GMT)
For Summer Time add ONE hour in non-shaded areas

Lat 52°28′ N Long 1°45′ E

TIMES AND HEIGHTS OF HIGH AND LOW WATERS

YEAR **1992**

SEPTEMBER

Date	Time	m	Date	Time	m
1 Tu	0552 1158 1830	0·5 2·7 0·3	**16** W	0516 1131 1745	0·7 2·4 0·7
2 W	0035 0633 1246 1911	2·3 0·6 2·6 0·6	**17** Th	0001 0550 1209 1816	2·3 0·8 2·4 0·7
3 Th ☽	0122 0718 1341 1956	2·2 0·8 2·4 0·8	**18** F	0037 0630 1250 1854	2·2 0·8 2·3 0·8
4 F	0213 0811 1446 2048	2·1 0·9 2·2 1·1	**19** Sa ☾	0120 0718 1346 1946	2·2 0·9 2·2 1·0
5 Sa	0315 0922 1613 2207	2·1 1·0 2·1 1·2	**20** Su	0216 0824 1503 2058	2·1 0·9 2·1 1·1
6 Su	0424 1115 1746 2345	2·1 1·0 2·1 1·2	**21** M	0328 0948 1631 2228	2·1 0·9 2·1 1·1
7 M	0541 1235 1901	2·1 0·9 2·1	**22** Tu	0443 1118 1746 2346	2·1 0·8 2·2 1·0
8 Tu	0050 0650 1330 1954	1·2 2·2 0·7 2·2	**23** W	0548 1231 1852	2·2 0·6 2·2
9 W	0135 0741 1411 2035	1·1 2·2 0·6 2·2	**24** Th	0046 0648 1331 1950	0·9 2·4 0·4 2·3
10 Th	0211 0818 1446 2109	1·0 2·3 0·6 2·2	**25** F	0141 0743 1426 2039	0·8 2·5 0·2 2·4
11 F	0239 0850 1518 2141	0·9 2·4 0·5 2·3	**26** Sa ●	0231 0833 1515 2122	0·7 2·7 0·1 2·5
12 Sa ○	0307 0922 1550 2209	0·8 2·5 0·5 2·3	**27** Su	0320 0922 1558 2203	0·6 2·8 0·1 2·5
13 Su	0337 0952 1620 2237	0·7 2·5 0·5 2·3	**28** M	0405 1007 1641 2245	0·5 2·8 0·2 2·5
14 M	0411 1024 1650 2301	0·7 2·5 0·5 2·3	**29** Tu	0448 1052 1722 2324	0·5 2·8 0·3 2·4
15 Tu	0443 1058 1718 2330	0·7 2·5 0·6 2·3	**30** W	0531 1139 1801	0·5 2·7 0·6

OCTOBER

Date	Time	m	Date	Time	m
1 Th	0003 0615 1226 1841	2·4 0·6 2·5 0·8	**16** F	0535 1150 1746	0·7 2·4 0·8
2 F	0046 0700 1320 1920	2·3 0·7 2·3 1·0	**17** Sa	0011 0618 1237 1828	2·4 0·7 2·3 0·9
3 Sa ☽	0133 0750 1428 2009	2·2 0·9 2·2 1·2	**18** Su	0054 0715 1337 1924	2·3 0·8 2·2 1·1
4 Su	0228 0856 1550 2115	2·2 1·0 2·1 1·4	**19** M ☾	0146 0820 1456 2037	2·2 0·8 2·1 1·2
5 M	0331 1035 1713 2305	2·1 1·0 2·1 1·4	**20** Tu	0252 0935 1620 2200	2·2 0·8 2·1 1·2
6 Tu	0443 1156 1826	2·1 0·9 2·1	**21** W	0407 1056 1731 2318	2·2 0·7 2·2 1·1
7 W	0013 0554 1250 1920	1·3 2·2 0·8 2·2	**22** Th	0518 1203 1835	2·3 0·5 2·3
8 Th	0056 0656 1333 2003	1·2 2·2 0·7 2·2	**23** F	0020 0620 1303 1928	1·0 2·4 0·4 2·3
9 F	0131 0739 1409 2037	1·1 2·3 0·6 2·3	**24** Sa	0115 0718 1358 2015	0·9 2·5 0·3 2·4
10 Sa	0201 0815 1441 2109	0·9 2·4 0·6 2·3	**25** Su ●	0207 0811 1446 2058	0·8 2·7 0·3 2·5
11 Su ○	0233 0848 1513 2135	0·8 2·4 0·6 2·4	**26** M	0258 0901 1533 2139	0·7 2·7 0·3 2·5
12 M	0309 0922 1543 2200	0·8 2·5 0·6 2·4	**27** Tu	0346 0948 1616 2218	0·6 2·7 0·4 2·5
13 Tu	0345 0958 1613 2228	0·7 2·5 0·6 2·4	**28** W	0431 1035 1656 2256	0·6 2·7 0·6 2·5
14 W	0420 1033 1643 2300	0·7 2·5 0·7 2·4	**29** Th	0516 1122 1733 2335	0·6 2·5 0·8 2·5
15 Th	0458 1111 1713 2333	0·7 2·4 0·7 2·4	**30** F	0600 1211 1809	0·6 2·4 1·0
			31 Sa	0015 0645 1303 1846	2·4 0·7 2·3 1·1

NOVEMBER

Date	Time	m	Date	Time	m
1 Su	0056 0731 1403 1928	2·4 0·8 2·1 1·3	**16** M	0037 0716 1333 1916	2·4 0·6 2·2 1·1
2 M ☽	0145 0824 1513 2020	2·3 0·9 2·1 1·3	**17** Tu ☾	0128 0815 1445 2018	2·4 0·6 2·2 1·1
3 Tu	0243 0931 1624 2133	2·2 0·9 2·1 1·4	**18** W	0228 0918 1601 2130	2·3 0·6 2·1 1·2
4 W	0345 1056 1731 2305	2·2 0·9 2·1 1·3	**19** Th	0337 1028 1709 2243	2·3 0·6 2·2 1·2
5 Th	0448 1158 1831	2·2 0·8 2·2	**20** F	0448 1133 1811 2348	2·4 0·5 2·2 1·1
6 F	0001 0550 1243 1920	1·2 2·2 0·8 2·2	**21** Sa	0556 1235 1903	2·4 0·5 2·3
7 Sa	0045 0645 1322 2000	1·1 2·3 0·7 2·3	**22** Su	0048 0658 1330 1952	1·0 2·5 0·5 2·4
8 Su	0122 0731 1358 2030	1·0 2·3 0·7 2·3	**23** M	0148 0754 1422 2035	0·8 2·6 0·5 2·5
9 M	0201 0813 1431 2056	0·9 2·4 0·7 2·4	**24** Tu ●	0245 0846 1509 2115	0·7 2·6 0·6 2·5
10 Tu ○	0241 0854 1505 2126	0·8 2·4 0·7 2·4	**25** W	0335 0937 1552 2154	0·6 2·5 0·7 2·5
11 W	0324 0933 1541 2200	0·8 2·5 0·7 2·5	**26** Th	0422 1024 1633 2231	0·6 2·5 0·8 2·5
12 Th	0405 1015 1615 2235	0·7 2·5 0·7 2·5	**27** F	0505 1111 1709 2309	0·6 2·4 0·9 2·5
13 F	0448 1056 1652 2313	0·7 2·4 0·8 2·5	**28** Sa	0546 1156 1741 2346	0·6 2·3 1·0 2·5
14 Sa	0535 1141 1731 2352	0·6 2·4 0·9 2·5	**29** Su	0628 1245 1813	0·6 2·2 1·1
15 Su	0624 1231 1818	0·6 2·3 1·0	**30** M	0024 0707 1333 1850	2·4 0·7 2·1 1·2

DECEMBER

Date	Time	m	Date	Time	m
1 Tu	0107 0750 1428 1935	2·4 0·8 2·1 1·2	**16** W ☾	0113 0800 1424 2000	2·5 0·4 2·2 1·0
2 W ☽	0156 0839 1528 2028	2·3 0·8 2·1 1·3	**17** Th	0207 0854 1531 2056	2·4 0·5 2·1 1·1
3 Th	0250 0937 1630 2131	2·2 0·9 2·1 1·3	**18** F	0311 0956 1639 2205	2·4 0·6 2·1 1·1
4 F	0352 1046 1730 2250	2·2 0·9 2·1 1·3	**19** Sa	0424 1103 1741 2318	2·4 0·6 2·2 1·1
5 Sa	0456 1146 1824 2356	2·2 0·9 2·1 1·2	**20** Su	0535 1207 1839	2·4 0·7 2·2
6 Su	0556 1233 1907	2·2 0·8 2·2	**21** M	0031 0643 1309 1930	1·0 2·4 0·7 2·3
7 M	0046 0652 1315 1945	1·1 2·2 0·8 2·3	**22** Tu	0141 0748 1403 2016	0·9 2·4 0·8 2·4
8 Tu	0133 0741 1354 2020	1·0 2·3 0·8 2·4	**23** W	0239 0845 1452 2058	0·7 2·4 0·8 2·4
9 W ○	0220 0828 1435 2056	0·9 2·3 0·7 2·4	**24** Th ●	0328 0933 1535 2135	0·6 2·4 0·8 2·5
10 Th	0309 0915 1516 2135	0·7 2·4 0·7 2·5	**25** F	0413 1018 1613 2213	0·5 2·3 0·9 2·5
11 F	0400 1001 1600 2215	0·6 2·4 0·7 2·6	**26** Sa	0452 1101 1646 2248	0·5 2·3 0·9 2·5
12 Sa	0448 1048 1645 2256	0·5 2·4 0·7 2·6	**27** Su	0530 1141 1716 2324	0·5 2·2 0·9 2·5
13 Su	0535 1135 1731 2339	0·4 2·4 0·8 2·6	**28** M	0605 1220 1746 2358	0·5 2·2 0·9 2·5
14 M	0622 1228 1818	0·4 2·3 0·9	**29** Tu	0641 1300 1818	0·6 2·1 1·0
15 Tu	0024 0709 1322 1907	2·5 0·4 2·2 0·9	**30** W	0035 0715 1341 1858	2·4 0·7 2·1 1·0
			31 Th	0115 0754 1428 1941	2·4 0·7 2·0 1·1

Chart Datum: 1.50 metres below Ordnance Datum (Newlyn)

LOWESTOFT *continued*

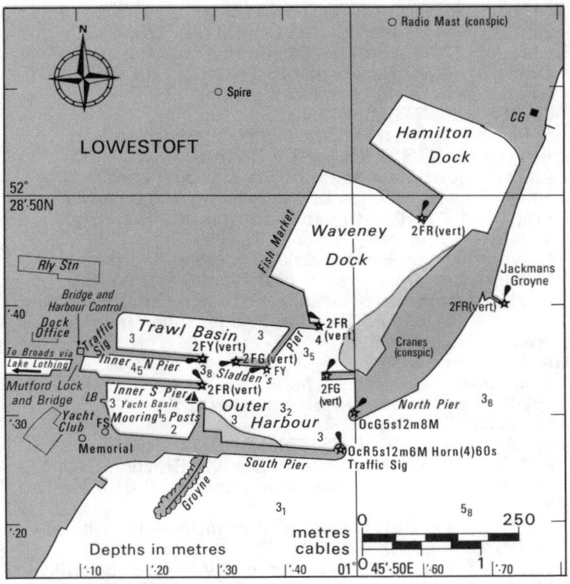

N
Radio Mast (conspic)
Spire
LOWESTOFT
CG
Hamilton Dock
52° 28'·50N
Fish Market
Waveney Dock
2FR(vert)
Rly Stn
Bridge and Harbour Control
Jackmans Groyne
2FR(vert)
'40
Dock Office
Traffic Sig
Trawl Basin
2FY(vert)
2FR 4(vert)
Pier
Cranes (conspic)
To Broads via Lake Lothing
Inner N Pier
2FG(vert)
FY
Sladden's
Mutford Lock and Bridge
LB
Inner S Pier
2FR(vert)
2FG (vert)
3 Yacht Basin
Outer Harbour
North Pier
'30
Yacht Club
FS
Mooring Posts
Memorial
OcG5s12m8M
OcR5s12m6M Horn(4)60s
Traffic Sig
South Pier
Groyne
'20
Depths in metres
metres
cables
250
'·10
'·20
'·30
'·40
01° 45'·50E
'·60
'·70

NAVIGATION

Sands are continually shifting. Beware shallows and drying areas, and do not cross banks in bad weather or strong tidal conditions. From S, waypoint East Barnard E cardinal buoy, Q(3) 10s, 52°24'·60N 01°46'·20E; then follow buoyed channel inshore of S Newcome and Pakefield buoys. From N or E, waypoint Corton E cardinal buoy, Q(3) 10s Bell, 52°31'·10N 01°51'·50E; then follow Holm Channel Bell (buoyed) into Corton Road. Speed limit in harbour 4 kn. Passage to Oulton Broad Wednesday p.m., passing two swing bridges and a lock; give Oulton Broad Hr Mr at least 48 hours notice.

LIGHTS AND MARKS

Entry Signals: Fl W Lt (obsc 232°-286°) below the Oc R Lt on South Pier Lt Ho – vessels may proceed to sea (with clearance from harbour control on Ch 14 or tel 572286) but entry prohibited. When signal not shown: No vessel to proceed to sea but entry permitted.

Bridge Signals: when bridge is lifting, vessels may not approach within 137m until G Lt is shown on N wall of entrance channel. When G Lt shown: vessels may enter or leave Inner Harbour.

RADIO TELEPHONE

VHF Ch **14** 16; 14 (H24). Pilot Ch 14.

TELEPHONE (0502)

Hr Mr 572286; Hr Mr Oulton Broad 574946; MRCC Great Yarmouth 851338; Bridge Control 572286; Pilot 560277; ⌗ (0473) 219481; Weather Norwich 660779; Marinecall 0898 500 455; Police 562121; Ⓗ 600611.

FACILITIES

EC Thursday; **Royal Norfolk & Suffolk YC** ☎ 566726, Slip, M, D, L, FW, C (2ton), R, Bar; **Oulton Broad — Jeckells Y. Co.** ☎ 565007, L, ME, El, Sh, CH, SM; **Oulton Broad Calor Centre** Gas, Gaz; **Knights Creek** ☎ 572599, El, CH; **J. E. Fletcher** ☎ 574951, Slip, Sh; **F. Newson** ☎ 574902, Slip, M, L, El, Sh; **A. D. Truman** ☎ 565950, Slip, M, L, ME, El, Sh; **Lowestoft Cruising Club** ☎ 574376, Slip, M, L, FW, AB; **Charity and Taylor** ☎ 581529, ACA. **Town** V, R, Bar. ✉; Ⓑ; ⇌; ✈ (Norwich).

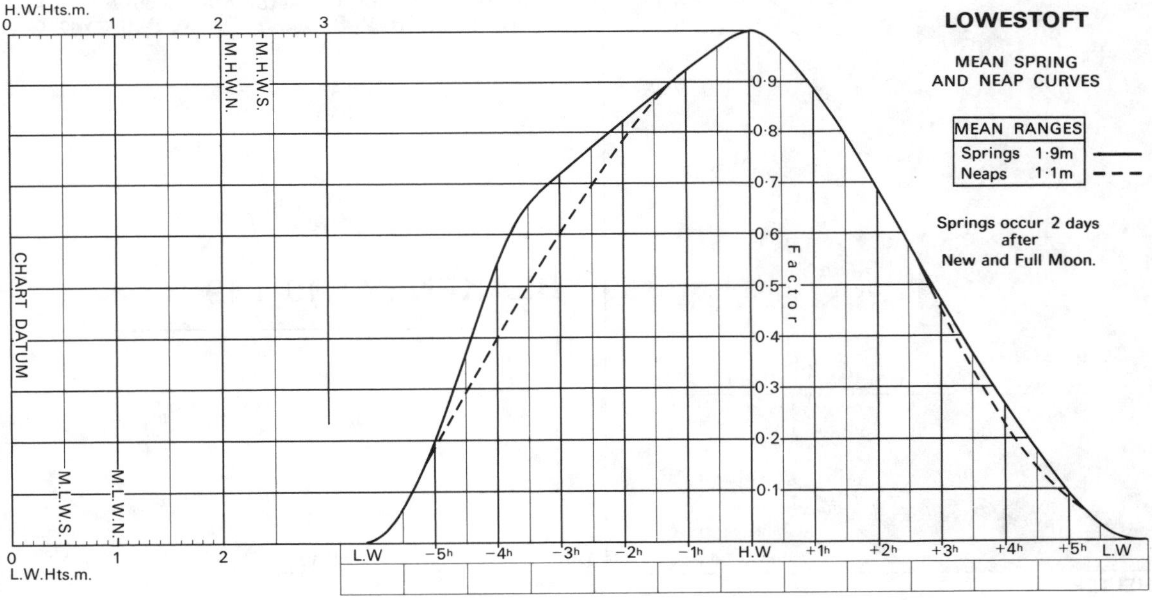

H.W.Hts.m.
0
1
2
3
M.H.W.S.
M.H.W.N.
CHART DATUM
M.L.W.S.
M.L.W.N.
0
1
2
L.W.Hts.m.
Factor
0·9
0·8
0·7
0·6
0·5
0·4
0·3
0·2
0·1
L.W
−5h
−4h
−3h
−2h
−1h
H.W
+1h
+2h
+3h
+4h
+5h
L.W
LOWESTOFT
MEAN SPRING AND NEAP CURVES
MEAN RANGES
Springs 1·9m
Neaps 1·1m
Springs occur 2 days after New and Full Moon.

GREAT YARMOUTH 10-4-18

Norfolk

CHARTS

Admiralty 1536, 1543; Stanford 3; Imray C28; OS 134

TIDES

−0210 Dover; ML 1·5; Duration 0620; Zone 0 (GMT).

Standard Port LOWESTOFT (⟵)

Times				Height (metres)			
HW		LW		MHWS	MHWN	MLWN	MLWS
0300	0900	0200	0800	2·4	2·1	1·0	0·5
1500	2100	1400	2000				
Differences GORLESTON							
−0035	−0035	−0030	−0030	0·0	−0·1	0·0	0·0
CAISTER-ON-SEA							
−0130	−0130	−0100	−0100	0·0	−0·1	0·0	0·0

Rise of tide occurs mainly during 3½ hours after LW. Level is usually within 0·3m of predicted HW height, from 3 hours before HW Lowestoft, until HW Lowestoft. Flood tide runs for about 1½ hrs after predicted HW and Ebb for about 2-2½ hrs after predicted LW.

GREAT YARMOUTH *continued*

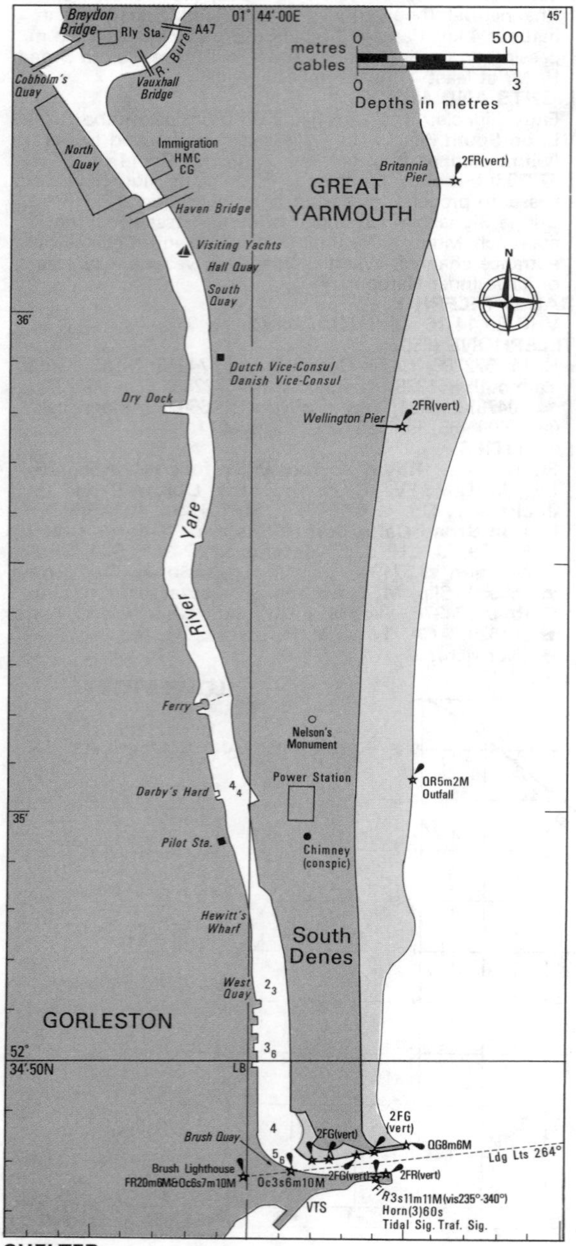

Breydon Bridge
Rly Sta.
A47
R. Bure
01° 44'·00E
45'
metres 0 500
cables 0 3
Depths in metres
Cobholm's Quay
Vauxhall Bridge
North Quay
Immigration
HMC
CG
Britannia Pier
2FR(vert)
GREAT YARMOUTH
Haven Bridge
Visiting Yachts
Hall Quay
South Quay
N
36'
Dutch Vice-Consul
Danish Vice-Consul
Dry Dock
Wellington Pier
2FR(vert)
River Yare
Ferry
Nelson's Monument
Power Station
QR5m2M
Outfall
Darby's Hard
35'
Pilot Sta.
Chimney (conspic)
Hewitt's Wharf
South Denes
West Quay
GORLESTON
52° 34'·50N
LB
Brush Quay
2FG (vert)
2FG(vert)
QG8m6M
Ldg Lts 264°
Brush Lighthouse
FR20m6M&Oc6s7m10M
Oc3s6m10M
2FG(vert)
2FR(vert)
VTS
FlR3s11m11M(vis235°-340°)
Horn(3)60s
Tidal Sig. Traf. Sig.

SHELTER

Anchoring is prohibited within the harbour but shelter is excellent on the East side on Town Hall Quay which is immediately south of the Haven Bridge.

NAVIGATION

Waypoint 52°34'·40N 01°45'·67E, 084°/264° from/to front Ldg Lt 264°, 1·0M. Subject to clearance, the harbour is available at all times but small craft should not attempt entrance when strong SE winds cause dangerous seas especially on the ebb tide. Other than at slack water there are strong tidal streams at the entrance. Temporary shoaling is liable to occur in the harbour entrance during strong easterly winds when depths of 1m less than those charted may be expected. The harbour is a busy commercial port, traffic signals and instructions from the Vessel Traffic Service (VTS) should be complied with at all times. Beware the strong tidal streams that sweep through the Haven Bridge.

Bridge clearances (at MHWS)

Haven Bridge (C/L centre span closed)	2·3m
Vauxhall (old railway bridge)	2·3m
Bure (A47 road bridge)	2·3m
Breydon (C/L centre span closed)	4·0m
Breydon (side spans)	4·5m

LIGHTS AND MARKS

Main Lt (S Pier) Fl R 3s. 11m 11M vis. 235°-340°. Fog sig Horn (3) 60s. N Pier Lt Q G 8m 6M vis. 176°-078° (through 270°). Ldg Lts 264°-Front Oc 3s 6m 10M. Rear Oc 6s 7m 10M. Tidal signal (S Pier) Q Y vis. 235°-340°, when tide flooding between the piers.

TRAFFIC CONTROL SIGNALS

S Pier 3 F R (vert) vis. 235°-295°. Entrance to Port Prohibited. VTS Office – 3 F R (vert) no vessel to proceed down river south of the Life-boat shed.

Haven Bridge – when bridge is lifting and passage prohibited 3 F R (vert) exhibited from the Eastern or Western Buttresses.

Breydon Bridge – when bridge is lifting and passage through the centre span is prohibited 3 F R (vert) exhibited from the S Buttress or Bridge Control Building.

Both the Haven and Breydon Bridges when manned operate on VHF Ch 12

RADIO TELEPHONE

Call: *Great Yarmouth Harbour* VHF Ch 12, 16; 09 11 12 (H24). Breydon and Haven Bridges Ch 12.

TELEPHONE (0493)

Hr Mr 855151; MRCC 851338; # (0473) 219481; Police 842222; Port Health Authority 856100; Breydon Bridge 651275; Broads Navigation Authority (0603) 610734.

FACILITIES

EC Thursday; **Burgh Castle Marina** (90 + 10 visitors) ☎ 780263, Slip, D, FW, ME, El, Sh, C (6 ton), ◎, Gas, Gaz, CH, V, R, Bar, Access HW∓4; **Goodchild Marine** 852442; BY, D, ME, El, FW, Slip, Diving; **Bure Marine** 656996, Slip, AB, FW, L, M, ME, El, Sh; **Breydon Marine** 780379, AB, P, D, L, FW; **Paul Williment** ☎ 662710 (by LB station) D; **Yarmouth Stores** 842289, SM; **Gorleston Marine** 661883, ACA; **Town** P, D, CH, V, R, Bar, ⊠, Ⓑ, ≷, ✈ (Norwich).

BLAKENEY 10-4-19

Norfolk

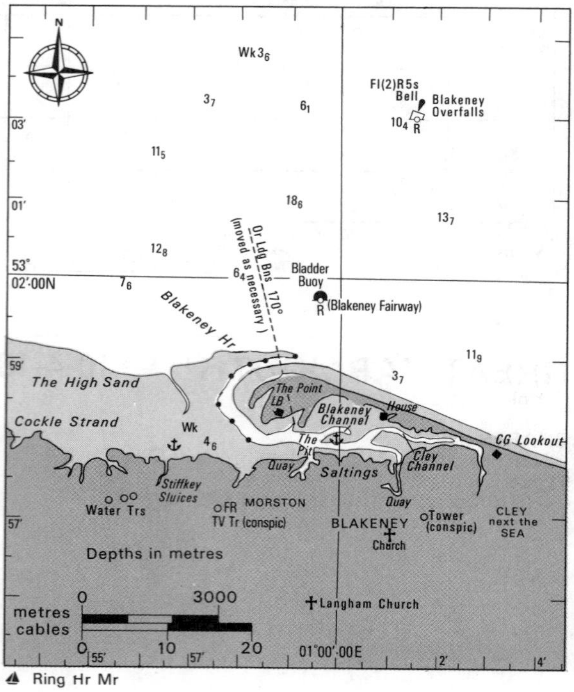

N
Wk 3_6
Fl(2)R5s Bell
Blakeney Overfalls
03'
01'
53° 02'·00N
Or Ldg Bns 170° (moved as necessary)
Bladder Buoy
(Blakeney Fairway)
Blakeney Hr
59'
The High Sand
Cockle Strand
The Point
LB
Blakeney Channel
House
CG Lookout
The Pit
Quay
Saltings
Cley Channel
Quay
Stiffkey Sluices
Water Trs
FR TV Tr (conspic)
MORSTON
BLAKENEY
Church
Tower (conspic)
CLEY next the SEA
57'
Depths in metres
metres 0 3000
cables 0 10 20
Langham Church
55'
57'
01°00'·00E
2'
4'

▲ Ring Hr Mr

BLAKENEY *continued*

CHARTS
Admiralty 108; Imray C28; OS 133

TIDES
−0445 Dover; Duration 0530; Zone 0 (GMT).

Standard Port IMMINGHAM (⟶)

Times				Height (metres)			
HW		LW		MHWS	MHWN	MLWN	MLWS
0100	0700	0100	0700	7·3	5·8	2·6	0·9
1300	1900	1300	1900				
Differences BLAKENEY							
+0115	+0055	No data		−3·9	−3·8	No data	
BLAKENEY BAR							
+0035	+0025	+0030	+0040	−1·6	−1·3	No data	
CROMER							
+0050	+0030	+0050	+0130	−2·1	−1·7	−0·5	−0·1

SHELTER
Very good shelter but harbour inaccessible with fresh on-shore winds. Conditions in the entrance deteriorate very quickly with on-shore winds, especially on the ebb. Entry, springs HW ∓2½, neaps HW ∓1. Moorings in The Pit or at Stiffkey Sluices.

NAVIGATION
Waypoint 53°00′·00N 00°58′·20E, 350°/170° from/to channel entrance 0·97M. Large wreck to W of harbour entrance channel; very dangerous, unlit, marked by buoy. The bar is shallow and changes frequently. The channel is marked by B buoys to be left to stbd. Beware mussel lays in the channel off Blakeney spit. Speed limit 8 kn. For pilotage contact Stratton Long Marine (below).

LIGHTS AND MARKS
Orange leading beacons established on dunes at Blakeney Pt, moved according to changes in the channel (not always reliable). Conspic marks are Blakeney Church and Langham Church. There is a conspic chimney on the house on Blakeney Point neck. A Lt buoy, QY, is placed (April-Oct) marking entrance, 1½ ca N of wreck.

RADIO TELEPHONE
None.

TELEPHONE (0263)
Hr Mr 740362; MRCC Great Yarmouth 851338; # (0473) 219481; Marinecall 0898 500 455; Dr 740314.

FACILITIES
EC Wednesday; **Blakeney Quay** Slip, M, D, L, FW, El, C (15 ton), CH, AB; **Stratton Long Marine** ☎ 740362, M, P, D, FW, ME, El, Sh, CH, Slip, L, C, AB, BY, SM, Gas, Gaz, AC; **Village** V, R, Bar. ⊠; Ⓑ; ⇌ (Sherringham); ✈ (Norwich).
Note: The areas of Blakeney Point and Dunes are National Trust Property and contain a bird sanctuary.
Note 2: There is a plan to build a marina at Cromer.

WELLS-NEXT-THE-SEA 10-4-20

Norfolk

CHARTS
Admiralty 108; Imray C28, Y9; OS 132

TIDES
−0445 Dover; ML 1·2 Duration 0540; Zone 0 (GMT).

Standard Port IMMINGHAM (⟶)

Times				Height (metres)			
HW		LW		MHWS	MHWN	MLWN	MLWS
0100	0700	0100	0700	7·3	5·8	2·6	0·9
1300	1900	1300	1900				
Differences WELLS-NEXT-THE-SEA							
+0035	+0045	+0340	+0310	−3·8	−3·8	No data	
WELLS BAR							
+0020	+0020	+0020	+0020	−1·3	−1·0	No data	
HUNSTANTON							
+0010	+0020	+0105	+0025	+0·1	−0·2	−0·1	0·0
BURNHAM OVERY STAITHE							
+0045	+0055	No data		−5·0	−4·9	No data	

SHELTER
The shelter is good except in strong N winds. Max draft 3m at springs. Entrance possible from HW −1½ to HW +1 but recommended on the flood. Entrance impossible to small craft with strong on-shore winds.

NAVIGATION
Waypoint Wells Fairway buoy, 53°00′·20N, 00°51′·15E, 020°/200° from/to channel entrance, 1M. The bar and entrance vary in depth and position. The position of buoys is altered to suit. Channel is marked with Q buoys to stbd, QR to port, reaching No. 16 (port). Keep to port side of channel from No 12 to quay. Advisable to take a pilot or follow fishing boat.

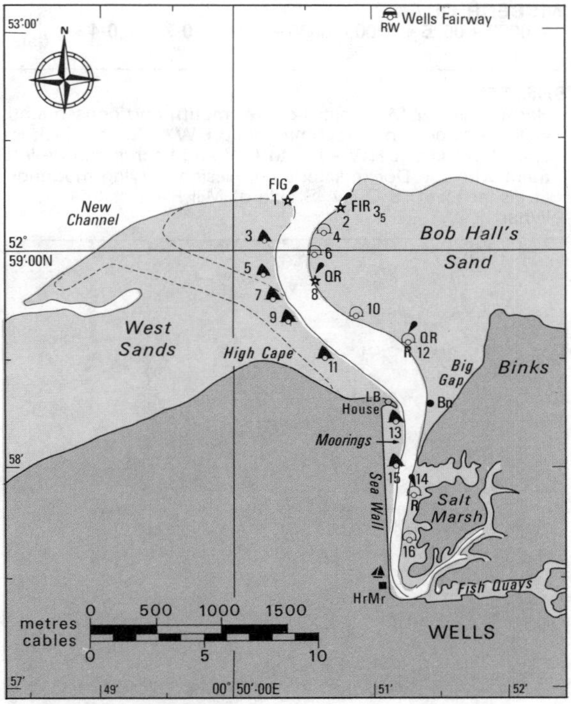
53°00′
Wells Fairway
RW
N
FIG
1
New Channel
FIR
2
3
5
Bob Hall's Sand
4
6
52′
59′00N
QR
8
7
9
10
West Sands
QR
12
High Cape
11
Big Gap
Binks
LB House
Bn
13
Moorings
58′
Sea Wall
15
14
Salt Marsh
16
HrMr
Fish Quays
0 500 1000 1500
metres
cables
0 5 10
WELLS
57′
49′
00° 50′·00E
51′
52′

LIGHTS AND MARKS
Harbour ent has a conspic W Lifeboat Ho with R roof on the West point.

RADIO TELEPHONE
VHF Ch 16; 06 08 12 (when vessels expected)

TELEPHONE (0328 – Fakenham)
Hr Mr 711744; Pilot 710550; MRCC Gt. Yarmouth 851338; # (0473) 219481; Marinecall 0898 500 455; Police 710212; Ⓗ 710218.

FACILITIES
EC Thursday; **East Quay** Slip, M, L; **Main Quay** M (see Hr Mr), L, FW, ME, El, Sh, C (5 ton mobile), CH, AB, V, R, Bar; **Wells SC** Slip, Bar; **Standard House Chandlery** ☎ 710593, M, L, ME, El, Sh, CH, AB, V, ACA; **J. Crook** ☎ 710593, CH; **M. Walsingham** ☎ 710438, Gas; **Preston** ☎ 2414, Ⓔ; **Town** P and D (bowser on quay – up to 500 galls), CH, V, R, Bar. ⊠; Ⓑ; ⇌ (bus to Norwich or King's Lynn); ✈ (Norwich).

KING'S LYNN 10-4-21

Norfolk

CHARTS
Admiralty 1200, 108, 1190; Imray Y9; OS 132

TIDES
−0443 Dover; ML 3·6; Duration 0340 Sp, 0515 Np; Zone 0 (GMT).

Standard Port IMMINGHAM (⟶)

Times				Height (metres)			
HW		LW		MHWS	MHWN	MLWN	MLWS
0100	0700	0100	0700	7·3	5·8	2·6	0·9
1300	1900	1300	1900				
Differences KING'S LYNN							
+0030	+0030	+0305	+0140	−0·5	−0·8	−0·8	+0·1
WISBECH CUT							
+0020	+0025	+0200	+0030	−0·3	−0·7	−0·4	No data

SHELTER
Harbour is 1½ M within the river mouth and consequently well sheltered. Entry recommended HW ∓3. The dock is open from about HW−1½ to HW and yachts can be left there with the Dockmaster's permission. Drying moorings at Fisher Fleet, S Quay, S side of Mill Fleet or Friar's Wharf.

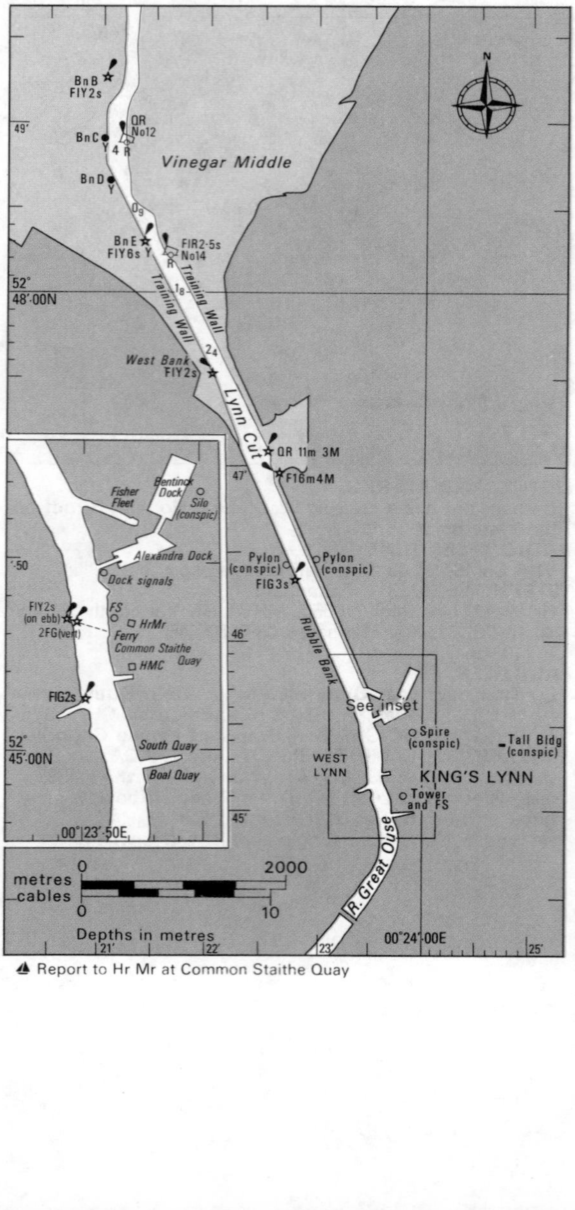

BnB
FlY2s
QR
No12
BnC
Y 4 R
Vinegar Middle
BnD
Y
9
BnE
FlY6s Y
FlR2·5s
No14
R
18
Training Wall
Training Wall
West Bank
FlY2s
24
Lynn Cut
QR 11m 3M
F16m4M
Pylon (conspic)
Pylon (conspic)
FlG3s
Rubble Bank
See inset
Spire (conspic)
Tall Bldg (conspic)
WEST LYNN
KING'S LYNN
Tower and FS
R. Great Ouse
Fisher Fleet
Bentinck Dock
Silo (conspic)
Alexandra Dock
Dock signals
FlY2s (on ebb)
2FG(vert)
FS
HrMr
Ferry
Common Staithe Quay
HMC
FlG2s
South Quay
Boal Quay
52° 48'·00N
52° 45'·00N
49'
47'
46'
45'
00°23'·50E
00°24'·00E
21'
22'
23'
25'
N
metres 0 2000
cables 0 10
Depths in metres

⚠ Report to Hr Mr at Common Staithe Quay

NAVIGATION
Waypoint North Well (RW) buoy LFl 10s Horn Racon 53°03'·00N, 00°00'·28E, 022°/202° From/to Cork Hole 7·0M. Extensive shifting sand banks extend several miles into the Wash. The best and safest approach is via the Cork Hole route, marked by Lt buoys. Channels are subject to frequent changes particularly between No 7 Light Buoy and Lynn Cut. S of West Stones Bn the deeper water is on E side of channel.

LIGHTS AND MARKS
Ldg Lts 155°. Front QR 11m 3M, Rear FW 16m 4M, both on masts.
Entry signals for Alexander Dock:
Bu flag or R Lt — Vessels can enter
R flag or G Lt — Vessels leaving dock.

RADIO TELEPHONE
VHF Ch 16; 11 14 (Mon-Fri: 0800-1730 LT. Other times: HW−4 to HW+1).
King's Lynn Docks Ch **14** 16; 11 (HW−2½ to HW+1).
Other station: Wisbech Ch 16; 09 **14** (HW−4 to HW when vessel expected).

TELEPHONE (0553)
Hr Mr 773411, Dock 691555; MRCC Gt. Yarmouth 851338; # (0473) 219481; Marinecall 0898 500 455; Dr Ring Hr Mr.

FACILITIES
EC Wednesday; There are virtually no facilities for visiting yachts; **Docks** ☎ 691555, M, L, FW, C (32 ton), AB; **N.C. Shipp** ☎ 772831, ME, El; **V. Pratt** ☎ 764058, El, CH; **Downham Components** ☎ (0366) 500737, Ⓔ. **Commercial and Marine Communications** ☎ 672206 El, Ⓔ; **Town** P, D, ME, El, Sh, CH, V, R, Bar. ✉; Ⓑ; ⇄; ✈ (Humberside or Norwich).
Note 24 miles up the Great Ouse river **Ely Marina** ☎ Ely 664622, (Lock at Denver Sluice and low bridges above this point), Slip, M, P, D, FW, ME, El, Sh, C (10 ton), CH.

MINOR HARBOURS AND ANCHORAGES 10.4.22

RIVER ROACH, Essex 51°35′·00N, 00°43′·00E, Zone 0 (GMT), Admty chart 3750. At Rochford HW +0115 on Dover, −0010 on Sheerness; HW height −2·4m on Sheerness. Excellent shelter. Very good anchorage and shelter about ¼M up R Roach close to W bank. River runs into R Crouch and is ¼M wide at the mouth, but mud extends from both banks, the Wallasea Ness bank being marked by Branklet Spit Buoy (Y spher). Few boats go above Barling Ness. For moorings and anchorages, see chartlet 10.3.23 and 10.4.8. A riding light is needed when anchored since R Roach is used by freighters day and night. Facilities: most facilities in **Rochford** EC Wed. **Shuttlewoods** (100) ☎ 226, D, BY, Slip, M; **Paglesham** FW, (from yard), V (at East End), Sh, Bar. **Wakering** El, FW, ME, Sh; Stores at **Great Wakering**; **Wakering YC**.

NORFOLK BROADS. There are about 130 miles of navigable rivers and tributaries in Norfolk and Suffolk together with meres and lakes, known as Broads. The main rivers are the Bure, the Yare and the Waveney which all flow into Breydon Water and thence into the sea at Great Yarmouth (see 10.4.18). This is the principal entrance. Licences are compulsory and Norfolk Broads temporary licences are obtainable from The Broads Authority Thomas Harvey House 18 Colegate Norwich NR3 1BQ ☎ (0603) 610734. Pass up R Yare, under Haven Bridge (headroom when closed 2·4m at MHWS) which is a lifting bridge (contact the Bridge Officer on Yarmouth 663476 or on VHF Ch 12). Bridge is manned 0800-1700 Mon-Thurs, 0800-1600 Fri. It does not open 0800-0900 or 1700-1800. Lifts are co-ordinated to pass small craft in groups. Thence to Breydon Water or to the R Bure, under two bridges (headroom 2m at MHWS.) Once past the two fixed bridges, some other bridges on the broads open − to open swing bridges, give three long blasts. A number of broads are closed to navigation. Tides: LW at Breydon (mouth of R Yare) is 1 hour before LW at Yarmouth Yacht Station (mouth of R Bure). Tide will start to flood on Breydon Water whilst still ebbing from R Bure. LW R Bure mouth = HW at Yarmouth Bar +0700. Tidal differences are quoted on LW at Yarmouth Yacht Station, which is Gorleston (see 10.4.18) +0100. For LW times at the following, add to time of LW at Yarmouth Yacht Station

Acle Bridge +0230	St Olaves +0115
Horning +0300	Beccles +0320
Reedham +0115	Oulton Broad +0300
Cantley +0200	Potter Heigham +0400
Norwich +0430	Burney Arms +0100

The Broads can also be entered at Lowestoft from the sea, via Oulton Dyke and Mutford Lock (opens Wed) into the R Waveney (see 10.4.17).

BURNHAM OVERY STAITHE, Norfolk, 52°59′·00N, 00°45′·00E, Zone 0 (GMT), Admty chart 108. HW −0420 on Dover, +0021 on Immingham; HW height −2·6m on Immingham. See 10.4.20. Small harbour which dries; anchorage off the Staithe only suitable in good weather. No lights. Scolt Hd conspic to W and Gun Hill to E. Channel varies constantly and buoys moved to suit. Local knowledge advisable. Facilities: (0328) **Burnham Overy Staithe SC** ☎ 738348, M, L; **The Boathouse** ☎ 738348, CH, M, ME, Sh, Slip, FW; **Burnham Market** EC Wed; Bar, P and D (cans), R, V.

BRANCASTER STAITHE, Norfolk, 52°58′·00N, 00°39′·00E, Zone 0 (GMT), Admty chart 108. HW −0425 on Dover, Hunstanton +0020 on Immingham; HW height −0·6m on Immingham. Small unlit harbour which dries; dangerous to enter except in daylight in fine weather. Speed limit 6 kn. Approach from due N. Conspic Golf Club House with Lt Fl 5s 8m 3M marks the start of channel buoys. Beware wreck shown on chart. Sandbanks vary continuously and buoys changed to suit. Scolt Hd conspic to E. Pilot advised. Facilities: (0485) Hr Mr ☎ 210638, visitors mooring available occasionally; Bar, BY, CH, D, El, FW, P and D (cans), ME, R, Sh, V; **Brancaster Staithe SC** ☎ 210249, R, Bar; **Scolt Head Nat Trust Warden** ☎ 210330 (Access HW∓3); **Brancaster Sailing Centre** ☎ 210236, CH.

WISBECH, Cambridgeshire, 52°40′·00N, 00°10′·00E, Zone 0 (GMT), Admty charts 1200. HW −0450 on Dover, Wisbech Cut +0020 on Immingham; HW height −0·5m on Immingham; ML 3·5m; Duration 0520. See 10.4.21. Excellent shelter. Vessels of 4·8m draught at sp can reach Wisbech (3·4m at nps). Entrance to R Nene and inland waterways. Moorings W bank ½M downstream from Sutton Bridge at Sutton Port or at Wisbech Town Quay. Entrance well marked from wreck to Nene Towers with lit stbd Bns. Best entrance HW −3. Wisbech Cut to Sutton Br is 3½M call on VHF Ch 16 09 14 or ☎ Holbeach 350364. Sutton Br to Wisbech 12M with Fl R Lts to port. Take care when ships entering or leaving the berthing area. Facilities: (0945) Hr Mr ☎ 582125; EC Wed; **Bodger Bros** ☎ 582864, Gas; **Town** P and D (cans), Bar, R, V, L at Western Tower.

WELLAND RIVER, Lincolnshire, 52°56′·00N, 00°05′·00E, Zone 0 (GMT), Admty charts 1200, 1190. At Welland Cut HW −0440 on Dover, +0030 on Immingham; HW height −0·1m on Immingham; ML 0·3m; Duration 0520. Enter by Welland Cut, Iso R 2s to SE and Iso G 2s to NW. Entrance HW ∓3. Beware tides of up to 5 kn on flood at sp. Secure at small quay ½M NE of bridge on stbd side. Dries.
Recommended for short stay only (at Fosdyke). Very limited facilities.

Area 5

North-East England
The Wash to Berwick-on-Tweed

10-5-2

North-East England

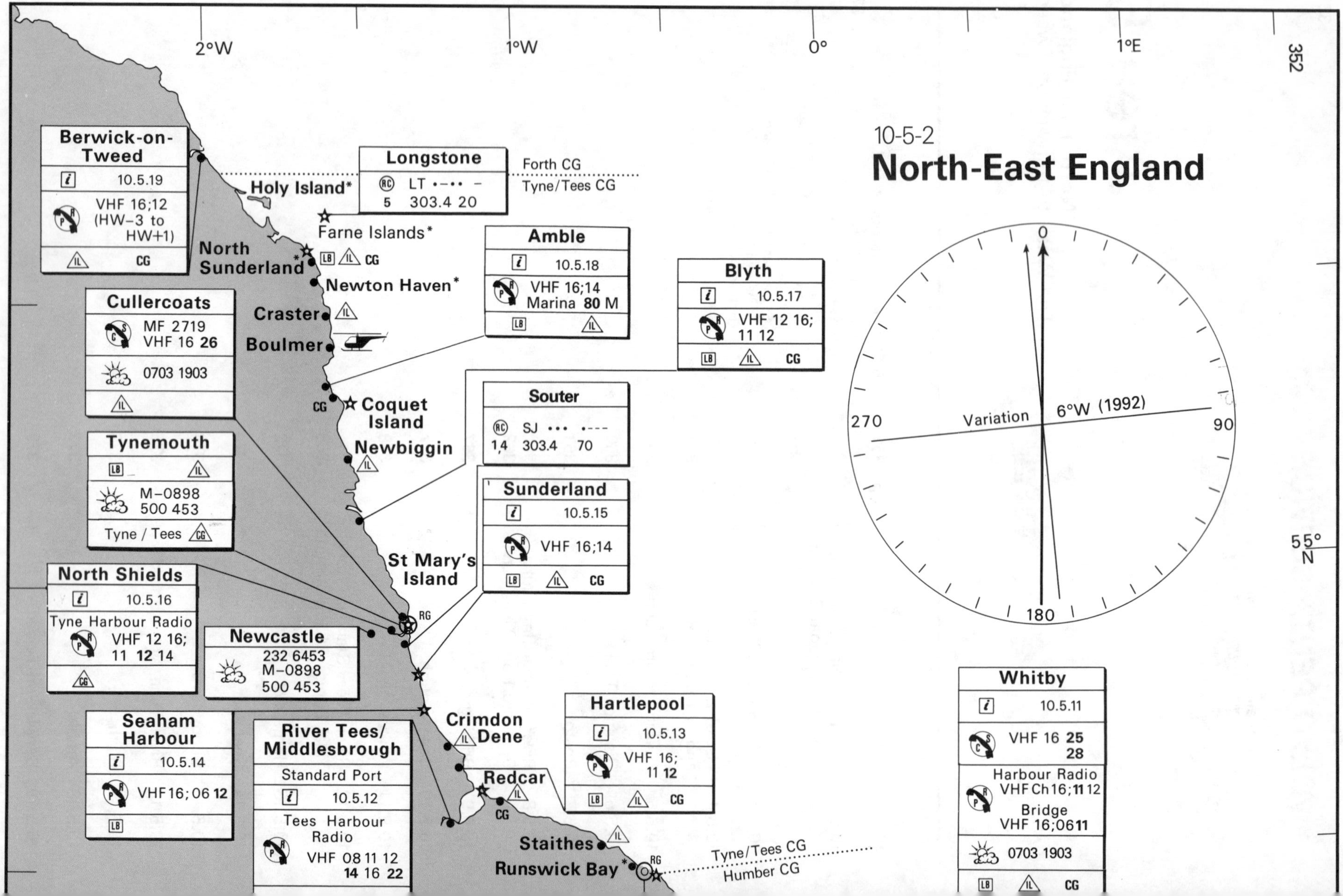
2°W
1°W
0°
1°E
55° N
Berwick-on-Tweed
10.5.19
VHF 16;12 (HW–3 to HW+1)
CG
Longstone
LT •–•• –
5 303.4 20
Forth CG
Tyne/Tees CG
Holy Island*
Farne Islands*
CG
North Sunderland
Newton Haven*
Craster
Boulmer
Amble
10.5.18
VHF 16;14
Marina 80 M
Blyth
10.5.17
VHF 12 16; 11 12
CG
Cullercoats
MF 2719
VHF 16 26
0703 1903
CG
Coquet Island
Newbiggin
Souter
SJ ••• •–––
1,4 303.4 70
Tynemouth
M–0898
500 453
Tyne / Tees
Sunderland
10.5.15
VHF 16;14
CG
St Mary's Island
North Shields
10.5.16
Tyne Harbour Radio
VHF 12 16; 11 12 14
RG
Newcastle
232 6453
M–0898
500 453
Seaham Harbour
10.5.14
VHF 16; 06 12
River Tees/ Middlesbrough
Standard Port
10.5.12
Tees Harbour Radio
VHF 08 11 12 14 16 22
Crimdon Dene
Redcar
CG
Hartlepool
10.5.13
VHF 16; 11 12
CG
Staithes
Runswick Bay*
RG
Tyne/Tees CG
Humber CG
Whitby
10.5.11
VHF 16 25 28
Harbour Radio
VHF Ch 16; 11 12
Bridge
VHF 16; 06 11
0703 1903
CG
0
90
180
270
Variation 6°W (1992)

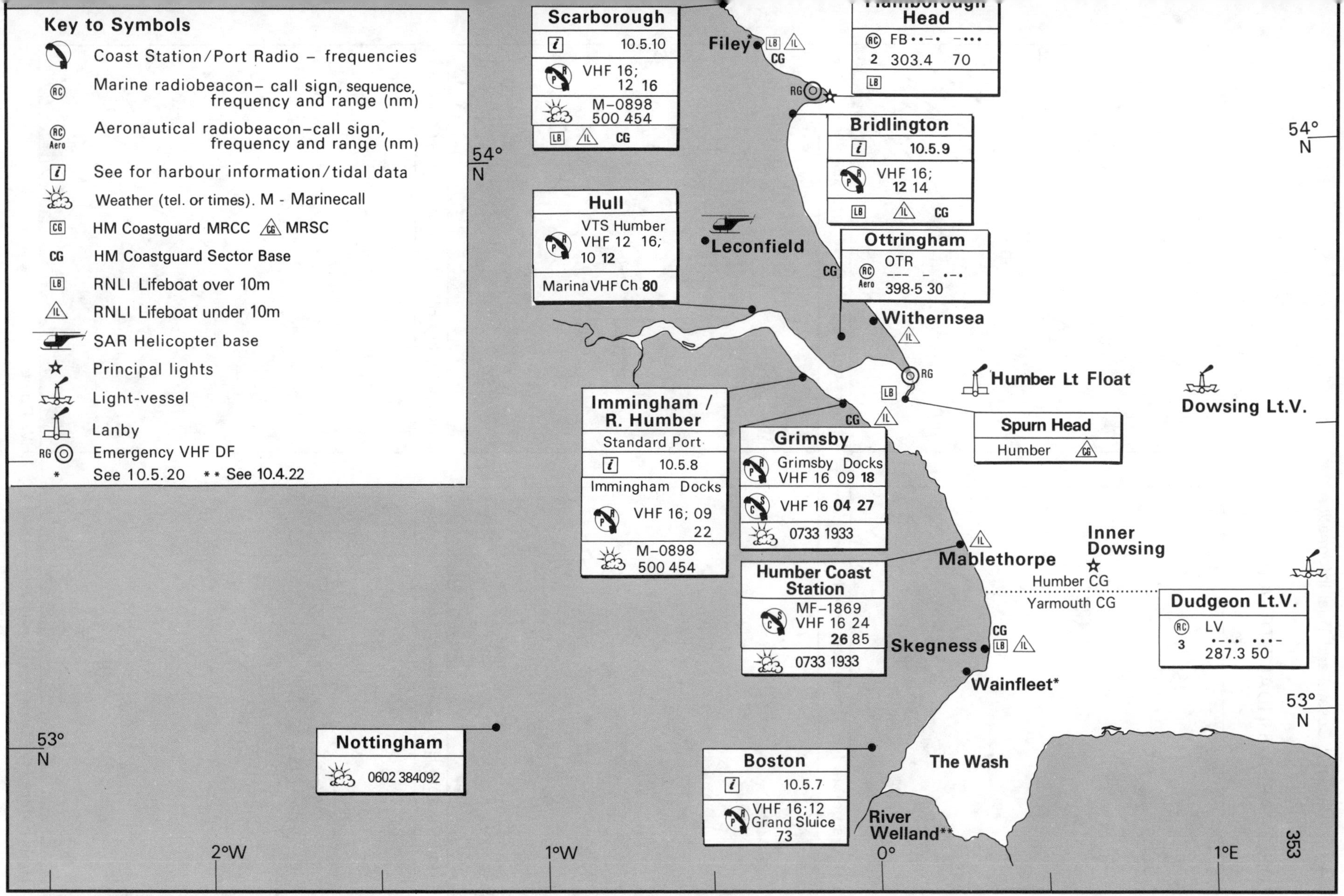
Key to Symbols
Coast Station/Port Radio – frequencies
Marine radiobeacon– call sign, sequence, frequency and range (nm)
Aeronautical radiobeacon–call sign, frequency and range (nm)
See for harbour information/tidal data
Weather (tel. or times). M - Marinecall
HM Coastguard MRCC MRSC
HM Coastguard Sector Base
RNLI Lifeboat over 10m
RNLI Lifeboat under 10m
SAR Helicopter base
Principal lights
Light-vessel
Lanby
Emergency VHF DF
See 10.5.20 ** See 10.4.22
Scarborough
10.5.10
VHF 16; 12 16
M–0898 500 454
CG
Filey*
CG
Flamborough Head
FB
2 303.4 70
RG
Bridlington
10.5.9
VHF 16; 12 14
CG
Hull
VTS Humber VHF 12 16; 10 12
Marina VHF Ch 80
Leconfield
Ottringham
OTR
Aero 398·5 30
CG
Withernsea
RG
Humber Lt Float
Dowsing Lt.V.
Spurn Head
Humber
Immingham / R. Humber
Standard Port
10.5.8
Immingham Docks
VHF 16; 09 22
M–0898 500 454
CG
Grimsby
Grimsby Docks VHF 16 09 18
VHF 16 04 27
0733 1933
Mablethorpe
Inner Dowsing
Humber CG
Yarmouth CG
Humber Coast Station
MF–1869 VHF 16 24 26 85
0733 1933
Dudgeon Lt.V.
LV
3 287.3 50
CG
Skegness
Wainfleet*
The Wash
Nottingham
0602 384092
Boston
10.5.7
VHF 16;12 Grand Sluice 73
River Welland**
54° N
53° N
2°W
1°W
0°
1°E

10.5.3 AREA 5 TIDAL STREAMS

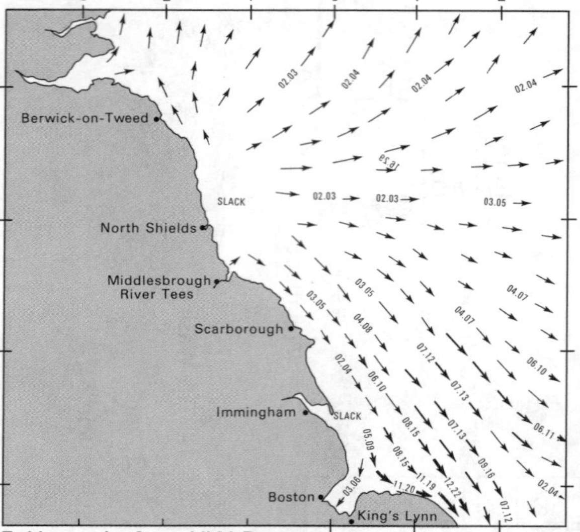
3°
2°
1°
0°
1°
2°
56°
55°
54°
53°
Berwick-on-Tweed
SLACK
North Shields
Middlesbrough
River Tees
Scarborough
Immingham
SLACK
Boston
King's Lynn

5 Hours before HW Dover (0030 after HW Immingham)

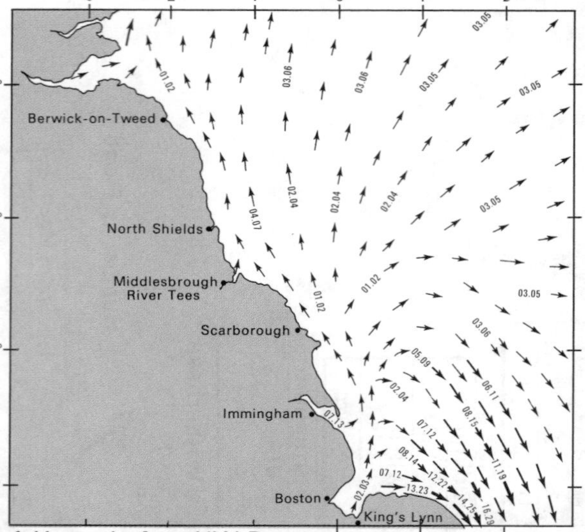
3°
2°
1°
0°
1°
2°
56°
55°
54°
53°
Berwick-on-Tweed
North Shields
Middlesbrough
River Tees
Scarborough
Immingham
Boston
King's Lynn

4 Hours before HW Dover (0130 after HW Immingham)

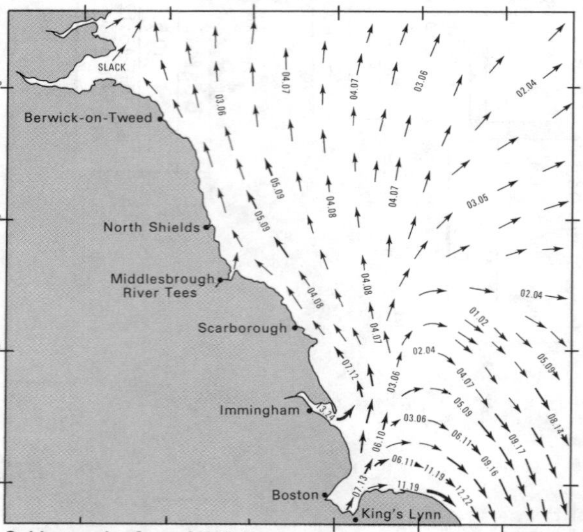
SLACK
56°
55°
54°
53°
Berwick-on-Tweed
North Shields
Middlesbrough
River Tees
Scarborough
Immingham
Boston
King's Lynn

3 Hours before HW Dover (0230 after HW Immingham)

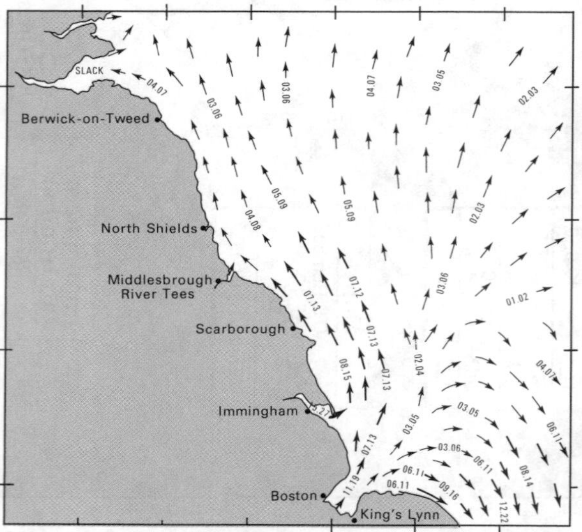
SLACK
56°
55°
54°
53°
Berwick-on-Tweed
North Shields
Middlesbrough
River Tees
Scarborough
Immingham
Boston
King's Lynn

2 Hours before HW Dover (0330 after HW Immingham)

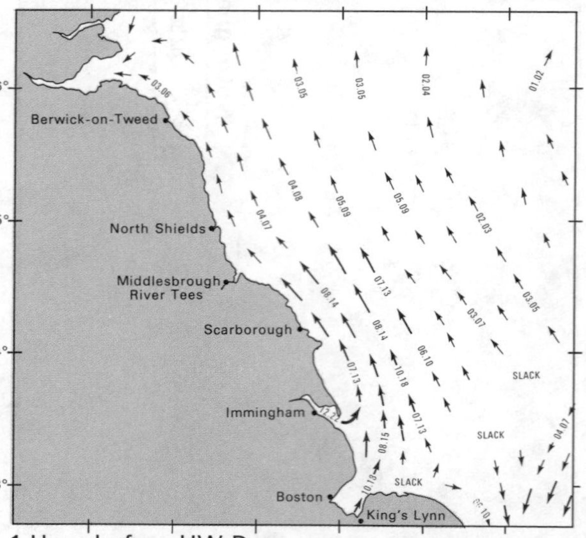
56°
55°
54°
53°
Berwick-on-Tweed
North Shields
Middlesbrough
River Tees
Scarborough
Immingham
SLACK
SLACK
SLACK
Boston
King's Lynn

1 Hour before HW Dover (0430 after HW Immingham)

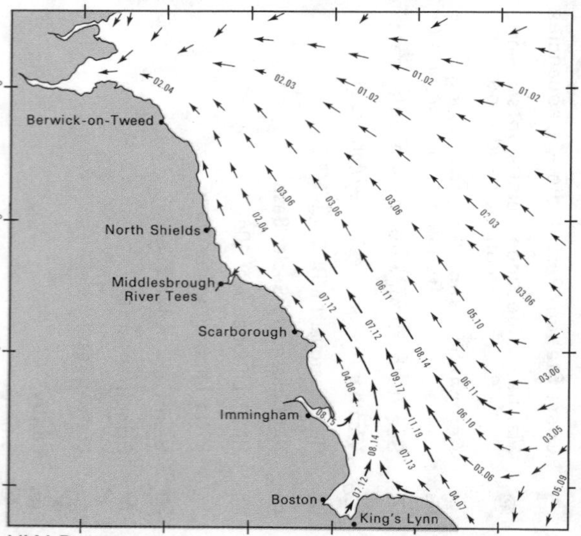
56°
55°
54°
53°
Berwick-on-Tweed
North Shields
Middlesbrough
River Tees
Scarborough
Immingham
Boston
King's Lynn

HW Dover (0530 after HW Immingham)

Northward 10.6.3 Southward 10.4.3

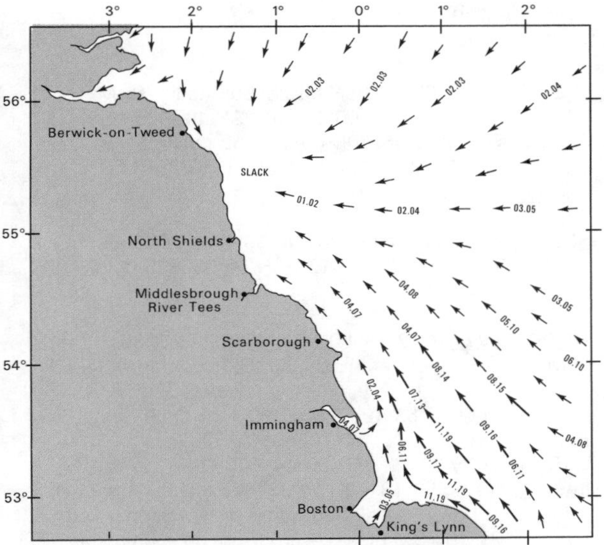
3°
2°
1°
0°
1°
2°
56°
55°
54°
53°
Berwick-on-Tweed
North Shields
Middlesbrough
River Tees
Scarborough
Immingham
Boston
King's Lynn
SLACK

1 Hour after HW Dover (0555 before HW Immingham)

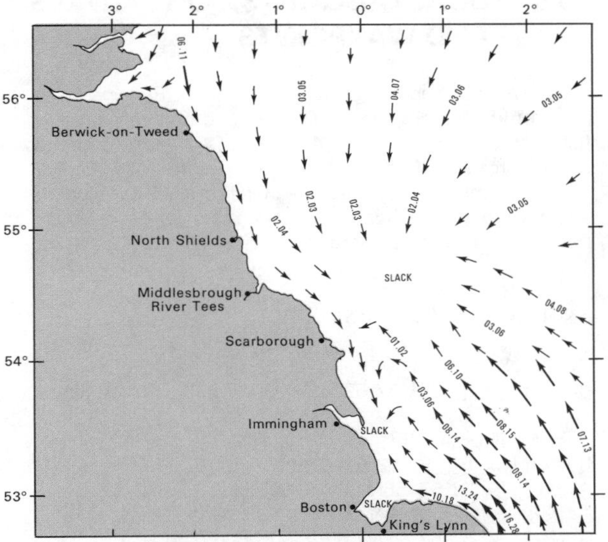
Berwick-on-Tweed
North Shields
Middlesbrough
River Tees
Scarborough
Immingham
Boston
King's Lynn
SLACK

2 Hours after HW Dover (0455 before HW Immingham)

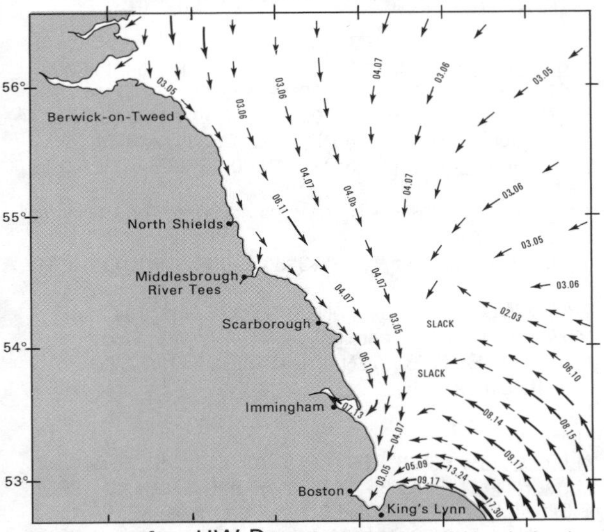
Berwick-on-Tweed
North Shields
Middlesbrough
River Tees
Scarborough
Immingham
Boston
King's Lynn
SLACK

3 Hours after HW Dover (0355 before HW Immingham)

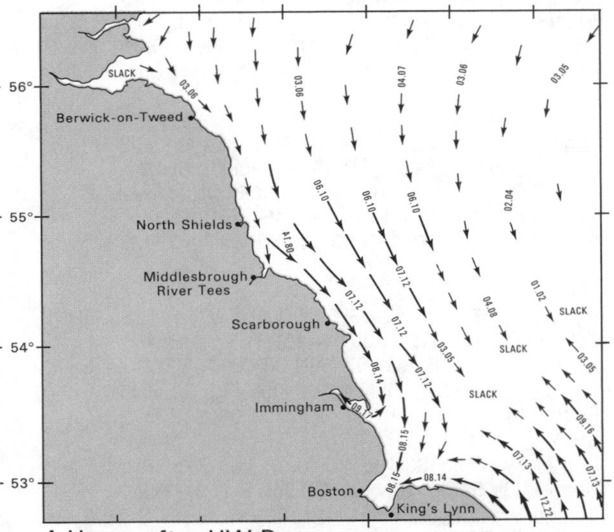
Berwick-on-Tweed
North Shields
Middlesbrough
River Tees
Scarborough
Immingham
Boston
King's Lynn
SLACK

4 Hours after HW Dover (0255 before HW Immingham)

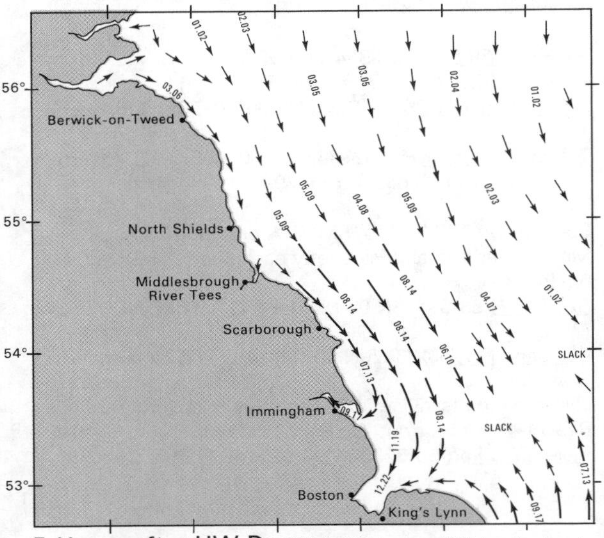
Berwick-on-Tweed
North Shields
Middlesbrough
River Tees
Scarborough
Immingham
Boston
King's Lynn
SLACK

5 Hours after HW Dover (0155 before HW Immingham)

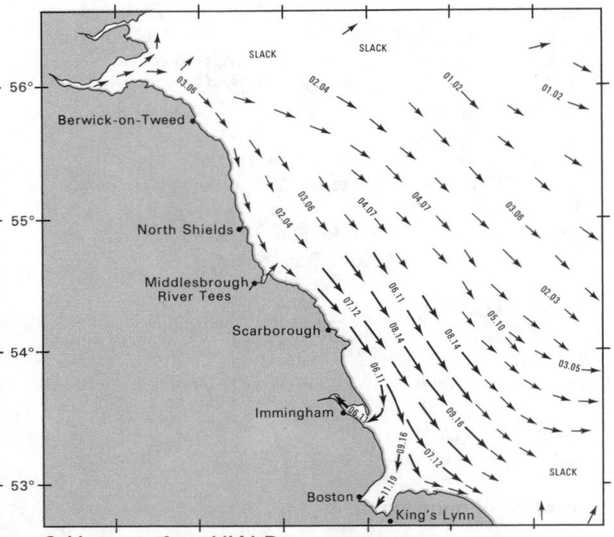
Berwick-on-Tweed
North Shields
Middlesbrough
River Tees
Scarborough
Immingham
Boston
King's Lynn
SLACK

6 Hours after HW Dover (0055 before HW Immingham)

10.5.4 COASTAL LIGHTS, FOG SIGNALS AND WAYPOINTS

Abbreviations used below are given in 1.4.1. Principal lights are in **bold** print, places in CAPITALS, and light-vessels, light floats and Lanbys in *CAPITAL ITALICS*. Unless otherwise stated lights are white. m—elevation in metres; M—nominal range in n. miles. Fog signals are in *italics*. Useful waypoints are underlined - use those on land with care. All geographical positions should be assumed to be approximate. See 4.2.2.

ENGLAND—NORTH–EAST COAST

BOSTON.
Boston Roads Lt By 52°57'·55N 00°16'·23E L Fl 10s; SWM.

FREEMAN CHANNEL.
Boston No. 1 Lt By 52°57'·87N 00°15'·16E Fl G 3s; SHM.
Alpha Lt By 52°57'·66N 00°15'·06E Fl R 3s; PHM.
No. 3 Lt By 52°58'·10N 00°14'·15E Fl G 6s; SHM.
Bravo Lt By 52°57'·98N 00°14'·00E Fl R 6s; PHM.
No. 5 Lt By 52°58'·52N 00°12'·78E Fl G 3s; SHM.
Charlie Lt By 52°58'·43N 00°12'·54E Fl R 3s; PHM.
Freeman Inner Lt By 52°58'·45N 00°11'·50E Q (9) 15s; WCM.
Delta Lt By 52°58'·34N 00°11'·68E Fl R 6s; PHM.

BOSTON DEEP.
Lynn Knock Lt By 53°04'·35N 00°27'·30E QG; SHM.
Pompey By 53°02'·20N 00°19'·37E (unlit); SHM.
Long Sand By 53°01'·10N 00°18'·30E (unlit); SHM.
Friskney By 53°00'·48N 00°16'·68E (unlit); SHM.
Scullridge By 52°59'·68N 00°14'·00E (unlit); SHM.

LOWER ROAD.
Boston No. 7 Lt By 52°58'·57N 00°10'·05E Fl G 3s; SHM.
Echo Lt By 52°58'·34N 00°10'·15E Fl R 3s; PHM.
Boston No. 9 Lt By 52° 57'·58N 00°08'·45E Fl G 3s; SHM.
Foxtrot Lt By 52°57'·55N 00°09'·00E Fl R 3s; PHM.
Boston No. 11 Lt By 52°56'·65N 00°08'·10E Fl G 6s; SHM.
Golf Lt By 52°56'·80N 00°07'·90E Fl (2) R 6s; PHM.
Hotel Lt By 52°56'·28N 00°07'·54E Fl R 3s; PHM.
Boston No.13 Lt By 52°56'·18N 00°06'·93E Fl G 3s; SHM.
India Lt By 56°12'·05N 00°06'·72E Fl R 6s; PHM.
Juliett Lt By 52°56'·08N 00°06'·72E Fl R 3s; PHM.
Boston No.15 Lt By 52°56'·29N 00°05'·74E Fl G 3s; SHM.
Welland 52°56'·06N 00°05'·37E QR 5m; R ■ on Bn.
Ent N side, Dollypeg 52°56'·10N 00°05'·15E QG 4m 1M; B ▲ on Bn; Ra refl.

BOSTON NEW CUT AND RIVER WITHAM.
Tabs Hd Q WG 4m 1M; R ■ on W mast; vis W shore-251°, G251°-shore; Ra refl.
New Cut 52°56'·0N 00°04'·8E Fl G 3s; ▲ on pile.
New Cut Ldg Lts 240°. Both F 5/8m 5M.

WELLAND CUT.
SE side Iso R 2s; NW side Iso G 2s. Lts QR (to port) and QG (to stbd) mark the chan upstream.
Wainfleet Range UQ R, with FR on Trs SW & NE.

WAINFLEET ROADS.
Swatchway By 53°03'·76N 00°19'·80E (unlit); SHM.

(Direction of buoyage S).

Inner Knock By 53°04'·85N 00°20'·50E (unlit); PHM.
Wainfleet Roads By 53°06'·20N 00°21'·40E (unlit); PHM.
Skegness S By 53°06'·70N 00°23'·35E (unlit); SHM.
Skegness By 53°08'·42N 00°23'·80E (unlit); SHM.
Skegness Pier 2 FR (vert).

Scott Patch Lt By 53°11'·10N 00°36'·50E VQ (3) 5s; ECM.
S Inner Dowsing Lt By 53°12'·10N 00°33'·80E Q (6) + LFl 15s; SCM; *Bell.*

DUDGEON Lt V 53°16'·60N 01°17'·00E Fl (3) 30s 12m **25M**; R hull with Lt Tr amidships; RC; Racon; *Horn (4) 60s.*

E Dudgeon Lt By 53°19'·70N 00°58'·80E Q (3) 10s; ECM; *Bell* .
W Ridge Lt By 53°19'·05N 00°44'·60E Q (9) 15s; WCM.
Inner Dowsing 53°19'·70N 00°33'·96E Fl 10s 41m **21M**; R pylon on W house, on platform on B piles; Racon; *Horn 60s*; Fl R 2s 31m 3M Lts (synchronised) on each corner of house, when main Lt is not displayed.

HUMBER APPROACHES.
Protector Lt By 53°24'·83N 00°25'·25E Fl R 2·5s; PHM.
DZ No. 4 Lt By 53°27'·12N 00°19'·17E Fl Y 5s; SPM.
DZ No. 3 Lt By 53°28'·40N 00°19'·20E Fl Y 2·5s; SPM.
Rosse Spit Lt By 53°30'·40N 00°17'·05E Fl (2) R 5s; PHM.
Haile Sand No. 2 Lt By 53°32'·14N 00°12'·80E Fl (3) R 10s; PHM.
Mid Outer Dowsing Lt By 53°24'·80N 01°07'·90E Fl (3) G 10s; SHM; *Bell.*
N Outer Dowsing Lt By 53°33'·50N 00°59'·70E Q; NCM.

DOWSING Lt V 53°34'·00N 00°50'·17E Fl (2) 10s 12m **23M**; R hull with Lt Tr amidships; *Horn (2) 60s*; Racon.
Humber Lt By 53°36'·72N 00°21'·60E L Fl 10s; SWM; *Bell;* Racon.

HUMBER.
N Binks Lt By 53°36'·22N 00°18'·70E Fl Y 2·5s; SPM.
Outer Haile Lt By 53°35'·25N 00°19'·00E Fl (4) Y 15s; SPM.
S Binks Lt By 53°34'·70N 00°16'·60E Fl Y 5s; SPM.
SPURN Lt F 53°33'·53N 00°14'·33E Q (3) 10s 10m 8M; ECM; *Horn 20s*; Racon.

E CHEQUER Lt F 53°33'·4N 00°12'·6E VQ (6) + L Fl 10s 6m 6M; SCM; Ra refl; *Horn 30s*. FW Riding Lt.
No. 3 Chequer Lt By 53°33'·05N 00°10'·70E Q (6) + LFl 15s; SCM.
Tetney Monobuoy 53°32'·34N 00°06'·85E 2 VQ Y (vert); Y SBM; *Horn Mo (A) 60s*; QY on 290m floating hose.

Spurn Pt Bn Fl G 3s 11m 5M; G ▲ on tripod.
Military Pier (Hd) and Pilot Jetty each show 2 FG (vert) Lts 6m 2M.
BULL Lt F 53°33'·78N 00°05'·64E VQ 8m 6M; NCM; *Horn (2) 20s.*
Bull Sand Fort 53°33'·70N 00°04'·14E Fl (2) 5s 20m 4M; *Horn 20s.*
Killingholme Lts in line 292°. Front Iso R 2s 10m 14M. Rear, 189m from front, Oc R 4s 21m 14M.
Haile Sand Fort 53°32'·05N 00°02'·14E Fl R 5s 21m 3M.

HUMBER TO BRIDLINGTON.
Wreck Lt By 53°42'·35N 00°07'·30E VQ(3) 5s; ECM.
DZ Lt By 53°47'·82N 00°00'·25E QY; SPM.
DZ S Lt By 53°50'·35N 00°01'·50W Fl Y 2s; SPM.
DZ No 5 Lt By 53°50'·40N 00°04'·00W Fl Y 5s; SPM.
DZ No 4 Lt By 53°51'·50N 00°00'·00 Fl Y 10s; SPM.
DZ No 3 Lt By 53°54'·10N 00°02'·00W Fl Y 10s; SPM.
DZ No. 2 Lt By 53°54'·05N 00°04'·00W Fl Y 10s; SPM.
DZ N Lt By 53°53'·10N 00°05'·50W Fl Y 2s; SPM.
Hornsea Sewer Outfall Lt By 53°55'·00N 00°01'·70E Fl Y 20s; SPM.
Atwick Sewer Outfall Lt By 53°57'·10N 00°10'·20W Fl Y 10s; SPM.

BRIDLINGTON.
SW Smithic Lt By 54°02'·40N 00°09'·10W Q (9) 15s; WCM.
N Pier Hd 54°04'·77N 00°11'·08W Fl 2s 7m 9M; *Horn 60s.*
S Pier FR or G R 12m, G8m, G3M, R12m, R4M, (Tidal Lts).
N Smithic Lt By 54°06'·20N 00°03'·80W Q; NCM.

Flamborough Hd 54°06'·95N 00°04'·87W Fl (4) 15s 65m **29M**; W ● Tr; RC; Horn *(2) 90s.*

FILEY.
On cliff above CG Stn FR 31m 1M; vis 272°-308°.
Filey Brigg Lt By 54°12'·74N 00°14'·48W Q (3) 10s; ECM; *Bell.*

SCARBOROUGH.
E Pier Hd 54°16'·87N 00°23'·27W QG 8m 3M.
Lighthouse Pier Iso 5s 17m 9M; W ● Tr; vis 219°-039° and FY 8m; vis 233°-030°; (tide sigs); *Dia 60s.*

WHITBY.
Whitby Lt By 54°30'·32N 00°36'·48W Q; NCM; *Bell.*
High Lt, Ling Hill 54°28'·67N 00°34'·00W Iso WR 10s 73m **23M**; W 8-sided Tr and dwellings; vis R128°-143°, W143°-319°.
E Pier Hd FR 14m 3M; R Tr.
W Pier Hd FG 14m; G Tr; *Horn 30s.*

Redcar, The High. Outfall Lt By 54°36'·63N 01°00'·30W Fl Y 10s; SPM.
Salt Scar Lt By 54°38'·15N 01°00'·00W Q; NCM; *Horn(1) 15s; Bell.*

REDCAR.
Luff Way Ldg Lts 197°. Front, on Esplanade, FR 8m 7M; vis 182°-212°. Rear, 115m from front, FR 12m 7M; vis 182°-212°.
High Stone Ldg Lts 247°. Both Oc R 2·5s 9/11m 7M; vis 232°-262°.

Tees Fairway Lt By 54°40'·93N° 01°06'·37W Iso 4s 9m 8M; SWM; *Horn (1) 5s*; Racon.
Tees N (Fairway) Lt By 54°40'·28N 01°07'·20W Fl G 5s; SHM.
Tees S (Fairway) Lt By 54°40'·17N 01°06'·95W Fl R 5s; PHM.

RIVER TEES.
Breakwater Hd, **S Gare**. 54°38'·83N 01°08'·16W Fl WR 12s 16m **W20M**, **R17M**; W ● Tr; vis W020°-274°, R274°-357°; *Horn 30s.*
Ldg Lts 210·1°. Both FR 18/20m 13/10M.

HARTLEPOOL.
Longscar Lt By 54°40'·85N 01°09'·80W Q(3) 10s; ECM; *Bell.*
The Heugh 54°41'·78N 01°10'·47W Fl (2) 10s 19m **19M** (H24); W Tr.
Old Pier Hd 54°41'·59N 01°10'·99W QG 13m 7M; B Tr.
N Sands, PipeJetty Hd 54°42'·80N 01°12'·40W 2 FR (vert) 1M; *Bell(1) 15s.*

SEAHAM HARBOUR.
N Pier Hd 54°50'·25N 01°19'·15W Fl G 10s 12m 5M; W col, B bands; Di*a 30s.*
S Pier Hd 2 FR (vert) 10m 5M.

SUNDERLAND.
Roker Pier Hd 54°55'·27N 01°21'·05W Fl 5s 25m **23M**; W ● Tr, 3 R bands and cupola: vis 211°-357°; *Siren 20s.*
New S Pier Hd Fl 10s 14m 10M; W Tr.
S side Fl R 5s 9m 2M.
Old N Pier Hd QG 12m 8M; Y Tr; *Horn 10s.*

Whitburn Steel By 54°56'·30N 01°20'·80W (unlit); PHM.

WHITBURN FIRING RANGE.
54°57'·2N 01°21'·3W and 54°57'·7N 01°21'·2W both FR when firing is taking place.
Special Bys 54°57'·04N 01°18'·81W and 54°58'·58N 01°19'·80W, both Fl Y 2·5s.

Lizard Pt Souter 54°58'·23N 01°21'·80W F W 43m; W ●Tr, Or Band and Lantern; vis 230°-270°.
Lt By 55°00'·17N 01°23'·60W Fl (3) R 10s; PHM.
Eugena Chandris Lt By 55°00'·26N 01°23'·58W Fl (3) R 10s; PHM.

TYNEMOUTH.
Ent N Pier Hd 55°00'·87N 01°24'·08W Fl (3) 10s 26m **26M**; Gy ■ Tr, W lantern; *Horn 10s.*
S Pier Hd Oc WRG 10s 15m W13M, R9M, G8M; Gy ● Tr, R&W lantern; vis W075°-161°, G161°-179° over Bellhues rk, W179°-255°, R255°-075°; *Bell (1) 10s* (TD 1988).
Herd Groyne Hd Oc WR 10s 13m W13M, R11M, R1M; R pile structure, R&W lantern; vis R (unintens) 080°-224°, W224°-255°, R255°-277°; *Bell (1) 5s (TD 1988).*

NORTH SHIELDS.
Fish Quay Ldg Lts 258°. **Front** F 25m **20M**; W ■ Tr. **Rear** 220m from front F 39m **20M**; W ■ Tr.

CULLERCOATS.
Ldg Lts 256°. Front 55°02'·1N 01°25'·8W FR 27m 3M.
Rear 38m from front FR 35m 3M.

BLYTH.
Fairway Lt By 55°06'·58N 01°28'·50W Fl G 3s; SHM; *Bell.*
E Pier Hd Fl (4) 10s 19m **21M**; W Tr. FR 13m 13M (same Tr); vis 152°-249°; *Horn (3) 30s.*
W Pier Hd 2FR(vert) 7m 8M; W Tr.
Training wall S end Fl R 6s 6m 1M.
S Harbour Inner W Pier, N end 2 Fl (2) R 6s (vert) 5m 5M; W metal structure.
Hauxley By 55°19'·28N 01°31'·54W (unlit); PHM.

COQUET ISLAND AND AMBLE.
Coquet 55°20'·01N 01°32'·25W Fl (3) WR 30s 25m **W23M**, **R19M**; W ■ Tr, turreted parapet, lower half Gy; vis R330°-140°, W140°-163°, R163°-180°, W180°-330°; *Horn 30s.*
NE Coquet By 55°20'·55N 01°32'·00W (unlit); PHM.
NW Coquet By 55°20'·41N 01°32'·71W (unlit); SHM.
Pan Bush By 55°20'·67N 01°33'·22W (unlit); PHM.
Outfall Lt By 55°20'·32N 01°33'·63W Fl R 10s; PHM; *Bell.*

WARKWORTH/AMBLE.
S Pier Hd Fl R 5s 9m 5M; W I Tr, R bands, W base.
N Breakwater Hd 55°20'·38N 01°34'·15W Fl G 6s 12m 6M; W pylon.

ALNMOUTH BAY.
Boulmer Stile By 55°23'·75N 01°32'·60W (unlit); PHM.

BEADNELL BAY.
Newton Rock By 55°32'·08N 01°35'·45W (unlit); PHM.

N SUNDERLAND/SEAHOUSES.
NW Pier Hd FG 11m 3M; W Tr; vis 159°-294°; *Siren 90s* (occas).
Breakwater Hd 55°35'·05N 01°38'·79W Fl R 2·5s 6m.
Shoreston Outcars By 55°35'·67N 01°39'·18W; PHM.
Black Rocks Pt, **Bamburgh** 55°37'·00N 01°43'·35W Oc (2) WRG 15s 12m **W17M**, R13M, G13M; W bldg; vis G122°-165°, W165°-175°, R175°-191°, W191°-238°, R238°-275°, W275°-289°, G289°-300°.

FARNE ISLANDS.
Near SW Pt 55°36'·93N 01°39'·25W L Fl (2) WR 15s 27m W13M, R9M; W ● Tr; vis R119°-277°, W277°-119°.
Longstone W side 55°38'·63N 01°36'·55W Fl 20s 23m **24M**; R Tr, W band; RC; *Horn (2) 60s.*

Swedman By 55°37'70N 01°41'·50W (unlit); SHM.

HOLY ISLAND APPROACHES.
Goldstone By 55°40'·14N 01°43'·42W; SHM.
Ridge By 55°39'·70N 01°45'87W (unlit); ECM.
Triton By 55°39'·61N 01°46'49W (unlit); SHM.

BERWICK.
Breakwater Hd 55°45'·88N 01°58'·95W Fl 5s 15m 10M; W ● Tr, R cupola and base; vis 154°-010°. FG (same Tr) 8m 1M; vis 010°-154°; *Reed 60s* (occas).

10.5.5 PASSAGE INFORMATION

THE WASH (charts 108, 1200)

For general notes on The Wash see 10.4.5. The W shore of The Wash is fronted by extensive flats which extend 2–3M offshore and which dry up to 4m, and provide a bombing range. The Wainfleet Swatchway should only be used in good vis: the chan shifts constantly, and beware the various dangers off Gibraltar Pt, 3M S of Skegness. For Wainfleet see 10.5.20. The better route N from Boston (10.5.7) is through Freeman chan into Lynn Deep which, if bound E, also gives access to Sledway which runs S of Woolpack and Burnham Flats. Near N end of Lynn Deep there are overfalls over Lynn Knock at sp tides.

Inner Dowsing is a narrow N/S sandbank with a least depth of 1·2m, 10M off Mablethorpe. There are overfalls off the W side of the bank at the N end. Inner Dowsing Lt Ho (Lt, fog sig) stands close NE of the bank.

In the outer approaches to R. Humber and The Wash there are many offlying banks, but few of them are of direct danger to yachts. The sea however breaks on some of them in bad weather, when they should be avoided. Fishing vessels may be encountered, and there are oil/gas installations offshore (see below).

TIDAL STREAMS IN RIVERS

Tidal streams in rivers are influenced by local weather conditions as well as by the phases of the Moon. At or near sp, in a river which is obstructed, for example, by sandbanks at the entrance, the time of HW gets later going up river: the time of LW also gets later, but more rapidly. So the duration of rise of tide becomes shorter, and duration of fall of tide becomes longer. At the entrance the flood stream starts at an interval after LW which increases with the degree of obstruction of the chan: this interval between local LW and the start of the flood increases with the distance up river. The ebb begins soon after local HW along the length of the river. Hence the duration of the flood is less than that of the ebb, and the difference increases with distance up river.

The flood stream is normally stronger than the ebb, and runs harder during the first half of the rise of tide.

At nps the flood and ebb both start soon after local LW and HW respectively, and their durations and rates are roughly equal.

Both at sps and nps, the streams can be affected by recent precipitation, whereby the duration and rate of the ebb are increased, and of the flood are reduced.

OIL AND GAS INSTALLATIONS

Any yacht crossing the North Sea is likely to encounter oil or gas installations. These are shown on Admiralty charts where the scale permits, and are listed in the Annual Summary of Admiralty Notices to Mariners and in the Admiralty List of Lights and Fog Signals. Safety zones of radius 500m are established round all permanent platforms, mobile exploration rigs, and tanker loading moorings. Yachts must not enter these zones except in emergency or due to stress of weather.

Platforms show a main Lt, Fl Mo (U) 15s 15M. In addition there are secondary Lts, Fl R Mo (U) 15 s 3M synchronised with the main Lt and situated at each corner of the platform if not marked by a W Lt. Platforms sound a fog signal, Horn Mo (U) 30 s.

RIVER HUMBER (charts 109, 1188, 3497)

R. Humber is formed by R. Ouse and R. Trent, which join 15M above Kingston upon Hull, and is important for the access provided to the inland waterways by these rivers. By the time R. Humber reaches the sea between Donna Nook and Spurn Hd it is 6M wide, draining as it does most of Yorkshire and the Midlands.

Approaching from the S, a yacht should make for Rosse Spit By and then for Haile Sand By, before altering course any more W to meet and follow the main buoyed chan, which leads in from a NE direction through New Sand Hole. Beyond Bull Sand Fort (Lt, fog sig) it is advisable to follow one of the buoyed chans, since shoals are liable to change.
If proceeding to or coming from the N, beware The Binks – a shoal (dries in places) extending 3M E from Spurn Hd, with a rough sea when wind is against tide.

10M E of Spurn Hd the tidal streams are not affected by the river; the S-going stream begins at HW Immingham –0455, and the N-going at HW Immingham +0130. Nearer the entrance the direction of the S-going stream becomes more W, and that of the N-going stream more E. 0·5M S of Spurn Hd the in-going stream runs NW and begins about HW Immingham –0520, sp rate 3·5 kn: the out-going stream runs SE and begins about HW Immingham, sp rate 4 kn. In this area the worst seas are experienced in NW gales on a strong flood tide.

HUMBER TO WHITBY (charts 107, 121, 129)

For the coast, hbrs, anchs N from R. Humber refer to *Sailing Directions Humber Estuary to Rattray Hd* (Royal Northumberland YC). Bridlington B (chart 1882) is clear of dangers apart from Smithic Shoals (buoyed), about 3M off Bridlington (10.5.9): the seas break on these shoals in strong N or E winds.

Flamborough Hd (Lt, fog sig, RC) is a steep, W cliff with conspic Lt Ho on summit. The Lt may be obsc by cliffs when close inshore. An old Lt Ho, also conspic, is 0·25M WNW. From here the coast runs NW, with no offshore dangers until Filey Brigg where rky ledges extend 0·5M ESE, marked by By. There is anch in Filey B (10.5.20) in N or offshore winds. NW of Filey Brigg beware Horse Rk and foul ground 0·5M offshore; maintain this offing past Scarborough (10.5.10) to Whitby High Lt. Off Whitby (10.5.11) beware Whitby Rk and The Scar (dry in places) to E of Hr, and Upgang Rks (dry in places) 1M to WNW: the sea breaks on all these rks.

WHITBY TO COQUET ISLAND (charts 134, 152, 156)

From Whitby to Hartlepool (10.5.13) there are no dangers more than 1M offshore. Runswick B (10.5.20 and chart 1612), 5M NW of Whitby, provides anch in winds from S and W but is dangerous in onshore winds. The little hbr of Staithes is only suitable for yachts which can take the ground, and only in good weather and offshore winds.

Redcliff, dark red and 205m high is a conspic feature of this coast which, along to Hunt Cliff is prone to landslides and is fringed with rky ledges which dry for about 0·3M. There is a conspic radio mast 0·4M SW of Redcliff. Off Redcar and Coatham beware W Scar and Salt Scar – detached rky ledges (dry) lying 0·1 - 0·8M offshore. Other ledges lie close SW and S of Salt Scar which is marked by By.

Between R. Tees (10.5.12) and Hartlepool (10.5.13) beware Long Scar – detached rky ledge (dries) with extremity marked by By. From the Heugh an offing of 1M clears all dangers until approaching Sunderland (10.5.15), where White Stones, rky shoals with depth 3·0m, lie 1·75M SSE of Roker Pier Lt Ho, and Hendon Rk, depth 1·5m, lies 1·25M SE of the Lt Ho. N of Sunderland, Whitburn Steel, a rk with less than 2m over it, lies 1M S of Souter Pt, and an obstruction (dries) lies 0·1MSE of Whitburn Steel. Along this stretch of coast industrial smoke haze may reduce vis and obsc Lts.

The coast N of Tynemouth (10.5.16) is foul, and on passage to Blyth (10.5.17) it should be given an offing of 1M. 3·5M N of Tynemouth is St Mary's Is (with disused Lt Ho), connected to land by causeway. The hbr of Seaton Sluice, 1M NW of St Mary's Is, is closed.

Proceeding N from Blyth, keep well seaward of The Sow and Pigs By, and set course to clear Newbiggin Pt and Beacon Pt by about 1M. Vessels conduct trials on measured distance here. Near Beacon Pt is conspic chy of aluminium smelter. Snab Pt is 2M NNW of Beacon Pt. Cresswell Skeres, rky patches with depth 3·0m, lie 1·25M and 1.75m NNE of Snab Pt. Cresswell Pt is 0·8M NW of Snab Pt, and between the two are rks extending 0·3M seaward. S of Hauxley Hd rks extend 0·6M offshore, with depths of 1·2m, marked by By.

COQUET ISLAND TO FARNE ISLANDS (chart 156)

Coquet Is (Lt, fog sig) lies about 0·5M offshore at SE end of Alnmouth B, and nearly 1M NNE of Hauxley Pt – off which drying ledges extend 0·55M E and 0·65M NNE towards the Is (marked by Bys). On passage, normally pass 1M E of Coquet Is, but Coquet chan inshore is available in good vis by day. It is very narrow, and no longer buoyed, with least depth of 1·2m near the centre, and the stream runs strongly, S-going from HW Tyne –0515 and N-going from HW Tyne +0045. There are good anchs in Coquet Road, W of the Is, in winds from S or W.

Amble (Warkworth) hbr ent (10.5.18) is about 1M W of Coquet Is, and 1·5M SE of Warkworth Castle (conspic). 0·4M NE and ENE of ent is Pan Bush, rky shoal with least depth of 0·3m on which dangerous seas can build in any swell. The bar off ent has varying depths, down to less than 1m. Once inside, the hbr is safe, but the ent is dangerous in strong winds from N or E when broken water may extend to Coquet Is.

Between Coquet Is and the Farne Is, 19M to N, keep at least 1M offshore to avoid various dangers. To seaward, Dicky Shad and Newton Skere lie 1·75M and 4·5M E of Beadnell Pt, and Craster Skeres lie 5M E of Castle Pt: these are three rky banks on which the sea breaks heavily in bad weather. For Newton Haven and Seahouses (N Sunderland) see 10.5.20.

FARNE ISLANDS AND HOLY ISLAND (charts 1612, 111, 160)

The coast between N Sunderland Pt and Berwick-upon-Tweed, 16M NW, is a dangerous area. The Farne Is and offlying shoals extend 4·5M offshore, and are worth visiting in good weather. The area is a bird sanctuary, owned and operated by the National Trust, with large colonies of sea birds and also grey seals. For details of this area refer to Royal Northumberland YC sailing directions. The group of Is, rks and shoals is divided by Farne Sound running NE/SW, and by Staple Sound running NW/SE. Farne Is (Lt) is the innermost Is, separated from mainland by Inner Sound, which in good conditions is a better N/S route than keeping outside the whole group: but the stream runs 3 kn at sp, and with strong wind against tide there is rough water. Beware Swedman reef (dries, marked by By) 0·4 WSW of Megstone, which is a rk 5m high 1M NW of Farne Lt Ho. N of Inner Sound, off Holy Is, Goldstone chan passes between Goldstone Rk (dries) on E side and Plough Seat Reef and Plough Rk (both dry) on W side. See 10.5.20.

On NE side of Farne Is there is anch called The Kettle, sheltered except from NW, but anch out of stream close to The Bridges connecting Knock's Reef and W Wideopen.
If course is set outside Farne Is, pass 1M E of Longstone (Lt, fog sig, RC) to clear Crumstone Rk 1M to S, and Knivestone (dries) and Whirl Rks (depth 0·6m) respectively 0·5M and 0·6M NE of Longstone Lt Ho. The sea breaks on these rks.

Near the Farne Is and Holy Is the SE-going stream begins at HW Tyne –0430, and the NW-going at HW Tyne +0130. 1M NE of Longstone the sp rate is about 3·5 kn, decreasing seaward. There is an eddy S of Longstone on NW-going stream.

Holy Is (Lindisfarne) lies 6M WNW of Longstone, and is linked to mainland by a causeway covered at HW. There is a good anch on S side (chart 1612). From a point about 0·5M S of Plough Seat Reef, obelisks on Old Law lead 260° S of Triton Shoal (least depth 0·4m, 0·4M SSE of Castle Pt) to the bar, from where Heugh Bn on with belfry of St Mary's Ch leads 310° to anch. The stream runs strongly in and out of hbr, W-going from HW Tyne +0510, and E-going from HW Tyne –0045. See 10.5.20.

10.5.6 DISTANCE TABLE

Approximate distances in nautical miles are by the most direct route while avoiding dangers and allowing for traffic separation schemes etc. Places in *italics* are in adjoining areas.

1 *North Foreland*	**1**																			
2 *Goeree Tower*	91	**2**																		
3 *IJmuiden*	137	46	**3**																	
4 *Brunsbüttel*	337	263	221	**4**																
5 Boston	160	161	175	344	**5**															
6 Grimsby	169	169	182	332	58	**6**														
7 Bridlington	194	188	196	329	83	44	**7**													
8 Flamborough Head	192	186	193	325	84	45	5	**8**												
9 Scarborough	206	200	207	336	98	59	19	14	**9**											
10 Whitby	222	116	223	345	114	75	35	30	16	**10**										
11 River Tees	243	237	244	367	135	96	56	50	37	21	**11**									
12 Hartlepool	245	239	246	370	137	98	58	53	39	24	4	**12**								
13 Seaham	253	247	254	373	145	106	66	61	47	33	15	11	**13**							
14 Sunderland	257	251	258	375	149	110	70	65	51	36	20	16	5	**14**						
15 Tynemouth	262	256	262	378	154	115	75	70	56	41	27	23	12	7	**15**					
16 Blyth	270	264	267	382	162	123	83	78	64	49	35	31	20	15	8	**16**				
17 Longstone (Farne)	298	292	295	388	190	151	111	105	92	76	67	63	52	46	40	32	**17**			
18 Berwick-on-Tweed	313	307	310	402	205	166	126	120	107	91	82	78	67	61	55	47	15	**18**		
19 *St Abbs Head*	322	316	322	410	214	175	135	129	116	110	91	87	76	70	64	56	24	12	**19**	
20 *Peterhead*	404	391	378	439	296	257	217	212	200	186	173	170	161	155	149	143	112	105	97	**20**

BOSTON 10-5-7

Lincs.

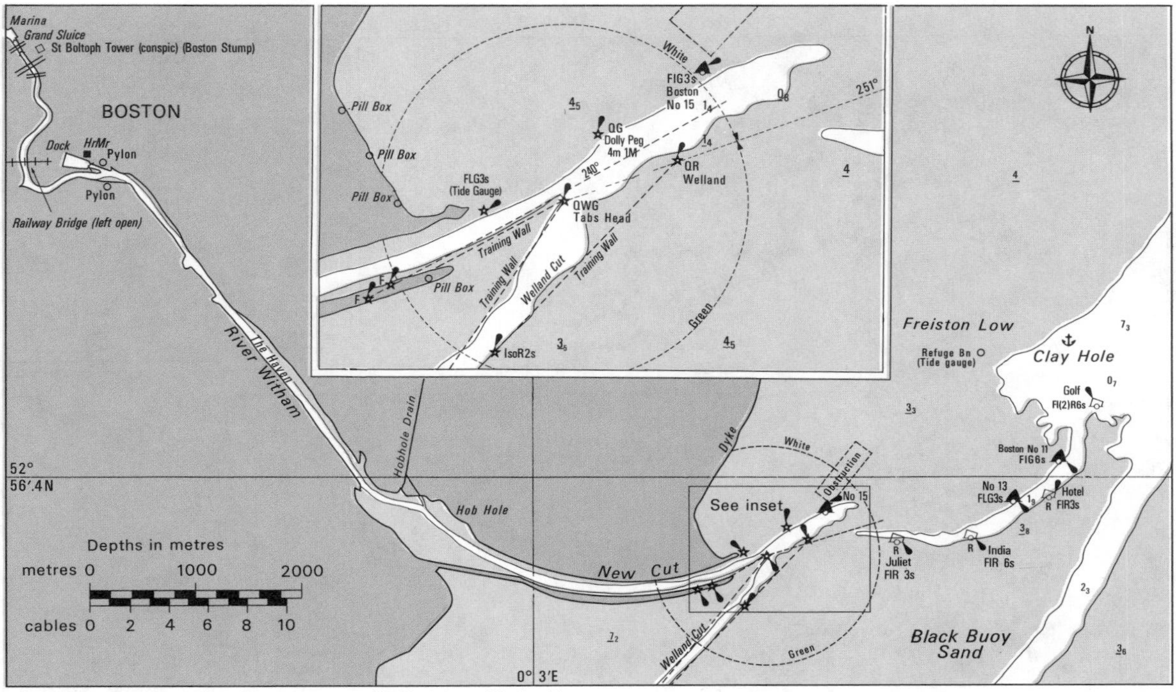
Marina
Grand Sluice
St Boltoph Tower (conspic) (Boston Stump)
BOSTON
Dock
HrMr
Pylon
Pylon
Railway Bridge (left open)
The Haven
River Witham
Hobhole Drain
Hob Hole
52°
56'.4N
Depths in metres
metres 0 1000 2000
cables 0 2 4 6 8 10
New Cut
Welland Cut
0° 3'E
Dyke
White
Green
See inset
Obstruction
No 15
R Juliet FlR 3s
R India FlR 6s
No 13 FLG3s
Hotel R FlR3s
Boston No 11 FlG6s
Golf Fl(2)R6s
Refuge Bn (Tide gauge)
Freiston Low
Clay Hole
Black Buoy Sand
Pill Box
Pill Box
Pill Box
Pill Box
FLG3s (Tide Gauge)
QG Dolly Peg 4m 1M
QWG Tabs Head
QR Welland
FlG3s Boston No 15
251°
240°
Training Wall
Training Wall
Training Wall
IsoR2s
N

⛵ Visitors berths at River Quay, report to Hr Mr (alongside Lock)

CHARTS

Admiralty 1200, 108; Imray Y9; OS 131

TIDES

−0415 Dover; ML 3·4; Duration Flood 0500, Ebb 0700; Zone 0 (GMT).

Standard Port IMMINGHAM (⟶)

Times				Height (metres)			
HW		LW		MHWS	MHWN	MLWN	MLWS
0100	0700	0100	0700	7·3	5·8	2·6	0·9
1300	1900	1300	1900				
Differences BOSTON							
0000	+0010	+0140	+0050	−0·5	−1·0	−0·9	−0·5
SKEGNESS							
+0010	+0015	+0030	+0020	−0·4	−0·5	−0·1	0·0

SHELTER

Very good but mooring in the Dock is not permitted except in emergency. Yachts which can lower masts should pass through the Grand Sluice into fresh water (24 hrs notice required); marina is on the stbd side immediately beyond the sluice. This leads into the R Witham Navigation which goes 31 miles up to Lincoln. The lock is 22·7m x 4·6m and opens approx HW∓2. Moorings may be possible (on S side) below first fixed bridge. British Waterways have 50 moorings, with FW and AC, above the sluice.

NAVIGATION

Waypoint Boston Roads safe water buoy, LFl 10s, 52°57'·53N 00°16'·23E, 100°/280° from/to Freeman Channel entrance, 0·70M. The channel is liable to change but is well marked. Tabs Head marks the entrance to the river which should be passed not earlier than HW−3 to enable the Grand Sluice to be reached before the start of the ebb. On reaching Boston Dock, masts should be lowered to negotiate swing bridge (cannot always be opened) and three fixed bridges. Channel through town is narrow and un-navigable at LW.

LIGHTS AND MARKS

New Cut and R Witham are marked by Bns with topmarks. FW Lts mark leading lines — six pairs going upstream and six pairs going downstream. St Boltoph's Church tower, known as the Boston Stump is conspicuous landmark. Entry signals for Boston Dock are not given since yachts are not allowed in. Yachts in difficulty secure just above dock entrance and see Hr Mr. The port is administered by Port of Boston Ltd.

RADIO TELEPHONE

Call: *Boston Dock* VHF Ch 16; 12 (Mon to Fri 0700-1700 LT and HW−3 to HW+2). All boats seaward of Grand Sluice must listen on Ch 12. Call: *Grand Sluice* Ch 73.

TELEPHONE (0205)

Hr Mr 362328; MRCC Great Yarmouth 851338; Port Signal Stn 362328; # 363070; Lock Keeper 364864; Marinecall 0898 500 455; Police 366222; Ⓗ 364801.

FACILITIES

EC Thursday; **Boston Marina** (50 and some visitors) ☎ 364420, D, ACA, FW, CH; C in dock by arrangement with Hr Mr (emergency only) Access HW∓2; **Keightley & Son** ☎ 63616, ME, El, Sh; **Boston Diesel** ☎ 355450, ME, El, Sh, Gas; **Town** V, R, Bar, ✉, Ⓑ, ≹, ✈ (Norwich or Humberside).

RIVER HUMBER 10-5-8

Humberside

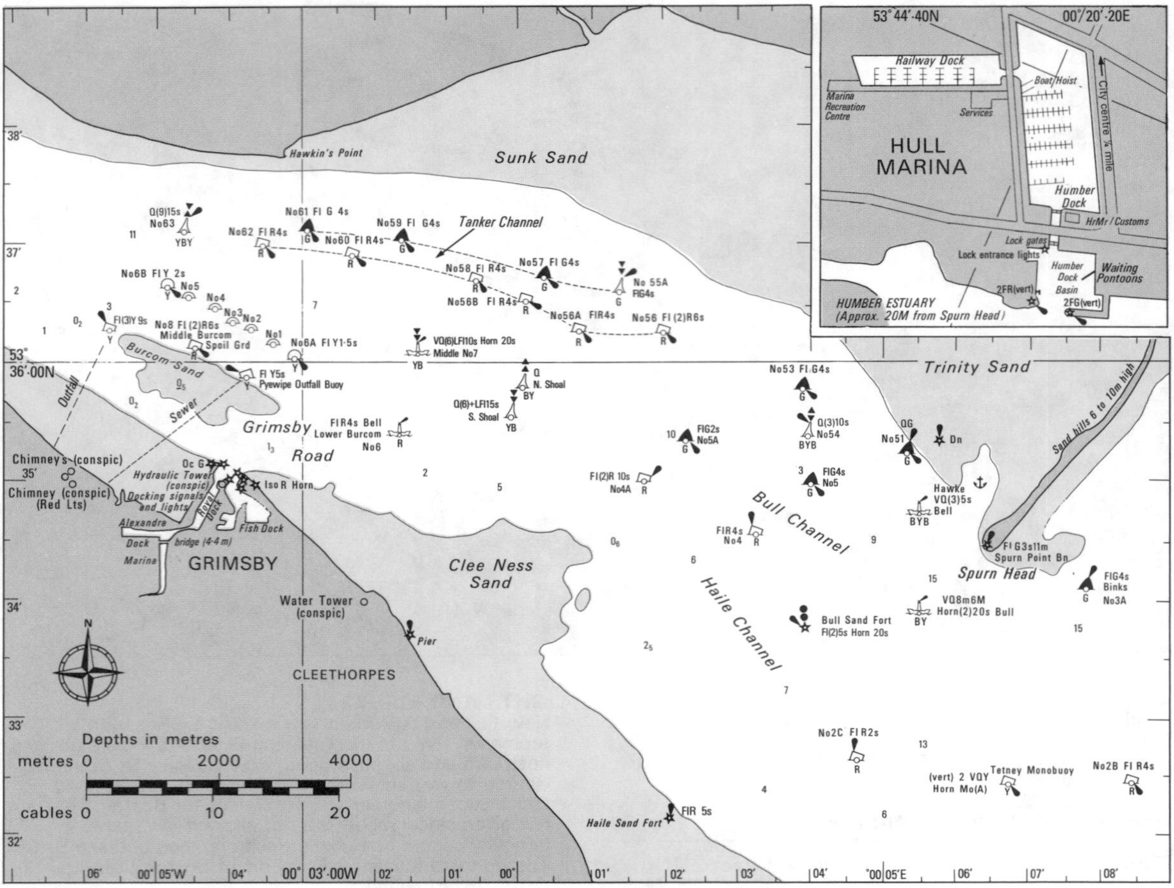

Sunk Sand
Hawkin's Point
Tanker Channel
HULL MARINA
Railway Dock
Marina Recreation Centre
Services
Boat Hoist
City centre ¼ mile
Humber Dock
HrMr / Customs
Lock gates
Lock entrance lights
Humber Dock Basin
Waiting Pontoons
HUMBER ESTUARY (Approx. 20M from Spurn Head)
53°44'·40N
00°20'·20E
Trinity Sand
Sand hills 6 to 10m high
Burcom Sand
Grimsby Road
Outfall
Sewer
Pyewipe Outfall Buoy
Chimneys (conspic)
Chimney (conspic) (Red Lts)
Hydraulic Tower (conspic)
Docking signals and lights
Royal Dock
Fish Dock
Alexandra Dock
Marina
GRIMSBY
Bull Channel
Haile Channel
Clee Ness Sand
Water Tower (conspic)
Pier
CLEETHORPES
Spurn Head
Spurn Point Bn
Bull Sand Fort Fl(2)5s Horn 20s
Tetney Monobuoy
Haile Sand Fort
Depths in metres
metres 0 2000 4000
cables 0 10 20
00° 03'·00W
00°05'E

CHARTS

Admiralty 109, 3497, 1188; Associated British Ports; Imray C29; OS 107

TIDES

−0510 Immingham, −0452 Hull, Dover; ML 4·1; Duration 0555; Zone 0 (GMT).

Standard Port IMMINGHAM (⟶)

Times				Height (metres)			
HW		LW		MHWS	MHWN	MLWN	MLWS
0100	0700	0100	0700	7·3	5·8	2·6	0·9
1300	1900	1300	1900				
Differences HULL							
+0005	+0015	+0010	+0020	+0·2	0·0	−0·2	−0·2
GRIMSBY							
−0003	−0011	−0015	−0002	−0·3	−0·2	0·0	+0·1
BULL SAND FORT							
−0020	−0030	−0035	−0015	−0·4	−0·3	+0·1	+0·2
BURTON STATHER							
+0105	+0045	+0335	+0305	−2·1	−2·3	−2·3	Dries
KEADBY							
+0135	+0125	+0415	+0355	−2·7	−3·1	Dries	Dries
BLACKTOFT							
+0055	+0050	+0310	+0255	−1·5	−1·8	−1·9	−0·8
GOOLE							
+0130	+0115	+0355	+0350	−1·6	−2·1	−1·9	−0·6

NOTE: Immingham is a standard Port and details of daily HW and LW times and heights are given below.

SHELTER

R Humber is the estuary of R Ouse and R Trent. Yachts can anchor inside Spurn Head except in strong SW to NW winds. There are marinas at Hull, Grimsby, South Ferriby and Naburn. In Grimsby, visiting yachts now use the Fish Dock. The approach to South Ferriby Marina should not be attempted without reference to up-to-date Associated British Ports Chart. Immingham should be used only in emergency. South Ferriby available HW∓2½, Grimsby Dock HW∓2½, Hull Marina HW∓3. Yachts are welcome at Brough and Winteringham (30M up river from Spurn Head), but contact club first.

NAVIGATION

Waypoint 53°33'·50N 00°08'·00E, 095°/275° from/to Bull Sand Fort, 2·3M. There is a whirlpool effect at confluence of Rivers Hull and Humber. In flood it runs W into Humber and NE into Hull (reaches 2½ kn at springs).
N.B. Associated British Ports is the Navigational and Conservancy Authority for the Humber Estuary and are owners of the ports of Hull, Grimsby, Immingham and Goole. They issue up-to-date information about the buoyed channel up river from Hull which is constantly changing.

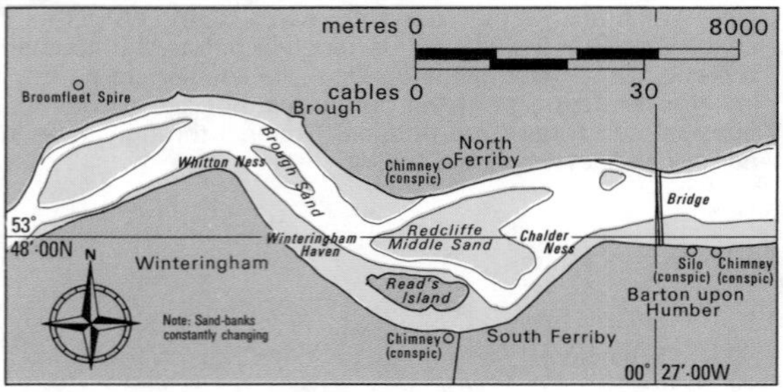

metres 0 8000
cables 0 30
Broomfleet Spire
Brough
North Ferriby
Chimney (conspic)
Whitton Ness
Brough Sand
Bridge
53° 48'·00N
Winteringham
Winteringham Haven
Redcliffe Middle Sand
Chalder Ness
Read's Island
Silo (conspic)
Chimney (conspic)
Barton upon Humber
Note: Sand-banks constantly changing
South Ferriby
00° 27'·00W

RIVER HUMBER *continued*

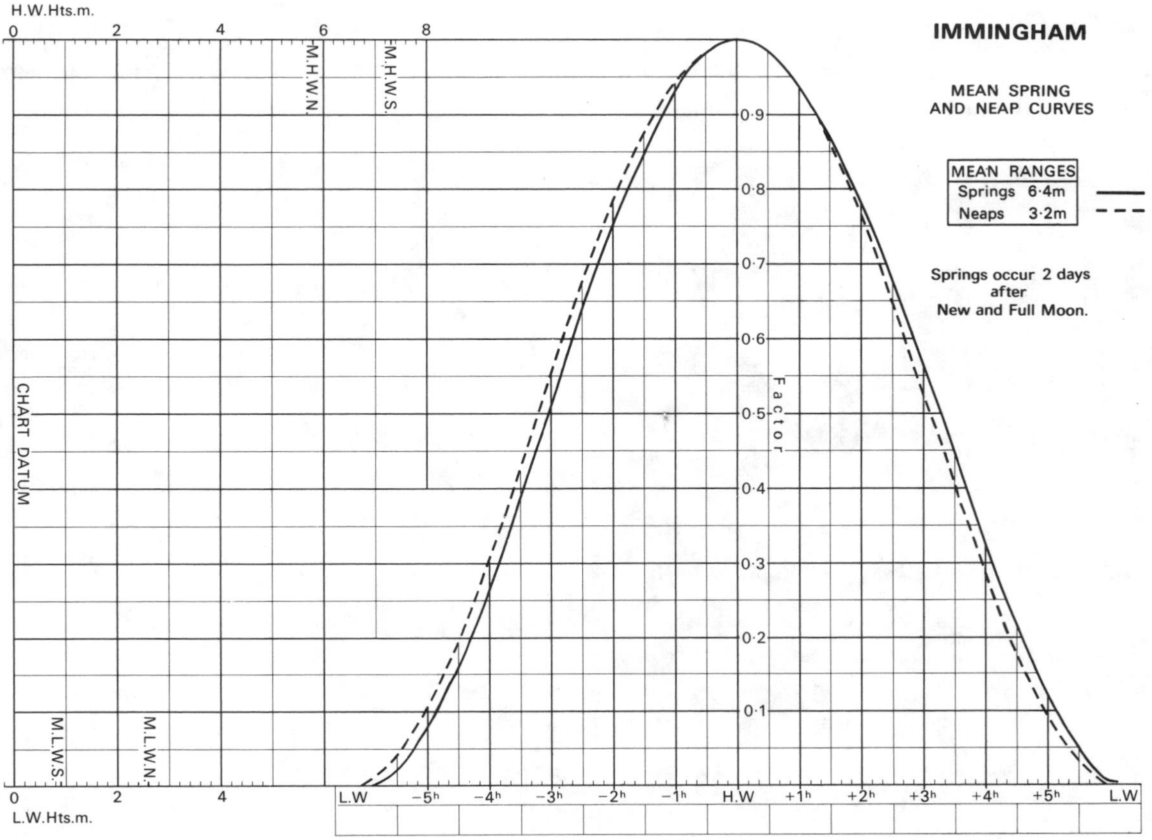
IMMINGHAM
MEAN SPRING AND NEAP CURVES
MEAN RANGES
Springs 6·4m
Neaps 3·2m
Springs occur 2 days after New and Full Moon.
H.W.Hts.m.
L.W.Hts.m.
CHART DATUM
M.H.W.N.
M.H.W.S.
M.L.W.S.
M.L.W.N.
Factor
L.W
H.W
L.W

LIGHTS AND MARKS

The Humber is well marked for its whole length. International Port Traffic Signals control entry to Grimsby (Royal Dock) shown W of entrance; Immingham; Killingholme; Hull; Goole. Entry to Winteringham Haven and Brough Haven should not be attempted without first contacting Humber Yawl Club for up-to-date approach channel details and mooring availability. Havens available HW∓1½ approx.

RADIO TELEPHONE

Humber Vessel Traffic Service – call: *VTS Humber* (Queen Elizabeth Dock, Hull, ☎ Hull 701787) VHF Ch 12, 16; **10 12**. Weather reports, tidal information and navigational warnings broadcast every odd H+03 on Ch 12. Grimsby Docks call *Royal Dock* Ch 16; 09 **18** (H24). Immingham Docks Ch 16; 09 22 (H24). River Hull Port Operations Service call: *Drypool Radio* Ch 16; 06 **14** (Mon-Fri: 0800–1800; Sat 0900–1100 LT. HW–2 to HW+1). Goole Docks Ch 16; 14 (H24). Booth Ferry Bridge Ch 09 (H24). Selby Railway Bridge Ch 09; **09** 12. Selby Toll Bridge Ch 09; 09. South Ferriby Yacht Harbour, Humber Yawl Club Ch 37, Hull Marina, Ch **80** (0700-2200). Grimsby Marina Ch 09 18.

TELEPHONE (Hull 0482 Grimsby 0472)

HULL Hr Mr 783538; Lock Tower 215357; MRSC Bridlington 672317; ⋕ 796161; Marinecall 0898 500 454; Police 26111; Dr – contact Humber Vessel Traffic Service 701787.

GRIMSBY Port Manager 359181; ⋕ 45441; MRSC Bridlington 672317; Marinecall 0898 500 454; Police 59171; Ⓗ 74111.

FACILITIES

HULL **Hull Marina** (310+20 visitors) ☎ 25048 (open 0700-2200 LT Fri, Sat, Sun, 0800–1800 LT weekdays), P, D, FW, CH, BH (50 ton), C (2 ton), AC, Gas; ⋕, ME, El, Sh, Slip, ▣, SM, (Access HW∓3); **B. Cooke** ☎ 223454, ACA; **Locat Developments** ☎ 25163, Ⓔ.

GRIMSBY EC Thursday; **Grimsby Marina** (150+25 visitors). ☎ 360404, D, FW, ME, AC, Gas, Gaz, El, Sh, BH (30 ton), R, CH, Bar, (Access HW∓3, bridge clearance 4·45m); **Grimsby and Cleethorpes YC** ☎ 356678; Bar, R, M, FW, ▣; **Grahams** ☎ 46673, ACA; **Fish Dock** ☎ 361343, M; **Royal Dock** ☎ 361344.

SOUTH FERRIBY **South Ferriby Marina** (100+20 visitors) ☎ Barton-on-Humber 635620, D, FW, ME, El, Sh, C (30 ton), CH, Gas, Gaz, (Access HW∓3). **Village** V, Bar, P.

WINTERINGHAM HAVEN (belongs to Humber Yawl Club) ☎ Scunthorpe 734452, ✉.

BROUGH HAVEN **Humber Yawl Club** ☎ Hull 667224, Slip, FW, AB*, Bar. *Limited – contact club.

Note. There is a marina at Naburn, up R Ouse near York (approx 80M from Spurn Pt). **Naburn Marina** (450+50 visitors) ☎ York 21021, VHF Ch **80** 37, CH, P, D, FW, AC, Sh, ME, BH (16 ton), R.

TIME ZONE **UT(GMT)**

For Summer Time add ONE hour in non-shaded areas

ENGLAND, EAST COAST – IMMINGHAM

Lat 53°38′ N Long 0°11′ W

TIMES AND HEIGHTS OF HIGH AND LOW WATERS

YEAR **1992**

JANUARY

Day	Time	m	Day	Time	m
1 W	0301 0917 1536 2145	6·1 2·2 6·1 2·3	16 Th	0144 0809 1434 2051	5·9 2·3 6·0 2·3
2 Th	0403 1012 1624 2238	6·2 2·1 6·3 2·1	17 F	0304 0924 1541 2202	6·2 2·1 6·4 1·9
3 F	0454 1057 1704 2323	6·3 2·0 6·6 1·8	18 Sa	0413 1028 1637 2304	6·5 1·8 6·8 1·4
4 Sa ●	0536 1137 1740	6·5 1·9 6·8	19 Su ○	0513 1126 1727	6·9 1·5 7·1
5 Su	0004 0615 1215 1815	1·6 6·6 1·8 6·9	20 M	0000 0607 1218 1815	1·0 7·2 1·2 7·4
6 M	0039 0650 1249 1848	1·5 6·7 1·7 7·0	21 Tu	0052 0656 1306 1900	0·6 7·4 1·1 7·6
7 Tu	0113 0723 1323 1920	1·4 6·7 1·7 7·0	22 W	0140 0742 1349 1944	0·4 7·4 1·0 7·7
8 W	0145 0755 1354 1951	1·4 6·6 1·7 7·0	23 Th	0223 0827 1432 2027	0·4 7·3 1·1 7·6
9 Th	0216 0827 1425 2023	1·4 6·6 1·8 6·9	24 F	0305 0911 1510 2110	0·6 7·0 1·3 7·3
10 F	0247 0900 1456 2056	1·5 6·4 2·0 6·7	25 Sa	0345 0952 1549 2153	1·0 6·7 1·6 7·0
11 Sa	0319 0932 1528 2131	1·6 6·2 2·1 6·5	26 Su ☾	0424 1035 1630 2242	1·4 6·3 2·0 6·5
12 Su	0353 1009 1604 2212	1·8 6·0 2·3 6·3	27 M	0508 1125 1720 2342	1·9 5·9 2·4 6·0
13 M ☽	0435 1055 1654 2304	2·0 5·9 2·5 6·1	28 Tu	0605 1229 1832	2·4 5·6 2·7
14 Tu	0530 1157 1801	2·2 5·7 2·7	29 W	0104 0723 1349 2005	5·7 2·7 5·6 2·8
15 W	0017 0646 1317 1930	5·9 2·4 5·7 2·6	30 Th	0237 0844 1507 2127	5·6 2·7 5·8 2·5
			31 F	0350 0949 1603 2224	5·8 2·5 6·1 2·2

FEBRUARY

Day	Time	m	Day	Time	m
1 Sa	0444 1040 1648 2311	6·1 2·2 6·4 1·8	16 Su	0407 1016 1624 2255	6·4 1·9 6·7 1·2
2 Su	0526 1120 1725 2349	6·4 2·0 6·7 1·6	17 M	0506 1115 1715 2350	6·9 1·4 7·1 0·8
3 M ●	0601 1158 1758	6·6 1·7 6·9	18 Tu ○	0557 1205 1801	7·2 1·1 7·5
4 Tu	0024 0634 1232 1829	1·4 6·7 1·6 7·0	19 W	0039 0642 1250 1843	0·4 7·4 0·9 7·7
5 W	0056 0704 1304 1900	1·2 6·8 1·5 7·1	20 Th	0123 0724 1331 1926	0·3 7·5 0·8 7·8
6 Th	0127 0733 1335 1931	1·2 6·8 1·4 7·1	21 F	0204 0804 1409 2005	0·3 7·3 0·9 7·7
7 F	0157 0802 1405 2001	1·2 6·8 1·5 7·1	22 Sa	0240 0842 1444 2044	0·6 7·1 1·1 7·4
8 Sa	0226 0832 1433 2032	1·2 6·6 1·6 6·9	23 Su	0314 0918 1519 2125	1·0 6·7 1·4 7·0
9 Su	0254 0901 1503 2103	1·4 6·5 1·7 6·8	24 M	0348 0955 1555 2207	1·5 6·4 1·8 6·4
10 M	0322 0932 1535 2139	1·6 6·3 1·9 6·5	25 Tu ☾	0424 1035 1640 2301	2·0 6·0 2·3 5·9
11 Tu ☽	0357 1010 1617 2227	1·8 6·1 2·2 6·2	26 W	0513 1132 1744	2·5 5·6 2·7
12 W	0447 1105 1720 2339	2·1 5·8 2·5 5·9	27 Th	0025 0632 1259 1928	5·4 2·9 5·4 2·9
13 Th	0600 1229 1853	2·5 5·7 2·6	28 F	0211 0811 1430 2101	5·4 3·0 5·6 2·6
14 F	0119 0737 1406 2032	5·7 2·5 5·8 2·3	29 Sa	0329 0924 1536 2202	5·7 2·7 5·9 2·2
15 Sa	0253 0905 1522 2150	6·0 2·2 6·2 1·8			

MARCH

Day	Time	m	Day	Time	m
1 Su	0423 1016 1623 2247	6·0 2·3 6·3 1·8	16 M	0357 1000 1607 2240	6·5 1·9 6·7 1·1
2 M	0504 1058 1702 2325	6·3 2·0 6·6 1·5	17 Tu	0452 1057 1658 2333	6·9 1·4 7·1 0·7
3 Tu	0539 1134 1736	6·5 1·7 6·8	18 W ○	0540 1146 1742	7·2 1·1 7·4
4 W ●	0000 0610 1208 1807	1·3 6·7 1·5 7·0	19 Th	0019 0621 1228 1824	0·4 7·3 0·8 7·6
5 Th	0032 0638 1241 1836	1·1 6·8 1·3 7·1	20 F	0100 0659 1307 1903	0·3 7·4 0·7 7·7
6 F	0103 0707 1312 1907	1·0 6·9 1·2 7·2	21 Sa	0138 0735 1345 1942	0·5 7·3 0·8 7·5
7 Sa	0133 0735 1342 1938	1·0 6·9 1·2 7·1	22 Su	0212 0811 1419 2020	0·8 7·1 1·0 7·2
8 Su	0202 0805 1412 2009	1·1 6·8 1·3 7·0	23 M	0243 0844 1451 2058	1·2 6·8 1·3 6·8
9 M	0230 0834 1443 2043	1·3 6·7 1·5 6·8	24 Tu	0314 0918 1527 2141	1·6 6·5 1·7 6·3
10 Tu	0258 0905 1515 2121	1·5 6·5 1·7 6·5	25 W	0348 0956 1607 2231	2·1 6·1 2·1 5·8
11 W	0334 0943 1557 2212	1·8 6·2 2·0 6·2	26 Th ☾	0433 1047 1706 2349	2·6 5·7 2·6 5·4
12 Th ☽	0421 1038 1702 2327	2·2 5·9 2·3 5·8	27 F	0543 1207 1843	3·0 5·4 2·8
13 F	0536 1205 1839	2·5 5·7 2·4	28 Sa	0128 0726 1342 2019	5·3 3·1 5·5 2·6
14 Sa	0113 0720 1347 2019	5·7 2·6 5·8 2·1	29 Su	0250 0844 1454 2122	5·5 2·8 5·8 2·2
15 Su	0247 0850 1507 2138	6·0 2·3 6·2 1·6	30 M	0345 0941 1546 2210	5·9 2·4 6·1 1·8
			31 Tu	0428 1024 1627 2251	6·2 2·1 6·4 1·5

APRIL

Day	Time	m	Day	Time	m
1 W	0504 1102 1704 2327	6·5 1·7 6·7 1·3	16 Th	0516 1120 1719 2353	7·0 1·2 7·2 0·7
2 Th	0537 1139 1737	6·7 1·5 6·9	17 F ○	0556 1204 1801	7·1 1·0 7·4
3 F ●	0003 0608 1214 1810	1·1 6·8 1·3 7·1	18 Sa	0034 0632 1243 1841	0·7 7·2 0·9 7·4
4 Sa	0035 0638 1248 1842	1·0 6·9 1·1 7·1	19 Su	0110 0707 1320 1921	0·8 7·2 1·0 7·2
5 Su	0107 0709 1321 1916	1·0 7·0 1·1 7·1	20 M	0144 0741 1355 2001	1·1 7·0 1·1 6·9
6 M	0140 0741 1354 1952	1·1 6·9 1·2 7·0	21 Tu	0216 0816 1429 2040	1·4 6·8 1·4 6·6
7 Tu	0211 0813 1429 2032	1·3 6·8 1·3 6·8	22 W	0247 0850 1504 2121	1·8 6·6 1·7 6·2
8 W	0243 0850 1507 2117	1·5 6·6 1·5 6·5	23 Th	0321 0927 1543 2209	2·2 6·3 2·0 5·8
9 Th	0322 0932 1553 2214	1·8 6·3 1·8 6·1	24 F ☾	0402 1013 1637 2313	2·5 5·9 2·3 5·5
10 F ☽	0413 1031 1701 2333	2·2 6·0 2·1 5·8	25 Sa	0501 1119 1753	2·9 5·6 2·5
11 Sa	0530 1156 1835	2·5 5·8 2·1	26 Su	0034 0625 1242 1919	5·4 3·0 5·5 2·5
12 Su	0107 0706 1327 2004	5·8 2·6 6·0 1·8	27 M	0151 0748 1357 2026	5·5 2·9 5·7 2·2
13 M	0232 0829 1444 2117	6·1 2·3 6·3 1·4	28 Tu	0251 0850 1456 2119	5·7 2·6 6·0 1·9
14 Tu	0338 0936 1545 2217	6·5 1·9 6·7 1·1	29 W	0341 0939 1543 2206	6·0 2·2 6·3 1·7
15 W	0431 1033 1635 2308	6·8 1·5 7·0 0·8	30 Th	0423 1024 1626 2249	6·3 1·9 6·5 1·4

Chart Datum: 3.90 metres below Ordnance Datum (Newlyn)

ENGLAND, EAST COAST – IMMINGHAM

Lat 53°38′ N Long 0°11′ W

TIMES AND HEIGHTS OF HIGH AND LOW WATERS

YEAR **1992**

TIME ZONE **UT(GMT)**
For Summer Time add ONE hour in non-shaded areas

MAY

Day	Time	m
1 F	0501 1105 1705 2329	6·6 1·6 6·7 1·3
2 Sa ●	0534 1144 1742	6·8 1·4 6·9
3 Su	0007 0610 1224 1819	1·2 6·9 1·2 7·0
4 M	0043 0643 1302 1859	1·1 7·0 1·1 7·1
5 Tu	0120 0720 1341 1942	1·2 7·0 1·1 7·0
6 W	0157 0759 1422 2029	1·3 7·0 1·2 6·8
7 Th	0236 0842 1507 2121	1·6 6·8 1·3 6·6
8 F	0321 0931 1559 2221	1·8 6·6 1·5 6·3
9 Sa ☽	0416 1030 1705 2333	2·1 6·3 1·7 6·1
10 Su	0525 1143 1822	2·4 6·2 1·7
11 M	0050 0643 1302 1938	6·0 2·4 6·2 1·6
12 Tu	0205 0759 1415 2047	6·2 2·2 6·4 1·4
13 W	0310 0905 1517 2148	6·4 2·0 6·6 1·3
14 Th	0403 1003 1610 2240	6·6 1·7 6·8 1·2
15 F	0448 1055 1658 2325	6·7 1·5 6·9 1·1
16 Sa ○	0529 1140 1742	6·9 1·3 7·0
17 Su	0007 0605 1222 1824	1·1 7·0 1·2 7·0
18 M	0045 0642 1300 1906	1·2 7·0 1·2 6·9
19 Tu	0120 0717 1338 1947	1·4 7·0 1·3 6·7
20 W	0154 0752 1412 2026	1·6 6·8 1·4 6·5
21 Th	0226 0827 1447 2105	1·8 6·7 1·6 6·2
22 F	0300 0904 1525 2148	2·1 6·5 1·8 6·0
23 Sa	0338 0946 1610 2237	2·4 6·2 2·0 5·7
24 Su ☾	0424 1037 1705 2337	2·6 6·0 2·2 5·6
25 M	0525 1140 1812	2·8 5·8 2·3
26 Tu	0043 0636 1249 1920	5·5 2·9 5·7 2·3
27 W	0147 0747 1355 2022	5·6 2·7 5·9 2·1
28 Th	0246 0847 1453 2118	5·8 2·5 6·1 1·9
29 F	0336 0941 1545 2207	6·1 2·1 6·3 1·7
30 Sa	0421 1031 1633 2255	6·4 1·8 6·5 1·5
31 Su	0504 1118 1718 2340	6·7 1·5 6·8 1·3

JUNE

Day	Time	m
1 M ●	0543 1203 1803	6·9 1·2 6·9
2 Tu	0024 0624 1249 1849	1·3 7·1 1·1 7·0
3 W	0107 0706 1334 1938	1·2 7·1 1·0 7·0
4 Th	0151 0751 1422 2029	1·3 7·2 0·9 7·0
5 F	0234 0836 1510 2121	1·5 7·1 1·0 6·8
6 Sa	0321 0927 1600 2217	1·7 6·9 1·2 6·6
7 Su ☽	0412 1021 1657 2318	1·9 6·7 1·3 6·3
8 M	0509 1122 1758	2·1 6·5 1·5
9 Tu	0022 0612 1229 1904	6·2 2·2 6·4 1·6
10 W	0130 0723 1341 2012	6·1 2·3 6·3 1·7
11 Th	0236 0833 1449 2115	6·1 2·2 6·4 1·7
12 F	0334 0936 1550 2212	6·3 2·0 6·4 1·6
13 Sa	0424 1033 1644 2301	6·4 1·8 6·5 1·6
14 Su	0506 1122 1732 2344	6·6 1·6 6·6 1·5
15 M ○	0546 1207 1814	6·8 1·4 6·7
16 Tu	0024 0622 1246 1856	1·5 6·9 1·4 6·7
17 W	0100 0659 1324 1934	1·6 6·9 1·3 6·6
18 Th	0135 0734 1359 2011	1·7 6·9 1·4 6·5
19 F	0209 0808 1432 2047	1·8 6·8 1·5 6·4
20 Sa	0242 0843 1507 2122	1·9 6·7 1·6 6·2
21 Su	0315 0919 1542 2200	2·1 6·5 1·7 6·0
22 M	0352 1000 1623 2244	2·3 6·3 1·9 5·8
23 Tu ☾	0434 1045 1712 2336	2·5 6·1 2·1 5·7
24 W	0527 1142 1811	2·7 5·9 2·3
25 Th	0038 0636 1249 1919	5·6 2·7 5·8 2·3
26 F	0145 0751 1401 2027	5·7 2·6 5·9 2·2
27 Sa	0250 0858 1507 2129	5·9 2·3 6·1 2·0
28 Su	0346 1000 1606 2226	6·2 2·0 6·4 1·7
29 M	0437 1055 1701 2319	6·6 1·6 6·7 1·5
30 Tu ●	0523 1149 1753	6·9 1·2 6·9

JULY

Day	Time	m
1 W	0010 0608 1241 1843	1·3 7·1 0·9 7·1
2 Th	0057 0655 1330 1934	1·2 7·3 0·7 7·2
3 F	0144 0740 1418 2022	1·1 7·4 0·6 7·2
4 Sa	0229 0826 1504 2111	1·2 7·4 0·7 7·0
5 Su	0312 0914 1549 2200	1·3 7·3 0·8 6·8
6 M	0356 1002 1635 2251	1·6 7·1 1·1 6·5
7 Tu ☽	0444 1055 1726 2346	1·8 6·8 1·5 6·2
8 W	0537 1156 1827	2·1 6·4 1·8
9 Th	0049 0643 1307 1935	6·0 2·3 6·2 2·1
10 F	0159 0801 1427 2046	5·9 2·4 6·1 2·1
11 Sa	0307 0917 1539 2149	6·0 2·2 6·1 2·1
12 Su	0404 1019 1637 2241	6·2 2·0 6·3 1·9
13 M	0451 1111 1725 2326	6·5 1·7 6·4 1·8
14 Tu ○	0530 1156 1807	6·7 1·5 6·6
15 W	0007 0607 1234 1843	1·7 6·9 1·4 6·6
16 Th	0043 0642 1309 1919	1·6 7·0 1·3 6·7
17 F	0117 0714 1341 1951	1·6 7·0 1·3 6·7
18 Sa	0149 0747 1412 2022	1·6 7·0 1·3 6·6
19 Su	0220 0819 1443 2053	1·7 6·9 1·4 6·4
20 M	0250 0851 1514 2125	1·8 6·7 1·6 6·3
21 Tu	0321 0925 1545 2159	2·0 6·5 1·7 6·1
22 W ☾	0355 1002 1621 2238	2·2 6·3 2·0 5·9
23 Th	0435 1048 1709 2332	2·4 6·0 2·2 5·7
24 F	0534 1153 1817	2·6 5·8 2·4
25 Sa	0046 0657 1316 1940	5·6 2·7 5·8 2·4
26 Su	0208 0825 1439 2057	5·8 2·5 6·0 2·2
27 M	0317 0936 1550 2204	6·1 2·0 6·3 1·9
28 Tu	0416 1040 1651 2304	6·5 1·6 6·7 1·6
29 W ●	0508 1137 1746 2357	6·9 1·1 7·0 1·3
30 Th	0556 1231 1835	7·3 0·7 7·3
31 F	0045 0641 1319 1921	1·0 7·5 0·5 7·4

AUGUST

Day	Time	m
1 Sa	0130 0724 1405 2006	0·9 7·7 0·4 7·4
2 Su	0213 0809 1447 2050	0·9 7·7 0·5 7·2
3 M	0253 0853 1528 2134	1·1 7·5 0·8 6·9
4 Tu	0332 0938 1607 2217	1·3 7·2 1·2 6·5
5 W ☽	0413 1024 1651 2305	1·7 6·8 1·6 6·2
6 Th	0502 1122 1744	2·1 6·3 2·1
7 F	0005 0605 1238 1856	5·8 2·5 5·9 2·5
8 Sa	0123 0734 1411 2019	5·7 2·6 5·8 2·6
9 Su	0243 0901 1529 2131	5·8 2·4 6·0 2·4
10 M	0346 1007 1628 2224	6·1 2·1 6·2 2·2
11 Tu	0434 1058 1713 2309	6·4 1·8 6·4 1·9
12 W	0513 1139 1751 2347	6·7 1·5 6·6 1·7
13 Th ○	0549 1215 1824	6·9 1·4 6·7
14 F	0022 0621 1248 1855	1·5 7·0 1·3 6·8
15 Sa	0055 0652 1319 1924	1·4 7·1 1·2 6·8
16 Su	0126 0723 1348 1952	1·4 7·1 1·2 6·8
17 M	0155 0752 1416 2022	1·4 7·0 1·3 6·6
18 Tu	0225 0823 1444 2050	1·6 6·9 1·5 6·5
19 W	0253 0854 1511 2119	1·8 6·7 1·7 6·3
20 Th	0322 0928 1542 2153	2·0 6·4 1·9 6·1
21 F ☾	0400 1010 1624 2241	2·2 6·1 2·2 5·8
22 Sa	0454 1115 1729 2357	2·5 5·8 2·6 5·6
23 Su	0621 1249 1904	2·7 5·7 2·7
24 M	0135 0801 1423 2034	5·7 2·5 5·9 2·4
25 Tu	0256 0921 1539 2148	6·1 2·0 6·4 2·0
26 W	0357 1027 1640 2247	6·6 1·4 6·8 1·6
27 Th	0451 1123 1732 2340	7·0 0·9 7·2 1·2
28 F ●	0537 1214 1818	7·4 0·6 7·4
29 Sa	0027 0621 1300 1900	0·9 7·7 0·3 7·5
30 Su	0110 0704 1342 1942	0·8 7·8 0·3 7·5
31 M	0151 0747 1422 2022	0·8 7·8 0·5 7·3

Chart Datum: 3.90 metres below Ordnance Datum (Newlyn)

TIME ZONE UT(GMT)
For Summer Time add ONE hour in non-shaded areas

ENGLAND, EAST COAST – IMMINGHAM

Lat 53°38′ N Long 0°11′ W

TIMES AND HEIGHTS OF HIGH AND LOW WATERS

YEAR **1992**

SEPTEMBER

Day	Time	m	Time	m	Time	m	Time	m
1 Tu	0229	1·0	0829	7·6	1500	0·9	2101	7·0
2 W	0305	1·3	0911	7·2	1535	1·4	2141	6·6
3 Th ☽	0343	1·6	0956	6·7	1613	1·9	2223	6·2
4 F	0428	2·1	1051	6·1	1702	2·5	2319	5·8
5 Sa	0530	2·5	1211	5·7	1817	2·9		
6 Su	0041	5·6	0707	2·7	1351	5·6	1951	2·9
7 M	0212	5·7	0842	2·5	1511	5·9	2107	2·7
8 Tu	0319	6·0	0946	2·1	1607	6·2	2202	2·3
9 W	0409	6·4	1033	1·8	1649	6·5	2244	2·0
10 Th	0448	6·6	1112	1·6	1725	6·7	2322	1·7
11 F	0523	6·9	1147	1·4	1756	6·8	2356	1·5
12 Sa ○	0554	7·0	1218	1·2	1825	6·9		
13 Su	0028	1·4	0625	7·1	1249	1·2	1853	6·9
14 M	0059	1·3	0655	7·2	1319	1·2	1921	6·9
15 Tu	0128	1·3	0726	7·1	1348	1·3	1949	6·8
16 W	0159	1·4	0757	7·0	1415	1·5	2018	6·7
17 Th	0227	1·6	0829	6·8	1443	1·7	2047	6·5
18 F	0258	1·8	0904	6·5	1514	2·0	2122	6·3
19 Sa ☾	0338	2·1	0950	6·2	1557	2·3	2210	6·0
20 Su	0433	2·4	1059	5·8	1702	2·7	2327	5·7
21 M	0601	2·6	1238	5·7	1841	2·8		
22 Tu	0110	5·8	0744	2·3	1412	6·0	2015	2·5
23 W	0233	6·2	0903	1·8	1524	6·5	2128	2·1
24 Th	0338	6·6	1007	1·3	1623	6·9	2227	1·6
25 F	0430	7·1	1104	0·9	1712	7·2	2318	1·2
26 Sa ●	0516	7·5	1151	0·6	1754	7·4		
27 Su	0004	0·9	0558	7·7	1236	0·5	1835	7·5
28 M	0046	0·8	0641	7·8	1316	0·5	1914	7·5
29 Tu	0126	0·8	0723	7·7	1354	0·8	1951	7·3
30 W	0204	1·0	0804	7·4	1429	1·2	2029	7·0

OCTOBER

Day	Time	m	Time	m	Time	m	Time	m
1 Th	0239	1·3	0846	7·0	1503	1·7	2105	6·7
2 F	0317	1·7	0931	6·5	1539	2·2	2145	6·3
3 Sa ☽	0359	2·1	1024	6·0	1624	2·7	2235	5·9
4 Su	0457	2·5	1140	5·6	1732	3·1	2353	5·6
5 M	0628	2·7	1313	5·5	1909	3·2		
6 Tu	0124	5·6	0802	2·6	1433	5·7	2029	2·9
7 W	0237	5·9	0907	2·2	1529	6·1	2125	2·5
8 Th	0331	6·2	0955	1·9	1613	6·4	2209	2·2
9 F	0413	6·5	1034	1·7	1649	6·6	2248	1·9
10 Sa	0449	6·8	1111	1·5	1722	6·8	2323	1·6
11 Su ○	0523	7·0	1146	1·3	1751	6·9	2357	1·4
12 M	0556	7·1	1218	1·3	1821	7·0		
13 Tu	0031	1·3	0627	7·1	1249	1·3	1850	7·0
14 W	0103	1·3	0700	7·1	1320	1·4	1921	7·0
15 Th	0137	1·4	0734	7·0	1351	1·6	1952	6·9
16 F	0209	1·5	0812	6·8	1422	1·8	2026	6·7
17 Sa	0246	1·7	0854	6·6	1458	2·0	2105	6·5
18 Su	0328	1·9	0946	6·2	1543	2·4	2157	6·2
19 M ☾	0427	2·2	1057	6·0	1651	2·7	2313	6·0
20 Tu	0553	2·3	1228	5·9	1822	2·8		
21 W	0046	6·0	0724	2·1	1352	6·1	1951	2·5
22 Th	0206	6·3	0839	1·7	1501	6·5	2101	2·1
23 F	0311	6·7	0942	1·3	1559	6·8	2200	1·7
24 Sa	0404	7·0	1037	1·0	1647	7·1	2252	1·4
25 Su ●	0452	7·3	1126	0·8	1729	7·3	2339	1·1
26 M	0537	7·5	1210	0·8	1808	7·4		
27 Tu	0021	1·0	0619	7·6	1249	0·9	1846	7·4
28 W	0102	1·0	0702	7·4	1327	1·1	1923	7·3
29 Th	0141	1·1	0744	7·2	1402	1·5	1959	7·0
30 F	0218	1·4	0827	6·8	1436	1·9	2036	6·8
31 Sa	0254	1·7	0911	6·4	1511	2·3	2114	6·5

NOVEMBER

Day	Time	m	Time	m	Time	m	Time	m
1 Su	0334	2·0	0959	6·0	1552	2·6	2159	6·1
2 M ☽	0424	2·4	1101	5·7	1647	3·0	2301	5·8
3 Tu	0534	2·6	1217	5·5	1805	3·2		
4 W	0021	5·7	0659	2·6	1333	5·6	1928	3·1
5 Th	0137	5·8	0809	2·4	1434	5·8	2033	2·8
6 F	0239	6·0	0904	2·2	1525	6·1	2124	2·5
7 Sa	0329	6·3	0949	1·9	1607	6·4	2209	2·1
8 Su	0412	6·5	1031	1·7	1644	6·6	2248	1·8
9 M	0451	6·8	1111	1·5	1718	6·8	2327	1·6
10 Tu ○	0527	6·9	1147	1·4	1751	7·0		
11 W	0005	1·4	0603	7·0	1222	1·4	1824	7·1
12 Th	0042	1·3	0641	7·0	1259	1·5	1859	7·1
13 F	0120	1·3	0721	7·0	1334	1·6	1935	7·1
14 Sa	0159	1·4	0805	6·9	1412	1·7	2015	6·9
15 Su	0242	1·5	0853	6·7	1453	2·0	2100	6·7
16 M	0328	1·7	0948	6·4	1542	2·2	2152	6·5
17 Tu ☾	0427	1·8	1052	6·2	1644	2·5	2259	6·3
18 W	0539	1·9	1207	6·1	1758	2·6		
19 Th	0017	6·2	0655	1·9	1323	6·2	1917	2·5
20 F	0133	6·4	0808	1·7	1432	6·4	2029	2·2
21 Sa	0242	6·6	0912	1·5	1531	6·6	2132	1·9
22 Su	0341	6·8	1009	1·4	1621	6·8	2227	1·6
23 M	0433	7·0	1059	1·3	1705	7·0	2316	1·4
24 Tu ●	0520	7·1	1144	1·2	1744	7·2		
25 W	0001	1·2	0604	7·2	1225	1·3	1822	7·2
26 Th	0043	1·2	0648	7·1	1304	1·4	1859	7·2
27 F	0123	1·3	0731	7·0	1340	1·7	1935	7·1
28 Sa	0201	1·4	0812	6·7	1413	1·9	2012	6·9
29 Su	0236	1·6	0851	6·5	1447	2·2	2049	6·7
30 M	0312	1·8	0934	6·2	1524	2·4	2128	6·4

DECEMBER

Day	Time	m	Time	m	Time	m	Time	m
1 Tu	0353	2·1	1019	5·9	1607	2·7	2216	6·2
2 W ☽	0442	2·3	1113	5·7	1701	2·9	2313	5·9
3 Th	0544	2·5	1217	5·6	1808	3·0		
4 F	0022	5·8	0655	2·5	1324	5·6	1923	3·0
5 Sa	0133	5·8	0801	2·4	1426	5·8	2029	2·7
6 Su	0236	6·0	0858	2·2	1519	6·1	2124	2·4
7 M	0329	6·2	0949	2·0	1604	6·4	2214	2·1
8 Tu	0419	6·5	1035	1·8	1647	6·7	2259	1·7
9 W ○	0502	6·7	1119	1·6	1725	6·9	2343	1·5
10 Th	0546	6·9	1201	1·5	1803	7·1		
11 F	0027	1·3	0628	7·0	1243	1·4	1842	7·2
12 Sa	0110	1·1	0714	7·1	1326	1·4	1923	7·3
13 Su	0155	1·1	0801	7·1	1408	1·5	2006	7·2
14 M	0240	1·1	0850	6·9	1451	1·7	2053	7·1
15 Tu	0328	1·2	0941	6·7	1538	1·9	2143	6·9
16 W ☾	0419	1·4	1037	6·5	1630	2·1	2240	6·7
17 Th	0516	1·6	1137	6·3	1729	2·3	2344	6·5
18 F	0619	1·8	1246	6·1	1838	2·4		
19 Sa	0056	6·3	0730	1·9	1357	6·1	1954	2·4
20 Su	0212	6·3	0840	1·9	1501	6·3	2105	2·2
21 M	0321	6·5	0943	1·8	1557	6·5	2207	1·9
22 Tu	0421	6·6	1037	1·7	1645	6·7	2302	1·7
23 W	0512	6·7	1125	1·6	1727	6·9	2350	1·4
24 Th ●	0558	6·8	1207	1·6	1805	7·1		
25 F	0032	1·3	0641	6·9	1246	1·6	1842	7·1
26 Sa	0110	1·3	0720	6·8	1323	1·6	1917	7·1
27 Su	0145	1·3	0755	6·7	1355	1·8	1951	7·0
28 M	0219	1·4	0830	6·6	1427	1·9	2026	6·9
29 Tu	0250	1·6	0904	6·4	1458	2·0	2100	6·7
30 W	0324	1·7	0939	6·2	1532	2·2	2136	6·5
31 Th	0400	1·9	1017	6·0	1610	2·5	2219	6·2

Chart Datum: 3.90 metres below Ordnance Datum (Newlyn)

5

BRIDLINGTON 10-5-9
Humberside

CHARTS
Admiralty 1882, 121, 129, 1191; Imray C29; OS 101
TIDES
+0553 Dover; ML 3·6; Duration 0610; Zone 0 (GMT).

Standard Port RIVER TEES ENT. (→)

Times				Height (metres)			
HW		LW		MHWS	MHWN	MLWN	MLWS
0000	0600	0000	0600	5·5	4·3	2·0	0·9
1200	1800	1200	1800				
Differences BRIDLINGTON							
+0100	+0050	+0055	+0050	+0·6	+0·4	+0·3	+0·2
FILEY BAY							
+0042	+0042	+0047	+0034	+0·3	+0·6	+0·4	+0·1

SHELTER
Good shelter except in winds from E, SE and S. Harbour available from HW∓3 (for draft of 2·7m).
NAVIGATION
Waypoint SW Smithic W cardinal buoy, Q(9) 15s, 54°02′·41N 00°09′·10W, 153°/333° from/to entrance, 2·6M. Beware bar, 1m at MLWN, could dry out at MLWS. Air gunnery and bombing practice is carried out off Cowden 17M south. Range marked by 5 small conical buoys; 3 seaward ones flashing every 10 secs, the 2 shoreward ones every 5 secs.
LIGHTS AND MARKS
Run in keeping the N Pier head light 002°. Tidal signals displayed from Sig Stn 50m from S Pierhead.
Less than 2·7m in harbour:- FG (No signal by day).
More than 2·7m in harbour:- FR (R flag by day).
When harbour is not clear, a W flag with a B circle in it below a R flag.
RADIO TELEPHONE
VHF Ch 16; **12** 14 (occas).
TELEPHONE (0262)
Hr Mr 670148; CG 672317; MRSC 672317; ⌗ Whitby 602047; Marinecall 0898 500 454; Police 672222; Ⓗ 673451.
FACILITIES
EC Thursday; **S Pier** ☎ 670148, FW, C (7 ton), CH; **Royal Yorkshire YC** ☎ 672041, L, FW, R, Bar; **West end of Harbour** Slip; **C & M Marine** ☎ 672212, Slip, M, Sh, C, CH. See Hr Mr for M, AB.
Town P, D, ME, El, V, R, Bar. ✉; Ⓑ; ⇌; ✈ (Humberside).

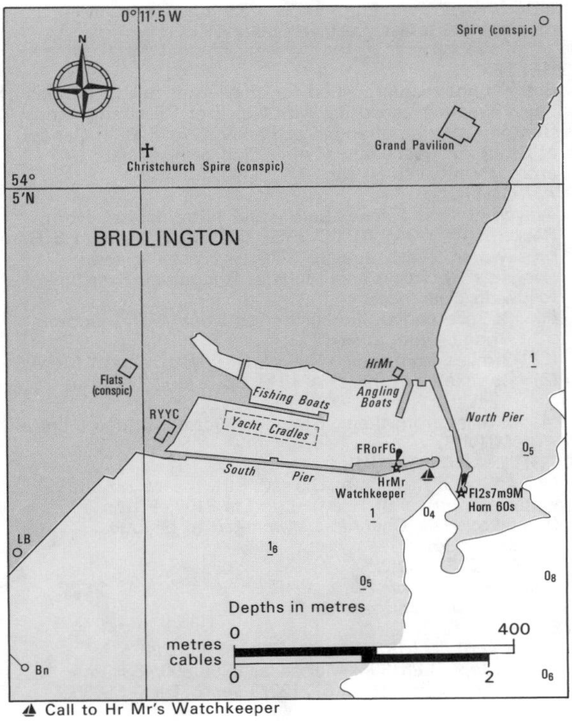
0°11′.5 W
N
Spire (conspic)
Grand Pavilion
Christchurch Spire (conspic)
54°
5′N
BRIDLINGTON
HrMr
Flats (conspic)
Fishing Boats
Angling Boats
RYYC
Yacht Cradles
North Pier
FRorFG
South Pier
HrMr Watchkeeper
Fl2s7m9M
Horn 60s
LB
Bn
Depths in metres
metres 0 400
cables 0 2

▲ Call to Hr Mr's Watchkeeper

SCARBOROUGH 10-5-10
N. Yorkshire

CHARTS
Admiralty 1612, 129, 1191; Imray C29; OS 101
TIDES
+0527 Dover; ML 3·5; Duration 0615; Zone 0 (GMT).

Standard Port RIVER TEES ENT. (→)

Times				Height (metres)			
HW		LW		MHWS	MHWN	MLWN	MLWS
0000	0600	0000	0600	5·5	4·3	2·0	0·9
1200	1800	1200	1800				
Differences SCARBOROUGH							
+0040	+0040	+0030	+0030	+0·2	+0·3	+0·3	0·0

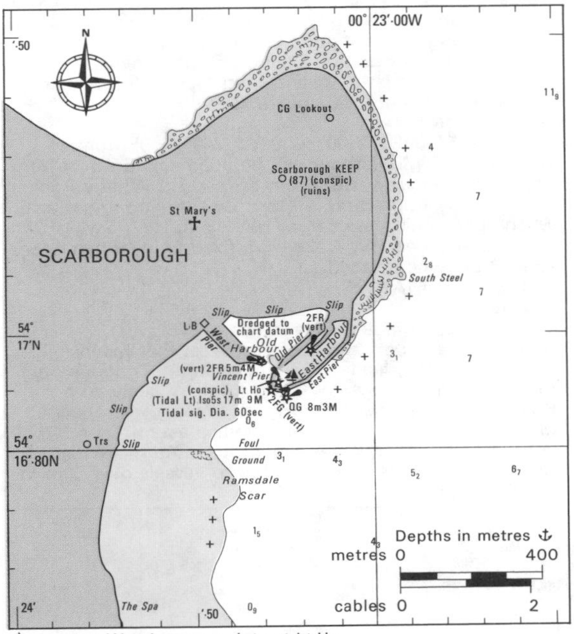
00° 23′·00W
N
CG Lookout
Scarborough KEEP (87) (conspic) (ruins)
St Mary's
SCARBOROUGH
South Steel
Dredged to chart datum
Old Harbour
Old Pier
East Harbour
West Pier
Vincent Pier
East Pier
2FR (vert)
(vert) 2FR 5m4M
(conspic) Lt Ho
(Tidal Lt) Iso5s 17m 9M
Tidal sig. Dia. 60sec
2FG (vert)
QG 8m3M
54° 17′N
54° 16′·80N
Trs
Foul Ground
Ramsdale Scar
The Spa
Depths in metres
metres 0 400
cables 0 2

▲ Contact Watchman on duty at Lt Ho

SHELTER
The old harbour is reserved strictly for fishing fleet. E harbour cannot be entered in strong E-SE winds, otherwise available HW∓3.
NAVIGATION
Waypoint 54°16′·50N 00°22′·00W, 122°/302° from/to East Pier Lt, 0·83M. Beware rocks SW of E pier running out for approx 20 m. Keep well clear of Ramsdale Scar. Keep careful watch for salmon nets to E and SE of entrance.
LIGHTS AND MARKS
No leading lights or marks. W pier head 2 FR (vert) 5m 4M when more than 1·8m. R flag — do not enter. These depths refer to Old Harbour; East Harbour entrance is about 1·5m less.
RADIO TELEPHONE
Call *Scarborough Lt Ho.* VHF Ch 16; 12 16 (H24).
TELEPHONE (0723)
Hr Mr Working hrs 373530, non-working hrs 360684; CG 372323; MRSC Bridlington 672317; ⌗ Whitby 602047; Marinecall 0898 500 454; Police 500300; Ⓗ 368111.
FACILITIES
EC Wednesday; **North Wharf** Slip; **Scarborough YC** ☎ 373821, Slip, M*, L, FW, ME, El, AB; **Old Pier** M*, L, FW, ME, El, AB; **Scarborough Marine** ☎ 375199, L, ME, El, Sh, CH, P and D (cans); **Vincent Pier** 3 ton; **A. H. Parcell** ☎ 375754, Ⓔ; **G. Kendall** ☎ 367021, Ⓔ; **West Pier** Slip, D, L; **Quay Marine** P, D, ME, El, Sh, CH; **Fisherman's Chandlers** ☎ 365266 CH; *Long waiting list — some berths available for visitors.
Town P, D, V, R, Bar, ✉; Ⓑ; ⇌; ✈ (Humberside).

WHITBY 10-5-11

N. Yorkshire

CHARTS
Admiralty 1612, 134, 129; Imray C29; OS 94

TIDES
+0500 Dover; ML 3·2; Duration 0605; Zone 0 (GMT).

Standard Port RIVER TEES ENT. (⟶)

Times				Height (metres)			
HW		LW		MHWS	MHWN	MLWN	MLWS
0000	0600	0000	0600	5·5	4·3	2·0	0·9
1200	1800	1200	1800				
Differences WHITBY							
+0015	+0030	+0020	+0005	+0·1	0·0	−0·1	−0·1

SHELTER
Good shelter except in lower harbour in strong NW to NE winds. Harbour available from HW∓3 for drafts of approx 2m. In strong winds from NW through N to SE the sea breaks a long way out and entry is difficult. Marina is run by Scarborough Borough Council. Bridge opens at ½ hour intervals HW∓2; and from May to Sept inclusive on Sat and Sun at 0900 and 1800.

NAVIGATION
Waypoint 54°30′·30N 00°36′·90W, 349°/169° from/to entrance, 0·65M. Harbour can be approached safely from any direction except SE. From SE beware Whitby Rock; keep Whitby Rock Buoy to port. Beware strong set to E when approaching piers from HW−2 to HW. Swing bridge is manned HW∓2, shows fixed G Lts when open, fixed R Lts when closed.

LIGHTS AND MARKS
Leading lines
(1) Chapel spire in line with Lt Ho — 176°.
(2) FR Lt, seen between East and West Pier Extension, Lts (FR and FG), leads 169° into harbour. Continue on this line until beacons (W triangle and W circle with B stripe) on East Pier (two FY Lts at night) are abeam.
(3) On course 209° leave marks in line astern.
Entry signal G Lt by night shown from top of W Pier Lt Ho indicating 'Enter', only applies to vessels over 30m in length.

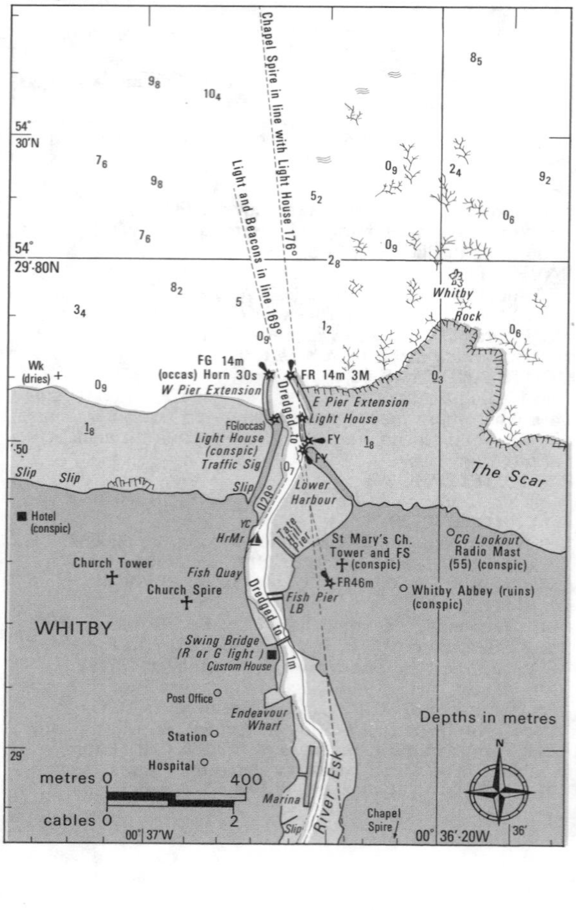
Chapel Spire in line with Light House 176°
Light and Beacons in line 169°
54° 30'N
54° 29'·80N
29'
Whitby Rock
Wk (dries)
FG 14m (occas) Horn 30s
W Pier Extension
FR 14m 3M
E Pier Extension
Light House
FY
FG(occas)
Light House (conspic)
Traffic Sig
Slip
Slip
Slip
Lower Harbour
The Scar
Hotel (conspic)
YC
HrMr
Tate Hill Pier
St Mary's Ch. Tower and FS (conspic)
CG Lookout Radio Mast (55) (conspic)
Church Tower
Fish Quay
Church Spire
FR46m
Fish Pier
LB
Whitby Abbey (ruins) (conspic)
WHITBY
Dredged 1.0
Swing Bridge (R or G light)
Custom House
Post Office
Endeavour Wharf
Depths in metres
Station
Hospital
metres 0 400
cables 0 2
Marina
River Esk
Chapel Spire
00° 37'W
00° 36'·20W
36'
N

RADIO TELEPHONE
VHF Ch 16; **11** 12 (0830-1730 LT). Whitby Bridge Ch 16; 06 **11** (listens on Ch 16 HW−2 to HW+2).

TELEPHONE (0947)
Hr Mr 602354; MRSC Humber Bridlington 672317; # 602074; Marinecall 0898 500 454/453; Police 603443; Dr 820888.

FACILITIES
EC Wednesday; **Whitby Marina** (200+10 visitors) ☎ 600165, Slip, P, AC, D, FW, ME, El, Sh, C, CH, Access HW∓2; **Fish Quay** M, D, L, FW, C (1 ton), CH, AB, R, Bar; **Whitby Marine Services** ☎ 600361, ME, El, Sh, CH; **M.R. Coates Marine** ☎ 604486, ME, El, Sh, CH, BH, ACA; **Whitby Port Services** ☎ 602272, Sh (up to 30 ton); **Whitby YC** ☎ 603623, M, L, Bar; **North East Sails** ☎ 604710 SM; **Endeavour Marine** ☎ 603484, ME, Sh, CH; **Collier** ☎ 602068 Gas, Gaz;
Town ✉; Ⓑ; ⇄; ✈ (Teesside).

RIVER TEES MIDDLESBROUGH 10-5-12

Cleveland

CHARTS
Admiralty 2566, 2567, 152; Imray C29; OS 93

TIDES
+0450 Dover; ML 3·2; Duration 0605; Zone 0 (GMT).

Standard Port RIVER TEES ENT. (⟶)

Times				Height (metres)			
HW		LW		MHWS	MHWN	MLWN	MLWS
0000	0600	0000	0600	5·5	4·3	2·0	0·9
1200	1800	1200	1800				
Differences MIDDLESBROUGH (Dock Ent)							
0000	+0002	0000	−0003	+0·1	+0·2	+0·1	−0·1

NOTE: River Tees Entrance is a Standard Port and detailed tide tables are given below.

SHELTER
Entry is not recommended for small craft during periods of heavy weather especially with NE, E or SE strong winds. Berthing may be arranged at Paddy's Hole (Bran Sands), at Stockton Castlegate Marine Club or elsewhere by arrangement with Hr Mr.

NAVIGATION
Waypoint Tees Fairway safe water buoy, Iso 4s, Horn, Racon, 54°40′·94N 01°06′·39W, 030°/210° from/to S Gare breakwater, 2·4M. Beware Saltscar, Eastscar and Longscar Rocks on approaching. Bridges up river have following clearances:-
(1) ½ mile above Middlesbrough Dock — Transporter Bridge—49m at MHWS;
(2) 2 miles from there, Newport Bridge, 6·4m at MHWS.
(3) ½ mile from there, A 19 Road Bridge 18·3m at MHWS;
(4) 2 miles from there, Stockton-Victoria Bridge 5·6m at MHWS.

LIGHTS AND MARKS
QW Lt, or 3FR (vert) at Old CG Stn, means no entry without approval of Hr Mr. Ldg Lts 210°, FR on framework Trs. Channel well marked to beyond Middlesbrough.

RADIO TELEPHONE
Call: *Tees Harbour Radio* VHF Ch 16; 08 11 12 **14 22** (H24). Information service Ch 14 22.

TELEPHONE (0642)
Hr Mr 468127; MRSC North Shields 257 2691; # Hartlepool 861390; Marinecall 0898 500 453; Police 248184; Ⓗ (North Tees) 672122, (South Tees) 850850.

RIVER TEES/MIDDLESBROUGH *continued*

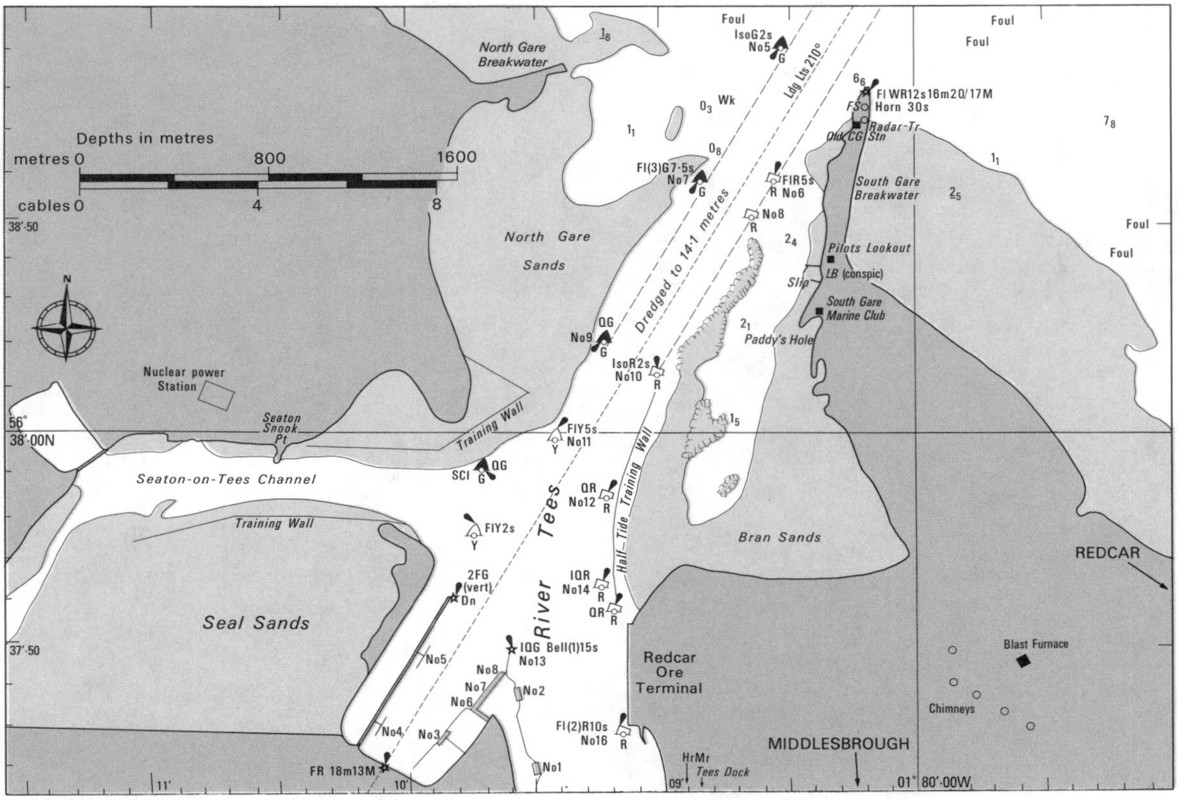
North Gare Breakwater
Foul
IsoG2s No5 G
Ldg Lts 210°
Foul
Foul
Fl WR12s16m20/17M
Horn 30s
FS
Radar Tr
Old CG Stn
Wk
Depths in metres
metres 0 800 1600
cables 0 4 8
38'·50
Fl(3)G7·5s No7 G
FIR5s R No6
South Gare Breakwater
No8 R
Foul
Foul
North Gare Sands
Pilots Lookout
LB (conspic)
Slip
South Gare Marine Club
Dredged to 14·1 metres
QG No9 G
Paddy's Hole
IsoR2s No10 R
Nuclear power Station
Seaton Snook Pt
Training Wall
56° 38'·00N
FlY5s No11 Y
Half Tide Training Wall
Seaton-on-Tees Channel
SCl QG
QR No12 R
Training Wall
FlY2s Y
River Tees
Bran Sands
REDCAR
2FG (vert) Dn
IQR No14 R
QR R
Seal Sands
37'·50
IQG Bell(1)15s No13
Blast Furnace
No5
No8
No7
No6
No2
Redcar Ore Terminal
Chimneys
No4
No3
Fl(2)R10s No16 R
MIDDLESBROUGH
FR 18m13M
No1
HrMr Tees Dock
11'
10'
09'
01° 80'·00W

Contact HrMr

FACILITIES

EC Wednesday; Limited accommodation on River Tees for small pleasure craft. Prior arrangements must be made with Club secretaries or Hr Mr. **South Gare Marine Club** ☎ 482015, Slip, M (check with Warden), L, FW, Bar; **Castlegate Marine Club** ☎ 583299 Slip, M, FW, ME, El, Sh, CH, L, V; **Tees Motor Boat Club** M (check with secretary); **Tees Docks** ☎ 452541, M (check), L, FW, C (30 ton), AB (check); **CTC Marine** ☎ 211756, Ⓔ, CH, ACA; **D.A.V. Engineering and Marine** ☎ 468272, El, ME.
Town ✉; Ⓑ; ≷; ✈.

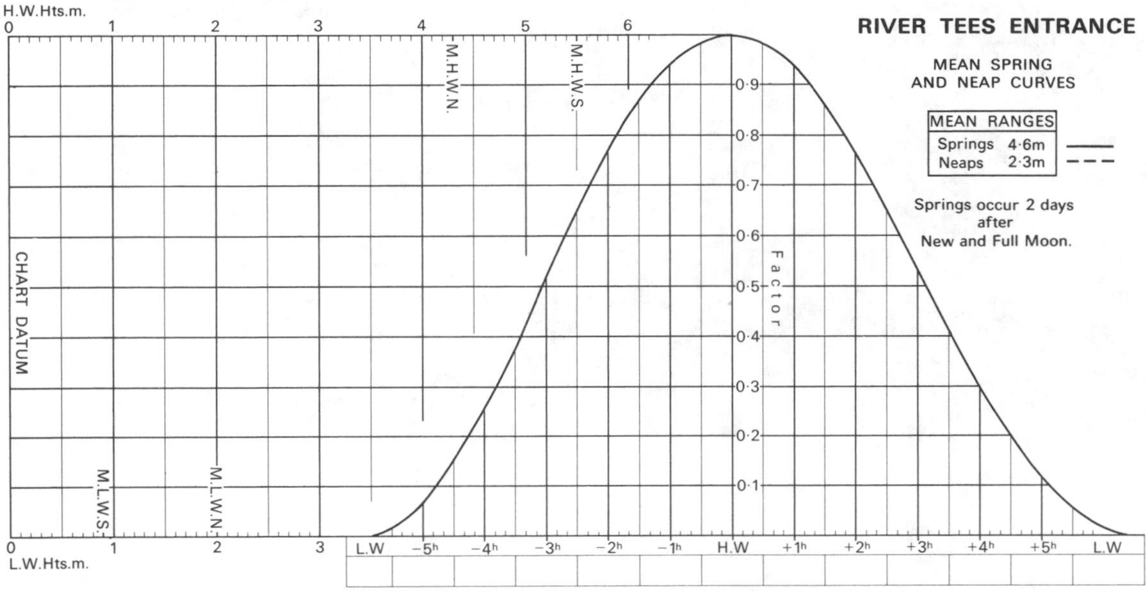
H.W.Hts.m.
0 1 2 3 4 5 6
M.H.W.N.
M.H.W.S.
0·9
0·8
0·7
0·6
0·5
0·4
0·3
0·2
0·1
Factor
CHART DATUM
M.L.W.S.
M.L.W.N.
0 1 2 3
L.W.Hts.m.
L.W −5h −4h −3h −2h −1h H.W +1h +2h +3h +4h +5h L.W

RIVER TEES ENTRANCE

MEAN SPRING AND NEAP CURVES

MEAN RANGES		
Springs	4·6m	——
Neaps	2·3m	– – –

Springs occur 2 days after New and Full Moon.

5

TIME ZONE UT(GMT)

For Summer Time add ONE hour in non-shaded areas

ENGLAND, EAST COAST – RIVER TEES ENTRANCE

Lat 54°38′ N Long 1°09′ W

TIMES AND HEIGHTS OF HIGH AND LOW WATERS

YEAR **1992**

JANUARY

Day	Time	m	Time	m	Time	m	Time	m
1 W	0041	4·6	0706	1·8	1313	4·6	1940	1·8
2 Th	0140	4·6	0758	1·7	1404	4·7	2030	1·6
3 F	0232	4·7	0843	1·6	1449	4·9	2114	1·4
4 Sa	0317	4·8	0921	1·6	1527	5·0	● 2152	1·3
5 Su	0355	4·9	0956	1·5	1602	5·1	2227	1·2
6 M	0430	4·9	1028	1·4	1634	5·2	2259	1·1
7 Tu	0502	4·9	1101	1·4	1705	5·2	2332	1·1
8 W	0536	4·9	1134	1·4	1739	5·2		
9 Th	0004	1·1	0610	4·8	1208	1·5	1812	5·1
10 F	0038	1·2	0645	4·7	1243	1·6	1849	4·9
11 Sa	0114	1·3	0724	4·6	1321	1·7	1928	4·8
12 Su	0154	1·5	0809	4·4	1402	1·9	2013	4·6
13 M	0240	1·7	0901	4·3	1454	2·1	☽ 2111	4·5
14 Tu	0336	1·9	1003	4·2	1602	2·2	2220	4·4
15 W	0448	2·0	1113	4·3	1725	2·2	2336	4·4
16 Th	0610	1·9	1224	4·5	1848	1·9		
17 F	0050	4·6	0723	1·7	1327	4·8	1957	1·5
18 Sa	0157	4·9	0823	1·4	1423	5·1	2054	1·1
19 Su	0254	5·3	0914	1·1	1514	5·4	○ 2145	0·6
20 M	0345	5·5	1002	0·9	1600	5·7	2231	0·3
21 Tu	0433	5·7	1045	0·8	1644	5·9	2318	0·2
22 W	0518	5·7	1129	0·8	1727	5·9		
23 Th	0003	0·2	0603	5·6	1211	0·9	1812	5·8
24 F	0046	0·3	0648	5·4	1255	1·1	1857	5·5
25 Sa	0131	0·7	0735	5·1	1338	1·4	1945	5·2
26 Su	0219	1·1	0825	4·8	1426	1·7	☾ 2040	4·9
27 M	0310	1·5	0919	4·5	1522	2·0	2143	4·5
28 Tu	0409	1·9	1023	4·3	1635	2·2	2258	4·3
29 W	0522	2·1	1134	4·2	1807	2·2		
30 Th	0017	4·2	0641	2·2	1246	4·3	1927	2·0
31 F	0127	4·3	0744	2·0	1347	4·5	2022	1·7

FEBRUARY

Day	Time	m	Time	m	Time	m	Time	m
1 Sa	0222	4·5	0832	1·9	1434	4·7	2104	1·5
2 Su	0305	4·6	0908	1·7	1512	4·9	2139	1·2
3 M	0342	4·8	0942	1·5	1546	5·1	● 2212	1·0
4 Tu	0414	4·9	1013	1·3	1616	5·2	2241	0·9
5 W	0442	4·9	1044	1·2	1645	5·3	2311	0·9
6 Th	0511	5·0	1115	1·1	1713	5·3	2342	0·9
7 F	0540	4·9	1144	1·1	1744	5·2		
8 Sa	0012	0·9	0612	4·9	1217	1·2	1817	5·1
9 Su	0045	1·1	0648	4·8	1250	1·4	1853	5·0
10 M	0120	1·3	0727	4·6	1328	1·6	1935	4·8
11 Tu	0201	1·5	0815	4·4	1416	1·8	☽ 2032	4·5
12 W	0254	1·8	0917	4·2	1519	2·0	2143	4·3
13 Th	0406	2·0	1031	4·2	1647	2·1	2309	4·3
14 F	0539	2·0	1153	4·3	1827	1·9		
15 Sa	0035	4·5	0707	1·8	1307	4·6	1944	1·4
16 Su	0145	4·8	0811	1·5	1408	5·0	2042	0·9
17 M	0243	5·2	0901	1·1	1458	5·4	2131	0·5
18 Tu	0331	5·5	0946	0·9	1543	5·7	○ 2216	0·2
19 W	0416	5·6	1028	0·7	1627	5·9	2258	0·0
20 Th	0458	5·7	1109	0·6	1708	5·9	2340	0·1
21 F	0539	5·6	1149	0·7	1749	5·8		
22 Sa	0021	0·3	0618	5·4	1228	0·9	1831	5·6
23 Su	0102	0·7	0659	5·1	1307	1·2	1914	5·2
24 M	0141	1·2	0742	4·8	1349	1·6	2004	4·8
25 Tu	0225	1·7	0832	4·5	1437	1·9	☾ 2104	4·4
26 W	0317	2·1	0931	4·2	1542	2·2	2219	4·1
27 Th	0427	2·4	1044	4·1	1722	2·3	2346	4·0
28 F	0603	2·5	1205	4·1	1900	2·1		
29 Sa	0103	4·1	0719	2·3	1314	4·3	1957	1·8

MARCH

Day	Time	m	Time	m	Time	m	Time	m
1 Su	0159	4·3	0806	2·0	1405	4·6	2037	1·5
2 M	0242	4·5	0844	1·7	1444	4·8	2111	1·3
3 Tu	0317	4·7	0917	1·5	1518	5·0	2142	1·0
4 W	0346	4·9	0948	1·3	1548	5·2	● 2213	0·9
5 Th	0414	5·0	1019	1·1	1617	5·3	2242	0·8
6 F	0441	5·0	1049	1·0	1645	5·3	2313	0·8
7 Sa	0511	5·1	1120	1·0	1716	5·3	2344	0·8
8 Su	0542	5·0	1153	1·0	1750	5·2		
9 M	0018	1·0	0617	4·9	1228	1·1	1829	5·1
10 Tu	0055	1·2	0657	4·7	1309	1·3	1916	4·8
11 W	0137	1·5	0747	4·5	1358	1·6	2013	4·6
12 Th	0232	1·8	0849	4·3	1503	1·8	☽ 2128	4·3
13 F	0343	2·0	1003	4·2	1628	1·9	2254	4·3
14 Sa	0518	2·1	1126	4·3	1807	1·7		
15 Su	0019	4·5	0648	1·9	1242	4·6	1923	1·3
16 M	0128	4·8	0749	1·5	1344	5·0	2020	0·8
17 Tu	0223	5·1	0840	1·2	1436	5·3	2108	0·5
18 W	0310	5·4	0924	0·9	1521	5·6	○ 2152	0·3
19 Th	0352	5·5	1006	0·7	1603	5·8	2233	0·2
20 F	0431	5·6	1045	0·7	1642	5·8	2312	0·3
21 Sa	0508	5·5	1123	0·7	1723	5·7	2350	0·6
22 Su	0546	5·3	1200	0·9	1804	5·4		
23 M	0028	1·0	0624	5·1	1238	1·2	1848	5·1
24 Tu	0104	1·4	0704	4·8	1319	1·5	1935	4·7
25 W	0145	1·8	0751	4·6	1405	1·8	2033	4·4
26 Th	0232	2·2	0847	4·3	1504	2·1	☾ 2142	4·1
27 F	0335	2·5	0956	4·1	1624	2·2	2302	4·0
28 Sa	0502	2·6	1112	4·1	1800	2·2		
29 Su	0018	4·1	0627	2·4	1222	4·3	1906	1·9
30 M	0116	4·3	0723	2·2	1319	4·5	1951	1·6
31 Tu	0159	4·5	0805	1·9	1402	4·7	2029	1·4

APRIL

Day	Time	m	Time	m	Time	m	Time	m
1 W	0237	4·7	0842	1·6	1439	5·0	2104	1·1
2 Th	0310	4·9	0917	1·3	1512	5·1	2138	1·0
3 F	0339	5·0	0950	1·1	1545	5·3	● 2212	0·9
4 Sa	0410	5·1	1023	1·0	1617	5·3	2244	0·8
5 Su	0441	5·2	1057	0·9	1652	5·3	2319	0·9
6 M	0516	5·1	1133	1·0	1732	5·3	2356	1·0
7 Tu	0554	5·0	1212	1·0	1817	5·1		
8 W	0036	1·3	0639	4·9	1259	1·2	1909	4·9
9 Th	0124	1·5	0731	4·7	1352	1·4	2012	4·6
10 F	0222	1·8	0834	4·5	1458	1·5	☽ 2125	4·4
11 Sa	0332	2·0	0946	4·4	1619	1·6	2244	4·4
12 Su	0458	2·1	1104	4·5	1744	1·4	2358	4·6
13 M	0619	1·9	1214	4·7	1855	1·2		
14 Tu	0103	4·8	0721	1·6	1316	5·0	1951	0·9
15 W	0155	5·1	0812	1·3	1408	5·2	2039	0·7
16 Th	0242	5·3	0857	1·1	1454	5·4	2124	0·6
17 F	0322	5·4	0939	0·9	1538	5·5	○ 2204	0·6
18 Sa	0402	5·4	1020	0·9	1619	5·5	2242	0·8
19 Su	0438	5·4	1058	0·9	1659	5·4	2319	1·0
20 M	0515	5·3	1136	1·0	1742	5·2	2356	1·3
21 Tu	0553	5·1	1214	1·2	1825	5·0		
22 W	0034	1·6	0635	4·9	1256	1·5	1914	4·7
23 Th	0113	1·9	0721	4·7	1341	1·7	2009	4·4
24 F	0201	2·2	0816	4·5	1436	1·9	☾ 2110	4·2
25 Sa	0258	2·4	0918	4·3	1541	2·0	2217	4·2
26 Su	0409	2·5	1024	4·3	1654	2·0	2322	4·2
27 M	0523	2·4	1127	4·4	1801	1·9		
28 Tu	0019	4·4	0628	2·2	1225	4·5	1856	1·7
29 W	0109	4·6	0719	2·0	1314	4·7	1941	1·5
30 Th	0151	4·8	0802	1·7	1358	4·9	2023	1·3

Chart Datum: 2.85 metres below Ordnance Datum (Newlyn)

5

ENGLAND, EAST COAST – RIVER TEES ENTRANCE

TIME ZONE UT(GMT)
For Summer Time add ONE hour in non-shaded areas

Lat 54°38′ N Long 1°09′ W

TIMES AND HEIGHTS OF HIGH AND LOW WATERS

YEAR **1992**

MAY

Date	Time	m	Date	Time	m
1 F	0230 0843 1437 2103	4·9 1·4 5·1 1·1	16 Sa ○	0256 0917 1517 2136	5·2 1·1 5·2 1·0
2 Sa ●	0305 0921 1515 2141	5·1 1·2 5·2 1·0	17 Su	0336 0959 1600 2216	5·2 1·1 5·2 1·1
3 Su	0341 1000 1555 2219	5·2 1·1 5·3 1·0	18 M	0414 1038 1642 2252	5·2 1·1 5·2 1·3
4 M	0419 1040 1637 2259	5·3 1·0 5·3 1·0	19 Tu	0452 1118 1725 2330	5·2 1·1 5·0 1·5
5 Tu	0458 1120 1722 2342	5·3 0·9 5·2 1·2	20 W	0530 1157 1808	5·1 1·2 4·9
6 W	0542 1207 1812	5·2 0·9 5·1	21 Th	0008 0612 1238 1855	1·7 5·0 1·4 4·7
7 Th	0027 0629 1256 1909	1·3 5·1 1·0 4·9	22 F	0049 0659 1321 1944	1·9 4·8 1·5 4·5
8 F	0117 0724 1352 2011	1·6 4·9 1·2 4·8	23 Sa	0134 0748 1411 2036	2·0 4·7 1·7 4·4
9 Sa ☽	0215 0825 1456 2118	1·8 4·8 1·3 4·6	24 Su ☾	0226 0842 1504 2132	2·2 4·6 1·8 4·3
10 Su	0321 0932 1606 2227	1·9 4·7 1·3 4·6	25 M	0324 0939 1602 2230	2·3 4·5 1·9 4·3
11 M	0434 1040 1718 2333	2·0 4·7 1·3 4·7	26 Tu	0427 1038 1702 2326	2·3 4·5 1·9 4·4
12 Tu	0547 1147 1824	1·9 4·8 1·2	27 W	0530 1134 1801	2·2 4·5 1·8
13 W	0034 0650 1248 1920	4·8 1·7 4·9 1·0	28 Th	0019 0629 1228 1855	4·5 2·1 4·6 1·6
14 Th	0126 0744 1342 2011	5·0 1·5 5·1 1·0	29 F	0109 0723 1319 1945	4·7 1·8 4·8 1·5
15 F	0213 0833 1432 2056	5·1 1·3 5·2 1·0	30 Sa	0154 0811 1406 2032	4·9 1·6 5·0 1·3
			31 Su	0237 0857 1454 2117	5·1 1·3 5·1 1·2

JUNE

Date	Time	m	Date	Time	m
1 M ●	0319 0942 1541 2202	5·2 1·1 5·3 1·1	16 Tu	0359 1027 1630 2234	5·1 1·1 5·0 1·4
2 Tu	0402 1028 1628 2247	5·3 0·9 5·3 1·1	17 W	0437 1105 1711 2311	5·2 1·1 4·9 1·5
3 W	0447 1115 1718 2332	5·4 0·8 5·3 1·1	18 Th	0515 1142 1750 2347	5·1 1·2 4·8 1·5
4 Th	0533 1203 1810	5·4 0·7 5·3	19 F	0554 1219 1829	5·1 1·2 4·7
5 F	0019 0622 1255 1904	1·3 5·3 0·8 5·1	20 Sa	0025 0635 1259 1912	1·6 5·0 1·3 4·6
6 Sa	0110 0714 1348 2001	1·4 5·2 0·9 5·0	21 Su	0106 0717 1340 1958	1·8 4·9 1·5 4·5
7 Su ☽	0204 0812 1446 2101	1·6 5·1 1·0 4·8	22 M	0149 0804 1425 2046	1·9 4·7 1·6 4·4
8 M	0303 0912 1546 2203	1·7 4·9 1·1 4·7	23 Tu ☾	0237 0853 1514 2138	2·0 4·6 1·7 4·3
9 Tu	0406 1016 1651 2304	1·8 4·8 1·2 4·7	24 W	0331 0948 1609 2234	2·2 4·5 1·8 4·3
10 W	0513 1120 1754	1·8 4·8 1·3	25 Th	0433 1047 1709 2333	2·2 4·5 1·9 4·4
11 Th	0004 0621 1224 1853	4·7 1·8 4·8 1·3	26 F	0540 1147 1814	2·1 4·5 1·8
12 F	0100 0721 1323 1947	4·8 1·6 4·9 1·3	27 Sa	0031 0646 1248 1916	4·6 2·0 4·7 1·6
13 Sa	0151 0815 1416 2034	4·9 1·5 4·9 1·3	28 Su	0126 0747 1345 2011	4·8 1·7 4·9 1·5
14 Su	0237 0903 1504 2118	5·0 1·3 5·0 1·3	29 M	0216 0840 1439 2103	5·0 1·3 5·1 1·3
15 M ○	0319 0946 1549 2157	5·1 1·2 5·0 1·4	30 Tu ●	0304 0932 1531 2150	5·2 1·0 5·3 1·1

JULY

Date	Time	m	Date	Time	m
1 W	0350 1020 1620 2237	5·4 0·7 5·4 1·0	16 Th	0423 1049 1652 2252	5·2 1·0 4·9 1·3
2 Th	0435 1108 1709 2322	5·6 0·5 5·5 1·0	17 F	0457 1123 1726 2326	5·2 1·0 4·9 1·3
3 F	0522 1156 1758	5·6 0·4 5·5	18 Sa	0530 1157 1800	5·2 1·0 4·8
4 Sa	0008 0608 1243 1848	1·0 5·6 0·4 5·3	19 Su	0000 0604 1231 1835	1·4 5·1 1·1 4·7
5 Su	0055 0657 1333 1940	1·1 5·5 0·6 5·1	20 M	0035 0641 1306 1914	1·5 5·0 1·3 4·6
6 M	0144 0751 1425 2033	1·3 5·3 0·8 4·9	21 Tu	0112 0720 1344 1957	1·6 4·9 1·5 4·5
7 Tu ☽	0236 0847 1519 2131	1·5 5·1 1·1 4·7	22 W ☾	0152 0805 1427 2046	1·8 4·7 1·6 4·3
8 W	0334 0949 1620 2233	1·8 4·8 1·4 4·6	23 Th	0240 0857 1518 2142	2·0 4·5 1·8 4·3
9 Th	0441 1057 1726 2336	1·9 4·7 1·6 4·5	24 F	0339 0959 1621 2248	2·1 4·4 2·0 4·3
10 F	0556 1205 1832	1·9 4·6 1·7	25 Sa	0454 1111 1737 2356	2·2 4·4 2·0 4·4
11 Sa	0039 0706 1310 1931	4·5 1·8 4·6 1·7	26 Su	0615 1224 1853	2·0 4·5 1·8
12 Su	0137 0806 1408 2023	4·7 1·6 4·7 1·6	27 M	0100 0728 1330 1957	4·6 1·7 4·8 1·6
13 M	0226 0856 1457 2105	4·8 1·4 4·8 1·5	28 Tu	0158 0829 1427 2050	4·9 1·2 5·1 1·3
14 Tu ○	0310 0938 1541 2143	5·0 1·2 4·9 1·4	29 W ●	0249 0919 1519 2138	5·3 0·8 5·4 1·0
15 W	0348 1016 1617 2219	5·1 1·1 4·9 1·4	30 Th	0335 1007 1607 2223	5·6 0·4 5·6 0·8
			31 F	0420 1054 1652 2306	5·8 0·2 5·7 0·7

AUGUST

Date	Time	m	Date	Time	m
1 Sa	0504 1139 1737 2349	5·9 0·2 5·6 0·8	16 Su	0501 1127 1726 2332	5·3 0·9 5·0 1·2
2 Su	0549 1224 1822	5·8 0·3 5·5	17 M	0530 1158 1757	5·2 1·0 4·9
3 M	0032 0634 1309 1910	0·9 5·7 0·5 5·2	18 Tu	0003 0604 1231 1832	1·2 5·1 1·1 4·8
4 Tu	0116 0723 1355 1959	1·1 5·4 0·9 4·9	19 W	0038 0639 1304 1910	1·4 5·0 1·3 4·6
5 W ☽	0204 0816 1447 2053	1·4 5·1 1·3 4·7	20 Th	0114 0721 1345 1958	1·6 4·7 1·6 4·4
6 Th	0258 0918 1545 2155	1·8 4·7 1·7 4·4	21 F ☾	0201 0813 1434 2056	1·8 4·5 1·9 4·2
7 F	0407 1030 1654 2305	2·0 4·5 2·0 4·3	22 Sa	0300 0922 1542 2207	2·0 4·3 2·1 4·2
8 Sa	0533 1149 1812	2·1 4·4 2·1	23 Su	0419 1042 1708 2325	2·1 4·3 2·1 4·3
9 Su	0018 0657 1302 1920	4·4 1·9 4·4 2·0	24 M	0553 1205 1835	2·0 4·4 2·0
10 M	0121 0758 1359 2011	4·5 1·7 4·6 1·8	25 Tu	0036 0713 1316 1941	4·6 1·6 4·7 1·6
11 Tu	0212 0844 1446 2051	4·8 1·4 4·7 1·6	26 W	0137 0812 1413 2033	5·0 1·1 5·1 1·3
12 W	0254 0922 1525 2127	5·0 1·2 4·8 1·4	27 Th	0229 0903 1503 2119	5·3 0·6 5·4 0·9
13 Th ○	0329 0956 1559 2159	5·1 1·0 4·9 1·3	28 F ●	0314 0948 1548 2202	5·7 0·3 5·7 0·7
14 F	0402 1027 1628 2230	5·2 0·9 5·0 1·2	29 Sa	0357 1031 1630 2244	5·9 0·1 5·8 0·6
15 Sa	0431 1057 1657 2301	5·3 0·9 5·0 1·1	30 Su	0440 1115 1711 2325	6·0 0·1 5·7 0·7
			31 M	0522 1156 1753	5·9 0·3 5·6

Chart Datum: 2.85 metres below Ordnance Datum (Newlyn)

ENGLAND, EAST COAST – RIVER TEES ENTRANCE

TIME ZONE UT(GMT)
For Summer Time add ONE hour in non-shaded areas

Lat 54°38′ N Long 1°09′ W

TIMES AND HEIGHTS OF HIGH AND LOW WATERS

YEAR **1992**

SEPTEMBER

Day	Time	m	Day	Time	m
1 Tu	0005	0·8	16 W	0530	5·2
	0605	5·7		1157	1·1
	1238	0·6		1756	4·9
	1835	5·3			
2 W	0048	1·1	17 Th	0008	1·3
	0653	5·4		0607	5·0
	1321	1·1		1232	1·3
	1921	5·0		1835	4·8
3 Th	0133	1·4	18 F	0048	1·5
	0745	5·0		0652	4·8
	1408	1·6		1313	1·6
	☽ 2012	4·6		1921	4·5
4 F	0225	1·8	19 Sa	0135	1·7
	0847	4·6		0748	4·5
	1503	2·0		1404	1·9
	2114	4·4		☾ 2022	4·3
5 Sa	0332	2·1	20 Su	0237	1·9
	1003	4·3		0900	4·3
	1614	2·3		1512	2·2
	2227	4·2		2136	4·3
6 Su	0506	2·2	21 M	0359	2·0
	1129	4·2		1024	4·3
	1746	2·4		1641	2·2
	2347	4·3		2257	4·3
7 M	0639	2·0	22 Tu	0533	1·8
	1245	4·3		1149	4·4
	1859	2·2		1812	2·0
8 Tu	0055	4·5	23 W	0011	4·6
	0737	1·7		0652	1·4
	1341	4·5		1257	4·8
	1949	2·0		1919	1·7
9 W	0145	4·7	24 Th	0113	5·0
	0819	1·5		0749	0·9
	1425	4·7		1352	5·1
	2027	1·7		2011	1·3
10 Th	0226	5·0	25 F	0204	5·4
	0854	1·2		0839	0·6
	1500	4·8		1440	5·5
	2100	1·5		2056	1·0
11 F	0301	5·1	26 Sa	0250	5·7
	0925	1·0		0924	0·3
	1531	5·0		1522	5·7
	2132	1·3		● 2138	0·8
12 Sa	0332	5·3	27 Su	0334	5·9
	0956	0·9		1006	0·2
	1557	5·0		1603	5·7
	○ 2202	1·2		2219	0·7
13 Su	0400	5·3	28 M	0416	5·9
	1026	0·8		1047	0·3
	1626	5·1		1642	5·7
	2233	1·1		2259	0·7
14 M	0428	5·3	29 Tu	0457	5·8
	1055	0·9		1126	0·5
	1652	5·1		1722	5·6
	2302	1·1		2339	0·9
15 Tu	0458	5·3	30 W	0540	5·6
	1125	0·9		1205	0·9
	1722	5·0		1803	5·3
	2334	1·2			

OCTOBER

Day	Time	m	Day	Time	m
1 Th	0019	1·2	16 F	0549	5·1
	0625	5·3		1208	1·4
	1246	1·3		1811	4·9
	1845	5·0			
2 F	0104	1·5	17 Sa	0031	1·4
	0717	4·9		0636	4·8
	1330	1·8		1252	1·6
	1934	4·7		1900	4·7
3 Sa	0155	1·8	18 Su	0123	1·5
	0818	4·5		0737	4·6
	1420	2·2		1345	1·9
	☽ 2034	4·4		2001	4·5
4 Su	0258	2·1	19 M	0226	1·7
	0931	4·2		0849	4·4
	1528	2·5		1454	2·2
	2145	4·3		☾ 2112	4·4
5 M	0426	2·2	20 Tu	0345	1·8
	1054	4·1		1009	4·4
	1657	2·6		1617	2·2
	2302	4·3		2230	4·5
6 Tu	0557	2·1	21 W	0511	1·6
	1210	4·2		1127	4·5
	1818	2·5		1743	2·1
				2343	4·7
7 W	0011	4·5	22 Th	0624	1·3
	0657	1·9		1234	4·8
	1306	4·4		1850	1·8
	1912	2·2			
8 Th	0106	4·7	23 F	0045	5·0
	0740	1·6		0723	1·0
	1348	4·7		1327	5·1
	1952	1·9		1944	1·4
9 F	0148	4·9	24 Sa	0140	5·3
	0816	1·4		0812	0·7
	1425	4·8		1415	5·4
	2027	1·6		2032	1·1
10 Sa	0226	5·1	25 Su	0227	5·6
	0849	1·2		0857	0·5
	1456	5·0		1458	5·6
	2101	1·4		● 2115	0·9
11 Su	0258	5·2	26 M	0312	5·7
	0921	1·0		0939	0·5
	1525	5·1		1538	5·6
	○ 2134	1·2		2156	0·8
12 M	0329	5·3	27 Tu	0355	5·7
	0952	0·9		1020	0·6
	1553	5·2		1617	5·6
	2204	1·1		2237	0·9
13 Tu	0359	5·4	28 W	0437	5·6
	1024	0·9		1059	0·9
	1623	5·2		1655	5·5
	2237	1·1		2318	1·0
14 W	0431	5·3	29 Th	0520	5·4
	1057	1·0		1137	1·2
	1654	5·2		1734	5·3
	2311	1·1		2358	1·2
15 Th	0508	5·2	30 F	0605	5·1
	1130	1·2		1215	1·5
	1730	5·1		1817	5·1
	2349	1·2			
			31 Sa	0042	1·5
				0655	4·8
				1257	1·9
				1904	4·8

NOVEMBER

Day	Time	m	Day	Time	m
1 Su	0130	1·7	16 M	0119	1·3
	0751	4·5		0731	4·8
	1345	2·2		1335	1·8
	1959	4·6		1947	4·8
2 M	0226	2·0	17 Tu	0219	1·4
	0856	4·3		0837	4·6
	1443	2·5		1439	2·0
	☽ 2103	4·4		☾ 2053	4·7
3 Tu	0335	2·1	18 W	0328	1·5
	1006	4·2		0949	4·5
	1556	2·6		1552	2·1
	2212	4·4		2203	4·7
4 W	0451	2·1	19 Th	0442	1·4
	1115	4·2		1059	4·6
	1715	2·6		1709	2·0
	2319	4·4		2315	4·8
5 Th	0558	2·0	20 F	0554	1·3
	1214	4·4		1204	4·8
	1819	2·4		1819	1·8
6 F	0017	4·6	21 Sa	0019	5·0
	0650	1·8		0655	1·1
	1303	4·6		1302	5·0
	1909	2·1		1919	1·6
7 Sa	0106	4·8	22 Su	0117	5·2
	0733	1·6		0748	1·0
	1344	4·8		1352	5·2
	1951	1·8		2011	1·3
8 Su	0148	5·0	23 M	0209	5·3
	0812	1·4		0836	0·9
	1420	5·0		1437	5·3
	2030	1·6		2057	1·1
9 M	0226	5·1	24 Tu	0257	5·4
	0849	1·2		0919	0·9
	1454	5·1		1519	5·4
	2107	1·4		● 2142	1·0
10 Tu	0303	5·2	25 W	0342	5·5
	0924	1·1		0959	1·0
	1528	5·2		1559	5·5
	○ 2142	1·2		2223	1·0
11 W	0338	5·3	26 Th	0426	5·4
	0959	1·1		1038	1·2
	1600	5·3		1637	5·4
	2219	1·1		2304	1·0
12 Th	0416	5·3	27 F	0508	5·3
	1035	1·1		1115	1·4
	1635	5·3		1716	5·3
	2258	1·1		2343	1·2
13 F	0457	5·3	28 Sa	0550	5·1
	1113	1·2		1153	1·6
	1715	5·3		1756	5·2
	2339	1·1			
14 Sa	0542	5·1	29 Su	0024	1·3
	1156	1·4		0635	4·8
	1758	5·1		1232	1·8
				1839	5·0
15 Su	0025	1·2	30 M	0106	1·6
	0634	5·0		0723	4·6
	1242	1·6		1314	2·0
	1849	5·0		1927	4·8

DECEMBER

Day	Time	m	Day	Time	m
1 Tu	0152	1·8	16 W	0206	1·0
	0815	4·4		0819	4·8
	1402	2·3		1419	1·7
	2020	4·6		☾ 2030	5·0
2 W	0246	1·9	17 Th	0307	1·2
	0911	4·3		0921	4·7
	1458	2·4		1522	1·9
	☽ 2119	4·5		2136	4·8
3 Th	0343	2·1	18 F	0412	1·4
	1013	4·2		1027	4·6
	1604	2·5		1634	2·0
	2221	4·4		2247	4·7
4 F	0448	2·1	19 Sa	0522	1·4
	1113	4·3		1134	4·6
	1713	2·4		1750	1·9
	2322	4·4		2357	4·8
5 Sa	0550	2·0	20 Su	0629	1·4
	1211	4·4		1238	4·7
	1818	2·3		1859	1·7
6 Su	0019	4·6	21 M	0102	4·9
	0646	1·9		0728	1·4
	1302	4·6		1334	4·9
	1913	2·0		1958	1·5
7 M	0112	4·7	22 Tu	0201	5·0
	0735	1·7		0820	1·3
	1347	4·8		1425	5·0
	2001	1·8		2050	1·3
8 Tu	0158	4·9	23 W	0251	5·1
	0820	1·5		0907	1·3
	1427	5·0		1508	5·2
	2044	1·5		2135	1·1
9 W	0242	5·1	24 Th	0336	5·2
	0901	1·3		0948	1·3
	1507	5·2		1549	5·3
	○ 2127	1·2		● 2216	1·0
10 Th	0325	5·2	25 F	0419	5·2
	0943	1·2		1024	1·3
	1545	5·3		1626	5·3
	2209	1·0		2254	1·0
11 F	0407	5·3	26 Sa	0457	5·1
	1024	1·1		1059	1·3
	1624	5·4		1701	5·3
	2251	0·9		2330	1·0
12 Sa	0452	5·4	27 Su	0534	5·0
	1105	1·1		1133	1·4
	1706	5·5		1737	5·3
	2336	0·8			
13 Su	0539	5·3	28 M	0005	1·1
	1149	1·2		0611	4·9
	1750	5·4		1208	1·6
				1814	5·1
14 M	0022	0·8	29 Tu	0041	1·3
	0628	5·2		0650	4·7
	1235	1·3		1245	1·7
	1838	5·3		1853	5·0
15 Tu	0113	0·9	30 W	0119	1·5
	0721	5·0		0731	4·6
	1324	1·5		1324	1·9
	1931	5·1		1937	4·8
			31 Th	0159	1·7
				0818	4·4
				1408	2·1
				2023	4·6

Chart Datum: 2.85 metres below Ordnance Datum (Newlyn)

HARTLEPOOL 10-5-13

Cleveland

CHARTS
Admiralty 2566, 2567, 152; Imray C29; OS 93

TIDES
+0437 Dover; ML 3·0; Duration 0600; Zone 0 (GMT).

Standard Port RIVER TEES ENT. (⟵)

Times				Height (metres)			
HW		LW		MHWS	MHWN	MLWN	MLWS
0000	0600	0000	0600	5·5	4·3	2·0	0·9
1200	1800	1200	1800				
Differences HARTLEPOOL							
−0004	−0004	−0006	−0006	−0·1	−0·1	−0·2	−0·1

SHELTER
Strong winds from E cause swell to build up making entrance channel hazardous. Once inside there is good shelter. Best berth at Hartlepool YC pontoons, SE corner of Victoria Dock, depth 5m (apply Dock Office Tel. 66127). West Harbour (dries) available for small craft. Access to enclosed docks HW∓1.

NAVIGATION
Waypoint Longscar E cardinal buoy, Q(3) 10s, Bell, 54°40′·85N 01°09′·79W, 137°/317° from/to entrance, 1·0M. Beware from S — Longscar rocks, 6 ca S of bottom of chartlet (Buoy BYB. Q (3) 10s). From N — 'The Stones' NE of breakwater head, 1 ca.

LIGHTS AND MARKS
Leading line 324°53′ into main harbour (Dir Iso WRG 3s 42m). Amber Lt on NW corner of Fish Quay means vessels may not enter or leave. When no light is shown vessels may pass in or out. Traffic to and from enclosed docks 1G Lt — Vessel may enter N Basin. 2G Lts — Vessel may pass through N Basin. 1R Lt — Vessel may not approach dock.

RADIO TELEPHONE
Call: *Hartlepool Dock Radio* VHF Ch 16; 11 **12** (HJ and on HW. Information service navigation advice, tidal service on Ch 12 HJ). Yacht Haven Ch 80

TELEPHONE (0429)
Hr Mr 266127; MRSC North Shields 257 2691; Tees & Hartlepool Port Authority 276771; ⋕ 861390; Marinecall 0898 500 453; Police 221151; Dr 274570.

FACILITIES
EC Wednesday; **Hartlepool Yacht Haven** ☎ 865744, ME, El, Sh, FW, AC, Access HW∓4½; **Harbour** (400) ☎ 266127, FW, D, Slip, C (10 ton); **Irvings Quay** Slip, M, L, AB; **Fish Quay** P (in cans), D, FW, CH; **A. M. Marine** ☎ 233820 ME, El, Sh, CH, C (Mobile); **Cliff Reynolds** ☎ 272049, ME, El, CH; **Dock** ☎ 266127, M, FW, ME, El, C (3 ton, 10 ton), AB; **Hartlepool YC** ☎ 274931, Bar; **Tees SC** ☎ 267151, ME, El; **Town** P, V, R, ▣, Bar. Gas, Gaz, ✉; Ⓑ; ⇌; ✈ (Teesside).

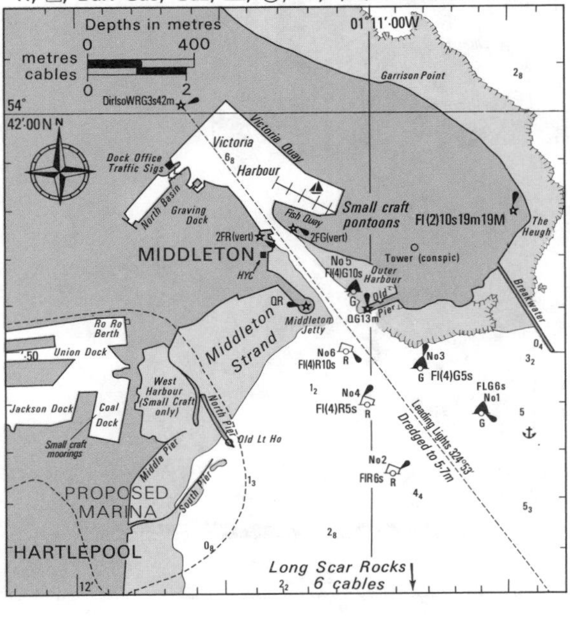
Depths in metres
metres
cables
0 400
0 2
01°11′·00W
54° 42′·00N
DirIsoWRG3s42m
Garrison Point
Victoria Quay
Victoria Harbour
Dock Office Traffic Sigs
North Basin
Graving Dock
Fish Quay
Small craft pontoons
Fl(2)10s19m19M
The Heugh
2FR(vert)
2FG(vert)
MIDDLETON
HYC
Tower (conspic)
No5 Fl(4)G10s
Outer Harbour
Old Pier
Breakwater
QR
Middleton Jetty
QG13m
Ro Ro Berth
Union Dock
Middleton Strand
No6 Fl(4)R10s
No3 Fl(4)G5s
FLG6s No1
West Harbour (Small Craft only)
Jackson Dock
Coal Dock
North Pier
Small craft moorings
No4 Fl(4)R5s
Leading Lights 324°53′ Dredged to 5·7m
Old Lt Ho
Middle Pier
South Pier
No2 FlR6s
PROPOSED MARINA
HARTLEPOOL
Long Scar Rocks 6 cables

Note: — South docks are being converted into a marina complex.

SEAHAM 10-5-14

Durham

CHARTS
Admiralty 1627, 152; Imray C29; OS 88

TIDES
+0435 Dover; ML 3·0; Duration 0600; Zone 0 (GMT).

Standard Port RIVER TEES ENT. (⟵)

Times				Height (metres)			
HW		LW		MHWS	MHWN	MLWN	MLWS
0000	0600	0000	0600	5·5	4·3	2·0	0·9
1200	1800	1200	1800				
Differences SEAHAM							
−0015	−0015	−0015	−0015	−0·3	−0·2	0·0	−0·2

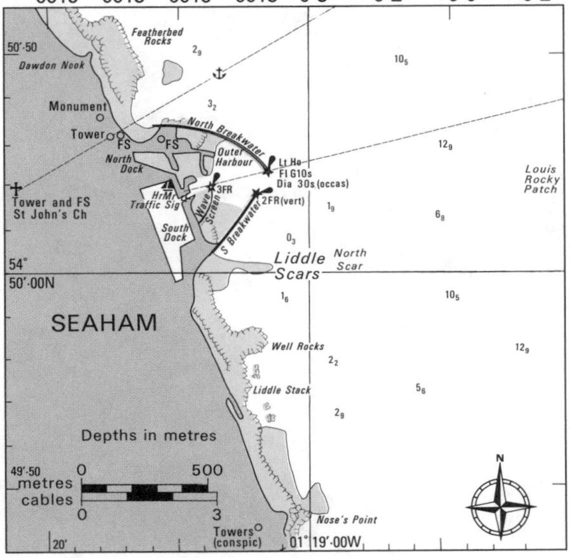
50′·50
Featherbed Rocks
Dawdon Nook
Monument
Tower
North Breakwater
FS
North Dock
Outer Harbour
Lt Ho Fl G10s Dia 30s (occas)
Louis Rocky Patch
Tower and FS St John's Ch
HrMr Traffic Sig
3FR
Wave Screen
2FR(vert)
South Dock
S Breakwater
54° 50′·00N
Liddle Scars
North Scar
SEAHAM
Well Rocks
Liddle Stack
Depths in metres
49′·50
metres
cables
0 500
0 3
Towers (conspic)
Nose's Point
20′
01°19′·00W

SHELTER
Small boats normally berth in N Dock where shelter is excellent but it dries. Larger boats may enter S Dock; gates open from HW−2 to HW+1.

NAVIGATION
Waypoint 54°50′·20N 01°18′·50W, 094°/274° from/to entrance, 0·40M. Shallow water and rocks to S of S breakwater (Liddle Scars). Entrance should not be attempted during strong on-shore winds. Speed limit 5 kn.

LIGHTS AND MARKS
No leading lights or marks but harbour is easily identified by lighthouse on N Pier Fl G 10s 12m 5M Dia 30s (W with B bands). FS at NE corner of S dock in line with N Lt Ho leads in clear of Tangle Rks. Anchorage good ¾ M off shore with Clock Tower in transit with St John's church tower.
Traffic signals, S Dock:
R Lt — Vessels enter
G Lt — Vessels leave

RADIO TELEPHONE
VHF Ch 16; 06 **12** (HW−2½ to HW+1½ — office hours 0800−1800 LT Mon−Fri).

TELEPHONE (091)
Hr Mr 581 3246; MRSC North Shields 257 2691; Seaham Harbour Operations Office 581 3877; ⋕ Sunderland 565 7113; Marinecall 0898 500 453; Police 581 2255; Dr 581 2332.

FACILITIES
EC Wednesday; **South Dock** ☎ 581 3877, L, FW, C (40 ton), AB; **North Dock** M; **Town** (½ M) P, D, FW, ME, El, CH (5 M), V, R, Bar. ✉; Ⓑ; ⇌; ✈ (Teesside or Newcastle).

SUNDERLAND 10-5-15

Tyne and Wear

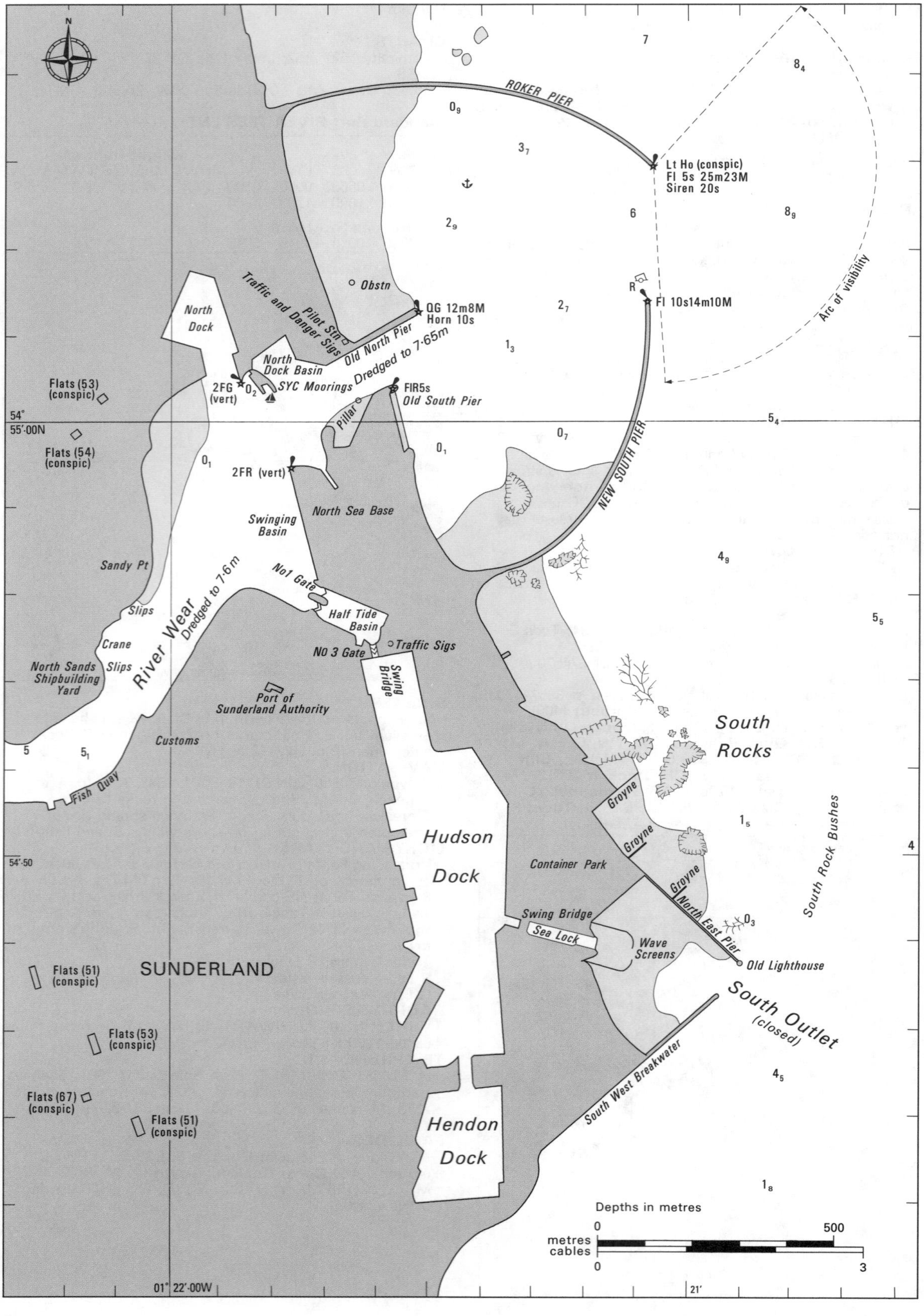

N
ROKER PIER
Lt Ho (conspic)
Fl 5s 25m23M
Siren 20s
Arc of visibility
Obstn
Traffic and Danger Sigs
Pilot Stn
QG 12m8M
Horn 10s
Old North Pier
Dredged to 7·65m
R
Fl 10s14m10M
North Dock
North Dock Basin
SYC Moorings
2FG (vert)
FlR5s
Old South Pier
Flats (53) (conspic)
Flats (54) (conspic)
54° 55'·00N
Pillar
NEW SOUTH PIER
2FR (vert)
North Sea Base
Swinging Basin
Sandy Pt
No1 Gate
Half Tide Basin
Slips
Crane
Slips
River Wear
Dredged to 7·6m
Traffic Sigs
NO 3 Gate
Swing Bridge
North Sands Shipbuilding Yard
Port of Sunderland Authority
Customs
Fish Quay
South Rocks
Groyne
Groyne
Groyne
Hudson Dock
Container Park
54°·50
South Rock Bushes
North East Pier
Swing Bridge
Sea Lock
Wave Screens
Old Lighthouse
SUNDERLAND
Flats (51) (conspic)
Flats (53) (conspic)
Flats (67) (conspic)
Flats (51) (conspic)
South Outlet (closed)
South West Breakwater
Hendon Dock
Depths in metres
metres 0 500
cables 0 3
01° 22'·00W
21'

SUNDERLAND *continued*

CHARTS
Admiralty 1627, 152; Imray C29; OS 88

TIDES
+0430 Dover; ML 2·9; Duration 0600; Zone 0 (GMT).

Standard Port RIVER TEES ENT. (⟵)

Times				Height (metres)			
HW		LW		MHWS	MHWN	MLWN	MLWS
0000	0600	0000	0600	5·5	4.3	2·0	0·9
1200	1800	1200	1800				
Differences SUNDERLAND							
−0017	−0017	−0016	−0016	−0·3	−0·1	0·0	−0·1

SHELTER
Shelter is good but no facilities for private yachts except through Sunderland YC, or Wear Boating Association. Strong winds between NE and SE cause heavy swell in entrance and outer harbour. Yachts normally berthed in North Dock, just up river from North Dock Basin.

NAVIGATION
Waypoint 54°55′·20N 01°20′·00W, 098°/278° from/to Roker Pier Lt, 0·61M. Beware wreck at Whitburn Steel about 1 M N of entrance, and Hendon Rk (0·9m), 1.2M SE of entrance.

LIGHTS AND MARKS
Three flashing R Lts from Pilot Station on Old North Pier indicate danger in harbour – no entry or departure.

RADIO TELEPHONE
VHF Ch 16; 14 (H24)

TELEPHONE (091)
Hr Mr 567 2626; MRSC North Shields 257 2691; # 565 7113; Marinecall 0898 500 453; Police 586 2621; Ⓗ 565 6256.

FACILITIES
EC Wednesday; **Sunderland YC** ☎ 567 5133, Slip (Dinghy), FW, AB, Bar; **Wear Boating Association** ☎ 567 5313, AB; **Town** P, D, V, R, Bar. ✉; Ⓑ; ⇌; ✈ (Newcastle).

RIVER TYNE/NORTH SHIELDS
Tyne and Wear

10-5-16

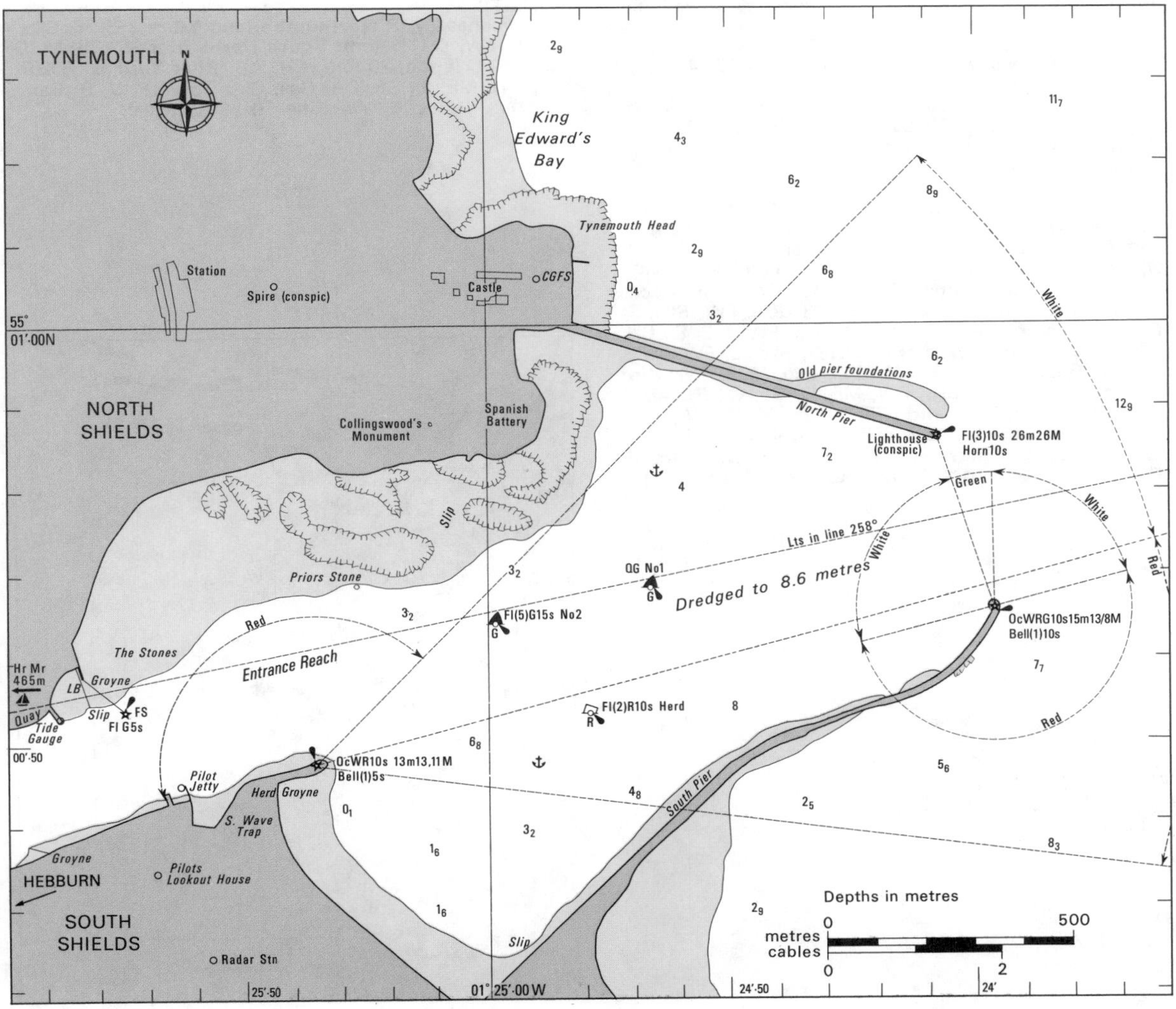
TYNEMOUTH
N
King Edward's Bay
Tynemouth Head
Station
Spire (conspic)
Castle
CGFS
55° 01'·00N
Old pier foundations
North Pier
Lighthouse (conspic)
Fl(3)10s 26m26M Horn10s
White
NORTH SHIELDS
Collingswood's Monument
Spanish Battery
Green
Red
Slip
Lts in line 258°
Priors Stone
QG No1
Dredged to 8.6 metres
Fl(5)G15s No2
OcWRG10s15m13/8M Bell(1)10s
The Stones
Entrance Reach
Hr Mr 465m
LB
Groyne
Quay
Slip
FS
Fl G5s
Tide Gauge
00'·50
Fl(2)R10s Herd
OcWR10s 13m13,11M Bell(1)5s
Pilot Jetty
Herd Groyne
S. Wave Trap
South Pier
Groyne
HEBBURN
Pilots Lookout House
SOUTH SHIELDS
Radar Stn
Slip
Depths in metres
metres 0 500
cables 0 2
25'·50
01° 25'·00W
24'·50
24'

RIVER TYNE / NORTH SHIELDS *continued*

CHARTS
Admiralty 1934, 152; Imray C29; OS 88

TIDES
+0430 Dover; ML 2·9; Duration 0604; Zone 0 (GMT)

Standard Port RIVER TEES ENT. (←)

Times				Height (metres)			
HW		LW		MHWS	MHWN	MLWN	MLWS
0000	0600	0000	0600	5·5	4·3	2·0	0·9
1200	1800	1200	1800				
Differences NORTH SHIELDS							
−0016	−0018	−0017	−0022	−0·5	−0·4	−0·2	−0·2
NEWCASTLE-UPON-TYNE							
−0013	−0015	−0009	−0014	−0·2	−0·2	−0·1	−0·1

SHELTER
Good shelter in all weathers. The approach is difficult for small craft in E and NE strong winds. Yachts may go into Albert Edward Dock giving excellent shelter and protection from heavy river traffic; obtain permission from Hr Mr by VHF or telephone first. Entrance 1M up river from Fl G 5s Lt on No 1 Groyne, on N bank.

NAVIGATION
Waypoint 55°01′·00N 01°22′·22W, 078°/258° from/to front Ldg Lt 258°, 2·2M. From S — No dangers. From N — Beware Bellhues Rock (approx 1 M N of harbour and ¾ M off shore) — Beware old N Pier; give it a wide berth.

LIGHTS AND MARKS
Ldg Lts 258° — FW 25/39m **20M** two W Trs with W Lts. Buoys mark the dredged channel in Lower Harbour. Tynemouth Castle forms prominent landmark on cliff 26m high on N side of harbour.

RADIO TELEPHONE
Call: *Tyne Harbour Radio* VHF Ch 12 16; 11 **12** 14 (H24).

TELEPHONE (091)
Hr Mr 257 0407; MRSC 257 2691; ⌗ 257 9441; Weather: 232 6453; Marinecall 0898 500 453; Police 232 3451; Dr Radio through Tyne Harbour 257 2080.

FACILITIES
EC Wednesday
Limited berthing accommodation on the River Tyne for small pleasure craft. Prior arrangements must be made with club Secretaries or Harbour Master.
St Peter's Basin Marina (140 + 20 visitors) ☎ 265 4472 Approx 7·8M upriver from hbr ent. AC, FW, D, P, Access HW∓4. **Hebburn Marina** (50) ☎ 483 2876, FW, Slip; **Friars Goose Marina** (50) ☎ 469 2545, FW, ME, El, CH, Slip; **Robsons Boatyard** ☎ 455 5187, Slip, L, FW, ME, El, AB; **Tyne Slipway** ☎ 456 6209, Slip, M, L, FW; **Jim Marine** ☎ 257 7610, Slip, FW, ME, El, Sh, C, CH, AB, V, R, Bar; **John Lillie and Gillie** ☎ 257 2217 ACA; **A.N.D. Electronics** ☎ 258 1635, Ⓔ; **Kelvin Hughes** ☎ 257 1318, Ⓔ; **Sperry** ☎ 257 1413, Ⓔ; **Town**, P (cans), D, V, R, Bar. ✉; Ⓑ; ⇌ (Tynemouth or South Shields), ✈ (Newcastle).

BLYTH 10-5-17
Northumberland

CHARTS
Admiralty 1626, 152; Imray C29; OS 81, 88

TIDES
+0430 Dover; ML 2·8; Duration 0558; Zone 0 (GMT).

Standard Port RIVER TEES ENT. (←)

Times				Height (metres)			
HW		LW		MHWS	MHWN	MLWN	MLWS
0000	0600	0000	0600	5·5	4·3	2·0	0·9
1200	1800	1200	1800				
Differences BLYTH							
−0011	−0025	−0018	+0013	−0·5	−0·4	−0·3	−0·1

SHELTER
Very good — Yachts normally berth in South Harbour, eastern section. At low tide in strong SE winds, seas break across entrance.

NAVIGATION
Waypoint Fairway stbd-hand buoy, FlG 3s, Bell, 55°06′·58N 01°28′·50W, 140°/320° from/to East Pier Lt, 0·53M. Beware The Pigs, The Sow and Seaton Sea Rocks when approaching from the N. No dangers from the S.

LIGHTS AND MARKS
Ldg Lts 324°, F Bu on framework Trs with Or diamonds 11/17m. Second pair of Ldg Lts 338°, F Bu at 5m and 11m respectively.

RADIO TELEPHONE
Call: *Blyth Harbour Control* VHF Ch 12 16; 11 12 (H24).

TELEPHONE (0670)
Hr Mr 352678; MRSC North Shields 257 2691; ⌗ 361521; Marinecall 0898 500 453; Police (0661) 72555; Dr 353226.

FACILITIES
EC Wednesday; **R Northumberland YC** ☎ 353636, Slip, M, L, FW, C (1½ ton); **South Harbour** ☎ 352678, M, D, L. FW, C (6 ton, 30 ton), CH, AB; **Boat Yard** ☎ 353207, Slip, D, ME, El, Sh, CH, Gas, Gaz; **Town** P, V, R, Bar. ✉; Ⓑ; ⇌ (bus to Newcastle); ✈ (Newcastle).

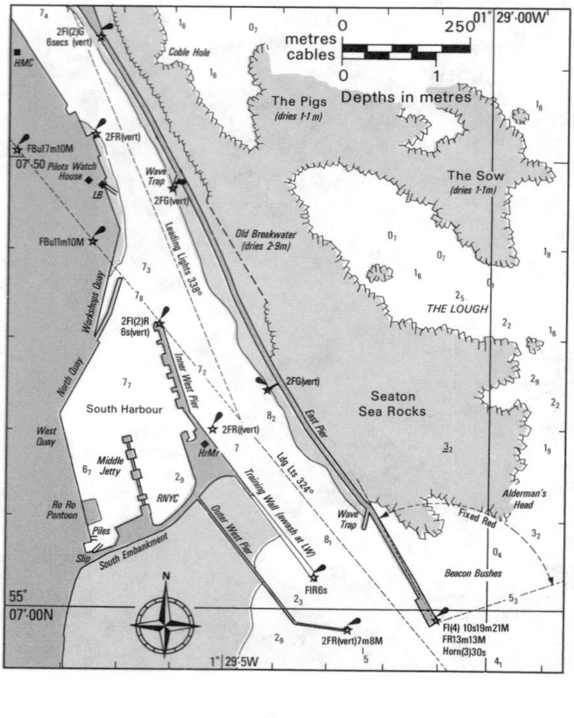

metres
cables
0
250
1
Depths in metres
01° 29′·00W
The Pigs
(dries 1·1 m)
The Sow
(dries 1·1m)
Coble Hole
HMC
2Fl(2)G 6secs (vert)
2FR(vert)
FBu17m10M
07′·50
Pilots Watch House
LB
Wave Trap
2FG(vert)
FBu11m10M
Old Breakwater (dries 2·9m)
Leading Lights 338°
Workshops Quay
2Fl(2)R 6s(vert)
THE LOUGH
Inner West Pier
2FG(vert)
North Quay
South Harbour
Seaton Sea Rocks
East Pier
2FR(vert)
West Quay
HrMr
Middle Jetty
Ldg Lts 324°
RNYC
Training Wall (awash at LW)
Alderman's Head
Ro Ro Pontoon
Piles
Outer West Pier
Wave Trap
Fixed Red
Slip
South Embankment
Beacon Bushes
FlR6s
55° 07′·00N
Fl(4) 10s19m21M
FR13m13M
Horn(3)30s
2FR(vert)7m8M
1° 29′·5W
N

AMBLE 10-5-18

Northumberland

CHARTS
Admiralty 1627, 156; Imray C29; OS 81

TIDES
+0412 Dover; ML 3·0; Duration 0606; Zone 0 (GMT).

Standard Port RIVER TEES ENT. (←)

Times				Height (metres)			
HW		LW		MHWS	MHWN	MLWN	MLWS
0000	0600	0000	0600	5·5	4·3	2·0	0·9
1200	1800	1200	1800				
Differences AMBLE							
−0039	−0033	−0040	−0036	−0·5	−0·2	0·0	−0·1
NORTH SUNDERLAND							
−0104	−0102	−0115	−0124	−0·7	−0·6	−0·4	−0·2
HOLY ISLAND							
−0059	−0057	−0122	−0132	−0·7	−0·6	−0·5	−0·3

SHELTER
The harbour, known as Warkworth Harbour, is safe in all weathers but entrance is dangerous in strong N to E winds or in swell which causes breakers on the bar (Pan Bush). In NE gales, broken water can extend to Coquet Island. Yachts should go to the Braid Yacht Marina on S bank of Coquet River, approx 1000m from ent; or the river above fish dock (ask at Coquet YC). There is a speed limit throughout the harbour of 4 kn.

NAVIGATION
Waypoint 55°21′·00N 01°33′·00W, 045°/225° from/to harbour entrance, 0·9M. Entrance recommended from NE, passing N and W of Pan Bush shoal. A wreck, min depth 1·7m, lies 1·75 ca ENE of breakwater head. Alternative approach in good conditions and with sufficient rise of tide through Coquet channel (buoyed, min depth 0·3m). The S-going stream sets strongly across entrance.

LIGHTS AND MARKS
Coquet Island Lt Ho, (conspic) W square Tr, turreted parapet, lower half grey; Fl (3) WR 30s 25m 23/19M R330°-140°, W140°-163°, R163°-180°, W180°-330°. Horn 30s.

RADIO TELEPHONE
Call *Amble Harbour* VHF Ch 16; 14 (Mon-Fri 0900-1700 LT). Coquet YC Ch 16. Marina, Call *Amble Braid Marina* Ch **80** (H24).

TELEPHONE (0665)
Hr Mr 710306; MRSC North Shields 257·2691; # Blyth 361521; Marinecall 0898 500 453; H 602661.

FACILITIES
EC Wednesday; **Braid Marina** (250+40 visitors) ☎ 712168 AC, BY, C, Gas, FW, D, P, R, Gaz, Slip, BH (20 ton), ME, El, Sh, Bar; V, CH, ◙; Access HW∓4 via sill; **Harbour** D, AB; **Marshall Branson Marine** ☎ 710267 ME, Slip, CH, El, Sh, D; **Coquet YC** Slip, Bar, M, FW, L; **Marshall Branson Chandlery** ☎ 711069 CH, SM, El, Ⓔ; **Marina Filling Station** P (cans); **Town** V, R, Bar, ✉, ≹ (Alnmouth), ✈ (Newcastle).

AGENTS WANTED
Ploumanac'h
Trébeurden
Le Touquet
Norderney
Dornumersiel
Langeoog
Wangerooge
Hooksiel
Bremerhaven

If you are interested in becoming our agent please write to the Editors and get your free copy annually. You do not have to be a resident in a port to be the agent but at least a fairly regular visitor.

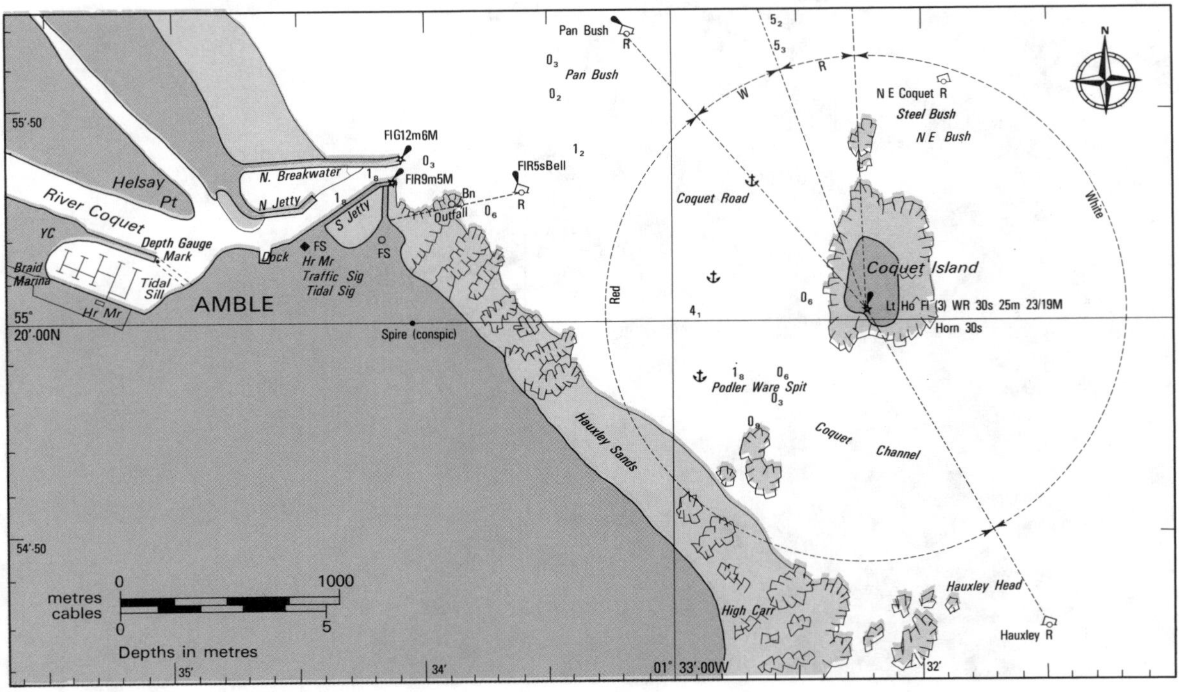

Pan Bush
Steel Bush
N E Bush
N E Coquet R
FlG12m6M
FlR9m5M
FlR5sBell
N. Breakwater
N Jetty
S Jetty
Helsay Pt
River Coquet
YC
Braid Marina
Depth Gauge Mark
Tidal Sill
Hr Mr
Dock
FS
Traffic Sig
Tidal Sig
Outfall
Bn
AMBLE
Spire (conspic)
Coquet Road
Coquet Island
Lt Ho Fl (3) WR 30s 25m 23/19M
Horn 30s
Podler Ware Spit
Coquet Channel
Hauxley Sands
High Carr
Hauxley Head
Hauxley R
Red
White
55°20′·00N
55′·50
54′·50
35′
34′
01° 33′·00W
32′
metres
cables
Depths in metres

BERWICK-ON-TWEED 10-5-19

Northumberland

CHARTS
Admiralty 1612, 111, 160; OS 75

TIDES
+0348 Dover; ML 2·5; Duration 0620; Zone 0 (GMT).

Standard Port RIVER TEES ENT. (⟵)

Times				Height (metres)			
HW		LW		MHWS	MHWN	MLWN	MLWS
0000	0600	0000	0600	5·5	4·3	2·0	0·9
1200	1800	1200	1800				
Differences BERWICK							
−0109	−0111	−0126	−0131	−0·8	−0·5	−0·7	−0·3

SHELTER
Good shelter or anchorage except in strong winds from E and SE. Yachts lie at W end of Fish Jetty or in Tweed Dock (opens HW−2 to HW). There are also good anchorages at Holy Is. See 10.5.20.

NAVIGATION
Waypoint 55°45′·80N 01°58′·00W, 098°/278° from/to breakwater Lt Ho, 0·54M. On-shore winds and ebb tides cause very confused state over the bar. From HW−2 to HW+1 strong flood tide sets across the entrance — keep well up to breakwater. The sands at the mouth of the Tweed shift so frequently that local knowledge is useful when entering Berwick Harbour.

LIGHTS AND MARKS
Town hall clock tower and lighthouse in line at 294°. When past Crabwater Rock, pick up transit beacons at Spittal in line at 207°. Beacons are B and Y with triangular top marks.

RADIO TELEPHONE
VHF CG: Ch 16 (0900-1700 LT); Pilot and Hr Mr; Ch 16; 12 (HW−3 to HW+1, when shipping expected).

TELEPHONE (0289)
Hr Mr 307404; MRSC North Shields 257·2691; # 307547; Marinecall 0898 500 453/452; Police 307111; Dr 307484

FACILITIES
EC Thursday; **Dock** ☎ 7404, Slip, M (See Hr Mr), P, D, L, FW, ME, El, Sh, C (Mobile 3 ton), AB; **Town** P, V, R, Bar. ✉; Ⓑ; ⇌; ✈ (Newcastle or Edinburgh).

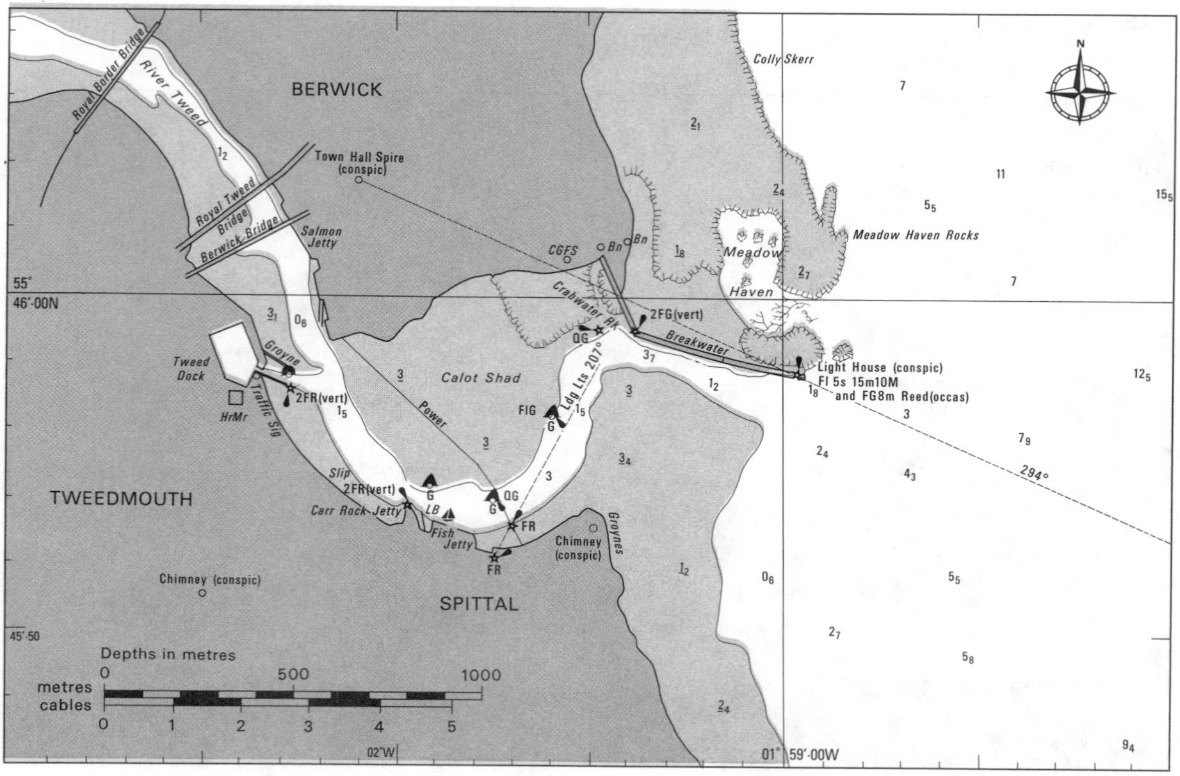
BERWICK
River Tweed
Royal Border Bridge
Royal Tweed Bridge
Berwick Bridge
Town Hall Spire (conspic)
Salmon Jetty
CGFS
Bn
Colly Skerr
Meadow Haven Rocks
Meadow Haven
Crabwater Rk
2FG(vert)
QG
Breakwater
Light House (conspic) Fl 5s 15m10M and FG8m Reed(occas)
294°
Tweed Dock
Groyne
2FR(vert)
HrMr
Traffic Sig
Calot Shad
Power
Ldg Lts 207°
FlG
TWEEDMOUTH
Slip
2FR(vert)
Carr Rock Jetty
LB
Fish Jetty
QG
FR
Chimney (conspic)
Groynes
SPITTAL
55° 46′·00N
45′·50
02°W
01° 59′·00W
Depths in metres
0 500 1000
metres
cables
0 1 2 3 4 5
N

MINOR HARBOURS AND ANCHORAGES 10.5.20

WAINFLEET, Lincolnshire, 53°06′·00N, 00°20′·00E, Zone 0 (GMT), Admty chart 108. Skegness HW +0500 on Dover, −0009 on Immingham; HW height −0·4m on Immingham; ML 4·0m; Duration 0600. Shelter good. Swatchway buoyed but not lit; channel through saltings marked with posts with radar reflectors, R can tops to port, G triangular tops to stbd. Enter HW∓1½. No lights. Facilities: EC Thurs, M, AB (larger boats at fishing jetties, smaller at YC), FW at Field Study Centre on stbd side at entrance. All shore facilities at Skegness (3½ miles).

FILEY, N Yorkshire, 54°13′·00N, 00°16′·00W, Zone 0 (GMT), Admty charts 1882, 129. HW +0532 on Dover, +0042 on River Tees Ent; HW height + 0·4m on River Tees Ent.; ML 3·5m; Duration 0605. See 10.5.9. Good anchorage in winds from NNE through W to S. Anchor in 4 to 5m on hard sandy bottom. Light on cliff above CG Station, G metal column, FR 31m 1M vis 272°−308°. The natural breakwater, Filey Brigg marked by Lt Buoy, Q(3)10s, Bell. Beware the Horse Rock, N of Filey Brigg, foul ground extending ½M from shore. Facilities; EC Wed, V, R, Bar, L, Ⓗ. ☎ 68111, ✉, Ⓑ, ⇌.

RUNSWICK BAY, N. Yorkshire, 54°32′·00N,00°45′·00W; Zone 0 (GMT). Admty chart 1612. HW +0505 on Dover: +0010 on River Tees Ent; HW height −0·1m on River Tees Ent; ML 3·1m; Duration 0605. Good shelter in all winds from NW by W to SSE. Enter bay at 270° keeping clear of many rocks at base of cliffs. Two white posts (2FY by night when required by lifeboat) 18m apart are leading marks to LB house and can be used to lead into anchorage. Good holding in 6m to 9m in middle of bay. Facilities: **Runswick Bay Rescue Boat Station** ☎ Whitby 840965; **Runswick Bay Hotel** ☎ 840210 Bar, R; **Runswick Bay Stores** ☎ 840880 V.

NEWTON HAVEN (St Mary's), Northumberland, 55° 31′·00N, 00° 36′·50W, Zone 0 (GMT), Admty chart 156. HW +0342 on Dover, −0102 on River Tees Ent; HW height −0·7m on River Tees Ent.; ML 2·6m; Duration 0625. A safe anchorage in winds from NNW to SE via S but susceptible to swell. Entrance to S of Newton Point. Beware Fills Rks. Anchor between Fills Rks and Low Newton by the Sea in 4/5m. A very attractive anchorage with no lights, marks or facilities except a pub.

SEAHOUSES (North Sunderland Harbour), Northumberland, 55°35′·00N, 01°39′·00W, Zone 0 (GMT), Admty chart 1612. HW +0340 on Dover, −0103 on River Tees Ent; HW height −0·7m on River Tees Ent.; ML 2·7m; Duration 0618. See 10.5.18. Good shelter except in on-shore winds when swell makes outer harbour berths very uncomfortable and dangerous. Access HW∓3. Inner harbour has excellent berths but usually full of fishing boats. Beware The Tumblers (rocks) to the W of entrance and rocks protruding NE from E breakwater. Lights − Breakwater head Fl R 2·5s 6m; NW pier head FG 11m 3M; vis 159°−294°, on W Tr; traffic signals; Siren 90s when vessels expected. When it is dangerous to enter a R Lt is shown over the G Lt (or R flag over a Bu flag) on NW pier head. Facilities: EC Wed; **J. Davidson** ☎ 720347, Gas; all facilities available.

FARNE ISLANDS, Northumberland, 55°37′·00N, 01°39′·00W, Zone 0 (GMT), Admty chart 111. HW +0345 on Dover, −0102 on River Tees Ent.; HW height −0·7m on River Tees Ent; ML 2·6m; Duration 0630. The islands are a nature reserve belonging to the National Trust. Landing is only allowed on Inner Farne, Staple I and Longstone. In the Inner Islands, yachts can anchor in The Kettle on the E side of Inner Farne, near the Bridges (which connect Knox Reef to West Wideopens) or to the S of West Wideopens. In the Outer Islands yachts can anchor in Pinnacle Haven (between Staple I and Brownsman). Beware turbulence over Knivestone and Whirl Rks and eddy S of Longstone during NW tidal streams. Lights Black Rock Point Oc(2) WRG 15s 12m 17/13M; G122°−165°, W165°−175°, R175°−191°, W191°−238°, R238°−275°, W275°−289°, G289°−300°. Farne Is Lt Ho at SW Pt LFl(2) WR 15s 27m 13/9M; W round Tr; R119°−277°, W277°−119°. Longstone Fl 20s 23m 29M, R Tr with W band, RC, Siren (2) 60s. It is a beautiful area with no facilities, and should only be attempted in good weather.

HOLY ISLAND, Northumberland, 55°40′·00N, 01°47′·00W, Zone 0 (GMT), Admty charts 1612, 111. HW +0344 on Dover, −0058 on River Tees Ent.; HW height −0·7m on River Tees Ent; ML 2·6m; Duration 0630. See 10.5.18. Shelter is complete in The Ooze (or Ouse) aground on soft mud; anchorage good just to E of St Cuthbert's I to the S of The Heugh except in W winds. Beware Plough Rks and the rocks all round them. Keep to Ldg Line 260° with Old Law Bns in line until church and Bn come in line at 310° which leads in to the anchorage S of The Heugh. There are no lights. Facilities: FW from tap on village green; P and D at Beal (5 miles); limited provisions in village. Hr Mr ☎ Holy Island 207 or 217. Note Lindisfarne is the ancient name for Holy Island; it is linked to the mainland by a causeway which is covered at HW.

Area 6

South-East Scotland
Eyemouth to Peterhead

10-6-2

South-East Scotland

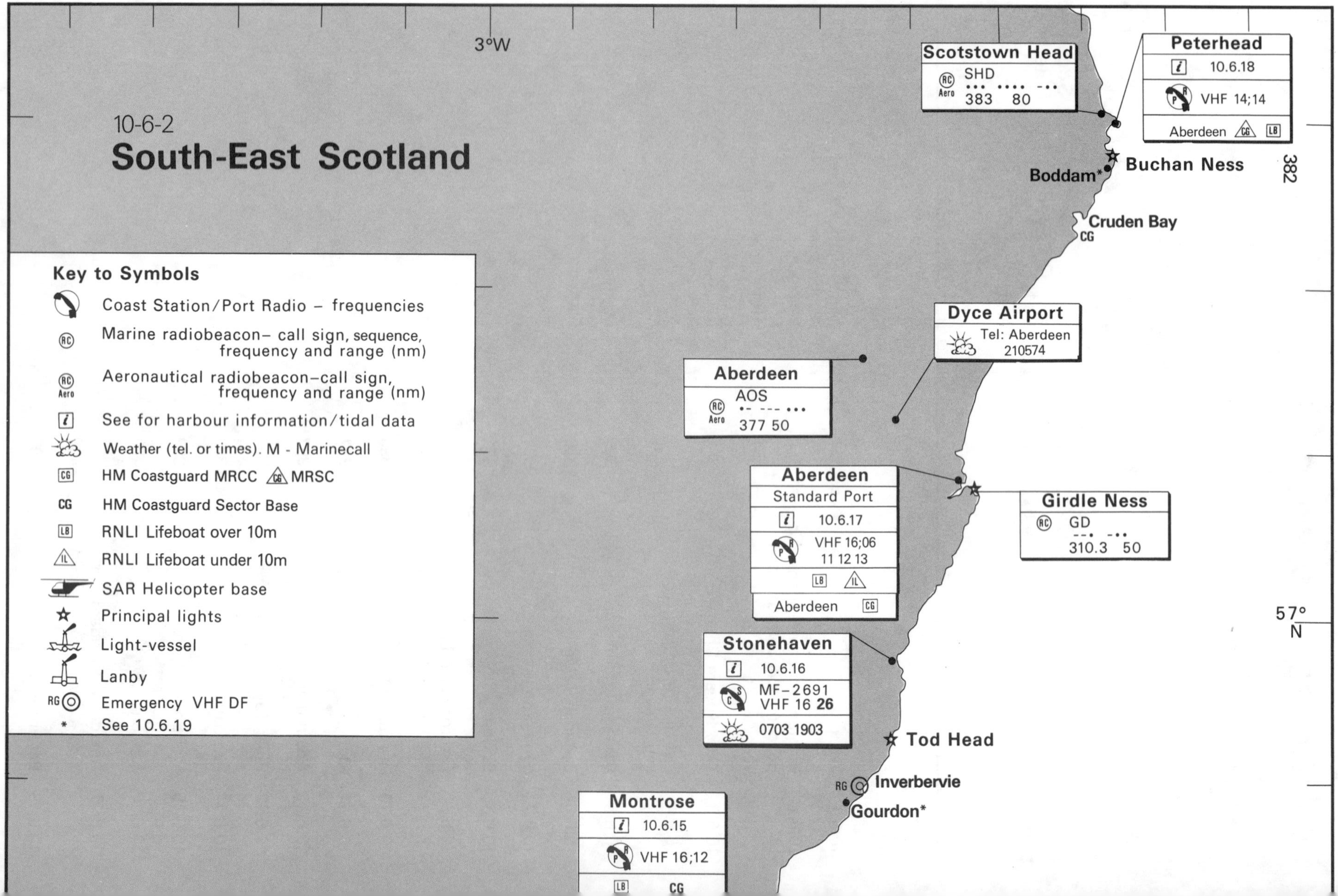

3°W
57° N
382
Key to Symbols
Coast Station/Port Radio – frequencies
Marine radiobeacon– call sign, sequence, frequency and range (nm)
Aeronautical radiobeacon–call sign, frequency and range (nm)
See for harbour information/tidal data
Weather (tel. or times). M - Marinecall
HM Coastguard MRCC MRSC
HM Coastguard Sector Base
RNLI Lifeboat over 10m
RNLI Lifeboat under 10m
SAR Helicopter base
Principal lights
Light-vessel
Lanby
Emergency VHF DF
See 10.6.19
Scotstown Head
SHD
383 80
Peterhead
10.6.18
VHF 14;14
Aberdeen
Buchan Ness
Boddam*
Cruden Bay
CG
Dyce Airport
Tel: Aberdeen 210574
Aberdeen
AOS
377 50
Aberdeen
Standard Port
10.6.17
VHF 16;06
11 12 13
Aberdeen
Girdle Ness
GD
310.3 50
Stonehaven
10.6.16
MF–2691
VHF 16 26
0703 1903
Tod Head
Inverbervie
Gourdon*
Montrose
10.6.15
VHF 16;12
CG

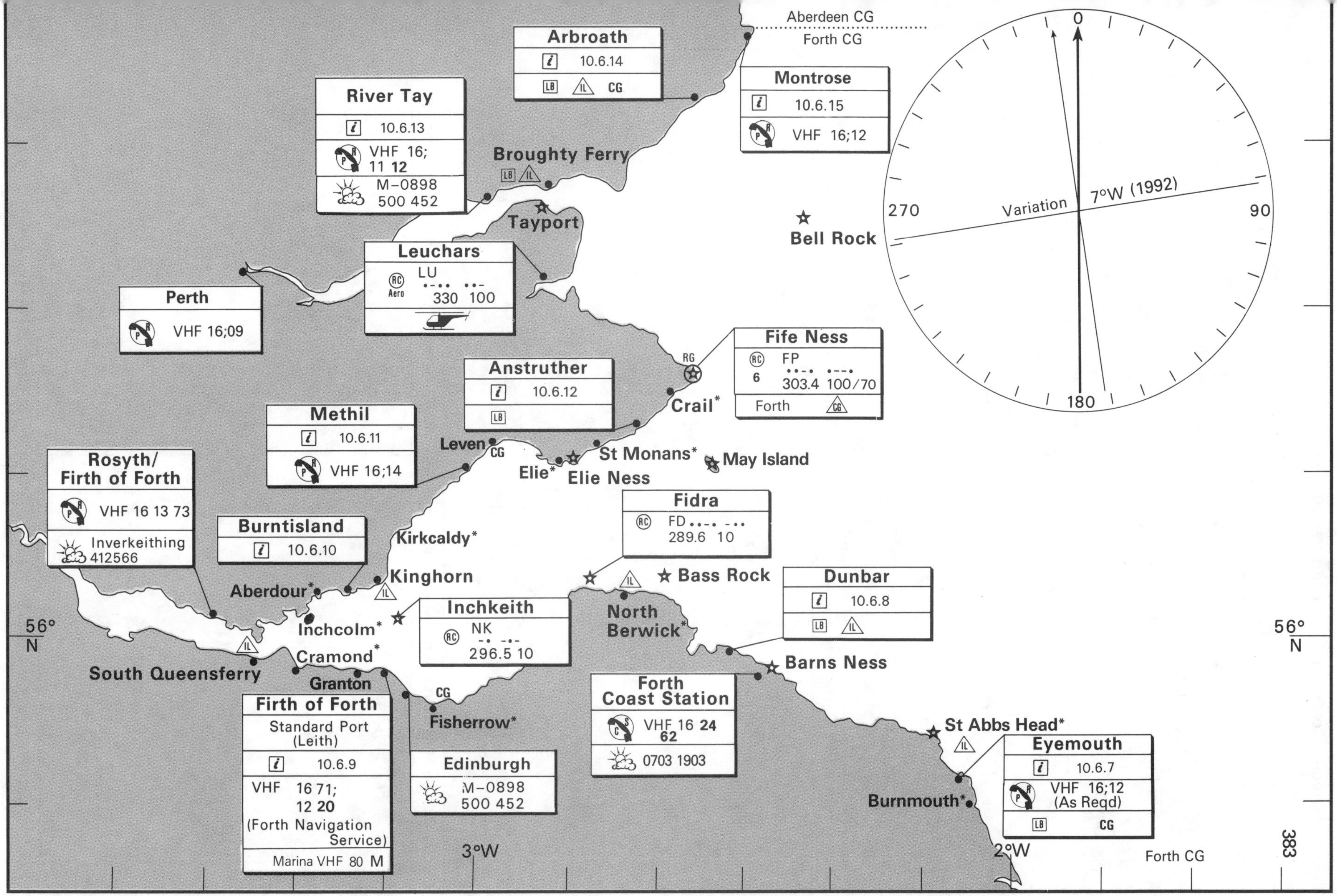
Aberdeen CG
Forth CG
Arbroath
10.6.14
LB IL CG
Montrose
10.6.15
VHF 16;12
River Tay
10.6.13
VHF 16; 11 12
M-0898 500 452
Broughty Ferry
LB IL
Tayport
Leuchars
RC Aero
LU
330 100
Perth
VHF 16;09
Bell Rock
270
90
0
180
Variation
7°W (1992)
Fife Ness
RG
RC FP
6 303.4 100/70
Forth CG
Anstruther
10.6.12
LB
Crail*
Methil
10.6.11
VHF 16;14
Leven
CG
Elie*
Elie Ness
St Monans*
May Island
Rosyth/
Firth of Forth
VHF 16 13 73
Inverkeithing 412566
Burntisland
10.6.10
Kirkcaldy*
Fidra
RC FD
289.6 10
Bass Rock
Dunbar
10.6.8
LB IL
Kinghorn
IL
Aberdour*
Inchkeith
RC NK
296.5 10
North Berwick*
Inchcolm*
56° N
Cramond*
South Queensferry
Granton
Barns Ness
Forth Coast Station
VHF 16 24 62
0703 1903
Firth of Forth
Standard Port (Leith)
10.6.9
VHF 16 71; 12 20
(Forth Navigation Service)
Marina VHF 80 M
CG
Fisherrow*
Edinburgh
M-0898 500 452
St Abbs Head*
IL
Eyemouth
10.6.7
VHF 16;12 (As Reqd)
LB CG
Burnmouth*
3°W
2°W
Forth CG

10.6.3 AREA 6 TIDAL STREAMS

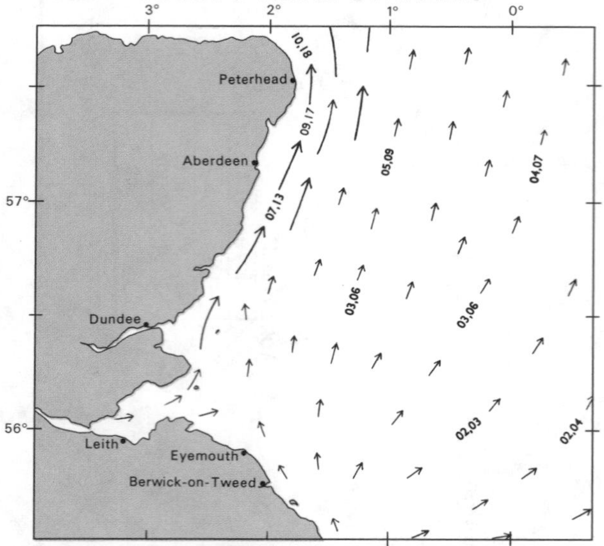
3°
2°
1°
0°
57°
56°
Peterhead
Aberdeen
Dundee
Leith
Eyemouth
Berwick-on-Tweed
10,18
09,17
07,13
05,09
04,07
03,06
03,06
02,03
02,04

5 Hours before HW Dover (0340 after HW Leith)

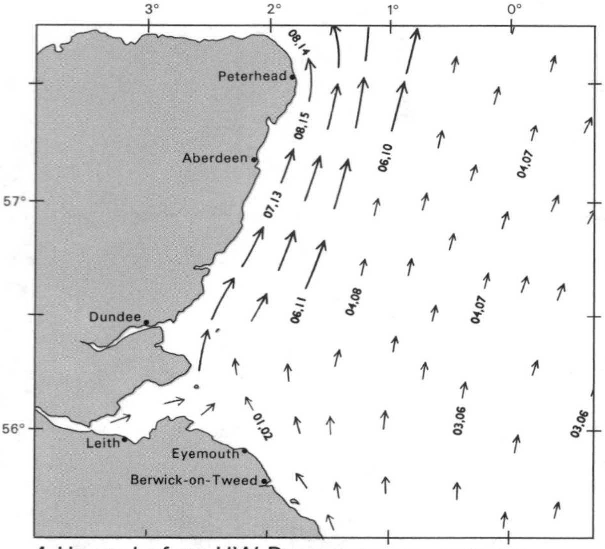
3°
2°
1°
0°
57°
56°
Peterhead
Aberdeen
Dundee
Leith
Eyemouth
Berwick-on-Tweed
08,14
08,15
07,13
06,10
04,07
06,11
04,08
04,07
01,02
03,06
03,06

4 Hours before HW Dover (0440 after HW Leith)

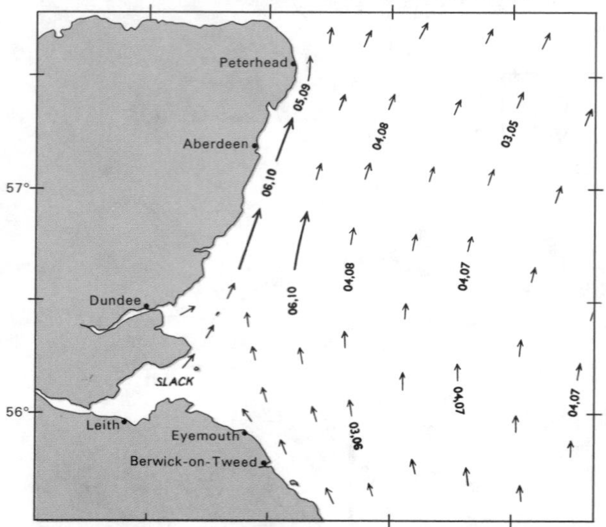
57°
56°
Peterhead
Aberdeen
Dundee
Leith
Eyemouth
Berwick-on-Tweed
SLACK
05,09
04,08
03,05
06,10
06,10
04,08
04,07
04,07
03,06
04,07

3 Hours before HW Dover (0540 after HW Leith)

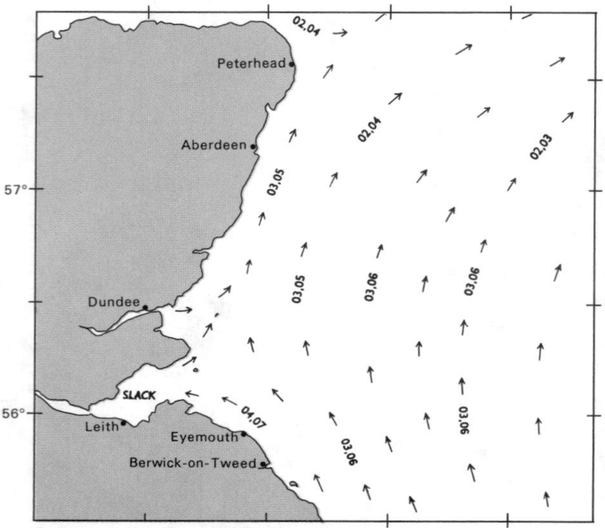
57°
56°
Peterhead
Aberdeen
Dundee
Leith
Eyemouth
Berwick-on-Tweed
SLACK
02,04
02,04
02,03
03,05
03,05
03,06
03,06
04,07
03,06
03,06

2 Hours before HW Dover (0545 before HW Leith)

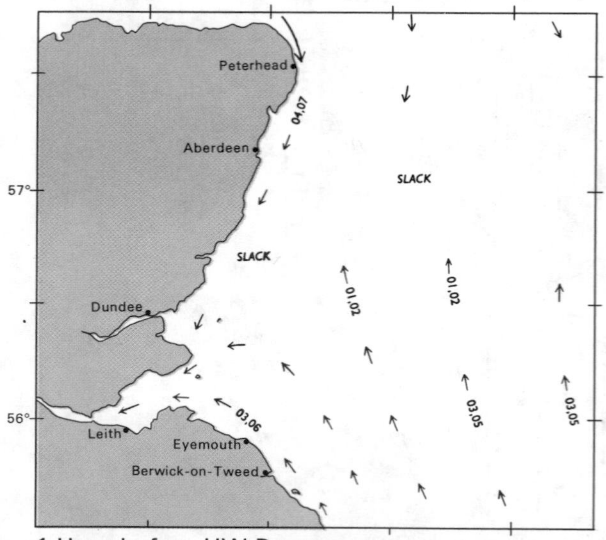
57°
56°
Peterhead
Aberdeen
Dundee
Leith
Eyemouth
Berwick-on-Tweed
SLACK
SLACK
04,07
01,02
01,02
03,06
03,05
03,05

1 Hour before HW Dover (0445 before HW Leith)

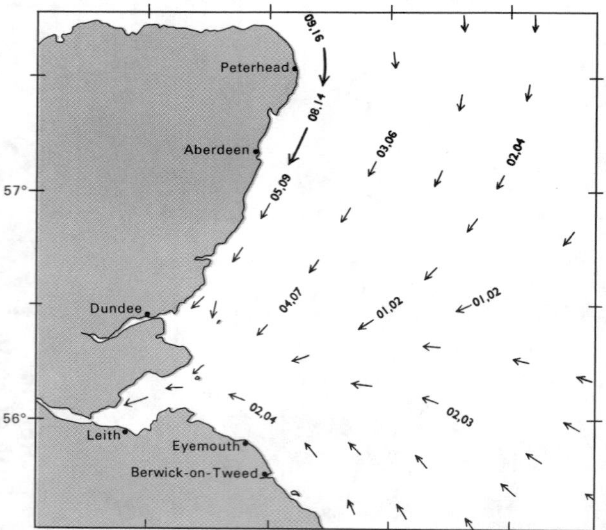
57°
56°
Peterhead
Aberdeen
Dundee
Leith
Eyemouth
Berwick-on-Tweed
09,16
08,14
05,09
03,06
02,04
04,07
01,02
01,02
02,04
02,03

HW Dover (0345 before HW Leith)

Northward 10.7.3 Southward 10.5.3

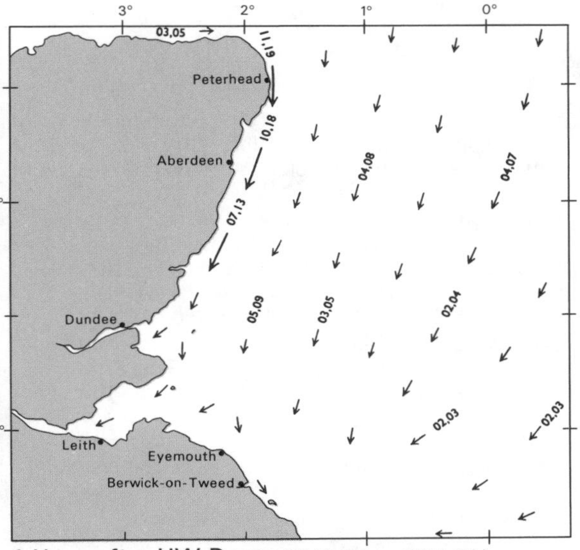
3°
2°
1°
0°
57°
56°
03,05
11,19
Peterhead
10,18
Aberdeen
04,08
04,07
07,13
Dundee
05,09
03,05
02,04
Leith
Eyemouth
Berwick-on-Tweed
02,03
02,03

1 Hour after HW Dover (0245 before HW Leith)

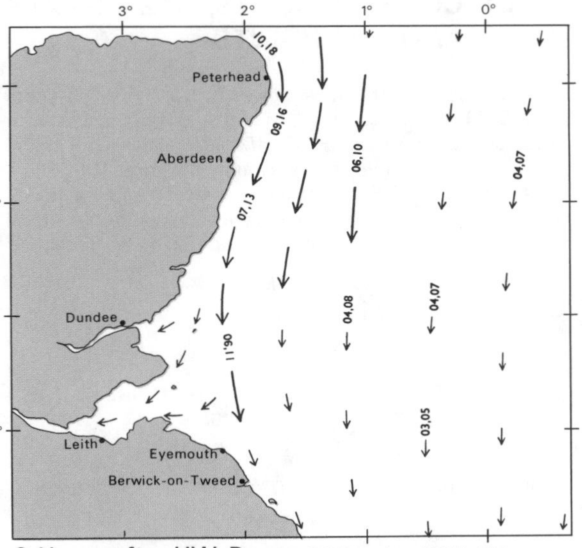
3°
2°
1°
0°
57°
56°
10,18
Peterhead
09,16
Aberdeen
06,10
04,07
07,13
Dundee
04,08
04,07
11,06
Leith
Eyemouth
Berwick-on-Tweed
03,05

2 Hours after HW Dover (0145 before HW Leith)

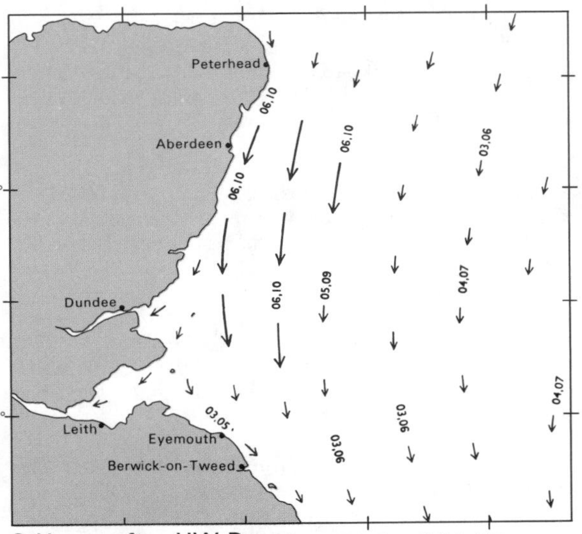
57°
56°
Peterhead
06,10
Aberdeen
06,10
03,06
06,10
Dundee
06,10
05,09
04,07
Leith
Eyemouth
Berwick-on-Tweed
03,05
03,06
03,06
04,07

3 Hours after HW Dover (0045 before HW Leith)

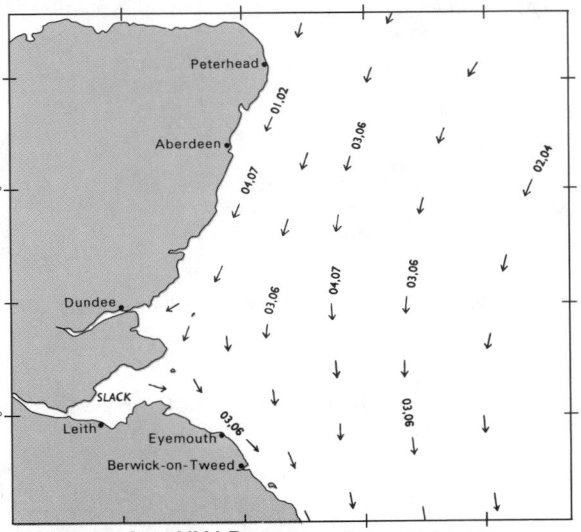
57°
56°
Peterhead
01,02
Aberdeen
03,06
02,04
04,07
Dundee
03,06
04,07
03,06
SLACK
Leith
Eyemouth
Berwick-on-Tweed
03,06
03,06

4 Hours after HW Dover (0015 after HW Leith)

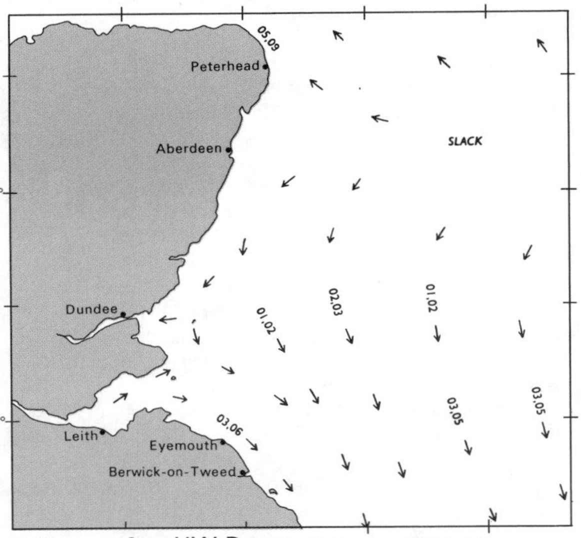
57°
56°
05,09
Peterhead
Aberdeen
SLACK
Dundee
01,02
02,03
01,02
Leith
Eyemouth
Berwick-on-Tweed
03,06
03,05
03,05

5 Hours after HW Dover (0115 after HW Leith)

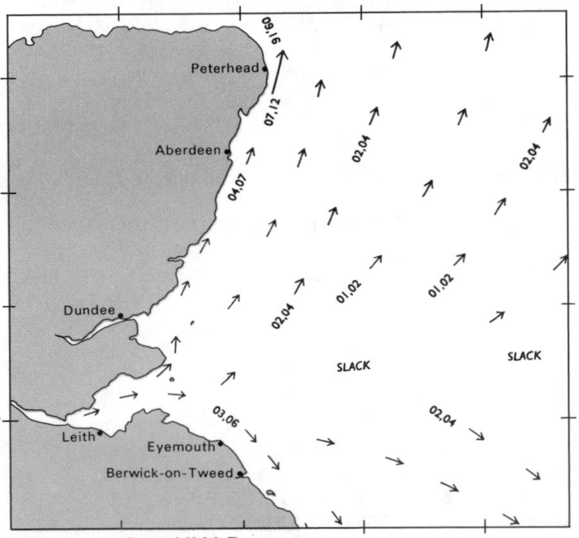
57°
56°
09,16
Peterhead
07,12
Aberdeen
02,04
02,04
04,07
Dundee
02,04
01,02
01,02
SLACK
SLACK
Leith
Eyemouth
Berwick-on-Tweed
03,06
02,04

6 Hours after HW Dover (0215 after HW Leith)

10.6.4 COASTAL LIGHTS, FOG SIGNALS AND WAYPOINTS

Abbreviations used below are given in 1.4.1. Principal lights are in **bold** print, places in CAPITALS, and light-vessels, light floats and Lanbys in *CAPITAL ITALICS*. Unless otherwise stated lights are white. m—elevation in metres; M—nominal range in n. miles. Fog signals are in *italics*. Useful waypoints are underlined – use those on land with care. All geographical positions should be assumed to be approximate. See 4.2.2.

SCOTLAND—SOUTH-EAST COAST

BURNMOUTH.
Ldg Lts. Front 55°50'·6N 02°04'·1W FR 29m 4M. Rear 45m from front FR 35m 4M. Both on W posts.

EYEMOUTH.
E Breakwater Hd 55°52'·51N 02°05'·18W Iso R 2s 8m 8M; *Siren 30s* (TD).

ST ABB'S.
St Abb's Hd 55°54'·97N 02°08'·20W Fl 10s 68m **29M**; W Tr; Racon.
Torness Power Station Pier Hd Fl R 5s 10m 5M.
Barns Ness 55°59'·2N 02°26'·6W Iso W 4s 30s 36m 10M; W ● Tr.

DUNBAR.
Bayswell Hill Ldg Lts 198°. Front Oc G 6s 15m 3M; W ▲ on Or col; intens 188°-208°. Rear Oc G 6s 22m 3M; ▼ on Or Col; synchronised with front, intens 188°-208°.
Victoria Hbr, middle quay, QR 6m 3M; vis through cliffs at hbr ent.
Bass Rock, S side, 56°04'·60N 02°38'·37W Fl(3) 20s 46m 10M; W Tr; vis 241°-107°.

NORTH BERWICK.
N Pier Hd 56°03'·73N 02°42'·92W F WR 7m 3M; vis R seaward, W over hbr. Not lit if ent closed by weather.

FIRTH OF FORTH, SOUTH SHORE.
Fidra, near summit 56°04'·40N 02°47'·00W Fl (4) 30s 34m **24M**; W Tr; RC; obsc by Bass Rk, Craig Leith and Lamb Is.
Wreck Lt By 56°04'·40N 02°52'·30W Fl (2) R 10s; PHM.
Port Seton, E Pier Hd, Iso WR 4s 10m W9M, R6M; R shore-105°, W105°-225°, R225°-shore; *Bell (occas)*.
Cockenzie Power Station, jetty Hd QR 6m 1M.
Fisherrow, E Pier Hd Oc W 6s 5m 6M; framework Tr.
South Channel Approach Lt By 56°01'·42N 03°02'·14W L Fl 10s; SWM.
Narrow Deep Lt By 56°01'·48N 03°04'·51W Fl (2) R 10s; PHM.
Herwit Lt By 56°01'·05N 03°06'·43W Fl (3) G 10s; SHM; *Bell*.
Craigh Waugh Lt By 56°00'·27N 03°04'·38W Q; NCM.
Leith Approach Lt By 55°59'·95N 03°11'·42W Fl R 3s; PHM.
Inchkeith Fairway Lt By 56°03'·50N 03°00'·00W Iso 2s; SWM; Racon.
No. 1 Lt By 56°03'·23N 03°03'·63W Fl G 9s; SHM.
No. 2 Lt By 56°02'·91N 03°03'·63W Fl R 9s; PHM.
No. 3 Lt By 56°03'·23N 03°06'·00W Fl G 6s; SHM.
No. 4 Lt By 56°02'·91N 03°06'·00W Fl R 6s; PHM.
No. 5 Lt By 56°03'·20N 03°07'·80W Fl G 3s; SHM.
No. 6 Lt By 56°03'·05N 03°08'·35W Fl R 3s; PHM.
No. 8 Lt By 56°02'·95N 03°09'·54W FlR 9s; PHM.
Inchkeith, summit 56°02'·01N 03°08'·09W Fl 15s 67m **22M**; stone Tr; RC.
Stell Pt *Horn 15s*.
Pallas Rock Lt By 56°01'·50N 03°09'·21W VQ (9) 10s; WCM.
East Gunnet Lt By 56°01'·42N 03°12'·29W Q (3) 10s; ECM.
West Gunnet Lt By 56°01'·35N 03°10'·98W Q (9) 15s; WCM.

North Channel (cont).
No. 7 Lt By 56°02'·80N 03°10'·87W QG; *Bell*; Racon.
No. 9 Lt By 56°02'·37N 03°13'·38W Fl G 6s; SHM.
No. 10 Lt By 56°02'·05N 03°13'·30W Fl R 6s; PHM.
No. 11 Lt By 56°02'·08N 03°15'·15W Fl G 3s; SHM.
No. 12 Lt By 56°01'·77N 03°15'·05W Fl R 3s; PHM.
No. 13 Lt By 56°01'·77N 03°16'·94W Fl G 9s; SHM.
No. 14 Lt By 56°01'·52N 03°16'·82W Fl R 9s; PHM.

LEITH.
E Breakwater Hd 55°59'·48N 03°10'·85W Iso R 4s 7m 9M; *Horn (3) 30s*.
W Breakwater Hd LFl G 6s.

GRANTON.
E Pier Hd 55°59'·28N 03°13'·17W Fl R 2s 5m 6M; W ■ Bldg.
W Pier Hd Fl G 2s 5m 7M; W Tr.
Oxcars 56°01'·36N 03°16'·74W Fl (2) WR 7s 16m W13M, R12M; W Tr, R band; vis W072°-087°, R087°-196°, W196°-313°, R313°-072°; Ra refl.

PORT EDGAR.
Dir Lt 244°. W Breakwater Hd 55°59'·85N 03°24'·69W Dir Fl R 4s 4m 8M; W blockhouse; 4 QY mark floating breakwater.
3 x 2 FR (vert) mark N ends of Marina pontoons inside hbr.
Beamer Rock 56°02'·28N 03°24'·66W Fl 3s 6m 9M; W Tr, R top; *Horn 20s*.

FIRTH OF FORTH, NORTH SHORE (INWARD).
Hawkcraig Pt Ldg Lts 292°. Front 56°03'·04N 03°16'·98W Q 12m 14M; W Tr; vis 282°-302°. Rear, 96m from front, Iso 5s 16m 14M; W Tr; vis 282°-302°.
Braefoot Bay Terminal.
Western Jetty. Ldg Lts 247°. **Front** 56°02'·15N 03°18'·63W Fl 3s 6m **15M**; W ▲ on E dolphin; vis 237·2°-257·2°; four dolphins marked by 2 FG (vert). **Rear**, 88m from front, Fl 3s 12m **15M**; W ▼ on appr gangway; vis 237·2°-257·2°; synchronised with front.

Mortimer's Deep.
No. 1 Lt By 56°02'·82N 03°15'·65W QG; SHM.
No. 2 Lt By 56°02'·65N 03°16'·08W QR; PHM.
No. 3 Lt By 56°02'·51N 03°17'·44W Fl (2) G 5s; SHM.
No. 4 Lt By 56°02'·38N 03°17'·35W Fl (2) R 5s; PHM.
No. 5 Lt By 56°02'·37N 03°17'·86W Fl G 4s; SHM.
No. 6 Lt By 56°02'·28N 03°17'·78W Fl R 4s; PHM.
No. 7 Lt By 56°01'·94N 03°18'·92W Fl (2) G 5s; SHM.
No. 8 Lt By 56°02'·10N 03°18'·17W Fl R 2s; PHM.
No. 9 Lt By 56°01'·69N 03°19'·08W QG; SHM.
No. 10 Lt By 56°01'·83N 03°18'·48W Fl (2) R 5s; PHM.
No. 14 Lt By 56°01'·56N 03°18'·96W Q (9) 15s; WCM.
Inchcolm E Pt, 56°01'·73N 03°17'·75W Fl (3) 15s 20m 10M; Gy Tr; part obsc 075°-145°; *Horn (3) 45s*.
Inchcolm S Lts in line 066°. Front, 84m from rear, Q 7m 7M; W Tr; vis 062·5°-082·5°. Common Rear 56°01'·80N 03°18'·13W Iso 5s 11m 7M; W Tr; vis 062°-082°.
N Lts in line 077°. Front, 80m from rear, Q 7m 7M; W Tr; vis 062·5°-082·5°.

Deep Channel
No. 15 Lt By 56°01'·43N 03°18'·70W Fl G 6s; SHM.
No. 16 Lt By 56°00'·75N 03°19'·81W Fl R 3s; PHM.
No. 17 Lt By 56°01'·17N 03°20'·12W Fl G 3s; SHM.
No. 19 Lt By 56°00'·72N 03°22'·40W Fl G 9s; SHM.
Hound Pt Terminal.
NE dolphin 56°00'·37N 03°21'·52W FR 7m 5M; Dn; *Siren (3) 90s.*
Centre Pier 2 Aero FR 47m 5M.
SW dolphin FR 7m 5M, Dn.
Inch Garvie, NW end 56°00'·01N 03°23'·29W L Fl 5s 9m 11M; B ● Bn, W lantern.
N Queensferry. Oc 5s and QR or QG tfc signals.
Forth Rail Bridge. Centres of spans have W Lts and ends of cantilevers R Lts, defining N and S chans.
Forth Road Bridge. N suspension Tr Iso G 4s 7m 6M on E and W sides; 2 Aero FR 155m 11M and 2 FR 109m 7M on same Tr. Main span, N part QG 50m 6M on E and W sides. Main span, centre Iso 4s 52m 8M on E and W sides. Main span, S part QR 50m 6M on E and W sides. S suspension Tr Iso R 4s 7m 6M on E and W sides; 2 Aero FR 155m and 2 Fr 109m 7M on same Tr.

HM NAVAL BASE, ROSYTH.
Main Chan Dir Lt 323·5°. Bn A 56°01'·19N 03°25'·53W Dir Oc WRG 7m 4M; R ■ on W post with R bands, on B&W diagonal ■ on W Bn; vis G318°-322°, W322°-325°, R325°-328° (H24).
Dir Lt 115°, Bn C Dir Oc WRG 6s 7m 4M; W ▼ on W Bn; vis R110°-114°, W114°-116°, G116°-120°.
Dir Lt 295°, Bn E Dir Oc 6s 11m 4M: vis 293·5°-296·5°.
S Arm Jetty Hd 56°01'·08N 03°26'·48W L Fl (2) WR 12s 5m W9M; R6M; vis W010°-280°, R280°-010°.
Rosyth Main Channel.
Whale Bank No. 2 Lt By 56°00'·70N 03°25'·10W Q (3) 10s; ECM.
No. 3 Lt By 56°00'·87N 03°24'·98W Fl G 5s; SHM.
No. 4 Lt By 56°00'·82N 03°25'·18W Fl R 3s; PHM.
No. 5 Lt By 56°01'·08N 03°25'·80W QG; SHM.
No. 6 Lt By 56°01'·01N 03°25'·94W QR; PHM.
Charlestown. Lts in line. Front 56°02'·2N 03°30'·6W FG 4m 10M; Y ▲ on Y pile; vis 017°-037°; marks line of HP gas main. Rear FG 6m 10M; Y ▼ on Y pile; vis 017°-037°.
Crombie Jetty, downstream dolphin 2 FG (vert) 8m 4M.
Crombie Jetty, upstream dolphin 2 FG (Vert) 8m 4M.
Bo'ness. Carriden outfall 56°01'·3N 03°33'·6W FlY 5s 3M; Y ■ on Y Bn.
Torry 56°02'·5N 03°35'·2W Fl G 10s 5m 7M; G ● structure.
Bo'ness Platform 56°01'·9N 03°36'·1W QR 3m 2M; R pile Bn.

GRANGEMOUTH.
No. 1 pile 56°02'·2N 03°37'·9W Fl (3) R 20s 4m 6M.
No. 2 pile 56°02'·4N 03°38'·8W Fl G 5s 4m 6M; G ■ on pile.
No. 3 pile Fl R 5s 4m 6M.
No. 4 pile Fl G 2s 4m 5M.
No. 5 pile Fl R 2s 4m 5M.
Dock entrance, E jetty *Horn 30s*; docking signals.
Longannet Power Station, intake L Fl G 10s 5m 6M.

KINCARDINE.
Swing bridge 56°03'·9N 03°43'·5W FW at centre of each span; FR Lts mark each side of openings.

BURNTISLAND
W Pier outer Hd 56°03'·2N 03°22'·2W Fl (2) R 6s 7m; W Tr.
E Pier outer Hd Fl (2) G 6s 6m 5M.

KIRKCALDY.
East Pier Hd 56°06'·78N 03°08'·81W Fl WG 10s 12m 8M; vis G156°-336°, W336°-156°; S pier Hd 2 FR (vert) 7m 5M.
W Rockheads By 56°07'·00N 03°06'·90W (unlit); SHM.
E Rockheads By 56°07'°15N 03°06'·33W (unlit); SHM.
Kirkcaldy Wreck Lt By 56°07'·26N 03°05'·20W Fl (3) G 18s; SHM.

METHIL.
Outer Pier Hd 56°10'·77N 03°00'·39W Oc G 6s 8m 5M; W Tr; vis 280°-100°.
Elie Ness 56°11'·05N 02°48'·65W Fl 6s 15m **18M**; W Tr.

ST MONANCE.
Breakwater Hd 56°12'·20N 02°45'·80W Oc WRG 6s 5m W7M, R4M, G4M; vis G282°-355°, W355°-026°, R026°-038°.
E Pier Hd 2 FG(vert) 6m 4M; Or tripod; *Bell* (occas).
W Pier near Hd, 2 FR (vert) 6m 4M.

PITTENWEEM.
Ldg Lts 037° Middle Pier Hd. Front FR 4m 5M. Rear FR 8m 5M. Both Gy Cols, Or stripes.
E Pier Hd extn 56°12'·68N 02°43'·53W Oc G 6s 5m 5M.
Beacon Rock QR 3m 2M.
W Pier, Elbow, *Horn 90s (occas)*.

ANSTRUTHER.
W Pier Hd 2 FR (vert) 5m 4M; Gy mast; *Reed (3) 60s (occas)*.
E Pier Hd 56°13'·15N 02°41'·72W Fl G 3s 6m 4M; R col.

Isle of May, Summit. 56°11'·13N 02°33'·30W Fl (2) 15s 73m **22M**; ■ Tr on stone dwelling.

CRAIL.
Ldg Lts 295°. Front FR 24m 6M (not lit when hbr closed). Rear 30m from front FR 30m 6M.
Fife Ness 56°16'·73N 02°35'·10W Iso WR 10s 12m **W21M, R20M**; W bldg; vis W143°-197°, R197°-217°, W217°-023°; RC.
N Carr Lt By 56°18'·07N 02°32'·85W Q (3) 10s; ECM.
Bell Rock 56°26'·05N 02°23'·07W Fl 5s 28m **18M**; W ● Tr; Racon.

RIVER TAY.
Tay Fairway Lt By 56°28'·60N 02°37'·15W L Fl 10s; SWM; *Whis.*
Middle Lt By (N) 56°28'·28N 02°38'·84W Fl (3) G 18s; SHM.
Middle Lt By (S) 56°28'·00N 02°38'·59W Fl (2) R 12s; PHM.
Abertay Lt By 56°27'·41N 02°40'·66W Q (3) 10s; ECM; Racon.
Abertay (Elbow) Lt By 56°27'·15N 02°40'·70W Fl R 6s; PHM.
Inner Lt Buoy 56°27'·10N 02°44'·23W Fl (2) R 12s; PHM.
N Lady Lt By 56°27'·36N 02°46'·80W Fl (3) G 18s; SHM.
S Lady Lt By 56°27'·20N 02°46'·76W Fl (3) R 18s; PHM.
Pool Lt By 56°27'·15N 02°48'·50W Fl R 6s; PHM.
Horse Shoe Lt By 56°27'·28N 02°50'·11W VQ (6) + LFl 10s; SCM.
Scalp Lt By 56°27'·18N 02°51'·50W Fl (2) R 12s; PHM; *Bell.*
Newcombe Shoal Lt By 56°27'·73N 02°53'·50W Fl R 6s; PHM.
E Deep Lt By 56°27'·45N 02°55'·65W QR; PHM.
Middle Bank Lt By 56°27'·40N 02°56'·39W Q (3) 10s; ECM.
Tentsmuir Pt 56°26'·6N 02°49'·5W Fl Y 5s; Y Bn; vis 198°-208°; marks gas pipeline.

6

Monifieth 56°28'·9N 02°47'·8W Fl Y 5s; Y Bn; vis 018°-028°; marks gas pipeline.
Broughty Castle 56°27'·76N 02°52'·10W 2 FG (vert) 10m 4M; Gy col; FR is shown at foot of old Lt Ho at Buddon Ness, 4M to E, and at other places on firing range when practice is taking place.

TAYPORT.
High Lt Ho Dir Lt 269°, 56°27'·17N 02°53'·85W Dir Iso WRG 3s 24m **W22M**, **R17M**, **G16M**; W Tr; vis G267°-268°, W268°-270°, R270°-271°.

ARBROATH.
Outfall Lt By 56°32'·66N 02°34'·96W Fl Y 3s; SPM.
Ldg Lts 299·2°. Front FR 7m 5M; W col. Rear, 50m from front, FR 13m 5M; W col.
W Breakwater E end, VQ (2) 6s 6m 4M; W post.
E Pier S elbow 56°33'·26N 02°34'·89W Fl G 3s 8m 5M; W Tr; shows FR when hbr closed; *Siren (3) 60s (occas)*.
Scurdie Ness 56°42'·12N 02°26'·15W Fl (3) 20s 38m **23M**; W Tr; Racon.

MONTROSE.
Scurdie Rocks Lt By 56°42'·15N 02°25'·42W QR; PHM.
Annat Lt By 56°42'·38N 02°25'·53W Fl G 3s; SHM.
Annat Shoal Lt By 56°42'·38N 02°25'·50W QG; SHM.
Ldg Lts 271·5°. Front FR 11m 5M; W twin pillars, R bands. Rear, 272m from front, FR 18m 5M; W Tr, R cupola.

JOHNSHAVEN.
Ldg Lts 316°. Front FR 5m; R structure. Rear, 85m from front, FG 20m; shows R when unsafe to enter hbr.

GOURDON HARBOUR.
Ldg Lts 358°. Front 56°49'·6N 02°17'·1W FR 5m 5M; W Tr; shows G when unsafe to enter; *Siren (2) 60s (occas)*. Rear 120m from front FR 30m 5M; W Tr.
W Pier Hd Fl WRG 3s 5m W9M, R7M, G7M; vis G180°-344°, W344°-354°, R354°-180°.
E breakwater Hd Q 3m 7M.

Tod Head 56°53'·0N 02°12'·8W Fl (4) 30s 41m **29M**; W Tr.

STONEHAVEN.
Outer Pier Hd 56°57'·59N 02°11'·89W Iso WRG 4s 7m W11M, R7M, G8M; vis G214°-246°, W246°-268°, R268°-280°.
Inner harbour Ldg Lts 273°. Front F 6m 5M. Rear 10m from front FR 8m 5M.

Girdle Ness 57°08'·35N 02°02'·82W Fl (2) 20s 56m **22M**; W ● Tr; obsc by Greg Ness when bearing more than about 020°; RC; Racon.

ABERDEEN.
Fairway Lt By 57°09'·33N 02°01'·85W L Fl 10s; SWM; Racon.
Torry. Ldg Lts 235·7°. Front FR or G 14m 5M; W Tr; R when ent safe, FG when dangerous to navigation; vis 195°-279°. Rear 205m from front FR 19m 5M; W Tr; vis 195°-279°.
S Breakwater Hd Fl (3) R 8s 23m 7M; W Tr.
N Pier Hd Oc WR 6s 11m 9M; W Tr; vis W145°-055°, R055°-145°. In fog FY 10m (same Tr) vis 136°-336°; *Bell (3) 12s*.
Old S Breakwater QR 3m 2M; ■ on R col.
Abercromby Jetty Hd Oc G 4s 5m 4M; ▲ on G col; vis 230°-080°.
S Jetty Hd, QR 5m 4M; ■ on R col; vis 063°-243°.

Buchan Ness 57°28'·23N 01°46'·37W Fl 5s 40m **28M**; W Tr, R bands; Racon; *Horn (3) 60s*.

PETERHEAD.
Kirktown Ldg Lts 314°. Front 57°30'·2N 01°47'·1W FR 13m 8M; R mast, W ▲ on Or mast. Rear 91m from front FR 17m 8M; W ▼ on Or mast.
S Breakwater Hd Fl (2) R 12s 24m 7M; W ●Tr with B base.
N Breakwater Hd 57°29'·85N 01°46'·22W Iso RG 6s 19m 11M; W tripod; vis R165°-230°, G230°-165°; *Horn 30s*.

Rattray Hd. Ron Rock. 57°36'·6N 01°48'·9W Fl(3) 30s 28m **24M**; W Tr; Racon; *Horn (2) 45s*.

10.6.5 PASSAGE INFORMATION

Throughout this area reference should be made to *North Sea (West) Pilot* and *Sailing Directions Humber Estuary to Rattray Head* (R Northumberland YC). For the Firth of Forth, refer to the *Forth Yacht Clubs Association Pilot Handbook*, which also covers the coast from Berwick to Fraserburgh.

BERWICK-UPON-TWEED TO BASS ROCK (charts 160,175)

From Berwick-upon-Tweed to the Firth of Forth there is no good hbr which can be approached with safety in strong onshore winds. So, if on passage with strong winds from N or E, it is advisable to keep well to seaward.

The coast N from Berwick is rky with cliffs rising in height to Burnmouth. Keep 0·5M offshore to avoid outlying rks. Burnmouth has more alongside berths than Eyemouth, which is a busy fishing hbr. N of Burnmouth the cliffs fall gradually to Eyemouth B (10.6.7),

Close S of St Abb's Hd is St Abb's hbr (10.6.19): the inner hbr dries, but outer hbr has depth of 2m in places. Do not approach in strong onshore wind or sea, and beware rky ledges close each side of Ldg line. Temp anch in offshore winds in Coldingham B.

St Abb's Hd (Lt) is a bold, steep headland, 92m high, with no offlying dangers. The stream runs strongly round the Hd, causing turbulence with wind against tide; this can be largely avoided by keeping well inshore. The ESE-going stream begins at HW Leith –0345, and the WNW-going at HW Leith +0240. There is a good anch in Pettico Wick, on NW side of Hd, in S winds, but dangerous if the wind shifts onshore. There are no off-lying dangers between St Abb's Hd and Fast Castle Hd, 3M WNW. Between Fast Castle Hd and Barns Ness, about 8M NW, is the attractive little hbr of Cove, which however dries and should only be approached in very good conditions.

Barns Ness (Lt) lies 2·5M ESE of Dunbar (10.6.8) and is fringed with rks: tidal streams as for St Abb's Hd. A conspic chy is 0·75M WSW of Barns Ness, and Torness Power Station (conspic) is 1·75M SE of Barns Ness. Between here and Dunbar keep at least 0·25M offshore to clear rky patches. Sicar Rk lies about 1·25M ENE of Dunbar, and sea breaks on it in onshore gales.

The direct course from Dunbar to Bass Rk (Lt) is clear of all dangers: inshore of this line beware Wildfire Rks (dry) on NW side of Bellhaven B. In offshore winds there is anch in Scoughall Road. Great Car is ledge of rks, nearly covering at HW, 1M ESE of Gin Hd, with Car Bn (stone Tr surmounted by cross) at its N end. Drying ledges of rks extend 1M SE of Great Car, up to 0·3M offshore. Keep at least 0·5M off Car Bn in strong onshore winds. Tantallon Castle (ruins) is on cliff edge 1M W of Great Car. Bass Rk lies 1·25M NNE of Gin Hd, and is a steep, conspic rk with no offlying dangers.

BASS ROCK TO INCHKEITH (chart 734)

Westward of Bass Rk Craigleith, Lamb Is and Fidra lie 0·5M or more offshore, while the coast is generally foul. Craigleith is steep-to, but temporary anchorage can be found on SE and SW sides; if passing inshore of it keep well to N side of Chan. N Berwick hbr (dries) lies S of Craigleith, but is unsafe in onshore winds. Lamb Is is 1·5M WNW of N Berwick (10.6.19) and has a rky ledge extending 0·25M SW. Inshore, between Craigleith and Lamb Is, beware drying rks up to 0·3M from land. Fidra Is (Lt, RC) is a bird reserve, nearly connected to the shore by rky ledges, and should be passed to the N. There are anchorages on E, S or W sides, depending on wind, in good weather.

In the B between Fidra and Edinburgh some shelter can be found in SE winds in Aberlady B and Gosford B. The best anch is SW of Craigielaw Pt. Port Seton is 0·75M E of the conspic chys of Cockenzie Power Station, and the E side of this fishing hbr (dries) can be entered HW–3 to HW+3, but not advisable in strong onshore wind or sea. Cockenzie (dries) is close to power station; beware Corsik Rk 400m to E. Access HW–2·5 to HW+2·5, but no attractions except boatyard. For Fisherrow see 10.6.19.

There are no dangers on the direct course from Fidra to Inchkeith (Lt, RC), which stands in the centre of ent to Leith, Granton (10.6.9), and the higher reaches of Firth of Forth. Rks extend 0·75M SE from Inchkeith, and 0·5M off the SW side. There is a small hbr on W side, below the Lt Ho; landing is forbidden without permission. N Craig and Craig Waugh (least depth 0·6m) are shallow patches 2·5M SE from Inchkeith Lt Ho, and are buoyed. The deep water chans N and S of Inchkeith are buoyed. In N chan, close to Inchkeith the W-going (flood) stream begins about HW Leith –0530, and the E-going at HW Leith +0030, sp rates about 1 kn. The streams gather strength towards the Forth bridges, where they reach 2·25kn and there may be turbulence. For Cramond and Inchcolm see 10.6.19.

INCHKEITH TO FIFE NESS (charts 734, 190)

From Burntisland (10.6.10) the N shore of Firth of Forth leads E to Kinghorn Ness. 1M SSW of Kinghorn Ness Blae Rk (buoyed) has least depth of 4·6m, but the sea breaks on it in E gales. Rost Bank lies halfway between Kinghorn Ness and Inchkeith, with tide rips at sp tides or in strong winds.

Between Kinghorn Ness and Kirkcaldy, drying rks lie up to 0·3M offshore. Kirkcaldy hbr (10.6.19) is primarily commercial but by arrangement yachts can enter inner dock near HW. The ent is dangerous in strong E winds, when the sea breaks a long way out.

Between Kirkcaldy and Methil (10.6.11) the only dangers more than 0·2M offshore are The Rockheads, extending 0·4M SE of Dysart, and marked by Bys. Largo B provides anch near E side, well sheltered from N and E. Off Chapel Ness beware W Vows (dries) and E Vows (dries, marked by refuge Bn). There is anch close W of Elie Ness (10.6.19). Ox Rk (dries) lies 0·5M ENE of Elie Ness, and 0·25M offshore: otherwise there are no dangers more than 0·2M offshore past St Monans (10.6.19), Pittenweem and Anstruther (10.6.12), but in bad weather the sea breaks on Shield Rk 0·4M off Pittenweem. From Ansthruther to Crail (10.16.9) and on to Fife Ness keep 0·3M offshore to clear Caiplie Rk and other dangers.

May Is (Lt, RC) (10.6.19) lies about 5M S of Fife Ness: its shores are bold except at NW end where rks extend 0·1M off. In good weather it is possible to land. Anch on W side, near N end, in E winds; or on E side, near N end, in W winds. Lt Ho boats use Kirkhaven, close SE of Lt Ho.

FIFE NESS TO MONTROSE (chart 190)

Northward from Firth of Forth to Rattray Hd the coast is mostly rky and steep-to, and there are no out-lying dangers within 2M of the coast except those off R. Tay, and Bell Rk.

Fife Ness is fringed by rky ledges, and a reef extends 1M NE to N Carr Rk (dries, marked by Bn). In strong onshore winds keep to seaward of N Carr Lt By. From here keep 0·5M offshore to clear dangers entering St Andrews B, where there is anch: the little hbr dries, and should not be approached in onshore winds.

R. Tay (10.6.13) ent is between Tentsmuir Pt and Buddon Ness (chart 1481), and has many sandbanks which are liable to shift. Abertay Sands extend nearly 4M E of Tentsmuir Pt on S side of chan (buoyed), and Gaa Sands run 1·75M E from

Buddon Ness. Passage across Abertay and Gaa Sands is very dangerous. Abertay Lt By (Racon) is on N side of chan 1·75M ESE of Buddon Ness. Elbow is an extension of Abertay Sands, to S and SE of Lt By. The Bar, NE of Abertay Lt By, is dangerous in heavy weather, particularly in strong onshore wind or swell. S of Buddon Ness the W-going (flood) stream begins about HW Aberdeen –0400, and the E-going at about HW Aberdeen +0230, sp rates 2 kn.

Bell Rk (Lt, Racon) lies about 11·5M E of Buddon Ness. 2M E of Bell Rk the S-going stream begins HW Aberdeen –0220, and the N-going at HW Aberdeen +0405, sp rates 1 kn. W of Bell Rk the streams begin earlier.

N from Buddon Ness the coast is sandy. 1·25M SW of Arbroath (10.6.14) beware Elliot Houses, rky patches with depth 1·8m, which extend about 0·5M offshore. Between Whiting Ness and Scurdie Ness, 9·5M NNE, the coast is clear of out-lying dangers, but is mostly fringed with drying rks up to 0·1M off. In offshore winds there is anch in Lunan B, off Ethie Haven.

Scurdie Ness (Lt, Racon) stands on S side of ent to Montrose (10.6.15). Scurdie Rks (dry) extend 0·2M E of the Ness. On N side of chan Annat Bank dries up to about 0·5M E of the shore, opposite Scurdie Ness (chart 1438). The in-going stream begins at HW Aberdeen –0500, and the outgoing at HW Aberdeen +0115; both streams are very strong, up to 7 kn at sp, and there is turbulence off the ent on the ebb. The ent is dangerous in strong onshore winds, with breaking seas extending to Scurdie Ness on the ebb. In marginal conditions the last quarter of the flood is best time to enter.

MONTROSE TO RATTRAY HEAD (charts 210, 213)

N from Montrose the coast is sandy for 5M to Milton Ness, where there is anch on S side in N winds. Johnshaven, 2·25M SW of Gourdon, is a small hbr (dries), which should not be approached with onshore wind or swell. 0·5M NE, off Brotherton Cas, drying rks extend 0·4M offshore. Gourdon (10.6.19) has a small hbr (mostly dries) approached by winding chan marked by Bns: inner hbr has storm gates. Outside Gourdon hbr rks extend 0·75M S of entrance, and the sea breaks heavily in strong E winds.

N to Inverbervie the coast is fringed with rky ledges up to 0·2M offshore. Just N of Tod Hd (Lt) is Catterline, a small B which forms a natural anch in W winds, but open to E. Downie Pt lies close SE of Stonehaven (10.6.16). The B has a sandy bottom, but is encumbered by rky ledges up to 0·2M from shore. Anch 0·6M E of Bay Hotel. In E gales the B is dangerous, and sea breaks well outside hbr ent.

From Garron Pt to Girdle Ness the coast is mostly steep-to. Fishing nets may be met off headlands during fishing season. Craigmaroinn and Seal Craig (dry) are parts of reef 0·3M offshore SE of Portlethen, a fishing village with landing sheltered by rks. Cove B has a very small fishing hbr, off which there is anch in good weather: Cove Rks (dry) lie 0·15M offshore. From Cove to Girdle Ness keep 0·5M offshore, avoiding The Hasman, a rk which dries 0·1M off Altens village.

Greg Ness and Girdle Ness (Lt, RC, Racon) are fringed by rks. Girdlestone is a rky patch, depth less than 2m, 0·2M ENE of Lt Ho. A drying patch lies 0·2M SE of Lt Ho. Off Girdle Ness the S-going stream begins at HW Aberdeen –0430, and the N-going at HW Aberdeen +0130, sp rates 2·5kn. A race forms on S-going stream. Girdle Ness lies at SE corner of Aberdeen B (10.6.17).

From Aberdeen there are few offshore dangers to Buchan Ness. R. Ythan, 1·75M SSW of Hackley Hd, is navigable by small craft, but chan shifts constantly. 3M N is the very small hbr of Collieston (mostly dries), only accessible in fine weather. 4·75M NNE of Hackley Hd lie The Skares, rks (marked by By) extending 0·35M from S point of Cruden B – where there is anch in offshore winds. On N side of Cruden B is Port Erroll (dries).

Buchan Ness (Lt, fog sig, Racon) is a rky peninsula. 0·2M N is the Is Meikle Mackie, close W of which is the small hbr of Boddam (dries) (10.6.19). 0·3M NE of Meikle Mackie is The Skerry, a rk 6m high on S side of Sandford B; rks on which the sea breaks extend 0·2M NNE. There is a chan between The Skerry and the coast, which can be used when making for Peterhead (10.6.18).

Rattray Hd (Lt, fog sig on Ron Rk, 0·3M E of Hd) has rky foreshore, drying for 0·2M Rattray Briggs is a detached reef, depth 0·6m, 0·2M E of Lt Ho. Rattray Hard is a rky patch, depth 0·2m, 1·5M ENE of Lt Ho, which raises a dangerous sea during strong onshore winds. Off Rattray Hd the S-going stream begins at HW Aberdeen –0420, and the N-going at HW Aberdeen +0110, sp rates 3 kn. In normal conditions keep about 1M E of Rattray Hd, but in bad weather pass 5M off, preferably at slack water. Conspic radio masts with R Lts lie 2·5M WNW and 2·2M W of Lt Ho.

For notes on offshore oil and gas installations, see 10.5.5.

10.6.6 DISTANCE TABLE

Approximate distances in nautical miles are by the most direct route while avoiding dangers and allowing for traffic separation schemes etc. Places in *italics* are in adjoining areas.

	1	2	3	4	5	6	7	8	9	10	11	12	13	14	15	16	17	18	19	20
1 *Brunsbüttel*																				
2 *Flamborough Head*	325																			
3 *Longstone (Farne)*	388	105																		
4 Eyemouth	406	126	21																	
5 St Abbs Head	408	129	24	3																
6 Dunbar	422	143	38	17	14															
7 Granton	449	170	65	44	41	27														
8 Port Edgar	456	177	72	51	48	34	7													
9 Burntisland	448	169	64	43	40	26	5	8												
10 Methil	441	162	57	36	33	20	14	20	12											
11 Anstruther	431	155	50	29	26	14	23	29	22	11										
12 Fife Ness	428	155	50	29	26	17	28	34	27	16	5									
13 Dundee	446	174	69	49	46	37	48	54	47	36	25	20								
14 Arbroath	433	169	64	44	41	34	45	51	44	33	22	17	15							
15 Montrose	433	175	69	51	48	43	55	61	54	43	32	27	27	12						
16 Stonehaven	434	185	82	66	63	60	72	78	71	60	49	44	45	30	20					
17 Aberdeen	436	194	93	78	75	73	84	90	83	72	61	56	57	42	32	13				
18 Peterhead	439	212	112	98	95	93	106	112	105	94	83	78	80	64	54	35	25			
19 *Duncansby Head*	504	292	192	179	176	174	186	192	185	174	163	158	161	145	135	115	105	82		
20 *Lerwick*	514	358	271	256	253	251	264	270	263	252	241	236	238	222	212	193	183	158	110	

6

EYEMOUTH 10-6-7

Berwick

CHARTS
Admiralty 1612, 160; OS 67

TIDES
+0330 Dover; ML No data; Duration 0610; Zone 0 (GMT).

Standard Port LEITH (⟶)

Times				Height (metres)			
HW		LW		MHWS	MHWN	MLWN	MLWS
0300	0900	0300	0900	5·6	4·5	2·1	0·8
1500	2100	1500	2100				
Differences EYEMOUTH							
−0015	−0025	−0014	−0004	−0·9	−0·8	No data	

SHELTER
Good shelter in harbour in all weathers but entry should not be attempted in strong winds from N through NE to E. There are many fishing boats. Yachts limited berth at outer end of E pier in 2m approx. Anchor in bay only in off-shore winds.

NAVIGATION
Waypoint 55°53′·00N 02°05′·28W, 354°/174° from/to E breakwater Lt, 0·50M. Approach can be made N or S of Hurcar Rocks but there are no leading marks to the S. To the N, beware Blind Buss. Entrance and basin dredged to 0·9m.

LIGHTS AND MARKS
Ldg Lts 174° (pillars painted orange) both FG 9/10m 6M on West pier. FR or red flag – unsafe to enter.

RADIO TELEPHONE
VHF Ch 16; 12 (No regular watch).

TELEPHONE (08907)
Hr Mr 50223; MRSC Crail 50666; # Edinburgh 554 2421; Marinecall 0898 500 452; Police 50217; Dr 50599.

FACILITIES
EC Wednesday; **Jetty** Slip, D (By delivery), P (cans), FW, AB; **Fishermans Mutual Assoc.** ☎ 50360 CH, Gas; **Eyemouth BY** ☎ 50231, Slip, BH, ME, El, Sh, C (12 ton mobile); **Collins** ☎ 50308, El; **Eyemouth Marine** ☎ 50594, ME; **Leith & Son** ☎ Berwick 307264 SM; **Ken's Electronics Marine** ☎ 51252 Ⓔ; **Coastal Marine** ☎ 50328 ME, Sh; **The Boat Shop** ☎ 51327 CH; **Town** LB, P, D, CH, V, R, Bar. ✉, ⊡, Gas, Gaz, Ⓑ, ⇌ (bus to Berwick-on-Tweed); ✈ (Edinburgh).
Note:– limited facilities in town on Sundays.

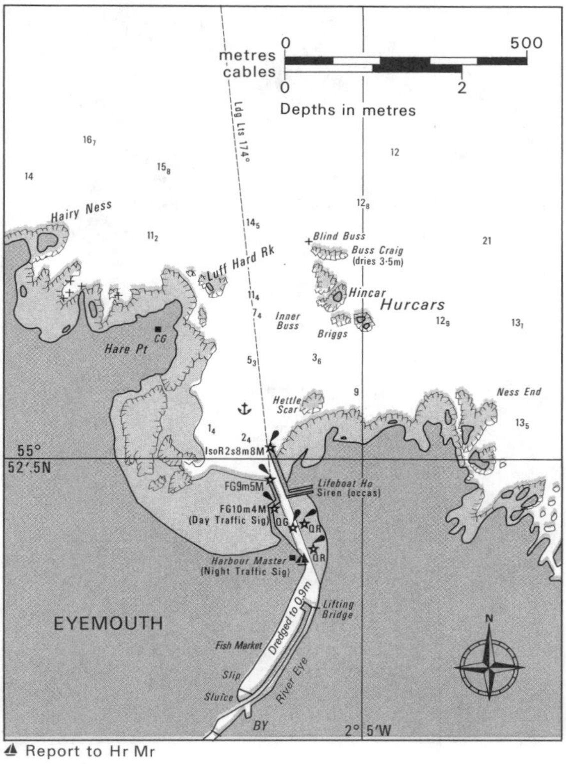

metres
cables
0
500
0
2
Depths in metres
Ldg Lts 174°
Hairy Ness
Luff Hard Rk
Blind Buss
Buss Craig (dries 3·5m)
Hincar
Hurcars
Inner Buss
Briggs
Hare Pt
CG
Hettle Scar
Ness End
55° 52′.5N
IsoR2s8m8M
FG9m5M
FG10m4M (Day Traffic Sig)
Lifeboat Ho Siren (occas)
QG
QR
Harbour Master (Night Traffic Sig)
Lifting Bridge
Dredged to 0·9m
EYEMOUTH
Fish Market
Slip
Sluice
River Eye
BY
2° 5′W
N

▲ Report to Hr Mr

DUNBAR 10-6-8

East Lothian

CHARTS
Admiralty 734, 175; Imray 27; OS 67

TIDES
+0330 Dover; ML 3·1; Duration 0600; Zone 0 (GMT).

Standard Port LEITH (⟶)

Times				Height (metres)			
HW		LW		MHWS	MHWN	MLWN	MLWS
0300	0900	0300	0900	5·6	4·5	2·1	0·8
1500	2100	1500	2100				
Differences DUNBAR							
−0005	−0010	+0010	+0017	−0·4	−0·3	−0·1	−0·1
FIDRA							
−0005	−0005	−0010	−0010	−0·4	−0·1	0·0	−0·2

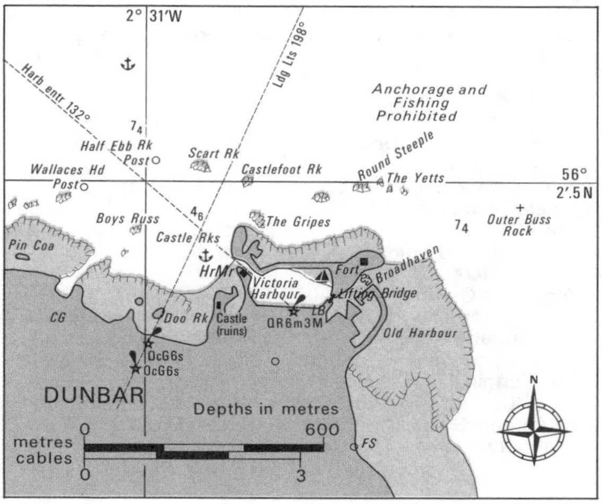

2° 31′W
Ldg Lts 198°
Harb entr 132°
Anchorage and Fishing Prohibited
Half Ebb Rk Post
Scart Rk
Castlefoot Rk
Round Steeple
The Yetts
Wallaces Hd Post
56° 2′.5N
Boys Russ
The Gripes
Outer Buss Rock
Castle Rks
Pin Coa
HrMr
Victoria Harbour
Fort
Broadhaven
Lifting Bridge
CG
Doo Rk
Castle (ruins)
QR6m3M
LB
Old Harbour
OcG6s
OcG6s
DUNBAR
Depths in metres
metres
cables
0
600
0
3
FS
N

SHELTER
Outer (Victoria) Harbour is dangerous in strong NW to NE winds but Inner (Old or Cromwell) Harbour (dries) is safe at all times: entry through a bridge which is opened on request to Hr Mr.

NAVIGATION
Waypoint 56°00′·70N 02°30′·80W, 018°/198° from/to front Ldg Lt 198°, 0·50M. Min depth at entrance 0·9m. Entrance is unsafe in heavy on-shore swell. N side of Victoria harbour dries but pool 1·25m at LWS in SW corner. Beware Outer Buss Rk (0·6m). Keep to port on entry to avoid rockfall off castle.

LIGHTS AND MARKS
The entrance from the NE is on the 198° leading lights which is marked by two W triangles on Or columns to S of Doo Rocks, both Oc G 6s 15/22m 3M at night, intens 188°-208° (synchronised). From the NW the leading line 132° allows direct passage between the posts. Entrance on Ldg line 132°, QR 6m 3M seen between high cliffs. Port Authority is the Lothian Regional Council.

RADIO TELEPHONE
None.

TELEPHONE (0368)
Hr Mr 63005; CG 63342; MRSC Crail 50666; # Edinburgh 554 2421; Marinecall 0898 500 452; Police 62718; H (0620) 824141; Dr 62327.

FACILITIES
EC Wednesday; **Quay** Slip, L, FW, D (delivery), P (cans); **North Wall** M, L, AB; **Inner Harbour** Slip, L, AB; **F & P Blair** ☎ 62371 ME; **Lawrence Turnbull** ☎ 63228 Gas, Gaz; **Town** LB, P, ⊡, V, R, Bar. ✉; Ⓑ; ⇌; ✈ (Edinburgh).

FIRTH OF FORTH 10-6-9

Lothian/Fife

CHARTS

Admiralty 734, 735, 736; Imray C27; OS 66

TIDES

+0350 (Granton) Dover; ML 3·3; Duration 0620; Zone 0 (GMT).

Standard Port LEITH (⟶)

Times				Height (metres)			
HW		LW		MHWS	MHWN	MLWN	MLWS
0300	0900	0300	0900	5·6	4·5	2·1	0·8
1500	2100	1500	2100				
Differences COCKENZIE							
−0007	−0015	−0013	−0005	−0·2	0·0	No data	
GRANTON							
0000	0000	0000	0000	0·0	0·0	0·0	0·0

Kincardine:— Time difference Leith +0030.
Alloa:— Time difference Leith +0048.
Leith is a Standard Port and tidal predictions for each day of the year are given below.

SHELTER

Rosyth does not offer any facilities to yachts except in emergency. Leith Docks are an impounded dock and accordingly yachts are not normally accepted. Yachts are advised to shelter in Granton or Port Edgar at S Queensferry or in Forth Yacht Marina at N Queensferry.
Granton — Yachts go to E of Middle Pier. Buoys are run by Royal Forth and Forth Corinthian YCs.

NAVIGATION

Waypoint Granton 56°00′·00N 03°13′·22W, 000°/180° from/to entrance, 0·72M. Beware Forth Railway Bridge — Forth Road Bridge — H.M. Ships entering and leaving Rosyth Dockyard — Hound Pt Oil Terminal — Braefoot Gas Terminal.
Note: Control of Forth Estuary, all commercial impounded docks and Granton Harbour is exercised by Forth Ports Authority.

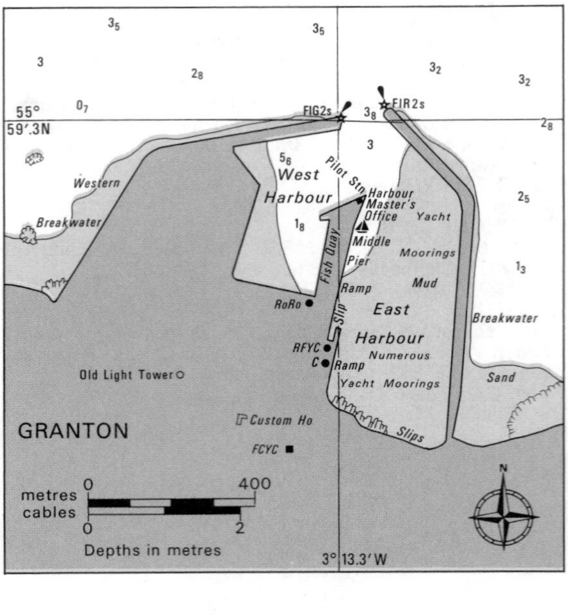
55° 59′.3N
FlG2s
FlR2s
West Harbour
Pilot Stn
Harbour Master's Office
Yacht Moorings
Middle Pier
Fish Quay
Ramp
Mud
East Harbour
Slip
RoRo
RFYC
C
Numerous Yacht Moorings
Breakwater
Sand
Western Breakwater
Old Light Tower
Slips
GRANTON
Custom Ho
FCYC
metres 0 400
cables 0 2
Depths in metres
3° 13.3′W

LIGHTS AND MARKS

Granton — R Flag with W diagonal cross (or G Lt by night) on signal mast at middle pierhead — Entry prohibited.
Leith — R Lt on both walls — Port closed.
— G Lt on both walls — Vessels may proceed.
— G Lt on one wall — Vessels moor on that side.
Port Edgar — On West Pier Dir Lt Fl R 4s 4m 8M 244°; 4 QY Lts mark floating breakwater; 3 x 2 FR (vert) mark N ends of marina pontoons inside harbour.
A Protected Channel 150m wide extends from Nos 13 & 14 light-buoys NNW of Oxcars, under the bridges (N of Inch Garvie and Beamer Rk), to the entrance of Rosyth Dockyard. When the Protected Channel is in operation an Oc 5s Lt and a QR Lt are shown from N Queensferry Naval Sig Stn, and all other vessels must clear the channel for naval traffic.

RADIO TELEPHONE

North Queensferry Naval Signal Station at Battery Point (call: *Queensferry*) VHF Ch 16; 13 **71** (H24).
Rosyth Naval Base (call: *QHM*) Ch 16; 13 73 (Mon-Fri: 0730-1700 LT).
Forth Navigation Service (at Leith) Ch 16 **71** (H24); **20** 12 (use 71 within area for calling and for short messages).
Grangemouth Docks Ch 16; 14 (H24).
Port Edgar Marina Ch **37** (Apl – Sept 0900 – 1930; Oct – Mar 0900 – 1630 LT).

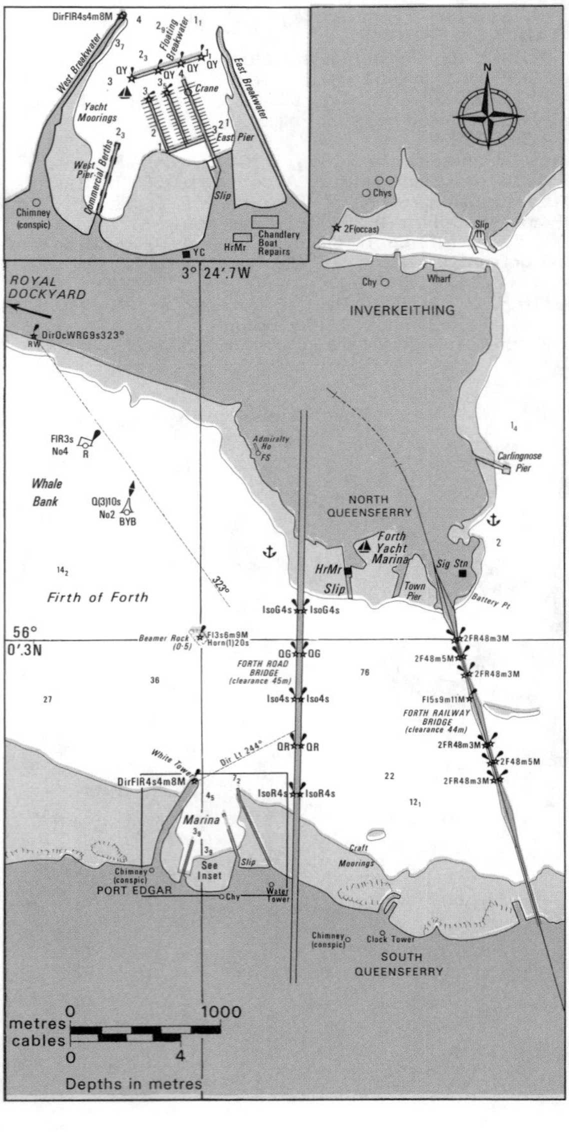
DirFlR4s4m8M
West Breakwater
Floating Breakwater
East Breakwater
QY
Crane
Yacht Moorings
East Pier
West Pier
Commercial Berths
Slip
Chimney (conspic)
Chandlery Boat Repairs
HrMr
YC
3° 24′.7W
ROYAL DOCKYARD
DirOcWRG9s323°
INVERKEITHING
Chys
2F(occas)
Wharf
Slip
FlR3s No4
Whale Bank
Q(3)10s No2 BYB
Admiralty No FS
Carlingnose Pier
NORTH QUEENSFERRY
Forth Yacht Marina
HrMr
Slip
Town Pier
Sig Stn
Battery Pt
Firth of Forth
IsoG4s
56° 0′.3N
Beamer Rock
Fl3s6m9M Horn(1)20s
QG
FORTH ROAD BRIDGE (clearance 45m)
Iso4s
QR
IsoR4s
2FR48m3M
2FR48m5M
Fl5s9m11M
FORTH RAILWAY BRIDGE (clearance 44m)
White Tower
Dir Lt 244°
DirFlR4s4m8M
Marina
See Inset
Slip
Water Tower
Chimney (conspic)
PORT EDGAR
Chy
Craft Moorings
Chimney (conspic)
Clock Tower
SOUTH QUEENSFERRY
metres 0 1000
cables 0 4
Depths in metres

TIME ZONE UT(GMT)

For Summer Time add ONE hour in non-shaded areas

SCOTLAND, EAST COAST – LEITH

Lat 55°59′ N Long 3°10′ W

TIMES AND HEIGHTS OF HIGH AND LOW WATERS

YEAR **1992**

JANUARY

Day	Time	m	Day	Time	m
1 W	0541 1200 1807	1·9 4·7 1·8	16 Th	0441 1103 1715 2331	1·9 4·6 1·9 4·8
2 Th	0035 0633 1254 1901	4·9 1·8 4·9 1·6	17 F	0545 1205 1818	1·7 4·8 1·5
3 F	0128 0715 1341 1946	4·9 1·7 5·0 1·4	18 Sa	0037 0643 1303 1916	5·1 1·4 5·2 1·1
4 Sa ●	0213 0750 1420 2022	5·0 1·6 5·1 1·3	19 Su ○	0137 0735 1358 2011	5·4 1·1 5·5 0·7
5 Su	0250 0820 1452 2056	5·1 1·5 5·2 1·2	20 M	0233 0824 1450 2101	5·7 0·9 5·8 0·4
6 M	0324 0850 1522 2126	5·1 1·4 5·3 1·1	21 Tu	0326 0911 1541 2146	5·9 0·7 5·9 0·2
7 Tu	0358 0920 1552 2156	5·1 1·4 5·3 1·1	22 W	0415 0954 1631 2231	5·9 0·7 6·0 0·2
8 W	0430 0952 1622 2226	5·1 1·3 5·2 1·1	23 Th	0503 1033 1718 2313	5·8 0·7 5·9 0·4
9 Th	0505 1026 1658 2258	5·0 1·4 5·2 1·2	24 F	0550 1113 1807 2354	5·6 0·9 5·7 0·7
10 F	0545 1100 1735 2331	4·9 1·5 5·1 1·3	25 Sa	0637 1152 1856	5·3 1·2 5·4
11 Sa	0626 1135 1820	4·8 1·6 4·9	26 Su ☾	0039 0726 1239 1946	1·2 5·0 1·6 5·1
12 Su	0007 0713 1215 1913	1·5 4·6 1·8 4·8	27 M	0131 0816 1341 2043	1·6 4·7 1·9 4·8
13 M ☽	0052 0805 1305 2011	1·7 4·4 2·1 4·6	28 Tu	0241 0913 1507 2146	2·0 4·4 2·2 4·5
14 Tu	0154 0901 1422 2116	1·9 4·4 2·2 4·6	29 W	0401 1016 1637 2301	2·2 4·4 2·1 4·4
15 W	0322 1001 1558 2222	2·0 4·4 2·1 4·6	30 Th	0516 1126 1756	2·2 4·4 1·9
			31 F	0016 0616 1233 1854	4·5 2·1 4·6 1·7

FEBRUARY

Day	Time	m	Day	Time	m
1 Sa	0115 0701 1322 1937	4·7 1·9 4·8 1·4	16 Su	0026 0631 1248 1909	5·0 1·4 5·2 0·9
2 Su	0158 0737 1401 2011	4·9 1·7 5·0 1·2	17 M	0126 0726 1345 2001	5·4 1·0 5·6 0·5
3 M ●	0233 0807 1433 2041	5·1 1·4 5·2 1·1	18 Tu ○	0220 0813 1437 2046	5·7 0·7 5·9 0·2
4 Tu	0305 0835 1501 2109	5·2 1·3 5·3 0·9	19 W	0309 0854 1524 2130	5·9 0·5 6·1 0·0
5 W	0335 0905 1531 2137	5·2 1·1 5·4 0·8	20 Th	0354 0933 1611 2209	5·9 0·5 6·1 0·1
6 Th	0407 0935 1603 2205	5·2 1·0 5·4 0·8	21 F	0439 1009 1656 2245	5·8 0·5 6·0 0·3
7 F	0441 1005 1635 2231	5·2 1·0 5·3 0·9	22 Sa	0522 1043 1741 2320	5·6 0·7 5·7 0·7
8 Sa	0516 1033 1711 2300	5·0 1·1 5·2 1·0	23 Su	0605 1118 1826 2354	5·3 1·0 5·4 1·2
9 Su	0554 1105 1750 2330	4·8 1·3 5·1 1·2	24 M	0648 1158 1913	4·9 1·4 5·0
10 M	0635 1139 1837	4·7 1·5 4·8	25 Tu ☾	0035 0735 1250 2007	1·7 4·6 1·8 4·6
11 Tu ☽	0005 0722 1222 1937	1·5 4·5 1·7 4·6	26 W	0137 0828 1420 2109	2·2 4·3 2·2 4·3
12 W	0054 0820 1324 2045	1·8 4·3 2·0 4·5	27 Th	0315 0931 1609 2226	2·5 4·2 2·2 4·2
13 Th	0215 0926 1518 2158	2·1 4·3 2·1 4·5	28 F	0446 1045 1733 2348	2·4 4·2 2·0 4·3
14 F	0409 1035 1658 2315	2·1 4·5 1·8 4·7	29 Sa	0552 1200 1830	2·2 4·4 1·7
15 Sa	0530 1145 1811	1·8 4·8 1·4			

MARCH

Day	Time	m	Day	Time	m
1 Su	0050 0637 1254 1911	4·6 1·9 4·7 1·4	16 M	0011 0616 1231 1854	5·0 1·4 5·2 0·8
2 M	0131 0711 1333 1943	4·8 1·6 4·9 1·1	17 Tu	0111 0707 1328 1943	5·4 1·0 5·6 0·4
3 Tu	0205 0743 1405 2015	5·0 1·3 5·1 0·9	18 W ○	0201 0750 1416 2026	5·6 0·7 5·9 0·2
4 W ●	0237 0813 1435 2043	5·2 1·1 5·3 0·7	19 Th	0246 0831 1503 2103	5·8 0·5 6·0 0·1
5 Th	0309 0843 1507 2111	5·3 0·9 5·4 0·6	20 F	0330 0907 1546 2139	5·8 0·4 6·0 0·2
6 F	0341 0913 1539 2137	5·3 0·9 5·4 0·6	21 Sa	0413 0941 1631 2213	5·7 0·5 5·8 0·5
7 Sa	0415 0941 1613 2203	5·2 0·8 5·4 0·7	22 Su	0452 1015 1713 2243	5·4 0·7 5·5 0·9
8 Su	0448 1009 1648 2230	5·1 0·9 5·3 0·8	23 M	0531 1048 1756 2313	5·2 1·0 5·2 1·3
9 M	0524 1041 1730 2300	4·9 1·0 5·1 1·1	24 Tu	0611 1126 1841 2346	4·8 1·3 4·8 1·8
10 Tu	0603 1115 1818 2335	4·7 1·2 4·8 1·4	25 W	0654 1213 1931	4·5 1·8 4·4
11 W	0650 1158 1920	4·6 1·5 4·6	26 Th ☾	0035 0745 1333 2031	2·2 4·3 2·1 4·2
12 Th ☽	0022 0752 1303 2028	1·7 4·4 1·8 4·4	27 F	0215 0845 1530 2141	2·6 4·1 2·2 4·1
13 F	0141 0900 1505 2143	2·1 4·4 2·0 4·4	28 Sa	0400 0954 1648 2258	2·5 4·1 2·0 4·2
14 Sa	0348 1015 1646 2300	2·1 4·5 1·7 4·6	29 Su	0509 1107 1746	2·3 4·3 1·7
15 Su	0515 1126 1756	1·8 4·8 1·2	30 M	0005 0558 1205 1830	4·5 1·9 4·5 1·4
			31 Tu	0050 0635 1250 1905	4·7 1·6 4·8 1·1

APRIL

Day	Time	m	Day	Time	m
1 W	0128 0711 1328 1939	5·0 1·3 5·0 0·9	16 Th	0137 0726 1354 1958	5·5 0·8 5·7 0·4
2 Th	0203 0745 1403 2011	5·1 1·1 5·2 0·7	17 F ○	0222 0805 1441 2037	5·6 0·7 5·7 0·4
3 F ●	0237 0816 1437 2039	5·2 0·9 5·3 0·6	18 Sa	0305 0843 1526 2109	5·6 0·6 5·7 0·6
4 Sa	0311 0846 1515 2109	5·2 0·8 5·4 0·6	19 Su	0345 0918 1609 2139	5·4 0·7 5·5 0·8
5 Su	0345 0918 1552 2135	5·2 0·7 5·3 0·7	20 M	0424 0952 1650 2209	5·3 0·8 5·3 1·1
6 M	0420 0950 1633 2205	5·1 0·8 5·2 0·8	21 Tu	0500 1026 1731 2239	5·1 1·0 5·0 1·4
7 Tu	0458 1024 1720 2239	5·0 0·9 5·1 1·1	22 W	0535 1103 1813 2313	4·8 1·3 4·7 1·8
8 W	0541 1103 1815 2318	4·9 1·1 4·9 1·4	23 Th	0615 1148 1900 2358	4·6 1·6 4·4 2·1
9 Th	0633 1154 1913	4·7 1·4 4·7	24 F ☾	0701 1252 1954	4·4 1·9 4·2
10 F ☽	0011 0735 1309 2020	1·8 4·6 1·7 4·5	25 Sa	0111 0800 1431 2056	2·4 4·2 2·1 4·2
11 Sa	0137 0845 1501 2131	2·1 4·5 1·7 4·5	26 Su	0258 0903 1552 2201	2·5 4·2 2·0 4·2
12 Su	0333 0956 1628 2245	2·1 4·6 1·5 4·7	27 M	0415 1009 1652 2305	2·3 4·3 1·8 4·4
13 M	0452 1107 1733 2350	1·8 4·9 1·1 5·0	28 Tu	0509 1111 1741	2·0 4·5 1·5
14 Tu	0552 1209 1828	1·4 5·2 0·8	29 W	0000 0556 1201 1824	4·6 1·7 4·7 1·2
15 W	0048 0643 1305 1916	5·3 1·1 5·5 0·5	30 Th	0045 0635 1246 1901	4·8 1·4 4·9 1·0

Chart Datum: 2.90 metres below Ordnance Datum (Newlyn)

TIME ZONE UT(GMT)
For Summer Time add ONE hour in non-shaded areas

SCOTLAND, EAST COAST – LEITH

Lat 55°59′ N Long 3°10′ W

TIMES AND HEIGHTS OF HIGH AND LOW WATERS

YEAR **1992**

MAY

Day	Time	m	Day	Time	m
1 F	0124 0713 1330 1935	5·0 1·2 5·1 0·9	16 Sa ○	0200 0746 1424 2011	5·3 0·9 5·4 0·9
2 Sa ●	0201 0748 1411 2009	5·1 1·0 5·2 0·8	17 Su	0241 0826 1509 2045	5·3 0·9 5·4 1·0
3 Su	0239 0824 1452 2041	5·2 0·8 5·3 0·8	18 M	0320 0903 1550 2115	5·3 0·9 5·2 1·2
4 M	0318 0900 1537 2115	5·2 0·7 5·3 0·8	19 Tu	0358 0937 1630 2143	5·2 1·0 5·1 1·3
5 Tu	0358 0937 1626 2150	5·2 0·7 5·2 0·9	20 W	0431 1013 1709 2216	5·0 1·1 4·9 1·5
6 W	0441 1018 1716 2230	5·1 0·8 5·1 1·1	21 Th	0503 1048 1746 2252	4·9 1·3 4·7 1·7
7 Th	0530 1105 1811 2316	5·0 0·9 5·0 1·4	22 F	0541 1130 1830 2335	4·7 1·5 4·6 1·9
8 F	0626 1203 1907	4·9 1·2 4·9	23 Sa	0624 1220 1918	4·6 1·7 4·4
9 Sa ☽	0015 0726 1320 2009	1·7 4·8 1·4 4·8	24 Su ☾	0030 0716 1328 2013	2·1 4·4 1·9 4·3
10 Su	0137 0830 1445 2115	1·9 4·7 1·4 4·7	25 M	0148 0816 1446 2111	2·3 4·3 1·9 4·3
11 M	0309 0935 1600 2220	1·9 4·8 1·3 4·8	26 Tu	0311 0918 1554 2211	2·3 4·3 1·8 4·4
12 Tu	0422 1043 1703 2324	1·8 4·9 1·2 4·9	27 W	0416 1018 1652 2307	2·1 4·4 1·6 4·5
13 W	0524 1145 1800	1·5 5·1 1·0	28 Th	0511 1115 1741 2358	1·9 4·6 1·5 4·7
14 Th	0022 0616 1243 1850	5·1 1·3 5·3 0·9	29 F	0558 1207 1824	1·6 4·8 1·3
15 F	0113 0703 1335 1933	5·2 1·1 5·4 0·9	30 Sa	0045 0641 1258 1903	4·8 1·3 4·9 1·1
			31 Su	0128 0724 1346 1943	5·0 1·1 5·1 1·0

JUNE

Day	Time	m	Day	Time	m
1 M ●	0211 0807 1435 2022	5·1 0·9 5·2 0·9	16 Tu	0301 0856 1535 2056	5·2 1·0 5·1 1·4
2 Tu	0254 0850 1526 2101	5·3 0·7 5·3 0·9	17 W	0335 0930 1611 2126	5·1 1·0 5·0 1·4
3 W	0341 0935 1616 2145	5·3 0·6 5·4 1·0	18 Th	0407 1001 1646 2200	5·1 1·1 5·0 1·4
4 Th	0430 1022 1709 2230	5·3 0·6 5·4 1·1	19 F	0437 1033 1720 2233	5·0 1·2 4·9 1·5
5 F	0522 1113 1801 2318	5·3 0·7 5·3 1·3	20 Sa	0511 1109 1800 2313	4·9 1·3 4·8 1·6
6 Sa	0616 1207 1856	5·2 0·9 5·2	21 Su	0552 1148 1843 2354	4·8 1·4 4·6 1·8
7 Su ☽	0015 0713 1309 1952	1·5 5·1 1·1 5·0	22 M	0639 1233 1931	4·7 1·6 4·5
8 M	0120 0811 1416 2052	1·7 5·0 1·3 4·9	23 Tu ☾	0045 0733 1331 2026	2·0 4·5 1·8 4·4
9 Tu	0235 0913 1526 2152	1·8 4·9 1·4 4·8	24 W	0152 0831 1445 2122	2·2 4·4 1·9 4·3
10 W	0346 1016 1633 2254	1·8 4·9 1·4 4·8	25 Th	0313 0933 1556 2220	2·2 4·4 1·9 4·4
11 Th	0454 1120 1733 2354	1·7 4·9 1·4 4·9	26 F	0424 1033 1656 2315	2·0 4·5 1·7 4·5
12 F	0554 1224 1826	1·5 5·0 1·4	27 Sa	0522 1133 1748	1·8 4·6 1·6
13 Sa	0048 0648 1320 1913	5·0 1·3 5·1 1·3	28 Su	0007 0615 1231 1837	4·7 1·5 4·8 1·4
14 Su	0139 0737 1411 1952	5·1 1·2 5·1 1·3	29 M	0058 0705 1328 1924	5·0 1·2 5·1 1·2
15 M ○	0222 0818 1454 2026	5·2 1·1 5·1 1·4	30 Tu ●	0146 0756 1422 2009	5·2 0·8 5·3 1·0

JULY

Day	Time	m	Day	Time	m
1 W	0237 0845 1515 2056	5·4 0·6 5·5 0·9	16 Th	0315 0918 1550 2111	5·2 1·0 5·1 1·3
2 Th	0328 0933 1605 2141	5·6 0·4 5·6 0·8	17 F	0343 0946 1620 2141	5·2 1·0 5·1 1·3
3 F	0418 1020 1656 2226	5·7 0·3 5·6 0·8	18 Sa	0411 1015 1654 2213	5·2 1·0 5·0 1·3
4 Sa	0511 1105 1746 2309	5·7 0·4 5·6 1·0	19 Su	0443 1045 1730 2246	5·2 1·0 4·9 1·4
5 Su	0601 1154 1837 2356	5·6 0·6 5·4 1·2	20 M	0520 1115 1809 2320	5·0 1·1 4·8 1·5
6 M	0654 1245 1930	5·4 0·9 5·1	21 Tu	0603 1150 1854 2358	4·9 1·3 4·6 1·7
7 Tu ☽	0050 0748 1343 2024	1·5 5·2 1·2 4·9	22 W ☾	0652 1228 1943	4·7 1·6 4·4
8 W	0154 0846 1448 2120	1·7 5·0 1·6 4·7	23 Th	0043 0748 1320 2037	2·0 4·5 1·9 4·3
9 Th	0311 0948 1600 2222	1·9 4·8 1·8 4·6	24 F	0150 0852 1443 2135	2·2 4·4 2·0 4·3
10 F	0430 1058 1709 2326	1·9 4·7 1·8 4·7	25 Sa	0331 0958 1611 2237	2·2 4·4 2·0 4·4
11 Sa	0543 1207 1811	1·7 4·7 1·8	26 Su	0452 1105 1720 2337	1·9 4·5 1·8 4·7
12 Su	0030 0645 1309 1900	4·8 1·5 4·9 1·7	27 M	0558 1211 1816	1·6 4·8 1·5
13 M	0122 0733 1400 1941	4·9 1·3 5·0 1·6	28 Tu	0035 0654 1311 1909	5·0 1·1 5·1 1·2
14 Tu ○	0205 0815 1441 2013	5·1 1·2 5·0 1·5	29 W ●	0130 0746 1407 1958	5·3 0·7 5·5 0·9
15 W	0243 0848 1516 2041	5·2 1·1 5·1 1·4	30 Th	0222 0835 1500 2045	5·6 0·4 5·7 0·7
			31 F	0313 0922 1548 2128	5·9 0·1 5·8 0·6

AUGUST

Day	Time	m	Day	Time	m
1 Sa	0401 1005 1637 2209	6·0 0·1 5·8 0·6	16 Su	0345 0948 1626 2148	5·4 0·8 5·2 1·1
2 Su	0450 1046 1724 2248	6·0 0·2 5·7 0·7	17 M	0416 1015 1700 2218	5·3 0·8 5·1 1·2
3 M	0541 1128 1813 2330	5·8 0·5 5·5 1·0	18 Tu	0450 1043 1735 2248	5·2 1·0 4·9 1·3
4 Tu	0630 1211 1901	5·6 0·9 5·2	19 W	0530 1111 1816 2322	5·0 1·2 4·7 1·5
5 W ☽	0015 0722 1301 1952	1·4 5·2 1·4 4·9	20 Th	0615 1143 1901	4·8 1·5 4·5
6 Th	0113 0818 1405 2046	1·7 4·9 1·8 4·6	21 F ☾	0000 0713 1226 1956	1·8 4·6 1·8 4·4
7 F	0235 0920 1528 2150	2·0 4·6 2·1 4·5	22 Sa	0054 0820 1330 2100	2·1 4·4 2·1 4·3
8 Sa	0411 1033 1650 2300	2·1 4·5 2·2 4·5	23 Su	0245 0931 1531 2205	2·2 4·4 2·2 4·5
9 Su	0535 1152 1758	1·9 4·5 2·1	24 M	0431 1043 1658 2313	2·0 4·5 2·0 4·7
10 M	0009 0637 1256 1846	4·6 1·6 4·7 1·9	25 Tu	0543 1154 1801	1·5 4·8 1·6
11 Tu	0103 0722 1343 1924	4·9 1·4 4·9 1·7	26 W	0015 0641 1256 1854	5·1 1·0 5·2 1·2
12 W	0146 0800 1420 1954	5·1 1·2 5·1 1·5	27 Th	0111 0731 1350 1941	5·5 0·6 5·6 0·8
13 Th ○	0220 0828 1452 2022	5·2 1·0 5·2 1·3	28 F ●	0203 0818 1439 2026	5·8 0·2 5·8 0·6
14 F	0248 0856 1522 2050	5·3 0·9 5·2 1·2	29 Sa	0252 0901 1526 2105	6·1 0·0 5·9 0·5
15 Sa	0316 0922 1554 2118	5·4 0·8 5·2 1·1	30 Su	0341 0941 1613 2145	6·1 0·0 5·9 0·5
			31 M	0428 1020 1658 2222	6·1 0·2 5·7 0·6

Chart Datum: 2.90 metres below Ordnance Datum (Newlyn)

6

SCOTLAND, EAST COAST – LEITH

Lat 55°59′ N Long 3°10′ W

TIMES AND HEIGHTS OF HIGH AND LOW WATERS

YEAR **1992**

TIME ZONE UT(GMT)

For Summer Time add ONE hour in non-shaded areas

SEPTEMBER

Day	Time	m	Time	m	Time	m	Time	m
1 Tu	0515	5·9	1056	0·6	1743	5·5	2300	0·9
2 W	0603	5·5	1133	1·0	1830	5·1	2341	1·3
3 Th ☽	0654	5·1	1215	1·6	1918	4·8		
4 F	0033	1·8	0748	4·7	1313	2·1	2011	4·5
5 Sa	0201	2·1	0852	4·4	1450	2·5	2115	4·3
6 Su	0352	2·2	1005	4·3	1626	2·5	2226	4·4
7 M	0516	2·0	1128	4·4	1733	2·3	2339	4·5
8 Tu	0613	1·7	1231	4·7	1820	2·0		
9 W	0035	4·8	0654	1·4	1316	4·9	1856	1·7
10 Th	0116	5·0	0728	1·2	1350	5·1	1926	1·5
11 F	0148	5·2	0758	1·0	1422	5·2	1956	1·2
12 Sa ○	0218	5·4	0824	0·8	1452	5·3	2024	1·1
13 Su	0246	5·4	0852	0·7	1522	5·3	2054	1·0
14 M	0318	5·4	0918	0·7	1556	5·3	2124	1·0
15 Tu	0350	5·4	0945	0·8	1628	5·1	2152	1·1
16 W	0426	5·3	1011	0·9	1701	5·0	2222	1·2
17 Th	0505	5·1	1039	1·1	1739	4·8	2256	1·4
18 F	0554	4·8	1111	1·4	1826	4·6	2335	1·6
19 Sa ☾	0652	4·6	1154	1·8	1924	4·5		
20 Su	0031	1·9	0801	4·5	1256	2·1	2031	4·5
21 M	0224	2·1	0913	4·4	1501	2·3	2141	4·6
22 Tu	0413	1·9	1026	4·6	1637	2·0	2250	4·8
23 W	0524	1·4	1135	5·0	1741	1·6	2354	5·2
24 Th	0620	1·0	1237	5·3	1833	1·2		
25 F	0052	5·6	0711	0·6	1330	5·7	1920	0·9
26 Sa ●	0143	5·9	0754	0·3	1416	5·9	2001	0·6
27 Su	0231	6·1	0835	0·2	1501	5·9	2041	0·5
28 M	0318	6·1	0915	0·2	1546	5·9	2120	0·5
29 Tu	0405	6·0	0950	0·5	1630	5·7	2156	0·7
30 W	0452	5·7	1024	0·8	1713	5·4	2233	1·0

OCTOBER

Day	Time	m	Time	m	Time	m	Time	m
1 Th	0539	5·4	1056	1·3	1756	5·1	2313	1·3
2 F	0628	5·0	1131	1·8	1841	4·8		
3 Sa ☽	0003	1·8	0720	4·6	1220	2·3	1933	4·5
4 Su	0126	2·1	0820	4·4	1354	2·6	2033	4·3
5 M	0315	2·2	0928	4·3	1541	2·7	2141	4·3
6 Tu	0433	2·1	1043	4·4	1652	2·4	2250	4·5
7 W	0530	1·8	1148	4·6	1741	2·1	2350	4·7
8 Th	0613	1·5	1235	4·9	1818	1·8		
9 F	0035	5·0	0648	1·3	1313	5·1	1854	1·5
10 Sa	0111	5·2	0720	1·0	1346	5·3	1928	1·3
11 Su ○	0145	5·3	0752	0·9	1420	5·3	1958	1·1
12 M	0218	5·4	0820	0·8	1452	5·4	2030	1·0
13 Tu	0254	5·4	0848	0·8	1526	5·3	2101	1·0
14 W	0330	5·4	0916	0·9	1558	5·2	2131	1·0
15 Th	0411	5·3	0945	1·0	1633	5·1	2205	1·1
16 F	0456	5·1	1016	1·2	1715	5·0	2243	1·3
17 Sa	0546	4·9	1054	1·5	1803	4·8	2328	1·5
18 Su	0645	4·7	1139	1·8	1903	4·7		
19 M ☾	0031	1·8	0750	4·6	1246	2·1	2011	4·7
20 Tu	0216	1·9	0858	4·6	1441	2·3	2120	4·7
21 W	0350	1·7	1009	4·8	1613	2·0	2230	5·0
22 Th	0500	1·4	1115	5·0	1716	1·7	2333	5·3
23 F	0556	1·0	1213	5·3	1809	1·3		
24 Sa	0030	5·6	0645	0·7	1305	5·6	1856	1·0
25 Su ●	0122	5·8	0730	0·5	1354	5·7	1941	0·8
26 M	0211	5·9	0811	0·5	1439	5·8	2020	0·7
27 Tu	0300	5·9	0848	0·6	1522	5·7	2100	0·7
28 W	0346	5·8	0922	0·8	1603	5·6	2137	0·9
29 Th	0431	5·5	0954	1·1	1645	5·4	2215	1·1
30 F	0516	5·3	1026	1·5	1724	5·1	2254	1·4
31 Sa	0601	5·0	1101	1·9	1805	4·9	2341	1·7

NOVEMBER

Day	Time	m	Time	m	Time	m	Time	m
1 Su	0650	4·7	1145	2·2	1852	4·6		
2 M ☽	0045	2·0	0743	4·4	1250	2·5	1948	4·5
3 Tu	0216	2·2	0843	4·3	1433	2·6	2050	4·4
4 W	0335	2·1	0946	4·4	1554	2·5	2154	4·4
5 Th	0435	1·9	1050	4·5	1652	2·2	2254	4·6
6 F	0524	1·7	1145	4·8	1739	1·9	2346	4·8
7 Sa	0607	1·4	1230	5·0	1820	1·7		
8 Su	0031	5·0	0645	1·2	1309	5·1	1858	1·4
9 M	0113	5·2	0718	1·1	1346	5·3	1933	1·2
10 Tu ○	0154	5·3	0752	1·0	1422	5·3	2009	1·1
11 W	0233	5·3	0824	1·0	1458	5·3	2045	1·0
12 Th	0316	5·3	0856	1·0	1535	5·3	2120	1·0
13 F	0401	5·3	0930	1·1	1616	5·3	2200	1·0
14 Sa	0450	5·2	1005	1·2	1701	5·2	2243	1·1
15 Su	0541	5·1	1048	1·5	1754	5·1	2333	1·3
16 M	0637	5·0	1139	1·7	1852	5·0		
17 Tu ☾	0037	1·5	0737	4·9	1245	2·0	1956	4·9
18 W	0200	1·6	0841	4·8	1415	2·1	2100	4·9
19 Th	0318	1·5	0945	4·9	1539	2·0	2205	5·0
20 F	0428	1·4	1048	5·0	1646	1·8	2309	5·2
21 Sa	0528	1·2	1148	5·2	1745	1·5		
22 Su	0009	5·4	0620	1·1	1243	5·4	1837	1·2
23 M	0105	5·6	0707	1·0	1333	5·5	1924	1·1
24 Tu ●	0158	5·6	0750	1·0	1418	5·6	2009	1·0
25 W	0246	5·6	0830	1·0	1501	5·6	2050	0·9
26 Th	0331	5·5	0903	1·2	1543	5·5	2130	1·0
27 F	0415	5·4	0935	1·4	1620	5·3	2205	1·1
28 Sa	0456	5·2	1005	1·6	1656	5·2	2241	1·3
29 Su	0537	5·0	1041	1·8	1731	5·0	2320	1·5
30 M	0618	4·8	1120	2·0	1813	4·8		

DECEMBER

Day	Time	m	Time	m	Time	m	Time	m
1 Tu	0005	1·8	0703	4·6	1209	2·2	1901	4·7
2 W ☽	0105	1·9	0754	4·5	1316	2·4	2000	4·5
3 Th	0222	2·1	0852	4·4	1441	2·4	2100	4·5
4 F	0333	2·0	0952	4·5	1554	2·3	2200	4·5
5 Sa	0433	1·9	1050	4·6	1654	2·1	2258	4·6
6 Su	0524	1·7	1143	4·7	1745	1·9	2352	4·8
7 M	0609	1·5	1230	4·9	1830	1·6		
8 Tu	0043	5·0	0650	1·4	1313	5·1	1911	1·4
9 W ○	0130	5·1	0728	1·2	1354	5·2	1952	1·1
10 Th	0216	5·3	0805	1·1	1435	5·4	2033	0·9
11 F	0303	5·4	0845	1·1	1518	5·5	2116	0·8
12 Sa	0352	5·4	0924	1·1	1605	5·5	2200	0·8
13 Su	0443	5·5	1005	1·1	1654	5·5	2246	0·8
14 M	0533	5·4	1048	1·2	1745	5·4	2335	0·9
15 Tu	0626	5·3	1137	1·4	1839	5·3		
16 W ☾	0030	1·1	0720	5·1	1233	1·6	1937	5·2
17 Th	0133	1·3	0816	5·0	1341	1·9	2037	5·1
18 F	0243	1·5	0916	4·9	1500	1·9	2139	5·0
19 Sa	0354	1·6	1018	4·9	1616	1·9	2245	5·0
20 Su	0501	1·5	1122	4·9	1724	1·7	2352	5·1
21 M	0601	1·5	1222	5·1	1826	1·5		
22 Tu	0054	5·2	0654	1·4	1316	5·2	1920	1·3
23 W	0148	5·3	0739	1·4	1405	5·3	2007	1·1
24 Th ●	0237	5·4	0818	1·4	1448	5·4	2050	1·1
25 F	0320	5·4	0850	1·4	1526	5·4	2126	1·1
26 Sa	0400	5·3	0920	1·4	1600	5·4	2156	1·1
27 Su	0435	5·2	0950	1·4	1631	5·3	2226	1·2
28 M	0509	5·1	1022	1·5	1701	5·2	2258	1·3
29 Tu	0545	5·0	1056	1·6	1737	5·1	2331	1·4
30 W	0624	4·8	1135	1·8	1820	4·9		
31 Th	0013	1·6	0711	4·6	1220	2·0	1911	4·7

Chart Datum: 2·90 metres below Ordnance Datum (Newlyn)

FIRTH OF FORTH *continued*

TELEPHONE (031)
Hr Mr Leith 554-3661; MRSC Crail 50666; # 554-2421; Forth Yacht Clubs Assn 331 1118. Weather, Glasgow 248-3451 or for Port Edgar Inverkeithing 412475; Marinecall 0898 500 452; Police (S. Queensferry) 331 1798; Dr (Hosps) Dunfermline 73777, Leith 332 2525.

FACILITIES
SOUTH QUEENSFERRY EC Wednesday; **Port Edgar Marina** (300 + 8 visitors) ☎ 331-3330, Slip, AC, CH, D, El, Ⓔ, ME, Sh, SM, Gas, FW, R, C (5 ton); Access H24; **Forth Area Marine Electronics** ☎ 331 4343, El, Ⓔ, **Port Edgar Marine Services** ☎ 331 1233, ME; **Bosun's Locker** ☎ 331-3875, D, Sh, Gas, Gaz, CH; **Town** P, V, R, Bar. ✉, Ⓑ, ≹ (Dalmeny), ✈ (Edinburgh).
NORTH QUEENSFERRY **Forth Yacht Marina** (15 + some visitors) ☎ Inverkeithing 416101, Slip, D (cans), ME, El, Sh, C (20 ton), CH, SM; **Town** D, V, R, Bar, ✉, Ⓑ, ≹ (Inverkeithing), ✈ (Edinburgh).
GRANTON Hr Mr ☎ 552-3385, Slip, AB, FW; **Royal Forth YC** ☎ 552-3006, Slip, M, L, FW, C (5 ton), D, ME, El, Sh, Bar; **Forth Corinthian YC** ☎ 552-5939, Slip, M, L, Bar; Access HW ∓ 3½; **Seaspan** ☎ 552-2224, Gas, Gaz, Sh, CH; **Scott, Walter and Watson** ☎ 552-6695, ME; **J C Forbes** ☎ 552-8201, Sh; **Granton Marine Engineering** ☎ 552-0164 ME **Town** D, P, V, R, Bar. ✉, Ⓑ, ≹, ✈ (Edinburgh).
EDINBURGH **Chattan Shipping Services** ☎ 557-0988, ACA.

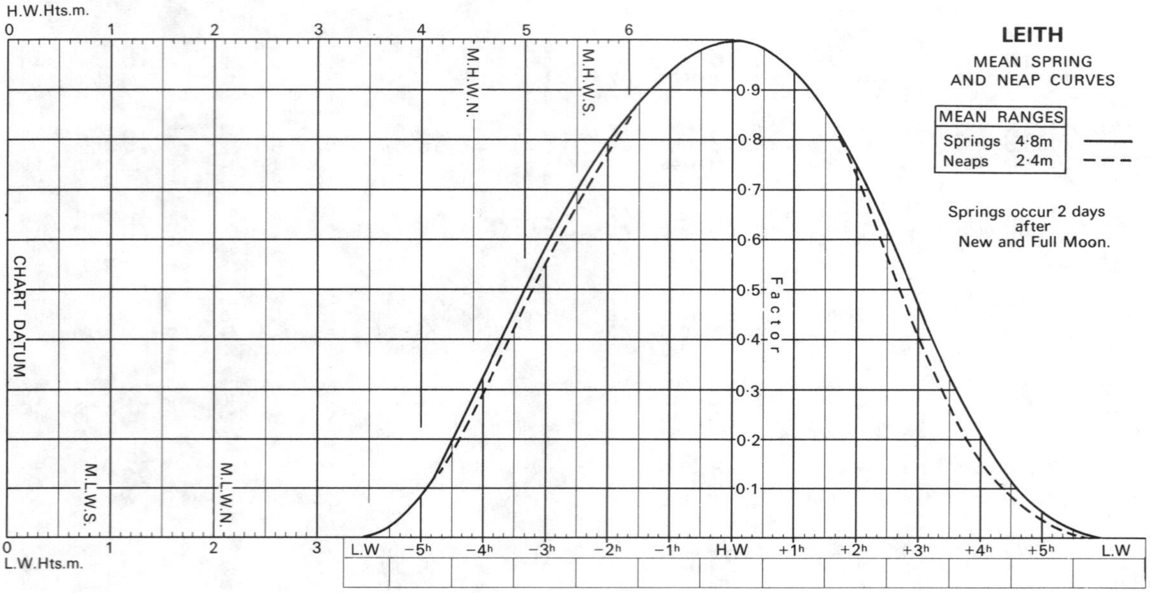
H.W.Hts.m.
0 1 2 3 4 5 6
M.H.W.N.
M.H.W.S.
LEITH
MEAN SPRING AND NEAP CURVES
MEAN RANGES
Springs 4·8m
Neaps 2·4m
Springs occur 2 days after New and Full Moon.
CHART DATUM
Factor
0·9 0·8 0·7 0·6 0·5 0·4 0·3 0·2 0·1
M.L.W.S.
M.L.W.N.
L.W.Hts.m.
L.W −5h −4h −3h −2h −1h H.W +1h +2h +3h +4h +5h L.W

BURNTISLAND 10-6-10
Fife

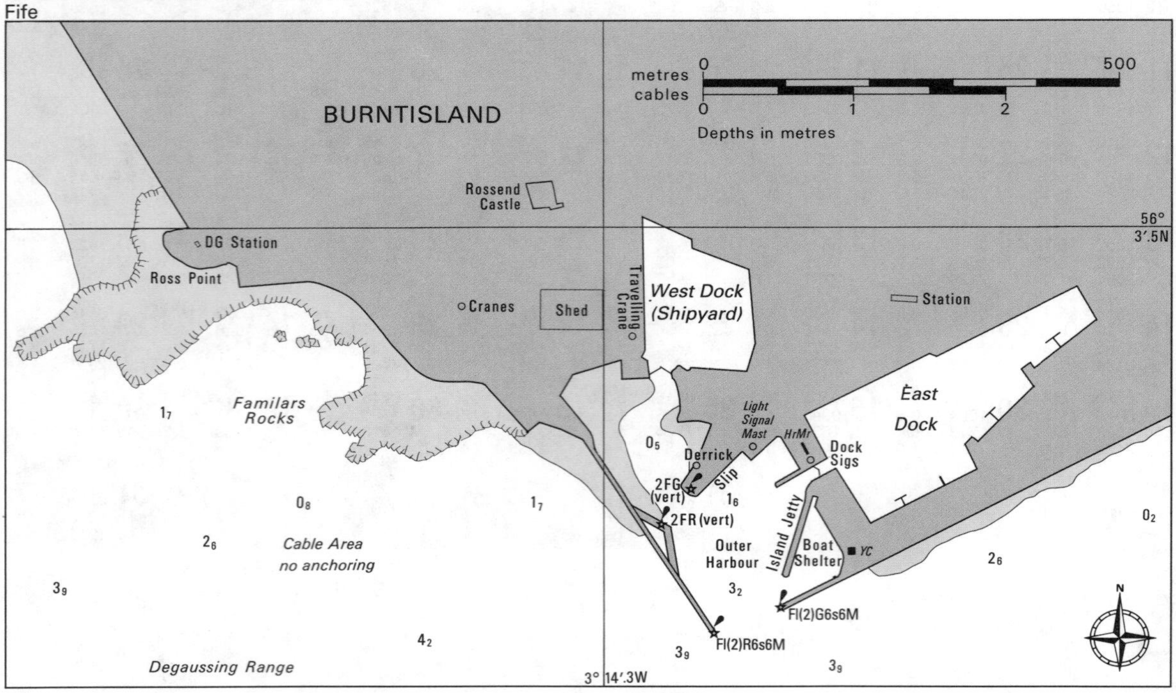
BURNTISLAND
metres
cables
0 500
0 1 2
Depths in metres
Rossend Castle
56°
3′.5N
DG Station
Ross Point
Cranes
Shed
Travelling Crane
West Dock (Shipyard)
Station
East Dock
Familars Rocks
Light Signal Mast
HrMr
Dock Sigs
Derrick
Slip
2FG (vert)
2FR (vert)
Outer Harbour
Island Jetty
Boat Shelter
YC
Cable Area no anchoring
Fl(2)G6s6M
Fl(2)R6s6M
Degaussing Range
3° 14′.3W

BURNTISLAND *continued*

CHARTS
Admiralty 739, 735; Imray C27; OS 66

TIDES
+0340 Dover; ML 2·9; Duration 0625; Zone 0 (GMT).

Standard Port LEITH (⟵)

Times				Height (metres)			
HW		LW		MHWS	MHWN	MLWN	MLWS
0300	0900	0300	0900	5·6	4·5	2·1	0·8
1500	2100	1500	2100				
Differences BURNTISLAND							
+0002	−0002	−0002	−0004	0·0	0·0	0·0	0·0

SHELTER
Shelter is very good in the docks but only fair in the outer harbour; unsuitable for yachts in strong winds. E dock can be entered from HW−2 to HW.

NAVIGATION
Waypoint 56°03′·00N 03°14′·00W, 163°/343° from/to entrance, 0·23M. To the E of the port, beware Black Rocks (off chartlet) and to the W, Familars Rocks. Keep clear of ships using DG ranges SW of port. Commercial barge operations can cause delays.

LIGHTS AND MARKS
By night and day
FR – Docks closed, bring up in roads
FG – Clear to enter Outer harbour
FR } FG } – Dangerous to enter
FR } FW } – Clear to enter E dock
FR } 2FW } – Clear to enter W dock
The above signals are shown from HW −3 until both dock gates are closed at HW.

RADIO TELEPHONE
Forth Navigation VHF Ch 16; 71 12 20 (H24).

TELEPHONE (0592)
Hr Mr (Port Superintendent) Leven 26725; MRSC Crail 50666; ⌗ 260730; Marinecall 0898 500 452; Police 872708; Dr 872761.

FACILITIES
EC Wednesday; **Dock** ☎ 872236, L, FW, C (10 ton), AB (Limited); **Outer Harbour** ☎ 872236, Slip, L, FW, AB (Limited); **Briggs Marine** ☎ 872939 D, ME, El, Sh, C (30 ton); **Burntisland Warehousing** ☎ 873708 CH; **Testpoint** ☎ 630220 Ⓔ; **Burntisland YC** ☎ 873375, M, L, FW, C (5 cwt); **Starlyburn BY** Slip, L, FW, ME, El, Sh, C, (25 ton); **Pop's Stores** ☎ 873524, Gas; **Town** P, D, ME, El, C, V, R, Bar. ✉; Ⓑ; ⇌; ✈ Edinburgh.

METHIL 10-6-11
Fife

CHARTS
Admiralty 739, 734; Imray C27; OS 59

TIDES
+0330 Dover; ML 3·2; Duration 0615; Zone 0 (GMT)

Standard Port LEITH (⟵)

Times				Height (metres)			
HW		LW		MHWS	MHWN	MLWN	MLWS
0300	0900	0300	0900	5·6	4·5	2·1	0·8
1500	2100	1500	2100				
Differences METHIL							
−0006	−0012	−0007	−0001	−0·1	−0·1	−0·1	−0·1

SHELTER
Principally a commercial port but good shelter in emergency.

NAVIGATION
Waypoint 56°10′·50N 03°00′·00W, 140°/320° from/to pier head Lt, 0·34M. Beware silting. A sand bar forms rapidly to seaward of the lighthouse and the dredged depth cannot always be maintained.

LIGHTS AND MARKS
By day and night
FR over FG Dangerous to enter. Bring up in roads.
FR over FW Clear to enter No 2 dock
FR Remain in roads until another signal is made.

RADIO TELEPHONE
VHF Ch 16; 14 (HW−3 to HW).

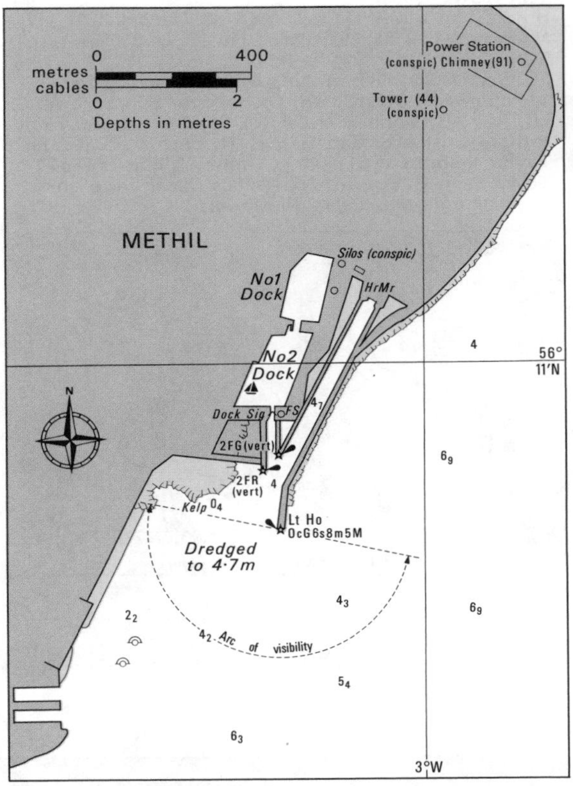

0 400
metres
cables
0 2
Depths in metres
Power Station
(conspic) Chimney(91)
Tower (44)
(conspic)
METHIL
Silos (conspic)
No1 Dock
HrMr
No2 Dock
Dock Sig
FS
2FG(vert)
2FR (vert)
Kelp
Lt Ho
OcG6s8m5M
Dredged to 4·7m
Arc of visibility
56°
11′N
3°W
N

TELEPHONE (0592)
Hr Mr (Port Superintendent) Leven 26725; MRSC Crail 50666; ⌗ (031) 554 2421; Marinecall 0898 500 452; Police 712881; Dr Leven 26913.

FACILITIES
EC Thursday; **Harbour** 2 Docks; C (7 ton); **Jas Donaldson** ☎ 26118, Gas; **Testpoint** ☎ 630220 Ⓔ; **Town** P, D, V, R, Bar, ✉; Ⓑ; ⇌ (bus to Markinch or Kirkcaldy); ✈ (Edinburgh).

ANSTRUTHER 10-6-12
Fife

CHARTS
Admiralty 734, 175; Imray C27; OS 59

TIDES
+0315 Dover; ML 3·2; Duration 0620; Zone 0 (GMT).

Standard Port LEITH (⟵)

Times				Height (metres)			
HW		LW		MHWS	MHWN	MLWN	MLWS
0300	0900	0300	0900	5·6	4·5	2·1	0·8
1500	2100	1500	2100				
Differences ANSTRUTHER							
−0010	−0035	−0020	−0020	−0·1	−0·1	−0·1	−0·1

SHELTER
Good shelter but entry should not be attempted when strong winds are blowing from the E and S.

ANSTRUTHER *continued*

NAVIGATION
Waypoint 56°12′·60N 02°42′·10W, 198°/018° from/to entrance, 0·60M. Harbour dries. Beware lobster pots and fishing vessels.
LIGHTS AND MARKS
Conspic Lt Tr on W Pier. Ldg Lts 019°, both FG 7/11m 4M. Fog horn (Reed) (3) 60s
RADIO TELEPHONE
Forth Navigation Service. See 10.6.9.
TELEPHONE (0333)
Hr Mr 310836; MRSC Crail 50666; ⌗ Dundee 22412; Marinecall 0898 500 452; Police 310333; Dr 310352.
FACILITIES
EC Wednesday; **Fisherman's Mutual Association** ☎ Pittenweem 311263, CH, D; **Harbour** Slip, M, FW, CH, LB, AC, AB; **Christie & Co** Tel. 311339, ME; **Gray and Pringle** ☎ 310508, Gas, Gaz; **R. R. Bett** ☎ 310369, El; **Taylor Inshore** ☎ 611459 Ⓔ; **James Miller** ☎ 7864 Sh; **Town** P, V, R, Bar, ✉; Ⓑ; ⇄ (bus Cupar or Leuchars); ✈ Edinburgh, or Dundee (Riverside).

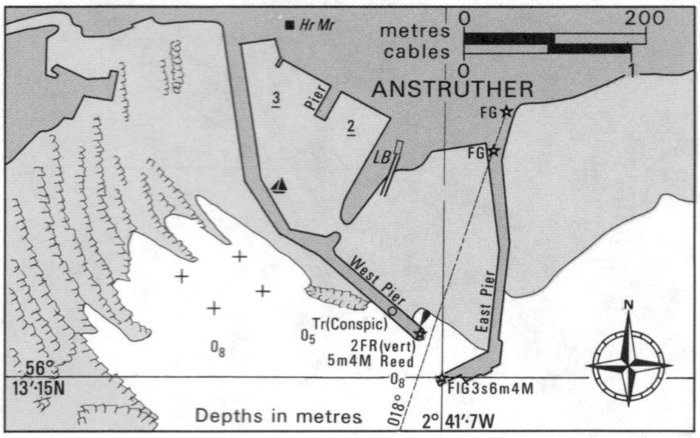

Hr Mr
metres 0 200
cables 0 1
ANSTRUTHER
3
Pier
2
LB
FG
FG
West Pier
East Pier
Tr(Conspic)
2FR(vert)
5m4M Reed
FlG3s6m4M
56°
13′15N
Depths in metres
018°
2° 41′·7W

RIVER TAY 10-6-13
Fife/Angus

CHARTS
Admiralty 1481, 190; OS 54, 59
TIDES
+0401 (Dundee) Dover; ML 3·0; Duration 0610; Zone 0 (GMT).

Standard Port ABERDEEN (⟶)

Times				Height (metres)			
HW		LW		MHWS	MHWN	MLWN	MLWS
0000	0600	0100	0700	4·3	3·4	1·6	0·6
1200	1800	1300	1900				
Differences BAR							
+0100	+0100	+0050	+0110	+0·9	+0·8	+0·3	+0·1
DUNDEE							
+0140	+0120	+0055	+0145	+1·1	+0·9	+0·3	+0·1
NEWBURGH							
+0215	+0200	+0250	+0335	−0·2	−0·4	−1·1	−0·5

SHELTER
Good shelter in the Tay estuary but the entrance is dangerous in strong winds from SE to E or in an on-shore swell. Tayport is best place for yachts on passage, access HW∓2½. Dundee docks (commercial) gates open HW−2 to HW. A R Fl Lt on Port Control Bldg at the lock ent indicates no entry or exit to/from Camperdown Dock. Anchorages as shown on chartlet; the one off the city is exposed and landing difficult. There are anchorages up river at Balmerino, Newburgh, Inchyra and Perth. Note:- Area is administered by the Dundee Port Authority.
NAVIGATION
Waypoint Tay Fairway safe water buoy, LFl 10s, Whis, 56°28′·62N 02°37′·15W, 060°/240° from/to Middle Bar buoys, 1·0M. The river is navigable right up to Perth. Entrance to river across Abertay sands is forbidden due to stakes. Channel is well buoyed but caution should be exercised as depths are liable to change. Tayport harbour dries except W side of NE pier; S side is full of yacht moorings.
LIGHTS AND MARKS
There are no leading lights but channel is well marked. The high focal plane buoy *"Abertay"* (Racon) at E end of Gaa Sands is a clear visual mark.
RADIO TELEPHONE
Dundee Harbour Radio VHF Ch 16; 11 **12** (H24). Perth Harbour Ch 16; 09.

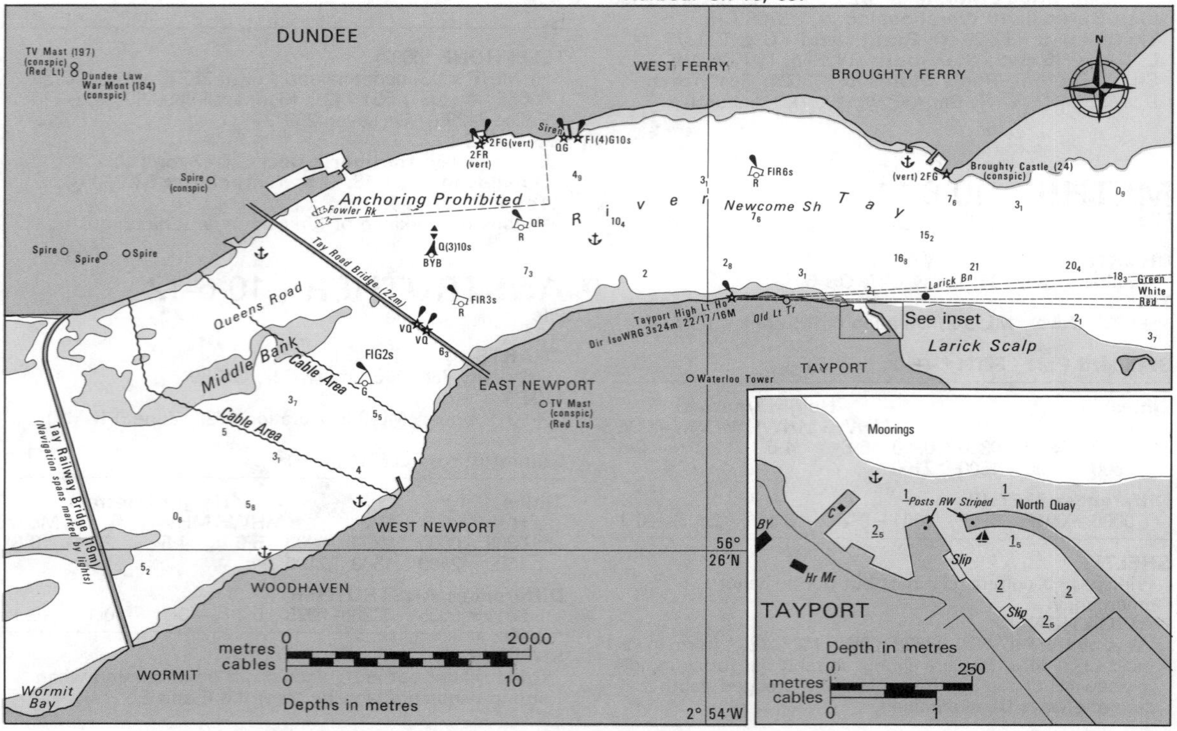

DUNDEE
TV Mast (197) (conspic) (Red Lt)
Dundee Law War Mont (184) (conspic)
WEST FERRY
BROUGHTY FERRY
Spire (conspic)
Spire
Spire
Spire
2FG(vert)
2FR (vert)
Siren
QG
Fl(4)G10s
FlR6s
(vert) 2FG
Broughty Castle (24) (conspic)
Anchoring Prohibited
Fowler Rk
QR
Q(3)10s
BYB
River Tay
Newcome Sh
Tay Road Bridge (22m)
FlR3s
Queens Road
VQ
VQ
Middle Bank
Cable Area
FlG2s
Larick Bn
Green
White
Red
Tayport High Lt Ho
Dir IsoWRG 3s24m 22/17/16M
Old Lt Tr
See inset
Larick Scalp
TAYPORT
Waterloo Tower
EAST NEWPORT
TV Mast (conspic) (Red Lts)
Cable Area
Tay Railway Bridge (19m) (Navigation spans marked by lights)
WEST NEWPORT
WOODHAVEN
56° 26′N
metres 0 2000
cables 0 10
Depths in metres
WORMIT
Wormit Bay
2° 54′W
Moorings
Posts RW Striped
North Quay
Slip
Slip
Hr Mr
TAYPORT
Depth in metres
metres 0 250
cables 0 1

RIVER TAY *continued*

TELEPHONE (0382)
Hr Mr (Dundee) 24121; Perth Hr Mr Perth 24056; MRSC Crail 50666; # 22412; Tayport Boatowners' Assn 553679; Marinecall 0898 500 452; Police (Tayport) 552222 (Dundee) 23200; Dr 21953; Ⓗ 23125.

FACILITIES
NORTH BANK: EC Dundee Wednesday; **Camperdown Dock** FW, ME, El, C (8 ton), AB; **Victoria Dock** FW, ME, C (8 ton), AB; **Royal Tay YC** (Broughty Ferry) ☎ 77516, M, L, R, Bar; **Allison-Gray** ☎ 27444, CH, ACA, SM; **Scotcraig Boat Co** ☎ 553230, M, L, ME, El, Sh, C (2 ton), CH; **Broughty Ferry** Slip, M; **Sea and Shore** ☎ 451816; **Dundee Town** P, D, CH, V, R, Bar, ✉, Ⓑ, ⇄, ✈.
SOUTH BANK: **Tayport Harbour** ☎ 553679 Slip, L, FW, AB, AC; **Wormit Boating Club** ☎ 541400 Slip, L, FW, V.

ARBROATH 10-6-14

Angus

CHARTS
Admiralty 1438, 190; OS 54

TIDES
+0317 Dover; ML 2·9; Duration 0620; Zone 0 (GMT).

Standard Port ABERDEEN (⟶)

Times				Height (metres)			
HW		LW		MHWS	MHWN	MLWN	MLWS
0000	0600	0100	0700	4·3	3·4	1·6	0·6
1200	1800	1300	1900				
Differences ARBROATH							
+0056	+0037	+0034	+0055	+0·7	+0·7	+0·2	+0·1

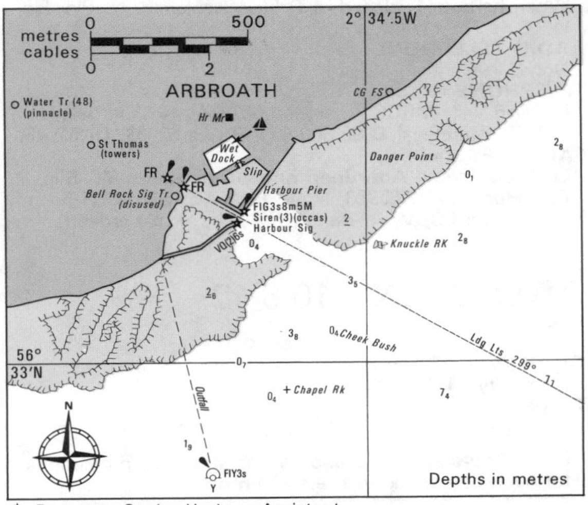
metres
cables
0
500
0
2
2° 34'.5W
ARBROATH
Water Tr (48) (pinnacle)
St Thomas (towers)
Hr Mr
Wet Dock
Slip
CG FS
Danger Point
FR
FR
Bell Rock Sig Tr (disused)
Harbour Pier
FlG3s8m5M
Siren(3)(occas)
Harbour Sig
Knuckle RK
Cheek Bush
Ldg Lts 299°
56° 33'N
Outfall
Chapel Rk
N
FlY3s
Y
Depths in metres

▲ Report to Senior Harbour Assistant

SHELTER
Good, especially in Dock, but entrance can be dangerous in moderate SE swell. Dock gates normally remain open, but will be closed on request. Entry should not be attempted LW ∓ 2½.

NAVIGATION
Waypoint 56°33'·00N 02°34'·10W, 119°/299° from/to entrance, 0·50M. Beware Knuckle rocks to stbd and Cheek Bush rocks to port on entering. Arbroath is a very busy fishing harbour so beware heavy traffic.

LIGHTS AND MARKS
Leading lights (FR) in line at 299°. By day St Thomas' church towers in line with the gap between Lt Ho on N pier and Bn on West breakwater.
Entry signals:- Fl G — Entry safe
FR — Entry dangerous

RADIO TELEPHONE
Contact AFA on VHF Ch 16.

TELEPHONE (0241)
Hr Mr 72166; MRSC Crail 50666; # Dundee 22412; Marinecall 0898 500 452; Police 72222; Dr 76836.

FACILITIES
EC Wednesday; **Pier** Slip, D, L, FW, AB; **Mackays BY** ☎ 72879, Slip, L, ME, El, Sh, C (8 ton) Ⓔ; **Arbroath Fisherman's Association** ☎ 72928, M, D, Gas, CH; **Gerrards** ☎ 73177, Slip, Sh; **W. M. Teviotdale** ☎ 73104, ME; **Elbar Shop** ☎ 73141, Gas; **A. Copland** ☎ 73212 ME; **J. Connely** ☎ 70121 ME; **Town** P, D, V, R, Bar. ✉; Ⓑ; ⇄; ✈ (Dundee).

MONTROSE 10-6-15

Angus

CHARTS
Admiralty 1438, 190; OS 54

TIDES
+0320 Dover; ML 2·8; Duration 0645; Zone 0 (GMT).

Standard Port ABERDEEN (⟶)

Times				Height (metres)			
HW		LW		MHWS	MHWN	MLWN	MLWS
0000	0600	0100	0700	4·3	3·4	1·6	0·6
1200	1800	1300	1900				
Differences MONTROSE							
+0100	+0100	+0030	+0040	+0·5	+0·5	+0·3	+0·1

SHELTER
Good with quayside berths usually available but beware wash from other traffic. Channel depth min 5m; best entry LW to LW+1; tidal streams are strong (up to 6 kn). It is a busy commercial port. Call up Hr Mr or report to Port Control Office on North Quay.

NAVIGATION
Waypoint 56°42'·20N 02°25'·00W, 091°/271° from/to front Ldg Lt, 1·25M. Beware Annat Bank to N and Scurdie Rks to S on entering. Entrance to harbour is dangerous with strong on-shore winds during ebb tide as heavy overfalls develop.

LIGHTS AND MARKS
Two sets of Ldg Lts. Outer 271·5°, both FR 5M. Inner 265°, both FG, 5M.

RADIO TELEPHONE
VHF Ch 16; 12 (H24).

TELEPHONE (0674)
Hr Mr 72302, 73153; MRCC Aberdeen 586258; # 74444; Marinecall 0898 500 452; Police 72222; Dr 73400.

FACILITIES
EC Wednesday; **North Quay** ☎ 72302, D, L, FW, ME, El, C (1½ to 40 ton), CH, AB; **SIM** ☎ 72696 Gas; **Town** V, R, P, Bar. ✉; Ⓑ; ⇄; ✈ (Aberdeen).

MONTROSE *continued*

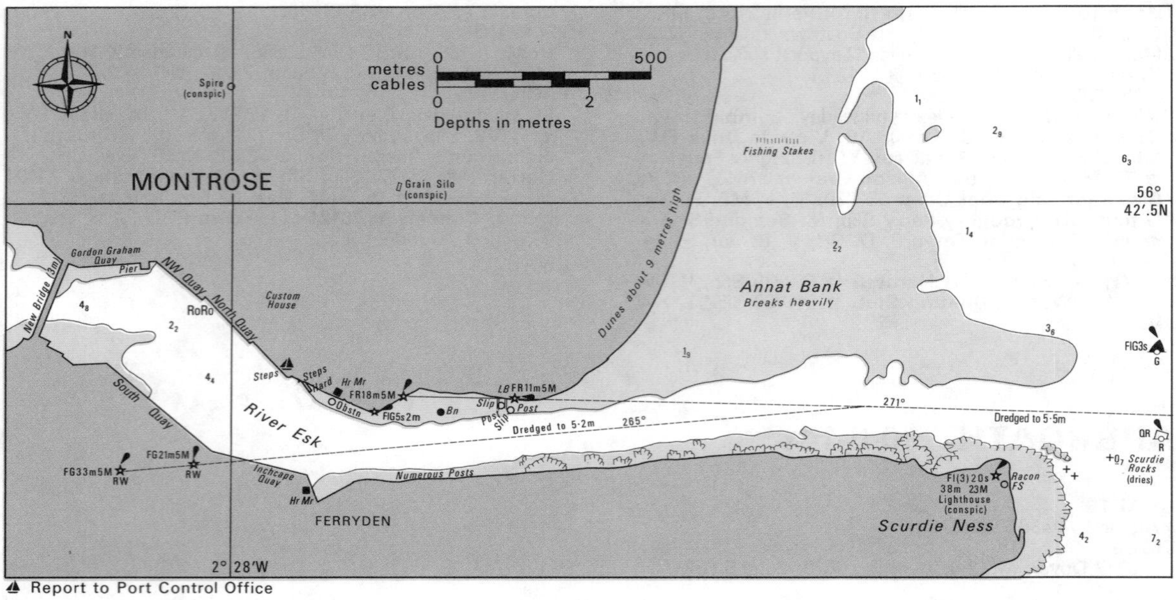

metres
cables
0
500
0
2
Depths in metres
Spire (conspic)
MONTROSE
Grain Silo (conspic)
Fishing Stakes
56°
42′.5N
Gordon Graham Quay
Pier
NW Quay
North Quay
New Bridge (3m)
RoRo
Custom House
Dunes about 9 metres high
Annat Bank
Breaks heavily
Steps
Hard
Hr Mr
FR18m5M
Obstn
FlG5s2m
Bn
FR11m5M
Slip
Post
Dredged to 5·2m
265°
271°
Dredged to 5·5m
FlG3s
G
QR
R
Scurdie Rocks (dries)
South Quay
River Esk
FG33m5M
RW
FG21m5M
RW
Inchcape Quay
Numerous Posts
Hr Mr
FERRYDEN
Fl(3)20s 38m 23M Lighthouse (conspic)
Racon
FS
Scurdie Ness
2° 28′W

▲ Report to Port Control Office

STONEHAVEN 10-6-16

Kincardine

CHARTS
Admiralty 1438, 210; OS 45

TIDES
+0235 Dover; ML 2·7; Duration 0620; Zone 0 (GMT).

Standard Port ABERDEEN (⟶)

Times				Height (metres)			
HW		LW		MHWS	MHWN	MLWN	MLWS
0000	0600	0100	0700	4·3	3·4	1·6	0·6
1200	1800	1300	1900				
Differences STONEHAVEN							
+0013	+0008	+0013	+0009	+0·2	+0·2	+0·1	0·0

SHELTER
Good shelter especially from S through W to N winds. Inner harbour dries; storm gates closed in severe weather. Speed limit in harbour 3 kn.

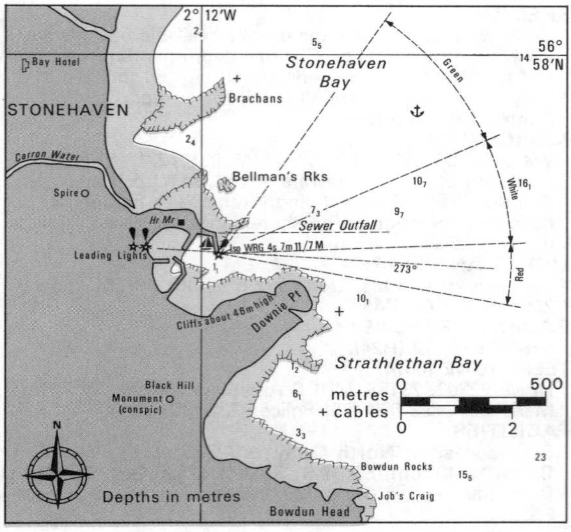

2° 12′W
56°
58′N
Bay Hotel
Stonehaven Bay
Brachans
STONEHAVEN
Carron Water
Green
White
Red
Bellman's Rks
Spire
Hr Mr
Sewer Outfall
Leading Lights
Iso WRG 4s 7m 11/7M
273°
Cliffs about 46m high
Downie Pt
Strathlethan Bay
Black Hill Monument (conspic)
metres
cables
0
500
0
2
Bowdun Rocks
Job's Craig
Bowdun Head
Depths in metres

NAVIGATION
Waypoint 56°57′·60N 02°10′·50W, 090°/270° from/to breakwater Lt, 0·77M. Give Downie Pt a wide berth. Do not enter in strong on-shore winds.

LIGHTS AND MARKS
When harbour is closed, a G Lt is displayed. N. Pier Iso WRG 4s 7m 11/7M.

RADIO TELEPHONE
None.

TELEPHONE (0569)
Hr Mr 62741; MRCC Aberdeen 592334; # Aberdeen 586258; Marinecall 0898 500 452; Police 62963; Dr 62945.

FACILITIES
EC Wednesday; **Aberdeen and Stonehaven YC** Slip, Bar; **Harbour** ☎ 65323, M, L, FW, AC, Slip, C (1·5 ton), AB; **Town** LB, V, R, Bar. ✉; Ⓑ; ⇄; ✈ (Aberdeen).

ABERDEEN 10-6-17

Aberdeen

CHARTS
Admiralty 1446, 210; OS 38

TIDES
+0231 Dover; ML 2·5; Duration 0620; Zone 0 (GMT).

Note: Aberdeen is a Standard Port and tidal predictions for each day of the year are given below.

SHELTER
Good shelter in harbour. Entry should not be attempted when winds are strong from NE through E to ESE. Yachts are not encouraged and it is very expensive. A busy commercial port and although all facilities are available, they are geared to commercial traffic. There are no special berths for yachts, so using commercial berths entails all the usual obligations and risks. Yachtsmen intending to call should contact the Hr Mr beforehand. Harbour open at all states of tide. Anchorage in Aberdeen Bay.

NAVIGATION
Waypoint Fairway safe water buoy, LFl 10s, Racon, 57°09′·34N 02°01′·83W, 058°/238° from/to N pier Lt, 1·1M. Give Girdle Ness a berth of at least ¼M (more in bad weather) and do not pass close round pier heads. Strong tidal streams and, with river in spate, possible overfalls. Channel dredged to 6m on leading line.

ABERDEEN *continued*

LIGHTS AND MARKS
Leading Lts 236° (FR when port open — FG when port closed).
Traffic signals at root of N Pier:
FG Entry prohibited
FR Departure prohibited
FR & FG Port closed

RADIO TELEPHONE
VHF Ch 16; 06 11 12 13 (H24).

TELEPHONE (0224)
Hr Mr 592571; MRCC 592334; ⌗ 586258; Weather: Dyce 722334; Marinecall 0898 500 452; Police 639111; Dr 55142.

FACILITIES
EC Wednesday/Saturday; **Enterprise Ship Stores** ☎ 590329, CH; **Woodsons of Aberdeen** ☎ 722884, El, Ⓔ; **Kelvin Hughes** ☎ 580823, CH, ACA; **North Sea Stores** ☎ 591896, CH; **Furuno (UK)** ☎ 595351, Ⓔ; **Seametrix** ☎ 873060, Ⓔ; **Town** P, D, V, R, Bar. ✉; Ⓑ; ⇌; ✈.

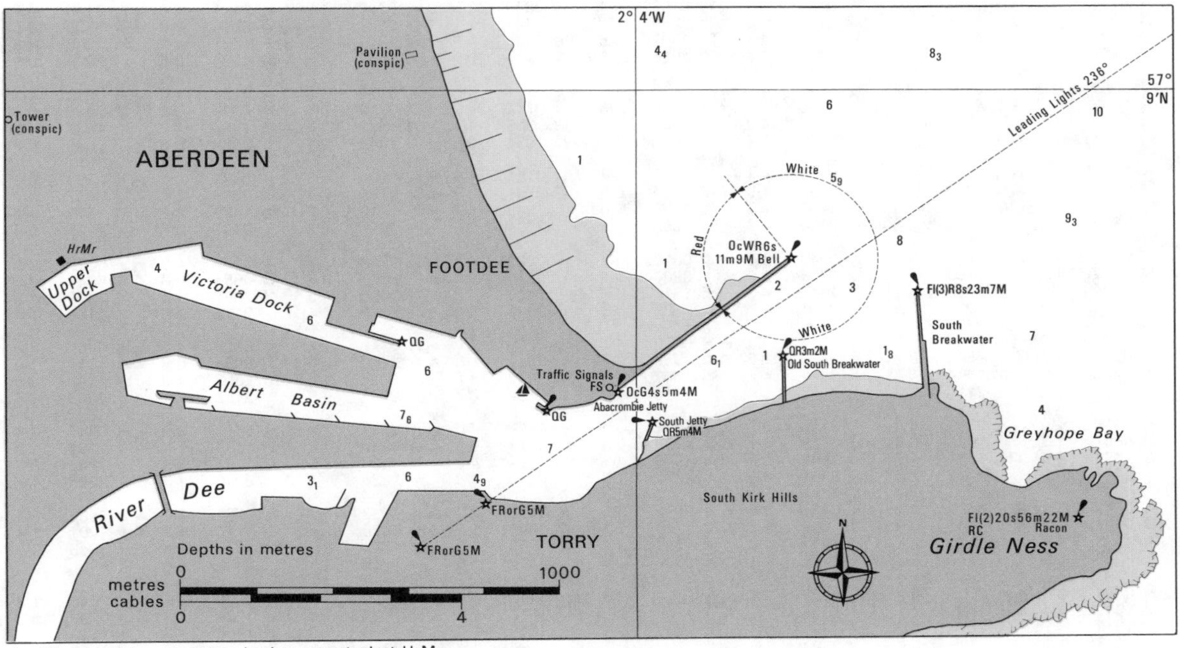

2° 4'W
57° 9'N
Pavilion (conspic)
Tower (conspic)
ABERDEEN
FOOTDEE
HrMr
Upper Dock
Victoria Dock
Albert Basin
River Dee
TORRY
South Kirk Hills
Girdle Ness
Greyhope Bay
Leading Lights 236°
White
Red
OcWR6s 11m9M Bell
Fl(3)R8s23m7M
South Breakwater
QR3m2M
Old South Breakwater
Traffic Signals
FS
OcG4s5m4M
Abacrombie Jetty
South Jetty QR5m4M
QG
FRorG5M
Fl(2)20s56m22M RC Racon
Depths in metres
metres
cables
1000

▲ After berthing, report to harbour control at HrMr

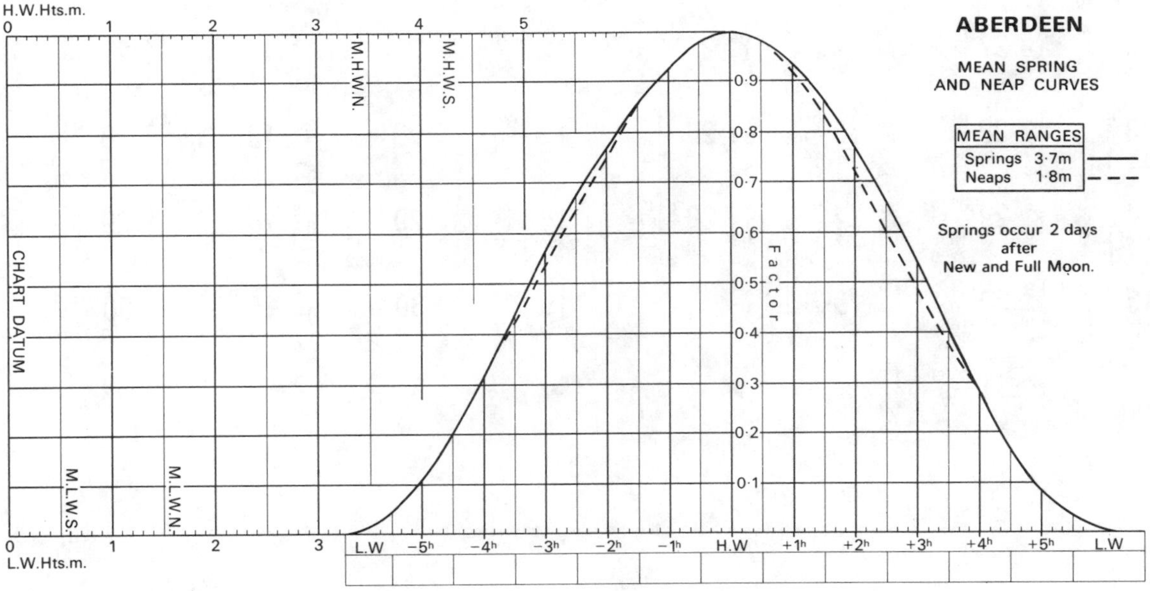

H.W.Hts.m.
M.H.W.N.
M.H.W.S.
CHART DATUM
M.L.W.S.
M.L.W.N.
L.W.Hts.m.
Factor
L.W -5h -4h -3h -2h -1h H.W +1h +2h +3h +4h +5h L.W
ABERDEEN
MEAN SPRING AND NEAP CURVES
MEAN RANGES
Springs 3·7m
Neaps 1·8m
Springs occur 2 days after New and Full Moon.

SCOTLAND, EAST COAST – ABERDEEN

TIME ZONE UT(GMT)
For Summer Time add ONE hour in non-shaded areas

Lat 57°09′ N Long 2°04′ W

TIMES AND HEIGHTS OF HIGH AND LOW WATERS

YEAR **1992**

JANUARY

Day	Time	m	Day	Time	m
1 W	0434 1054 1705 2319	1·4 3·6 1·4 3·6	16 Th	0327 0956 1604 2219	1·5 3·6 1·6 3·7
2 Th	0525 1142 1754	1·3 3·8 1·2	17 F	0435 1055 1709 2323	1·4 3·9 1·3 3·9
3 F	0008 0607 1221 1838	3·7 1·3 3·9 1·1	18 Sa	0534 1149 1805	1·2 4·1 0·9
4 Sa ●	0052 0645 1257 1914	3·8 1·3 4·1 1·0	19 Su ○	0021 0625 1236 1856	4·2 1·0 4·4 0·6
5 Su	0130 0720 1330 1948	3·9 1·2 4·1 0·9	20 M	0113 0713 1323 1944	4·4 0·8 4·6 0·3
6 M	0205 0752 1401 2020	4·0 1·2 4·2 0·9	21 Tu	0202 0758 1409 2030	4·5 0·7 4·7 0·2
7 Tu	0240 0825 1432 2053	4·0 1·2 4·2 0·8	22 W	0250 0842 1454 2117	4·5 0·7 4·7 0·2
8 W	0314 0857 1504 2127	4·0 1·2 4·2 0·9	23 Th	0336 0924 1541 2202	4·4 0·8 4·7 0·3
9 Th	0349 0931 1538 2200	3·9 1·3 4·1 0·9	24 F	0423 1007 1628 2248	4·2 0·9 4·5 0·6
10 F	0424 1006 1614 2237	3·8 1·4 4·1 1·1	25 Sa	0509 1052 1718 2337	3·9 1·1 4·2 0·9
11 Sa	0504 1044 1655 2318	3·7 1·5 3·9 1·2	26 Su ☾	0558 1142 1814	3·6 1·3 3·9
12 Su	0546 1127 1742	3·5 1·6 3·8	27 M	0031 0655 1242 1919	1·3 3·4 1·6 3·6
13 M ☽	0005 0638 1221 1839	1·4 3·4 1·7 3·6	28 Tu	0137 0802 1404 2037	1·6 3·3 1·7 3·4
14 Tu	0103 0740 1328 1948	1·5 3·4 1·8 3·5	29 W	0256 0917 1538 2159	1·7 3·3 1·7 3·3
15 W	0212 0849 1449 2104	1·6 3·4 1·8 3·5	30 Th	0412 1026 1651 2306	1·7 3·4 1·5 3·4
			31 F	0509 1120 1743 2357	1·6 3·6 1·3 3·6

FEBRUARY

Day	Time	m	Day	Time	m
1 Sa	0554 1203 1824	1·4 3·8 1·1	16 Su	0523 1132 1753	1·2 4·0 0·7
2 Su	0038 0631 1239 1859	3·7 1·3 3·9 0·9	17 M	0011 0614 1221 1842	4·1 0·9 4·3 0·4
3 M ●	0113 0704 1312 1930	3·9 1·2 4·1 0·8	18 Tu ○	0100 0659 1307 1928	4·4 0·7 4·6 0·2
4 Tu	0145 0735 1342 2001	4·0 1·1 4·2 0·7	19 W	0145 0740 1351 2011	4·5 0·6 4·7 0·1
5 W	0218 0805 1412 2030	4·1 1·0 4·2 0·7	20 Th	0227 0820 1434 2053	4·4 0·5 4·8 0·1
6 Th	0249 0836 1442 2101	4·0 1·0 4·3 0·7	21 F	0310 0900 1518 2135	4·3 0·5 4·7 0·3
7 F	0319 0905 1514 2132	4·0 1·0 4·2 0·8	22 Sa	0350 0939 1602 2216	4·1 0·7 4·4 0·6
8 Sa	0350 0938 1546 2204	3·9 1·1 4·2 0·9	23 Su	0431 1020 1648 2257	3·9 0·9 4·1 1·0
9 Su	0424 1013 1623 2241	3·8 1·2 4·0 1·1	24 M	0515 1105 1739 2342	3·6 1·2 3·7 1·4
10 M	0502 1052 1706 2323	3·7 1·3 3·8 1·3	25 Tu ☾	0604 1158 1839	3·4 1·5 3·4
11 Tu ☽	0549 1142 1803	3·5 1·5 3·6	26 W	0038 0704 1314 1959	1·7 3·2 1·7 3·2
12 W	0015 0649 1246 1914	1·5 3·4 1·7 3·5	27 Th	0204 0825 1507 2132	1·9 3·1 1·7 3·1
13 Th	0127 0805 1412 2042	1·6 3·4 1·7 3·4	28 F	0345 0948 1628 2245	1·9 3·2 1·6 3·3
14 F	0257 0924 1543 2204	1·7 3·5 1·5 3·6	29 Sa	0449 1051 1720 2336	1·7 3·4 1·3 3·5
15 Sa	0420 1034 1657 2315	1·5 3·7 1·1 3·9			

MARCH

Day	Time	m	Day	Time	m
1 Su	0533 1137 1800	1·5 3·6 1·1	16 M	0508 1113 1736 2356	1·2 4·0 0·6 4·1
2 M	0015 0610 1215 1834	3·7 1·3 3·8 0·9	17 Tu	0556 1203 1824	0·9 4·3 0·3
3 Tu	0049 0642 1248 1904	3·9 1·1 4·0 0·7	18 W ○	0042 0639 1249 1907	4·2 0·6 4·5 0·1
4 W ●	0121 0712 1319 1934	4·0 1·0 4·1 0·6	19 Th	0124 0719 1331 1948	4·3 0·5 4·6 0·1
5 Th	0151 0741 1348 2004	4·0 0·9 4·2 0·6	20 F	0204 0758 1413 2027	4·3 0·4 4·6 0·2
6 F	0220 0811 1418 2033	4·1 0·8 4·2 0·6	21 Sa	0243 0837 1456 2105	4·2 0·5 4·5 0·4
7 Sa	0250 0842 1450 2104	4·0 0·8 4·2 0·7	22 Su	0319 0915 1538 2143	4·1 0·6 4·2 0·8
8 Su	0319 0914 1524 2136	4·0 0·9 4·2 0·8	23 M	0357 0955 1623 2220	3·9 0·8 3·9 1·1
9 M	0352 0949 1602 2212	3·9 1·0 4·0 1·0	24 Tu	0437 1038 1711 2259	3·7 1·1 3·6 1·5
10 Tu	0430 1030 1648 2254	3·8 1·1 3·8 1·3	25 W	0520 1127 1808 2349	3·5 1·4 3·3 1·8
11 W	0516 1120 1747 2347	3·6 1·3 3·6 1·5	26 Th ☾	0614 1234 1921	3·3 1·6 3·1
12 Th ☽	0618 1227 1904	3·4 1·5 3·4	27 F	0104 0726 1419 2053	2·0 3·1 1·7 3·1
13 F	0103 0737 1357 2033	1·7 3·4 1·5 3·4	28 Sa	0300 0854 1548 2209	2·0 3·1 1·5 3·2
14 Sa	0244 0901 1531 2157	1·7 3·4 1·3 3·6	29 Su	0414 1009 1642 2302	1·8 3·2 1·3 3·4
15 Su	0409 1014 1641 2304	1·5 3·7 1·0 3·8	30 M	0501 1101 1725 2343	1·5 3·4 1·1 3·6
			31 Tu	0539 1142 1800	1·3 3·7 0·9

APRIL

Day	Time	m	Day	Time	m
1 W	0018 0612 1217 1832	3·8 1·1 3·8 0·8	16 Th	0019 0617 1229 1845	4·1 0·7 4·3 0·3
2 Th	0050 0643 1249 1903	3·9 0·9 4·0 0·7	17 F ○	0102 0657 1313 1926	4·1 0·5 4·4 0·3
3 F ●	0121 0714 1321 1934	4·0 0·8 4·1 0·6	18 Sa	0140 0738 1355 2004	4·2 0·5 4·3 0·5
4 Sa	0151 0745 1354 2005	4·0 0·8 4·2 0·6	19 Su	0218 0818 1437 2040	4·1 0·5 4·2 0·7
5 Su	0222 0819 1429 2037	4·1 0·7 4·2 0·7	20 M	0254 0857 1519 2115	4·0 0·7 4·0 0·9
6 M	0254 0854 1507 2112	4·0 0·8 4·1 0·9	21 Tu	0329 0936 1603 2150	3·9 0·8 3·8 1·2
7 Tu	0329 0934 1552 2152	4·0 0·9 4·0 1·1	22 W	0406 1017 1649 2230	3·7 1·0 3·5 1·5
8 W	0410 1019 1644 2240	3·9 1·0 3·8 1·3	23 Th	0447 1104 1742 2315	3·6 1·2 3·3 1·7
9 Th	0501 1113 1749 2337	3·7 1·2 3·6 1·6	24 F ☾	0536 1201 1843	3·4 1·4 3·2
10 F ☽	0604 1224 1904	3·5 1·3 3·5	25 Sa	0018 0636 1320 1958	1·9 3·2 1·5 3·1
11 Sa	0056 0721 1351 2027	1·7 3·4 1·3 3·5	26 Su	0148 0752 1446 2112	2·0 3·2 1·5 3·2
12 Su	0232 0842 1515 2143	1·7 3·5 1·1 3·6	27 M	0314 0910 1552 2213	1·8 3·2 1·4 3·3
13 M	0348 0953 1621 2245	1·5 3·7 0·8 3·8	28 Tu	0413 1012 1640 2301	1·6 3·4 1·2 3·5
14 Tu	0445 1052 1715 2336	1·2 3·9 0·6 3·9	29 W	0457 1059 1720 2340	1·4 3·5 1·0 3·6
15 W	0533 1143 1803	0·9 4·1 0·4	30 Th	0534 1140 1757	1·2 3·7 0·9

Chart Datum: 2.25 metres below Ordnance Datum (Newlyn)

TIME ZONE UT(GMT)

For Summer Time add ONE hour in non-shaded areas

SCOTLAND, EAST COAST – ABERDEEN

Lat 57°09′ N Long 2°04′ W

TIMES AND HEIGHTS OF HIGH AND LOW WATERS

YEAR **1992**

MAY

Day	Time	m
1 F	0015	3·8
	0611	1·0
	1217	3·9
	1831	0·8
2 Sa ●	0049	3·9
	0646	0·9
	1255	4·0
	1904	0·7
3 Su	0123	4·0
	0723	0·8
	1333	4·1
	1940	0·7
4 M	0157	4·1
	0801	0·7
	1413	4·1
	2018	0·8
5 Tu	0234	4·1
	0842	0·7
	1458	4·1
	2058	0·9
6 W	0315	4·1
	0927	0·7
	1549	4·0
	2143	1·1
7 Th	0402	4·0
	1016	0·8
	1645	3·9
	2234	1·3
8 F	0455	3·8
	1113	0·9
	1749	3·7
	2334	1·5
9 Sa ☽	0557	3·7
	1221	1·0
	1857	3·6
10 Su	0046	1·6
	0707	3·6
	1338	1·1
	2009	3·5
11 M	0206	1·6
	0820	3·6
	1453	1·0
	2118	3·6
12 Tu	0318	1·4
	0929	3·7
	1557	0·8
	2219	3·6
13 W	0417	1·2
	1030	3·9
	1652	0·7
	2312	3·8
14 Th	0509	1·0
	1123	4·0
	1740	0·6
	2357	3·9
15 F	0556	0·8
	1212	4·1
	1824	0·6
16 Sa ○	0039	4·0
	0641	0·7
	1257	4·1
	1903	0·6
17 Su	0119	4·0
	0723	0·7
	1341	4·0
	1941	0·8
18 M	0155	4·0
	0802	0·7
	1423	4·0
	2018	0·9
19 Tu	0230	4·0
	0842	0·7
	1504	3·8
	2053	1·1
20 W	0305	3·9
	0921	0·8
	1546	3·7
	2129	1·3
21 Th	0342	3·8
	1000	1·0
	1628	3·6
	2207	1·4
22 F	0421	3·7
	1042	1·1
	1715	3·4
	2249	1·6
23 Sa	0505	3·6
	1130	1·2
	1805	3·3
	2342	1·7
24 Su ☾	0557	3·4
	1228	1·4
	1903	3·2
25 M	0043	1·8
	0657	3·3
	1335	1·4
	2008	3·2
26 Tu	0157	1·8
	0805	3·3
	1444	1·4
	2111	3·2
27 W	0307	1·7
	0911	3·3
	1543	1·3
	2207	3·4
28 Th	0403	1·5
	1009	3·5
	1634	1·2
	2255	3·5
29 F	0452	1·4
	1059	3·6
	1718	1·1
	2337	3·7
30 Sa	0537	1·2
	1144	3·8
	1758	0·9
31 Su	0017	3·9
	0619	1·0
	1229	3·9
	1839	0·9

JUNE

Day	Time	m
1 M ●	0056	4·0
	0702	0·8
	1316	4·1
	1920	0·8
2 Tu	0135	4·2
	0747	0·7
	1402	4·1
	2004	0·8
3 W	0218	4·2
	0832	0·6
	1453	4·2
	2049	0·9
4 Th	0304	4·2
	0919	0·6
	1545	4·1
	2136	1·0
5 F	0352	4·2
	1012	0·6
	1640	4·0
	2227	1·1
6 Sa	0445	4·1
	1106	0·7
	1737	3·9
	2322	1·3
7 Su ☽	0543	4·0
	1207	0·8
	1836	3·7
8 M	0024	1·4
	0646	3·8
	1313	0·9
	1941	3·6
9 Tu	0131	1·4
	0754	3·7
	1422	1·0
	2046	3·5
10 W	0242	1·4
	0903	3·7
	1528	1·0
	2149	3·5
11 Th	0349	1·3
	1007	3·7
	1627	1·0
	2245	3·6
12 F	0448	1·1
	1106	3·8
	1719	1·0
	2336	3·7
13 Sa	0542	1·0
	1158	3·8
	1805	1·0
14 Su	0019	3·8
	0628	0·9
	1246	3·8
	1846	1·0
15 M ○	0059	3·9
	0712	0·8
	1330	3·9
	1924	1·0
16 Tu	0135	4·0
	0751	0·8
	1411	3·9
	2001	1·1
17 W	0211	4·0
	0827	0·8
	1449	3·8
	2034	1·1
18 Th	0244	4·0
	0903	0·8
	1527	3·8
	2110	1·2
19 F	0318	3·9
	0939	0·8
	1604	3·7
	2145	1·3
20 Sa	0355	3·9
	1016	0·9
	1644	3·6
	2223	1·4
21 Su	0435	3·8
	1057	1·1
	1726	3·5
	2305	1·5
22 M	0519	3·6
	1142	1·2
	1812	3·4
	2353	1·6
23 Tu ☾	0610	3·5
	1234	1·3
	1906	3·3
24 W	0050	1·7
	0707	3·4
	1333	1·4
	2006	3·2
25 Th	0157	1·7
	0811	3·4
	1437	1·4
	2108	3·3
26 F	0305	1·6
	0917	3·4
	1541	1·4
	2206	3·4
27 Sa	0410	1·5
	1020	3·5
	1637	1·3
	2258	3·6
28 Su	0506	1·3
	1118	3·7
	1729	1·1
	2346	3·9
29 M	0557	1·0
	1211	3·9
	1818	1·0
30 Tu ●	0032	4·1
	0646	0·8
	1302	4·1
	1904	0·9

JULY

Day	Time	m
1 W	0116	4·3
	0734	0·5
	1352	4·3
	1951	0·8
2 Th	0202	4·4
	0820	0·4
	1442	4·3
	2037	0·8
3 F	0249	4·4
	0908	0·3
	1532	4·3
	2122	0·8
4 Sa	0338	4·4
	0957	0·3
	1623	4·2
	2209	0·9
5 Su	0427	4·3
	1048	0·5
	1713	4·0
	2258	1·0
6 M	0520	4·2
	1142	0·7
	1807	3·8
	2351	1·2
7 Tu ☽	0619	4·0
	1241	0·9
	1904	3·5
8 W	0053	1·4
	0723	3·8
	1345	1·2
	2009	3·4
9 Th	0205	1·4
	0834	3·6
	1456	1·3
	2115	3·4
10 F	0322	1·4
	0948	3·5
	1603	1·3
	2220	3·5
11 Sa	0433	1·3
	1054	3·5
	1702	1·3
	2315	3·6
12 Su	0532	1·1
	1150	3·6
	1750	1·3
13 M	0001	3·7
	0619	1·0
	1236	3·7
	1832	1·2
14 Tu ○	0041	3·9
	0700	0·9
	1317	3·8
	1909	1·1
15 W	0117	4·0
	0735	0·8
	1354	3·9
	1942	1·1
16 Th	0149	4·0
	0809	0·7
	1429	3·9
	2015	1·1
17 F	0222	4·1
	0842	0·7
	1503	3·9
	2047	1·1
18 Sa	0254	4·1
	0914	0·7
	1536	3·9
	2119	1·1
19 Su	0328	4·0
	0948	0·8
	1610	3·8
	2153	1·2
20 M	0403	4·0
	1021	0·9
	1647	3·7
	2230	1·3
21 Tu	0441	3·8
	1059	1·1
	1726	3·5
	2311	1·4
22 W ☾	0525	3·7
	1142	1·3
	1812	3·4
	2358	1·6
23 Th	0618	3·5
	1232	1·4
	1909	3·3
24 F	0059	1·7
	0721	3·4
	1337	1·6
	2013	3·3
25 Sa	0215	1·7
	0834	3·4
	1451	1·6
	2121	3·4
26 Su	0334	1·6
	0950	3·5
	1604	1·5
	2224	3·6
27 M	0442	1·3
	1058	3·7
	1708	1·3
	2320	3·9
28 Tu	0540	1·0
	1156	4·0
	1801	1·1
29 W ●	0011	4·2
	0631	0·6
	1248	4·2
	1849	0·9
30 Th	0057	4·4
	0719	0·4
	1337	4·4
	1934	0·7
31 F	0144	4·6
	0805	0·2
	1425	4·4
	2018	0·6

AUGUST

Day	Time	m
1 Sa	0229	4·7
	0850	0·1
	1511	4·4
	2101	0·6
2 Su	0315	4·7
	0936	0·2
	1556	4·3
	2145	0·7
3 M	0403	4·5
	1021	0·4
	1644	4·0
	2230	0·9
4 Tu	0454	4·3
	1111	0·7
	1732	3·8
	2318	1·1
5 W ☽	0549	4·0
	1203	1·1
	1827	3·5
6 Th	0015	1·4
	0652	3·7
	1303	1·4
	1928	3·4
7 F	0130	1·5
	0806	3·4
	1420	1·6
	2042	3·3
8 Sa	0303	1·6
	0929	3·3
	1542	1·7
	2155	3·4
9 Su	0424	1·4
	1042	3·4
	1647	1·6
	2255	3·5
10 M	0522	1·2
	1139	3·5
	1736	1·5
	2343	3·7
11 Tu	0605	1·1
	1222	3·7
	1815	1·3
12 W	0021	3·9
	0642	0·9
	1259	3·8
	1849	1·2
13 Th ○	0056	4·0
	0714	0·8
	1331	3·9
	1921	1·1
14 F	0127	4·1
	0745	0·7
	1404	4·0
	1951	1·0
15 Sa	0158	4·2
	0816	0·6
	1434	4·0
	2022	1·0
16 Su	0227	4·2
	0846	0·7
	1505	4·0
	2053	1·0
17 M	0258	4·2
	0917	0·7
	1536	3·9
	2124	1·1
18 Tu	0332	4·1
	0948	0·9
	1609	3·8
	2157	1·2
19 W	0407	4·0
	1021	1·1
	1645	3·7
	2235	1·3
20 Th	0448	3·8
	1101	1·3
	1727	3·6
	2322	1·5
21 F ☾	0540	3·6
	1149	1·5
	1822	3·4
22 Sa	0021	1·6
	0648	3·4
	1252	1·7
	1931	3·4
23 Su	0140	1·7
	0809	3·4
	1418	1·7
	2049	3·5
24 M	0311	1·6
	0932	3·5
	1545	1·6
	2200	3·7
25 Tu	0427	1·3
	1044	3·7
	1651	1·4
	2259	4·0
26 W	0525	0·9
	1142	4·0
	1744	1·1
	2351	4·3
27 Th	0615	0·5
	1231	4·3
	1831	0·8
28 F ●	0038	4·5
	0700	0·2
	1317	4·4
	1914	0·6
29 Sa	0123	4·7
	0745	0·1
	1401	4·5
	1955	0·5
30 Su	0208	4·8
	0827	0·1
	1444	4·4
	2036	0·5
31 M	0253	4·7
	0911	0·2
	1528	4·3
	2118	0·6

Chart Datum: 2.25 metres below Ordnance Datum (Newlyn)

SCOTLAND, EAST COAST – ABERDEEN

TIME ZONE UT(GMT)
For Summer Time add ONE hour in non-shaded areas

Lat 57°09′ N Long 2°04′ W

TIMES AND HEIGHTS OF HIGH AND LOW WATERS

YEAR **1992**

SEPTEMBER

Day	Time	m	Day	Time	m
1 Tu	0338 0953 1612 2202	4·6 0·5 4·0 0·8	16 W	0305 0917 1535 2131	4·2 0·9 3·9 1·1
2 W	0427 1037 1657 2248	4·3 0·9 3·8 1·1	17 Th	0342 0950 1610 2210	4·0 1·1 3·8 1·3
3 Th ☽	0520 1123 1747 2343	3·9 1·3 3·6 1·4	18 F	0426 1030 1654 2257	3·8 1·3 3·7 1·4
4 F	0622 1219 1848	3·5 1·7 3·4	19 Sa ☾	0520 1119 1751 2358	3·6 1·6 3·6 1·6
5 Sa	0057 0740 1340 2004	1·6 3·3 1·9 3·3	20 Su	0634 1228 1904	3·5 1·8 3·5
6 Su	0243 0910 1518 2125	1·7 3·2 1·9 3·3	21 M	0123 0757 1359 2026	1·6 3·4 1·8 3·5
7 M	0407 1024 1627 2230	1·5 3·3 1·8 3·5	22 Tu	0256 0921 1529 2139	1·5 3·6 1·7 3·7
8 Tu	0502 1118 1713 2318	1·3 3·5 1·6 3·7	23 W	0410 1030 1634 2241	1·2 3·8 1·4 4·0
9 W	0543 1158 1751 2357	1·1 3·7 1·3 3·9	24 Th	0506 1125 1725 2332	0·8 4·1 1·1 4·3
10 Th	0617 1232 1824	0·9 3·9 1·2	25 F	0556 1211 1810	0·5 4·3 0·8
11 F	0031 0649 1304 1855	4·0 0·8 4·0 1·0	26 Sa ●	0018 0639 1256 1852	4·6 0·2 4·4 0·6
12 Sa ○	0102 0719 1335 1926	4·1 0·7 4·1 1·0	27 Su	0103 0723 1337 1933	4·7 0·2 4·4 0·5
13 Su	0131 0748 1405 1955	4·2 0·7 4·1 0·9	28 M	0147 0804 1419 2013	4·8 0·2 4·4 0·5
14 M	0201 0816 1434 2025	4·2 0·7 4·1 1·0	29 Tu	0232 0844 1458 2054	4·7 0·4 4·3 0·7
15 Tu	0232 0846 1504 2057	4·2 0·8 4·0 1·0	30 W	0317 0924 1539 2138	4·4 0·7 4·1 0·9

OCTOBER

Day	Time	m	Day	Time	m
1 Th	0404 1004 1621 2223	4·1 1·1 3·9 1·1	16 F	0328 0929 1546 2156	4·1 1·2 4·0 1·2
2 F	0455 1047 1709 2316	3·8 1·5 3·6 1·4	17 Sa	0417 1013 1634 2247	3·9 1·4 3·9 1·3
3 Sa ☽	0556 1137 1805	3·5 1·8 3·4	18 Su	0518 1106 1733 2351	3·7 1·7 3·7 1·5
4 Su	0027 0709 1252 1917	1·7 3·3 2·1 3·3	19 M ☾	0629 1217 1846	3·6 1·8 3·6
5 M	0206 0834 1437 2042	1·7 3·2 2·1 3·3	20 Tu	0113 0748 1347 2006	1·5 3·6 1·9 3·7
6 Tu	0331 0949 1552 2152	1·6 3·3 1·9 3·4	21 W	0239 0905 1508 2118	1·3 3·7 1·7 3·8
7 W	0427 1044 1641 2244	1·4 3·5 1·6 3·6	22 Th	0348 1010 1612 2220	1·1 3·9 1·4 4·1
8 Th	0509 1125 1720 2326	1·2 3·7 1·4 3·8	23 F	0444 1104 1702 2312	0·8 4·1 1·1 4·3
9 F	0546 1201 1754	1·0 3·9 1·2	24 Sa	0533 1151 1749	0·6 4·2 0·9
10 Sa	0001 0618 1235 1827	4·0 0·9 4·0 1·1	25 Su ●	0000 0618 1234 1832	4·5 0·4 4·3 0·7
11 Su ○	0034 0649 1306 1857	4·1 0·8 4·1 1·0	26 M	0046 0700 1316 1914	4·6 0·4 4·4 0·6
12 M	0106 0719 1335 1928	4·2 0·8 4·1 1·0	27 Tu	0131 0741 1355 1957	4·6 0·5 4·4 0·6
13 Tu	0137 0748 1405 2001	4·2 0·8 4·1 1·0	28 W	0215 0820 1433 2037	4·5 0·7 4·3 0·7
14 W	0211 0819 1436 2036	4·2 0·9 4·1 1·0	29 Th	0300 0858 1512 2121	4·3 1·0 4·1 0·9
15 Th	0247 0853 1508 2114	4·2 1·0 4·1 1·1	30 F	0346 0936 1552 2204	4·0 1·3 4·0 1·1
			31 Sa	0435 1017 1634 2252	3·8 1·6 3·8 1·3

NOVEMBER

Day	Time	m	Day	Time	m
1 Su	0529 1104 1725 2351	3·5 1·9 3·6 1·5	16 M	0515 1059 1722 2344	3·9 1·6 3·9 1·2
2 M ☽	0631 1204 1825	3·4 2·0 3·4	17 Tu ☾	0619 1204 1828	3·8 1·7 3·8
3 Tu	0107 0742 1330 1940	1·7 3·3 2·1 3·4	18 W	0057 0730 1321 1941	1·2 3·7 1·8 3·8
4 W	0230 0856 1454 2056	1·6 3·3 2·0 3·4	19 Th	0212 0842 1437 2053	1·2 3·7 1·7 3·9
5 Th	0336 0956 1556 2157	1·5 3·5 1·8 3·5	20 F	0321 0945 1543 2156	1·1 3·8 1·5 4·0
6 F	0426 1045 1641 2247	1·4 3·6 1·6 3·7	21 Sa	0420 1041 1640 2254	0·9 3·9 1·2 4·2
7 Sa	0506 1126 1722 2327	1·2 3·8 1·4 3·9	22 Su	0512 1130 1730 2346	0·8 4·1 1·0 4·3
8 Su	0543 1201 1757	1·1 3·9 1·2	23 M	0558 1215 1818	0·7 4·2 0·9
9 M	0004 0617 1235 1832	4·0 1·0 4·1 1·1	24 Tu ●	0034 0642 1256 1902	4·3 0·8 4·3 0·8
10 Tu ○	0041 0649 1307 1907	4·1 1·0 4·2 1·0	25 W	0120 0723 1335 1945	4·3 0·8 4·3 0·7
11 W	0117 0723 1340 1942	4·2 1·0 4·2 1·0	26 Th	0205 0801 1413 2026	4·2 1·0 4·3 0·8
12 Th	0155 0758 1413 2022	4·2 1·0 4·3 0·9	27 F	0247 0837 1450 2107	4·1 1·2 4·2 0·9
13 F	0237 0836 1450 2104	4·2 1·1 4·3 0·9	28 Sa	0331 0914 1527 2146	4·0 1·4 4·1 1·0
14 Sa	0324 0918 1534 2150	4·1 1·3 4·2 1·0	29 Su	0413 0952 1604 2228	3·8 1·5 4·0 1·2
15 Su	0416 1004 1623 2242	4·0 1·4 4·1 1·1	30 M	0458 1034 1648 2315	3·7 1·7 3·8 1·3

DECEMBER

Day	Time	m	Day	Time	m
1 Tu	0549 1122 1737	3·5 1·8 3·6	16 W ☾	0600 1143 1805	3·9 1·5 4·1
2 W ☽	0008 0645 1221 1836	1·5 3·4 2·0 3·5	17 Th	0032 0702 1248 1912	1·0 3·7 1·6 3·9
3 Th	0114 0748 1334 1944	1·6 3·3 2·0 3·4	18 F	0140 0809 1401 2023	1·1 3·6 1·6 3·9
4 F	0225 0856 1449 2054	1·6 3·4 1·9 3·4	19 Sa	0250 0915 1514 2134	1·2 3·7 1·5 3·8
5 Sa	0328 0955 1552 2156	1·5 3·5 1·8 3·5	20 Su	0356 1017 1621 2238	1·2 3·7 1·4 3·9
6 Su	0420 1044 1642 2248	1·4 3·6 1·6 3·7	21 M	0454 1112 1719 2336	1·1 3·9 1·2 4·0
7 M	0504 1126 1727 2333	1·3 3·8 1·4 3·8	22 Tu	0543 1200 1810	1·1 4·0 1·0
8 Tu	0544 1204 1808	1·2 4·0 1·2	23 W	0027 0628 1242 1855	4·0 1·1 4·2 0·9
9 W ○	0017 0624 1241 1849	4·0 1·1 4·2 1·0	24 Th ●	0113 0707 1320 1937	4·1 1·1 4·2 0·8
10 Th	0059 0702 1317 1930	4·1 1·1 4·3 0·9	25 F	0154 0745 1355 2015	4·1 1·1 4·3 0·8
11 F	0142 0742 1357 2012	4·2 1·0 4·4 0·8	26 Sa	0233 0820 1430 2050	4·0 1·2 4·3 0·8
12 Sa	0229 0825 1437 2056	4·3 1·1 4·5 0·7	27 Su	0311 0854 1504 2125	4·0 1·2 4·2 0·9
13 Su	0317 0908 1522 2143	4·3 1·1 4·4 0·7	28 M	0348 0929 1538 2202	3·9 1·3 4·1 1·0
14 M	0407 0955 1612 2234	4·2 1·2 4·3 0·8	29 Tu	0426 1004 1616 2238	3·8 1·4 4·0 1·1
15 Tu	0502 1045 1705 2330	4·1 1·4 4·2 0·9	30 W	0506 1044 1657 2320	3·7 1·6 3·9 1·3
			31 Th	0551 1129 1744	3·5 1·7 3·7

Chart Datum: 2.25 metres below Ordnance Datum (Newlyn)

PETERHEAD 10-6-18

Aberdeen

CHARTS
Admiralty 1438, 213; OS 30

TIDES
+0140 Dover; ML 2·3; Duration 0620; Zone 0 (GMT).

Standard Port ABERDEEN (⟵)

Times				Height (metres)			
HW		LW		MHWS	MHWN	MLWN	MLWS
0000	0600	0100	0700	4·3	3·4	1·6	0·6
1200	1800	1300	1900				
Differences PETERHEAD							
−0035	−0045	−0035	−0040	−0·5	−0·3	−0·1	−0·1

SHELTER
Excellent shelter. Can be entered in any weather at any tide. The bay is enclosed by breakwaters behind which yachts can anchor. Alongside berths in the inner harbours are sometimes available. Contact Hr Mr on VHF before entering or leaving.

NAVIGATION
Waypoint 57°29′·14N 01°45′·00W, 134°/314° from/to entrance, 1·0M. Peterhead is a major fishing port with all the implications. No navigational dangers.

LIGHTS AND MARKS
Leading lights into Peterhead Bay 314°.
Fishing Harbour signals (on Control Tower over Hr office on West pier)
3 Fl R (hor) – Bay closed to inward traffic
3 FR (hor) – Fishing Hr closed to inward traffic
2 Fl R (hor) – No exit from Bay to sea
2 FR (hor) – No exit from Fishing Hr
4 Fl R (hor) – Bay and harbour closed – No traffic movement permitted.
4 FR (hor) – Fishing harbour closed
When no signals showing, vessels may enter or leave with permission from Control Tower, call on Ch 16.

RADIO TELEPHONE
VHF Ch Port, Ch 14; 14. Emergency only, Ch 16.

TELEPHONE (0779)
Hr Mr 74281/3; MRCC Aberdeen 592334; # 74867; Marinecall 0898 500 452; Police 72571; Dr 74841.

FACILITIES
EC Wednesday; **A.J. Buchan** ☎ 72348, Slip, ME, El, Sh, C; **Northern Engineering** ☎ 72406, ME, El, Sh, C; **R. Irvin** ☎ 72044, ME, El, Sh, C; **Racal Decca** ☎ 73005, Ⓔ; **Woodsons** ☎ 70931, Ⓔ; **A. M. Campbell** ☎ 76433, El; **Murisons** ☎ 72173, Gas; **Town** P, D, V, R, Bar, ✉; Ⓑ; ≷ (bus to Aberdeen); ✈ (Aberdeen).

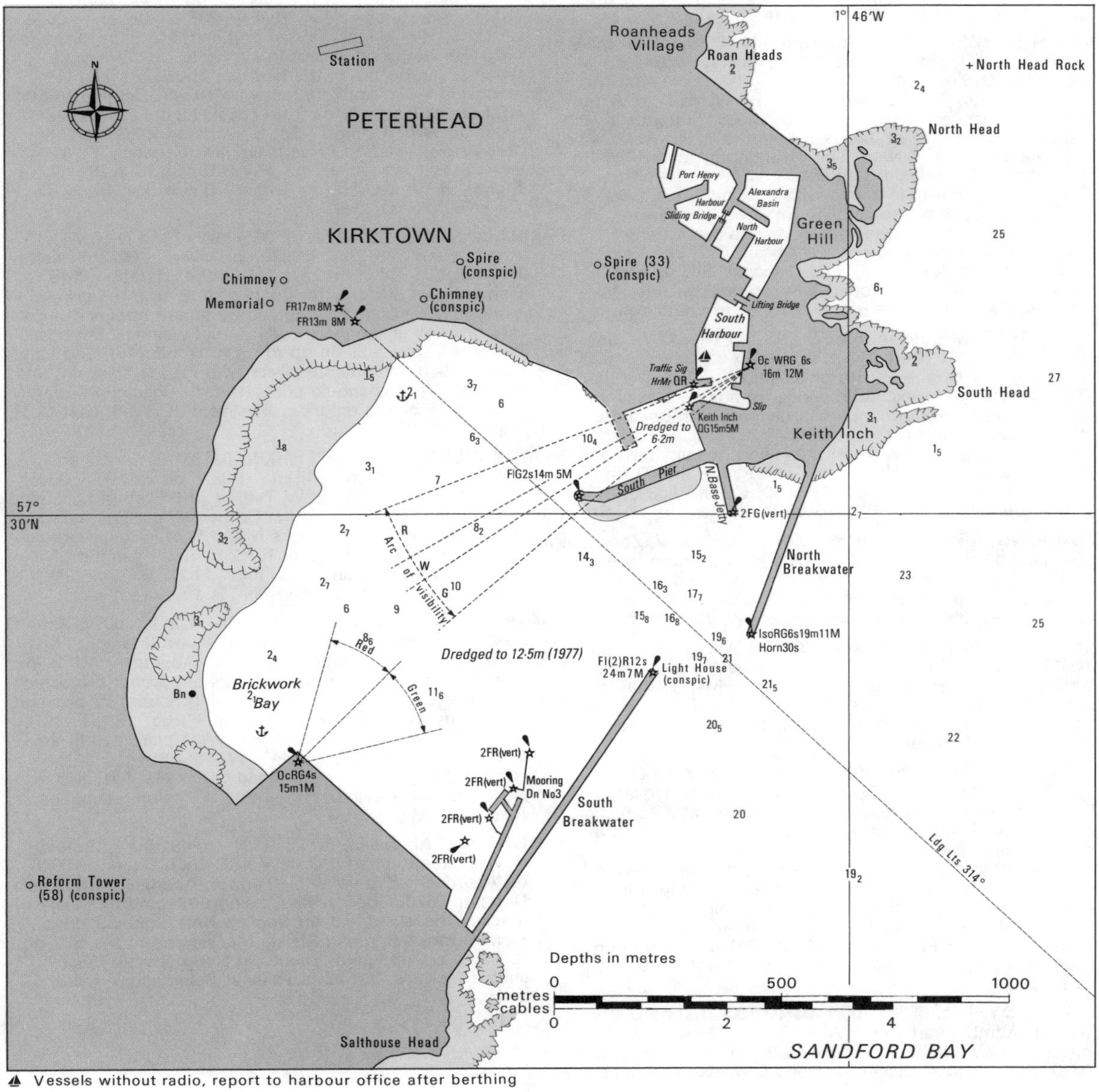

1° 46′W
Roanheads Village
Roan Heads
Station
+North Head Rock
North Head
PETERHEAD
Port Henry Harbour
Sliding Bridge
Alexandra Basin
North Harbour
Green Hill
KIRKTOWN
Spire (conspic)
Spire (33) (conspic)
Chimney
Memorial
FR17m 8M
FR13m 8M
Chimney (conspic)
Lifting Bridge
South Harbour
Traffic Sig HrMr QR
Oc WRG 6s 16m 12M
Slip
Keith Inch QG15m5M
Keith Inch
South Head
Dredged to 6·2m
FIG2s14m 5M
South Pier
N.Base Jetty
2FG(vert)
57° 30′N
R
W
G
Arc of visibility
North Breakwater
IsoRG6s19m11M Horn30s
Red
Green
Dredged to 12·5m (1977)
Fl(2)R12s 24m7M
Light House (conspic)
Brickwork Bay
Bn
OcRG4s 15m1M
2FR(vert)
Mooring Dn No3
South Breakwater
Ldg Lts 314°
Reform Tower (58) (conspic)
Depths in metres
metres
cables
Salthouse Head
SANDFORD BAY

▲ Vessels without radio, report to harbour office after berthing

MINOR HARBOURS AND ANCHORAGES 10.6.19

BURNMOUTH, Berwick, 55°50′·00N, 02°04′·00W, Zone O (GMT), Admty chart 160. HW +0315 on Dover, −0025 on Leith; Duration 0615. Good shelter especially in inner harbour (dries). With on-shore winds a swell makes outer harbour uncomfortable. Min depth at entrance at LWS is 0·6m. From S beware Quarry Shoal Rocks; from N beware East and West Carrs. Leading line at 274° with two Bns or FR at night 29/35m 4M, 45m apart run in towards the harbour mouth until the Lts in the inner basin at root of W pier (2FG (vert)) come in line with outer harbour entrance. Facilities: FW, limited stores, Bar at top of valley.

ST ABBS, Berwick, 55°54′·00N, 02°08′·00W, Zone O (GMT), Admty chart 175. HW +0330 on Dover, −0017 on Leith; HW height −0·6m on Leith; Duration 0605; Shelter good. In strong on-shore winds outer harbour suffers from waves breaking over E pier. Inner harbour is best but often full of fishing boats and dries out. Hr Mr will direct visitors. On E side of entrance channel, beware Hog's Nose and on W side the Maw Carr, Ldg Line S face of Maw Carr on village hall (conspic) runs in until the harbour entrance opens to port when the second Ldg Line can be seen, front on head of jetty FR 4m 1M, rear on SW corner of old harbour FR 8m 1M. Access HW∓3. Facilities: FW on quay (tap), V (local grocer), LB, R, more facilities including bar at Coldingham (½ M).

NORTH BERWICK, East Lothian, 56°04′·00N, 02°43′·00W Zone O (GMT), Admty chart 734. Fidra HW +0344 on Dover, −0005 on Leith; HW height −0·2m on Leith; ML 3·1m; Duration 0625. Shelter good with winds S to W but harbour is dangerous with on-shore winds. Entrance is closed by boom in bad weather. Entrance is 8m wide. Harbour dries out. Beware The Maidenfoot, marked by Bn 1 ca NW of N pierhead. Ldg line – W face of North Berwick Law (conspic) in line with post on N pierhead (160°). Lights; N pierhead FWR 7m 3M R to seaward, W over harbour. Extinguished when vessels cannot enter harbour due to bad weather. Facilities: EC Thurs; **East Lothian YC** ☎ 2698 Bar, P and D (cans), FW on pier, stores etc obtainable in town; **Lawrence Turnbull** ☎ 2134, Gas; Ⓑ, ✉, ≠ & Bus services to Edinburgh.

FISHERROW, Midlothian, 55°57′·00N, 03°04′·00W, Zone O (GMT), Admty chart 734. HW +0345 on Dover, −0005 on Leith; HW height −0·1m on Leith; ML 3·0m; Duration 0620. Shelter good except in winds from NW. Mainly a pleasure craft harbour. Approach dangerous in on-shore winds. Harbour dries; available HW∓2. Light – E pier head, Oc 6s 5m 6M on metal framework tower. Berth on E pier. Facilities: EC Wed; stores and FW. P and D from garage. Hr Mr ☎ Edinburgh 665-5900; CG 665-5639; **Fisherrow YC** ☎ 665-2576; **Town** V, R, Bar, Ⓑ, ✉, SM.

CRAMOND, Midlothian, 55°59′·00N, 03°18′·00W, Zone O (GMT), Admty chart 736. Tidal details as Granton (see 10.6.9). Enter R Almond, W of Cramond Island, marked by buoys and posts. Access HW∓2. **Cramond Boat Club** ☎ 336-1356 FW, M, Bar; **Village** V, R, Pub, Bus.

INCHCOLM, Fife, 56°02′·00N, 03°18′·00W, Zone O (GMT), Admty chart 736. Tidal details as Aberdour. Best anchorage N of abbey (conspic). Beware Meadulse Rocks (dry). Ends of island foul. Lt Fl(3) 15s (obsc 075°–145°) at SE point, Horn(3) 45s. Land at jetty E of abbey (fee payable). No facilities.

ABERDOUR, Fife, 56°03′·00N, 03°18′·00W, Zone O (GMT), Admty charts 735, 736. HW +0345 on Dover; +0005 on Leith; HW height 0·0m on Leith; ML 3·3m; Duration 0630. Good shelter except in SE winds when a swell occurs. The anchorage between The Little Craigs and the disused pier is good but exposed to winds from E to SW. Temporary berths are available in harbour (dries) alongside the quay wall. Beware Little Craigs (dries 2·1m) and outfall 2ca N marked by Bn. There are no lights or marks. Facilities: EC Wed; Hr Mr ☎ 860140, FW (tap on pier), P, R, V, Bar in village. **Aberdour Boat Club** ☎ 860206.

KIRKCALDY, Fife, 56°07′·00N, 03°09′·00W, Zone O (GMT), Admty chart 739. HW +0345 on Dover, −0005 on Leith; HW height −0·1m on Leith; ML 3·2m; Duration 0620. Shelter good except in strong E winds. Yachts can berth on E pier in outer harbour (known as Pier Harbour) or, by arrangement with Hr Mr, enter the Wet Dock (HW−2 to HW) if space allows. If possible make arrangements before arrival (Methil Hr. Radio Ch 16, 14 will relay messages). A special Lt Buoy FlY 5s, lies ½ M E of harbour. If approaching from E, keep S of the Bn 60m SSE of East Pier Lt. Lights; E pier head, Fl WG 10s 10m 8M; G156°–336°, W336°–156°. S pier head 2 FR (vert) 7m, 5M. W pier, inner head FW 5m. Dock entrance W side FR 6m, E side FG 6m. Entry signals, day and night: FR-Port closed, bring up in roads. FG-Entry permitted. Harbour is administered by Forth Ports Authority. Contact Methil ☎ 26725. Facilities: EC Wed; Bar, D (by road tanker); FW, R, V. Small repairs can be arranged. ✉, Ⓑ.

ELIE, Fife, 56°11′·00N, 02°46′·00W, Zone O (GMT), Admty chart 734. HW +0325 on Dover, −0015 on Leith; HW height −0·1m on Leith; ML 3·2m; Duration 0620; Elie Bay provides good shelter from winds in the N sectors to small craft but local knowledge is needed. Anchor to W of pier or take the mud alongside it. Beware ledge off end of pier which dries. Coming from E beware Ox Rock (dries 1m) ½ M ENE of Elie Ness; coming from W beware rocks off Chapel Ness, West Vows, East Vows (surmounted by cage Bn) and Thill Rock, the E extremity of the latter pair marked by R can buoy. Light; Elie Ness Fl 6s 15m 18M, white Tr. Facilities: In villages of Elie and Earlsferry, FW, R, V, Bar, ✉, Ⓑ; **Shell Bay** ☎ 330283, Gas.

ST MONANS, Fife, 56°12′·00N, 02°46′·00W, Zone O (GMT), Admty chart 734. HW +0335 on Dover, −0020 on Leith; HW height −0·1m on Leith; ML 3·2m; Duration 0620. Shelter good except in strong SE to SW winds when scend occurs in the harbour. Harbour dries. Lie alongside E pier until contact with Hr Mr. Coming from NE keep at least 2½ ca from coast. Lights Breakwater head Oc WRG 6s 5m 7/4M; E pier head 2 FG (vert) 6m 4M. W pier head 2 FR (vert) 6m 4M. Facilities: EC Wed; Bar, D (by road tanker), El, FW, ME, Sh, Slip (by root of E pier), R, V, ✉, AC, Ⓑ; **Millers BY** ☎ 864; **Bass Rk Oil** ☎ 501, P, D, Gas.

CRAIL, Fife, 56°15′·00N, 02°38′·00W, Zone O (GMT), Admty chart 175. HW +0320 on Dover, −0020 on Leith; HW height −0·2m on Leith; ML 3·0m; Duration 0615. Good shelter but only for boats able to take the ground alongside. Harbour is protected by timber booms dropped into grooves at the pier heads in foul weather. Entrance between S pier and Bn on rocks to S following Ldg Line 295° – two W concrete pillars with FR Lts, 24m 6M and 30m 6M. Vessels should contact Forth Coastguard on VHF Ch 16 before entering. Facilities: EC Wed; Bar, C, R, Slip, V, ✉, Ⓑ.

MAY ISLAND, Fife, 56°11′·00N, 02°33′·00W, Zone O (GMT), Admty chart 734. HW +0325 on Dover, −0025 on Leith. Anchorages at W Tarbert or E Tarbert according to the wind. Landing at Altar Stones. There is a harbour at Kirk Haven. Beware rocks N and S of island, Norman Rock to N and Maiden Hair Rock to S. At summit of island, a square Tr on stone house Fl(2) 15s 73m 22M. There are no facilities. The island is a nature reserve.

GOURDON, Kincardine, 56°50′·00N, 002°17′·00W, Zone O (GMT), Admty chart 210. HW +0240 on Dover; +0020 on Aberdeen; HW height +0·4m on Aberdeen; ML 2·7m; Duration 0620. Shelter good and inner harbour protected by storm gates. Beware rocks running S from W pier end marked by Bn. Lights – Ldg Lts 358°, both FR. Front Lt shows G when not safe to enter. West pier head Fl WRG 3s 5m 9/7M, vis G180°–344°, W344°–354°, R354°–180°. E breakwater head Q 3m 7M. Facilities: Hr Mr ☎ Inverbervie 61779 – Slip, FW from standpipe, V, R, Bar, D, ME, AC, M.

BODDAM, Aberdeen, 57°28′·00N, 01°46′·00W, Zone O (GMT), Admty chart 213. HW +0145 on Dover, −0040 on Aberdeen; HW height −0·4m on Aberdeen; ML 2·3m; Duration 0620. Good shelter, being protected by Meikle Mackie, the island just off Buchan Ness; harbour dries. Beware rocks all round Meikle Mackie and to the SW of it. There are no lights. Yachts lie along N wall. Very limited facilities, but all facilities at Peterhead, 4 miles away.

Area 7

North-East Scotland

Rattray Head to Cape Wrath
including Orkney and Shetland Islands

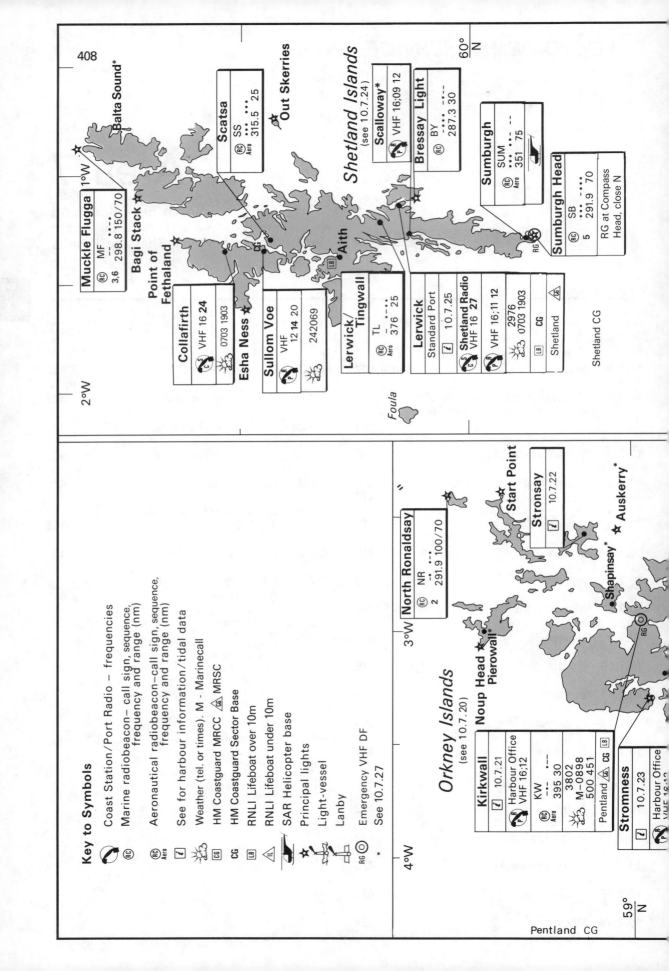

Key to Symbols

- Coast Station/Port Radio – frequencies
- Marine radiobeacon– call sign, sequence, frequency and range (nm)
- Aeronautical radiobeacon–call sign, sequence, frequency and range (nm)
- See for harbour information/tidal data
- Weather (tel. or times). M - Marinecall
- HM Coastguard MRCC / MRSC
- CG HM Coastguard Sector Base
- RNLI Lifeboat over 10m
- RNLI Lifeboat under 10m
- SAR Helicopter base
- Principal lights
- Light-vessel
- Lanby
- RG Emergency VHF DF
- * See 10.7.27

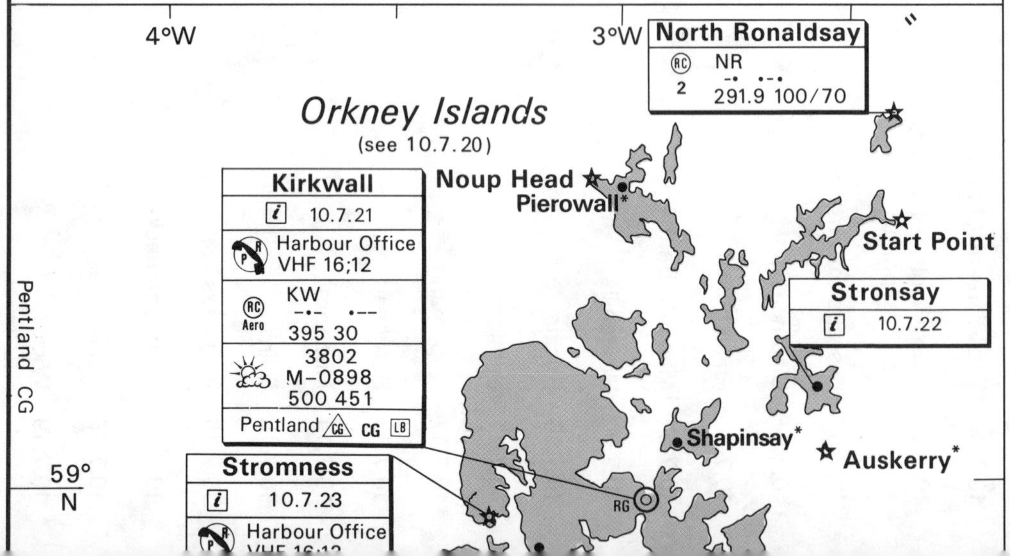

4°W
3°W
59° N
Orkney Islands
(see 10.7.20)
North Ronaldsay
NR
2
291.9 100/70
Noup Head
Pierowall*
Start Point
Stronsay
10.7.22
Kirkwall
10.7.21
Harbour Office
VHF 16;12
KW
395 30
3802
M–0898
500 451
Pentland CG
Shapinsay*
Auskerry*
Stromness
10.7.23
Harbour Office
RG
Pentland CG

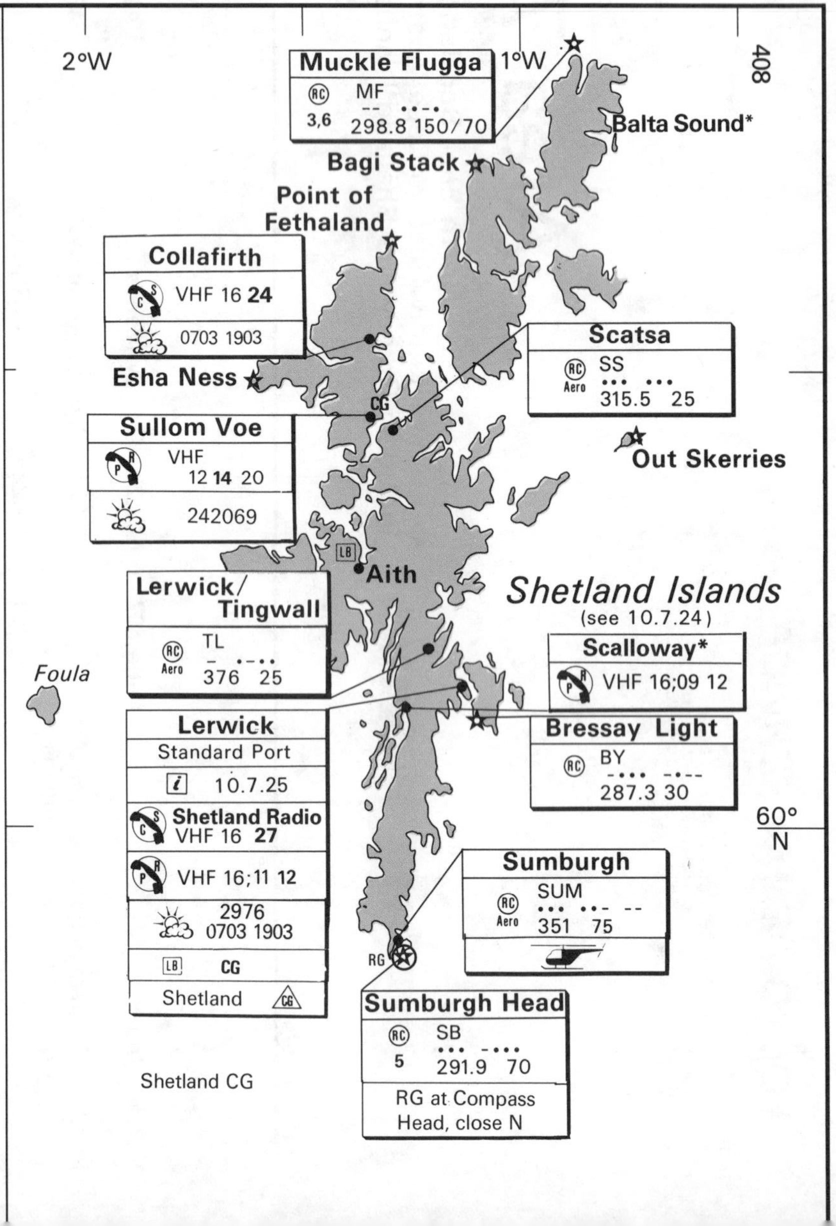

2°W
1°W
60° N
Muckle Flugga
MF
3,6
298.8 150/70
Balta Sound*
Bagi Stack
Point of Fethaland
Collafirth
VHF 16 24
0703 1903
Esha Ness
Scatsa
SS
315.5 25
Out Skerries
Sullom Voe
VHF
12 14 20
242069
CG
Aith
Shetland Islands
(see 10.7.24)
Lerwick/ Tingwall
TL
376 25
Foula
Scalloway*
VHF 16;09 12
Lerwick
Standard Port
10.7.25
Shetland Radio
VHF 16 27
VHF 16;11 12
2976
0703 1903
CG
Shetland
Bressay Light
BY
287.3 30
Sumburgh
SUM
351 75
Sumburgh Head
SB
5
291.9 70
RG at Compass Head, close N
RG
Shetland CG

10-7-2
North-East Scotland, Orkney and Shetland

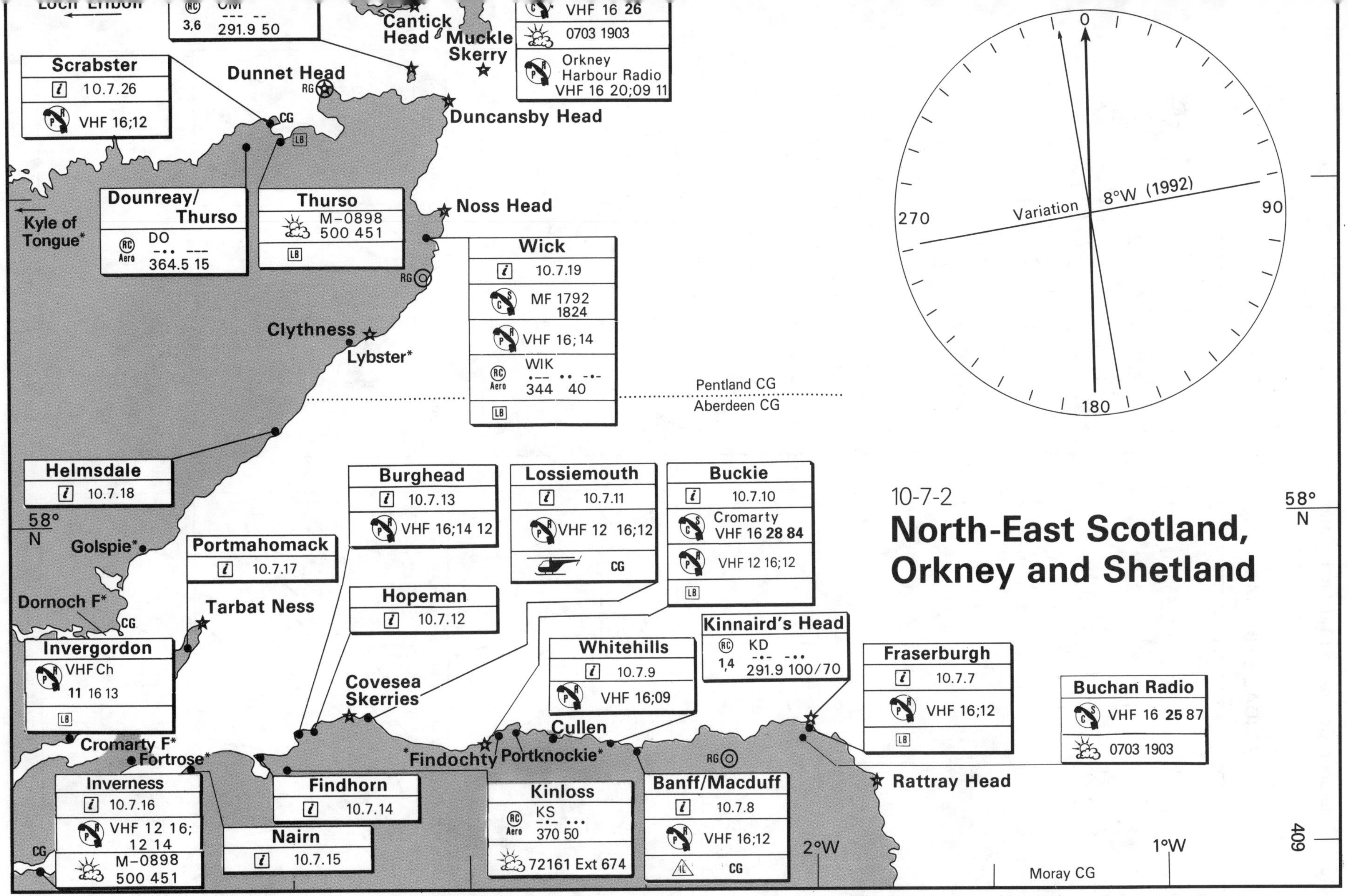
Scrabster
10.7.26
VHF 16;12
3,6 291.9 50
Dunnet Head
Cantick Head
Muckle Skerry
VHF 16 26
0703 1903
Orkney Harbour Radio VHF 16 20;09 11
Duncansby Head
Dounreay/ Thurso
DO
364.5 15
Thurso
M-0898 500 451
Kyle of Tongue*
Noss Head
Wick
10.7.19
MF 1792 1824
VHF 16;14
WIK
344 40
Clythness
Lybster*
Pentland CG
Aberdeen CG
Helmsdale
10.7.18
58° N
Golspie*
Portmahomack
10.7.17
Dornoch F*
Tarbat Ness
Invergordon
VHF Ch 11 16 13
Cromarty F*
Fortrose*
Inverness
10.7.16
VHF 12 16; 12 14
M-0898 500 451
Nairn
10.7.15
Findhorn
10.7.14
Burghead
10.7.13
VHF 16;14 12
Hopeman
10.7.12
Covesea Skerries
Lossiemouth
10.7.11
VHF 12 16;12
Buckie
10.7.10
Cromarty VHF 16 28 84
VHF 12 16;12
Whitehills
10.7.9
VHF 16;09
Cullen
Findochty
Portknockie*
Kinloss
KS
370 50
72161 Ext 674
Banff/Macduff
10.7.8
VHF 16;12
Kinnaird's Head
KD
1,4 291.9 100/70
Fraserburgh
10.7.7
VHF 16;12
Buchan Radio
VHF 16 25 87
0703 1903
Rattray Head
2°W
1°W
Moray CG
58° N
Variation
8°W (1992)
0
90
180
270

10.7.3 AREA 7 TIDAL STREAMS

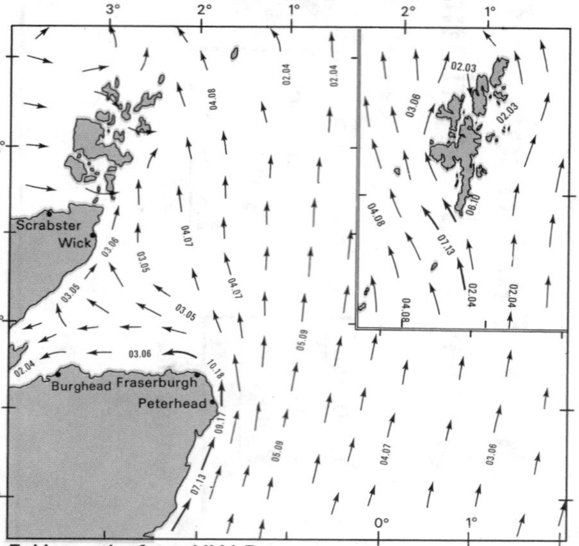
Scrabster
Wick
Burghead
Fraserburgh
Peterhead

5 Hours before HW Dover (0500 after HW Aberdeen)

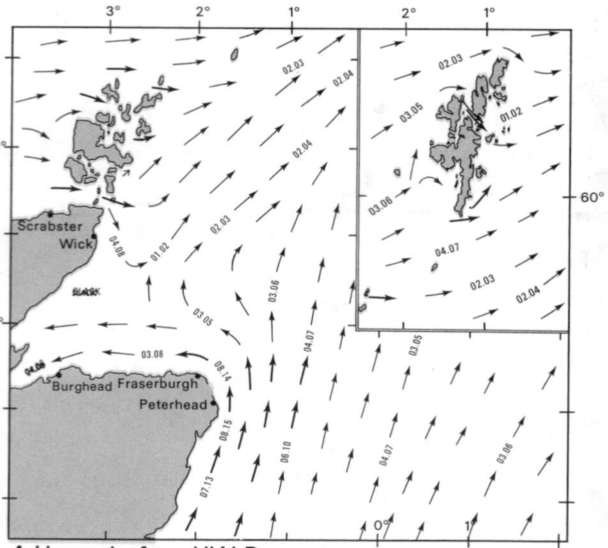
Scrabster
Wick
SLACK
Burghead
Fraserburgh
Peterhead

4 Hours before HW Dover (0600 after HW Aberdeen)

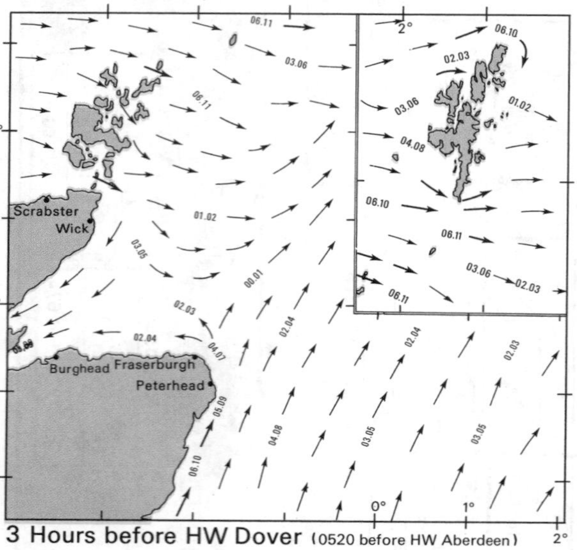
Scrabster
Wick
Burghead
Fraserburgh
Peterhead

3 Hours before HW Dover (0520 before HW Aberdeen)

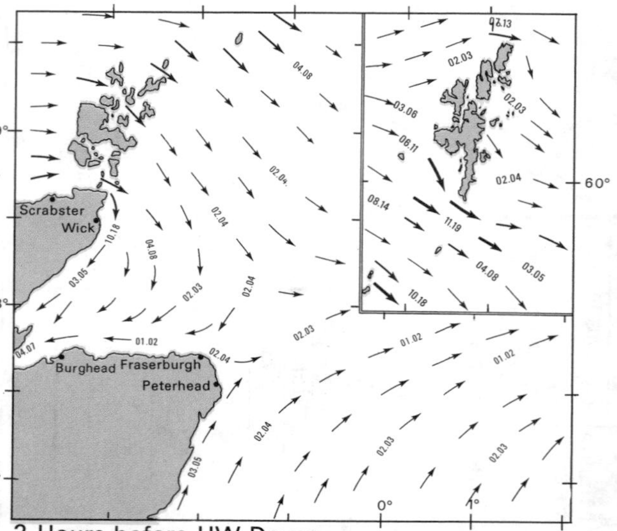
Scrabster
Wick
Burghead
Fraserburgh
Peterhead

2 Hours before HW Dover (0420 before HW Aberdeen)

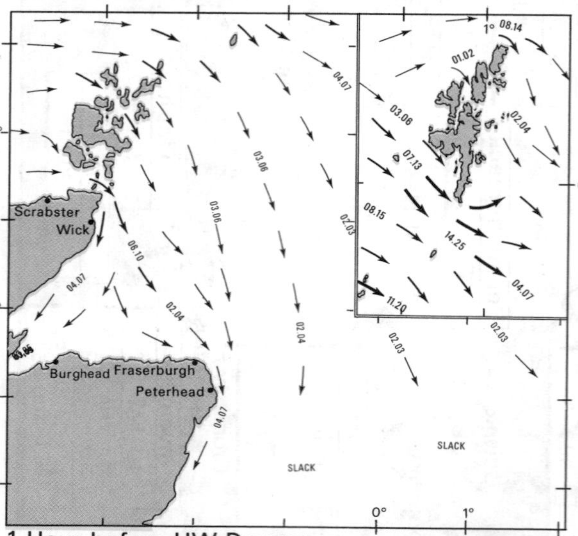
Scrabster
Wick
Burghead
Fraserburgh
Peterhead
SLACK
SLACK

1 Hour before HW Dover (0320 before HW Aberdeen)

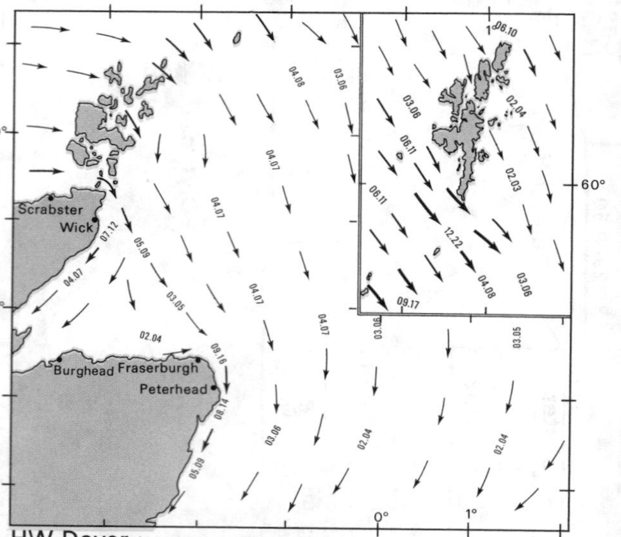
Scrabster
Wick
Burghead
Fraserburgh
Peterhead

HW Dover (0220 before HW Aberdeen)

Southward 10.6.3 Westward 10.8.3

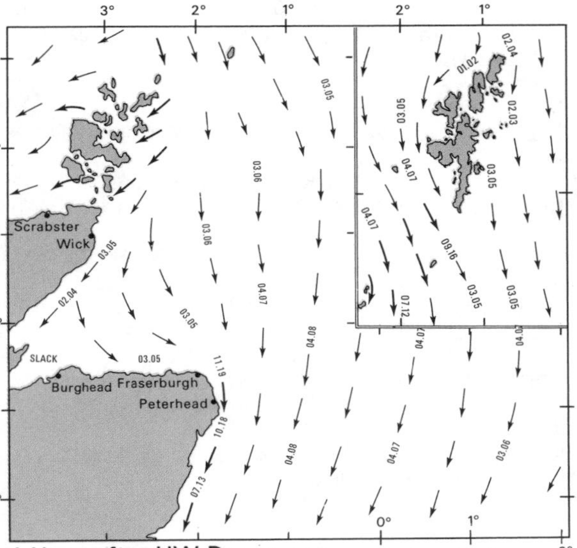
Scrabster
Wick
SLACK
Burghead
Fraserburgh
Peterhead

1 Hour after HW Dover (0120 before HW Aberdeen)

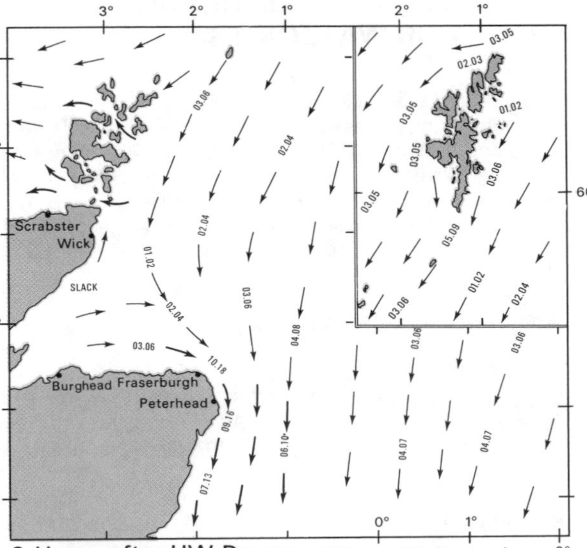
Scrabster
Wick
SLACK
Burghead
Fraserburgh
Peterhead

2 Hours after HW Dover (0020 before HW Aberdeen)

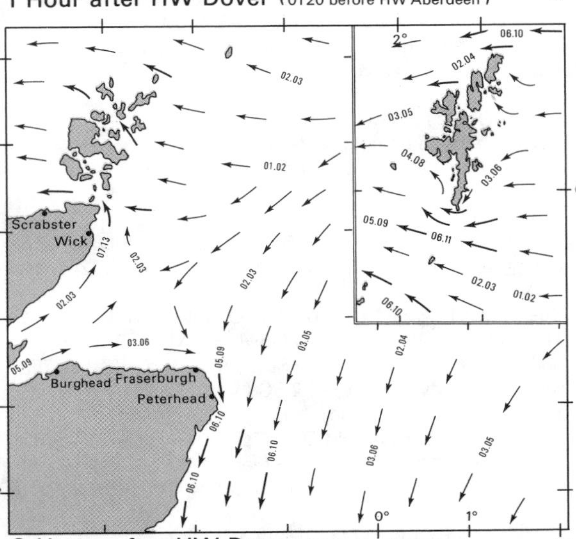
Scrabster
Wick
Burghead
Fraserburgh
Peterhead

3 Hours after HW Dover (0040 after HW Aberdeen)

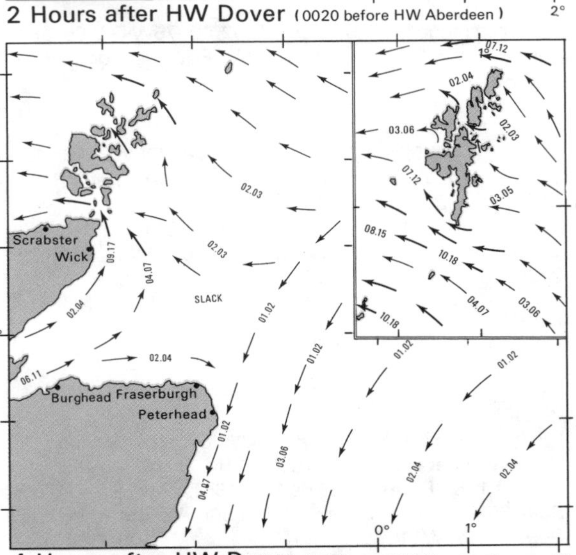
Scrabster
Wick
SLACK
Burghead
Fraserburgh
Peterhead

4 Hours after HW Dover (0140 after HW Aberdeen)

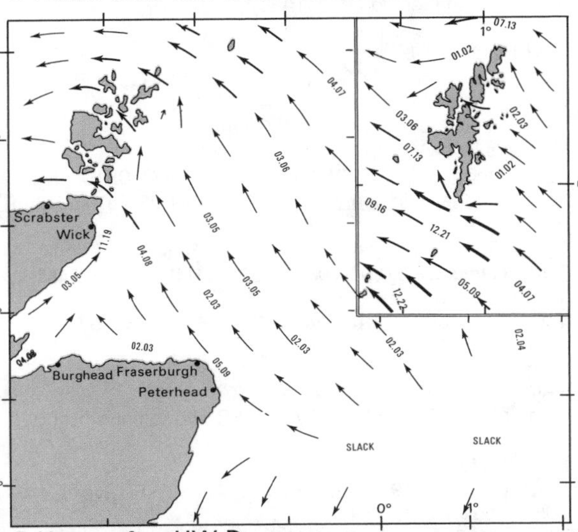
Scrabster
Wick
Burghead
Fraserburgh
Peterhead
SLACK
SLACK

5 Hours after HW Dover (0240 after HW Aberdeen)

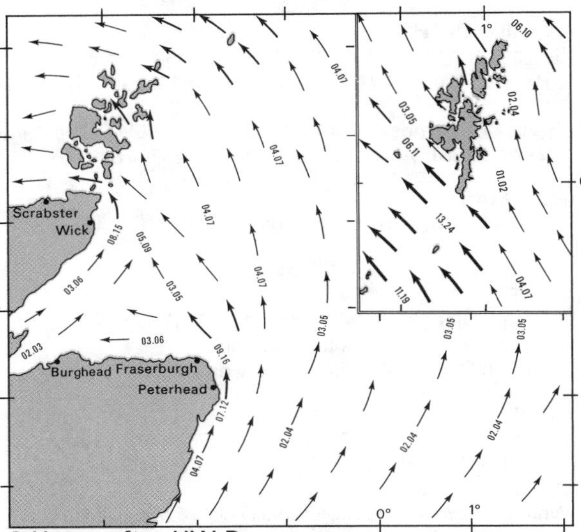
Scrabster
Wick
Burghead
Fraserburgh
Peterhead

6 Hours after HW Dover (0340 after HW Aberdeen)

10.7.4 COASTAL LIGHTS, FOG SIGNALS AND WAYPOINTS

Abbreviations used below are given in 1.4.1. Principal lights are in **bold** print, places in CAPITALS, and light-vessels, light floats and Lanbys in *CAPITAL ITALICS*. Unless otherwise stated lights are white. m—elevation in metres; M—nominal range in n. miles. Fog signals are in *italics*. Useful waypoints are underlined - use those on land with care. All geographical positions should be assumed to be approximate. See 4.2.2.

SCOTLAND—NORTH-EAST COAST

FRASERBURGH.
Cairnbulg Briggs 57°41'·12N 01°56'·37W Fl 3s 9m 5M; Bn.
Balaclava Breakwater Hd 57°41'·53N 01°59'·63W Fl (2) G 8s 26m 6M; dome on W Tr; vis 178°-326°; *Siren 20s* (occas).
S Breakwater Hd L Fl R 6s 9m 5M.

Kinnaird's Hd 57°41'·87N 02°00'·15W Fl 15s 37m **25M**; W Tr; RC.
Bombing range Lt By 57°43'·80N 02°00'·75W Fl Y 5s; SPM.
Target float 57°42'·00N 02°10'·00W Fl Y 10s; bombing target; Ra refl.

MACDUFF.
Lt Ho Pier Hd 57°40'·26N 02°29'·90W Fl (2) WRG 6s 12m W9M, R7M; W Tr; vis G shore-115°, W115°-174°, R174°-210°; *Horn (2) 20s* .
W Pier Hd 57°40'·2N 02°29'·9W QG 4m 5M.
Whitehills Pier Hd Fl WR 3s 7m W9M, R6M; W Tr; vis R132°-212°, W212°-245°.

PORTSOY.
Pier Ldg Lts 160°. Front 57°41'·2N 02°41'·3W F 12m 5M; Tr.
Rear FR 17m 5M; X on mast.

BUCKIE.
West Muck 57°41'·07N 02°57'·93W QR 5m7M; tripod.
N Breakwater Hd 2 FR (vert) 7m 11M; R col.
Ldg Lts 125°. **Front** Oc R 10s 15m **15M**; W Tr; *Siren (2) 60s*.
Rear 365m from front Iso WG 2s 30m **W16M**, G12M; vis G090°-110°, W110°-225°.
W Pier, NW corner 2 FG (vert) 4m 9M; G col.

LOSSIEMOUTH.
Sewer outfall Lt By 57°43'·78N 03°15'·83W FlY 5s; SPM.
S Pier Hd 57°43'·44N 03°16'·59W Fl R 6s 11m 5M; *Siren 60s*

Covesea Skerries 57°43'·5N 03°20'·2W Fl WR 20s 49m **W24M**, **R20M**; W Tr; vis W076°-267°, R267°-282°.

HOPEMAN.
S Pier Hd 57°42'·71N 03°26'·20W Oc G 4s 8m 4M shown 1/8-30/4.

BURGHEAD.
N Breakwater Hd 57°42'·10N 03°29'·94W Oc 8s 7m 5M.
Spur Hd QR 3m 5M; vis from SW only.
S pier Hd QG 3m 5M; vis from SW only.

NAIRN.
W Pier Hd 57°35'·62N 03°51'·56W QG 5m 1M; Gy post.
E Pier Hd Oc WRG 4s 6m 5M; 8-sided Tr; vis G shore-100°, W100°-207°, R207°-shore.
Whiteness Hd, McDermott Base Dir Lt 142·5°. Dir Iso WRG 4s 6m 10M; vis G138°-141°, W141°-144°, R144°-147°.

INVERNESS FIRTH.
Riff Bank E Lt By 57°38'·40N 03°58'·07W Fl Y 10s; SPM.
Navity Bank Lt By 57°38'·20N 04°01'·10W Fl (3) G 15s; SHM.
Riff Bank N Lt By 57°37'·18N 04°02'·30W Fl (2) R 12s; PHM.
Riff Bank W Lt By 57°35'·80N 04°03'·95W Fl Y 5s; SPM.

South Channel,
Riff Bank S Lt By 57°36'·75N 04°00'·87W Q (6) + LFl 15s; SCM.
Craigmee Lt By 57°35'·32N 04°04'·95W Fl R 6s; PHM.
Chanonry 57°34'·46N 04°05'·48W Oc 6s 12m **15M**; W Tr; vis 148°-073°.
Avoch 57°34'·0N 04°09'·8W 2 FR (vert) 7/5m 5M; (ocasl).
Munlochy Lt By 57°32'·93N 04°07'·55W L Fl 10s; SWM.
Meikle Mee Lt By 57°30'·27N 04°11'·94W Fl G 3s; SHM.
Longman Pt 57°30'·02N 04°13'·22W Fl WR 2s 7m W5M, R4M; R ▲ Bn; vis W078°-258°, R258°-078°.
Craigton Pt 57°30'·07N 04°14'·01W Fl WRG 4s 6m W11M, R7M, G7M; vis W312°-048°, R048°-064°, W064°-085°, G085°-shore.
Kessock Bridge. N Trs Oc G 6s 28m 5M and QG 3m 3M; S Trs Oc R 6s 28m 5M and QR 3m 3M.

INVERNESS.
R. Ness Outer Bn 57°29'·84N 04°13'·85W QR 3m 4M.
Inner Bn 57°29'·7N 04°14'·0W QR 3m 4M.
Embankment Hd Fl G 2s 8m 4M; G framework Tr.
E side Fl R 3s 7m 6M.

CALEDONIAN CANAL.
Clachnaharry, S training wall Hd 57°29'·5N 04°15'·8W Iso 4s 5m; W ▲ on W mast; tfc signals.

CROMARTY.
Fairway Lt By 57°39'·98N 03°54'·10W L Fl 10s; SWM; Racon.
Cromarty Bank Lt By 57°40'·68N 03°56'·69W Fl (2) G 10s; SHM.
Buss Bank Lt By 57°41'·00N 03°59'·45W Fl R 3s; PHM.
The Ness Oc WR 10s 18m **W15M**, R11M; W Tr; vis R079°-088°, W088°-275°, obsc by N Sutor when brg less than 253°.
Nigg Ferry jetty, SE corner, 2 FG (vert) 6m 2M.
SW corner 2 FG (vert) 6m 2M.
Nigg Oil Terminal Pier Hd Oc G 5s 31m 5M; Gy Tr, floodlit.
E and W ends marked by 2 FG (vert) 9 4M.
Nigg Sands E Lt By 57°41'·62N 04°04'·20W Fl (2) G 10s SHM.
Nigg Sands E Lt By 57°41'·35N 04°06'·78W Fl G 3s; SHM.
British Alcan Pier Hd QG 17m 5M.

INVERGORDON.
Dockyard Pier Hd 57°41'·2N 04°09'·6W Fl (3) G 10s 15m 4M.
Supply Base SE corner Iso G 4s 9m 6M; Gy mast.
Quay, W end Oc G 8s 9m 6M; Gy mast.
Queen's Dock W Arm Iso G 2s 9m 6M.
Three Kings Lt By 57°43'·75N 03°54'·17W Q (3) 10s; ECM.
Tarbat Ledge/Culloden Rk By 57°52'·45N 03°45'·45W (unlit); PHM.
Lt By 57°53'·00N 03°47'·00W Fl Y 5s; SPM.
Tarbat Ness 57°51'·92N 03°46'·52W Fl (4) 30s 53m **24M**; W Tr, R bands; Racon.
Tain Bar By (moved as required) 57°51'·6N° 03°52'·9W (unlit); SWM.

TAIN
Firing range 57°49'·5N 03°57'·4W FR, when firing occurs.

HELMSDALE.
Ben-a-chielt 58°19'·8N 03°22'·8W Aero 5 FR (vert) 448-265m; radio mast.
Lybster, S Pier Hd Oc R 6s 10m 3M; W Tr; occas.

Clythness 58°19'N 03°13'W Fl (2) 30s 45m **16M**; W Tr, R band.

WICK.
S Pier Hd 58°26'·36N 03°04'·65W Fl WRG 3s 12m W5M, R3M, G3M; W 8-sided Tr; vis G253°-269°, W269°-286°, R286°-329°; *Bell (2) 10s* (occas).
Dir Lt 290·5° 58°26'·6N 03°05'·2W Dir F WRG 9m W10M, R7M, G7M; col on N end of bridge; vis G285·5°-289·2°, W289·2°-291·7°, R291·7°-295·5°.
Noss Hd 58°28'·8N 03°03'·0W Fl WR 20s 53m **W25M**, **R21M**; W Tr; vis R shore-191°, W191°-shore.

SCOTLAND—NORTH COAST

Duncansby Hd 58°38'·67N 03°01'·43W Fl 12s 67m **24M**; W Tr; Racon.
Pentland Skerries 58°41'·4N 02°55'·4W Fl (3) 30s 52m **25M**; W Tr; *Horn 45s.*
Lother Rock 58°43'·80N 02°58'·58W Q 11m 6M; Racon.
S Ronaldsay, Burwick Jetty Hd 2 FG (vert) 6m 2M.
Swona, near SW end Fl 8s 17m 9M; W col; vis 261°-210°.
N Hd Fl (3) 10s 16m 10M.
Stroma, Swilkie Pt 58°41'·78N 03°06'·92W Fl (2) 20s 32m **26M**; W Tr; RC; *Horn (2) 60s* .
Inner sound, John O'Groats, Pier Hd Fl R 3s 4m 2M; W post; Ra refl.
Dunnet Hd Fl (4) 30s 105m **23M**; W Tr; RG.

THURSO.
Holburn Hd Fl WR 10s 23m **W15M**, R11M; W Tr; vis W198°-358°, R358°-shore. Breakwater Hd QG 5m 4M; G post; shown 1/9-30/4.
Ldg Lts 195°. Front FG 5m 4M; Gy post. Rear FG 6m 4M; Gy mast.

SCRABSTER.
Outer Pier Hd 58°36'·63N 03°32'·48W QG 6m 4M.
E Pier Hd 2 FG (vert) 6m 4M; shown 1/8-31/5.
W Pier Hd 2 FR (vert) 6m 4M; shown 1/8-31/5.
Strathy Pt 58°36'N 04°01'W Fl 20s 45m **27M**; W Tr on W dwelling.
Sule Skerry 59°05'·10N 04°24'·30W Fl (2) 15s 34m **19M**; W Tr; RC; Racon.
North Rona 59°07'·3N 05°48'·8W Fl (3) 20s 114m **24M**; W Tr.
Sula Sgeir 59°05'·65N 06°09'·50W Fl 15s 74m 11M; ■ structure.
Loch Eriboll, White Hd 58°31'·1N 04°38'·8W Fl WR 3s 18m W13M, R12M; W Tr and bldg; vis W030°-172°, R172°-191°, W191°-212°.
Cape Wrath 58°37'·55N 04°59'·87W Fl (4) 30s 122m **24M**; W Tr; RC; *Horn (3) 45s.*

ORKNEY ISLANDS

Tor Ness 58°46'·7N 03°17'·6W Fl 3s 21m 10M; W Tr.
S Walls, SE end, **Cantick Hd** 58°47'·2N 03°07'·8W Fl 20s 35m **18M**; W Tr.

SCAPA FLOW AND APPROACHES.
Ruff Reef, off Cantick Hd, Fl (2) 10s 10m 6M; B Bn.
Long Hope, S Ness Pier Hd, 58°48'·1N 03°12'·2W Fl WRG 3s 6m W7M, R5M, G5M; vis G082°-242°, W242°-252°, R252°-082°.
Hoxa Hd 58°49'·3N 03°02'·0W Fl WR 3s 15m W9M, R6M; W Tr; vis W026°-163°, R163°-201°, W201°-215°.
Stanger Hd 58°49'·0N 03°04'·6W Fl R 5s 25m 8M.
Roan Hd 58°50'·8N 03°03'·8W Fl (2) R 6s 12m 7M.
Nevi Skerry 58°50'·7N 03°02'·6W Fl (2) 6s 7m 6M; IDM.
Calf of Flotta 58°51'·3N 03°03'·9W QR 8m 4M.
Flotta Terminal. N end of E Jetty. 2 FR (vert) 10m 3M.
W 2 FR (vert) 10m 3M; *Bell (1)10s.*
Mooring dolphins, E and W, both QR 8m 3M.
SPM Tr No. 1 58°52'·2N 03°07'·3W Fl Y 5s 12m 3M; *Horn Mo(A) 60s.*
SPM Tr No. 2 58°52'·3N 03°05'·8W Fl (4) Y 15s 12m 3M; *Horn Mo(N) 60s.*
Gibraltar Pier 58°50'29N 03°07'·77W 2 FG (vert) 7m 3M.
Golden Wharf N end 58°50'·16N 03°11'·36W 2 FR (vert) 7m 3M.
Lyness Wharf S end 58°50'·04N 03°11'·31W 2 FR (vert) 7m 3M.
St Margaret's Hope, Needle Pt Reef 58°50'·1N 02°57'·3W Fl G 3s 6m 3M; ◆ on post.
Pier Hd 2 FG (vert) 6m 2M.
Ldg Lts 196°, both FR 7/11m.
Rose Ness 58°52'·4N 02°49'·9W Fl 6s 24m 8M; W Tr.
Scapa Pier W end 58°57'·4N 02°58'·3W Fl G 3s 6m 8M; W mast.
Barrel of Butter 58 53'·4N 03°07'·5W Fl (2) 10s 6m 7M; Gy platform on ● Tr.

Cava 58°53'·2N 03°10'·6W Fl WR 3s 12m W10M, R8M; W ● Tr; vis W351°-143°, R143°-196°, W196°-251°, R251°- 271°, W271°-298°.
Houton Bay Ldg Lts 316°. Front 58°55'·00N 03°11'·46W Fl G 3s 8m. Rear 200m from front FG 16m both R ▲ on W pole, B bands, vis 312°-320°.
Ro-Ro terminal, S end Iso R 4s 7m 5M.

CLESTRAN SOUND.
Peter Skerry Lt By 58°55'·32N 03°13'·43W Fl G 6s; SHM.
Riddock Shoal Lt By 58°55'·88N 03°15'·07W Fl (2) R 12s; PHM.

HOY SOUND.
Ebbing Eddy Rks Lt By 58°56'·62N 03°16'·90W Q; NCM.
Graemsay Is Ldg Lts 104°. **Front** 58°56'·46N 03°18'·50W Iso 3s 17m **15M**; W Tr; vis 070°-255°. **Rear** 1·2M from front Oc WR 8s 35m **W20M**, **R16M**; W Tr; vis R097°-112°, W112°-163°, R163°-178°, W178°-332°; obsc on Ldg line within 0·5M.
Skerry of Ness 58°56'·98N 03°17'·73W Fl WG 4s 7m W7M, G4M; vis W shore-090°, G 090°-shore.

STROMNESS.
Ldg Lts 317°. Front 58°57'·6N 03°18'·0W FR 29m 11M; post on W Tr. Rear, 55m from front FR 39m 11M; both vis 307°-327°.
N Pier Hd Fl R 3s 8m 5M.
Copinsay 58°53'·8N 02°40'·2W Fl (5) 30s 79m **21M**; W Tr; *Horn (4) 60s.*
Auskerry 59°01'·6N 02°34'·2W Fl 20s 34m **18M**; W Tr.
Helliar Holm S end 59°01'·17N 02°53'·95W Fl WRG 10s 18m W14M, R10M; W Tr; vis G256°-276° W276°-292° R292°-098° W098°-116° G116°-154°.
Balfour Pier 59°01'·9N 02°54'·4W Q WRG 5m W3M, R2M, G2M; vis G270°-010°, W010°-020°, R020°-090°.

KIRKWALL.
Scargun Shoal By 59°00'·83N 02°58'·57W (unlit); SHM.
Pier N end 58°59'·32N 02°57'·62W Iso WRG 5s 8m **W15M**, R13M, G13M; W Tr; vis G153°-183°, W183°-192°, R192°-210°.
Pier E end 2FG (vert) 6m 3M.

WIDE FIRTH.
Linga Skerry Lt By 59°02'·42N 02°57'·46W Q (3) 10s; ECM.
Boray Skerries Lt By 59°03'·68N 02°57'·55W Q (6) + L Fl 15s; SCM.
Skertours Lt By 59°04'·15N 02°56'·61W Q; NCM.
The Galt Lt By 59°05'·25N 02°54'·15W Q; NCM.
Brough of Birsay 59°08'·25N 03°20'·30W Fl (3) 25s 52m **18M**; W castellated Tr and Bldg.
Papa Stronsay NE end, The Ness 59°09'·38N 02°34'·80W Iso 4s 8m 9M; W Tr.

STRONSAY, PAPA SOUND.
Quiabow By 59°09'·85N 02°36'·20W (unlit); SHM.
No. 1 Lt By (off Jacks Reef) 59°09'·20N 02°36'·40W FlG 5s; SHM.
No. 2 Lt By 59°08'·95N 02°36'·50W Fl R 5s; PHM.
No. 3 Lt By 59°08'·73N 02°36'·08W Fl (2) G 5s; SHM.
No. 4 Lt By 59°08'·80N 02°36'·37W Fl (2) R 5s; PHM.
Whitehall Pier 50°08'·61N 02°35'·79W 2 FG (vert) 8/6m 4M.

SANDAY.
Start Pt 59°16'·70N 02°22'·50W Fl (2) 20s 24m **19M**; W Tr, B stripes.
Kettletoft Pier Fl WRG 3s 7m W7M, R5M, G5M; W Tr; vis W351°-011°, R011°-180°, G180°-351°.
N Ronaldsay, NE end, 59°23'·40N 02°22'·80W Fl 10s 43m **19M**; R Tr, W bands; RC; Racon; *Horn 60s*.
Nouster Pier Hd 59°21'·4N 02°26'·3W QR 5m.

EDAY.
Calf of Eday 59°14'·2N 02°45'·7W Iso WRG 5s 8m W8M, R7M, G6M; W Tr; vis R shore-216°, W216°-223°, G223°-302°, W302°-307°.
Backaland Pier Fl R 3s 5m 4M; vis 192°-250°.

WESTRAY.
Noup Hd 59°19'·90N 03°04'·10W Fl 30s 79m **22M**; W Tr; vis 335°-242°, 248°-282°; obsc on E bearings within 0·8M, part obsc 240°-275°.
Pierowall E Pier Hd Fl WRG 3s 7m W11M, R7M, G7M; vis G254°-276°, W276°-291°, R291°-308°, G308°-215°.
W Pier Hd 2 FR (vert) 6m 3M.
Papa Westray Moclett Bay Pier Hd Fl WRG 5s 7m W5M, R3M, G3M; vis G306°-341°, W341°-040°, R040°-074°.
EgilsayPier S end Fl G 3s 4m 4M.

SHETLAND ISLES

FAIR ISLE.
Skadan S end 59°30'·85N 01°39'·08W Fl (4) 30s 32m **24M**; W Tr; vis 260°-146°, obsc inshore 260°-282°; *Horn(2) 60s*.
Skroo N end 59°33'·16N 01°36'·49W Fl (2) 30s 80m **22M**; W Tr; vis 087°-358°; *Horn (3) 45s*.

MAINLAND.
Sumburgh Hd 59°51'·30N 01°16'·37W Fl (3) 30s 91m **23M**; W Tr; RC.

HOSWICK and SANDWICK.
Mousa, Perie Bard, Fl 3s 20m 10M; W Tr.

BRESSAY.
Kirkabister Ness, 60°07'·25N 01°07'·18W Fl (2) 20s 32m **23M**; W Tr; RC; FR Lts on radio masts 0·95M NE.

LERWICK.
Twageos Pt 60°08'·95N 01°07'·83W L Fl 6s 8m 6M; W Bn.
Maryfield, Ferry Terminal Oc WRG 6s 5m 5M; vis W008°-013°, R013°-111°, G111°-008°.
Breakwater N Hd 60°09'·27N 01°08'·29W 2 FR (vert) 5m 4M.
Victoria Pier, N Hd, Fl R 3s 5m 1M.
Victoria Pier E Elbow, 2 FG (vert) 5m 4M.
N Jetty QR 5m 1M.
N Ness 60°09'·6N 01°08'·7W Iso WG 4s 4m 5M; vis G158°-216°, W216°-158°.
Loofa Baa 60 09.75N°1 08.67W Q (6) + L Fl 15s 4m 5M; SCM.
N ent Dir Lt 215°. Dir Oc WRG 6s 27m 8M; Y ▲, Or stripe; vis R211°-214°, W214°-216°, G216°-221°.
Gremista Marina S breakwater Hd 60°10'·23N 01°09'·49W Iso R 4s 3m 2M.
Greenhead Q (4) R 10s 4m 3M.
Rova Hd 60°11'·45N 01°08'·45W Fl (3) WRG 18s 10m W8M, R7M, G6M; W Tr; vis R shore-180°, W180°-194°, G194°-213°, R213°-241°, W241°-261·5°, G261·5°-009°, W009°-shore.
Bretheran Rock Lt By 60°12'·38N 01°08'·12W Q (9) 15s; WCM.
Dales Voe 60°11'·8N 01°11'·1W Fl (2) WRG 8s 5m W4M, R3M, G3M; vis G220°-227°, W227°-233°, R233°-240°.
Dales Voe Quay 2 FR (vert) 9m 3M.
Laxfirth Pier Hd 2 FG (vert) 4m 2M.
Hoo Stack 60°14'·99N 01°05'·25W Fl (4) WRG 12s 40m W7M, R5M, G5M; W pylon; vis R169°-180°, W180°-184°, G184°-193°, W193°-169°.
Dir Lt 182°. Dir Fl (4) WRG 12s 40m W9M, R6M, G6M; same structure; vis R177°-180°, W180°-184°, G184°-187°; synchronised with upper Lt.
Mull (Moul) of Eswick Fl WRG 3s 50m W9M, R6M, G6M; W Tr; vis R shore-200°, W200°-207°, G207°-227°, R227°-241°, W241°-028°, R028°-shore.

WHALSAY.
Symbister Ness 60°20'·46N 01°02'·15W Fl (2) WG 12s 11m W8M, G6M;W Tr; vis W shore-203°, G203°-shore.
Symbister Bay S Breakwater Hd 60°20'·6N 01°01'·5W QG 4m 2M.
N Breakwater Hd Oc G 7s 3m 3M.
E Breakwater Hd Oc R 7s 3m 3M.
Marina N pontoon 2 FG (vert) 2m 3M.
Skate of Marrister 60°21'·4N 01°01'·3W Fl G 6s 4m 4M; G mast with platform.
Suther Ness Fl WRG 3s 8m W10M, R8M, G7M; vis W shore-038°, R038°-173°, W173°-206°, G206°-shore.
Mainland. Laxo Voe ferry terminal 60°21'·1N 01°10'·0W 2 FG (vert) 4m 2M.
Out Skerries 60°25'·50N 00°43'·50W Fl 20s 44m **20M**; W Tr.
Bruray ferry berth 60°25'·4N 00°45'·0W 2 FG (vert) 6m 4M
Muckle Skerry 60°26'·4N 00°51'·7W Fl (2) WRG 10s 13m W7M, R5M, G5M; W Tr; vis W046°-192°, R192°-272°, G272°-348°, W348°-353°, R353°-046°.

YELL SOUND.
S ent, Lunna Holm 60°27'·38N 01°02'·39W Fl (3) WRG 15s 19m W10M, R7M, G7M; W ● Tr; vis R shore-090°, W090°-094°, G094°-209°, W209°-275°, R275°-shore.
Firths Voe, N shore 60°27'·2N 01°10'·6W Oc WRG 8s 9m **W15M**, R10M, G10M; W Tr; vis W189°-194°, G194°-257°, W257°-263°, R263°-339°, W339°-066°.

Linga Is. Dir Lt Dir Q (4) WRG 8s 10m W9M, R9M, G9M; concrete col; vis R145°-148°, W148°-152°, G152°-155°. Q (4) WRG 8s 10m W7M, R4M, G4M; same structure; vis R052°-146°, G154°-196°, W196°-312°; synchronized with Dir Lt.
Yell, Ulsta Ferry Terminal Breakwater Hd Oc RG 4s 7m R5M, G5M; vis G shore-354°, R044°-shore. Oc WRG 4s 5m W8M, R5M, G5M; same structure; vis G shore-008°, W008°-036°, R036°-shore.
Toft ferry terminal 60°28'·0N 01°12'·4W 2 FR (vert) 5m 2M.
Ness of Sound, W side, Iso WRG 5s 18m W9M, R6M, G6M; vis G shore-345°, W345°-350°, R350°-160°, W160°-165°, G165°-shore.
Brother Is Dir Lt 329°, Dir Fl (4) WRG 8s 16m W10M, R7M, G7M; vis G323·5°-328°, W328°-330°, R330°-333·5°.
Mio Ness 60°29'·7N 01°13'·5W Q (2) WR 10s 12m W7M, R4M; W ● Tr; W282°-238°, R238°-282°.
Tinga Skerry 60°30'·5N 01°14'·7W Q (2) G 10s 9m 5M; W ● Tr.

YELL SOUND, NORTH ENTRANCE.
Bagi Stack 60°43'·55N 01°07'·40W Fl (4) 20s 45m 10M; W Tr.
Gruney Is 60°39'·20N 01°18'·03W Fl WR 5s 53m W7M, R4M; W Tr; vis R064°-180°, W180°-012°; Racon.
Point of Fethaland Fl (3) WR 15s 65m **W24M, R20M**; W Tr; vis R080°-103°, W103°-160°, R160°-206°, W206°-340°.
Muckle Holm 60°34'·85N 01°15'·90W Fl (2) 10s 32m 10M; W Tr.
Little Holm Iso 4s 12m 6M; W Tr.
Outer Skerry 60°33'·08N 01°18'·20W Fl 6s 12m 8M; W col, B bands.
Quey Firth Oc WRG 6s 22m W12M, R8M, G8M; W Tr; vis W shore (through S and W)-290°, G290°-327°, W327°-334°, R334°-shore.
Lamba, S side, Fl WRG 3s 30m W8M, R5M, G5M; W Tr; vis G shore-288°, W288°-293°, R293°-327°, W327°-044°, R044°-140°, W140°-shore. Dir Lt 290·5° Dir Fl WRG 3s 24m W10M, R7M, G7M; vis 285·5°-288°, W288°-293°, R293°-295·5°.

SULLOM VOE.
Gluss Is Ldg Lts 194·7° (H24). **Front** F 39m **19M**; ■ on Gy Tr. **Rear** F 69m **19M**; ■ on Gy Tr. Both Lts 9M by day.
Little Roe 60°30'·05N 01°16'·35W Fl (3) WR 10s 16m W5M, R4M; Y and W structure; vis R036°-095·5°, W095·5°-036°.
Skaw Taing 60°29'·1N 01°16'·7W Fl (2) WRG 5s 21m W8M, R5M, G5M; Or and W structure; vis W049°-078°, G078°-147°, W147°-154°, R154°-169°, W169°-288°.
Ness of Bardister 60°28'·2N 01°19'·5W Oc WRG 8s 20m W9M, R6M, G6M; Or and W structure; vis W180·5°-240°, R240°-310·5°, W310·5-314·5°, G314·5°-030·5°.
Vats Houllands 60°28'·0N 01°17'·5W Oc WRGY 3s 73m 6M; Gy Tr; vis W343·5°-029·5°, Y029·5°-049°, G049°-074·5°, R074·5°-098·5°, G098·5°-123·5°, Y123·5°-148°, W148°-163·5°.
Fugla Ness. Lts in line 212·3°. Rear 60°27'·3N 01°19'·7W Iso 4s 45m 14M. Common front 60°27'·5N 01°19'·4W Iso 4s 27m 14M; synchronized with rear Lts. Lts in line 203°. Rear 60°27'·3N 01°19'·6W Iso 4s 45m 14M.
Sella Ness. Upper Lt 60°26'·9N 01°16'·5W Q WRG 14m 7M; Gy Tr; vis G084·5°-098·7°, W098·7°-099·7°, W126°-128·5°, R128·5°-174·5°; by day F WRG 2M (occas).
Sella Ness. Lower Lt. Q WRG 10m 7M; vis G084·5°-106·5°, W106·5°-115°, R115°-174·5°; by day F WRG 2M (occas).
Tug jetty finger, pier Hd Iso G 4s 4m 3M.
Garth Pier N arm Hd 60°26'·7N 01°16'·2W Fl (2) G 5s 4m 3M.
Scatsa Ness Upper Lt 60°26'·5N 01°18'·1W Oc WRG 5s 14m 7M; Gy Tr; vis G161·5°-187·2°, W187·2°-188·2°, W207·2°-208·2°, R208·2°-251·5°; by day F WRG 2M (occas).
Scatsa Ness. Lower Lt Oc WRG 5s 10m 7M; vis G161·5°-197·2°, W197·2°-202·2°, R202·2°-251·5°; by day F WRG 2M (occas).
Ungam Is 60°27'·3N 01°18'·5W VQ (2) 5s 2m 2M; W col; Ra refl.
Whitehill 60°34'·85N 01°00'·01W Fl WR 3s 24m W9M, R6M; vis W shore-163°, R163°-211°, W211°-349°, R349°-shore.
Uyea Sound 60°41'·2N 00°55'·3W Fl (2) 8s 8m 7M; R & W Tr.
Balta Sound 60°44'·5N 00°47'·6W Fl WR 10s 17m 10M, R7M; vis W249°-010°, R010°-060°, W060°-154°; Q Lt (occas) marks Unst Aero RC 0·7M W.

NORTH UNST.
Muckle Flugga 60°51'·33N 00°53'·00W Fl (2) 20s 66m **25M**; W Tr; RC. **Auxiliary Lt** FR 52m **15M** (same Tr); vis 276°-311°.
Yell. Cullivoe breakwater Hd 60°41'·9N 00°59'·7W Oc R 7s 5m 2M; Gy col.
Esha Ness 60°29'·35N 01°37'·55W Fl 12s 61m **25M**; W ■ Tr.
Hillswick, S end of Ness 60°27'·2N 01°29'·7W Fl (4) WR 15s 34m W9M, R6M; W house: vis W217°-093°, R093°-114°.
Muckle Roe, Swarbacks Minn, 60°21'·05N 01°26'·90W Fl WR 3s 30m W9M, R6M; vis W314°-041°, R041°-075°, W075°-137°.
Aith breakwater. RNLI berth 60°17'·2N 01°22'·3W QG 5m 3M.
W Burra Firth. Transport Pier Hd 60°17'·7N 01°32'·3W Iso G 4s 4m 4M.
Ve Skerries 60°22'·40N 01°48'·67W Fl (2) 20s 17m 11M; W Tr; Racon.

VAILA SOUND.
Rams Hd 60°12'·00N 01°33'·40W Fl WG 8s 16m W9m, G6M, R6M; W house; vis G265°-355°, W355°-012°, R012°-090°, W090°-136°, obsc by Vaila I when brg more than 030°.
Vaila Pier 60°13'·5N 01°34'·0W 2 FR (vert) 4m.
Skeld Voe. Skeld Pier Hd 60°11'·2N 01°26'·1W 2 FR (vert) 4m 3M.
North Havra 60°09'·88N 01°20'·17W Fl WRG 12s 24m W7M, R5M, G5M; W Tr; vis G 001°-053·5°, W053·5°-060·5°, G274°-334°, W334°-337·5°, R337·5°-001°.
Pt of the Pund 60°08'·02N 01°18'·20W Fl WRG 5s 20m W7M, R5M, G5M; W Tr; vis R350°-090°, G090°-111°, R111°-135°, W135°-140°, G140°-177°, W267°-350°.

SCALLOWAY.
Whaleback Skerry Lt By 60°07'·98N 01°18'·79W Q; NCM.
Moores slipway, Jetty Hd 60°08'·2N 01°16'·7W 2 FR (vert) 4m 1M.
Blacksness W Pier Hd 2 FG (vert) 6m 3M.
E Pier Hd Oc R 7s 5m 3M.
Centre Pier Oc WRG 10s 7m W14M, G11M, R11M; vis G045·7°- 056·8°, W056·8°-058·8°, R058·8°-069·9°.
Fugla Ness 60°06'·40N 01°20'·75W Fl (2) WRG 10s 20m W10M, R7M, G7M; W Tr; vis G014°-032°, W032°-082°, R082°-134°, W134°-shore.

FOULA.
60°06'·78N 02°03'·72W Fl (3) 15s 36m **18M**; W Tr. Obscured 123°-221°.

7

10.7.5 PASSAGE INFORMATION

RATTRAY HEAD TO INVERNESS (charts 115, 222, 223)

On direct route from Rattray Hd (Lt, fog sig) to Duncansby Hd (Lt, Racon) heavy seas may be met in strong W winds. For oil installations see 10.5.5. Tidal streams are moderate off Rattray Hd and strong in inner part of Moray Firth, but weak elsewhere in the firth. 5M NE of Rattray Hd the NE-going stream begins at HW Aberdeen +0140, and the SE-going stream at HW Aberdeen –0440, sp rates 2 kn.

In strong winds the sea breaks over Steraton Rk in the E approach to Fraserburgh (10.7.7), and over Colonel Rk 1·75M E of Kinnairds Hd (Lt). Banff B is shallow: beware Collie Rks N of Macduff (10.7.8). Banff hbr dries, and should not be approached in fresh NE-E winds, when sea breaks well offshore.

From Meavie Pt to Scarnose dangers extend up to 0·3M from shore in places. Beware Caple Rk (depth 0·2m) 0·75M W of Logie Hd. Spey B is clear of dangers more than 0·75M from shore: anch here, but only in offshore winds. Beware E Muck (dries) 0·5M SW of Craigan Roan, an above-water rky patch 0·5M SW of Craig Hd, and Middle Muck and W Muck in approach to Buckie (10.7.10). For Portknockie see 10.7.27.

Halliman Skerries (dry) lie 1·5M WNW of Stotfield Hd, and are marked by Bn. Covesea Skerries Lt Ho is 2M W of Stotfield Hd, and Covesea Skerries (dry) lie 0·5M NW of the Lt Ho.

Inverness Firth is approached between Nairn (10.7.15) and S Sutor. In heavy weather there is a confused sea with overfalls on Guillam Bank, 9M S of Tarbat Ness. The sea also breaks on Riff Bank (S of S Sutor) which dries in places. Chans run both N and S of Riff Bank. Off Fort George, on E side of ent to Inverness Firth (chart 1078), the SW-going stream begins HW Aberdeen +0605, sp rate 2·5kn; the NE- going stream begins at HW Aberdeen –0105, sp rate 3·5kn. There are eddies and turbulence between Fort George and Chanonry Pt when stream is running hard. Most of Inverness Firth is shallow, but a deeper chan skirts the NW shore to within 1M of Craigton Pt, NE of which is a bank called Meikle Mee with depths of less than 1m.

INVERNESS TO DUNCANSBY HEAD (chart 115)

Cromarty Firth (charts 1889, 1890) is entered between N Sutor and S Sutor, both fringed by Rks, some of which dry. Off the entrance the in-going stream begins at HW Aberdeen +0605, and the out-going at HW Aberdeen –0105, sp rates 1·5kn. Good sheltered anchs within the firth. See 10.7.27.

The coast running NE to Tarbat Ness (Lt) is fringed with rks. Beware Three Kings (dries) about 3M NE of N Sutor. Culloden Rk, a shoal with depth of 1·8m, extends 0·25M NE of Tarbat Ness, where stream is weak. Beware salmon nets on coast between Tarbat Ness and Portmahomack (10.7.17). Dornoch Firth (10.7.27) is shallow, with shifting banks, and in strong E winds the sea breaks heavily on the bar E of Dornoch Pt.

At Lothbeg Pt, between Brora Pt and Helmsdale (10.7.18), there is a rk ledge extending 0·5M offshore. Near Berriedale, 7M NE of Helmsdale, is The Pinnacle, a detached rk 61m high, standing close offshore. The Beatrice oil field lies on Smith Bank, 28M NE of Tarbat Ness, and 11M off Caithness coast. Between Dunbeath and Lybster (10.7.27) there are no dangers more than 0·2M offshore. Clyth Ness is fringed by detached and drying rks. From here to Wick (10.7.19) the only dangers are close inshore. There is anch in Sinclair's B in good weather, but Freswick B further N is better while waiting for tide in Pentland Firth (beware Wk in centre of bay). Baxter Rk (depth 2·7m) lies 0·4M S of Duncansby Hd, and Stacks of Duncansby 0·6M further SSW.

PENTLAND FIRTH (charts 2162, 2581)

This dangerous chan should only be attempted in moderate winds and good vis, and not at sp tides. At E end the firth is entered between Duncansby Hd and Old Hd (S Ronaldsay), between which lie Pentland Skerries. At W end the firth is entered between Dunnet Hd and Tor Ness (Hoy). Near the centre of firth are the Is of Swona (N side) and Stroma (S side). Outer Sound is between Swona and Stroma; Inner Sound is between Stroma and the Scottish coast E of St John's Pt. Other than as above there are no dangers more than about 0·2M offshore, but the tide runs extremely strongly, and causes very severe eddies and races and a most confused sea at different times and places depending on conditions. See *N Coast of Scotland Pilot*.

In general the E-going stream begins at HW Aberdeen +0500, and the W-going at HW Aberdeen –0105. On both streams eddies form S of Muckle Skerry and around Stroma. Between Pentland Skerries and Duncansby Hd the sp rate is 8-10 kn. On the SE-going stream Duncansby Race extends first towards Muckle Skerry but then swings anti-clockwise until by HW Aberdeen –0440 it extends in a NW direction from Duncansby Hd. At HW Aberdeen –0140 it starts to subside. By HW Aberdeen +0245 the race forms again for about 2h in a ENE direction towards Muckle Skerry. This race is violent in strong E or SE winds against SE going stream.

The stream runs 8-9 kn at sp through Outer Sound, causing a persistent and dangerous race off Swilkie Pt at N end of Stroma, especially with a W-going stream and a strong W wind.

The most dangerous and extensive race in the firth is Merry Men of Mey, which forms off St John's Pt on W-going stream at HW Aberdeen –0150 and for a while extends right across to Tor Ness with heavy breaking seas even in fine weather. By HW Aberdeen +0315 the SE end of race detaches from Men of Mey Rks off St John's Pt, and by HW Aberdeen +0435 the race begins to subside off Tor Ness. With the start of the E-going stream, at about HW Aberdeen +0515, the race subsides in mid-chan.

Any yacht going through Pentland Firth, even in ideal conditions, must avoid Duncansby Race, Swilkie Race, and Merry Men of Mey. A safe passage depends on correct timing and positioning to avoid the worst races mentioned above, regular fixes to detect any dangerous set, and sufficient power to cope with the very strong tidal stream.

DUNCANSBY HEAD TO CAPE WRATH (chart 1954)

Dunnet B, S of Dunnet Hd (Lt) gives temp anch in E or S winds, but dangerous seas roll in from NW. On W side of Thurso B is Scrabster (10.7.26).

Between Holborn Hd and Strathy Pt the E-going stream begins at HW Ullapool –0150, and the W-going at HW Ullapool +0420, sp rates 2·5kn. Close to Brims Ness off Ushat Hd the sp rate is 3 kn, and there is often turbulence. SW of Ushat Hd the buildings of Dounreay are conspic, near shore. Dangers extend 0·25M seaward off this coast.

Along E side of Strathy Pt an eddy gives almost continuous N-going stream, but there is usually turbulence off the Pt where this eddy meets the main E or W stream. Several small B's along this coast give temp anch in offshore winds, but must not be used or approached with wind in a N quarter.

Kyle of Tongue (10.7.27) is entered from E through Caol Raineach, S of Eilean nan Ron, or from N between Eilean Iosal and Cnoc Glass. There is no chan into the kyle W of Rabbit Is, to which a drying spit extends 0·5M NNE from the mainland shore. Further S there is a bar across entrance to inner part of kyle. There are anchs on SE side of Eilean nan Ron, SE side of Rabbit Is, off Skullomie, or S of Eilean Creagach off Talmine. Approach to the latter runs close W of Rabbit Islands, but beware rks to N and NW of them.

Loch Eriboll (see chart 2076 and 10.7.27) provides secure anchs, but in strong winds violent squalls blow down from mountains. Eilean Cluimhrig lies on W side of entrance; the E shore is fringed with rks up to 0·2M offshore. At White Hd (Lt) the loch narrows to 0·6M. There are chans W and E of Eilean Choraidh. Best anchs in Camas an Duin (S of Ard Neackie) or in Rispond B close to entrance (but not in E winds, and beware Rispond Rk which dries).

Westward to C Wrath (see 10.8.5) the coast is indented, with dangers extending 0·3M from the shore and from offlying rks and Is. Once a yacht has left Loch Eriboll she is committed to a long and exposed passage until reaching Loch Inchard. The Kyle of Durness would be dangerous if the wind or sea is onshore. A firing exercise area extends 8M E of C Wrath, and 4M offshore. When in use, R flags or pairs of R Lts (vert) are shown from E and W limits, and yachts should keep clear.

ORKNEY ISLANDS (10.7.20 and charts 2249, 2250)

The Is are mostly indented and rky, but with sandy beaches especially on NE sides. Pilotage is easy in good vis, but in other conditions great care is needed since tides run strongly. For details refer to Clyde Cruising Club sailing directions and *N Coast of Scotland Pilot.*

When cruising in Orkney it is essential to understand and use the tidal streams to the best advantage, while at the same time considering the various tide races and overfalls, particularly near sp. A good engine is needed since, for example, there are many places where it is dangerous to get becalmed. It must also be remembered that swell from the Atlantic or North Sea can contribute to dangerous sea conditions, or penetrate to some of the anchorages. During summer months winds are not normally unduly strong, and can be expected to be Force 7 or more on about two days a month. But in winter the wind reaches this strength for 10-15 days per month, and gales can be very severe in late winter and early spring. Cruising conditions are best near midsummer, when of course the hours of daylight are much extended.

Stronsay Firth and Westray Firth run from SE to NW through the group. Races and/or tide rips, often dangerous in bad weather with wind against tide, occur off Mull Hd, over Dowie Sand, between Muckle Green Holm and War Ness (where violent turbulence may extend right across the firth), between Faraclett Hd and Wart Holm, and off Sacquoy Hd. Off War Ness the SE-going stream begins at HW Aberdeen +0435, and the NW-going at HW Aberdeen –0200, sp rates 7kn.

Tide races and dangerous seas occur at the entrances to most of the firths or sounds when the stream is against strong winds. This applies particularly to Hoy Sound, Eynhallow Sound, Papa Sound (Westray), Lashy Sound, and North Ronaldsay Firth.

There are many good anchs among the islands, including: Deer Sound (W of Deer Ness); B of Firth, B of Isbister, and off Balfour in Elwick B (all leading from Wide Firth); Rysa Sound, B of Houton, Hunda Sound (in Scapa Flow); Rousay Sound; and Pierowall Road (Westray). Plans for some of these are on chart 2622. For Shapinsay, Auskerry, Houton Bay and Pierowall see 10.7.27. There is a major oil terminal and prohibited area at Flotta, on S side of Scapa Flow.

SHETLAND ISLANDS (10.7.24 and charts 3281, 3282, 3283)

These Islands mostly have bold cliffs and are relatively high, separated by narrow sounds through which the tide runs strongly, so that in poor vis great care is needed. The Clyde Cruising Club sailing directions and *N Coast of Scotland Pilot* are almost indispensable.

As an introduction to these waters, a most violent and dangerous race forms off Sumburgh Hd (at S end of mainland) on both streams. Other dangerous areas include between Ve Skerries and Papa Stour; the mouth of Yell Sound with strong wind against N-going stream; and off Holm of Skaw (N end of Unst).

Although there are many secluded and attractive anchs, it must be remembered that the weather can change very quickly, with sudden shifts of wind. Also beware salmon fisheries and mussel rafts (unlit) in many Voes, Sounds and hbrs. For Scalloway and Balta Sound see 10.7.27.

Fair Is (North Haven) is a useful port of call when bound to/from Shetland Is. Note that races form off both ends of the Is, especially S, during the strength of tidal stream in both directions. See 10.7.27.

10.7.6 DISTANCE TABLE

Approximate distances in nautical miles are by the most direct route while avoiding dangers and allowing for traffic separation schemes etc. Places in *italics* are in adjoining areas.

1 *Flamborough Head*	1																			
2 *Fife Ness*	155	2																		
3 *Peterhead*	212	78	3																	
4 Fraserburgh	227	94	16	4																
5 Banff	244	111	33	18	5															
6 Buckie	257	124	46	31	15	6														
7 Lossiemouth	267	134	56	41	25	11	7													
8 Findhorn	280	147	69	54	38	24	13	8												
9 Inverness	301	168	90	75	59	45	34	23	9											
10 Tarbat Ness	283	150	72	57	41	27	18	14	27	10										
11 Helmsdale	285	152	74	59	44	33	26	28	43	16	11									
12 Wick	283	150	72	57	50	46	44	51	69	42	29	12								
13 Duncansby Head	292	158	82	67	62	58	57	63	81	54	41	13	13							
14 Scrabster	310	176	100	85	80	76	75	81	99	72	59	31	18	14						
15 Kirkwall	325	191	115	100	95	91	90	96	114	87	74	46	34	50	15					
16 Stromness	314	180	104	89	84	80	79	85	103	76	63	35	22	25	32	16				
17 Noup Head	342	208	132	117	112	108	107	113	131	104	91	63	50	47	23	28	17			
18 Lerwick	356	238	160	150	156	160	162	170	190	162	148	120	109	124	95	110	82	18		
19 Sullom Voe	385	268	190	180	186	190	192	200	220	192	178	150	139	154	125	136	108	38	19	
20 *Cape Wrath*	355	221	145	130	125	121	120	126	144	117	104	76	63	47	79	58	73	155	176	20

7

FRASERBURGH 10-7-7

Aberdeen

CHARTS
Admiralty 1462, 222; OS 30

TIDES
+0120 Dover; ML 2·3; Duration 0615; Zone 0 (GMT).

Standard Port ABERDEEN (⟵)

Times				Height (metres)			
HW		LW		MHWS	MHWN	MLWN	MLWS
0000	0600	0100	0700	4·3	3·4	1·6	0·6
1200	1800	1300	1900				
Differences FRASERBURGH							
−0105	−0115	−0120	−0110	−0·6	−0·5	−0·2	0·0

SHELTER
Good shelter but entrance is dangerous in on-shore gales. Yachts normally use South Harbour.

NAVIGATION
Waypoint 57°41′·32N 01°58′·71W, 111°/291° from/to entrance, 0·57M. This is a very busy fishing port and fishing vessels come and go day and night. There are no particular facilities for yachtsmen but it is a safe refuge. Large boulders have been deposited in SW part of harbour ent, reducing depth over an area which extends NE to the 291° ldg line. Take care on entering or leaving.

LIGHTS AND MARKS
Entry signals at South Pier
2 B Balls or 2 R Lts (vert): No entry. R flag or one R Lt: Harbour open but special care needed.
Docking signals (from head of Burnett Pier, SE end of West Pier, and NE end of head of North Pier). By day, semaphore arm: 45° above horizontal – clear inwards; horizontal – closed to all traffic; 45° below horizontal – clear outwards. By night G Lt shows relevant basin open, R Lt shows relevant basin closed.

RADIO TELEPHONE
VHF Ch 16; 12 (H24).

TELEPHONE (0346)
Hr Mr 23323; Port Office 25858; MRCC Aberdeen 592334; ⌗ 28033; Marinecall 0898 500 451; Police 23121; Dr 22088.

FACILITIES
EC Wednesday; **Port** ☎ 25858, Slip, P, D, L, FW, ME, El, Sh, C (70 ton mobile), CH, AB, V, R, Bar; **Caleys** ☎ 23241, P, D; **Mitchells** ☎ 22021, ME, El; **Buchan, Hall and Mitchell** ☎ 23336, ME, El, Sh; **May & Bruce** ☎ 25222, ME; **C. Will** ☎ 23364, C (30 ton); **G Walker** ☎ 23211 Slip, SM, Sh, C; **J. Noble** ☎ 3179, El, Sh; **Murisons** ☎ 23376, Gas. **Town** ✉; Ⓑ; ⇌ (bus to Aberdeen); ✈ (Aberdeen).

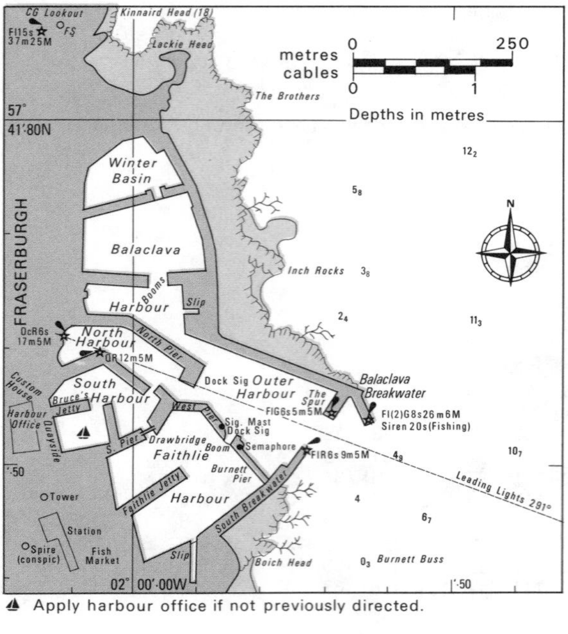
CG Lookout
Kinnaird Head (18)
Fl1 5s 37m25M
FS
Lackie Head
metres
cables
0
250
0
1
The Brothers
57°
41′·80N
Depths in metres
Winter Basin
Balaclava
FRASERBURGH
Booms
Harbour
Slip
Inch Rocks
North Harbour
North Pier
OcR6s 17m5M
QR12m5M
South Harbour
Custom House
Bruce's Jetty
Harbour Office
Quayside
Dock Sig
Outer Harbour
The Spur
Balaclava Breakwater
West Pier
FlG6s5m5M
Fl(2)G8s26m6M Siren 20s(Fishing)
Sig. Mast Dock Sig
Drawbridge
Boom
Semaphore
S. Pier
Faithlie
FlR6s 9m5M
Burnett Pier
Leading Lights 291°
Faithlie Jetty
Harbour
South Breakwater
Tower
Station
Spire (conspic)
Fish Market
Slip
Boich Head
Burnett Buss
02° 00′·00W
′·50
N

⚠ Apply harbour office if not previously directed.

MACDUFF 10-7-8

(BANFF)
Banff

CHARTS
Admiralty 1462, 222; OS 29

TIDES
+0055 Dover; ML 2·0; Duration 0615; Zone 0 (GMT).

Standard Port ABERDEEN (⟵)

Times				Height (metres)			
HW		LW		MHWS	MHWN	MLWN	MLWS
0200	0900	0400	0900	4·3	3·4	1·6	0·6
1400	2100	1600	2100				
Differences BANFF							
−0100	−0150	−0150	−0050	−0·8	−0·6	−0·5	−0·2

SHELTER
Reasonably good shelter but the entrance is open to westerly winds. Entry not recommended in strong NW winds. Harbour is three basins with entrance 17m wide. A busy cargo and fishing port.

NAVIGATION
Waypoint 57°40′·50N 02°30′·50W, 307°/127° from/to Macduff ent, 0·40M. Same waypoint 056°/236° from/to Banff entrance, 0·44M.
Beware rocky coast to the N and S of harbour entrance. There is a slight to moderate surge in the outer harbour with N to NE gales.

LIGHTS AND MARKS
A B ball (FG Lt at night) over pierhead Lt means harbour closed.

RADIO TELEPHONE
VHF Ch 16; 12 (H24).

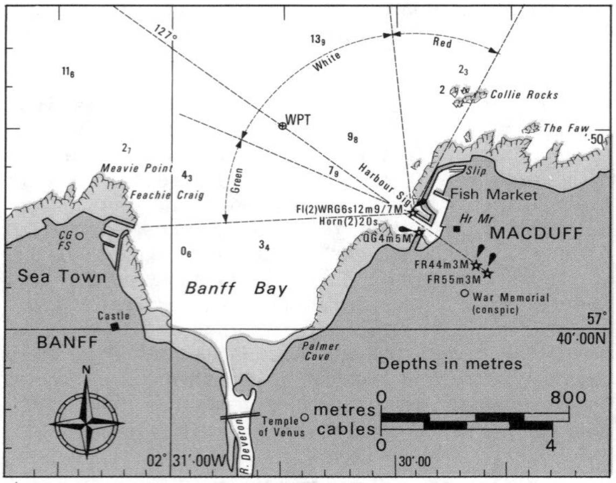
127°
White
Red
Collie Rocks
The Faw
WPT
Green
Harbour Slip
Meavie Point
Feachie Craig
Fl(2)WRG6s12m9/7M
Horn(2)20s
QG4m5M
Slip
Fish Market
Hr Mr
MACDUFF
CG FS
Sea Town
Banff Bay
FR44m3M
FR55m3M
War Memorial (conspic)
Castle
BANFF
57°
40′·00N
Palmer Cove
Depths in metres
metres
cables
800
4
Temple of Venus
R. Deveron
02° 31′·00W
30′·00
N

⚠ Apply to harbour office if not previously directed

TELEPHONE (Macduff 0261, Banff 02612)
Hr Mr (Macduff) 32236; Hr Mr (Banff) 5093; MRCC Aberdeen 592334; ⌗ 32217; Marinecall 0898 500 451; Police (Macduff) 32222, (Banff) 2555; Dr Banff 2021.

FACILITIES
EC Wednesday; **Harbour** ☎ 32236, Slip, P, D, FW, ME, El, Sh, CH, V, R, Bar; **Macduff Boat Building & Engineering Co** ☎ 32234, ME, El, Sh. **Banff SC. W. Thompson** ☎ 32388, Gas; **Town** ✉ (Macduff, Banff); Ⓑ (Banff); ⇌ (bus to Keith); ✈ (Aberdeen).
Note: Banff harbour, controlled by Grampian Region Council, is a popular yachting port. When entrance to Macduff is very rough with winds from SW to N, Banff can be a safe refuge. When winds are strong between N and ENE, Banff is unapproachable. Harbour dries. FW on quays. Town has P, D, ⇌, V, R, Bar.

WHITEHILLS 10-7-9
Banff

CHARTS
Admiralty 115, 222; OS 29

TIDES
+0050 Dover; ML 2·4; Duration 0610; Zone 0 (GMT).

Standard Port ABERDEEN (←)

Times				Height (metres)			
HW		LW		MHWS	MHWN	MLWN	MLWS
0200	0900	0400	0900	4·3	3·4	1·6	0·6
1400	2100	1600	2100				
Differences WHITEHILLS							
−0122	−0137	−0117	−0127	−0·4	−0·3	+0·1	+0·1

SHELTER
Safe. Swell in the outer basin in strong N to W winds.

NAVIGATION
Waypoint 57°42′·00N 02°34′·80W, 000°/180° from/to breakwater Lt, 1·2M. Reefs on S side of channel marked by two beacons. Beware numerous fishing floats.

LIGHTS AND MARKS
Fl WR 3s 7m 9/6M on pier head — approach in R sector vis R132°-212°, W212°-245°.

RADIO TELEPHONE
Whitehills Harbour Radio VHF Ch 16; 09.

TELEPHONE (026 17)
Hr Mr 5229; MRCC Aberdeen 592334; # Peterhead 74867; Marinecall 0898 500 451; Police (0542) 32222; Dr Banff 2027.

FACILITIES
EC Wednesday; **Pier** ☎ 5229, P, D, FW, ME, El, CH, V, Bar; **End of Harbour** Slip; **Paterson** ☎ 5219, P, D, CH. **Town** V, R, Bar. ✉; Ⓑ (AM only); ⇌ (bus to Keith); ✈ (Aberdeen).

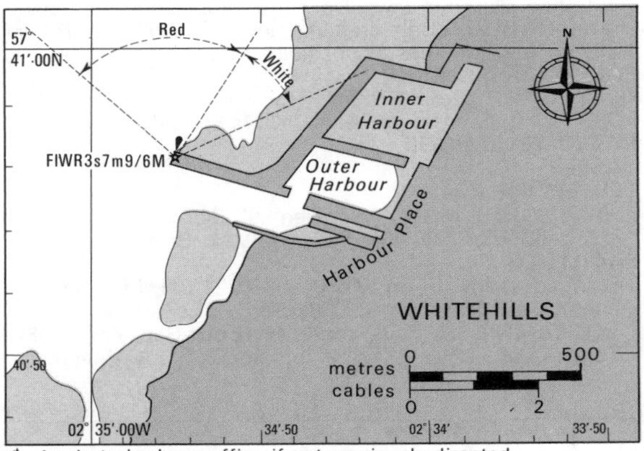
Red
White
57°
41′·00N
Inner Harbour
Outer Harbour
FlWR3s7m9/6M
Harbour Place
WHITEHILLS
metres
cables
0
500
0
2
40′·50
02° 35′·00W
34′·50
02° 34′
33′·50
▲ Apply to harbour office if not previously directed

BUCKIE 10-7-10
Banff

CHARTS
Admiralty 1462, 222; OS 28

TIDES
+0040 Dover; ML 2·4; Duration 0550; Zone 0 (GMT).

Standard Port ABERDEEN (←)

Times				Height (metres)			
HW		LW		MHWS	MHWN	MLWN	MLWS
0200	0900	0400	0900	4·3	3·4	1·6	0·6
1400	2100	1600	2100				
Differences BUCKIE							
−0130	−0145	−0125	−0140	−0·2	−0·2	0·0	+0·1

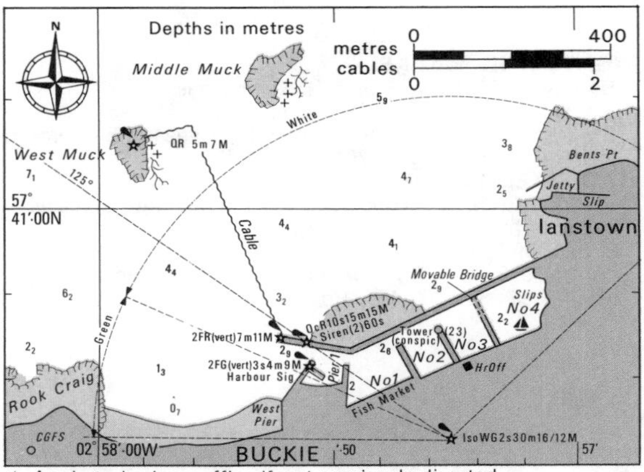
Depths in metres
Middle Muck
metres
cables
0
400
0
2
West Muck
QR 5m7M
White
125°
57°
41′·00N
Cable
Bents Pt
Jetty
Slip
Ianstown
Movable Bridge
Slips
No4
Green
2FR(vert)7m11M
OcR10s15m15M
Siren(2)60s
Tower (conspic)
No2
No3
HrOff
2FG(vert)3s4m9M
Harbour Sig
Pier
No1
Fish Market
Rook Craig
West Pier
CGFS
02° 58′·00W
BUCKIE
′50
IsoWG2s30m16/12M
57′
▲ Apply to harbour office if not previously directed

SHELTER
Overnight only. Good shelter and can be entered in all weathers. Hr entrance is 9m wide. Portknockie has good shelter. See 10.7.27.

NAVIGATION
Waypoint 57°41′·32N 02°58′·80W, 306°/126° from/to entrance, 0·80M. Beware West Muck, Middle Muck and East Muck Rocks, 3 ca off shore. There is a dangerous swell over the bar in harbour entrance in strong N to W winds.

LIGHTS AND MARKS
Lights in line at 125° lead SW of West Muck. Oc R 10s 15m 15M Entry signals:
W Pier B ball or Fl G Lt — Entrance depth less than 3m
B ball or FG over Fl G Lts — Entrance dangerous
2 B balls or 2 FR Lts — Harbour closed.

RADIO TELEPHONE
VHF Ch 12 16; 12. (Ch 16 H24)

TELEPHONE (0542)
Hr Mr 31700; MRCC Aberdeen 592334; # 32254; Marinecall 0898 500 451; Police 32222; Dr 31555.

FACILITIES
EC Wednesday; **No 4 Basin (East)** ☎ 31700, Slip, D, (Lorry delivery), AB, FW; **Aberdeen Boat Centre** Sh, CH; **Herd and Mackenzie** ☎ 31245, Slip, ME, El, Sh, C (15 ton); **Jones, Buckie SY** ☎ 32727, ME, El, Sh, CH, ACA, SM, BH; **Moravian Motors** ☎ 33977, Gas. **Town** ✉; Ⓑ; ⇌ (bus to Elgin); ✈ (Aberdeen or Inverness).

LOSSIEMOUTH 10-7-11
Moray

CHARTS
Admiralty 1462, 223; OS 28

TIDES
+0040 Dover; ML 2·3; Duration 0605; Zone 0 (GMT)

Standard Port ABERDEEN (←)

Times				Height (metres)			
HW		LW		MHWS	MHWN	MLWN	MLWS
0200	0900	0400	0900	4·3	3·4	1·6	0·6
1400	2100	1600	2100				
Differences LOSSIEMOUTH							
−0125	−0200	−0130	−0130	−0·2	−0·2	0·0	0·0

SHELTER
Very good from winds from N through W to SSE. From NE to SE it is dangerous and E winds bring swell in outer harbour. Visiting yachts moor in East Basin.

NAVIGATION
Waypoint 57°43′·40N 03°16′·00W, 097°/277° from/to entrance, 0·30M. Rocks to N & S of harbour entrance — approach from East. At night leading lights (FR 292°) are shown when safe to enter. When entering the harbour, beware current from R Lossie setting in northerly direction and causing confused water.

7

LOSSIEMOUTH *continued*

LIGHTS AND MARKS
By day — B ball at S pier } Dangerous
By night — R Lt over G Lt } to enter
R Flag at South Jetty when merchant vessels entering or leaving. Leading lights 292°, both FR.
RADIO TELEPHONE
VHF Ch 12 16; 12 (0800-1700 LT, and 1h before vessel expected).
TELEPHONE (034 381)
Hr Mr 3066; MRCC Aberdeen 592334; # Elgin 547518; Marinecall 0898 500 451; Police 2022; Dr 2277.

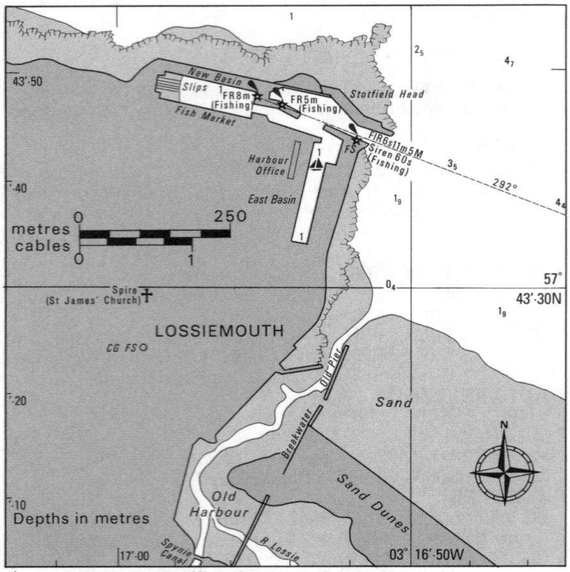
New Basin
Slips
FR8m (Fishing)
FR5m (Fishing)
Stotfield Head
Fish Market
FIR6s11m5M
FS
Siren 60s (Fishing)
Harbour Office
East Basin
292°
metres
cables
0
250
1
43′·50
·40
·20
·10
57°
43′·30N
Spire (St James' Church)
LOSSIEMOUTH
CG FS
Old Pier
Breakwater
Sand
Sand Dunes
Old Harbour
Spynie Canal
R Lossie
Depths in metres
17′·00
03° 16′·50W
⛵ Apply to harbour office if not previously directed

FACILITIES
EC Thursday; **Harbour** Slip, D, M (See Hr Mr), FW (on quay), ME, El, Sh, C, AB, SM, BH (15 ton); **Jones Buckie Shipyard** ☎ 2029, ME, El, Sh, CH. **Lossiemouth SC** ☎ 2928; **Mallard** ☎ 3001, Gas.
Town P, V, R, Bar. ✉; Ⓑ; ⇌ (bus to Elgin); ✈ (Inverness).
Note:- East Basin will probably become a marina.

HOPEMAN 10-7-12
Moray

CHARTS
Admiralty 1462, 223; OS 28
TIDES
+0050 Dover; ML 2·4; Duration 0610; Zone 0 (GMT)

Standard Port ABERDEEN (⟵)

Times				Height (metres)			
HW		LW		MHWS	MHWN	MLWN	MLWS
0200	0900	0400	0900	4·3	3·4	1·6	0·6
1400	2100	1600	2100				
Differences HOPEMAN							
−0120	−0150	−0135	−0120	−0·2	−0·2	0·0	0·0

SHELTER
A popular yachting harbour with alongside berths and good facilities; controlled by Grampian Regional Council. Entrance is difficult in winds from NE to SE. Once in SW basin, shelter good from all winds. Harbour dries. Access HW∓2 (for 1·5m draught).
NAVIGATION
Waypoint 57°42′·68N, 03°26′·50W, 263°/083° from/to entrance, 0·17M. Dangerous rocks lie off harbour entrance. Harbour dries. Do not attempt entry in heavy weather. Beware salmon stake nets E and W of harbour Mar to Aug and lobster pot floats.
LIGHTS AND MARKS
Ldg Lts 081°, Front FR 3m, Rear FR 4m (1 August – 30th April). South Pier head OcG 4s 8m 4M.
RADIO TELEPHONE
None.
TELEPHONE (0343)
Hr Mr 830650; MRCC Aberdeen 592334; # Elgin 547518; Marinecall 0898 500 451; Police 830222; Dr Elgin 543141.
FACILITIES
EC Wednesday. **John More** ☎ 830221 CH, ME, Gas; **North East Sailing** ☎ 830889 Sh; **J Sutherland** ☎ 830236 ME, El, D, P (cans); **Harbour** Slip, AB, D, FW; **Town** V, R, Bar, ✉; Ⓑ; ⇌ (bus to Elgin); ✈ (Inverness).

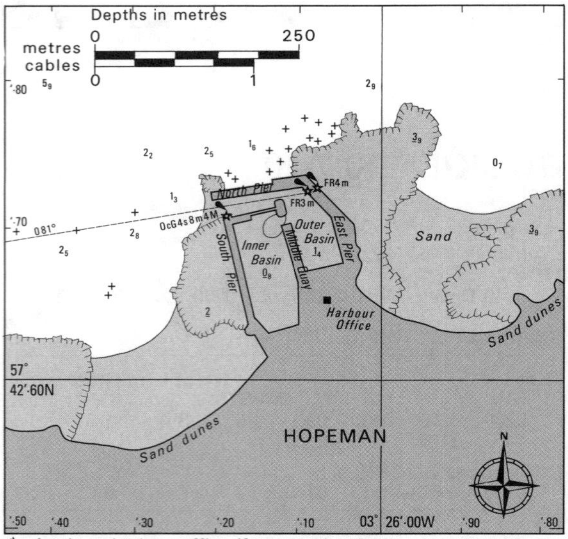
Depths in metres
metres
cables
0
250
1
·80
·70
North Pier
FR4m
FR3m
081°
OcG4s8m4M
South Pier
Inner Basin
Middle Quay
Outer Basin
East Pier
Harbour Office
Sand
Sand dunes
57°
42′·60N
HOPEMAN
·50
·40
·30
·20
·10
03° 26′·00W
·90
·80
⛵ Apply to harbour office if not previously directed

BURGHEAD 10-7-13
Moray

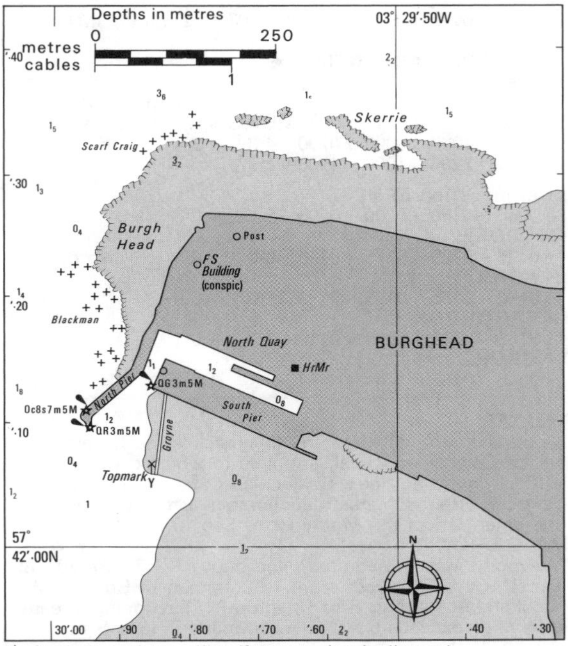
Depths in metres
metres
cables
0
250
1
03° 29′·50W
Skerrie
Scarf Craig
Burgh Head
Post
FS Building (conspic)
Blackman
North Quay
BURGHEAD
HrMr
North Pier
QG3m5M
Oc8s7m5M
QR3m5M
South Pier
Groyne
Topmark Y
57° 42′·00N
30′·00
N

▲ Apply to harbour office if not previously directed

CHARTS
Admiralty 1462, 223; OS 28

TIDES
+0035 Dover; ML 2·4; Duration 0610; Zone 0 (GMT).

Standard Port ABERDEEN (⟵)

Times				Height (metres)			
HW		LW		MHWS	MHWN	MLWN	MLWS
0200	0900	0400	0900	4·3	3·4	1·6	0·6
1400	2100	1600	2100				
Differences BURGHEAD							
−0120	−0150	−0135	−0120	−0·2	−0·2	0·0	0·0

SHELTER
One of the few harbours open in Moray Firth with strong E winds. NE wall of basin dries. Go alongside where available and contact Hr Mr's office. Can become very congested with fishing vessels.

NAVIGATION
Waypoint 57°42′·30N 03°30′30W, 317°/137° from/to N Pier Lt, 0·28M. Channel is subject to variations due to sand movement. Details from Hr Mr. Approach from SW. Access HW∓4.

LIGHTS AND MARKS
No leading lights but night entrance is safe after identifying the two outer pier Lts, QR 3m 5M and Oc 8s 7m 5M. South Pier head QG 3m 5M.

RADIO TELEPHONE
Hr Mr VHF Ch 16; 12 14 (office hours and when vessel expected).

TELEPHONE (0343)
Hr Mr 835337; MRCC Aberdeen 592334; # Elgin 547518; Marinecall 0898 500 451; Dr Lossiemouth 2277.

FACILITIES
EC Thursday; **Harbour** D, FW, AB, C (15 ton mobile), L, Slip. **Ernest Colburn** ☎ 835088 BY, Sh; **Town** Bar, ✉; V, P (cans), Ⓑ; ≠ (bus to Elgin); ✈ (Inverness).

FINDHORN 10-7-14
Moray

CHARTS
Admiralty 223; OS 27

TIDES
+0110 Dover; ML 2·5; Duration 0615; Zone 0 (GMT)

Standard Port ABERDEEN (⟵)

Times				Height (metres)			
HW		LW		MHWS	MHWN	MLWN	MLWS
0200	0900	0400	0900	4·3	3·4	1·6	0·6
1400	2100	1600	2100				
Differences FINDHORN							
−0120	−0150	−0135	−0130	0·0	−0·1	0·0	+0·1

SHELTER
Anchor off north pier and enquire at YC. Do not attempt entry in strong winds from NW to NE or when big swell is running.
THE OLD BAR. The original mouth of Findhorn River 4M SW of Findhorn gives excellent shelter in all weathers. Channel changes – local knowledge needed.

NAVIGATION
Waypoint 57°41′·00N 03°38′·80W 328°/148° from/to Ee Point, 1·4M. From waypoint, proceed to safe water mark which is a spar buoy, thence ESE to the buoys which mark the gap in the sand bar. Thence to three poles with R can top marks to be left a boat's length to port. Once past The Ee turn to port, leaving green buoys to stbd.

LIGHTS AND MARKS
There are no lights. There is a windsock on a flagpole by The Ee.

RADIO TELEPHONE
VHF Ch M (when yacht racing in progress).

TELEPHONE (0309)
MRCC Aberdeen 592334; # Elgin 547518; G. Mackenzie (Findhorn Pilot) 30546; Marinecall 0898 500 451; Police 72224; Dr 72221.

FACILITIES
Royal Findhorn YC ☎ 30247, M, FW, Bar; **Findhorn BY** ☎ 30099, C (16 ton), CH, D and P (cans), El, FW, L, M, ME, ACA, R, Slip, Gas; **Reids Engineering** (Forres) ☎ 72175, ME, El; **Norman Whyte** ☎ 30504, AC, L, ME, FW, BY, Sh; **Town** V, R, Bar, ✉; Ⓑ (Nairn and Forres); ≠ (Forres), ✈ (Inverness).

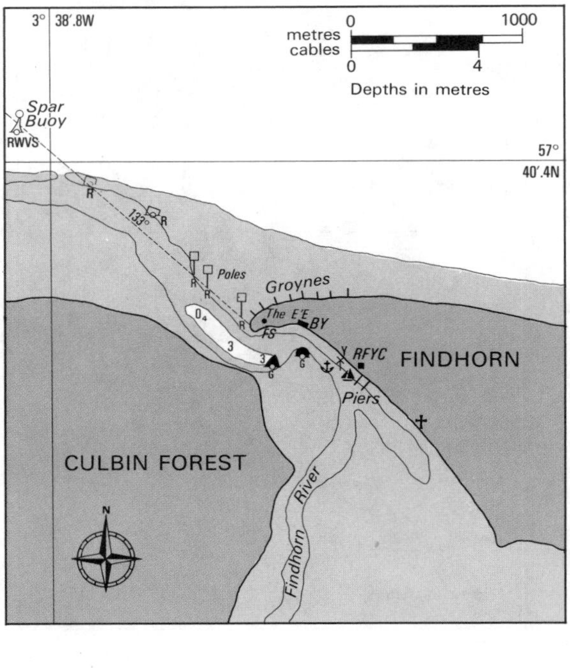
3° 38′.8W
metres
cables
0
1000
4
Depths in metres
Spar Buoy
RWVS
57° 40′.4N
132°
Poles
Groynes
The E'E
BY
FS
RFYC
FINDHORN
Piers
CULBIN FOREST
Findhorn River
N

7

NAIRN 10-7-15

Nairn

CHARTS
Admiralty 1462, 223; OS 27

TIDES
+0110 Dover; ML 2·2; Duration 0615; Zone 0 (GMT).

Standard Port ABERDEEN (⟵)

Times				Height (metres)			
HW		LW		MHWS	MHWN	MLWN	MLWS
0200	0900	0400	0900	4·3	3·4	1·6	0·6
1400	2100	1600	2100				
Differences NAIRN							
−0120	−0150	−0135	−0130	0·0	−0·1	0·0	+0·1
McDERMOTT BASE							
−0110	−0140	−0120	−0115	−0·1	−0·1	+0·1	+0·3

SHELTER
Entry channel faces NNE so winds from that direction make entry difficult. Pontoons in harbour with six visitors places.

NAVIGATION
Waypoint 57°35′·90N, 03°51′·80W, 335°/155° from/to entrance, 0·30M. Advisable to enter between HW∓1½. Harbour is no longer used by commercial shipping.

LIGHTS AND MARKS
Lt Ho on E pier head, sectored Oc WRG 4s, 6m 5M G shore-100°, W100°-207°, R207°-shore. Keep in W sector.

RADIO TELEPHONE
None. Ch 37 (weekends only).

TELEPHONE (0667)
Hr Mr 54704; MRCC Aberdeen 592334; ⌗ Inverness 222787; Marinecall 0898 500 451; Police 52222; Dr 53421; Clinic 5092.

FACILITIES
EC Wednesday: **Grants** ☎ 52243 D and P (drums); **Nairn Basin** FW (standpipes), Slip, AC (110 volts), P, D; **Nairn SC** ☎ 53897, Bar; **Town** V, R, Bar, ✉; Ⓑ; ≷; ✈ (Inverness).
A major marina – village project is under way (1990).

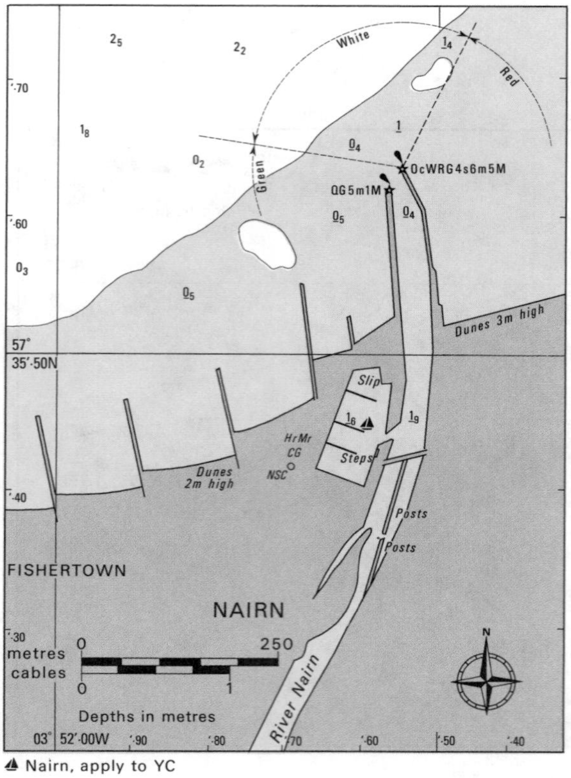
White
Red
Green
OcWRG4s6m5M
QG5m1M
Dunes 3m high
Slip
Steps
HrMr
CG
NSC
Dunes
2m high
Posts
Posts
FISHERTOWN
NAIRN
River Nairn
metres
cables
0
250
0
1
Depths in metres
57°
35′·50N
03° 52′·00W
N

⛵ Nairn, apply to YC

INVERNESS 10-7-16

Inverness

CHARTS
Admiralty 1078, 1077, 223; OS 26/27

TIDES
+0100 Dover; ML 2·7; Duration 0620; Zone 0 (GMT).

Standard Port ABERDEEN (⟵)

Times				Height (metres)			
HW		LW		MHWS	MHWN	MLWN	MLWS
0300	1000	0000	0700	4·3	3·4	1·6	0·6
1500	2200	1200	1900				
Differences INVERNESS							
−0050	−0150	−0200	−0105	+0·5	+0·3	+0·2	+0·1
FORTROSE							
−0125	−0125	−0125	−0125	0·0	0·0	No data	
CROMARTY							
−0120	−0155	−0155	−0120	0·0	0·0	+0·1	+0·2
INVERGORDON							
−0105	−0200	−0200	−0110	+0·1	+0·1	+0·1	+0·1
DINGWALL							
−0045	−0145	No data		+0·1	+0·2	No data	

SHELTER
Good shelter in all weathers. Inverness is the NE entrance to the Caledonian Canal, entrance to which can be difficult in strong tides. Caledonian Canal — See 10.8.15. Fortrose offers some safe anchorages at the entrance to the inner part of the Moray Firth. See 10.7.27.

NAVIGATION
Waypoint Meikle Mee stbd-hand buoy, FlG 3s, 57°30′·28N 04°11′·93W, 070°/250° from/to Longman Pt Bn, 0·74M. Tidal streams strong S of Craigton Pt (East going stream at springs exceeds 5 kn). Beware marine farms S of Avoch. (Off chartlet).

LIGHTS AND MARKS
Entrance to river is very narrow but deep. Craigton Pt Lt is Fl WRG 4s 6m 11/7M vis W312°-048°, R048°-064°, W064°-085°, G085°-shore.

RADIO TELEPHONE
Call: *Inverness Harbour Office* VHF Ch 12 16; 12 14 (Mon-Fri: 0800-1700 LT). Caley Marina Ch **80** M. Inverness Boat Centre Ch **80** M (0900-1800 LT). Other station: Cromarty Firth Port Control Ch 16; **11** 16 13 (H24).
Call: *Clachnaharry Sea Lock* Ch 74. For canal office call: *Caledonian Canal* Ch 74.

TELEPHONE (0463)
Hr Mr 233291 (after hours 234478); Clachnaharry Sea Lock 235439; MRCC Aberdeen 592334; ⌗ 222787; Marinecall 0898 500 451; Police 239191; Dr 234151.

FACILITIES
EC Wednesday; **Caley Marina** (25+25 visitors) ☎ 236539 ACA, AC, C (20 ton), CH, D, ME, El, Sh, FW, (Access H24); **Muirtown Marina** (20+20 visitors) ☎ 239745 AC, D, FW, Gas, Gaz, ME, ▣, C (4 ton), CH, Sh, El; Access HW∓4; **Shore Street Quay** ☎ 233291, Slip, P, D, L, FW, ME, El, C (2 mobiles), CH, AB; **Citadel Quay** ☎ 233291, Slip, P, D, L, FW, ME, El, AB; **Inverness Boatbuilding and Engineering** ☎ 243585, Slip, M, ME, El, Sh, C (100 ton); **P. T. McHardy** ☎ 233632, Gas; **Inverness Boat Centre** ☎ 73383, CH, FW, L, M, ME, P, Slip, SM. **Town** V, R, Bar. ✉; Ⓑ; ≷; ✈.

INVERNESS *continued*

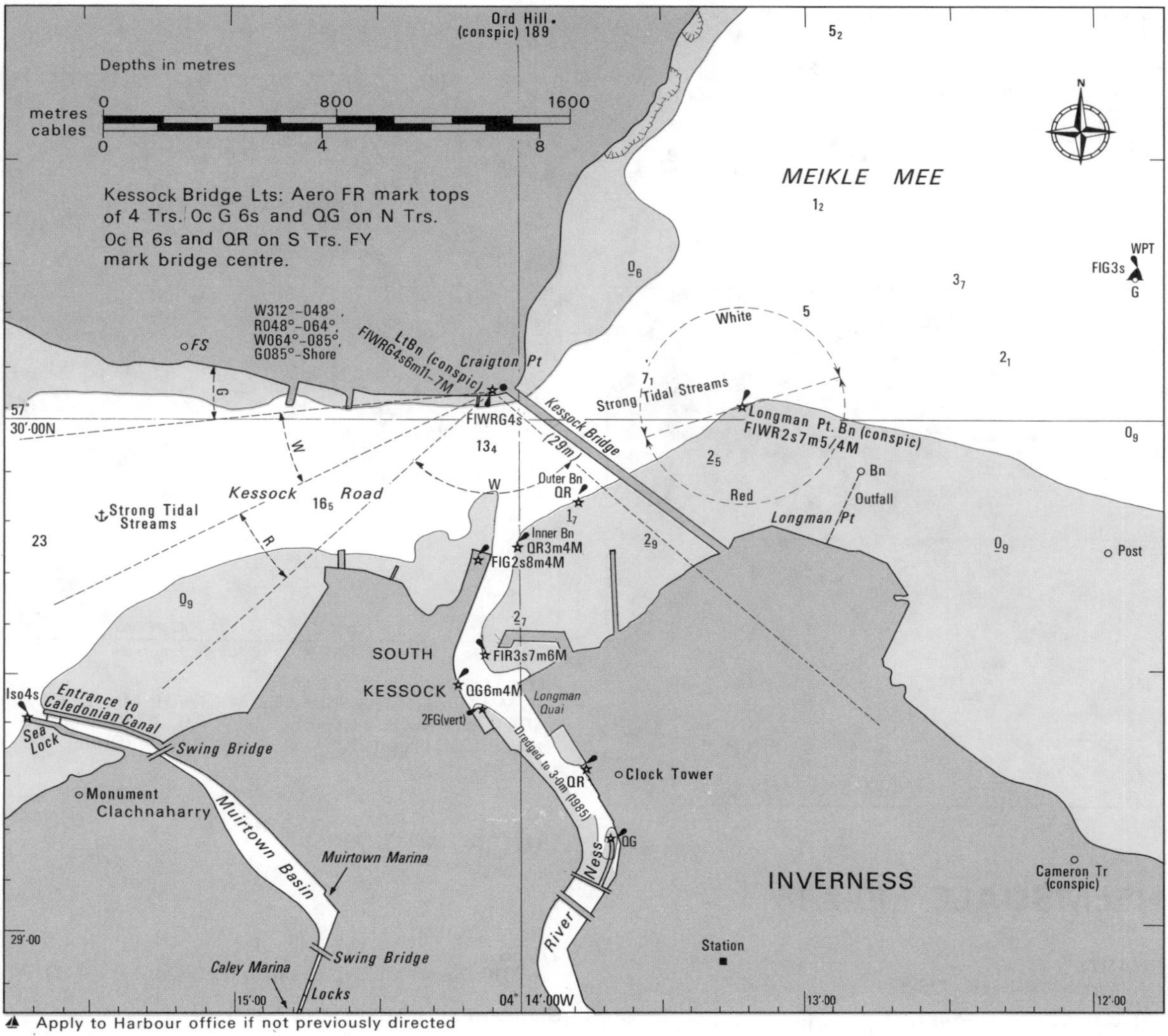
Ord Hill
(conspic) 189
Depths in metres
metres 0 800 1600
cables 0 4 8
Kessock Bridge Lts: Aero FR mark tops of 4 Trs. Oc G 6s and QG on N Trs. Oc R 6s and QR on S Trs. FY mark bridge centre.
W312°-048°, R048°-064°, W064°-085°, G085°-Shore
LtBn (conspic) FlWRG4s6m11-7M
Craigton Pt
FlWRG4s
MEIKLE MEE
WPT
FlG3s
G
White
Strong Tidal Streams
Longman Pt. Bn (conspic) FlWR2s7m5/4M
Kessock Bridge (29m)
Kessock Road
Strong Tidal Streams
Outer Bn QR
Inner Bn QR3m4M
FlG2s8m4M
Red
Bn
Outfall
Longman Pt
Post
SOUTH KESSOCK
FlR3s7m6M
QG6m4M
Longman Quai
2FG(vert)
Iso4s
Entrance to Caledonian Canal
Sea Lock
Swing Bridge
Monument
Clachnaharry
Muirtown Basin
Muirtown Marina
Dredged to 3·0m (1985)
QR
QG
Clock Tower
River Ness
INVERNESS
Cameron Tr (conspic)
Station
Caley Marina
Swing Bridge
Locks
57° 30'·00N
29'·00
15'·00
04° 14'·00W
13'·00
12'·00

Apply to Harbour office if not previously directed

PORTMAHOMACK 10-7-17

Ross and Cromarty

CHARTS
Admiralty 223, 115; OS 21

TIDES
+0035 Dover; ML 2·5; Duration 0600; Zone 0 (GMT).

Standard Port ABERDEEN (⟵)

Times				Height (metres)			
HW		LW		MHWS	MHWN	MLWN	MLWS
0300	0800	0200	0800	4·3	3·4	1·6	0·6
1500	2000	1400	2000				
Differences PORTMAHOMACK							
−0120	−0210	−0140	−0110	−0·2	−0·1	+0·1	+0·1

SHELTER
Uncomfortable in NW to SW winds, but otherwise good shelter. Access to harbour at HW only. Harbour dries but good anchorage close SW of pier.

NAVIGATION
Waypoint Special buoy, FlY 5s, 57°53'·03N 03°47'·02W, 346°/166° from/to Tarbat Ness Lt, 1·13M. Beware Curach Rocks which lie from 2ca SW of pier to the shore. Rocks extend to N and W of the pier. Beware lobster pot floats and salmon nets to N of harbour.

PORTMAHOMACK *continued*

LIGHTS AND MARKS
There are no lights or marks.
RADIO TELEPHONE
None.
TELEPHONE (086 287)
Hr Mr 446; MRCC Aberdeen 592334; ⌗ Invergordon 852221; Marinecall 0898 500 451; Dr Tain 2759.
FACILITIES
EC Wednesday; **Harbour** C (6 ton), M, L, FW, AB; **Town** ✉; Ⓑ (Mobile from Tain Monday 1500-1600); ⇄ (bus to Tain); ✈ (Inverness).

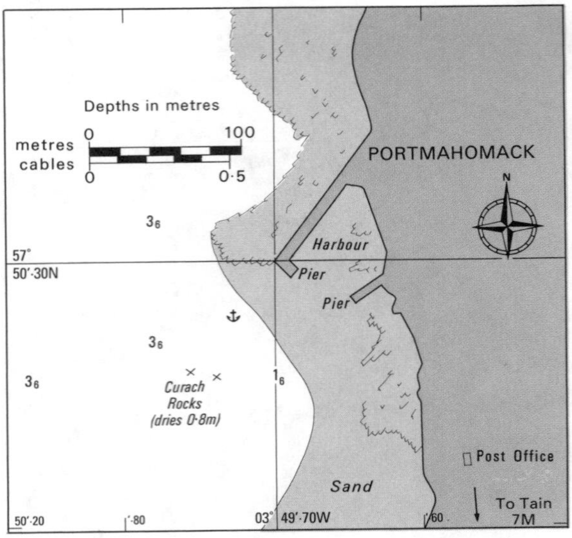

Depths in metres
metres 0 100
cables 0 0·5
PORTMAHOMACK
Harbour
Pier
Pier
57° 50′·30N
Curach Rocks (dries 0·8m)
Post Office
Sand
To Tain 7M
50′·20
·80
03° 49′·70W
·60

HELMSDALE 10-7-18

Sutherland

CHARTS
Admiralty 1462, 115; OS 17
TIDES
+0035 Dover; ML 2·2; Duration 0615; Zone 0 (GMT).

Standard Port ABERDEEN (⟵)

Times				Height (metres)			
HW		LW		MHWS	MHWN	MLWN	MLWS
0300	0800	0200	0800	4·3	3·4	1·6	0·6
1500	2000	1400	2000				
Differences HELMSDALE							
−0140	−0200	−0150	−0135	−0·5	−0·4	−0·1	−0·1
GOLSPIE							
−0130	−0215	−0155	−0130	−0·3	−0·3	−0·1	0·0

SHELTER
Good in all weathers except strong E to SE winds.
NAVIGATION
Waypoint 58°06′·61N 03°38′·30W, 133°/313° from/to entrance, 0·35M. Beware spate coming down river after heavy rains. Shallow both sides of channel and bar builds up when river in spate.
LIGHTS AND MARKS
Ldg Lts 313°. Front FG (harbour open) or FR (harbour closed). Rear FG; both on W masts. By day Or disc on each mast.
RADIO TELEPHONE
VHF Ch 16, 12.
TELEPHONE (043 12)
Hr Mr 347; MRCC Aberdeen 592334; ⌗ Wick 3650; Marinecall 0898 500 451; Dr 225 (Home) or 221 (Surgery).

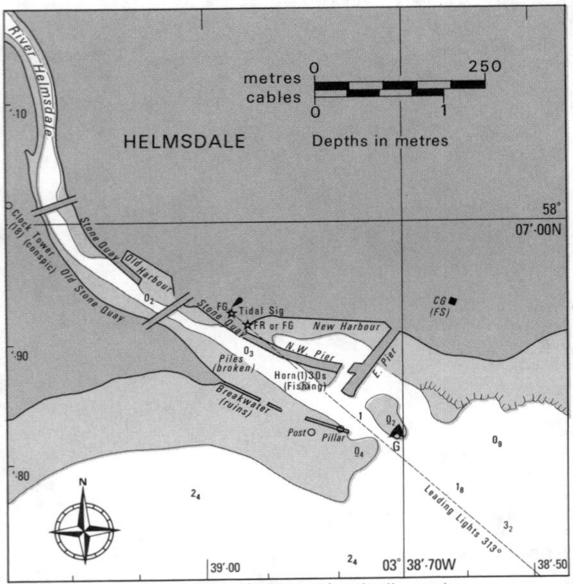

River Helmsdale
metres 0 250
cables 0 1
HELMSDALE
Depths in metres
58° 07′·00N
Clock Tower (18) (conspic)
Stone Quay
Old Harbour
Old Stone Quay
Tidal Sig
FR or FG
New Harbour
N.W. Pier
E. Pier
CG (FS)
Piles (broken)
Horn(1)30s (Fishing)
Breakwater (ruins)
Post
Pillar
Leading Lights 313°
39′·00
03° 38′·70W
38′·50

⚠ Apply to Harbour office if not previously directed

FACILITIES
EC Wednesday; **NW Pier** Slip, M (See Hr Mr), L, FW, AB; **E Pier** M (See Hr Mr), L, FW, AB; **A. R. McLeod** ☎ 338, Gas; **Town** P, D, V, R, Bar. ✉; Ⓑ (Brora); ⇄; ✈ (Wick).

WICK 10-7-19

Caithness

CHARTS
Admiralty 1462, 115; OS 12
TIDES
+0010 Dover; ML 2·0; Duration 0625; Zone 0 (GMT).

Standard Port ABERDEEN (⟵)

Times				Height (metres)			
HW		LW		MHWS	MHWN	MLWN	MLWS
0300	0800	0200	0800	4·3	3·4	1·6	0·6
1500	2000	1400	2000				
Differences WICK							
−0155	−0220	−0210	−0220	−0·9	−0·7	−0·2	−0·1
DUNCANSBY HEAD							
−0320	−0320	−0320	−0320	−1·2	−1·0	No data	

SHELTER
Shelter good except in strong NNE to SSE winds. NB. The river harbour is leased and must *not* be entered without prior permission.
NAVIGATION
Waypoint 58°26′·20N 03°03′·30W, 104°/284° from/to South Pier Lt, 0·72M. Harbour entrance dangerous in strong easterly winds as boats have to make a 90° turn at the end of S Pier. Unlit pole beacon S side of bay marks seaward end of ruined breakwater.
LIGHTS AND MARKS
Harbour inaccessible — a black ball (G light at night) on top of CG Station on South Head.
South pier Lt — Fl WRG 3s 12m 5/3M G253°-269°, W269°-286°, R286°-329°
Dir Lt on N end of bridge, W sector 289°-292°. Dir Lt 290·5°. Dir FWRG 9m 10/7M.
When harbour temporarily obstructed B ball or R Lt at S Pier head. Leading Lts 234°, both FR.

WICK *continued*

RADIO TELEPHONE
VHF Ch 16; 14 (when vessel expected).

TELEPHONE (0955)
Hr Mr 2030; MRSC Kirkwall 3268; # 3650; Police 3551; Ⓗ 2434, 2261.

FACILITIES
EC Wednesday; **Inner N Pier** Slip, L, ME, AB (see Hr Mr), V; **Harbour Quays** L, ME; **Outer S Pier** L; **Jetty** ☎ Tel. 2689, D, L, FW, CH; **James McCaughey** ☎ 3701 or 2858, ME, El, Sh, CH, Slip, Gas; **Town** Slip, P, ME, El, Sh, C (15 to 100 ton), CH, V, R, Bar. ✉; Ⓑ; ⇌; ✈.

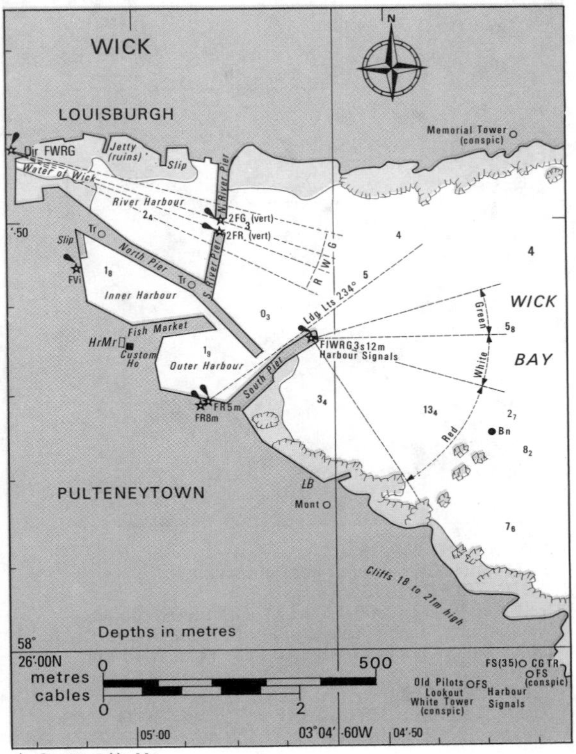

WICK
N
LOUISBURGH
Memorial Tower (conspic)
Dir FWRG
Jetty (ruins)
Slip
Water of Wick
River Harbour
N River Pier
2FG (vert)
2FR (vert)
North Pier
Slip
FVi
Inner Harbour
S River Pier
Ldg Lts 234°
R W G
Fish Market
HrMr
Custom Ho
Outer Harbour
South Pier
FIWRG3s12m
Harbour Signals
Green
White
Red
WICK
BAY
Bn
FR5m
FR8m
LB
Mont
PULTENEYTOWN
Cliffs 18 to 21m high
Depths in metres
58°
26'·00N
metres
cables
500
FS(35)
CG TR
FS (conspic)
Old Pilots Lookout White Tower (conspic)
Harbour Signals
05'·00
03°04'·60W
04'·50

⛵ Contact Hr Mr

ORKNEY ISLANDS 10-7-20

The Orkneys consist of some 70 islands, of which about 24 are inhabited. They extend 5 to 50M NNE from Duncansby Head, and are mostly low-lying, but Hoy in the SW of the group reaches 475m (1560ft). Coasts are generally rocky and much indented, but there are many sandy beaches. A passage with least width of about 3M runs from NW to SE through the group. The islands are divided from Scotland by Pentland Firth, a very dangerous stretch of water (see 10.7.5). The climate is mild but windy, and very few trees grow. The principal island is Mainland (or Pomona) on which stands Kirkwall, the capital. There is a small naval base at Lyness in Scapa Flow.

Beware the many lobster pots (creels) all round the coast. Severe gales blow in winter and early spring (see 10.7.5). There are lifeboats at Longhope, Stromness and Kirkwall. There is a MRSC at Kirkwall, ☎ (0856) 3268, with Auxiliary (Watch and Rescue) Stations at Longhope (South Walls), Brough Ness (South Ronaldsay), Stromness (Mainland), Deerness (Mainland), Westray, Papa Westray, Sanday, North Ronaldsay and all inhabited islands except Egilsay and Wyre.

CHARTS
Charts 2249 and 2250 cover the islands. For larger scale charts, see under individual harbours.

TIDES
Tidal information is related to Aberdeen (10.6.17) as Standard Port. Tidal streams are strong, particularly in Pentland Firth and in the firths and sounds among the islands (see 10.7.5.).

SHELTER
There are piers at all the main islands, and there are many anchorages, of which the following are a selection.

MAINLAND
SCAPA BAY: good except in S winds. No yacht berths alongside pier due to heavy harbour traffic.
STROMNESS: see 10.7.23
KIRKWALL: see 10.7.21
HOUTON BAY: see 10.7.27
ST MARY'S: N side of Kirk Sound; anchor in Bay of Ayre or go alongside E side of pier.
KIRK SOUND (E entrance): anchor N or E end of Lamb Holt.
DEER SOUND: anchor in Pool of Mirkady or off pier on NW side of sound; very good shelter, no facilities.

BURRAY
EAST WEDDEL SOUND: excellent anchorage E side of Churchill Barrier in centre of Weddel Bay.
HUNDA SOUND: good anchorage in all winds.

SOUTH RONALDSAY
ST MARGARET'S HOPE: anchor in centre of bay; beware Flotta ferries using the pier.

HOY
LONG HOPE: anchor E of the pier on South Ness, which is used by steamers/ferries or go alongside pier (safest at slack water). Facilities: FW, ✉, V.
PEGAL BAY: good anchorage except in strong W winds.

ROUSAY
WYRE SOUND: anchor to E of Rousay pier, or go alongside pier. Facilities: ✉, shop.

EDAY
FERS NESS BAY: good holding, and shelter from all S winds.

WESTRAY
PIEROWALL: see 10.7.27
BAY OF MOCLETT: Excellent anchorage but open to S winds.
SOUTH WICK: Small vessel anchorage on E of Papa Westray, off the old pier or ESE of pier off Holm of Papa.

SANDAY
OTTERSWICK: good anchorage except in N or E winds.
NORTH BAY: on NW side of island, exposed to NW.
KETTLETOFT BAY: anchor in bay or go alongside pier; very exposed to SE winds. Facilities: ✉, shop, hotel.

NORTH RONALDSAY
SOUTH BAY: anchor in middle of bay or go alongside pier; open to S and E, and subject to swell.
LINKLET BAY: not a safe anchorage, open to E.
STRONSAY: see 10.7.22
AUSKERRY: see 10.7.27

NAVIGATION
Apart from the strong tidal streams and associated races, navigation is easy in clear weather; see 10.7.5.

LIGHTS AND MARKS
The main harbours and sounds are well lit; for details see 10.7.4. Powerful lights are shown from Cantick Head, Graemsay Island, Copinsay, Auskerry, Kirkwall, Brough of Birsay, Sanday Island, North Ronaldsay and Noup Head.

RADIO TELEPHONE
Orkney Harbours Navigation Service (call: *Orkney Harbour Radio*, Ch 16 20; 09 11 (H24)) covers Scapa Flow, Wide Firth and Shapinsay Sound; see 10.7.21. For other local stations see individual harbours. The local Coast Radio Station is Orkney Radio (VHF Ch 16 26 (H24)), remotely controlled from Wick Radio.

MEDICAL SERVICES
There are doctors available at Kirkwall, Stromness, Rousay, Shapinsay, Eday, North Ronaldsay, Stronsay, Sanday and Westray (Pierowall). Papa Westray is looked after from Westray. The only hospital is at Kirkwall. Serious cases are flown to Aberdeen (1 hour). The only dental services are at Kirkwall.

ORKNEY ISLANDS *continued*

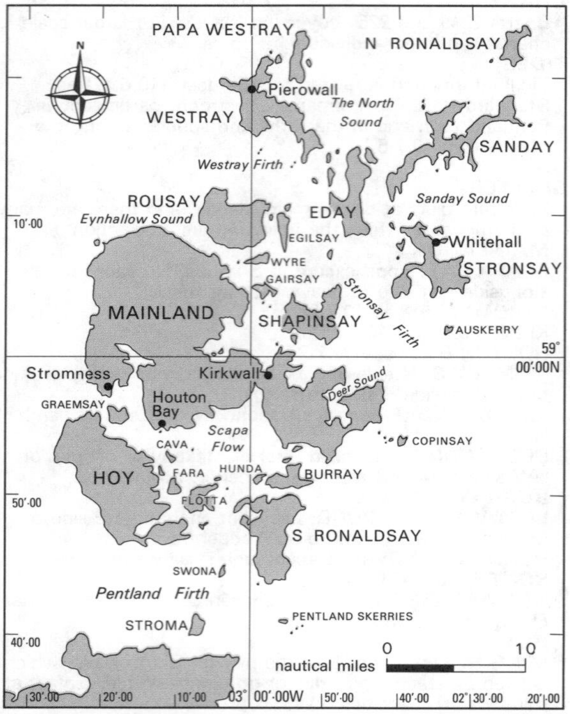
PAPA WESTRAY
N RONALDSAY
Pierowall
The North Sound
WESTRAY
SANDAY
Westray Firth
ROUSAY
Eynhallow Sound
EDAY
Sanday Sound
EGILSAY
Whitehall
WYRE
STRONSAY
GAIRSAY
Stronsay Firth
MAINLAND
SHAPINSAY
AUSKERRY
Stromness
Kirkwall
Deer Sound
GRAEMSAY
Houton Bay
Scapa Flow
COPINSAY
CAVA
HOY
FARA
HUNDA
BURRAY
FLOTTA
S RONALDSAY
SWONA
Pentland Firth
STROMA
PENTLAND SKERRIES
nautical miles
0
10
10'·00
50'·00
40'·00
59° 00'·00N
30'·00
20'·00
10'·00
03° 00'·00W
50'·00
40'·00
02° 30'·00
20'·00

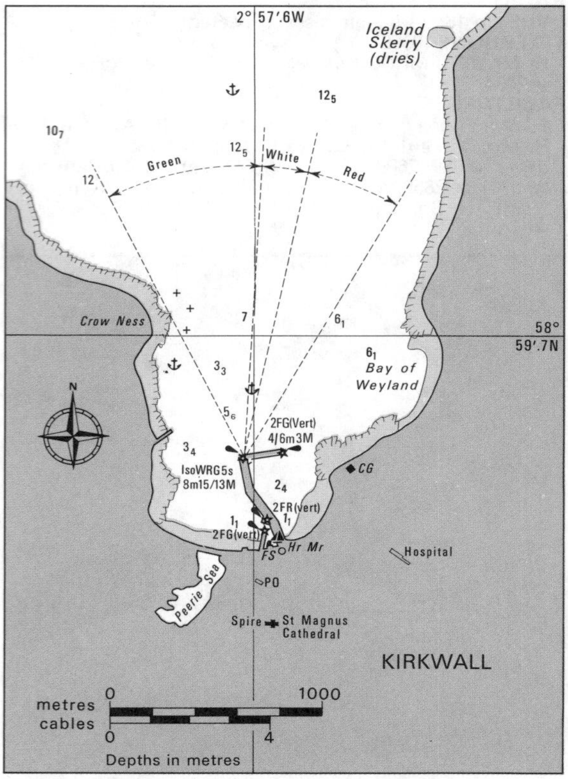
2° 57'.6W
Iceland Skerry (dries)
Green
White
Red
Crow Ness
58° 59'.7N
Bay of Weyland
2FG(Vert) 4/6m3M
IsoWRG5s 8m15/13M
2FR(vert)
2FG(vert)
CG
Hr Mr
FS
Hospital
PO
Peerie Sea
Spire
St Magnus Cathedral
KIRKWALL
metres
cables
0
1000
0
4
Depths in metres

SALMON CAGES

Beware salmon cages in the following areas: –

Rysa Sound	Pegal Bay
Lyrawa Bay	Hunda Sound
Ore Bay	Kirk Sound
Widewall Bay	Carness Bay
St Margaret's Hope	Bay of Ham

OYSTERS AND LONGLINES

Beware Oysters and Longlines located as follows: –

Widenall Bay	Bay of Firth
Swandister Bay	Damsay Sound
Water Sound	Gairsay Milldurnday
Hunda Sound	Pierowall
Deer Sound	Bay of Skaill (Westray)
Inganess Bay	Longhope

KIRKWALL 10-7-21

Orkney Islands

CHARTS

Admiralty 1553, 2584, 2250; OS 6

TIDES

–0045 Dover; ML 1·7; Duration 0620; Zone 0 (GMT).

Standard Port ABERDEEN (⟵)

Times				Height (metres)			
HW		LW		MHWS	MHWN	MLWN	MLWS
0300	1100	0200	0900	4·3	3·4	1·6	0·6
1500	2300	1400	2100				
Differences KIRKWALL							
–0305	–0245	–0305	–0250	–1·4	–1·2	–0·5	–0·2
MUCKLE SKERRY							
–0230	–0230	–0230	–0230	–1·7	–1·4	–0·6	–0·2
BURRAYNESS							
–0200	–0200	–0155	–0155	–1·0	–0·9	–0·3	0·0

SHELTER

Harbour well sheltered except in N winds or W gales when there is a surge at the entrance. Safe anchorage for small yachts between W pier head and Crowness Pt.

NAVIGATION

Waypoint 59°01'·40N 02°57'·00W, 008°/188° from/to pierhead Lt, 2·2M. SW of the bay is a shoal.

LIGHTS AND MARKS

St Magnus Cathedral is very conspic.

RADIO TELEPHONE

VHF Ch 16; 12 (0900-1700 LT). Orkney Harbours Navigation Service, call: *Orkney Harbour Radio* Ch 16 20; 09 11 (H24). Local Weather on Ch 11 at 0915 and 1715 LT.

TELEPHONE (0856)

Hr Mr 2292; Port Office 3636; MRSC 3268; # 2108; Weather 3802; Marinecall 0898 500 451; Police 2241; Dr 2763 or 3201.

FACILITIES

EC Wednesday; **Pier** P, D, FW CH; **N & E Quays** M; **Ellewick (Pier)** M, D, FW, V; **Orkney SC** ☎ 2331, M, L, C, AB; **Hatston** Slip; **John Scott and Millar** ☎ 3146, Gas; **Town** P, D, ME, El, Sh, CH, V, Gas, R, Bar. ✉; Ⓑ; ⇄ (Ferry to Scrabster, bus to Thurso); ✈.

STRONSAY 10-7-22

Orkney Islands

CHARTS

Admiralty 2622, 2250; OS 6

TIDES

–0140 Dover; ML 1·7; Duration 0620; Zone 0 (GMT).

Standard Port ABERDEEN (⟵)

Times				Height (metres)			
HW		LW		MHWS	MHWN	MLWN	MLWS
0300	1100	0200	0900	4·3	3·4	1·6	0·6
1500	2300	1400	2100				
Differences DEER SOUND							
–0245	–0245	–0245	–0245	–1·1	–0·9	–0·3	0·0

SHELTER

Good from winds in all directions. Good anchorage between seaward end of piers. Many other good sheltered anchorages round the bay.

STRONSAY *continued*

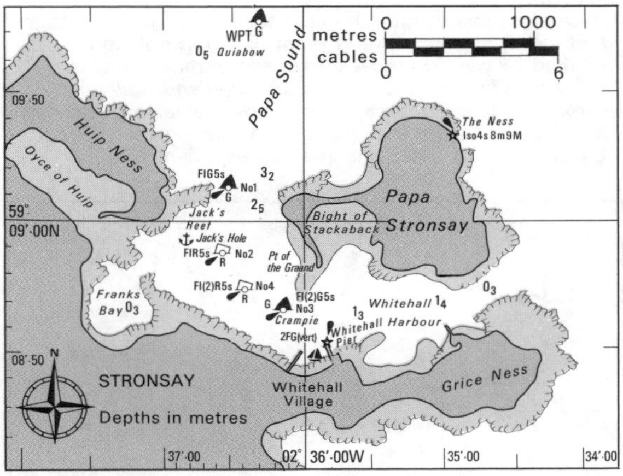
WPT G
05 Quiabow
Papa Sound
metres 0 1000
cables 0 6
09'·50
Huip Ness
Oyce of Huip
59°
09'·00N
FlG5s No1 G
32
Jack's Reef
25
Jack's Hole
FlR5s No2 R
Pt of the Graand
Bight of Stackaback
Papa Stronsay
The Ness Iso4s 8m9M
Franks Bay 03
Fl(2)R5s No4 R
Fl(2)G5s No3 G
Crampie
2FG(vert)
Whitehall Pier
13
Whitehall Harbour
Whitehall 14
03
08'·50
STRONSAY
Depths in metres
Whitehall Village
Grice Ness
37'·00
02° 36'·00W
35'·00
34'·00

NAVIGATION
Waypoint Quiabow stbd-hand buoy, 59°09'·83N 02°36'·20W, 009°/189° from/to No 1 Lt Buoy, 6·5 ca. 800m NE of Huip Ness is Quiabow, a submerged rock marked by G conical buoy.
Jack's Reef extends 400m E from Huip Ness, and is marked by G conical buoy.
A bank extends 350m SW from Papa Stronsay. Crampie Shoal is in mid-channel, marked by a buoy. The buoyed channel to Whitehall pier is dredged to 3·5 m.
Spit to E of Whitehall pier extends 400m N.
The E entrance is narrow and shallow.
LIGHTS AND MARKS
Pierhead Lts, 2FG (vert).
RADIO TELEPHONE
See Kirkwall.
TELEPHONE (085 76)
Hr Mr 257; MRSC Kirkwall 3268; # Kirkwall 2108; Marinecall 0898 500 451; Police (0856) 2251; Dr 321.
FACILITIES
EC Thursday; **W. Pier** M, L, AB; **Main Pier** M, L, FW, AB; **Village (Whitehall)** P, D, V, Bar. ✉; Ⓑ; ⇌ (ferry to Scrabster, bus to Thurso); ✈.

STROMNESS 10-7-23
Orkney Islands

CHARTS
Admiralty 2568, 2249; OS 6
TIDES
−0145 Dover; ML 2·0; Duration 0620; Zone 0 (GMT).

Standard Port ABERDEEN (⟵)

Times				Height (metres)			
HW		LW		MHWS	MHWN	MLWN	MLWS
0300	1100	0200	0900	4·3	3·4	1·6	0·6
1500	2300	1400	2100				
Differences STROMNESS							
−0430	−0355	−0415	−0420	−0·7	−0·8	−0·1	−0·1
KETTLETOFT PIER							
−0230	−0230	−0225	−0225	−1·1	−0·9	−0·3	0·0
TINGWALL							
−0355	−0345	−0355	−0340	−1·2	−1·0	−0·3	−0·1
WIDEWALL BAY							
−0400	−0400	−0400	−0400	−0·7	−0·7	−0·3	−0·2
PIEROWALL							
−0355	−0355	−0355	−0355	−0·6	−0·6	−0·2	0·1

SHELTER
Very good shelter with no tidal stream in harbour. Anchorage in harbour or berth alongside.
The southern pier is the Northern Lights Pier and is for no other use. Berthing piers further N.

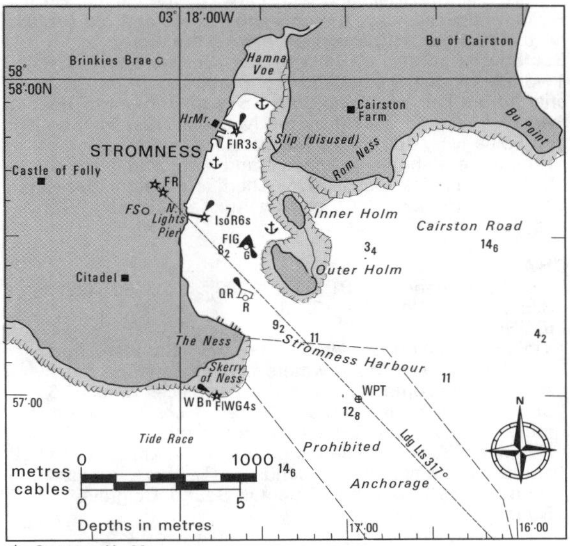
03° 18'·00W
Brinkies Brae
58°
58'·00N
Hamna Voe
Bu of Cairston
Cairston Farm
Bu Point
HrMr.
FlR3s
STROMNESS
Slip (disused)
Rom Ness
Castle of Folly
FR
FSo
N. Lights Pier
Iso R6s
Inner Holm
Cairston Road
FlG
82
34
146
Outer Holm
Citadel
QR R
The Ness
92
11
42
Stromness Harbour
Skerry of Ness
W Bn FlWG4s
11
WPT
128
57'·00
Tide Race
Prohibited
Ldg Lts 317°
Anchorage
metres 0 1000
cables 0 5
146
Depths in metres
17'·00
16'·00

▲ Contact Hr Mr

NAVIGATION
Waypoint 58°57'·00N 03°16'·90W, 137°/317° from/to front Ldg Lt, 0·88M. Tides in Hoy sound are very strong, entry should not be attempted in bad weather or when strong winds are against the tide. Spring tides can exceed 7 kn.
LIGHTS AND MARKS
Ldg Lts 317°, both FR 29/39m 11M (H24); W Trs; vis 307°-327°. Skerry of Ness Lt, Fl WG 4s 7m 7/4M; W shore-090°, G090°-shore.
RADIO TELEPHONE
VHF Ch 16; 12 (0900-1700 LT). (See also Kirkwall).
TELEPHONE (0856)
Hr Mr 850744; MRSC Kirkwall 3268; # Kirkwall 2108; Marinecall 0898 500 451; Police 850222; Dr 850205.
FACILITIES
EC Thursday; **I. Richardson** ☎ 850321, Sh; **R. J. Merriman** ☎ 850361, El; **Walker Stewart** ☎ 850613, Ⓔ; **Marine Electronics** ☎ 850247, Ⓔ; **Town** FW, D, V, R, Bar, Gas, ✉; Ⓑ; ⇌ (Ferry to Scrabster, bus to Thurso); ✈ (Kirkwall).
Note: Yachtsmen may contact, for help, **J. Stout** ☎ 850100, **I. Mackenzie** ☎ 850587 or **S. Mowat** ☎ 850624

SHETLAND ISLANDS 10-7-24

The Shetland Islands consist of approx 100 islands, holms and rocks of which fewer than 20 are inhabited. They lie 90 to 150 miles NNE of the Scottish mainland. By far the biggest island is Mainland with Lerwick, the capital, on the E side and Scalloway, the only other town and old capital, on the W side. At the very S there is the airport at Sumburgh and also at Balta Sound, Scalsta and Tingwall. Two islands of the Shetland group not shown on the chartlet are Fair Isle, lying 20M SSW of Sumburgh Head (see 10.7.27) and owned by the National Trust for Scotland, and Foula lying 16M W of Mainland.

There are lifeboats at Lerwick and Aith, and there is a MRSC at Lerwick (0595) 2976. There is a Sector Base at Sella Ness (Sullom Voe), and an Auxiliary Station (Watch and Rescue) at Fair Isle.

CHARTS

Admiralty; general 3281, 3282, 3283; also 3290, 3291, 3292, 3294, 3295, 3297, 3298.

TIDES

Tidal information is related to Lerwick, Standard Port, see 10.7.25 below. In open waters tidal streams are mostly weak but in some sounds and other places rates of 6 kn or more can be attained and there are some dangerous races and overfalls. Tidal streams run mostly N and S or NW and SE, and cause dangerous disturbances at the N and S extremities of the islands and in the two main sounds (Yell Sound and Bluemull Sound/Colgrave Sound).

SHELTER

Weather conditions are bad in winter, and yachts should restrict visits to April to September. Around mid-summer it is light during all 24 hours. There are numerous anchorages but the following are those which it is safe to enter in all weathers.

LERWICK: see 10.7.25

CAT FIRTH: excellent shelter, anchor in approx 6m. Facilities: ✉ (Skellister), FW, V (both at Lax Firth).

GRUNNA VOE: off S side of Dury Voe, good shelter, anchor in 5-10m, good holding, beware prohibited anchoring areas. Facilities: V, FW, ✉ (Lax Firth).

SCALLOWAY: see 10.7.27.

VAILA SOUND: on SW of Mainland, use Easter Sound entrance (Wester Sound entrance is dangerous), very good shelter, anchor N of Salt Ness in 4 to 5m in mud. Facilities: FW, V, ✉.

GRUTING VOE: tides −0150 on Lerwick, anchor in main voe or in Browland, Seli or Scutta voes. Facilities: Stores and ✉ at Bridge of Walls (at head of Browland Voe).

SWARBACKS MINN: a large complex of voes and islands SE of St Magnus Bay. Best anchorages Uyea Sound or Aith Voe, both well sheltered and good holding. Facilities: former none; Aith FW, ✉, V, Bar, LB.

OLNA FIRTH: NE of Swarbacks Minn, beware rk 1 ca off S shore which dries. Anchor in firth, 4-8m or in Gon Firth or go alongside pier at Voe. Facilities: (Voe) FW, V, D, ✉, Bar.

URA FIRTH: NE of St Magnus Bay, anchor in Hills Wick on W side or in Hamar Voe on E side. The latter has excellent shelter in all weathers and good holding. Facilities: Hamar Voe, none; Hills Wick V, R, FW, V, ✉, D, ME, El, Sh, Bar.

HAMNA VOE: tides − 0200 on Lerwick, very good shelter, ldg line 153° old house on S shore with prominent rk on pt of W shore 3 ca within ent. Facilities: ✉ (½M), Stores, D (1½M), L (at pier).

S OF YELL SOUND: in the complex there are a number of good anchorages; Hamna Voe, Boatsroom Voe, West Lunna Voe, Dales Voe, Colla Firth. Tides −0025 on Lerwick; all well protected and good holding. Facilities: none except at West Lunna Voe where there is a small hotel.

SULLOM VOE: tides −0130 on Lerwick. 6½M long deep water voe which has partly been taken over by the oil industry. Anchor above the narrows. Facilities at Brae, FW, V, ✉, D, ME, El, Sh, Bar.

MID YELL VOE: tides −0040 on Lerwick, enter through South Sd or Hascosay Sd, good anchorage in wide part of voe 2½-10m. Facilities: ✉, FW at pier on S side, D, Stores, ME, Sh, El.

BASTA VOE: good anchorage above shingle bank in 5-15m; good holding in places. Facilities: FW, Stores, Motel, ✉.

BALTA SOUND; see 10.7.27.

NAVIGATION

A careful lookout must be kept for salmon farming cages and low lying mussel rafts (approx 100 in no), mostly marked by plastic yellow buoys and combinations of Y lights. The Clyde Cruising Club *Shetland Sailing Directions and Anchorages* is a most valuable publication for visitors. For general passage information see 10.7.5. Local magnetic anomalies may be experienced.

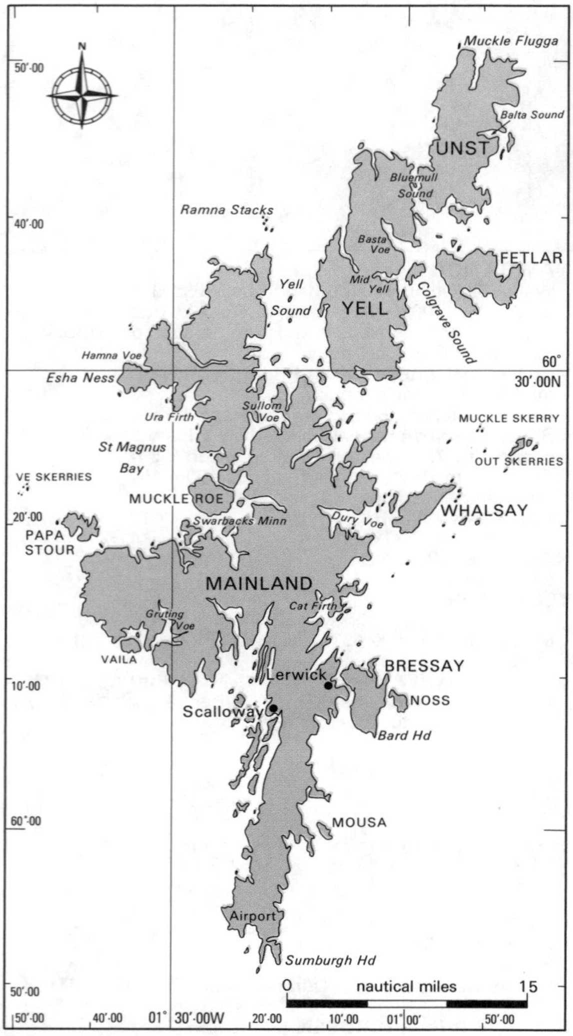

N
Muckle Flugga
Balta Sound
UNST
Bluemull Sound
Ramna Stacks
Basta Voe
FETLAR
Mid Yell
Yell Sound
YELL
Colgrave Sound
Hamna Voe
Esha Ness
Ura Firth
Sullom Voe
St Magnus Bay
MUCKLE SKERRY
OUT SKERRIES
VE SKERRIES
MUCKLE ROE
Swarbacks Minn
Dury Voe
WHALSAY
PAPA STOUR
MAINLAND
Cat Firth
Gruting Voe
VAILA
BRESSAY
Lerwick
NOSS
Scalloway
Bard Hd
MOUSA
Airport
Sumburgh Hd
0 nautical miles 15
50'·00
40'·00
20'·00
10'·00
60°·00
60°
30'·00N
50'·00
40'·00
01° 30'·00W
20'·00
10'·00
01° 00'
50'·00

LIGHTS AND MARKS

See 10.7.4.

RADIO TELEPHONE

For Port Radio services see 10.7.25. Local Coast Radio Stations are Shetland Radio (Ch 16 27), and Collafirth Radio (Ch 16 24). Weather messages are broadcast by Shetland Radio (Ch 27) and Collafirth Radio (Ch 24) at 0703 and 1903 GMT. Gale warnings after next silence period and at 0303 0903 1503 2103 GMT.

TELEPHONE (0595)

Hr Mr Lerwick 5911; Sullom Voe 242551; Scalloway 574; Weather 2239.

FACILITIES

See shelter above.

LERWICK 10-7-25

Shetland Islands

CHARTS
Admiralty 3290, 3291, 3283; OS 4

TIDES
−0001 Dover; ML 1·3; Duration 0620; Zone 0 (GMT).

Standard Port LERWICK (⟶)

Times				Height (metres)			
HW		LW		MHWS	MHWN	MLWN	MLWS
0000	0600	0100	0800	2·2	1·6	0·9	0·5
1200	1800	1300	2000				
Differences FAIR ISLE							
−0020	−0025	−0020	−0035	0·0	+0·1	0·0	−0·1
BLUE MULL SOUND							
−0135	−0135	−0155	−0155	+0·4	+0·3	+0·1	0·0

Lerwick is a Standard Port and tidal predictions for each day of the year are given below.

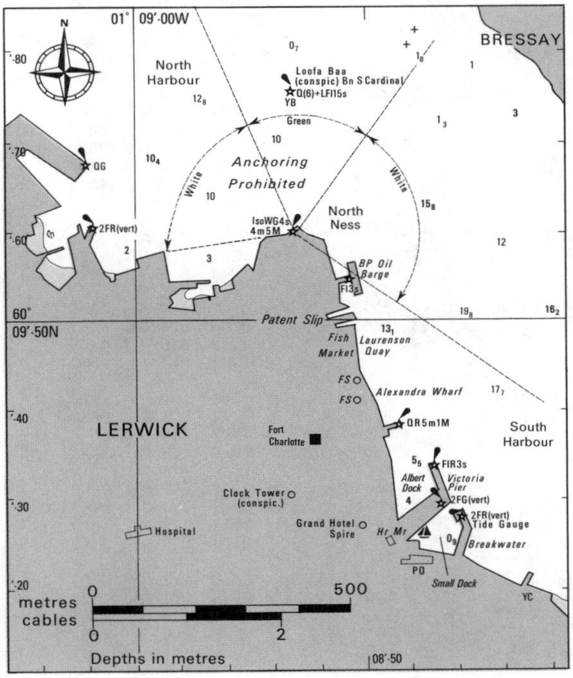

01° 09'·00W
N
North Harbour
BRESSAY
Loofa Baa (conspic) Bn S Cardinal
Q(6)+LFl15s
YB
Green
Anchoring Prohibited
White
White
IsoWG4s 4m5M
North Ness
2FR(vert)
QG
BP Oil Barge
Fl3s
60° 09'·50N
Patent Slip
Fish Market
Laurenson Quay
Alexandra Wharf
LERWICK
Fort Charlotte
QR5m1M
South Harbour
FlR3s
Albert Dock
Victoria Pier
2FG(vert)
2FR(vert)
Tide Gauge
Clock Tower (conspic.)
Grand Hotel Spire
Hr Mr
Breakwater
Hospital
PO
Small Dock
YC
metres 0 500
cables 0 2
Depths in metres
08'·50

SHELTER
Good. Hr Mr allocates berths in Small Dock or Albert Dock. Fishing boats occupy most alongside space. Anchoring prohibited for about 2 ca off the waterfront. Gremista marina is in North Harbour, mainly for local boats, and is a long way from the town.

NAVIGATION
Waypoint 60°06'·00N 01°08'·45W, 185°/005° from/to Twageos Pt Lt, 3·0M. From S, Bressay Sound is clear of dangers. From N, beware Soldian Rock (dries), Nive Baa (0·6m) and Green Holm (10m high) and the Brethren (two rocks 2m and 1·5m high).

LIGHTS AND MARKS
Kirkabister Ness Lt Fl(2) 20s 32m 23M on Bressay. Twageos Pt Lt LFl 6s 8m 6M. Loofa Baa S Cardinal Bn marks shoal between North and South Harbours. Light-buoys mark Middle Ground in North Harbour.

RADIO TELEPHONE
VHF Ch 16; 11 **12** (H24).
Other stations: Sullom Voe Ch 16; 12 **14** 20 (H24). Traffic information is available on request on Ch 14 or 16. Local weather forcasts will be broadcast on request on Ch 14 or 16. Scalloway Ch 16; 12 (Mon-Fri: 0800-1700. Sat: 0800-1200 LT). Balta Sound Ch 16 20 (occas).

TELEPHONE (0595)
Hr Mr 5911; MRSC 2976; # 4040 (2835 after hours); Weather 2239; Police 2110; Dr 3201.

FACILITIES
EC Wednesday (all day); **Harbour** Slip, M, P, D, L, FW, ME, Sh, Gas; **Malakoff** ☎ 5544, ME, El, Ⓔ, Sh, Slip, BY, CH, Sh, SM; **Thulecraft** ☎ 3192, CH, ME, Gas; **Hay** ☎ 3057, ACA; **Lerwick Harbour Trust** ☎ 2991, M, FW, D, P, AB; **Rearo Supplies** ☎ 2636, Gas; **Lerwick Boating Club** ☎ 2407, L, C, Bar, ⊡; **Town** V, R, Bar, CH, ✉; Ⓑ; ⇌ (ferry to Aberdeen); ✈.

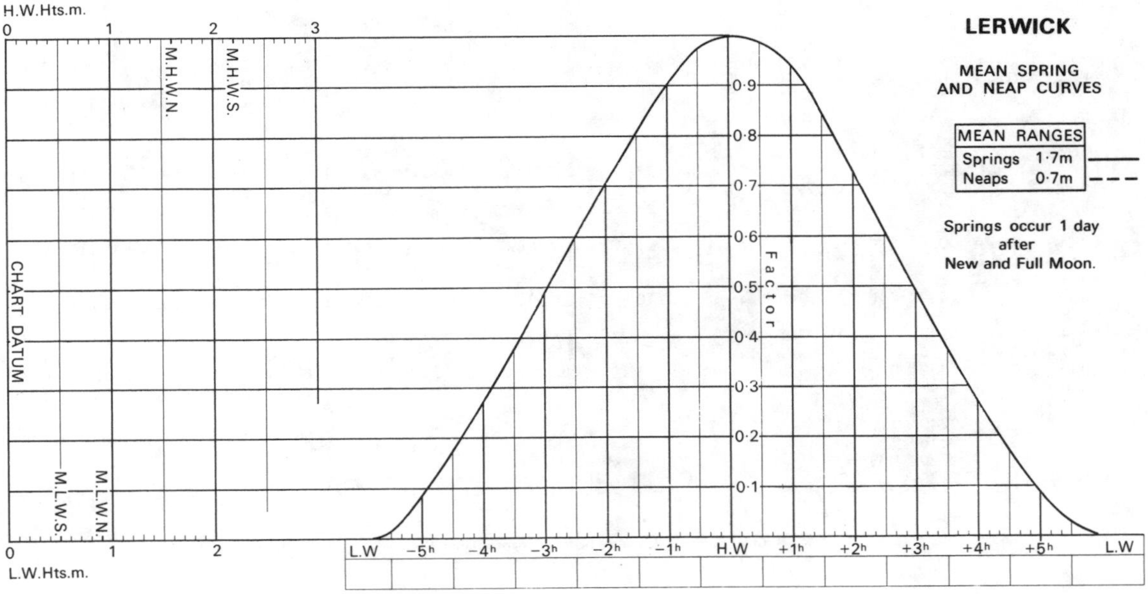

H.W.Hts.m.
0 1 2 3
M.H.W.N.
M.H.W.S.
CHART DATUM
M.L.W.S.
M.L.W.N.
0 1 2
L.W.Hts.m.
Factor
0·9 0·8 0·7 0·6 0·5 0·4 0·3 0·2 0·1
L.W −5h −4h −3h −2h −1h H.W +1h +2h +3h +4h +5h L.W
LERWICK
MEAN SPRING AND NEAP CURVES
MEAN RANGES
Springs 1·7m
Neaps 0·7m
Springs occur 1 day after New and Full Moon.

SHETLAND ISLANDS - LERWICK

TIME ZONE **UT(GMT)**

For Summer Time add ONE hour in non-shaded areas

LAT 60°09'N **LONG 1°08'W**

TIMES AND HEIGHTS OF HIGH AND LOW WATERS

YEAR **1992**

JANUARY

Day	Time	m	Day	Time	m
1 W	0208 0820 1441 2052	0.9 1.8 0.8 1.8	**16** TH	0101 0731 1344 2001	0.9 1.8 0.9 1.8
2 TH	0256 0906 1529 2139	0.9 1.9 0.8 1.9	**17** F	0211 0832 1446 2104	0.9 2.0 0.7 2.0
3 F	0337 0947 1611 2220	0.9 2.0 0.7 1.9	**18** SA	0307 0924 1539 2157	0.8 2.1 0.5 2.1
4 SA	0414 1025 1649 ● 2258	0.8 2.1 0.6 1.9	**19** SU	0357 1011 1628 ○ 2246	0.7 2.2 0.4 2.2
5 SU	0449 1101 1724 2335	0.8 2.1 0.6 2.0	**20** M	0444 1057 1715 2332	0.6 2.4 0.2 2.2
6 M	0522 1136 1757	0.8 2.2 0.6	**21** TU	0528 1141 1801	0.5 2.4 0.2
7 TU	0009 0554 1210 1829	2.0 0.8 2.2 0.6	**22** W	0017 0611 1226 1847	2.2 0.5 2.4 0.2
8 W	0044 0627 1244 1901	1.9 0.8 2.1 0.6	**23** TH	0102 0655 1311 1933	2.1 0.5 2.4 0.2
9 TH	0119 0700 1318 1933	1.9 0.8 2.1 0.6	**24** F	0146 0739 1356 2020	2.0 0.6 2.2 0.4
10 F	0154 0734 1353 2008	1.8 0.8 2.0 0.7	**25** SA	0230 0825 1444 2110	1.9 0.7 2.1 0.6
11 SA	0231 0811 1431 2045	1.8 0.9 1.9 0.7	**26** SU	0317 0916 1536 ☾ 2205	1.8 0.8 1.9 0.7
12 SU	0312 0854 1513 2129	1.7 1.0 1.9 0.8	**27** M	0411 1022 1641 2316	1.7 0.9 1.7 0.9
13 M	0359 0947 1604 ☽ 2224	1.7 1.0 1.8 0.9	**28** TU	0520 1158 1811	1.6 1.0 1.6
14 TU	0458 1057 1711 2337	1.7 1.0 1.7 0.9	**29** W	0039 0646 1328 1939	1.0 1.6 0.9 1.6
15 W	0614 1224 1839	1.7 1.0 1.7	**30** TH	0148 0756 1432 2042	1.0 1.7 0.9 1.7
			31 F	0240 0848 1520 2128	1.0 1.8 0.8 1.7

FEBRUARY

Day	Time	m	Day	Time	m
1 SA	0323 0931 1559 2207	0.9 1.9 0.7 1.8	**16** SU	0255 0906 1526 2145	0.8 2.0 0.4 2.0
2 SU	0359 1008 1634 2242	0.8 2.0 0.6 1.9	**17** M	0344 0955 1614 2231	0.6 2.2 0.2 2.1
3 M	0433 1042 1705 ● 2315	0.8 2.1 0.5 1.9	**18** TU	0428 1040 1659 ○ 2314	0.5 2.3 0.1 2.2
4 TU	0504 1115 1735 2347	0.7 2.1 0.5 2.0	**19** W	0511 1124 1743 2356	0.4 2.4 0.1 2.2
5 W	0534 1148 1804	0.7 2.2 0.5	**20** TH	0552 1207 1825	0.4 2.4 0.1
6 TH	0018 0604 1220 1832	2.0 0.6 2.2 0.5	**21** F	0036 0633 1250 1907	2.1 0.4 2.3 0.3
7 F	0050 0635 1253 1902	2.0 0.7 2.1 0.5	**22** SA	0117 0714 1334 1949	2.0 0.5 2.2 0.4
8 SA	0123 0708 1327 1934	1.9 0.7 2.1 0.6	**23** SU	0157 0756 1418 2031	1.9 0.6 2.0 0.6
9 SU	0157 0742 1403 2009	1.9 0.8 2.0 0.7	**24** M	0239 0842 1506 2116	1.8 0.7 1.8 0.8
10 M	0235 0822 1443 2049	1.8 0.8 1.9 0.8	**25** TU	0324 0940 1603 ☾ 2215	1.7 0.9 1.6 1.0
11 TU	0318 0911 1533 ☽ 2141	1.8 0.9 1.8 0.9	**26** W	0422 1118 1733 2355	1.6 1.0 1.5 1.1
12 W	0413 1018 1640 2255	1.7 1.0 1.7 1.0	**27** TH	0554 1308 1921	1.6 0.9 1.5
13 TH	0529 1153 1816	1.7 1.0 1.7	**28** F	0124 0727 1414 2026	1.1 1.6 0.8 1.6
14 F	0036 0700 1327 1949	1.0 1.7 0.8 1.8	**29** SA	0221 0825 1501 2110	1.0 1.7 0.7 1.7
15 SA	0157 0811 1433 2053	0.9 1.9 0.6 1.9			

MARCH

Day	Time	m	Day	Time	m
1 SU	0303 0908 1537 2146	0.9 1.8 0.6 1.8	**16** M	0239 0847 1510 2128	0.7 2.0 0.3 2.0
2 M	0338 0944 1608 2218	0.8 1.9 0.5 1.9	**17** TU	0326 0936 1556 2211	0.6 2.2 0.2 2.0
3 TU	0410 1018 1637 2249	0.7 2.0 0.5 1.9	**18** W	0409 1021 1639 ○ 2252	0.4 2.3 0.1 2.1
4 W	0440 1050 1705 ● 2319	0.6 2.1 0.4 2.0	**19** TH	0450 1105 1721 2332	0.4 2.3 0.1 2.1
5 TH	0510 1122 1734 2350	0.6 2.1 0.4 2.0	**20** F	0531 1147 1801	0.3 2.3 0.2
6 F	0540 1155 1803	0.5 2.1 0.4	**21** SA	0010 0611 1230 1839	2.1 0.3 2.2 0.3
7 SA	0021 0611 1229 1833	2.0 0.6 2.1 0.5	**22** SU	0048 0651 1312 1917	2.0 0.4 2.1 0.5
8 SU	0054 0644 1304 1905	2.0 0.6 2.1 0.6	**23** M	0126 0732 1354 1954	2.0 0.5 1.9 0.7
9 M	0129 0720 1342 1941	1.9 0.6 2.0 0.7	**24** TU	0205 0816 1439 2034	1.8 0.7 1.7 0.8
10 TU	0207 0801 1425 2023	1.9 0.7 1.9 0.8	**25** W	0247 0909 1533 2122	1.7 0.8 1.6 1.0
11 W	0250 0852 1518 2117	1.8 0.8 1.8 0.9	**26** TH	0338 1032 1651 ☾ 2247	1.6 0.9 1.4 1.1
12 TH	0345 1001 1629 ☽ 2235	1.7 0.9 1.7 1.0	**27** F	0451 1232 1847	1.5 0.9 1.4
13 F	0500 1138 1807	1.7 0.8 1.6	**28** SA	0046 0637 1341 1955	1.1 1.6 0.8 1.5
14 SA	0022 0633 1312 1938	1.0 1.7 0.7 1.7	**29** SU	0149 0747 1427 2039	1.0 1.6 0.7 1.6
15 SU	0143 0749 1417 2039	0.9 1.8 0.5 1.8	**30** M	0233 0834 1503 2115	0.9 1.7 0.6 1.7
			31 TU	0308 0912 1534 2146	0.8 1.8 0.5 1.8

APRIL

Day	Time	m	Day	Time	m
1 W	0340 0947 1603 2217	0.7 1.9 0.5 1.9	**16** TH	0349 1002 1617 2228	0.4 2.2 0.2 2.0
2 TH	0411 1021 1632 2248	0.6 2.0 0.4 2.0	**17** F	0431 1046 1657 ○ 2307	0.4 2.2 0.3 2.1
3 F	0442 1055 1702 ● 2320	0.5 2.1 0.4 2.0	**18** SA	0511 1128 1735 2345	0.3 2.2 0.4 2.1
4 SA	0515 1130 1734 2354	0.5 2.1 0.4 2.1	**19** SU	0552 1210 1812	0.3 2.1 0.5
5 SU	0549 1207 1808	0.5 2.1 0.5	**20** M	0022 0632 1252 1848	2.0 0.4 2.0 0.6
6 M	0029 0626 1246 1844	2.0 0.5 2.0 0.6	**21** TU	0100 0713 1334 1924	2.0 0.5 1.8 0.7
7 TU	0107 0706 1328 1924	2.0 0.5 2.0 0.7	**22** W	0139 0757 1418 2002	1.9 0.6 1.7 0.8
8 W	0148 0752 1417 2010	1.9 0.6 1.9 0.8	**23** TH	0220 0846 1507 2047	1.8 0.7 1.5 0.9
9 TH	0234 0847 1514 2108	1.8 0.7 1.7 0.9	**24** F	0306 0949 1610 ☾ 2148	1.7 0.8 1.4 1.0
10 F	0330 0958 1626 ☽ 2226	1.7 0.7 1.6 1.0	**25** SA	0403 1125 1741 2330	1.6 0.8 1.4 1.0
11 SA	0442 1128 1757	1.7 0.7 1.6	**26** SU	0520 1245 1903	1.5 0.8 1.5
12 SU	0004 0607 1253 1919	1.0 1.7 0.6 1.7	**27** M	0056 0644 1337 1954	1.0 1.6 0.7 1.6
13 M	0122 0724 1357 2018	0.8 1.8 0.4 1.8	**28** TU	0148 0744 1416 2034	0.9 1.6 0.7 1.7
14 TU	0218 0824 1449 2106	0.7 1.9 0.3 1.9	**29** W	0228 0830 1451 2109	0.8 1.7 0.6 1.8
15 W	0305 0915 1534 2148	0.6 2.1 0.2 2.0	**30** TH	0304 0911 1523 2142	0.7 1.8 0.5 1.9

Chart Datum: 1.22 metres below Ordnance Datum (Newlyn)

SHETLAND ISLANDS - LERWICK

TIME ZONE UT(GMT)
For Summer Time add ONE hour in non-shaded areas

LAT 60°09'N LONG 1°08'W

TIMES AND HEIGHTS OF HIGH AND LOW WATERS

YEAR **1992**

MAY

Day	Time	m	Time	m	Time	m	Time	m
1 F	0339	0.6	0950	1.9	1557	0.5	2217	2.0
2 SA	0415	0.5	1028	2.0	1632	0.5	● 2252	2.0
3 SU	0452	0.5	1108	2.1	1709	0.5	2330	2.1
4 M	0532	0.4	1150	2.1	1748	0.5		
5 TU	0009	2.1	0613	0.4	1234	2.0	1829	0.6
6 W	0050	2.1	0658	0.4	1321	2.0	1914	0.7
7 TH	0135	2.0	0748	0.5	1412	1.9	2004	0.8
8 F	0223	1.9	0845	0.5	1509	1.7	2102	0.8
9 SA	0318	1.8	0952	0.5	1616	1.6	☽ 2213	0.9
10 SU	0423	1.8	1110	0.5	1734	1.6	2337	0.9
11 M	0540	1.7	1227	0.5	1851	1.6		
12 TU	0052	0.8	0656	1.8	1332	0.4	1951	1.7
13 W	0153	0.7	0800	1.9	1425	0.4	2040	1.8
14 TH	0244	0.6	0855	1.9	1512	0.4	2124	1.9
15 F	0330	0.5	0944	2.0	1554	0.4	2205	1.9
16 SA	0414	0.4	1029	2.0	1634	0.5	○ 2244	2.0
17 SU	0456	0.4	1112	2.0	1712	0.5	2322	2.0
18 M	0537	0.4	1154	1.9	1749	0.6		
19 TU	0000	2.0	0618	0.4	1235	1.9	1824	0.7
20 W	0039	2.0	0658	0.5	1316	1.8	1900	0.7
21 TH	0117	1.9	0739	0.6	1358	1.7	1938	0.8
22 F	0157	1.8	0823	0.6	1442	1.6	2020	0.9
23 SA	0239	1.7	0910	0.7	1531	1.5	2108	0.9
24 SU	0325	1.7	1006	0.7	1630	1.5	☾ 2209	1.0
25 M	0419	1.6	1113	0.8	1740	1.5	2325	1.0
26 TU	0524	1.6	1220	0.8	1848	1.5		
27 W	0040	0.9	0636	1.6	1315	0.7	1941	1.6
28 TH	0137	0.9	0739	1.7	1400	0.7	2026	1.7
29 F	0224	0.8	0832	1.8	1443	0.6	2107	1.9
30 SA	0308	0.7	0920	1.9	1524	0.6	2147	2.0
31 SU	0351	0.6	1005	1.9	1606	0.5	2228	2.1

JUNE

Day	Time	m	Time	m	Time	m	Time	m
1 M	0434	0.5	1051	2.0	1649	0.5	● 2310	2.1
2 TU	0518	0.4	1136	2.1	1733	0.5	2352	2.1
3 W	0604	0.3	1223	2.0	1819	0.6		
4 TH	0036	2.1	0651	0.3	1312	2.0	1905	0.6
5 F	0122	2.1	0742	0.3	1403	1.9	1955	0.7
6 SA	0211	2.0	0837	0.3	1456	1.8	2049	0.7
7 SU	0303	1.9	0937	0.4	1555	1.7	☽ 2150	0.8
8 M	0402	1.9	1045	0.5	1702	1.6	2302	0.8
9 TU	0511	1.8	1157	0.5	1813	1.6		
10 W	0019	0.8	0627	1.8	1304	0.5	1919	1.6
11 TH	0128	0.7	0738	1.8	1401	0.6	2014	1.7
12 F	0226	0.6	0838	1.8	1450	0.6	2102	1.8
13 SA	0316	0.6	0930	1.8	1534	0.6	2145	1.9
14 SU	0402	0.5	1016	1.9	1615	0.6	2225	2.0
15 M	0445	0.5	1059	1.9	1653	0.6	○ 2304	2.0
16 TU	0526	0.4	1139	1.9	1729	0.7	2342	2.0
17 W	0605	0.5	1218	1.8	1805	0.7		
18 TH	0019	2.0	0641	0.5	1256	1.8	1840	0.7
19 F	0056	2.0	0718	0.5	1334	1.7	1915	0.7
20 SA	0133	1.9	0754	0.6	1413	1.7	1952	0.8
21 SU	0210	1.9	0832	0.6	1453	1.6	2032	0.8
22 M	0250	1.8	0913	0.7	1537	1.6	2118	0.9
23 TU	0334	1.7	0959	0.7	1627	1.5	☾ 2213	0.9
24 W	0425	1.6	1054	0.8	1727	1.6	2321	1.0
25 TH	0528	1.6	1159	0.8	1836	1.6		
26 F	0038	0.9	0644	1.6	1307	0.8	1940	1.7
27 SA	0145	0.8	0756	1.7	1406	0.8	2033	1.8
28 SU	0241	0.7	0855	1.8	1459	0.7	2122	2.0
29 M	0331	0.6	0947	1.9	1547	0.6	2207	2.1
30 TU	0418	0.4	1036	2.0	1634	0.6	● 2252	2.2

JULY

Day	Time	m	Time	m	Time	m	Time	m
1 W	0505	0.3	1124	2.1	1720	0.5	2336	2.2
2 TH	0552	0.2	1210	2.1	1806	0.5		
3 F	0021	2.3	0639	0.2	1258	2.1	1851	0.5
4 SA	0107	2.2	0728	0.2	1345	2.0	1938	0.6
5 SU	0154	2.2	0819	0.3	1434	1.9	2027	0.6
6 M	0243	2.1	0913	0.4	1526	1.8	2122	0.7
7 TU	0338	1.9	1013	0.5	1623	1.7	☽ 2227	0.8
8 W	0442	1.8	1122	0.6	1731	1.6	2347	0.8
9 TH	0600	1.7	1234	0.7	1844	1.6		
10 F	0107	0.8	0720	1.7	1339	0.8	1949	1.7
11 SA	0214	0.7	0826	1.7	1433	0.8	2042	1.8
12 SU	0308	0.7	0920	1.7	1518	0.8	2128	1.9
13 M	0354	0.6	1005	1.8	1559	0.8	2209	2.0
14 TU	0435	0.5	1045	1.8	1636	0.7	○ 2247	2.0
15 W	0512	0.5	1122	1.9	1711	0.7	2323	2.1
16 TH	0546	0.5	1157	1.9	1745	0.7	2358	2.1
17 F	0619	0.5	1232	1.9	1817	0.7		
18 SA	0032	2.1	0650	0.5	1306	1.8	1849	0.7
19 SU	0107	2.0	0722	0.5	1341	1.8	1923	0.7
20 M	0141	2.0	0754	0.6	1416	1.8	1958	0.8
21 TU	0218	1.9	0829	0.7	1454	1.7	2038	0.9
22 W	0257	1.8	0909	0.8	1537	1.7	☾ 2125	0.9
23 TH	0343	1.7	0957	0.8	1628	1.6	2226	1.0
24 F	0441	1.7	1059	0.9	1735	1.7	2347	1.0
25 SA	0600	1.6	1221	0.9	1856	1.7		
26 SU	0113	0.9	0729	1.7	1339	0.9	2004	1.8
27 M	0220	0.8	0838	1.8	1440	0.8	2059	2.0
28 TU	0314	0.6	0933	2.0	1532	0.7	2148	2.1
29 W	0403	0.4	1022	2.1	1619	0.6	● 2234	2.3
30 TH	0450	0.2	1108	2.2	1704	0.5	2318	2.4
31 F	0536	0.1	1153	2.2	1748	0.5		

AUGUST

Day	Time	m	Time	m	Time	m	Time	m
1 SA	0003	2.4	0621	0.1	1238	2.2	1831	0.5
2 SU	0048	2.4	0707	0.2	1322	2.1	1916	0.5
3 M	0134	2.3	0754	0.3	1406	2.0	2002	0.6
4 TU	0221	2.1	0843	0.5	1453	1.8	2052	0.7
5 W	0313	2.0	0937	0.7	1544	1.7	☽ 2153	0.8
6 TH	0413	1.8	1042	0.8	1645	1.7	2317	0.9
7 F	0534	1.7	1203	0.9	1806	1.6		
8 SA	0053	0.9	0707	1.6	1320	1.0	1926	1.7
9 SU	0205	0.8	0818	1.7	1418	0.9	2025	1.8
10 M	0258	0.7	0909	1.7	1504	0.9	2111	1.9
11 TU	0341	0.7	0950	1.8	1543	0.8	2151	2.0
12 W	0418	0.6	1026	1.9	1618	0.8	2227	2.1
13 TH	0450	0.5	1100	1.9	1650	0.7	○ 2301	2.1
14 F	0521	0.5	1132	2.0	1721	0.7	2334	2.2
15 SA	0550	0.5	1204	2.0	1752	0.6		
16 SU	0006	2.1	0619	0.5	1236	2.0	1822	0.7
17 M	0039	2.1	0648	0.6	1308	1.9	1854	0.7
18 TU	0113	2.1	0718	0.6	1341	1.9	1928	0.8
19 W	0148	2.0	0751	0.7	1417	1.9	2005	0.8
20 TH	0227	1.9	0829	0.8	1457	1.8	2051	0.9
21 F	0313	1.8	0915	0.9	1547	1.7	☾ 2151	1.0
22 SA	0412	1.7	1019	1.0	1653	1.7	2315	1.0
23 SU	0536	1.7	1151	1.1	1820	1.7		
24 M	0051	0.9	0713	1.7	1322	1.0	1939	1.9
25 TU	0203	0.7	0823	1.9	1425	0.9	2038	2.0
26 W	0257	0.5	0917	2.0	1516	0.7	2128	2.2
27 TH	0346	0.4	1004	2.1	1601	0.6	2214	2.3
28 F	0432	0.2	1048	2.2	1645	0.5	● 2259	2.4
29 SA	0516	0.2	1131	2.2	1727	0.4	2343	2.5
30 SU	0600	0.2	1213	2.2	1810	0.4		
31 M	0027	2.4	0643	0.3	1255	2.2	1852	0.5

Chart Datum: 1.22 metres below Ordnance Datum (Newlyn)

SHETLAND ISLANDS - LERWICK

TIME ZONE UT(GMT)

For Summer Time add ONE hour in non-shaded areas

LAT 60°09'N LONG 1°08'W

TIMES AND HEIGHTS OF HIGH AND LOW WATERS

YEAR **1992**

SEPTEMBER

Date	Time	m	Date	Time	m
1 TU	0113	2.3	16 W	0048	2.1
	0726	0.4		0647	0.7
	1336	2.1		1311	2.0
	1937	0.6		1903	0.8
2 W	0159	2.2	17 TH	0125	2.1
	0811	0.6		0721	0.8
	1419	1.9		1347	2.0
	2025	0.7		1943	0.8
3 TH	0248	2.0	18 F	0206	2.0
	0859	0.8		0800	0.9
	1506	1.8		1429	1.9
	☽ 2123	0.8		2030	0.9
4 F	0346	1.8	19 SA	0256	1.9
	0958	1.0		0849	1.0
	1603	1.7		1519	1.8
	2250	0.9		☾ 2133	1.0
5 SA	0508	1.6	20 SU	0359	1.8
	1128	1.1		0958	1.1
	1723	1.7		1626	1.8
				2258	1.0
6 SU	0037	1.0	21 M	0525	1.7
	0652	1.6		1135	1.1
	1259	1.1		1752	1.8
	1857	1.7			
7 M	0149	0.9	22 TU	0033	0.9
	0803	1.7		0659	1.8
	1359	1.0		1306	1.0
	2002	1.8		1913	1.9
8 TU	0239	0.8	23 W	0144	0.7
	0850	1.7		0806	1.9
	1444	1.0		1407	0.9
	2048	1.9		2015	2.1
9 W	0318	0.7	24 TH	0238	0.5
	0928	1.8		0858	2.0
	1521	0.9		1457	0.7
	2127	2.0		2107	2.2
10 TH	0351	0.6	25 F	0326	0.4
	1001	1.9		0943	2.2
	1554	0.8		1542	0.6
	2202	2.1		2154	2.4
11 F	0421	0.6	26 SA	0411	0.3
	1032	2.0		1026	2.2
	1625	0.7		1624	0.5
	2235	2.1		● 2239	2.4
12 SA	0450	0.5	27 SU	0454	0.3
	1103	2.1		1107	2.3
	1655	0.7		1707	0.4
	○ 2307	2.2		2323	2.5
13 SU	0518	0.5	28 M	0536	0.3
	1133	2.1		1147	2.3
	1725	0.7		1749	0.4
	2339	2.2			
14 M	0546	0.6	29 TU	0007	2.4
	1204	2.1		0617	0.4
	1756	0.7		1227	2.2
				1831	0.5
15 TU	0013	2.2	30 W	0052	2.3
	0615	0.6		0657	0.6
	1237	2.1		1308	2.1
	1828	0.7		1915	0.6

OCTOBER

Date	Time	m	Date	Time	m
1 TH	0137	2.1	16 F	0109	2.1
	0739	0.8		0700	0.8
	1349	2.0		1326	2.1
	2002	0.7		1930	0.8
2 F	0226	1.9	17 SA	0154	2.0
	0822	0.9		0744	0.9
	1434	1.9		1410	2.0
	2059	0.9		2022	0.8
3 SA	0321	1.8	18 SU	0247	1.9
	0915	1.1		0837	1.0
	1525	1.8		1502	1.9
	☽ 2219	1.0		2125	0.9
4 SU	0436	1.6	19 M	0352	1.8
	1036	1.2		0946	1.1
	1635	1.7		1606	1.9
				☾ 2245	0.8
5 M	0007	1.0	20 TU	0512	1.8
	0620	1.6		1116	1.1
	1224	1.2		1725	1.9
	1811	1.7			
6 TU	0119	0.9	21 W	0011	0.8
	0733	1.7		0638	1.8
	1329	1.1		1242	1.0
	1925	1.8		1845	1.9
7 W	0207	0.8	22 TH	0121	0.6
	0820	1.7		0744	1.9
	1415	1.0		1345	0.9
	2015	1.9		1951	2.1
8 TH	0245	0.8	23 F	0217	0.5
	0857	1.8		0836	2.0
	1452	0.9		1436	0.7
	2055	2.0		2046	2.2
9 F	0318	0.7	24 SA	0305	0.4
	0930	1.9		0921	2.1
	1525	0.8		1522	0.6
	2131	2.1		2135	2.3
10 SA	0347	0.6	25 SU	0350	0.4
	1001	2.0		1003	2.2
	1556	0.7		1606	0.5
	2205	2.1		● 2221	2.4
11 SU	0416	0.6	26 M	0432	0.4
	1032	2.1		1043	2.3
	1627	0.7		1649	0.5
	○ 2239	2.2		2306	2.4
12 M	0445	0.6	27 TU	0513	0.5
	1103	2.2		1123	2.3
	1659	0.7		1731	0.5
	2314	2.2		2350	2.3
13 TU	0516	0.6	28 W	0553	0.6
	1136	2.2		1203	2.3
	1733	0.7		1814	0.5
	2350	2.2			
14 W	0548	0.7	29 TH	0034	2.2
	1210	2.2		0631	0.7
	1808	0.7		1243	2.2
				1858	0.6
15 TH	0027	2.2	30 F	0118	2.0
	0622	0.8		0710	0.9
	1247	2.1		1324	2.1
	1847	0.7		1944	0.7
			31 SA	0204	1.9
				0751	1.0
				1406	2.0
				2035	0.8

NOVEMBER

Date	Time	m	Date	Time	m
1 SU	0255	1.8	16 M	0239	1.9
	0837	1.1		0828	1.0
	1453	1.9		1448	2.0
	2138	0.9		2116	0.7
2 M	0356	1.6	17 TU	0339	1.8
	0938	1.2		0931	1.0
	1549	1.8		1547	2.0
	☽ 2305	1.0		☾ 2226	0.7
3 TU	0518	1.6	18 W	0450	1.8
	1112	1.2		1048	1.1
	1701	1.7		1657	1.9
				2344	0.7
4 W	0026	0.9	19 TH	0607	1.8
	0641	1.6		1210	1.0
	1239	1.1		1815	1.9
	1824	1.7			
5 TH	0121	0.9	20 F	0055	0.6
	0737	1.7		0715	1.9
	1334	1.1		1319	0.9
	1928	1.8		1926	2.0
6 F	0202	0.8	21 SA	0154	0.6
	0818	1.8		0811	1.9
	1416	1.0		1415	0.8
	2016	1.9		2027	2.1
7 SA	0238	0.8	22 SU	0245	0.6
	0854	1.9		0858	2.0
	1452	0.9		1505	0.7
	2057	2.0		2119	2.2
8 SU	0310	0.7	23 M	0330	0.6
	0928	2.0		0942	2.1
	1527	0.8		1552	0.6
	2136	2.1		2207	2.2
9 M	0342	0.7	24 TU	0413	0.6
	1002	2.1		1023	2.2
	1601	0.7		1636	0.5
	2213	2.1		● 2252	2.2
10 TU	0415	0.7	25 W	0453	0.6
	1036	2.2		1104	2.2
	1637	0.7		1719	0.5
	○ 2252	2.2		2336	2.2
11 W	0450	0.7	26 TH	0532	0.7
	1112	2.2		1143	2.2
	1715	0.6		1802	0.5
	2331	2.2			
12 TH	0527	0.7	27 F	0018	2.1
	1149	2.3		0609	0.8
	1754	0.6		1223	2.2
				1843	0.6
13 F	0013	2.2	28 SA	0100	2.0
	0606	0.8		0647	0.8
	1229	2.2		1302	2.1
	1836	0.6		1926	0.7
14 SA	0058	2.1	29 SU	0142	1.9
	0649	0.8		0725	0.9
	1311	2.2		1342	2.1
	1923	0.6		2009	0.7
15 SU	0146	2.0	30 M	0226	1.8
	0735	0.9		0806	1.0
	1357	2.1		1423	2.0
	2015	0.7		2055	0.8

DECEMBER

Date	Time	m	Date	Time	m
1 TU	0313	1.7	16 W	0318	1.9
	0852	1.1		0910	0.9
	1508	1.9		1526	2.0
	2148	0.9		☾ 2201	0.6
2 W	0408	1.6	17 TH	0419	1.8
	0948	1.1		1015	0.9
	1559	1.8		1630	2.0
	☽ 2252	0.9		2312	0.7
3 TH	0515	1.6	18 F	0529	1.8
	1103	1.1		1134	1.0
	1702	1.7		1745	1.9
4 F	0004	0.9	19 SA	0026	0.7
	0629	1.7		0642	1.8
	1226	1.1		1253	0.9
	1817	1.7		1904	1.9
5 SA	0103	0.9	20 SU	0132	0.7
	0727	1.7		0745	1.8
	1328	1.0		1359	0.8
	1926	1.8		2012	1.9
6 SU	0150	0.9	21 M	0227	0.7
	0814	1.8		0839	1.9
	1415	1.0		1454	0.7
	2020	1.9		2109	2.0
7 M	0232	0.8	22 TU	0315	0.7
	0854	2.0		0925	2.0
	1458	0.9		1544	0.6
	2107	2.0		2158	2.0
8 TU	0311	0.8	23 W	0358	0.7
	0933	2.1		1008	2.1
	1538	0.8		1628	0.6
	2151	2.0		2242	2.0
9 W	0351	0.8	24 TH	0438	0.7
	1012	2.2		1048	2.2
	1619	0.7		1710	0.5
	○ 2234	2.1		● 2323	2.0
10 TH	0431	0.7	25 F	0515	0.7
	1052	2.3		1127	2.2
	1700	0.6		1750	0.5
	2317	2.2			
11 F	0512	0.7	26 SA	0002	2.0
	1132	2.3		0551	0.7
	1743	0.5		1205	2.2
				1827	0.5
12 SA	0001	2.2	27 SU	0040	2.0
	0554	0.7		0626	0.8
	1214	2.3		1242	2.2
	1827	0.5		1903	0.6
13 SU	0047	2.2	28 M	0118	1.9
	0639	0.7		0701	0.8
	1258	2.3		1318	2.1
	1914	0.4		1938	0.6
14 M	0134	2.1	29 TU	0155	1.8
	0725	0.8		0736	0.9
	1343	2.2		1354	2.0
	2004	0.5		2014	0.7
15 TU	0224	2.0	30 W	0233	1.8
	0814	0.8		0813	0.9
	1432	2.1		1432	1.9
	2059	0.5		2052	0.8
			31 TH	0315	1.7
				0855	1.0
				1513	1.8
				2134	0.9

Chart Datum: 1.22 metres below Ordnance Datum (Newlyn)

SCRABSTER 10-7-26

Caithness

CHARTS
Admiralty 1462, 2162, 1954; OS 12

TIDES
−0240 Dover; ML 3·2; Duration 0615; Zone 0 (GMT).

Standard Port ABERDEEN (⟵)

Times				Height (metres)			
HW		LW		MHWS	MHWN	MLWN	MLWS
0300	1000	0100	0800	4·3	3·4	1·6	0·6
1500	2200	1300	2000				
Differences SCRABSTER							
−0455	−0510	−0500	−0445	+0·7	+0·3	+0·5	+0·2
STROMA							
−0320	−0320	−0320	−0320	−1·2	−1·1	−0·3	−0·1

SHELTER
Very good except in strong NE winds. Anchoring is not recommended. Secure alongside NE wall and contact Hr Mr. Yachts normally use Inner Basin.

NAVIGATION
Waypoint 58°36′·60N 03°32′·00W, 098°/278° from/to E pier Lt, 0·25M. Can be entered at all tides in all weathers. Do not confuse harbour lights with those of Thurso. Beware fishing vessels, merchant ships and the Orkney ferries.

LIGHTS AND MARKS
There are no leading marks or lights. Entry is straightforward once the Lt on end of pier QG 6m 4M has been located.

RADIO TELEPHONE
VHF Ch 16; 12 (0800-2200 LT).

TELEPHONE (0847)
Hr Mr 62779; MRSC Kirkwall 3268; ⋕ Wick 3650; Marinecall 0898 500 451; Police 63222; Dr. 63154.

FACILITIES
EC Thurso — Thursday; **Harbour** Slip, D, L, FW, ME, El, C (30 ton mobile), CH, AB, R, Bar; **Pentland Firth YC** M, R, Bar; **Thurso** V, R, Bar. ✉; Ⓑ; ≹; ✈ (Wick).

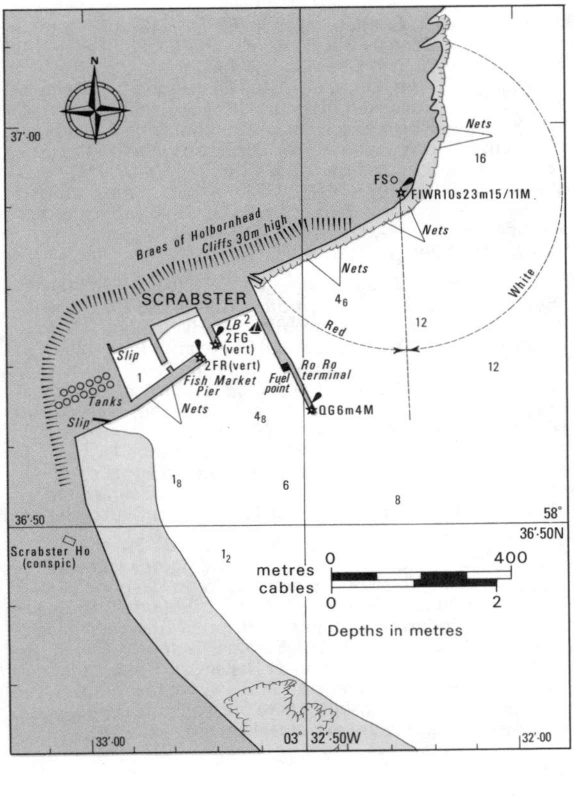
N
37′·00
Nets
16
FS
FlWR10s23m15/11M
Braes of Holbornhead Cliffs 30m high
Nets
Nets
White
SCRABSTER
LB 2
2FG (vert)
2FR(vert)
Red
12
Slip
1
Fish Market Pier
Fuel point
Ro Ro terminal
12
Tanks
Nets
QG6m4M
Slip
1₈
6
8
36′·50
58°
36′·50N
Scrabster Ho (conspic)
1₂
metres 0 400
cables 0 2
Depths in metres
33′·00
03° 32′·50W
32′·00

MINOR HARBOURS AND ANCHORAGES 10.7.27

CULLEN, Banff, 57°41′·00N, 02°49′·00W, Zone 0 (GMT), Admty Chart 222. HW +0045 on Dover, −0135 on Aberdeen; HW height −0·3m on Aberdeen; ML 2·4m; Duration 0555. Shelter good but entrance hazardous in strong winds from N and W. Harbour, consisting of two basins, dries, access HW∓4 approx. Moor in inner basin if under 1m draught. Beware local boat mooring right across inner basin entrance. There are no lights or marks. Popular recreational harbour. Facilities: Hr Mr ☎ 41116; **Cullen Bay Hotel** ☎ 40432 R, Bar; **Town** V, R, Bar, ✉.

PORTKNOCKIE, Banff, 57°42′·00N, 02°51′·00W, Zone 0 (GMT), Admty chart 222. HW +0045 on Dover, −0135 on Aberdeen; HW height −0·3m on Aberdeen; ML 2·3m; Duration 0555. Shelter is good and is one of the safest harbours on S side of Moray Firth but care is needed entering in strong N winds. Scend is often experienced. Most of inner harbour dries but berth on W or N wall – firm sandy bottom. W Tr on S pier head. Yachts use NW jetties. Orange street lights surround the harbour – two conspic white lights are the leading lights of approx 130°, on S pier. Facilities: Hr Mr ☎ Cullen 40705; EC Wed; AB, FW, C (15 ton), CH; **D Reid** Slip, L, Sh. Dr. ☎ Cullen 40272, **Town** Ⓑ, P, ✉, V, Bar.

FINDOCHTY, Banff, 57°42′·00N, 02°54′·00W, Zone 0 (GMT), Admty chart 222. HW +0045 on Dover, −0140 on Aberdeen; HW height −0·2m on Aberdeen; ML 2·3m; Duration 0550. Good shelter in inner basin which has pontoon berths for 60 yachts. Access (1·5m draught) HW∓4. Outer basin dries and has numerous rocky outcrops. Entrance faces N and is 20m wide. There are two FW Ldg Lts leading into Outer Basin. Facilities: Hr Mr ☎ Cullen 40715. **Town** V, R, Bar, ✉.

FORTROSE, Ross and Cromarty, 57°35′·00N, 04°08′·00W, Zone 0 (GMT), Admty charts 1078, 223. HW +0055 on Dover, −0125 on Aberdeen; HW height 0·0m on Aberdeen; ML 2·5m; Duration 0620. See 10.7.16. Small Hr which dries, well protected by Chanonry Ness on E. Beware Craigan Rock ESE of Hr entrance. Ldg line 296°, Broomhill House (conspic on hill to NW) in line with school house spire. Follow line until just beyond G buoy Iso G, then turn W to avoid Craigan Rock. There are no Hr Lts. Lt Ho on Chanonry Pt Oc 6s 12m 15M, vis 148°–073°. Facilities: EC Thurs; AB, P, ✉, Ⓑ, D, Dr, L, M, R, YC, Slip, V;
Chanonry SC (near pier); **Fortrose YC**; **Pagwari** ☎ 20356, Gas.

CROMARTY FIRTH, Ross and Cromarty, 57°41′·00N, 04°02′·00W, Zone 0 (GMT), Admty charts 1889, 1890. HW +0100 on Dover, −0135 on Aberdeen; HW height 0·0m on Aberdeen; ML 2·5m; Duration 0625. See 10.7.16. Excellent harbour extending 7·5M W and then 9M SW. Good shelter can always be found depending on the direction of the wind. The harbour is run by Cromarty Firth Ports Authority. Visitors should report to the Port Manager (VHF Ch 11). Beware rocks and reefs round N and S Sutor, N and S of entrance. Also beware many unlit oil rig mooring buoys and fish cages within the firth. Cromarty harbour is protected by two piers, and dries. Cromarty Lt Ho, on the Ness, Oc WR 10s 18m 14/11M, R079°–088°, W088°–275°, obsc by N Sutor when bearing less than 253°. A Lt is shown 5m from head of S pier 1st Oct to 31st Mar. Anchorage in approx 6m 2 ca W of S pier head. Cromarty Firth Port Control VHF Ch 11 16 13 (H24). Facilities: EC Wed; AB, Bar, C(3 ton) D, FW, ✉, P, R, V, L; **Invergordon Boating Club**; **Tomlinson** ☎ 852233, Gas.

7

MINOR HARBOURS AND ANCHORAGES *Continued*

DORNOCH FIRTH, Ross and Cromarty/Sutherland 57°51′·00N, 04°08′·00W, Zone 0 (GMT), Admty charts 223, 115. HW + 0115 on Dover, −0120 on Aberdeen; HW height +0·1m on Aberdeen; ML 2·5m; Duration 0605. Excellent shelter but difficult entrance. Firth extends 15M inland, entered between N edge of Whiteness Sands and S edge of Gizzen Briggs. There are many shifting sandbanks, especially near the entrance. Anchorages in 7m ¾M ESE of Dornoch Pt (sheltered from NE swell by Gizzen Briggs), in 7m 2 ca SSE of Ard na Cailc, in 3·3m 1M below Bonar Bridge. (Admiralty chart coverage ceases ¼M E of Ferry Pt.) Light on Tarbat Ness Fl(4) 30s 53m 24M. R Lt shown on Tain bombing range when firing in progress. Very limited facilities at Ferrytown and Bonar Bridge. Dornoch:- EC Thur; V, P, ✉, Dr, Ⓑ, R, Bar. Note: A bridge is under construction southwards from Ard na Cailc which will have min clearance of 11m at MHWS under the centre arch.

GOLSPIE, Sutherland, 57°58′·00N, 03°59′·00W, Zone 0 (GMT), Admty chart 223. HW +0045 on Dover, −0130 sp, −0215 np on Aberdeen; HW height −0·3m on Aberdeen; ML 2·3m; Duration 0610. See 10.7.18. Golspie pier projects 60m across foreshore with arm projecting SW at the head, giving shelter during NE winds. Beware The Bridge, a bank (0·3m to 1·8m) running parallel to the shore ¼M to seaward of pier head. Seas break heavily over The Bridge in NE winds. There are no lights. To enter, keep Duke of Sutherlands Memorial in line with boathouse SW of pier at 316° until Church spire in middle of village is in line with head of pier at 006°, then keep on those marks. Harbour gets very congested; good anchorage off pier. Facilities: EC Wed; **Lindsay** ☎ 3212, Gas; **Town** Bar, D, Dr, Ⓗ, L, M, P, ✉, R, ≹, V, Ⓑ.

LYBSTER, Caithness, 58°18′·00N, 03°17′·00W, Zone 0 (GMT), Admty chart 115. HW +0020 on Dover, −0150 sp −0215 np on Aberdeen; HW height −0·6m on Aberdeen; ML 2·1m; Duration 0620. Excellent shelter in Inner Hr. Berth on E side of W pier at N end. Beware rocks on E side of entrance; entrance difficult in strong E winds. Min depth 2·5m in entrance. S pier head Lt Oc R 6s 10m 3M shown during fishing season. Facilities: EC Thurs; FW on S quay, **Town** Bar, D, P, R, V.

HOUTON BAY, Orkney Islands, 58°55′·00N, 03°11′·00W, Zone 0 (GMT), Admty charts 2568, 35. HW −0140 on Dover, −0400 on Aberdeen; HW height +0·3m on Kirkwall; ML 1·8m; Duration 0615. Anchorage in the bay in approx 5·5m at centre, sheltered from all winds. The entrance is to the E of the island Holm of Houton; entrance channel dredged 3·5m for 15m each side of Ldg line. Care should be taken not to obstruct merchant vessels & ferries plying to Flotta. Ldg Lts in line at 316°, Front Fl G 3s 8m, Rear FG 16m. Ro Ro terminal in NE corner marked by Iso R 4s. There are no facilities, except a slip close E of piers.

SHAPINSAY, Orkney Islands, 59°03′·00N, 02°54′·00W, Zone 0 (GMT), Admty charts 2584, 2249. HW −0015 on Dover, −0330 on Aberdeen; HW height −1·0m on Aberdeen. Good shelter in Ellwick Bay off Balfour on SW end of island in 2½ to 3m. Enter bay passing W of Helliar Holm which has Lt (Fl WRG 10s) on S end. Keep mid-channel. Balfour Pier Lt Q WRG 5m 3/2M; vis G270°-010°, W010°-020°, R020°-090°. Tides in The String reach 5 kn at springs. Facilities: ✉, P (from garage), shop.

PIEROWALL, Orkney Islands, 59°19′·00N, 02°58′·00W, Zone 0 (GMT), Admty chart 2622, 2250. HW −0135 on Dover, −0355 on Aberdeen; HW height +0·7m on Kirkwall; ML 2·2m; Duration 0620. See 10.7.23. The bay is a good anchorage in 2m to 7m and well protected. Deep water berths at Gill Pt. are available – consult Hr Mr (Tel. Westray 273). Beware Skelwick Skerry rocks approaching from S and the rocks off Vest Ness (extent approx 1 ca off shore) coming from the N. The N entrance through Papa Sound should not be used unless local knowledge is available. There is a dangerous tide race off Mull Head at the N of Papa Westray. Lights; E pier head Fl WRG 3s 7m 11/7M; G254°−276°, W276°−291°, R291°−308°, G308°−215°. W pier head 2 FR (vert) 4/6m 3M. Facilities: Hr Mr VHF Ch 16 FW (at Gill Pier) P and D at garage in Pierowall, Bar, ✉, R, V.

AUSKERRY, Orkney Islands 59°02′·00N, 02°34′·00W, Zone 0 (GMT), Admty chart 2250. HW −0010 on Dover, −0315 on Aberdeen; HW height −1·0m on Aberdeen. Small island at entrance to Stronsay Firth has small harbour on W side. Safe entrance and good shelter except in SW winds. Auskerry Sound and Stronsay Firth are dangerous with wind over tide. Ent min 3·5m and alongside pier 1·2m. Yachts can lie secured between ringbolts at entrance and the pier. Auskerry Lt at S end Fl 20s 34m 18M from W Tr. There are no facilities.

FAIR ISLE, Shetland Islands, 59°32′·00N, 01°37′·00W, Zone 0 (GMT), Admty chart 2622. HW −0030 on Dover, −0020 on Lerwick; HW height −0·1m on Lerwick; ML 1·4m; Duration 0620. See 10.7.25. Good shelter in North Haven although open to NE winds. Lie alongside pier or anchor in approx 2m. Beware rocks all round the island particularly in the 'so called' South Harbour which is not recommended. There is a light at each end; Skadan in the S Fl (4) 30s 32m 24M; vis 260°−146° but obscured close inshore from 260°−282°; Horn(2) 60s. In the N, Skroo Fl (2) 30s 80m 22M (vis about 087°−358°), Horn (3) 45s. Ldg Marks at 199°, the Stack of North Haven in line with top of Sheep Craig leads into North Haven. Facilities: there is a shop and ✉ at N Shriva, and a bi-weekly ferry to Shetland.

SCALLOWAY, Shetland Islands, 60°08′·00N, 01°17′·00W, Zone 0 (GMT), Admty chart 3294. HW −0200 on Dover, −0150 on Lerwick; HW height −0·5m on Lerwick; ML 0·9m; Duration 0620. A good sheltered anchorage available in all weathers but care is needed passing through the islands in strong SW winds. Anchor off Scalloway 6 to 10m, in Hamna Voe (W Burra), almost land-locked, in 6m approx, but bottom foul with old moorings. Lights; Scalloway Hr, Moores Slipway jetty head 2 FR (vert) 4/2m 3M; Blacksness W pier head 2 FG (vert) 6/4m 3M; E pier head Oc R 7s 5m 3M; Fugla Ness Fl (2) WRG 10s 20m 10/7M; W Tr; vis G014°−032°, W032°−082°, R082°−134°, W134°−shore. Lt Oc WRG 10s 7m 14/11M, in posn 60°08′.11N 01°16′.39W, vis G045·7°−056·8°, W056·8°−058·8°, R058·8°−069.9°. VHF Ch 16; 09 **12** (Mon-Fri 0600-1800 LT; Sat 0600-1230 LT). Hr Mr & Port Control ☎ (0806) 242551 (H24). Facilities: EC Thurs; Bar, C, D, El, FW, ME, ✉, Sh, Slip, R, V, AB, SM, BY, CH, M, P; **Scalloway Boating Club** ☎ 408; **W. Moore** ☎ 215, Slip, ME, El, Sh; **H. Williamson** ☎ 645, El.

BALTA SOUND, Shetland Islands, 60°44′·00N, 00°48′·00W, Zone 0 (GMT), Admty chart 3293. HW −0105 on Dover, −0055 on Lerwick; HW height +0·2m on Lerwick; ML 1·3m; Duration 0640. The Sound and Balta Hr form a large landlocked harbour with good shelter from all winds. Beware kelp which causes bad holding. R can buoys mark 4m patches. Anchor near Sandisons Wharf in approx 6m. Light on S end of Balta I Fl WR 10s 17m 10/7M; W249°−010°, R010°−060°, W060°−154°. Safest entry is between Huney I and Balta I. VHF Ch 16; 20 (office hours) Facilities: at BY FW, D, El, ME, Sh; Hotel by pier; **Baltasound village**, Bar, R, V, ✉.

KYLE OF TONGUE, Sutherland, 58°32′·00N, 04°24′·00W (Rabbit Is.), Zone 0 (GMT), Admty Charts 1954, 2720. HW −0325 on Dover, +0050 on Ullapool; HW height −0·4m on Ullapool. The Kyle runs about 7M inland. Entry (see 10.7.5) should not be attempted in strong N winds. Anchorages at Talmine (W of Rabbit Is.) protected from all but NE winds; at Skullomie Hr, protected from E winds; off Mol na Coinne, a small bay on SE side of Eilean nan Ron, protected from W and N winds; off S of Rabbit Is., protected from W to N winds. There are no lights or leading marks. Facilities: Limited supplies at Talmine shop (½M from slip) or at Coldbachie (1½M from Skullomie).

LOCH ERIBOLL, Sutherland, 58°29′·00N, 04°39′·00W, Zone 0 (GMT), Admty chart 2076. Tidal figures taken at Rispond: HW −0345 on Dover, +0035 on Ullapool; HW height −0·5m on Ullapool; ML 2·7m; Duration 0610. See 10.8.7. Two good anchorages; in Rispond Bay on W side of loch, entrance good in all but E winds, in approx 5m; in bays to N and S of peninsular at Heilam on E side of loch. Yachts can enter Rispond Hr, access approx HW ∓3, where they can dry out alongside. There are no lights or marks. Facilities at Rispond are extremely limited.

Area 8

North-West Scotland
Cape Wrath to Craobh Haven

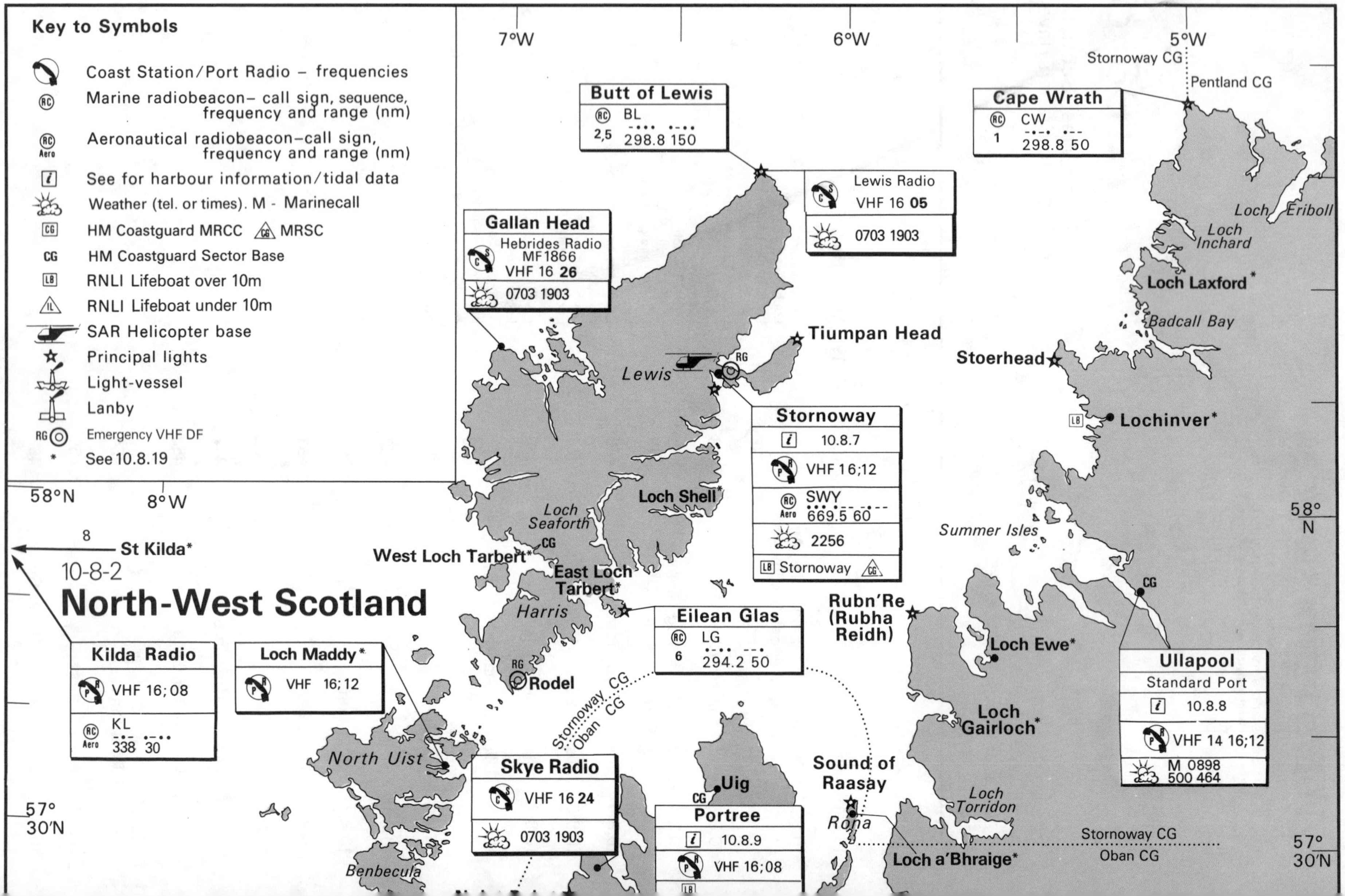

10-8-2
North-West Scotland
Key to Symbols
Coast Station/Port Radio – frequencies
Marine radiobeacon– call sign, sequence, frequency and range (nm)
Aeronautical radiobeacon–call sign, frequency and range (nm)
See for harbour information/tidal data
Weather (tel. or times). M - Marinecall
HM Coastguard MRCC
MRSC
HM Coastguard Sector Base
RNLI Lifeboat over 10m
RNLI Lifeboat under 10m
SAR Helicopter base
Principal lights
Light-vessel
Lanby
Emergency VHF DF
* See 10.8.19
7°W
6°W
5°W
8°W
58°N
58° N
57° 30'N
Butt of Lewis
BL
2,5 298.8 150
Lewis Radio
VHF 16 05
0703 1903
Cape Wrath
CW
1 298.8 50
Stornoway CG
Pentland CG
Gallan Head
Hebrides Radio
MF1866
VHF 16 26
0703 1903
Stornoway
10.8.7
VHF 16;12
SWY
Aero
669.5 60
2256
Stornoway
Tiumpan Head
Stoerhead
Lochinver*
Loch Eriboll
Loch Inchard
Loch Laxford*
Badcall Bay
Lewis
Loch Shell*
Loch Seaforth
Summer Isles
8
St Kilda*
West Loch Tarbert*
East Loch Tarbert*
Harris
Rodel
Eilean Glas
LG
6 294.2 50
Rubn'Re (Rubha Reidh)
Loch Ewe*
Loch Gairloch*
Ullapool
Standard Port
10.8.8
VHF 14 16;12
M 0898 500 464
Kilda Radio
VHF 16; 08
KL
Aero
338 30
Loch Maddy*
VHF 16; 12
Stornoway CG
Oban CG
North Uist
Benbecula
Skye Radio
VHF 16 24
0703 1903
Uig
Portree
10.8.9
VHF 16;08
Sound of Raasay
Rona
Loch Torridon
Loch a'Bhraige*

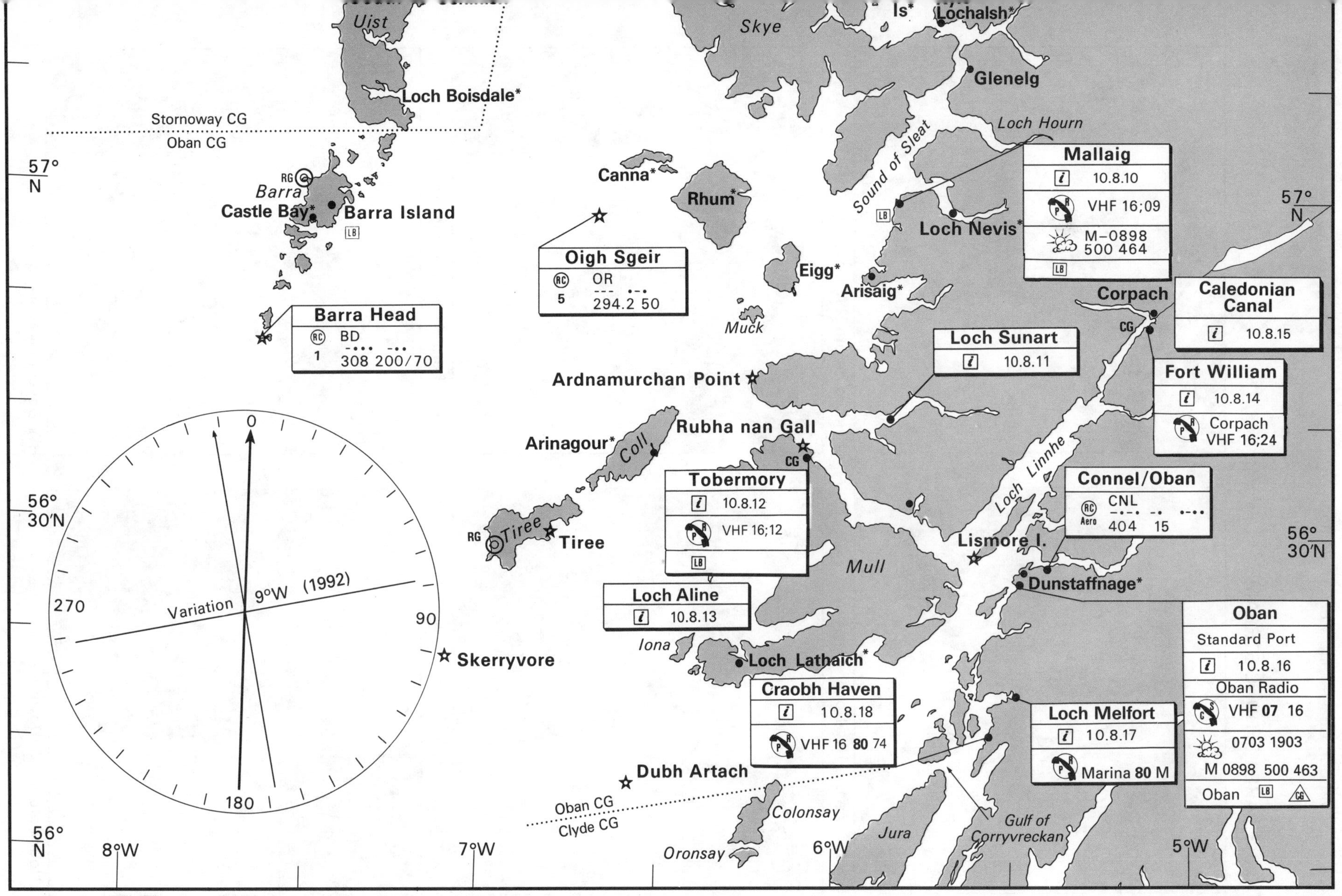

Uist
Loch Boisdale*
Stornoway CG
Oban CG
57° N
Barra
Castle Bay*
Barra Island
Barra Head
BD
1 308 200/70
Canna*
Rhum*
Oigh Sgeir
OR
5 294.2 50
Skye
Is*
Lochalsh*
Glenelg
Loch Hourn
Sound of Sleat
Mallaig
10.8.10
VHF 16;09
M-0898 500 464
Loch Nevis*
Eigg*
Arisaig*
Muck
Corpach
Caledonian Canal
10.8.15
Loch Sunart
10.8.11
Fort William
10.8.14
Corpach VHF 16;24
Ardnamurchan Point
Rubha nan Gall
Arinagour*
Coll
Tobermory
10.8.12
VHF 16;12
Loch Linnhe
Connel/Oban
CNL
Aero
404 15
Lismore I.
Dunstaffnage*
56° 30′N
Tiree
Mull
Loch Aline
10.8.13
Iona
Loch Lathaich*
Oban
Standard Port
10.8.16
Oban Radio
VHF 07 16
0703 1903
M 0898 500 463
Oban
Skerryvore
Craobh Haven
10.8.18
VHF 16 80 74
Loch Melfort
10.8.17
Marina 80 M
Dubh Artach
Oban CG
Clyde CG
Colonsay
Jura
Gulf of Corryvreckan
Oronsay
0
90
180
270
Variation 9°W (1992)
56° N
8°W
7°W
6°W
5°W

10.8.3 AREA 8 TIDAL STREAMS

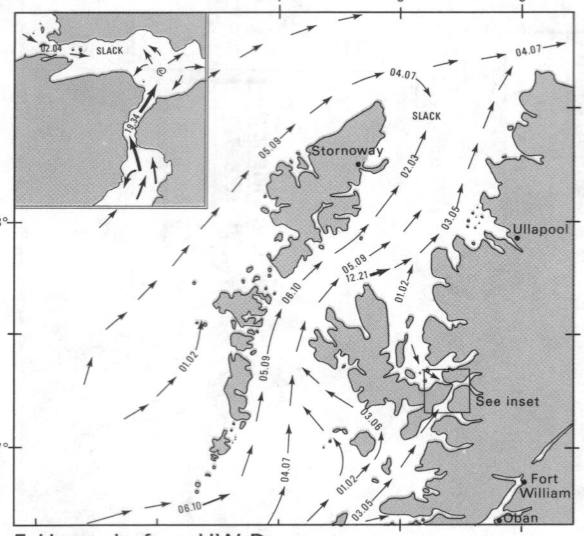
7°
6°
5°
58°
57°
SLACK
Stornoway
Ullapool
See inset
Fort William
Oban

5 Hours before HW Dover (0050 before HW Ullapool)

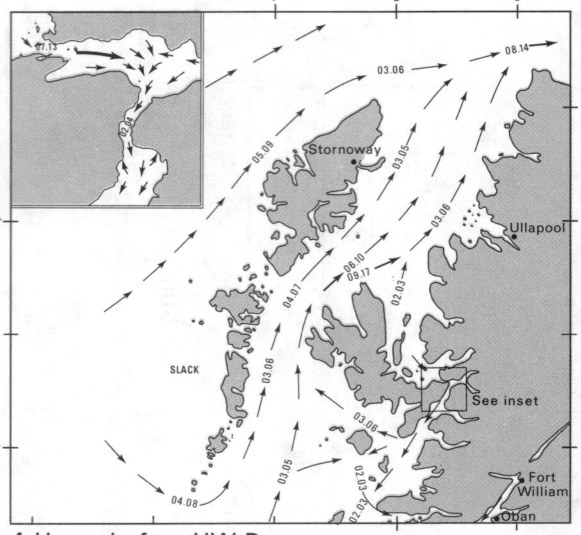
7°
6°
5°
58°
57°
SLACK
Stornoway
Ullapool
See inset
Fort William
Oban

4 Hours before HW Dover (0010 after HW Ullapool)

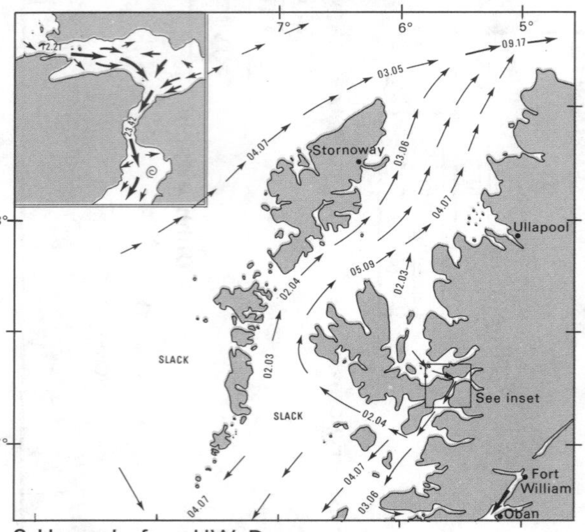
7°
6°
5°
58°
57°
SLACK
SLACK
Stornoway
Ullapool
See inset
Fort William
Oban

3 Hours before HW Dover (0110 after HW Ullapool)

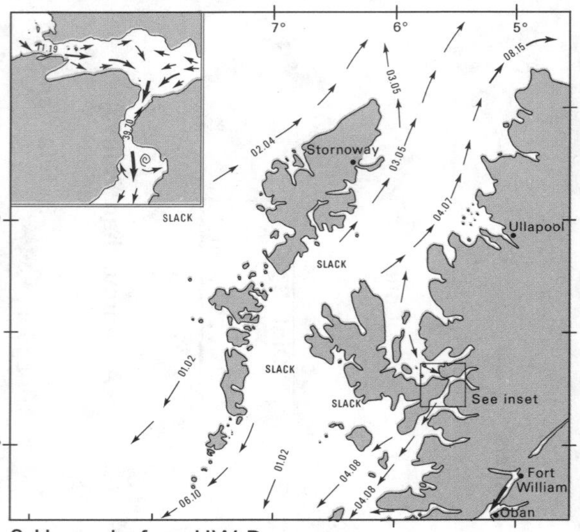
7°
6°
5°
58°
57°
SLACK
SLACK
SLACK
SLACK
Stornoway
Ullapool
See inset
Fort William
Oban

2 Hours before HW Dover (0210 after HW Ullapool)

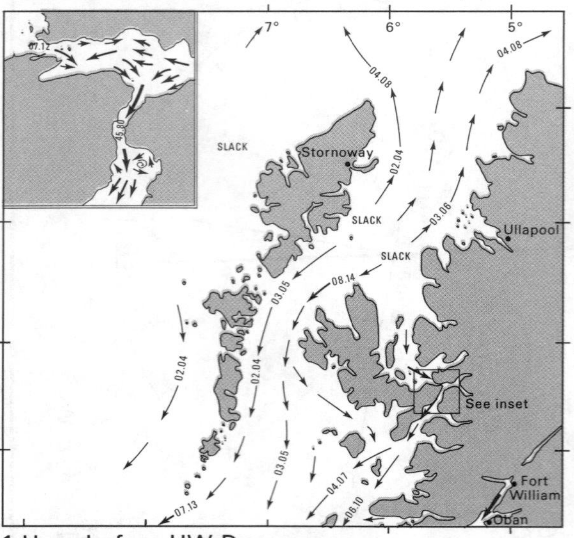
7°
6°
5°
58°
57°
SLACK
SLACK
SLACK
Stornoway
Ullapool
See inset
Fort William
Oban

1 Hour before HW Dover (0310 after HW Ullapool)

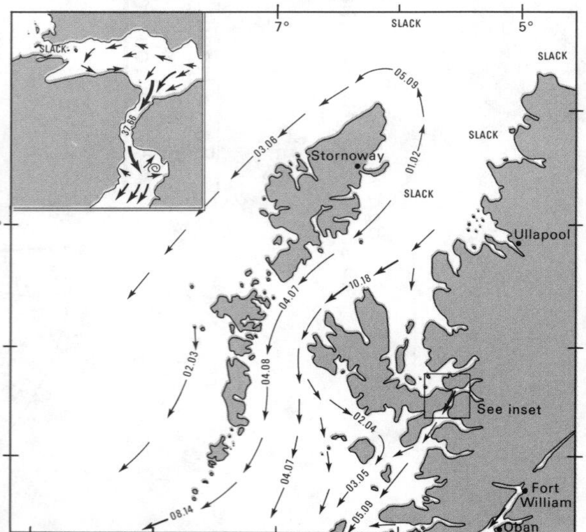
7°
6°
5°
58°
57°
SLACK
SLACK
SLACK
SLACK
SLACK
Stornoway
Ullapool
See inset
Fort William
Oban

HW Dover (0410 after HW Ullapool)

Eastward 10.7.3 Southward 10.9.3

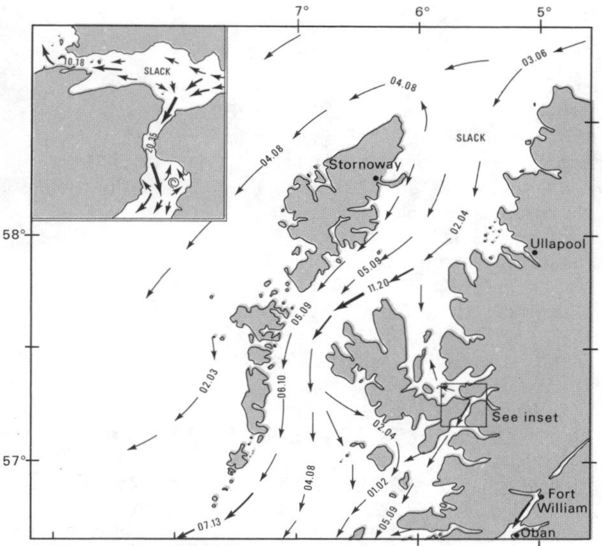
7°
6°
5°
58°
57°
Stornoway
Ullapool
See inset
Fort William
Oban
SLACK

1 Hours after HW Dover (0510 after HW Ullapool)

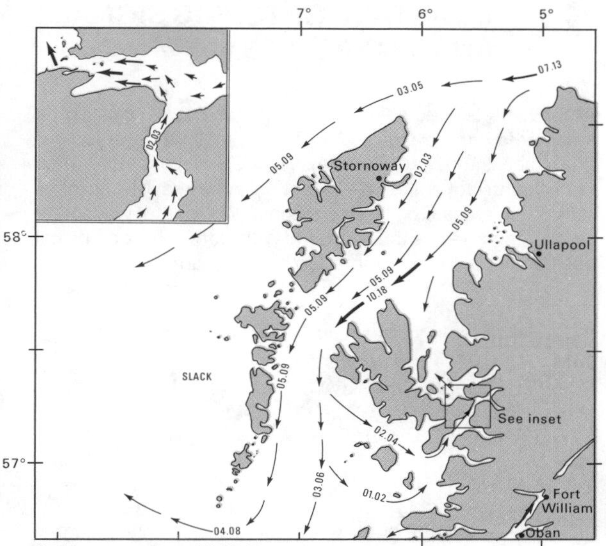
7°
6°
5°
58°
57°
Stornoway
Ullapool
See inset
Fort William
Oban
SLACK

2 Hours after HW Dover (0615 before HW Ullapool)

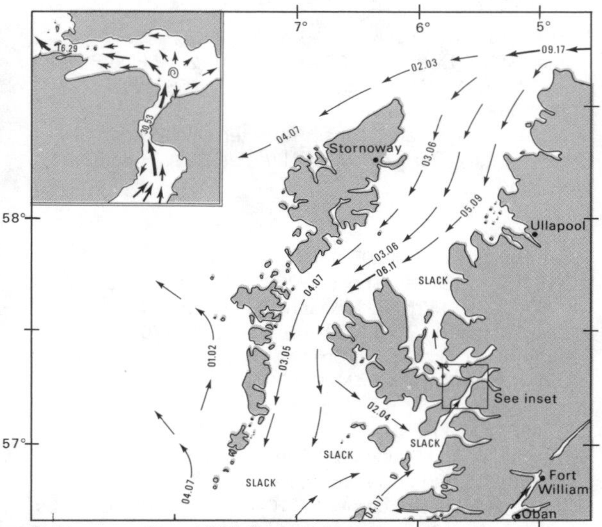
7°
6°
5°
58°
57°
Stornoway
Ullapool
See inset
Fort William
Oban
SLACK

3 Hours after HW Dover (0515 before HW Ullapool)

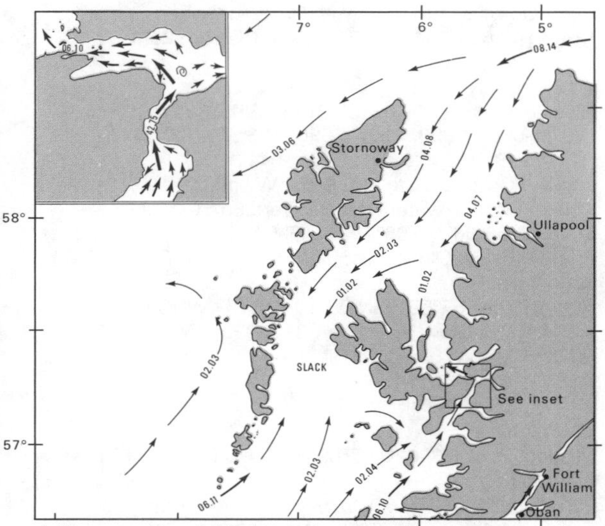
7°
6°
5°
58°
57°
Stornoway
Ullapool
See inset
Fort William
Oban
SLACK

4 Hours after HW Dover (0415 before HW Ullapool)

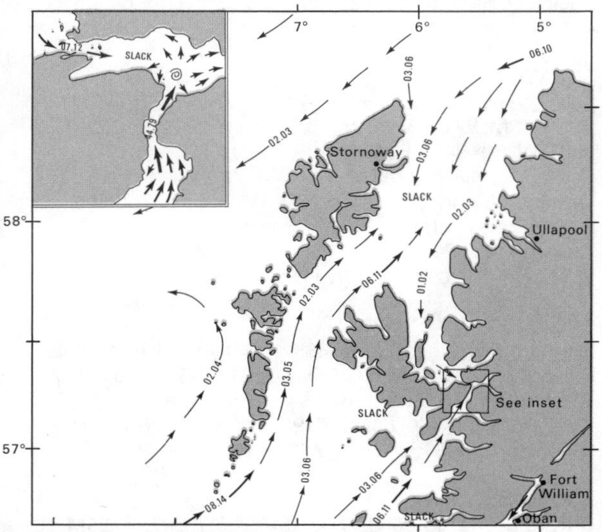
7°
6°
5°
58°
57°
Stornoway
Ullapool
See inset
Fort William
Oban
SLACK

5 Hours after HW Dover (0315 before HW Ullapool)

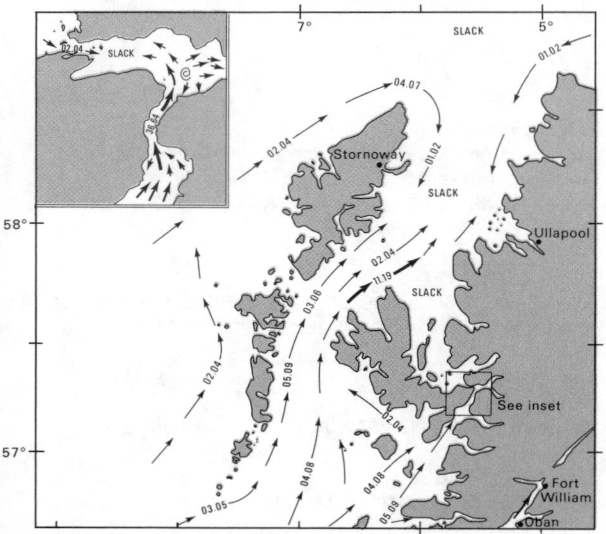
7°
6°
5°
58°
57°
Stornoway
Ullapool
See inset
Fort William
Oban
SLACK

6 Hours after HW Dover (0215 before HW Ullapool)

10.8.4 COASTAL LIGHTS, FOG SIGNALS AND WAYPOINTS

Abbreviations used below are given in 1.4.1. Principal lights are in **bold** print, places in CAPITALS, and light-vessels, light floats and Lanbys in *CAPITAL ITALICS*. Unless otherwise stated lights are white. m—elevation in metres; M—nominal range in n. miles. Fog signals are in *italics*. Useful waypoints are <u>underlined</u> - use those on land with care. All geographical positions should be assumed to be approximate. See 4.2.2.

<u>Cape Wrath</u> 58°37'·55N 04°59'·87W Fl (4) 30s 122m **24M**; W Tr; RC; *Horn (3) 45s*.
Rockall 57°35'·8N 13°41'·3W Fl 15s 19m 13M (unreliable).

SCOTLAND—WEST COAST

LOCH INCHARD
<u>Rubha na Lecaig</u> 58°27'·43N 05°04'·51W Fl (2) 10s 30m 8M.
Loch Bervie Ldg Lts 327°. Front 58°27'·5N 05°03'·1W Oc G 8s 16m 9M W ■, Or ▲ on Gy Tr. Rear, 330m from front, Oc G 8s 26m 9M; W ■, Or ▼ on Gy Tr.
<u>Stoer Hd</u> 58°14'·4N 05°24'·0W Fl 15s 59m **24M**; W Tr.

LOCH INVER.
Glas Leac 58°08'·7N 05°16'·3W Fl WRG 3s 7m; Gy col; vis W071°-080°, R080°-090°, G090°-103°, W103°-111°, R111°-243°, W243°-251°, G251°-071°.
Off Aird Ghlas QG 3m 1M; B col, W bands.
Culag Hbr breakwater Hd 2 FG (vert) 6m; Gy col.
Soyea Is 58°08'·6N 05°19'·6W Fl (2) 10s 34m 6M; Gy post.
Summer Isles, Old Dornie, new Pier Hd Fl G 3s 5m; B & W ▲ on Gy pole..
<u>Rubha Cadail</u> 57°55'·53N 05°13'·30W Fl WRG 6s 11m W9M, R6M, G6M; W Tr; vis G311°-320°, W320°-325°, R325°-103°, W103°-111°, G111°-118°, W118°-127°, R127°-157°, W157°-199°.

ULLAPOOL.
<u>Ullapool Pt</u> 57°53'·62N 05°09'·85W Iso R 4s 8m 6M; vis 258°-108°.
Ferry Pier 57°37'·7N 05°09'·5W 2 FR (vert) 6m; on post.
Extension, SE corner 57°53'·7N 05°09'·3W Fl R 3s 6m 1M; on pole.

<u>Cailleach Hd</u> 57°55'·83N 05°24'·15W Fl (2) 12s 60m 9M; W Tr; vis 015°-236°.

LOCH EWE.
Loch Ewe, NATO Jetty, NW corner Fl G 4s 5m 3M.
Dolphins off N and S ends of jetty Fl G 4s.
Rubha Reidh 57°51'·4N 05°48'·6W Fl (4) 15s 37m **24M**; W Tr.

LOCH GAIRLOCH.
Glas Eilean 57°42'·8N 05°42'·3W Fl WRG 6s 9m W6M, R 4M; vis W080°-102°, R102°-296°, W296°-333°, G333°-080°.

RONA.
NE point Fl 12s 69m **19M**; W Tr; W Tr; vis 050°-358°.

LOCH A'BHRAIGE.
Sgeir Shuas 57°35'·04N 05°58'·54W Fl R 2s 6m 3M; vis 070°-199°.
Jetty, NE end 57°34'·7N 05°57'·9W 2FR (vert).
57°34'·6N 05°57'·9W Fl R 5s 4m 3M.
Ldg Lts 136·5° Front. No 9 Bn Q WRG 3m W4M, R3M; W and Or Bn; vis W135°-138°, R138°-318°, G318°-135°. Rear, No 10 Iso 6s 28m 5M; W Bn.
No 1 Bn Fl G 3s 91m 3M, Or Bn.
Rubha Chùil-tairbh Fl 3s 6m 5M; W Bn.
No. 11 Bn QY 6m 4M; Or Bn.
No. 3 Bn Fl (2) 10s 9m 4M; W Bn and Or stripes.
No. 12 Bn QR 5m 3M; Or Bn.
Garbh Eilean SE Pt No. 8 Bn Fl 3s 8m 5M; W Bn.

SOUND OF RAASAY.
<u>Portree Pier Hd</u> 57°24'·66N 06°11'·34W 2 FR (vert) 6m 4M; occas.
<u>Ru Na Lachan</u> 57°29'·04N 05°52'·07W Oc WR 8s 21m 10M; Tr; vis W 337°-022°, R022°-117°, W117°-162°.
Applecross Pier Fl G 3s 3m 3M; G ▲ on post.
<u>McMillan's Rock Lt By</u> 57°21'·13N 06°06'·24W Fl (2) G 12s; SHM.
Raasay Suisnish 2 FG (vert) 8/6m 2M.
Raasay SE Pt, <u>Eyre Pt</u> 57°20'·03N 06°01'·22W Fl WR 3s 5m W9M, R6M; W Tr; vis W215°-266°, R266°-288°, W288°-063°.
Skye, Loch Sligachan, Sconser ferry terminal QR 8m 3M.
Crowlin, <u>Eilean Beag</u> 57°21'·23N 05°51'·33W Fl 6s 32m 6M; W Bn.

KYLE AKIN.
<u>Eilean Ban</u> 57°16'·68N 05°44'·48W Iso WRG 4s 16m W9M, R6M, G6M; W Tr; vis W278°-282°, R282°-096°, W096°-132°, G132°-182°; Racon.
Allt-an-Avaig Jetty 2 FR (vert) 10m; vis 075°-270°.
S shore, ferry slipway QR 6m (vis in Kyle of Loch Alsh).
Mooring dolphin 57°16'·4N 05°43'·4W Q 5m 3M.

KYLE OF LOCH ALSH.
Ferry Pier, W and E sides, 2 FG (vert) 6/5m 5/4M
Fishery Pier E end Fl G 3s 6m 2M.
Butec Jetty W end N corner 57°16'·7N 05°42'·4W Oc G 6s 5m 3M each end, synchronized.
<u>Sgeir-na-Caillich</u> 57°15'·63N 05°38'·83W Fl (2) R 6s 3m 4M; Bn.

SOUND OF SLEAT.
<u>Kyle Rhea</u> 57°14'·20N 05°39'·90W Fl WRG 3s 7m W11M, R9M, G8M; W Bn; vis R shore-219°, W219-228°, G228°-338°, W338°-346°, R346°-shore.
Sandaig Is, NW point Fl 6s 12m 8M; W 8-sided Tr.
Ornsay, SE end Oc 8s 18m **15M**; W Tr; vis 157°-030°.
Eilean Iarmain, off Pier Hd 2 FR (vert) 3/2m 2M.
Armadale Bay Pier Centre Oc R 6s 6m 6M.
Pt of Sleat 57°01'N 06 01'W Fl 3s 20m 9M; W Tr.

MALLAIG.
<u>Northern Pier E end</u> 57°00'·48N 05°49'·45W Iso WRG 4s 6m W9M, R6M, G6M; Gy Tr; vis G181°-185°, W185°-197°, R197°-201°. Fl G 3s 14m 6M; same structure.
<u>Sgeir Dhearg 57°00'·6</u>4N 05°49'·53W Fl (2) WG 8s 6m 5M; Gy Bn; vis G190°-055°, W055°-190°.

SCOTLAND—THE HEBRIDES
<u>Butt of Lewis</u> 58°30'·93N 06°15'·72W Fl 5s 52m **25M**; R Tr; vis 056°-320°; RC; *Horn (2) 30s*.

Tiumpan Hd 58°15'·6N 06°08'·3W Fl (2) 15s 55m **25M**; W Tr.
Eitshal 58°10'·7N 06°35'·0W 4 FR (vert) on radio mast.

STORNOWAY.
Arnish Pt 58°11'·50N 06°22'·17W Fl WR 10s 17m **W19M**, **R15M**; W ● Tr; vis W088°-198°, R198°-302°, W302°-013°.
Sandwick Bay, NW side Oc WRG 6s 10m 9M; vis G334°-341°, W341°-347°, R347°-354°.

LOCH ERISORT.
Tavag Beag 58° 07'·22N 06°23'·15W Fl 3s 13m 3M.
Eilean Chalabrigh 58°06'·81N 06°26'·62W QG 5m 3M.
Gob na Milaid Pt 58°01'·0N 06°21'·8W Fl 15s 14m 10M; W Tr.
Rubh' Uisenis 57°56'·2N 06°28'·2W Fl 5s 24m 11M; W Tr.

EAST LOCH TARBERT.
Scalpay, **Eilean Glas** 57°51'·43N 06°38'·45W Fl (3) 20s 43m **23M**; W Tr, R bands; RC; Racon.
Sgeir Griadach Lt By 57°50'·38N 06°41'·31W Q (6) + LFl 15s; SCM.
Sgeir Ghlas 57°52'·38N 06°45'·18W Iso WRG 4s 9m W9M, R6M, G6M; W ● Tr; vis G282°-319°, W319°-329°, R329°-153°, W153°-164°. G164°-171°.
Scalpay N Harbour Lt By 57°52'·58N 06°42'·16W Fl G 2s; SHM.
Dun Cor Mor Fl R 5s 10m 5M.

SOUND OF HARRIS
Dubh Sgeir 57°45'·5N 07°02'·6W Q (2) 5s 9m 6M; R Tr, B bands.
Jane's Tr 57°45'·8N 07°02'·0W Q (2) G 5s 6m 4M; obsc 273°-318°.
Leverburgh Pier Hd 57°46'·0N 07°01'·6W Oc WRG 8s 5m 2M; Gy col; vis G305°-059°, W059°-066°, R066°-125°.

Berneray Breakwater Hd 57°42'·9N 07°10'·0W Iso R 4s 4M; Gy col.
Drowning Rock Q 2) G 8s 2m 2M; G pillar.
Reef Chan No 1 QG 2m 4M.
Reef Chan No. 2 Iso G 4s 2m 4M.
Eilean Fuam 57°41'·9N 07°10'·6W Q 6m 2M; W col.
N Uist, Newton Jetty Root 57°41'·5N 07°11'·5W 2 FG (vert) 9m 8M; Gy col.
Griminish Hbr Sgeir Dubh Mor 57°40'·0N 07°26'·8W Q (2) G 10s 4m 4M (shown Mar-Oct).
Pier Hd 57°39'·3N 07°26'·3W 2 FG (vert) 4m G. Metal col (shown Mar-Oct).

LOCH MADDY,
Weaver's Pt 57°36'·61N 07°05'·95W Fl 3s 21m 7M; W hut.
Glas Eilean Mòr 57°35'·98N 07°06'·64W Fl (2) 6s 8m.
Rudna Nam Pleac 57°35'·8N 07°06'·7W Fl R 4s 7m 5M; W post.
Ruigh Liath Islet 57°35'·73N 07°08'·36W QG 6m.
Vallaquie Is 57°35'·5N 07°09'·3W Fl (3) WRG 8s 11m W7M, R5M, G5M; W pillar; vis G shore-205°, W205°-210°, R210°-240°, G240°-254°, W254°-257°, R257°-shore.
Lochmaddy Ldg Lts 298°. Front, Ro Ro pier 57°35'·8N 07°09'·3W 2 FG (vert) 8/6m 4M. Rear, 110m from front, Oc G 8s 10m 4M; col on dolphin; vis 284°-304°.
Grimsay. Kallin Hbr Breakwater NE corner 57°28'·9N 07°12'·3W 2 FR (vert) 6m 5M; Gy col.

LOCH CARNAN.
Landfall Lt By 57°22'·30N° 07°11'·45W L Fl 10s; SWM.
No. 2 Lt By 57°22'·33N 07°14'·87W Fl R 2s; PHM.
No. 3 Lt By 57°22'·35N 07°15'·55W Fl R 5s; PHM.
No. 4 Lt By 57°22'·27N 07°16'·13W QR; PHM.
Ldg Lts 222°. Front 57°22'·00N 07°16'·28W Fl R 2s 7m 5M; W ◆ on post. Rear 58m from front Iso R 10s 11m 5M; W ◆ on post.

Usinish (S Uist) 57°17'·91N 07°11'·50W Fl WR 20s 54m **W19M**, **R15M**; W Tr; vis W193°-356°, R356°-013°.

LOCH BOISDALE,
Calvay E End 57°08'·5N 07°15'·3W Fl (2) WRG 10s 16m W7M, R4M, G4M; W Tr; vis G190°-202°, W202°-286°, R286°-111°, W111°-190°.
N side QG 3m 3M.
Gasay Is Fl WR 5s 10m W7M, R4M; W Tr; vis R284°-120°, W120°-284°.
Jetty Hd 57°09'·2N 07°18'·2W Iso RG 4s 12m 2M; vis G shore-283°, R283°-shore; 2 FG (vert) 8m 3M on dolphin 84m W.
Ludaig Dir Lt 297° 57°06'·2N 07°19'·7W Dir Oc WRG 6s 8m W7M, R4M, G4M; vis G287°-296°, W296°-298°, R298°-307°.
Ludaig Pier 2 FG (vert) 5/3m 3M.
Stag Rk 57°05'·9N 07°18'·3W Fl (2) 8s 7m 4M.
Bank Rk 57°05'·6N 07°17'·5W Q (2) 4s 5m 4M.

BARRA.
Curachan Lt By 56°58'·58N 07°20·45W Q (6) + LFl 15s; SCM.
Drover Rks Lt By 57°04'·18N 07°23'·58W Fl (2) 10s; IDM.

ERISKAY.
The Witches Lt By 57°05'·75N 07°20'·77W Fl R 5s; PHM.
Haun Dir Lt 236° Dir Oc WRG 3s 9m W7M, R4M, G4M; vis G226°-234.5°, W234·5°-237·5°, R237·5°-246°.
Eriksay Pier 2 FG(vert) 5m 5M.
Acairseid Mhor Ldg Lts 285°. Front 57°03'·9N 07°17'·2W Oc R 6s 9m 4M. Rear 24m from front Oc R 6s 10m 4M. Both Gy cols.

VATERSAY SOUND,
Sgeir Dubh 56°56'·4N 07°28'·9W Fl (2) WG 6s 6m W7M, G5M; vis W280°180°, G180°-280°. Destroyed, marked by Lt By (T).
Sgeir Leadh (Liath) 56°56'·7N 07°30'·7W Fl 3s 7m 8M; W bldg.
Rubha Glas. Ldg Lts 295°. Front 56°56'·78N 07°30'·59W FG 9m 11M; Or ▲ on W Tr. Rear 457m from front FG 15m 11M; Or ▼ on W Tr.

South Uist. Falconet Tr 57°21'·5N 07°23'·6W FR 25m 8M (3M by day); shown 1h before firing, changes to Iso R 2s 15min before firing until completion; similar Lts 1·2M NNW and 7·5M SSW.

BERNERAY.
W side, **Barra Hd** 56°47'·13N 07°39'·18W Fl 15s 208m **21M**; W Tr; obsc by islands to NE; RC.
Flannan Is, Eilean Mór 58°17'·32N 07°35'·23W Fl (2) 30s 101m **20M**; W Tr; obsc in places by Is to W of Eilean Mór.

EAST LOCH ROAG.
Aird Laimishader Carloway 58°17'·1N 06°49'·5W L Fl 12s 61m 8M; W hut; obsc on some brgs.

8

Ardvanich Pt 58°13'·5N 06°47'·7W Fl G 3s 2m 2M.
Tidal Rk 58°13'·5N 06°47'·6W Fl R 3s 2m 2M (synchronised with previous Lt).
Gt Bernera Kirkibost Jetty 2 FG (vert) 6/5m 2M.
Greinam 58°13'·3N 06°46'·2W Fl WR 6s 8m W8M, R7M; W Bn; vis R143°-169°, W169°-143°.
Rudha Arspaig Jetty 2 FR (vert) 10/7m 4M.

ST KILDA.
Ldg Lts 270°. Front 57°48'·36N 08°34'·27W Oc 5s 26m 3M. Rear, 100m from front, Oc 5s 38m 3M; synchronised.

SCOTLAND—WEST COAST

Eilean Trodday 57°43'·6N 06°17'·8W Fl (2) WRG 10s 49m W12M, R9M, G9M; W Bn; vis W062°-088°, R088°-130°, W130°-322°, G322°-062°.

SKYE.
Uig Pier Hd Iso WRG 4s 9m W7M, R4M, G4M; vis W180°-008°, G008°-052°, W052°-075°, R075°-180°.
Waternish Pt 57°36'·5N 06°38'·0W Fl 20s 21m 8M; W Tr.
Loch Dunvegan Uiginish Pt 57°26'·8N 06°36'·5W Fl WG 3s 14m W7M, G5M; W hut; vis G040°-128°, W128°-306°, obsc by Fiadhairt Pt when brg more than 148°.
Neist Pt 57°25'·4N 06°47'·2W Fl 5s 43m **16M**; W Tr.
Loch Harport Ardtreck Pt 57°20'·4N 06°25'·8W Iso 4s 17m 9M; small W Tr.

CANNA.
E end Sanday Is 57°02'·8N 06°27'·9W Fl 6s 32m 9M; W Tr; vis 152°-061°.

Oigh Sgeir, near S end, **Hyskeir** 56°58'·13N 06°40'·80W Fl (3) 30s 41m **24M**; W Tr; RC. N end *Horn 30s*.

EIGG.
SE point of Eilean Chathastail 56°52'·25N 06°07'·20W Fl 6s 24m 8M; W Tr; vis 181°-shore.

Bo Faskadale Lt By 56°48'·18N 06°06'·35W Fl (3) G 18s; SHM.
Ardnamurchan 56°43'·64N 06°13'·46W Fl (2) 20s 55m **24M**; Gy Tr; vis 002°-217°; *Horn (2) 20s*.
Cairns of Coll, Suil Ghorm 56°42'·27N 06°26'·70W Fl 12s 23m 10M; W Tr.

COLL.
Loch Eatharna, Bogha Mor Lt By 56°36'·67N 06°30'·90W Fl G 6s; SHM.
Arinagour Pier 2 FR (vert) 10m.

TIREE.
Scarinish, S side of ent 56°30'·02N 06°48'·20W Fl 3s 11m **16M**; W ■ Tr; vis 210°-030°.
Ldg Lts 286·5°. Front 56°30'·6N 06°47'·9W FR (when vessel expected). Rear 30m from front FR.

Skerryvore 56°19'·40N 07°06'·75W Fl 10s 46m **26M**; Gy Tr; Racon; *Horn 60s*.
Dubh Artach 56°08'·0N 06°37'·9W Fl (2) 30s 44m **20M**; Gy Tr, R band; *Horn 45s*.
Eileanan na Liathanaich, SE end, Bunessan 56°20'·5N 06°16'·2W Fl WR 6s 12m W8M, R6M; W Bn; vis R088°-108°, W108°-088°.

SOUND OF MULL.
Ardmore Pt 56°39'·4N 06°07'·6W Fl (2) 10s 17m 8M; W col.
Rubha nan Gall 56°38'·33N 06°03'·91W Fl 3s 17m **15M**, W Tr.
Eileanan Glasa, Green Is 56°32'·3N 05°54'·7W Fl 6s 7m 8M; W ● Tr.

Ardtornish Pt 56°31'·1N 05°45'·1W Fl (2) WRG 10s 7m W8M, R5M, G5M; W Tr; vis G shore-302°, W302°-310°, R310°-342°, W342°-057°, R057°-095°, W095°-108°, G108°-shore.
Glas Eileanan Grey Rks 56°29'·8N 05°42'·7W Fl 3s 10m 6M; W ● Tr on W base.

LOCH LINNHE.
Ent W side, Corran Pt 56°43'·27N 05°14'·47W Iso WRG 4s 12m W10M, R7M; W Tr; vis R shore-195°, W195°-215°, G215°-305°, W305°-030°, R030°-shore.
Corran Narrows NE 56°43'·62N 05°13'·83W Fl 5s 4m 4M; W Tr; vis S shore-214°.
Jetty 56°43'·42N 05°14'·56W Fl R 5s 7m 3M; Gy mast.

FORT WILLIAM,
Pier Hd Fl G 2s 6m 4M.
Corpach, Caledonian Canal lock ent Iso WRG 4s 6m 5M; W Tr; vis G287°-310°, W310°-335°, R335°-030°.

Sgeir Bhuidhe Appin 56°33'·6N 05°24'·6W Fl (2) WR 7s 7m 9M; W Bn; vis R184°-220°, W220°-184°.

LOCH CRERAN,
off Airds Pt Fl WRG 2s 2m W3M, R1M, G1M; R col; vis R196°-246°, W246°-258°, G258°-041°, W041°-058°, R058°-093°, W093-139°.
Eriska NE Pt, QG 2m 2M; G col; vis 128°-329°.
Lismore SW end 56°27'·4N 05°36'·4W Fl 10s 31m **19M**; W Tr; vis 237°-208°.
Lady's Rk 56°27'·0N 05°37'·0W Fl 6s 12m 5M; R ● on W Bn.
Duart Pt 56°26'·9N 05°38'·7W Fl (3) WR 18s 14m W5M, R3M; Gy bldg; vis W162°-261°, R261°-275°, W275°-353°, R353°-shore.

DUNSTAFFNAGE BAY.
Pier Hd, NE end 2 FG (vert) 4m 2M.

OBAN,
N spit of Kerrera 56°25'·50N 05°29'·50W Fl R 3s 9m 5M; W col. R bands.
Dunollie Fl (2) WRG 6s 7m W5M, G4M, R4M; vis G351°-009°, W009°-047°, R047°-120°, W120°-138°, G138°-143°.
Rubbh'a' Chruidh QR 3m 2M.

Kerrera Sound, Dubh Sgeir 56°22'·82N 05°32'·20W Fl (2) 12s 7m 5M; W ● Tr.
Port Lathaich 56°22'·8N 05°31'·3W Oc G 6s 6M; Bn; vis 037°-072°.

Fladda 56°14'·90N 05°40'·80W Fl (3) WRG 18s 13m W11M, R9M, G9M; W Tr; vis R169°-186°, W186°-337°, G337°-344°. W344°-356°, R356°-026°, obsc 026°-169°..
Dubh Sgeir (Luing) 56°14'·78N 05°40'·12W Fl WRG 6s 9m W6M, R4M. G4M; W Tr; vis W000°-010°, R010°-025°, W025°-215°, G215°-000°; Racon.
The Garvellachs, Eileach an Naoimh, SW end 56°13'·1N 05°48'·9W Fl 6s 21m 9M; W Bn; vis 240°-215°.

COLONSAY,
Scalasaig, Rubha Dubh 56°04'·02N 06°10'·83W Fl (2) WR 10s 6m W8M, R5M; W bldg; vis R shore-230°, W230°-337°, R337°-354°.
Pier Hd Ldg Lts 262°, FR 8/10m (occas).

Loch Melfort, Fearnach Bay Pier 56°16'·2N 05°30'·1W 2 FR (vert) 6/5m 3M; shown 1/4 to 31/10.

► **For Sound of Jura and Sound of Islay see 10.9.4.**

10.8.5 PASSAGE INFORMATION

SCOTLAND – WEST COAST

This provides splendid, if sometimes boisterous, sailing and unmatched scenery. In summer the long hours of daylight and warmth of the Gulf Stream compensate for lower air temp and higher wind speeds experienced when depressions run typically N of Scotland. Inshore the wind is often unpredictable, due to geographical effects of lochs, mountains and islands offshore: calms and squalls can occur in rapid succession. Magnetic anomalies occur.

A yacht must rely on good anchors. Particularly in N of area, facilities are very dispersed. It is essential to carry good large scale charts, and pilotage information as in *West Coast of Scotland Pilot* or as provided by the Clyde Cruising Club. Also useful is *Scottish West Coast Pilot* by Mark Brackenbury.

It is helpful to know at least some of the more common Gaelic terms, as follows. *Acairseid*: anchorage. *Ailean*: meadow. *Aird, ard*: promontory. *Aisir, aisridh*: passage between rocks. *Beag*: litttle. *Beinn*: mountain. *Bo, boghar, bodha*: rock. *Cala*: harbour. *Camas*: channel, bay. *Caol*: strait. *Cladach*: shore, beach. *Creag*: cliff. *Cumhamn*: narrows. *Dubh, dhubh*: black. *Dun*: castle. *Eilean, eileanan*: island. *Garbh*: rough. *Geal, gheal*: white. *Glas, ghlas*: grey, green. *Inis*: island. *Kyle*: narrow strait. *Linn, Linne*: pool. *Mor, mhor*, large. *Mull*: promontory. *Rinn, roinn*: point. *Ruadh*: red, brown. *Rubha, rhu*: cape. *Sgeir*: rock. *Sruth*: current. *Strath*: river valley. *Tarbert*: isthmus. *Traigh*: beach. *Uig*: bay.

CAPE WRATH TO LOCH TORRIDON (charts 1785, 1794, 2210)

C Wrath (Lt, fog sig, RC) is a steep headland (110m). To N of it the E-going stream begins at HW Ullapool –0350, and W-going at HW Ullapool +0235, sp rates 3 kn. Eddies close inshore cause almost continuous W-going stream E of cape, and N-going stream SW of it. Where they meet is turbulence, with dangerous sea in bad weather. Duslic Rk, 0·7M NE of Lt Ho, dries. 6M SW of C Wrath is Is of Am Balg (45m), foul for 0·2M offshore.

There are anchs in Loch Inchard (chart 2503), the most sheltered being in Loch Bervie on N shore. Good anchs among Is along S shore of Loch Laxford, entered between Ardmore Pt and Rubha Ruadh (see 10.8.19). Handa I to WSW is bird sanctuary. Handa Sound is navigable with care, but beware Bogha Morair in mid-chan and associated overfalls. Tide turns 2h earlier in the sound than offshore.

With strong wind against tide there is bad sea off Pt of Stoer. S lies Enard B. The best shelter is Loch Inver (10.8.19 and chart 2504), with good anch off hotel near head of loch.

Summer Is (chart 2501) lie NW of Ullapool (10.8.8) and provide several good anchs, but approaches are often difficult. The best include the B on E side of Tanera Mor; off NE of Tanera Beg (W of Eilean Fada Mor); and in Caolas Eilean Ristol, between the Is and mainland.

Loch Ewe (chart 3146) provides good shelter and is easy of access. Best anchs are in Poolewe B (beware Boor Rks off W shore) and in SW corner of Loch Thuirnaig (entering, keep close to S shore to avoid Rks extending from N side). See 10.8.19.

Off Rubha Reidh (Lt) the NE-going stream begins at HW Ullapool –0335, and the SW-going at HW Ullapool +0305. Sp rates 3 kn, but streams lose strength SW of pt.

Longa Is lies N of ent to Loch Gairloch (10.8.19 and chart 2528). The chan N of it is navigable but narrow at E end. Outer loch is free of dangers, but exposed to swell. Best anch is Caolas Bad a Chrotha on W side of Eilean Horrisdale, on S side of loch.

Loch Torridon (chart 2210) has few dangers, and streams are weak except in narrows between Loch Shieldaig and Upper Loch Torridon, where they run 2-3 kn. Entering Loch Torridon from S or W beware Murchadh Breac (dries) 0·3M NNW of Rubha na Fearna. Best anchs are SW of Eilean Mor (to W of Ardheslaig); in Loch a 'Chracaich, on S shore 3M from entrance; E of Shieldaig Is in Loch Shieldaig; and near head of Upper Loch Torridon.

OUTER HEBRIDES (charts 1785, 1794, 1795)

The E sides of these Is have many good, sheltered anchs, but W coasts give little shelter. The *Outer Hebrides sailing directions* of Clyde Cruising Club are recommended. The Sea of the Hebrides and the Little Minch can be very rough, particularly between Skye and Harris, and around Shiant Is where tide runs locally 4 kn at sp, and heavy overfalls can be met. Beware fish farms in many inlets.

Between Skerryvore and Neist Pt the stream runs generally N and S, starting N-going at HW Ullapool +0550, and S-going at HW Ullapool –0010. Mostly it does not exceed 1 kn; but it is stronger near Skerryvore, around headlands of The Small Is, and over rks and shoals. Between N point of Skye and S Harris the NE-going stream begins at HW Ullapool –0335, and the SW-going stream at HW Ullapool +0250, sp rates 2·5 kn.

From N to S, the better hbrs in Outer Hebrides include: *Lewis*. Stornoway (see 10.8.7); Loch Grimshader (beware Sgeir a'Chaolais, dries in entrance); Loch Erisort; Loch Odhairn; Loch Shell (10.8.19). Proceeding S from here, or to E Loch Tarbert beware Sgeir Inoe (dries) 3M ESE of Eilean Glas Lt Ho at SE end of Scalpay.

Harris. E Loch Tarbert (10.8.19); Loch Scadaby; Loch Stockinish; Loch Finsby. W Loch Tarbert (10.8.19). *N Uist*. Loch Maddy (10.8.19); Loch Eport. *S Uist*. Loch Skiport; Loch Eynort; Loch Boisdale (10.8.19). *Barra*. Castlebay (10.8.19). Berneray. On N side, E of Shelter Rk.

SKYE (charts 1795, 2210, 2209, 2208)

Skye and the Is around it provide many good and attractive anchs, of which the most secure are: Acairseid Mhor on the W side of Rona; Portree (10.8.9); Isleornsay; Portnalong, near the ent to Loch Harport, and Carbost at the head: Dunvegan; and Uig B in Loch Snizort.

Anch behind Fladday Is near the N end of Raasay can be squally and uncomfortable except in settled weather, and Loch Scavaig more so, though the latter is so spectacular as to warrant a visit in fair weather. Soay has a small, safe hbr on its N side, but the bar at ent almost dries at LW sp.

Tides are strong off Rubha Hunish at N end of Skye, and heavy overfalls occur with weather-going tide against fresh or strong winds.

Between Skye and the coast there is the choice of Sound of Raasay and Inner Sound. Using the former, coming S from Portree, beware Sgeir Chnapach (3m) and Ebbing Rk (dries 2·4m) NNW of Oskaig Pt. At the Narrows (chart 2534) the S-going stream begins at HW Ullapool –0605, and the N-going at HW Ullapool –0040. Sp rate 1·5 kn in mid-chan, but more near shoals each side. Beware McMillan's Rk in mid-chan, marked by By. **The direction of buoyage here is now N-wards**.

The chan between Scalpay and Skye narrows to 0·25M 2M W of Guillamon Is, where a reef has least depth of 0·3m. There is a Lt Bn on N side of narrows, where N-going stream begins at HW Ullapool +0550, and S-going at HW Ullapool –0010, sp rates about 1 kn.

8

Inner Sound is a wider, easier chan than Sound of Raasay: the two are connected by Caol Rona and Caol Mor, respectively N and S of Raasay. Dangers extend about 1M N of Rona, and Cow Is lies off the mainland 8M to S; otherwise approach from N is clear to Crowlin Is, which should be passed to W. There is a platform construction site with prohib area S of Crowlin Is. There is a good anch between the two S Is, More and Meadhonach. See 10.8.19.

The British Underwater Test and Evaluation Centre (BUTEC) torpedo range exists in the Inner Sound. While passage through the Sound is normally unrestricted, vessels passing through the area may be requested to keep to the E side of the Sound while the range is active. This is indicated by R Flags and International Code NE4 flown at the range head building at Applecross, by all range vessels and at the naval pier at Kyle of Lochalsh.

Approaching Kyle Akin (chart 2540) from W, beware dangerous rks to N, off Bleat Is (at S side of entrance to Loch Carron); Bogha Beag (dries 0·6m) on S side of chan, 0·62M W of Kyle Akin LtHo; and Black Eye Rk 0·4M W of Lt Ho with least depth 3·8m. For Plockton (Loch Carron) see 10.8.19.

Pass at least 0·05 distant either N or S of Eileanan Dubha off Kyle of Lochalsh. On S side of main chan String Rk (dries) is marked by By. For Loch Alsh see 10.8.19.

Kyle Rhea connects Loch Alsh with NE end of Sound of Sleat. The tidal streams are very strong: N-going stream begins HW Ullapool +0600, sp rate 6-7 kn; S-going stream begins at HW Ullapool, sp rate 8 kn. Eddies form both sides of the Kyle and there are heavy overfalls off S end in strong S winds on S-going stream. Temp anch in Sandaig Bay.

THE SMALL ISLES (charts 2207, 2208)

These consist of Canna Rhum, Eigg (10.8.19) and Muck. Dangers extend SSW from Canna: at 1M Jemina Rk (depth 1·5m) and Belle Rk (depth 3·6m); at 2M Humla Rk (5m high), marked by Lt By and with offlying shoals close W and 0·05 N of it; at 5M Oigh Sgeir (Lt, fog sig, RC), the largest of a group of small Is; and at 7M Mill Rks (with depths of 1·8m). The tide runs hard in these areas, and in bad weather the sea breaks heavily up to 15M SW of Canna.

On the N side of Muck, 1M offshore, are Godag Rks, some above water but with submerged dangers extending 0·2M further to N. Most other dangers around The Small Isles are closer inshore, but there are banks on which the sea breaks heavily in bad weather. Local magnetic anomalies exist around the islands.

The best hbr is Eigg (10.8.19). Others are Loch Scresort (Rhum) and Canna hbr (between Canna and Sanday), but both are exposed to E.

S OF ARDNAMURCHAN PT & MULL (chart 2171)

6M NE of Ardnamurchan Pt (Lt, fog sig) is Bo Faskadale, with two heads, the N one awash and the S with depth of 1·2m, marked by By. Ardnamurchan Pt has no offlying dangers, but it is exposed, and a heavy sea can build up even in moderate winds. Here the N-going stream begins at HW Oban –0525, and the S-going at HW Oban +0100, sp rates 1·5 kn.

Proceeding S (chart 2171) there is the choice of Passage of Tiree (exposed to SW, and with heavy overfalls in bad weather) or the sheltered route via Sound of Mull, Firth of Lorne and Sound of Jura. The former permits a visit to Coll or Tiree, where best anchs are at Arinagour and Gott B respectively. Beware Cairns of Coll, off the N point.

The W coast of Mull is rewarding in really calm and settled weather, but careful pilotage is needed. Beware tide rip off Caliach Pt (NW corner) and Torran Rks off SW end of Mull. Bunessan, N side of Ross of Mull, is an anch with boatyard etc. (see 10.8.19). Apart from the attractions of Iona and of Staffa (Fingal's Cave), the remote Treshnish Is are worth visiting. The best anchs in this area are at Ulva, Gometra, and Bull Hole and Tinker's Hole in Iona Sound. Passage through Iona Sound avoids overfalls W of Iona, but care is needed.

The Sound of Mull gives access to Tobermory (10.8.12), Dunstaffnage (10.8.19), Oban (10.8.16), and up Loch Linnhe through Corran Narrows (where tide runs strongly) to Fort William (10.8.14) and to Corpach for the Caledonian Canal (10.8.15). But, apart from these places, there are dozens of lovely anchs in the sheltered lochs inside Mull, as for example in Loch Sunart (10.8.11). For Loch Aline see 10.8.13.

On the mainland shore Eilean nam Beathach is a sheltered anch. For Loch Melfort see 10.8.17. For passage S through Sound of Jura, and Gulf of Corryvreckan, see 10.9.5.

10.8.6 DISTANCE TABLE

Approximate distances in nautical miles are by the most direct route while avoiding dangers and allowing for traffic separation schemes etc. Places in *italics* are in adjoining areas.

1 *Lerwick*	**1**																			
2 *Kirkwall*	95	**2**																		
3 *Duncansby Head*	109	34	**3**																	
4 Cape Wrath	155	79	63	**4**																
5 Butt of Lewis	183	118	103	40	**5**															
6 Stornoway	208	132	116	53	30	**6**														
7 Ullapool	208	132	116	53	52	43	**7**													
8 Portree	238	162	146	83	69	50	53	**8**												
9 Neist Point	247	171	155	92	72	49	65	48	**9**											
10 Mallaig	265	189	173	110	100	83	82	38	41	**10**										
11 Barra Head	295	219	203	140	120	97	113	96	48	63	**11**									
12 Oigh Sgeir	274	198	182	119	99	76	92	67	27	29	33	**12**								
13 Ardnamurchan Pt	284	218	202	139	119	96	104	60	47	22	47	21	**13**							
14 Tobermory	304	228	212	149	129	106	114	70	57	32	56	31	10	**14**						
15 Fort William	347	271	255	192	171	149	157	113	100	75	99	74	53	43	**15**					
16 Oban	328	252	236	173	153	130	138	94	81	56	80	55	34	24	29	**16**				
17 *Crinan*	344	268	252	189	169	146	154	110	97	72	92	71	50	42	50	24	**17**			
18 *Mull of Kintyre*	387	311	295	232	212	189	203	159	140	111	112	103	99	89	98	70	51	**18**		
19 *Altacarry Head*	379	303	287	224	204	181	197	151	132	103	104	95	91	92	101	73	54	12	**19**	
20 *Tory Island*	385	309	293	230	210	187	203	170	138	132	95	113	110	115	143	114	110	86	74	**20**

STORNOWAY 10-8-7

Lewis (Outer Hebrides)

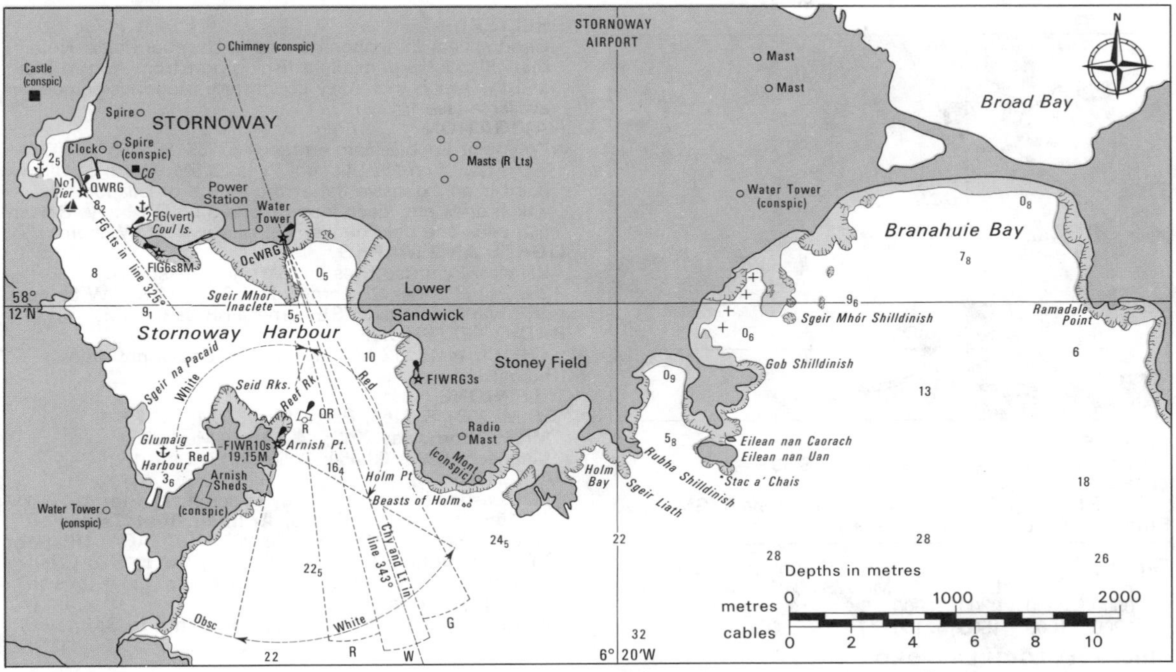
STORNOWAY AIRPORT
Chimney (conspic)
Castle (conspic)
Spire
STORNOWAY
Clock
Spire (conspic)
CG
No 1 Pier
QWRG
Power Station
Water Tower
2FG(vert)
Coul Is.
FIG6s8M
FG Lts in line 325°
OcWRG
Masts (R Lts)
Mast
Mast
Broad Bay
Water Tower (conspic)
Branahuie Bay
Lower
Sandwick
Sgeir Mhor Inaclete
58° 12'N
Stornoway Harbour
Sgeir na Pacaid
White
Seid Rks.
Reef Rk.
QR
R
Red
FIWRG3s
Stoney Field
Radio Mast
Mont (conspic)
Glumaig Harbour
FIWR10s 19.15M
Arnish Pt.
Arnish Sheds (conspic)
Holm Pt
Beasts of Holm
Holm Bay
Water Tower (conspic)
Chy and Lt in line 343°
Obsc
White
R
W
G
Sgeir Mhór Shilldinish
Gob Shilldinish
Ramadale Point
Eilean nan Caorach
Eilean nan Uan
Stac a' Chais
Rubha Shilldinish
Sgeir Liath
6° 20'W
Depths in metres
metres 0 1000 2000
cables 0 2 4 6 8 10
N

8

CHARTS
Admiralty 2529, 1794; OS 8

TIDES
−0428 Dover; ML 2.9; Duration 0610; Zone 0 (GMT).

Standard Port ULLAPOOL (⟶)

Times				Height (metres)			
HW		LW		MHWS	MHWN	MLWN	MLWS
0100	0700	0300	0900	5.2	3.9	2.1	0.7
1300	1900	1500	2100				
Differences STORNOWAY							
−0010	−0010	−0010	−0010	−0.4	−0.2	−0.1	0.0
LOCH ERIBOLL (Portnancon)							
+0055	+0105	+0055	+0100	0.0	+0.1	+0.1	+0.2
KYLE OF DURNESS							
+0030	+0030	+0050	+0050	−0.6	−0.4	−0.3	−0.1
LOCH SHELL (Hebrides)							
−0023	−0010	−0010	−0027	−0.4	−0.3	−0.2	0.0
EAST LOCH TARBERT (Hebrides)							
−0035	−0020	−0020	−0030	−0.2	−0.2	0.0	+0.1
LOCH MADDY (Hebrides)							
−0054	−0024	−0026	−0040	−0.4	−0.3	−0.2	0.0
LOCH SKIPORT (Hebrides)							
−0110	−0035	−0034	−0034	−0.6	−0.6	−0.4	−0.2
LOCH BOISDALE (Hebrides)							
−0105	−0040	−0030	−0050	−1.1	−0.9	−0.4	−0.2
CASTLEBAY (Hebrides)							
−0125	−0050	−0055	−0110	−0.9	−0.8	−0.4	−0.1
BARRA HEAD (Hebrides)							
−0125	−0050	−0055	−0105	−1.2	−0.9	−0.3	+0.1
WEST LOCH TARBERT (Hebrides)							
−0103	−0043	−0024	−0044	−1.0	−0.7	−0.8	−0.3
LITTLE BERNERA (Hebrides)							
−0031	−0021	−0027	−0037	−0.9	−0.8	−0.5	−0.2
CARLOWAY (Hebrides)							
−0050	+0010	−0045	−0025	−1.0	−0.7	−0.5	−0.1

Standard Port ULLAPOOL (⟶)

Times				Height (metres)			
HW		LW		MHWS	MHWN	MLWN	MLWS
0000	0600	0300	0900	5.2	3.9	2.1	0.7
1200	1800	1500	2100				
VILLAGE BAY (St Kilda)							
−0110	−0040	−0100	−0100	−1.9	−1.4	−0.9	−0.3
FLANNAN ISLES							
−0036	−0026	−0026	−0036	−1.3	−0.9	−0.7	−0.2
ROCKALL							
−0115	−0115	−0125	−0125	−2.4	−1.8	−1.0	−0.3

SHELTER
Good except S swells make the anchorages uncomfortable. Anchorages: Poll nam Portan opposite commercial quays, clear of LB moorings; Glumaig Harbour in W sector is best anchorage but oil industry works may preclude this; Eilean na Gobhail in bay NW of island; or yachts can go alongside Cromwell Street Quay. It is possible to berth alongside fishing boats in the inner harbour. Visitors land at steps N of FG Ldg Lts and report to Hr Mr or enter Inner Harbour and berth at Cromwell St quay.

NAVIGATION
Waypoint 58°10′.00N 06°20′.80W, 163°/343° from/to Oc WRG Lt, 2.3M. Reef rocks, W side of entrance marked by lighted R can buoy. The rocky patch off Holm Point is marked by an unlit R beacon. Ferries to Ullapool use the harbour. A local magnetic anomaly exists over a small area 1.75 ca N of Seid Rks.

LIGHTS AND MARKS
Arnish Point Fl WR 10s 17m 19/15M; W Tr; vis W088°−198°, R198°−302°, W302°−013°. R can buoy QR marking Reef Rock. Stoney Field Fl WRG 3s 8m 11M; vis G shore−073°, R073°−102°, W102°−109°, G109°−shore. Sandwick Bay, NW side (close E of power station and water Tr) Oc WRG 6s 10m 9M; vis G334°−341°, W341°−347°, R347°−354°; in line with conspic chy bears 343°. Ldg Lts 325° to Ro Ro jetty, both FG. No 1 Pier Q WRG 5m 11M, R shore −352°, W352°-335°, G335°-shore.

RADIO TELEPHONE
VHF Ch 16; 12 (H24)

TELEPHONE (0851)
Hr Mr 2688; MRSC 2013; # 3626; Marinecall 0898 500 464; Police 2222; Dr 3145

FACILITIES
EC Wednesday; **Pier N end of Bay** FW, C(10 ton), CH, AB; **W Pier** Slip, P, FW; **Steamer Pier** FW; **Duncan MacIver** ☎ 2010 CH, ACA; **Electronic Services** ☎ 2909 El, Ⓔ; **Stornoway Boatbuilding Co.** ☎ 3488, ME, El, Sh; **Town** P, D, El, V, R, Bar, Gas, ✉; Ⓑ; ⇌ (ferry to Ullapool, bus to Garve); ✈.

ULLAPOOL 10-8-8

Ross and Cromarty

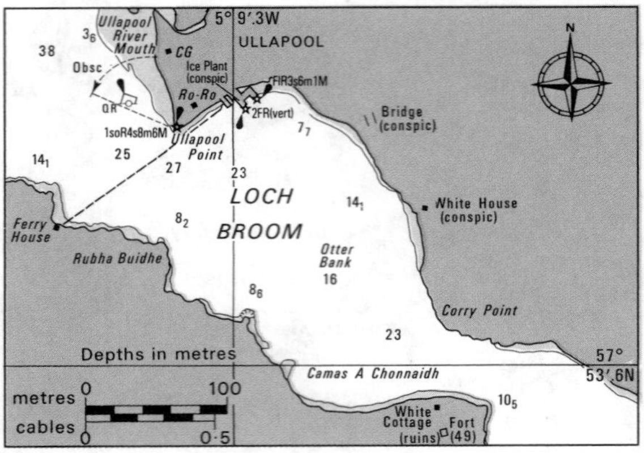
5° 9'.3W
ULLAPOOL
Ullapool River Mouth
CG
Ice Plant (conspic)
Ro-Ro
Obsc
QR
FlR3s6m1M
2FR(vert)
IsoR4s8m6M
Ullapool Point
Bridge (conspic)
LOCH BROOM
White House (conspic)
Otter Bank
Ferry House
Rubha Buidhe
Corry Point
Camas A Chonnaidh
White Cottage
Fort (ruins) (49)
Depths in metres
57° 53'.6N
metres 0 100
cables 0 0·5

CHARTS

Admiralty 2500, 2501, 2509, 1791; OS 19

TIDES

−0415 Dover; ML 3.0; Duration 0610; Zone 0 (GMT).

Standard Port ULLAPOOL (⟶)

Times				Height (metres)			
HW		LW		MHWS	MHWN	MLWN	MLWS
0000	0600	0300	0900	5.2	3.9	2.1	0.7
1200	1800	1500	2100				
Differences LOCH LAXFORD							
+0015	+0015	+0005	+0005	−0.3	−0.4	−0.2	0.0
LOCH BERVIE							
+0030	+0010	+0010	+0020	−0.3	−0.3	−0.2	0.0
LOCH INVER							
−0005	−0005	−0005	−0005	−0.2	0.0	0.0	+0.1
BADCALL BAY							
+0005	+0005	+0005	+0005	−0.7	−0.5	−0.5	+0.2
LOCH EWE (Mellon Charles)							
−0010	−0010	−0010	−0010	−0.1	−0.1	−0.1	0.0
LOCH GAIRLOCH							
−0020	−0020	−0010	−0010	0.0	+0.1	−0.3	−0.1
SUMMER ISLES (Tanera Mor)							
−0005	−0005	−0010	−0010	−0.1	+0.1	0.0	+0.1

Ullapool is a Standard Port and detailed tidal predictions for each day of the year are given below.

SHELTER

Good shelter in anchorage behind Ullapool Point. Note that Ullapool is primarily a fishing port from Aug to Mar and the pier is extremely congested. Moorings sometimes available (see Hr Mr).

NAVIGATION

Waypoint Loch Broom entrance 57°55'.80N 05°15'.00W, 309°/129° from/to Ullapool Pt Lt, 3.5M. North of Ullapool point is an extensive flat at the mouth of Ullapool River which dries out: deep water marked by QR buoy. Beware fish pens and unlit buoys S of narrows off W shore.

LIGHTS AND MARKS

Ullapool Point Iso R 4s 8m 6M; grey mast; vis 258° – 108°. Pier SE corner, Fl R 3s 6m 1M; SW corner 2FR (vert). Extension SE corner Fl R 3s 6m 1M.

RADIO TELEPHONE

VHF Ch 14 16; 12 (July-Nov: H24. Dec-June: office hours).

TELEPHONE (0854)

Hr Mr 2091 & 2165; Port Officer 2724; CG 2014; MRSC Stornoway 2013; # (Aug – Mar) 2253; Marinecall 0898 500 464; Police 2017; Dr 2015.

FACILITIES

EC Tuesday (but open all day in summer); **Pier** ☎ 2091 & 2165, D, L, FW, CH, AB; **Ardmair Boat Centre** ☎ 2054, Sh, CH; **Ullasport** ☎ 2621, CH, ACA; **Ullapool YC** Gas; **Highland Coastal Trading Co** ☎ 2488 CH; **Village** P, ⊡, ME, El, Ⓔ, V, R, Bar. ✉; Ⓑ; ≷ (bus to Garve); ✈ (Inverness).

Note: daily buses to Inverness and ferries to Stornoway.

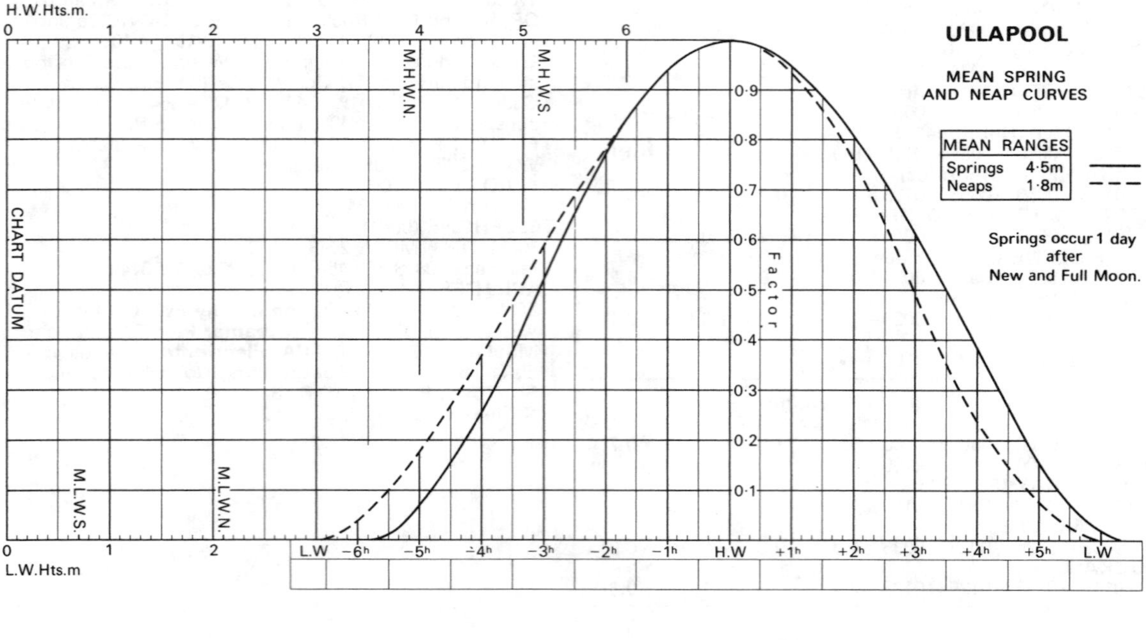
ULLAPOOL
MEAN SPRING AND NEAP CURVES
MEAN RANGES
Springs 4·5m
Neaps 1·8m
Springs occur 1 day after New and Full Moon.
H.W.Hts.m.
L.W.Hts.m
CHART DATUM
M.H.W.N.
M.H.W.S.
M.L.W.S.
M.L.W.N.
Factor
L.W −6h −5h −4h −3h −2h −1h H.W +1h +2h +3h +4h +5h L.W

SCOTLAND, WEST COAST - ULLAPOOL

TIME ZONE **UT(GMT)**

For Summer Time add ONE hour in non-shaded areas

LAT 57°54'N **LONG 5°10'W**

TIMES AND HEIGHTS OF HIGH AND LOW WATERS

YEAR **1992**

JANUARY

Day	Time	m	Day	Time	m
1 W	0435 1049 1704 2315	4.2 1.9 4.2 1.7	**16** TH	0342 1000 1608 2223	4.2 2.0 4.4 1.7
2 TH	0521 1141 1748 2358	4.4 1.7 4.2 1.6	**17** F	0439 1106 1705 2322	4.5 1.6 4.6 1.4
3 F	0600 1223 1826	4.6 1.5 4.3	**18** SA	0529 1200 1756	4.9 1.1 4.9
4 SA ●	0036 0635 1301 1858	1.5 4.7 1.4 4.4	**19** SU ○	0013 0615 1249 1843	1.1 5.2 0.7 5.1
5 SU	0112 0708 1336 1930	1.4 4.9 1.3 4.5	**20** M	0101 0700 1335 1929	0.8 5.4 0.4 5.2
6 M	0146 0741 1410 2002	1.3 5.0 1.2 4.5	**21** TU	0146 0744 1419 2015	0.6 5.6 0.2 5.3
7 TU	0219 0813 1444 2035	1.3 5.0 1.1 4.5	**22** W	0229 0828 1503 2100	0.5 5.5 0.2 5.1
8 W	0253 0847 1517 2108	1.3 5.0 1.2 4.5	**23** TH	0313 0912 1547 2146	0.6 5.4 0.3 4.9
9 TH	0327 0920 1552 2143	1.4 4.8 1.2 4.4	**24** F	0356 0957 1632 2234	0.8 5.1 0.6 4.6
10 F	0402 0956 1628 2221	1.5 4.7 1.4 4.2	**25** SA	0441 1046 1719 2330	1.1 4.7 1.0 4.3
11 SA	0440 1034 1707 2304	1.7 4.5 1.5 4.1	**26** SU ☾	0528 1146 1809	1.4 4.3 1.4
12 SU	0521 1120 1751 2358	1.9 4.3 1.7 4.0	**27** M	0038 0620 1310 1909	4.0 1.8 4.0 1.8
13 M ☽	0610 1221 1844	2.1 4.1 1.9	**28** TU	0159 0729 1440 2028	3.9 2.1 3.8 2.1
14 TU	0111 0712 1341 1949	3.9 2.2 4.1 2.0	**29** W	0313 0911 1553 2156	3.9 2.2 3.8 2.1
15 W	0233 0834 1501 2109	4.0 2.2 4.1 1.9	**30** TH	0414 1041 1651 2301	4.0 2.1 3.9 2.0
			31 F	0503 1136 1736 2346	4.2 1.9 4.0 1.8

FEBRUARY

Day	Time	m	Day	Time	m
1 SA	0543 1215 1812	4.4 1.6 4.2	**16** SU	0513 1149 1743	4.8 1.0 4.8
2 SU	0023 0617 1249 1843	1.6 4.7 1.4 4.4	**17** M	0000 0559 1236 1828	1.1 5.2 0.5 5.1
3 M ●	0057 0649 1320 1912	1.4 4.9 1.2 4.5	**18** TU ○	0046 0643 1319 1911	0.7 5.4 0.2 5.3
4 TU	0128 0719 1350 1941	1.2 5.0 1.0 4.6	**19** W	0129 0725 1400 1953	0.4 5.6 0.0 5.3
5 W	0159 0749 1420 2010	1.1 5.1 0.9 4.7	**20** TH	0210 0806 1441 2034	0.3 5.5 0.0 5.2
6 TH	0230 0819 1451 2039	1.1 5.1 0.9 4.7	**21** F	0251 0846 1522 2115	0.4 5.3 0.2 5.0
7 F	0302 0850 1523 2110	1.1 5.0 0.9 4.6	**22** SA	0331 0927 1602 2157	0.6 5.0 0.6 4.7
8 SA	0335 0922 1556 2142	1.2 4.9 1.1 4.5	**23** SU	0412 1010 1644 2243	0.9 4.6 1.0 4.3
9 SU	0410 0956 1632 2218	1.4 4.7 1.3 4.3	**24** M	0455 1059 1728 2343	1.3 4.2 1.5 4.0
10 M	0448 1037 1713 2303	1.6 4.4 1.5 4.1	**25** TU ☾	0543 1223 1819	1.8 3.8 2.0
11 TU ☽	0533 1132 1801	1.9 4.2 1.8	**26** W	0113 0645 1412 1935	3.8 2.2 3.6 2.3
12 W	0012 0631 1304 1903	4.0 2.1 4.0 2.0	**27** TH	0238 0840 1530 2129	3.8 2.4 3.6 2.3
13 TH	0156 0756 1442 2031	3.9 2.2 4.0 2.1	**28** F	0345 1029 1630 2243	3.9 2.2 3.7 2.1
14 F	0319 0941 1555 2204	4.1 2.0 4.2 1.9	**29** SA	0437 1120 1715 2327	4.1 1.9 3.9 1.9
15 SA	0421 1055 1653 2309	4.5 1.5 4.5 1.5			

MARCH

Day	Time	m	Day	Time	m
1 SU	0517 1155 1749	4.4 1.6 4.2	**16** M	0454 1131 1725 2343	4.8 0.8 4.8 1.0
2 M	0002 0551 1225 1818	1.6 4.6 1.3 4.4	**17** TU	0540 1215 1808	5.1 0.4 5.0
3 TU	0034 0622 1254 1845	1.3 4.8 1.0 4.6	**18** W ○	0026 0622 1257 1849	0.6 5.3 0.2 5.2
4 W ●	0104 0651 1322 1912	1.1 5.0 0.9 4.7	**19** TH	0108 0703 1337 1928	0.4 5.4 0.1 5.2
5 TH	0133 0720 1351 1940	1.0 5.1 0.7 4.8	**20** F	0148 0742 1416 2006	0.3 5.3 0.1 5.1
6 F	0204 0750 1421 2008	0.9 5.1 0.7 4.8	**21** SA	0227 0821 1454 2044	0.4 5.1 0.4 4.9
7 SA	0235 0820 1453 2038	0.9 5.0 0.8 4.8	**22** SU	0306 0859 1532 2123	0.6 4.8 0.7 4.7
8 SU	0309 0852 1527 2109	1.0 4.9 0.9 4.7	**23** M	0346 0939 1611 2204	0.9 4.4 1.2 4.4
9 M	0344 0927 1603 2145	1.2 4.7 1.2 4.5	**24** TU	0427 1025 1651 2257	1.3 4.0 1.6 4.0
10 TU	0424 1010 1644 2229	1.4 4.4 1.5 4.3	**25** W	0513 1141 1739	1.8 3.7 2.0
11 W	0510 1111 1733 2340	1.7 4.1 1.8 4.0	**26** TH ☾	0022 0612 1335 1846	3.8 2.1 3.5 2.4
12 TH ☽	0610 1256 1837	1.9 3.9 2.1	**27** F	0154 0756 1455 2044	3.7 2.3 3.5 2.4
13 F	0135 0740 1432 2011	3.9 2.0 4.0 2.1	**28** SA	0304 0951 1555 2208	3.8 2.1 3.7 2.2
14 SA	0300 0928 1541 2148	4.1 1.8 4.2 1.9	**29** SU	0358 1044 1640 2255	4.0 1.9 3.9 1.9
15 SU	0402 1039 1636 2253	4.4 1.3 4.5 1.5	**30** M	0441 1120 1715 2331	4.2 1.6 4.1 1.6
			31 TU	0517 1150 1745	4.5 1.3 4.4

APRIL

Day	Time	m	Day	Time	m
1 W	0003 0548 1220 1812	1.4 4.7 1.0 4.6	**16** TH	0005 0602 1234 1826	0.7 5.0 0.4 5.0
2 TH	0034 0619 1249 1841	1.1 4.8 0.8 4.8	**17** F ○	0046 0642 1313 1904	0.6 5.1 0.3 5.0
3 F ●	0105 0650 1320 1910	1.0 5.0 0.7 4.9	**18** SA	0126 0721 1351 1941	0.5 5.0 0.4 5.0
4 SA	0137 0722 1352 1940	0.9 5.0 0.7 4.9	**19** SU	0205 0800 1428 2018	0.6 4.8 0.7 4.9
5 SU	0211 0755 1426 2012	0.9 5.0 0.8 4.9	**20** M	0244 0838 1506 2057	0.8 4.6 1.0 4.7
6 M	0247 0832 1502 2047	0.9 4.9 0.9 4.8	**21** TU	0324 0918 1543 2138	1.0 4.3 1.3 4.4
7 TU	0325 0912 1542 2127	1.1 4.7 1.2 4.6	**22** W	0405 1005 1624 2227	1.4 4.0 1.7 4.2
8 W	0409 1003 1626 2217	1.3 4.4 1.5 4.3	**23** TH	0451 1111 1709 2335	1.7 3.7 2.0 3.9
9 TH	0500 1117 1718 2337	1.5 4.1 1.8 4.1	**24** F ☾	0546 1243 1809	2.0 3.5 2.2
10 F ☽	0604 1254 1825	1.7 3.9 2.0	**25** SA	0058 0703 1402 1936	3.8 2.1 3.5 2.4
11 SA	0119 0732 1416 1955	4.0 1.8 4.0 2.0	**26** SU	0210 0838 1504 2108	3.8 2.1 3.7 2.2
12 SU	0237 0906 1521 2125	4.2 1.6 4.2 1.8	**27** M	0308 0946 1552 2207	3.9 1.9 3.8 2.0
13 M	0339 1015 1616 2230	4.4 1.2 4.4 1.4	**28** TU	0355 1031 1632 2250	4.1 1.6 4.1 1.7
14 TU	0432 1107 1703 2320	4.7 0.8 4.7 1.0	**29** W	0436 1107 1706 2326	4.3 1.4 4.3 1.5
15 W	0519 1152 1746	4.9 0.5 4.9	**30** TH	0512 1141 1738	4.5 1.2 4.5

Chart Datum: 2.75 metres below Ordnance Datum (Newlyn)

SCOTLAND, WEST COAST - ULLAPOOL

TIME ZONE UT(GMT)

For Summer Time add ONE hour in non-shaded areas

LAT 57°54′N LONG 5°10′W

TIMES AND HEIGHTS OF HIGH AND LOW WATERS

YEAR **1992**

MAY

Day		Moon	Time	m	Time	m	Time	m	Time	m
1	F		0001	1.3	0547	4.7	1216	1.0	1810	4.7
2	SA	●	0036	1.1	0623	4.8	1250	0.9	1843	4.9
3	SU		0113	0.9	0700	4.9	1327	0.8	1918	5.0
4	M		0151	0.8	0739	4.9	1405	0.8	1955	5.0
5	TU		0231	0.8	0822	4.8	1445	0.9	2036	4.9
6	W		0315	0.9	0911	4.7	1529	1.1	2123	4.7
7	TH		0402	1.1	1008	4.4	1617	1.4	2220	4.5
8	F		0456	1.2	1120	4.2	1711	1.6	2334	4.3
9	SA	☽	0600	1.4	1239	4.1	1815	1.8		
10	SU		0056	4.2	0715	1.5	1352	4.1	1932	1.8
11	M		0211	4.2	0835	1.4	1456	4.2	2053	1.7
12	TU		0315	4.4	0944	1.2	1552	4.3	2201	1.5
13	W		0411	4.5	1040	1.0	1642	4.5	2256	1.2
14	TH		0501	4.6	1128	0.8	1726	4.7	2344	1.0
15	F		0546	4.7	1211	0.7	1807	4.8		
16	SA	○	0027	0.9	0628	4.7	1251	0.7	1845	4.8
17	SU		0109	0.8	0707	4.7	1330	0.8	1923	4.9
18	M		0149	0.8	0746	4.6	1407	1.0	2000	4.8
19	TU		0228	0.9	0825	4.4	1445	1.1	2039	4.7
20	W		0308	1.1	0905	4.2	1523	1.4	2119	4.5
21	TH		0348	1.3	0949	4.0	1602	1.6	2204	4.4
22	F		0431	1.5	1040	3.9	1645	1.8	2256	4.2
23	SA		0519	1.7	1142	3.7	1734	2.0	2356	4.0
24	SU	☾	0613	1.9	1251	3.6	1834	2.2		
25	M		0102	3.9	0717	1.9	1357	3.7	1946	2.2
26	TU		0206	3.9	0826	1.9	1454	3.8	2058	2.1
27	W		0302	4.0	0927	1.8	1543	4.0	2157	1.9
28	TH		0352	4.2	1018	1.6	1626	4.2	2246	1.7
29	F		0437	4.3	1102	1.4	1706	4.4	2330	1.5
30	SA		0520	4.5	1144	1.2	1745	4.7		
31	SU		0012	1.2	0603	4.7	1226	1.0	1824	4.9

JUNE

Day		Moon	Time	m	Time	m	Time	m	Time	m
1	M	●	0054	1.0	0646	4.9	1308	0.9	1904	5.0
2	TU		0137	0.8	0731	4.9	1350	0.9	1947	5.1
3	W		0221	0.7	0818	4.9	1434	0.9	2032	5.1
4	TH		0307	0.7	0909	4.8	1520	1.0	2120	5.0
5	F		0356	0.7	1003	4.6	1608	1.1	2214	4.8
6	SA		0448	0.9	1104	4.4	1700	1.3	2316	4.6
7	SU	☽	0544	1.0	1210	4.3	1757	1.5		
8	M		0026	4.4	0646	1.2	1320	4.1	1901	1.6
9	TU		0140	4.2	0756	1.3	1426	4.1	2014	1.7
10	W		0250	4.2	0908	1.4	1528	4.2	2129	1.7
11	TH		0353	4.2	1012	1.3	1622	4.3	2234	1.5
12	F		0449	4.3	1107	1.3	1711	4.4	2328	1.3
13	SA		0538	4.4	1153	1.2	1754	4.6		
14	SU		0015	1.2	0621	4.4	1236	1.2	1833	4.7
15	M	○	0058	1.1	0700	4.4	1315	1.1	1911	4.8
16	TU		0137	1.0	0737	4.4	1352	1.2	1947	4.8
17	W		0215	1.0	0812	4.4	1428	1.2	2023	4.8
18	TH		0253	1.1	0848	4.4	1504	1.3	2059	4.7
19	F		0330	1.1	0925	4.3	1541	1.4	2137	4.6
20	SA		0407	1.3	1004	4.1	1619	1.5	2218	4.4
21	SU		0446	1.4	1047	4.0	1659	1.7	2302	4.3
22	M		0528	1.6	1137	3.9	1744	1.9	2353	4.1
23	TU	☾	0615	1.8	1236	3.8	1836	2.1		
24	W		0054	4.0	0709	1.9	1343	3.8	1939	2.2
25	TH		0203	3.9	0813	1.9	1449	3.9	2054	2.1
26	F		0308	4.0	0923	1.9	1547	4.1	2205	2.0
27	SA		0407	4.2	1026	1.7	1638	4.3	2303	1.7
28	SU		0500	4.4	1119	1.5	1725	4.6	2354	1.3
29	M		0550	4.7	1208	1.2	1810	4.9		
30	TU	●	0041	1.0	0636	4.9	1254	1.0	1853	5.1

JULY

Day		Moon	Time	m	Time	m	Time	m	Time	m
1	W		0126	0.7	0722	5.1	1339	0.8	1937	5.3
2	TH		0211	0.5	0809	5.1	1423	0.7	2022	5.3
3	F		0256	0.3	0856	5.1	1508	0.7	2108	5.3
4	SA		0342	0.4	0944	4.9	1553	0.8	2156	5.1
5	SU		0430	0.5	1036	4.7	1640	1.0	2248	4.8
6	M		0519	0.8	1133	4.4	1730	1.2	2349	4.5
7	TU	☽	0613	1.1	1239	4.2	1826	1.5		
8	W		0104	4.2	0715	1.5	1353	4.0	1933	1.8
9	TH		0226	4.0	0829	1.7	1504	4.0	2056	1.9
10	F		0340	4.0	0947	1.8	1607	4.1	2220	1.8
11	SA		0443	4.0	1053	1.7	1700	4.2	2323	1.7
12	SU		0534	4.1	1144	1.6	1745	4.4		
13	M		0011	1.5	0616	4.3	1226	1.4	1823	4.6
14	TU	○	0051	1.3	0652	4.4	1303	1.3	1858	4.8
15	W		0127	1.1	0723	4.5	1337	1.2	1931	4.9
16	TH		0200	1.0	0754	4.5	1410	1.1	2003	4.9
17	F		0233	1.0	0824	4.6	1443	1.1	2035	4.9
18	SA		0305	1.0	0855	4.5	1516	1.2	2107	4.9
19	SU		0338	1.0	0927	4.5	1549	1.3	2141	4.7
20	M		0411	1.2	1001	4.3	1624	1.5	2216	4.5
21	TU		0447	1.4	1038	4.2	1701	1.7	2256	4.3
22	W	☾	0526	1.6	1122	4.0	1744	1.9	2347	4.1
23	TH		0612	1.8	1224	3.9	1838	2.1		
24	F		0102	3.9	0710	2.0	1352	3.8	1952	2.3
25	SA		0232	3.9	0829	2.1	1515	4.0	2128	2.1
26	SU		0346	4.1	0956	2.0	1618	4.3	2245	1.8
27	M		0446	4.4	1102	1.7	1709	4.6	2341	1.3
28	TU		0537	4.7	1155	1.3	1756	5.0		
29	W	●	0029	0.9	0623	5.0	1241	0.9	1839	5.3
30	TH		0113	0.5	0707	5.2	1325	0.6	1922	5.5
31	F		0157	0.2	0751	5.3	1408	0.4	2004	5.6

AUGUST

Day		Moon	Time	m	Time	m	Time	m	Time	m
1	SA		0239	0.1	0834	5.3	1450	0.4	2047	5.5
2	SU		0322	0.1	0917	5.1	1532	0.5	2131	5.3
3	M		0405	0.4	1003	4.9	1616	0.7	2217	4.9
4	TU		0450	0.8	1052	4.5	1701	1.1	2310	4.5
5	W	☽	0538	1.2	1153	4.2	1751	1.5		
6	TH		0025	4.1	0632	1.7	1315	3.9	1851	1.9
7	F		0205	3.8	0746	2.0	1440	3.8	2025	2.2
8	SA		0329	3.8	0927	2.2	1551	3.9	2217	2.1
9	SU		0435	3.9	1046	2.0	1647	4.1	2322	1.8
10	M		0526	4.0	1136	1.8	1732	4.4		
11	TU		0004	1.6	0604	4.2	1214	1.6	1808	4.6
12	W		0038	1.3	0635	4.4	1247	1.3	1839	4.8
13	TH	○	0109	1.1	0702	4.6	1318	1.1	1908	5.0
14	F		0138	0.9	0729	4.7	1348	1.0	1937	5.1
15	SA		0207	0.8	0756	4.8	1417	1.0	2006	5.1
16	SU		0236	0.8	0823	4.8	1448	1.0	2036	5.0
17	M		0306	0.9	0852	4.7	1519	1.1	2106	4.9
18	TU		0338	1.0	0921	4.6	1551	1.3	2137	4.7
19	W		0411	1.3	0953	4.4	1626	1.5	2212	4.5
20	TH		0447	1.5	1029	4.2	1706	1.8	2257	4.2
21	F	☾	0530	1.8	1121	4.0	1756	2.1		
22	SA		0014	3.9	0625	2.1	1302	3.8	1909	2.3
23	SU		0209	3.9	0747	2.3	1450	4.0	2104	2.2
24	M		0331	4.1	0934	2.1	1559	4.3	2231	1.8
25	TU		0431	4.4	1047	1.7	1652	4.7	2327	1.2
26	W		0521	4.8	1139	1.2	1738	5.1		
27	TH		0013	0.7	0605	5.1	1225	0.8	1821	5.4
28	F	●	0056	0.3	0647	5.4	1307	0.4	1902	5.6
29	SA		0137	0.0	0728	5.5	1348	0.2	1943	5.7
30	SU		0217	0.0	0808	5.4	1428	0.2	2023	5.6
31	M		0257	0.1	0849	5.3	1508	0.4	2104	5.3

Chart Datum: 2.75 metres below Ordnance Datum (Newlyn)

SCOTLAND, WEST COAST - ULLAPOOL

TIME ZONE UT(GMT)

For Summer Time add ONE hour in non-shaded areas

LAT 57°54′N LONG 5°10′W

TIMES AND HEIGHTS OF HIGH AND LOW WATERS

YEAR 1992

SEPTEMBER

Day	Time	m	Day	Time	m
1 TU	0338 0930 1549 2146	0.4 5.0 0.7 4.9	16 W	0307 0849 1524 2107	1.0 4.8 1.2 4.8
2 W	0419 1013 1632 2233	0.9 4.6 1.1 4.4	17 TH	0341 0920 1600 2144	1.2 4.6 1.5 4.6
3 TH	0503 1107 1718 ☽ 2343	1.4 4.2 1.6 4.0	18 F	0418 0956 1641 2231	1.5 4.4 1.7 4.3
4 F	0553 1232 1816	1.9 3.9 2.1	19 SA	0502 1048 1734 ☾ 2358	1.9 4.1 2.0 4.0
5 SA	0141 0703 1411 1956	3.7 2.3 3.8 2.4	20 SU	0559 1235 1851	2.2 3.9 2.2
6 SU	0311 0904 1527 2210	3.7 2.4 3.9 2.2	21 M	0154 0723 1427 2047	3.9 2.3 4.0 2.1
7 M	0418 1031 1625 2309	3.8 2.2 4.1 1.9	22 TU	0312 0913 1536 2212	4.1 2.2 4.3 1.7
8 TU	0506 1118 1709 2345	4.0 1.9 4.4 1.6	23 W	0411 1027 1630 2307	4.5 1.7 4.7 1.1
9 W	0541 1153 1744	4.2 1.6 4.6	24 TH	0500 1119 1717 2352	4.8 1.2 5.1 0.7
10 TH	0014 0609 1223 1813	1.4 4.4 1.4 4.8	25 F	0544 1203 1801	5.1 0.8 5.4
11 F	0042 0634 1252 1841	1.1 4.6 1.1 5.0	26 SA	0033 0625 1245 ● 1841	0.3 5.3 0.5 5.6
12 SA	0110 0700 1321 ○ 1909	0.9 4.8 1.0 5.1	27 SU	0114 0705 1326 1921	0.1 5.5 0.3 5.6
13 SU	0137 0726 1350 1937	0.8 4.9 0.9 5.2	28 M	0153 0744 1405 2000	0.1 5.4 0.3 5.5
14 M	0206 0752 1419 2006	0.8 5.0 0.9 5.1	29 TU	0232 0822 1445 2040	0.3 5.3 0.5 5.2
15 TU	0236 0820 1451 2035	0.9 4.9 1.0 5.0	30 W	0311 0901 1526 2120	0.6 5.0 0.8 4.8

OCTOBER

Day	Time	m	Day	Time	m
1 TH	0351 0942 1607 2205	1.1 4.7 1.2 4.3	16 F	0319 0902 1544 2133	1.3 4.8 1.4 4.6
2 F	0432 1031 1653 2309	1.5 4.3 1.7 3.9	17 SA	0400 0944 1630 2230	1.5 4.6 1.6 4.3
3 SA ☽	0519 1147 1749	2.0 4.0 2.1	18 SU	0447 1044 1727 2359	1.8 4.3 1.9 4.1
4 SU	0104 0622 1329 1922	3.6 2.4 3.8 2.4	19 M ☾	0546 1224 1844	2.1 4.1 2.0
5 M	0236 0816 1449 2132	3.6 2.5 3.9 2.3	20 TU	0135 0707 1400 2023	4.0 2.2 4.2 1.9
6 TU	0343 0953 1549 2233	3.7 2.3 4.1 2.0	21 W	0249 0844 1510 2143	4.2 2.1 4.4 1.5
7 W	0432 1044 1634 2310	4.0 2.0 4.3 1.7	22 TH	0348 0959 1606 2240	4.5 1.7 4.7 1.1
8 TH	0508 1121 1710 2341	4.2 1.8 4.5 1.4	23 F	0438 1054 1656 2328	4.8 1.3 5.0 0.8
9 F	0537 1152 1741	4.4 1.5 4.7	24 SA	0523 1141 1741	5.0 0.9 5.2
10 SA	0009 0604 1222 1810	1.2 4.7 1.3 4.9	25 SU	0010 0604 1224 ● 1822	0.5 5.2 0.7 5.3
11 SU	0037 0630 1252 ○ 1840	1.0 4.8 1.1 5.1	26 M	0051 0644 1305 1903	0.4 5.3 0.5 5.3
12 M	0106 0657 1322 1909	0.9 5.0 1.0 5.1	27 TU	0131 0723 1346 1942	0.4 5.3 0.5 5.2
13 TU	0137 0725 1354 1941	0.9 5.0 1.0 5.1	28 W	0210 0801 1426 2022	0.6 5.2 0.7 5.0
14 W	0208 0755 1428 2014	0.9 5.0 1.0 5.0	29 TH	0248 0840 1507 2102	0.9 5.0 1.0 4.6
15 TH	0242 0827 1504 2050	1.0 5.0 1.2 4.9	30 F	0327 0921 1549 2146	1.2 4.7 1.3 4.3
			31 SA	0408 1007 1634 2243	1.6 4.5 1.7 3.9

NOVEMBER

Day	Time	m	Day	Time	m
1 SU	0452 1108 1727	2.0 4.2 2.0	16 M	0439 1045 1723 2348	1.6 4.5 1.5 4.2
2 M	0008 0547 1230 ☽ 1837	3.7 2.3 4.0 2.2	17 TU ☾	0537 1204 1831	1.8 4.4 1.6
3 TU	0139 0706 1350 2014	3.6 2.5 3.9 2.3	18 W	0107 0646 1328 1950	4.2 2.0 4.3 1.6
4 W	0250 0844 1455 2132	3.7 2.4 4.0 2.1	19 TH	0220 0807 1440 2107	4.2 1.9 4.4 1.5
5 TH	0344 0952 1547 2221	3.9 2.2 4.2 1.9	20 F	0322 0925 1542 2211	4.4 1.7 4.6 1.2
6 F	0426 1038 1629 2258	4.1 2.0 4.4 1.6	21 SA	0416 1027 1637 2303	4.6 1.5 4.8 1.0
7 SA	0501 1116 1706 2332	4.3 1.7 4.6 1.4	22 SU	0505 1120 1725 2349	4.8 1.2 4.9 0.9
8 SU	0532 1150 1740	4.6 1.5 4.8	23 M	0548 1206 1810	5.0 1.0 5.0
9 M	0004 0602 1224 1813	1.2 4.8 1.3 4.9	24 TU	0032 0629 1250 ● 1851	0.8 5.1 0.9 5.0
10 TU	0037 0633 1258 ○ 1847	1.1 5.0 1.1 5.0	25 W	0112 0708 1332 1931	0.8 5.1 0.8 4.9
11 W	0111 0705 1334 1923	1.0 5.1 1.1 5.1	26 TH	0151 0746 1412 2010	0.9 5.1 0.9 4.7
12 TH	0147 0739 1412 2002	1.0 5.1 1.0 5.0	27 F	0230 0825 1453 2049	1.1 5.0 1.1 4.5
13 F	0225 0816 1452 2045	1.1 5.1 1.1 4.9	28 SA	0308 0904 1534 2130	1.3 4.9 1.3 4.3
14 SA	0305 0857 1537 2134	1.2 4.9 1.2 4.7	29 SU	0347 0946 1616 2215	1.5 4.6 1.5 4.1
15 SU	0349 0945 1626 2233	1.4 4.8 1.4 4.4	30 M	0428 1033 1701 2310	1.8 4.4 1.7 3.9

DECEMBER

Day	Time	m	Day	Time	m
1 TU	0514 1128 1752	2.0 4.2 1.9	16 W ☾	0521 1137 1808	1.5 4.6 1.3
2 W	0019 0608 1235 ☽ 1853	3.7 2.2 4.0 2.1	17 TH	0034 0620 1253 1914	4.3 1.7 4.4 1.5
3 TH	0134 0716 1345 2003	3.7 2.3 4.0 2.1	18 F	0148 0730 1411 2028	4.2 1.8 4.3 1.5
4 F	0241 0835 1448 2111	3.8 2.3 4.0 2.0	19 SA	0256 0849 1522 2140	4.2 1.8 4.3 1.5
5 SA	0335 0943 1542 2206	4.0 2.2 4.2 1.9	20 SU	0357 1003 1623 2241	4.4 1.7 4.4 1.4
6 SU	0420 1035 1629 2251	4.2 2.0 4.4 1.7	21 M	0450 1105 1717 2333	4.5 1.5 4.5 1.3
7 M	0500 1119 1711 2332	4.4 1.7 4.6 1.5	22 TU	0537 1156 1803	4.7 1.3 4.6
8 TU	0537 1159 1752	4.7 1.5 4.8	23 W	0018 0618 1242 1844	1.2 4.9 1.1 4.6
9 W	0011 0613 1240 ○ 1831	1.3 4.9 1.3 4.9	24 TH	0059 0656 1323 ● 1922	1.1 5.0 1.0 4.6
10 TH	0051 0650 1320 1913	1.1 5.1 1.1 5.0	25 F	0137 0733 1402 1957	1.1 5.0 1.0 4.6
11 F	0131 0729 1402 1955	1.0 5.2 0.9 5.1	26 SA	0214 0808 1439 2032	1.1 5.0 1.0 4.5
12 SA	0213 0809 1445 2040	1.0 5.2 0.8 5.0	27 SU	0250 0844 1516 2107	1.2 5.0 1.1 4.4
13 SU	0256 0852 1530 2129	1.0 5.2 0.8 4.9	28 M	0326 0920 1553 2144	1.3 4.8 1.2 4.3
14 M	0341 0940 1618 2223	1.1 5.0 0.9 4.6	29 TU	0402 0958 1630 2224	1.5 4.7 1.4 4.1
15 TU	0429 1034 1710 2324	1.3 4.8 1.1 4.4	30 W	0441 1039 1710 2310	1.7 4.4 1.6 4.0
			31 TH	0523 1127 1754	1.9 4.2 1.8

8

Chart Datum: 2.75 metres below Ordnance Datum (Newlyn)

PORTREE 10-8-9

Skye

CHARTS

Admiralty 2534, 2209; Imray C66; OS 23

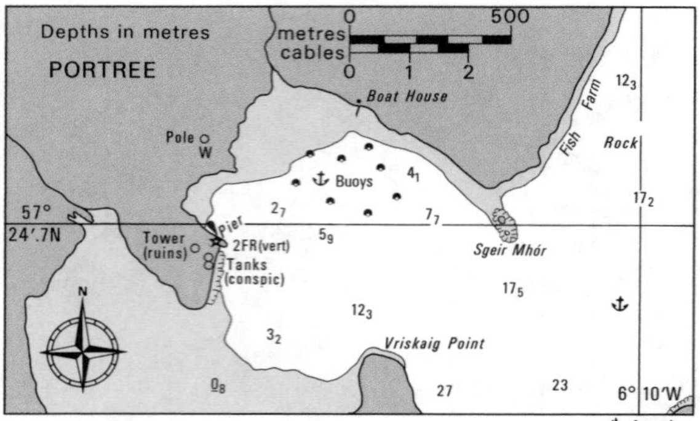

Depths in metres
PORTREE
metres
cables
0
500
0 1 2
Boat House
Pole
W
Buoys
Fish Farm
Rock
57° 24'.7N
Tower (ruins)
Pier
2FR(vert)
Tanks (conspic)
Sgeir Mhór
Vriskaig Point
6° 10'W

At pier

TIDES

−0445 Dover; ML 2.9; Duration 0610; Zone 0 (GMT).

Standard Port ULLAPOOL (←)

Times				Height (metres)			
HW		LW		MHWS	MHWN	MLWN	MLWS
0000	0600	0300	0900	5.2	3.9	2.1	0.7
1200	1800	1500	2100				
Differences PORTREE (Skye)							
−0025	−0025	−0025	−0025	+0.1	−0.2	−0.2	0.0
SHEILDAG (Loch Torridon)							
−0020	−0020	−0015	−0015	+0.4	+0.3	+0.1	0.0
PLOCKTON (Loch Carron)							
+0005	−0025	−0005	−0010	+0.5	+0.5	+0.5	+0.2
LOCH SNIZORT-(Uig Bay, Skye)							
−0045	−0020	−0005	−0025	+0.1	−0.4	−0.2	0.0
LOCH DUNVEGAN (Skye)							
−0105	−0030	−0020	−0040	0.0	−0.1	0.0	0.0
LOCH HARPORT (Skye)							
−0115	−0035	−0020	−0100	−0.1	−0.1	0.0	+0.1
KYLE OF LOCHALSH							
−0040	−0020	−0005	−0025	+0.1	0.0	+0.1	+0.1
GLENELG BAY (Kyle Rhea)							
−0105	−0034	−0034	−0054	−0.4	−0.4	−0.9	−0.1
LOCH HOURN							
−0125	−0050	−0040	−0110	−0.2	−0.1	−0.1	+0.1

SHELTER

Secure shelter in all but strong SW winds but holding ground not reliable. There are eight HIDB moorings for visitors for vessels up to 15 tons, in Portree. There are a number of anchorages round Skye, so choose one according to wind direction and forecast. There are four HIDB moorings off Stein in NW.

NAVIGATION

Waypoint 57°24′.70N 06°07′.50W, 090°/270° from/to Sgeir Mhor rock, 1.6M. Approaching from S, keep clear of shore round An Tom Pt (off chartlet) where there are rocks.

LIGHTS AND MARKS

The only lights in the harbour are 2 FR (vert) 6m 4M (occas) on the pier.

RADIO TELEPHONE

VHF Ch 16; 08 (occas).

TELEPHONE (0478)

Hr Mr office on pier ☎ 2926; MRSC Oban 63720; # Inverness 222787; Marinecall 0898 500 464; Police 2888; Dr 2013; Ⓗ 2704

FACILITIES

EC Wednesday; **Pier** D (cans), L, FW; **West End Garage** P, Gas; **Town** P, V, Gaz, ⊡, R, Bar. ✉; Ⓑ; ⇄ (bus to Kyleakin, ferry to Kyle of Lochalsh); ✈ (Inverness).

MALLAIG 10-8-10

Inverness

CHARTS

Admiralty 2541, 2208; Imray C65, C66; OS 40

TIDES

−0515 Dover; ML 2.9; Duration 0605; Zone 0 (GMT).

Standard Port OBAN (⟶)

Times				Height (metres)			
HW		LW		MHWS	MHWN	MLWN	MLWS
0000	0600	0100	0700	4.0	2.9	1.8	0.7
1200	1800	1300	1900				
Differences MALLAIG							
+0040	+0020	+0035	+0030	+1.0	+0.9	+0.3	0.0
INVERIE BAY							
+0030	+0020	+0035	+0020	+1.0	+0.9	+0.2	0.0
BAY OF LAIG (Eigg)							
+0015	+0030	+0040	+0005	+0.7	+0.6	−0.2	−0.2
LOCH MOIDART							
+0015	+0015	+0040	+0020	+0.8	+0.6	−0.2	−0.2
LOCH EATHARNA (Coll)							
+0025	+0010	+0015	+0025	+0.4	+0.3	No data	
GOTT BAY (Tiree)							
0000	+0010	+0005	+0010	0.0	+0.1	0.0	0.0

SHELTER

Good shelter in SW winds but open to the N. Anchor near the head or go alongside Fish Pier. Access H24.

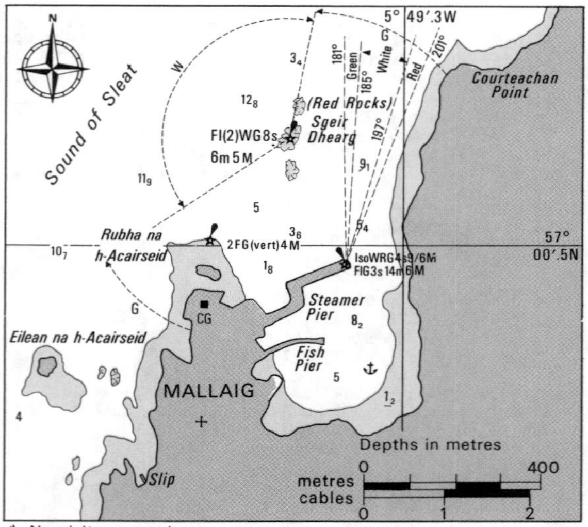

N
5° 49'.3W
Sound of Sleat
W
G
Green
White
Red
181°
185°
197°
201°
Courteachan Point
(Red Rocks)
Sgeir Dhearg
Fl(2)WG8s 6m5M
Rubha na h-Acairseid
2FG(vert)4M
IsoWRG4s9/6M
FlG3s14m6M
57° 00'.5N
Steamer Pier
CG
Eilean na h-Acairseid
Fish Pier
MALLAIG
Slip
Depths in metres
metres
cables
0
400
0 1 2

No visitors moorings

NAVIGATION

Waypoint 57°00′.70N 05°49′.80W, 330°/150° from/to Steamer Pier Lt, 0.28M. Red Rocks lie in entrance to the harbour (marked by beacon on centre rock) but can be passed either side, the E side being easier. Harbour is often congested with fishing boats. Also used by car ferry service to Skye.

LIGHTS AND MARKS

Sgeir Dhearg Fl(2)WG 8s 6m 5M; vis G190° − 055°, W055° − 190° (liable to be obsc by town lights). Steamer Pier, E end Iso WRG 4s 6m 9/6M; vis G181° − 185°, W185° − 197°, R197° − 201°. On same structure Fl G 3s 14m 6M. Int Port Traffic Sigs for ferries (May − Sep).

RADIO TELEPHONE

Call: *Mallaig Harbour Radio* VHF Ch 16; 09 (office hours).

TELEPHONE (0687)

Hr Mr 2154; MRSC Oban 63720; # Fort William 2948; Marinecall 0898 500 464; Police 2177; Dr 2202

FACILITIES

EC Wednesday; **Jetty** Slip, M, P, D, L, FW, ME, El, Sh, C (10 ton mobile), CH, AB; **Mallaig Boat Bldg Co.** ☎ 2304, ME, El, Sh, CH; **Western Battery Service** ☎ 2044, Ⓔ; **Johnson Bros** ☎ 2215 CH, ACA; **Town** V, R, Gas, Gaz, Bar. ✉; Ⓑ; ⇄; ✈ (Inverness).

LOCH SUNART (Drumbuie and Salen) 10-8-11

Argyll

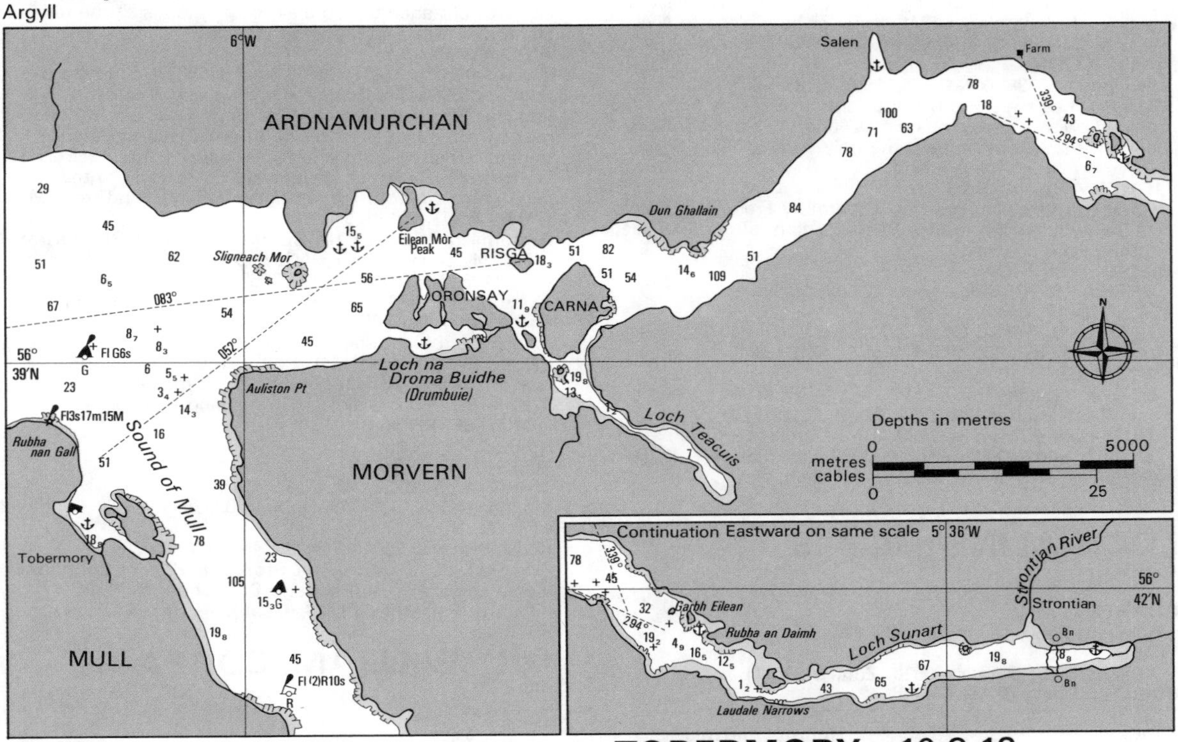

6°W
ARDNAMURCHAN
Salen
Farm
Dun Ghallain
Sligneach Mor
Eilean Mòr Peak
RISGA
ORONSAY
CARNA
083°
052°
339°
294°
56°
39'N
Fl G6s
Fl3s17m15M
Rubha nan Gall
Auliston Pt
Loch na Droma Buidhe (Drumbuie)
Loch Teacuis
Sound of Mull
MORVERN
Tobermory
MULL
Fl (2)R10s
Depths in metres
0
5000
metres
cables
0
25
Continuation Eastward on same scale
5° 36'W
Strontian River
Strontian
56°
42'N
Garbh Eilean
Rubha an Daimh
Loch Sunart
Laudale Narrows
Bn

CHARTS
Admiralty 2394, 2392, 2171; Imray C65; OS 45, 47, 49

TIDES
Salen −0500 Dover; ML 2.0; Zone 0 (GMT).

Standard Port OBAN (⟶)

Times				Height (metres)			
HW		LW		MHWS	MHWN	MLWN	MLWS
0100	0700	0100	0800	4.0	2.9	1.8	0.7
1300	1900	1300	2000				
Differences SALEN							
−0015	+0015	+0010	+0005	+0.6	+0.5	−0.1	−0.1

SHELTER
Anchorages in Loch na Droma Buidhe (S of Oronsay) sheltered in all winds, between Oronsay and Carna, in Loch Teacuis (very difficult entrance), E of Carna, Salen Bay, Garbh Eilean (NW of Rubha an Daimh), and E of sand spit near head of loch by Strontian R.

NAVIGATION
Waypoints – from W 56°39'.70N 06°03'.00W, 263°/083° from/to Creag nan Sgarbh 3.7M: from S 56°38'00N, 06°00'65W 1M to S of Auliston Pt. Beware Ross Rk S of Risga; Broad Rk E of Risga; Dun Ghallain Rk; shoals extending 3 ca NNW from Eilean mo Shlinneag off S shore; rk which dries 1 ca W of S end of Garbh Eilean and strong streams at sp in Laudale Narrows.

LIGHTS AND MARKS
There are no Lts. There are numbers of transits shown on the chart. Coming from S, Eilean Mor Peak at 052°; from W, Risga in line with N point of Oronsay at 083°. Further up the loch, 339° and 294°, as shown in chartlet are useful.

RADIO TELEPHONE
None.

TELEPHONE (096 785)
MRSC Oban 63720; # Oban 63079; Marinecall 0898 500 463; Ⓗ Fort William 2481; Dr 231.

FACILITIES
SALEN EC Monday **Jack Walters** ☎ 648, M, V, Gas; **The Jetty Shop** ☎ 648, CH, V, Gas, M, (ME, El, Sh, P, D by arrangement); **Conyer Marine** ☎ 654, M, ME, Sh, El, CH; **Salen Hotel** ☎ 661 R, Bar; **Village** V, FW (at pier), CH, ✉, Ⓑ (mobile Tues and Wed), ⇄ (bus to Loch Ailort), ✈ (Oban).
STRONTIAN V, hotel, ✉, Gas, Bar, FW.

TOBERMORY 10-8-12

Mull

CHARTS
Admiralty 2474, 2390, 2171; Imray C65; OS 47

TIDES
−0519 Dover; ML 2.5; Duration 0610; Zone 0 (GMT).

Standard Port OBAN (⟶)

Times				Height (metres)			
HW		LW		MHWS	MHWN	MLWN	MLWS
0100	0700	0100	0800	4.0	2.9	1.8	0.7
1300	1900	1300	2000				
Differences TOBERMORY (Mull)							
+0025	+0010	+0015	+0025	+0.4	+0.4	0.0	0.0
IONA (Mull)							
−0010	−0005	−0020	+0015	0.0	+0.1	−0.3	−0.2
LOCH LATHAICH (Bunessan, Mull)							
−0015	−0015	−0010	−0015	+0.3	+0.1	0.0	−0.1
ULVA SOUND (Mull)							
−0010	−0015	0000	−0005	+0.4	+0.3	0.0	−0.1

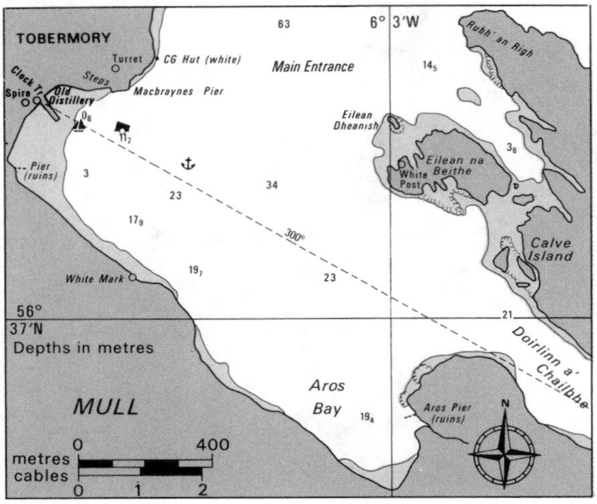

TOBERMORY
6° 3'W
Turret
CG Hut (white)
Main Entrance
Steps
Macbraynes Pier
Clock Tr
Spire
Old Distillery
Rubh' an Righ
Eilean Dheanish
Pier (ruins)
Eilean na Beithe
White Post
300°
Calve Island
White Mark
56°
37'N
Depths in metres
Doirlinn a' Chailbhe
Aros Bay
MULL
Aros Pier (ruins)
0
400
metres
cables
0
1
2

TOBERMORY *Continued*

SHELTER
Good except for some swell when strong winds from NW or N. Anchor off Old Distillery pierhead (where there are some Bu spherical mooring buoys marked 'HIDB visitors only'), off Aros pier in SW corner of bay, close to NW side of Calve Is or in bay at NW end of Calve Is.

NAVIGATION
Waypoint 56°38'.00N 06°02'.00W, 058°/238° from/to MacBraynes Pier, 1.1M. South entrance is only 80m wide at HW, with a dangerous wreck, and dries at LW. North entrance is recommended, the only danger being Sgeit Calve on NE of Calve Island.

LIGHTS AND MARKS
Coming up Doirlinn passage Tobermory Free Church spire in line with West entrance Pt to Doirlinn, about 300° leads through the channel.

RADIO TELEPHONE
VHF Ch 16; 12 (office hours. Listens only).

TELEPHONE (0688)
Hr Mr 2017; MRSC Oban 63720; ⌗ Oban 63079; Marinecall 0898 500 463; Police 2016; Dr 2013

FACILITIES
EC Wednesday; **Pier** P, FW, AB, V: **Seafare** (listens on Ch 16 office hours) ☎ 2277, M, P, D, Sh, CH, V, ACA; **Archebald Brown** ☎ 2020, FW, AB; **Western Isles YC** ☎ 2097; **Iain MacDonald** ☎ 2023 Gas. **Town** V, R, Bar, ✉; Ⓑ; ⊡, ⇌ (ferry to Oban); ✈ (Mull).

LOCH ALINE 10-8-13

Argyll

CHARTS
Admiralty 2390; Imray C65; OS 49

TIDES
−0523 Dover; Duration 0610; Zone 0 (GMT).

Standard Port OBAN (⟶)

Times				Height (metres)			
HW		LW		MHWS	MHWN	MLWN	MLWS
0100	0700	0100	0800	4.0	2.9	1.8	0.7
1300	1900	1300	2000				
Differences LOCH ALINE							
No data	+0012	+0012	No data	+0.5	+0.3	No data	No data
CRAIGNURE							
+0030	+0005	+0010	+0015	0.0	+0.1	−0.1	−0.1

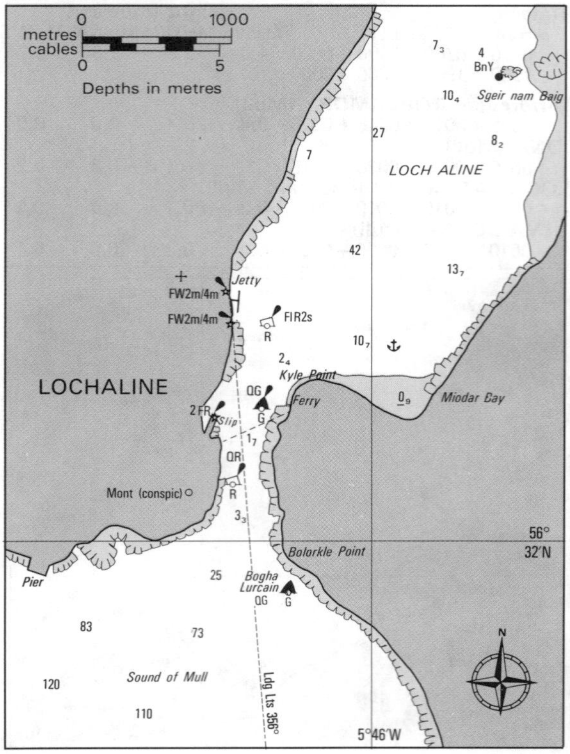
metres 0 1000
cables 0 5
Depths in metres
LOCH ALINE
Sgeir nam Baig
BnY
Jetty
FW2m/4m
FW2m/4m
FIR2s
LOCHALINE
Kyle Point
Ferry
Miodar Bay
2FR
Slip
QG
QR
Mont (conspic)
Bolorkle Point
Bogha Lurcain
Pier
Sound of Mull
Ldg Lts 356°
5°46'W
56° 32'N

SHELTER
Very good shelter but only good anchorage is in S end of loch to E of entrance. There are numerous hazards in N part of loch. Yachts can use the pier outside the loch, 3 ca W of entrance temporarily, or go alongside the old stone pier in the entrance on W side.

NAVIGATION
Waypoint 56°31'.50N, 05°46'30W 356°/176° from/to front Ldg Bn, 0.9M. The entrance is easy and is buoyed. The Ldg Bns 356° lead 0.5 ca W of Bogha Lurcain, a drying rock off Bolorkle Pt on E side of ent. Beyond Bolorkle Pt the ent is narrow with a bar (min depth 2.1m, 1985). Here stream runs 2½ kn at sp. Beware coasters from the sand mine going to/from the jetty and ferries to and from Mull.

LIGHTS AND MARKS
Ardtormish Pt Lt Ho, 1M SE of ent, Fl (2) WRG 10s 7m 8/5M; vis G shore-302°, W302°-310°, R310°-342°, W342°-057°, R057°-095°, W095°-108°, G108°-shore. Three buoys mark entrance channel QR, QG and Fl R 2s. End of ferry slip 2FR (vert). A War Memorial Cross (conspic 9m high) stands on W side of entrance. The Ldg Lts are FW 2m/4m (H24). Half mile up the loch on E side is a Y iron Bn with spherical topmark marking a reef, and ½M further up is a similar Bn marking a larger reef.

RADIO TELEPHONE
None.

TELEPHONE (096 784)
MRSC Oban 63720; ⌗ Oban 63079; Marinecall 0898 500 463; Ⓗ Oban 63636; Dr 252.

FACILITIES
K. Masters ☎ 2301, Gas; **J. Hodgson** ☎ 204, M, P, D, FW, Gas, R, ⊡; **Lochaline Stores** ☎ 220, V; **Lochaline Hotel** ☎ 657, R, Bar; **Village** Bar, Shop, V, P, ✉, Ⓑ (Oban or Fort William), ⇌ (Oban); ✈ (Oban); Ferry to Fishmish.

FORT WILLIAM/CORPACH 10-8-14

Inverness

CHARTS
Admiralty 2372, 2380; Imray C65; OS 41

TIDES
−0535 Dover; ML 2.5; Duration 0610; Zone 0 (GMT).

Standard Port OBAN (⟶)

Times				Height (metres)			
HW		LW		MHWS	MHWN	MLWN	MLWS
0100	0700	0100	0800	4.0	2.9	1.8	0.7
1300	1900	1300	2000				
Differences CORPACH							
0000	+0020	+0040	0000	0.0	0.0	−0.2	−0.2
CORRAN NARROWS							
+0007	+0007	+0004	+0004	+0.4	+0.4	−0.1	0.0
LOCH LEVEN HEAD							
+0045	+0045	+0045	+0045	No data		No data	
LOCH LINNHE (Port Appin)							
−0005	−0005	−0030	0000	+0.2	+0.2	+0.1	+0.1
BARCALDINE PIER (Loch Creran)							
+0010	+0020	+0040	+0015	+0.1	+0.1	0.0	+0.1

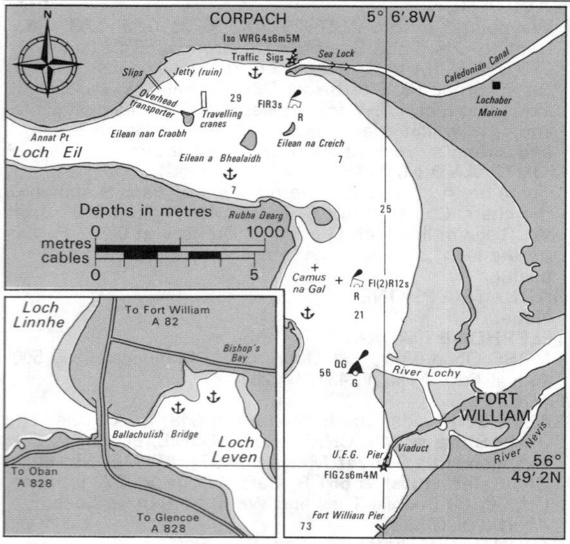
CORPACH
5° 6'.8W
Iso WRG4s6m5M
Traffic Sigs
Sea Lock
Caledonian Canal
Lochaber Marine
Slips
Jetty (ruin)
Overhead transporter
Travelling cranes
FIR3s
Annat Pt
Eilean nan Craobh
Eilean na Creich
Loch Eil
Eilean a Bhealaidh
Depths in metres
Rubha Dearg
metres 0 1000
cables 0 5
Camus na Gal
Fl(2)R12s
River Lochy
FORT WILLIAM
River Nevis
Viaduct
U.E.G. Pier
FIG2s6m4M
Fort William Pier
56° 49'.2N
Loch Linnhe
To Fort William A 82
Bishop's Bay
Ballachulish Bridge
Loch Leven
To Oban A 828
To Glencoe A 828

FORT WILLIAM/CORPACH *Continued*

SHELTER
Exposed to NE through N to SW winds. Anchorages in Bishop's Bay (Loch Leven), Ardgour Bay (beware ferry moorings and fish farm), Camus na Gal Bay (good shelter), Corpach Basin or SW of Eilean A Bhealaidh.

NAVIGATION
Corpach waypoint 56°50'.30N 05°07'.00W, 135°/315° from/to lock entrance, 0.30M. There are no dangers round Fort William but when coming up Loch Linnhe, the Corran Narrows may present a danger. On the port side is Salachan shoal running from Salachan Pt to the narrows and on the starboard is Culchenna spit. These are well marked and buoyed. Spring tide makes up to 6 kn through the narrows.

LIGHTS AND MARKS
There is a Fl G 2s Lt at Fort William pierhead.
NOTE: Corpach is the entrance to the Caledonian Canal (see 10.8.15). There is an Iso WRG 4s Lt at N jetty of lock entrance.

RADIO TELEPHONE
Call: *Corpach Lock* VHF Ch 16; 24 (0800-1700 LT Mon-Sat).

TELEPHONE (0397)
Hr Mr 707249; MRSC Oban 63720; # 702948; Marinecall 0898 500 463; Police 702361; Dr 703136, 702947.

FACILITIES
FORT WILLIAM. EC Wednesday; **Pier** ☎ 3881, L, AB; **Slip** ☎ 3701, L; **Town** P, ME, El, Sh, YC, V, R, Bar; Ⓗ; ✉; Ⓑ; ⇌.
CORPACH. **Corpach Basin** ☎ 772249, AB, L, FW; **Lochaber Marine** ☎ 772861, ME, El, Sh, D (cans), M, CH, C, (18 ton), Slip, Divers; **Lochaber YC** ☎ 703576, M, FW, L, Slip; **Village** P, V, R, Bar, ✉; Ⓑ; ⇌; ✈ (Oban).

CALEDONIAN CANAL 10-8-15

Inverness

CHARTS
Admiralty 1791. OS 41 34 26

TIDES
Tidal differences: Clachnaharry +0116 on Dover, −0104 on Aberdeen; Corpach −0455 on Dover, +0035 on Oban.

SHELTER
Corpach is the SW end of the Caledonian Canal. It is best to pass through the sea lock and lie between that and the first canal lock. The canal consists of three lochs, Lochs Lochy, Oich and Ness connected by canals with 29 locks totalling in all 60M. There are 14 locks between Loch Linnhe (Corpach), through Lochs Lochy and Oich to the summit (100' above sea level) and 15 locks from the summit through Loch Ness to Inverness. 22 miles are through canals and 38 through lochs. It normally takes two full days to pass through and in the summer it may take longer.

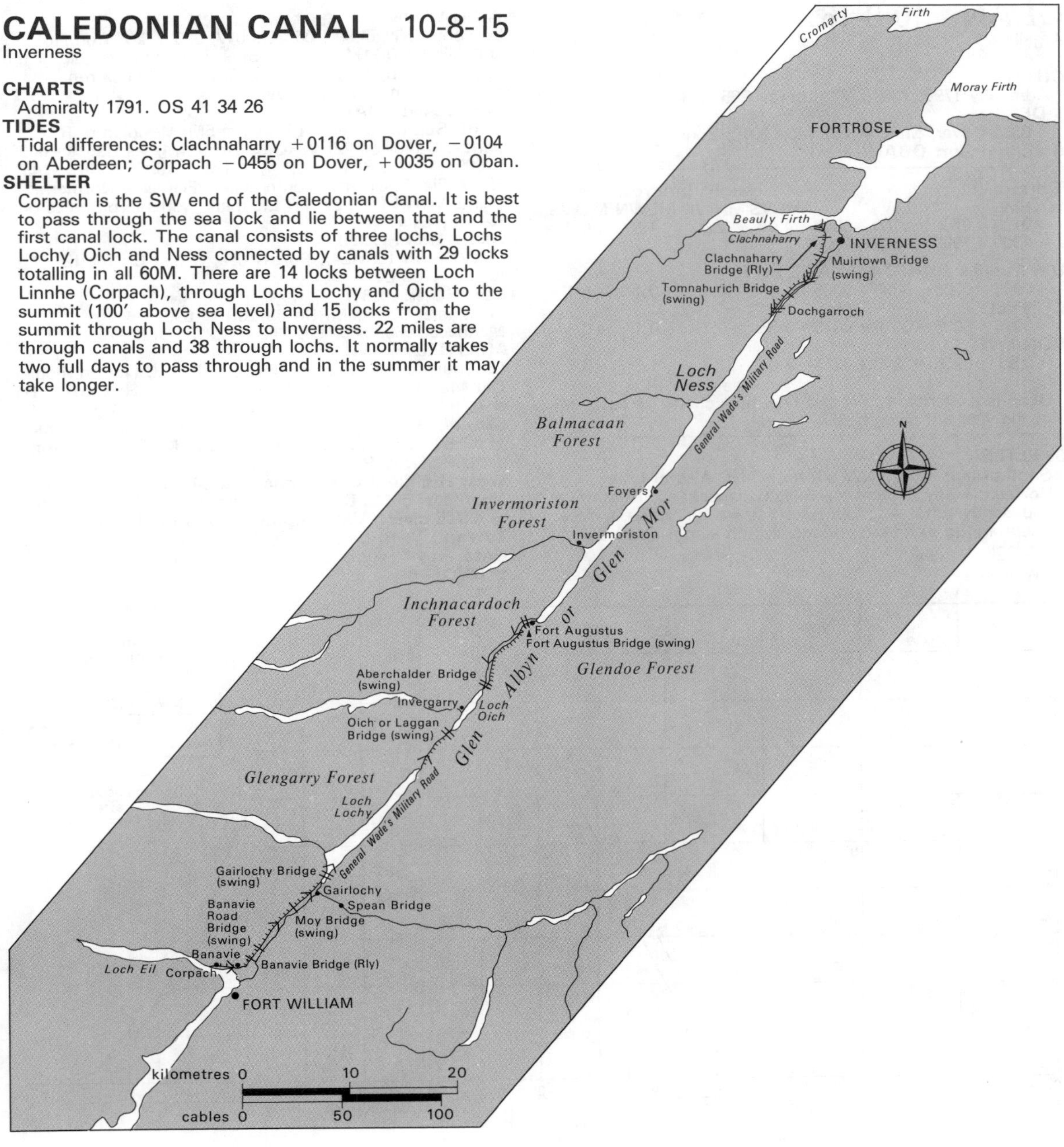
Cromarty Firth
Moray Firth
FORTROSE
Beauly Firth
Clachnaharry
INVERNESS
Clachnaharry Bridge (Rly)
Muirtown Bridge (swing)
Tomnahurich Bridge (swing)
Dochgarroch
Loch Ness
General Wade's Military Road
Balmacaan Forest
N
Foyers
Invermoriston Forest
Invermoriston
Glen Mor or Glen Albyn
Inchnacardoch Forest
Fort Augustus
Fort Augustus Bridge (swing)
Glendoe Forest
Aberchalder Bridge (swing)
Invergarry
Loch Oich
Oich or Laggan Bridge (swing)
Glengarry Forest
Loch Lochy
Gairlochy Bridge (swing)
Gairlochy
Spean Bridge
Banavie Road Bridge (swing)
Moy Bridge (swing)
Banavie
Banavie Bridge (Rly)
Loch Eil
Corpach
FORT WILLIAM
kilometres 0 10 20
cables 0 50 100

CALEDONIAN CANAL *Continued*

NAVIGATION
There is a speed limit of 5.2 kn in the canal sections. There are eight swing bridges. All locks are manned and operate Mid May-early Oct 0800-1800 LT, Autumn and Spring 0800-1650 LT and Winter 0915-1600 LT. Sea locks will open outside these hours for extra payment. Dues are payable at the Corpach end. Canal is available for vessels up to 48m LOA, 11m beam and 4m draught, max mast height 36.5m. Entrance is available HW − 4 to HW + 4 (springs); H24 (neaps). Ring Lockkeeper on Corpach 772249. For rules and regulations etc apply to the Engineer and Manager, Caledonian Canal Office, Clachnaharry, Tel. Inverness 233140.
Loch Oich is part of an Hydro-Electric Scheme and for this reason the water level can vary. Do not pass bridges at either end without keeper's instructions.

LIGHTS & MARKS
Channel is marked by posts, cairns and buoys, R on the NW side of the channel and G on the SE side — none are lit. There is an Iso WRG 4s light at canal entrance at Corpach, and an Iso 4s at the sea lock in Inverness.

RADIO TELEPHONE
Call: *Corpach Lock* VHF Ch 16; 24. Call: *Laggan Lock* Ch 74. Call: *Fort Augustus Lock* Ch 74. Call: *Dochgarroch Lock* Ch 74. For Clachnaharry office, call: *Caledonian Canal* Ch 74. Call: *Clachnaharry Sea Lock* Ch 74.

TELEPHONES
Head Office Inverness 233140; Corpach Sea Lock Corpach 772249; Clachnaharry Sea Lock Inverness 235439.

FACILITIES
- Corpach see 10.8.14.
- Gairlochy AB.
- NE end of Loch Lochy V, M, AB, R.
- Oich Bridge D, AB, R.
- Invergarry V, L, FW, AB.
- Fort Augustus FW, P, L, ME, El, AB, P, V, ✉, Dr, Bar
- Dochgarroch FW, P, V.
- Caley Marina (25 + 25 visitors) ☎ Inverness 236539 (Muirtown top lock) FW, C, ACA, CH, D, ME, El, Sh, AC.
- Muirtown Marina (20 visitors) (Muirtown basin) ☎ Inverness 239745, D, El, ME, Sh, FW, Gas, Gaz, ⊡, C (4 ton), CH, AC.

OBAN 10-8-16
Argyll

CHARTS
Admiralty 1790, 2387, 2171; Imray C65; OS 49

TIDES
−0530 Dover; ML 2.4; Duration 0610; Zone 0 (GMT).

Standard Port OBAN (⟶)

Times				Height (metres)			
HW		LW		MHWS	MHWN	MLWN	MLWS
0100	0700	0100	0800	4.0	2.9	1.8	0.7
1300	1900	1300	2000				
Differences DUNSTAFFNAGE BAY							
+0005	0000	0000	+0005	+0.1	+0.1	+0.1	+0.1
CONNEL							
+0020	+0005	+0010	+0015	−0.3	−0.2	−0.1	+0.1
BONAWE							
+0150	+0205	+0240	+0210	−2.0	−1.7	−1.3	−0.5

Oban is a Standard Port and tidal predictions for each day of the year are given below.

SHELTER
Good except in SW-NW strong winds. Also at Little Horseshoe Bay, Horseshoe Bay, Gallanachbeg, Ardantrive and Bandystone. Anchorages off town, but water is deep. There are no visitors moorings and no alongside berths available.

NAVIGATION
Waypoint 56°25′.80N 05°30′.00W, 306°/126° from/to Dunollie Lt, 0.71M. Beware Sgeir Rathaid in middle of the bay marked by buoys, also MacBraynes ferries run services from Railway Quay.

LIGHTS AND MARKS
North Spit of Kerrera Fl R 3s 9m 5M; W column, R bands. Dunollie Fl(2) WRG 6s 7m 5/4M; vis G351° − 009°, W009° − 047°, R047° − 120°, W120° − 138°, G138° − 143°. North Pier 2FG(vert). South Quay 2FG(vert). Northern Lights Wharf OcG 6s. FR Lts mark works in progress on Railway Quay (T).

RADIO TELEPHONE
CG-VHF Ch 16 (H24). Port Office, N pier Ch 16; 12 (0900 − 1700 LT).

TELEPHONE (0631)
Piermaster 62892; MRSC 63720; # 63079; Marinecall 0898 500 463; Police 62213; Dr 63175.

FACILITIES
EC Thursday; **N. Pier** ☎ 62892, L, FW, C (15 ton mobile); **Cal Mac Pier** ☎ 62285, Slip, D, L, FW, CH; **Curries BY** ☎ 62102, Slip, CH; **Oban Yacht Services BY** ☎ 63666, Slip, M, D, L, FW, ME, Sh, C, CH, AB; **Nancy Black** ☎ 62550, CH, ACA; **Ardantrive Bay** M, P, D, FW (on pier); **Railway Pier** D.
West Highland Gas Services ☎ 64050 Gas; **Ardoran Marine** ☎ 66123 D, Sh, ME, Slip, C, M; **Oban Divers** ☎ 62755 divers; **Vale Engineering** ☎ 64531 ME, El; **Town** P, V, R, Bar. ✉; Ⓑ; ⇌; ✈.
Note: Royal Highland YC, Andentallan, by Oban, ☎ 63309.

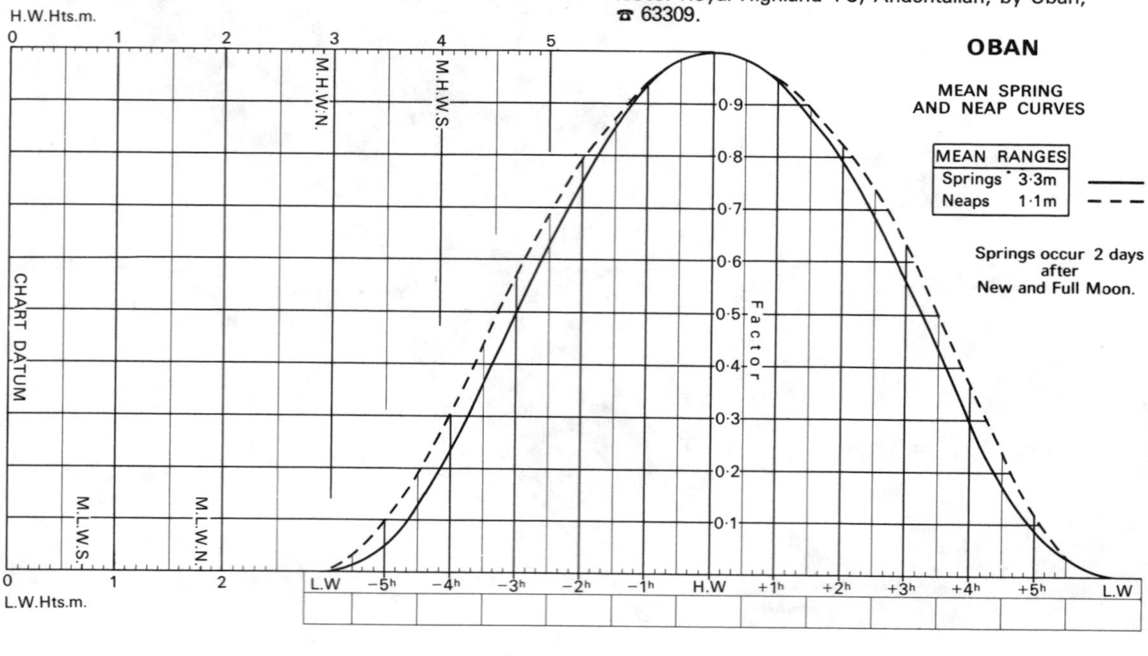

H.W.Hts.m.
0 1 2 3 4 5
M.H.W.N.
M.H.W.S.
CHART DATUM
M.L.W.S.
M.L.W.N.
L.W.Hts.m.
Factor
0·9 0·8 0·7 0·6 0·5 0·4 0·3 0·2 0·1
L.W −5h −4h −3h −2h −1h H.W +1h +2h +3h +4h +5h L.W
OBAN
MEAN SPRING AND NEAP CURVES
MEAN RANGES
Springs 3·3m
Neaps 1·1m
Springs occur 2 days after New and Full Moon.

OBAN *continued*

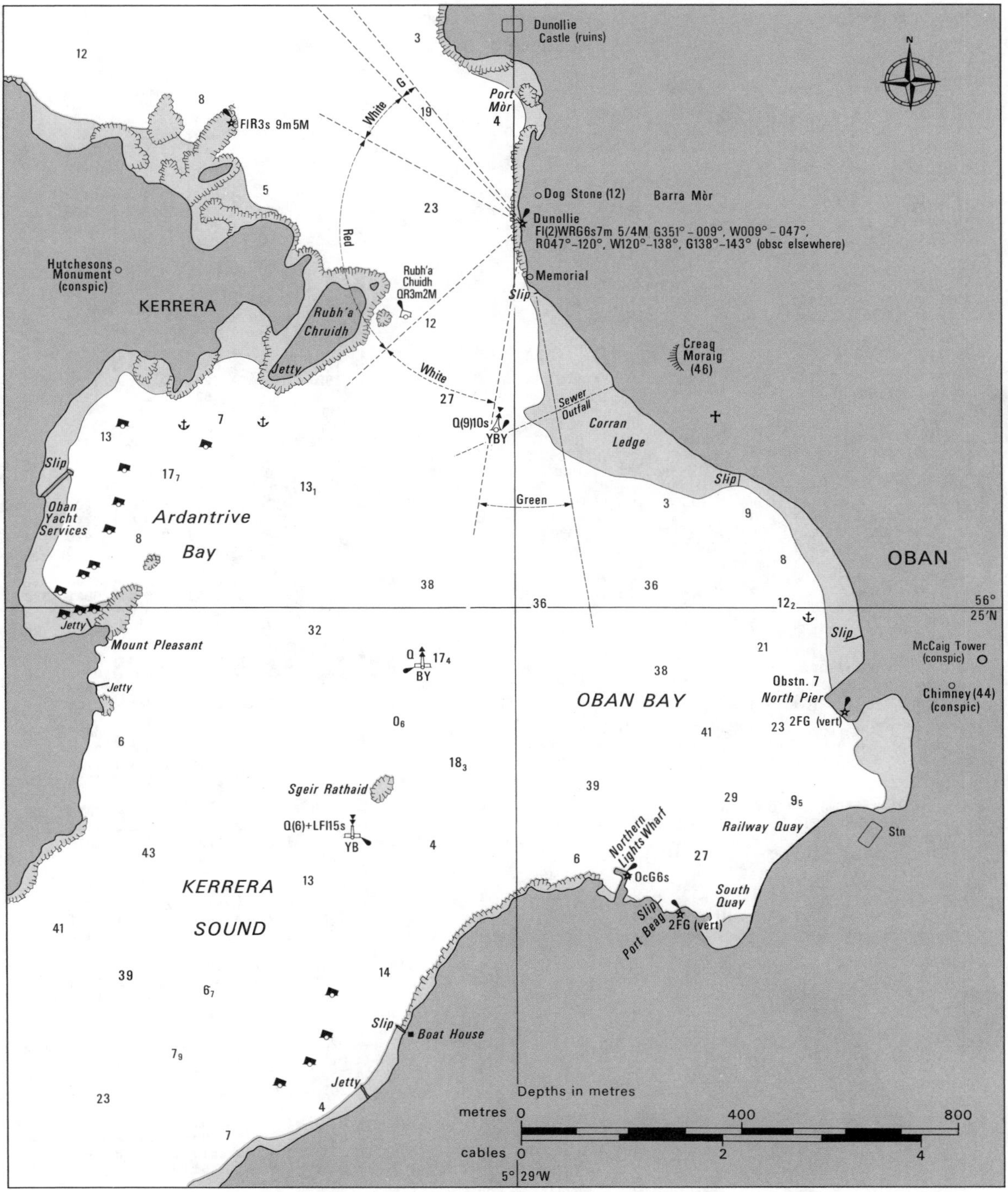
Dunollie Castle (ruins)
Port Mòr
FlR3s 9m5M
White
G
Red
Dog Stone (12)
Barra Mòr
Dunollie
Fl(2)WRG6s7m 5/4M G351° - 009°, W009° - 047°, R047°–120°, W120°–138°, G138°–143° (obsc elsewhere)
Hutchesons Monument (conspic)
KERRERA
Rubh'a Chuidh QR3m2M
Rubh'a Chruidh
Jetty
Memorial
Slip
Creag Moraig (46)
White
Sewer Outfall
Q(9)10s
YBY
Corran Ledge
Slip
Oban Yacht Services
Ardantrive Bay
Green
OBAN
Jetty
Mount Pleasant
Jetty
Q
BY
56° 25′N
McCaig Tower (conspic)
Chimney (44) (conspic)
Obstn. 7
North Pier
2FG (vert)
OBAN BAY
Sgeir Rathaid
Q(6)+LFl15s
YB
Railway Quay
Stn
Northern Lights Wharf
OcG6s
KERRERA
SOUND
South Quay
Slip
Port Beag
2FG (vert)
Slip
Boat House
Jetty
Depths in metres
metres 0 400 800
cables 0 2 4
5° 29′W
8

SCOTLAND, WEST COAST - OBAN

TIME ZONE UT(GMT)

For Summer Time add ONE hour in non-shaded areas

LAT 56°25′N LONG 5°29′W

TIMES AND HEIGHTS OF HIGH AND LOW WATERS

YEAR **1992**

JANUARY

Day	Time	m	Day	Time	m
1 W	0328	3.3	**16** TH	0159	3.1
	0908	1.7		0825	1.7
	1605	3.2		1512	3.3
	2156	1.7		2054	1.5
2 TH	0415	3.4	**17** F	0321	3.3
	1008	1.6		0942	1.4
	1641	3.3		1612	3.5
	2239	1.5		2156	1.2
3 F	0453	3.6	**18** SA	0419	3.6
	1056	1.5		1042	1.1
	1711	3.5		1701	3.7
	2318	1.4		2249	0.9
4 SA	0527	3.8	**19** SU	0507	3.9
	1137	1.4		1133	0.9
	1741	3.6		1745	3.9
	● 2354	1.2		○ 2338	0.6
5 SU	0600	3.9	**20** M	0552	4.2
	1214	1.4		1219	0.6
	1812	3.7		1827	4.1
6 M	0030	1.2	**21** TU	0023	0.4
	0633	4.0		0634	4.3
	1250	1.3		1304	0.6
	1844	3.8		1907	4.1
7 TU	0105	1.2	**22** W	0108	0.3
	0707	4.0		0714	4.3
	1324	1.3		1347	0.6
	1915	3.8		1946	4.0
8 W	0139	1.2	**23** TH	0152	0.4
	0739	4.0		0755	4.2
	1357	1.4		1429	0.7
	1945	3.7		2025	3.9
9 TH	0210	1.3	**24** F	0236	0.5
	0811	3.9		0834	4.0
	1428	1.5		1512	1.0
	2014	3.6		2104	3.7
10 F	0240	1.4	**25** SA	0321	0.8
	0841	3.8		0914	3.7
	1500	1.5		1557	1.2
	2042	3.5		2146	3.4
11 SA	0310	1.5	**26** SU	0408	1.1
	0913	3.6		0957	3.4
	1536	1.6		1646	1.5
	2114	3.4		☾ 2235	3.2
12 SU	0345	1.6	**27** M	0500	1.4
	0950	3.4		1047	3.1
	1619	1.7		1745	1.8
	2154	3.2		2345	3.0
13 M	0429	1.8	**28** TU	0603	1.7
	1039	3.3		1212	2.9
	1714	1.8		1858	1.9
	☽ 2248	3.1			
14 TU	0531	1.8	**29** W	0139	2.9
	1157	3.1		0721	1.9
	1824	1.8		1504	2.8
				2024	1.9
15 W	0011	3.0	**30** TH	0313	3.1
	0654	1.9		0852	1.9
	1350	3.1		1605	3.0
	1942	1.7		2137	1.8
			31 F	0408	3.3
				1006	1.8
				1641	3.2
				2227	1.6

FEBRUARY

Day	Time	m	Day	Time	m
1 SA	0446	3.5	**16** SU	0414	3.6
	1053	1.6		1039	1.0
	1708	3.4		1653	3.6
	2306	1.4		2236	0.7
2 SU	0517	3.7	**17** M	0500	3.9
	1129	1.4		1126	0.7
	1734	3.5		1733	3.9
	2341	1.2		2324	0.4
3 M	0547	3.9	**18** TU	0541	4.1
	1201	1.3		1207	0.5
	1802	3.7		1811	4.0
	●			○	
4 TU	0014	1.1	**19** W	0008	0.2
	0617	4.0		0619	4.3
	1233	1.2		1247	0.4
	1829	3.8		1847	4.1
5 W	0046	1.0	**20** TH	0050	0.1
	0647	4.0		0656	4.3
	1302	1.1		1326	0.4
	1856	3.8		1922	4.1
6 TH	0116	1.0	**21** F	0131	0.2
	0716	4.0		0732	4.2
	1331	1.1		1404	0.6
	1922	3.8		1956	3.9
7 F	0144	1.0	**22** SA	0212	0.4
	0743	4.0		0807	3.9
	1359	1.1		1443	0.8
	1947	3.7		2031	3.7
8 SA	0210	1.1	**23** SU	0254	0.7
	0810	3.8		0842	3.6
	1428	1.2		1522	1.1
	2012	3.6		2108	3.5
9 SU	0238	1.2	**24** M	0337	1.0
	0839	3.7		0918	3.3
	1502	1.3		1606	1.4
	2041	3.5		2150	3.2
10 M	0310	1.4	**25** TU	0426	1.4
	0912	3.5		0958	3.0
	1542	1.5		1659	1.7
	2117	3.3		☾ 2248	2.9
11 TU	0352	1.5	**26** W	0526	1.8
	0954	3.2		1100	2.7
	1634	1.6		1811	1.9
	☽ 2205	3.1			
12 W	0452	1.7	**27** TH	0043	2.8
	1102	3.0		0648	2.0
	1744	1.7		1444	2.6
	2320	2.9		1944	1.9
13 TH	0621	1.8	**28** F	0251	2.9
	1334	2.9		0838	2.0
	1910	1.7		1548	2.8
				2113	1.8
14 F	0133	2.9	**29** SA	0349	3.1
	0811	1.7		0958	1.8
	1509	3.1		1622	3.1
	2033	1.5		2207	1.6
15 SA	0316	3.2			
	0941	1.4			
	1607	3.3			
	2141	1.1			

MARCH

Day	Time	m	Day	Time	m
1 SU	0425	3.4	**16** M	0402	3.5
	1037	1.5		1026	0.9
	1647	3.3		1635	3.5
	2246	1.3		2217	0.6
2 M	0454	3.6	**17** TU	0445	3.8
	1108	1.3		1109	0.6
	1712	3.5		1713	3.8
	2319	1.1		2303	0.4
3 TU	0523	3.8	**18** W	0523	4.0
	1137	1.1		1147	0.4
	1738	3.7		1748	4.0
	2350	1.0		○ 2346	0.2
4 W	0552	3.9	**19** TH	0558	4.1
	1205	1.0		1224	0.4
	1804	3.8		1821	4.0
	●				
5 TH	0019	0.9	**20** F	0027	0.1
	0620	4.0		0632	4.1
	1234	0.9		1300	0.4
	1829	3.8		1854	4.0
6 F	0047	0.8	**21** SA	0108	0.2
	0647	4.0		0705	4.0
	1301	0.9		1336	0.6
	1853	3.8		1927	3.9
7 SA	0114	0.8	**22** SU	0147	0.4
	0714	4.0		0738	3.8
	1330	0.9		1413	0.8
	1917	3.8		2002	3.7
8 SU	0141	0.9	**23** M	0227	0.7
	0742	3.8		0811	3.5
	1401	0.9		1451	1.1
	1944	3.7		2038	3.5
9 M	0211	1.0	**24** TU	0309	1.1
	0811	3.6		0845	3.2
	1436	1.1		1533	1.3
	2016	3.5		2119	3.2
10 TU	0247	1.2	**25** W	0356	1.5
	0846	3.4		0923	2.9
	1518	1.2		1625	1.6
	2054	3.3		2215	3.0
11 W	0332	1.4	**26** TH	0455	1.8
	0929	3.1		1019	2.7
	1611	1.4		1734	1.8
	2143	3.1		☾ 2356	2.8
12 TH	0435	1.6	**27** F	0615	2.0
	1043	2.8		1326	2.6
	1722	1.6		1902	1.9
	☽ 2302	2.9			
13 F	0610	1.7	**28** SA	0201	2.9
	1333	2.7		0759	2.0
	1848	1.5		1502	2.7
				2030	1.8
14 SA	0130	2.9	**29** SU	0307	3.1
	0809	1.6		0920	1.8
	1457	3.0		1541	3.0
	2013	1.3		2130	1.6
15 SU	0308	3.2	**30** M	0347	3.3
	0934	1.2		1001	1.5
	1551	3.3		1611	3.2
	2122	1.0		2211	1.3
			31 TU	0419	3.5
				1033	1.3
				1638	3.4
				2245	1.1

APRIL

Day	Time	m	Day	Time	m
1 W	0450	3.7	**16** TH	0500	3.9
	1102	1.1		1122	0.6
	1705	3.6		1722	3.8
	2317	1.0		2322	0.4
2 TH	0520	3.9	**17** F	0534	3.9
	1131	0.9		1158	0.5
	1731	3.7		1755	3.9
	2346	0.8		○	
3 F	0549	3.9	**18** SA	0003	0.4
	1201	0.8		0606	3.9
	1757	3.8		1234	0.6
	●			1828	3.9
4 SA	0015	0.8	**19** SU	0044	0.5
	0618	4.0		0639	3.8
	1231	0.7		1310	0.7
	1823	3.8		1902	3.8
5 SU	0045	0.8	**20** M	0123	0.7
	0648	3.9		0712	3.6
	1303	0.7		1347	0.9
	1851	3.8		1938	3.7
6 M	0117	0.8	**21** TU	0204	0.9
	0719	3.8		0746	3.4
	1338	0.8		1426	1.1
	1923	3.7		2016	3.5
7 TU	0153	0.9	**22** W	0246	1.2
	0753	3.6		0821	3.2
	1418	0.9		1508	1.3
	1959	3.6		2100	3.3
8 W	0235	1.1	**23** TH	0332	1.5
	0833	3.3		0902	3.0
	1504	1.1		1558	1.5
	2043	3.4		2154	3.1
9 TH	0326	1.3	**24** F	0427	1.8
	0924	3.0		0957	2.8
	1600	1.3		1700	1.7
	2139	3.1		☾ 2315	2.9
10 F	0435	1.5	**25** SA	0538	1.9
	1054	2.7		1146	2.6
	1709	1.4		1815	1.8
	☽ 2305	2.9			
11 SA	0608	1.6	**26** SU	0052	2.9
	1315	2.7		0701	2.0
	1828	1.4		1341	2.7
				1932	1.8
12 SU	0121	3.0	**27** M	0206	3.0
	0756	1.5		0816	1.8
	1432	2.9		1441	2.9
	1948	1.2		2036	1.7
13 M	0248	3.2	**28** TU	0256	3.2
	0913	1.2		0908	1.6
	1526	3.2		1522	3.1
	2056	1.0		2124	1.5
14 TU	0342	3.5	**29** W	0336	3.4
	1003	0.9		0947	1.4
	1610	3.4		1556	3.3
	2151	0.7		2203	1.3
15 W	0424	3.7	**30** TH	0412	3.6
	1045	0.7		1022	1.2
	1647	3.7		1626	3.5
	2239	0.5		2238	1.1

Chart Datum: 2.10 metres below Ordnance Datum (Newlyn)

SCOTLAND, WEST COAST - OBAN

TIME ZONE UT(GMT)

For Summer Time add ONE hour in non-shaded areas

LAT 56°25′N LONG 5°29′W

TIMES AND HEIGHTS OF HIGH AND LOW WATERS

YEAR **1992**

MAY

Day	Time	m	Day	Time	m
1 F	0446 1055 1656 2311	3.8 1.0 3.6 0.9	16 SA ○	0513 1133 1733 2342	3.7 0.8 3.7 0.7
2 SA ●	0520 1129 1727 2346	3.8 0.8 3.7 0.8	17 SU	0545 1210 1808	3.7 0.8 3.8
3 SU	0553 1204 1759	3.9 0.7 3.8	18 M	0023 0618 1248 1844	0.8 3.6 0.9 3.8
4 M	0021 0628 1242 1833	0.8 3.8 0.7 3.8	19 TU	0104 0653 1326 1922	1.0 3.5 0.9 3.7
5 TU	0101 0705 1322 1911	0.8 3.7 0.7 3.7	20 W	0145 0729 1406 2002	1.1 3.4 1.1 3.6
6 W	0143 0746 1406 1954	0.9 3.5 0.8 3.6	21 TH	0226 0806 1448 2045	1.3 3.3 1.3 3.4
7 TH	0232 0833 1455 2043	1.0 3.3 0.9 3.5	22 F	0310 0847 1533 2133	1.6 3.1 1.5 3.3
8 F	0328 0931 1551 2143	1.2 3.1 1.1 3.3	23 SA	0359 0934 1623 2232	1.7 3.0 1.6 3.1
9 SA ☽	0435 1055 1655 2303	1.4 2.9 1.2 3.1	24 SU ☾	0455 1037 1721 2342	1.9 2.8 1.8 3.1
10 SU	0557 1238 1805	1.5 2.8 1.2	25 M	0558 1201 1825	1.9 2.8 1.8
11 M	0051 0725 1356 1917	3.1 1.4 2.9 1.2	26 TU	0055 0704 1321 1928	3.1 1.9 2.8 1.8
12 TU	0219 0839 1455 2024	3.2 1.3 3.1 1.0	27 W	0158 0804 1421 2025	3.2 1.7 3.0 1.6
13 W	0317 0934 1542 2123	3.4 1.1 3.3 0.9	28 TH	0249 0854 1507 2114	3.3 1.5 3.1 1.5
14 TH	0402 1018 1622 2213	3.5 1.0 3.5 0.8	29 F	0334 0939 1547 2159	3.5 1.3 3.3 1.3
15 F	0439 1057 1658 2259	3.6 0.9 3.6 0.7	30 SA	0416 1020 1625 2241	3.6 1.1 3.5 1.1
			31 SU	0456 1101 1703 2324	3.7 0.9 3.7 0.9

JUNE

Day	Time	m	Day	Time	m
1 M ●	0537 1143 1743	3.8 0.7 3.8	16 TU	0009 0607 1232 1833	1.1 3.5 1.0 3.8
2 TU	0007 0617 1226 1824	0.8 3.8 0.6 3.9	17 W	0050 0641 1310 1910	1.2 3.5 1.0 3.8
3 W	0053 0700 1311 1907	0.8 3.7 0.6 3.9	18 TH	0129 0716 1348 1948	1.2 3.5 1.1 3.7
4 TH	0140 0745 1357 1953	0.8 3.6 0.6 3.8	19 F	0208 0752 1426 2026	1.4 3.4 1.2 3.6
5 F	0230 0833 1446 2043	0.9 3.4 0.7 3.7	20 SA	0247 0828 1504 2105	1.5 3.3 1.3 3.5
6 SA	0325 0927 1538 2139	1.1 3.3 0.8 3.5	21 SU	0326 0904 1542 2146	1.6 3.2 1.5 3.4
7 SU ☽	0425 1031 1635 2244	1.3 3.1 1.0 3.3	22 M	0408 0943 1623 2234	1.7 3.1 1.6 3.2
8 M	0532 1148 1737	1.4 3.0 1.1	23 TU ☾	0457 1031 1711 2333	1.8 3.0 1.8 3.1
9 TU	0007 0645 1310 1843	3.2 1.5 3.0 1.2	24 W	0553 1135 1810	1.8 2.9 1.8
10 W	0141 0758 1420 1951	3.2 1.5 3.0 1.2	25 TH	0047 0657 1258 1918	3.1 1.8 2.9 1.8
11 TH	0254 0901 1517 2055	3.2 1.4 3.2 1.2	26 F	0201 0801 1414 2026	3.2 1.7 3.0 1.7
12 F	0346 0952 1604 2153	3.3 1.3 3.3 1.2	27 SA	0303 0859 1514 2128	3.3 1.5 3.2 1.5
13 SA	0427 1035 1644 2243	3.4 1.2 3.5 1.1	28 SU	0356 0952 1604 2223	3.5 1.2 3.4 1.2
14 SU	0501 1115 1721 2328	3.4 1.1 3.6 1.1	29 M	0444 1040 1651 2313	3.6 0.9 3.7 1.0
15 M ○	0534 1153 1757	3.5 1.0 3.7	30 TU ●	0528 1127 1735	3.8 0.7 3.9

JULY

Day	Time	m	Day	Time	m
1 W	0001 0611 1213 1819	0.8 3.8 0.5 4.0	16 TH	0037 0629 1252 1854	1.2 3.6 0.9 3.9
2 TH	0048 0654 1259 1903	0.7 3.9 0.4 4.1	17 F	0112 0701 1327 1927	1.2 3.7 1.0 3.9
3 F	0135 0737 1344 1947	0.7 3.8 0.4 4.0	18 SA	0145 0732 1400 2000	1.2 3.6 1.1 3.8
4 SA	0222 0821 1431 2033	0.8 3.7 0.5 3.9	19 SU	0218 0802 1431 2031	1.3 3.5 1.2 3.7
5 SU	0311 0907 1519 2120	0.9 3.5 0.6 3.7	20 M	0250 0830 1500 2103	1.4 3.4 1.4 3.5
6 M	0402 0957 1611 2213	1.1 3.3 0.9 3.4	21 TU	0324 0900 1531 2136	1.5 3.3 1.5 3.4
7 TU ☽	0459 1056 1706 2316	1.3 3.1 1.1 3.2	22 W ☾	0404 0935 1609 2218	1.6 3.1 1.7 3.2
8 W	0602 1214 1809	1.5 3.0 1.3	23 TH	0453 1021 1702 2324	1.7 3.0 1.8 3.0
9 TH	0050 0713 1345 1919	3.0 1.6 2.9 1.5	24 F	0558 1133 1818	1.8 2.9 1.8
10 F	0238 0827 1501 2034	3.0 1.6 3.0 1.5	25 SA	0115 0713 1323 1950	3.0 1.7 2.9 1.8
11 SA	0344 0931 1558 2143	3.1 1.5 3.2 1.5	26 SU	0245 0827 1455 2113	3.1 1.5 3.1 1.5
12 SU	0428 1021 1641 2237	3.2 1.4 3.4 1.4	27 M	0347 0930 1555 2216	3.3 1.2 3.4 1.2
13 M	0501 1102 1716 2322	3.3 1.2 3.6 1.3	28 TU	0436 1024 1644 2307	3.6 0.9 3.7 0.9
14 TU ○	0530 1140 1749	3.4 1.1 3.7	29 W ●	0520 1112 1728 2354	3.8 0.6 4.0 0.7
15 W	0000 0558 1217 1821	1.2 3.5 1.0 3.8	30 TH	0601 1158 1810	3.9 0.3 4.2
			31 F	0038 0641 1243 1850	0.5 4.0 0.2 4.3

AUGUST

Day	Time	m	Day	Time	m
1 SA	0121 0720 1327 1931	0.5 4.0 0.2 4.2	16 SU	0117 0706 1329 1929	1.1 3.8 1.0 4.0
2 SU	0204 0759 1411 2011	0.6 3.9 0.3 4.1	17 M	0146 0732 1356 1956	1.1 3.7 1.1 3.8
3 M	0248 0839 1456 2052	0.7 3.7 0.5 3.8	18 TU	0215 0757 1422 2023	1.2 3.6 1.2 3.7
4 TU	0333 0921 1543 2136	1.0 3.5 0.8 3.5	19 W	0246 0824 1451 2053	1.3 3.5 1.4 3.5
5 W ☽	0423 1010 1635 2226	1.3 3.2 1.2 3.1	20 TH	0323 0857 1527 2129	1.5 3.3 1.6 3.2
6 TH	0520 1117 1736 2343	1.6 3.0 1.5 2.9	21 F ☾	0410 0940 1619 2224	1.6 3.1 1.7 3.0
7 F	0631 1312 1852	1.7 2.9 1.7	22 SA	0515 1045 1741	1.7 2.9 1.9
8 SA	0233 0754 1454 2023	2.8 1.8 3.0 1.8	23 SU	0045 0637 1251 1933	2.8 1.7 2.9 1.8
9 SU	0344 0913 1554 2146	2.9 1.7 3.2 1.7	24 M	0238 0801 1447 2109	3.0 1.5 3.1 1.5
10 M	0426 1008 1634 2237	3.1 1.5 3.4 1.5	25 TU	0338 0910 1547 2211	3.2 1.2 3.5 1.2
11 TU	0454 1048 1705 2314	3.3 1.3 3.6 1.4	26 W	0425 1006 1633 2258	3.5 0.8 3.8 0.8
12 W	0519 1124 1733 2346	3.5 1.1 3.8 1.2	27 TH	0506 1055 1714 2340	3.8 0.5 4.1 0.5
13 TH ○	0544 1157 1802	3.6 1.0 3.9	28 F ●	0544 1140 1753	4.0 0.2 4.3
14 F	0017 0611 1230 1831	1.1 3.7 0.9 4.0	29 SA	0020 0620 1223 1831	0.4 4.1 0.1 4.4
15 SA	0047 0639 1300 1900	1.1 3.8 0.9 4.0	30 SU	0100 0657 1305 1908	0.4 4.1 0.1 4.3
			31 M	0140 0733 1348 1945	0.5 4.0 0.3 4.1

Chart Datum: 2.10 metres below Ordnance Datum (Newlyn)

SCOTLAND, WEST COAST - OBAN

TIME ZONE UT(GMT)

For Summer Time add ONE hour in non-shaded areas

LAT 56°25'N LONG 5°29'W

TIMES AND HEIGHTS OF HIGH AND LOW WATERS

YEAR 1992

SEPTEMBER

Day	Time	m	Day	Time	m
1 TU	0220 0810 1431 2021	0.7 3.8 0.6 3.8	16 W	0143 0728 1351 1951	1.0 3.7 1.2 3.7
2 W	0302 0849 1516 2059	1.0 3.6 0.9 3.4	17 TH	0216 0757 1423 2022	1.2 3.6 1.3 3.5
3 TH ☽	0347 0933 1606 2142	1.3 3.3 1.3 3.1	18 F	0254 0832 1504 2100	1.3 3.4 1.5 3.2
4 F	0441 1033 1707 2243	1.6 3.0 1.7 2.8	19 SA ☾	0343 0917 1600 2156	1.5 3.2 1.7 2.9
5 SA	0550 1232 1827	1.8 2.9 1.9	20 SU	0448 1025 1728	1.6 3.0 1.9
6 SU	0219 0719 1438 2017	2.7 1.9 3.0 2.0	21 M	0037 0610 1236 1926	2.8 1.7 3.0 1.8
7 M	0329 0847 1536 2143	2.9 1.8 3.2 1.8	22 TU	0224 0735 1432 2101	2.9 1.5 3.2 1.5
8 TU	0407 0945 1612 2223	3.1 1.6 3.4 1.6	23 W	0321 0847 1531 2157	3.2 1.2 3.6 1.1
9 W	0433 1025 1640 2253	3.3 1.3 3.7 1.4	24 TH	0406 0945 1615 2240	3.5 0.8 3.9 0.8
10 TH	0456 1059 1706 2321	3.5 1.2 3.9 1.2	25 F	0446 1033 1655 2320	3.8 0.5 4.1 0.6
11 F	0520 1131 1734 2349	3.7 1.0 4.0 1.1	26 SA ●	0522 1118 1732 2358	4.0 0.3 4.3 0.4
12 SA ○	0546 1201 1803	3.8 0.9 4.1	27 SU	0558 1201 1808	4.2 0.2 4.3
13 SU	0017 0612 1231 1830	1.0 3.9 0.9 4.1	28 M	0035 0632 1243 1843	0.4 4.2 0.3 4.2
14 M	0046 0637 1258 1857	0.9 3.9 1.0 4.0	29 TU	0114 0707 1325 1918	0.5 4.1 0.4 4.0
15 TU	0114 0702 1324 1924	1.0 3.8 1.1 3.9	30 W	0152 0744 1407 1953	0.7 3.9 0.7 3.7

OCTOBER

Day	Time	m	Day	Time	m
1 TH	0232 0822 1451 2029	1.0 3.7 1.1 3.4	16 F	0155 0739 1409 2006	1.1 3.8 1.3 3.5
2 F	0316 0905 1540 2108	1.3 3.4 1.5 3.1	17 SA	0237 0819 1456 2050	1.2 3.6 1.5 3.2
3 SA ☽	0407 1001 1639 2202	1.6 3.2 1.8 2.8	18 SU	0328 0909 1557 2156	1.4 3.4 1.7 3.0
4 SU	0512 1139 1758	1.8 3.0 2.1	19 M ☾	0431 1019 1722	1.5 3.2 1.8
5 M	0111 0635 1349 1942	2.7 2.0 3.0 2.1	20 TU	0014 0546 1213 1907	2.8 1.6 3.2 1.7
6 TU	0250 0803 1454 2106	2.8 1.9 3.2 1.9	21 W	0155 0706 1404 2035	3.0 1.5 3.3 1.5
7 W	0330 0908 1533 2147	3.1 1.7 3.4 1.7	22 TH	0256 0819 1507 2132	3.2 1.2 3.6 1.2
8 TH	0358 0952 1604 2218	3.3 1.5 3.7 1.5	23 F	0343 0919 1554 2217	3.5 1.0 3.8 0.9
9 F	0424 1028 1633 2247	3.5 1.3 3.8 1.3	24 SA	0423 1011 1634 2256	3.8 0.7 4.0 0.8
10 SA	0450 1100 1703 2316	3.7 1.2 4.0 1.1	25 SU ●	0500 1057 1711 2334	4.0 0.6 4.1 0.6
11 SU ○	0517 1131 1733 2345	3.8 1.1 4.1 1.0	26 M	0536 1140 1746	4.1 0.5 4.1
12 M	0543 1200 1802	3.9 1.0 4.1	27 TU	0012 0610 1223 1821	0.6 4.1 0.6 4.0
13 TU	0015 0609 1229 1830	0.9 4.0 1.0 4.0	28 W	0050 0646 1305 1855	0.7 4.1 0.7 3.9
14 W	0046 0636 1259 1859	0.9 3.9 1.1 3.9	29 TH	0128 0723 1347 1931	0.9 4.0 1.0 3.7
15 TH	0118 0706 1331 1931	1.0 3.9 1.2 3.7	30 F	0208 0802 1430 2007	1.1 3.8 1.3 3.4
			31 SA	0251 0845 1517 2047	1.3 3.6 1.6 3.2

NOVEMBER

Day	Time	m	Day	Time	m
1 SU	0338 0937 1612 2138	1.6 3.4 1.9 3.0	16 M	0317 0907 1555 2158	1.2 3.6 1.6 3.1
2 M ☽	0436 1048 1718 2306	1.8 3.2 2.1 2.8	17 TU ☾	0416 1012 1708 2332	1.4 3.4 1.7 3.0
3 TU	0546 1222 1838	2.0 3.1 2.1	18 W	0522 1139 1833	1.4 3.3 1.7
4 W	0117 0704 1345 1956	2.9 2.0 3.2 2.0	19 TH	0111 0634 1323 1955	3.1 1.4 3.4 1.6
5 TH	0228 0814 1439 2052	3.0 1.9 3.4 1.9	20 F	0222 0747 1440 2100	3.2 1.3 3.5 1.4
6 F	0311 0908 1521 2133	3.2 1.8 3.6 1.7	21 SA	0317 0852 1535 2151	3.4 1.2 3.7 1.2
7 SA	0345 0950 1558 2209	3.4 1.6 3.7 1.4	22 SU	0402 0949 1619 2234	3.7 1.0 3.8 1.1
8 SU	0417 1027 1632 2242	3.6 1.4 3.9 1.3	23 M	0443 1039 1657 2314	3.8 0.9 3.9 1.0
9 M	0447 1101 1706 2315	3.8 1.3 4.0 1.1	24 TU ●	0520 1125 1733 2353	4.0 0.9 3.9 0.9
10 TU ○	0516 1134 1739 2348	3.9 1.2 4.0 1.0	25 W	0556 1208 1807	4.1 0.9 3.9
11 W	0546 1207 1812	4.0 1.1 4.0	26 TH	0031 0632 1250 1842	0.9 4.1 1.0 3.8
12 TH	0023 0618 1243 1846	0.9 4.0 1.1 3.9	27 F	0110 0709 1331 1917	1.0 4.0 1.2 3.7
13 F	0101 0653 1322 1924	0.9 4.0 1.2 3.8	28 SA	0149 0748 1413 1954	1.1 3.9 1.4 3.5
14 SA	0142 0732 1406 2005	1.0 3.9 1.3 3.6	29 SU	0230 0829 1456 2033	1.3 3.8 1.6 3.4
15 SU	0226 0816 1456 2054	1.1 3.8 1.4 3.3	30 M	0313 0913 1542 2115	1.5 3.6 1.8 3.2

DECEMBER

Day	Time	m	Day	Time	m
1 TU	0400 1003 1633 2208	1.7 3.4 2.0 3.1	16 W ☾	0358 0956 1644 2249	1.1 3.6 1.5 3.2
2 W ☽	0454 1105 1732 2321	1.9 3.3 2.1 3.0	17 TH	0457 1102 1753	1.3 3.4 1.6
3 TH	0557 1220 1838	2.0 3.2 2.1	18 F	0013 0602 1231 1909	3.1 1.4 3.3 1.7
4 F	0051 0705 1333 1943	3.0 2.1 3.3 2.0	19 SA	0142 0713 1415 2024	3.2 1.5 3.3 1.6
5 SA	0205 0811 1433 2039	3.1 2.0 3.4 1.8	20 SU	0253 0827 1527 2126	3.3 1.5 3.4 1.5
6 SU	0259 0906 1523 2126	3.3 1.9 3.5 1.6	21 M	0349 0933 1618 2217	3.5 1.4 3.5 1.3
7 M	0341 0953 1606 2208	3.4 1.7 3.7 1.4	22 TU	0434 1030 1658 2300	3.7 1.3 3.6 1.2
8 TU	0419 1035 1647 2248	3.6 1.5 3.8 1.2	23 W	0514 1117 1732 2340	3.8 1.2 3.6 1.1
9 W ○	0455 1115 1726 2327	3.8 1.3 3.9 1.0	24 TH ●	0549 1200 1803	3.9 1.2 3.7
10 TH	0531 1155 1804	4.0 1.2 4.0	25 F	0018 0623 1240 1834	1.0 4.0 1.2 3.7
11 F	0007 0608 1236 1843	0.9 4.1 1.1 3.9	26 SA	0056 0658 1318 1907	1.0 4.1 1.2 3.7
12 SA	0049 0648 1319 1923	0.8 4.1 1.0 3.9	27 SU	0133 0733 1355 1941	1.1 4.0 1.3 3.7
13 SU	0132 0729 1404 2005	0.8 4.1 1.1 3.7	28 M	0210 0809 1432 2014	1.2 3.9 1.5 3.6
14 M	0217 0813 1452 2052	0.8 4.0 1.2 3.6	29 TU	0247 0845 1509 2049	1.4 3.8 1.6 3.5
15 TU	0306 0901 1545 2144	1.0 3.8 1.3 3.4	30 W	0325 0923 1548 2124	1.6 3.6 1.8 3.3
			31 TH	0403 1004 1631 2204	1.7 3.4 1.9 3.2

Chart Datum: 2.10 metres below Ordnance Datum (Newlyn)

LOCH MELFORT 10-8-17

Argyll

CHARTS
Admiralty 2326, 2169; Imray C65; OS 55

TIDES
Loch Shuna −0615 Dover; ML Seil Sound 1.4; Duration Seil Sound 0615; Zone 0 (GMT).

Standard Port OBAN (⟵)

Times				Height (metres)			
HW		LW		MHWS	MHWN	MLWN	MLWS
0100	0700	0100	0800	4.0	2.9	1.8	0.7
1300	1900	1300	2000				
Differences SEIL SOUND							
−0035	−0015	−0040	−0015	−1.3	−0.9	−0.7	−0.3
SCALASAIG (Colonsay)							
−0020	−0005	−0015	+0005	−0.1	−0.2	−0.2	−0.2
GLENGARRISDALE BAY (Jura)							
−0020	0000	−0010	0000	−0.4	−0.2	0.0	−0.2

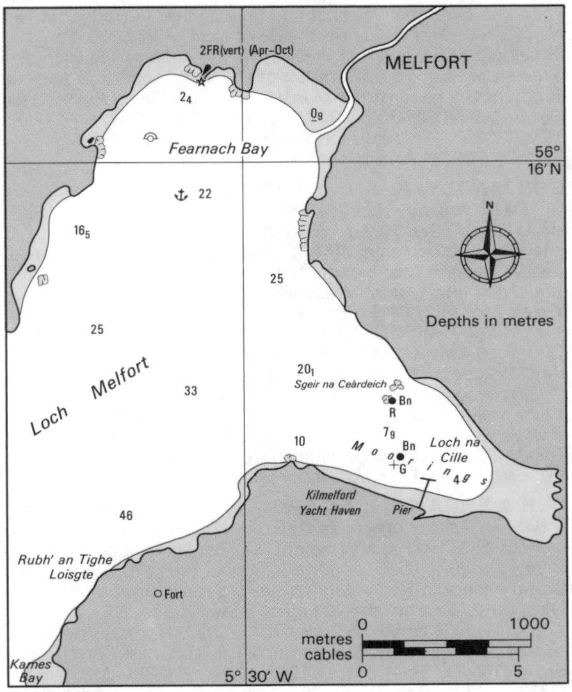
2FR(vert) (Apr–Oct)
MELFORT
Fearnach Bay
56° 16′N
Depths in metres
Loch Melfort
Sgeir na Ceàrdeich
Loch na Cille
Moorings
Kilmelford Yacht Haven
Pier
Rubh' an Tighe Loisgte
Fort
metres
cables
0
1000
5
Kames Bay
5° 30′ W

SHELTER
Loch Melfort provides several sheltered anchorages. There is a bay with moorings ½M inside the entrance on S shore, but beware rock which dries 1.5m. 1M further E is Kames Bay with some room to anchor clear of moorings, rocks and fish farm, and sheltered from S and W. Fearnach Bay at NE end of loch is a good anchorage in N winds and moorings are available. Best shelter of all is in Loch na Cille, where Kilmelford Yacht Haven provides swinging and pontoon moorings.

NAVIGATION
Waypoint 56°14′.00N 05°35′.00W, 210°/030° from/to summit Eilean Gamhna, 4ca. Pass either side of Eilean Gamhna. 8ca NE lies Campbell Rock (1.8m). A rock which dries 0.9m lies 1½ca ESE of the FS on Eilean Coltair. The S side of Loch Melfort is mostly steep-to, except in Kames Bay. Approaching Kilmelford Yacht Haven beware drying reef which extends ¾ca from NE shore and is marked by a red and black (port-hand) perch, and also a rock near S shore marked by green (stbd-hand) perch.

LIGHTS AND MARKS
2FR(vert) 6m 3M on the pier in Fearnach Bay, (1 Apl to 31 Oct).

RADIO TELEPHONE
Kilmelford Yacht Haven VHF Ch **80** M (working hours).

TELEPHONE (085 22)
Hr Mr 248; MRSC Oban 63720; ⋕ Oban 63079; Marinecall 0898 500 463; Police (0631) 62213; Ⓗ Lochgilphead 2323.

FACILITIES
Kilmelford Yacht Haven ☎ 248, BH (12 ton), Slip, ME, El, Sh, CH, Gas, Gaz, D, FW. **Melfort Marine** (Fearnach Bay) ☎ 257, M, AB, Gas, D, FW, R, Bar, P, D, AC, Sh, V; **Village** (¾M) V, Bar, ✉.

CRAOBH HAVEN (Loch Shuna) 10-8-18

Argyll

CHARTS
Admiralty 2326, 2169; Imray C65; OS 55

TIDES
HW Loch Shuna −0615 Dover; ML Seil Sound 1.4; Duration Seil Sound 0615; Zone 0 (GMT). For tidal figures see 10.8.17 opposite.

SHELTER
Craobh (pronounced Creuve) Haven is a yacht harbour on E shore of Loch Shuna. It is enclosed by Eilean Buidhe on the NE side, and by Eilean an Duin and Fraoch Eilean to the NW and W. Each island has a causeway to the shore. The entrance on the N side is formed by breakwaters. Very good shelter within. There are anchorages in Asknish Bay 1M to the N, and in the bays S of Craobh Haven — E of Eilean Arsa and in Bagh an Tight-Stoir.

NAVIGATION
Waypoint 56°12′.84N 05°33′.40W, 270°/090° from/to entrance, 0.5M. Tidal streams in Loch Shuna are weak. Beware un-marked reefs Eich Donna NE of the island Eilean Gamhna. A stbd-hand buoy marks a rock (1m) which lies ¾ca NNW of the N breakwater head. Port-hand buoys mark a shoal area close S of the E breakwater. A pink perch on W corner of harbour marks a spit. Elsewhere there is ample depth in the marina.

LIGHTS AND MARKS
There are no lights or marks.

RADIO TELEPHONE
VHF Ch 16, M, 74, **80** (summer 0800−1900 LT; winter 0900−1700 LT).

TELEPHONE (085 25)
Hr Mr 222; MRSC Oban 63720; ⋕ Oban 63079; Marinecall 0898 500 463; Police (0631) 62213; Ⓗ Lochgilphead 2323.

FACILITIES
Craobh Haven Marina (175+25 visitors) ☎ 222, AC, FW, D, P, SM, V, Bar, BY ☎ 225; CH ☎ 622, Access H24; **Camus Marine Services** (200) ☎ Slip, BH (15 ton), C (12 ton), Gas, Gaz, CH, ME, El, Sh.
Craobh Haven Bank (Wednesday or at Lochgilphead), ✉ (Kilmelford); ⇌ (Oban by bus); ✈ (Glasgow).

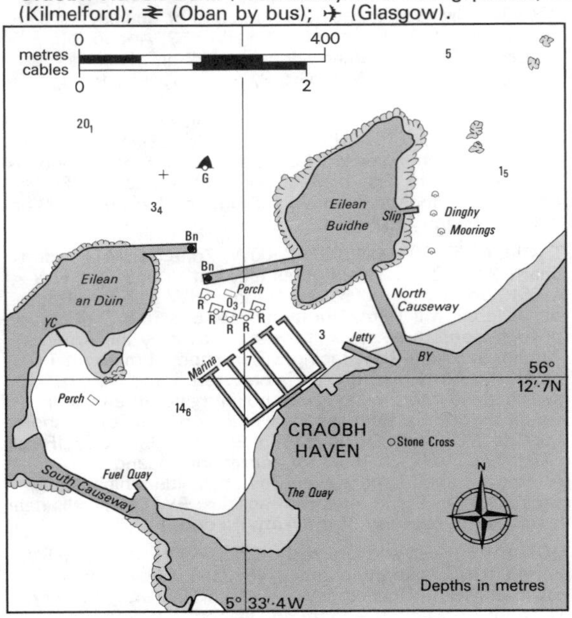
metres
cables
0
400
2
Eilean Buidhe
Slip
Dinghy Moorings
Eilean an Dùin
Perch
North Causeway
YC
Jetty
BY
Marina
56° 12′·7N
CRAOBH HAVEN
Stone Cross
Fuel Quay
South Causeway
The Quay
Depths in metres
5° 33′·4W

8

MINOR HARBOURS AND ANCHORAGES 10-8-19

LOCH LAXFORD, Sutherland, 58°25′·00N, 05°08′·00W, Zone 0 (GMT), Admty chart 2503. HW −0410 on Dover, +0010 on Ullapool. See 10.8.8. Ent between Rubha Ruadh and Ardmore Pt, 1M ENE, clearly identified by three isolated mountains Ben Stack, Ben Arkle and Foinaven inland. There are many anchorages in the loch including: Loch a'Chadh-fi on NE side (John Ridgway's Adventure School has moorings − check with school on Pt on W side of narrows); Bagh nah-Airde Beag, next bay to E, (beware rk ½ ca off SE shore which covers at MHWS); Fanagmore Bay on SW shore (beware head of bay foul with old moorings); Bagh na Fionndalach Mor on SW shore (4-6m); Weaver's Bay on SW shore, 3M from ent (beware drying rock off NW Pt of ent). Beware many fish farming cages. Facilities: none, nearest at Scourie (5M).

LOCH INVER, Sutherland, 58°09′·00N, 05°15′·00W, Zone 0 (GMT), Admty chart 2504. HW −0433 on Dover, −0005 on Ullapool; HW height −0·1m on Ullapool; ML 3·1m. See 10.8.8. Entrance between Soya I and Kirkaig Pt. Beward rk about 50m off Kirkaig Pt which dries. About 1M up the loch is the islet Glas Leac with a Lt Fl WRG 3s 7m; W071°-080°, R080°-090°, G090°-103°, W103°-111°, R111°-243°, W243°-251°, G251°-071°. Anchor at top of loch in 6m approx in middle of bay off the pier. Perfect shelter from all winds. Facilities: Shop, ✉, Hotel, Gas, FW, P, D.

LOCH SHELL, Harris, 58°00′·00N, 06°25′·00W, Zone 0 (GMT), Admty chart 1794. HW −0437 on Dover, −0016 on Ullapool; HW height −0·4m on Ullapool; ML 2·7m. See 10.8.7. Pass S of Eilean Iuvard; beware rks to W of Is. Anchor in Tob Eishken, 2½M up loch on N shore (beware rk awash on E side of ent), or at head of loch (exposed to E winds, and dries some distance). Facilities: ✉/Stores at Lemrevay.

WEST LOCH TARBERT, Harris, 57°55′·00N, 06°55′·00W, Zone 0 (GMT) Admty chart 2841. HW −0515 on Dover, −0055 on Ullapool; HW height −0·8m on Ullapool; Duration 0550. See 10.8.7. Good shelter once beyond Taransay. Safest entrance to N of Taransay thence up the S side of loch. Beware rks and islets on N shore. Anchor at head of loch in approx 10m off Tarbert village. There are three small lochs off N shore which provide good alternative anchorages − Lochs Leosavay, Meavaig and Bunavoneadar. Facilities: FW only but Tarbert is only ¼M aay.

EAST LOCH TARBERT, Harris, 57°51′·00N, 06°45′·00W, Zone 0 (GMT), Admty chart 2905. HW −0446 on Dover, −0026 on Ullapool; HW height −0·2m on Ullapool; ML 2·8m; Duration 0605. See 10.8.7. Approach through Sound of Scalpay; beware Elliot Rk (depth 2m) 2½ ca SSW of Rubha Crago. Eilean Glas Lt Ho at E end of Scalpay, Fl (3) 20s 43m 23M; W Tr, R bands. In sound of Scalpay, stream sets W from HW +3, and E from HW −3. Anchor off Tarbert WSW of steamer pier in about 2·5m. Facilities: EC Thurs; Bar, D, Dr, FW at pier, P, ✉, R, V, ferry to Uig (Skye).
Alternatively Scalpay North Harbour gives good shelter. Beware rk ½ ca off Aird an Aiseig, E side of entrance. Stbd hand buoy marks wreck off Coddem. ½ ca E of the buoy is a rk, depth 1·1m. Fish pier at S end of harbour has 2FG (vert) lights; anchor ¾ ca N, in about 3m. Facilities: FW at pier, ✉, V, ferry to Harris.

ST KILDA, 57°50′·00N, 08°30′·00W, Zone 0 (GMT), Admty charts 2721, 2524. Tidal figures taken at Village Bay; HW −0510 on Dover, −0055 on Ullapool; HW height −1·6m on Ullapool; ML 1·9m; Duration 0615. See 10.8.7. A group of four Is and three stacks now taken over by the Army. Anchor in Village Bay, facing SE, in approx 5m about 1·5 ca off the Army pier. If wind is between S and NE big swells come into the bay; poor holding and untenable if winds are strong. Reef lies parallel to and ½ ca off N shore. Ldg Lts 270°, both Oc 5s 26/38m 3M. Yachts with VHF call *Kilda Radio* VHF Ch 16;08 for permission to land. Alternative anchorage is Glen Bay on N side which is only satisfactory in S and E winds. Facilities: FW from wells near landings (by courtesy of the Army); Food, FW, ☎.

LOCH EWE, Ross and Cromarty, 57°51′·00N, 05°38′·00W, Zone 0 (GMT), Admty charts 3146, 2509. Tidal figures taken at Mellon Charles; HW −0415 on Dover, −0010 on Ullapool; HW height −0·1m on Ullapool; ML 2·9m; Duration 0610. See 10.8.8. Excellent shelter in all winds except N. Easy entrance with no dangers in loch except Boor Rks on W shore about 0·7M from loch head. Loch approx 7M long with Isle Ewe with two small Islets about 2M from entrance in centre of loch which can be passed on either side. Beware unlit mooring buoys and also dolphins near MoD (Navy) pier E side of entrance. Loch divides beyond Isle Ewe. MoD fuelling pier, dolphins and marker buoys opposite E end of Isle Ewe. Excellent anchorage in Loch Thurnaig to E. Aultbea Pier, partly derelict, to NE. Beware fish farming cages. Fairway Lt buoy LFl 10s; No 1 Lt buoy Fl(3) G 10s; NATO fuelling jetty and dolphins, all Fl G 4s. Facilities: Dr., P, ✉, R, V, Bar. On pier D, L, S of Poolewe Bay (3·5m), **Inverewe Gdns** FW, Bar, D, L, P (at garage), ✉, R, V, Gas.

LOCH GAIRLOCH, Ross and Cromarty, 57°43′·00N, 05°45′·00W, Zone 0 (GMT), Admty charts 2528, 2210. HW −0440 on Dover, −0020 on Ullapool; HW height +0·1m on Ullapool; ML 2·9m; Duration 0600. See 10.8.8. A wide loch facing W. Entrance clear of dangers. Quite heavy seas roll in bad weather. Yachts can take shelter in Badachro to W of Eilean Horrisdale on S side of loch or in Loch Shieldaig at SE end of the loch. At the head of the loch, Flowerdale Bay, the N branch of the loch, anchor in approx 6m near the head of the pier. Lights: Glas Eilean Fl WRG 6s 9m 6/4M W080°-102°, R102°-296°, W296°-333°, G333°-080°. Pierhead, QR 9m. Facilities: Loch Shirlaig Hotel (½M), P, D, FW; stores ½M.

LOCH MADDY, North Uist, 57°36′·00N, 07°08′·00W, Zone 0 (GMT), Admty chart 2825 HW −0500 on Dover, −0039 on Ullapool. See 10.8.7. With strong wind against tide there can be bad seas off ent. Approaches clear but from S inside Madadh Mor beware submerged rk ½ ca N of Leac nam Madadh. Lights: Weaver's Pt Fl 3s 21m 7M; Glas Eilean Mor Fl(2) 6s 8m;Rudna Nam Fl R 4s 7m 5M; inside loch Ruigh Liath QG, Lochmaddy pier Ldg Lts 298°. Front 2FG(vert) 4M. Rear OcG 8s 10m 4M; vis 284° − 304°. Anchorages: off Steamer Pier; in Charles Harbour; Oronsay − go alongside private pier but anchoring not recommended owing to moorings; Sponish Harbour; Loch Portain; Vallaquie. VHF Ch 16; 12. Port Manager ☎ 63337 (day), 63226 (night). Facilities: Lochmaddy, EC Wed, Shop, Ⓑ, Gas, ✉, P, D, FW; Loch Portain ✉, Shop.

LOCH A'BHRAIGE, Rona, 57°34′·00N, 05°58′·00W, Zone 0 (GMT), Admty charts 2534, 2749. HW −0438 on Dover, −0023 on Ullapool; HW height +0·2m on Ullapool; ML 2·9m; Duration 0605. A good safe anchorage in NW of the island except in NNW winds. Beware rocks on the NE side lying up to a ca off shore. Lights Sgeir Shuas, NE of entrance, Fl R 2s 6m 3M; vis 070° − 199°. Harbour in NE corner of loch, Lt on SW corner 2 FR (vert). Ldg Lts 137°. Front Q WRG 3m 4/3M, W135° − 138°, R138° − 318°, G318° − 135°. Rear Iso 6s 28m 5M. Facilities very limited. There is a pier, FW and a helipad. Alternative shelter at Acarseid Mhor at SW of Island. (Sketch chart of rocks at entrance is necessary). Loch is used by MoD (Navy) − call on VHF Ch 16 to Rona Naval Establishment before entering.

CROWLIN ISLANDS, Ross and Cromarty, 57°21′·00N, 05°51′·00W. Zone 0 (GMT), Admty charts 2498, 2209. HW −0435 on Dover, −0020 on Ullapool; HW height +0·3m on Ullapool. Anchor between Eilean Meadhonach and Eilean Mor, approaching from N, keep E of Eilean Beg. Excellent shelter except in strong N winds. There is an inner anchorage with 3½m but entrance channel dries. Eilean Beg Lt Ho FlW 6s 32m 6M. There are no facilities.

LOCH HARPORT, Isle of Skye, 57°20′·00N, 06°25′·00W, Zone 0 (GMT), Admty chart 1795. HW −0447 (Sp), −0527 (Np) on Dover, −0035 (Sp) −0115 (Np) on Ullapool; HW height −0·1m on Ullapool. See 10.8.9. On E side of Loch Bracadale, entered between Oronsay I and Ardtreck Pt (W Lt Ho, Iso 4s 17m 9M). SW end of Oronsay has conspic rock pillar, called The Castle; keep ¼M off-shore here and off E coast of Oronsay which is joined to Ullinish Pt by drying reef. Anchorages: Oronsay Is, N side of drying reef (4m), or on E side, but beware rk (dries) 0·5ca off N shore of Oronsay. Fiskavaig Bay 1M S of Ardtreck (7m); Loch Beag on N side of loch, exposed to W winds; Port na Long E of Ardtreck, sheltered except from E winds (beware fish farm); Carbost on SW shore. Facilities: (Carbost) EC Wed; V (local shop), Bar, R, P (garage), ✉, FW. (Port na Long) Bar, FW.

MINOR HARBOURS AND ANCHORAGES *Continued*

PLOCKTON, LOCH CARRON, Ross and Cromarty, 57°20′·00N, 05°39′·00W, Zone 0 (GMT), Admty charts 2528, 2209. HW −0435 on Dover, −0020 on Ullapool; HW height +0·3m on Ullapool; ML 3·2m; Duration 0600. See 10.8.9. Good anchorage on S side of Outer Loch Carron. Safest entrance between Sgeir Bhuidhe and Sgeir Golach, thence S to pass between Dubgh Sgeir and Hawk Rks off Cat Is. (with conspic stone tower). Beware Plockton Rks off Yellow Cliff Isle. Lts established 57°21′·93N, 05°37′·32W Dir Fl (3) WRG 10s 8m 6/4M vis: G060°-063°, W063°-067°, R067°-070°. Duncraig Dir Lt at 57°20′·33N 05°37′·65 W Dir Fl (3) WRG 10s 5m 6/4M vis G157°-162°, W162°-166°, R166°-171°. Leacanashie Dir Lt 042·5° 4m 6/4M At 57°21′·58N, 05°34′·53W Dir Fl (3) WRG 10s 4m 6/4M G318°-041°, W041°-044°, R044°-050°. Sgeir Golach marked by G Bn with cone. Anchor in centre of bay in approx 3·5m. Facilities: **Leisure Marine** D, CH; **Village** Bar, FW, ✉, R, ⇌, Gas, V, airstrip.

LOCH ÀLSH, Ross and Cromarty, 57°17′·00N, 05°34′·00W, Zone 0 (GMT), Admty charts 2540, 2541. Tidal figures taken at Dornie Bridge; HW −0450 on Dover, −0025 on Ullapool; HW height 0·0 on Ullapool; ML 3·0m; Duration 0555. See 10.8.9. Almost land-locked between the SE corner of Skye and the mainland. Safe anchorages can be found for most winds; off the hotel at Kyle of Lochalsh in 11m; in Ardintoul Bay on S shore opposite Racoon Rk in 5·5m; in Totaig (or Ob Aonig) opposite Loch Long entrance in 3·5m; in Ratigan Bay in SW corner of the loch in 7m; in Avernish Bay, W of Rubh' an Aisig in 3m (open to SW); inside the pier at Kyleakin. Kyle of Lochalsh is an important ferry port and railhead; yachts can go alongside E end of pier to fuel. Pier head Lts 2 FG (vert) 6/5m 5M on W side, 2 FG (vert) 6/5m 4M on E side. Facilities (at Kyle of Lochalsh): Hr Mr ☎ Kyle 4167, Bar, D, FW, ✉, R, ⇌, V, airstrip, CH, P. Bus to Glasgow or Inverness.

LOCH BOISDALE, South Uist, 57°09′·00N, 07°18′·00W, Zone 0 (GMT), Admty chart 2770. HW −0455 on Dover, −0045 on Ullapool; HW height −0·9m on Ullapool; ML 2·4m; Duration 0600. See 10.8.7. Good shelter except in SE gales when swell runs right up the 2M loch. Safest entrance from N passing between Rubha na Cruibe and Calvay Is. From S beware Clan Ewan Rk, dries 1m, and McKenzie Rk, marked by R can Lt buoy Fl(3) R 15s. Channel up to Boisdale Hr N of Gasay Is. (beware rks off E end). Anchor off pier in approx 4m, or SW of Gasay Is. in approx 9m. There are fish cages W of Ru Bhuaitt. Calvay Is. E end Fl(2) WRG 10s 16m 7/4M; vis G190°−202°, W202°−286°, R286°−111°, W111°−190°. Gasay I Fl WR 5s 10m 7/4M; vis W120°−284°, R284°−120°. Gasay I, N side QG. Ludaig Dir Lt 297°, Dir Oc WRG 6s 8m 7/4M; G287°−296°, W296°−298°, R298°−307°. N pier 2 FG (vert). Ro Ro terminal Iso RG 4s 12m 2M Gshore−283°, R283°−shore. N entrance Ldg line, pier in line with Hollisgeir at 245°. Facilities: EC Tues; Bar, FW (tap on pier); P, ✉, R, V, ferry to mainland.

RHUM (The Small Islands) Inverness, 57°01′·00N, 05°55′·00W, Zone 0 (GMT), Admty charts 2207, 2208. HW−0500 on Dover, −0035 on Ullapool; HW height −0·3m on Ullapool, ML 2·4 m, Duration 0600. Only landing allowed at Loch Scresort on E side; no dogs. Island belongs to Nature Conservancy Council. Beware drying rocks off N point up to ¼ M off shore and off W point up to 1 ca offshore. Harbour exposed to E. winds. Facilities: Hotel, ✉, FW, V, R, Bar, Ferry to Mallaig.

CANNA, The Small Islands, 57°03′·00N, 06°29′·00W, Zone 0 (GMT), Admty charts 2208, 1796. HW −0457 (Sp), −0550 (Np) on Dover, −0035 on Ullapool; HW height −0·4m on Ullapool; Duration 0605. Good shelter except in strong E winds. Hr lies between Canna and Sanday Is. Most of Hr dries. Anchor in 3m to 4m having entered Hr along Sanday Is. shore: beware drying patch W of pier on Canna side. Lights: Sanday Is. Fl 6s 32m 9M, vis 152°−061°. Beware abnormal magnetic variations off NE Canna. Facilities: FW only. **Note:** Canna is a National Trust for Scotland island and yachtsmen are asked to refrain from ditching rubbish.

LOCH NEVIS, Inverness, 57°02′·00N, 05°44′·00W, Zone 0 (GMT), Admty charts 2541, 2208. HW −0515 on Dover, +0030 on Oban. HW height +1·0m on Oban. Anchorage NE of Eilean na Glaschoille, good except in S winds. Beware rocks Bogha cas Sruth (dries 1·8m), Bogha Don and Sgeirean Glasa both marked by Bns. Upper parts of the loch subject to very violent unpredictable squalls. Yachts can pass into the inner loch with care, and anchor N or SE of Eilean Maol, but this passage should be undertaken with caution.

CASTLEBAY, Barra, 56°57′·00N, 07°29′·00W, Zone 0 (GMT), Admty chart 2769. HW −0525 on Dover, −0105 on Ullapool; HW height −0·8m on Ullapool; ML 2·3m; Duration 0600. See 10.8.7. Very good shelter and holding ground. Best anchorage NW of Kiessimul Castle (on an Island) in approx 8m; NE of castle are rocks: There are HIDB visitors buoys to W of pier. Alternative anchorage in Vattersay Bay in approx 9m. Vatersay Sound has been closed by a causeway across its W end. Beware rks NNW of Dubh Sgeir; Dubh Sgeir Lt Fl(2) WG 6s 6m 7/5M; vis W280°-180°, G180°-280°. Sgeir Liath Lt Fl 3s 7m 8M. Ldg Lts 295°, Front on Rubha Glas, FG 9m 4M, Or Δ on W framework Tr, rear, 550m from front, FG 15m 4M, Or Δ on W framework Tr. Facilities: Bar, D, FW, P, ✉, R, V. Ferry to mainland.

EIGG HARBOUR, Eigg, 56°53′·00N, 06°08′·00W, Zone 0 (GMT), Admty chart 2207. HW −0523 on Dover, +0025 on Oban, HW height +0.7m on Oban. See 10.8.10. Most of Hr dries but yachts can anchor NE of Galmisdale Pt which is good anchorage, except in NE winds when yachts should go through the narrows and anchor in South Bay in 6/8m. Tide runs strongly in the narrows. Coming from N beware Garbh Sgeir and Flod Sgeir, both marked by Bns. SE point of Eilean Chathastail Fl 6s 24m 8M, vis 181°−shore. VHF, call *Eigg Harbour*, Ch 16; 08. Facilities: FW, D, repairs can be arranged by Hr Mr; **Village** (2M) Bar, ✉, R, V, Gas.

ARISAIG, (Loch Nan Ceall), Inverness, 56°54′·00N, 05°55′·00W, Zone 0 (GMT), Admty chart 2207. HW −0515 on Dover, +0030 on Oban; HW height +0·9m on Oban; ML 2·9m; Duration 0605. Anchorage above Cave Rock, approx 1M within the entrance, is well sheltered. South channel is winding but is marked by perches. Ldg line into loch is S point of Eigg and N point of Muck. There are numerous unmarked rocks. There are no lights. VHF, Call *Arisaig Harbour* Ch 16. Facilities: EC Thurs; FW at hotel; **Sea Leisure Centre** ☎ 224 C (10 ton), CH, D, El, M, ME, P, Sh, V. **Village** Bar, ✉, R, ⇌, V.

ARINAGOUR, Loch Eatharna, Coll, 56°37′·00N, 06°31′·00W. Zone 0 (GMT). Admty charts 2474, 2171. HW −0530 on Dover, +0015 on Oban; HW height +0·4m on Oban; ML 1·4m; Duration 0600; see 10.8.10. Good shelter except with SE swell or strong S winds. Entrance marked by Arinagour pier, NW of G buoy (Fl G 6s) marking Bogha Mor. Continue N towards old pier, pick up a buoy or anchor to S of it. Beware McQuarry's Rock (dries) 1 ca E of Arinagour pier. Lt on Arinagour pier head 2 FR(vert), 10m on metal column. Facilities: six visitors moorings on W side of harbour, N of pier. Alternative anchorage N of Eilean Eatharna. Facilities: Pinmester ☎ (087 93) 347 VHF Ch 31. **Highlands and Islands Development Board Trading Post** M, D, FW, Gas, V, CH, R; **Village** ◙, FW, P, Hotel, ✉.

DUNSTAFFNAGE, Argyll, 56°27′·00N, 05°26′·00W, Zone 0 (GMT), Admty charts 1790, 2387. HW −0500 on Dover; local tidal figures approx as for Oban. See 10.8.16. Good sheltered anchorage approached between Rubhagarbh and Eilean Mor. No navigational hazards. Anchor near castle in approx 5m or S part of bay or enter yacht harbour. Lts on pier head on NW side of bay 2 FG (vert) 4m 2M. Facilities: Land at pier; **Dunstaffnage Yacht Haven** ☎ Oban 66555 CH, R, BH (20 ton), Gas; **Ardtalla Yachts** ☎ Oban 65630 ME, El, Sh, ◙, SM, CH.

LOCH LATHAICH, Mull, 56°19′·00N, 06°14′·00W, Zone 0 (GMT), Admty chart 2617. HW −0545 on Dover, −0015 on Oban; HW height +0·2m on Oban. ML 2·4. See 10.8.12. Excellent shelter with easy access. Eileanan na Liathanaich (a group of islets) lie off the ent marked by a W Bn at the E end, Fl WR 6s 12m 8/6M, R088°-108°, W108°-088°. Keep to W side of loch and anchor behind White Is. at the head of loch (approx 5m). Facilities: (Bunessan) Shop, ✉, Bar, R, P (cans, 3M), FW (90m).

8

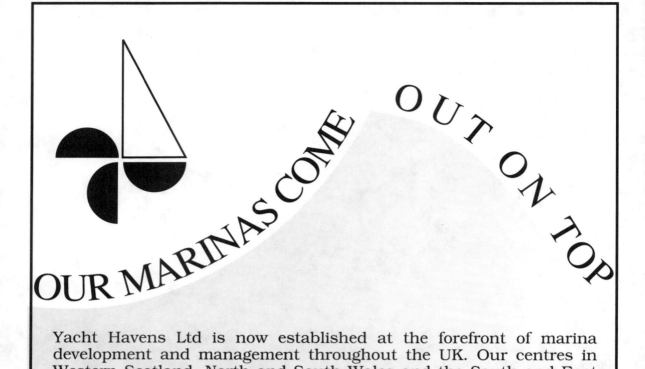

Area 9

South-West Scotland
Loch Craignish to Kirkcudbright

9

10-9-2

South West Scotland

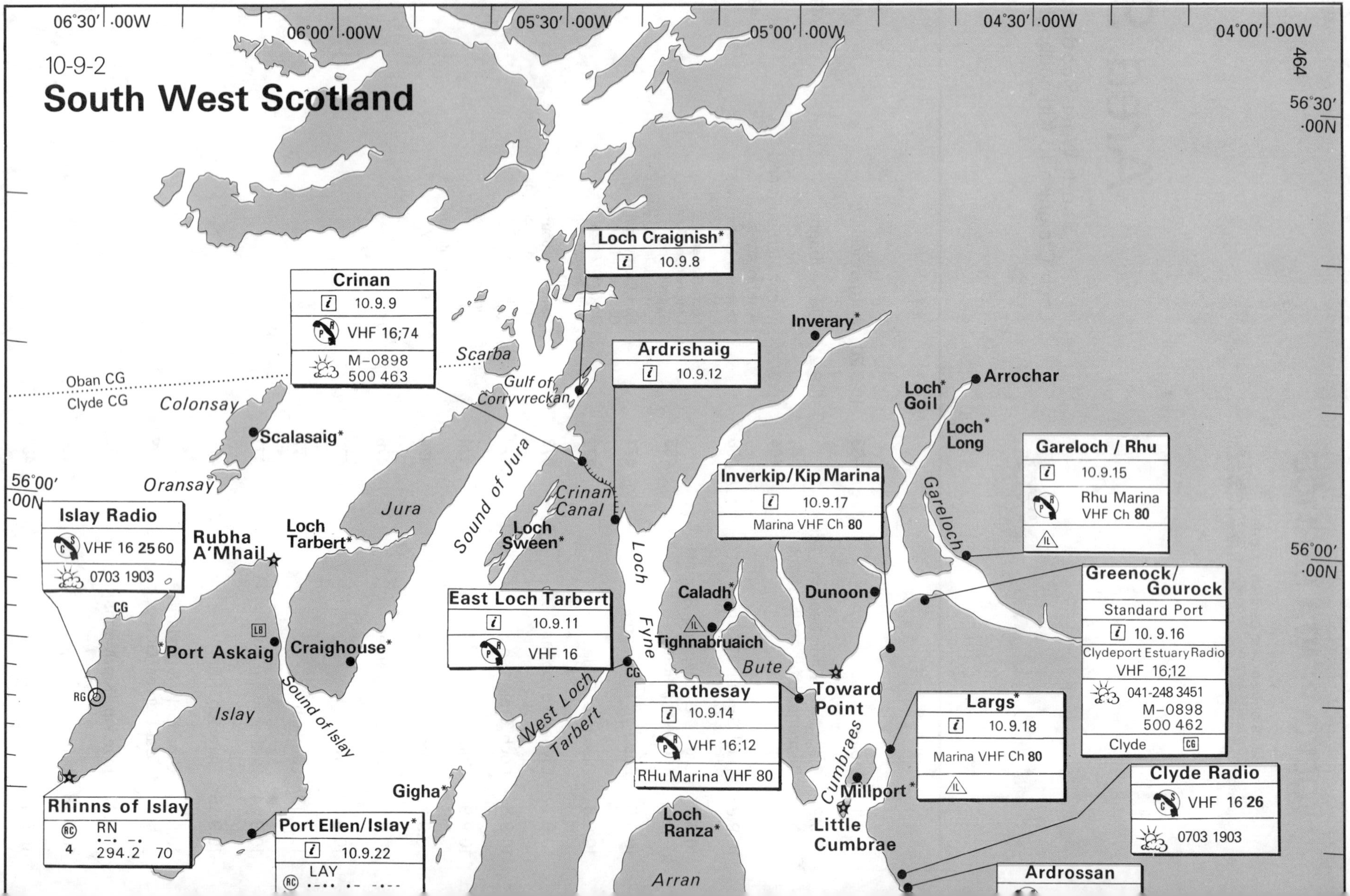
06°30'·00W
06°00'·00W
05°30'·00W
05°00'·00W
04°30'·00W
04°00'·00W
56°30'·00N
56°00'·00N
Loch Craignish*
10.9.8
Crinan
10.9.9
VHF 16;74
M-0898
500 463
Ardrishaig
10.9.12
Inverary*
Arrochar
Loch* Goil
Loch* Long
Gareloch / Rhu
10.9.15
Rhu Marina
VHF Ch 80
Gareloch
Inverkip/Kip Marina
10.9.17
Marina VHF Ch 80
Greenock/Gourock
Standard Port
10.9.16
Clydeport Estuary Radio
VHF 16;12
041-248 3451
M-0898
500 462
Clyde
CG
Oban CG
Clyde CG
Scarba
Gulf of Corryvreckan
Colonsay
Scalasaig*
Oransay
Jura
Sound of Jura
Crinan Canal
Loch Sween*
Loch Fyne
Caladh*
Dunoon
Tighnabruaich
Bute
Toward Point
Islay Radio
VHF 16 25 60
0703 1903
Rubha A'Mhail
Loch Tarbert*
CG
Port Askaig
LB
Craighouse*
East Loch Tarbert
10.9.11
VHF 16
CG
Rothesay
10.9.14
VHF 16;12
RHu Marina VHF 80
Largs*
10.9.18
Marina VHF Ch 80
RG
Islay
Sound of Islay
West Loch Tarbert
Cumbraes
Millport*
Little Cumbrae
Clyde Radio
VHF 16 26
0703 1903
Rhinns of Islay
RN
4
294.2
70
Gigha*
Port Ellen/Islay*
10.9.22
LAY
Loch Ranza*
Arran
Ardrossan

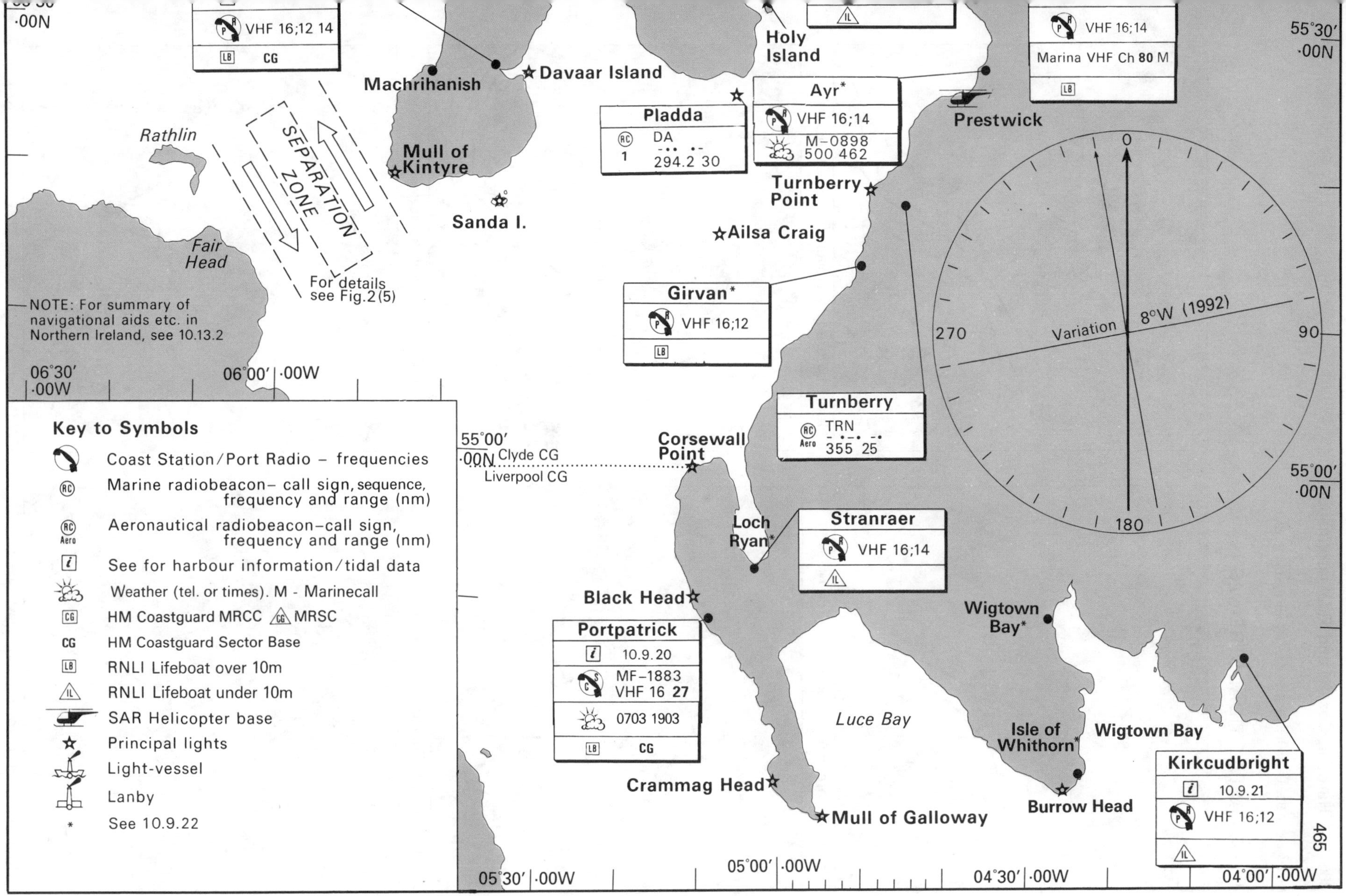
55°30′ ·00N
VHF 16;12 14
LB CG
Machrihanish
Davaar Island
Holy Island
Pladda
RC DA 1 294.2 30
Ayr*
VHF 16;14
M–0898 500 462
Prestwick
VHF 16;14
Marina VHF Ch 80 M
LB
Rathlin
SEPARATION ZONE
Mull of Kintyre
Sanda I.
Fair Head
For details see Fig.2(5)
Turnberry Point
Ailsa Craig
NOTE: For summary of navigational aids etc. in Northern Ireland, see 10.13.2
Girvan*
VHF 16;12
LB
0
8°W (1992)
Variation
270
90
180
06°30′ ·00W
06°00′ ·00W
Turnberry
RC Aero TRN 355 25
55°00′ ·00N
Clyde CG
Liverpool CG
Corsewall Point
Key to Symbols
Coast Station/Port Radio – frequencies
Marine radiobeacon– call sign, sequence, frequency and range (nm)
Aeronautical radiobeacon–call sign, frequency and range (nm)
See for harbour information/tidal data
Weather (tel. or times). M - Marinecall
HM Coastguard MRCC MRSC
HM Coastguard Sector Base
RNLI Lifeboat over 10m
RNLI Lifeboat under 10m
SAR Helicopter base
Principal lights
Light-vessel
Lanby
See 10.9.22
Loch Ryan*
Stranraer
VHF 16;14
Black Head
Portpatrick
10.9.20
MF–1883
VHF 16 27
0703 1903
LB CG
Wigtown Bay*
Luce Bay
Isle of Whithorn*
Wigtown Bay
Burrow Head
Kirkcudbright
10.9.21
VHF 16;12
Crammag Head
Mull of Galloway
05°30′ ·00W
05°00′ ·00W
04°30′ ·00W
04°00′ ·00W

Northward 10.8.3 Irish Sea 10.10.3 North Ireland 10.13.3

10.9.3. AREA 9 TIDAL STREAMS

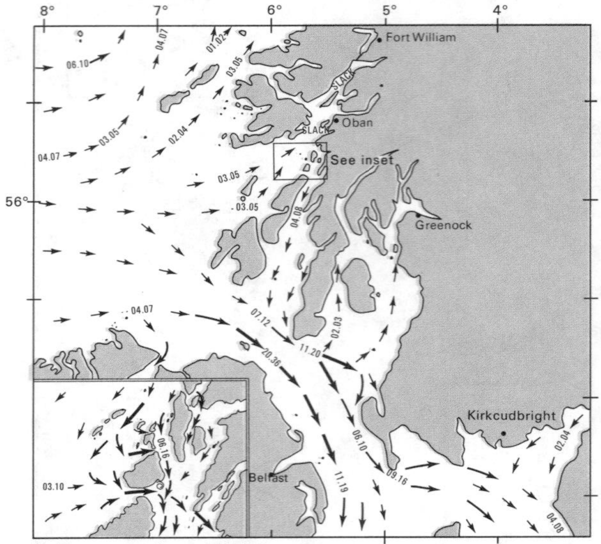
8°
7°
6°
5°
4°
56°
55°
Fort William
Oban
SLACK
See inset
Greenock
Kirkcudbright
Belfast

5 Hours before HW Dover (0050 before HW Ullapool)

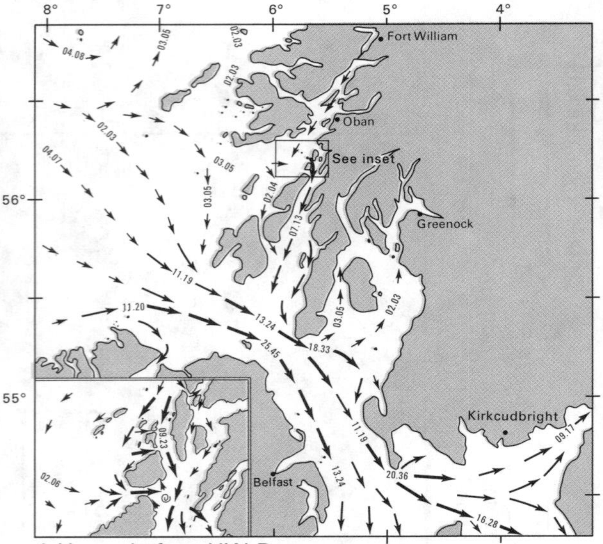
8°
7°
6°
5°
4°
56°
55°
Fort William
Oban
See inset
Greenock
Kirkcudbright
Belfast

4 Hours before HW Dover (0010 after HW Ullapool)

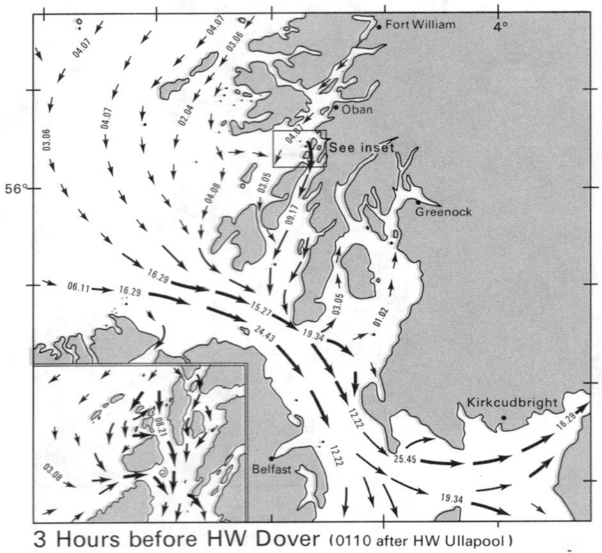
4°
56°
Fort William
Oban
See inset
Greenock
Kirkcudbright
Belfast

3 Hours before HW Dover (0110 after HW Ullapool)

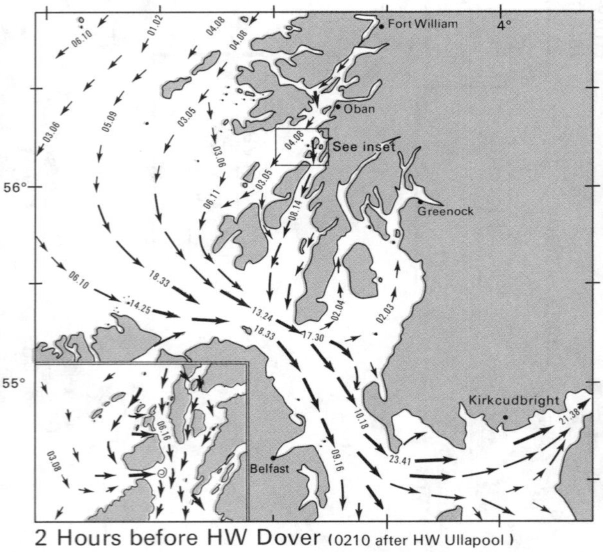
4°
56°
55°
Fort William
Oban
See inset
Greenock
Kirkcudbright
Belfast

2 Hours before HW Dover (0210 after HW Ullapool)

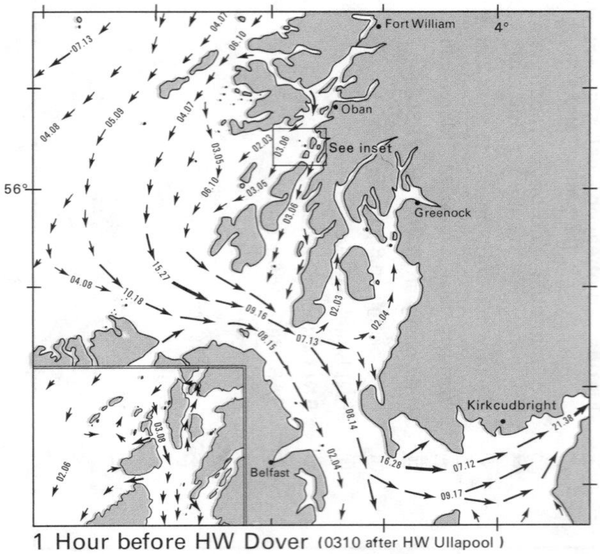
4°
56°
Fort William
Oban
See inset
Greenock
Kirkcudbright
Belfast

1 Hour before HW Dover (0310 after HW Ullapool)

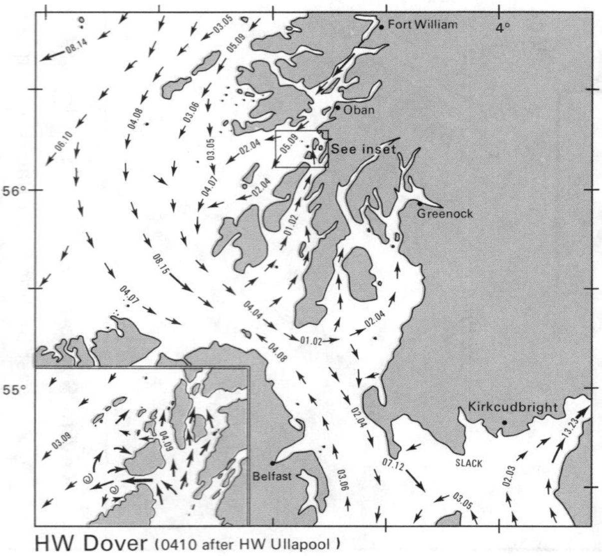
4°
56°
55°
Fort William
Oban
See inset
Greenock
Kirkcudbright
Belfast
SLACK

HW Dover (0410 after HW Ullapool)

Northward 10.8.3 Irish Sea 10.10.3 North Ireland 10.13.3

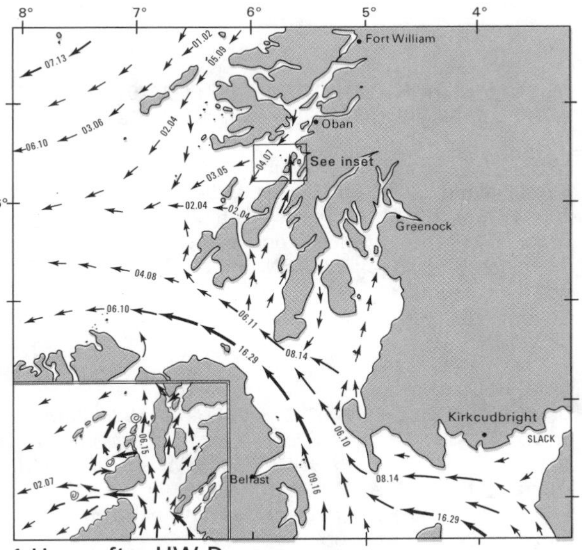
Fort William
Oban
See inset
Greenock
Kirkcudbright
SLACK
Belfast
1 Hour after HW Dover (0510 after HW Ullapool)

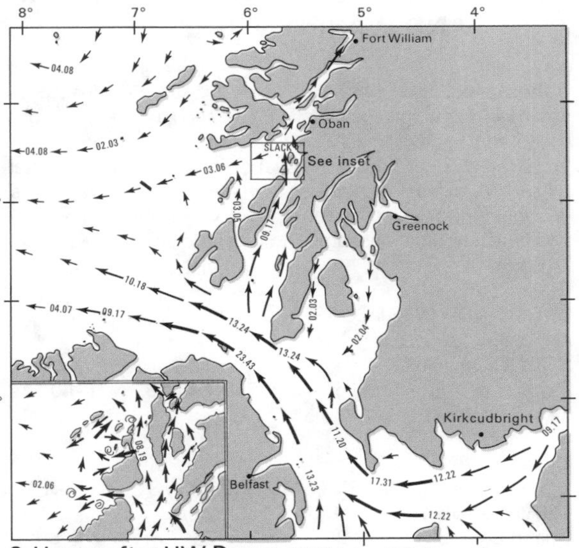
Fort William
Oban
SLACK
See inset
Greenock
Kirkcudbright
Belfast
2 Hours after HW Dover (0615 before HW Ullapool)

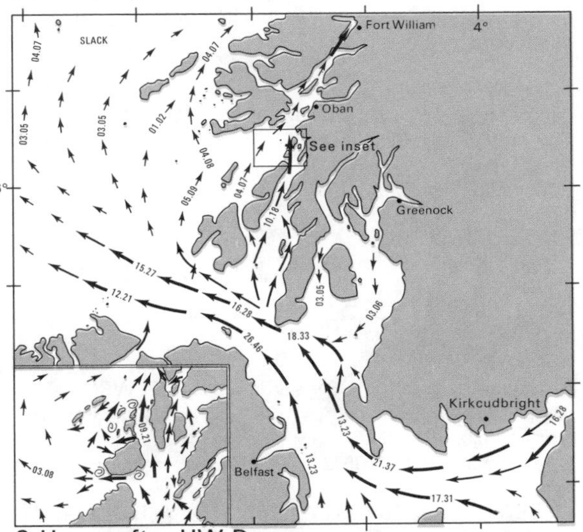
SLACK
Fort William
Oban
See inset
Greenock
Kirkcudbright
Belfast
3 Hours after HW Dover (0515 before HW Ullapool)

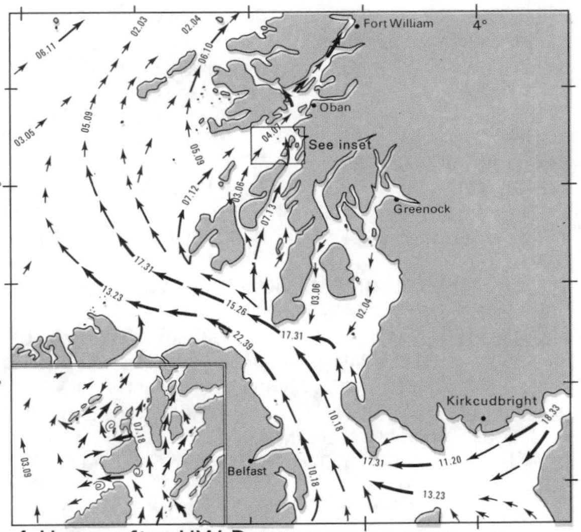
Fort William
Oban
See inset
Greenock
Kirkcudbright
Belfast
4 Hours after HW Dover (0415 before HW Ullapool)

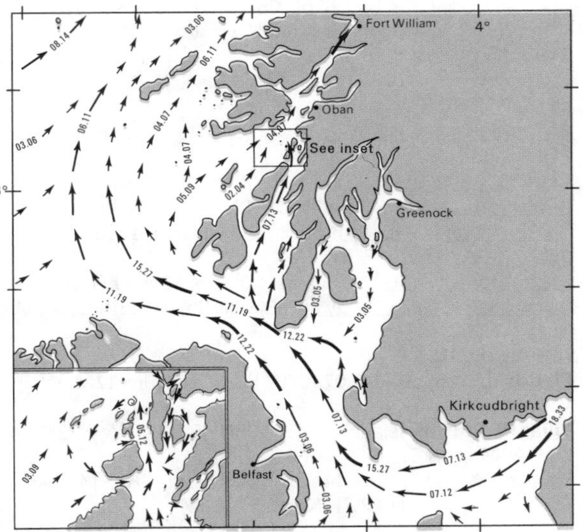
Fort William
Oban
See inset
Greenock
Kirkcudbright
Belfast
5 Hours after HW Dover (0315 before HW Ullapool)

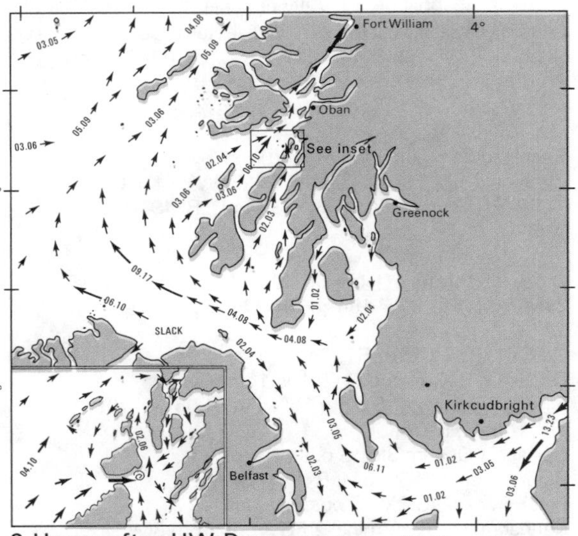
Fort William
Oban
See inset
Greenock
SLACK
Kirkcudbright
Belfast
6 Hours after HW Dover (0215 before HW Ullapool)

10.9.4 COASTAL LIGHTS, FOG SIGNALS AND WAYPOINTS

Abbreviations used below are given in 1.4.1. Principal lights are in **bold** print, places in CAPITALS, and light-vessels, light floats and Lanbys in *CAPITAL ITALICS*. Unless otherwise stated lights are white. m—elevation in metres; M—nominal range in n. miles. Fog signals are in *italics*. Useful waypoints are underlined - use those on land with care. All geographical positions should be assumed to be approximate. See 4.2.2.

SCOTLAND—WEST COAST

SOUND OF JURA.
Reisa an t-Sruith, S end of Is 56°07'·8N 05°38'·8W Fl (2) 12s 12m 7M; W col.

CRINAN CANAL.
E of lock ent 56°05'·48N 05°33'·30W Fl WG 3s 8m 4M; W Tr, R band; vis W shore-146°, G146°-shore.
Ruadh Sgeir 56°04'·3N 05°39'·7W Fl 6s 13m 8M; W ●Tr.
Skervuile 55°52'·47N 05°49'·80W Fl 15s 22m 9M; W Tr.
Eilean nan Gabhar 55°50'·05N 05°56'·15W Fl 5s 7m 8M; framework Tr; vis 225°-010°.
Na Cùiltean 55°48'·65N 05°54'·85W Fl 10s 9m 9M; col on W bldg.

SOUND OF ISLAY.
Rhuda Mhail 55°56'·20N 06°07'·35W Fl (3) WR 15s 45m **W24M**, **R21M**; W Tr; vis R075°-180°, W180°-075°.
Carragh an t'Struith 55°52.'·3N 06°05'·7W Fl WG 3s 8m W9M, G6M, W Tr; vis W354°-078°, G078°-170°, W170°-185°.
Carragh Mòr 55°50'·4N 06°06'·0W Fl (2) WR 6s 7m W8M, R6M; W Tr; vis R shore-175°, W175°-347°, R347°-shore.
McArthur's Hd S end 55°45'85N 06°02'·80W Fl (2) WR 10s 39m W14M, R11M; W Tr; W in Sound of Islay from NE coast—159°, R159°-244°, W244°-E coast of Islay.
Eilean a Chùirn 55°40'·14N 06°01'·15W Fl (3) 18s 26m 8M; W Bn; obsc when brg more than 040°.
Otter Rock Lt By 55°33'·92N 06°07'·85W Q (6) + LFl 15s; SCM.

PORT ELLEN.
Lt By 55°37'·00N 06°12'·22W QG; SHM.
Carraig Fhada Fl WRG 3s 20m W8M, R6M, G6M; W ■ Tr; vis W shore-248°, G248°-311°, W311°-340°, R340°-shore.
Ro Ro terminal 2 FG (vert) 7/6m 3M.

LOCH INDAAL.
Bruichladdich Pier Hd 2 FR (vert) 6m 5M.
Rubh'an Dùin 55°44'·70N 06°22'·35W Fl (2) WR 7s 15m W13M, R12M; W Tr; vis W218°-249°, R249°-350°, W350°-036°.

Orsay Is, **Rhinns of Islay** 55°40'·38N 06°30'·70W Fl 5s 46m **24M**; W Tr; vis 256°-184°; *Horn (3) 45s*. RC.

WEST LOCH TARBERT.
Dunskeig Bay, N end Q (2) 10s 11m 8M.
Eileen Traighe (off S side) 55°45'·40N 05°35'·70W QR 5m 3M; R post; Ra refl.
Corran Pt QG 3m 3M; G post; Ra refl.
Sgeir Mhein QR 3m 3M; R post; Ra refl.
Black Rocks QG 3M; G post; Ra refl.
Kennacraig ferry terminal 2 FG (vert) 7/6m 3M; silver post.

Mull of Kintyre 55°18'·6N 05°48'·1W Fl (2) 20s 91m **29M**; W Tr on W Bldg; vis 347°-178°; *Horn Mo(N) 90s*.

Macosh Rk Lt By 55°17'·95N 05°36'·90W Fl R 6s; PHM.
Sanda Island, S side 55°16'·50N 05°34'·90W L Fl WR 24s 50m **W19M**, **R16M**; W Tr; vis R245°-267°, W267°-shore; Racon. (Fl 10s 55m 15M with no R sector (T) ufn).
Patersons Rk Lt By 55°16'·88N 05°32'·40W Fl (3) R 18s; PHM.
Arranman Barrels Lt By 55°19'·40N 05°32'·80W Fl (2) R 12s; PHM.

CAMPBELTOWN LOCH.
Davaar N Pt 55°25'·69N 05°32'·37W Fl (2) 10s 37m **23M**; W Tr; vis 073°-330°; *Horn (2) 20s*.
Methe Bank Lt By 55°25'·30N 05°34'·36W Iso 10s; SWM.
Otterard Lt By 55°27'·07N 05°31'·05W Q (3) 10s; ECM.
Kilbrannan Sound. Port Crannaich, breakwater Hd 55°35'·7N 05°27'·8W Fl R 10s 5m 6M; vis 099°-279°.
Skipness range 55°46'·7N 05°19'·0W Iso R 8s 7m 10M; Y ◆ on bldg; vis 292·2°-312·2°. Oc (2) Y 10s **24M** when range in use (occas).

LOCH FYNE.
Lamont Shelf Lt By 55°48'·40N 05°13'·84W Fl (2) 10s; IDM.
Sgat Mór (S end) 55°50'·85N 05°18'·42W Fl 3s 9m 12M; W ● Tr.
Portavadie Breakwater 2 FG (vert) 6/4m 4M.

EAST LOCH TARBERT.
Madadh Maol ent S side 55°52'·02N 05°24'·18W Fl R 2·5s 4m3M; R col.
Eilean a'Choic SE side QG 3m 2M; G col.

ARDRISHAIG.
Breakwater Hd 56°00'·76N 05°26'·53W L Fl WRG 6s 9m 4M; W Tr; vis G287°-339°, W339°-350°, R350°-035°. 2 FG (vert) on pier 120m NW.
Otter Spit 56°00'·63N 05°21'·03W Fl G 3s 7m 8M; G tank on pyramid.
Glas Eilean S end 56°01'·10N 05°21'·10W Fl R 5s 12m 7M; R col on pedestal.
Sgeir an Eirionnaich 56°06'·5N 05°13'·5W Fl WR 3s 7m 8M; B Tr on B I Tr, W stripes; vis R044°-087°, W087°-192°, R192°-210°, W210°-044°.

KYLES OF BUTE.
Ardlamont Pt No. 47 Lt By 55°49'·59N 05°11'·70W Fl R 4s; PHM.
Carry Pt No. 46 Lt By 55°51'·40N 05°12'·18W Fl R 4s; PHM.
Rubha Ban Lt By 55°54'·95N 05°12'·33W Fl R 4s; PHM.
Burnt Islands No. 42 Lt By (S of Eilean Buidhe) 55°55'·77N 05°10'·32W Fl R 2s; PHM.
Rubha Bodach Lt By 55°55'·39N 05°09'·53W Fl G; SHM.
Ardmaleish Pt No. 41 Lt By 55°53'·03N 05°04'·63W Q; NCM.

ARRAN ISLAND.
Pladda 55°25'·50N 05°07'·07W Fl (3) 30s 40m **17M**; W Tr; RC.
Pillar Rk Pt (Holy Island), 55°31'·05N 05°03'·57W Fl (2) 20s 38m **25M**; W ■ Tr.
Holy Is SW end Fl G 3s 14m 10M; W Tr; vis 282°-147°.
Brodick Bay, Pier Hd 2 FR (vert) 9/7m 4M.

FIRTH OF CLYDE.
Runnaneun Pt 55°43'·79N 05°00'·17W Fl R 6s 8m 12M; W Tr.
Little Cumbrae 55°43'·27N 04°57'·95W Fl 3s 31m **23M**; W Tr; vis 334°-210°; shown by day if fog signal operating; *Horn (3) 40s* (TD 1989)..
Portachur Lt By 55°44'·35N 04°58'·44W Fl G 3s; SHM.
Mountstuart Lt By 55°48'·00N 04°57'·50W L Fl 10s; SWM.

GREAT CUMBRAE

MILLPORT.
Eileans W end 55°44'·89N 04°55'·52W QG 5m 2M; shown 1/9-30/4.
Ldg Lts 333°. Pier Hd front FR 7m 5M. Rear 137m from front FR 9m 5M.

FAIRLIE.
Hunterston Jetty S end 55°45'·10N 04°52'·80W 2 FG (vert).
Pier N end 2 FG (vert) 7m 5M.
NATO Pier Hd 2 FG (vert) N and S ends.

LARGS.
Marina S Breakwater Hd 55°46'·35N 04°51'·67W OcG 10s 4m 4M; G s on col.
W Breakwater Hd OcR 10s 4m 4M; R ■ on col.
Approach Lt By 55°46'·50N 04°51'·78W L Fl 10s; SWM.
Largs Pier Hd N end 2 FG (vert) 7/5m 5M (H24).
Ascog Patches No. 13 Lt Bn 55°49'·71N 05°00'·17W Fl (2) 10s 5m 5M; IDM.

Toward Pt 55°51'·73N 04°58'·73W Fl 10s 21m **22M**; W Tr; shown by day if fog signal operating; *Horn 20s.*
Toward Bank No 35 Lt By 55°51'·05N 04°59'·93W Fl G 3s; SHM.

ROTHESAY.
Front Pier E end 55°50'·32N 05°03'·03W 2 FG (vert) 7m 5M.
Pier W end 2 FR (vert) 7m 5M.
Albert Quay, near N end 2 FR (vert) 8m 5M.
Skelmorlie Lt By 55°51'·65N 04°56'·28W Iso 5s; SWM.
Wemyss Bay, pier 2 FG (vert) 7/5m 5M.
Inverkip oil jetty, S and N ends 2 FG (vert) 11m 2M.
No. 12 55°52'·9N 04°53'·7W Oc (2) Y 10s 5m 3M; SPM.
Kip Lt By 55°54'·49N 04°52'·95W QG; SHM.
Cowal Lt By 55°56'·00N 04°54'·77W L Fl 10s; SWM.
Lunderston Bay No. 8 55°55'·5N 04°52'·9W Fl (4) Y 10s 5m 3M.

Gantock Beacon 55°56'·46N 04°55'·00W Fl R 2·5s 12m **18M**; W ● Tr.

DUNOON.
Pier, S end and N end 2 FR (vert) 5m 6M.
Cloch Pt Fl 3s 24m 8M; W ● Tr, B band, W dwellings; *Horn (2) 30s* .
McInroy's Pt Ro Ro terminal 2 FG (vert) 5/3m 6M.
No. 5 55°57'·0N 04°51'·6W Oc (2) Y 10s 5m 3M; SPM.
Hunter's Quay Ro Ro terminal 2 FR (vert) 6/4m 6M.

Holy Loch Pier (SE end) 55°59'·0N 04°56'·7W 2 FR (vert) 6/4m 3M.

LOCH LONG.
Loch Long Lt By 55°59'·17N 04°52'·33W Oc 6s; SWM.
Baron's Pt No. 3 55°59'·2N 04°51'·0W Oc (2) Y 10s 5m 3M.
Ravenrock Pt 56°02'·1N 04°54'·3W Fl 4s 12m 10M; W Tr on W col.
Dir Lt 204°, Dir WRG 9m (same Tr); vis R201·5°-203°, Al WR203°-203·5° (W phase incr with brg), F W203·5°-204·5°, Al WG204·5°-205° (G phase incr with brg), FG205°-206·5°.
Port Dornaige 56°03·76N 04° 53'·60W Fl 6s 8m 11M; W col; vis 026°-206°.
Carraig nan Ron (Dog Rock) 56°06'·01N 04°51'·60W Fl 2s 7m 11M; W col.
Finnart Oil Terminal, Cnap Pt 56°07'·41N 04°49'·88W Ldg Lts 031°. Front Q 8m 10M; W col. Rear, 87m from front F 13m; R line on W Tr.

Ashton Lt By 55°58'·11N 04°50'·58W Iso 5s; SWM.

GOUROCK.
Railway Pier Hd 55°57'·8N 04°49'·0W 2 FG (vert) 10/8m 3M; Gy Tr.
Kempock Pt No. 4 55°57'·7N 04°49'·3W Oc (2) Y 10s 6m 3M.
Whiteforeland Lt By 55°58'·11N 04°47'·20W L Fl 10s; SWM.
Rosneath Patch, S end 55°58'·52N 04°47'·37W Fl (2) 10s 5m 10M.
Ldg Lts 356·3° Front Bn No. 7N 56°00'·06N 04°45'·29W Oc G 6s 3m 3M; G s on pile; SHM on pile..
Ardencaple Castle Centre 2 FG (vert) 26m 12M; Tr on Castle NE corner; vis 335°-020°.
Rear, 822m from front FG 10M; Or daymark.

ROSNEATH.
Gareloch No. 8N Lt Bn 55°59'·09N 04°44'·13W Fl Y 3s 3m 3M; SPM.
Gareloch No. 1 Lt Bn 55°59'·12N 04°43'·81W VQ (4) Y 5s 9m and Dir Q WRG 7m W3M, R2M, G2M; vis G077·5°-079·5°, W079·5°-080·5°, G080·5°-082·5°.
Row Lt By 55°59'·85N 04°45'·05W Fl G 5s; SHM.
Cairndhu Lt By 56°00'·36N 04°45'·93W Fl G 2.5s; SHM.
Rosneath. Dir Lt 290·7°. Dir Oc WRG 3s 7m 14M; vis G288·2°-289·7°, W289·7°-291·7°, R291·7°-296·2°; (H24).
Ldg Lts 290·7°. Front 56°00'·6N 04°47'·7W FR 4m. Rear 0·66M from front FR; both vis 275·5°-305·7°.
Castle Pt 56°00'·20N 04°46'·43W Fl(2) R 10s 8m 6M; R mast.
Rosneath DG Jetty 2 FR (vert) 5M; W col; vis 150°-330°.
Rhu Narrows 56°00'·9N 04°47'·1W Q (3) WRG 6s 9m W10M, R7M, G7M; vis G270°-000°, W000°-114°, R114°-188°.
Dir Lt 318°. Dir Oc WRG 6s; same Tr; vis G313·5°-317°, W317°-319°, R319°-323·5°; (H24).

Rosneath Bay Ldg Lts 163·4°. Front 56°00'·0N 04°47'·1W FG 11m 12M; Tr; vis 149·4°-177·4°. Rear 683m from front FG 24m 12M; stone Tr; vis 149·4°-177·4°.

GARELOCH/RHU.
Rhu S Lt By 56°00'·66N 04°47'·35W Fl G 3s; SHM.
Mambeg Dir Lt 330°, Dir Q (4) WRG 8s 8m 14M; W col; vis G327·5°-329°, W329°-331°, R331°-332°; (H24).
Faslane Base, wharf, S elbow Fl G 5s 11m 5M.
Floating dock, E side Fl R 3m 2M, middle 2FG (vert) 14m 5M, N side Q WRG 14m W9M, R6M, G6M; vis G333°-084°, W084°-161°, R161°-196°; (H24).
Garelochhead, S fuel jetty 56°04'·23N 04°49'·62W 2 FG (vert) 10m 5M.
N fuel jetty, elbow Iso WRG 4s 10m; vis G351°-356°, W356°-006°, R006°-011°.

9

GREENOCK.
Anchorage Lts in line 196°. Front 55°57'·6N 04°46'·5W FG 7m 12M; Y col. Rear 32m from front FG 9m 12M. Y col.
Lts in line 194°·5'. Front 55°57'·4N 04°45'·8W FG 18m. Rear 360m from front FG 33m.
Clydeport Container Terminal NW corner QG 8m 8M.
Victoria Hbr ent W side 2 FG 5m (vert).
Garvel Embankment, W end 55°56'·81N 04°43'·48W Oc G 10s 9m 4M.
E end, Maurice Clark Pt 55°56'·61N 04°42'·78W QG 7m 2M; G Tr.

PORT GLASGOW.
Bn off ent 55°56'·3N 04°41'·2W FG 7m 9M; B&W chequered Tr and cupola.
Steamboat Quay W end FG 12m 12M; B&W chequered col; vis 210°-290°. From here to Glasgow Lts on S bank are Fl G and Lts on N bank are Fl R.

SCOTLAND—WEST COAST

ARDROSSAN.
Approach Dir Lt 055°. 55°38'·7N 04°49'·1W Dir F WRG 15m 9M; vis G048·5°-053·5°, W053·5°-056·5°, R056·5°-061·5°. FR 9m 9M (same Tr); vis 340°-130°.
NBreakwater Hd Fl WR 2s 7m 5M; R gantry; vis R041°-126°, W126°-041°.
Lighthouse Pier Hd 55°38'·47N 04°49'·50W Iso WG 4s 11m 9M; W Tr; vis W035°-317°, G317°-035°.

IRVINE.
Ent N side 55°36'·21N 04°42'·00W Fl R 3s 6m 5M; R col.
S side Fl G 3s 6m 5M; G col.
Ldg Lts 051°. Front FG 10m 5M. Rear 101m from front FR 15m 5M; both on G masts, vis 019°-120°.

TROON.
Troon Lt By 55°30'·07N 04°41'·28W Fl G 4s; SHM.
West Pier Hd 55°33'·07N 04°40'·95W Oc WR 6s 11m 5M; W Tr; vis R036°-090°, W090°-036°; *Siren 30s.*
14m SE Fl WG 3s 7m 5M; post on dolphin; vis G146°-318°, W318°-146°.
E pier Hd Fl R 10s 6m 3M; R col; obsc brg more than 199°.

Lady Is 55°31'·63N 04°43'·95W Fl (4) 30s 19m 8M; W Bn.

AYR.
Bar Lt By 55°28'·12N 04°39'·38W Fl G 2s; SHM.
N Breakwater Hd 55°28'·22N 04°38'·71W QR 9m 5M.
S Pier Hd Q 7m 7M; R Tr; vis 012°-161°. FG 5m 5M; same Tr; vis 012°-066°.
Ldg Lts 098°. Front 55°28'·2N 04°38'·3W FR 10m 5M; R Tr. Rear 130m from front Oc R 10s 18m 9M.

Turnberry Pt, near castle ruins 55°19'·55N 04°50'·60W Fl 15s 29m **24M**; W Tr.

Ailsa Craig 55°15'·12N 05°06'·42W Fl 4s 18m **17M**; W Tr; vis 145°-028°.

GIRVAN.
N groyne Hd 55°14'·75N 04°51'·70W Iso 4s 3m 4M.
S pier Hd 2 FG (vert) 8m 4M; W Tr.
N breakwater Hd 55°14'·74N 04°51'·77W Fl (2) R 6s 7m 4M.

LOCH RYAN.
Cairn Pt 54°58'·5N 05°01'·8W Fl(2) R 10s 14m 12M; W Tr.
Cairnryan 54°57'·8N 05°00'·9W Fl R 5s 5m 5M.

Stranraer approach No. 1 Bn 54°56'·6N 05°01'·3W Oc G 6s.
No. 3 Bn 54°55'·9N 05°01'·6W QG.
No. 5 54°55'·1N 05°01'·8W Fl G 3s.

STRANRAER.
Ross Pier Hd 2 F Bu (vert).
E pier Hd 2 FR (vert) 9m.
W Pier Hd 2 FG (vert) 8m 4M; Gy col.

Corsewall Pt 55°00'·43N 05°09'·50W Al Fl WR 74s 34m **18M**; W Tr; vis 027°-257°.

Killantringan Black Hd 54°51'·71N 05°08'·75W Fl (2) 15s 49m **25M**; W Tr.

PORTPATRICK.
Ldg Lts 050·5°. Front 54°50'·5N 05°06'·9W FG (occas). Rear, 68m from front, FG 8m (occas).

Crammag Hd 54°39'·90N 04°57'·80W Fl 10s 35m **18M**; W Tr.
Mull of Galloway, SE end 54°38'·05N 04°51'·35W Fl 20s 99m **28M**; W Tr; vis 182°-105°.

PORT WILLIAM.
Ldg Lts 105°. Front Pier Hd 54°45'·65N 04°35'·10W Fl G 3s 7m 3M. Rear, 130m from front, FG 10m 2M.

Isle of Whithorn Hbr E Pier Hd 54°41'·8N 04°21'·7W QG 4m 5M; Gy col.
Ldg Lts 335°. Front Oc R 8s 7m 7M; Or ◆. Rear, 35m from front, OcR 8s 9m 7M; Or ◆, synchronised.

Little Ross 54°45'·93N 04°05'·02W Fl 5s 50m 12M; W Tr; obsc in Wigton B when brg more than 103°.

KIRKCUDBRIGHT BAY.
No. 1 Lifeboat House 54°'·47.68N 04°03'·66W Fl 3s 7m 3M.
Perch No.12 54°49'·1N 04°04'·8W Fl R 3s 3m.
Perch No.14 54°49'·25N 04°04'·76W Fl 3s 5m.
Perch No. 22 54°50'·1N 04°03'·9W Fl R 3s 2m.
Outfall 54°50'·2N 04°03'·8W Fl Y 5s 3m 2M; Y Tr.

Hestan Island E end 54°50'·0N 03°48'·4W Fl (2) 10s 38m 7M; W house.
Annan, S end of quay 54°59'N 03°16'W 2 FR (vert) 6m 5M.

10.9.5 PASSAGE INFORMATION

SCOTLAND – SOUTH-WEST COAST

Although conditions in the South-West of Scotland are in general less rugged than from Mull northwards, some of the remarks at the start of 10.8.5 are equally applicable to this area.

The W coasts of Colonsay and Oronsay (chart 2169) are fringed with dangers up to 2M offshore. The two Islands are separated by a narrow chan which dries and has an overhead cable (10m). For Scalasaig see 10.9.22.

Sound of Luing (chart 2326) between Scarba, Lunga, Fiola Meadlonach, Rubha Fiola and Pladda (or Fladda) on the W side, and Luing and Dubh Sgeir on the E side, is the normal chan to or from Sound of Jura – despite dangers at the N end and strong tidal streams. The N-going stream begins at HW Oban +0430, and the S-going at HW Oban –0155. Sp rates are 2·5-3 kn at S end of sound, increasing to 6 kn or more in Is off N entrance – where there are eddies, races and overfalls. Good shelter in Ardinamar B, SW of Torsa.

CORRYVRECKAN/CRINAN (charts 2326, 2343)

Between Scarba and Jura is the Gulf of Corryvreckan (chart 2343), with a least width of 0·6M and free of dangers, but noted for its very strong tides which, in conjunction with an uneven bottom, cause extreme turbulence. This is particularly dangerous with strong W winds over a W-going (flood) tide which spews out several miles to seaward of the gulf, with overfalls extending 3M from the W of ent. The gulf is best avoided, and should never be attempted by yachts except at slack water and in calm conditions. Keep to the S side of the gulf to avoid the whirlpool known as The Hag. The W-going stream in the gulf begins at HW Oban +0410, and the E-going at HW Oban –0210. Sp rate W-going is 8·5 kn, and E-going rather less.

The range of tide at sp can vary nearly 2m between the E end of the gulf (1·5m) and the W end (3·4m), with HW 0·5h earlier at the E end. Slack water lasts about 1 hour at nps, but only 0·5h at sps. On the W-going (flood) stream eddies form both sides of the gulf, but the one on the N (Scarba) shore is more important. Where this eddy meets the main stream off Camas nam Bairneach there is violent turbulence, with heavy overfalls extending W at the division of the eddy and the main stream. There are temp anchs with the wind in the right quarter in Bagh Gleann a Mhaoil in the SE corner of Scarba, and in Bagh Gleann nam Muc at N end of Jura but the latter has rks in approaches E and SW of Eilean Beag.

At N end of Sound of Jura (chart 2326) is Loch Craignish (10.9.8). There are very strong tides in Dorus Mor, if approaching from the N. The W-going stream begins at HW Oban +0330, and the E-going at HW Oban –0215, sp rates 8 kn. The main chan up Loch Craignish is clear 0·15M offshore, but beware charted rks off Eilean Dubh and Eilean Mhic Chrion when approaching head of loch and the Ardfern Yacht Centre, which is behind Eilean Inshaig on W shore.

S of Loch Craignish is Loch Crinan, which leads to the Crinan Canal (10.9.9). Beware Black Rk, 2m high and 0·2M N of the canal sea lock, and dangers extending 0·05M from the rk.

ISLAY (charts 2481, 2168)

An alternative N/S route is through the Sound of Islay. The chan presents no difficulty: hold to the Islay shore, where all dangers are close in. The N-going stream begins at HW Oban +0440, and the S-going at HW Oban –0140. The sp rates are 2·5 kn at N entrance and 1·5 kn at S entrance, but increasing in the narrows and reaching 5 kn off Port Askaig. There are overfalls off McArthur's Hd (Islay side of S entrance) during the S-going stream. There are anchs in the sound, but mostly holding ground is poor. The best places are alongside at Port Askaig (10.9.22), or at anch off the distillery in Bunnahabhan B, 2·5M to N.

The W coast of Islay is very exposed. Off Orsay, Frenchman's Rks and W Bank the NW-going stream begins at HW Oban +0530, and the SE-going at HW Oban –0040. Sp rates are 8 kn off Orsay and Frenchman's Rks, and 6 kn over W bank, but decrease to 3 kn 5M offshore. There are races and overfalls in these areas. In the N of Islay there is anch E of Nave Is at entrance to Loch Gruinart: beware Balach Rks which dry, just to N. Loch Indaal gives some shelter: beware rks extending from Laggan Hd on E side of ent. Port Ellen (chart 2474) has several dangers in approach, and is exposed to S. See 10.9.22.

SOUND OF JURA TO MULL OF KINTYRE

From Crinan to Gigha the Sound of Jura is safe if a mid-chan course is held. Skervuile (Lt) is a reef roughly in middle of sound. Loch Sween (chart 2397) can be approached N or SE of MacCormaig Islands, where there is an attractive anch on NE side of Eilean Mor, but exposed to NE. Coming from N beware Keills Rk and Danna Rk. Sgeirean a Mhain is a rk in fairway 1·5M NE of Castle Sween (conspic on SE shore). Anch at Tayvallich, near head of loch on W side. See 10.9.22.

W Loch Tarbert (chart 2477) is long and narrow, with good anchs but unmarked shoals. On entry give a berth of at least 0·25M to Eilean Traighe off N shore, E of Ardpatrick Pt. Dun Skeig, an isolated hill, is conspic on S shore. Good anch near head of loch, 1M by road from E Loch Tarbert (see 10.9.11).

On other side of sound, near S end of Jura, are The Small Is (chart 2396) between Rubh' an Leanachais and Rubha na Caillich. Beware Goat Rk (dries) 0·15M off southernmost Is, Eilean nan Gabhar, behind which is good anch. Also possible to go alongside Craighouse Pier (10.9.22). Another anch exists in Lowlandman's B, about 3M to N, but exposed to S winds: Ninefoot Rks with depth of 2·4m lie off ent.

S of W Loch Tarbert, and about 2M off the Kintyre shore, is Gigha Is (chart 2475), with Cara Is and Gigalum Is off its S end. See 10.9.22. Dangers extend 1M W off S end of Gigha Is. Outer and Inner Red Rks (least depth 2m) lie 2M SW of N end of Gigha Is.

Gigha Sound need very careful pilotage, since there are several dangerous rks. The N-going stream begins at HW Oban +0430, and S-going at HW Oban –0155, sp rates 1·5 kn. Good anchs in Druimyeon B and Ardminish B, respectively N and S of Ardminish Pt on E side of Gigha.

From Crinan to Mull of Kintyre is about 50M, and this long peninsula has great effect on tidal stream in North chan. Off Mull of Kintyre (Lt, fog sig) the N-going stream begins at HW Oban +0400, and the S-going at HW Oban –0225, sp rates 5 kn. A strong race and overfalls exist S and SW of Mull of Kintyre, dangerous in strong S winds against S-going tide. Careful timing is needed. There is a Traffic Separation Scheme in North chan – see Fig. 2(5). For notes on crossing the Irish Sea, see 10.13.5.

Sanda Sound separates Sanda Is (Lt) and its neighbouring rks and Is, from Kintyre. Beware Macosh Rks (dry) forming part of Barley Ridges, 0·2M offshore, E of Rubha McShannuick; Arranman Barrels, drying and submerged, 0·25M E from Duna-h-Oighe and marked by By; and Blindman Rk (depth 2m) 0·2M off Ru Stafnish, where there are 3 radio masts 0·5M to W. 0·3M off N of Sanda Is is Sheep Is. Paterson's Rk (dries) is 1M E of Sheep Is. There is anch in Sanda hbr. In Sanda Sound the E-going stream begins at HW Greenock +0340, and the W-going at HW Greenock –0230, sp rates 5 kn. Tide races extend N and W from Sheep Is, and in strong S or SW winds the Sound is dangerous. In these conditions pass E of Paterson's Rk, and 2M S of Sanda and Mull of Kintyre.

MULL OF KINTYRE TO FIRTH OF CLYDE (charts 2126, 2383, 2381).

Once E of Mull of Kintyre, tidal and pilotage conditions improve greatly. Campbeltown (10.9.10) is entered N of

9

Davaar Is (Lt, fog sig). 1·5M N of Lt Ho is Otterard Rk (depth 3m), with Long Rk (dries) 0·5M W of it; both are marked by Bys. E of Davaar Is tide runs 4 kn at sp, and there are overfalls.

Kilbrannan Sound runs 21M from Davaar Is to Skipness Pt, where it joins Inchmarnock Water and Bute Sound. There are few dangers apart from overfalls on Erins Bank, 10M S of Skipness, on S-going stream. Good anch in Carradale B (10.9.22), off Torrisdale Castle. There are overfalls off Carradale Pt on S-going stream.

Loch Fyne (chart 2381) is relatively clear of dangers to E Loch Tarbert (10.9.11). On E shore beware rks off Ardlamont Pt, and 4M to NW is Skate Is which is best passed to W.

3M from Ardrishaig (10.9.12) beware Big Rk (depth 2·1m). Further N, at entrance to Loch Gilp (much of which dries) note shoals round Gulnare Rk with least depth 1·5m, and Duncuan Is with dangers extending SW to Sgeir Sgalag (depth 0·8m) marked by By.

Where Loch Fyne turns NE it is largely obstructed by Otter Spit (dries), extending 0·8M WNW from E shore. Outer end of spit is marked by Bn (lit), but dangers extend somewhat beyond. The stream runs up to 2 kn here. A rk with depth less than 2m lies about 0·75M SW of Otter Spit Bn. In Upper Loch Fyne (chart 2382) Minard Narrows are formed by rks and Is in the fairway, but there are charted chans between. For Inveraray see 10.9.22.

Bute Sound leads into Firth of Clyde, and is clear in fairway. Sannox Rk (depth 1·2m) is 0·25M off Arran coast 8M N of Lamlash (10.9.13). 0·1M off W side of Inchmarnock is Tra nah-uil, a rk which dries. In Inchmarnock Sound, Shearwater Rk (depth 0·9m) lies in centre of S entrance.

Arran's mountains tend to cause squalls or calms, but it has good anchs at Lamlash (10.9.13), Brodick (10.9.22) and Loch Ranza (10.9.22).

FIRTH OF CLYDE TO KIRKCUDBRIGHT (charts 2131, 2126, 2199, 2198, 2094)

Kyles of Bute are attractive chan between Inchmarnock Water and Firth of Clyde, and straightforward apart from Burnt Is. Here it is best to take N chan, narrow but well buoyed, passing S of Eilean Buidhe, and N of Eilean Fraoich and Eilean Mor. Care is needed, since stream may reach 5 kn at sp.

In contrast, the N lochs in Firth of Clyde are less attractive. Loch Goil is worth a visit but Loch Long is squally and has few anchs, while Gareloch has little to attract cruising yachts. For Millport (Great Cumbrae) see 10.9.22. There is anch in Kilchattan Bay (E Bute) sheltered from SSE to WNW.

Navigation in Firth of Clyde presents few problems since chans are well marked, but beware unlit moorings and also the considerable amount of commercial and naval shipping (see 10.9.15). Tidal streams are generally weak, seldom exceeding 1 kn.

S of Largs (10.9.18) the coast is generally uninviting, with mostly commercial hbrs until Troon (10.9.19). There are various dangers in Ayr B (10.9.22); beware Troon Rk (depth 5·6m, but sea can break), Lappock Rk (dries, marked by Bn), and Mill Rk (dries, buoyed).

There is a serious race off Bennane Hd (8M SSE of Ailsa Craig) when tide is running strongly. Loch Ryan offers little for yachtsmen but there is anch S of Kirkcolm Pt, inside the drying spit which runs in SE direction 1·5M from the point. There is also useful anch in Lady Bay, sheltered except from NE. Between Corsewall Pt and Mull of Galloway the S-going stream begins HW Greenock +0310, and the N-going at HW Greenock −0250. Sp rate off and S of Black Hd is 5 kn; N of Black Hd it decreases, to 2-3 kn off Corsewall Pt. Races occur off Morroch B, Money Hd, Mull of Logan and SE of Crammag Hd.

Mull of Galloway (Lt) is S point of Scotland, a tall headland (83m) and steep-to, but beware dangerous race extending nearly 3M to S. On E-going stream the race extends NNE into Luce B; on W-going stream it extends SW and W.

The Scares are rks in middle of Luce B. Elsewhere Bay is clear more than 0·25M offshore, but there is practice bombing range. Best anch at E Tarbert B, or alongside in Drummore which is sheltered but dries. Off Burrow Hd there is bad race in strong W winds with W-going tide. In Wigtown B (10.9.22) the best anch is in Is of Whithorn B, but exposed to S. It is also possible to dry out in Garlieston.

There is a tank firing range extending 14M offshore between Kirkcudbright (10.9.21) and Abbey Head, 4M to E. If unable to avoid the area, cross it at N end close inshore. For information telephone 'Range control' Dundrennan 055 723236 or contact the Range safety boat "Gallovidian" which keeps watch on VHF Ch 16. The range operates from 0900-1600 LT Mon-Fri, but weekend and night firing may also take place.

10.9.6 DISTANCE TABLE

Approximate distances in nautical miles are by the most direct route while avoiding dangers and allowing for traffic separation schemes etc. Places in *italics* are in adjoining areas.

1 *Tory Island*	**1**																			
2 *Barra Head*	95	**2**																		
3 *Oigh Sgeir*	113	33	**3**																	
4 *Ardnamurchan Pt*	110	47	21	**4**																
5 Port Askaig	87	77	75	60	**5**															
6 Mull of Kintyre	86	112	103	99	33	**6**														
7 Campbeltown	106	132	123	119	53	20	**7**													
8 E Loch Tarbert	131	157	148	144	78	45	31	**8**												
9 Ardrishaig	140	166	157	153	87	54	39	10	**9**											
10 Toward Point	139	165	156	152	86	53	45	23	31	**10**										
11 Kip Marina	144	170	161	157	91	58	50	28	36	5	**11**									
12 Helensburgh	153	179	170	166	100	67	59	37	45	14	9	**12**								
13 Lamlash	120	146	137	133	67	34	24	25	34	21	25	33	**13**							
14 Troon	130	156	147	143	77	44	33	33	40	24	29	38	16	**14**						
15 Portpatrick	119	148	139	135	69	36	39	66	74	65	68	77	44	49	**15**					
16 Mull of Galloway	134	164	155	151	85	52	56	82	90	81	84	93	60	65	16	**16**				
17 Kirkcudbright	164	196	187	183	117	84	88	114	122	113	116	125	92	97	48	32	**17**			
18 *Mew Island*	116	149	140	136	69	37	44	72	80	74	77	86	54	60	16	22	54	**18**		
19 *Point of Ayre*	160	186	177	173	107	74	78	104	112	103	106	115	82	87	38	22	25	44	**19**	
20 *St Bees Head*	177	207	198	194	128	95	99	125	133	124	127	136	103	108	59	43	24	65	26	**20**

CLYDE AREA WAYPOINTS 10-9-7

Selected waypoints for use in the Clyde area are listed in alphabetical order below. Further waypoints for use in coastal waters are given in section 4 of each relevant area.

AE Lt Buoy	55°51'·68N 05°02'·31W
Ailsa Craig Lt	55°15'·12N 05°06'·42W
Ardgowan Pt By	55°54'·93N 04°54'·00W
Ardmaleish No.41 Lt By	55°53'·03N 05°04'·62W
Ardmore No.4 Lt By	55°58'·75N 04°48'·30W
Ardmore No.5 Lt By	55°58'·67N 04°47'·44W
Ardmore No. 8 Lt By	55°58'·95N 04°46'·66W
Ardmore No.10 Lt By	55°59'·03N 04°45'·62W
Ardyne Lt By	55°52'·00N 05°03'·16W
Arranman Barrels Lt By	55°19'·40N 05°32'·80W
Ascog Patches Lt Bn (No. 13)	55°49'·71N 05°00'·17W
Ashton Lt By	55°58'·11N 04°50'·58W
Ayr Bar Lt By	55°28'·12N 04°39'·38W
Cairndhu Lt By	56°00'·36N 04°45'·93W
Cowal Lt By	55°56'·00N 04°54'·77W
Dunoon Bank Lt By	55°56'·63N 04°54'·09W
Eagle Rock Lt By	55°38'·21N 04°49'·62W
Fairlie Patch Lt By	55°45'·48N 00°52'·30W
Fullerton Rk Lt By	55°30'·64N 05°04'·50W
Gantock Bn Lt	55°56'·46N 04°55'·00W
Hun 1 Lt By	55°48'·10N 05°54'·15W
Hun 3 Lt By	55°47'·60N 04°53'·43W
Hun 5 Lt By	55°45'·86N 04°52'·45W
Hun 7 Lt By	55°44'·96N 04°53'·86W
Hun 8 Lt By	55°44'·80N 04°53'·62W
Hun 9 Lt By	55°44'·68N 04°54'·38W
Hun 10 Lt By	55°44'·15N 04°54'·79W
Hun 11 Lt By	55°43'·45N 04°55'·09W
Hun 12 Lt By	55°43'·45N 04°55'·55W
Hun 13 Lt By	55°42'·52N 04°55'·10W
Hun 14 Lt By	55°42'·52N 04°55'·54W
Kip Lt By	55°54'·49N 04°52'·95W
Kilcreggan No.1 Lt By	55°58'·68N 04°50'·19W
Kilcreggan No.2 Lt By	55°59'·20N 04°51'·39W
Lady Isle Lt	55°31'·63N 04°43'·95W
Lamont Shelf Lt By	55°48'·40N 05°13'·84W
Largs Lt By	55°46'·50N 04°51'·78W
Loch Long Lt By	55°59'·17N 04°52'·33W
Macosh Rk Lt By	55°17'·95N 05°36'·90W
Methe Bank Lt By	55°25'·30N 05°34'·36W
Millbeg Bank Lt By	55°25'·53N 05°33'·93W
Mountstuart Lt By	55°27'·07N 05°31'·04W
Outer St Nicholas Lt By	55°28'·11N 04°39'·37W
Outfall Lt By	55°43'·56N 04°54'·74W
Patersons Rk Lt By	55°16'·90N 05°32'·40W
Pillar Rk Lt Ho	55°31'·05N 05°03'·57W
Pladda Lt Ho	55°25'·50N 05°11'·70W
Perch Rock By	55°59'·45N 04°45'·58W
Portachur Lt By	55°44'·35N 04°58'·44W
Portachur Spit Lt By	55°44'·42N 04°57'·05W
Rhu South Lt By	56°00'·67N 04°47'·34W
Row Lt By	55°59'·85N 04°45'·05W
Skelmorlie Lt By	55°51'·65N 04°56'·28W
Skipness Pt No. 51 Lt By	55°45'·57N 05°19'·60W
Toward Bank Lt By No.35	55°51'·05N 04°59'·93W
Troon Lt By	55°33'·07N 04°41'·27W
Warden Bank Lt By	55°57'·78N 04°54'·48W
West Crinan Lt By	55°38'·46N 04°49'·82W
Whiteforeland Lt By	55°58'·12N 04°47'·20W
7N Lt By	56°00'·06N 04°45'·29W
8N Lt By	55°59'·09N 04°44'·13W

9

LOCH CRAIGNISH 10-9-8

Argyll

CHARTS
Admiralty 2326, 2169; Imray C63, C65; OS 55

TIDES
+0600 Dover; ML (Seil Sound) 1·4;
Duration (Seil Sound) 0615; Zone 0 (GMT).

Standard Port OBAN (⟵)

Times				Height (metres)			
HW		LW		MHWS	MHWN	MLWN	MLWS
0100	0700	0100	0800	4·0	2·9	1·8	0·7
1300	1900	1300	2000				
Differences SEIL SOUND							
−0035	−0015	−0040	−0015	−1·3	−0·9	−0·7	−0·3
GLENGARRISDALE BAY (Jura)							
−0020	0000	−0010	0000	−0·4	−0·2	0·0	−0·2

Tidal heights are very much affected by wind and barometric pressure causing differences of up to 1m above or below predicted height.

SHELTER
Entrance between Garbh Reisa and Liath-sgier Mhor. Beware squalls in easterlies, especially on E side of loch. Yachts can go to Ardfern Yacht Centre or anchor off. Anchorages include
- Goat Island (Eilean nan Gabhar), approach from E channel and anchor between the island and the skerry
- Eilean Righ, off the E side in middle of the Is.
- Bagh na Cille, NE of Craignish Pt.
- Eilean Dubh in the "lagoon" between the Is and Craignish peninsular.

NAVIGATION
Waypoint 56°07′·00N, 05°35′·05W. Beware strong tidal streams (up to 8kn) in the Dorus Mor. Beware a reef extending one ca SSW of the SE chain of islands. Also beware rock 1½ca SSW of Eilean Dubh. The main fairway is free from hazards, except a rock Sgeir Dubh due E of the easterly point of Mhic Chrion which has a reef extending about ½ ca all round it. Beware fish cages especially on E side of loch. At Ardfern, beware drying rock at N end of anchorage with a rock awash ¼ca E of it. These two are ½ca S of the more southerly of little islets close to the mainland.

LIGHTS AND MARKS
There are no lights.

RADIO TELEPHONE
VHF Ch 16 37 watched by Ardfern Yacht Centre during working hours and Ch **80** M (0830 – 1800 LT).

TELEPHONE (085 25)
Hr Mr (Yacht Centre) 247; MRSC Oban 63720; Marinecall 0898 500 463; # Oban 63079; Dr (0546) 2921; H (0546) 2449

FACILITIES
Ardfern Yacht Centre (87 + 20 visitors); ☎ 247, AC, BH (16 ton), Slip, ME, El, Sh, ACA, C (6 ton), FW, D, CH, Gas, Gaz, R; **Galley of Lorne Hotel** ☎ 284, R, V, P (cans); **Ardfern Village Store** V; **Ardfern Village** Ⓑ (Wednesday); ✉ (AM only); ⇌ (Oban); ✈ (Glasgow).

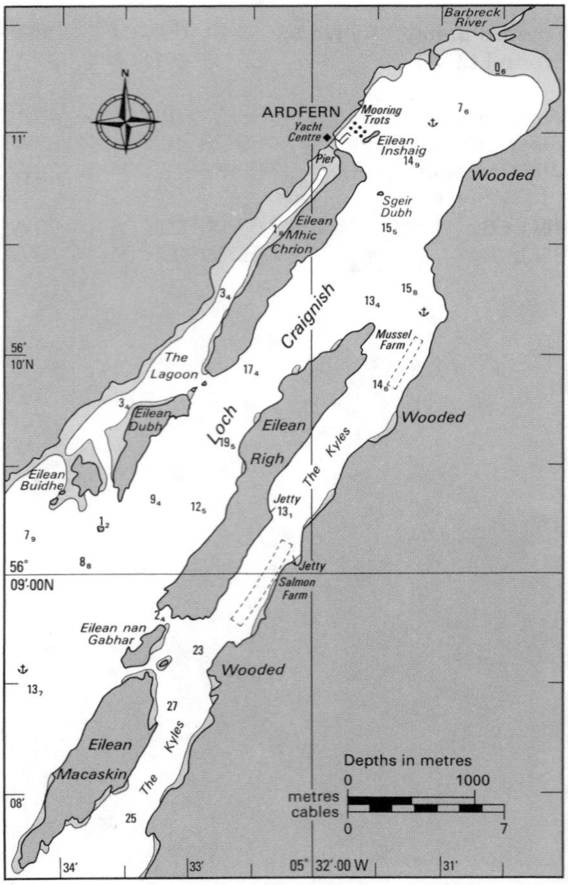

Barbreck River
ARDFERN
Yacht Centre
Mooring Trots
Eilean Inshaig
Pier
Wooded
Sgeir Dubh
Eilean Mhic Chrion
Craignish
Mussel Farm
The Lagoon
Eilean Dubh
Loch
Eilean Righ
The Kyles
Wooded
Eilean Buidhe
Jetty
Salmon Farm
Eilean nan Gabhar
Wooded
Eilean Macaskin
The Kyles
Depths in metres
metres
cables
0
1000
7
11′
56° 10′N
56° 09′·00N
08′
34′
33′
05° 32′·00 W
31′

CRINAN 10-9-9

Argyll

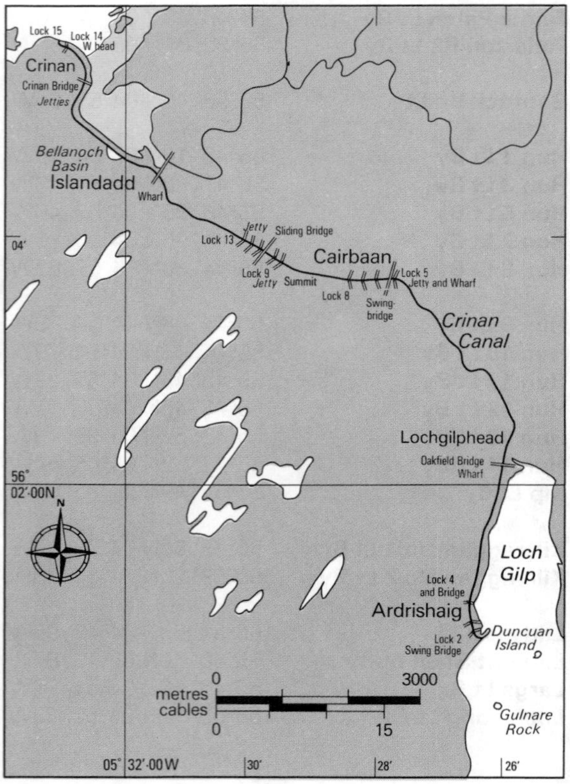

Lock 15
Lock 14 W head
Crinan
Crinan Bridge
Jetties
Bellanoch Basin
Islandadd
Wharf
Jetty
Sliding Bridge
Lock 13
Cairbaan
Lock 9
Jetty
Summit
Lock 8
Lock 5
Jetty and Wharf
Swing-bridge
Crinan Canal
Lochgilphead
Oakfield Bridge
Wharf
Loch Gilp
Lock 4 and Bridge
Ardrishaig
Lock 2
Swing Bridge
Duncuan Island
Gulnare Rock
metres
cables
0
3000
15
04′
56° 02′·00N
05° 32′·00W
30′
28′
26′

CRINAN *continued*

CHARTS
Admiralty 2320, 2326; Imray C65; OS 55

TIDES
−0608 Dover; ML 2·1; Duration 0605; Zone 0 (GMT)

Standard Port OBAN (⟵)

Times				Height (metres)			
HW		LW		MHWS	MHWN	MLWN	MLWS
0100	0700	0100	0800	4·0	2·9	1·8	0·7
1300	1900	1300	2000				
SCALASAIG (Colonsay)							
−0020	−0005	−0015	+0005	−0·1	−0·2	−0·2	−0·2
RUBHA A'MHAIL (Islay)							
−0020	0000	+0005	−0015	−0·3	−0·1	−0·3	−0·1
ORSAY ISLAND (Islay)							
−0110	−0110	−0040	−0040	−1·4	−0·6	−0·5	−0·2
BRUICHLADDICH (Islay)							
−0100	−0005	−0110	−0040	−1·7	−1·4	−0·4	+0·1
PORT ELLEN (Islay)							
−0530	−0050	−0045	−0530	−3·1	−2·1	−1·3	−0·4
PORT ASKAIG (Islay)							
−0110	−0030	−0020	−0020	−1·9	−1·4	−0·8	−0·3
CRAIGHOUSE (Sound of Jura)							
−0430	−0130	−0050	−0500	−2·8	−2·0	−1·4	−0·4
LOCH BEAG (Sound of Jura)							
−0110	−0045	−0035	−0045	−1·6	−1·2	−0·8	−0·4
GIGHA SOUND (Sound of Jura)							
−0450	−0210	−0130	−0410	−2·5	−1·6	−1·0	−0·1
MACHRIHANISH							
−0520	−0350	−0340	−0540	Mean range 0·5 metres.			

High water in Loch Crinan is 0045 before HW Oban.

SHELTER
Complete shelter in canal basin, but often many fishing boats lie there. Good shelter in Crinan Harbour to E of Eilean da Mheim, but full of moorings. Except in strong winds from W or N there is anchorage off the canal entrance, clear of fairway.

NAVIGATION
Waypoint 56°05′·80N 05°33′·69W, 326°/146° from/to Fl WG 3s Lt, 0·38M. Beware the Black Rocks and other nearby rocks in approach and near Ldg line.

CRINAN CANAL. Canal runs from Crinan, 9 miles to Ardrishaig and has 15 locks. All bridges open and canal can be entered at any tide. Max size, 26·5m length, 6m beam, 2·9m draught, mast height 28·9m. Vessels proceeding West have right of way. Canal dues are payable at Ardrishaig or Crinan sea lock. Passage time is between 5 to 6 hours. Lock opening times can be obtained from Canal Office (0546) 3210.

Crinan Bridge and sea locks operate until 1930 on Fri, Sat and Sun during summer.

Sea lock outer gates are left open after hours for yachts to shelter in the locks.

LIGHTS AND MARKS
W wing of entrance 2 FG (vert)
E wing of entrance 2 FR (vert)
Light to E of entrance Fl WG 3s 8m 4M, W shore-146°, G146°-shore.

RADIO TELEPHONE
VHF Ch 16; 74.

TELEPHONE (054 683)
Lock-keeper 211 MRSC Oban 63720; # Oban 63079; Marinecall 0898 500 463; Canal HQ (0546) 3210; Police Lochgilphead (0546) 2222; Dr Lochgilphead 2921

FACILITIES
Canal Office ☎ Lochgilphead 3210, M, L, FW; **Crinan Boats** ☎ 232, Slip, M, L, FW, ME, El, Sh, Gas, C, (5 ton) ◎, CH, ACA; **Sea Basin** P (cans), D, AB, V, R, Bar; **Crinan Hotel** ☎ 235, D, R, Bar; **Fyneside Service Station** ☎ Lochgilphead 2229, C. **M. Murray** ☎ 238 M; **Village** ✉; Ⓑ (Ardrishaig); ⇌ (Oban); ✈ (Glasgow or Campbeltown).
Note: There are some Bu spherical buoys marked 'HIDB visitors only'.
There is a boat park at Cairnbaan.

9

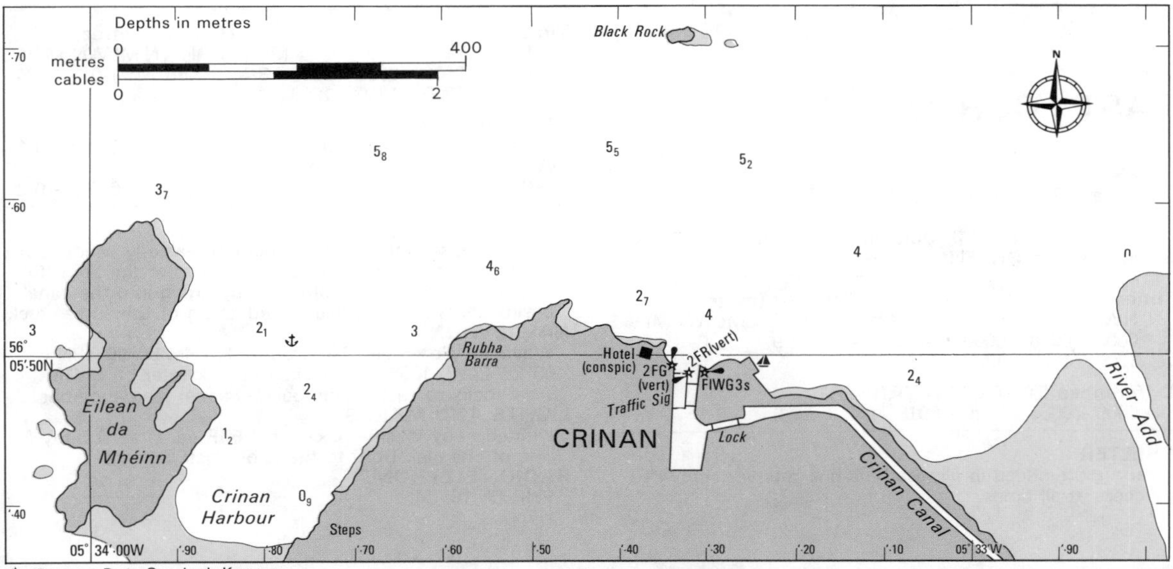
Depths in metres
metres
cables
0
400
0
2
Black Rock
N
Eilean
da
Mhéinn
Crinan
Harbour
Steps
Rubha
Barra
Hotel
(conspic)
2FG
(vert)
Traffic Sig
2FR(vert)
FlWG3s
CRINAN
Lock
Crinan Canal
River Add
56°
05′50N
05° 34′·00W
05° 33′W

▲ Contact Duty Sea lock Keeper

CAMPBELTOWN 10-9-10

Argyll

CHARTS
Admiralty 1864 2126; Imray C63; OS 68

TIDES
+0125 Dover; ML 1·8; Duration 0630; Zone 0 (GMT).
Standard Port GREENOCK (⟶)

Times				Height (metres)			
HW		LW		MHWS	MHWN	MLWN	MLWS
0000	0600	0000	0600	3·4	2·9	1·0	0·4
1200	1800	1200	1800				
Differences CAMPBELTOWN							
+0010	+0005	+0005	+0020	−0·5	−0·3	+0·1	+0·2
SANDA ISLAND							
−0040	−0040	No data		−1·0	−0·9	No data	
SOUTHEND, KINTYRE							
−0020	−0040	−0040	+0035	−1·3	−1·2	−0·5	−0·2

SHELTER
Good shelter from all directions. Excellent anchorage.

NAVIGATION
Waypoint 55°26′·30N 05°31′·39W, 060°/240° from/to front Ldg Bn 240°, 2·6M. Strong winds gust over the hills to the SW when wind in that direction.

LIGHTS AND MARKS
Davaar Fl(2) 10s 37m 23M. Ldg Lts 240°, Front FY 7m 6M, Rear FY 28m 6M.

RADIO TELEPHONE
VHF Ch 16; 12 14 (0845-1645 LT)

TELEPHONE (0586)
Hr Mr 52552; Campbeltown Loch Berthing 54381; MRCC Greenock 29988; ⌗ 52261; Marinecall 0898 500 462; Police 52253; Dr 52105

FACILITIES
EC Wednesday; **Piers** ☎ 52552, Slip, P, D, L, FW, ME, El, Sh, C (4 ton mobile), CH, AB, V, R, Bar; **Town Jetty** L, FW, ME, CH, AB; **New Quay** Slip; **Campbeltown Shipyard** ☎ 52881 L, FW, ME, Sh, CH, AB; **New Quay Chandlers** ☎ 54381 CH; **Campbeltown S.C.** Slip (dinghies only), M, L, FW, ME, CH, AB; **Duncan McPhee** ☎ 52115/52772, Slip, M, ME, El, Sh, C, CH;

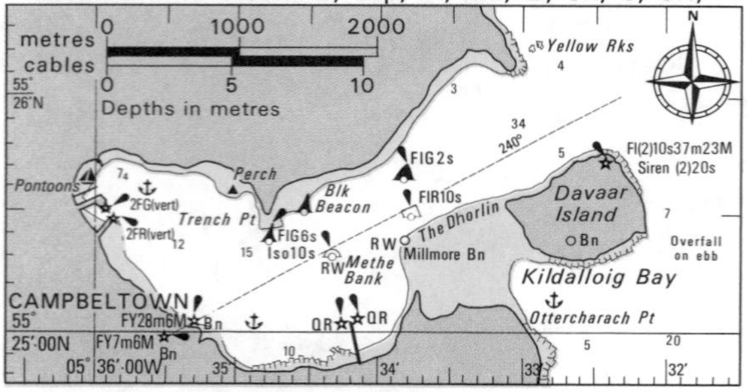

metres 0 1000 2000
cables 0 5 10
Depths in metres
Yellow Rks
Pontoons
Perch
Trench Pt
Blk Beacon
Fl G 2s
Fl R 10s
Fl G 6s
Iso 10s
Methe Bank
Millmore Bn
The Dhorlin
Davaar Island
Fl(2)10s37m23M
Siren (2)20s
Overfall on ebb
Kildalloig Bay
Ottercharach Pt
CAMPBELTOWN
FY28m6M
FY7m6M
QR
2FG(vert)
2FR(vert)
55° 26′N
55° 25′·00N
05° 36′·00W

County Garage ☎ 52235 Gas; **Town** P, D, V, R, Bar. ✉; Ⓑ; ⇌ (Air or bus to Glasgow); ✈.

EAST LOCH TARBERT 10-9-11

Argyll

CHARTS
Admiralty 2381; Imray C63; OS 62

TIDES
+0120 Dover; ML 1·9; Duration 0640; Zone 0 (GMT).
Standard Port GREENOCK (⟶)

Times				Height (metres)			
HW		LW		MHWS	MHWN	MLWN	MLWS
0000	0600	0000	0600	3·4	2·9	1·0	0·4
1200	1800	1200	1800				
Differences EAST LOCH TARBERT							
+0005	+0005	−0020	+0015	0·0	0·0	+0·1	−0·1

SHELTER
Very good indeed in all weathers but gets very crowded. Access at all times.

NAVIGATION
Waypoint 55°52′·02N 05°22′·96W, 090°/270° from/to FlR 2·5s Lt, 0·70M. Entrance is very narrow. Cock Isle divides the entrance into two. Buteman's Hole to the N, Main harbour to the S. N anchorages are fouled by heavy moorings and lost chains.

LIGHTS AND MARKS
Leading marks, Bn, G column (QG Lt) in line with tower (conspic) at 239°

RADIO TELEPHONE
VHF Ch 16 (0900-1700 LT)

TELEPHONE (0880)
Hr Mr 820344; MRCC Greenock 29988; ⌗ Greenock 28311; Marinecall 0898 500 462; Police 820200; Ⓗ Lochgilphead 2323.

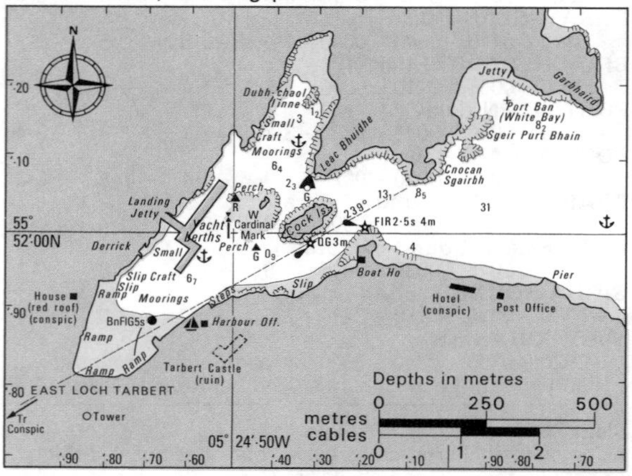

N
Dubh-chaol Linne
Small Craft Moorings
Leac Bhuidhe
Jetty
Garbhaird
Port Ban (White Bay)
Sgeir Port Bhain
Cnocan Sgairbh
Landing Jetty
Perch
Yacht Berths
W Cardinal Mark
Cock Is
FlR2·5s 4m
QG3m
Derrick
Small
Slip Craft Moorings
Ramp
Slip
Boat Ho
Pier
Hotel (conspic)
Post Office
House (red roof) (conspic)
BnFlG5s
Harbour Off.
Tarbert Castle (ruin)
EAST LOCH TARBERT
Tower
Tr Conspic
55° 52′·00N
05° 24′·50W
Depths in metres
metres 0 250 500
cables 0 1 2

FACILITIES
EC Wednesday; **Old Quay** D, FW; **Tarbert YC** Slip, L; **W. B. Leitch & Son** ☎ 820287, SM, ⊡, ACA; **M. Elliot** ☎ 820560, ME; **A. MacCallum** ☎ 820209, Sh. **Tarbert (Argyll) Fishermen** ☎ 820421, D, V, CH; **Yacht Berthing Facility** AB, FW, L, AC; **A. McKay** ☎ 820215 Gas;
Town P and D (cans), Gas, Gaz, L, V, R, Bar. ✉ (Tarbert); Ⓑ (Tarbert); ⇌ (bus to Glasgow); ✈ (Glasgow or Campbeltown).

ARDRISHAIG 10-9-12

Argyll

CHARTS
Admiralty 2381; Imray C63; OS 55

TIDES
+0120 Dover; ML 1·9; Duration 0640; Zone 0 (GMT).
Standard Port GREENOCK (⟶)

Times				Height (metres)			
HW		LW		MHWS	MHWN	MLWN	MLWS
0000	0600	0000	0600	3·4	2·9	1·0	0·4
1200	1800	1200	1800				
Differences ARDRISHAIG							
+0006	+0006	−0015	+0020	0·0	0·0	+0·1	−0·1
INVERARY							
+0011	+0011	+0034	+0034	−0·1	+0·1	−0·5	−0·2

SHELTER
Harbour is sheltered except in strong easterly winds. Lock into the Crinan Canal opens at all states of the tide. (See 10·9·9). Shelter can be obtained by going into the canal basin. Canal tolls payable at Ardrishaig or Crinan sea lock.

NAVIGATION
Waypoint No 48 port-hand buoy, FlR 4s, 56°00′·18N 05°26′·24W, 165°/345° from/to breakwater Lt, 0·61M. Tidal rocks to east of approach channel are dangerous.

LIGHTS AND MARKS
Lighted buoy W side of channel Fl R 4s. Unlit B buoy E side of channel. Both to the S of Sgeir Sgalag.

RADIO TELEPHONE
VHF Ch 16; 74.

ARDRISHAIG *continued*

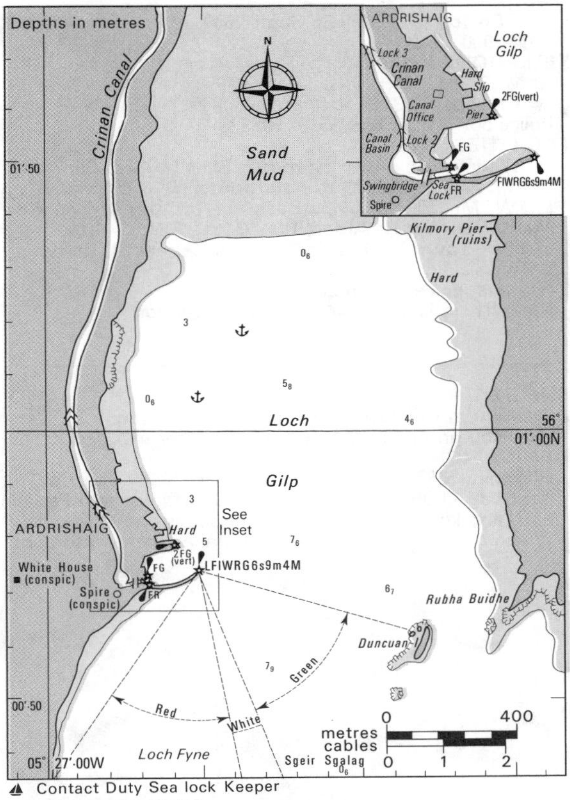
Depths in metres
Crinan Canal
Sand
Mud
Loch
Gilp
ARDRISHAIG
Loch Gilp
Lock 3
Crinan Canal
Hard
Slip
2FG(vert)
Canal Office
Pier
Canal Basin
Lock 2
FG
Swingbridge
Sea Lock
FR
FlWRG6s9m4M
Spire
Kilmory Pier (ruins)
Hard
01'·50
56° 01'·00N
See Inset
ARDRISHAIG
Hard
White House ■ (conspic)
Spire (conspic)
2FG (vert)
FG
FR
LFlWRG6s9m4M
Rubha Buidhe
Duncuan
Green
Red
White
00'·50
05° 27'·00W
Loch Fyne
Sgeir Sgalag
metres
cables
0
400
1
2

▲ Contact Duty Sea lock Keeper

TELEPHONE (0546)
Hr Mr 3210; MRCC Greenock 29988; ⵌ Greenock 28311; Marinecall 0898 500 462; Police 3233; Dr 2921.

FACILITIES
EC Wednesday; **Ardrishaig Pier/Harbour** ☎ 3210, Slip, L, FW, AB; **Crinan Canal** M, L, FW, AB, R, Bar; **Crinan BY** ☎ 83 232, Slip, L, FW, ME, El, Sh, CH, V; **Ardrishaig BY** ☎ 3280 ME, El, Sh, CH, C, D (cans); Cranes up to 20 ton available Lochgilphead (2 M); **Mid-Argyll Caravans** ☎ 2003 Gas. **Village** P and D (cans), CH, V, R, Bar. ✉; Ⓑ; ⇌ (bus to Oban); ✈ (Glasgow or Campbeltown).

LAMLASH 10-9-13

Isle of Arran, Bute

CHARTS
Admiralty 1864, 2220; Imray C63; OS 69

TIDES
+0115 Dover; ML no data; Duration 0635; Zone 0 (GMT).

Standard Port GREENOCK (⟶)

Times				Height (metres)			
HW		LW		MHWS	MHWN	MLWN	MLWS
0000	0600	0000	0600	3·4	2·9	1·0	0·4
1200	1800	1200	1800				
Differences LAMLASH							
−0016	−0036	−0024	−0004	−0·2	−0·2	No data	
BRODICK BAY							
0000	0000	+0005	+0005	−0·2	−0·2	0·0	0·0
LOCH RANZA							
−0015	−0005	−0005	−0010	−0·4	−0·3	−0·1	0·0

SHELTER
Very good in all weathers. Anchorages — off Lamlash except in E. winds; off Kingscross, good except in N or NW strong winds; off the Farm on NW of Holy Is in E winds. Alternative Loch Ranza to the N (where new marina is planned see 10·9·22).

NAVIGATION
Waypoint 55°32′·63N 05°03′·00W, 090°/270° from/to North Channel buoy (FlR 5s), 1·0M. Beware submarines which exercise frequently in this area, and also wreck of landing craft (charted) off farmhouse on Holy Island.

LIGHTS AND MARKS
Lights as shown on chartlet. There are two consecutive measured miles marked by poles north of Sannox, courses 322° or 142° (about 12 miles N of Lamlash).

RADIO TELEPHONE
None.

TELEPHONE (077 06)
MRCC Greenock 29988; ⵌ Ayr 262088; Marinecall 0898 500 462; Police Brodick 2573; Ⓗ 214.

FACILITIES
EC Wednesday (Brodick and Lamlash); **Lamlash Old Pier** Slip, M, L, FW; **Johnston's Marine Stores** ☎ 333, CH. **Village** Bar, R, ME, P and D (cans), V, ✉; Ⓑ; ⇌ (bus to Brodick, ferry to Ardrossan); ✈ (Glasgow or Prestwick).

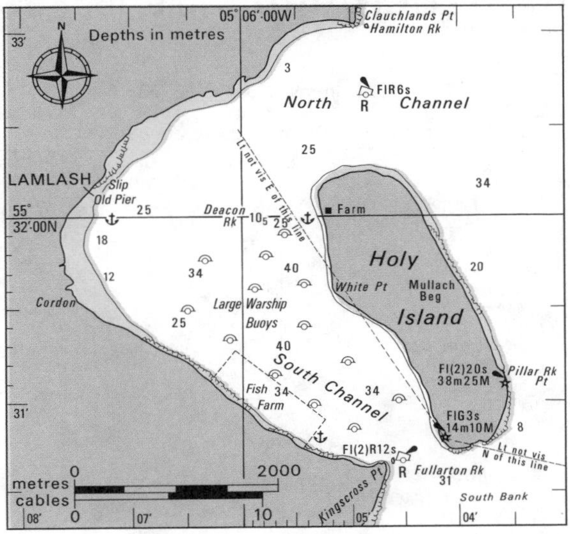
05° 06'·00W
Clauchlands Pt
Hamilton Rk
33'
Depths in metres
North
Channel
FlR6s
LAMLASH
Slip
Old Pier
55° 32'·00N
Deacon Rk
Farm
Holy
Island
White Pt
Mullach Beg
Cordon
Large Warship Buoys
South Channel
Fish Farm
Fl(2)20s 38m25M
Pillar Rk Pt
FlG3s 14m10M
Fl(2)R12s
Fullarton Rk
Kingscross Pt
South Bank
Lt not vis E of this line
Lt not vis N of this line
31'
metres
cables
0
2000
10
08'
07'
05'
04'

ROTHESAY 10-9-14

Isle of Bute, Bute

CHARTS
Admiralty 1867, 1907; Imray C63; OS 63

TIDES
+0100 Dover; ML 1·9; Duration 0640; Zone 0 (GMT).

Standard Port GREENOCK (⟶)

Times				Height (metres)			
HW		LW		MHWS	MHWN	MLWN	MLWS
0000	0600	0000	0600	3·4	2·9	1·0	0·4
1200	1800	1200	1800				
Differences ROTHESAY BAY							
−0020	−0015	−0010	−0002	+0·2	+0·2	+0·2	+0·2

SHELTER
Good shelter except in strong N to NE winds. Good anchorage in bay. In N to NE winds, yachts advised to go to Kyles of Bute or Kames Bay. Major pier reconstruction in progress.

NAVIGATION
Waypoint 55°51′·00N 05°02′·69W, 014°/194° from/to Albert Pier Lt, 0·69M. Keep 1 ca off Bogany Pt coming from E, and Ardbeg Pt coming from W. Admiralty mooring buoys, unlit, in Rothesay Bay (painted with Dayglo paint).

LIGHTS AND MARKS
Approaching the harbour, 'A' buoy Fl Y 2s is the most southerly of the mooring buoys.

ROTHESAY *continued*

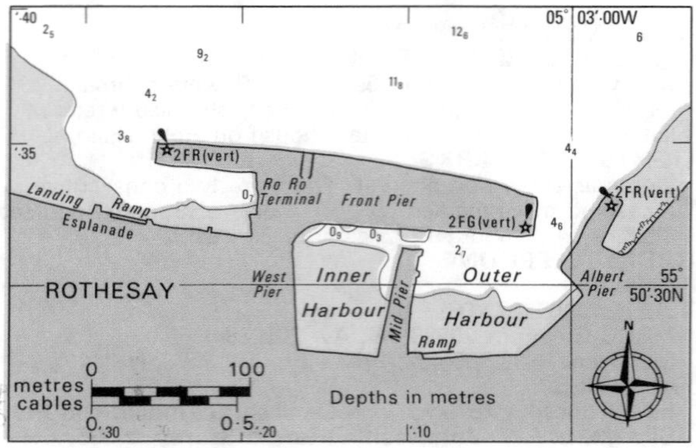
05° 03'·00W
2FR(vert)
Ro Ro Terminal
Front Pier
Landing Ramp
Esplanade
2FG(vert)
2FR(vert)
ROTHESAY
West Pier
Inner Harbour
Mid Pier
Outer Harbour
Ramp
Albert Pier
55° 50'·30N
metres
cables
Depths in metres

RADIO TELEPHONE
VHF Ch 16; 12 (1 May-30 Sept; 0600-2100, 1 Oct-30 Apl, 0600-1900 LT).
TELEPHONE (0700)
Hr Mr 503842; MRCC Greenock 29988;
Greenock 28311; Marinecall 0898 500 462;
Police 502121; Dr 503985; H 503938
FACILITIES
EC Wednesday; **Outer Harbour (E)** ☎ 503842, Slip, D*, L, FW, ME, El, AB; **Outer Harbour (W)** ☎ 503842, D*, L, FW, ME, El, Sh, CH, AB; **Inner Harbour** L, FW, AB; **Main Pier** FW, R; **Albert Pier** D*, L, FW, C (4 ton mobile); **Town** P, D, CH, V, R, Bar; ✉; Ⓑ; ⇌ (ferry to Wemyss Bay); ✈ (Glasgow).
*By arrangement (min 200 galls).
Note: There is a marina planned for Dunoon.

GARELOCH/RHU 10-9-15

Dumbarton

CHARTS
Admiralty 2000, 1994; Imray C63; OS 56, 63
TIDES
+0110 Dover; ML 1·9; Duration 0640; Zone 0 (GMT).

SHELTER
Excellent in Gareloch — Entrance not difficult.
Helensburgh Pier may be used, but rather exposed.
NAVIGATION
Waypoint 55°59'·30N 04°45'·19W, 176°/356° from/to front Ldg Lt 356°, 1·3M. Beware submarines from Faslane Base and large unlit MoD mooring buoys and barges off W shore of Gareloch. Gareloch entrance narrows to about

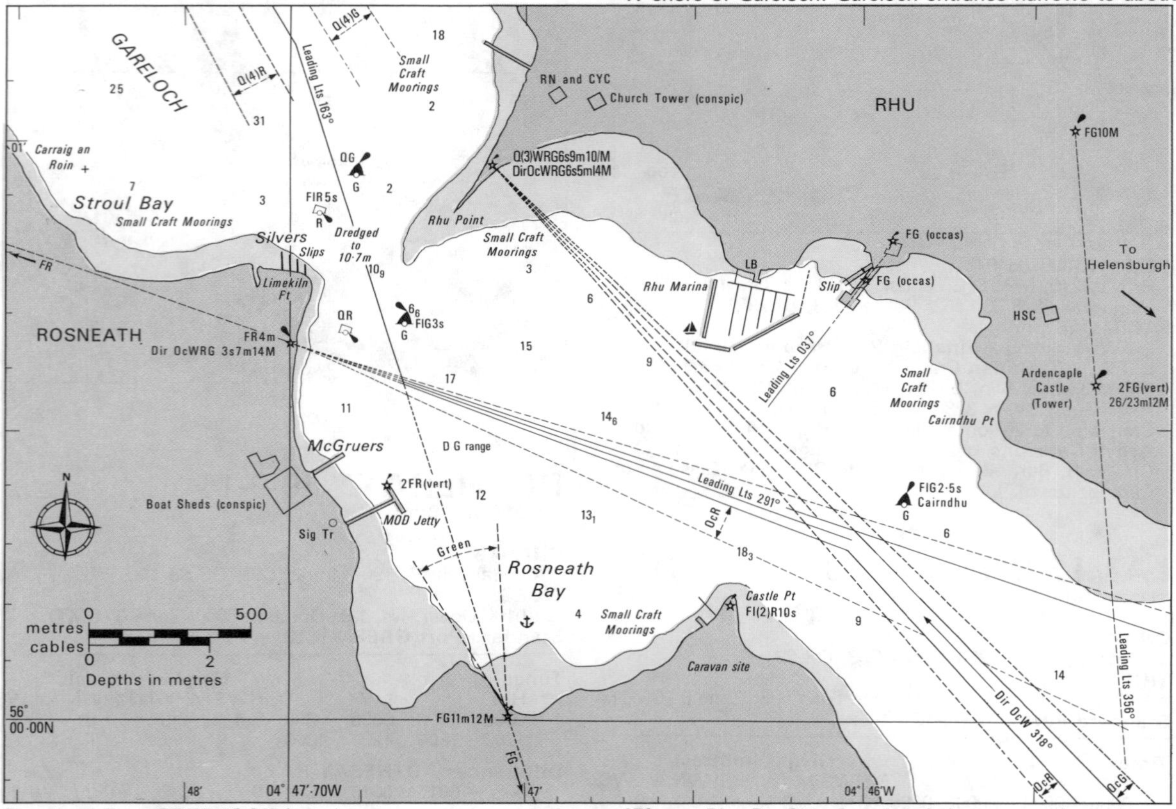
GARELOCH
Leading Lts 163°
Q(4)G
Q(4)R
Small Craft Moorings
RN and CYC
Church Tower (conspic)
RHU
FG10M
Carraig an Roin
Stroul Bay
Small Craft Moorings
QG
Q(3)WRG6s9m10/M
DirOcWRG6s5ml4M
FlR5s
Silvers
Slips
Dredged to 10·7m
Rhu Point
Small Craft Moorings
FG (occas)
To Helensburgh
Limekiln Pt
Rhu Marina
LB
Slip
FG (occas)
ROSNEATH
FR4m
Dir OcWRG 3s7m14M
QR
Fl G3s
HSC
Leading Lts 037°
Small Craft Moorings
Cairndhu Pt
Ardencaple Castle (Tower)
2FG(vert) 26/23m12M
McGruers
D G range
Boat Sheds (conspic)
2FR(vert)
MOD Jetty
Sig Tr
Leading Lts 291°
OcR
Fl G2·5s
Cairndhu
Green
Rosneath Bay
Small Craft Moorings
Castle Pt
Fl(2)R10s
Caravan site
Leading Lts 356°
Dir OcW 318°
metres
cables
Depths in metres
56° 00·00N
FG11m12M
FG
OcR
OcG
04° 47'·70W
04° 46'W

150m at Rhu Pt. Shingle spit is being removed to widen channel. If using Helensburgh Pier keep outside line of pierhead. Beware occasional steamer.
Beaches between Helensburgh Pier and Cairndhu Pt strewn with large boulders above and below MLWS.
Major construction and marine works are in hand at Faslane Naval Base. Faslane Bay area contains numerous obstructions and underwater cables. Gareloch Fuel Depot area immediately to N. of Base is included.
Craft proceeding to Garelochhead keep to W shore until well clear of Base area.
Construction lights and unlit obstructions make night passages in the Base area most inadvisable. Gareloch Oil Fuel Depot sectored light is clearly visible from S of construction areas.

Standard Port GREENOCK (⟶)

Times				Height (metres)			
HW		LW		MHWS	MHWN	MLWN	MLWS
0000	0600	0000	0600	3·4	2·9	1·0	0·4
1200	1800	1200	1800				
Differences GARELOCHHEAD							
0000	0000	0000	0000	0·0	0·0	0·0	0·1
COULPORT							
−0005	−0005	−0005	−0005	0·0	0·0	−0·1	−0·1
ARROCHAR							
−0005	−0005	−0005	−0005	0·0	0·0	−0·1	−0·1
HELENSBURGH							
0000	0000	0000	0000	0·0	0·0	0·0	−0·0

GARELOCH/RHU *continued*

LIGHTS AND MARKS
Leading lights into Gareloch 356°, 318°, 291° and 163°.

RADIO TELEPHONE
VHF Ch 16. Rhu Marina Ch **80** M (H24). See also Greenock/Gourock.

TELEPHONE (0436)
Queen's Hr Mr 74321; MRCC Greenock 29988 & 29014; # Greenock 28311; Marinecall 0898 500 462; Police 72141; H Alexandria 54121; Dr 72277.

FACILITIES
EC Wednesday; **Rhu Marina** (150) ☎ 820652, D, FW, CH, AC, BH (4½ ton), Gas, Gaz; **Royal Northern & Clyde YC** ☎ 820322, L, R, Bar; **Helensburgh SC** ☎ 72778 Slip (dinghies) L, FW; **McGruer (Rosneath)** ☎ 831313, Sh, ME, El, M, L, BH (25 ton), Slip; **Timbacraft** ☎ 810391, Sh, ME, El, Slip; **Silvers Marine** ☎ 831222 FW, Sh, ME, El, Ⓔ, L, M, BH (18 ton); **Nicolson Hughes** ☎ 831356, SM; **Gareloch Moorings and Engineers** ☎ 820062 ME, El, M; **R. McAlister** ☎ Dumbarton 62396 Sh, ME, El, M, Slip, BH (10 ton), AB, FW, CH, D; **Harken Barbarossa** ☎ 71415, CH: **Machspeed** ☎ 76351 CH; **Helensburgh** EC Wednesday, Slip, FW, CH, V, R, Bar, P, D, L, ✉; Ⓑ; ⇌; ✈ (Glasgow).

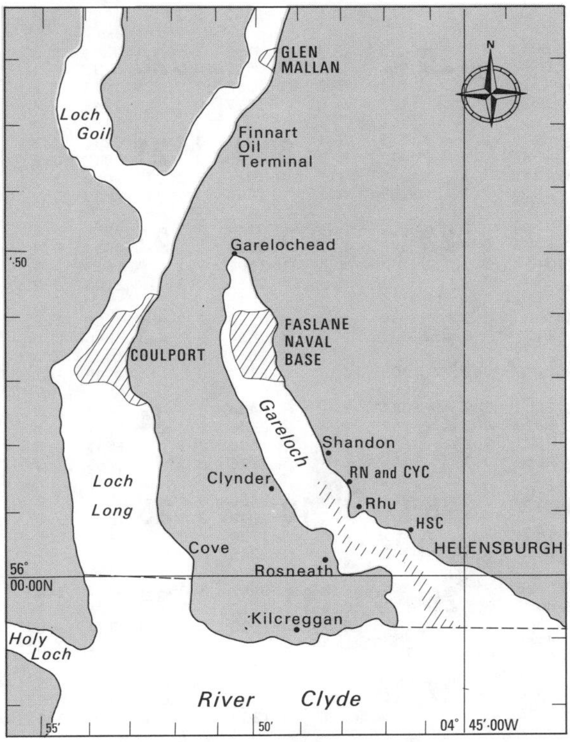

GLEN MALLAN
Loch Goil
Finnart Oil Terminal
Garelochead
COULPORT
FASLANE NAVAL BASE
Gareloch
Shandon
Loch Long
Clynder
RN and CYC
Rhu
HSC
HELENSBURGH
Cove
Rosneath
Kilcreggan
Holy Loch
River Clyde
56° 00·00N
04° 45'·00W

▨ Restricted Area-Max Speed 7Kn
– – – Southern Limit of Dockyard Port

NOTE: There are many restricted areas which are closed to all vessels during Nuclear Submarine movements (see W Coast of Scotland Pilot APP 2). Vessels are never allowed within 150m of naval installations; MoD police launches patrol area.
The S limit of restricted area marked by two Or posts with St Andrews Cross topmarks on Shandon foreshore. The W limit marked by three-sectored Lt at Gareloch Oil fuel depot N jetty. When restrictions are in force

1. Holy Loch, Coulport, Faslane
   by day : 3 G Lts (vert) supplemented by International Code pendant over pendant Nine.
   by night : 3 FG (vert) in conspic position
2. Entrance to Gareloch
   by day : R G G Lts (vert) supplemented by R flag with W diagonal bar.
   by night : R G G Lts (vert)

GREENOCK/GOUROCK
Renfrew

10-9-16

CHARTS
Admiralty 1994; Imray C63; OS 63

TIDES
+0122 Dover; ML 2·0; Duration 0640; Zone 0 (GMT)

Standard Port GREENOCK (→)

Times				Height (metres)			
HW		LW		MHWS	MHWN	MLWN	MLWS
0000	0600	0000	0600	3·4	2·9	1·0	0·4
1200	1800	1200	1800				
Differences PORT GLASGOW							
+0010	+0005	+0010	+0020	+0·2	+0·1	0·0	0·0
BOWLING							
+0020	+0010	+0030	+0055	+0·6	+0·5	+0·3	+0·1

NOTE: Harbours are all controlled by Clyde Port Authority, 16 Robertson St., Glasgow. Tel. Glasgow 221-8733. Greenock is a Standard Port and tidal predictions for each day of the year are given below.

SHELTER
Greenock — Commercial port
Gourock — very good anchorages on W side of bay but exposed to NE to N winds.

NAVIGATION
Gourock waypoint 55°58'·00N 04°49'·00W, 000°/180° from/to Kempock Pt Lt, 0·22M. No navigational dangers except the continuous shipping using the Clyde estuary and steamers using Railway Pier. Beware the bottom being fouled with lost tackle.

9

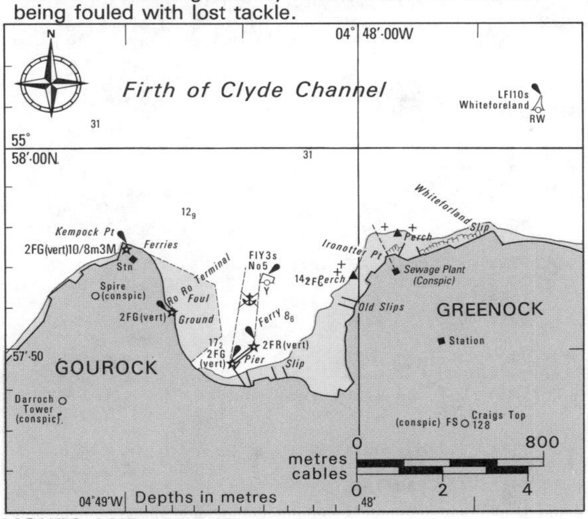

04° 48'·00W
Firth of Clyde Channel
LFl10s Whiteforeland RW
55° 58'·00N
Whiteforland Slip
Kempock Pt
2FG(vert)10/8m3M
Ferries
Stn
Ro Ro Terminal
FlY3s No5
Ironotter Pt
Perch
Sewage Plant (Conspic)
Spire (conspic)
2FG(vert)
Foul Ground
Ferry
2FR(vert)
Old Slips
GREENOCK
Station
57'·50
GOUROCK
2FG (vert)
Pier
Slip
Darroch Tower (conspic)
(conspic) FS
Craigs Top 128
metres
cables
04°49'W
Depths in metres
48'

LIGHTS AND MARKS
(Gourock). At the end of the pier 2 FG (vert).
(Greenock) Ldg Lts to dredged channel, 194°30' on Clydeport Control Tr, both FG.

RADIO TELEPHONE
Call: *Clydeport Estuary Radio* VHF Ch 16; 12 (H24). Other station: Dunoon (call: *Dunoon Pier*) Ch 31; 12 16 **31** (0700-2035 LT Mon-Sat; 0900-2015 LT Sun).

TELEPHONE (0475)
Hr Mr 25775; Estuary Control 26221; MRCC 29988; # 28311; Weather Glasgow 246 8091; Marinecall 0898 500 462; Police 24444; Dr 20000.

FACILITIES
EC Wednesday; **Greenock** All facilities available by prior arrangement with Harbour Dept, but small craft not particularly welcome; **Jas. Adam & Son** ☎ 31346 Slip, ME, El, C (5 ton), Ⓔ; **R. McAlister & Son** ☎ Dumbarton 62396, CH, D, Gas, ME, Sh; **Garvel Dry Dock** ☎ 25372, AB, AC, C (45 ton), El, Ⓔ, FW, L, ME, M, Sh; **Mackenzie** ☎ 36196, SM; **Royal Gourock YC** ☎ 32983 M, L, FW, ME, V, R, Bar; **Ritchie Bros** ☎ 32125, M; **Mackenzie** ☎ 36196, SM; **Ashton Bay** M; **Gourock Bay** M, L; **Maybank** Slip; **Town (Gourock)** P, D, V, R, Bar. ✉; Ⓑ; ⇌; ✈ (Glasgow).
Note: Clyde Yacht Clubs Assn is at Anchor House, Blackhall Lane, Paisley 041-887-8296. The Clyde Cruising Club is aboard S.V. Carrick, Glasgow 041-552-2183.

SCOTLAND, WEST COAST - GREENOCK

TIME ZONE UT(GMT)

For Summer Time add ONE hour in non-shaded areas

LAT 55°57′N LONG 4°46′W

TIMES AND HEIGHTS OF HIGH AND LOW WATERS

YEAR **1992**

JANUARY

Day	Time	m	Day	Time	m
1 W	0300 0946 1528 2157	1.0 3.1 0.9 3.0	16 TH	0218 0837 1437 2121	0.8 2.9 0.9 2.9
2 TH	0354 1042 1619 2258	1.0 3.2 0.8 3.0	17 F	0321 0950 1539 2238	0.7 3.1 0.7 3.0
3 F	0440 1129 1705 2348	0.9 3.3 0.7 3.0	18 SA	0415 1051 1633 2337	0.6 3.3 0.5 3.2
4 SA ●	0522 1211 1747	0.9 3.4 0.7	19 SU ○	0503 1143 1722	0.4 3.5 0.2
5 SU	0030 0558 1249 1824	3.0 0.9 3.4 0.6	20 M	0028 0549 1231 1808	3.4 0.3 3.8 0.1
6 M	0107 0632 1323 1858	3.0 1.0 3.4 0.6	21 TU	0114 0634 1316 1854	3.5 0.3 3.9 0.0
7 TU	0140 0703 1355 1931	3.1 1.0 3.4 0.6	22 W	0158 0718 1400 1939	3.6 0.3 4.1 0.0
8 W	0212 0734 1427 2004	3.1 0.9 3.4 0.6	23 TH	0241 0802 1443 2024	3.6 0.3 4.1 0.1
9 TH	0245 0807 1459 2040	3.2 0.9 3.4 0.6	24 F	0323 0847 1526 2110	3.5 0.4 4.0 0.2
10 F	0320 0844 1534 2118	3.2 0.9 3.4 0.6	25 SA	0406 0934 1610 2158	3.4 0.5 3.8 0.5
11 SA	0359 0924 1611 2202	3.2 1.0 3.3 0.7	26 SU ☾	0451 1025 1655 2251	3.3 0.7 3.6 0.8
12 SU	0441 1010 1653 2252	3.1 1.0 3.2 0.8	27 M	0539 1126 1744 2357	3.1 0.9 3.3 1.0
13 M ☽	0528 1102 1739 2351	3.1 1.1 3.1 0.8	28 TU	0634 1244 1840	2.9 1.0 3.0
14 TU	0621 1206 1833	3.0 1.1 2.9	29 W	0130 0749 1410 2000	1.2 2.8 1.0 2.8
15 W	0103 0722 1323 1945	0.9 2.9 1.1 2.8	30 TH	0248 0916 1514 2143	1.1 2.9 0.9 2.7
			31 F	0343 1023 1606 2253	1.1 3.0 0.8 2.8

FEBRUARY

Day	Time	m	Day	Time	m
1 SA	0429 1115 1651 2342	1.0 3.1 0.7 2.9	16 SU	0357 1031 1617 2327	0.6 3.2 0.4 3.1
2 SU	0508 1158 1730	1.0 3.2 0.7	17 M	0445 1126 1705	0.4 3.5 0.1
3 M ●	0021 0542 1235 1804	3.0 0.9 3.3 0.6	18 TU ○	0014 0530 1214 1750	3.3 0.3 3.7 0.0
4 TU	0054 0613 1308 1835	3.0 0.9 3.4 0.6	19 W	0058 0613 1258 1833	3.5 0.1 3.9 -0.1
5 W	0124 0642 1339 1906	3.1 0.8 3.4 0.5	20 TH	0138 0655 1340 1916	3.5 0.1 4.0 -0.1
6 TH	0154 0711 1408 1937	3.2 0.7 3.4 0.4	21 F	0218 0737 1421 1958	3.5 0.1 3.9 0.0
7 F	0224 0743 1439 2010	3.2 0.6 3.4 0.4	22 SA	0256 0820 1502 2040	3.5 0.2 3.8 0.2
8 SA	0257 0817 1511 2047	3.2 0.6 3.3 0.4	23 SU	0335 0903 1543 2123	3.3 0.3 3.6 0.5
9 SU	0333 0855 1546 2127	3.2 0.6 3.3 0.4	24 M	0415 0950 1624 2210	3.2 0.5 3.3 0.8
10 M	0412 0937 1624 2213	3.1 0.7 3.2 0.6	25 TU ☾	0457 1045 1708 2306	3.0 0.8 3.0 1.1
11 TU ☽	0454 1025 1706 2309	3.1 0.8 3.0 0.7	26 W	0544 1203 1756	2.8 1.0 2.7
12 W	0541 1125 1754	3.0 0.9 2.9	27 TH	0056 0645 1347 1903	1.3 2.7 1.0 2.5
13 TH	0024 0635 1246 1857	0.9 2.9 1.0 2.7	28 F	0228 0836 1453 2126	1.3 2.6 0.9 2.5
14 F	0154 0747 1416 2059	0.9 2.8 0.9 2.7	29 SA	0322 0958 1544 2237	1.2 2.8 0.8 2.6
15 SA	0303 0920 1523 2228	0.8 3.0 0.6 2.9			

MARCH

Day	Time	m	Day	Time	m
1 SU	0406 1053 1626 2323	1.0 3.0 0.7 2.8	16 M	0336 1008 1556 2309	0.6 3.2 0.3 3.1
2 M	0443 1136 1703 2359	0.9 3.1 0.6 2.9	17 TU	0423 1104 1644 2354	0.4 3.4 0.1 3.3
3 TU	0516 1212 1736	0.8 3.2 0.6	18 W ○	0507 1152 1728	0.2 3.6 0.0
4 W ●	0030 0545 1245 1806	3.0 0.7 3.3 0.5	19 TH	0035 0550 1236 1810	3.4 0.1 3.7 -0.1
5 TH	0059 0614 1315 1836	3.1 0.6 3.3 0.4	20 F	0114 0631 1318 1851	3.4 0.0 3.8 0.0
6 F	0128 0644 1345 1908	3.2 0.5 3.3 0.3	21 SA	0151 0712 1357 1931	3.4 0.0 3.7 0.1
7 SA	0159 0716 1415 1941	3.2 0.4 3.3 0.2	22 SU	0228 0753 1436 2011	3.3 0.1 3.5 0.3
8 SU	0232 0751 1448 2018	3.2 0.3 3.2 0.2	23 M	0304 0835 1515 2050	3.2 0.2 3.3 0.5
9 M	0307 0829 1523 2059	3.2 0.3 3.2 0.3	24 TU	0341 0920 1554 2132	3.1 0.4 3.1 0.8
10 TU	0345 0911 1601 2145	3.2 0.4 3.1 0.5	25 W	0420 1011 1635 2221	2.9 0.7 2.8 1.1
11 W	0426 0959 1643 2240	3.1 0.5 2.9 0.7	26 TH ☾	0502 1122 1720 2349	2.8 0.9 2.6 1.3
12 TH ☽	0511 1059 1730 2359	3.0 0.7 2.8 0.9	27 F	0554 1307 1817	2.7 1.0 2.4
13 F	0602 1224 1833	2.9 0.8 2.6	28 SA	0149 0724 1418 2037	1.3 2.6 1.0 2.4
14 SA	0134 0710 1358 2052	0.9 2.9 0.7 2.6	29 SU	0246 0914 1508 2158	1.2 2.7 0.9 2.5
15 SU	0243 0853 1504 2214	0.8 2.9 0.5 2.8	30 M	0330 1015 1550 2245	1.1 2.8 0.7 2.7
			31 TU	0408 1101 1627 2323	0.9 3.0 0.6 2.9

APRIL

Day	Time	m	Day	Time	m
1 W	0441 1139 1701 2356	0.8 3.1 0.5 3.0	16 TH	0444 1128 1704	0.2 3.5 0.1
2 TH	0512 1214 1733	0.6 3.1 0.4	17 F ○	0009 0527 1213 1746	3.3 0.1 3.5 0.1
3 F ●	0027 0543 1247 1806	3.1 0.5 3.2 0.3	18 SA	0048 0609 1255 1827	3.3 0.0 3.5 0.1
4 SA	0059 0616 1319 1840	3.2 0.3 3.2 0.2	19 SU	0125 0650 1335 1906	3.3 0.0 3.4 0.3
5 SU	0132 0651 1352 1917	3.2 0.2 3.2 0.1	20 M	0201 0731 1413 1945	3.2 0.1 3.2 0.4
6 M	0207 0729 1427 1956	3.2 0.1 3.1 0.2	21 TU	0236 0813 1450 2023	3.2 0.2 3.1 0.7
7 TU	0244 0809 1505 2039	3.2 0.1 3.1 0.3	22 W	0312 0857 1529 2103	3.1 0.4 2.9 0.9
8 W	0323 0854 1546 2127	3.2 0.2 3.0 0.5	23 TH	0350 0946 1608 2149	3.0 0.6 2.8 1.1
9 TH	0404 0946 1630 2226	3.2 0.4 2.9 0.7	24 F ☾	0431 1047 1653 2253	2.9 0.9 2.6 1.3
10 F ☽	0450 1049 1723 2345	3.1 0.6 2.8 0.9	25 SA	0518 1208 1747	2.8 1.0 2.5
11 SA	0542 1212 1838	3.0 0.7 2.6	26 SU	0037 0621 1324 1911	1.4 2.7 1.0 2.5
12 SU	0111 0649 1337 2037	0.9 3.0 0.6 2.7	27 M	0151 0800 1419 2051	1.3 2.6 0.9 2.5
13 M	0217 0824 1440 2150	0.8 3.0 0.4 2.9	28 TU	0241 0919 1505 2151	1.1 2.7 0.7 2.7
14 TU	0310 0941 1532 2243	0.6 3.2 0.3 3.1	29 W	0323 1014 1546 2237	1.0 2.8 0.6 2.9
15 W	0359 1039 1620 2328	0.4 3.3 0.1 3.2	30 TH	0401 1059 1624 2316	0.8 2.9 0.5 3.0

Chart datum: 1.62 metres below Ordnance Datum (Newlyn)

SCOTLAND, WEST COAST - GREENOCK

TIME ZONE UT(GMT)

For Summer Time add ONE hour in non-shaded areas

LAT 55°57'N LONG 4°46'W

TIMES AND HEIGHTS OF HIGH AND LOW WATERS

YEAR 1992

MAY

Date	Day	Moon	Time	m	Time	m	Time	m	Time	m
1	F		0437	0.6	1139	3.0	1701	0.3	2353	3.1
2	SA	●	0514	0.4	1217	3.1	1738	0.2		
3	SU		0030	3.2	0551	0.2	1255	3.1	1817	0.2
4	M		0107	3.2	0631	0.1	1333	3.1	1857	0.2
5	TU		0145	3.3	0712	0.0	1412	3.1	1940	0.2
6	W		0225	3.3	0757	0.1	1454	3.1	2027	0.4
7	TH		0306	3.4	0845	0.1	1539	3.0	2118	0.6
8	F		0350	3.4	0939	0.3	1628	3.0	2217	0.7
9	SA	☽	0438	3.3	1042	0.4	1726	2.9	2328	0.8
10	SU		0531	3.2	1155	0.5	1841	2.8		
11	M		0042	0.8	0635	3.2	1309	0.5	2006	2.9
12	TU		0147	0.7	0754	3.1	1413	0.4	2116	3.0
13	W		0244	0.6	0909	3.2	1508	0.3	2212	3.1
14	TH		0335	0.4	1011	3.2	1557	0.3	2300	3.2
15	F		0423	0.3	1104	3.3	1643	0.3	2344	3.2
16	SA	○	0508	0.2	1152	3.2	1727	0.3		
17	SU		0024	3.2	0551	0.1	1236	3.2	1808	0.4
18	M		0102	3.2	0634	0.1	1316	3.1	1847	0.5
19	TU		0139	3.2	0715	0.2	1355	3.0	1926	0.6
20	W		0215	3.2	0757	0.3	1432	2.9	2003	0.8
21	TH		0251	3.1	0839	0.5	1510	2.9	2042	0.9
22	F		0328	3.1	0923	0.6	1549	2.8	2125	1.1
23	SA		0407	3.0	1013	0.8	1632	2.8	2217	1.2
24	SU	☾	0451	2.9	1110	0.9	1722	2.7	2320	1.3
25	M		0543	2.9	1214	0.9	1821	2.7		
26	TU		0032	1.2	0645	2.8	1317	0.9	1933	2.7
27	W		0137	1.1	0803	2.7	1413	0.8	2045	2.7
28	TH		0232	1.0	0914	2.7	1503	0.6	2144	2.8
29	F		0320	0.8	1013	2.8	1549	0.5	2235	2.9
30	SA		0404	0.6	1104	2.9	1633	0.4	2320	3.1
31	SU		0448	0.4	1150	3.0	1716	0.3		

JUNE

Date	Day	Moon	Time	m	Time	m	Time	m	Time	m
1	M	●	0003	3.2	0531	0.2	1235	3.1	1759	0.3
2	TU		0045	3.3	0615	0.1	1319	3.1	1843	0.3
3	W		0127	3.4	0700	0.0	1403	3.2	1929	0.3
4	TH		0210	3.5	0747	0.0	1448	3.2	2016	0.4
5	F		0254	3.6	0837	0.0	1535	3.2	2107	0.5
6	SA		0339	3.6	0929	0.1	1625	3.2	2202	0.6
7	SU	☽	0427	3.6	1026	0.3	1719	3.1	2302	0.7
8	M		0519	3.5	1129	0.4	1819	3.0		
9	TU		0008	0.8	0616	3.4	1238	0.5	1928	3.0
10	W		0115	0.7	0722	3.2	1345	0.5	2037	3.0
11	TH		0218	0.7	0835	3.1	1445	0.6	2139	3.0
12	F		0314	0.5	0944	3.1	1539	0.6	2234	3.1
13	SA		0406	0.4	1045	3.0	1628	0.6	2322	3.1
14	SU		0454	0.4	1137	3.0	1713	0.6		
15	M	○	0006	3.2	0539	0.3	1224	3.0	1755	0.7
16	TU		0047	3.2	0621	0.3	1305	3.0	1834	0.7
17	W		0124	3.2	0702	0.4	1343	2.9	1911	0.8
18	TH		0200	3.2	0741	0.4	1419	2.9	1947	0.9
19	F		0235	3.2	0818	0.5	1454	3.0	2023	0.9
20	SA		0310	3.2	0857	0.6	1531	3.0	2100	1.0
21	SU		0347	3.2	0938	0.7	1610	3.0	2142	1.0
22	M		0426	3.1	1023	0.7	1654	2.9	2230	1.1
23	TU	☾	0509	3.0	1114	0.8	1742	2.9	2325	1.1
24	W		0558	2.9	1213	0.8	1837	2.8		
25	TH		0029	1.1	0655	2.8	1319	0.8	1939	2.8
26	F		0137	1.0	0806	2.7	1422	0.7	2048	2.8
27	SA		0240	0.9	0925	2.7	1519	0.6	2153	2.9
28	SU		0335	0.7	1033	2.8	1610	0.5	2249	3.1
29	M		0426	0.5	1130	3.0	1658	0.4	2340	3.2
30	TU	●	0515	0.3	1220	3.1	1745	0.3		

JULY

Date	Day	Moon	Time	m	Time	m	Time	m	Time	m
1	W		0027	3.4	0601	0.1	1308	3.3	1830	0.3
2	TH		0112	3.6	0648	0.0	1353	3.4	1915	0.3
3	F		0156	3.7	0734	0.0	1438	3.4	2001	0.3
4	SA		0241	3.8	0822	0.0	1523	3.4	2048	0.4
5	SU		0326	3.8	0910	0.1	1609	3.4	2138	0.5
6	M		0412	3.8	1002	0.3	1656	3.3	2232	0.6
7	TU	☽	0500	3.6	1058	0.5	1748	3.2	2332	0.7
8	W		0551	3.4	1202	0.7	1846	3.0		
9	TH		0041	0.8	0649	3.2	1317	0.8	1954	3.0
10	F		0154	0.8	0800	3.0	1428	0.8	2107	3.0
11	SA		0259	0.7	0922	2.9	1528	0.8	2211	3.0
12	SU		0354	0.6	1034	2.9	1619	0.8	2306	3.1
13	M		0443	0.5	1131	2.9	1704	0.8	2353	3.2
14	TU	○	0528	0.5	1217	2.9	1744	0.8		
15	W		0034	3.3	0607	0.5	1257	3.0	1821	0.8
16	TH		0112	3.3	0645	0.5	1331	3.0	1854	0.8
17	F		0146	3.3	0719	0.5	1403	3.1	1926	0.8
18	SA		0218	3.3	0752	0.5	1435	3.1	1958	0.8
19	SU		0250	3.3	0826	0.6	1508	3.1	2031	0.8
20	M		0323	3.3	0902	0.6	1544	3.1	2108	0.8
21	TU		0358	3.2	0941	0.6	1623	3.1	2150	0.9
22	W	☾	0437	3.1	1026	0.7	1705	3.0	2237	0.9
23	TH		0519	3.0	1120	0.8	1753	2.9	2334	1.0
24	F		0607	2.9	1227	0.9	1847	2.9		
25	SA		0045	1.0	0706	2.8	1346	0.9	1953	2.8
26	SU		0205	0.9	0837	2.7	1455	0.8	2112	2.9
27	M		0313	0.8	1010	2.8	1552	0.7	2223	3.1
28	TU		0409	0.5	1115	3.0	1641	0.5	2319	3.3
29	W	●	0458	0.3	1207	3.2	1727	0.4		
30	TH		0009	3.6	0545	0.1	1254	3.4	1811	0.3
31	F		0055	3.8	0630	0.0	1337	3.5	1855	0.2

AUGUST

Date	Day	Moon	Time	m	Time	m	Time	m	Time	m
1	SA		0139	3.9	0715	-0.1	1420	3.6	1939	0.2
2	SU		0223	4.0	0800	0.0	1501	3.6	2024	0.2
3	M		0306	4.0	0845	0.1	1544	3.5	2110	0.4
4	TU		0350	3.9	0933	0.3	1627	3.4	2200	0.5
5	W	☽	0435	3.6	1023	0.6	1712	3.2	2256	0.7
6	TH		0522	3.4	1124	0.9	1803	3.1		
7	F		0007	0.9	0614	3.1	1249	1.1	1906	2.9
8	SA		0134	0.9	0723	2.9	1417	1.1	2034	2.9
9	SU		0246	0.9	0908	2.8	1518	1.1	2152	3.0
10	M		0341	0.8	1028	2.8	1607	1.0	2251	3.1
11	TU		0428	0.7	1123	2.9	1649	1.0	2339	3.2
12	W		0510	0.6	1205	3.0	1727	0.9		
13	TH	○	0019	3.3	0547	0.6	1241	3.1	1800	0.9
14	F		0055	3.4	0620	0.6	1312	3.2	1830	0.8
15	SA		0126	3.4	0651	0.6	1341	3.2	1859	0.8
16	SU		0156	3.4	0721	0.6	1410	3.2	1929	0.7
17	M		0226	3.3	0753	0.5	1441	3.3	2001	0.7
18	TU		0257	3.3	0827	0.5	1515	3.3	2036	0.7
19	W		0330	3.2	0905	0.6	1552	3.2	2115	0.7
20	TH		0406	3.2	0948	0.7	1632	3.2	2201	0.8
21	F	☾	0447	3.0	1039	0.8	1716	3.1	2255	0.9
22	SA		0531	2.9	1145	1.0	1806	3.0		
23	SU		0006	1.0	0625	2.8	1317	1.1	1906	2.9
24	M		0139	1.0	0801	2.7	1435	1.0	2034	3.0
25	TU		0253	0.8	0957	2.9	1532	0.8	2158	3.2
26	W		0350	0.5	1100	3.1	1621	0.6	2258	3.4
27	TH		0439	0.3	1150	3.3	1706	0.4	2348	3.7
28	F	●	0525	0.1	1234	3.5	1750	0.3		
29	SA		0034	3.9	0609	0.0	1316	3.6	1832	0.2
30	SU		0118	4.0	0652	0.0	1355	3.7	1915	0.1
31	M		0200	4.0	0735	0.1	1435	3.6	1958	0.2

Chart Datum: 1.62 metres below Ordnance Datum (Newlyn)

9

SCOTLAND, WEST COAST - GREENOCK

TIME ZONE UT(GMT)

For Summer Time add ONE hour in non-shaded areas

LAT 55°57'N LONG 4°46'W

TIMES AND HEIGHTS OF HIGH AND LOW WATERS

YEAR **1992**

SEPTEMBER

Day	Time	m	Day	Time	m
1 TU	0242 0817 1514 2042	3.9 0.2 3.5 0.3	16 W	0230 0757 1447 2009	3.3 0.5 3.4 0.5
2 W	0324 0901 1555 2129	3.8 0.5 3.4 0.5	17 TH	0304 0835 1524 2049	3.2 0.6 3.4 0.6
3 TH	0407 0948 1637 ☽ 2223	3.5 0.8 3.3 0.7	18 F	0341 0918 1604 2135	3.2 0.7 3.3 0.7
4 F	0451 1043 1723 2335	3.3 1.1 3.1 1.0	19 SA	0422 1010 1647 ☾ 2231	3.1 0.9 3.2 0.9
5 SA	0541 1213 1819	3.0 1.4 2.9	20 SU	0508 1118 1735 2345	3.0 1.1 3.2 1.0
6 SU	0113 0645 1358 1952	1.1 2.7 1.4 2.9	21 M	0604 1253 1834	2.8 1.2 3.1
7 M	0226 0854 1458 2126	1.0 2.7 1.3 3.0	22 TU	0120 0757 1411 2002	1.0 2.8 1.1 3.1
8 TU	0320 1013 1544 2228	0.9 2.8 1.2 3.1	23 W	0233 0941 1508 2131	0.8 3.0 0.9 3.3
9 W	0405 1103 1625 2315	0.8 3.0 1.1 3.3	24 TH	0328 1040 1557 2233	0.5 3.2 0.7 3.6
10 TH	0444 1142 1700 2354	0.8 3.1 1.0 3.4	25 F	0417 1128 1642 2324	0.3 3.5 0.5 3.8
11 F	0519 1214 1732	0.7 3.2 0.9	26 SA ●	0502 1210 1726	0.1 3.6 0.3
12 SA	0028 0550 1244 ○ 1800	3.4 0.6 3.3 0.8	27 SU	0010 0545 1250 1808	3.9 0.1 3.7 0.2
13 SU	0100 0620 1313 1829	3.4 0.6 3.3 0.7	28 M	0054 0627 1329 1851	4.0 0.1 3.7 0.1
14 M	0129 0650 1342 1900	3.4 0.5 3.4 0.6	29 TU	0136 0709 1407 1933	3.9 0.2 3.7 0.2
15 TU	0159 0722 1413 1933	3.3 0.5 3.4 0.6	30 W	0217 0750 1445 2017	3.8 0.4 3.6 0.3

OCTOBER

Day	Time	m	Day	Time	m
1 TH	0258 0832 1524 2103	3.6 0.7 3.5 0.5	16 F	0244 0814 1501 2032	3.2 0.6 3.5 0.5
2 F	0339 0916 1604 2156	3.4 1.0 3.3 0.8	17 SA	0324 0900 1542 2121	3.2 0.8 3.5 0.6
3 SA	0422 1006 1648 ☽ 2304	3.1 1.3 3.2 1.0	18 SU	0408 0954 1626 2219	3.1 1.0 3.4 0.8
4 SU	0510 1123 1739	2.9 1.5 3.1	19 M	0458 1103 1715 ☾ 2333	3.0 1.2 3.4 0.9
5 M	0039 0610 1319 1856	1.2 2.7 1.6 3.0	20 TU	0603 1229 1815	2.9 1.3 3.3
6 TU	0154 0813 1423 2042	1.1 2.7 1.5 3.0	21 W	0058 0751 1343 1936	0.9 2.9 1.1 3.3
7 W	0248 0937 1511 2150	1.0 2.8 1.4 3.1	22 TH	0208 0915 1441 2101	0.7 3.1 1.0 3.4
8 TH	0332 1027 1552 2239	0.9 3.0 1.2 3.2	23 F	0304 1013 1532 2205	0.5 3.3 0.7 3.6
9 F	0411 1106 1627 2320	0.8 3.2 1.1 3.3	24 SA	0353 1101 1619 2259	0.4 3.5 0.5 3.7
10 SA	0446 1140 1659 2356	0.7 3.3 1.0 3.4	25 SU	0440 1145 1704 ● 2346	0.3 3.6 0.4 3.8
11 SU ○	0518 1211 1730	0.7 3.4 0.8	26 M	0523 1225 1748	0.2 3.7 0.3
12 M	0029 0549 1243 1801	3.4 0.6 3.4 0.7	27 TU	0031 0605 1304 1830	3.8 0.3 3.7 0.2
13 TU	0101 0622 1314 1834	3.3 0.5 3.5 0.6	28 W	0114 0647 1342 1913	3.7 0.4 3.7 0.3
14 W	0134 0656 1348 1910	3.3 0.5 3.5 0.5	29 TH	0154 0727 1420 1957	3.6 0.6 3.6 0.4
15 TH	0208 0734 1423 1949	3.3 0.5 3.5 0.5	30 F	0235 0808 1458 2043	3.4 0.8 3.5 0.6
			31 SA	0315 0850 1537 2133	3.2 1.1 3.4 0.8

NOVEMBER

Day	Time	m	Day	Time	m
1 SU	0357 0936 1619 2232	3.1 1.3 3.3 1.0	16 M	0403 0944 1613 2210	3.2 1.0 3.7 0.6
2 M	0444 1036 1706 ☽ 2347	2.9 1.5 3.2 1.2	17 TU	0457 1047 1703 ☾ 2317	3.2 1.1 3.6 0.7
3 TU	0539 1206 1806	2.8 1.7 3.1	18 W	0602 1159 1801	3.1 1.2 3.5
4 W	0103 0659 1328 1932	1.2 2.8 1.6 3.0	19 TH	0030 0724 1311 1911	0.8 3.1 1.1 3.5
5 TH	0203 0832 1424 2053	1.1 2.9 1.5 3.1	20 F	0139 0841 1413 2028	0.7 3.2 1.0 3.5
6 F	0251 0934 1510 2152	1.0 3.0 1.3 3.1	21 SA	0239 0943 1508 2137	0.6 3.3 0.8 3.5
7 SA	0333 1021 1549 2240	0.9 3.1 1.2 3.2	22 SU	0332 1034 1558 2235	0.5 3.5 0.6 3.5
8 SU	0411 1101 1625 2321	0.8 3.3 1.0 3.2	23 M	0420 1121 1646 2327	0.5 3.5 0.5 3.5
9 M	0447 1138 1700	0.7 3.4 0.8	24 TU ●	0506 1203 1732	0.5 3.6 0.4
10 TU	0000 0522 1214 ○ 1736	3.3 0.6 3.5 0.7	25 W	0013 0549 1244 1815	3.5 0.5 3.6 0.4
11 W	0037 0559 1249 1814	3.3 0.5 3.5 0.5	26 TH	0057 0630 1323 1859	3.5 0.6 3.6 0.4
12 TH	0114 0637 1326 1853	3.3 0.5 3.6 0.4	27 F	0138 0710 1400 1942	3.4 0.8 3.6 0.5
13 F	0152 0718 1404 1936	3.3 0.6 3.7 0.4	28 SA	0218 0750 1438 2025	3.3 0.9 3.6 0.6
14 SA	0233 0802 1444 2022	3.3 0.7 3.7 0.4	29 SU	0257 0829 1515 2110	3.2 1.1 3.5 0.8
15 SU	0316 0850 1527 2113	3.3 0.8 3.7 0.5	30 M	0337 0911 1555 2158	3.1 1.3 3.4 0.9

DECEMBER

Day	Time	m	Day	Time	m
1 TU	0420 0958 1637 2252	3.0 1.4 3.3 1.1	16 W	0448 1025 1650 ☾ 2252	3.3 0.9 3.8 0.6
2 W	0508 1054 1726 ☽ 2353	3.0 1.5 3.2 1.2	17 TH	0544 1127 1743 2357	3.2 1.0 3.6 0.7
3 TH	0604 1203 1824	2.9 1.6 3.1	18 F	0648 1236 1844	3.2 1.0 3.5
4 F	0058 0711 1315 1936	1.2 2.9 1.5 3.0	19 SA	0108 0800 1345 1955	0.7 3.2 0.9 3.4
5 SA	0158 0824 1416 2051	1.1 2.9 1.4 3.0	20 SU	0216 0909 1447 2110	0.8 3.2 0.8 3.3
6 SU	0250 0927 1507 2155	1.0 3.0 1.2 3.0	21 M	0315 1009 1543 2218	0.7 3.3 0.7 3.3
7 M	0336 1019 1552 2247	0.8 3.2 1.0 3.1	22 TU	0407 1101 1634 2315	0.7 3.4 0.5 3.3
8 TU	0419 1105 1634 2334	0.7 3.3 0.8 3.1	23 W	0454 1147 1721	0.7 3.5 0.5
9 W ○	0501 1147 1716	0.6 3.4 0.6	24 TH	0005 0538 1230 ● 1804	3.3 0.7 3.5 0.4
10 TH	0018 0542 1228 1758	3.2 0.5 3.6 0.5	25 F	0049 0618 1309 1846	3.3 0.8 3.6 0.5
11 F	0100 0624 1309 1841	3.3 0.5 3.7 0.3	26 SA	0129 0657 1346 1926	3.2 0.8 3.6 0.5
12 SA	0143 0707 1350 1926	3.4 0.5 3.8 0.3	27 SU	0205 0733 1422 2004	3.2 0.9 3.6 0.6
13 SU	0226 0752 1432 2012	3.4 0.6 3.9 0.3	28 M	0241 0809 1456 2042	3.2 1.0 3.5 0.7
14 M	0310 0839 1515 2101	3.4 0.7 3.9 0.3	29 TU	0316 0844 1532 2121	3.2 1.1 3.5 0.8
15 TU	0357 0929 1601 2154	3.4 0.8 3.9 0.4	30 W	0354 0922 1609 2203	3.1 1.1 3.4 0.9
			31 TH	0435 1005 1649 2250	3.1 1.2 3.2 1.0

Chart datum: 1.62 metres below Ordnance Datum (Newlyn)

GREENOCK/GOUROCK *continued*

Note: There is a scheme to re-open the Forth and Clyde Canal from Dalmuir (on the Clyde) via Kirkintilloch, Castlecary, Bonnybridge to the Carron R flowing into the Forth at Grangemouth.

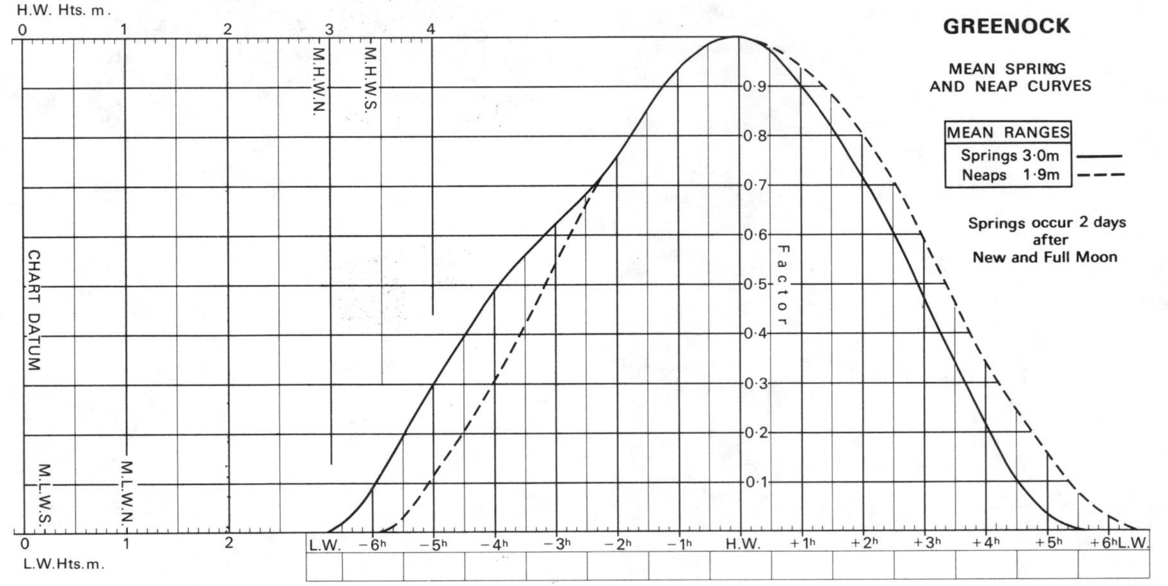
H.W. Hts. m.
0
1
2
3
4
M.H.W.N.
M.H.W.S.
CHART DATUM
M.L.W.S.
M.L.W.N.
L.W.Hts.m.
Factor
0·9
0·8
0·7
0·6
0·5
0·4
0·3
0·2
0·1
L.W.
−6h
−5h
−4h
−3h
−2h
−1h
H.W.
+1h
+2h
+3h
+4h
+5h
+6h L.W.
GREENOCK
MEAN SPRING AND NEAP CURVES
MEAN RANGES
Springs 3·0m
Neaps 1·9m
Springs occur 2 days after New and Full Moon

INVERKIP (KIP MARINA)

Renfrew

10-9-17

CHARTS
Admiralty 1907; Imray C63; OS 63

TIDES
+0110 Dover; ML 1·8; Duration 0640; Zone 0 (GMT).

Standard Port GREENOCK (←)

Times				Height (metres)			
HW		LW		MHWS	MHWN	MLWN	MLWS
0000	0600	0000	0600	3·4	2·9	1·0	0·4
1200	1800	1200	1800				
Differences WEMYSS BAY							
−0005	−0005	−0005	−0005	0·0	0·0	+0·1	+0·1

SHELTER
Excellent and is navigable at all states of the tide (2·2m at MLWS). Inverkip Bay is exposed to winds NW through W to SW.

NAVIGATION
Waypoint Kip stbd-hand buoy, QG, 55°54′·48N 04°52′·95W, at entrance to buoyed channel. Entrance ½M N of conspic chimney (238m). Beware shifting bank to N of entrance to buoyed channel. No areas in marina dry.

LIGHTS AND MARKS
From Kip G buoy, QG, three G buoys to starboard and three R buoys to port, 30m apart form navigable channel 365 metres long.

RADIO TELEPHONE
VHF Ch **80** M (H24).

TELEPHONE (0475)
Hr Mr 521485; MRCC 29988; ⊞ 28311; Marinecall 0898 500 462; Police 521222; Dr 520248; Ⓗ 33777.

FACILITIES
EC Wednesday; **Kip Marina** (700+40 visitors) ☎ 521485, D, FW, AC, ME, El, Ⓔ, Sh, BH (40 ton), ACA, SM, CH, V, R, Bar, ◎, Gas, Gaz, YC; **Town** ✉; Ⓑ (Gourock); ⇌; ✈ (Glasgow).

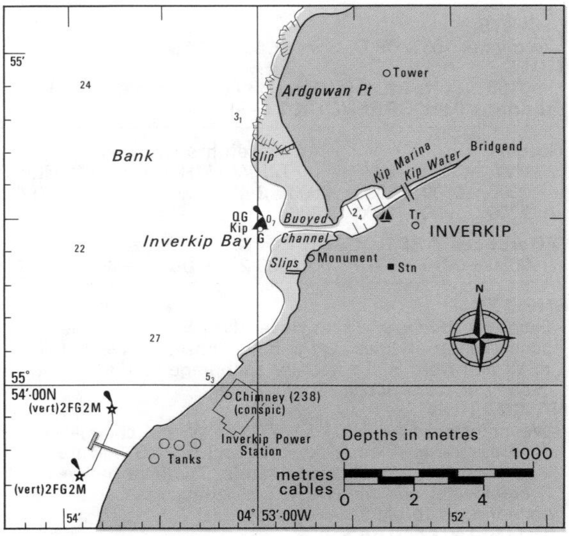
55′
24
Tower
Ardgowan Pt
Bank
Slip
Kip Marina
Kip Water
Bridgend
QG
Kip
G
Buoyed
Channel
Tr
INVERKIP
22
Inverkip Bay
Slips
Monument
Stn
N
27
55°
54′·00N
(vert)2FG2M
Chimney (238)
(conspic)
Inverkip Power Station
Tanks
(vert)2FG2M
Depths in metres
0
1000
metres
cables
0
2
4
54′
04° 53′·00W
52′

LARGS 10-9-18

Ayr

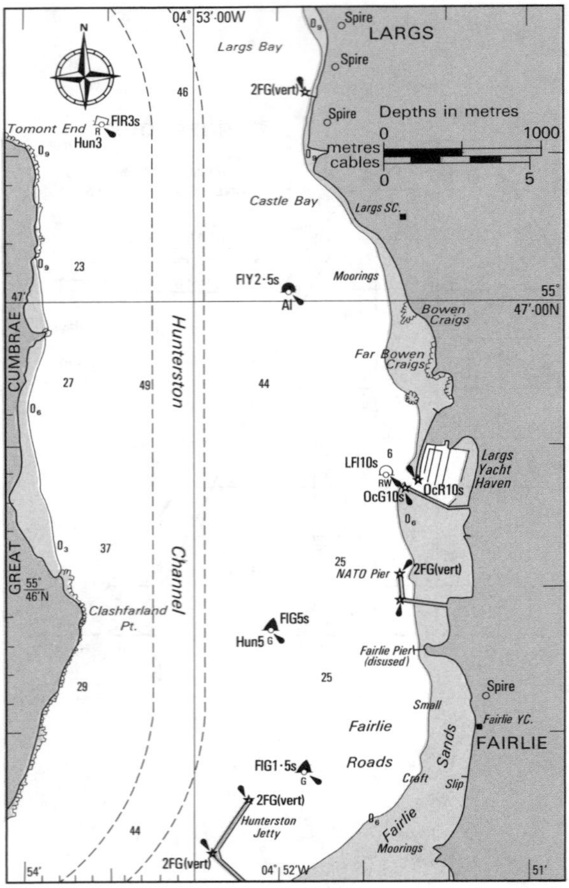

04° 53'·00W
LARGS
Largs Bay
Spire
2FG(vert)
Depths in metres
0 1000
metres
cables
0 5
Tomont End
FlR3s
Hun3
Castle Bay
Largs SC.
Moorings
FlY2·5s
Al
55° 47'·00N
Bowen Craigs
Far Bowen Craigs
CUMBRAE
GREAT
Hunterston Channel
LFl10s
RW
OcR10s
OcG10s
Largs Yacht Haven
NATO Pier
2FG(vert)
55° 46'N
Clashfarland Pt.
FlG5s
Hun5
Fairlie Pier (disused)
Spire
Small
Fairlie YC.
FAIRLIE
Fairlie Roads
Fairlie Sands
Craft
Slip
FlG1·5s
2FG(vert)
Hunterston Jetty
Moorings
54'
04° 52'W
51'

CHARTS
Admiralty 1867, 1907; Imray C63; OS 63

TIDES
+0105 Dover; ML 1·9; Duration 0640; Zone 0 (GMT).

Standard Port GREENOCK (⟵)

Times				Heights (metres)			
HW		LW		MHWS	MHWN	MLWN	MLWS
0000	0600	0000	0600	3·4	2·9	1·0	0·4
1200	1800	1200	1800				
Differences ARDROSSAN							
−0020	−0010	−0010	−0010	−0·2	−0·2	+0·1	+0·1

SHELTER
Excellent shelter in Yacht Haven (1M S of Largs pier) accessible at all tides. Largs bay exposed to winds from N to W and from S. Temporary anchorage in 10m about ½ca N of pier opposite Royal Hotel.

NAVIGATION
Waypoint 55°46'·40N 04°51'·77W; RW mid channel buoy off entrance to marina. Approaching from S beware Hunterston and Southannan sands. The area between the S breakwater and the NATO pier is restricted and anchoring is forbidden.

LIGHTS AND MARKS
Yacht Haven (1M S of Largs pier): entrance buoy RW LFl 10s; S breakwaterhead Oc G 10s; N breakwaterhead Oc R 10s. Largs; N end of pier, 2 FG (vert) 7/5m 5M, shown when vessel expected.

RADIO TELEPHONE
Yacht Haven Ch **80** M (H24).

TELEPHONE (0475)
Hr Mr (Yacht Haven) 675333; MRCC 29988; # 28311; Marinecall 0898 500 462; Dr 673380; ⊞ 33777.

FACILITIES
EC Wednesday. **Largs Yacht Haven** (500 – some visitors) ☎ 675333, FW, D, P, BH (45 ton), ⊡, CH, AC, SM, BY, C (17 ton), Gas, Gaz, Slip (Access H24); **Marine Sales Engineering** ☎ 687139 ME; **C and C Marine** ☎ 687180 Divers; **DDZ Marine** ☎ 686072 ME, El, Sh; **Largs Chandlers** ☎ 686026, CH; **Yacht Electrical and Electronic Services** ☎ 686463, El, Ⓔ; **Regattas** ☎ 686684, Bar, R; **The Ship's Galley** ☎ 675625, V; **Largs SC** ☎ 674782; **Town** LB, V, R, Bar, ✉, Ⓑ; ⇌; ✈ (Glasgow).

TROON 10-9-19

Ayr

CHARTS
Admiralty 1866 2220; Imray C63; OS 70

TIDES
+0050 Dover; ML 1·9; Duration 0630; Zone 0 (GMT).
Standard Port GREENOCK (⟵)

Times				Height (metres)			
HW		LW		MHWS	MHWN	MLWN	MLWS
0000	0600	0000	0600	3·4	2·9	1·0	0·4
1200	1800	1200	1800				
Differences TROON							
−0025	−0025	−0020	−0020	−0·2	−0·2	0·0	0·0
IRVINE							
−0020	−0020	−0030	−0010	−0·3	−0·3	−0·1	0·0
AYR							
−0025	−0025	−0030	−0015	−0·4	−0·3	+0·1	+0·1
GIRVAN							
−0025	−0040	−0035	−0010	−0·3	−0·3	−0·1	0·0

SHELTER
Completely sheltered from all winds. Strong SW winds cause heavy seas in the approaches. Berth in Yacht Marina.

NAVIGATION
Waypoint 55°33′·20N 04°42′·00W, 283°/103° from/to West Pier Lt, 0·61M. Beware the Mill Rock ½ M NE of West Pier (R buoy on S side). Keep clear of water off Ailsa Shipbuilding yard.

LIGHTS AND MARKS
As on chartlet. No leading lights. Sheds of Ailsa shipyard (35m) are conspic. Recommended approach Troon on bearing S to SW. Entry signals: Day—2B balls, Night—2RLts (vert) Entry and Exit prohibited: these refer to commercial traffic only.

RADIO TELEPHONE
Marina VHF Ch **80** M (H24). Other stations: Ardrossan Ch 16; 12 14 (H24). Girvan Ch 16; 12 (Mon-Fri: 0900-1700 LT).

TELEPHONE (0292)
Hr Mr 313412; MRCC Greenock 29988; # Greenock 28311; Marinecall 0898 500 462; Police 313100; Ⓗ 68621; Marina officials will give telephone numbers of doctors on call 315553.

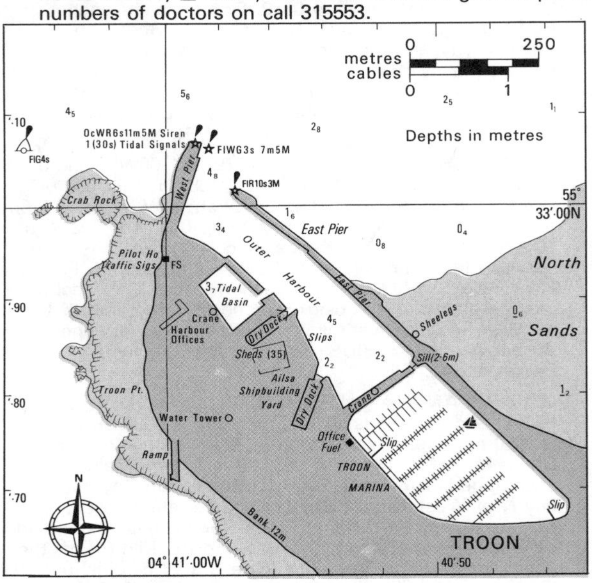

metres
cables
0
250
0
1
Depths in metres
OcWR6s11m5M Siren 1(30s) Tidal Signals
FIWG3s 7m5M
FIR10s3M
FIG4s
Crab Rock
West Pier
East Pier
Outer Harbour
Pilot Ho Traffic Sigs
Tidal Basin
Crane
Harbour Offices
Dry Dock
Slips
Sheds (35)
Ailsa Shipbuilding Yard
Sheelegs
Sill(2·6m)
North
Sands
Troon Pt.
Water Tower
Ramp
Office Fuel
Slip
TROON MARINA
Bank 12m
TROON
55° 33′·00N
04° 41′·00W
40′·50

FACILITIES
EC Wednesday; **Marina** (345+40 visitors) ☎ 315553 (Access all tides), Slip, D, FW, ME, El, Sh (on-site repairs ☎ 316180), BH (12 ton), C (2 ton), CH, AC, V, R, Bar; ⊡, Gas, Gaz; **Harbour Pier** FW, Sh, AB, V. **Ailsa Shipyard** has all normal 'big ship' repair facilities. **Troon Cruising Club** ☎ 311190; **Marine Mechanical** ☎ 313400, ME; **Boat Electrics and Electronics** ☎ 315355, El, Ⓔ. **Town** ✉; Ⓑ; ⇌; ✈ (Glasgow).

PORTPATRICK 10-9-20

Wigtown

CHARTS
Admiralty 2198; Imray C62; OS 82

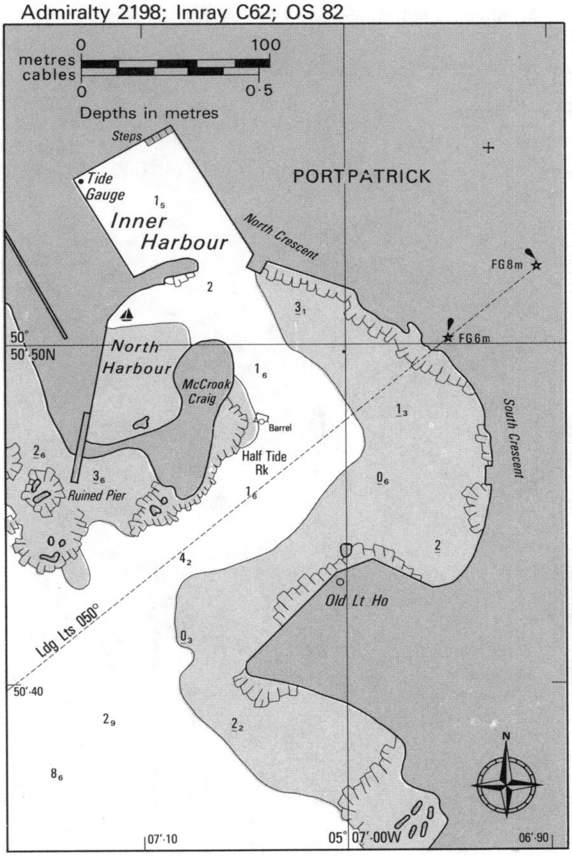

metres
cables
0
100
0
0·5
Depths in metres
Steps
Tide Gauge
Inner Harbour
PORTPATRICK
North Crescent
FG8m
FG6m
North Harbour
McCrook Craig
Barrel
Half Tide Rk
Ruined Pier
South Crescent
Old Lt Ho
Ldg Lts 050°
50′·50N
50′·40
07′·10
05° 07′·00W
06′·90
N

TIDES
+0032 Dover; ML 2·1; Duration 0615; Zone 0 (GMT).
Standard Port LIVERPOOL (⟶)

Times				Heights (metres)			
HW		LW		MHWS	MHWN	MLWN	MLWS
0000	0600	0200	0800	9·3	7·4	2·9	0·9
1200	1800	1400	2000				
Differences PORTPATRICK							
+0018	+0026	0000	−0035	−5·5	−4·4	−2·0	−0·6

Stranraer Differences Liverpool +0046 (see 10·10·11)

SHELTER
Good but is a difficult entrance in winds from SW to NW when strong. Inner harbour has good shelter and berthing facilities.

NAVIGATION
Waypoint 54°50′·00N 05°08′·00W, 235°/055° from/to entrance, 0·70M. Entrance to outer harbour by way of short narrow entrance with adjacent hazards including rocky shelf submerged at HW. Barrel marks end of rocks.

LIGHTS AND MARKS
Two FG Ldg Lts 050°, 6 and 8m: Front on sea wall, Rear on building; 2 vert orange lines by day. There is a conspic hotel approx 100m NW of Inner Harbour.

RADIO TELEPHONE
None. Other station: Stranraer VHF Ch 16; 14 (H24). Portpatrick Coast Radio Station VHF Ch 16; 27.

TELEPHONE (077 681)
Hr Mr 355; MRSC Greenock 29988; # Newton Stewart 2718; Marinecall 0898 500 462; Police 222; Ⓗ Stranraer 2323

FACILITIES
EC Thursday. **Harbour** Slip (very small craft), M, FW, L, AB. **Village** P and D (cans), Gas, V, R, Bar. ✉; Ⓑ (Stranraer); ⇌ (bus to Stranraer); ✈ (Carlisle).

9

KIRKCUDBRIGHT 10-9-21

Kirkcudbrightshire

CHARTS

Admiralty 1344, 1346, 2094; Imray C62; OS 84

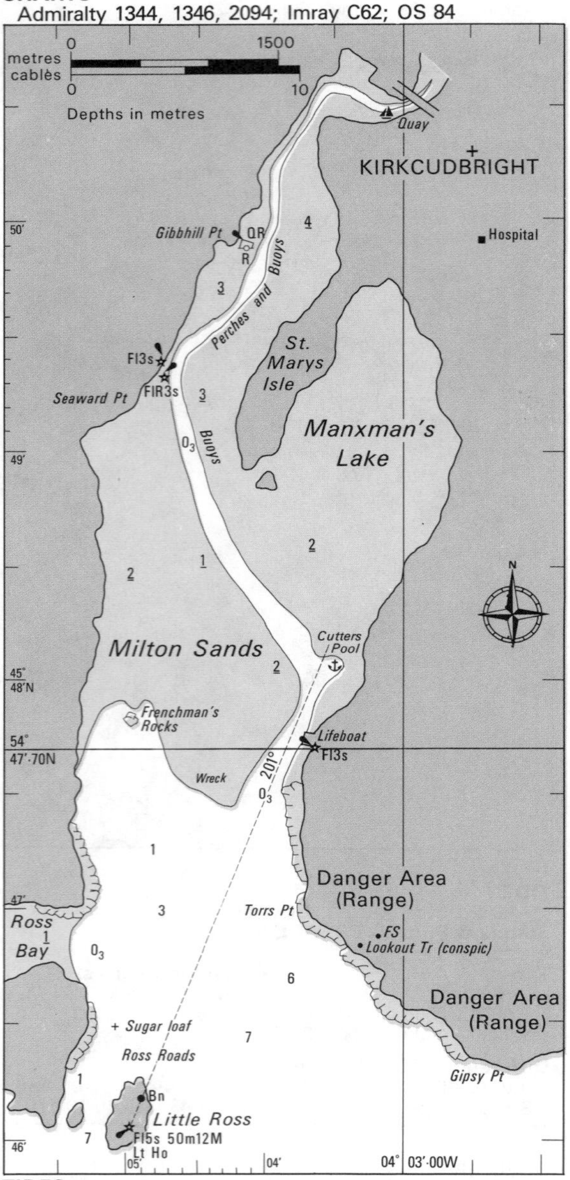

metres
cables
0
1500
10
Depths in metres
Quay
KIRKCUDBRIGHT
Hospital
Gibbhill Pt
QR
R
Perches and Buoys
St. Marys Isle
Manxman's Lake
Fl3s
FlR3s
Seaward Pt
Buoys
Milton Sands
Cutters Pool
Frenchman's Rocks
Lifeboat
Fl3s
Wreck
201°
Danger Area (Range)
Torrs Pt
FS
Lookout Tr (conspic)
Ross Bay
Danger Area (Range)
Sugar loaf
Ross Roads
Gipsy Pt
Bn
Little Ross
Fl5s 50m12M
Lt Ho
50'
49'
45' 48'N
54° 47'·70N
47'
46'
05'
04'
04° 03'·00W

TIDES

+0030 Dover; ML 4·1; Duration 0545; Zone 0 (GMT).

Standard Port LIVERPOOL (⟶)

Times				Heights (metres)			
HW		LW		MHWS	MHWN	MLWN	MLWS
0000	0600	0200	0800	9·3	7·4	2·9	0·9
1200	1800	1400	2000				
Differences KIRKCUDBRIGHT BAY							
+0015	+0015	+0010	0000	−1·8	−1·5	−0·5	−0·1
DRUMMORE							
+0030	+0040	+0015	+0020	−3·4	−2·5	−0·9	−0·3
ISLE OF WHITHORN							
+0020	+0025	+0025	+0005	−2·4	−2·0	−0·8	−0·2

SHELTER

Very good shelter. Complete shelter at town quays, which dry. Boats can stay afloat in 2m off the wooden jetty. Good shelter behind Ross Is and in Flint Bay ½ ca N of Torrs Pt except in winds between SSW and ESE which cause heavy swell.

NAVIGATION

Waypoint 54°45'·50N 04°04'·00W, 185°/005° from/to Torrs Pt, 1·4M. The Bar is 1 ca N of Torrs Pt. Note that spring tides run up to 3 kn. A firing range crosses the entrance. Details can be obtained either from Range Safety Officer (055 732) 236 or from Range Safety Vessel on VHF Ch 16 73.

LIGHTS AND MARKS

Little Ross Lt Ho West of entrance Fl 5s 50m 12M, (obsc in Wigtown bay when bearing more than 103°).

Note: The harbour authority is the Dumfries & Galloway Regional Council.

RADIO TELEPHONE

VHF Ch 12, 16. (HW∓2).

TELEPHONE (0557)

Hr Mr 31135; # Newton Stewart 2718; MRCC Liverpool 931 3341; Marinecall 0898 500 461; Police 30600; Dr 30755.

FACILITIES

EC Thursday. **Town Quay** P, D, L, FW, AB, El, CH; **Gordon Burns** ☎ 30420, ME; **Wooden Pier** AB; **Kirkcudbright YC** ☎ 30963; **SC** ☎ 30032, Slip, M, FW; **Scallop Gear** ☎ 30399, CH; **Town** V, R, Bar. ✉; Ⓑ; ⇌ (bus to Dumfries); ✈ (Glasgow).

MINOR HARBOURS AND ANCHORAGES 10-9-22

SCALASAIG, Colonsay, 56°04'·00N, 06°11'·00W, Zone 0 (GMT), Admty charts 2474, 2169. HW −0542 on Dover, −0012 on Oban; HW height −0·1m on Oban; ML 2·2m. See 10·9·9. Inner harbour safe, but dries. Beware group of rocks N of pier head marked by Bn. Lts: Rubha Dubh to S of harbour, Fl (2) WR 10s 6m 8/5M; R shore −230°, W230° −337°, R337° −354°. Ldg Lts 262°, front on pier head FR 8m, rear 60m from front, FR 10m. Facilities: D, P, V (all at ✉), FW.

LOCH TARBERT, Jura, 55°57'·00N, 06°00'·00W, Zone 0 (GMT), Admty charts 2481, 2169. Tides at Rubha A'Mhail HW −0540 on Dover, −0010 on Oban; HW height −0·2m on Oban; ML 2·1m; Duration 0600. Excellent shelter inside the loch; anchor outside in Glenbatrick Bay in approx 6m in S winds, or at Bagh Gleann Righ Mor in approx 2m in N winds. To enter inner loch there are four pairs of ldg marks (white stones) at approx 120°, 150°, 077°, and 188°, the latter astern, to be picked up in sequence. There are no facilities.

LOCH SWEEN, TAYVALLICH, Argyll, 56°01'·00N, 05°37'·00W, Zone 0 (GMT), Admty chart 2397. HW +0550 on Dover, −0015 on Oban; HW height −1·1m on Oban; ML 1·5m; Duration 0610. Good shelter; anchor in Port Lunna SSW of Barr Mor, in Loch a Bhealaich (outside Tayvallich in approx 7m) or enter inner harbour and anchor by central reef. Beware Sgeirean a Mhain, a rock in the middle of the loch to S of Taynish I, 3M from entrance. There are no lights. Facilities: **Livingstone** ☎ 226, Gas, Bar, FW (tap by ✉), ✉, R, V.

CRAIGHOUSE, Jura, 55°50'·00N, 05°57'·00W, Zone 0 (GMT), Admty charts 2396, 2481, 2168. HW +0600 on Dover, −0430 np, −0130 sp on Oban; HW height −2·0m on Oban; ML 0·7m; Duration 0640 np 0530 sp. See 10·9·9. Good shelter but squalls occur in W winds. Enter between Lt Bn on SW end of Eilean nan Gabhar, Fl 5s 7m 8M vis 225° −010°, and the beacon to the SW. Yachts may go alongside the pier or anchor in 5m N end of Loch na Mile. Facilities: very limited. There are eight spherical Bu buoys marked 'HIDB visitors only'. Bar, FW, ✉, R, V; **Paton** ☎ 242, Gas.

GIGHA ISLAND, Argyll, 55°41'·00N, 05°44'·00W, Zone 0 (GMT), Admty charts 2475, 2168. HW +0600 on Dover, −0450 np, −0210 sp on Oban; HW height −2·0m on Oban; ML 0·9m; Duration 0530. See 10·9·9. Main anchorage is Ardminish Bay but Druimyeon Bay and the bay N of West Tarbert Bay are popular alternatives. Beware numerous rocks in Gigha Sound, reefs extending off both points of Ardminish Bay and the Kiln Rk off the jetty. There are no lights but there is a W cardinal buoy Fl (9) 15s marking Gigalum Rks, opposite N end of Gigalum I. There are 12 spherical buoys marked 'HIDB for visitors' in Ardminish Bay. Facilities are limited; Bar, FW in hut at end of jetty, ✉, R, V; **Gigha Engineering Services** ☎ 261, ME. **Bannatyne** ☎ 220, Gas.

PORT ASKAIG, Islay, 55°51'·00N, 06°07'·00W, Zone 0 (GMT), Admty charts 2481, 2168. HW +0610 on Dover, −0050 on Oban; HW height −1·6m on Oban; ML 1·2m. Harbour on W side of Sound of Islay. Anchor close inshore in 4m or secure to ferry pier. Beware strong tides with eddies. Facilities: Hotel, Gas, FW (hose on pier), P, R, Bar, V, ✉, ferries to Jura and Kintyre.

MINOR HARBOURS AND ANCHORAGES *Continued*

PORT ELLEN, Islay, 55°38′·00N, 06°12′·00W, Zone 0 (GMT), Admty charts 2474, 2168. HW −0620 sp +0130 np on Dover; −0050 sp −0530 np on Oban; the tide seldom exceeds 0·6m and the level of the sea is greatly affected by the weather; at neaps the tide is often not appreciable. See 10·9·9. Good shelter except in S winds when a swell sets into the bay. In these conditions, anchor N of Carraig Fhada. At other times anchor in 3m in NE corner. Beware rocks all along E side of entrance. Carraig Fhada, Lt Ho (conspic) on W side Fl WRG 3s 20m 8/6M; W shore-248°, G248°−311°, W311°−340°, R340°−shore. Keep in W sector until past the G can buoy, QG; Ro Ro terminal shows 2 FG (vert). Facilities: **Bridgend Sawmills** ☎ 598, Gas; **Village** Bar, FW, ✉, R, V.

CARRADALE BAY, Argyll, 55°32′·00N, 05°27′·00W, Zone O (GMT), Admty chart 2131, HW+0115 on Dover, 0000 on Greenock, HW height −0·2m on Greenock. Good anchorage in 7m off Torrisdale Castle in SW corner of bay. With S winds a swell sets into bay and better anchorage to be found N of Carradale Pt, in Port Cranaig. Off Carradale Pt is R buoy Fl(2)R 12s marks outer end of foul ground. Good shelter inside breakwater. Facilities: V, R, Bar, ✉.

BRODICK, Arran, 55°35′·00N, 05°09′·00W, Zone 0 (GMT), Admty charts 1864, 2220. HW +0115 on Dover, 0000 on Greenock. HW height −0·2m on Greenock; ML 1·8m; Duration 0635. See 10·9·13. Shelter is good except in E winds. Anchor W of pier in approx 3m, just below the Castle in 4·5m or further N off Merkland Pt in 3 to 4m. There are no navigational dangers but the bay is in a submarine exercise area. Only Lts are 2FR (vert) 9/7m 4M on pier head and Fl Y on two Admiralty buoys. Facilities: EC Wed; Ⓑ, Bar, P and D in cans, FW (at pier head), ME, ✉, R, V.

LOCH RANZA, Arran, 55°43′·00N, 05°17′·00W, Zone 0 (GMT), Admty charts 2221, 2383. HW +0120 on Dover, −0005 on Greenock; HW height −0·3m on Greenock; ML 1·7m; Duration 0635. See 10·9·13. Good shelter but swell comes into the harbour with N winds. The 850m mountain 4M to S causes fierce squalls in the loch with S winds. Beware rocky spit extending seaward from S of Newton Pt. Anchor off castle in 5m. Facilities: Bar, FW (tap near pier), ✉, R, V. Marina is planned.

INVERARY, Argyll, 56°14′·00N, 05°04′·00W, Zone 0 (GMT), Admty chart 2382. HW +0126 on Dover, +0011 on Greenock; HW height −0·1m (sp), +0·1m (np) on Greenock (see 10·9·12). For Upper Loch Fyne see 10·9·5. Beware An Oitir extending 2 ca offshore, ½M S of pier. Anchor NNE of pier in 4m or pick up a buoy (some reserved for visitors). Facilities: FW (on pier), ✉, V, R, Bar, Gas, bus to Glasgow.

CALADH HARBOUR, Argyll, 55°56′·00N, 05°12′·00W, Zone 0 (GMT), Admty chart 1906. HW (Tighnabruaich) +0015 on Dover; as Greenock; HW height +0·1m on Greenock; ML 2·1m. Perfectly sheltered natural harbour on W side of mouth of Loch Riddon. There are two passages into Caladh Harbour, N and S of Eilean Dush; keep to the middle of the S passage; between R and G beacons when using the N. It is best to fetch up in the middle of the harbour, avoiding a nasty drying rock which lurks off the N shore. Land at a stone slip on the S side. There are no facilities or stores. Tighnabruaich has all stores, a yacht yard and D in cans.

LOCH LONG/LONG GOIL, Argyll/Dumbartonshire, 56°02′ to 12′·00N, 04°45′·00W; Zone 0 (GMT); Admty chart 3746. HW (Arrochar) +0010, (Lochgoilhead) +0022 on Dover; (Arrochar) −0005, (Lochgoilhead) +0007 on Greenock; HW height (Arrochar) 0·0m, (Lochgoilhead) −0·3m on Greenock; ML 1·75m; Duration 0645. See 10·9·15. Loch Long is about 15M long and there are anchorages at Cove, Portincaple, Blairmore (unsuitable in S winds), Ardentinny, Coilessan (about 1M S of Ardgartan Pt), Arrochar (anchor N of the pier or opposite, off the W shore). In Loch Goil by Carrick Castle (Anchor S of the pier, in N winds a swell develops), or at Lochgoilhead; the whole of the head of the loch is crowded with moorings, so find a free one or anchor with tripping line. Avoid anchoring near Douglas Pier. Lights: Coulport Jetty, 2FG (vert) each end; Port Dornaige Fl W6s 8m 11M, vis. 026°-206°; Dog Rock (Carraig nan Ron) Fl 2s 11M; Finnart Ocean Oil Terminal has numerous lights for the benefit of tankers. Facilities: Loch Long (Cove) shops, FW (on pier); (Portincaple) shops, hotel, ✉, FW; (Ardentinny) shop, V.R. hotel, M; (Blairmore) shops, ✉, Slip, FW; (Arrochar) shops, hotel, FW, Gas, ✉. Loch Goil (Carrick Castle) has ✉, shop, hotel; (Lochgoilhead) has all stores, ✉, hotel, FW, Gas.

MILLPORT, Great Cumbrae, Bute, 55°45′·00N, 04°55′·00W, Zone 0 (GMT), Admty charts 1867, 1907. HW +0100 on Dover, −0015 on Greenock; HW height 0·0m on Greenock; ML 1·9m; Duration 0640. Good shelter except with S winds. Anchor E of the inner of The Eileans in approx 3m, or off pier in approx 3m. Beware The Spoig and The Clach to W of Ldg Line, and the rocks off The Eileans to E of Ldg Line. Ldg Lts 333°, front FR 7m 5M, rear FR 9m 5M. Facilities: EC Wed; Hr Mr ☎ Largs 530826; Town CH, Bar, Gas, D, P, FW, ✉, R, Slip, V.

AYR, Ayr, 55°28′·00N, 04°38′·00W, Zone 0 (GMT), Admty charts 1866, 2220. HW +0050 on Dover, −0025 on Greenock; HW height −0·3m on Greenock; ML 1·8m. Duration 0630. See 10·9·19. Good shelter except in W winds when shelter can be found in the dock. Beware St Nicholas Rock to S of entrance and large amounts of debris being washed down the R Ayr after heavy rains. Entrance is not easy for larger yachts. Ldg Lts 098° Front, by Pilot Stn, FR 10m 5M R Tr, also traffic signals; rear (130m from front) Oc R 10s 18m 10M. N breakwater head QR 9m 5M. S pier head QW 7m 7M; vis 012°−161°, and FG 5m 5M; vis 012°−066°, over St Nicholas Rocks. North Quay head, 2 B balls (vert) or 2FR (vert) = harbour closed. 1 B ball (1 R Lt or 1 GLt) = proceed with caution. Hr Mr Tel. 281687. VHF Ch 16 14. Facilities: EC Wed; Ⓑ, Bar, CH, Gas, D, El, FW, ME, ✉, R, ⇌, Sh, V; **Saturn Sails** ☎ 286241 SM; **Ayr Yacht & Cruising Club** (40) ☎ 267963, Bar, R, M. **J. W. Mackay** ☎ 281586, Sh, ME, El; **J. Goodwin** ☎ 263837, CH.

GIRVAN, Ayr, 55°15′·00N, 04°52′·00W, Zone 0 (GMT), Admty chart 1866 2199. HW +0043 on Dover, −0032 on Greenock; HW height −0·3m on Greenock; ML 1·8m; Duration 0630. See 10·9·19. Good shelter. Harbour used by fishing vessels and coasters but yachts may find berths available on quay. Beware Girvan Patch, 2·4m, 4 ca SW of entrance, and Brest Rocks, 3·5M N of harbour extending 6 ca offshore, marked by W Lt Bn Fl(2) 6s 7m 4M. Entrance between breakwater to N and pier to S. Lts: N. Breakwater head Fl(2) R 6s 7m 4M; pier head 2FG (vert) 8m 4M South pier head – 2 B discs (hor), at night 2FR (hor) = harbour closed. VHF Ch 16; 12 (office hours). Facilities: EC Wed; Harbour Office ☎ 3048; FW, Slip; **Town** Ⓑ, Bar, ✉, R, ⇌, V.

LOCH RYAN, Wigtown, 54°55′·00N, 05°03′·00W, Zone 0 (GMT), Admty charts 1403, 2198. HW (Stranraer) +0055 on Dover, −0020 on Greenock; HW height −0·4m on Greenock; ML 1·6m; Duration 0640. Very good shelter except in strong NW winds. Entrance between Milleur Pt and Finnarts Pt. Anchorages in Lady Bay, 1·3M SSE of Milleur Pt; in The Wig in 3m; off Stranraer NE of steamer pier in 3m or lie alongside quay at Stranraer. Beware The Beef Barrel, rk 1m high 6 cables SSE of Milleur Pt; the sand spit running 1·5M to SE from W shore opposite Cairn Pt Lt Ho Fl (2) R 10s 14m 12M. Lt at Cairnryan ferry terminal Fl R 5s 5m 5M. Lts at Stranraer – centre pier head 2FBu (vert), E pier head 2FR (vert), W Ross pier head 2 FVi (vert) 10m 4M. Facilities (Stranraer): EC Wed; Ⓑ, Bar, D, FW, P, ✉, R, ⇌, V.

ISLE OF WHITHORN, Wigtown, 54°42′·00N, 04°22′·00W, Zone 0 (GMT), Admty chart 2094. HW +0035 on Dover, +0020 on Liverpool; HW height −2·2m on Liverpool; ML 3·7m; Duration 0545. See 10·9·21. Shelter good but Hr dries having approx 2·5m at HW∓3. Beware the Skerries, a ledge on W side of entrance marked by a perch. E pier head has QG 4m 5M; Ldg Lts 335°, front Oc R 8s 7m 7M; orange mast; Rear, 35m from front, Oc R 8s 9m 7M; orange mast; synchronised with front. Each has Dayglo Orange Diamond atop. Berth alongside quay. Facilities: Hr Mr ☎ Whithorn 246, Slip, P, D, FW, ME, Sh, CH, V, Bar, ✉, VHF Ch 80 (occas).

WIGTOWN BAY, Kirkcudbrightshire, 54°47′·00N, 04°21′·00W, Zone 0 (GMT), Admty chart 2094. HW (Garlieston) +0100 on Dover, +0030 on Liverpool; HW height −2·0m on Liverpool; ML 3·8m; Duration 0545. Garlieston harbour affords complete shelter but dries. Access (2m) HW∓3. Pier head Lt 2FR (vert) 5m 3M. Beware rocky outcrops in W side of bay marked by a perch. Facilities. Hr Mr ☎ Garlieston 259. FW, AC on quay & visitors moorings; stores, ME, P, D and slip in town.

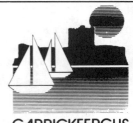

Area 10

North-West England, Isle of Man and North Wales

Solway Firth to Bardsey Island

10-10-2

North-West England, Isle of Man and North Wales

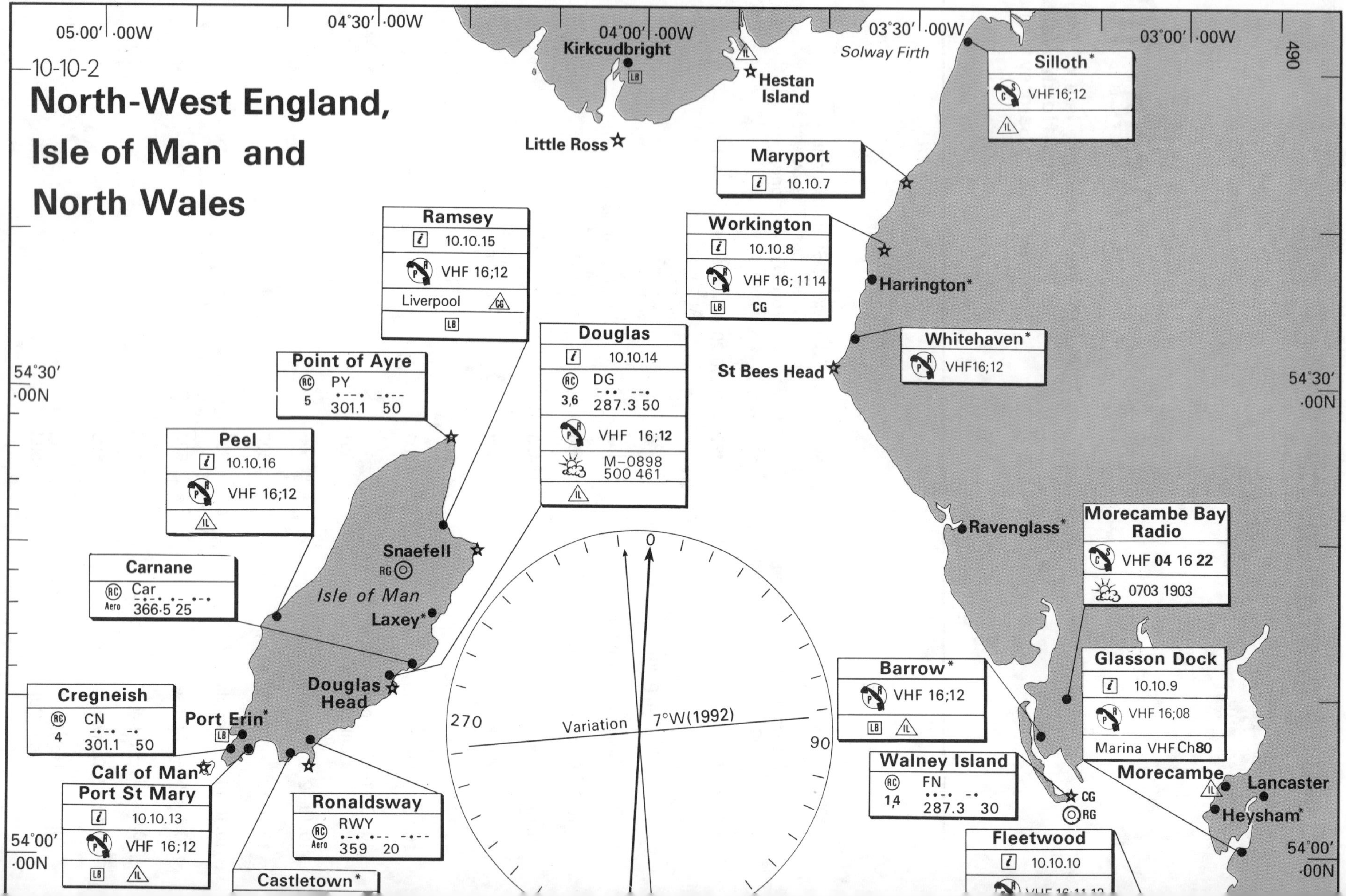
05·00′ ·00W
04°30′ ·00W
04°00′ ·00W
03°30′ ·00W
03°00′ ·00W
54°30′ ·00N
54°00′ ·00N
Kirkcudbright
Hestan Island
Little Ross
Solway Firth
Silloth*
VHF16;12
Maryport
10.10.7
Workington
10.10.8
VHF 16; 11 14
CG
Harrington*
Whitehaven*
VHF16;12
St Bees Head
Ravenglass*
Morecambe Bay Radio
VHF 04 16 22
0703 1903
Glasson Dock
10.10.9
VHF 16;08
Marina VHF Ch80
Morecambe
Lancaster
Heysham*
Barrow*
VHF 16;12
Walney Island
FN
1,4
287.3 30
CG
RG
Fleetwood
10.10.10
Ramsey
10.10.15
VHF 16;12
Liverpool
Point of Ayre
PY
5
301.1 50
Douglas
10.10.14
DG
3,6
287.3 50
VHF 16;12
M–0898
500 461
Peel
10.10.16
VHF 16;12
Carnane
Car
366·5 25
Snaefell
RG
Isle of Man
Laxey*
Douglas Head
Cregneish
CN
4
301.1 50
Port Erin*
Calf of Man
Port St Mary
10.10.13
VHF 16;12
Ronaldsway
RWY
359 20
Castletown*
0
90
270
Variation
7°W(1992)

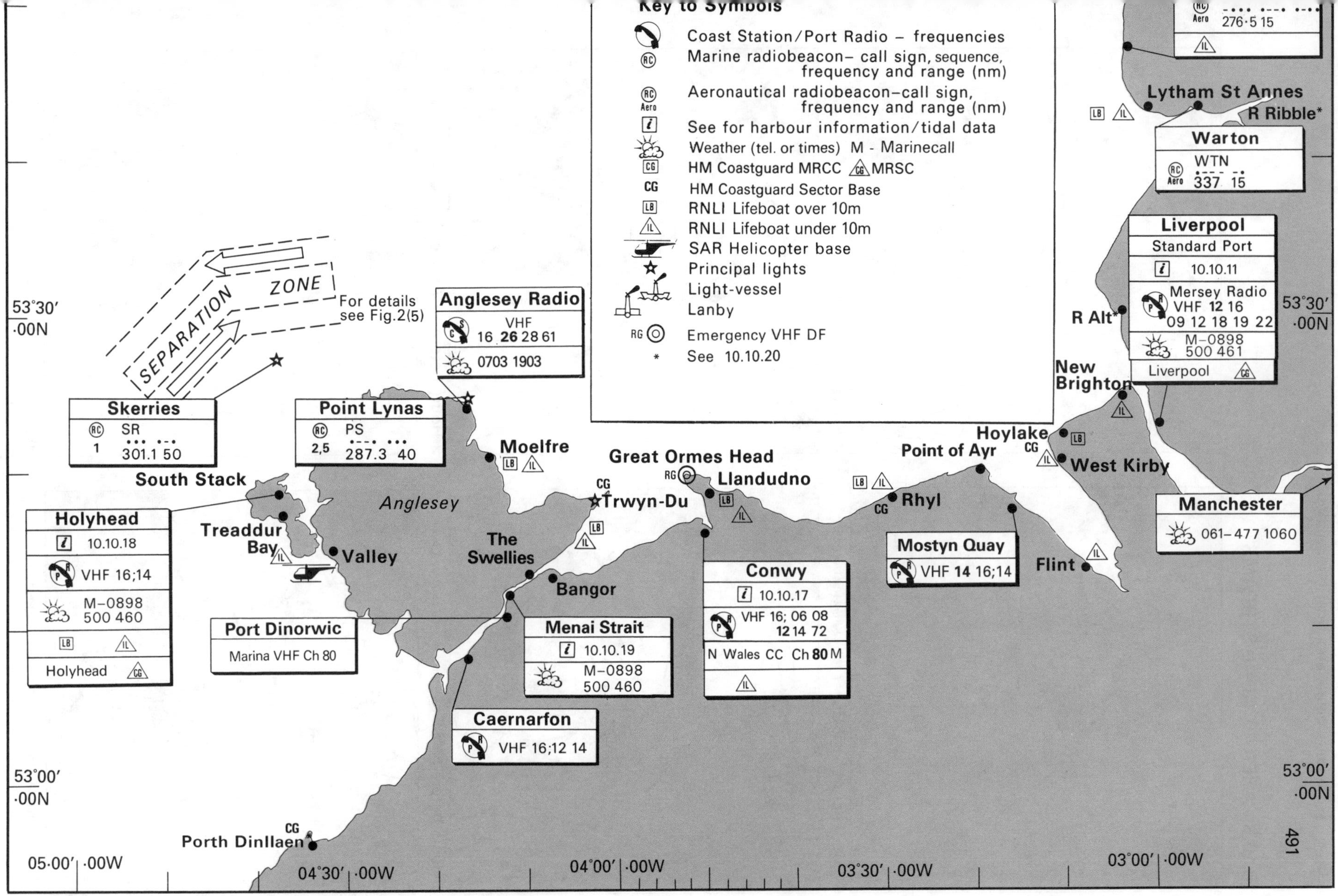
Key to Symbols
Coast Station/Port Radio – frequencies
Marine radiobeacon– call sign, sequence, frequency and range (nm)
Aeronautical radiobeacon–call sign, frequency and range (nm)
See for harbour information/tidal data
Weather (tel. or times) M - Marinecall
HM Coastguard MRCC MRSC
HM Coastguard Sector Base
RNLI Lifeboat over 10m
RNLI Lifeboat under 10m
SAR Helicopter base
Principal lights
Light-vessel
Lanby
Emergency VHF DF
* See 10.10.20
Aero 276·5 15
Lytham St Annes
R Ribble*
Warton
WTN
337 15
Liverpool
Standard Port
10.10.11
Mersey Radio
VHF 12 16
09 12 18 19 22
M–0898
500 461
Liverpool
R Alt*
New Brighton
Hoylake
West Kirby
Manchester
061–477 1060
Point of Ayr
Rhyl
Flint
Mostyn Quay
VHF 14 16;14
Great Ormes Head
Llandudno
Conwy
10.10.17
VHF 16; 06 08
12 14 72
N Wales CC Ch 80 M
Trwyn-Du
Anglesey Radio
VHF
16 26 28 61
0703 1903
Skerries
SR
1
301.1 50
Point Lynas
PS
2,5
287.3 40
SEPARATION ZONE
For details see Fig.2(5)
Moelfre
South Stack
Anglesey
Holyhead
10.10.18
VHF 16;14
M–0898
500 460
Holyhead
Treaddur Bay
Valley
The Swellies
Bangor
Port Dinorwic
Marina VHF Ch 80
Menai Strait
10.10.19
M–0898
500 460
Caernarfon
VHF 16;12 14
Porth Dinllaen
53°30′ ·00N
53°00′ ·00N
05·00′ ·00W
04°30′ ·00W
04°00′ ·00W
03°30′ ·00W
03°00′ ·00W

10.10.3 AREA 10 TIDAL STREAMS

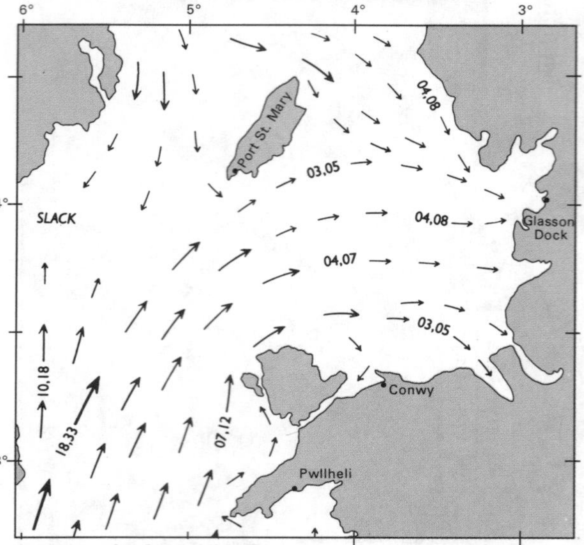
6°
5°
4°
3°
54°
53°
Port St. Mary
SLACK
04,08
03,05
04,08
04,07
03,05
Glasson Dock
Conwy
Pwllheli
10,18
18,33
07,12
5 Hours before HW Dover (0515 before HW Liverpool)

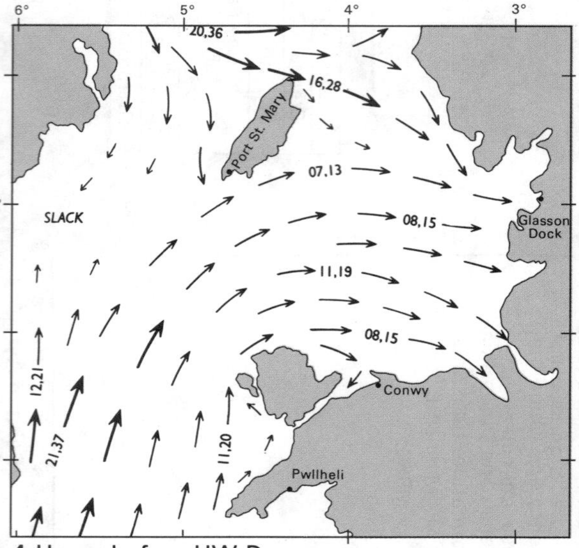
6°
5°
4°
3°
54°
53°
20,36
16,28
Port St. Mary
SLACK
07,13
08,15
11,19
08,15
Glasson Dock
Conwy
Pwllheli
12,21
21,37
11,20
4 Hours before HW Dover (0415 before HW Liverpool)

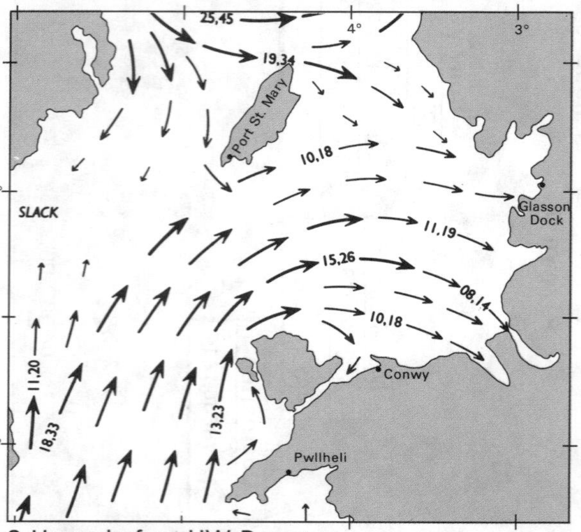
4°
3°
54°
53°
25,45
19,34
Port St. Mary
SLACK
10,18
11,19
15,26
08,14
10,18
Glasson Dock
Conwy
Pwllheli
11,20
18,33
13,23
3 Hours before HW Dover (0315 before HW Liverpool)

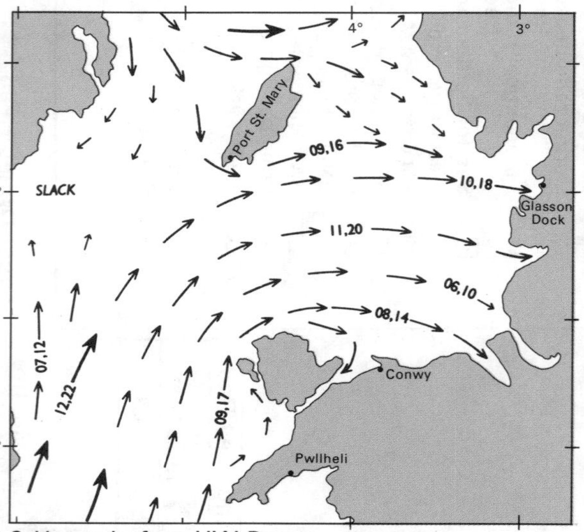
4°
3°
54°
53°
Port St. Mary
SLACK
09,16
10,18
11,20
06,10
08,14
Glasson Dock
Conwy
Pwllheli
07,12
12,22
09,17
2 Hours before HW Dover (0215 before HW Liverpool)

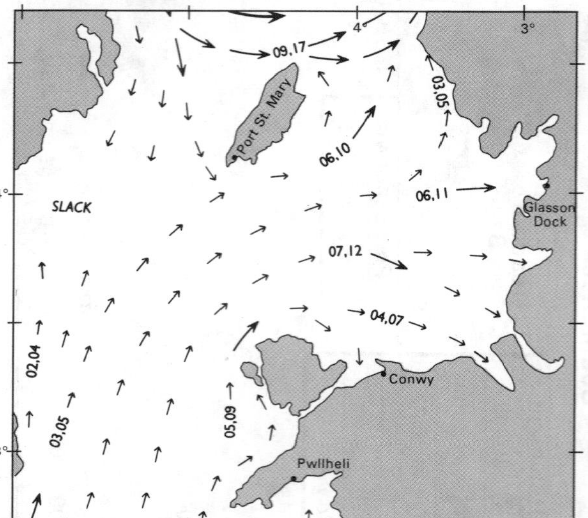
4°
3°
54°
53°
09,17
03,05
Port St. Mary
SLACK
06,10
06,11
07,12
04,07
Glasson Dock
Conwy
Pwllheli
02,04
03,05
05,09
1 Hour before HW Dover (0115 before HW Liverpool)

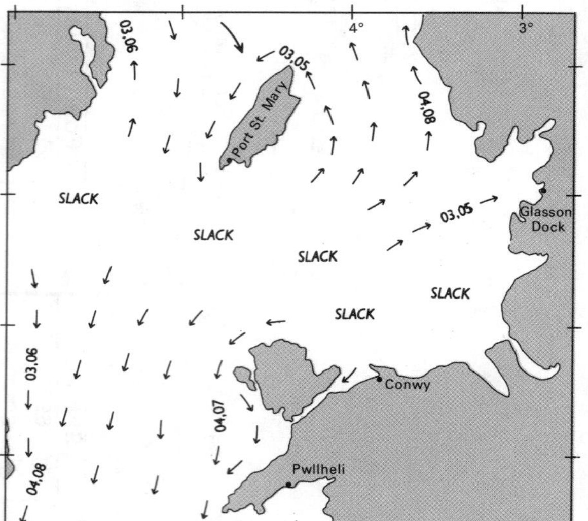
4°
3°
54°
53°
03,06
03,05
04,08
Port St. Mary
SLACK
SLACK
SLACK
SLACK
SLACK
03,05
Glasson Dock
Conwy
Pwllheli
03,06
04,07
04,08
HW Dover (0015 before HW Liverpool)

Northward 10.9.3 Southward 10.11.3 North Ireland 10.13.3 South Ireland 10.12.3

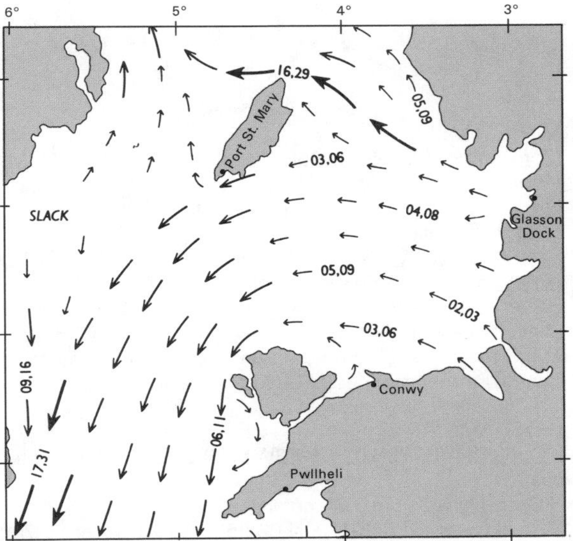
6°
5°
4°
3°
54°
53°
16,29
05,09
Port St. Mary
03,06
SLACK
04,08
Glasson Dock
05,09
02,03
03,06
09,16
Conwy
06,11
17,31
Pwllheli
1 Hour after HW Dover (0045 after HW Liverpool)

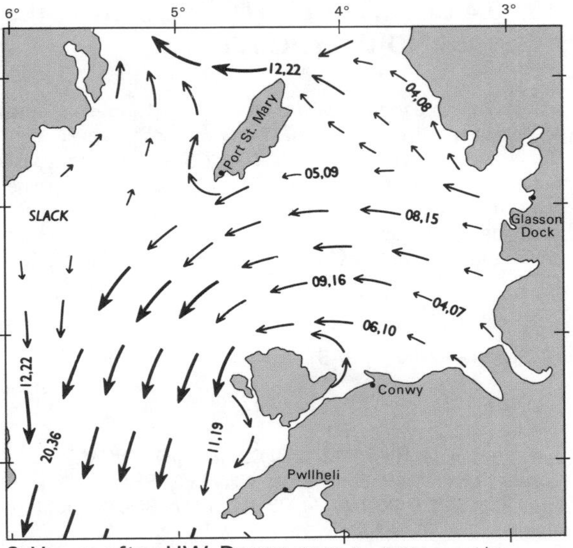
6°
5°
4°
3°
54°
53°
12,22
04,08
Port St. Mary
05,09
SLACK
08,15
Glasson Dock
09,16
04,07
06,10
12,22
Conwy
20,36
11,19
Pwllheli
2 Hours after HW Dover (0145 after HW Liverpool)

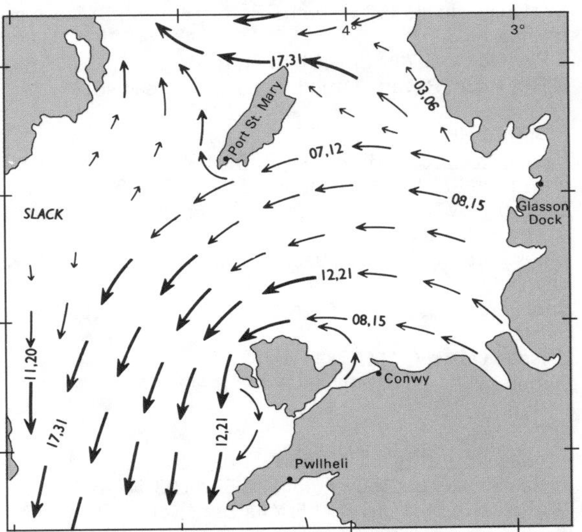
4°
3°
54°
53°
17,31
03,06
Port St. Mary
07,12
09,15
SLACK
Glasson Dock
12,21
08,15
11,20
Conwy
17,31
12,21
Pwllheli
3 Hours after HW Dover (0245 after HW Liverpool)

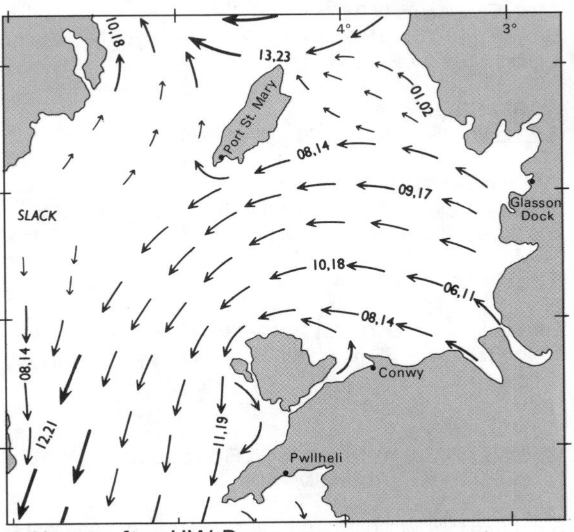
4°
3°
54°
53°
10,18
13,23
01,02
Port St. Mary
08,14
09,17
SLACK
Glasson Dock
10,18
06,11
08,14
08,14
Conwy
12,21
11,19
Pwllheli
4 Hours after HW Dover (0345 after HW Liverpool)

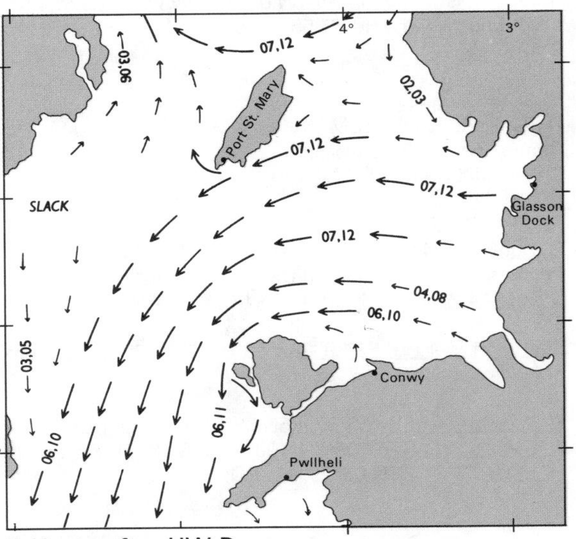
4°
3°
54°
53°
07,12
03,06
02,03
Port St. Mary
07,12
SLACK
07,12
Glasson Dock
07,12
04,08
06,10
03,05
Conwy
06,10
06,11
Pwllheli
5 Hours after HW Dover (0445 after HW Liverpool)

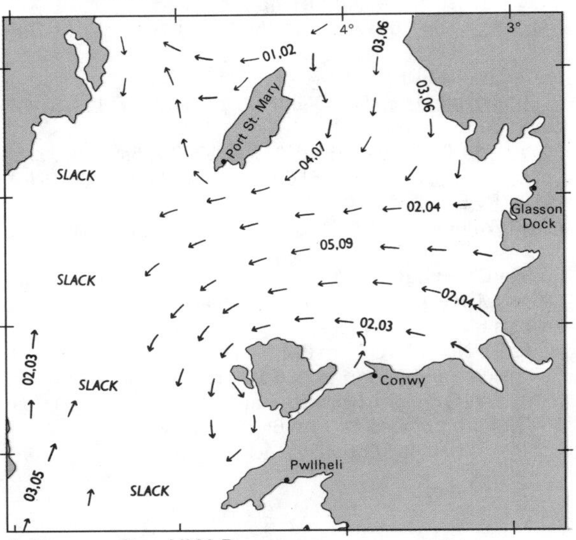
4°
3°
54°
53°
01,02
03,06
03,06
Port St. Mary
04,07
SLACK
02,04
Glasson Dock
05,09
SLACK
02,04
02,03
02,03
Conwy
SLACK
03,05
SLACK
Pwllheli
6 Hours after HW Dover (0545 after HW Liverpool)

10

10.10.4 COASTAL LIGHTS, FOG SIGNALS AND WAYPOINTS

Abbreviations used below are given in 1.4.1. Principal lights are in **bold** print, places in CAPITALS, and light-vessels, light floats and Lanbys in *CAPITAL ITALICS*. Unless otherwise stated lights are white. m—elevation in metres; M—nominal range in n. miles. Fog signals are in *italics*. Useful waypoints are underlined – use those on land with care. All geographical positions should be assumed to be approximate. See 4.2.2.

ENGLAND—WEST COAST

SILLOTH.

Two Feet Bank By 54°42'·40N 03°44'·40W; WCM.
Corner Lt By 54°49'·00N 03°30'·40W Fl G; SHM.
Lees Scar 54°51'·80N 03°24'·75W QG 11m 8M; W structure on piles; vis 005°-317°.
E Cote Dir Lt 052°, Dir FG 15m 12M; W structure on piles; vis 046°-058°, intens 052°.
Groyne Hd 54°52'·1N 03°24'·0W 2 FG (vert) 4m 4M; Fl Bu tfc signals close by.

MARYPORT.
S Pier Hd 54°43'·05N 03°30'·60W Fl 1·5s 10m 4M.

WORKINGTON.
N Workington By 54°40'·10N 03°38'·10W; NCM.
S Workington Lt By 54°37'·00N 03°38'·50W Q (6) + L Fl 15s; SCM.
S Pier 54°39'·13N 03°34'·71W Fl 5s 11m 8M; R bldg; *Siren 20s*.
Ldg Lts 131·8°. Front 54°38'·9N 03°34'·1W FR 10m 3M. Rear 134m from front FR 12m 3M; both on W pyramidal Tr, Or bands.

WHITEHAVEN.
W Pier Hd 54°33'·16N 03°35'·84W Fl G 5s 16m 13M; W ● Tr.
N Pier Hd 2 FR (vert) 8m 9M; W ● Tr.

Saint Bees Hd 54°30'·80N 03°38'·15W Fl (2) 20s 102m **21M**; W ● Tr; obsc shore-340°; (H24).
Selker Lt By 54°16'·13N 03°29'·50W Fl (3) G 10s; SHM; *Bell*.

BARROW-IN-FURNESS.
Lightning Knoll Lt By 53°59'·83N 03°14'·20W L Fl 10s; SWM; *Bell*.
Halfway Lt By 54°01'·40N 03°11'·87W Fl R 5s; PHM.
Outer Bar Lt By 54°01'·99N 03°11'·05W Fl (4) R 10s; PHM.
Bar Lt By 54°02'·61N 03°10'·13W Fl (2) R 5s; PHM.
Isle of Walney 54°02'·92N 03°10'·65W Fl 15s 21m **23M**; stone Tr; obsc 122°-127° within 3M of shore; RC.
Walney Chan Ldg Lts 040·8°. No. 1 Front 54°03'·3N 03°08'·9W Q 6m 6M; B pile, W daymark. No. 2 Rear 640m from front Iso 2s 12m 6M; R col, W face.
Haws Pt, NE of Pt QR 8m 6M.
Rampside Sands Ldg Lts 006·2°. No. 3 Front 54°04'·4N 03°09'·7W Q 6m 6M; B pile structure, W daymark. No. 4 Rear 0·77M from front Iso 2s 14m 6M; R col, W face.
No. 3A 54°04'·4N 03°09'·7W QG 8m 9M.

MORECAMBE.
Morecambe Lt By 53°52'·00N 03°24'·00W Q (9) 15s; WCM; *Whis*.
Lune Deep Lt By 53°55'·80N 03°11'·00W Q (6) + LFl 15s; SCM; *Whis*; Racon.
Shell Wharf Lt By 53°55'·45N 03°08'·89W Fl G 2·5s; SHM.
King Scar Lt By 53°56'·95N 03°04'·30W Fl G 2·5s; SHM.
Sewer outfall 54°04'·3N 02°53'·7W Fl G 2s 4m 2M; metal Tr.
Lts in line about 090°. Front 54°04'·4N 02°52'·5W FR 10m 2M; G mast. Rear 140m from front FR 14m 2M; G mast.
Central Promenade Pier 2 FG (vert) 9m 4M.

HEYSHAM.
S Outfall 54°01'·73N 02°55'·73W Fl (2) G 10s 5m 2M; metal post.
N Outfall Fl G 5s 5m 2M; metal post.
S Breakwater Hd 54°01'·90N 02°55'·64W 2 FG (vert) 9/7m 5M; W Tr; Ra refl; *Siren 30s*.
SW Quay Ldg Lts 102·2°, both F Bu 11/14m 2M; Or & B ◆ on masts.
S Pier Hd Oc G 7·5s 9m 6M; W Tr, R base.
N Pier Hd 2 FR (vert) 11m 2M; obsc from seaward.

RIVER LUNE.
R.Lune No.1 Lt By 53°58'·62N 02°59'·99W Q (9) 15s; WCM.
Ldg Lts 083·7°. Front, Plover Scar 53°58'·87N 02°52'·88W Fl 2s 6m 6M; W Tr, B lantern. Rear 854m from front, Cockersand Abbey F 18m 8M; R Tr.
Crook Perch, No. 7 53°59'·5N 02°52'·3W Fl G 5s 3M; G ▲ on mast.
Bazil Perch, No. 16 54°00'·2N 02°51'·6W Fl (3) R 10s 3M; R mast.
Glasson Quay FG 1M.
Outfall 54°01'·3N 02°49'·7W Fl (TE 1985).

FLEETWOOD.
Fairway No 1 Lt By 53°57'·65N 03°02'·15W Q; NCM; *Bell*.
Esplanade Ldg Lts 156°. Front 53°55'·7N 03°00'·4W Fl Y 2s 14m. Rear 320m from front Fl Y 4s 28m. Both buff-coloured ■ Trs, B bases, R lanterns and vis on Ldg line only.
Steep Breast Perch 53°55'·8N 03°00'·5W Iso G 2s 3m 2M.
Knott End slipway, Hd 53°55'·7N 03°00'·0W 2 FR (vert) 3m 2M.

BLACKPOOL.
N Pier Hd 2 FG (vert) 3M.
Central Pier Hd 2 FG (vert) 4M.
S Pier Hd 2 FG (vert) 4M.

RIVER RIBBLE.
Gut Lt By 53°41'·74N 03°08'·91W L Fl 10s, SWM.
Perches show Fl R on N side, and Fl G on S side of chan.
S side, 14·25M Perch 53°42.75N 03°04'·85W Fl G 5s 6m 3M.
Southport Pier Hd, 52°39'·35N 03°01'·25W 2 FG (vert) 6m 5M; W post; vis 033°-213°.

El Oso Wreck Lt By 53°37'·55N 03°23'·45W Q; NCM.
Jordan's Spit Lt By 53°35'·74N 03°19'·20W Q (9) 15s; WCM.
FT Lt By 53°34'·55N 03°13'·12W Q; NCM.

Spoil Ground Lt By 53°34'·25N 03°17'·30W Fl Y 3s; SPM.

ENGLAND—WEST COAST, RIVER MERSEY

RIVER MERSEY.
BAR LANBY 53°32'·00N 03°20'·90W Fl 5s 12m **21M**; R structure on By; Racon; *Horn*.
FORMBY Lt F 53°31'·10N 03°13'·45W Iso 4s 11m 6M; R hull, W stripes.
CROSBY Lt F 53°30'·7N 03°06'·2W Oc 5s 11m 8M; R hull, W stripes.

SEACOMBE FERRY.
N and S corners 3 FG 5m 5M; near N corner FY 8m 6M; *Bell (3) 20s*.

BIRKENHEAD.
Cammell Laird slip, SE corner Fl (2) G 6s 5m 5M.
Woodside Landing Stage N end 3 FG 5m 4M and S end 2 FG (vert) with *Bell (4) 15s*.

TRANMERE TERMINAL.
N dolphin 53°22'·9N 03°00'·0W Fl G 3s 7m 7M.
N stage, S end 2 FG (vert) 10m 3M; *Bell (2) 10s*.

ENGLAND—WEST COAST

RIVER DEE.

HE2 Lt By 53°26'·20N 03°16'·80W QR; PHM.
HE1 Lt By 53°25'·00N 03°13'·10W Q (3) 10s; WCM.
HE3 Lt By 53°23'·27N 03°14'·22W Fl G 2·5s; SHM.
Welshman Lt By 53°22'·30N 03°14'·20W Q (3) 10s; ECM.
Hilbre Island, N end 53°22'·97N 03°13'·70W Fl R 3s 14m 5M; W metal Tr.

MOSTYN.
Training wall Hd Fl R 1·3s 8m 4M; B mast.
E Hoyle Lt By 53°22'·0N 03°21'·03W Fl (4) R 15s; PHM.
NE Mostyn Lt By 51°21'·48N 03°17'·73W Fl (3) G 10s; SHM.
Ldg Lts 215·7°. Front 53°19'·2N 03°16'·1W FR 12m; W ◆ on B mast. Rear 135m from front FR 22m; W ◆ on B mast.
N training wall Hd Fl R 3s 4m 6M; Tr.
S training wall Hd Fl G 10s 3m 6M; Tr.
Summersby Wharf FR.
Connah's Quay, power station 2 FR (vert).
S Hoyle Lt By 53°21'·40N 03°24'·78W Fl (3) R 10s; PHM.

ISLE OF MAN.
King William Bank Lt By 54°26'·00N 04°00'·00W Q (3) 10s; ECM.
Point of Ayre 54°24'·95N 04°22'·03W Al L Fl WR 60s 32m **19M**; W Tr, two R bands; RC; Racon.
Low Lt 54°25'·1N 04°21'·8W Fl 3s 10m 8M; R Tr, lower part W, on B Base; part obsc 335°-341°; *Siren (3) 90s*.

JURBY.
Cronk y Cliwe 54°22'·3N 04°31'·4W 2 Fl R 5s (vert); synchronised, 2m apart.
Orrisdale 54°19'·3N 04°34'·1W 2 Fl R 5s (vert); synchronised, 2m apart.
North DZ By 54°23'·6N 04°36'·7W Fl Y 10s (unreliable).
South DZ By 54°21'·5N 04°38'·8W Fl Y 10s (unreliable); with QY on target floats 1·5M ENE and 2·1M E.

PEEL.
Pier Hd, E side of ent Oc R 7s 8m 5M; W Tr with R band; vis 156°-249°.
Groyne Hd Iso R 2s 4m.
Castle Jetty Hd Oc G 7s 5m 4M; W Tr, 3 G bands.
Breakwater Hd 54°13'·67N 04°41'·62W Oc 7s 11m 6M; W Tr; *Bell (4) 12s* (occas).

PORT ERIN.
Ldg Lts 099·1°. Front 54°05'·3N 04°45'·4W FR 10m 5M; W Tr, R band. Rear 39m from front FR 19m 5M; W col, R band.
Raglan Pier Hd Oc G 5s 8m 5M; W Tr, G band.
Thousla Rk 54°03'·7N 04°48'·0W Fl R 3s 9m 4M; 8-sided tapered pillar.

Calf of Man, W Pt Fl 15s 93m 28M; W 8-sided Tr; vis 274°-190°; FR Lts on conspic radio mast 3·2M NE; *Horn 45s*.
Chicken Rk 54°02'·3N 04°50'·1W Fl 5s 38m 13M; Tr; *Horn 60s*.

PORT ST MARY.
The Carrick 54°04'·30N 04°42'·60W Q (2) 5s 6m 3M; IDM.
Alfred Pier Hd Oc R 10s 8m 6M; W Tr, R band; B*ell* (3) 12s (occas).
Inner Pier Hd Oc R 3s 8m 5M; W Tr, R band.

CASTLETOWN.
New Pier Hd 54°04'·3N 04°38'·8W Oc R 15s 8m 5M; W Tr, R band.
N side of ent Oc G 4s 3m.
Irish Quay Oc R 4s 5m 5M; W Tr, R band; vis 142°-322°.

Langness, Dreswick Pt 54°03'·28N 04°37'·45W Fl (2) 30s 23m **21M**; W Tr.

Derby Haven, Breakwater SW end Iso G 2s 5m 5M; W Tr, G band.
Douglas Hd 54°08'·58N 04°27'·88W Fl 10s 32m **24M**; W Tr; obsc brg more than 037°. FR Lts on radio masts 1 and 3M West.

DOUGLAS.
Princess Alexandra Pier Hd 54°08'·85N 04°27'·80W Fl R 5s 16m 8M; R mast; *Whis (2) 40s*.
Battery Pier, 140m from breakwater Hd, QR 12m 1M; W Tr, R band; vis 038°-218°.
Ldg Lts 229·3°, Front Oc 10s 9m 5M; W ▲ R border on mast. Rear, 62m from front, Oc 10s 12m 5M; W ▼ on R border; synchronised with front.
Victoria Pier Hd Oc G 8s 10m 3M; W col; vis 225°-327°; RC; Intnl Port Tfc Signals; B*ell (1) 2s*.
Fort Anne Jetty Hd Oc R 4s 6m 2M; W Tr, R band; vis 107°-297°.
King Edward VIII Pier S side Hd Oc G 4s 6m 2M; W Tr, G band; vis 253°-005°.
FR each side of swing bridge, 365m W, when closed.

LAXEY.
Pier Hd Oc R 3s 7m 5M; W Tr, R band; obsc when brg less than 318°.
Breakwater Hd Oc G 3s 7m; W Tr, G band.

Maughold Hd 54°17'·70N 04°18'·50W Fl (3) 30s 65m **22M**; W Tr.
Bahama Lt By 54°20'·00N 04°08'·50W Q (6) + LFl 15s; SCM; *Bell*.

10

RAMSEY.
S Pier Hd 54°19'·42N 04°22'·42W Oc R 5s 8m 4M; W Tr, R band, B base; *Bell (2)10s (occas).*
N Pier Hd Oc G 5s 9m 5M; W Tr, B base.

WALES—NORTH COAST

Chester Flat Lt By 53°21'·65N 03°27'·40W Fl (2) R 5s;PHM.
Middle Patch Spit Lt By 53°21'·80N 03°31'·50W Fl R 5s; PHM.
N Rhyl Lt By 53°22'·75N 03°34'·50W Q; NCM.
W Constable Lt By 53°23'·13N 03°49'·17W Q (9) 15s; WCM.

RHYL.
River Clwyd Breakwater Hd 53°19'·50N 03°30'·30W QR 7m 2M; Bn.
Llanddulas, Llysfaen Jetty 53°17'·55N 03°39'·45W Fl G 10s.
Raynes Quarry Jetty Hd 2 FG (vert).
Llandudno Pier Hd 53°19'·90N 03°49'·40W 2 FG (vert) 8/6m 4M.
Great Ormes Hd Lt Ho 53°20'·55N 03°52'·10W (unlit).

CONWY.
Conway R. ent S side 53°178'·0N 03°50'·9W Fl WR 5s 5m 2M; vis W076°-088°, R088°-171°, W171°-319°, R319°-076°

MENAI STRAIT.
Trwyn-Du 53°18'·76N 04°02'·38W Fl 5·5s 19m **15M**; W ● castellated Tr, B bands; vis 101°-023°; *Bell (1) 30s*, sounded continuously. FR on radio mast 2M SW.

Beaumaris Pier F WG 5m 6M; vis G212°-286°, W286°-041°, G041°-071°.
St George's Pier Fl G 10s.
E side of chan 53°13'·2N 04°09'·5W QR 4m; R mast; vis 064°-222°.
Price Pt Fl WR 2s 5m 3M; W Bn; vis R059°-239°, W239°-259°.
Britannia tubular bridge, S chan Ldg Lts 231° E side. Front FW. W side, Rear 45m from front FW. Centre span of bridge Iso 5s 27m 3M, one either side.
S end of bridge, FR 21m 3M either side, N end of bridge FG 21m 3M either side.
Port Dinorwic Pier Hd F WR 5m 2M; vis R225°-357°, W357°-225°.

Pt Lynas 53°24'·97N 04°17'·30W Oc 10s 39m **20M**; W castellated Tr; vis 109°-315°; (H24); Fog Det Lt F 25m 16M vis 211·8°-214·3°; *Horn 45s*; RC.
Pilot Station Pier 54°24'·9N 04°17'·1W 2 FR (vert).
Amlwch SBM 53°26'·7N 04°19'·8W Mo (U) 15s 8M; mooring By; Ra refl.
Fl Y 5s 3M marks floating hose 285m from By; *Horn Mo(U) 30s.*

AMLWCH.
Main Breakwater 53°25'·0N 04°19'·8W 2 FG (vert) 11/9m 5M; W mast; vis 141°-271°.
Inner breakwater 2 FR (vert) 12°10m 5M; W mast; vis 164°-239°.
Inner Hbr FW 9m 8M; W post; vis 233°-257°.

Wylfa power station 2 FG (vert) 13m 6M.
Ethel Rk By 53°26'·63N 04°33'·60W; NCM.
Coal Rk By 53°25'·90N 04°32'·72W; SCM.
Victoria Bank By 53°25'·60N 04°31'·30W; NCM.

The Skerries 53°25'·25N 04°36'·45W Fl (2) 10s 36m **22M**; W ● Tr, R band; RC; Racon. FR 26m 16M; same Tr; vis 231°-254°; *Horn (2) 20s.*

HOLYHEAD.
Langdon Lt By 53°22'·74N 04°38'·58W Q (9) 15s; WCM.
Clipera Lt By 53°20'·08N 04°36'·14W Fl (4) R 15s; PHM; *Bell.*
Breakwater Hd 53°19'·83N 04°37'·08W Fl (3) 15s 21m 14M; W ■ Tr, B band; *Siren 20s.*
Old Hbr, Admiralty Pier dolphin 53°18'·85N 04°37'·00W 2 FG (vert) 8m 5M; *Bell* (occas).

S Stack 53°18'·4N 04°41'·9W Fl 10s 60m **28M**; (H24); W ● Tr; obsc to N by N Stack and part obsc in Penrhos bay. *Horn 30s.* Fog Det Lt vis 145°-325°.
Ynys Meibion 53°11'·4N 04°30'·2W Fl R 5s 37m 10M; (occas) 2 FR (vert) shown from flagstaffs 550m NW and 550m SE when firing taking place.

WALES—WEST COAST

CAERNARFON BAY AND MENAI STRAIT (SOUTHERN PART).
Llanddwyn Is S end 53°08'·04N 04°24'·70W Fl WR 2·5s 12m W7M, R4M; W Tr; vis R280°-015°, W015°-120°.
C1 Lt By 53°07'·46N 04°24'·90W Fl G 5s; SHM.
Abermenai Pt 53°07'·60N 04°19'·64W Fl WR 3·5s 6m 3M; W mast; vis R065°-245°, W245°-065°.
Caernarfon Hbr Tidal Basin S Pier Hd 2 FG (vert) 5m 2M.
Poole Lt By 53°00'·00N 04°34'·00W Fl Y 6s; SPM (Apr-Oct).
Port Dinoric Pier Hd 53°11'·2N 04°12'·6W F WR 5m 2M; vis R225°-357°, W357°-225°.
Porth Dinlläen (CG Stn) 52°56'·8N 04°33'·8W FR when firing taking place 10M N..
Careg y Chwislen 52°56'·96N 04°33'·44W; IDM (unlit).

Bardsey Is 52°44'·97N 04°47'·93W Fl (5) 15s 39m **26M**; W ■ Tr, R bands; obsc by Bardsey Is 198°-250° and in Tremadoc B when brg less than 260°; *Horn Mo(N) 45s*; RC.

10.10.5 PASSAGE INFORMATION

ENGLAND – NORTH WEST COAST (chart 1346)

On the boundaries of Areas 9 and 10 lies Solway Firth, most of which is encumbered by shifting sandbanks. There are navigable, buoyed chans as far as Annan on the N shore, but Bys are moved as conditions dictate. Particularly in the upper firth, the stream runs very strongly in the chans when the banks are dry, and less strongly over the banks when these are covered. In Powfoot chan for example the in-going stream begins at HW Liverpool –0300, and the outgoing at HW Liverpool +0100, sp rates up to 6 kn. Off the entrances to Firth of Solway, and in the approaches to Workington (10.10.8) beware shoals over which strong W winds raise a heavy sea. Southwards along the Cumbria coast past St Bees Hd to Walney Is there are no dangers more than 2M offshore, but no shelter either.

For Silloth, Harrington, Whitehaven and Ravenglass see 10.10.20.

BARROW TO RIVER MERSEY (charts 1961, 1981, 1951)

Ent to Barrow-in-Furness (chart 3164) is about 1M S of Hilpsford Pt at S end of Walney Island. Two chys of Roosecote power station are conspic, 3·25M N of Walney Lt Ho (Lt, RC). Coming from S it is possible to cross the sands between Fleetwood and Barrow with sufficient rise of tide. The stream sets across the chan, which is narrow and shallow but well marked. W winds cause rough sea in the ent. Moorings and anch off Piel Is, but space is limited and stream runs hard on ebb. See 10.10.20.

Lune Deep, 2M NW of Rossall Pt, is ent to Morecambe B (chart 2010), gives access to Fleetwood (10.10.10), Glasson Dock (10.10.9), and the commercial port of Heysham (10.10.20). It is well buoyed. Streams runs 3·5 kn at sp. Most of Bay is encumbered with drying sands, intersected by chans which are subject to change. S of Morecambe B, beware shoals extending 4M W of Rossall Pt.

Gut chan in estuary of R. Ribble gives access to the marina Preston.

Queen's chan and Crosby chan (charts 1951 and 1978) which are well buoyed, dredged and preserved by training banks, give main access to R. Mersey, and are entered E of the Bar Lanby. Be careful not to obstruct commercial shipping. From the N the old Formby chan is abandoned, but possible near HW. Towards HW and in moderate winds a yacht can cross the training bank (level of which varies between 2m and 3m above CD) E of Great Burbo Bank, if coming from the W. Rock Chan, parts of which dry and which is unmarked, may also be used but beware wrecks.

In good weather and at nps, the Dee Estuary (charts 1953, 1978) is interesting for boats prepared to take the ground. Most of estuary dries and banks extend 6M seaward. Chans shift, and Bys are moved as required. Stream runs hard in chans when banks are dry. Main ent is Welsh chan, but if coming from N Hilbre Swash runs W of Hilbre Is (lit).

Sailing W from the Dee on the ebb, it is feasible to take the inshore passage (buoyed) S of West Hoyle Spit, and this enjoys some protection from onshore winds at half tide or below. Rhyl is a tidal hbr, not accessible in strong onshore winds, but gives shelter for yachts able to take the ground. Abergele Road, Colwyn B and Llandudno B are possible anchs in settled weather and S winds.

Between Pt of Ayr and Great Ormes Hd the E-going stream begins at HW Liverpool +0600, and the W-going at HW Liverpool –0015, sp rates 3 kn.

ISLE OF MAN (charts 2094, 2696)

There are four choices when rounding South of Isle of Man (IOM). In bad weather or at night, keep S of Chicken Rk (Lt, fog sig). In good conditions, take chan between Chicken Rk and Calf of Man (Lt, fog sig). Alternatively use Calf Sound between Calf of Man and coast, passing S of Kitterland Is but N of Thousla Is, which is marked by lit Bn and is close to Calf of Man shore. There is also a minor chan, called Little Sound, N of Kitterland Is.

The stream runs strongly through Calf Sound, starting N-going at HW Liverpool –0145, and S-going at HW Liverpool +0345, sp rates 3·5 kn. W of Calf of Man the stream runs N and S, but changes direction off Chicken Rk and runs W and E between Calf of Man and Langness Pt 6M to E. Overfalls extend E from Chicken Rk on E-going stream, which begins at HW Liverpool +0610, and N from the rk on W-going stream, which begins at HW Liverpool.

Off Langness Pt (Lt) the Skerranes (dry) extend 0·1M SW, and tidal stream runs strongly, with eddies and a race. E side of Langness peninsula is foul ground, over which a dangerous sea can build in strong winds. Here the NE-going stream begins at HW Liverpool +0545, and the SW-going at HW Liverpool –0415, sp rates 2·25 kn.

There is anch in Derby Haven, N of St Michael's Is, but exposed to E. Between Derby Is and Douglas (10.10.14) and on to Maughold Hd, there are no dangers more than 0·4M offshore. Near the land the SW-going stream runs for 9 hours and the NE-going for 3 hours, since an eddy forms during the second half of the main NE-going stream. Off Maughold Hd the NE-going stream begins at HW Liverpool +0500, and the SW-going at HW Liverpool –0415.

SE, E and NW of Pt of Ayre are dangerous shoals, over which the sea breaks in bad weather. They are Bahama Bank (least depth 1·5m), Whitestone Bank (0·6m), Ballacash Bank (2·4m), King William Banks (3·7m), and Strunakill Bank (5·5m).

The W coast of IOM has few pilotage features. A spit with depths less than 1·8m runs 0·4M offshore 0·5M E of Rue Pt. Jurby Rk (depth 2·7m) lies 0·4M off Jurby Hd, and up to 3M offshore there is a target area marked by Bys and Y Lts: yachts are advised to pass to seaward or to keep well inshore by passing close to Jurby Rk (above). Craig Rk (depth 3·7m) and shoals lie 2·5M NNE of St Patricks Is.

For general pilotage information, tidal streams and hbr details of IOM, see *IOM Sailing Directions, Tidal Streams and Anchorages*, published by the Manx Sailing and Cruising Club. For notes on crossing the Irish Sea, see 10.13.5.

MENAI STRAIT (10.10.19 and chart 1464)

The main features of this narrow chan are: Puffin Is, seaward of NE end; Beaumaris; Garth Pt at Bangor, where NE end of Strait begins; Menai Suspension Bridge (30·5m); The Swellies, a narrow 1M stretch with strong tide and dangers mid-stream; Britannia Rail Bridge, with cables close W at elevation of 24m; Port Dinorwic; Caernarfon; Abermenai Pt, where narrows mark SW end of Strait; and Caernarfon Bar.

The Swellies should be taken near HW slack, and an understanding of tidal streams is essential. The tide is about 1 hour later, and sp range about 2·7m more, at NE end of Strait than at SW end. Levels differ most about HW +0100 at NE end (when level there is more than 1·8m above level at SW end), and about HW –0445 at NE end (when level there is more than 1·8m below level at SW end). Normally the stream runs as follows (times referred to HW Holyhead). HW–0040 to HW +0420: SW between Garth Pt and Abermenai Pt. HW

10

+0420 to HW +0545: outwards from about The Swellies, NE towards Garth Pt and SW towards Abermenai Pt. HW +0545 to HW –0040: NE between Abermenai Pt and Garth Pt. Sp rates generally about 3 kn, but more in narrows, e.g. 5 kn off Abermenai Pt, 6 kn between the bridges, and 8 kn at The Swellies. The timings and rates of streams may be affected by strong winds in either direction.

Note that direction of lateral buoyage changes at Caernarfon.

The following brief notes only cover very basic pilotage. From NE, enter chan W of Puffin Island, taking first of ebb to arrive Swellies at slack HW (HW Holyhead –0100). Slack HW only lasts about 20 mins at sps, a little more at nps. Pass under centre of suspension bridge span, and steer to leave Swelly By close to stbd, and Platters (dry) on mainland shore to port. From Swelly By to Britannia Bridge hold mainland shore, leaving Bn on Price Pt to port, and Gored Goch and Gribbin Rk to stbd. Leave Britannia Rk (centre pier of bridge) to stbd. Thence to SW hold to buoyed chan near mainland shore. Port Dinorwic is useful to await right tidal conditions for onward passage in either direction. Caernarfon Bar is impassable even in moderately strong winds against ebb, but narrows at Abermenai Pt demand a fair tide, or slackish water, since tide runs strongly here. Going seaward on first of ebb, when there is water over the banks, it may not be practicable to return to the Strait if conditions on the bar are bad. Then it is best to anch near Mussel Bank By and await slack water, before returning to Caernarfon (say). Leaving Abermenai Pt on last of ebb means banks to seaward are exposed and there is little water in chan or over bar.

Going NE it is safe to arrive at Swellies with last of flood, leaving Caernarfon about HW Holyhead –0230. Do not leave too late, or full force of ebb will be met before reaching Bangor. For detailed instructions see *W Coasts of England and Wales Pilot*, or *Cruising Anglesey* (NW Venturers Yacht Club).

ANGLESEY TO BARDSEY ISLAND (charts 1977, 1970, 1971)

On N of Anglesey, off Lynas Pt (Lt, fog sig, RC) a race extends 0·5M on E-going stream. Off Amlwch is a mooring/unloading By for supertankers, which must be given a wide berth. Amlwch is a small commercial hbr (mostly dries) 1·5M W of Lynas Pt. A drying rk lies 0·05M offshore on W side of approach, which should not be tried in strong onshore winds. From here to Carmel Hd beware E Mouse (and shoals to SE), Middle Mouse, Harry Furlong's Rks (dry), Victoria Bank (least depth 1·6m), Coal Rk (awash), and W Mouse (with dangers to W and SW). The outermost of these dangers is 2M offshore. There are overfalls and races at headlands and over many rks and shoals along this coast.

Between Carmel Hd and the Skerries (Lt, fog sig, Racon, RC) the NE-going stream begins at HW Holyhead +0550, and the SW-going at HW Holyhead –0010, sp rates 5 kn. 1M NW of Skerries the stream turns 1·5 hours later, and runs less strongly. Simplest passage, or at night or in bad weather, is to pass 1M off Skerries, remembering traffic scheme off shore – see Fig. 2(5). In good conditions by day the inshore passage may be taken, close round Carmel Hd, but there is a confused sea here with wind against tide, and good timing is then needed.

Races also occur off N Stack and (more severe) off S Stack (Lt, fog sig), up to 1·5M offshore on NNE-going stream which begins at HW Holyhead –0605, sp rate 5 kn. Races do not extend so far on SSW-going stream which begins at HW Holyhead +0020, sp rate 5 kn.

Along W coast of Anglesey, S from Holyhead (10.10.18), coast is rugged with rks, some drying, up to 1·5M offshore. There are races off Penrhyn Mawr and Rhoscolyn Hd. Pilot's Cove, E of Llanddwyn Is, is good anch while waiting right conditions for Menai Strait.

Porth Dinllaen (10.10.20) is good anch, but exposed to N and NE. Beware rks off the Trwyn Porth Dinlläen Pt, and Carreg-y-chad 0·75M to SW. Give Carreg-y-Chwislen (a drying rk with Bn, and with shoals extending 0·25M E) a berth of at least 0·35M in rough weather.

Braich y Pwll is a steep and rky point at end of Lleyn Peninsula (chart 1971). About 1M N of it and about 1M offshore lie The Tripods, a bank on which there are overfalls and a bad sea with wind against tide.

Bardsey Sound can be used in daylight and moderate winds. Stream reaches 6 kn at sp, and passage should be made at slack water, 0·5h before HW or LW Holyhead. Avoid Carreg Ddu on N side and Maen Bugail on S side of Sound, where there are dangerous races. Passing outside Bardsey Is (Lt, fog sig, RC) make a good offing to avoid overfalls which extend 1·5M W of Is and 2·5M S of it. Turbulence occurs over Bastram Shoal, Devil's Tail and Devil's Ridge, which lie S and E of Bardsey Is.

10.10.6 DISTANCE TABLE

Approximate distances in nautical miles are by the most direct route while avoiding dangers and allowing for traffic separation schemes etc. Places in *italics* are in adjoining areas.

1 *Strangford*	**1**																			
2 *Mew Island*	29	**2**																		
3 *Mull of Galloway*	34	23	**3**																	
4 St Bees Head	70	65	43	**4**																
5 Point of Ayre	44	43	21	26	**5**															
6 Douglas	63	62	40	37	19	**6**														
7 Barrow	95	96	74	39	53	52	**7**													
8 Glasson Dock	109	107	85	53	64	63	22	**8**												
9 Fleetwood	103	113	79	47	58	57	17	10	**9**											
10 Liverpool	109	121	101	75	80	70	50	52	46	**10**										
11 Conwy	90	105	94	77	72	59	59	62	56	46	**11**									
12 Beaumaris	89	102	91	77	71	58	62	66	60	49	12	**12**								
13 Holyhead	74	90	79	80	68	50	72	79	73	68	36	32	**13**							
14 Caernarfon	92	111	105	87	81	68	72	76	70	59	22	10	26	**14**						
15 Bardsey Island	103	120	115	116	107	88	103	107	101	90	53	41	38	31	**15**					
16 Abersoch	117	134	129	126	121	102	117	121	115	104	67	55	52	45	14	**16**				
17 Pwllheli	121	138	133	130	125	106	121	125	119	108	71	59	56	49	18	5	**17**			
18 *South Bishop*	151	172	169	174	159	143	163	167	161	150	113	101	98	91	60	70	74	**18**		
19 *Tuskar Rock*	136	155	152	163	152	132	159	170	164	152	115	103	91	93	63	75	79	36	**19**	
20 *Dun Laoghaire*	71	90	93	113	93	78	119	126	120	118	88	84	56	69	61	75	79	90	70	**20**

MARYPORT 10-10-7
Cumbria

CHARTS
Admiralty 2013, 1346; Imray C62; OS 89
TIDES
+0038 Dover; ML 4·7; Duration 0550; Zone 0 (GMT).
Standard Port LIVERPOOL (⟶)

Times				Height (metres)			
HW		LW		MHWS	MHWN	MLWN	MLWS
0000	0600	0200	0800	9·3	7·4	2·9	0·9
1200	1800	1400	2000				
Differences MARYPORT							
+0017	+0032	+0020	+0005	−0·7	−0·8	−0·4	0·0
SILLOTH							
+0030	+0040	+0045	+0055	−0·1	−0·3	−0·6	−0·1
TORDUFF POINT							
+0105	+0140	+0520	+0410	−4·1	−4·9	—	—

SHELTER
Complete shelter in Senhouse Dock, (Maryport Marina) Access HW ∓2½. Nearest anchorage Workington Basin. Complete shelter in Elizabeth Dock (commercial) which dries.
NAVIGATION
Waypoint 54°43′·08N 03°32′·39W, 270°/090° from/to South Pier Lt, 1·0M. 1·8m over bar between piers at entrance at half tide and in river channel. Mud banks cover HW−2. Channel not buoyed.
LIGHTS AND MARKS
South Pier. Fl 1·5s, 10m 4M.
RADIO TELEPHONE
VHF Ch 16; 12 (occas). Maryport Marina Ch 16, M.

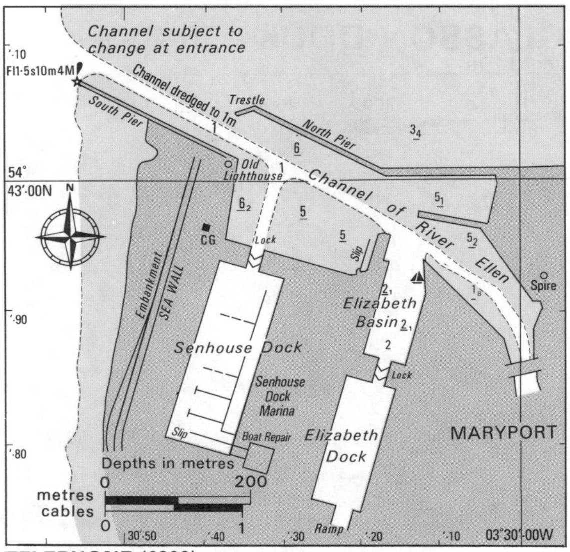

Channel subject to change at entrance
Fl1·5s10m4M
Channel dredged to 1m
South Pier
Trestle
North Pier
Old Lighthouse
Channel of River Ellen
CG
Lock
Slip
Spire
Elizabeth Basin
Embankment
SEA WALL
Senhouse Dock
Senhouse Dock Marina
Boat Repair
Elizabeth Dock
MARYPORT
Depths in metres
metres
cables
Ramp
54°
43′·00N
03°30′·00W

TELEPHONE (0900)
Hr Mr 817440; CG 2238; MRSC Liverpool 931-3341; # 604611; Marinecall 0898 500 461; Police 812601; Dr 815544; Ⓗ 812634.
FACILITIES
EC Wednesday. **Maryport Marina** (200) ☎ 813331, AC, BY, CH, El, FW, ◙, ME, Slip Access over sill 1·75m HW∓2½ (P and D from Fisherman's Co-op via marina); **Elizabeth Dock** Slip (at HW), M, Sh, AB. **Town** P, D, ME, V, R, Bar; ✉; Ⓑ; ⇌; ✈ (Newcastle)

10

WORKINGTON 10-10-8
Cumbria

CHARTS
Admiralty 2013, 1346; Imray C62; OS 89
TIDES
+0025 Dover; ML 4·4; Duration 0545; Zone 0 (GMT).
Standard Port LIVERPOOL (⟶)

Times				Height (metres)			
HW		LW		MHWS	MHWN	MLWN	MLWS
0000	0600	0200	0800	9·3	7·4	2·9	0·9
1200	1800	1400	2000				
Differences WORKINGTON							
+0020	+0020	+0020	+0010	−1·1	−1·0	−0·1	+0·3
WHITEHAVEN							
+0005	+0015	+0010	+0005	−1·3	−1·1	−0·5	+0·1
TARN POINT							
+0005	+0005	+0010	0000	−1·0	−1·0	−0·4	0·0

SHELTER
Good shelter in Turning Basin. Tidal harbour dries and bridge clearance is only 1·8m.
NAVIGATION
Waypoint 54°39′·58N 03°35′·30W, 311°/131° from/to front Ldg Lt, 1·0M. No navigational dangers but in periods of heavy rain a strong freshet may be encountered. Debris from collapsed wall marked by sign-boards river-side wall of dock.
LIGHTS AND MARKS
End of breakwater QG, end of S pier Fl 5s. Leading Lts on W pyramidal Trs with Y bands both FR at 132°.
RADIO TELEPHONE
VHF Ch 16; 11, 14 (HW−2½ to HW+2).
TELEPHONE (0900)
Hr Mr 602301; CG 2238; # 604611;
MRSC Liverpool 931-3341; Police 812601; Dr 64866; Hosp 602244.
FACILITIES
EC Thursday; **Dock** D, FW, ME, El; **Vanguard SC** ☎ 826886, M, FW; **Town** P, V, R, Bar. ✉; Ⓑ; ⇌; ✈ (Carlisle or Newcastle).

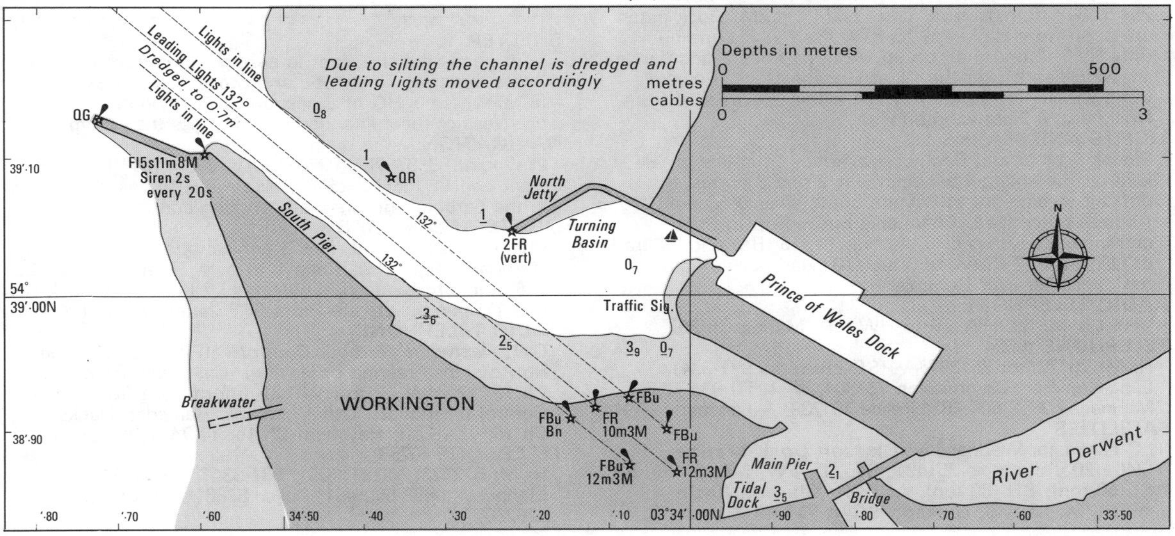

Lights in line
Leading Lights 132°
Dredged to 0·7m
Lights in line
Due to silting the channel is dredged and leading lights moved accordingly
Depths in metres
metres
cables
QG
Fl5s11m8M
Siren 2s every 20s
QR
North Jetty
Turning Basin
2FR (vert)
South Pier
Prince of Wales Dock
Traffic Sig.
Breakwater
WORKINGTON
FBu Bn
FR 10m3M
FBu
FBu 12m3M
FR 12m3M
Main Pier
Tidal Dock
Bridge
River Derwent
54°
39′·00N
03°34′·00N

GLASSON DOCK 10-10-9

Lancashire

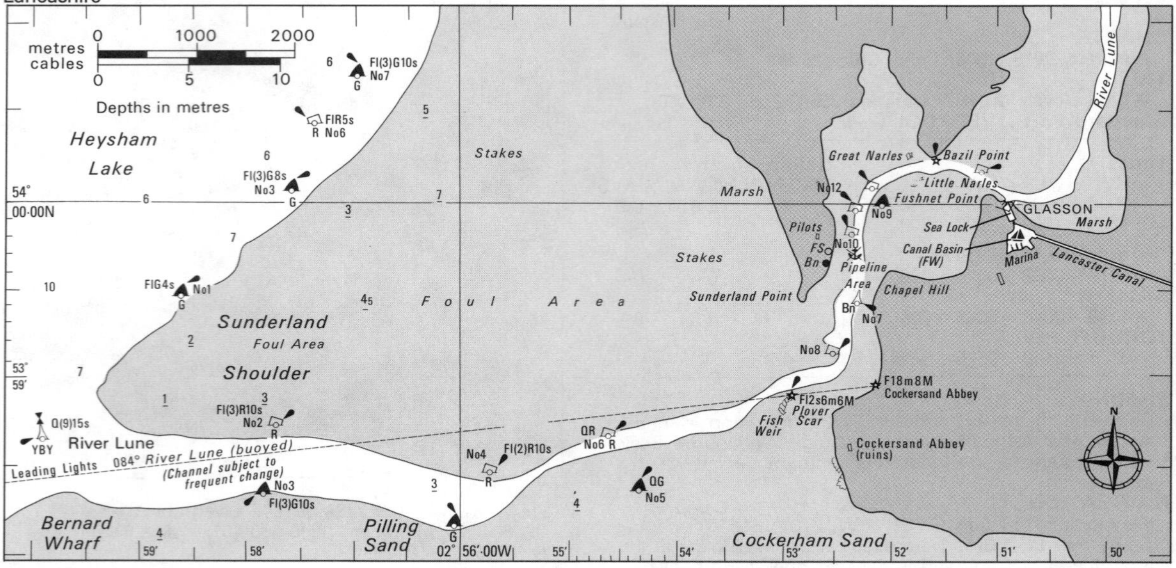
metres
cables
0 1000 2000
0 5 10
Depths in metres
Heysham
Lake
54°
00·00N
53°
59'
Sunderland
Foul Area
Shoulder
Stakes
Foul Area
Fl(3)G10s
No7
FlR5s
R No6
Fl(3)G8s
No3
FlG4s
No1
Fl(3)R10s
No2
Q(9)15s
YBY
River Lune
Leading Lights 084° River Lune (buoyed)
(Channel subject to frequent change)
No3
Fl(3)G10s
Bernard
Wharf
Pilling
Sand
No4
Fl(2)R10s
QR
No6 R
QG
No5
Cockerham Sand
Cockersand Abbey
(ruins)
Fl8m8M
Cockersand Abbey
Fl2s6m6M
Plover
Scar
Fish
Weir
No8
Bn
No7
Chapel Hill
Sunderland Point
Pipeline
Area
Pilots
FS
Bn
No10
No12
No9
Marsh
Great Narles
Bazil Point
Little Narles
Fushnet Point
Sea Lock
Canal Basin
(FW)
Marina
GLASSON
Marsh
Lancaster Canal
River Lune
59' 58' 02° 56'·00W 55' 54' 53' 52' 51' 50'

CHARTS

Admiralty 1552, 2010; Imray C62; OS 102, 97

TIDES

+0020 Dover; ML Wyre Lt Ho 11·7, Lancaster 5·2; Duration 0535; Zone 0 (GMT).

Standard Port LIVERPOOL (⟶)

Times				Height (metres)			
HW		LW		MHWS	MHWN	MLWN	MLWS
0000	0600	0200	0700	9·3	7·4	2·9	0·9
1200	1800	1400	1900				
Differences GLASSON DOCK							
+0020	+0030	+0220	+0240	−2·7	−3·0	No data	
LANCASTER							
+0110	+0030	No data		−5·0	−4·9	Dries out	
BARROW-IN-FURNESS (Ramsden Dock)							
+0015	+0015	+0015	+0015	−0·2	−0·3	−0·1	+0·1
MORECAMBE							
+0005	+0010	+0030	+0015	+0·2	0·0	0·0	+0·2
HEYSHAM							
+0005	+0005	+0015	0000	+0·1	0·0	0·0	+0·2

SHELTER

Very sheltered anchorage. Even more so up towards Lancaster; navigable for small boats but pilot is advised. Dock connects with British Waterways basin of Lancaster canal. Marina is in canal.

NAVIGATION

Waypoint R Lune entrance 53°58′·40N 03°00′·00W, 264°/084° from/to front Ldg Lt 084°, 4·2M. Dock gates are open from HW−1½ to HW. Wait at R Lune buoy until HW−2 and then go up. Abbey Lt has a tide gauge showing depth over the sill at Glasson Dock. Beware three wrecks on Bernard Wharf within 2½ miles E from Nos 2 and 8 Fleetwood buoys.

LIGHTS AND MARKS

Plover Scar Lt and Cockersand Abbey Lt in line at 084° lead up the channel between Nos 2 and 3 buoys. Lts difficult to pick out at R Lune buoy; steer 085° until Abbey Lt identified. Channel is buoyed up to dock entrance. Buoys no 6, 8, 10, 12, 14, 16 (Bn) and 18 are Fl or QR; no 5, 7 (Bn) and 9 are QG. Harbour authority is the Lancaster Port Commission.

RADIO TELEPHONE

VHF Ch 16; 08 (HW−2 to HW+1). Marina Ch 80.

TELEPHONE (0524)

Hr Mr 751724 or 751307; MRSC Liverpool 931-3341; Lancaster Port Commission 751304; # (051) 933 7075; Marinecall 0898 500 461; Police 791239; [H] Lancaster 65944.

FACILITIES

EC Lancaster Wednesday; **Glasson Dock Marina** (240+20 visitors) ☎ 751491, Slip, D, FW, ME, El, Ⓔ, Sh, C, (50 ton), BH (50 ton), AC, CH; **Glasson Basin** ☎ 751724, M, AB; **Glasson SC** ☎ 751089 Slip, M, C; **Lune Cruising Club** Access HW∓2; **Town** P, V, R, Bar, ⊠; Ⓑ (Lancaster); ≷ (bus to Lancaster); ✈ (Blackpool).

Note: There is a proposal to build a 500 berth marina at Morecambe.

FLEETWOOD 10-10-10

Lancashire

CHARTS

Admiralty 1552, 2010; Imray C62; OS 102

TIDES

+0015 Dover; ML 5·0; Duration 0540; Zone 0 (GMT).

Standard Port LIVERPOOL (⟶)

Times				Height (metres)			
HW		LW		MHWS	MHWN	MLWN	MLWS
0000	0600	0200	0700	9·3	7·4	2·9	0·9
1200	1800	1400	1900				
Differences FLEETWOOD							
0000	0000	+0005	0000	−0·1	−0·1	+0·1	+0·3
BLACKPOOL							
−0015	−0005	−0005	−0015	−0·4	−0·4	−0·1	+0·1

SHELTER

Very good shelter except in strong winds from N to W. Boats can pass Fleetwood and proceed up to Skipool (5 M) where is HQ of Blackpool & Fleetwood YC. Passage up river not recommended on tides less than 8·0m.

NAVIGATION

Waypoint 53°57′·78N 03°01′·90W, 338°/158° from/to front Ldg Lt 156°, 2·25M. Beware Ro Ro vessels turning in the harbour and dredgers working continuously.

LIGHTS AND MARKS

Channel well buoyed, five G conical buoys and one Bn to starboard, eight R can buoys to port. Fleetwood Ldg Lts 156° (only to be used between No 7 buoy and Black Scar (No 11) perch). Lts are Front Fl Y 2s and Rear Fl Y 4s.

RADIO TELEPHONE

Call: *Fleetwood Harbour Control* VHF Ch 16; **12** (when Ro Ro ships entering or leaving). Call: *Fleetwood Docks* Ch 16; 12 (HW−2 to HW+2). Information from Harbour Control on request. Other stations: Ramsden Docks Ch 16; 12 (H24); Heysham Ch 16; 14 74 (H24).

TELEPHONE (0253)

Hr Mr 872323; MRSC (051) 931-3341; # 779211; Marinecall 0898 500 461; Police 876611; Dr Cleveleys 826280.

FLEETWOOD *continued*

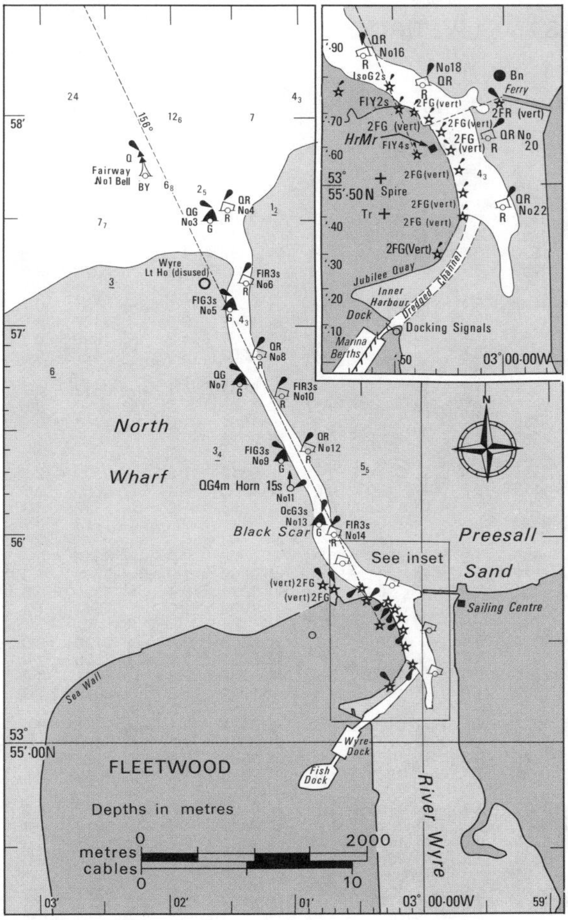
See inset
North
Wharf
Black Scar
Preesall
Sand
Sailing Centre
Sea Wall
FLEETWOOD
Depths in metres
metres
cables
0
2000
0
10
River Wyre
Wyre Dock
Fish Dock
Fairway No1 Bell
Wyre Lt Ho (disused)
QG4m Horn 15s
HrMr
Spire
Jubilee Quay
Inner Harbour
Dock
Marina Berths
Dredged Channel
Docking Signals
Ferry
03° 00·00W
53° 55'·00N
53° 55'·50N

FACILITIES

EC Wednesday; **Harbour** ☎ 872323, FW, ME, El, CH; **Wyre dock** (70) M (No deep water moorings), FW, ME, El, Sh, C (by arrangement 25 ton); **Blackpool and Fleetwood YC (Skipool Creek)** ☎ Blackpool 884205, Slip (at Stanah), L, FW, AB (Skipool), Bar, M; **Fleetwood Trawler Supply Co** ☎ 873470, CH, ACA; **Wardleys Marine** ☎ Hambleton 700117, AB, CH, D, El, FW, L, M (drying), ME, Sh, Slip; **David Moss** ☎ Blackpool 893830, D (cans), FW, ME, El, Sh, C (mobile 50 ton), CH; **Marine Electronics** ☎ 779174, Ⓔ
Town P, D, ME, El, Sh, CH, V, R, Bar. ✉; Ⓑ; ⇌ (bus to Poulton-le-Fylde or Blackpool); ✈ (Blackpool).

Note: – The Wyre Dock area is to be converted to a Marina Village with berths for 400 yachts.

POULTON-LE-FYLDE. P, D, ME, El, Sh, V, R, Bar; **Lytham Marine** ☎ 735531, Slip, D, FW, ME, El, Sh, C (4 ton), CH, AB; **Fylde Coast Sailmaking Co** ☎ 873476, SM, CH.

LIVERPOOL 10-10-11

Merseyside

CHARTS

Admiralty 3490, 1951, 1978; Imray C62; OS 108

TIDES

+0015 Dover; ML 5·2; Duration 0535; Zone 0 (GMT).

Standard Port LIVERPOOL (→)

Times				Height (metres)			
HW		LW		MHWS	MHWN	MLWN	MLWS
0000	0600	0200	0700	9·3	7·4	2·9	0·9
1200	1800	1400	1900				
Differences FORMBY							
–0015	–0010	–0020	–0020	–0·3	–0·1	0·0	+0·1
ROCK CHANNEL							
–0030	–0030	–0030	–0030	–0·4	–0·2	–0·2	0·0
Differences R. MERSEY							
EASTHAM							
+0003	+0006	+0015	+0030	+0·4	+0·3	–0·1	–0·1
WIDNES							
+0040	+0045	+0400	+0345	–4·2	–4·4	–2·5	–0·3
Differences R. DEE							
MOSTYN QUAY							
–0020	–0015	–0020	–0020	–0·8	–0·7	No data	
CHESTER							
+0105	+0105	+0500	+0500	–5·3	–5·4	Dries out	

NOTE: Liverpool is a Standard Port and tidal predictions for each day of the year are given below.

SHELTER

Yachts should go to Liverpool Marina in the Coburg and Brunswick docks. The entrance is abeam the Pluckington Bank buoy; access HW ∓2 approx. Shelter is good in all winds. Good shelter is also available in Stanley, Canning and Albert Docks but access very limited. There are no other facilities for berthing or anchoring on the NE side of the river. Anchoring is possible on the SW side of the river but only in fair weather.

NAVIGATION

Liverpool waypoint Bar Lanby 53°32'·00N 03°20'·90W, Fl 5s, Horn, Racon, 280°/100° from/to Queen's Channel, 3·0M. River Dee waypoint Hilbre Swash HE2 port-hand buoy, QR, 53°26'·20N 03°16'·80W (channel shifts). Wind against tide causes steep seas in outer reaches of Mersey. Do not go outside buoys marking fairway. Advisable to enter by Bar and Queens Channel. The whole area from River Dee, River Mersey to River Alt and up to Morecambe Bay is littered with sandbanks. R Mersey is safe within commercial channel, but everywhere else great

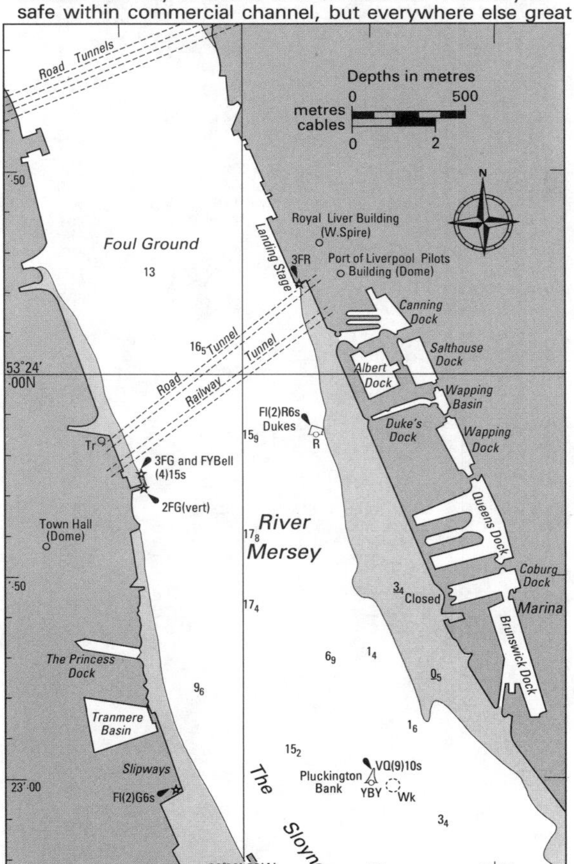
Road Tunnels
Depths in metres
0
500
metres
cables
0
2
Foul Ground
Landing Stage
Royal Liver Building (W.Spire)
3FR
Port of Liverpool Pilots Building (Dome)
Canning Dock
Salthouse Dock
Albert Dock
Wapping Basin
Duke's Dock
Wapping Dock
Road Tunnel
Railway Tunnel
Fl(2)R6s Dukes
3FG and FYBell (4)15s
2FG(vert)
Town Hall (Dome)
River Mersey
Queens Dock
Coburg Dock
Marina
Brunswick Dock
Closed
The Princess Dock
Tranmere Basin
Slipways
Fl(2)G6s
The Sloyne
Pluckington Bank
VQ(9)10s
YBY
Wk
53°24'·00N
23'·00
03°00'·00W

10

ENGLAND, WEST COAST – LIVERPOOL

Lat 53°25′ N Long 3°00′ W

TIMES AND HEIGHTS OF HIGH AND LOW WATERS

YEAR **1992**

TIME ZONE UT(GMT)
For Summer Time add ONE hour in non-shaded areas

JANUARY

Day	Time	m	Day	Time	m
1 W	0246	2·5	16 Th	0138	2·7
	0830	7·9		0727	7·7
	1514	2·6		1420	2·7
	2058	8·0		2001	8·0
2 Th	0342	2·3	17 F	0251	2·3
	0924	8·3		0837	8·2
	1610	2·3		1529	2·1
	2150	8·2		2107	8·5
3 F	0430	2·1	18 Sa	0355	1·8
	1010	8·6		0936	8·8
	1657	2·1		1631	1·5
	2235	8·4		2206	9·0
4 Sa	0511	2·0	19 Su	0451	1·3
	1051	8·8		1030	9·3
	1736	1·9		1727	0·9
●	2313	8·6	○	2258	9·4
5 Su	0546	1·8	20 M	0543	0·9
	1127	9·0		1120	9·7
	1812	1·7		1818	0·4
	2349	8·7		2347	9·7
6 M	0618	1·8	21 Tu	0631	0·6
	1201	9·1		1207	10·0
	1845	1·6		1907	0·1
7 Tu	0021	8·7	22 W	0034	9·8
	0649	1·7		0716	0·5
	1235	9·1		1253	10·1
	1916	1·6		1952	0·1
8 W	0052	8·7	23 Th	0119	9·7
	0720	1·7		0759	0·6
	1307	9·0		1337	10·0
	1947	1·6		2034	0·3
9 Th	0124	8·6	24 F	0202	9·4
	0752	1·8		0840	0·9
	1340	8·9		1420	9·6
	2019	1·7		2117	0·8
10 F	0157	8·4	25 Sa	0246	9·0
	0827	2·0		0922	1·4
	1412	8·7		1504	9·2
	2054	1·9		2157	1·4
11 Sa	0229	8·2	26 Su	0331	8·5
	0903	2·3		1006	1·9
	1447	8·5		1552	8·5
	2131	2·2	☾	2244	2·1
12 Su	0307	8·0	27 M	0421	8·0
	0943	2·6		1058	2·5
	1529	8·2		1648	7·9
	2213	2·5		2342	2·7
13 M	0353	7·8	28 Tu	0525	7·5
	1031	2·9		1207	3·0
	1620	7·9		1800	7·3
☽	2305	2·7			
14 Tu	0452	7·6	29 W	0056	3·1
	1134	3·1		0643	7·3
	1726	7·7		1333	3·2
				1928	7·2
15 W	0017	2·9	30 Th	0216	3·1
	0608	7·5		0805	7·5
	1259	3·0		1454	2·9
	1845	7·7		2043	7·4
			31 F	0324	2·8
				0907	7·9
				1557	2·5
				2139	7·8

FEBRUARY

Day	Time	m	Day	Time	m
1 Sa	0414	2·4	16 Su	0341	1·9
	0956	8·3		0925	8·7
	1644	2·1		1620	1·3
	2221	8·2		2156	8·9
2 Su	0457	2·1	17 M	0440	1·3
	1035	8·7		1019	9·3
	1723	1·8		1716	0·6
	2258	8·5		2247	9·5
3 M	0530	1·8	18 Tu	0530	0·7
	1111	9·0		1106	9·8
	1756	1·6		1805	0·1
●	2330	8·7	○	2332	9·8
4 Tu	0603	1·6	19 W	0617	0·4
	1143	9·1		1151	10·1
	1827	1·4		1849	–0·1
5 W	0001	8·8	20 Th	0015	9·9
	0632	1·4		0659	0·2
	1215	9·2		1234	10·2
	1856	1·3		1931	–0·1
6 Th	0031	8·9	21 F	0056	9·8
	0702	1·3		0738	0·3
	1245	9·2		1314	10·0
	1926	1·2		2009	0·2
7 F	0100	8·9	22 Sa	0135	9·6
	0734	1·4		0816	0·6
	1316	9·2		1355	9·7
	1957	1·3		2046	0·8
8 Sa	0130	8·8	23 Su	0215	9·1
	0805	1·5		0854	1·2
	1345	9·0		1434	9·1
	2027	1·5		2122	1·5
9 Su	0159	8·6	24 M	0254	8·6
	0837	1·8		0934	1·8
	1418	8·8		1517	8·4
	2100	1·8		2202	2·2
10 M	0233	8·4	25 Tu	0339	8·0
	0912	2·1		1019	2·5
	1454	8·5		1606	7·6
	2135	2·2	☾	2251	3·0
11 Tu	0315	8·1	26 W	0435	7·4
	0953	2·5		1120	3·1
	1542	8·1		1716	7·0
☽	2221	2·6			
12 W	0409	7·8	27 Th	0005	3·5
	1052	2·9		0557	7·0
	1645	7·7		1255	3·4
	2329	2·9		1856	6·8
13 Th	0526	7·4	28 F	0144	3·5
	1219	3·0		0733	7·1
	1814	7·5		1427	3·2
				2022	7·1
14 F	0103	3·0	29 Sa	0258	3·1
	0659	7·5		0843	7·6
	1357	2·7		1532	2·7
	1944	7·7		2118	7·6
15 Sa	0232	2·6			
	0820	8·0			
	1515	2·1			
	2057	8·3			

MARCH

Day	Time	m	Day	Time	m
1 Su	0352	2·6	16 M	0325	1·9
	0932	8·1		0908	8·7
	1620	2·2		1604	1·2
	2159	8·1		2141	8·9
2 M	0433	2·1	17 Tu	0423	1·2
	1012	8·6		1000	9·3
	1658	1·8		1658	0·5
	2234	8·5		2228	9·4
3 Tu	0508	1·7	18 W	0512	0·7
	1045	8·9		1047	9·8
	1730	1·4		1744	0·2
	2305	8·8	○	2312	9·7
4 W	0539	1·4	19 Th	0556	0·4
	1118	9·2		1130	10·0
	1800	1·2		1827	0·0
●	2334	9·0		2353	9·8
5 Th	0608	1·2	20 F	0636	0·3
	1149	9·3		1211	10·0
	1831	1·0		1904	0·1
6 F	0004	9·1	21 Sa	0031	9·7
	0641	1·1		0714	0·4
	1218	9·4		1250	9·8
	1902	1·0		1941	0·5
7 Sa	0034	9·1	22 Su	0109	9·5
	0712	1·1		0751	0·7
	1249	9·3		1328	9·4
	1931	1·1		2015	1·0
8 Su	0103	9·1	23 M	0145	9·1
	0744	1·2		0827	1·2
	1320	9·2		1405	8·9
	2002	1·3		2049	1·7
9 M	0134	8·9	24 Tu	0222	8·6
	0816	1·5		0904	1·9
	1354	9·0		1446	8·2
	2033	1·6		2124	2·4
10 Tu	0209	8·7	25 W	0304	8·1
	0851	1·8		0945	2·5
	1432	8·7		1532	7·5
	2108	2·0		2206	3·1
11 W	0250	8·3	26 Th	0357	7·5
	0934	2·3		1041	3·1
	1521	8·2		1637	6·9
	2156	2·5	☾	2312	3·6
12 Th	0345	7·9	27 F	0512	7·0
	1033	2·7		1207	3·4
	1627	7·7		1811	6·7
☽	2304	2·9			
13 F	0505	7·5	28 Sa	0056	3·7
	1201	2·9		0645	7·0
	1758	7·4		1341	3·2
				1942	6·9
14 Sa	0042	3·0	29 Su	0218	3·3
	0641	7·5		0801	7·4
	1341	2·5		1449	2·8
	1931	7·7		2042	7·5
15 Su	0213	2·6	30 M	0314	2·8
	0804	8·0		0854	7·9
	1501	1·9		1539	2·3
	2043	8·3		2124	8·0
			31 Tu	0356	2·3
				0935	8·4
				1619	1·8
				2200	8·4

APRIL

Day	Time	m	Day	Time	m
1 W	0433	1·8	16 Th	0448	0·9
	1012	8·8		1024	9·5
	1654	1·5		1719	0·5
	2231	8·7		2248	9·5
2 Th	0508	1·5	17 F	0532	0·7
	1045	9·0		1106	9·6
	1727	1·2		1800	0·5
	2302	9·0	○	2327	9·6
3 F	0542	1·2	18 Sa	0612	0·6
	1118	9·2		1147	9·6
	1801	1·0		1836	0·6
●	2333	9·1			
4 Sa	0615	1·0	19 Su	0005	9·5
	1150	9·4		0650	0·7
	1835	1·0		1227	9·4
				1913	0·9
5 Su	0005	9·2	20 M	0043	9·3
	0650	1·0		0728	1·0
	1224	9·4		1304	9·0
	1909	1·0		1947	1·4
6 M	0039	9·2	21 Tu	0120	9·0
	0726	1·1		0805	1·4
	1259	9·3		1341	8·6
	1941	1·2		2019	1·9
7 Tu	0114	9·1	22 W	0157	8·6
	0801	1·3		0840	1·9
	1337	9·0		1420	8·1
	2016	1·6		2053	2·4
8 W	0152	8·8	23 Th	0237	8·2
	0840	1·6		0919	2·4
	1420	8·7		1505	7·6
	2056	2·0		2131	3·0
9 Th	0239	8·5	24 F	0327	7·7
	0928	2·0		1007	2·8
	1514	8·2		1602	7·1
	2146	2·4	☾	2226	3·4
10 F	0338	8·0	25 Sa	0430	7·3
	1030	2·4		1115	3·1
	1623	7·7		1716	6·8
☽	2255	2·8		2349	3·6
11 Sa	0457	7·7	26 Su	0546	7·1
	1154	2·5		1236	3·1
	1750	7·6		1839	6·9
12 Su	0027	2·8	27 M	0114	3·4
	0624	7·8		0700	7·3
	1324	2·2		1347	2·8
	1914	7·8		1947	7·3
13 M	0152	2·5	28 Tu	0218	3·0
	0741	8·2		0801	7·7
	1439	1·7		1443	2·4
	2022	8·3		2036	7·7
14 Tu	0301	1·9	29 W	0308	2·5
	0844	8·7		0850	8·1
	1541	1·2		1531	2·0
	2118	8·9		2117	8·2
15 W	0359	1·4	30 Th	0352	2·1
	0938	9·2		0931	8·5
	1633	0·7		1613	1·7
	2204	9·2		2153	8·6

Chart Datum: 4·93 metres below Ordnance Datum (Newlyn)

ENGLAND, WEST COAST - LIVERPOOL

Lat 53°25′ N Long 3°00′ W

TIME ZONE UT(GMT)

For Summer Time add ONE hour in non-shaded areas

TIMES AND HEIGHTS OF HIGH AND LOW WATERS

YEAR **1992**

MAY

Day	Time	m	Day	Time	m
1 F	0433	1·7	16 Sa	0509	1·2
	1009	8·8		1045	9·1
	1652	1·4		1733	1·1
	2228	8·9	○	2305	9·2
2 Sa	0512	1·3	17 Su	0551	1·1
	1045	9·1		1127	9·1
	1732	1·2		1811	1·2
●	2304	9·1		2344	9·2
3 Su	0551	1·1	18 M	0631	1·1
	1123	9·3		1207	8·9
	1810	1·1		1848	1·4
	2342	9·3			
4 M	0632	1·0	19 Tu	0022	9·1
	1203	9·3		0709	1·3
	1848	1·1		1245	8·7
				1921	1·6
5 Tu	0019	9·3	20 W	0059	8·9
	0712	1·0		0745	1·6
	1243	9·3		1323	8·5
	1926	1·2		1955	1·9
6 W	0102	9·2	21 Th	0137	8·7
	0754	1·1		0820	1·9
	1328	9·1		1401	8·2
	2006	1·5		2029	2·3
7 Th	0147	9·0	22 F	0216	8·4
	0839	1·4		0857	2·2
	1418	8·7		1442	7·8
	2050	1·8		2105	2·6
8 F	0237	8·7	23 Sa	0300	8·0
	0931	1·7		0939	2·4
	1512	8·3		1528	7·5
	2143	2·2		2150	3·0
9 Sa	0336	8·3	24 Su	0350	7·7
	1033	1·9		1028	2·7
	1620	8·0		1624	7·2
☽	2249	2·5	☾	2248	3·2
10 Su	0447	8·1	25 M	0449	7·5
	1144	2·0		1130	2·8
	1733	7·9		1729	7·1
				2358	3·3
11 M	0007	2·5	26 Tu	0554	7·4
	0601	8·1		1236	2·8
	1259	1·9		1836	7·2
	1848	8·0			
12 Tu	0123	2·3	27 W	0110	3·1
	0713	8·3		0657	7·6
	1409	1·7		1341	2·6
	1954	8·3		1937	7·5
13 W	0232	2·0	28 Th	0212	2·8
	0816	8·6		0755	7·9
	1511	1·4		1439	2·3
	2050	8·6		2027	8·0
14 Th	0331	1·6	29 F	0307	2·3
	0911	8·8		0846	8·3
	1604	1·2		1531	1·9
	2139	8·9		2114	8·4
15 F	0423	1·4	30 Sa	0357	1·9
	1000	9·0		0932	8·6
	1651	1·1		1619	1·6
	2224	9·1		2156	8·8
			31 Su	0445	1·5
				1017	8·9
				1705	1·4
				2240	9·1

JUNE

Day	Time	m	Day	Time	m
1 M	0532	1·2	16 Tu	0617	1·5
	1102	9·2		1153	8·7
	1749	1·2		1828	1·6
●	2323	9·3			
2 Tu	0617	1·0	17 W	0007	9·0
	1147	9·3		0655	1·5
	1832	1·1		1229	8·6
				1902	1·7
3 W	0007	9·4	18 Th	0043	9·0
	0703	0·8		0730	1·6
	1234	9·3		1304	8·5
	1916	1·1		1934	1·8
4 Th	0053	9·4	19 F	0119	8·8
	0751	0·8		0802	1·7
	1323	9·2		1340	8·4
	2001	1·2		2006	2·0
5 F	0142	9·3	20 Sa	0155	8·7
	0839	0·9		0836	1·8
	1413	9·0		1416	8·2
	2047	1·5		2042	2·2
6 Sa	0233	9·1	21 Su	0232	8·4
	0929	1·1		0911	2·0
	1507	8·7		1454	7·9
	2139	1·7		2119	2·5
7 Su	0328	8·8	22 M	0312	8·2
	1024	1·4		0950	2·3
	1604	8·4		1536	7·7
☽	2235	2·0		2204	2·8
8 M	0427	8·6	23 Tu	0357	7·9
	1123	1·6		1037	2·5
	1706	8·1		1626	7·5
	2340	2·2	☾	2258	3·0
9 Tu	0532	8·3	24 W	0451	7·7
	1228	1·8		1133	2·7
	1814	8·0		1726	7·3
10 W	0049	2·3	25 Th	0004	3·1
	0641	8·2		0554	7·6
	1335	1·9		1241	2·7
	1921	8·1		1834	7·4
11 Th	0159	2·2	26 F	0117	3·0
	0748	8·2		0702	7·7
	1440	1·9		1351	2·6
	2023	8·3		1940	7·7
12 F	0304	2·1	27 Sa	0226	2·6
	0849	8·3		0805	8·0
	1538	1·8		1453	2·3
	2117	8·5		2039	8·2
13 Sa	0402	1·8	28 Su	0327	2·2
	0942	8·5		0903	8·4
	1628	1·7		1550	1·9
	2206	8·7		2131	8·6
14 Su	0452	1·7	29 M	0423	1·7
	1030	8·6		0956	8·8
	1712	1·6		1642	1·5
	2249	8·9		2221	9·0
15 M	0537	1·5	30 Tu	0516	1·2
	1113	8·7		1047	9·1
	1751	1·6		1733	1·2
○	2329	9·0	●	2309	9·4

JULY

Day	Time	m	Day	Time	m
1 W	0607	0·8	16 Th	0639	1·5
	1136	9·4		1212	8·7
	1821	0·9		1843	1·6
	2357	9·6			
2 Th	0656	0·5	17 F	0025	9·1
	1225	9·5		0710	1·4
	1907	0·8		1245	8·7
				1914	1·6
3 F	0045	9·8	18 Sa	0057	9·1
	0744	0·4		0740	1·4
	1313	9·5		1316	8·6
	1954	0·8		1945	1·7
4 Sa	0133	9·7	19 Su	0130	8·9
	0830	0·4		0811	1·5
	1401	9·4		1347	8·5
	2039	1·0		2018	1·8
5 Su	0219	9·6	20 M	0202	8·8
	0917	0·7		0843	1·7
	1449	9·1		1419	8·3
	2124	1·3		2051	2·1
6 M	0308	9·2	21 Tu	0236	8·5
	1003	1·1		0917	2·0
	1539	8·7		1454	8·1
	2213	1·7		2129	2·4
7 Tu	0400	8·8	22 W	0314	8·2
	1055	1·5		0955	2·3
	1634	8·3		1535	7·8
☽	2308	2·1	☾	2213	2·8
8 W	0458	8·3	23 Th	0359	7·9
	1153	2·0		1042	2·6
	1737	7·9		1627	7·6
				2309	3·0
9 Th	0014	2·5	24 F	0458	7·6
	0605	7·9		1144	2·9
	1300	2·3		1737	7·4
	1848	7·8			
10 F	0128	2·6	25 Sa	0027	3·1
	0721	7·8		0614	7·5
	1412	2·4		1306	2·9
	1958	7·9		1857	7·5
11 Sa	0243	2·5	26 Su	0151	2·8
	0832	7·8		0734	7·7
	1517	2·3		1422	2·6
	2100	8·1		2011	8·0
12 Su	0349	2·2	27 M	0303	2·3
	0931	8·1		0843	8·2
	1612	2·1		1528	2·1
	2152	8·5		2112	8·5
13 M	0442	2·0	28 Tu	0406	1·7
	1020	8·3		0942	8·7
	1658	1·9		1626	1·6
	2237	8·8		2206	9·1
14 Tu	0526	1·7	29 W	0504	1·1
	1101	8·5		1034	9·2
	1737	1·8		1719	1·1
○	2315	9·0	●	2257	9·6
15 W	0604	1·6	30 Th	0556	0·6
	1139	8·6		1123	9·6
	1811	1·7		1808	0·7
	2351	9·1		2343	9·9
			31 F	0643	0·2
				1210	9·8
				1855	0·5

AUGUST

Day	Time	m	Day	Time	m
1 Sa	0029	10·1	16 Su	0032	9·3
	0730	0·0		0713	1·2
	1256	9·8		1248	8·9
	1938	0·5		1920	1·4
2 Su	0114	10·1	17 M	0103	9·2
	0812	0·1		0742	1·3
	1340	9·6		1317	8·8
	2020	0·7		1952	1·6
3 M	0158	9·8	18 Tu	0133	9·0
	0854	0·5		0813	1·5
	1423	9·3		1347	8·6
	2101	1·0		2025	1·9
4 Tu	0242	9·4	19 W	0202	8·8
	0936	1·0		0844	1·9
	1508	8·8		1418	8·4
	2145	1·6		2058	2·2
5 W	0328	8·8	20 Th	0237	8·5
	1021	1·7		0919	2·2
	1557	8·3		1456	8·1
☽	2235	2·2		2138	2·6
6 Th	0423	8·2	21 F	0319	8·1
	1115	2·4		1002	2·6
	1657	7·8		1545	7·8
	2339	2·7	☾	2231	3·0
7 F	0532	7·6	22 Sa	0417	7·7
	1224	2·9		1101	3·0
	1812	7·5		1654	7·5
				2349	3·2
8 Sa	0103	3·0	23 Su	0540	7·4
	0657	7·3		1228	3·1
	1347	3·0		1825	7·4
	1935	7·5			
9 Su	0227	2·8	24 M	0124	2·9
	0819	7·5		0712	7·6
	1500	2·8		1358	2·8
	2044	7·9		1949	7·9
10 M	0336	2·5	25 Tu	0244	2·3
	0919	7·9		0827	8·1
	1557	2·4		1510	2·2
	2138	8·4		2056	8·6
11 Tu	0430	2·1	26 W	0350	1·6
	1006	8·2		0928	8·8
	1642	2·1		1610	1·5
	2220	8·8		2150	9·2
12 W	0511	1·7	27 Th	0448	0·9
	1044	8·5		1019	9·3
	1719	1·8		1702	1·0
	2257	9·0		2240	9·8
13 Th	0546	1·5	28 F	0539	0·4
	1118	8·7		1106	9·8
	1751	1·6		1750	0·6
○	2330	9·2	●	2325	10·1
14 F	0617	1·4	29 Sa	0624	0·0
	1149	8·9		1150	10·0
	1821	1·5		1835	0·3
15 Sa	0001	9·3	30 Su	0008	10·3
	0645	1·3		0707	−0·1
	1219	8·9		1232	9·9
	1850	1·4		1916	0·3
			31 M	0050	10·2
				0748	0·2
				1314	9·7
				1957	0·6

Chart Datum: 4·93 metres below Ordnance Datum (Newlyn)

10

TIME ZONE UT(GMT)

For Summer Time add ONE hour in non-shaded areas

ENGLAND, WEST COAST – LIVERPOOL

Lat 53°25′ N Long 3°00′ W

TIMES AND HEIGHTS OF HIGH AND LOW WATERS

YEAR **1992**

SEPTEMBER

Day	Time	m	Time	m	Time	m	Time	m
1 Tu	0133	9·9	0826	0·6	1354	9·4	2036	1·0
2 W	0213	9·3	0904	1·3	1436	8·9	2118	1·7
3 Th	0258	8·7	0946	2·0	1521	8·3	☽ 2204	2·4
4 F	0349	7·9	1035	2·8	1619	7·7	2308	3·0
5 Sa	0458	7·2	1147	3·3	1736	7·3		
6 Su	0036	3·3	0634	7·0	1321	3·4	1909	7·3
7 M	0206	3·0	0801	7·2	1437	3·1	2022	7·8
8 Tu	0314	2·6	0900	7·8	1534	2·6	2114	8·3
9 W	0403	2·1	0943	8·2	1617	2·2	2155	8·7
10 Th	0442	1·8	1019	8·6	1652	1·8	2230	9·0
11 F	0516	1·5	1051	8·8	1725	1·6	2302	9·2
12 Sa	0546	1·3	1120	9·0	1754	1·4	○ 2333	9·4
13 Su	0615	1·2	1150	9·1	1824	1·3		
14 M	0003	9·4	0645	1·2	1218	9·1	1856	1·3
15 Tu	0034	9·3	0714	1·3	1246	9·0	1927	1·5
16 W	0103	9·1	0745	1·5	1317	8·9	2001	1·8
17 Th	0134	8·9	0816	1·8	1349	8·7	2034	2·1
18 F	0211	8·6	0850	2·2	1427	8·3	2114	2·5
19 Sa	0256	8·1	0932	2·7	1518	7·9	☾ 2209	2·9
20 Su	0356	7·7	1034	3·1	1630	7·6	2329	3·1
21 M	0520	7·4	1203	3·2	1804	7·5		
22 Tu	0106	2·8	0655	7·6	1337	2·9	1928	8·0
23 W	0226	2·2	0811	8·2	1450	2·2	2036	8·7
24 Th	0332	1·5	0910	8·9	1549	1·6	2129	9·3
25 F	0427	0·8	0959	9·4	1641	1·0	2217	9·8
26 Sa	0516	0·4	1044	9·8	1727	0·6	● 2302	10·1
27 Su	0600	0·2	1126	10·0	1811	0·4	2344	10·2
28 M	0641	0·2	1207	9·9	1852	0·5		
29 Tu	0027	10·0	0720	0·5	1248	9·7	1933	0·7
30 W	0107	9·7	0757	1·0	1327	9·4	2012	1·5

OCTOBER

Day	Time	m	Time	m	Time	m	Time	m
1 Th	0148	9·1	0834	1·6	1406	8·9	2053	1·8
2 F	0230	8·5	0912	2·3	1450	8·3	2138	2·5
3 Sa	0319	7·8	0959	3·0	1545	7·8	☽ 2237	3·1
4 Su	0423	7·2	1106	3·5	1657	7·3		
5 M	0000	3·3	0553	6·9	1241	3·7	1825	7·3
6 Tu	0127	3·2	0723	7·1	1359	3·3	1942	7·6
7 W	0233	2·8	0825	7·6	1456	2·9	2037	8·1
8 Th	0324	2·3	0910	8·1	1541	2·4	2119	8·6
9 F	0403	1·9	0946	8·5	1619	2·0	2156	8·9
10 Sa	0438	1·6	1019	8·8	1652	1·7	2230	9·1
11 Su	0511	1·4	1048	9·0	1725	1·5	○ 2302	9·3
12 M	0543	1·3	1118	9·2	1757	1·4	2333	9·3
13 Tu	0615	1·2	1149	9·2	1832	1·4		
14 W	0005	9·3	0648	1·3	1221	9·2	1906	1·5
15 Th	0039	9·2	0721	1·5	1253	9·1	1942	1·7
16 F	0114	9·0	0755	1·8	1330	8·9	2020	2·0
17 Sa	0155	8·6	0832	2·2	1413	8·5	2104	2·3
18 Su	0244	8·2	0918	2·6	1507	8·1	2202	2·6
19 M	0346	7·8	1020	3·0	1617	7·8	☾ 2319	2·8
20 Tu	0508	7·6	1144	3·1	1743	7·8		
21 W	0046	2·5	0634	7·8	1312	2·8	1903	8·2
22 Th	0202	2·0	0747	8·3	1425	2·2	2009	8·7
23 F	0305	1·5	0846	8·8	1524	1·7	2105	9·2
24 Sa	0402	1·0	0935	9·3	1617	1·2	2155	9·6
25 Su	0449	0·7	1020	9·6	1705	0·9	● 2240	9·8
26 M	0534	0·6	1104	9·8	1749	0·8	2323	9·9
27 Tu	0615	0·7	1144	9·7	1831	0·8		
28 W	0005	9·7	0653	0·9	1224	9·6	1912	1·0
29 Th	0046	9·3	0731	1·3	1303	9·3	1951	1·4
30 F	0126	8·9	0808	1·8	1342	8·9	2032	1·9
31 Sa	0206	8·4	0844	2·4	1425	8·4	2114	2·4

NOVEMBER

Day	Time	m	Time	m	Time	m	Time	m
1 Su	0253	7·8	0925	3·0	1514	8·0	2204	2·9
2 M	0348	7·3	1020	3·4	1614	7·6	☽ 2311	3·2
3 Tu	0458	7·0	1137	3·7	1726	7·3		
4 W	0025	3·2	0621	7·0	1259	3·6	1842	7·5
5 Th	0134	3·0	0731	7·3	1402	3·2	1945	7·8
6 F	0229	2·6	0823	7·8	1453	2·8	2034	8·2
7 Sa	0315	2·2	0904	8·2	1536	2·3	2117	8·6
8 Su	0357	1·9	0941	8·6	1616	2·0	2155	8·9
9 M	0435	1·7	1014	8·9	1654	1·7	2230	9·1
10 Tu	0512	1·5	1048	9·1	1733	1·5	○ 2306	9·2
11 W	0549	1·4	1123	9·3	1811	1·4	2343	9·3
12 Th	0627	1·3	1200	9·3	1850	1·4		
13 F	0022	9·3	0703	1·4	1239	9·3	1931	1·5
14 Sa	0103	9·1	0742	1·7	1321	9·1	2015	1·7
15 Su	0148	8·8	0823	2·0	1408	8·8	2103	1·9
16 M	0240	8·5	0912	2·3	1501	8·5	2159	2·1
17 Tu	0341	8·1	1012	2·6	1606	8·3	☾ 2305	2·3
18 W	0451	7·9	1123	2·7	1718	8·2		
19 Th	0019	2·2	0605	7·9	1241	2·6	1832	8·3
20 F	0131	2·0	0716	8·2	1352	2·3	1940	8·6
21 Sa	0236	1·7	0818	8·6	1457	1·9	2040	8·9
22 Su	0334	1·4	0911	8·9	1553	1·6	2134	9·2
23 M	0426	1·2	1000	9·2	1644	1·3	2221	9·3
24 Tu	0511	1·1	1044	9·4	1730	1·2	● 2306	9·3
25 W	0553	1·1	1126	9·5	1814	1·2	2349	9·2
26 Th	0632	1·3	1207	9·4	1855	1·3		
27 F	0029	9·0	0709	1·5	1245	9·2	1934	1·5
28 Sa	0109	8·8	0745	1·9	1324	9·0	2012	1·8
29 Su	0147	8·4	0819	2·3	1402	8·7	2050	2·2
30 M	0227	8·1	0856	2·6	1446	8·3	2131	2·5

DECEMBER

Day	Time	m	Time	m	Time	m	Time	m
1 Tu	0311	7·7	0936	3·0	1532	7·9	2216	2·8
2 W	0403	7·4	1028	3·3	1628	7·6	☽ 2312	3·0
3 Th	0505	7·1	1136	3·5	1730	7·5		
4 F	0018	3·1	0614	7·1	1250	3·4	1838	7·5
5 Sa	0124	2·9	0720	7·4	1355	3·1	1940	7·8
6 Su	0222	2·6	0815	7·8	1450	2·7	2032	8·1
7 M	0314	2·3	0901	8·2	1541	2·3	2118	8·5
8 Tu	0400	2·0	0943	8·6	1627	1·9	2202	8·8
9 W	0445	1·7	1024	9·0	1712	1·6	○ 2244	9·1
10 Th	0527	1·4	1105	9·3	1756	1·3	2327	9·3
11 F	0610	1·3	1146	9·5	1841	1·1		
12 Sa	0011	9·4	0652	1·2	1229	9·5	1926	1·1
13 Su	0056	9·3	0735	1·3	1314	9·5	2012	1·1
14 M	0142	9·2	0819	1·5	1402	9·3	2058	1·3
15 Tu	0232	8·9	0905	1·7	1453	9·1	2149	1·5
16 W	0325	8·6	0957	2·0	1548	8·8	☾ 2244	1·8
17 Th	0424	8·3	1057	2·3	1649	8·5	2347	2·0
18 F	0532	8·0	1205	2·5	1758	8·3		
19 Sa	0056	2·1	0642	8·0	1320	2·5	1910	8·2
20 Su	0206	2·1	0751	8·2	1432	2·3	2018	8·4
21 M	0310	1·9	0851	8·5	1535	2·0	2118	8·6
22 Tu	0406	1·8	0945	8·8	1631	1·7	2210	8·8
23 W	0455	1·6	1031	9·1	1720	1·5	2257	8·9
24 Th	0537	1·5	1115	9·2	1804	1·4	● 2339	8·9
25 F	0617	1·5	1154	9·3	1843	1·4		
26 Sa	0017	8·9	0652	1·6	1231	9·2	1920	1·5
27 Su	0052	8·8	0726	1·7	1306	9·1	1952	1·6
28 M	0126	8·6	0757	1·9	1341	8·9	2025	1·8
29 Tu	0201	8·4	0827	2·2	1416	8·7	2057	2·0
30 W	0236	8·1	0903	2·5	1454	8·4	2132	2·3
31 Th	0315	7·8	0941	2·8	1536	8·0	2213	2·6

Chart Datum: 4.93 metres below Ordnance Datum (Newlyn)

LIVERPOOL *continued*

caution and local knowledge is needed. R Alt is only available HW∓2 and only suitable for shallow draught (1·2m) boats. See 10·10·22.

LIGHTS AND MARKS
The entrance to the Mersey is marked by the Bar Lanby Fl 5s 12m 21M, Horn 20s, Racon.

RADIO TELEPHONE
Call: *Mersey Radio* (Port of Liverpool Building) VHF Ch **12** 16; 09 12 18 19 22 (H24). Traffic movements, local navigational warnings and weather reports broadcast on Ch 09 at 3h and 2h before HW. Local navigational and gale warnings broadcast on receipt on Ch 12, and on Ch 09 every 4h commencing 0000 local time. Alfred Dock Ch 05 (H24). Tranmere Stages Ch 19 (H24). Garston Dock Ch 20 (H24). Waterloo Dock Ch 20 (H24). Langton Dock Ch 21 (H24). Gladstone Dock Ch 05 (H24). Eastham Locks (Manchester Ship Canal) Ch 07 14 (H24). Latchford Locks (Manchester Ship Canal) Ch 14 20 (H24). Weaver Navigation. Weston Point Dock, call *Weston Point* Ch 14; 71 73. Yachts entering or leaving Weaver Navigation should call on Ch 73 when approaching locks. Liverpool Marina Ch **80** M.

TELEPHONE (051)
Hr Mr 200 4124; MRSC 931 3341; # (051) 933 7075; Marinecall 0898 500 461; Police 709 6010; Ⓗ 709 0141.

FACILITIES
EC Wednesday; **Liverpool Marina** (500) ☎ 708 5228. 0600-2130 Mar to Oct. Min depth 3·5m. Slip, BH, AC, FW, C (60 ton), Bar, ◙, R, CH, V; Ent via Brunswick Dock lock; Access HW∓2; **Albert Dock** Access HW−2 to HW (VHF Ch 37 when entrance manned) AB, FW, AC; **West Kirby SC** ☎ 625 5579, Slip, M (in Dee Est), L, FW, C (30 ton), AB (at HW), Bar; **Blundellsands SC** ☎ 929 2101; Slip, L (at HW), FW, Bar; **Hoylake SC** ☎ 632 2616, Slip, M, FW, Bar; **Royal Mersey YC** ☎ 645 3204, Slip, M, P, D, L, FW, R, Bar; **Perrys Yacht Centre** ☎ 647 5751, CH; **Davey Jones Marine** ☎ 263 4700, ME, El, CH; **Ship Shape** ☎ 928 4471, Sh, CH; **J. Sewill** ☎ 207 2777, ACA, Nautical Instruments; **Dubois – Phillips and McCallum** ☎ 236 2776, CH, ACA; **MGR Services** ☎ 653 3437, Ⓔ; **Robins Marine** ☎ 709 5431, Ⓔ. **Town** ✉; Ⓑ; ⇌; ✈.
Note: Access to East Coast via Leeds and Liverpool Canal (British Waterways Board). Liverpool to Goole 161 miles, 103 locks. Maximum draught 3ft, air draught 8ft, beam 13ft 6in, length 60ft.

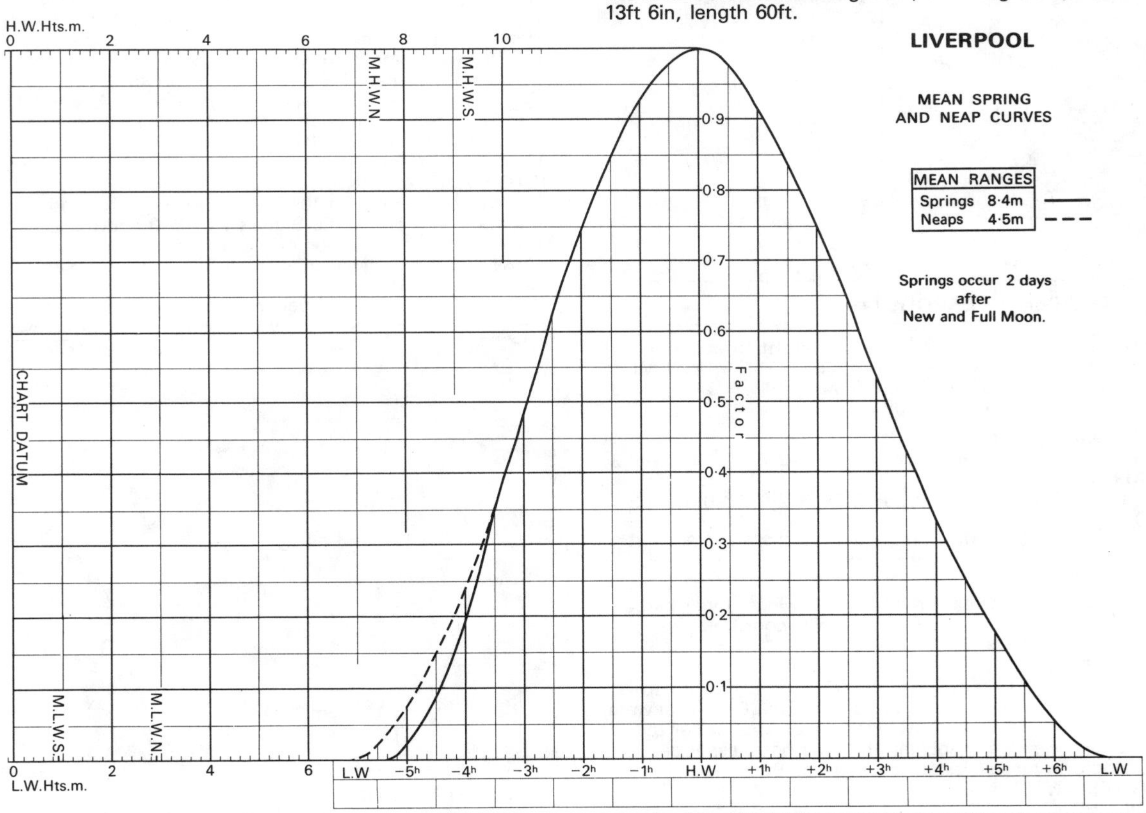
LIVERPOOL
MEAN SPRING AND NEAP CURVES
MEAN RANGES
Springs 8·4m
Neaps 4·5m
Springs occur 2 days after New and Full Moon.
H.W.Hts.m.
0
2
4
6
8
10
M.H.W.N.
M.H.W.S.
CHART DATUM
M.L.W.S.
M.L.W.N.
L.W.Hts.m.
Factor
0·9
0·8
0·7
0·6
0·5
0·4
0·3
0·2
0·1
L.W
−5h
−4h
−3h
−2h
−1h
H.W
+1h
+2h
+3h
+4h
+5h
+6h
L.W

ISLE OF MAN 10-10-12

CHARTS
Admiralty 2696, 2094

The Isle of Man is one of the British Islands, set in the Irish Sea almost equidistant from England, Scotland and Ireland but it is not part of the United Kingdom. It has a considerable degree of self-government. The island comes under the same customs umbrella as the rest of the United Kingdom, so no customs formalities are necessary on landing or returning to UK ports.
Manx harbours are administered by the Isle of Man Government and the lights are maintained by the Commissioners of Northern Lighthouses in Scotland.
Besides the four main harbours given below, there are good anchorages at Castletown in the SE, Laxey Bay in the E and Port Erin in the SW – see 10·10·22. There are also good anchorages in Derby Haven in the SE; this is a rather bleak area and the inner harbour dries. Most of the harbours are on the E and S sides but a visit to the W coast with its characteristic cliffs is worth while. For passage through Calf Sound, see 10·10·5.
When contact with local Harbour Masters cannot be established on VHF, vessels should call *Douglas Radio* Ch 16 12 for urgent messages or other information. Since the closure of MRSC Ramsey, calls have to be made to Liverpool but there is no loss of radio coverage on VHF as the existing Snaefell (IoM) aerial has been retained and linked to Liverpool by land line. Weather forecasts can be obtained from local radio programmes or by telephone from the Met Office Ronaldsway (0624) 823313 between 0630 and 2030 (LT). Visitors are recommended to obtain *Sailing directions, tidal streams and anchorages of the Isle of Man* produced by the Manx Sailing and Cruising Club in Ramsey, Tel. (0624) 813494.

PORT ST MARY 10-10-13

Isle of Man

CHARTS
Admiralty 2696, 2094; Imray C62, Y70; OS 95

TIDES
+0020 Dover; ML 3·2; Duration 0605; Zone 0 (GMT).

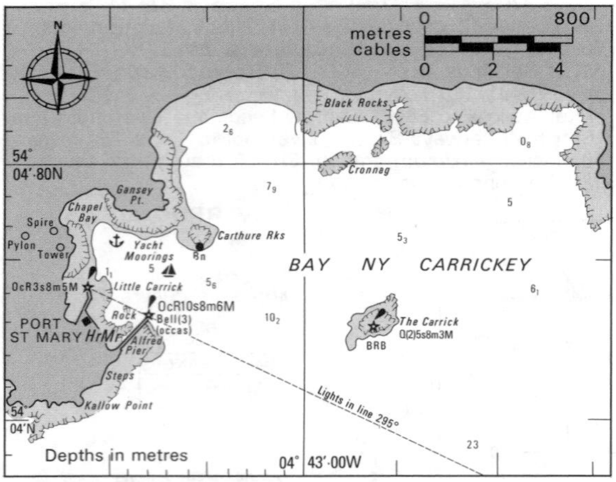

metres
cables
0
800
2
4
N
54°
04'·80N
Black Rocks
Cronnag
Gansey Pt.
Chapel Bay
Spire
Pylon
Tower
Yacht Moorings
Carthure Rks
BAY NY CARRICKEY
OcR3s8m5M
Little Carrick
OcR10s8m6M
Bell(3) (occas)
Rock
PORT ST MARY
HrMr
Alfred Pier
The Carrick
Q(2)5s8m3M
BRB
Steps
Kallow Point
Lights in line 295°
54°
04'N
Depths in metres
04° 43'·00W

Standard Port LIVERPOOL (⟵)

Times				Height (metres)			
HW		LW		MHWS	MHWN	MLWN	MLWS
0000	0600	0200	0700	9·3	7·4	2·9	0·9
1200	1800	1400	1900				
Differences PORT ST MARY							
+0005	+0015	−0010	−0030	−3·4	−2·7	−1·2	−0·3
CALF SOUND							
+0005	+0005	−0015	−0025	−3·2	−2·6	−0·9	−0·3
PORT ERIN							
−0005	+0015	−0010	−0050	−4·1	−3·2	−1·3	−0·5

SHELTER
Very good shelter except in E or SE winds. Inner harbour dries out. Anchorages off Gansey Pt; poor holding. Visitors moorings.

NAVIGATION
Waypoint 54°03'·60N 04°43'·00W, 150°/330° from/to breakwater Lt, 0·84M. Carrick Rock, 7 ca E of breakwater Q(2) 5s 6m 3M. Rock outcrops to E of breakwater to 2 ca offshore. Beware of lobster and crab pots, especially offshore from Calf Island to Langness Pt.

LIGHTS AND MARKS
Alfred Pier, head Oc R 10s 8m 6M; W Tr, R band. Inner Pier, head Oc R 3s 8m 5M; W Tr, R band. These two Lts in line 295° lead clear S of The Carrick.

RADIO TELEPHONE
Call: *Port St Mary Harbour* VHF Ch 16; 12 (0830-1630 LT when manned or through Douglas Harbour Radio).

TELEPHONE (0624)
Hr Mr 833206; MRSC Liverpool 931 3341; Weather 823313; # 74321; Marinecall 16622; Police 822222; Dr 832281.

FACILITIES
EC Thursday; **Breakwater** Slip, D (by road tanker), L, FW, C (20 ton mobile), AB; **Inner Harbour** Slip, D, L, FW, C (20 ton mobile), AB; **Bay** M, L; **Ballasalla Marine & Auto Eng** ☎ 822715, ME; **Island Boat Services** ☎ 832073 ME, SM; **Isle of Man YC** ☎ 832088, FW, Bar. **Town** CH, V, R, Bar. ✉; Ⓑ; ⇌ (bus to Douglas, ferry to Heysham); ✈ (I.o.M.).

DOUGLAS 10-10-14

Isle of Man

CHARTS
Admiralty 2696, 2094; Imray C62, Y70; OS 95

TIDES
+0009 Dover; ML 3·8; Duration 0600; Zone 0 (GMT).

Standard Port LIVERPOOL (⟵)

Times				Height (metres)			
HW		LW		MHWS	MHWN	MLWN	MLWS
0000	0600	0200	0700	9·3	7·4	2·9	0·9
1200	1800	1400	1900				
Differences DOUGLAS							
−0004	−0004	−0022	−0032	−2·4	−2·0	−0·5	−0·1

SHELTER
Shelter is good except with north-easterly winds. Very heavy seas run in during NE gales. The Harbour Board provides one B can buoy for visitors, between Lifeboat slip and Fort Anne Jetty, and a mooring pontoon at inner end of Battery Pier.

NAVIGATION
Waypoint 54°09'·00N 04°27'·60W, 049°/229° from/to front Ldg Lt, 0·47M. Inner harbour dries; access HW ∓2. It becomes very full in summer. There is no bar. Beware swing bridge and also concrete step at end of dredged area (diamond mark on King Edward pier). SE and SW corners of linkspan, SE of pier, marked with 2 FG (vert). Concrete dolphin at seaward end of Princess Alexandra Pier 2FR (vert). Approach to N of No 1 buoy and await port entry signal. If available call on VHF Ch 12. Keep clear of larger vessels and ferries.

LIGHTS AND MARKS
Ldg Lts 229°, both Oc 10s 9/12m 5M, synchronised. International Port Traffic Signals Nos 2, 3 and 5 shown from mast at head of Victoria Pier. Signals below are shown from near head of Victoria Pier in panels with FlY Lts in top corners.

X (red)	Unspecified vessels may not proceed
→ (white)	Vessels may proceed in direction shown

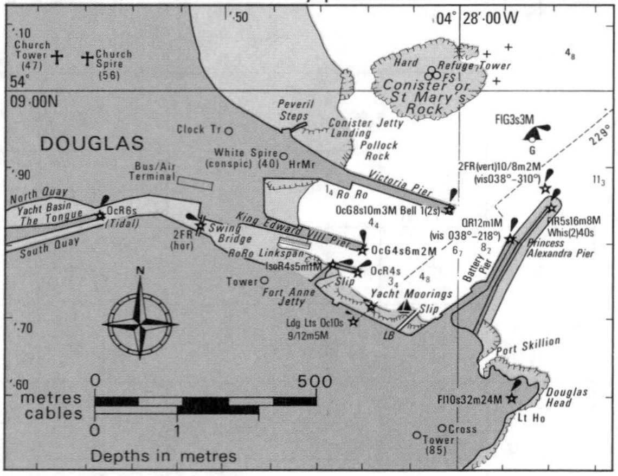

04° 28'·00W
Church Tower (47)
Church Spire (56)
54°
09·00N
Hard
Refuge Tower
FS
Conister or St Mary's Rock
Peveril Steps
Conister Jetty Landing
Pollock Rock
Clock Tr
DOUGLAS
White Spire (conspic) (40)
HrMr
Bus/Air Terminal
Victoria Pier
Fl G3s3M
229°
North Quay
Yacht Basin
The Tongue
OcR6s (Tidal)
South Quay
2FR (hor)
Swing Bridge
King Edward VIII Pier
Ro Ro
OcG8s10m3M Bell 1(2s)
2FR(vert)10/8m2M (vis038°-310°)
QR12m1M (vis 038°-218°)
FlR5s16m8M Whis(2)40s
Princess Alexandra Pier
Battery Pier
RoRo Linkspan
OcG4s6m2M
IsoR4s5m1M
OcR4s
Tower
Fort Anne Jetty
Slip
Yacht Moorings
Ldg Lts Oc10s 9/12m5M
LB
Port Skillion
metres
cables
0
500
1
Fl10s32m24M
Douglas Head
Lt Ho
Cross Tower (85)
Depths in metres

RADIO TELEPHONE
VHF Ch 16; 12 (H24). Broadcasts Ch 12 at 0133, 0533, 0733, 0933, 1333, 1733 and 2133 giving navigational warnings for IoM coastal waters.

TELEPHONE (0624)
Hr Mr 623813; MRSC Liverpool 931 3341; # 674321; Marinecall 0898 500 461; Police 631212; Dr 673661.

FACILITIES
EC Thursday; **Outer Harbour** ☎ 623813, Slip, M, P, D, L, FW, ME, El, Sh, C (10, 5 ton), CH; **Inner Harbour (N & S Quays)** ☎ 623813, Slip, M (N & S Quays), P, D, L, FW, ME, El, Sh, C, CH, AB; **Manx Marine** ☎ 674842, CH, ACA; **Auto Electrical Centre** ☎ 628123, El, Diving; **Douglas Motor Boat & Sailing Club** ☎ 673965, Bar, Slip, L; **Rileys** ☎ 675166, Gas, Gaz, Kos. **Town** V, R, Bar. ✉; Ⓑ; ⇌ (ferry to Heysham; also in summer to Belfast and Liverpool); ✈ (I.o.M.).

RAMSEY 10-10-15

Isle of Man

CHARTS
Admiralty 2696, 2094; Imray C62, Y70; OS 95

TIDES
+0020 Dover; ML 4·0; Duration 0545; Zone 0 (GMT).

Standard Port LIVERPOOL (←)

Times				Height (metres)			
HW		LW		MHWS	MHWN	MLWN	MLWS
0000	0600	0200	0700	9·3	7·4	2·9	0·9
1200	1800	1400	1900				
Differences RAMSEY							
+0005	+0015	−0005	−0015	−1·7	−1·5	−0·6	+0·1

SHELTER
Very good except in strong winds between NE and SE, through E. The harbour dries. Access HW−2½ to HW+2. Berth alongside SW quay — instructions given by Hr Mr as vessels enter between piers. The Manx S.C. has visitors moorings N of Queens Pier.

NAVIGATION
Waypoint 54°19′·40N 04°21′·60W, 095°/275° from/to entrance, 0·48M. The foreshore dries out 100m to seaward of the pier heads. Entrance to the harbour is only permitted from HW−2½ to HW+2.

LIGHTS AND MARKS
There are no leading lights or marks. Lights as shown on chartlet. There is FR Lt in centre of swing bridge.

RADIO TELEPHONE
VHF Ch 16; 12 (0830-1630 LT when manned or through Douglas Harbour Radio).

TELEPHONE (0624)
Hr Mr 812245; MRSC Liverpool (051) 931 3341; # 674321; Marinecall 0898 500 461; Police 812234; Dr 813881; Ⓗ 813254.

FACILITIES
EC Wednesday; **Entrance Channel** L, FW, AB; C*, **North Quay** L, FW, ME, El, Sh, AB; **East Quay** ☎ 812245, L, FW, ME, El, Sh, AB; **West Quay** Slip (Grid), L, FW, ME, El, AB, ⊡; **Shipyard Quay** Slip, ME, El, Sh; **Old Harbour** Slip, M, L, ME, AB; **Calor Manx Gas** ☎ 813143, Gas; **Booth W. Kelly** ☎ 812322, ME; **Bevan** ☎ 812583, El, Ⓔ; **Manx Sailing and Cruising Club** ☎ 813494, Bar, D, P, Ⓔ, FW, L, ⊡, Slip, V; **Town** P, D, V, R, Gas, Gaz, Kos, Bar, ✉; Ⓑ; ⇌ (bus to Douglas, ferry to Heysham); ✈ (I.o.M.).
Fuels from local suppliers but none situated on harbour estate.
*Various mobile cranes on hire from suppliers through Douglas.

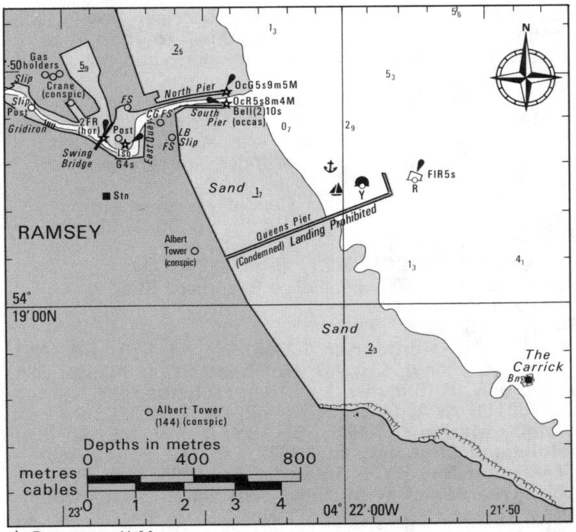
RAMSEY
Gas holders
Crane (conspic)
Slip
Post
Gridiron
2FR (hor)
Swing Bridge
Iso G4s
North Pier
South Pier
OcG5s9m5M
OcR5s8m4M
Bell(2)10s (occas)
East Quay
LB Slip
Stn
Sand
Queens Pier (Condemned) Landing Prohibited
FIR5s
Albert Tower (conspic)
Albert Tower (144) (conspic)
The Carrick
54° 19′00N
04° 22′·00W
21′·50
Depths in metres
metres
cables

Report to HrMr

PEEL 10-10-16

Isle of Man

CHARTS
Admiralty 2696, 2094; Imray C62, Y70; OS 95

TIDES
+0005 Dover; ML 2·9; Duration 0540; Zone 0 (GMT).

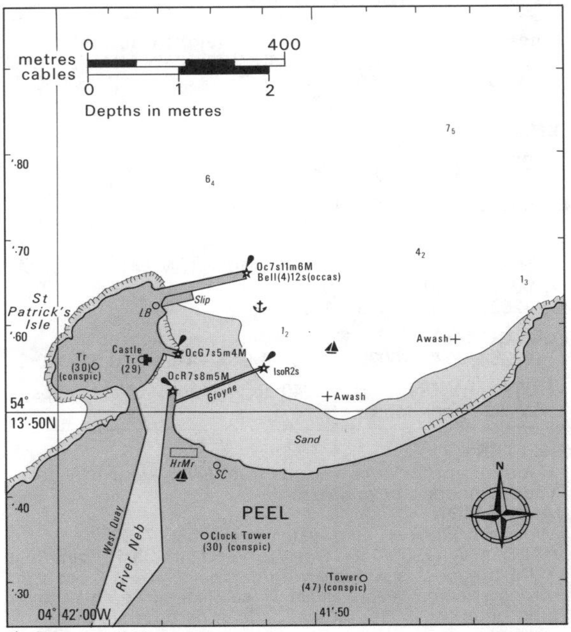
metres
cables
Depths in metres
Oc7s11m6M
Bell(4)12s(occas)
St Patrick's Isle
Slip
LB
Castle Tr (29)
Tr (30) (conspic)
OcG7s5m4M
OcR7s8m5M
IsoR2s
Groyne
Awash
Sand
HrMr
SC
PEEL
Clock Tower (30) (conspic)
Tower (47) (conspic)
West Quay
River Neb
54° 13′·50N
04° 42′·00W
41′·50

Report to HrMr

Standard Port LIVERPOOL (←)

Times				Height (metres)			
HW		LW		MHWS	MHWN	MLWN	MLWS
0000	0600	0200	0700	9·3	7·4	2·9	0·9
1200	1800	1400	1900				
Differences PEEL							
−0015	+0010	0000	−0010	−4·0	−3·2	−1·4	−0·4

SHELTER
Good shelter except in strong NW to NE winds. Inner harbour has water HW∓3; bottom is flat sand.

NAVIGATION
Waypoint 54°14′·00N 04°41′·20W, 037°/217° from/to breakwater Lt, 0·42M. Entry should not be attempted in strong NW to NE winds. Beware groyne running ENE from mouth of River Neb submerged at half tide. Harbour dries out and is very crowded from June to October.

LIGHTS AND MARKS
There are no leading marks or lights. Lt on end of groyne, Iso R 2s. Pier head Oc R 7s 8m 5M; vis 156°-249°. Breakwater Oc 7s 11m 6M.

RADIO TELEPHONE
VHF Ch 16; 12 (0830-1630 LT when manned or through Douglas Harbour Radio).

TELEPHONE (0624)
Hr Mr 842338; MRSC Liverpool 931 3341; # 674321; Weather 16622; Marinecall 0898 500 461; Police 842208; Dr 843636.

FACILITIES
EC Thursday; **Breakwater** Slip, L, FW, ME, El, Sh, C (7½ ton mobile), AB; **Inner Pier** ☎ 842338, L, FW, ME, El, Sh, AB; **East Quay** Slip, L, FW, ME, El, C (7½ ton mobile), AB; **West Quay** L, FW, ME, El, Sh, Slip, C (7½ ton mobile), AB; **J. D. Faulkner** ☎ 842296, ME, D (cans); **Manx Gas Service Centre** ☎ 842281, Gas; **West Marine** ☎ 842604, BY, CH, ME; **Manx Marine** ☎ 674842, CH, ACA; **Peel Sailing and Cruising Club** ☎ 842390, P and D (cans), R, ⊡, Bar; **T and J Autos** ☎ 842096, ME; **D.P. Oils, Total I.o.M.** ☎ 844000 P, D; **Town** P and D (cans), CH, V, R, Bar, ✉; Ⓑ; ⇌ (bus to Douglas, ferry to Heysham); ✈ (I.o.M.).

10

CONWY 10-10-17

Gwynedd

CHARTS
Admiralty 1978, 1977; Imray C61; OS 115

TIDES
−0015 Dover; ML 4·3; Duration 0545; Zone 0 (GMT).

Standard Port HOLYHEAD (→)

Times				Height (metres)			
HW		LW		MHWS	MHWN	MLWN	MLWS
0000	0600	0500	1100	5·7	4·5	2·0	0·7
1200	1800	1700	2300				
Differences CONWY							
+0020	+0020	No data	+0050	+2·1	+1·6	+0·3	No data

Standard Port LIVERPOOL (←)

Times				Height (metres)			
HW		LW		MHWS	MHWN	MLWN	MLWS
0000	0600	0200	0700	9·3	7·4	2·9	0·9
1200	1800	1400	1900				
LLANDUDNO							
−0035	−0025	−0025	−0035	−1·9	−1·5	−0·5	−0·2

NOTE: HW Conwy is −0040 springs and −0020 neaps HW Liverpool approx.

SHELTER
Good except for strong winds from NW. Ask Hr Mr for vacant mooring or pontoon.

NAVIGATION
Waypoint Fairway (safe water) buoy, 53°17′·90N 03°55′·47W, 290°/110° from/to Penmaen-bach Point, 1·7M. Channel is variable with depths of about 0·5m and strong stream. Keep at least ¼ ca clear of Perch Lt to stbd on entry. Many mussel beds in harbour entrance. Beware unlit moorings. Entry recommended during daylight only and between HW−2 and HW. Entry via 'Inshore Passage' not recommended. Speed limit from the Perch Lt to ½ M above bridges is 10 kn.
Vessels must proceed only within the buoyed channel.
Vessels must check with harbour authorities before arrival.

LIGHTS AND MARKS
None of the channel marks has either light or bell except the most inshore one, Fl WR 5s 5m 2M; W 076°-088°, R 088°-171°; W 171°-319°, R 319°-076°. The 'Inshore Passage' to E of Perch Lt can be used for vessels up to 2m draught, Neaps HW ∓1, Springs HW ∓3, passing inshore of Or liferaft (on station Apl-Oct).

RADIO TELEPHONE
VHF Ch 16; 06 08 **12** 14 72 (Apl-Sept 0900-1700. Oct-Mar Mon-Fri 0900-1700 LT). N Wales Cruising Club Ch **80** M Llanddulas Ch 16; 14 (0900−1230, 1400-1700 LT).

TELEPHONE (0492)
Hr Mr 596253; MRSC Holyhead 762051; ⊞ (0407) 2336; Marinecall 0898 500 460; Police 2222; Dr 593385.

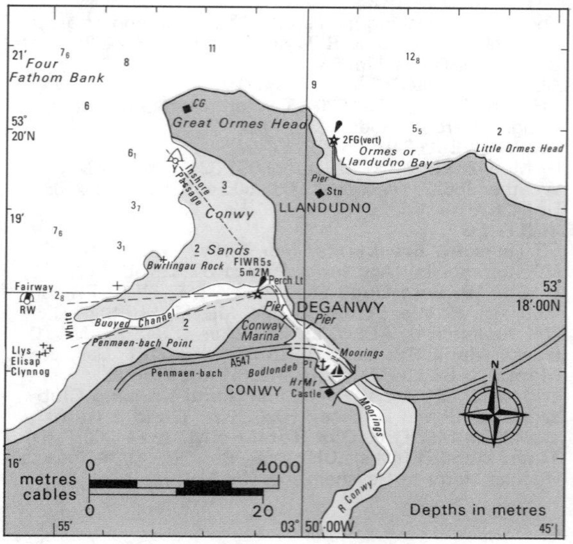

Four Fathom Bank
Great Ormes Head
2FG(vert)
Ormes or Llandudno Bay
Little Ormes Head
Pier
Stn
Inshore Passage
Conwy
LLANDUDNO
Sands
Bwrlingau Rock
FlWR5s 5m2M
Perch Lt
Fairway RW
White
Buoyed Channel
Pier
DEGANWY
Pier
Conwy Marina
Penmaen-bach Point
Llys Elisap
Clynnog
Penmaen-bach
A547
Bodlondeb Pt
CONWY
Hr Mr
Castle
Moorings
R Conwy
N
53° 18′·00N
03° 50′·00W
metres 0 4000
cables 0 20
Depths in metres

FACILITIES
EC Wednesday; **Conwy Marina** (450) (due to open April 1992) CH, YC, R, Bar, D, BH; **Conwy Quay Harbour** ☎ 596253, (dries − limited stay for loading, watering, etc.), M, D, L, FW, AB (up to 40 ft); **Conwy Harbour Boat Shop** ☎ 592366, D, ME, Gas, Gaz, CH; **Conwy River Boatyard** ☎ 592489, M, ME, El, Slip, Gas, Gaz, Sh; **Deganwy Dock** (dries), L, FW, C (mobile), AB; **Sailtronic Marine** ☎ Glanconwy 536, El, Ⓔ; **Deganwy Entrance** Slip, L; **Beacons** Slip, L; **Conwy YC** ☎ 83690, Slip, M, L, FW, R, Bar; **N Wales Cruising Club** ☎ 593481, M, L, FW, AB, Bar; **Town** P and D (in cans), V, R, Bar. ✉; Ⓑ; ⇌; ✈ (Liverpool).

HOLYHEAD 10-10-18

Gwynedd

CHARTS
Admiralty 2011, 1413, 1970; Imray C61; OS 114

TIDES
−0035 Dover; ML 3·2; Duration 0615; Zone 0 (GMT).

Standard Port HOLYHEAD (→)

Times				Height (metres)			
HW		LW		MHWS	MHWN	MLWN	MLWS
0000	0600	0500	1100	5·7	4·5	2·0	0·7
1200	1800	1700	2300				
Differences AMLWCH							
+0020	+0010	+0035	+0025	+1·6	+1·3	+0·5	+0·2
PORTH TRECASTEL							
−0045	−0025	−0005	−0015	−0·6	−0·6	0·0	0·0

Holyhead is a Standard Port and tidal predictions for each day of the year are given below.

SHELTER
Very good. Anchor in New Harbour only. NE winds cause a slight sea.

NAVIGATION
Waypoint 53°20′·00N 04°36′·47W, 019°/199° from/to Admiralty Pier Old Lt Ho, 1·2M. Cliperau Rks (R can bell buoy) Fl (4) R 15s. Beware ferries, especially crossing the entrance to New Harbour passing down to go to Inner Harbour. Also beware large unlit mooring buoys in NW part of harbour.

LIGHTS AND MARKS
Entrance between Cliperau Rks and breakwater lighthouse.
Entry signals:- R Lt or R Flag − Inner harbour closed.
2R Lts or 2R Flags − Old and Inner harbours blocked.

RADIO TELEPHONE
VHF Ch 16 14 (H24). Other station: Anglesey Marine Terminal (Amlwch) Ch 10 12 16 19. SC Ch 80 M.

TELEPHONE (0407)
Hr Mr 2304; MRSC 762051; ⊞ (0407) 762714; Marinecall 0898 500 460; Police Beaumaris 810222; Dr via MRSC.

FACILITIES
EC Tuesday; **Harbour** ☎ 762304, Slip, M, D, L, FW, ME, El, Sh, C (many), CH, AB; **Holyhead SC** ☎ 762526, Slip, M, L, FW, R (Summer only), Bar; **Holyhead BY** ☎ 760111, ACA, FW, CH, D, ME, El, Sh, C (20 ton); **Trinity Marine** ☎ 763855, BH, BY, D, FW, ME, Sh, Slip; **Holyhead Chandlery** ☎ 763632, CH, ME, El, Ⓔ, ACA; **Trearddur Bay BY** ☎ Trearddur Bay 860501, D, FW, Sh, CH; **Trearddur Bay** M (Small craft only), L; **Trearddur Bay Village** P, V, R, Bar. **Town** P, V, R, Bar, ⊡. ✉; Ⓑ; ⇌; ✈ (Liverpool). Ferry to Dun Laoghaire.

HOLYHEAD *continued*

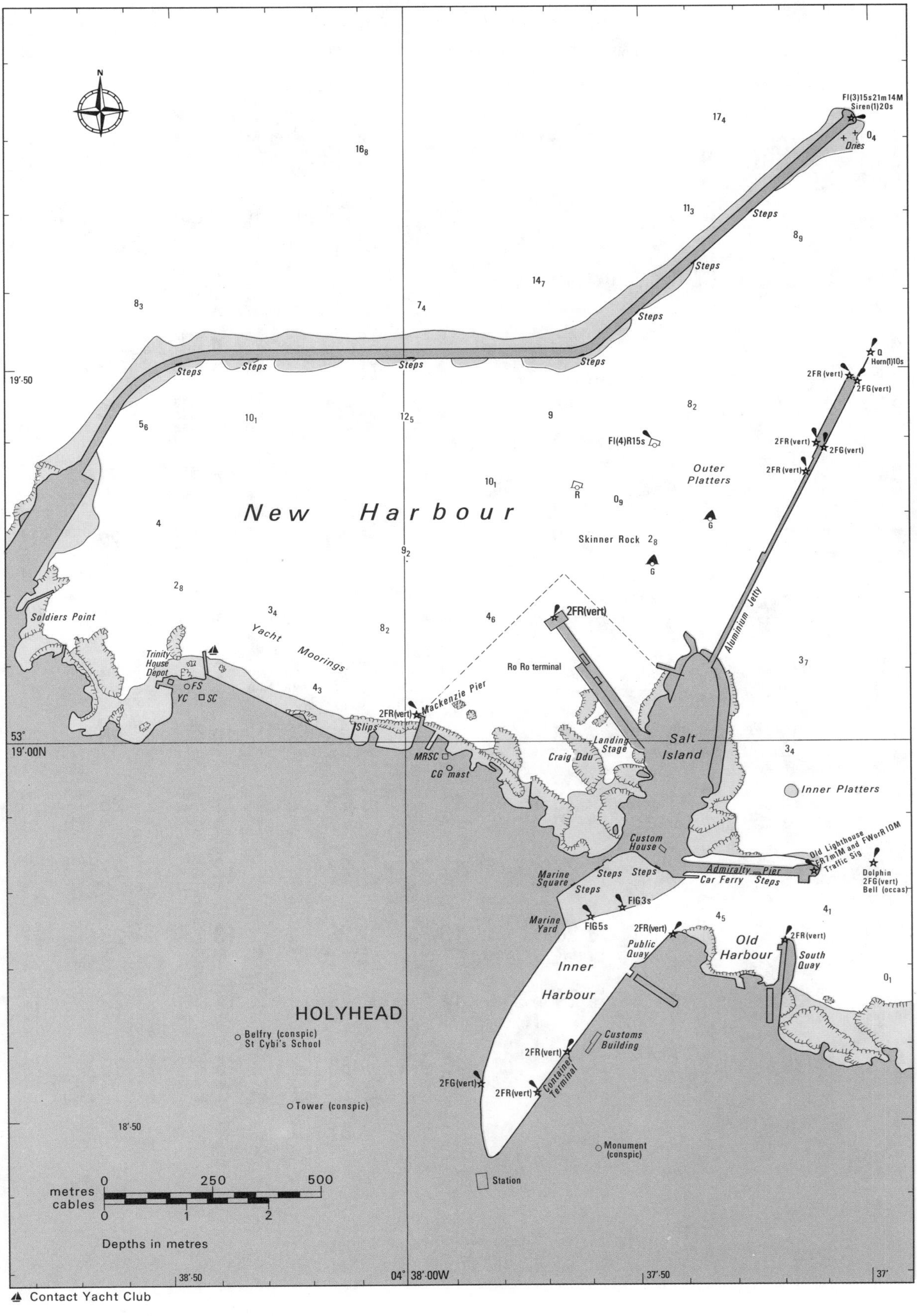
N
Fl(3)15s21m14M
Siren(1)20s
Dries
Steps
New Harbour
Q
Horn(1)10s
2FR(vert)
2FG(vert)
Fl(4)R15s
R
G
Outer Platters
Skinner Rock
Aluminium Jetty
Soldiers Point
Trinity House Depot
FS
YC
SC
Yacht Moorings
Mackenzie Pier
Slips
Ro Ro terminal
MRSC
CG mast
Craig Ddu
Landing Stage
Salt Island
Inner Platters
Custom House
Old Lighthouse
FR7m1M and FWorR10M
Traffic Sig
Dolphin
2FG(vert)
Bell (occas)
Marine Square
Admiralty Pier
Car Ferry
Marine Yard
FlG3s
FlG5s
Public Quay
Inner Harbour
Old Harbour
South Quay
HOLYHEAD
Belfry (conspic)
St Cybi's School
Customs Building
Container Terminal
Tower (conspic)
Monument (conspic)
Station
metres
cables
0
250
500
1
2
Depths in metres
19'·50
53°
19'·00N
18'·50
38'·50
04° 38'·00W
37'·50
37'

▲ Contact Yacht Club

WALES – HOLYHEAD

Lat 53°18′ N Long 4°38′ W

TIME ZONE UT(GMT)

For Summer Time add ONE hour in non-shaded areas

TIMES AND HEIGHTS OF HIGH AND LOW WATERS

YEAR **1992**

JANUARY

Date	Day	Time	m
1	W	0130 0749 1359 2016	1·7 4·8 1·7 4·8
2	Th	0225 0839 1453 2104	1·6 5·0 1·5 4·9
3	F	0310 0919 1536 2145	1·5 5·1 1·4 5·0
4	Sa ●	0349 0957 1614 2221	1·4 5·3 1·2 5·1
5	Su	0424 1031 1649 2255	1·3 5·4 1·1 5·1
6	M	0458 1105 1723 2329	1·2 5·5 1·1 5·1
7	Tu	0530 1137 1756	1·2 5·5 1·1
8	W	0001 0603 1211 1828	5·1 1·2 5·4 1·1
9	Th	0034 0636 1245 1902	5·0 1·3 5·4 1·2
10	F	0107 0712 1320 1937	4·9 1·4 5·2 1·3
11	Sa	0144 0749 1358 2016	4·8 1·6 5·1 1·5
12	Su	0225 0832 1442 2101	4·7 1·8 4·9 1·6
13	M ☽	0314 0924 1535 2156	4·6 2·0 4·7 1·8
14	Tu	0417 1028 1645 2306	4·5 2·1 4·6 1·9
15	W	0536 1147 1805	4·5 2·0 4·6
16	Th	0022 0650 1302 1917	1·8 4·6 1·8 4·8
17	F	0128 0754 1405 2020	1·6 4·9 1·4 5·1
18	Sa	0227 0847 1501 2114	1·3 5·3 1·0 5·3
19	Su ○	0318 0935 1552 2202	1·0 5·6 0·6 5·6
20	M	0407 1020 1640 2248	0·7 5·9 0·3 5·8
21	Tu	0454 1105 1727 2334	0·5 6·1 0·1 5·8
22	W	0539 1150 1812	0·4 6·1 0·1
23	Th	0019 0624 1236 1859	5·7 0·5 6·0 0·3
24	F	0106 0710 1321 1945	5·5 0·7 5·8 0·6
25	Sa	0152 0757 1409 2034	5·2 1·0 5·4 1·0
26	Su ☾	0242 0847 1503 2128	4·9 1·4 5·0 1·4
27	M	0339 0948 1607 2234	4·6 1·7 4·7 1·8
28	Tu	0449 1104 1729 2351	4·4 2·0 4·4 2·0
29	W	0612 1229 1859	4·4 2·1 4·3
30	Th	0107 0730 1345 2009	2·0 4·5 1·9 4·5
31	F	0211 0826 1443 2058	1·9 4·8 1·7 4·7

FEBRUARY

Date	Day	Time	m
1	Sa	0257 0908 1525 2136	1·7 5·0 1·4 4·8
2	Su	0336 0943 1600 2207	1·4 5·2 1·2 5·0
3	M ●	0409 1016 1631 2238	1·2 5·4 1·0 5·1
4	Tu	0440 1045 1701 2306	1·1 5·5 0·9 5·2
5	W	0509 1116 1732 2336	1·0 5·5 0·9 5·2
6	Th	0540 1147 1801	1·0 5·5 0·9
7	F	0005 0611 1218 1832	5·2 1·0 5·5 0·9
8	Sa	0038 0642 1252 1903	5·2 1·1 5·4 1·1
9	Su	0110 0717 1326 1938	5·1 1·3 5·3 1·2
10	M	0147 0755 1405 2019	4·9 1·5 5·1 1·4
11	Tu ☽	0229 0843 1453 2111	4·8 1·7 4·8 1·7
12	W	0325 0946 1602 2221	4·5 1·9 4·6 1·9
13	Th	0448 1112 1734 2353	4·4 2·0 4·5 2·0
14	F	0622 1241 1903	4·5 1·8 4·6
15	Sa	0112 0737 1352 2011	1·7 4·8 1·4 5·0
16	Su	0215 0833 1450 2104	1·4 5·2 0·9 5·3
17	M	0307 0921 1539 2149	0·9 5·6 0·5 5·6
18	Tu ○	0353 1004 1624 2231	0·6 5·9 0·2 5·8
19	W	0435 1047 1708 2313	0·3 6·1 0·0 5·8
20	Th	0519 1130 1750 2356	0·2 6·2 0·1 5·8
21	F	0601 1212 1832	0·3 6·0 0·3
22	Sa	0036 0643 1256 1914	5·6 0·5 5·8 0·6
23	Su	0119 0727 1340 1958	5·3 0·8 5·4 1·1
24	M	0204 0813 1427 2047	5·0 1·2 4·9 1·6
25	Tu ☾	0253 0908 1525 2148	4·7 1·7 4·5 2·0
26	W	0356 1023 1648 2311	4·4 2·1 4·2 2·3
27	Th	0526 1157 1836	4·2 2·2 4·1
28	F	0038 0702 1321 1952	2·3 4·3 2·0 4·3
29	Sa	0148 0802 1420 2039	2·1 4·6 1·7 4·5

MARCH

Date	Day	Time	m
1	Su	0236 0846 1501 2115	1·8 4·9 1·4 4·8
2	M	0314 0919 1535 2145	1·5 5·1 1·2 5·0
3	Tu	0345 0950 1604 2212	1·2 5·3 1·0 5·1
4	W ●	0414 1020 1633 2238	1·0 5·4 0·8 5·3
5	Th	0442 1049 1701 2306	0·9 5·5 0·8 5·3
6	F	0512 1119 1730 2337	0·8 5·6 0·7 5·4
7	Sa	0543 1151 1801	0·8 5·6 0·8
8	Su	0008 0615 1224 1834	5·3 0·9 5·5 0·9
9	M	0042 0650 1300 1909	5·2 1·0 5·3 1·1
10	Tu	0119 0731 1341 1951	5·1 1·2 5·1 1·4
11	W	0201 0820 1432 2044	4·9 1·5 4·8 1·7
12	Th ☽	0258 0925 1542 2157	4·6 1·7 4·5 2·0
13	F	0421 1054 1720 2333	4·4 1·8 4·4 2·0
14	Sa	0601 1224 1852	4·5 1·6 4·6
15	Su	0056 0719 1335 1957	1·7 4·8 1·2 4·9
16	M	0158 0815 1432 2047	1·3 5·2 0·8 5·3
17	Tu	0249 0901 1519 2129	0·9 5·6 0·4 5·5
18	W ○	0334 0945 1603 2209	0·6 5·9 0·2 5·7
19	Th	0414 1026 1644 2249	0·3 6·0 0·1 5·8
20	F	0457 1108 1725 2329	0·2 6·0 0·2 5·7
21	Sa	0537 1150 1805	0·3 5·8 0·4
22	Su	0010 0619 1232 1845	5·6 0·5 5·6 0·8
23	M	0050 0702 1314 1927	5·3 0·8 5·2 1·2
24	Tu	0131 0747 1359 2011	5·1 1·2 4·8 1·6
25	W	0216 0839 1453 2105	4·7 1·6 4·4 2·1
26	Th ☾	0312 0945 1607 2223	4·4 2·0 4·1 2·4
27	F	0431 1113 1753 2356	4·2 2·1 4·0 2·4
28	Sa	0610 1238 1914	4·2 2·0 4·2
29	Su	0109 0721 1340 2005	2·2 4·4 1·8 4·4
30	M	0159 0808 1423 2042	1·9 4·7 1·5 4·7
31	Tu	0239 0844 1457 2111	1·6 5·0 1·2 4·9

APRIL

Date	Day	Time	m
1	W	0311 0917 1528 2139	1·3 5·2 1·0 5·1
2	Th	0342 0948 1557 2207	1·0 5·3 0·9 5·3
3	F ●	0413 1019 1628 2237	0·9 5·5 0·7 5·4
4	Sa	0444 1051 1659 2308	0·8 5·5 0·7 5·4
5	Su	0518 1125 1733 2342	0·7 5·5 0·7 5·4
6	M	0553 1203 1808	0·8 5·5 0·9
7	Tu	0019 0634 1242 1849	5·4 0·9 5·3 1·1
8	W	0100 0719 1330 1935	5·2 1·1 5·1 1·4
9	Th	0148 0812 1426 2033	5·0 1·3 4·8 1·7
10	F ☽	0249 0919 1539 2149	4·8 1·5 4·5 1·9
11	Sa	0409 1044 1712 2316	4·6 1·6 4·5 1·9
12	Su	0540 1205 1834	4·7 1·4 4·6
13	M	0034 0655 1313 1935	1·7 4·9 1·1 4·9
14	Tu	0135 0751 1409 2025	1·3 5·2 0·8 5·2
15	W	0226 0839 1457 2107	1·0 5·5 0·5 5·4
16	Th	0311 0922 1539 2146	0·7 5·7 0·4 5·6
17	F ○	0353 1004 1620 2226	0·5 5·7 0·4 5·6
18	Sa	0435 1047 1701 2306	0·4 5·7 0·5 5·6
19	Su	0518 1129 1740 2346	0·5 5·5 0·7 5·5
20	M	0600 1211 1819	0·7 5·3 1·0
21	Tu	0027 0642 1253 1900	5·3 0·9 5·0 1·3
22	W	0106 0726 1337 1942	5·1 1·2 4·7 1·7
23	Th	0148 0813 1426 2032	4·8 1·5 4·4 2·0
24	F ☾	0239 0910 1527 2135	4·6 1·8 4·2 2·3
25	Sa	0341 1020 1648 2255	4·4 2·0 4·0 2·4
26	Su	0501 1136 1811	4·3 2·0 4·1
27	M	0010 0617 1241 1912	2·2 4·4 1·8 4·3
28	Tu	0107 0714 1331 1955	2·0 4·6 1·6 4·6
29	W	0152 0759 1411 2030	1·7 4·8 1·4 4·8
30	Th	0232 0837 1447 2103	1·4 5·0 1·1 5·0

Chart Datum: 3.05 metres below Ordnance Datum (Newlyn)

TIME ZONE UT(GMT)
For Summer Time add ONE hour in non-shaded areas

WALES – HOLYHEAD

Lat 53°18′ N Long 4°38′ W

TIMES AND HEIGHTS OF HIGH AND LOW WATERS

YEAR **1992**

MAY

Day	Time	m	Day	Time	m
1 F	0307 0912 1521 2134	1·2 5·2 1·0 5·2	**16** Sa ○	0336 0948 1559 2207	0·8 5·4 0·8 5·4
2 Sa ●	0342 0948 1556 2207	1·0 5·4 0·8 5·4	**17** Su	0420 1031 1640 2247	0·7 5·4 0·8 5·5
3 Su	0419 1026 1633 2244	0·8 5·5 0·8 5·5	**18** M	0504 1113 1720 2327	0·7 5·3 1·0 5·4
4 M	0457 1105 1711 2323	0·7 5·5 0·8 5·5	**19** Tu	0544 1154 1800	0·8 5·1 1·1
5 Tu	0539 1147 1753	0·7 5·4 0·9	**20** W	0007 0625 1235 1838	5·3 1·0 4·9 1·3
6 W	0005 0624 1234 1839	5·5 0·8 5·3 1·0	**21** Th	0045 0706 1316 1919	5·2 1·2 4·7 1·6
7 Th	0052 0714 1326 1930	5·3 0·9 5·1 1·3	**22** F	0126 0748 1359 2002	5·0 1·4 4·5 1·8
8 F	0144 0811 1425 2029	5·2 1·1 4·8 1·5	**23** Sa	0209 0836 1449 2053	4·8 1·6 4·3 2·0
9 Sa ☽	0244 0915 1535 2139	5·0 1·2 4·7 1·7	**24** Su ☾	0300 0928 1548 2152	4·6 1·7 4·2 2·2
10 Su	0356 1028 1654 2254	4·8 1·3 4·6 1·7	**25** M	0400 1028 1655 2259	4·5 1·8 4·2 2·2
11 M	0515 1142 1807	4·8 1·2 4·7	**26** Tu	0508 1133 1801	4·4 1·8 4·3
12 Tu	0005 0625 1246 1907	1·6 5·0 1·1 4·9	**27** W	0004 0612 1231 1857	2·1 4·5 1·7 4·5
13 W	0109 0726 1344 1959	1·4 5·1 0·9 5·0	**28** Th	0100 0707 1321 1944	1·9 4·7 1·5 4·7
14 Th	0204 0816 1433 2044	1·1 5·3 0·8 5·2	**29** F	0148 0757 1406 2026	1·6 4·9 1·3 4·9
15 F	0251 0904 1518 2127	0·9 5·3 0·8 5·3	**30** Sa	0233 0840 1449 2105	1·3 5·1 1·1 5·2
			31 Su	0315 0922 1529 2145	1·1 5·2 1·0 5·4

JUNE

Day	Time	m	Day	Time	m
1 M ●	0357 1006 1612 2226	0·9 5·4 0·8 5·5	**16** Tu	0452 1101 1705 2312	0·9 5·1 1·1 5·4
2 Tu	0442 1049 1657 2309	0·7 5·5 0·8 5·6	**17** W	0532 1139 1742 2349	1·0 5·0 1·2 5·3
3 W	0529 1137 1743 2356	0·6 5·5 0·8 5·6	**18** Th	0608 1217 1818	1·0 4·9 1·3
4 Th	0618 1228 1832	0·6 5·4 0·9	**19** F	0025 0645 1252 1855	5·3 1·1 4·8 1·4
5 F	0045 0709 1320 1924	5·6 0·6 5·2 1·0	**20** Sa	0100 0721 1330 1933	5·2 1·2 4·7 1·5
6 Sa	0137 0804 1416 2019	5·4 0·8 5·0 1·2	**21** Su	0140 0801 1411 2013	5·0 1·4 4·6 1·7
7 Su ☽	0233 0901 1518 2119	5·3 0·9 4·8 1·4	**22** M	0222 0843 1456 2100	4·9 1·5 4·5 1·9
8 M	0335 1004 1626 2226	5·1 1·1 4·7 1·5	**23** Tu ☾	0310 0931 1549 2155	4·7 1·7 4·4 2·0
9 Tu	0445 1112 1734 2334	5·0 1·2 4·7 1·6	**24** W	0406 1027 1654 2258	4·6 1·8 4·3 2·1
10 W	0556 1218 1839	4·9 1·2 4·7	**25** Th	0512 1130 1800	4·5 1·8 4·4
11 Th	0042 0700 1319 1937	1·5 4·9 1·2 4·9	**26** F	0007 0618 1234 1900	2·0 4·6 1·7 4·6
12 F	0144 0759 1413 2027	1·4 4·9 1·2 5·0	**27** Sa	0109 0720 1331 1954	1·8 4·7 1·5 4·8
13 Sa	0239 0851 1501 2112	1·2 5·0 1·1 5·2	**28** Su	0204 0813 1422 2042	1·5 4·9 1·3 5·1
14 Su	0327 0938 1545 2155	1·1 5·1 1·1 5·3	**29** M	0254 0904 1510 2127	1·2 5·1 1·1 5·3
15 M ○	0412 1020 1626 2234	1·0 5·1 1·1 5·4	**30** Tu ●	0342 0952 1557 2212	0·9 5·3 0·8 5·6

JULY

Day	Time	m	Day	Time	m
1 W	0430 1038 1644 2257	0·6 5·5 0·7 5·8	**16** Th	0513 1119 1722 2329	1·0 5·1 1·1 5·4
2 Th	0519 1126 1732 2344	0·4 5·6 0·6 5·9	**17** F	0547 1151 1754	0·9 5·0 1·1
3 F	0607 1215 1819	0·3 5·6 0·6	**18** Sa	0001 0619 1224 1827	5·4 1·0 5·0 1·2
4 Sa	0031 0656 1304 1907	5·8 0·3 5·4 0·7	**19** Su	0035 0652 1257 1900	5·3 1·1 4·9 1·3
5 Su	0120 0745 1355 1958	5·7 0·5 5·2 0·9	**20** M	0109 0726 1333 1937	5·2 1·2 4·8 1·5
6 M	0212 0837 1450 2051	5·5 0·8 5·0 1·2	**21** Tu	0145 0802 1411 2016	5·1 1·3 4·7 1·7
7 Tu ☽	0308 0935 1550 2152	5·2 1·1 4·8 1·5	**22** W ☾	0225 0843 1454 2103	4·9 1·5 4·6 1·9
8 W	0413 1038 1658 2302	4·9 1·3 4·6 1·7	**23** Th	0314 0932 1550 2202	4·7 1·7 4·4 2·0
9 Th	0525 1149 1810	4·7 1·5 4·6	**24** F	0416 1035 1704 2316	4·5 1·9 4·4 2·1
10 F	0018 0642 1257 1919	1·7 4·6 1·6 4·7	**25** Sa	0534 1151 1821	4·5 1·9 4·5
11 Sa	0130 0751 1359 2016	1·7 4·7 1·6 4·8	**26** Su	0035 0650 1302 1928	1·9 4·6 1·7 4·7
12 Su	0230 0846 1451 2104	1·5 4·8 1·5 5·0	**27** M	0141 0757 1402 2025	1·6 4·8 1·4 5·1
13 M	0321 0932 1535 2143	1·3 4·9 1·3 5·2	**28** Tu	0239 0851 1456 2112	1·2 5·1 1·1 5·4
14 Tu ○	0403 1012 1613 2220	1·1 5·0 1·2 5·3	**29** W ●	0329 0939 1543 2157	0·8 5·4 0·8 5·7
15 W	0440 1047 1648 2255	1·0 5·0 1·1 5·4	**30** Th	0416 1024 1628 2241	0·4 5·6 0·5 6·0
			31 F	0502 1109 1713 2326	0·2 5·7 0·4 6·1

AUGUST

Day	Time	m	Day	Time	m
1 Sa	0549 1154 1800	0·1 5·7 0·4	**16** Su	0549 1153 1757	0·9 5·2 1·0
2 Su	0011 0634 1241 1845	6·1 0·2 5·6 0·5	**17** M	0004 0618 1224 1829	5·5 1·0 5·1 1·1
3 M	0057 0720 1327 1933	5·9 0·4 5·4 0·8	**18** Tu	0036 0649 1256 1902	5·4 1·1 5·0 1·3
4 Tu	0145 0808 1416 2022	5·6 0·8 5·1 1·1	**19** W	0110 0723 1331 1940	5·2 1·3 4·9 1·5
5 W ☽	0237 0901 1511 2119	5·2 1·2 4·8 1·5	**20** Th	0148 0801 1412 2023	5·0 1·5 4·8 1·7
6 Th	0339 1003 1619 2231	4·8 1·6 4·6 1·8	**21** F ☾	0233 0849 1503 2121	4·8 1·7 4·6 2·0
7 F	0457 1119 1740 2357	4·5 1·9 4·5 2·0	**22** Sa	0334 0952 1617 2240	4·5 2·0 4·4 2·1
8 Sa	0628 1238 1902	4·4 2·0 4·6	**23** Su	0501 1118 1750	4·4 2·1 4·5
9 Su	0119 0745 1347 2005	1·9 4·5 1·8 4·8	**24** M	0010 0631 1241 1907	1·9 4·5 1·9 4·8
10 M	0222 0840 1439 2051	1·6 4·6 1·6 5·0	**25** Tu	0123 0742 1345 2006	1·5 4·8 1·5 5·1
11 Tu	0308 0921 1521 2128	1·4 4·8 1·4 5·2	**26** W	0222 0836 1439 2054	1·1 5·2 1·1 5·5
12 W	0346 0955 1555 2202	1·2 5·0 1·2 5·3	**27** Th	0312 0922 1525 2138	0·6 5·5 0·7 5·9
13 Th ○	0419 1026 1627 2233	1·0 5·1 1·1 5·5	**28** F ●	0357 1004 1609 2220	0·3 5·7 0·4 6·1
14 F	0449 1054 1657 2302	0·9 5·1 1·0 5·5	**29** Sa	0441 1047 1652 2304	0·1 5·8 0·3 6·2
15 Sa	0519 1123 1726 2333	0·9 5·2 1·0 5·5	**30** Su	0525 1129 1736 2347	0·0 5·8 0·3 6·1
			31 M	0607 1212 1819	0·2 5·7 0·4

10

Chart Datum: 3.05 metres below Ordnance Datum (Newlyn)

TIME ZONE UT(GMT)

For Summer Time add ONE hour in non-shaded areas

WALES – HOLYHEAD

Lat 53°18′ N Long 4°38′ W

TIMES AND HEIGHTS OF HIGH AND LOW WATERS

YEAR **1992**

SEPTEMBER

Day	Time	m	Day	Time	m
1 Tu	0032 0652 1257 1906	5·9 0·5 5·5 0·7	16 W	0007 0615 1225 1834	5·4 1·1 5·2 1·2
2 W	0119 0737 1344 1954	5·6 0·9 5·2 1·1	17 Th	0041 0650 1300 1912	5·3 1·2 5·1 1·4
3 Th ☽	0209 0827 1436 2050	5·1 1·4 4·9 1·6	18 F	0120 0730 1341 1958	5·1 1·5 4·9 1·7
4 F	0308 0928 1539 2203	4·7 1·9 4·6 1·9	19 Sa ☾	0208 0819 1434 2058	4·8 1·8 4·7 1·9
5 Sa	0428 1047 1706 2333	4·3 2·2 4·4 2·1	20 Su	0312 0925 1549 2220	4·5 2·0 4·5 2·0
6 Su	0611 1212 1838	4·2 2·2 4·5	21 M	0442 1055 1725 2350	4·4 2·1 4·6 1·8
7 M	0059 0730 1324 1942	2·0 4·4 2·1 4·7	22 Tu	0617 1219 1846	4·6 1·9 4·9
8 Tu	0201 0822 1418 2027	1·7 4·6 1·8 5·0	23 W	0104 0726 1326 1945	1·4 4·9 1·5 5·3
9 W	0246 0858 1457 2104	1·5 4·8 1·5 5·2	24 Th	0202 0818 1418 2033	1·0 5·2 1·1 5·6
10 Th	0319 0929 1529 2135	1·2 5·0 1·3 5·4	25 F	0250 0901 1504 2117	0·6 5·5 0·7 5·9
11 F	0350 0957 1559 2204	1·1 5·1 1·1 5·5	26 Sa ●	0334 0942 1546 2157	0·3 5·8 0·5 6·1
12 Sa ○	0419 1024 1627 2233	0·9 5·2 1·0 5·6	27 Su	0417 1023 1628 2241	0·2 5·9 0·3 6·2
13 Su	0445 1052 1657 2304	0·9 5·3 1·0 5·6	28 M	0458 1104 1712 2325	0·2 5·9 0·4 6·0
14 M	0515 1120 1727 2334	0·9 5·3 1·0 5·5	29 Tu	0542 1147 1757	0·4 5·7 0·5
15 Tu	0544 1151 1758	0·9 5·3 1·1	30 W	0010 0624 1229 1842	5·8 0·7 5·5 0·8

OCTOBER

Day	Time	m	Day	Time	m
1 Th	0055 0709 1314 1931	5·4 1·1 5·3 1·2	16 F	0021 0627 1239 1856	5·3 1·2 5·3 1·3
2 F	0144 0757 1404 2025	5·0 1·6 4·9 1·6	17 Sa	0104 0710 1324 1945	5·1 1·5 5·1 1·5
3 Sa ☽	0240 0853 1503 2132	4·6 2·0 4·6 2·0	18 Su	0157 0804 1420 2049	4·9 1·8 4·9 1·7
4 Su	0356 1007 1621 2258	4·2 2·3 4·4 2·1	19 M ☾	0304 0911 1532 2206	4·6 2·0 4·7 1·8
5 M	0536 1134 1754	4·1 2·4 4·4	20 Tu	0431 1035 1702 2329	4·5 2·1 4·8 1·6
6 Tu	0019 0656 1248 1903	2·1 4·3 2·2 4·6	21 W	0556 1156 1818	4·7 1·9 5·0
7 W	0123 0748 1341 1952	1·8 4·5 2·0 4·9	22 Th	0039 0702 1300 1919	1·3 4·9 1·5 5·3
8 Th	0208 0826 1422 2029	1·6 4·8 1·7 5·1	23 F	0137 0754 1354 2009	1·0 5·2 1·2 5·6
9 F	0243 0857 1456 2101	1·4 5·0 1·4 5·3	24 Sa	0226 0839 1442 2054	0·7 5·5 0·9 5·8
10 Sa	0314 0925 1527 2132	1·2 5·2 1·2 5·4	25 Su ●	0311 0921 1527 2138	0·5 5·7 0·6 5·9
11 Su ○	0343 0952 1556 2202	1·0 5·3 1·1 5·5	26 M	0353 1002 1610 2221	0·4 5·8 0·5 5·9
12 M	0412 1021 1627 2234	0·9 5·4 1·0 5·6	27 Tu	0435 1042 1654 2305	0·5 5·8 0·6 5·8
13 Tu	0442 1051 1659 2306	0·9 5·5 1·0 5·6	28 W	0518 1125 1739 2350	0·7 5·7 0·7 5·5
14 W	0515 1125 1734 2342	1·0 5·5 1·0 5·5	29 Th	0601 1208 1824	1·0 5·5 1·0
15 Th	0549 1200 1812	1·1 5·4 1·2	30 F	0035 0643 1250 1910	5·2 1·3 5·3 1·3
			31 Sa	0121 0728 1335 2001	4·9 1·7 5·1 1·6

NOVEMBER

Day	Time	m	Day	Time	m
1 Su	0213 0819 1426 2057	4·6 2·0 4·8 1·9	16 M	0151 0755 1411 2040	5·0 1·6 5·1 1·4
2 M ☽	0314 0921 1529 2206	4·3 2·3 4·6 2·1	17 Tu ☾	0254 0858 1517 2149	4·8 1·8 5·0 1·5
3 Tu	0434 1037 1647 2322	4·2 2·4 4·5 2·1	18 W	0410 1012 1633 2302	4·7 1·9 5·0 1·4
4 W	0554 1151 1801	4·2 2·4 4·5	19 Th	0527 1126 1747	4·7 1·8 5·0
5 Th	0027 0656 1252 1900	2·0 4·4 2·2 4·7	20 F	0011 0634 1232 1852	1·3 4·9 1·6 5·2
6 F	0119 0741 1338 1945	1·8 4·7 1·9 4·9	21 Sa	0112 0730 1331 1948	1·1 5·1 1·3 5·4
7 Sa	0159 0818 1418 2023	1·5 4·9 1·6 5·1	22 Su	0205 0819 1423 2037	1·0 5·3 1·1 5·5
8 Su	0234 0850 1453 2058	1·3 5·1 1·4 5·3	23 M	0253 0903 1512 2124	0·9 5·5 0·9 5·6
9 M	0308 0921 1528 2134	1·2 5·3 1·2 5·4	24 Tu ●	0336 0945 1557 2209	0·8 5·6 0·8 5·6
10 Tu ○	0341 0953 1603 2209	1·1 5·4 1·1 5·5	25 W	0420 1027 1642 2252	0·8 5·7 0·8 5·5
11 W	0416 1027 1640 2245	1·0 5·5 1·0 5·5	26 Th	0501 1109 1726 2336	0·9 5·7 0·9 5·3
12 Th	0451 1104 1718 2326	1·0 5·6 1·0 5·5	27 F	0543 1150 1810	1·1 5·6 1·0
13 F	0530 1143 1801	1·0 5·6 1·0	28 Sa	0019 0624 1231 1852	5·1 1·3 5·4 1·2
14 Sa	0010 0614 1228 1848	5·4 1·2 5·5 1·1	29 Su	0100 0704 1310 1934	4·9 1·6 5·2 1·4
15 Su	0057 0702 1316 1941	5·2 1·4 5·3 1·3	30 M	0144 0747 1354 2020	4·7 1·8 5·0 1·7

DECEMBER

Day	Time	m	Day	Time	m
1 Tu	0230 0834 1442 2111	4·5 2·0 4·8 1·9	16 W ☾	0236 0839 1454 2124	5·0 1·4 5·3 1·2
2 W ☽	0327 0931 1539 2210	4·3 2·2 4·6 2·0	17 Th	0341 0942 1600 2230	4·8 1·6 5·1 1·3
3 Th	0433 1037 1647 2315	4·3 2·3 4·5 2·0	18 F	0451 1052 1715 2340	4·7 1·7 5·0 1·4
4 F	0542 1146 1754	4·3 2·3 4·6	19 Sa	0601 1204 1827	4·8 1·7 5·0
5 Sa	0017 0643 1246 1853	1·9 4·5 2·1 4·7	20 Su	0046 0706 1312 1931	1·4 4·9 1·6 5·0
6 Su	0109 0733 1337 1944	1·8 4·7 1·9 4·9	21 M	0147 0804 1412 2029	1·3 5·1 1·4 5·1
7 M	0155 0815 1420 2029	1·6 4·9 1·6 5·1	22 Tu	0240 0853 1505 2118	1·2 5·3 1·2 5·2
8 Tu	0236 0854 1503 2110	1·4 5·2 1·4 5·2	23 W	0327 0936 1553 2203	1·1 5·4 1·0 5·3
9 W ○	0315 0931 1543 2149	1·2 5·4 1·1 5·4	24 Th ●	0409 1017 1635 2244	1·1 5·5 0·9 5·3
10 Th	0355 1009 1624 2231	1·0 5·6 0·9 5·5	25 F	0449 1057 1716 2323	1·1 5·6 0·9 5·2
11 F	0435 1049 1708 2315	0·9 5·7 0·8 5·5	26 Sa	0527 1134 1754	1·1 5·6 1·0
12 Sa	0519 1132 1753	0·9 5·7 0·7	27 Su	0000 0604 1210 1831	5·2 1·2 5·5 1·1
13 Su	0000 0604 1218 1841	5·5 0·9 5·7 0·8	28 M	0036 0639 1245 1906	5·0 1·3 5·4 1·2
14 M	0049 0653 1306 1931	5·4 1·1 5·6 0·9	29 Tu	0112 0716 1321 1942	4·9 1·5 5·2 1·4
15 Tu	0140 0744 1357 2025	5·2 1·2 5·5 1·0	30 W	0149 0754 1401 2023	4·8 1·7 5·0 1·6
			31 Th	0232 0837 1446 2108	4·6 1·9 4·8 1·8

Chart Datum: 3.05 metres below Ordnance Datum (Newlyn)

HOLYHEAD *continued*

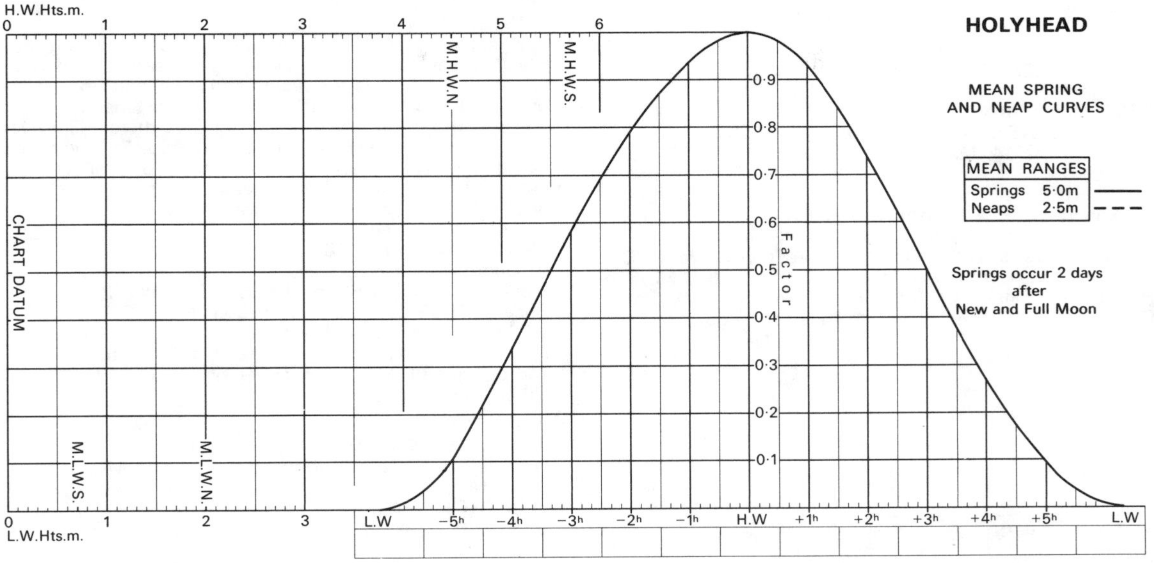
HOLYHEAD
MEAN SPRING AND NEAP CURVES
MEAN RANGES
Springs 5·0m
Neaps 2·5m
Springs occur 2 days after New and Full Moon
H.W.Hts.m.
L.W.Hts.m.
CHART DATUM
M.H.W.N.
M.H.W.S.
M.L.W.S.
M.L.W.N.
Factor
L.W −5h −4h −3h −2h −1h H.W +1h +2h +3h +4h +5h L.W

MENAI STRAIT 10-10-19

Gwynedd

CHARTS
Admiralty 1464; Imray C61; OS 114, 115

TIDES
Beaumaris — 0025, Caernarfon — 0105 Dover;
ML Beaumaris 3·9; Caernarfon 2·9; Duration 0540;
Zone 0 (GMT).

Standard Port HOLYHEAD (⟵)

Times				Height (metres)			
HW		LW		MHWS	MHWN	MLWN	MLWS
0000	0600	0500	1100	5·7	4·5	2·0	0·7
1200	1800	1700	2300				
Differences BEAUMARIS							
+0025	+0010	+0055	+0035	+2·0	+1·6	+0·5	+0·1
MENAI BRIDGE							
+0030	+0010	+0100	+0035	+1·7	+1·4	+0·3	0·0
PORT DINORWIC							
−0015	−0025	+0030	0000	0·0	0·0	0·0	+0·1
CAERNARFON							
−0030	−0030	+0015	−0005	−0·4	−0·4	−0·1	−0·1
PORTH DINLLAEN							
−0120	−0105	−0035	−0025	−1·0	−1·0	−0·2	−0·2
BARDSEY ISLAND							
−0220	−0240	−0145	−0140	−1·2	−1·2	−0·5	−0·1

HW in The Swellies −0045 HW Port Dinorwic; −0200 HW Liverpool; −0115 HW Holyhead.

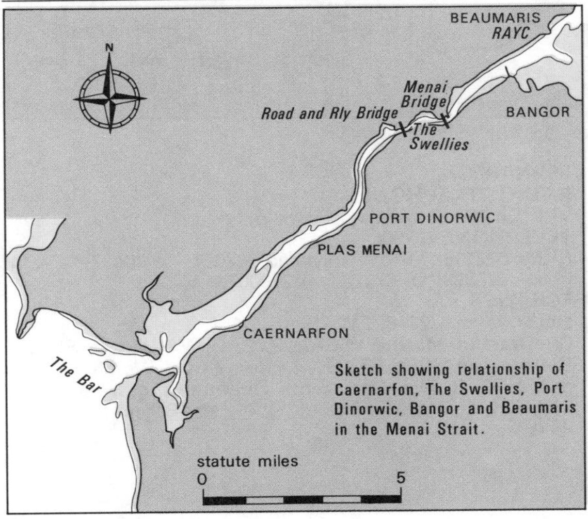
BEAUMARIS
RAYC
Menai Bridge
Road and Rly Bridge
The Swellies
BANGOR
PORT DINORWIC
PLAS MENAI
CAERNARFON
The Bar
Sketch showing relationship of Caernarfon, The Swellies, Port Dinorwic, Bangor and Beaumaris in the Menai Strait.
statute miles
0
5

SHELTER
Very good shelter and facilities at Beaumaris, Bangor, Port Dinorwic (fresh water marina), Caernarfon (only available near HW).

NAVIGATION
NE entrance waypoint 53°20′·00N 04°00′·00W, 045°/225° from/to NE end Puffin Island, 1·0M. Caernarfon Bar waypoint 53°07′·60N 04°26′·00W, 270°/090° from/to Abermenai Pt Lt, 3·8M. From N end of Strait keep to buoyed channel near Anglesey shore. Night pilotage not recommended – many unlit buoys. The bridges and power cables have minimum clearance of 24m at MHWS. Between the bridges is a stretch of water called the Swellies which should only be attempted at slack HW which normally occurs about one hour before HW Holyhead. For further notes see Menai Strait 10·10·5.

LIGHTS AND MARKS
A light FWG exhibited at the end of Beaumaris pier. Menai Strait is marked by lateral marks, lights and light buoys; direction of buoyage changes off Caernarfon. From N approach in G sector of Mountfield Lt. Between the bridges is Price Pt, Fl WR 2s 5m 3M; R059° – 239°, W239° – 259°. At S end of Strait, Abermenai Pt Lt, Fl WR 3·5s; R065° – 245°, W245° – 065°.

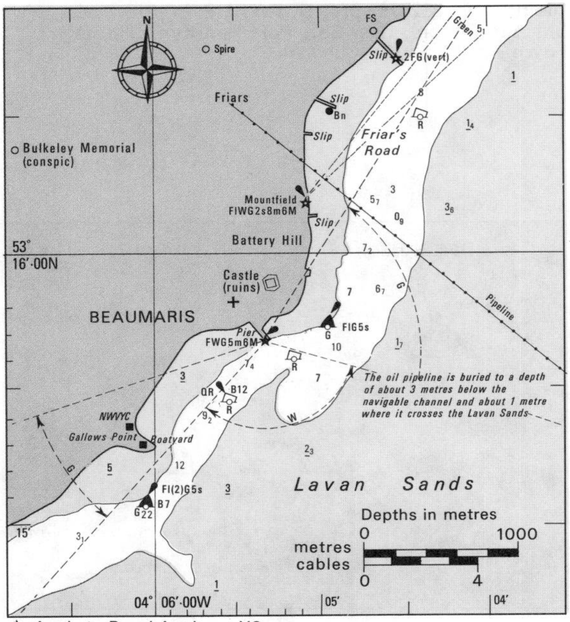
N
Spire
Friars
Bulkeley Memorial (conspic)
Slip
Bn
Friar's Road
Mountfield FlWG2s8m6M
Battery Hill
53° 16′·00N
Castle (ruins)
BEAUMARIS
Pier FWG5m6M
FlG5s
QR
B12
NWYC
Gallows Point
Boatyard
Fl(2)G5s
B7
G22
Pipeline
The oil pipeline is buried to a depth of about 3 metres below the navigable channel and about 1 metre where it crosses the Lavan Sands
Lavan Sands
Depths in metres
metres 0 1000
cables 0 4
04° 06′·00W
05′
04′
15′

▲ Apply to Royal Anglesey YC

MENAI STRAIT *continued*

BEAUMARIS
RADIO TELEPHONE
None.
TELEPHONE (0248)
Hr Mr 750057 Ex. 212; MRSC Holyhead 762051; # (0407) 762714; Marinecall 0898 500 460; Police 810222; Dr 810501.
FACILITIES
EC Beaumaris – Wednesday. **Pier** FW, L; **Royal Anglesey YC** ☎ 810295, Slip, M, L, R, Bar; P. **Brimecombe** ☎ 810310, M; **Northwest Venturers YC** ☎ 810023, M, L, FW; **Anglesey Boat Co** ☎ 810359, Slip, P and D (in cans), FW, ME, BH (20 ton), Sh, C (2 ton), CH, El, ⒺGas: **Town** ✉; Ⓑ; ≠ (bus to Bangor); ✈ (Liverpool).

BANGOR
RADIO TELEPHONE
None.

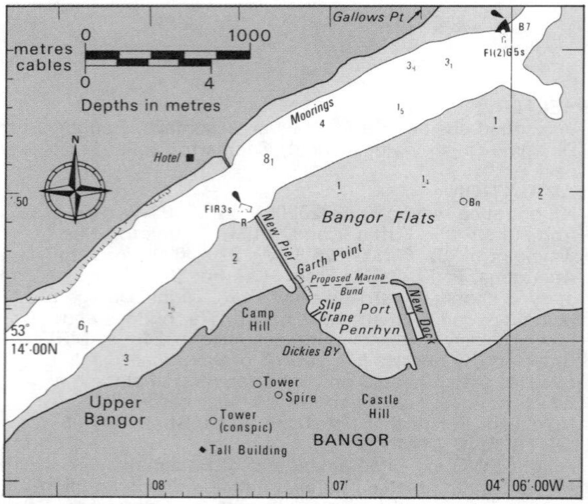
Gallows Pt
metres
cables
0
1000
0
4
Depths in metres
Moorings
Hotel
FlR3s
Bangor Flats
New Pier
Garth Point
Proposed Marina Bund
Slip
Crane
Port Penrhyn
New Dock
Camp Hill
Dickies BY
Tower
Spire
Castle Hill
Upper Bangor
Tower (conspic)
Tall Building
BANGOR
Fl(2)G5s
Bn
53°
14'·00N
08'
07'
04° 06'·00W

TELEPHONE (0248)
Hr Mr 722920 Ex. 212; MRSC Holyhead 762051; # (0407) 762714; Dr 364567.
FACILITIES
Dickies Tel. 352775, Slip, D, FW, ME, El, Sh, C, CH, Ⓔ, SM, BH (30 ton), Gas, Gaz; **Port Penrhyn**, Slip, D; **Town** ✉; Ⓑ; ≠; ✈ (Chester).

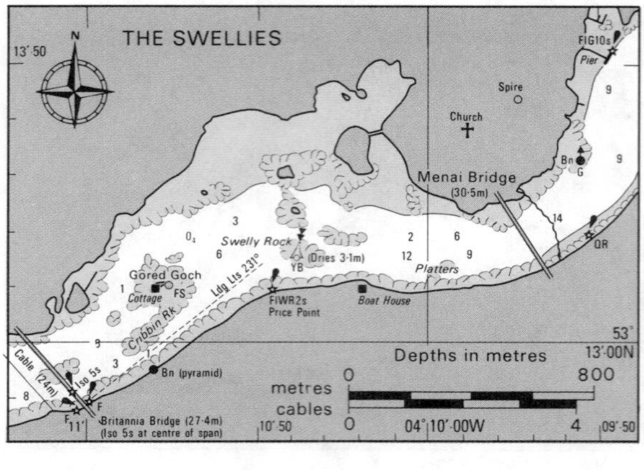
THE SWELLIES
FlG10s
Pier
Spire
Church
Menai Bridge
(30·5m)
Bn
QR
Swelly Rock
(Dries 3·1m)
YB
Platters
Gored Goch
Cottage
FS
Ldg Lts 231°
FlWR2s
Price Point
Boat House
Cribbin Rk
Cable (24m)
Iso 5s
Bn (pyramid)
Britannia Bridge (27·4m)
(Iso 5s at centre of span)
Depths in metres
metres
cables
0
800
0
4
13'50
53°
13'·00N
11'
10'50
04°10'·00W
09'50

THE SWELLIES
NAVIGATION
For general pilotage notes on Menai Strait, including the Swellies, see 10·10·5. The (Swellies) passage between the bridges is dangerous for yachts and small craft except at or immediately before slack HW. At other times the stream can run up to 8 kn. At slack HW there is 3m over The Platters and over the outcrop off Price Pt, and these can be ignored. Passage is also possible for shallow-draught boats at slack LW at neaps, but there are charted depths of 0·4m close E of Britannia Bridge. Passage at night not recommended.
LIGHTS AND MARKS
St George's Pier FlG 10s.
E side of channel QR 4m; R mast; vis 064°-222°.
Price Pt FlWR 2s 5m 3M; W Bn: vis R059°-239°, W239°-259°. Britannia Bridge, E side, Ldg Lts 231°. Both FW. Centre span of bridge Iso 5s 27m 3M; either side. S end of bridge FR 21m 3M; either side. N end FG 21m 3M; either side.

PORT DINORWIC
RADIO TELEPHONE
Port Dinorwic Yacht Harbour, Call *Dinorwic Marine* VHF Ch **80** M (office hours).
TELEPHONE (0248)
Hr Mr 670441; MRSC Holyhead 762051; # (0407) 762714; Dr 670423.
FACILITIES
Outer harbour dries. **Port Dinorwic Yacht Harbour** (230) ☎ 670559 D, AC, CH, SM; **J. Dawson** ☎ 670103, SM; **P. D. Marine** ☎ 670441, ME, El, Sh, Slip, C; **M. J. Stallard** ☎ 670010, El, CH; **Town** Ⓔ, ✉ (Bangor or Caernarfon); Ⓑ; ≠ (Bangor); ✈ (Liverpool).
Note: Between Port Dinorwic and Caernarfon is **Plas Menai** ☎ 670964, the Sport Council for Wales Sailing and Sports Centre. VHF Ch **80** 37.
Call: *Menai Base*. Day moorings only. All forms of water sport.

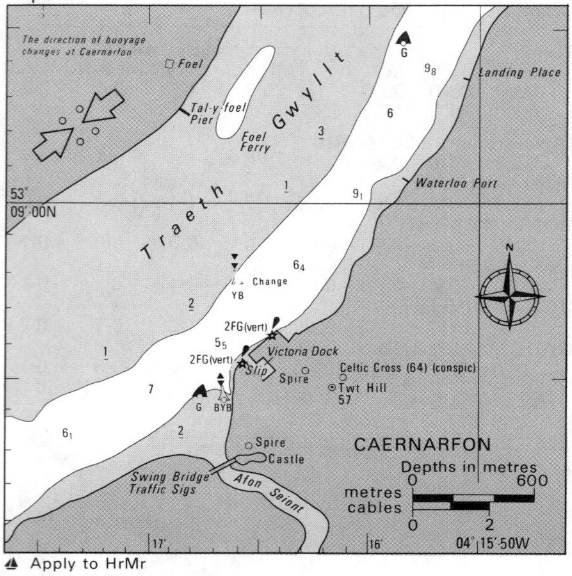
The direction of buoyage changes at Caernarfon
Foel
Tal-y-foel Pier
Foel Ferry
Traeth Gwyllt
Landing Place
Waterloo Port
Change
YB
2FG(vert)
Victoria Dock
Slip
Spire
Celtic Cross (64) (conspic)
Twt Hill
57
G
BYB
Spire
Castle
CAERNARFON
Swing Bridge
Traffic Sigs
Afon Seiont
Depths in metres
metres
cables
0
600
0
2
53°
09'·00N
17'
16'
04° 15'·50W

▲ Apply to HrMr

CAERNARFON
RADIO TELEPHONE
VHF Ch 16; 12 14 (day service only).
TELEPHONE (0286)
Hr Mr 672118; MRSC Holyhead 762051; # (0407) 762714; Police 673333; Dr 673224; Ⓗ 370007.
FACILITIES
Harbour ☎ 672118, FW, Slip, L, C (2 ton), V; **Caernarfon Marine** ☎ 674322, P, D, ME, El, Ⓔ, Sh, CH; **Caernarfon SC** ☎ 672861, L, Bar; **Royal Welsh YC** ☎ 672599, P, FW, Bar; **Arfon Oceaneering** ☎ 76055, Slip, CH, El, Ⓔ, ME; **Town** ✉; Ⓑ; ≠ (Bangor); ✈ (Liverpool).

MINOR HARBOURS AND ANCHORAGES 10-10-20

SILLOTH, Cumbria, 54°52′·00N, 03°24′·00W, Zone 0 (GMT), Admty charts 2013, 1346. HW −0050 on Dover, +0035 on Liverpool; HW height −0·3m on Liverpool; ML 4·9m; Duration 0520. See 10·10·7. Two channels marked on stbd side. Approx 8M long, East channel and Middle channel. Anchorage off Lees Scar in about 4m, exposed to SW winds; outer harbour dries; or berth in the new wet dock, but this is principally commercial. Beware constantly changing channels and sandbanks. East Cote Dir Lt 052° FG 15m 12M; vis 046°−058°, intens 052°. Lees Scar, S of entrance, QG 11m 8M; vis 005°−317°. Groyne head 2 FG (vert). Entry signals on mast at New Dock − no entry unless Y signal arm raised by day or Q Bu Lt by night. VHF Ch 16; 12 (HW−2½ to HW+1½). Facilities: EC Tues; Hr Mr ☎ 31358; FW on quays, all stores available, Ⓑ, Bar, ✉, R, V.

HARRINGTON, Cumbria, 54°37′·00N, 03°34′·00W, Zone 0 (GMT), Admty charts 2013, 1346. HW +0025 on Dover, +0015 on Liverpool; HW height −1·1m on Liverpool; ML 4·6m; Duration 0540. Good shelter in small harbour only used now by local fishermen and yachts. Entrance (difficult in strong W winds) by stone pier. Inner harbour dries. Contact Cockermouth 823741 Ext. 148 for moorings. Very limited facilities.

WHITEHAVEN, Cumbria, 54°33′·00N, 03°36′·00W, Zone 0 (GMT), Admty charts 2013, 1346. HW +0015 on Dover, +0010 on Liverpool; HW height −1·2m on Liverpool; ML 4·5m; Duration 0550. See 10·10·8. All harbour dries except Queens Dock, but outer harbour has over 5m at MHWS. Very good shelter and entrance safe in most conditions. Access HW∓2½. W pier head Fl G 5s 16m 13M. N pier head 2 FR (vert) 8m 9M. N Wall Quay 2 FR (vert) 8m 2M. Old Quay head 2 FG (vert) 8m 2M. VHF Ch 16; 12 (HW−2½ to HW+1½). Facilities: EC Wed; berthing see Hr Mr. ☎ 692435, FW, D, Slip, C (7½ ton), P (on Fish Quay), Bar, Ⓑ, CH, ✉, R, V.

RAVENGLASS, Cumbria, 54°21′·00N, 03°25′·00W, Zone 0 (GMT), Admty chart 1346. HW +0020 on Dover, +0005 on Liverpool; HW height −1·0m on Liverpool; ML 4·6m; Duration 0545. Large harbour formed by estuaries of R Mite, R Irt and R Esk, which dries; there is approx 2·5m in entrance at HW−2. From N beware Drigg Rock and from S Selker Rks. Local knowledge advised. Also beware gun testing range at Eskmeals (R flag when in use). There is a FG Lt (occas). Facilities: FW (in village), but no other facilities.

BARROW-IN-FURNESS, Cumbria, 54°06′·00N, 03°12′·00W, Zone 0 (GMT), Admty charts 3164, 2010. HW +0030 on Dover, +0015 on Liverpool; HW height −0·25m on Liverpool; ML 5·2m; Duration 0530. See 10·10·9. Good shelter. Harbour dries except for Walney Channel which must be kept clear. Landing places at Piel I and Roa I. Depths of under 2m may be encountered even on Ldg lines. Lights: Walney I Fl 15s 21m 23M (when within 3M of shore, obsc 122°−127°), RC. Ldg Lts leading in from Lightning Knoll By (RW LFl 10s) at 041° front Q 6m 6M (B structure with W daymark), rear (640m from front) Iso 2s 12m 6M (R column with W face). VHF *Ramsden Dock* Ch 16; 12 (H24). Facilities: EC Thurs; all facilities available in Barrow; **Rawlinson** ☎ 832806, SM.

HEYSHAM, Lancashire, 54°02′·00N, 02°55′·00W, Zone 0 (GMT), Admty charts 1552, 2010. HW +0015 on Dover, +0001 on Liverpool; HW height +0·1m on Liverpool; ML 5·3m; Duration 0545. See 10·10·9. Good shelter but yachts not normally accepted without special reason. Beware ferries and 'rig' supply vessels. Ldg Lts 102°, front FBu 11m 2M, Y+B diamond on mast; rear (137m from front) FBu 14m 2M, Y+B diamond on mast. S pier head Oc G 7·5s 9m 6M. N pier head 2FR (vert) 11m, obsc from seaward. Entry sigs; R flag or R Lt = no entry; no signal = no departure; 2R flags or 2R Lts = no entry or departure. VHF Ch 16; 14 74 (H24). Facilities: EC Wed (Heysham and Morecambe); Bar, FW, R, V. All stores at Morecambe (2M).

RIVER RIBBLE, Lancashire, 53°45′·00N, 02°47′·00W, Zone 0 (GMT), Admty chart 1981. HW +0013 on Dover; Preston 0000, St Anne's −0004 on Liverpool; HW height Preston −3·9m, St Anne's −0·1m on Liverpool; ML Preston 2·4m, St Anne's 5·4m; Duration St Anne's 0520. Preston closed as a commercial port in 1981. Many navigational aids in R Ribble have been withdrawn and silting has occurred. Entrance marked by Gut buoy, RW, lit. Training wall breached and channel now runs through S Gut (unmarked). Local knowledge needed. Contact **Ribble Cruising Club** ☎ Lytham 739983. Yachts berth nearby at Lytham, at Freckleton or near River Douglas entrance. Facilities: AB, C (7 ton), CH, D, FW, Sh, Slip. **Douglas Boatyard**, access HW∓2, ☎ Hesketh Bank 812462, ME, Sh, CH. Other facilities very limited except at Preston. Hr Mr (Preston) ☎ Preston 726711. **Preston Marina** (250) ☎ (0772) 733595, Lock in HW∓1½, VHF Ch 14 call *Riversway*; CH, D, C (250 ton), R, V.

RIVER ALT, Merseyside, 53°30′·00N, 03°04′·00W, Zone 0 (GMT), Admty charts 1951, 1978. HW −0008 on Dover, −0021 on Liverpool, see 10·10·11. Good shelter but only available to small craft. Access HW∓1½ for draught of 1·2m. Channel shifts frequently. Entrance channel marked by can buoy N side of groyne between Crosby and Hall Road beach marks. Channel from there marked by perches arranged by Blundellsands SC. Anchor between perches marking channel; local knowledge advised. Facilities very limited. **Blundellsands SC** at Hightown ☎ Liverpool 929 2101 (occas).

CASTLETOWN, Isle of Man, 54°04′·00N, 04°39′·00W, Zone 0 (GMT), Admty charts 2696, 2094. HW +0025 on Dover, +0010 on Liverpool; HW height −2·9m on Liverpool; ML 3·4m; Duration 0555. All 4 harbours dry. Secure in Inner Hr below fixed bridge or in Irish Hr below swing bridge. Anchorage between Lheeah−rio Rks and pier in 3m; at Langness Pt; in Derby Haven (drying). The bay gives good shelter except in SW to SE winds. Beware Lheeah-rio Rocks in W of bay, marked by R can buoy Fl R 3s, Bell. Beware race off Langness Pt, which should be given a good berth. Lt to E of Langness Pt, on Dreswick Pt Fl(2) 30s 23m 21M. N side of entrance Oc G 4s 3m (W metal post on concrete column). S side of entrance, Irish Quay, Oc R 4s 5m 5M vis 142°−322°. 150m NW is swing bridge marked by 2 FR (hor). To SE, New Pier head Oc R 15s 8m 5M. VHF Ch 16; 12 (when vessel expected). Facilities: EC Thurs; Hr Mr ☎ 823549; Dr 823597 **Outer Hr** Slip, L, C (20 ton) AB; **Irish Quay** AB, C, FW; **Inner Hr** AB, C, FW; **Moon's Garage** ☎ 823211 P, D, Gas; **Ballasalla Marine and Auto Eng** ☎ 822715, ME.

LAXEY, Isle of Man, 54°13′·00N, 04°23′·00W, Zone 0 (GMT), Admty chart 2094. HW +0025 on Dover, +0010 on Liverpool; HW height −2·0m on Liverpool; ML 4·0m; Duration 0550. The bay gives good shelter in N to SW winds through W. The harbour is only suitable for small yachts; it dries and has approx 2m at MHWN. Access HW∓3. Beware rocks on N side of the narrow entrance. Keep close to pier after entering to avoid training wall to N. Pier head Lt Oc R 3s 7m 5M, obsc when bearing less than 318°. Breakwater head Lt Oc G 3s 7m. Facilities are few other than FW, R, ✉, Ⓑ, Bar.

PORT ERIN, Isle of Man, 54°05′·00N, 04°46′·00W, Zone 0 (GMT), Admty charts 2696, 2094. HW −0020 on Dover, +0005 on Liverpool; HW height −3·7m on Liverpool; ML 2·9m; Duration 0555. See 10·10·13. The bay has good anchorage in 3m to 8m, and protection from winds except those from SW to NW. There is a small drying harbour on the S side which has 3·6m at MHWN. Beware the ruined breakwater running N from the SW corner, the end being marked with G con buoy. Ldg Lts 099°, front FR 10m 5M, rear FR 19m 5M, lead into middle of the bay. Raglan Pier (E arm of harbour) Oc G 5s 8m 5M. Facilities: EC Thurs; Bar, D, FW, P, R, Slip, V. Two visitors buoys W of Raglan Pier − Call Hr Mr Port St. Mary (VHF).

PORTH DINLLAEN, Gwynedd, 52°57′·00N, 04°34′·00W, Zone 0 (GMT), Admty charts 1512, 1971. HW −0240 on Dover, −0120 on Holyhead; HW height −1·0m on Holyhead; ML 2·5m; Duration 0535. Shelter good in S to W winds but strong NNW to NNE winds cause heavy seas in the bay. Beware Carreg-y-Chad (1·8m) 0·75M SW of the point, and Carreg-y-Chwislen (dries, with Bn unlit) 2 ca ENE of the point. Best anchorage 0·1M S of LB house in approx 2m. Facilities: EC Wed; Hr Mr ☎ Nefyn 720295; CG ☎ Nefyn 720204, Bar, V by landing stage; Other facilities are at Morfa Nefyn (IM), Bar, P. R. V.

Area 11

South Wales and Bristol Channel
Bardsey Island to Lands End

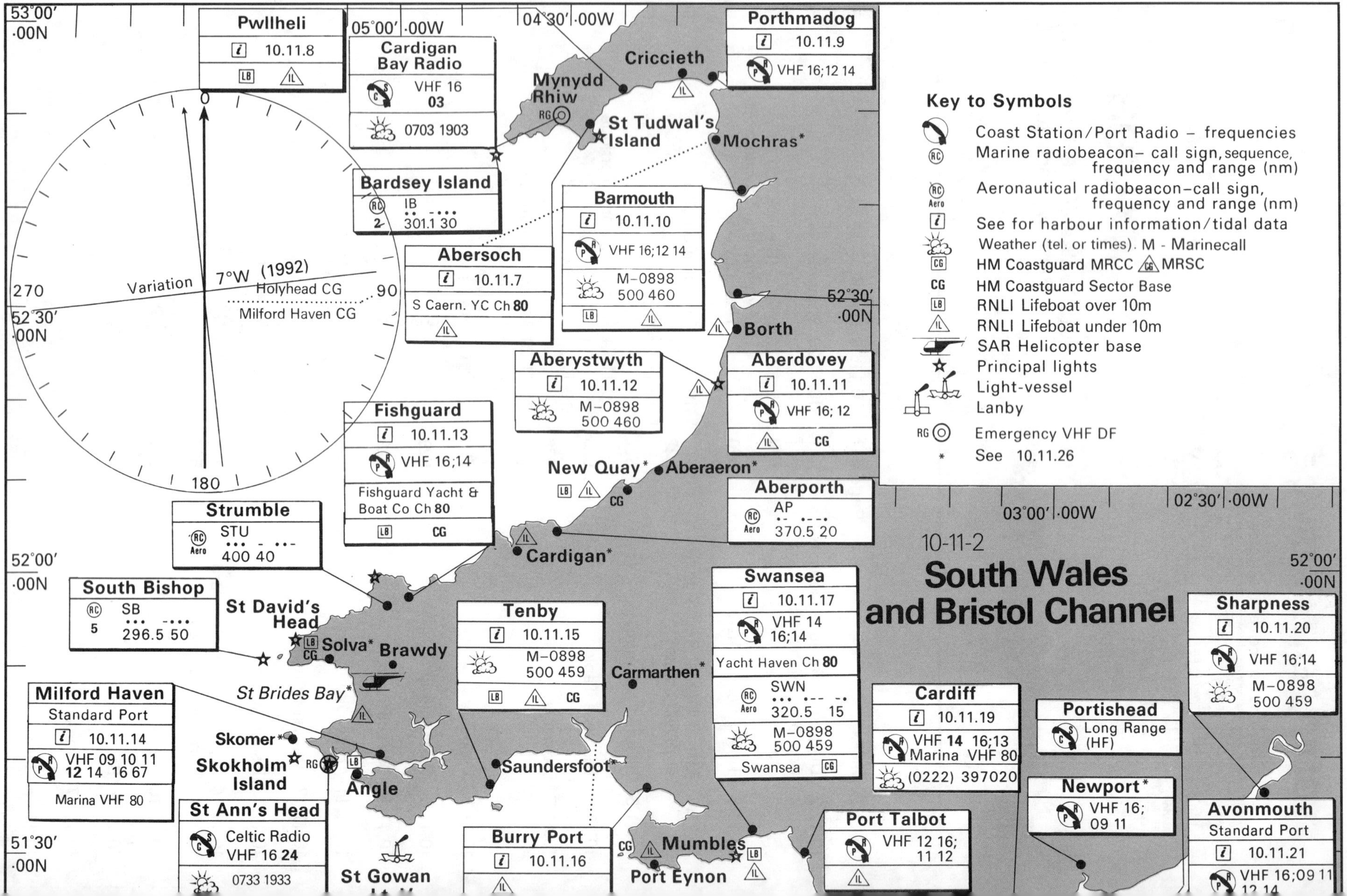

10-11-2
South Wales and Bristol Channel
Key to Symbols
Coast Station/Port Radio – frequencies
Marine radiobeacon– call sign, sequence, frequency and range (nm)
Aeronautical radiobeacon–call sign, frequency and range (nm)
See for harbour information/tidal data
Weather (tel. or times). M - Marinecall
HM Coastguard MRCC MRSC
HM Coastguard Sector Base
RNLI Lifeboat over 10m
RNLI Lifeboat under 10m
SAR Helicopter base
Principal lights
Light-vessel
Lanby
Emergency VHF DF
See 10.11.26
Pwllheli 10.11.8
Cardigan Bay Radio VHF 16 03 0703 1903
Porthmadog 10.11.9 VHF 16;12 14
Criccieth
Mynydd Rhiw
St Tudwal's Island
Mochras*
Bardsey Island IB 301.1 30 2
Barmouth 10.11.10 VHF 16;12 14 M–0898 500 460
Abersoch 10.11.7 S Caern. YC Ch 80
Borth
Aberystwyth 10.11.12 M–0898 500 460
Aberdovey 10.11.11 VHF 16; 12 CG
Fishguard 10.11.13 VHF 16;14 Fishguard Yacht & Boat Co Ch 80 CG
New Quay* Aberaeron* CG
Aberporth AP 370.5 20
Strumble STU 400 40
Cardigan*
South Bishop SB 5 296.5 50
St David's Head
Solva* Brawdy
Tenby 10.11.15 M–0898 500 459 CG
Swansea 10.11.17 VHF 14 16;14 Yacht Haven Ch 80 SWN 320.5 15 M–0898 500 459 Swansea
Carmarthen*
Sharpness 10.11.20 VHF 16;14 M–0898 500 459
Milford Haven Standard Port 10.11.14 VHF 09 10 11 12 14 16 67 Marina VHF 80
St Brides Bay*
Skomer*
Skokholm Island
Angle
Saundersfoot*
Cardiff 10.11.19 VHF 14 16;13 Marina VHF 80 (0222) 397020
Portishead Long Range (HF)
Newport* VHF 16; 09 11
Avonmouth Standard Port 10.11.21 VHF 16;09 11 12 14
St Ann's Head Celtic Radio VHF 16 24 0733 1933
St Gowan
Burry Port 10.11.16
Mumbles
Port Eynon
Port Talbot VHF 12 16; 11 12
Variation 7°W (1992)
Holyhead CG
Milford Haven CG
0 90 180 270
53°00'·00N
52°30'·00N
52°00'·00N
51°30'·00N
05°00'·00W
04°30'·00W
03°00'·00W
02°30'·00W

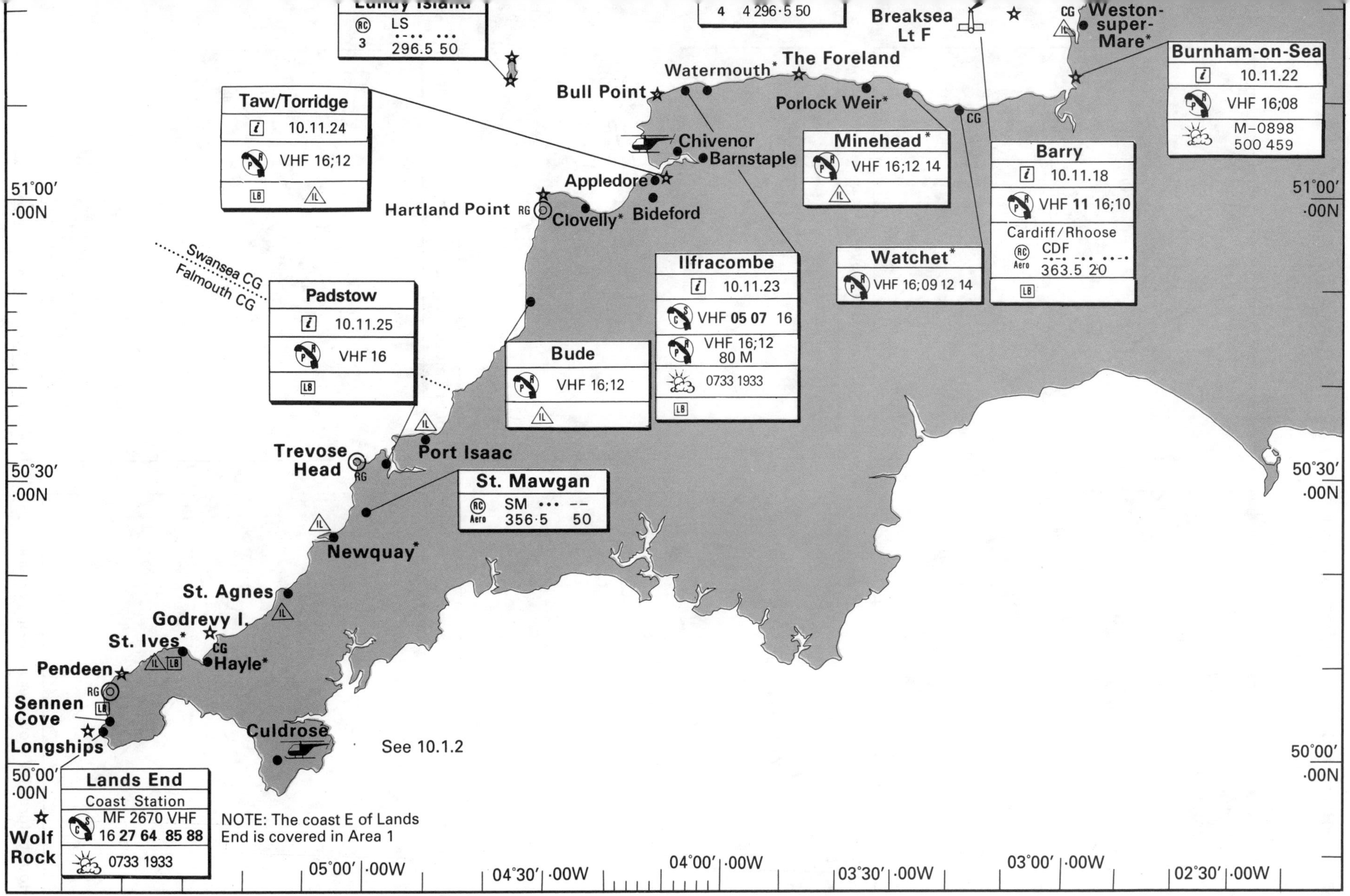

LS
3
296.5 50
4
4 296·5 50
Breaksea
Lt F
CG
Weston-
super-
Mare*
Burnham-on-Sea
10.11.22
VHF 16;08
M–0898
500 459
Watermouth*
The Foreland
Bull Point
Porlock Weir*
CG
Taw/Torridge
10.11.24
VHF 16;12
Chivenor
Barnstaple
Minehead*
VHF 16;12 14
Barry
10.11.18
VHF 11 16;10
Cardiff/Rhoose
CDF
363.5 20
Appledore
Hartland Point
RG
Clovelly*
Bideford
Swansea CG
Falmouth CG
Ilfracombe
10.11.23
VHF 05 07 16
VHF 16;12
80 M
0733 1933
Watchet*
VHF 16;09 12 14
Padstow
10.11.25
VHF 16
Bude
VHF 16;12
Trevose
Head
Port Isaac
St. Mawgan
SM
356·5 50
Newquay*
St. Agnes
Godrevy I.
St. Ives*
CG
Hayle*
Pendeen
Sennen
Cove
Longships
Culdrose
See 10.1.2
Lands End
Coast Station
MF 2670 VHF
16 27 64 85 88
0733 1933
Wolf
Rock
NOTE: The coast E of Lands
End is covered in Area 1
51°00′ ·00N
50°30′ ·00N
50°00′ ·00N
05°00′ ·00W
04°30′ ·00W
04°00′ ·00W
03°30′ ·00W
03°00′ ·00W
02°30′ ·00W

10.11.3 AREA 11 TIDAL STREAMS

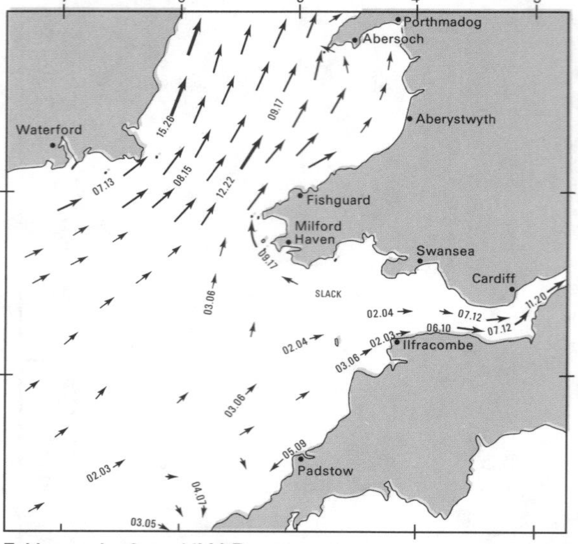
7°
6°
5°
4°
3°
52°
51°
Porthmadog
Abersoch
Aberystwyth
Waterford
Fishguard
Milford Haven
Swansea
Cardiff
SLACK
Ilfracombe
Padstow

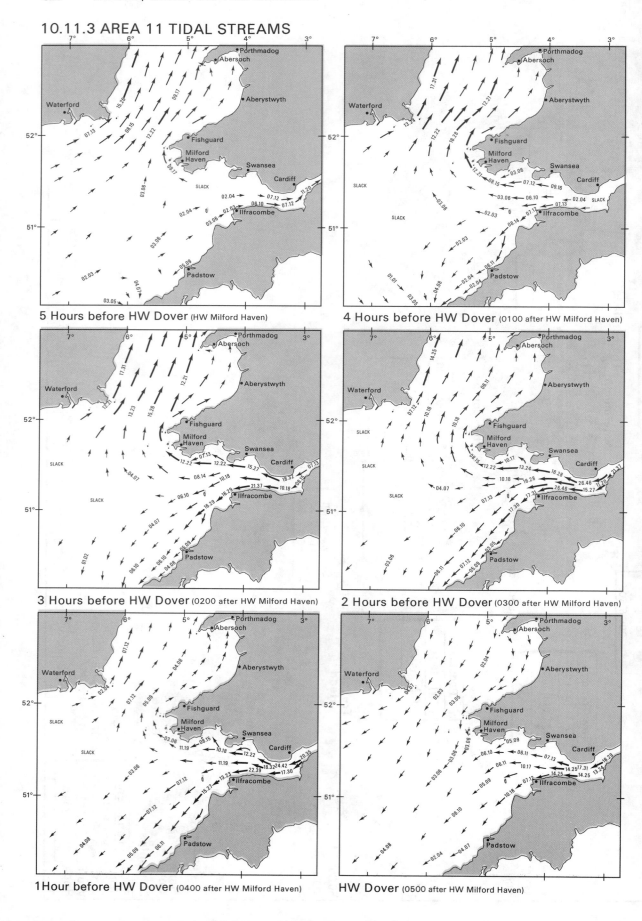

5 Hours before HW Dover (HW Milford Haven)

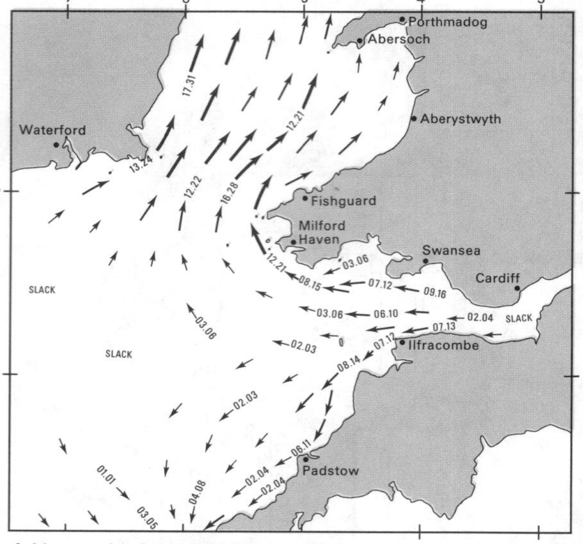
7°
6°
5°
4°
3°
52°
51°
Porthmadog
Abersoch
Aberystwyth
Waterford
Fishguard
Milford Haven
Swansea
Cardiff
SLACK
SLACK
SLACK
Ilfracombe
Padstow

4 Hours before HW Dover (0100 after HW Milford Haven)

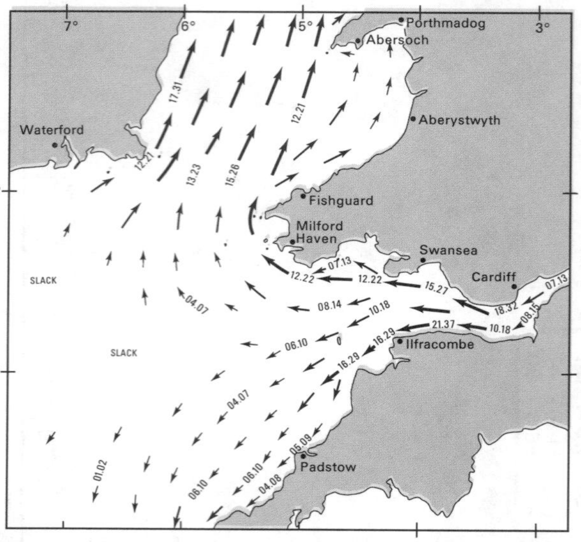
7°
6°
5°
4°
3°
52°
51°
Porthmadog
Abersoch
Aberystwyth
Waterford
Fishguard
Milford Haven
Swansea
Cardiff
SLACK
SLACK
Ilfracombe
Padstow

3 Hours before HW Dover (0200 after HW Milford Haven)

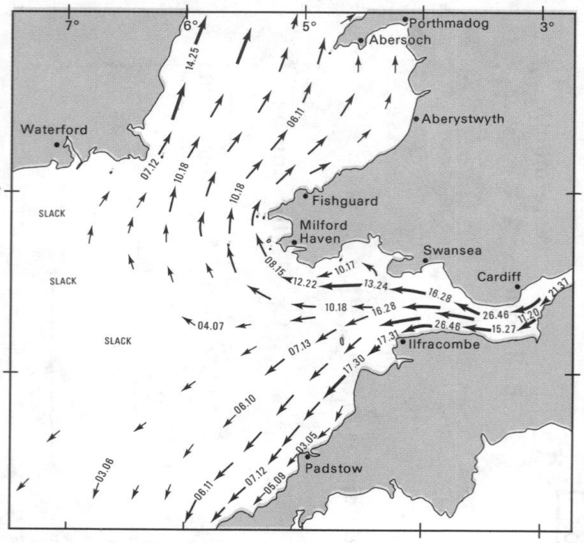
7°
6°
5°
4°
3°
52°
51°
Porthmadog
Abersoch
Aberystwyth
Waterford
Fishguard
Milford Haven
Swansea
Cardiff
SLACK
SLACK
SLACK
Ilfracombe
Padstow

2 Hours before HW Dover (0300 after HW Milford Haven)

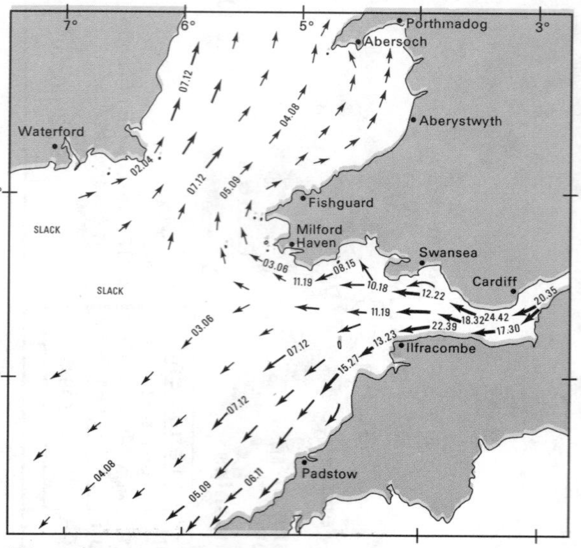
7°
6°
5°
4°
3°
52°
51°
Porthmadog
Abersoch
Aberystwyth
Waterford
Fishguard
Milford Haven
Swansea
Cardiff
SLACK
SLACK
Ilfracombe
Padstow

1 Hour before HW Dover (0400 after HW Milford Haven)

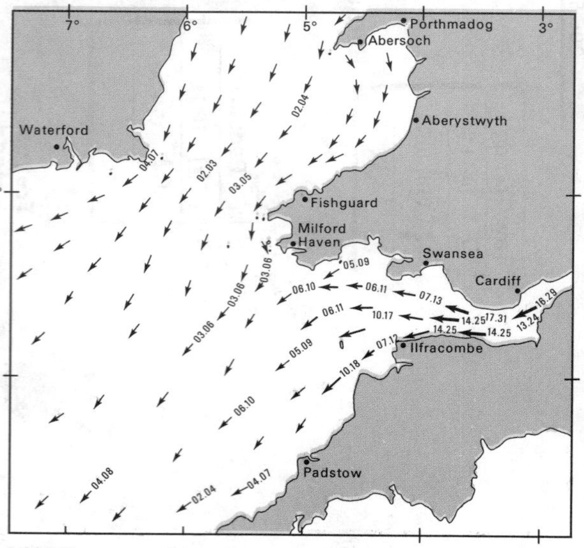
7°
6°
5°
4°
3°
52°
51°
Porthmadog
Abersoch
Aberystwyth
Waterford
Fishguard
Milford Haven
Swansea
Cardiff
Ilfracombe
Padstow

HW Dover (0500 after HW Milford Haven)

Southward 10.1.3 Northward 10.10.3 South Ireland 10.12.3

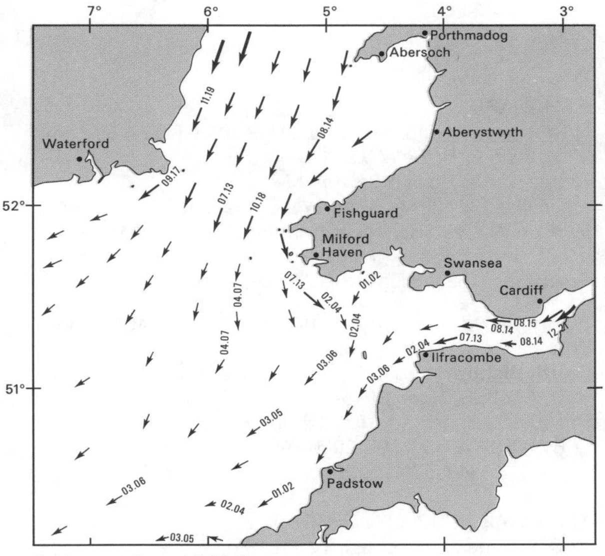
7°
6°
5°
4°
3°
52°
51°
Porthmadog
Abersoch
Aberystwyth
Waterford
Fishguard
Milford Haven
Swansea
Cardiff
Ilfracombe
Padstow

1 Hour after HW Dover (0600 after HW Milford Haven)

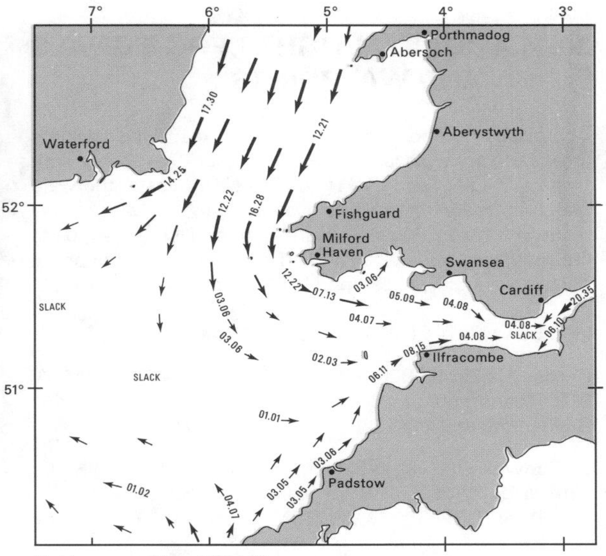
7°
6°
5°
4°
3°
52°
51°
Porthmadog
Abersoch
Aberystwyth
Waterford
Fishguard
Milford Haven
Swansea
Cardiff
Ilfracombe
Padstow
SLACK
SLACK
SLACK

2 Hours after HW Dover (0525 before HW Milford Haven)

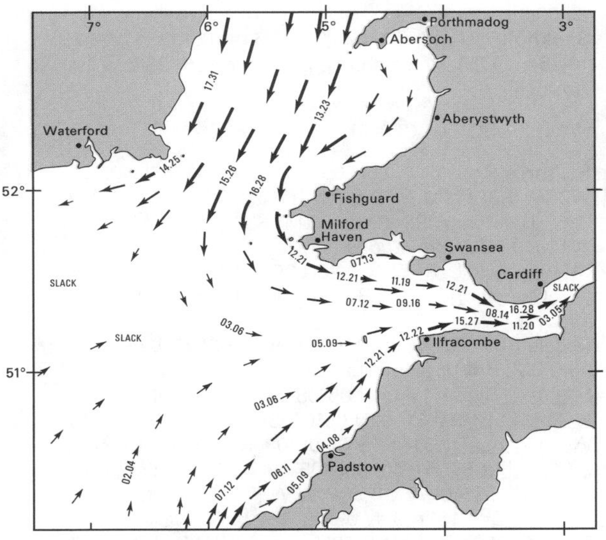
7°
6°
5°
4°
3°
52°
51°
Porthmadog
Abersoch
Aberystwyth
Waterford
Fishguard
Milford Haven
Swansea
Cardiff
Ilfracombe
Padstow
SLACK
SLACK
SLACK

3 Hours after HW Dover (0425 before HW Milford Haven)

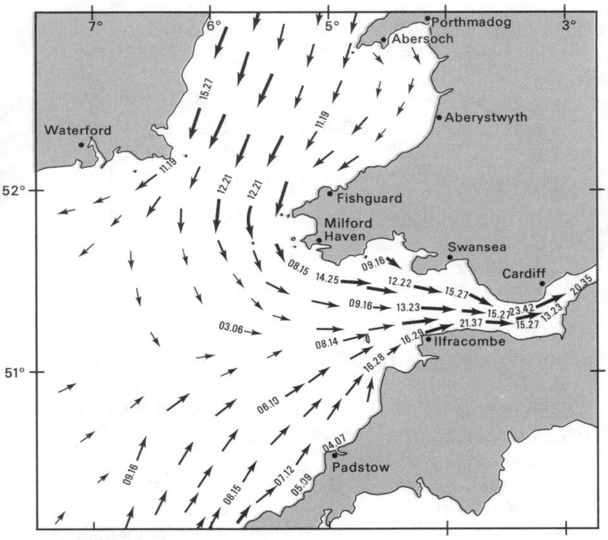
7°
6°
5°
4°
3°
52°
51°
Porthmadog
Abersoch
Aberystwyth
Waterford
Fishguard
Milford Haven
Swansea
Cardiff
Ilfracombe
Padstow

4 Hours after HW Dover (0325 before HW Milford Haven)

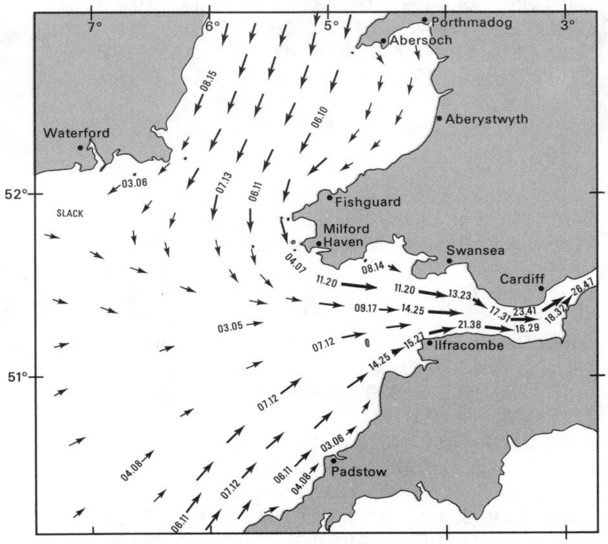
7°
6°
5°
4°
3°
52°
51°
Porthmadog
Abersoch
Aberystwyth
Waterford
Fishguard
Milford Haven
Swansea
Cardiff
Ilfracombe
Padstow
SLACK

5 Hours after HW Dover (0225 before HW Milford Haven)

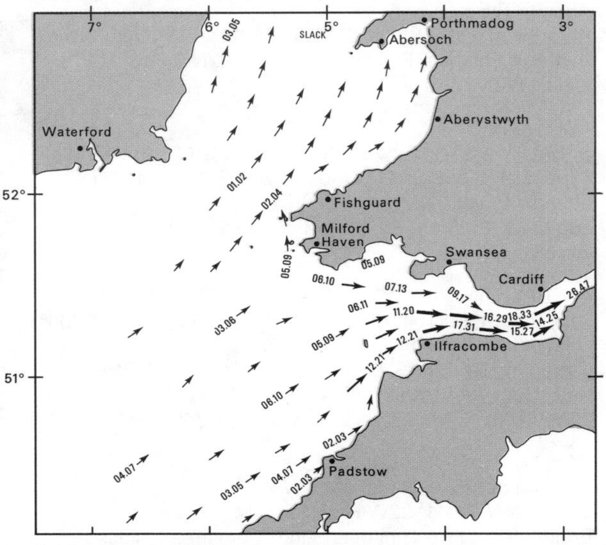
7°
6°
5°
4°
3°
52°
51°
Porthmadog
Abersoch
Aberystwyth
Waterford
Fishguard
Milford Haven
Swansea
Cardiff
Ilfracombe
Padstow
SLACK

6 Hours after HW Dover (0125 before HW Milford Haven)

10.11.4 COASTAL LIGHTS, FOG SIGNALS AND WAYPOINTS

Abbreviations used below are given in 1.4.1. Principal lights are in **bold** print, places in CAPITALS, and light-vessels, light floats and Lanbys in *CAPITAL ITALICS*. Unless otherwise stated lights are white. m—elevation in metres; M—nominal range in n. miles. Fog signals are in *italics*. Useful waypoints are underlined – use those on land with care. All geographical positions should be assumed to be approximate. See 4.2.2.

WALES—WEST COAST (see also 10.10.4)

Bardsey Is 52°44'·97N 04°47'·93W Fl (5) 15s 39m **26M**; W ■ Tr, R bands; obsc by Bardsey Is 198°-250° and in Tremadoc B when brg less than 260°; *Horn Mo(N) 45s*; RC.

St Tudwal's, W Island 52°47'·90N 04°28'·20W Fl WR 20s 46m **W15**, R13M; W ● Tr; vis W349°-169°, R169°-221°, W221°-243°, R243°-259°, W259°-293°, R293°-349°; obsc by East Island 211°-231°.

PWLLHELI.
No. 1 Lt By 52°33'·26N 04°23'·77W QG; SHM.
Pwllheli F WRG 12m; vis G155°-175°, R175°-245°, W245°-045°.
Sewer Outfall 52°53'·18N 04°23'·69W QR.
Abererch By 52°53'·50N 04°23'·00W; SPM (Apr-Oct).
Butlins By 52°53'·00N 04°22'·00W; SPM (Apr-Oct)
West End By 52°52'·40N 04°25'·50W; SPM (Apr- Oct).

Porthmadog Fairway Lt By 52°52'·87N 04°11'·02W L Fl 10s; SWM.
Shell Island 52°49'·54N 04°07'·64W Fl WRG 4s; vis G079°-124°, W124°-134°, R134°-179°; shown 15/3 - 30/11.

BARMOUTH.
Barmouth Outer Lt By 52°42'·60N 04°04'·76W L Fl 10s; SWM.
N Bank Y perch 52°42'·81N 04°03'·67W QR 4m 2M TE 1986.
Ynys y Brawd SE end 52°42'·97N 04°03'·07W Fl R 5s.
Bridge NW end 2 FR (hor).
Sarn Badrig Causeway Lt By 52°41'·17N 04°25'·30W Q (9) 15s; WCM; *Bell*.
Sarn-y-Bwch. Bwch By 52°34'·80N 04°13'·50W (unlit); WCM.

ABERDOVEY.
Aberdovey Outer By 52°31'·75N 04°06'·20W (unlit); SWM.
Cynfelyn Patches. Patches By 52°25'·82N 04°16'·30W (unlit); WCM.

ABERYSTWYTH.
S Breakwater Hd 52°24'·39N 04°05'·46W Fl (2) WG 10s 12m 10M; B col; vis G030°-053°, W053°-210°. 4 FR (vert) on radio tower 2·8M S.
Ldg Lts 138°. Front FR 4m 5M. Rear 52m from front FR 7m 6M.

ABERAERON.
S Pier 52°14'·60N 04°15'·87W Fl (3) G 10s 6M; vis 125°-200°.
N Pier Fl (4) R 15s 6M; vis 104°-178°.
Carreg Ina By 52° 13'.09N 04°20'·47W (unlit); NCM.
New Quay Pier Hd 52°12'·94N 04°21'·27W Fl WG 3s 12m W8M, G5M; G s vis W135°-252°, G252°-295°.

CARDIGAN.
CG Bldg 52°06'·98N 04°41'·14W 2 FR (vert).
52°06'·44N 04°41'·32W Fl (2) 5s; IDM.
Bridge, Iso Y 2s on upstream and downstream sides.

FISHGUARD.
N Breakwater Hd 52°00'·74N 04°58'·15W Fl G 4·5s 18m 13M; 8-sided Tr; *Bell (1) 8s* .
E Breakwater Hd Fl R 3s 10m 5M.
Lts in line 282°. Front 52°00'·7N 04°59'·2W FG 77m 5M; W ◆ on W mast. Rear 46m from front FG 89m 5M; W ◆ on W mast.
Penanglas, 152m S of Pt *Dia (2) 60s*; W obelisk.

Strumble Hd 52°01'·8N 05°04'·3W Fl (4) 15s 45m **29M**; W ● Tr; vis 038°-257°; (H24).
South Bishop 51°51'·15N 05°24'·65W Fl 5s 44m **24M**; W ● Tr; (H24); R; *Horn (3) 45s*.
Brawdy. St Brides Bay. Research Area, seaward Lt Bys.
Lt By A1 51°49'·30N 05°20'·00W Fl (4) Y 20s; SPM.
Lt By B1 51°48'·30N 05°20'·00W Fl (4) Y 20s; SPM.

The Smalls 51°43'·25N 05°40'·15W Fl (3) 15s 36m **25M**; W ● Tr, R bands; Racon. FR 33m 13M; same Tr; vis 253°-285° over Hats and Barrels Rk; both Lts shown H24; *Horn (2) 60s*.
Skokholm Island, SW end 51°41'·60N 05°17'·17W Fl R 10s 54m **17M**; W 8-sided Tr; part obsc 226°-258°; (H24); *Horn 15s*.

WALES—SOUTH COAST

St Ann's Hd 51°40'·85N 05°10'·35W Fl WR 5s 48m **W23M**, **R22/19M**; W 8-sided Tr; vis W233°-247°, R247°-285°, R (intens) 285°-314°, R314°-332°, W332°-124°, W129°-131°; *Horn (2) 60s*.
St Anne's Hd Lt By 51°40'·23N 05°10'·43W Fl R 2·5s; PHM.
Mid Channel Rocks Lt By 51°40'·17N 05°10'·07W Q (9) 15s; WCM.
Middle Chan Rocks Lt 51°40'·29N 05°09'·77W Fl (3) G 7s 18m 8M; B ●Tr, aluminium lantern.
Sheep Lt By 51°40'·04N 05°08'·26W QG; SHM.
Millbay Lt By 51°41'·02N 05°09'·38W Fl (2) R 5s; PHM.
W Chapel Lt By 51°40'·97N 05°08'·60W Fl G 10s; SHM.
E Chapel Lt By 51°40'·83N 05°08'·08W Fl R 5s; PHM.
Rat Lt By 51°40'·77N 05°07'·80W Fl G 5s; SHM.
Angle Lt By 51°41'·60N 05°08'·18W VQ; WCM.
Thorn Rock Lt By 51°41'·50N 05°07'·70W Q (9) 15s; WCM.
Dakotian Lt By 51°42'·13N 05°08'·22W Q (3) 10s; ECM.
Chapel Lt By 51°41'·63N 05°06'·80W Fl G 5s; SHM.
Stack Lt By 51°42'·00N 05°06'·47W Fl R 2·5s; PHM.
S Hook Lt By 51°40'·80N 05°06'·03W Q (6) +L Fl 15s; WCM.
Esso Lt By 51°41'·72N 05°05'·17W Q Fl; NCM.
E Angle Lt By 51°41'·68N 05°04'·20W Fl (3) G 10s; SHM.

MILFORD HAVEN.
W Blockhouse Pt 51°41'·27N 05°09·40W Ldg Lts 022·5° F 54m 13M; B stripe on W Tr; vis 004·5°-040·5°.
Watwick Pt Rear, 0·5M from front F 80m 15M; vis 013·5°-031·5°.
Dale Fort Fl (2) WR 5s 20m W5M, R3M; vis R222°-276°, W276°-019°.
Great Castle Hd 51°42'·65N 05°07'·00W F WRG 27m W5M, R3M, G3M; W ■ Tr, B stripe; vis R243°-281°, G281°-299°, W299°-029°. Same Tr Ldg Lts 039·8° Oc 4s 27m **15M**; ; vis 031·2°-048·2°.
Little Castle Hd 51°43'·02N 05°06'·52W rear, 890m from front Oc 8s 53m **15M**; vis 031·2°-048·2°.
Pembroke Dock Ldg Lts 153°. Front QG 5m; W ◆, B stripe. Rear, 82m from front, QG 9m; W ◆, B stripe.
Turbot Bank Lt By 51°37'·40N 05°10'·00W VQ (9) 10s; WCM.

WALES—SOUTH COAST—BRISTOL CHANNEL

SAINT GOWAN LT V 51°30'·50N 04°59'·80W Fl 20s 12m **26M**; R hull with Lt Tr amidships; *Horn (3) 60s*; Racon.
Caldey Is 51°37'·86N 04°41'·00W Fl(3) WR 20s 65m W14M, R12M; W ● Tr; vis R173°-212°, W212°-088°, R088°- 102°.
Eel Pt By 51°38'·83N 04°42'·17W (unlit); SHM.
Giltar Spit By 51°39'·00N 04°42'·05W (unlit); PHM.
Spaniel By 51°38'·03N 04°39'·67W (unlit); ECM.
Woolhouse By 51°39'·32N 04°39'·62W (unlit); WCM.
North Highcliff By 51°39'·35N 04°40'·70W (unlit); NCM.

TENBY.
Pier Hd 51°40'·37N 04°41'·81W FR 7m 7M.
Saundersfoot Pier Hd 51°42'·55N 04°41'·68W Fl R 5s 6m 7M.

CARMARTHEN BAY.
DZ1 By 51°42'·05N 04°35'·90W (unlit); SPM.
DZ2 Lt By 51°39'·95N 04°37'·62W Fl Y 2·5s; SPM.
DZ3 By 51°37'·35N 04°37'·70W (unlit); SPM.
DZ7 Lt By 51°38'·08N 04°30'·05W Fl Y 10s; SPM.
DZ4 Lt By 51°35'·70N 04°29'·95W Fl Y 5s; SPM.
DZ8 By 51°41'·50N 04°24'·30W (unlit); SPM.
DZ6 By 51°38'·00N 04°24'·30W (unlit); SPM.
DZ5 Lt By 51°36'·35N 04°24'·30W Fl Y 2·5s; SPM.

Burry Port 51°40'·5N 04°14'·9W Barrel Post QR 1M (occas). W breakwater FR 7M.
Whiteford Lt Ho Fl 5s 7m 7M; Tr; (occas).
West Helwick (W.HWK) Lt By 51°31'·37N 04°23'·58W Q (9) 15s; WCM; *Whis*; Racon.
East Helwick Lt By 51°31'·77N 04°12'·60W VQ (3) 5s; ECM; *Bell*.

SWANSEA BAY.
Ledge Lt By 51°29'·90N 03°58'·70W VQ (6) + L Fl 10s; WCM.
Mixon By 51°33'·10N 03°58.70W (unlit); PHM; *Bell*.
Grounds Lt By 51°32'°90N 03°53'·40W VQ (3) 5s; ECM.
Mumbles 51°34'·00N 03°58'·20W Fl (4) 10s 35m **17M**; W Tr; Fog Det Lt Fl 5s 28m; vis 331·5°-336·5°; *Horn(3) 60s*.
Railway Pier Hd 2 FR (vert) 11m 9M; W Tr.
SW Inner Green Grounds Lt By 51°34'·04N 03°56'·95W Q (6) + L Fl 15s; WCM; *Bell*.

SWANSEA.
Outer Fairway Lt By 51°35'·50N 03°56'·06W QG; SHM; *Bell*.
W Pier Hd Fl (2) R 10s 11m 9M; FR Lts on radio mast 1·3M NNE.
E Breakwater Hd 51°36'·35N 03°55'·55W 2 FG (vert) 10m 6M; W Tr; *Horn 30s*.
Lts in line 020°. Jetty Hd Front 2 FG (vert) 5m 2M. Rear 260m from front FG 6M (mark E limit of dredged area, obsc bearing less than 020°).

RIVER NEATH.
Approach Chan Lt By 51°35'·70N 03°52'·75W Fl G 5s; SHM.
SE training wall near S end 51°36'·30N 03°51'·89W 2 FG (vert) 6m 5M R mast.
Training wall, middle FG 6m 5M; R mast.
Training wall N end 3 FG (vert) 6m 5M; R mast.

PORT TALBOT.
Cabenda Lt By 51°33'·43N 03°52'·27W VQ (6) + L Fl 10s; WCM.
Outer chan Bys: 51°33'·67N 03°51'·22W Fl G 5s; SHM.
P.Talbot N Outer Lt By 51°33'·76N 03°51'·30W Fl R 5s; PHM.
P. Talbot N Inner Lt By 51°34'·19N 03°50'·17W Fl R 3s; PHM; *Horn*.
Ldg Lts 059·8° (occas). Front Oc R 4s 12m 6M; Y & Or ◆ on Tr. Rear 400m from front, Oc R 6s 32m 6M; Y & Or ◆ on Tr.
N Breakwater Hd Fl (4) R 10s 11m 3M; metal pylon.
S Breakwater Hd 51°34'·43N 03°48'·95W Fl G 3s 11m 3M.
Sker Pt. Kenfig Lt By 51°29'·71N 03°46'·52W Q (3) 10s; ECM.

BRISTOL CHANNEL—EASTERN PART (NORTH SHORE)

W Scarweather (W.SCAR) Lt By 51°28'·28N 03°55'·50W Q (9) 15s; WCM; *Bell*; Racon.
S Scarweather (S.SCAR) Lt By 51°27'·58N 03°51'·50W Q (6) + L Fl 15s; WCM.
Hugo By 51°28'·80N 03°48'·30W (unlit); PHM.
E Scarweather By 51°28'·12N 03°46'·23W (unlit); ECM.

PORTHCAWL.
Fairy By 51°27'·83N 03°42'·00W (unlit); WCM.
Tusker Lt By 51°26'·97N 03°40'·55W Fl (2) R 5s; PHM.
Porthcawl Breakwater Hd 51°28'·33N 03°41'·95W F WRG 10m W6M, R4M, G4M; W 6-sided Tr, B base; vis G302°-036°, W036°-082°, R082°-122°. In line with Saint Hilary radio mast (Aero QR) 094° leads through Shord chan.
W Nash Lt By 51°25'·95N 03°45'·88W VQ(9) 10s; WCM.
Middle Nash By 51°25'·00N 03°40'·00W (unlit); WCM.
E Nash Lt By 51°24'·03N 03°34'·03W Q (3) 10s; ECM.

Nash 51°24'·00N 03°33'·05W Fl (2) WR 10s 56m **W21M**, **R20/17M**; W ● Tr; vis R280°-290°, W290°-097°, R097°-100°, R (intens) 100°-104°, R104°-120°, W120°-128°; *Siren (2) 45s*; RC.
Saint Hilary 51° 27'·4N 03°24'·1W Aero QR 346m 11M; radio mast; 4 FR (vert) on same mast 6M.
Breaksea Pt intake 51°22'·5N 03°24'·5W Fl R 11m. FR Lt on radio mast 3·4M ENE.

BREAKSEA Lt Float 51°19'·85N 03°19'·00W Fl 15s 11m **16M**; Racon; F riding Lt 5M; *Horn (2) 30s*.
Wenvoe 51°27'·5N 03°16'·8W Aero Fl W 365m 12M; radio mast.
Merkur Lt By 51°21'·85N 03°15'·87W Fl R 2·5s; PHM.
Welsh Water Barry W Lt By 51°22'·23N 03°16'·84W Fl R 5s; PHM.

BARRY.
W Breakwater Hd Fl 2·5s 12m 10M; W ● Tr.
E Breakwater Hd 51°23'·50N 03°15'·37W QG 7m 8M.
W One Fathom Lt By 51°20'·40N 03°14'·50W Q (9) 15s; WCM.
N One Fathom Lt By 51°21'·10N 03°11'·75W Q; NCM.
Mackenzie Lt By 51°21'·72N 03°08'·15W QR; PHM.
Wolves Lt By 51°2310N 03°08'·81W VQ; NCM.

Flat Holm, SE Pt 51°22'·52N 03°07'·05W Fl (3) WR 10s 50m W16**M**, R13M; W ● Tr; vis R106°-140°, W140°-151°, R151°-203°, W203°-106°; (H24); *Horn 30s*.
Weston Lt By 51°22'·80N 03°05'·20W Fl (2) R 5s; PHM.
Monkstone Rock Lt 51°24'·86N 03°05'·93W Fl 5s 13m 13M; R col on ● Tr.

CARDIFF/PENARTH ROADS.
Ranie Lt By 51 24.22N° 3 09.30W Fl (2) R 5s; PHM.
S Cardiff Lt By 51°24'·15N 03°08'·48W Q (6) + L Fl 15s; WCM; *Bell* .
Mid Cardiff Lt By 51°25'·57N 03°08'·00W Fl (3) G 10s; SHM.

11

Cardiff Spit By 51°25'·53N 03°06'·42W (unlit); PHM.
N Cardiff Lt By 51°27'·77N 03°05'·28W QG; SHM.

PENARTH.
Promenade Pier near Hd 2 FR (vert) 8/6m 3M; *Reed Mo(BA) 60s*, sounded 10 min before a steamer expected.
Boat Club pontoon 51°26'·8N 03°10'·5W Q.

CARDIFF.
Outer Wrach Lt By 51°26'·17N 03°09'·38W Q (9) 15s; WCM.
Ldg Lts 349°. **Front** 51°27'·7N 03°09'·9W F 4m **17M**. **Rear** 520m from front F 24m **17M**.
Queen Alexandra Dock ent S Jetty Hd 2 FG (vert); Tfc sigs; *Dia 60s*.

Tail Patch Lt By 51°23'·50N 03°03'·59W QG; SHM.
Hope Lt By 51°24'·82N 03°02'·60W Q (3) 10s; ECM.
NW Elbow Lt By 51°26'·10N 02°59'·95W VQ (9) 10s; WCM; *Bell*.
English and Welsh Grounds Lt By 51°26'·90N 03°00'·10W L Fl 10s 7M; Racon; SWM; *Bell & Whis*.

NEWPORT DEEP.
Newport Deep Lt By 51°29'·33N 02°59'·03W Fl (3)G 10s; SHM; *Bell*.

RIVER USK.
East Usk 51°32'·38N 02°57'·93W Fl (2) WRG 10s 11m **W15M**, R11M, G11M; W ● Tr; vis W284°-290°, R290°-017°, W017°-037°, G037°-115°, W115°-120°. Also Oc WRG 10s 10m W11M, R9M, G9M; vis G018°-022°, W022°- 024°, R024°-028°.
Alexandra Dock, S Lock W Pier Hd 2 FR (vert) 9m 6M; *Horn 60s*.
E Pier Hd 2 FG (vert) 9m 6M.
Julians Pill Ldg Lts about 057°. 51°33'·3N 02°57'·9W. Rear, 61m from front, FG 8m 4M. Common Front FG 5m 4M. Ldg Lts 149°. Rear, 137m from front FG 9m 4M.
Bellport Jetty 51°33'·6N 02°58'·0W 2 FG (vert) 6m.
Dallimores Wharf 51°33'·8N 02°58'·4W 2 FG (vert).
Transporter Bridge W side 2 FR (vert); 2 FY (vert) shown on transporter car;
E side 2 FG (vert). Centres of George Street and Newport Bridges marked by FY Lts.

BRISTOL DEEP.
N Elbow Lt By 51°27'·12N 02°57'·08W QG; SHM; *Bell* .
S Mid Grounds Lt By 51°27'·78N 02°57'·13W Fl (4) R 15s; PHM.
E Mid Grounds Lt By 51°27'·93N 02°54'·58W Fl R 5s; PHM.
Clevedon Lt By 51°27'·33N 02°54'·18W VQ; NCM.
Welsh Hook Lt By 51°28'·40N 02°52'·00W Fl (2) R 5s; PHM; *Bell* .
Avon Lt By 51°27'·77N 02°51'·65W Fl G 2·5s; SHM.
Clevedon Pier detached Hd Fl G 10s 7m 3M.
Walton Bay, Old signal station Fl 2·5s 35m 2M.
Black Nore Pt 51°29'·05N 02°47'·95W Fl (2) 10s 11m **15M**; W ● Tr; obsc by Sand Pt when brg less than 049°; vis 044°-243°.
Newcome Lt By 51°29'·93N 02°46'·95W Fl (3) R 10s; PHM.
Cockburn Lt By 51°30'·43N 02°44'·00W Fl R 2·5s; PHM.

Portishead Pt 51°29'·64N 02°46'·34W Q (3) 10s 9m **16M**; B Tr, W base; vis 060°-262°; *Horn 20s*.

PORTISHEAD.
Pier Hd 51°29'·66N 02°45'·18W Iso G 2s 5m 3M; W col; *Horn 15s*, sounded when vessel expected.
Lock E side 2 FR (vert) 7m 1M; Gy col; (occasl).
Lock W side 2 FG (vert) 7m 1M; Gy col; (occasl).
Portbury Wharf. Lts in line 191·6°. Front 51°29'·5N 02°44'·1W Oc G 5s 7m 10M; vis 171·5°-211·5°. Rear 100m from front Oc G 5s 12m 10M; vis 171·5°-211·5°.
Seabank. Lts in line 103°. Front 51°30'·0N 02°43'·7W Oc (2) 10s 13m 5M; vis 086·5°-119·5°. Rear, 150m from front Oc (2) 10s 13m 5M; vis 086·5°-119·5°.
Royal Portbury Dock 51°30'·1N 02°43'·6W L Fl G 15s 5m 6M; Gy pillar.
Pier corner Fl G 2s 7m 7M; Gy pillar; *Dia 30s*, sounded HW-4 to HW+3.
Knuckle 51°29'·92N 02°43'·60W Oc G 5s 6m 6M.

AVONMOUTH.
Royal Edward Dock N Pier Hd Fl 10s 15m 10M; ● Tr; vis 060°-228·5°.
Ldg Lts 184·5°. Front QG 5m 6M; vis 129°-219°. Rear 220m from front, S pier Hd 51°30'·34N 02°43'·02W Oc RG 30s 9m 10M; ● Tr; vis R294°-036°, G036°-194°; *Bell 10s*.
King Road Ldg Lts 072·4°. N Pier Hd Front 51°30'·5N 02°43'·0W Oc R 5s 5m 9M; W obelisk, R bands; vis 062°-082°. Rear, 546m from front, QR 15m 10M; B&W striped ● on Tr, Or bands; vis 066°-078°.
Royal Edward Lock N side 2 FR (vert) 8m 1M, S side 2 FG (vert) 8m 1M.
Oil Jetty Hd, 51°30'·6N 02°42'·8W 2 FG (vert) 6m 2M.
Gypsum effluent pipe Fl Y 3s 3m 2M; Y Bn.

RIVER AVON.
Ldg Lts 127·2°. Front 51°30'·05N 02°42'·47W FR 7m 3M; W ■, R stripes; vis 010°-160°. Rear 142m from front FR 17m 3M; W ●, vis 048°-138°.
Monoliths 51°30'·2N 02°42'·7W Fl R 5s 5m 3M; W ■, B stripes on W col; vis 317°-137°.
Saint George Ldg Lts 173·3°, both Oc G 5s 6m 1M, on Or cols; vis 158°-305°; synchronised.
Nelson Pt 51°29'·82N 02°42'·43W F IR 3s 9m 3M; W mast.
Broad Pill 51°29'·6N 02°41'·8W QY 11m 1M; W Tr.
Avonmouth Bridge, NE end L Fl R 10s 5m 3M, SW end L Fl G 10s 5m 3M, showing up and downstream. From here to City Docks, Oc G Lts are shown on S bank, and R or Y Lts on N bank.

CUMBERLAND BASIN.
Ent N side 2 FR (vert) 6m 1M; S side W end 2 FG (vert) 7m 1M;
Plimsoll Bridge centre Iso 5s 6m each side.

AVON BRIDGE.
N side FR 6m 1M on bridge pier. Centre of span Iso 5s 6m 1M. S side FG 6m 1M on bridge pier.

ENGLAND—WEST COAST—RIVER SEVERN

Bedwin Lt By 51°32'·33N 02°43'·15W Q (3) 10s; ECM.

THE SHOOTS.
Lower Shoots Bn 51°33'·62N 02°42'·05W (unlit); SHM.
Upper Shoots Bn 51°34'·20N 02°41'·79W (unlit); WCM.
Charston Rk 51°35'·32N 02°41'·60W Fl 5s 5m 9M; W ● Tr, B stripe; vis 203°-049°.
Redcliffe Ldg Lts 012·9° Front F Bu 16m; vis 358°-028°. Rear 320m from front F Bu 33m 10M.
Chapel Rk 51°36'·40N 02°39'·13W Fl WRG 2·6s 6m W8M, G5M; B Tr, W lantern; vis W213°-284°, R284°-049°, W049°-051·5°, G051·5°-160°.

RIVER WYE.
Wye Bridge, 2F Bu (hor); centre of span.

SEVERN BRIDGE.
West Tr 3QR (hor) on upstream and downstream sides; Horn *(3) 45s*; Obscured 040°-065°.
Centre of span Q Bu, each side.
E Tr 3QG (hor) on upstream and downstream sides.

Aust 51°36'·1N 02°37'·9W 2 QG (vert) 11/5m 6M; power cable pylon.
Lyde Rk 51°36'·9N 02°38'·6W QR 5m 5M; B Tr, W lantern.
Sedbury 2 FR (vert) 10m 3M.
Slime Road Ldg Lts 210·4°. Front F Bu 9m 5M; W hut. Rear, 91 m from front, F Bu 16m 5M; B Tr, W lantern.
Inward Rocks Ldg Lts 252·5°. Front F 6m 6M; B Tr. Rear, 183m from front, F 13m 2M; W hut and mast.
Sheperdine Ldg Lts 070·4°. Front F 7m 5M; B Tr, W lantern. Rear, 168m from front, F 13m 5M; B Tr, W lantern; *Bell (26) 60s*.
Narlwood Rks Ldg Lts 224·9°. Front Fl 2s 5m 8M; Y Bn, B lantern. Rear, 198m from front Fl 2s 9m 8M; Y Bn, B lantern.
Conigre Ldg Lts 077·5°. Front F Vi 21m 8M. Rear, 213m from front F Vi 29m 8M.
Fishing House Ldg Lts 218·7°. Front F 5m 2M: W hut and post. Rear F 11m 2M; W hut and mast.

BERKELEY.
Power Station 3x2 FG (vert); *Siren (2) 30s*.
Bull Rk Iso 2s 6m 8M.
Berkeley Pill Ldg Lts 187·8°. Front FG 5m 2M. Rear, 152m from front, FG 11m 2M; both B Trs, W lanterns.
Panthurst Pill F Bu 6m 1M; Y pillar.
Lydney Docks Pier Hd FW or R (tidal); *Gong (tidal)*.

SHARPNESS DOCKS.
S Pier Hd 2 FG (vert) 6m 3M; *Siren 20s*.
N Pier 2 FR (vert) 6m 3M.
Old ent S side, *Siren 5s* (tidal).

ENGLAND—BRISTOL CHANNEL (SOUTH SHORE)

WESTON-SUPER-MARE.
Pier Hd 51°20'·85N 02°59'·17W 2 FG (vert) 6/5m.
E Culver Lt By 51°17'·70N 03°14'·50W Q (3) 10s; ECM.
W Culver Lt By 51°16'·85N 03°19'·20W VQ (9) 10s; WCM.
Gore Lt By 51°13'·93N 03°09'·70W Iso 5s; SWM; *Bell*.

BURNHAM-ON-SEA.
Entrance, 51°14'·90N 02°59'·85W Fl 7·5s 28m **17M**; W ● Tr, R stripe; vis 074°-164°.
Dir Lt 078°. Dir F WRG 24m **W16M**, R12M, G12M; same Tr; vis G073°-077°, W077°-079°, R079°-083°.
Seafront Lts in line 112°, moved for changing chan, Front FR 6m 3M W ■, Or stripe on sea wall. Rear FR 12m 3M; church Tr.
Brue 51°13'·5N 03°00'·2W QR 4m 3M; W mast, R bands.
Stert Reach 51°11'·3N 03°01'·9W Fl 3s 4m 7M; vis 187°-217°.
Hinkley Pt, water intake 51°12'·9N 03°07'·8W 2 FG (vert) 7/5m 3M.

WATCHET.
W Breakwater Hd 51°11'·03N 03°19'·67W FG 9m 9M; R 6-sided Tr, W lantern, G cupola.
FR Lts on radio masts 1·6M SSW.
E pier 2 FR (vert) 3M.

MINEHEAD.
Breakwater Hd Fl (2) G 5s 4M; vis 127°-262°.
Sewer Outfall 51°12'·95N 03°28'·22W QG 6m 7M; SHM Bn.

Lynmouth Foreland 51°14'·70N 03°47'·13W Fl (4) 15s 67m **26M**; W ● Tr; vis 083°-275° (H24).

LYNMOUTH.
River training arm 2 FR (vert) 6m 5M.
Harbour arm 2 FG (vert) 6m 5M.
Sand Ridge By 51°14'·98N 03°49'·70W (unlit); SHM.
Copperas Rock By 51°13'·77N 04°00'·50W (unlit); SHM.

ILFRACOMBE.
Lantern Hill 51°12'·64N 04°06'·70W FR 39m 6M; W lantern on chapel.
Promenade Pier N end 2 FG (vert) *Siren 30s (occas)*.
Horseshoe Lt By 51°15'·00N 04°12'·85W Q; NCM.

Bull Point 51°11'·95N 04°12'·05W Fl (3) 10s 54m **25M**; W ● Tr. FR 48m 12M; same Tr; vis 058°-096°.

Morte Stone By 51°11'·30N 04°14'·85W (unlit); SHM.
Baggy Leap By 51°08'·90N 04°16'·90W (unlit); SHM.

BIDEFORD.
Bideford Fairway Lt By 51°05'·23N 04°16'·17W L Fl 10s; SWM; *Bell*.
Bideford Bar By 51°04'·86N 04°14'·63W; SHM.
Instow Ldg Lts 118°. **Front** Oc 6s 22m **15M**. **Rear** 427m from front Oc 10s 38m **15M**. Both on W Trs and vis 103°-133°; (H24).
Crow Pt Fl R 5s 8m 4M; W Tr; vis 225°-045°.

LUNDY.
Near North Pt 51°12'·07N 04°40'·57W Fl (2) 20s 50m **24M**; W ● Tr; vis 009°-285°.
SE Pt 51°09'·70N 04°39'·30W Fl 5s 53m **24M**; W ● Tr; vis 170°-073°; RC; *Horn 25s*.

Hartland Pt 51°01'·3N 04°31'·4W Fl (6) 15s 37m **25M**; (H24); W ● Tr; *Horn 60s*.

PADSTOW.
Stepper Pt 50°34'·11N 04°56'·63W L Fl 10s 12m 4M.
St Saviour's Pt L Fl G 10s 1M; G ▲.
Kettle Rk QG 2m.
N Quay Hd 50°32'·5N 2 FG (vert) 6m 2M.
Trevose Hd 50°32'·93N 05°02'·06W Fl R 5s 62m **25M**; W ● Tr. *Horn (2) 30s*.

NEWQUAY.
N Pier Hd 2 FG (vert) 5m 2M.
S Pier Hd 2 FR (vert) 4m 2M; ● Tr.
The Stones Lt By 50°15'·60N 05°25'·40W Q; NCM; *Bell*; *Whis*.
Godrevy Is 50°14'·50N 05°23'·95W Fl WR 10s 37m W12M, R9M; W 8-sided Tr; vis W022°-101°, R101°-145°, W145°-272°.
4 FR(vert) Lts on radio mast 6·5M SE.

HAYLE.
Lts in line 180°. Front 50°11'·5N 05°26'·1W F 17m 4M. Rear 110m from front, F 23m 4M.

ST IVES.
E Pier Hd 2 FG (vert) 8m 5M; W ● Tr.
W Pier Hd 2 FR (vert) 5m 3M Gy col.

Pendeen 50°09'·8N 05°40'·2W Fl 4) 15s 59m **27M**; W ● Tr; vis 042°-240°; in B between Gurnard Hd and Pendeen it shows to coast; *Siren 20s*. For Lts further SW see 10.1.4.

11

10.11.5 PASSAGE INFORMATION

CARDIGAN BAY (charts 1971, 1972, 1973)

Hbrs are mostly on a lee shore, and most have bars which make them dangerous to approach in bad weather. In the approaches to St Tudwal's Is (lit) and Abersoch (10.11.7) there may be overfalls off Trwyn Cilan. In N part of bay there are three major dangers to coasting yachts, as described briefly below. St Patrick's Causeway runs 11M SW from Mochras Pt. It is mostly large loose stones, and dries for much of its length. In strong winds the sea breaks heavily at all states of tide. The outer end is marked by a Lt By. At the inner end there is a chan about 0·5M offshore, which can be taken with care at half tide.

Sarn-y-Bwch runs 4M WSW from Pen Bwch Pt. It is composed of rky boulders, drying in places 0·6M offshore and with depths of 0·3m extending nearly 3M seaward. There is a By off W end. Sarn Cynfelyn and Cynfelyn Patches extend a total of 6·5M offshore, with depths of 1·5m in places, from a point about 2M N of Aberystwyth (10.11.12). There is a By off outer end. Not quite halfway along the bank is Main Chan, 0·3M wide, running roughly N and S, but not marked.

Firing exercises take place in the S part of Cardigan B (chart 1973). Beware targets and mooring Bys, some unlit.

THE BISHOPS AND THE SMALLS (chart 1478)

If bound N or S along St George's Chan (ie not proceeding to Cardigan B or Milford Haven) the easiest route is W of the Bishops and the Smalls, but note the TSS (see Fig. 2(5)). This is the best route by night but, if bound to/from Milford Haven or S Wales hbrs, it is possible to pass inside both the Smalls and Grassholm Is. Even shorter is the route inside the Bishops, passing close W of Ramsey Is, and outside Skomer Is and Skokholm Is. The shortest route of all involves the passage of Ramsey Sound and Jack Sound, but this is not recommended except by daylight, in good weather, and with the right tidal conditions – preferably at nps. Only the main features of these various chans are described below, but for full directions refer to the *W Coasts of England and Wales Pilot*, or to *Irish Sea Cruising Guide*.

The Bishops and the Clerks (chart 1482) are Is and rks 2·5M W and NW of Ramsey Is, a bird sanctuary SSW of St David's Hd. N Bishop is the N Is of the group, but Bell Rk which has depth of 2·2m lies 0·3M ENE of N Bishop and between them is a ridge with heavy overfalls and tide rips. S Bishop (Lt, fog sig, RC) is the SW Is, with Rks extending 0·5M NE and NW.

Between S Bishop and Ramsey Is are several dangers, including Daufraich (Is 0·7M NE of S Bishop) with Maen Daufraich (dries) close N of it; Cribog (dries) and Moelyn (dries) respectively 0·2M and 0·35M ENE of Daufraich; there are heavy overfalls SE of Moelyn. There is however a chan 0·25M W of Ramsey Is, if care is taken to avoid dangers S and close W of Ramsey Is. This chan passes E of Llechau-uchaf (Rk 1·5m high) and Llechau-isaf (dries) which are near N and S ends respectively of foul ground with heavy overfalls about 0·65M W of Ramsey Is. Beware also Carreg Rhoson, with rks extending from it to NE and SW, roughly between N Bishop and S Bishop; Maen Rhoson (rk 9m high) 0·2M NW of Careg Rhoson; and Carreg-trai (dry) 1·75M NE of Carreg Rhoson. Note also Gwahan, a rk 1·5m high, about 0·4M N of Ramsey Is. 2M W of The Bishops the S-going stream begins at HW Milford Haven +0400, and the N-going at HW Milford Haven –0225, sp rates 2 kn. Between The Bishops and Ramsey Is the SW-going stream begins at HW Milford Haven +0330, and the NE-going at HW Milford Haven –0255, sp rates 5 kn.

Ramsey Sound (chart 1482) should be taken at slack water (see also above). The S-going stream begins at HW Milford Haven +0300, and the N-going at HW Milford Haven –0325, sp rates 6 kn at The Bitches where chan is narrowest (0·2M) and decreasing N and S. The Bitches are rks extending 0·2M E from middle of E side of Ramsey Is. Other dangers are Gwahan and Carreg-gafeiliog, respectively on W and E sides of N end of chan: Horse Rk (dries) and associated overfalls about 0·5M NNE of The Bitches; Shoe Rk (dries) on E side of chan at S end; and rks extending 0·5M SSE from S end of Ramsey Is.

St Brides B (10.11.26) provides anch in settled weather or offshore winds, but is a trap in westerlies. Solva is a little hbr with shelter for boat capable of taking ground, or anch E of Black Rk off the entrance.

If passing outside The Smalls (Lt, fog sig, Racon) beware SW Rk (dries) 0·3M SW of Lt Ho, the only danger W of it. Near The Smalls the S-going stream begins at HW Milford Haven +0515, and the N-going at HW Milford Haven –0045, sp rates 5 kn near the rks but decreasing to 3 kn when 2M S, W or N of them.

As mentioned above, there are various chans inside The Smalls. Hats and Barrels are shallow rky areas respectively about 1·75M and 4M E of The Smalls. They are usually marked by tide rips and overfalls, and by breaking seas in bad weather. The chan between The Smalls and Hats is over 1M wide, but beware E Rk 0·25M E of Lt Ho. Chan between Hats and Barrels is 2M wide. There are no Ldg marks for either of these chans.

Grassholm is 7M E of The Smalls, and has no dangers extending more than 1·05M, although there is a race either end and strong tidal eddies so that it is advisable to pass about 1M off. The chan between Barrels and Grassholm is 2·5M wide, and here the S-going stream begins at HW Milford Haven +0440, and the N-going at HW Milford Haven –0135, sp rates 5 kn. 5M of clear water lie between Grassholm and Skomer Is/Skokholm Is to the E. But Wildgoose Race, which forms W of Skomer and Skokholm is very dangerous, so it is necessary to keep 2M W of these two Islands.

To E of Skomer Is is Midland Is, and between here and Wooltack Pt is Jack Sound (chart 1482) which is only 0·1M wide and should not be attempted without detailed pilotage directions, and only at slack water. Among the dangers which should be identified on the chart are: The Crab Stones, extending E from Midland Is; The Cable, a drying rk on E side of chan; Tusker Rk, steep-to on its W side, off Wooltack Pt; the Black Stones; and The Anvil and other rks off Anvil Pt. In Jack Sound the S-going stream begins at HW Milford Haven +0200, and the N-going at HW Milford Haven –0425, sp rates 6 kn.

BRISTOL CHANNEL (chart 1179, 1076, 1165, 1164)

Sailing E from Milford Haven (10.11.14), along N shore of Bristol chan, there are few significant dangers to St Gowan's Hd. Crow Rk (dries) is 0·55M SSE of Linney Hd, and The Toes are dangerous submerged rks close W and SE of Crow Rk. There is a pass. inshore off these dangers. There are overfalls on St Gowan Shoals which extend 4M SW of St Gowan's Hd, and the sea breaks on the shallow patches in bad weather.

Caldy Is (Lt) lies S of Tenby (10.11.15). Off its NW pt is St Margaret's Is connected by a rky reef. Caldy Sound is between St Margaret's Is and Giltar Pt (chart 1482). It is buoyed, but beware Eel Spit near W end of Caldy Is where there can be a nasty sea with wind against tide, and Woolhouse Rks (dry) 0·12M NE of Caldy Is.

Carmarthen B (10.11.26) has no offshore dangers for yachts, other than the charted sands at head of B and on its E side off Burry Inlet (10.11.16). There is a hbr (dries) at Saundersfoot (10.11.26) 2M N of Tenby, with anch off well sheltered from N and W but subject to swell. Streams are weak here.

East of Worms Head, Helwick Sands extend 7M W from Port Eynon Pt. Near their W end are depths of 1·8 m. Stream sets across the sands. There is a narrow chan inshore, close to Port Eynon Pt. Between here and Mumbles Hd the stream runs roughly along coast, sp rates 3 kn off Pts, but there are eddies in Port Eynon B and Oxwich B, and overfalls off Oxwich Pt.

Off Mumbles Hd (Lt, fog sig) beware Mixon Shoal (dries), marked by By. In good conditions pass N of shoal, 0·1M off Mumbles Hd. Anch N of Mumbles Hd, good holding but exposed to swell. Green Grounds, rky shoals, cover W side of B in approach to Swansea (10.11.17).

Scarweather Sands, much of which dry and where sea breaks heavily, extend 7M W from Porthcawl (10.11.26) and are marked by Bys (chart 1161). There is a chan between the sands and coast to E, but beware Hugo Bank (dries) and rky patches with overfalls up to 0·75M offshore between Sker Pt and Porthcawl.

Nash Sands extend 7·5M WNW from Nash Pt. Depths vary and are least at inshore end (dries), but there is chan 0·1M wide between sand and rky ledge off Nash Pt. On E-going stream there are heavy overfalls off Nash Pt and at W end of Nash Sands. Between Nash Pt and Breaksea Pt the E-going stream begins at HW Avonmouth +0535, and the W-going at HW Avonmouth –0035, sp rates 3 kn. Off Breaksea Pt there may be overfalls.

From Rhoose Pt to Lavernock Pt the coast if fringed with foul ground. Lavernock Spit extends 1·75M from Lavernock Pt, and E of the spit is main chan to Cardiff (10.11.19), the other side of the chan being Cardiff Grounds – a drying bank which runs parallel with the shore and about 1·5M from it. Further offshore is Monkstone Rk (dries), and E of this runs the buoyed chan to Avonmouth and Bristol (10.11.21) S of extensive drying banks along the N shore (chart 1176).

Near the centre of Bristol Chan, and close to main fairway are the Is of Flat Holme (Lt, fog sig) and Steep Holme. 7M SW of Flat Holme lies Culver Sand (dries), 4M in length, marked by Bys. Between Flat Holme and Steep Holme the E-going stream begins at HW Avonmouth –0610, sp rate 3 kn, and the W-going at HW Avonmouth +0015, sp rate 4 kn.

W from Burnham-on-Sea (10.11.22), the S shore of Bristol Chan has fewer obstructions than N shore. There is also less shelter since hbrs such as Watchet, Minehead, Porlock Weir and Watermouth dry out. See 10.11.26. In bad weather dangerous overfalls occur NW and NE of Foreland Pt. 5M to W there is a race off Highveer Pt. Between Ilfracombe (10.11.23) and Bull Pt the E-going stream begins at HW Milford Haven +0540, and the W-going at HW Milford Haven –0025, sp rates 3 kn. Overfalls occur up to 1·5M N of Bull Pt and over Horseshoe Rks, which lie 3M N. There is a dangerous race off Morte Pt, 1·5M to W of Bull Pt.

NORTH CORNWALL (charts 1156, 1149)

The N coast of Cornwall and approachs to Bristol chan along are very exposed, with little shelter in bad weather. Shelter is available under lee of Lundy Is (10.11.26); but there are bad races to NE (White Horses), the NW (Hen and Chickens), and to SE; also overfalls over NW Bank. So in this area yachts need to be sturdy and well equipped, since if bad weather develops no shelter may be at hand. Streams are moderate W of Lundy, but strong round the Is. They get much stronger towards Bristol Chan proper.

Proceeding SW from Taw/Torridge (10.11.24), keep 3M off to avoid the race N of Hartland Pt (Lt, fog sig). There is shelter off Clovelly in winds S-SW. Bude (10.11.26) dries, and is not approachable in W winds; but it is accessible in calm weather or offshore winds.

Boscastle is a tiny hbr (dries) 3M NE of Tintagel Hd. Only approach in good weather or offshore winds: anch off or (if room) dry out alongside.

Padstow is a refuge, but in strong NW winds the sea breaks on bar and prevents entry. Off Trevose Hd (Lt) beware Quies Rks which extend 1M to W. From here S the coast is relatively clear to Godrevy Is, apart from Bawden Rks 1M N of St Agnes Hd. Newquay B (10.11.26) is good anch in offshore winds, and the hbr (dries) is sheltered but uncomfortable in N winds. Off Godrevy Is (Lt) are the Stones, extending 1M from Is and marked by By.

In St Ives B (chart 1168), Hayle (10.11.26) (dries) is a commercial port: seas break heavily on bar in strong onshore winds. Stream is strong, so enter just before HW. The bottom is mostly sand. St Ives (dries) (10.11.26) gives sheltered anch outside in winds from E to SW, but very exposed to N; there is sometimes room to dry out alongside.

From St Ives to Land's End coast is rugged and exposed. There are overfalls SW of Pendeen Pt (Lt, fog sig). Vyneck Rks lie awash about 0·3M NW of C Cornwall. The Brisons are two rky Is 0·5M SW of C Cornwall, and rky ledges extend inshore and to the S and SW. The Longships (Lt, fog sig) are a group of rks about 1M W of Land's End, with ledges 0·2M further seaward. The inshore passage is unwise.

For continuation south, see 10.1.5.

10.11.6 DISTANCE TABLE

Approximate distances in nautical miles are by the most direct route while avoiding dangers and allowing for traffic separation schemes etc. Places in *italics* are in adjoining areas.

1 *Bardsey Island*	**1**																			
2 *Abersoch*	14	**2**																		
3 Aberdovey	31	26	**3**																	
4 Aberystwyth	33	30	10	**4**																
5 Fishguard	45	54	47	40	**5**															
6 South Bishop	60	70	67	61	25	**6**														
7 Milford Haven	83	93	90	84	48	23	**7**													
8 Tenby	106	116	113	107	71	46	28	**8**												
9 Swansea	129	139	136	130	94	69	55	36	**9**											
10 Barry	151	161	158	152	116	91	77	57	37	**10**										
11 Newport	168	178	175	169	133	108	94	75	54	17	**11**									
12 Sharpness	191	201	198	192	156	131	117	106	75	39	32	**12**								
13 Avonmouth	174	184	181	175	139	114	100	89	58	22	15	17	**13**							
14 Burnham-on-Sea	168	178	175	169	133	108	94	70	48	18	28	50	33	**14**						
15 Minehead	148	158	155	149	113	88	76	55	32	14	29	51	34	20	**15**					
16 Ilfracombe	127	137	134	128	92	67	53	35	25	35	51	74	57	45	25	**16**				
17 Lundy Island	110	120	117	111	75	50	38	30	37	54	71	95	78	66	46	22	**17**			
18 *Longships*	168	178	175	169	133	108	105	110	120	130	146	169	152	140	121	95	82	**18**		
19 *Tuskar Rock*	63	75	84	80	48	36	59	82	105	127	144	167	150	144	124	103	85	130	**19**	
20 *Dun Laoghaire*	61	75	92	94	94	90	113	136	159	181	198	221	204	198	178	157	140	199	70	**20**

ABERSOCH 10-11-7

Gwynedd

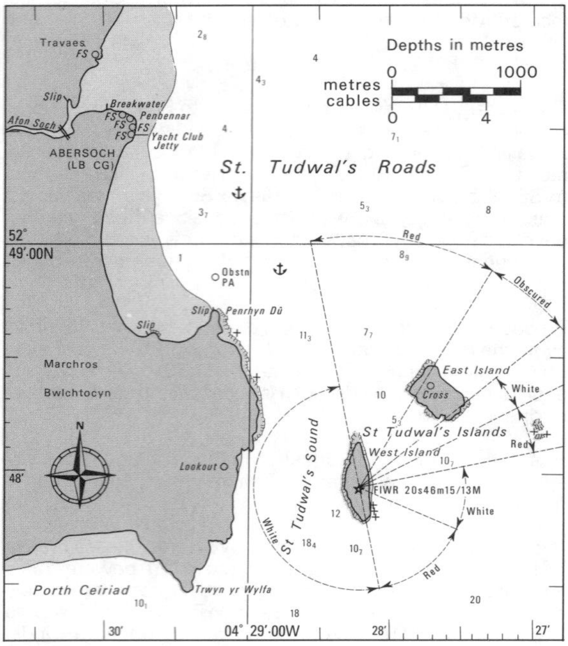
Depths in metres
metres 0 1000
cables 0 4
Travaes FS
Slip
Breakwater
FS
Penbennar
FS
FS
FS
Yacht Club Jetty
Afon Soch
ABERSOCH (LB CG)
St. Tudwal's Roads
52° 49'·00N
Obstn PA
Slip
Penrhyn Dû
Slip
Marchros
Bwlchtocyn
N
Red
Obscured
East Island
Cross
White
St Tudwal's Islands
West Island
Red
FlWR 20s46m15/13M
White
St Tudwal's Sound
White
Red
48'
Lookout
Porth Ceiriad
Trwyn yr Wylfa
30'
04° 29'·00W
28'
27'

CHARTS

Admiralty 1512, 1971; Imray C61; OS 123

TIDES

−0315 Dover; ML 2·5; Duration 0520; Zone 0 (GMT).

Standard Port MILFORD HAVEN (⟶)

Times				Height (metres)			
HW		LW		MHWS	MHWN	MLWN	MLWS
0100	0800	0100	0700	7·0	5·2	2·5	0·7
1300	2000	1300	1900				
Differences ST TUDWAL'S ROADS							
+0155	+0145	+0240	+0310	−2·2	−1·9	−0·7	−0·2
ABERDARON							
+0210	+0200	+0240	+0310	−2·4	−1·9	−0·6	−0·2

SHELTER

There are few moorings for visitors. Apply to Hr Mr or SC. Anchorage in St Tudwal's Roads clear of area of moored yachts is sheltered from SSE through S to NE.

NAVIGATION

Waypoint 52°48'·50N 04°26'·06W, 113°/293° from/to Yacht Club jetty, 2·4M. There are no navigational dangers but steer well clear of the rocks to the E of St Tudwal's Islands, which dry out. The islands themselves are fairly steep to, except at N ends. St Tudwal's Sound is clear of dangers.

LIGHTS AND MARKS

The only major light is that on St Tudwal's West Island as shown on the chartlet.

RADIO TELEPHONE

South Caernarfon YC Ch **80** M.

TELEPHONE (075 881)

Hr Mr 812684; MRSC Holyhead 762051; # (0407) 762714; Marinecall 0898 500 460; Police 2022; Dr Pwllheli 612535.

FACILITIES

EC Wednesday. **S. Caernarvonshire YC** ☎ 2338, Slip, M, L, FW, R, Bar (May-Sept), D; **Abersoch BY** ☎ 2213, Slip, ME, El, Sh, C (5 ton), ACA, CH; **Abersoch Land & Sea Services** ☎ 3434, ME, El, Sh, FW, P, D, C (12 ton), CH; **Hookes Marine** ☎ 2458, ME, El, Sh; **Abersoch Power Boat Club** ☎ 2027; **Town** CH, V, R, Bar. ✉; Ⓑ; ⇌ (Pwllheli); ✈ (Chester).

PWLLHELI 10-11-8

Gwynedd

CHARTS

Admiralty 1512, 1971; Imray C61; OS 123

TIDES

−0300 Dover; ML 2·6; Duration 0510; Zone 0 (GMT).

Standard Port MILFORD HAVEN (⟶)

Times				Height (metres)			
HW		LW		MHWS	MHWN	MLWN	MLWS
0100	0800	0100	0700	7·0	5·2	2·5	0·7
1300	2000	1300	1900				
Differences PWLLHELI							
+0210	+0150	+0245	+0320	−2·0	−1·8	−0·6	−0·2
CRICCIETH							
+0210	+0155	+0255	+0320	−2·0	−1·8	−0·7	−0·3

SHELTER

Strong winds from SW to E cause breakers off shore. Inner harbour has good shelter but dries. Entry HW ∓2. No anchoring in harbour. Yachts should go to the Marina where shelter is excellent.

NAVIGATION

Waypoint 52°52'·50N 04°23'·00W, 150°/330° from/to Pwllheli Pt Lt (QR), 0·80M. The bar has often less than 0·3m. It is safe to cross in any wind direction. Boats with 1·5m draught can cross HW∓2. Tide runs up to 3 kn at sp. Harbour speed limit 5 kn.

LIGHTS AND MARKS

Outer No 1 Lt Buoy, QG, G conical.

QG and QR Lts mark the start of ent channel. Channel well marked. S end of marina 2 Fl G (vert).

RADIO TELEPHONE

VHF Ch 16 (occas).

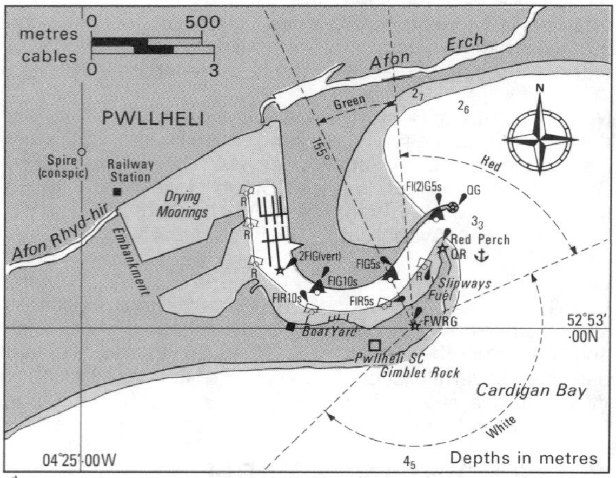
metres 0 500
cables 0 3
Afon Erch
PWLLHELI
Green
155°
N
Spire (conspic)
Railway Station
Drying Moorings
Red
Fl(2)G5s
QG
Afon Rhyd-hir
Embankment
2FlG(vert)
FlG5s
Red Perch
QR
FlG10s
FlR10s
FlR5s
Slipways
Fuel
FWRG
52°53'·00N
Boat Yard
Pwllheli SC
Gimblet Rock
Cardigan Bay
White
04°25'·00W
Depths in metres

⛵ Secure to mooring and see Hr Mr

TELEPHONE (0758)

Hr Mr 613131 ex 281; MRSC Holyhead 762051; # (0407) 762714; Marinecall 0898 500 460; Police Abersoch 2022; Dr 612535

FACILITIES

EC Thursday. **Pwllheli Marina** (265) ☎ 701219, FW, AC; **Pier**, P, D, L, FW, AB, V; **Pwllheli SC** ☎ 612219; **Marina Club** ☎ 612611, Slip, L, FW; **Partington BY** ☎ 612808, Slip, L, FW, ME, Gas, Sh, C (10 ton), CH, ACA; **Firmhelm BY** ☎ 612251, Slip, D, L, FW, ME, Sh, C (14 ton), CH; **Harbour Authority** Slip, M, L, FW, AB; **Tony Evans Marine Engineering** ☎ 613219, ME, El; **Rowlands Marine Electronics** ☎ 613193, Ⓔ, El; **J.K.A. Sails** ☎ 613266, SM; **Tudor Sails** ☎ 613141, SM; **Gimblet Rock Caravan Park Pier** ☎ 612770, P, D; **Town** V, R, Bar; ✉; Ⓑ; ⇌; ✈ (Chester).

PORTHMADOG 10-11-9

Gwynedd

CHARTS
Admiralty 1512, 1971; Imray C61; OS 124

TIDES
−0232 Dover; ML 2·8; Duration 0455; Zone 0 (GMT).
Standard Port MILFORD HAVEN (⟶)

Times				Height (metres)			
HW		LW		MHWS	MHWN	MLWN	MLWS
0100	0800	0100	0700	7·0	5·2	2·5	0·7
1300	2000	1300	1900				
Differences PORTHMADOG							
+0235	+0210	No data		−1·9	−1·8	No data	

Differences on Liverpool −0245

SHELTER
Inner Harbour — Good all year round. Outer Harbour — Summer only and exposed to S winds.

NAVIGATION
Waypoint Fairway (safe water) buoy, LFl 10s, 52°52′·87N 04°11′·02W (channel shifts). Depth at Bar MLWS is only 0·8m. When wind is in SW, waves are steep sided and close, especially on the ebb tide. Bar changes frequently. Up to date situation is supplied by Hr Mr upon request. Advise entering HW∓1½.

LIGHTS AND MARKS
Fairway buoy RW L Fl 10s. Remainder of channel markers (16) have reflective top marks, G to stbd, R to port.

RADIO TELEPHONE
Madoc YC: VHF Ch 16 **80** M. Hr Mr Ch 16; 14 12 (0900-1700 LT).

TELEPHONE (0766)
Hr Mr 512927; MRSC Holyhead 762051; Pilot 75684; Harbour Authority Dwyfor District Council, (0758) 613131; ⌗ (0407) 762714; Marinecall 0898 500 460; Police 512226; Dr 512239.

FACILITIES
EC Wednesday; **Harbour** (265) ☎ 512927, D, FW, C, Slip; **Pen-y-Cei** Slip, V, R, Bar; **Madoc YC** ☎ 512976, M, L, FW, AB, Bar; **Glaslyn Marine Supplies** ☎ 513545, CH, ACA; **Robert Owen** ☎ 513435, D, ME; **D. Hardie** ☎ 512776, Sh; **Kyffin BY** El, C (3½ ton), CH, AB; **Madog BY** ☎ 514205, AB; **Porthmadog & Transfynydd SC** ☎ 513546, Slip, AB, M, FW; **Harbour Filling Station** P (45 gall drums). **Town** ✉; Ⓑ; ⇄; ✈ (Chester).

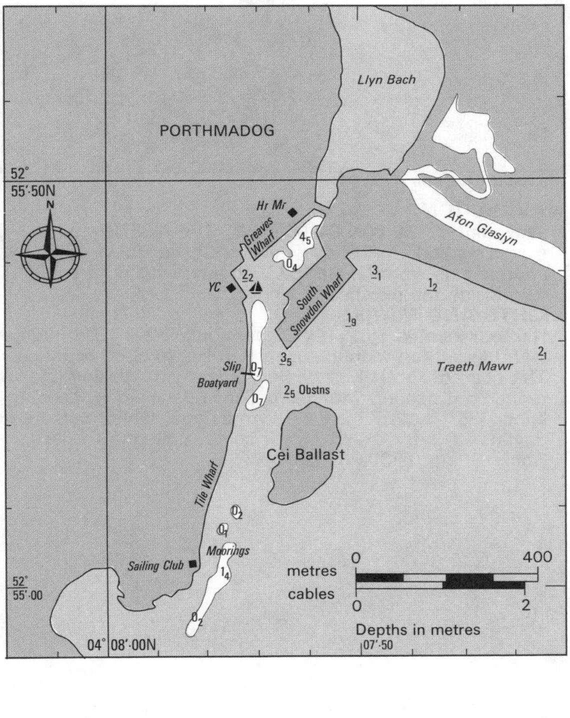
PORTHMADOG
Llyn Bach
52° 55′·50N
Hr Mr
Greaves Wharf
Afon Glaslyn
YC
South Snowdon Wharf
Slip
Boatyard
Traeth Mawr
2₅ Obstns
Cei Ballast
Tile Wharf
Moorings
Sailing Club
52° 55′·00
metres
cables
0
400
0
2
Depths in metres
04° 08′·00N
07′·50

BARMOUTH 10-11-10

Gwynedd

CHARTS
Admiralty 1484, 1971; Imray C61; OS 124

TIDES
−0250 Dover; ML 2·6; Duration 0515; Zone 0 (GMT).
Standard Port MILFORD HAVEN (⟶)

Times				Height (metres)			
HW		LW		MHWS	MHWN	MLWN	MLWS
0100	0800	0100	0700	7·0	5·2	2·5	0·7
1300	2000	1300	1900				
Differences BARMOUTH							
+0215	+0205	+0310	+0320	−2·0	−1·7	−0·7	0·0

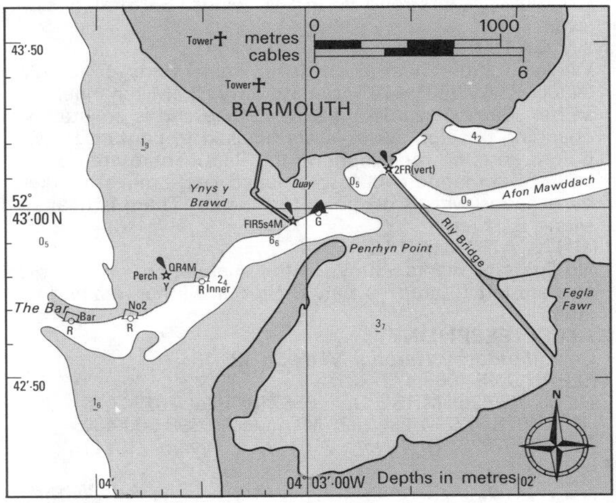
43′·50
Tower
metres
cables
0
1000
0
6
Tower
BARMOUTH
Ynys y Brawd
Quay
2FR(vert)
Afon Mawddach
52° 43′·00N
FlR5s4M
G
Penrhyn Point
Rly Bridge
QR4M
Perch
Y
R Inner
No2
The Bar
Bar
R
R
Fegla Fawr
42′·50
N
04′
04° 03′·00W
Depths in metres
02′

SHELTER
Good shelter. Entry HW∓2½ safe except in strong on-shore winds; entry impossible with strong SW winds. The river (Afon Mawddach) and estuary are tidal and river is navigable for about 7 miles above railway bridge. It is not buoyed and sandbanks move constantly. Local knowledge is essential. Clearance under railway bridge approx 5·5m. Exposed anchorage W of Barmouth Outer buoy in 6 to 10m. In harbour secure to mooring as directed by Hr Mr on account of submarine cables and strong tidal streams. A quay, which dries at half-tide, fronts the town.

NAVIGATION
Waypoint, Barmouth Outer (safe water) buoy, L Fl 10s, 52°42′·60N 04°04′·75W, 253°/073° from/to Y perch Lt, QR, 0·7M. Approach from SW between St Patrick's Causeway (Sarn Badrig) and Sarn-y-Bwch (see 10·11·5). Barmouth can be identified by Cader Idris, a mountain 890m high, 5M ESE. Fegla Fawr, a rounded hill, lies on S side of harbour. Bar lies 0·75M W of Penrhyn Pt, min depth 0·3m but subject to considerable change. Channel marked by three port-hand buoys, moved as necessary. Tidal stream runs 3 to 5 kn on ebb at springs.

LIGHTS AND MARKS
Y perch, QR 4m 4M marks S end of stony ledge extending 3 ca SW from Ynys y Brawd across North Bank. Ynys y Brawd groyne, SE end, marked by Bn with Lt, Fl R 5s 4M. NW end of Rly bridge 2 FR(vert).

RADIO TELEPHONE
Call *Barmouth Harbour* VHF Ch 12, 16; 12 (Apl-Sept 0900-2200 LT; Oct-Mar 0900-1600 LT).

TELEPHONE (0341)
Hr Mr 280671; MRSC Holyhead 762051; ⌗ (0407) 762714; Marinecall 0898 500 460; Police 280222; Dr 280521.

FACILITIES
EC Wednesday; There are some visitors' moorings; **Quay** D, FW, El, AC, Slip; **J. Stockford** ☎ 280742, Slip, M, D, L; **Seafarer Chandlery** ☎ 280978, CH, ACA; **F. Cocksey** ☎ 280425, M, CH; **Marine Stores** ☎ 280742, Slip, M; **Merioneth YC** ☎ 280000; **Town** P, D, V, R, Bar; ✉; Ⓑ; ⇄; ✈ (Chester); Ferry across to Penrhyn Pt.

11

ABERDOVEY 10-11-11

Gwynedd

CHARTS
Admiralty 1484, 1972; Imray C61; OS 135

TIDES
−0320 Dover; ML 2·6; Duration 0535; Zone 0 (GMT).

Standard Port MILFORD HAVEN (⟶)

Times				Height (metres)			
HW		LW		MHWS	MHWN	MLWN	MLWS
0100	0800	0100	0700	7·0	5·2	2·5	0·7
1300	2000	1300	1900				
Differences ABERDOVEY							
+0215	+0200	+0230	+0305	−2·0	−1·7	−0·5	0·0

SHELTER
Good except in strong W to SW winds. Berth alongside jetty.

NAVIGATION
Waypoint Aberdovey Outer (safe water) buoy, 52°31′·75N 04°06′·22W, 250°/070° from/to jetty, 2·3M (channel shifts). Bar is hazardous below ½ tide and is constantly changing position. Visitors are advised to contact Hr Mr before entering, or telephone the Pilot. There are no lights. Submarine cables (prohibited anchorages) marked by beacons with R diamond top marks. There is heavy silting E of jetty.

LIGHTS AND MARKS
No lights or marks. Buoys in the channel are all G conical and are left to stbd — Bar, S Spit and Inner, leading to jetty.

RADIO TELEPHONE
Call *Aberdovey Harbour* VHF Ch 12; 16.

TELEPHONE (065 472)
Hr Mr 767626; MRSC Dale 636218; Pilot 767247; # (0407) 762714 Ext 262; Marinecall 0898 500 460; Police 767222; Dr Tywyn 710414; Ⓗ Tywyn 710411.

FACILITIES
EC Wednesday (winter only); **Jetty** L, FW, AB; **Wharf** Slip, L, FW, C, AB; **West Wales Marina BY** ☎ 767475, ME, El, Sh, CH; **Frongoch BY** ☎ 767842, Slip (Patent 10 ton), ME, El, Sh, CH; **Dovey YC** ☎ (0827) 286514, Bar, Slip, L, FW; **Dovey Marine** ☎ 767581, CH, ACA; **Bruce Morris** ☎ Tywyn 711541, Ⓔ. **Town** P and D (in cans), ME, El, CH, V, R, Bar. ✉; Ⓑ; ⇄; ✈ (Chester).

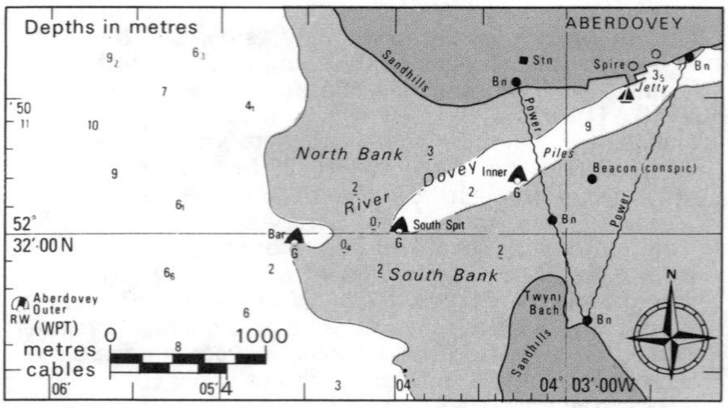
Depths in metres
ABERDOVEY
Sandhills
Stn
Spire
Bn
Jetty
Power
North Bank
River
Dovey
Inner
Piles
Beacon (conspic)
Power
Bar
South Spit
South Bank
Twyni Bach
Sandhills
52°
32′·00N
Aberdovey Outer
RW
(WPT)
metres
cables
0
1000
8
06′
05′
04′
04° 03′·00W
N

ABERYSTWYTH 10-11-12

Dyfed

CHARTS
Admiralty 1484, 1972; Imray C61; OS 135

TIDES
−0330 Dover; ML 2·7; Duration 0540; Zone 0 (GMT)

Standard Port MILFORD HAVEN (⟶)

Times				Height (metres)			
HW		LW		MHWS	MHWN	MLWN	MLWS
0100	0800	0100	0700	7·0	5·2	2·5	0·7
1300	2000	1300	1900				
Differences ABERYSTWYTH							
+0145	+0130	+0210	+0245	−2·0	−1·7	−0·7	0·0
NEW QUAY							
+0150	+0125	+0155	+0230	−2·1	−1·8	−0·6	−0·1
ABERPORTH							
+0135	+0120	+0150	+0220	−2·1	−1·8	−0·6	−0·1
PORT CARDIGAN							
+0140	+0120	+0220	+0130	−2·3	−1·8	−0·5	0·0

SHELTER
Good but harbour dries. Lie alongside quays. Advise entering between HW∓2; dangerous in strong on-shore winds. Visitors berth halfway up Town Quay, marked 'Visiting Yachts only' — Access HW∓3.

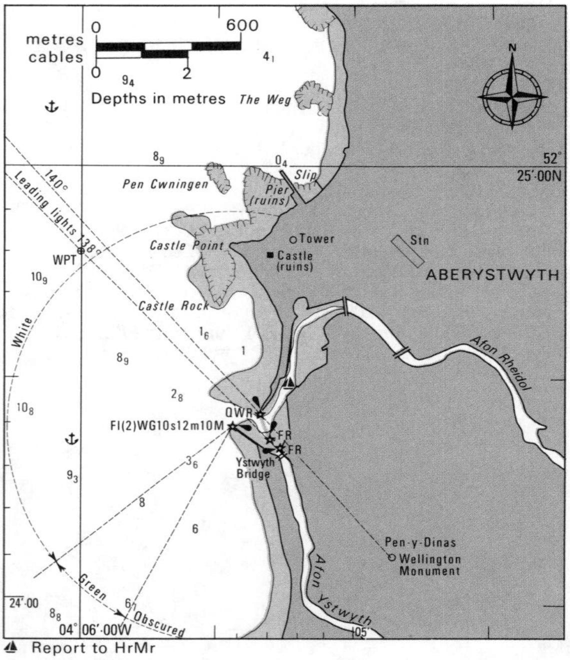
metres
cables
0
600
2
Depths in metres
The Weg
Pen Cwningen
Slip
Pier (ruins)
52°
25′·00N
140°
Leading lights 138°
Castle Point
Tower
Castle (ruins)
Stn
ABERYSTWYTH
WPT
Castle Rock
White
Afon Rheidol
QWR
Fl(2)WG10s12m10M
FR
FR
Ystwyth Bridge
Pen-y-Dinas
Wellington Monument
Afon Ystwyth
Green
Obscured
24′·00
04° 06′·00W
05′
N

▲ Report to HrMr

NAVIGATION
Waypoint 52°24′·80N 04°06′·00W, 318°/138° from/to front Ldg Lt 138°, 0·62M. Beware Castle Rocks when approaching from N. Narrow entrance with right-angle turn inside the pier head.

LIGHTS AND MARKS
Harbour located by Pen-y-Dinas, conspic hill 120m high, with Wellington monument, which lies to S of entrance. The head of the N breakwater in line with Wellington monument bearing 140° leads S of Castle Rock. Leading lights 138°, both FR on Ystwyth Bridge; white markers for daytime. N jetty Q WR 4M, R sector covering Castle Rock. S jetty Fl(2) WG 10s 10M.

ABERYSTWYTH *continued*

RADIO TELEPHONE
VHF (portable) Ch 16 14 (for harbour control only).

TELEPHONE (0970)
Hr Mr 611433; MRSC Dale 636218; # (0222) 399123; Marinecall 0898 500 460; Police 612791; Dr 4855.

FACILITIES
Town Quay Slip, CH, C (3 ton), L, FW, Access HW∓3; **Inner Basin** Slip, L, C (up to 15 ton by arrangement); **F. L. Steelcraft** ☎ Borth 713, CH, D, Ⓔ, ME, Sh, M, Slip; C (25 ton); **Lucas Service** ☎ 617013, El; **AJ Plant** ☎ 828983, C (25 ton mobile); **Aberystwyth YC** ☎ 612907, Slip, M, L, FW, Bar; **Primrose Gdn Centre** ☎ 4631, Gas; **Town** P and D (cans), CH, V, R, Bar. ✉; Ⓑ; ⇌; ✈ (Swansea).
Note:– A marina is planned here.

FISHGUARD 10-11-13
Dyfed

CHARTS
Admiralty 1484, 1973; Imray C61/60; OS 157

TIDES
–0347 Dover; ML 2·5; Duration 0550; Zone 0 (GMT).
Standard Port MILFORD HAVEN (→)

Times				Height (metres)			
HW		LW		MHWS	MHWN	MLWN	MLWS
0100	0800	0100	0700	7·0	5·2	2·5	0·7
1300	2000	1300	1900				
Differences FISHGUARD							
+0115	+0100	+0110	+0135	–2·2	–1·8	–0·5	+0·1
CARDIGAN TOWN							
+0140	+0120	+0220	+0130	–2·3	–1·8	–0·5	0·0
PORTHGAIN							
+0055	+0045	+0045	+0100	–2·5	–1·8	–0·6	0·0
RAMSEY SOUND							
+0030	+0030	+0030	+0030	–1·9	–1·3	–0·3	0·0
SOLVA							
+0015	+0010	+0035	+0015	–1·5	–1·0	–0·2	0·0
LITTLE HAVEN							
+0010	+0010	+0025	+0015	–1·1	–0·8	–0·2	0·0
MARTIN'S HAVEN							
+0010	+0010	+0015	+0015	–0·8	–0·5	+0·1	+0·1

SHELTER
Good shelter except in strong winds between NE & NW and can be entered at any time. There are two harbours, the North or upper harbour belonging to Sealink provides no facilities for visiting yachts. The lower harbour, at Goodwick, provides temporary moorings but dries. Access HW∓1.

NAVIGATION
Waypoint 52°01'·00N 04°57'·50W, 057°/237° from/to Northern Breakwater Lt, 0·48M. The harbour can be entered in any weather.
Beware large swell against quay near station especially in strong N winds, 340°-010°.

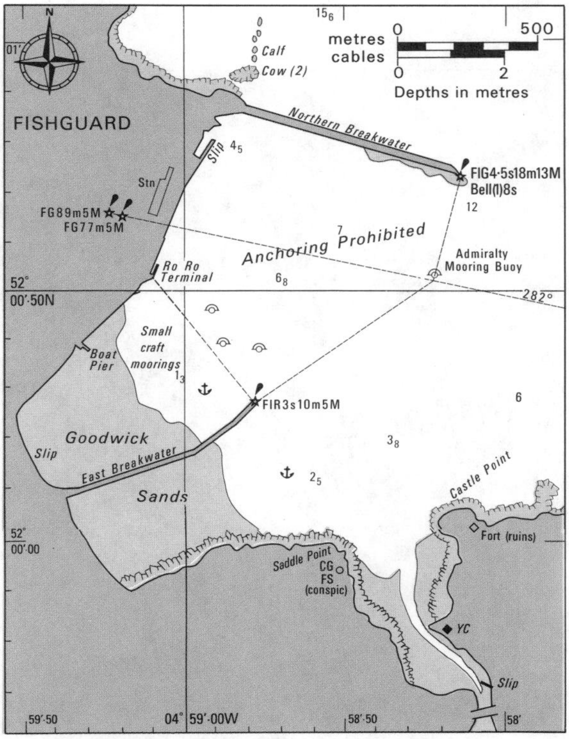
FISHGUARD
Calf
Cow (2)
metres
cables
Depths in metres
Northern Breakwater
FIG4·5s18m13M
Bell(I)8s
FG89m5M
FG77m5M
Stn
Slip
Anchoring Prohibited
Admiralty Mooring Buoy
282°
Ro Ro Terminal
Small craft moorings
Boat Pier
FIR3s10m5M
Goodwick
Slip
East Breakwater
Sands
Castle Point
Fort (ruins)
Saddle Point
CG
FS
(conspic)
YC
Slip
52° 00'·50N
52° 00'·00
59'·50
04° 59'·00W
58'·50
58'

LIGHTS AND MARKS
N Breakwater FIG 4·5s 18m 13M, Bell 8s. E Breakwater FIR 3s 10m 5M. Lts in line 282°, both FG; W diamonds on masts.

RADIO TELEPHONE
None.

TELEPHONE (0348)
Upper harbour Port Supervisor 872881; Lower Hr Mr 5203; MRSC Dale 636218; # (0222) 399123; Marinecall 0898 500 460; Police 873073; Dr 872802.

FACILITIES
EC Wednesday; **Goodwick Marine** ☎ 874590 D, Sh, ME, Slip, CH; **Fishguard Marine** ☎ 873377, Slip, ME, Sh, CH; **Lower Harbour** M; **Fishguard Bay YC** ☎ 872866, FW, Bar; **Fishguard Yacht and Boat Co.** ☎ 873377, BY, ACA; **Fishguard Harbour Garage** ☎ 873814, Gas; **Town** P, D, V, R, Bar. ✉; Ⓑ; ⇌; ✈ (Swansea).

11

MILFORD HAVEN 10-11-14

Dyfed

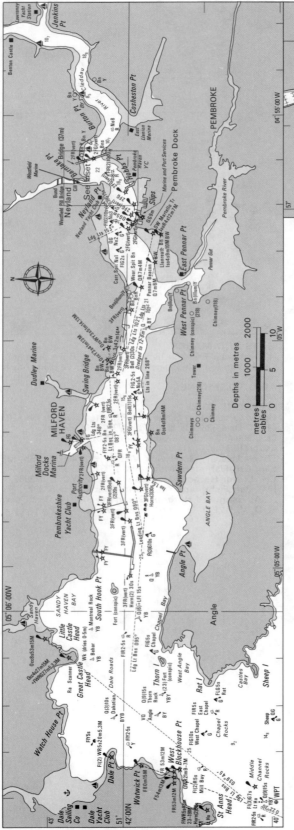

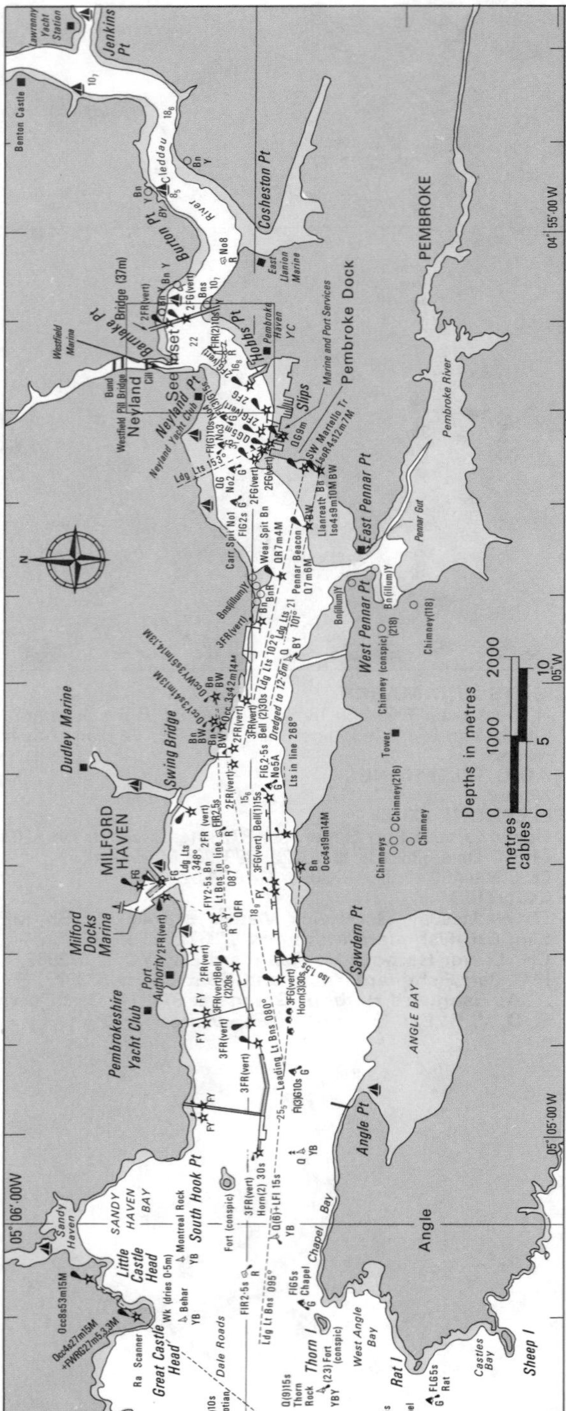
MILFORD HAVEN
PEMBROKE
Pembroke Dock
NEYLAND
Neyland Pt
Hobbs Pt
Barnlake Pt
Burton Pt
Cosheston Pt
Jenkins Pt
Benton Castle
Cleddau River
Westfield Marina
Neyland Yacht Club
Pembroke Haven YC
East Llanion Marine
Marine and Port Services
Pembroke River
East Pennar Pt
West Pennar Pt
Pennar Gut
Dudley Marine
Swing Bridge
Milford Docks Marina
Port Authority
Pembrokeshire Yacht Club
Sawdern Pt
ANGLE BAY
Angle Pt
Angle
South Hook Pt
SANDY HAVEN BAY
Sandy Haven
Little Castle Head
Great Castle Head
Dale Roads
Thorn I
West Angle Bay
Chapel Bay
Rat I
Sheep I
Castles Bay
Chapel Rocks
Mid Channel Rocks
Watch House Pt
Dale Pt
Dale Sailing Co
Dale Yacht Club
Watwick Pt
West Blockhouse Pt
St Anns Head
Mill Bay
Depths in metres
metres
cables

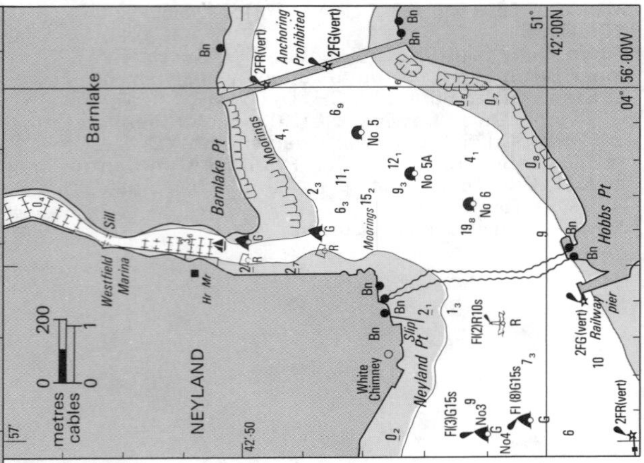
Barnlake
Barnlake Pt
Anchoring Prohibited
Moorings
No 5
No 5A
No 6
Westfield Marina
Hr Mr
NEYLAND
White Chimney
Neyland Pt
Slip
Hobbs Pt
Railway pier
metres
cables

▲ Contact Milford Haven Signal Station

CHARTS
Admiralty 3274, 3275, 2878, 1478; Imray C60; OS 157

TIDES
−0454 Dover; ML 3·8; Duration 0605; Zone 0 (GMT).

Standard Port MILFORD HAVEN (⟶)

Times				Height (metres)			
HW		LW		MHWS	MHWN	MLWN	MLWS
0100	0800	0100	0700	7·0	5·2	2·5	0·7
1300	2000	1300	1900				
Differences SKOMER IS							
−0005	−0005	+0005	+0005	−0·4	−0·1	0·0	0·0
DALE ROADS							
−0005	−0005	−0008	−0008	0·0	0·0	0·0	−0·1
NEYLAND							
+0002	+0010	0000	0000	0·0	0·0	0·0	0·0
HAVERFORDWEST							
+0010	+0025	No data		−4·8	−4·9	Dries out	
LLANGWM (Black Tar)							
+0010	+0020	+0005	0000	+0·1	+0·1	0·0	−0·1

NOTE: Milford Haven is a Standard Port and all tidal predictions for the year are given below.

SHELTER
Very good shelter in various places round the harbour, especially in Westfield Marina at Neyland. Anchorages – Dale Bay; Off Chapel Bay and Angle Point on S shore; Off Scotch Bay by Milford, above the town; and many others above Pembroke Dock. River Cleddau is navigable, at certain tides, up to Haverfordwest for boats with moderate draughts. Clearance under Cleddau Bridge above Neyland is 37m; under power cable 1M upstream, 25m. Check low headroom under bridges and cables approaching Haverfordwest. Contact Milford Haven Signal Station to ascertain most suitable anchorage or berth. Majority of moorings are 'all-tide afloat'. It is possible to dry out safely, depending on weather conditions at inshore areas of Dale, Sandy Haven and Angle Bay.

NAVIGATION
Waypoint 51°40'·00N, 05°10'·52W, 042°/222° from/to Angle N Cardinal Lt By, 2·17M. There is considerable tidal set across the entrance to the Haven particularly at springs. In bad weather avoid passing over Mid Channel Rocks in entrance, where a confused sea and swell will be found. Give St Ann's Head a wide berth, as there is a confused sea there in bad weather. Beware large tankers entering and leaving the haven.
NOTE: – The Port Authority is the Milford Haven Port Authority with jetty, Signal Station and offices near Hubberston Point. Their launches have green hulls and white upperworks and fly a Pilot flag (white over red horizontal) when on pilotage duties or a blue flag with the word 'Harbourmaster' in white letters while on patrol. Their instructions must be obeyed. No vessel may operate within 100 metres of any terminal or any tanker whether at anchor or under way. Milford Dock opens from HW−2 to HW and berths may be had on application to the Dockmaster (Tel. 692275).

TIME ZONE UT(GMT)

For Summer Time add ONE hour in non-shaded areas

WALES – MILFORD HAVEN

Lat 51°42′ N Long 5°01′ W

TIMES AND HEIGHTS OF HIGH AND LOW WATERS

YEAR **1992**

JANUARY

Date	Day	Time	m	Time	m	Time	m	Time	m
1	W	0324	5·7	0950	2·1	1552	5·7	2220	2·0
2	Th	0420	6·0	1045	1·9	1644	5·9	2308	1·8
3	F	0506	6·2	1130	1·6	1729	6·1	2349	1·6
4	Sa ●	0549	6·4	1210	1·5	1808	6·3		
5	Su	0025	1·4	0625	6·6	1245	1·3	1843	6·4
6	M	0057	1·3	0700	6·7	1319	1·2	1917	6·4
7	Tu	0130	1·3	0734	6·7	1349	1·2	1949	6·4
8	W	0201	1·3	0806	6·6	1422	1·2	2022	6·4
9	Th	0232	1·3	0839	6·5	1453	1·4	2053	6·2
10	F	0304	1·5	0911	6·4	1527	1·5	2127	6·1
11	Sa	0336	1·7	0946	6·2	1602	1·8	2202	5·9
12	Su	0414	2·0	1024	6·0	1642	2·0	2244	5·7
13	M ☽	0458	2·2	1111	5·7	1733	2·2	2337	5·5
14	Tu	0558	2·4	1211	5·5	1841	2·4		
15	W	0046	5·3	0717	2·5	1327	5·5	2002	2·3
16	Th	0208	5·5	0842	2·3	1450	5·7	2119	2·0
17	F	0325	5·8	0956	1·8	1602	6·1	2226	1·6
18	Sa	0430	6·4	1058	1·3	1701	6·5	2322	1·1
19	Su ○	0525	6·8	1153	0·8	1754	6·9		
20	M	0014	0·7	0615	7·3	1243	0·5	1843	7·2
21	Tu	0102	0·4	0703	7·5	1331	0·2	1930	7·4
22	W	0148	0·3	0749	7·6	1416	0·2	2013	7·3
23	Th	0232	0·4	0833	7·5	1500	0·4	2057	7·1
24	F	0314	0·6	0917	7·2	1542	0·8	2139	6·7
25	Sa	0356	1·0	1000	6·8	1624	1·2	2223	6·3
26	Su ☾	0440	1·5	1045	6·2	1709	1·8	2311	5·8
27	M	0527	2·0	1134	5·7	1800	2·2		
28	Tu	0007	5·4	0629	2·4	1239	5·3	1913	2·6
29	W	0126	5·2	0758	2·6	1409	5·1	2049	2·6
30	Th	0256	5·3	0929	2·5	1531	5·3	2202	2·3
31	F	0400	5·6	1030	2·1	1628	5·6	2252	2·0

FEBRUARY

Date	Day	Time	m	Time	m	Time	m	Time	m
1	Sa	0449	6·0	1116	1·8	1712	5·9	2332	1·6
2	Su	0530	6·3	1153	1·5	1750	6·2		
3	M ●	0007	1·4	0607	6·6	1227	1·2	1825	6·4
4	Tu	0039	1·2	0641	6·7	1257	1·1	1856	6·6
5	W	0110	1·0	0713	6·8	1327	0·9	1927	6·6
6	Th	0138	1·0	0742	6·9	1358	0·9	1957	6·6
7	F	0208	1·0	0813	6·8	1427	1·0	2026	6·6
8	Sa	0239	1·1	0843	6·7	1458	1·2	2057	6·4
9	Su	0308	1·3	0915	6·5	1529	1·4	2129	6·2
10	M	0341	1·6	0950	6·2	1604	1·7	2207	6·0
11	Tu ☽	0419	1·9	1031	5·9	1647	2·0	2254	5·6
12	W	0512	2·2	1127	5·5	1750	2·3		
13	Th	0001	5·4	0634	2·5	1249	5·3	1923	2·5
14	F	0134	5·3	0816	2·4	1429	5·4	2100	2·2
15	Sa	0307	5·7	0943	1·9	1549	5·9	2213	1·6
16	Su	0416	6·3	1048	1·2	1649	6·5	2311	1·1
17	M	0511	6·9	1142	0·7	1740	7·0		
18	Tu ○	0000	0·6	0600	7·3	1229	0·3	1827	7·3
19	W	0046	0·2	0646	7·6	1313	0·0	1910	7·5
20	Th	0128	0·1	0728	7·7	1355	0·0	1951	7·5
21	F	0209	0·2	0811	7·6	1434	0·3	2030	7·2
22	Sa	0249	0·4	0850	7·2	1512	0·7	2110	6·9
23	Su	0327	0·9	0928	6·8	1549	1·2	2148	6·4
24	M	0404	1·4	1009	6·2	1626	1·8	2230	5·9
25	Tu ☾	0445	1·9	1052	5·6	1708	2·3	2320	5·4
26	W	0539	2·5	1150	5·1	1810	2·7		
27	Th	0034	5·0	0704	2·8	1323	4·8	2002	2·9
28	F	0219	5·0	0900	2·6	1505	5·0	2135	2·5
29	Sa	0335	5·4	1006	2·2	1604	5·4	2227	2·1

MARCH

Date	Day	Time	m	Time	m	Time	m	Time	m
1	Su	0424	5·9	1051	1·8	1648	5·8	2308	1·7
2	M	0505	6·2	1127	1·4	1725	6·2	2342	1·3
3	Tu	0540	6·5	1200	1·1	1758	6·4		
4	W ●	0014	1·1	0614	6·7	1231	0·9	1831	6·7
5	Th	0043	0·9	0645	6·9	1300	0·8	1900	6·8
6	F	0113	0·8	0716	7·0	1330	0·7	1930	6·8
7	Sa	0142	0·8	0747	6·9	1401	0·8	1959	6·8
8	Su	0213	0·9	0818	6·8	1430	0·9	2030	6·7
9	M	0244	1·1	0850	6·6	1503	1·2	2104	6·4
10	Tu	0318	1·4	0927	6·3	1538	1·5	2142	6·1
11	W	0357	1·7	1009	5·9	1621	1·9	2231	5·7
12	Th ☽	0451	2·1	1106	5·5	1726	2·3	2340	5·4
13	F	0617	2·4	1232	5·2	1903	2·5		
14	Sa	0119	5·3	0805	2·3	1418	5·3	2046	2·2
15	Su	0254	5·7	0932	1·7	1536	5·9	2159	1·6
16	M	0400	6·3	1033	1·1	1633	6·5	2252	1·0
17	Tu	0454	6·9	1123	0·6	1722	6·9	2340	0·5
18	W ○	0540	7·3	1208	0·3	1805	7·3		
19	Th	0024	0·2	0624	7·5	1250	0·1	1848	7·4
20	F	0106	0·1	0706	7·6	1330	0·1	1926	7·4
21	Sa	0144	0·2	0745	7·4	1406	0·4	2004	7·2
22	Su	0222	0·5	0822	7·1	1442	0·8	2040	6·8
23	M	0258	0·9	0900	6·6	1515	1·3	2118	6·4
24	Tu	0334	1·4	0936	6·1	1549	1·8	2157	5·9
25	W	0413	1·9	1019	5·5	1627	2·2	2244	5·4
26	Th ☾	0501	2·4	1111	5·0	1723	2·7	2350	5·0
27	F	0617	2·7	1232	4·7	1900	2·9		
28	Sa	0128	4·9	0808	2·7	1420	4·8	2049	2·6
29	Su	0254	5·3	0925	2·3	1528	5·2	2149	2·2
30	M	0348	5·7	1013	1·8	1613	5·7	2231	1·7
31	Tu	0430	6·1	1051	1·4	1651	6·1	2308	1·4

APRIL

Date	Day	Time	m	Time	m	Time	m	Time	m
1	W	0508	6·4	1126	1·1	1726	6·4	2342	1·1
2	Th	0542	6·7	1200	0·9	1758	6·6		
3	F ●	0014	0·9	0615	6·9	1231	0·7	1831	6·8
4	Sa	0046	0·7	0648	7·0	1303	0·6	1903	6·9
5	Su	0119	0·7	0721	7·0	1335	0·7	1935	6·9
6	M	0151	0·8	0755	6·9	1409	0·9	2011	6·8
7	Tu	0227	1·0	0832	6·6	1444	1·1	2049	6·5
8	W	0305	1·3	0912	6·3	1525	1·4	2131	6·2
9	Th	0352	1·6	1002	5·9	1614	1·8	2224	5·8
10	F ☽	0452	1·9	1104	5·5	1723	2·2	2337	5·5
11	Sa	0617	2·1	1228	5·3	1855	2·3		
12	Su	0109	5·5	0754	2·0	1402	5·4	2026	2·0
13	M	0234	5·8	0911	1·6	1515	5·9	2135	1·5
14	Tu	0338	6·3	1010	1·1	1610	6·4	2230	1·0
15	W	0430	6·8	1059	0·7	1658	6·8	2318	0·7
16	Th	0518	7·0	1144	0·5	1742	7·0		
17	F ○	0001	0·5	0601	7·2	1225	0·4	1822	7·2
18	Sa	0042	0·4	0642	7·2	1304	0·5	1902	7·2
19	Su	0121	0·5	0721	7·0	1341	0·7	1940	7·0
20	M	0158	0·7	0758	6·8	1415	1·0	2016	6·7
21	Tu	0234	1·1	0836	6·4	1450	1·4	2054	6·4
22	W	0311	1·5	0912	6·0	1524	1·7	2134	6·0
23	Th	0349	1·8	0953	5·5	1602	2·1	2217	5·6
24	F ☾	0435	2·2	1041	5·2	1651	2·5	2315	5·2
25	Sa	0537	2·5	1147	4·9	1805	2·7		
26	Su	0031	5·1	0700	2·6	1314	4·8	1938	2·6
27	M	0154	5·2	0822	2·3	1433	5·1	2053	2·3
28	Tu	0257	5·5	0921	2·0	1527	5·5	2145	1·9
29	W	0346	5·9	1007	1·6	1610	5·9	2227	1·6
30	Th	0427	6·2	1047	1·3	1648	6·2	2306	1·3

Chart Datum: 3.71 metres below Ordnance Datum (Newlyn)

TIME ZONE UT(GMT)

For Summer Time add ONE hour in non-shaded areas

WALES – MILFORD HAVEN

Lat 51°42′ N Long 5°01′ W

TIMES AND HEIGHTS OF HIGH AND LOW WATERS

YEAR **1992**

MAY

Day	Time	m	Day	Time	m
1 F	0506 1125 1725 2343	6·5 1·1 6·5 1·0	**16** Sa ○	0539 1203 1801	6·7 0·9 6·8
2 Sa ●	0543 1201 1801	6·7 0·9 6·8	**17** Su	0022 0621 1242 1841	0·8 6·7 0·9 6·8
3 Su	0019 0621 1236 1838	0·8 6·9 0·7 6·9	**18** M	0102 0702 1319 1920	0·9 6·6 1·0 6·8
4 M	0056 0659 1314 1916	0·8 6·9 0·7 6·9	**19** Tu	0140 0740 1355 1958	1·0 6·5 1·2 6·6
5 Tu	0135 0740 1354 1957	0·8 6·8 0·8 6·8	**20** W	0216 0816 1429 2034	1·2 6·2 1·4 6·4
6 W	0218 0823 1436 2042	0·9 6·6 1·1 6·6	**21** Th	0253 0854 1504 2114	1·4 6·0 1·6 6·1
7 Th	0304 0910 1524 2129	1·1 6·3 1·3 6·4	**22** F	0331 0932 1542 2155	1·7 5·7 1·9 5·8
8 F	0356 1002 1617 2226	1·4 6·0 1·6 6·1	**23** Sa	0412 1014 1624 2241	1·9 5·4 2·2 5·6
9 Sa ☽	0458 1104 1722 2333	1·6 5·7 1·9 5·8	**24** Su ☾	0501 1105 1719 2337	2·2 5·2 2·4 5·3
10 Su	0611 1217 1839	1·8 5·5 2·0	**25** M	0601 1207 1828	2·3 5·1 2·5
11 M	0049 0728 1335 1957	5·8 1·8 5·6 1·9	**26** Tu	0042 0709 1317 1941	5·3 2·3 5·1 2·4
12 Tu	0205 0842 1446 2105	5·9 1·6 5·9 1·6	**27** W	0149 0816 1425 2046	5·4 2·2 5·3 2·2
13 W	0310 0941 1542 2203	6·2 1·3 6·2 1·3	**28** Th	0250 0914 1519 2139	5·6 1·9 5·6 1·9
14 Th	0404 1033 1633 2252	6·4 1·1 6·5 1·0	**29** F	0342 1003 1607 2227	5·9 1·6 6·0 1·6
15 F	0454 1119 1718 2339	6·6 0·9 6·7 0·9	**30** Sa	0428 1048 1651 2312	6·2 1·3 6·3 1·3
			31 Su	0513 1132 1734 2356	6·5 1·1 6·6 1·0

JUNE

Day	Time	m	Day	Time	m
1 M ●	0558 1215 1818	6·7 0·9 6·9	**16** Tu	0046 0645 1302 1903	1·1 6·4 1·2 6·6
2 Tu	0041 0643 1259 1903	0·8 6·8 0·8 7·0	**17** W	0124 0723 1337 1941	1·1 6·3 1·2 6·6
3 W	0127 0730 1345 1948	0·7 6·8 0·8 7·0	**18** Th	0159 0758 1411 2016	1·2 6·3 1·3 6·5
4 Th	0213 0816 1432 2036	0·7 6·7 0·9 6·9	**19** F	0233 0833 1444 2051	1·3 6·1 1·4 6·3
5 F	0304 0905 1521 2127	0·8 6·6 1·1 6·7	**20** Sa	0308 0908 1518 2128	1·4 6·0 1·6 6·1
6 Sa	0356 0957 1613 2220	1·0 6·3 1·3 6·4	**21** Su	0345 0945 1556 2206	1·6 5·8 1·8 5·9
7 Su ☽	0451 1052 1709 2318	1·3 6·0 1·5 6·2	**22** M	0424 1026 1637 2249	1·8 5·6 2·1 5·7
8 M	0550 1153 1812	1·5 5·8 1·7	**23** Tu ☾	0509 1111 1727 2339	2·1 5·4 2·3 5·5
9 Tu	0021 0656 1300 1921	6·0 1·7 5·7 1·8	**24** W	0604 1207 1829	2·2 5·2 2·4
10 W	0130 0804 1409 2032	5·9 1·7 5·7 1·8	**25** Th	0039 0709 1313 1940	5·4 2·3 5·2 2·4
11 Th	0237 0910 1514 2136	5·9 1·7 5·9 1·7	**26** F	0147 0816 1422 2049	5·4 2·2 5·4 2·2
12 F	0339 1009 1609 2233	6·0 1·5 6·1 1·5	**27** Sa	0254 0919 1525 2150	5·6 1·9 5·8 1·8
13 Sa	0434 1059 1659 2322	6·2 1·4 6·3 1·3	**28** Su	0355 1017 1621 2247	6·0 1·6 6·2 1·4
14 Su	0522 1144 1744	6·3 1·3 6·5	**29** M	0449 1109 1713 2339	6·3 1·2 6·6 1·1
15 M ○	0007 0605 1225 1825	1·2 6·3 1·2 6·6	**30** Tu ●	0542 1200 1803	6·6 0·9 6·9

JULY

Day	Time	m	Day	Time	m
1 W	0029 0631 1248 1850	0·7 6·9 0·7 7·1	**16** Th	0106 0704 1319 1921	1·1 6·4 1·2 6·6
2 Th	0119 0719 1335 1938	0·5 7·0 0·6 7·2	**17** F	0138 0737 1349 1954	1·1 6·4 1·1 6·6
3 F	0206 0806 1423 2026	0·4 7·0 0·6 7·2	**18** Sa	0209 0809 1420 2026	1·1 6·3 1·2 6·5
4 Sa	0254 0853 1510 2114	0·5 6·9 0·7 7·1	**19** Su	0242 0842 1451 2058	1·2 6·2 1·3 6·4
5 Su	0342 0941 1557 2202	0·7 6·6 0·9 6·8	**20** M	0314 0912 1524 2131	1·4 6·1 1·5 6·2
6 M	0430 1028 1647 2251	1·0 6·3 1·3 6·4	**21** Tu	0346 0946 1557 2206	1·6 5·9 1·8 5·9
7 Tu ☽	0520 1120 1740 2346	1·4 6·0 1·6 6·0	**22** W ☾	0423 1024 1637 2248	1·8 5·7 2·1 5·7
8 W	0617 1219 1842	1·8 5·7 1·9	**23** Th	0508 1111 1729 2340	2·1 5·4 2·3 5·5
9 Th	0050 0724 1331 1957	5·7 2·0 5·5 2·1	**24** F	0607 1212 1841	2·3 5·3 2·5
10 F	0205 0840 1447 2114	5·5 2·1 5·6 2·1	**25** Sa	0050 0723 1331 2006	5·3 2·4 5·3 2·4
11 Sa	0319 0949 1552 2219	5·6 2·0 5·8 1·9	**26** Su	0215 0844 1453 2125	5·4 2·2 5·6 2·0
12 Su	0419 1044 1644 2311	5·8 1·8 6·1 1·6	**27** M	0331 0955 1600 2230	5·8 1·8 6·1 1·5
13 M	0509 1130 1730 2354	6·0 1·5 6·3 1·4	**28** Tu	0433 1054 1657 2325	6·2 1·3 6·6 1·0
14 Tu ○	0551 1210 1810	6·2 1·4 6·5	**29** W ●	0527 1146 1749	6·7 0·8 7·0
15 W	0032 0629 1245 1846	1·2 6·3 1·2 6·6	**30** Th	0017 0617 1235 1836	0·6 7·0 0·5 7·4
			31 F	0104 0703 1321 1923	0·3 7·3 0·3 7·6

AUGUST

Day	Time	m	Day	Time	m
1 Sa	0151 0748 1406 2008	0·1 7·3 0·2 7·5	**16** Su	0142 0742 1352 1958	0·9 6·6 1·0 6·7
2 Su	0234 0832 1450 2051	0·2 7·2 0·4 7·3	**17** M	0212 0811 1422 2027	1·0 6·5 1·1 6·6
3 M	0318 0915 1534 2136	0·5 6·9 0·7 6·9	**18** Tu	0242 0840 1451 2058	1·2 6·4 1·4 6·4
4 Tu	0402 0959 1617 2221	0·9 6·5 1·2 6·5	**19** W	0312 0911 1524 2131	1·4 6·2 1·6 6·1
5 W ☽	0445 1047 1705 2311	1·4 6·0 1·7 5·9	**20** Th	0345 0946 1557 2209	1·7 5·9 1·9 5·8
6 Th	0536 1140 1803	2·0 5·6 2·1	**21** F ☾	0423 1030 1644 2259	2·0 5·6 2·2 5·5
7 F	0011 0641 1252 1923	5·4 2·4 5·3 2·4	**22** Sa	0519 1129 1758	2·3 5·3 2·5
8 Sa	0134 0812 1423 2058	5·1 2·5 5·3 2·4	**23** Su	0012 0645 1256 1938	5·2 2·5 5·2 2·5
9 Su	0303 0935 1536 2207	5·2 2·3 5·6 2·1	**24** M	0149 0822 1432 2110	5·2 2·3 5·5 2·0
10 M	0406 1031 1630 2258	5·5 1·9 6·0 1·7	**25** Tu	0317 0941 1545 2217	5·7 1·8 6·1 1·4
11 Tu	0454 1115 1712 2337	5·9 1·6 6·3 1·4	**26** W	0419 1040 1641 2311	6·3 1·2 6·7 0·9
12 W	0533 1151 1750	6·1 1·4 6·5	**27** Th	0511 1130 1732	6·8 0·7 7·2
13 Th ○	0011 0608 1224 1825	1·2 6·3 1·2 6·7	**28** F ●	0000 0558 1217 1818	0·4 7·2 0·3 7·6
14 F	0043 0641 1255 1857	1·1 6·5 1·0 6·8	**29** Sa	0045 0643 1302 1903	0·1 7·5 0·1 7·7
15 Sa	0113 0712 1324 1928	1·0 6·6 1·0 6·8	**30** Su	0128 0726 1344 1945	0·0 7·5 0·1 7·7
			31 M	0211 0808 1426 2027	0·2 7·3 0·3 7·4

Chart Datum: 3.71 metres below Ordnance Datum (Newlyn)

WALES – MILFORD HAVEN

TIME ZONE UT(GMT)
For Summer Time add ONE hour in non-shaded areas

Lat 51°42′ N Long 5°01′ W

TIMES AND HEIGHTS OF HIGH AND LOW WATERS

YEAR **1992**

SEPTEMBER

Date	Time	m	Time	m	Time	m	Time	m
1 Tu	0250	0·5	0849	7·0	1507	0·7	2108	6·9
2 W	0331	1·0	0929	6·6	1548	1·2	2150	6·4
3 Th ☽	0410	1·6	1013	6·0	1633	1·8	2237	5·7
4 F	0457	2·2	1104	5·5	1727	2·3	2333	5·2
5 Sa	0558	2·6	1215	5·1	1849	2·7		
6 Su	0100	4·9	0741	2·8	1357	5·1	2039	2·6
7 M	0243	5·0	0915	2·5	1515	5·5	2148	2·2
8 Tu	0346	5·4	1010	2·1	1606	5·9	2234	1·8
9 W	0430	5·9	1051	1·7	1648	6·3	2312	1·4
10 Th	0508	6·2	1126	1·4	1725	6·6	2344	1·2
11 F	0542	6·4	1158	1·1	1757	6·7		
12 Sa ○	0015	1·0	0614	6·6	1228	1·0	1829	6·9
13 Su	0045	0·9	0645	6·7	1257	0·9	1900	6·9
14 M	0113	0·8	0713	6·8	1326	0·9	1930	6·9
15 Tu	0142	0·9	0742	6·7	1355	1·0	1959	6·7
16 W	0212	1·1	0812	6·6	1425	1·3	2030	6·5
17 Th	0243	1·3	0844	6·4	1457	1·5	2104	6·2
18 F	0317	1·7	0919	6·1	1534	1·8	2145	5·9
19 Sa ☾	0356	2·0	1004	5·7	1623	2·2	2237	5·5
20 Su	0454	2·4	1108	5·4	1742	2·5	2354	5·2
21 M	0625	2·6	1239	5·3	1927	2·4		
22 Tu	0137	5·2	0808	2·3	1418	5·6	2057	2·0
23 W	0303	5·7	0925	1·8	1528	6·2	2202	1·3
24 Th	0402	6·3	1021	1·2	1623	6·8	2252	0·8
25 F	0452	6·9	1111	0·7	1712	7·3	2339	0·4
26 Sa ●	0537	7·3	1156	0·3	1757	7·6		
27 Su	0022	0·2	0621	7·5	1239	0·2	1841	7·7
28 M	0104	0·2	0702	7·5	1321	0·2	1921	7·6
29 Tu	0145	0·4	0742	7·4	1402	0·5	2002	7·2
30 W	0223	0·7	0822	7·0	1442	0·9	2043	6·8

OCTOBER

Date	Time	m	Time	m	Time	m	Time	m
1 Th	0301	1·2	0903	6·6	1522	1·4	2124	6·2
2 F	0341	1·8	0945	6·1	1604	1·9	2207	5·7
3 Sa ☽	0423	2·3	1034	5·6	1657	2·4	2302	5·2
4 Su	0519	2·7	1140	5·2	1811	2·7		
5 M	0021	4·8	0653	2·9	1313	5·1	1957	2·7
6 Tu	0204	4·9	0836	2·7	1437	5·4	2111	2·3
7 W	0312	5·3	0935	2·2	1532	5·8	2159	1·9
8 Th	0359	5·8	1019	1·8	1616	6·2	2237	1·6
9 F	0437	6·1	1054	1·5	1652	6·5	2312	1·3
10 Sa	0511	6·4	1127	1·2	1727	6·7	2344	1·1
11 Su ○	0544	6·6	1158	1·1	1800	6·8		
12 M	0015	0·9	0615	6·8	1229	1·0	1832	6·9
13 Tu	0046	0·9	0646	6·9	1300	0·9	1903	6·9
14 W	0117	0·9	0717	6·8	1333	1·0	1937	6·8
15 Th	0148	1·1	0751	6·7	1406	1·2	2012	6·6
16 F	0223	1·3	0826	6·5	1443	1·5	2050	6·3
17 Sa	0301	1·6	0907	6·2	1527	1·8	2135	6·0
18 Su	0348	1·9	0956	5·9	1623	2·1	2233	5·6
19 M ☾	0449	2·3	1102	5·6	1740	2·3	2349	5·3
20 Tu	0615	2·4	1228	5·5	1914	2·2		
21 W	0121	5·4	0748	2·2	1357	5·8	2036	1·8
22 Th	0242	5·8	0903	1·8	1505	6·3	2139	1·4
23 F	0339	6·3	0959	1·3	1600	6·7	2230	0·9
24 Sa	0430	6·8	1049	0·9	1649	7·1	2316	0·7
25 Su ●	0515	7·1	1134	0·6	1736	7·3		
26 M	0001	0·5	0558	7·3	1219	0·5	1819	7·4
27 Tu	0042	0·5	0641	7·3	1302	0·5	1902	7·3
28 W	0123	0·7	0721	7·2	1341	0·7	1941	7·0
29 Th	0201	1·0	0801	6·9	1422	1·0	2022	6·6
30 F	0239	1·4	0842	6·6	1501	1·5	2101	6·2
31 Sa	0315	1·8	0922	6·2	1542	1·9	2145	5·7

NOVEMBER

Date	Time	m	Time	m	Time	m	Time	m
1 Su	0356	2·2	1009	5·8	1630	2·3	2233	5·3
2 M ☽	0445	2·5	1104	5·4	1729	2·6	2334	5·0
3 Tu	0554	2·8	1215	5·2	1848	2·7		
4 W	0057	5·0	0726	2·8	1338	5·3	2009	2·5
5 Th	0218	5·2	0842	2·5	1444	5·6	2110	2·2
6 F	0314	5·6	0934	2·1	1534	5·9	2156	1·8
7 Sa	0357	5·9	1016	1·8	1616	6·2	2235	1·5
8 Su	0437	6·2	1054	1·5	1654	6·5	2312	1·3
9 M	0512	6·5	1130	1·3	1730	6·7	2347	1·1
10 Tu ○	0547	6·7	1205	1·1	1807	6·8		
11 W	0021	1·0	0622	6·9	1241	1·0	1842	6·9
12 Th	0056	1·0	0659	6·9	1317	1·0	1920	6·8
13 F	0134	1·1	0737	6·9	1357	1·1	2001	6·7
14 Sa	0213	1·2	0818	6·7	1440	1·3	2044	6·4
15 Su	0257	1·4	0904	6·5	1529	1·5	2134	6·2
16 M	0348	1·7	0956	6·2	1626	1·7	2231	5·9
17 Tu ☾	0448	2·0	1058	6·0	1733	1·9	2337	5·6
18 W	0600	2·1	1210	5·9	1849	2·0		
19 Th	0055	5·6	0719	2·1	1326	5·9	2005	1·8
20 F	0209	5·8	0832	1·8	1436	6·2	2111	1·6
21 Sa	0312	6·2	0934	1·5	1536	6·5	2206	1·3
22 Su	0407	6·5	1027	1·2	1630	6·7	2257	1·1
23 M	0455	6·8	1118	1·0	1718	6·9	2342	0·9
24 Tu ●	0542	7·0	1203	0·9	1803	6·9		
25 W	0025	0·9	0624	7·1	1246	0·9	1845	6·9
26 Th	0106	1·0	0704	7·0	1327	1·0	1926	6·8
27 F	0144	1·1	0745	6·9	1406	1·2	2005	6·5
28 Sa	0220	1·4	0823	6·6	1444	1·4	2043	6·2
29 Su	0256	1·6	0903	6·4	1521	1·7	2122	5·9
30 M	0332	1·9	0943	6·1	1602	2·0	2203	5·6

DECEMBER

Date	Time	m	Time	m	Time	m	Time	m
1 Tu	0413	2·2	1028	5·8	1647	2·2	2251	5·4
2 W ☽	0504	2·5	1120	5·5	1743	2·5	2347	5·2
3 Th	0607	2·6	1222	5·3	1849	2·5		
4 F	0057	5·1	0723	2·7	1333	5·4	2001	2·4
5 Sa	0209	5·3	0833	2·5	1437	5·5	2103	2·2
6 Su	0310	5·6	0931	2·2	1532	5·8	2153	1·9
7 M	0357	5·9	1019	1·9	1619	6·1	2238	1·6
8 Tu	0441	6·3	1102	1·6	1702	6·4	2320	1·4
9 W ○	0522	6·6	1143	1·3	1744	6·7		
10 Th	0001	1·1	0603	6·8	1225	1·0	1827	6·8
11 F	0042	1·0	0645	7·0	1307	0·9	1910	6·9
12 Sa	0124	0·9	0728	7·1	1352	0·8	1954	6·9
13 Su	0209	0·9	0813	7·0	1439	0·9	2040	6·8
14 M	0254	1·1	0900	6·9	1527	1·1	2128	6·5
15 Tu	0343	1·3	0949	6·7	1619	1·3	2219	6·3
16 W ☾	0435	1·5	1042	6·4	1713	1·5	2316	6·0
17 Th	0534	1·8	1143	6·1	1817	1·8		
18 F	0019	5·8	0642	2·0	1249	6·0	1926	1·9
19 Sa	0131	5·7	0755	2·0	1402	5·9	2039	1·9
20 Su	0243	5·9	0908	1·9	1512	6·0	2145	1·7
21 M	0346	6·1	1012	1·6	1613	6·2	2241	1·5
22 Tu	0441	6·4	1105	1·4	1705	6·4	2329	1·3
23 W	0529	6·7	1153	1·2	1751	6·6		
24 Th ●	0012	1·2	0612	6·8	1236	1·1	1834	6·6
25 F	0052	1·1	0652	6·9	1314	1·1	1912	6·6
26 Sa	0128	1·1	0730	6·9	1351	1·1	1948	6·5
27 Su	0202	1·2	0806	6·8	1425	1·2	2023	6·4
28 M	0234	1·4	0842	6·6	1457	1·4	2057	6·2
29 Tu	0308	1·6	0915	6·4	1531	1·6	2132	6·0
30 W	0342	1·8	0952	6·1	1607	1·9	2209	5·7
31 Th	0420	2·1	1031	5·8	1648	2·1	2249	5·5

Chart Datum: 3.71 metres below Ordnance Datum (Newlyn)

11

MILFORD HAVEN *continued*

LIGHTS AND MARKS
Middle Channel Rocks Fl(3)G 7s 18m 8M; B Tr, steel lantern. Ldg Lts (for West channel) 040°. Front Oc 4s 27m 15M. Rear Oc 8s 53m 15M; both vis 031°-048° (H24). Milford Dock Ldg Lts 348° both FG, with W circular daymarks. Dock entry signals on E side of lock: Blue flag or 2FG(vert) means gates open, vessels may enter. Exit signals are given via VHF Ch 12. VHF is used normally by day for entry instead of Bu flag.

RADIO TELEPHONE
Call: *Milford Haven Radio* (Port Signal Station), VHF Ch 11 12 14 16 (H24); 09 10 11 **12** 14 16 67. Local weather forecasts broadcast on Ch 12 and 14 at approx. 0300, 0900, 1500 and 2100 GMT. Gale Warnings broadcast on receipt Ch 12 and 14. Shipping movements for next 24 hours on Ch 12 between 0800 – 0830 and 2000 – 2030 LT.
Milford Haven Patrol/Pilot Launches, VHF Ch 11 16 12 (H24); Multi-Channel.
Milford Docks Ch 09 12 14 16 (HW – 2 to HW).
Westfield Marina Ch **80** M Lawrenny Yacht Stn Ch M.

TELEPHONE (0646) (06462 for 4 or 5 figures nos)
Hr Mr Milford Haven Signal Station 692342/3; Dock Master 692275; MRSC 636218; # 681310; Marinecall 0898 500 459; Police (Milford Haven) 692351; Police (Pembroke) 682121, (Neyland) 600221; Dr via Milford Haven Signal Station 692342/3.

FACILITIES
EC Wednesday (Pembroke Dock and Neyland): Thursday (Milford Haven, Haverfordwest); **Westfield Marina** (at Neyland) (380 + 40 visitors) ☎ 601601; FW, D, R, CH, V, AC, Ⓔ, P, Gas, Gaz, ▣, C (15 ton), SM, SC, ME, El, Sh; Access Lower basin H24, Upper basin HW ∓ 3½ **Milford Dock Marina** (151) ☎ 692271 AB, CH, C, El, Ⓔ, V, FW, D, ME; **Brunel Chandlery** ☎ 601667, ACA, CH, Gas, Gaz, V; **Dale SC** ☎ Dale 636349/Neyland 601061, C (23 ton), BY, ME, El, Sh, CH, D, V, FW, L, M, Ⓔ, P, R (Dale), Slip (Dale), Gas, Gaz, ACA; **Milford Haven Port Authority Jetty** ☎ 692342/3 (occasional use by visiting yachtsmen with special permission from Harbourmaster – contact Signal Station) AB, FW, L; **Milford Docks** ☎ 692271 (contact Pierhead ☎ 692275 for permission to enter, VHF Ch 14) AB, C (various), FW, #, D, L, ME, Sh; **Dudley Marine** ☎ 692787, BY, AB, FW, L, ME, CH, Sh, El; **Pennar Park Marine** ☎ 684608, AB, Bar, FW, L, M, R, Slip, V; **Marine and Port Services** ☎ 682271, AB, BY, C, D, El, FW, L, M, CH, ME, Sh, Slip; **Rudders BY** ☎ 600288, C, El, Ⓔ, FW, L, M, ME, Sh, Slip, SM, El, Gas, Gaz, V, ME. **Kelpie Boats** ☎ 683661, BY, CH, D, FW, L, ACA, SM, El, Gas, Gaz, V, ME; **Bridge Boats** ☎ 601661, ME, BY, El, CH; **Copp Sails** ☎ 601561, SM; **East Llanion Marine** ☎ 686866, BY, D (cans), Slip, Ⓔ, El, FW, Sh; **Lawrenny Yacht Station** (100) ☎ 651212, AB, Bar, BY, C (30 ton), CH, D, Sh, ▣, FW, L, M, ME, P, R, Slip, V (Sub ✉ in village). **Milford Haven Calor Gas Centre** ☎ 692252, Gas. **Haven Yachts** ☎ 684503 Sh, BY, Slip, M, SM;

Yacht Clubs – Dale YC ☎ Dale 636362,
Pembrokeshire YC ☎ 692799,
Neyland YC ☎ 600267,
Pembroke Haven YC ☎ 684403, Bar, M, L, FW, Slip;

Towns – Milford Haven, ✉; Ⓑ; ⇌.
Pembroke Dock, ✉; Ⓑ; ⇌; Ⓗ.
Neyland, ✉; Ⓑ.
Haverfordwest, ✉; Ⓗ; Ⓑ; ⇌; ✈ (Swansea or Cardiff).

There is a small airfield at Haverfordwest.

Note: The Castlemartin Range Danger Area extends 12M S from St Govans Head and from there in an arc to a point 12M WNW of Linney Head. The Danger Area operative on any one day however depends on the ranges used. Call Castlemartin Control Tower on Channel 16 VHF, ☎ 661321 Ext 4336, Range Safety Boats on Ch 16 or 12, or Milford Haven Coastguard. When firing is in progress R flags are flown (R flashing lights at night), along the coast from St Govans Head to Linney Head to Freshwater West. Times of firing are published locally and can be obtained from the Range Officer on 661321 Ext 4336 or 4287, or Ext 4364 (the Chief Clerk).

During the firing period (April to December) firing takes place between 0900 and 1630. Night firing takes place from 1830 to 2359 normally on Tuesdays and Thursdays. (These times vary according to the hours of darkness). Firing also takes place for two weeks in January and February.

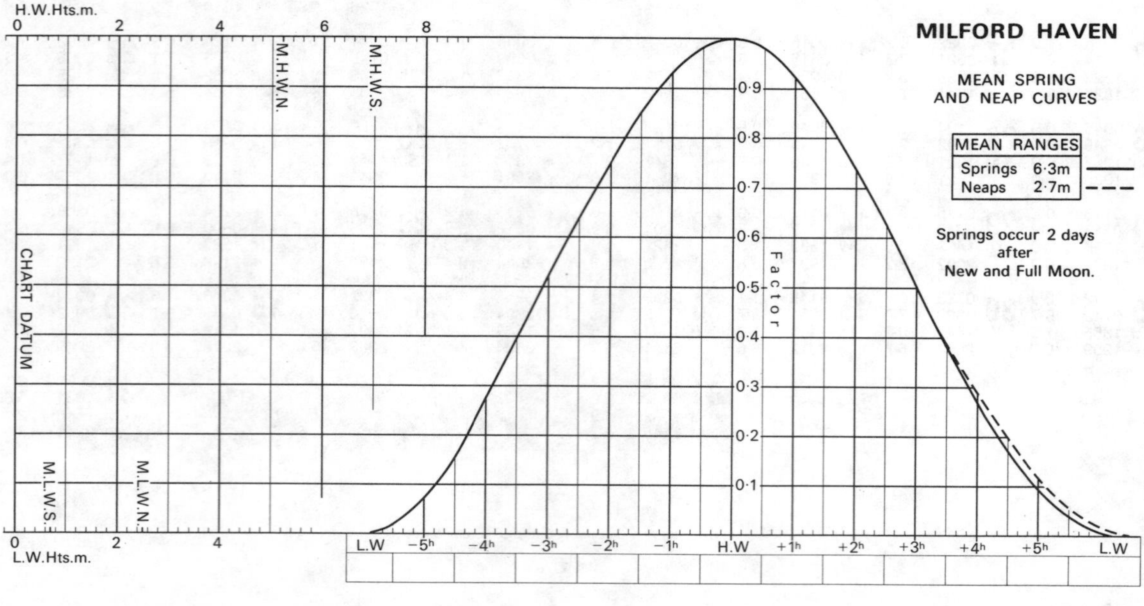
MILFORD HAVEN
MEAN SPRING AND NEAP CURVES
MEAN RANGES
Springs 6·3m
Neaps 2·7m
Springs occur 2 days after New and Full Moon.
H.W.Hts.m.
0 2 4 6 8
M.H.W.N.
M.H.W.S.
CHART DATUM
M.L.W.S.
M.L.W.N.
L.W.Hts.m.
Factor
0·9 0·8 0·7 0·6 0·5 0·4 0·3 0·2 0·1
L.W −5h −4h −3h −2h −1h H.W +1h +2h +3h +4h +5h L.W

TENBY 10-11-15

Dyfed

CHARTS
Admiralty 1482 1076; Stanford 14; Imray C60; OS 158

TIDES
−0510 Dover; ML 4·5; Duration 0610; Zone 0 (GMT)

Standard Port MILFORD HAVEN (←)

Times				Height (metres)			
HW		LW		MHWS	MHWN	MLWN	MLWS
0100	0800	0100	0700	7·0	5·2	2·5	0·7
1300	2000	1300	1900				
Differences TENBY							
−0015	−0010	−0015	−0020	+1·4	+1·1	+0·5	+0·2
STACKPOLE QUAY							
−0005	+0025	−0010	−0010	+0·9	+0·7	+0·2	+0·3

SHELTER
Harbour dries out but shelter good. (Access HW∓2½). Sheltered anchorages in Tenby Roads, Caldey Roads, Jones Bay or Lydstep Haven depending on wind direction.

NAVIGATION
Waypoint 51°40′·00N 04°38′·00W, 099°/279° from/to FS on Castle Hill, 2·2M. Beware Woolhouse Rocks (buoy unlit) and Sker Rocks (unbuoyed). It is recommended that boats enter Tenby harbour HW∓2½. On approaching Tenby Roads, keep outside the line of buoys.

LIGHTS AND MARKS
FR 7m 7M on pierhead. Inside Hr FW 6m 1M marks landing steps. Tenby church spire and N side of St Catherine's Is in line at 276°. R can Bn (unlit) marks rock outcrop off North Walk on north beach near Hr.

RADIO TELEPHONE
VHF Ch 16 (listening during office hours).

TELEPHONE (0834)
Hr Mr 2717 (end May-end Sept); MRSC (0646) 636218; ⌗ (0222) 399123; Marinecall 0898 500 459; Police 2303; Dr. 4161; Hosp 2040.

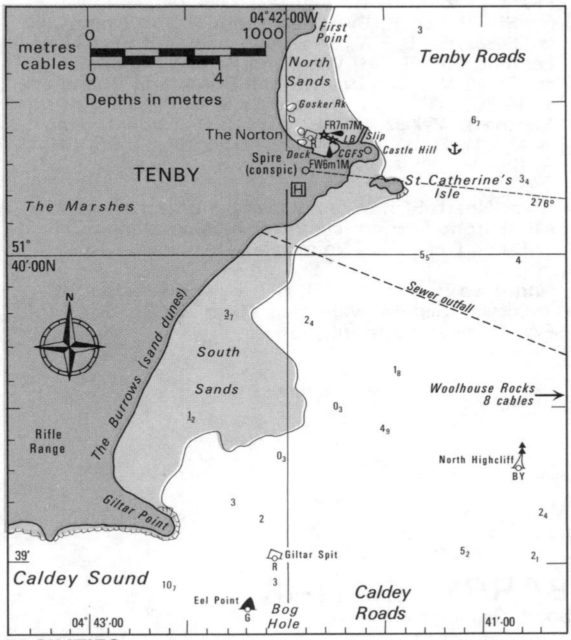
04°42′·00W
First Point
Tenby Roads
metres
cables
0
1000
4
Depths in metres
North Sands
Gosker Rk
The Norton
FR7m7M
Slip
Castle Hill
Spire (conspic)
Dock
CGFS
FW6m1M
TENBY
St Catherine's Isle
276°
The Marshes
51° 40′·00N
Sewer outfall
The Burrows (sand dunes)
South Sands
Woolhouse Rocks 8 cables
Rifle Range
North Highcliff
BY
Giltar Point
39′
Giltar Spit
Caldey Sound
Eel Point
Bog Hole
Caldey Roads
04° 43′·00
41′·00

FACILITIES
EC Wednesday; **Harbour** ☎ 2717, Slip (up to 4·2m), L, AB, Sh, FW; **Pier** L; **Tenby YC** ☎ 2762, M; **Morris Bros** ☎ 2105, Gas, CH;
Town P, D, ⊡, CH, V, R, Bar. ✉; Ⓑ; ≹; ✈ (Swansea). (There are small airports at Swansea and Haverfordwest).

BURRY PORT 10-11-16

Dyfed

CHARTS
Admiralty 1167, 1076; Stanford 14; Imray C59, C60; OS 159

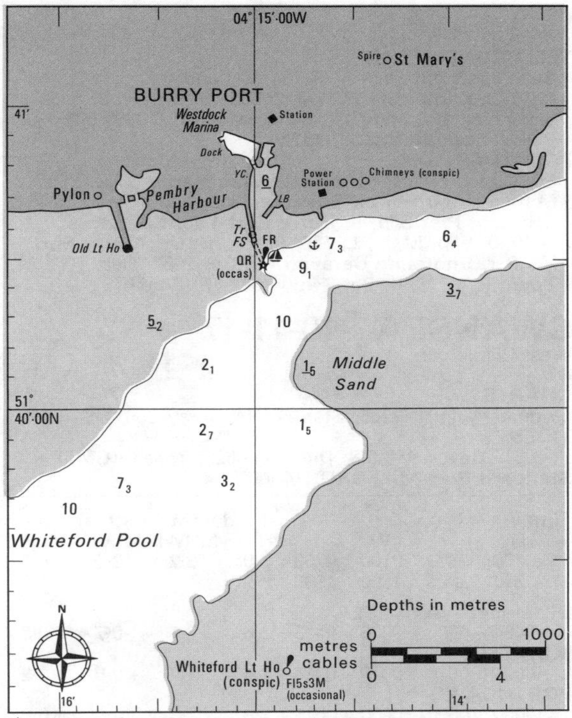
04° 15′·00W
Spire St Mary's
BURRY PORT
Westdock Marina
Station
41′
Dock
YC
Power Station
Chimneys (conspic)
Pylon
Pembry Harbour
LB
Tr FS
FR
QR (occas)
Old Lt Ho
Middle Sand
51° 40′·00N
Whiteford Pool
Depths in metres
metres
cables
0
1000
4
Whiteford Lt Ho (conspic)
Fl5s3M (occasional)
16′
14′

⚠ Report to Burry Port Yacht Services The above is under development

TIDES
−0500 Dover; ML 4·7; Duration 0555; Zone 0 (GMT).

Standard Port MILFORD HAVEN (←)

Times				Height (metres)			
HW		LW		MHWS	MHWN	MLWN	MLWS
0100	0800	0100	0700	7·0	5·2	2·5	0·7
1300	2000	1300	1900				
Differences BURRY PORT							
+0003	+0003	+0007	+0007	+1·6	+1·4	+0·5	+0·4
LLANELLI							
−0003	−0003	+0150	+0020	+0·8	+0·6	No data	
FERRYSIDE							
0000	−0010	+0220	0000	−0·3	−0·7	−1·7	−0·6
CARMARTHEN							
+0010	0000	No data		−4·4	−4·8	dries out	

SHELTER
Shelter in outer harbour is good but it dries out; as it is entirely filled with moorings, entry without prior inspection at LW is not practical. Can be approached HW∓2. Marina in West Dock due to open 1992 will give excellent shelter. Port is owned by Llanelli Borough Council and rate payers have first priority.

NAVIGATION
Waypoint 51°37′·10N 04°18′·20W. 320°/140° from/to Minor Pt 0·34M. Proceed on stern transit 198° with Worms Head in the Sound between Burry Holms and Limekiln Pt. When Whiteford Lt Ho bears E, head for three chimneys of Power Stn, approx NE, leading to barrel post off harbour. No dangers in Carmarthen Bay but ground swell develops into rollers on the bar. Bar should not be attempted by small craft in W winds of Force 5 or over. Best time to enter is HW−2 to HW+1, but the channel is not buoyed. Before entry, check which sections of Carmarthen Bay are closed for range practice. (See 10·11·12). Channel through the sandbanks is liable to vary and is unlit.

LIGHTS AND MARKS
A barrel post with a QR light is about 1 ca S of conspic Tr and FS on West breakwater. Entrance to Burry Inlet close N of Burry Holms marked by Y buoy Fl Y 2·5s. Three conspic chimneys east of harbour.

RADIO TELEPHONE
None.

BURRY PORT *continued*

TELEPHONE (055 46)
Superintendent Llanelli 758181; CG and MRCC Swansea 366534; ⌗ (0222) 399123; Proof and Experimental Station 09945-243; Marinecall 0898 500 459; Police (Llanelli) 772222; Dr 2240.

FACILITIES
EC Tuesday; **Outer Harbour West pier** ☎ 3342, Slip, M (ring Hr Mr); **West Basin** ☎ 3342, Slip (ring Hr Mr), L, CH; **East Pier** Slip, L; **Burry Port Yacht Services** ☎ 2740, Slip, M, D, L, ME, El, Sh, C, CH; **Burry Port YC** Bar; **Shoreline Caravan Park** ☎ 2657, Gas. **Town** P, D, V, R, Bar. ✉; Ⓑ; ⇌; ✈ (Cardiff).

SWANSEA 10-11-17

West Glamorgan

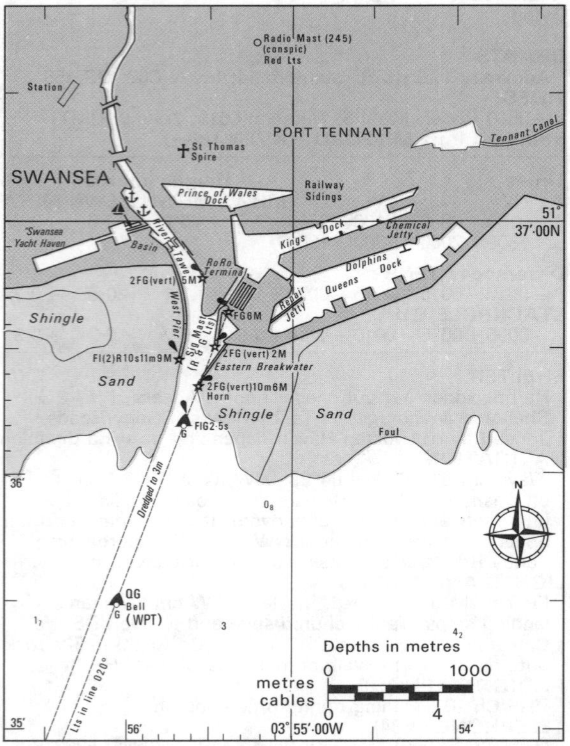

Radio Mast (245) (conspic) Red Lts
Station
PORT TENNANT
Tennant Canal
St Thomas Spire
SWANSEA
Prince of Wales Dock
Railway Sidings
51° 37'·00N
"Swansea Yacht Haven"
Basin
River Tawe
Kings Dock
Chemical Jetty
RoRo Terminal
Dolphins Dock
Queens Dock
Repair Jetty
2FG(vert)5M
West Pier
Sig Mast (R & G Lts)
FG6M
Shingle
Fl(2)R10s11m9M
Sand
2FG(vert)2M
Eastern Breakwater
2FG(vert)10m6M Horn
Shingle
Sand
Foul
FlG2·5s
G
36'
Dredged to 3m
QG Bell (WPT)
G
Depths in metres
metres 0 1000
cables 0 4
35'
56'
03°55'·00W
54'
Lts in line 020°

CHARTS
Admiralty 1161, 1165; Stanford 14; Imray C59; OS 159

TIDES
−0515 Dover; ML 5·3; Duration 0620; Zone 0 (GMT)

Standard Port MILFORD HAVEN (⟵)

Times				Height (metres)			
HW		LW		MHWS	MHWN	MLWN	MLWS
0100	0800	0100	0700	7·0	5·2	2·5	0·7
1300	2000	1300	1900				
Differences SWANSEA							
+0004	+0006	−0006	−0003	+2·6	+2·1	+0·7	+0·3
MUMBLES							
+0005	+0010	−0020	−0015	+2·3	+1·7	+0·6	+0·2
PORTHCAWL							
0000	0000	0000	−0015	+2·9	+2·3	+0·8	+0·3

SHELTER
Very good. Small craft may lie in the river below Tawe Lock but they dry out on mud at LW. Good anchorage off Mumbles in W wind. It is advised to enter the marina in South Dock, passing through Tawe Lock. Lock operates 0700 to 2200 HW∓4½. There are two buoys marked SYH for waiting yachts in mid-stream, below barrage; moor fore and aft between them.

NAVIGATION
Waypoint stbd-hand buoy, QG, Bell, 51°35'·50N 03°56'·06W, 200°/020° from/to Eastern Breakwater Lt, 0·92M. At springs, yachts should not enter river until LW+2. Yachts must be under power in the harbour and approaches, maximum speed 5 kn.

LIGHTS AND MARKS
Ldg Lts 020°. Front 2FG (vert) 5m 2M. Rear FG 6M; mark E side of dredged channel. When approaching from E, keep to seaward side of the inner fairway buoy (G conical, Fl G 2·5s). Marina Master will advise on movements on VHF Ch **80**. Traffic signals are shown at W side of entrance to King's Lock. Three FR Lts (vert) mean that dock and harbour are closed. Three FR Lts (hor) mean that docks are closed. Other signals consist of three rows of R or G Lts in three columns. Yachts entering are controlled by the light in the middle row of the left-hand column. When red this prohibits movement of yachts in the port or in the approach channel: when green, incoming craft may enter between breakwaters and proceed to river berth or marina, as below:

R R R   Yachts may enter river and proceed
G R R   to Tawe barrage
R R R

Traffic signals at lock as follows:

2FR – Lock closed. Do not proceed
R/G – Free flow operating; proceed with caution
R – Proceed only if instructed
G – Proceed into lock as instructed

RADIO TELEPHONE
Call: *Swansea Docks Radio* VHF Ch 14; 14 (H24). Marina Ch **80** M (working hours). Call: *Tawe Lock* Ch 18.

TELEPHONE (0792)
Hr Mr 650855 Ext 260; MRCC 366534; ⌗ (0222) 399123; Marinecall 0898 500 459; Police 456999; Ⓗ 205666; Dr 653452.

FACILITIES
Swansea Yacht Haven (350+50 visitors) ☎ 470310, D, FW, C (1 ton), BH (18 ton), AC, Gas, CH, Gaz, ME, El, Ⓔ, Sh, ⊡, Bar, R; **Swansea Yacht & Sub Aqua Club** ☎ 654863, M, L, FW, C (½ ton static), AB, Bar; **Near Landing** ME, El, CH; **Westland Engine Supplies** ☎ 873249 ME; **Cambrian Small Boats and Chandlery** ☎ 467263, ACA, CH; **Canard Sails** ☎ 367838, SM; **Barry Marine** ☎ 458057, ME, El, Ⓔ, CH; **Rainbow Sailing** ☎ 467804, El, Ⓔ, Sh, SM, V; **Town** ME, El, Sh, CH, V, R, Bar. ✉; Ⓑ; ⇌; ✈.

River Neath Slip, M (entry over bar after ½ flood)
Monkstone Marina (controlled by Monkstone SC) ☎ Briton Ferry 8722. No multihulls.

Mumbles P, D, CH, V, R, Bar; **Bristol Channel YC** ☎ 366000, Slip, M; **Mumbles YC** ☎ 369321, Slip, M, L, FW, C (by appointment);

BARRY 10-11-18

South Glamorgan

CHARTS
Admiralty 1182, 1152; Stanford 14; Imray C59; OS 171

TIDES
−0423 Dover; ML 6·1; Duration 0630; Zone 0 (GMT).

Standard Port BRISTOL (AVONMOUTH) (⟶)

Times				Height (metres)			
HW		LW		MHWS	MHWN	MLWN	MLWS
0600	1100	0300	0800	13·2	10·0	3·5	0·9
1800	2300	1500	2000				
Differences BARRY							
−0030	−0015	−0125	−0030	−1·8	−1·3	+0·2	0·0

BARRY *Continued*

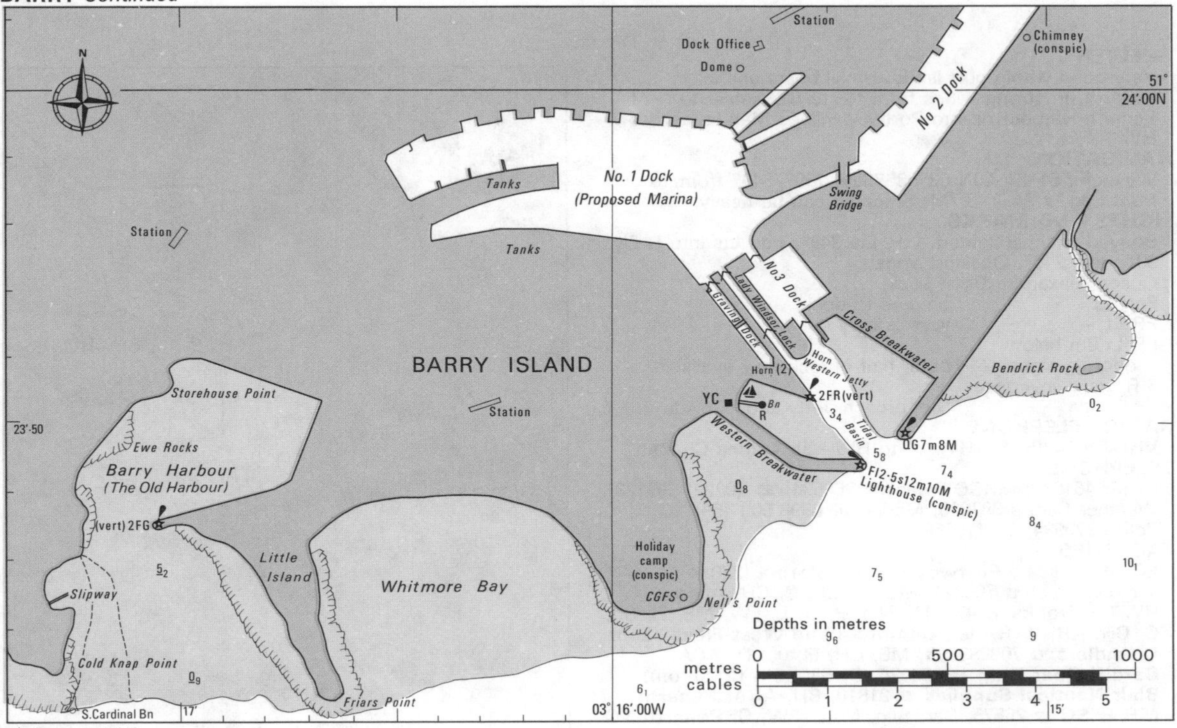

N
Station
Dock Office
Dome
Chimney (conspic)
51° 24'·00N
No 2 Dock
No. 1 Dock (Proposed Marina)
Tanks
Tanks
Swing Bridge
Station
No.3 Dock
Lady Windsor Lock
Graving Dock
Cross Breakwater
Horn Western Jetty
BARRY ISLAND
Bendrick Rock
Horn (2)
YC
Bn
R
2FR(vert)
Storehouse Point
Station
Tidal Basin
QG7m8M
Western Breakwater
Fl2·5s12m10M Lighthouse (conspic)
23'·50
Ewe Rocks
Barry Harbour (The Old Harbour)
(vert) 2FG
Little Island
Holiday camp (conspic)
Whitmore Bay
CGFS
Nell's Point
Slipway
Depths in metres
metres
cables
Cold Knap Point
Friars Point
S.Cardinal Bn
17'
03° 16'·00W
15'

⚠ Report to YC

SHELTER
Good shelter except in strong E to SE winds. In these winds yachts are advised to enter the dock (HW∓3) by prior arrangement. Outer harbour always available (free). Old harbour to W of Barry Island dries out and is no longer any use. A marina is planned for The Old Harbour.

NAVIGATION
Waypoint 51°23'.00N 03°15'.00W, 152°/332° from/to entrance, 0.53M. Beware heavy merchant traffic. Approaching from E keep well out from the shore. Strong tidal stream across entrance.

LIGHTS AND MARKS
W Breakwater Fl 2.5s 10M. E Breakwater QG 8M.

RADIO TELEPHONE
Call: *Barry Radio* VHF Ch **14**, 16; 13 (HW−4 to HW+3).

TELEPHONE (0446)
Hr Mr 732311; MRCC Swansea 366534; ⊞ (0222) 399123; Marinecall 0898 500 459; Police 734451; Dr 739543.

FACILITIES
EC Wednesday; **Ray Harris Marine** ☎ 740924, Slip, P, D, FW, Gas, ME, El, Sh, CH, SM; **Barry YC** (130) ☎ 735511, Slip, M, Bar, FW, Access HW∓3½. **Town** P, D, CH, V, R, Bar. ✉; Ⓑ; ⇌; ✈ (Cardiff).

CARDIFF 10-11-19

South Glamorgan

CHARTS
Admiralty 1182, 1176; Stanford 14; Imray C59; OS 171

TIDES
−0425 Dover; ML 6·4; Duration 0610; Zone 0 (GMT).

Standard Port BRISTOL (AVONMOUTH) (⟶)

Times				Height (metres)			
HW		LW		MHWS	MHWN	MLWN	MLWS
0600	1100	0300	0800	13·2	10·0	3·5	0·9
1800	2300	1500	2000				
Differences CARDIFF							
−0015	−0015	−0100	−0030	−1·0	−0·6	+0·1	0·0
NEWPORT							
−0020	−0010	0000	−0020	−1·1	−1·0	−0·6	−0·7

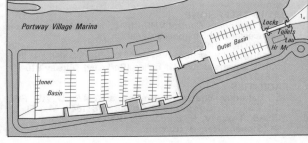

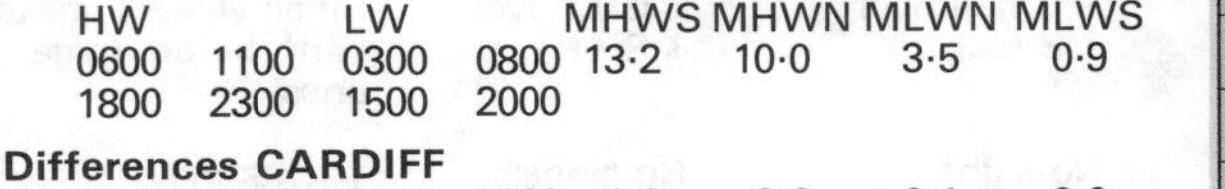

Portway Village Marina
Locks
Toilets
Lau
Hr Mr
Outer Basin
Inner Basin

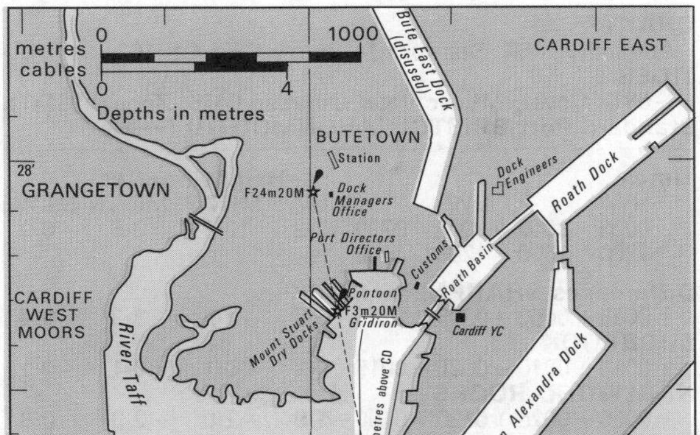

metres
cables
Depths in metres
Bute East Dock (disused)
CARDIFF EAST
BUTETOWN
Station
28'
GRANGETOWN
F24m20M
Dock Managers Office
Dock Engineers
Roath Dock
Port Directors Office
Customs
Roath Basin
CARDIFF WEST MOORS
Pontoon
F3m20M
Gridiron
Cardiff YC
Mount Stuart Dry Docks
River Taff
Queen Alexandra Dock
Dredged to 1·4 metres above CD
Jetties (disused)
2FR (vert)
F5m
F2m
Dia(occas)
2FG (vert)
51° 27'·00N
Penarth Flats
Cardiff Flats
Ely Tidal Harbour
Penarth MB + SC
Ldg Lts 246°
FlG5s
349°
R. Ely
The Patch
FW Y Bn
FW Y Bn
FlG2·5
Portway Village Marina
See inset
PENARTH
Ldg Lts 304°
11'
03° 10'·00W
09'

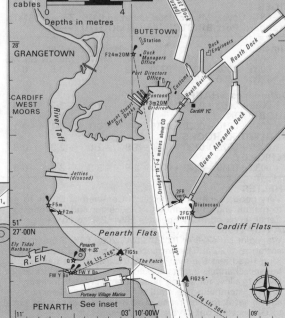

⚠ Contact Penarth YC or Cardiff YC

CARDIFF *continued*

SHELTER
Very good within port limits. Small boats anchor in Penarth. In strong winds from NE to SE, safest to N of Penarth Harbour or into Portway Village Marina (access HW∓3¾).
NAVIGATION
Waypoint 51°24'·00N 03°08'·73W, 169°/349° from/to front Ldg Lt 349°, 3·7M. Shipping can be heavy.
LIGHTS AND MARKS
Buoyed channel lighted. Ldg Lts 349°. Ldg Lts into R Ely 304° and 246°. Docking signals:-
Queen Alexandra Dock Lock;

Fl R Lt —	prepare to dock.
FR Lt —	vessels may dock.
FR Lt 9m below docking signal —	outer half of lock only available.
3 R Lts in inverted triangle —	S approach Jetty is occupied.

RADIO TELEPHONE
VHF Ch **14** 16; 13 (HW−4 to HW+3). Marina Ch **80** M.
TELEPHONE (0222)
Hr Mr 461083; MRCC Swansea 366534; # (0222) 399123; Weather Centre 397020; Marinecall 0898 500 459; Police 373934; Dr 415258.
FACILITIES
EC Wednesday; **Portway Village Marina** (220 + some visitors) ☎ 705021, ME, El, Sh, C, CH, Access HW∓4; **Docks** ☎ 471311, Slip, P, D, L, FW, ME, El, Sh, C, CH, AB, V, R, Bar; **Cambrian and West Fleet Yacht Chandlers** ☎ 709983 Sh, ME, CH, El, Ⓔ, D, ACA: **Cardiff Boat Bldg** ☎ 488034, D, SM, Sh, C (20 ton); **Blair Nautical Supplies** ☎ 21810, CH, ACA; **Penarth MB & SC** ☎ 26575, Bar, Slip, M, L, FW, C; **Penarth YC** ☎ 708196, Slip, FW, Bar; **Cardiff YC** ☎ 387697, Slip, M, L (Floating Pontoon), FW, Bar; **Barry Marine Centre** ☎ 562000, CH; **E.H. Hewett** ☎ 480624, ME, El; **Cambrian Marine Services** ☎ 43459, ME, El, Sh; **Barda Yachts** ☎ 705106, Sh; **ARG Ltd** ☎ 481076, Gas. **Town** P, D, ME, El, V, R, Bar. ⊠; Ⓑ; ⇌; ✈.

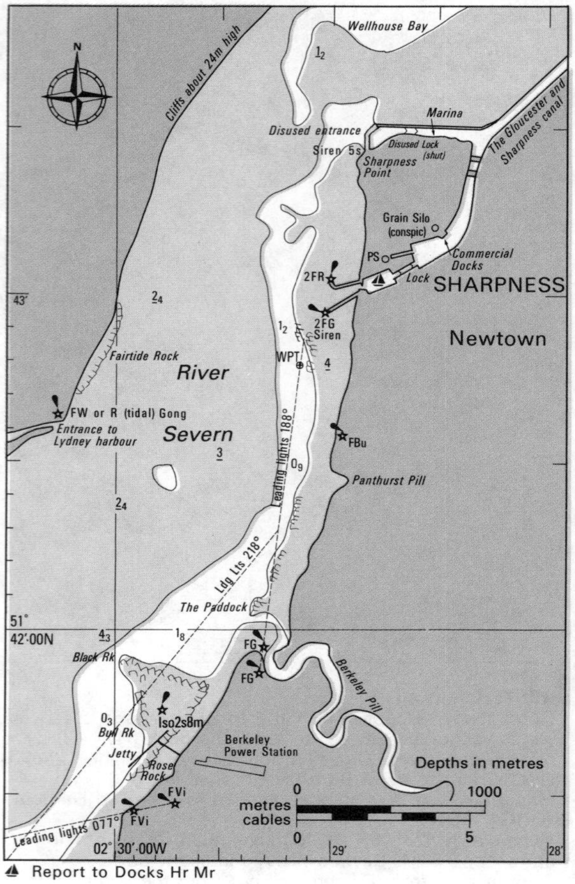

Wellhouse Bay
Cliffs about 24m high
Marina
The Gloucester and Sharpness canal
Disused entrance
Siren 5s
Disused Lock (shut)
Sharpness Point
Grain Silo (conspic)
PS
Commercial Docks
2FR
Lock
SHARPNESS
43'
2FG Siren
Newtown
Fairtide Rock
River
WPT
FW or R (tidal) Gong
Entrance to Lydney harbour
Severn
FBu
Leading lights 188°
Panthurst Pill
Ldg Lts 218°
The Paddock
51°
42'·00N
Black Rk
FG
FG
Berkeley Pill
Iso2s8m
Bull Rk
Jetty
Berkeley Power Station
Rose Rock
Depths in metres
FVi
FVi
metres
cables
0
1000
5
Leading lights 077°
02° 30'·00W
29'
28'

⛵ Report to Docks Hr Mr

SHARPNESS 10-11-20
Gloucestershire

CHARTS
Admiralty 1166; Stanford 14; Imray C59; OS 162
TIDES
−0315 Dover; ML No data; Duration 0415; Zone 0 (GMT).
Standard Port BRISTOL (AVONMOUTH) (⟶)

Times				Height (metres)			
HW		LW		MHWS	MHWN	MLWN	MLWS
0000	0600	0000	0700	13·2	10·0	3·5	0·9
1200	1800	1200	1900				
Differences SHARPNESS DOCK							
+0035	+0050	+0305	+0245	−3·9	−4·2	−3·3	−0·4
SUDBROOK							
+0010	+0010	+0025	+0015	+0·2	+0·1	−0·1	+0·1
NARLWOOD ROCKS							
+0025	+0025	+0120	+0100	−1·9	−2·0	−2·3	−0·8
BERKELEY							
+0030	+0045	+0245	+0220	−3·8	−3·9	−3·4	−0·5

SHELTER
Very good. Yachts pass through Commercial Docks to get to marina and to entrance to Gloucester and Sharpness Canal. Lock normally operates HW−2½ to HW+½.
NAVIGATION
Waypoint 51°42'·80N 02°29'·20W, 208°/028° from/to entrance, 0·20M. The entrance is 15 miles up river from King Road and the river dries out except for a narrow buoyed channel. Yachts should arrive off Sharpness about HW−1; allow for strong flood stream. Watch for entry signals, stemming tide south of the F Bu Lt. Beware strong set across entrance. There are no locks in the canal to Gloucester, but several swing bridges.

LIGHTS AND MARKS
Entry signals are as follows:—

Day	Night	
2 B balls	2 R Lts	Entrance closed
1 B ball	1 R Lt	Entrance not clear (traffic)
1 G flag	1 G Lt	Entrance clear for commercial shipping
1 G flag over 1 B ball	1 G Lt over 1 R Lt	Small vessels are to berth before large ones
No signals	No signals	Yachts may proceed in or out.
2 G flags (one at each yard arm)	2 G Lts	HW or tide ebbing

RADIO TELEPHONE
Call: *Sharpness Control* VHF Ch 16; 14 (H24). Bridges on Gloucester and Sharpness Canal Ch 74.
TELEPHONE (0453)
Hr Mr 811644; # (0453) 811302; Marinecall 0898 500 459; MRCC Swansea 366534; Police (Berkeley) Dursley 810477; Ⓗ 810777.
FACILITIES
EC Saturday; **Sharpness Marine** ☎ 811476, D, AC, FW, Sh, Gas, CH; **Commercial Docks** ☎ 811644, ME, El, Sh, C, AB. **Town** V, R, Bar. ⊠; Ⓑ (Berkeley); ⇌ (Stonehouse); ✈ (Bristol).

BRISTOL (CITY DOCKS)

Avon

10-11-21

CHARTS
Admiralty 1859, 1176; Stanford 14; Imray C59; OS 172

TIDES
−0401 (Avonmouth) Dover; ML 7·0; Duration 0620; Zone 0 (GMT).

Standard Port BRISTOL (AVONMOUTH) (⟶)

Times				Height (metres)			
HW		LW		MHWS	MHWN	MLWN	MLWS
0200	0800	0300	0800	13·2	10·0	3·5	0·9
1400	2000	1500	2000				
Differences CUMBERLAND BASIN (Ent)							
+0010	+0010	Dries out		−2·9	−3·0	Dries out	
PORTISHEAD							
−0002	0000	No data		−0·1	−0·1	No data	

NOTE: The Port of Bristol (Avonmouth) is a Standard Port and tidal predictions for each day are given below.

SHELTER
Except in emergency, neither Avonmouth, Royal Portbury or Portishead Docks are available for yachts. Some shelter is available in the approach channel to the locks at Portishead. Yachts must not anchor adjoining the pier or stone jetty and they must be prepared to dry out on soft mud 2 hours each side of MLWS.
The regulations for craft entering the Avon, Cumberland Basin, Floating Harbour or City Docks are set out in detail in a pamphlet called *Bristol City Docks — Information for Owners of Pleasurecraft*, obtainable from the Hr Mr's Office, Underfall Yard, Cumberland Road, Bristol BS1 6XG. ☎ 264797.

NAVIGATION
Avonmouth waypoint 51°30′·40N 02°43′·21W, 307°/127° from/to front Ldg Lt 127°, 0·58M. The channel from Flatholm is buoyed. Tidal stream can run at five knots or more. When approaching Walton Bay, contact Avonmouth Radio on Ch 12 and transfer to either Ch 09 or 14 low power, for instructions to pass Royal Portbury Dock and enter the River Avon. If no radio fitted, signal Avonmouth Signal Station with international flag R or flash morse letter R. The signal station will reply by light or loud hailer.

LIGHTS AND MARKS
R Avon is entered south of S Pier Lt Oc RG 30s; vis R 294°-036°, G036°-194°. Ldg Lts 127° both FR. Saint George Ldg Lts 173°, both Oc G 5s synchronised. Above Pill Creek stbd hand Lts are mostly Oc G 5s, and port hand are FY.
Yachts should arrive Cumberland Basin entrance by HW. Entry signals to Bristol City Docks are shown from two positions on E bank, 1½ and 2½ ca above Clifton Suspension Bridge. FG Lt — come ahead with caution. FR Lt — stop and await orders. Prince's Street and Redcliffe bridges are manned 0600-2230 summer, 0900-1645 winter. Other bridges HW−3 to HW+1. R Lts indicate bridges are closed. Inform Bridgemaster Tel. 299338 in advance, or sound one short blast followed by one long and one short.

RADIO TELEPHONE
Avonmouth Signal Station (South Pier, Royal Edward Dock) Call: *Avonmouth Radio*: VHF Ch **12** (VTS), Port Operations Ch 14 09 11 16 (H24): navigational information provided on request. Royal Portbury Dock Ch 16; 12 **14** (HW−4½ to HW+3½).
Portishead Dock Ch 16; 12 **14** (HW−2½ to HW+1½).
City Docks Radio Ch 14; 11 **14** (HW−3 to HW+1).
Bristol Floating Harbour Ch 16; 73 (Office hours).
Other station: Newport Ch 16; 09 11 (HW∓4). Marina Ch **80** M.

TELEPHONE (0272)
Hr Mr 264797; MRCC Swansea 366534; Netham Lock Keeper 776590; Princes St & Redcliffe Bridge Masters 299338; # (0272) 235200; Dock Master, Cumberland Basin 273633; Bristol Floating Harbour 297608; Weather Centre 279298; Marinecall 0898 500 459; Police 277777; Ⓗ 230000.

FACILITIES
EC Wednesday/Saturday; **Bristol Marina** (80 visitors) ☎ 265730, D, FW, ME, El, Sh, AC, SM, Slip, C, BH (30 ton), Access HW−3 to HW+1; **Baltic Wharf Leisure Centre** ☎ 297608, Slip, L, Bar; **Cabot Cruising Club** ☎ 268318, M, L, FW, AB, Bar; **Mud Dock** FW, C (4 ton); **City Dock** ☎ 264797, AB, C (4 ton), M; gridiron available outside Cumberland Basin — contact Dockmaster ☎ 273633; **Saltford Marine** ☎ Saltford 872226, Slip, C (8 ton), M, L, FW, ME, El, Sh, CH, R; **Marine Electronic Services** ☎ 227409, Ⓔ; **Portavon Marina** ☎ 861626, Slip, M, L, FW, ME, Sh, CH, R; **Enigma Chandlery** ☎ (0454) 416876, CH; **Bristol Boating Centre** ☎ 294160, CH; **Bristol Marine Engineering** ☎ 262923, BY, Gas, Gaz, Kos, ME, El, CH; **SW Petroleum Co** P, D; **W F Price** ☎ 823888, CH, ACA; **City** ✉; Ⓑ; ⇌; ✈.

11

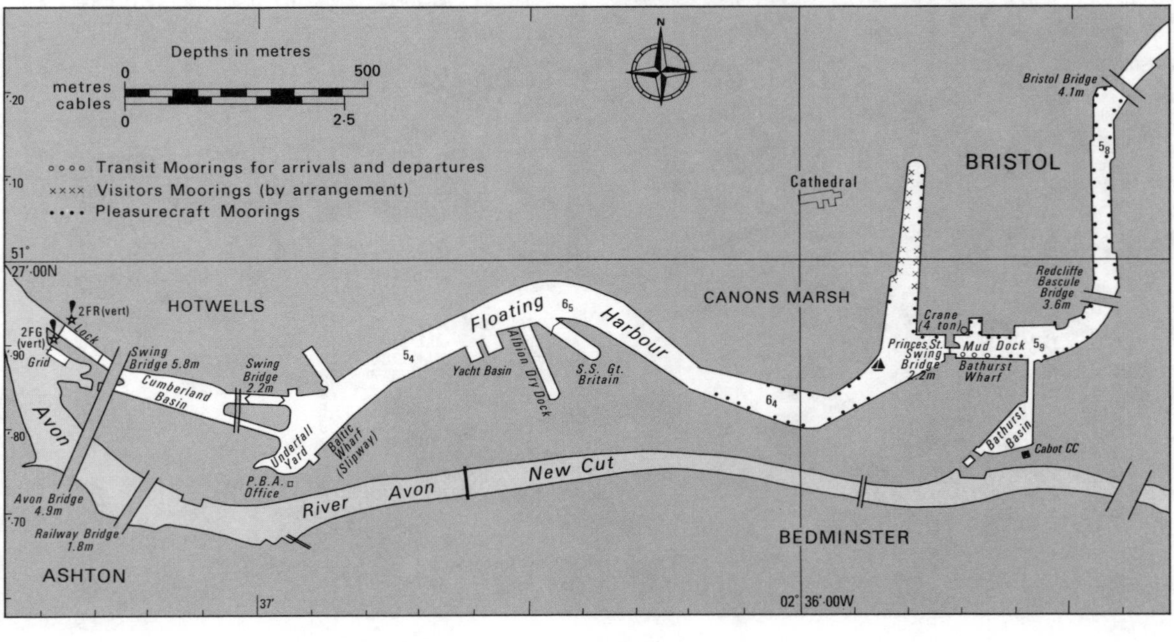
Depths in metres
metres
cables
0
500
0
2·5
○○○○ Transit Moorings for arrivals and departures
×××× Visitors Moorings (by arrangement)
•••• Pleasurecraft Moorings
51°
27′·00N
2FR(vert)
2FG (vert)
Grid
HOTWELLS
Lock
Swing Bridge 5.8m
Swing Bridge 2.2m
Cumberland Basin
Avon
Avon Bridge 4.9m
Railway Bridge 1.8m
ASHTON
P.B.A. Office
Underfall Yard
Baltic Wharf (Slipway)
Floating Harbour
Yacht Basin
Albion Dry Dock
S.S. Gt. Britain
River Avon
New Cut
CANONS MARSH
Cathedral
BRISTOL
Bristol Bridge 4.1m
Redcliffe Bascule Bridge 3.6m
Crane (4 ton)
Princes St. Swing Bridge 2.2m
Mud Dock
Bathurst Wharf
Bathurst Basin
Cabot CC
BEDMINSTER
37′
02° 36′·00W

ENGLAND, WEST COAST – PORT OF BRISTOL (AVONMOUTH)

TIME ZONE UT(GMT)
For Summer Time add ONE hour in non-shaded areas

Lat 51°30′ N Long 2°43′ W

TIMES AND HEIGHTS OF HIGH AND LOW WATERS

YEAR **1992**

JANUARY

Date	Day	Time	m	Time	m	Time	m	Time	m
1	W	0407	10·7	1034	3·2	1638	10·8	2308	3·0
2	Th	0511	11·2	1142	2·7	1737	11·3		
3	F	0011	2·6	0603	11·7	1236	2·3	1827	11·7
4	Sa ●	0100	2·2	0648	12·1	1324	2·0	1910	12·0
5	Su	0144	1·9	0728	12·4	1405	1·8	1947	12·1
6	M	0223	1·8	0804	12·5	1443	1·8	2020	12·2
7	Tu	0258	1·8	0834	12·5	1517	1·7	2050	12·2
8	W	0328	1·8	0904	12·5	1548	1·8	2119	12·2
9	Th	0357	1·9	0935	12·3	1616	1·8	2150	12·0
10	F	0424	2·0	1007	12·0	1645	2·0	2223	11·7
11	Sa	0452	2·2	1041	11·6	1713	2·3	2255	11·3
12	Su	0520	2·5	1115	11·2	1743	2·6	2330	10·8
13	M ☽	0554	2·9	1154	10·7	1821	3·0		
14	Tu	0017	10·4	0638	3·3	1252	10·3	1913	3·4
15	W	0126	10·2	0744	3·7	1419	10·3	2040	3·5
16	Th	0256	10·5	0932	3·5	1541	10·9	2219	3·0
17	F	0413	11·2	1054	2·7	1652	11·7	2332	2·3
18	Sa	0522	12·1	1211	2·1	1758	12·4		
19	Su ○	0048	1·7	0624	12·9	1324	1·4	1857	13·1
20	M	0151	1·1	0719	13·6	1422	0·8	1948	13·7
21	Tu	0244	0·6	0806	14·0	1511	0·5	2034	13·9
22	W	0331	0·4	0851	14·2	1555	0·4	2117	13·9
23	Th	0410	0·5	0934	14·1	1631	0·6	2159	13·6
24	F	0445	0·8	1016	13·6	1705	1·1	2240	12·9
25	Sa	0518	1·4	1057	12·8	1734	1·7	2320	12·1
26	Su ☾	0547	2·0	1137	11·9	1804	2·4		
27	M	0001	11·2	0619	2·7	1221	11·0	1838	3·1
28	Tu	0048	10·3	0700	3·5	1317	10·1	1926	3·8
29	W	0158	9·7	0813	4·1	1437	9·7	2105	4·2
30	Th	0327	9·8	0957	3·8	1607	10·0	2234	3·6
31	F	0445	10·5	1111	3·1	1716	10·7	2340	2·8

FEBRUARY

Date	Day	Time	m	Time	m	Time	m	Time	m
1	Sa	0543	11·4	1210	2·4	1808	11·4		
2	Su	0035	2·2	0629	12·0	1300	1·9	1852	11·9
3	M ●	0123	1·8	0709	12·4	1345	1·6	1928	12·3
4	Tu	0205	1·5	0744	12·6	1425	1·4	2001	12·5
5	W	0240	1·4	0813	12·8	1500	1·3	2029	12·7
6	Th	0312	1·3	0843	12·9	1531	1·3	2057	12·8
7	F	0342	1·4	0912	12·9	1600	1·3	2127	12·6
8	Sa	0410	1·5	0943	12·6	1627	1·5	2157	12·3
9	Su	0434	1·7	1014	12·2	1651	1·8	2227	11·9
10	M	0458	2·1	1044	11·7	1715	2·2	2257	11·4
11	Tu ☽	0525	2·4	1118	11·1	1746	2·6	2334	10·8
12	W	0603	2·9	1207	10·5	1831	3·1		
13	Th	0038	10·3	0659	3·5	1334	10·1	1945	3·6
14	F	0218	10·2	0853	3·7	1512	10·4	2149	3·3
15	Sa	0349	10·9	1031	2·9	1635	11·3	2312	2·4
16	Su	0506	11·9	1158	2·1	1747	12·3		
17	M	0036	1·7	0611	12·9	1314	1·2	1845	13·2
18	Tu ○	0141	0·9	0704	13·7	1411	0·5	1934	13·8
19	W	0232	0·3	0751	14·2	1457	0·1	2016	14·2
20	Th	0314	0·0	0832	14·4	1536	0·1	2056	14·2
21	F	0352	0·2	0911	14·2	1610	0·4	2134	13·8
22	Sa	0423	0·6	0950	13·7	1638	1·0	2212	13·1
23	Su	0449	1·2	1028	12·8	1702	1·6	2247	12·2
24	M	0515	1·9	1104	11·8	1726	2·3	2320	11·2
25	Tu ☾	0540	2·6	1137	10·8	1753	3·1	2357	10·2
26	W	0612	3·4	1224	9·7	1831	3·9		
27	Th	0100	9·3	0706	4·2	1348	9·1	1942	4·6
28	F	0246	9·2	0924	4·3	1534	9·4	2206	4·0
29	Sa	0417	10·1	1041	3·3	1648	10·3	2311	3·0

MARCH

Date	Day	Time	m	Time	m	Time	m	Time	m
1	Su	0515	11·1	1139	2·4	1742	11·2		
2	M	0007	2·2	0603	11·9	1232	1·8	1825	11·9
3	Tu	0056	1·6	0642	12·4	1320	1·4	1902	12·3
4	W ●	0140	1·3	0717	12·7	1401	1·1	1934	12·7
5	Th	0218	1·1	0748	13·0	1437	1·0	2002	12·9
6	F	0251	1·0	0816	13·1	1510	1·0	2030	13·1
7	Sa	0322	1·0	0847	13·1	1539	1·0	2101	13·0
8	Su	0350	1·2	0918	12·9	1606	1·2	2132	12·7
9	M	0416	1·4	0950	12·5	1628	1·5	2203	12·2
10	Tu	0437	1·8	1023	11·9	1652	1·9	2234	11·7
11	W	0504	2·1	1058	11·3	1722	2·3	2315	11·0
12	Th ☽	0542	2·7	1150	10·5	1808	3·0		
13	F	0019	10·3	0639	3·4	1317	10·0	1924	3·6
14	Sa	0158	10·1	0834	3·6	1456	10·3	2129	3·3
15	Su	0334	10·8	1014	2·8	1623	11·3	2255	2·4
16	M	0452	11·9	1144	1·9	1732	12·3		
17	Tu	0021	1·6	0556	12·9	1257	1·1	1827	13·1
18	W ○	0123	0·8	0646	13·6	1351	0·5	1914	13·7
19	Th	0212	0·3	0730	14·0	1436	0·2	1954	14·0
20	F	0253	0·2	0809	14·1	1512	0·3	2032	14·0
21	Sa	0327	0·4	0847	14·0	1543	0·7	2107	13·7
22	Su	0356	0·8	0924	13·4	1609	1·2	2143	13·0
23	M	0421	1·3	1000	12·6	1631	1·8	2217	12·1
24	Tu	0445	1·9	1033	11·6	1654	2·4	2248	11·1
25	W	0509	2·6	1105	10·6	1719	3·0	2320	10·2
26	Th ☾	0540	3·3	1144	9·6	1753	3·7		
27	F	0015	9·3	0627	4·1	1302	8·9	1850	4·5
28	Sa	0159	9·0	0815	4·5	1447	9·1	2124	4·4
29	Su	0332	9·7	1004	3·5	1606	10·0	2233	3·2
30	M	0435	10·7	1101	2·5	1702	10·9	2327	2·4
31	Tu	0525	11·6	1154	1·9	1747	11·7		

APRIL

Date	Day	Time	m	Time	m	Time	m	Time	m
1	W	0021	1·8	0607	12·2	1245	1·5	1827	12·2
2	Th	0107	1·4	0643	12·6	1330	1·2	1900	12·6
3	F ●	0148	1·1	0717	12·9	1408	1·0	1933	13·0
4	Sa	0225	1·0	0749	13·1	1443	0·9	2004	13·2
5	Su	0258	1·0	0822	13·2	1517	1·0	2037	13·1
6	M	0331	1·1	0857	13·0	1546	1·1	2111	12·9
7	Tu	0359	1·3	0934	12·6	1612	1·4	2146	12·4
8	W	0424	1·6	1012	12·0	1638	1·8	2226	11·8
9	Th	0455	2·0	1055	11·3	1713	2·3	2313	11·1
10	F ☽	0537	2·6	1153	10·6	1803	2·9		
11	Sa	0021	10·5	0642	3·1	1313	10·2	1926	3·4
12	Su	0148	10·4	0826	3·2	1442	10·5	2111	3·0
13	M	0317	11·1	0953	2·5	1603	11·3	2231	2·3
14	Tu	0433	11·9	1118	1·9	1709	12·2	2354	1·7
15	W	0533	12·6	1232	1·3	1804	12·8		
16	Th	0057	1·1	0624	13·1	1326	0·9	1849	13·2
17	F ○	0145	0·8	0707	13·4	1409	0·8	1930	13·5
18	Sa	0226	0·7	0747	13·5	1446	0·9	2006	13·5
19	Su	0300	0·9	0823	13·3	1515	1·2	2043	13·3
20	M	0329	1·2	0900	12·9	1542	1·5	2118	12·7
21	Tu	0356	1·6	0936	12·2	1606	2·0	2153	11·9
22	W	0421	2·0	1009	11·3	1630	2·4	2224	11·1
23	Th	0447	2·5	1042	10·5	1655	2·9	2258	10·3
24	F ☾	0518	3·1	1120	9·8	1729	3·4	2346	9·6
25	Sa	0601	3·6	1221	9·2	1818	4·0		
26	Su	0107	9·2	0706	4·0	1348	9·2	1937	4·3
27	M	0233	9·6	0903	3·7	1507	9·7	2136	3·7
28	Tu	0341	10·4	1012	2·9	1607	10·5	2238	2·9
29	W	0434	11·1	1106	2·3	1658	11·3	2333	2·3
30	Th	0520	11·8	1200	1·8	1743	11·9		

Chart Datum: 6.50 metres below Ordnance Datum (Newlyn)

ENGLAND, WEST COAST – PORT OF BRISTOL (AVONMOUTH)

TIME ZONE UT(GMT)
For Summer Time add ONE hour in non-shaded areas

Lat 51°30′ N Long 2°43′ W

TIMES AND HEIGHTS OF HIGH AND LOW WATERS

YEAR **1992**

MAY

Day	Time	m
1 F	0025	1·8
	0604	12·3
	1250	1·5
	1824	12·4
2 Sa ●	0113	1·4
	0643	12·7
	1335	1·2
	1902	12·8
3 Su	0157	1·2
	0723	12·9
	1418	1·0
	1940	13·1
4 M	0236	1·1
	0802	13·0
	1456	1·0
	2018	13·1
5 Tu	0314	1·1
	0843	12·9
	1532	1·2
	2058	13·0
6 W	0350	1·3
	0925	12·6
	1606	1·4
	2141	12·6
7 Th	0424	1·6
	1010	12·2
	1640	1·8
	2227	12·1
8 F	0501	1·9
	1059	11·6
	1719	2·2
	2319	11·6
9 Sa ☽	0547	2·3
	1157	11·0
	1811	2·6
10 Su	0022	11·1
	0650	2·7
	1304	10·7
	1924	2·9
11 M	0134	11·0
	0809	2·7
	1420	10·9
	2046	2·7
12 Tu	0251	11·3
	0924	2·4
	1535	11·3
	2159	2·3
13 W	0403	11·7
	1038	2·1
	1640	11·8
	2316	2·1
14 Th	0505	12·1
	1156	1·9
	1736	12·2
15 F	0025	1·8
	0558	12·4
	1253	1·7
	1824	12·5
16 Sa ○	0117	1·5
	0643	12·5
	1340	1·6
	1906	12·8
17 Su	0159	1·4
	0726	12·6
	1418	1·6
	1945	12·9
18 M	0236	1·5
	0804	12·6
	1451	1·6
	2023	12·7
19 Tu	0308	1·6
	0842	12·3
	1521	1·8
	2100	12·4
20 W	0338	1·8
	0918	11·9
	1549	2·1
	2134	11·9
21 Th	0406	2·1
	0952	11·4
	1614	2·4
	2207	11·3
22 F	0434	2·4
	1024	10·9
	1641	2·7
	2242	10·8
23 Sa	0504	2·7
	1102	10·4
	1713	3·0
	2323	10·3
24 Su ☾	0542	3·0
	1147	9·9
	1754	3·3
25 M	0018	9·9
	0629	3·3
	1246	9·7
	1848	3·6
26 Tu	0127	9·8
	0731	3·5
	1358	9·8
	1958	3·7
27 W	0237	10·1
	0853	3·3
	1505	10·2
	2128	3·4
28 Th	0338	10·7
	1007	2·8
	1603	10·9
	2237	2·8
29 F	0433	11·3
	1109	2·3
	1657	11·5
	2337	2·2
30 Sa	0523	11·9
	1207	1·9
	1747	12·2
31 Su	0035	1·8
	0612	12·4
	1303	1·5
	1834	12·7

JUNE

Day	Time	m
1 M ●	0128	1·4
	0700	12·7
	1354	1·3
	1920	13·0
2 Tu	0218	1·2
	0747	13·0
	1440	1·1
	2005	13·2
3 W	0304	1·1
	0833	13·0
	1525	1·2
	2051	13·2
4 Th	0348	1·2
	0921	12·9
	1606	1·3
	2138	13·0
5 F	0430	1·3
	1007	12·6
	1647	1·5
	2226	12·7
6 Sa	0511	1·6
	1057	12·2
	1727	1·8
	2316	12·3
7 Su ☽	0554	1·8
	1147	11·7
	1814	2·1
8 M	0010	11·8
	0642	2·2
	1245	11·3
	1907	2·4
9 Tu	0110	11·4
	0740	2·4
	1348	11·0
	2011	2·7
10 W	0219	11·2
	0846	2·6
	1458	11·0
	2121	2·7
11 Th	0328	11·2
	0956	2·7
	1606	11·2
	2234	2·6
12 F	0434	11·4
	1111	2·6
	1706	11·5
	2347	2·4
13 Sa	0533	11·6
	1219	2·4
	1800	11·9
14 Su	0046	2·2
	0624	11·8
	1312	2·2
	1846	12·2
15 M ○	0134	2·0
	0709	12·0
	1354	2·0
	1928	12·4
16 Tu	0215	1·9
	0749	12·1
	1432	1·9
	2008	12·4
17 W	0251	1·8
	0827	12·1
	1505	2·0
	2044	12·3
18 Th	0324	1·9
	0903	11·9
	1536	2·1
	2117	12·1
19 F	0355	2·0
	0934	11·7
	1604	2·2
	2149	11·8
20 Sa	0423	2·1
	1006	11·5
	1631	2·4
	2223	11·5
21 Su	0452	2·2
	1040	11·1
	1659	2·5
	2258	11·1
22 M	0523	2·4
	1115	10·7
	1733	2·8
	2337	10·7
23 Tu ☾	0600	2·7
	1156	10·3
	1811	3·1
24 W	0024	10·3
	0642	3·1
	1246	10·1
	1900	3·4
25 Th	0124	10·1
	0737	3·3
	1355	10·1
	2006	3·6
26 F	0239	10·3
	0900	3·3
	1510	10·5
	2142	3·3
27 Sa	0346	10·8
	1021	2·8
	1614	11·2
	2254	2·6
28 Su	0448	11·5
	1127	2·2
	1715	11·9
29 M	0000	2·1
	0549	12·1
	1234	1·8
	1812	12·5
30 Tu ●	0106	1·7
	0645	12·6
	1335	1·4
	1906	13·0

JULY

Day	Time	m
1 W	0206	1·3
	0737	13·0
	1430	1·1
	1955	13·4
2 Th	0258	1·0
	0825	13·3
	1519	0·9
	2043	13·6
3 F	0345	0·8
	0911	13·4
	1604	0·9
	2128	13·6
4 Sa	0428	0·9
	0956	13·2
	1644	1·0
	2214	13·3
5 Su	0506	1·1
	1042	12·8
	1722	1·3
	2259	12·9
6 M	0543	1·4
	1127	12·2
	1758	1·8
	2347	12·2
7 Tu ☽	0619	2·0
	1215	11·6
	1839	2·3
8 W	0038	11·5
	0702	2·5
	1309	10·9
	1927	2·9
9 Th	0138	10·8
	0758	3·1
	1415	10·5
	2037	3·3
10 F	0249	10·5
	0914	3·4
	1529	10·5
	2157	3·3
11 Sa	0404	10·6
	1034	3·2
	1641	10·9
	2313	2·9
12 Su	0512	11·0
	1146	2·8
	1740	11·5
13 M	0018	2·5
	0607	11·4
	1245	2·4
	1831	11·9
14 Tu ○	0110	2·1
	0655	11·8
	1333	2·1
	1914	12·2
15 W	0155	1·9
	0735	12·0
	1413	1·9
	1952	12·4
16 Th	0234	1·8
	0812	12·2
	1450	1·8
	2026	12·5
17 F	0308	1·7
	0843	12·2
	1522	1·8
	2057	12·5
18 Sa	0339	1·7
	0912	12·2
	1550	1·9
	2127	12·4
19 Su	0407	1·7
	0942	12·1
	1617	2·0
	2157	12·1
20 M	0435	1·9
	1012	11·8
	1642	2·1
	2230	11·7
21 Tu	0502	2·1
	1042	11·3
	1709	2·4
	2301	11·2
22 W ☾	0529	2·4
	1115	10·9
	1739	2·8
	2334	10·7
23 Th	0601	2·8
	1151	10·4
	1815	3·2
24 F	0021	10·3
	0643	3·3
	1249	10·1
	1909	3·6
25 Sa	0135	10·0
	0751	3·6
	1416	10·1
	2044	3·7
26 Su	0305	10·4
	0941	3·3
	1539	10·8
	2221	3·0
27 M	0421	11·2
	1058	2·6
	1651	11·7
	2334	2·3
28 Tu	0530	12·0
	1211	2·0
	1756	12·5
29 W ●	0052	1·8
	0631	12·7
	1324	1·4
	1853	13·2
30 Th	0157	1·2
	0724	13·3
	1422	0·9
	1942	13·8
31 F	0250	0·6
	0812	13·7
	1510	0·5
	2029	14·1

AUGUST

Day	Time	m
1 Sa	0335	0·4
	0856	13·9
	1552	0·5
	2111	14·1
2 Su	0414	0·5
	0938	13·7
	1630	0·7
	2155	13·8
3 M	0449	0·9
	1019	13·2
	1704	1·1
	2237	13·1
4 Tu	0520	1·4
	1101	12·5
	1733	1·7
	2318	12·3
5 W ☽	0549	2·1
	1142	11·6
	1804	2·4
6 Th	0001	11·3
	0621	2·8
	1227	10·7
	1842	3·2
7 F	0053	10·4
	0703	3·6
	1330	10·0
	1941	3·9
8 Sa	0208	9·8
	0826	4·1
	1456	9·9
	2128	3·9
9 Su	0338	9·9
	1007	3·7
	1620	10·5
	2248	3·2
10 M	0454	10·7
	1120	2·9
	1722	11·4
	2351	2·5
11 Tu	0550	11·4
	1219	2·3
	1812	12·0
12 W	0046	2·0
	0636	11·9
	1309	1·9
	1855	12·4
13 Th ○	0133	1·7
	0716	12·3
	1352	1·6
	1931	12·7
14 F	0212	1·5
	0749	12·5
	1429	1·5
	2004	12·8
15 Sa	0247	1·4
	0819	12·6
	1501	1·5
	2032	12·8
16 Su	0319	1·4
	0846	12·6
	1531	1·6
	2100	12·8
17 M	0348	1·5
	0914	12·5
	1557	1·7
	2129	12·5
18 Tu	0413	1·6
	0942	12·2
	1621	1·9
	2159	12·1
19 W	0437	1·9
	1012	11·7
	1645	2·3
	2228	11·5
20 Th	0501	2·3
	1040	11·2
	1709	2·7
	2258	11·0
21 F ☾	0527	2·7
	1112	10·7
	1742	3·1
	2339	10·4
22 Sa	0605	3·2
	1204	10·2
	1831	3·6
23 Su	0050	9·9
	0706	3·7
	1335	10·0
	1957	3·9
24 M	0234	10·0
	0907	3·7
	1514	10·6
	2156	3·3
25 Tu	0402	10·9
	1034	2·8
	1634	11·6
	2315	2·4
26 W	0515	12·0
	1156	2·0
	1742	12·6
27 Th	0041	1·6
	0617	12·9
	1310	1·3
	1838	13·5
28 F ●	0144	0·9
	0707	13·6
	1406	0·6
	1926	14·1
29 Sa	0233	0·4
	0752	14·0
	1453	0·3
	2009	14·4
30 Su	0317	0·2
	0833	14·2
	1534	0·3
	2050	14·3
31 M	0353	0·5
	0912	13·9
	1607	0·7
	2129	13·9

Chart Datum: 6.50 metres below Ordnance Datum (Newlyn)

ENGLAND, WEST COAST – PORT OF BRISTOL (AVONMOUTH)

TIME ZONE UT(GMT)

For Summer Time add ONE hour in non-shaded areas

Lat 51°30′ N Long 2°43′ W

TIMES AND HEIGHTS OF HIGH AND LOW WATERS

YEAR **1992**

SEPTEMBER

Day	Time	m	Day	Time	m
1 Tu	0424 0952 1638 2210	1·0 13·3 1·2 13·1	16 W	0350 0914 1600 2132	1·6 12·5 1·8 12·3
2 W	0451 1031 1705 2248	1·6 12·5 1·2 12·1	17 Th	0413 0945 1623 2203	1·9 12·1 2·2 11·7
3 Th ☽	0516 1109 1732 2327	2·3 11·5 2·6 11·0	18 F	0435 1014 1647 2235	2·2 11·5 2·5 11·1
4 F	0544 1149 1804	3·1 10·5 3·4	19 Sa ☾	0504 1049 1720 2319	2·6 11·0 3·0 10·5
5 Sa	0014 0621 1249 1853	9·9 3·9 9·6 4·2	20 Su	0543 1144 1810	3·2 10·3 3·6
6 Su	0131 0724 1423 2101	9·2 4·6 9·4 4·4	21 M	0035 0646 1317 1941	9·9 3·7 10·0 3·9
7 M	0311 0943 1556 2223	9·4 4·2 10·2 3·4	22 Tu	0216 0844 1456 2136	10·0 3·7 10·6 3·2
8 Tu	0430 1052 1658 2322	10·4 3·1 11·3 2·4	23 W	0346 1014 1617 2258	11·0 2·8 11·7 2·3
9 W	0525 1149 1746	11·4 2·2 12·1	24 Th	0458 1137 1723	12·1 2·0 12·7
10 Th	0015 0610 1239 1828	1·8 12·0 1·7 12·5	25 F	0022 0557 1252 1818	1·5 13·0 1·2 13·5
11 F	0103 0649 1324 1904	1·5 12·4 1·5 12·8	26 Sa ●	0123 0646 1345 1904	0·8 13·6 0·6 14·0
12 Sa ○	0145 0721 1402 1935	1·3 12·6 1·4 12·9	27 Su	0212 0730 1430 1947	0·4 14·0 0·4 14·2
13 Su	0222 0749 1436 2002	1·2 12·8 1·3 13·0	28 M	0253 0809 1508 2026	0·4 14·1 0·5 14·1
14 M	0253 0816 1507 2032	1·2 12·9 1·4 13·0	29 Tu	0328 0847 1542 2105	0·7 13·9 0·9 13·7
15 Tu	0322 0844 1535 2101	1·3 12·8 1·6 12·7	30 W	0357 0927 1612 2145	1·2 13·3 1·4 12·9

OCTOBER

Day	Time	m	Day	Time	m
1 Th	0423 1004 1637 2223	1·9 12·4 2·1 11·8	16 F	0356 0927 1607 2149	1·8 12·3 2·1 11·9
2 F	0448 1041 1704 2259	2·5 11·4 2·8 10·8	17 Sa	0421 1003 1635 2230	2·2 11·8 2·4 11·3
3 Sa ☽	0515 1119 1736 2343	3·2 10·4 3·5 9·8	18 Su	0451 1045 1713 2320	2·6 11·2 2·9 10·6
4 Su	0547 1215 1819	3·9 9·5 4·2	19 M ☾	0534 1146 1808	3·1 10·6 3·4
5 M	0053 0641 1345 1959	9·1 4·6 9·2 4·6	20 Tu	0034 0643 1309 1938	10·2 3·6 10·3 3·6
6 Tu	0229 0905 1515 2148	9·2 4·5 9·9 3·7	21 W	0201 0826 1437 2114	10·3 3·5 10·8 3·0
7 W	0350 1017 1621 2244	10·1 3·4 10·9 2·7	22 Th	0325 0950 1556 2233	11·1 2·7 11·8 2·3
8 Th	0448 1111 1711 2337	11·0 2·5 11·7 2·0	23 F	0435 1111 1659 2354	12·0 2·0 12·6 1·7
9 F	0533 1203 1753	11·8 2·0 12·3	24 Sa	0533 1225 1754	12·8 1·5 13·2
10 Sa	0027 0614 1249 1831	1·6 12·2 1·6 12·6	25 Su ●	0056 0624 1320 1842	1·2 13·3 1·0 13·5
11 Su ○	0112 0648 1330 1903	1·4 12·6 1·4 12·8	26 M	0145 0707 1405 1924	0·9 13·6 0·8 13·7
12 M	0149 0717 1406 1933	1·3 12·8 1·3 13·0	27 Tu	0226 0747 1444 2005	0·9 13·7 0·9 13·6
13 Tu	0225 0747 1440 2005	1·2 13·0 1·4 13·0	28 W	0301 0825 1518 2044	1·2 13·6 1·2 13·3
14 W	0257 0818 1512 2037	1·3 12·9 1·5 12·8	29 Th	0332 0904 1548 2124	1·6 13·1 1·6 12·6
15 Th	0328 0851 1542 2112	1·5 12·7 1·8 12·4	30 F	0400 0942 1616 2202	2·1 12·3 2·2 11·7
			31 Sa	0426 1020 1644 2238	2·6 11·4 2·8 10·8

NOVEMBER

Day	Time	m	Day	Time	m
1 Su	0452 1057 1715 2319	3·2 10·6 3·3 10·0	16 M	0457 1049 1722 2323	2·4 11·8 2·5 11·2
2 M ☽	0525 1144 1754	3·7 9·8 3·9	17 Tu ☾	0543 1147 1817	2·8 11·3 2·9
3 Tu	0014 0608 1255 1853	9·4 4·2 9·4 4·2	18 W	0025 0645 1255 1927	10·8 3·1 11·0 3·0
4 W	0130 0720 1416 2046	9·2 4·5 9·6 4·0	19 Th	0138 0802 1412 2044	10·7 3·1 11·1 2·8
5 Th	0249 0922 1525 2156	9·7 4·0 10·3 3·3	20 F	0256 0919 1527 2157	11·1 2·8 11·6 2·5
6 F	0353 1023 1621 2249	10·4 3·2 11·1 2·6	21 Sa	0406 1035 1633 2316	11·7 2·4 12·1 2·2
7 Sa	0445 1116 1708 2342	11·2 2·5 11·7 2·1	22 Su	0506 1151 1730	12·2 2·0 12·5
8 Su	0529 1205 1750	11·8 2·1 12·2	23 M	0025 0558 1252 1821	1·8 12·7 1·6 12·8
9 M	0031 0608 1252 1828	1·7 12·3 1·7 12·5	24 Tu ●	0117 0645 1340 1906	1·6 13·0 1·4 13·0
10 Tu ○	0116 0645 1335 1906	1·5 12·7 1·5 12·8	25 W	0201 0727 1420 1948	1·5 13·2 1·4 13·0
11 W	0157 0721 1415 1942	1·3 12·9 1·4 12·9	26 Th	0240 0808 1457 2029	1·5 13·2 1·5 12·8
12 Th	0234 0758 1454 2022	1·3 13·0 1·5 12·9	27 F	0312 0847 1531 2107	1·8 12·9 1·8 12·4
13 F	0312 0837 1531 2103	1·5 12·9 1·6 12·7	28 Sa	0343 0925 1600 2145	2·1 12·4 2·1 11·8
14 Sa	0348 0918 1606 2145	1·7 12·7 1·9 12·3	29 Su	0410 1000 1630 2219	2·5 11·8 2·5 11·2
15 Su	0420 1002 1641 2231	2·0 12·3 2·2 11·8	30 M	0437 1035 1658 2254	2·9 11·1 2·9 10·7

DECEMBER

Day	Time	m	Day	Time	m
1 Tu	0506 1115 1732 2334	3·2 10·6 3·2 10·2	16 W ☾	0546 1136 1812	2·1 12·1 2·2
2 W ☽	0542 1201 1814	3·5 10·1 3·5	17 Th	0008 0634 1232 1903	11·5 2·5 11·6 2·6
3 Th	0027 0628 1303 1907	9·8 3·9 9·8 3·8	18 F	0107 0730 1338 2005	11·1 2·8 11·2 2·9
4 F	0133 0730 1415 2026	9·6 4·1 9·9 3·8	19 Sa	0218 0842 1450 2119	10·9 3·0 11·1 3·0
5 Sa	0243 0905 1519 2152	9·9 3·9 10·3 3·4	20 Su	0331 0957 1602 2237	11·0 2·9 11·3 2·8
6 Su	0346 1021 1616 2251	10·5 3·3 10·9 2·7	21 M	0438 1116 1706 2353	11·5 2·6 11·7 2·5
7 M	0440 1118 1708 2347	11·2 2·6 11·6 2·2	22 Tu	0537 1224 1803	12·0 2·2 12·0
8 Tu	0530 1212 1756	11·9 2·1 12·2	23 W	0052 0628 1317 1852	2·1 12·4 1·8 12·3
9 W ○	0039 0617 1306 1842	1·7 12·5 1·7 12·6	24 Th ●	0140 0713 1402 1935	1·8 12·7 1·7 12·5
10 Th	0131 0702 1355 1927	1·4 12·9 1·5 12·9	25 F	0222 0755 1442 2016	1·7 12·9 1·6 12·6
11 F	0219 0745 1443 2012	1·3 13·2 1·3 13·1	26 Sa	0257 0833 1517 2051	1·7 12·8 1·7 12·5
12 Sa	0304 0829 1527 2057	1·3 13·3 1·3 13·1	27 Su	0329 0908 1548 2125	1·9 12·6 1·9 12·2
13 Su	0346 0912 1609 2142	1·3 13·2 1·4 12·9	28 M	0357 0941 1616 2156	2·1 12·3 2·0 11·9
14 M	0426 0959 1649 2227	1·5 13·0 1·6 12·6	29 Tu	0423 1012 1641 2227	2·3 11·9 2·2 11·5
15 Tu	0505 1045 1729 2316	1·8 12·6 1·9 12·1	30 W	0449 1044 1709 2259	2·5 11·4 2·5 11·0
			31 Th	0518 1119 1742 2334	2·8 10·9 2·8 10·5

Chart Datum: 6.50 metres below Ordnance Datum (Newlyn)

BRISTOL *continued*

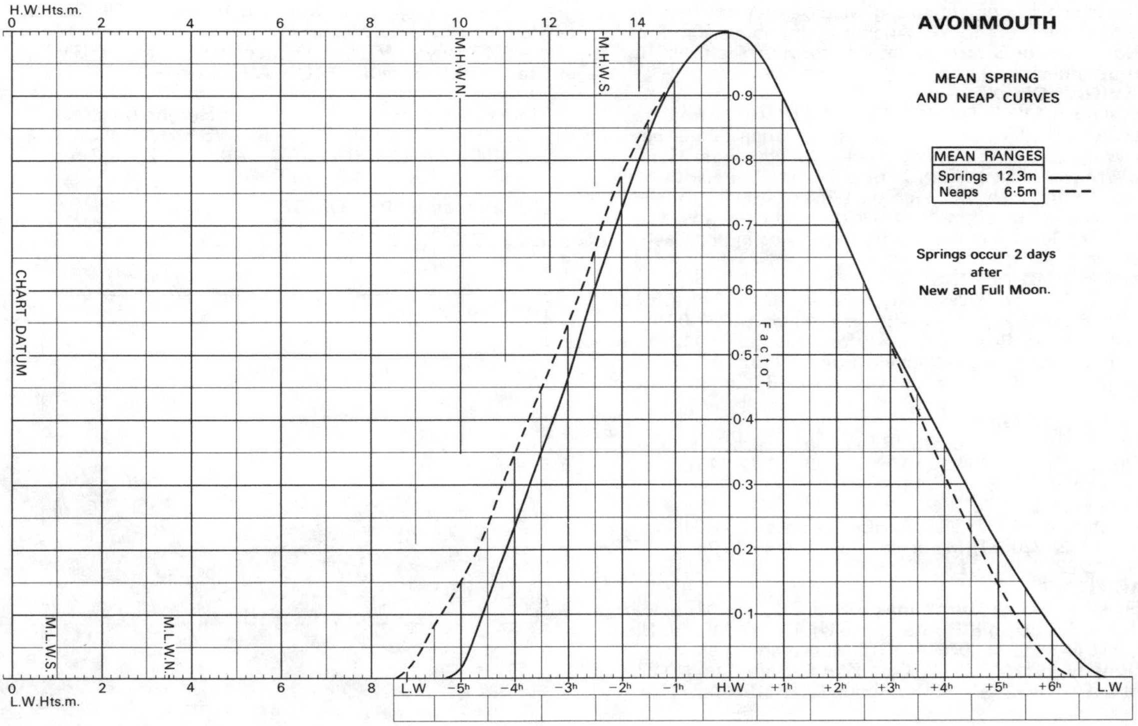
AVONMOUTH
MEAN SPRING AND NEAP CURVES
MEAN RANGES
Springs 12.3m
Neaps 6·5m
Springs occur 2 days after New and Full Moon.
H.W.Hts.m.
L.W.Hts.m.
CHART DATUM
M.H.W.N.
M.H.W.S.
M.L.W.S.
M.L.W.N.
Factor
L.W
−5h
−4h
−3h
−2h
−1h
H.W
+1h
+2h
+3h
+4h
+5h
+6h
L.W

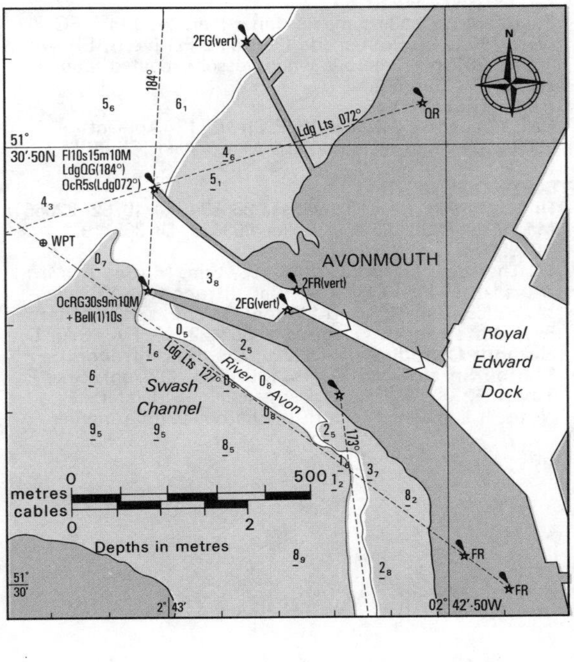
2FG(vert)
184°
Ldg Lts 072°
QR
51° 30′·50N
Fl10s15m10M
LdgQG(184°)
OcR5s(Ldg072°)
WPT
AVONMOUTH
2FR(vert)
2FG(vert)
OcRG30s9m10M
+Bell(1)10s
Ldg Lts 127°
River Avon
Swash Channel
Royal Edward Dock
173°
metres
cables
Depths in metres
51° 30′
2° 43′
02° 42′·50W
FR
FR

BURNHAM-ON-SEA 10-11-22

Somerset

CHARTS

Admiralty 1152; Stanford 14; Imray C59; OS 182

TIDES

−0435 Dover; ML 5·4; Duration 0620; Zone 0 (GMT).

Standard Port BRISTOL (AVONMOUTH) (⟵)

Times				Height (metres)			
HW		LW		MHWS	MHWN	MLWN	MLWS
0200	0800	0300	0800	13·2	10·0	3·5	0·9
1400	2000	1500	2000				
Differences BURNHAM							
−0020	−0025	−0030	0000	−2·3	−1·9	−1·4	−1·1
BRIDGWATER							
−0015	−0030	+0305	+0455	−8·6	−8·1	dries out	
WESTON-SUPER-MARE							
−0020	−0030	−0130	−0030	−1·2	−1·0	−0·8	−0·2
WATCHET							
−0035	−0050	−0145	−0040	−1·9	−1·5	+0·1	+0·1
MINEHEAD							
−0035	−0045	−0100	−0100	−2·6	−1·9	−0·1	0·0
PORLOCK BAY							
−0045	−0055	−0205	−0050	−3·0	−2·2	−0·1	−0·1

BURNHAM-ON-SEA *continued*

SHELTER
Ent is very choppy in strong winds, especially from W to SW and from N to NE. Anchor in 4m about 40m E of No 1 buoy or S of town jetty or for best shelter in R. Brue (dries).

NAVIGATION
Waypoint 51°13′·56N 03°10′·00W, 258°/078° from/to Upper Lt, 6·5M. Local knowledge essential. Enter between HW−3 and HW; not adviseable at night. From Gore SWM pick up transit 078° of old Lt structure with Main Lt Ho slightly open to S Approx 1·3M past No 1 By steer on transit 112° of Y stripe/W background on sea wall with Ch. Tr. Beware unmarked fishing stakes in approach channel.

LIGHTS AND MARKS
Fl 7·5s 28m 17M; W Tr, R stripe; vis 074°-164°. Dir Lt 078° F WRG 24m 16/12M; same Tr; vis G073°-077°, W077°-079°, R079°-083°. Seafront Lts in line 112° (moved to meet changes in channel). Front FR 6m 3M; Or stripe on W background on sea wall. Rear FR 12m 3M; church Tr.

RADIO TELEPHONE
Hr Mr and Pilot VHF Ch 16; 08 (when vessel expected). Other stations: Watchet VHF Ch 16; 09 12 14 (occas). Minehead Ch 16; 12, 14 (occas).

TELEPHONE (0278)
Hr Mr and Pilot 782180; MRCC Swansea 366534; # (0752) 220661; Marinecall 0898 500 459; Police 782288; H 782262.

FACILITIES
EC Wednesday; **Burnham-on-Sea SC** Slip, M, L, Bar; **Jetty** Slip; **Uphill Boats** ☎ (0934) 418017 ME, El, Sh; **RPM Marine** ☎ (02974) 5816 Mobile engineering; **Solway Ltd** ☎ 782908, Gas; **Wessex Marine** ☎ 42255, ME; **Town** ✉; Ⓑ; ⇌ (Highbridge); ✈ (Bristol).

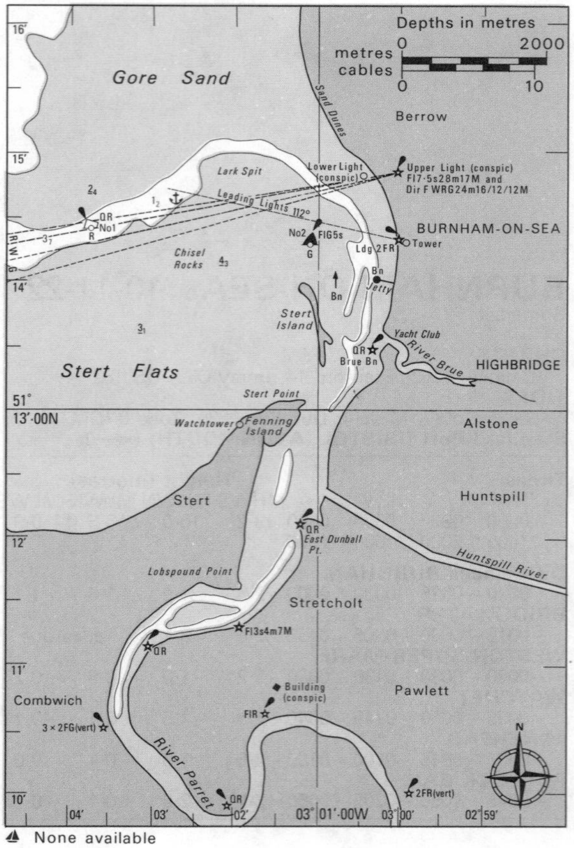
Depths in metres
metres
cables
Gore Sand
Sand Dunes
Berrow
Lark Spit
Lower Light (conspic)
Upper Light (conspic) Fl7·5s28m17M and Dir F WRG24m16/12/12M
Leading Lights 112°
BURNHAM-ON-SEA
Tower
Ldg 2FR
Chisel Rocks
Jetty
Stert Island
Yacht Club
River Brue
HIGHBRIDGE
Stert Flats
Stert Point
Watchtower
Fenning Island
Alstone
Stert
Huntspill
East Dunball Pt.
Huntspill River
Lobspound Point
Stretcholt
Fl3s4m7M
Combwich
3×2FG(vert)
Building (conspic)
Pawlett
River Parret
2FR(vert)
13′·00N
03°01′·00W

▲ None available

ILFRACOMBE 10-11-23
Devon

CHARTS
Admiralty 1160, 1165; Stanford 14; Imray C59; OS 180

TIDES
−0525 Dover; ML 5·0; Duration 0625; Zone 0 (GMT).

Standard Port MILFORD HAVEN (⟵)

Times				Height (metres)			
HW		LW		MHWS	MHWN	MLWN	MLWS
0100	0700	0100	0700	7·0	5·2	2·5	0·7
1300	1900	1300	1900				
Differences ILFRACOMBE							
−0030	−0015	−0035	−0055	+2·2	+1·7	+0·5	0·0

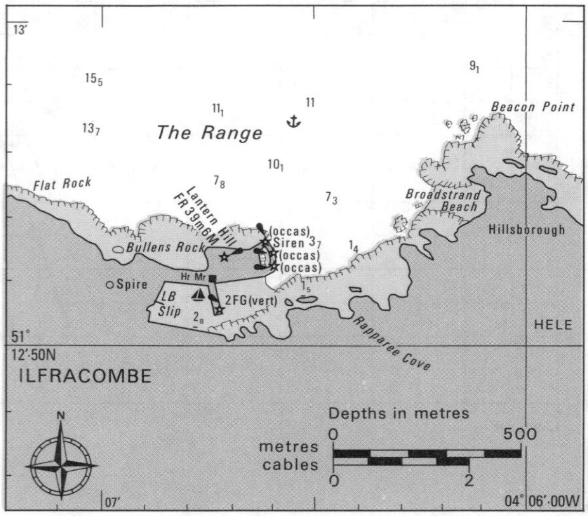
The Range
Beacon Point
Flat Rock
Lantern Hill FR39m6M
Broadstrand Beach
Hillsborough
Bullens Rock
(occas)
Siren
(occas)
(occas)
Hr Mr
2FG(vert)
Spire
LB Slip
Rapparee Cove
HELE
12′·50N
ILFRACOMBE
Depths in metres
metres
cables
04°06′·00W

SHELTER
Good except E to NE Winds. On entering obtain directions from pierhead gates on NE side. SW gales cause a very severe surge in the harbour. 12 visitors buoys in outer harbour.

NAVIGATION
Waypoint 51°13′·20N 04°06′·60W, 000°/180° from/to pierhead, 0·55M. Coming from E, beware Copperas Rocks (4M to E), marked by buoy. Do not anchor in line with LB Slip. 1 or 2 balls hoisted on flagpole yard indicates steamer is to berth alongside pier.

LIGHTS AND MARKS
There are no leading marks. Inner Pier Head Lt 2 FG (vert). 3 Lts on Promenade Pier, all 2 FG (vert). Shown 1 Sept-30 Apl. Siren 30s when vessel expected. Lantern Hill Lt FR, 39m 6M.

RADIO TELEPHONE
Call: *Ilfracombe Harbour* VHF Ch 16; 12 (Apl-Oct 0800-2000 when manned. Nov-Mar occas). Ch **80** M (occas).

TELEPHONE (0271)
Hr Mr 863969; MRCC Swansea 366534; # (0752) 220661; Marinecall 0898 500 459; Police 863633; Dr 863119.

FACILITIES
EC Thursday; **Harbour** ☎ 862108, Slip, M (See Hr.Mr.), D (cans), L, FW, CH, V, R, Bar; **Ilfracombe YC** ☎ 863969, Bar, R, M, C (35 ton), FW, L, ◻, CH; **Pier** FW; **Watermouth Harbour** ☎ 865422, M, FW, Slip, D; **Harbour Chandlery** ☎ 862299, CH, Gas; **Ilfracombe Marine Services** ☎ 866815, ME, El, C (12 ton), Sh; **Town** ✉; Ⓑ; ⇌ (bus to Barnstaple); ✈ (Exeter).
Note: It is planned to turn the harbour into a marina.

RIVERS TAW & TORRIDGE
Devon

10-11-24

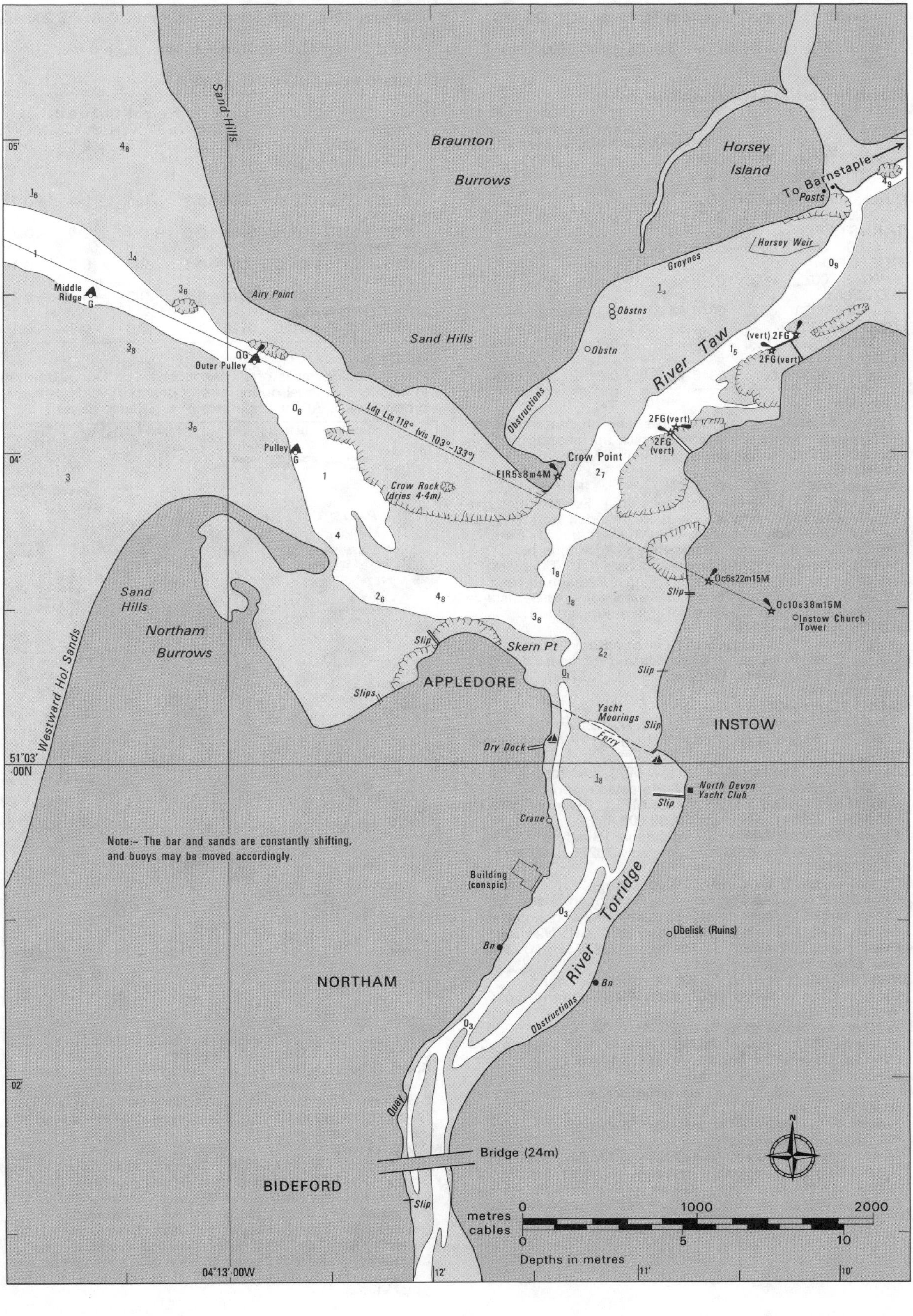
Sand-Hills
Braunton
Burrows
Horsey
Island
To Barnstaple
Posts
Horsey Weir
Groynes
Middle Ridge
G
Airy Point
Obstns
Obstn
Sand Hills
River Taw
(vert) 2FG
2FG (vert)
QG
Outer Pulley
Obstructions
Ldg Lts 118° (vis 103°–133°)
2FG (vert)
2FG (vert)
Pulley
G
FlR5s8m4M
Crow Point
Crow Rock (dries 4·4m)
Oc6s22m15M
Slip
Oc10s38m15M
Instow Church Tower
Sand Hills
Northam
Burrows
Westward Ho! Sands
Slip
Skern Pt
Slip
Slips
APPLEDORE
Yacht Moorings
Slip
INSTOW
Ferry
Dry Dock
51°03'·00N
North Devon Yacht Club
Slip
Crane
Note:- The bar and sands are constantly shifting, and buoys may be moved accordingly.
Building (conspic)
River Torridge
Obelisk (Ruins)
Bn
NORTHAM
Bn
Obstructions
Quay
Bridge (24m)
BIDEFORD
Slip
metres
cables
0
1000
2000
0
5
10
Depths in metres
04°13'·00W
12'
11'
10'
05'
04'
02'
N

RIVERS TAW & TORRIDGE *continued*

CHARTS
Admiralty 1160, 1164; Stanford 14; Imray C58; OS 180

TIDES
−0516 (Bideford) Dover; ML 3·6; Duration 0600; Zone 0 (GMT)

Standard Port MILFORD HAVEN (⟵)

Times				Height (metres)			
HW		LW		MHWS	MHWN	MLWN	MLWS
0100	0700	0100	0700	7·0	5·2	2·5	0·7
1300	1900	1300	1900				
Differences APPLEDORE							
−0020	−0025	+0015	−0045	+0·5	0·0	−0·9	−0·5
BARNSTAPLE							
0000	−0015	−0155	−0245	−2·9	−3·8	−2·2	−0·4
BIDEFORD							
−0020	−0025	0000	0000	−1·1	−1·6	−2·5	−0·7
CLOVELLY							
−0030	−0030	−0020	−0040	+1·3	+1·1	+0·2	+0·2
LUNDY ISLAND							
−0030	−0030	−0020	−0040	+1·0	+0·7	+0·2	+0·1
BUDE							
−0040	−0040	−0035	−0045	+0·7	+0·6	No data	

SHELTER
Very well protected, but entry in strong on-shore winds is dangerous. Yachts can anchor or pick up mooring buoy in Appledore Pool. A marina is planned at Northam.

NAVIGATION
Waypoint 51°05′·40N 04°16′·04W, 298°/118° from/to front Ldg Lt 118°, 3·8M (channel shifts). Estuary dries out at low water and entry is only recommended from HW−2 to HW. Once tide is running out, breakers quickly form between Bar Buoy and Middle Ridge. Advice on bar available from Hartlard/Swansea Coastguard. Tidal stream off Skern Pt can reach 5kts at springs. Passage up to Bideford is not difficult but boats proceeding to Barnstaple are advised to take a pilot (available at Appledore).

LIGHTS AND MARKS
Apart from jetties etc only the Fairway Buoy, Outer Pulley, Crow Point and the two leading marks are lit. The Torridge has no lights. Entry at night is NOT recommended.

RADIO TELEPHONE
Two Rivers Port/Pilots VHF Ch 16; 12 (Listens from HW−2). Other station: Bude VHF Ch 16; 12 (when vessel expected.)

TELEPHONE (Barnstaple + Instow 0271, Bideford 0237)
Hr Mr Bideford 476711 Ext 317, Barnstaple apply Amenities Officer 72511 Ext 7408; MRCC Swansea 366534; ⌗ (0752) 220661; Marinecall 0898 500 459; Police (Bideford) 476896; Dr Appledore (Bideford 474994), Bideford 476444 or 476363, Barnstaple 75221 or 473443.

FACILITIES
EC Barnstaple & Bideford — Wednesday;
APPLEDORE is a free port so no authority can charge for use of public facilities eg slip at town quay and alongside berths. **RNS Marine** ☎ Bideford 474167, CH; **Marine Electronics (Bideford)** ☎ Torrington 22870, El, Ⓔ; **The Sea Chest** ☎ Bideford 476191, CH;
BIDEFORD: AB (few), V, R, Bar; Berthing arranged through Capt V. Harris ☎ Bideford 474569; **Blanchards** ☎ 472084, Gas;
INSTOW: **F. Johns** ☎ Instow 860578, ACA, CH; **N. Devon YC** ☎ Instow 860367, Slip, R, Bar; **Instow Marine Services** ☎ 861081, D, ME, M, AB, Ⓔ, C (4 ton); **Town** V, R, FW, Bar;
BARNSTAPLE: AB, V, Bar; **Barnstaple Calor Centre** ☎ 75794, Gas.
Towns ✉ (all four); Ⓑ (Barnstaple, Bideford); ⇌ (Barnstaple); ✈ (Exeter).
Note: There are no alongside facilities for FW, D or P. Small quantities supplied in jerrycans. A larger quantity of D or P can be supplied by bowser from Plymouth (see Hr Mr). FW can be collected from the North Devon YC.

PADSTOW 10-11-25

Cornwall

CHARTS
Admiralty 1168, 1156; Stanford 13; Imray C58; OS 200

TIDES
−0550 Dover; ML 4·0; Duration 0600; Zone 0 (GMT)

Standard Port MILFORD HAVEN (⟵)

Times				Height (metres)			
HW		LW		MHWS	MHWN	MLWN	MLWS
0100	0700	0100	0700	7·0	5·2	2·5	0·7
1300	1900	1300	1900				
Differences PADSTOW							
−0055	−0050	−0040	−0050	+0·3	+0·4	+0·1	+0·1
NEWQUAY							
−0100	−0110	−0105	−0050	0·0	+0·1	0·0	−0·1
PERRANPORTH							
−0100	−0110	−0110	−0050	−0·1	0·0	0·0	+0·1
ST IVES							
−0050	−0115	−0105	−0040	−0·4	−0·3	−0·1	+0·1
CAPE CORNWALL							
−0130	−0145	−0120	−0120	−1·0	−0·9	−0·5	−0·1

SHELTER
Heavy breaking seas often encountered on Doom Bar and in adjacent channel during strong onshore winds or heavy ground swell. Allow ample rise of tide (least depth in

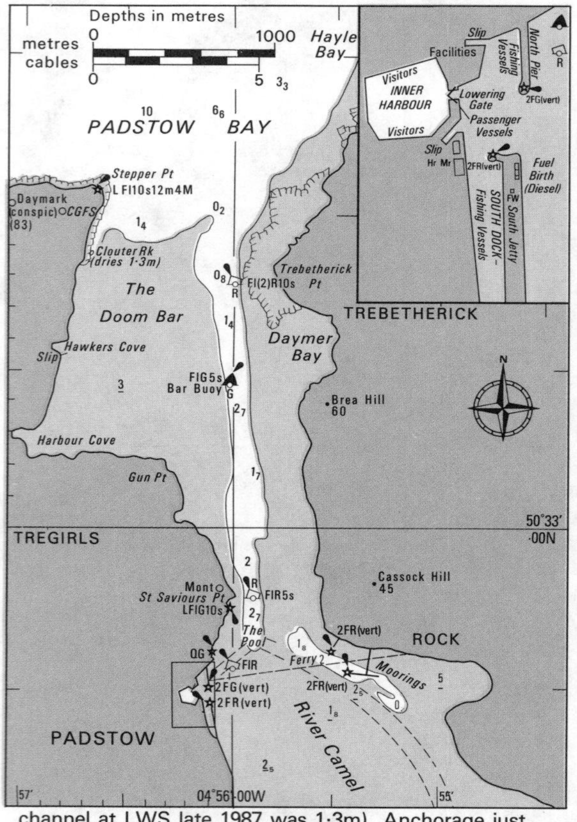

Depths in metres
metres
cables
0
1000
5
Hayle Bay
PADSTOW BAY
Stepper Pt
L Fl10s12m4M
Daymark (conspic) CGFS (83)
Clouter Rk (dries 1·3m)
Fl(2)R10s
Trebetherick Pt
The Doom Bar
Hawkers Cove
Slip
FlG5s
Bar Buoy
Daymer Bay
TREBETHERICK
Brea Hill 60
Harbour Cove
Gun Pt
TREGIRLS
50°33′·00N
Cassock Hill 45
Mont
St Saviours Pt
LFlG10s
FlR5s
The Pool
2FR(vert)
ROCK
QG
FlR
Ferry
Moorings
2FG(vert)
2FR(vert)
PADSTOW
River Camel
57′
04°56′·00W
55′
Slip
Fishing Vessels
North Pier
Facilities
Visitors
INNER HARBOUR
Lowering Gate
Passenger Vessels
Visitors
Hr Mr
Fuel Birth (Diesel)
SOUTH DOCK
Fishing Vessels
South Jetty
FW

channel at LWS late 1987 was 1·3m). Anchorage just down stream of The Pool in 1·5m LWS. Harbour itself gives alongside berthing in good shelter except in strong SE winds. Inner Harbour retains 3.5m. Access HW∓2. Swinging mooring (drying) sometimes available for small vessels on passage.

NAVIGATION
Waypoint 50°35′·00N 04°58′·50W, 305°/125° from/to Stepper Pt, 1·5M. Coming from S, beware Quies Rks, Gulland Rk, The Hen, Gurley Rk and Chimney Rks and the wreck 5 ca W of Stepper Pt. All are hazardous (off the chartlet). From N, keep well clear of Newland Is and its reefs jutting out. The sandbanks in the estuary change frequently, so local knowledge, care and a rising tide are recommended. Final approach S of St Saviours Pt is close to W shore.

PADSTOW *continued*

LIGHTS AND MARKS
Entrance marked by the stone tower (daymark) conspic, W of Stepper Point. Stepper Pt Lt L Fl 10s 12m 4M and harbour entrance marked by 2 FG (vert) to stbd and 2FR (vert) to port.

RADIO TELEPHONE
VHF Ch 16 (HW−2½ to HW+1½).

TELEPHONE (0841)
Hr Mr 532239; MRCC Falmouth 317515; ⌗ (0752) 220661; Marinecall 0898 500 458; Police Wadebridge 2216; Dr 532346.

FACILITIES
EC Wednesday; **Harbour** ☎ 532239, Access HW ∓2½, Slip, M, FW, El, C, D, AB, V, R, Bar; **Pier** ☎ 532239, D; **Dock** ☎ 532239, ME, C (6 ton), AB; **Rock SC** ☎ Trebetherick 2431, Slip; **Wadebridge Boat Centre** ☎ Wadebridge 3809, M, ME, El, CH; **Chapman & Hewitt** ☎ Wadebridge 2981, BY; **Westerly Boats** ☎ Trebetherick 3439, Slip, L, Sh; **Cornish Crabbers** ☎ Trebetherick 2666, Slip, ME, Sh, C; **Nettec Marine Chandlers** (on quay), CH, Gas, Gaz.
Town ⊡, P, ⊠; Ⓑ; ⇌ (bus to Bodmin Road); ✈ (Newquay or Plymouth).

MINOR HARBOURS AND ANCHORAGES 10-11-26

MOCHRAS, Gwynedd, 52°49′·00N, 04°07′·00W, Zone 0 (GMT), Admty charts 1512, 1971. HW −0245 on Dover, +0205 on Milford Haven. HW height −1·7m on Milford Haven. Small yacht harbour on E end of Shell Island. Mochras lagoon dries. See 10·11·5. Entrance between Shell Is (Lt Fl WRG 4s; G079°-124°, W124°-134°, R134°-179°; shown Apl-Nov) and sea wall. Bar, about 2 ca to seaward. Three R posts mark N side of channel. Tide runs strongly in the narrows on the ebb. Entry advised after HW∓2. Inside, the channel runs NE to Pen-Sarn, marked by posts. To S buoyed channel runs to Shell Island Yacht Harbour. Shallow draught boats can lie afloat below the railway bridge. Facilities (Pen-Sarn) Slip, AB, FW, ⇌. **Shell Island** ☎ Llanbedr 453 M, FW, R, Slip.

ABERAERON, Dyfed, 52°19′·00N, 04°09′·00W, Zone 0 (GMT), Admty Charts 1484, 1972. HW −0325 on Dover, +0140 on Milford Haven; HW height −1·9m on Milford Haven; ML 2·7m; Duration 0540. A small drying harbour at the mouth of the R. Aeron (or Ayron). Short piers extend each side of the river ent. Pierheads dry. In strong NW winds there is little shelter. Foul ground with depths of 1·5m extend 3 ca offshore to SW of Aberaeron. Beware Carreg Gloyn (0·3m) 4 ca WSW of harbour; Sarn Cadwgan (1·8m) extending ½M offshore from Cadwgan Pt to NE of Aberaeron. Lights:— N pier Fl(4)R 15s 6m 6M; vis 104°-178°. S pier Fl(3)G 10s 6m 7M; vis 125°-200°. No radio telephone. Facilities: Hr Mr ☎ 570407; **Aberaeron YC** ☎ 570077.

NEW QUAY, Dyfed, 52°13′00N, 04°21′·00W, Zone −0100. Admty charts 1484, 1972. HW −0335 on Dover, +0140 on Milford Haven. HW height −2·0m on Milford Haven; ML 2·6m; Duration 0540. The bay gives shelter in offshore winds, but NW winds make it untenable. On E side of bay is Carreg Ina, a rock which dries 1·6m marked by N cardinal buoy. Bns show alignment of sewer pipe extending 7ca NNW from Ina Point. There are moorings in the bay. The harbour (dries) is protected by a pier with a Lt, FlWG 3s 12m 8/5M; vis W135°-252°, G252°-295°. Rocks, marked by a Bn, extend 50m SSE from pierhead. Facilities: Hr Mr ☎ 560368; CG ☎ 560212; Dr ☎ 560203; YC ☎ 560516; D (from fishermen) ☎ 560375. **Town** D, FW, V, P (3M), ⊠, R, Bar.

CARDIGAN, Dyfed, 52°06′·00N, 04°41′·00W, Zone 0 (GMT), Admty charts 1484, 1973. HW −0350 on Dover, +0130 on Milford Haven; HW height −2·1m on Milford Haven; ML 2·7m; Duration 0550. See 10·11·12. Shelter is good but entrance dangerous in strong N to NW winds. Bar dries but has 2·5m at MHWS. Channel between Pen-y-Ergyd and Bryn Du changes continuously. Anchor in pools in R Teifi near St Dogmaels. Near Hotel on E side of entrance 2 FR (vert). Facilities: EC Wed; Hr Mr ☎ 612084; **Ynys Marine** ☎ 613179, ME, Sh; **Town** Ⓑ, Bar, CH, D, FW, ME, P, R, ⇌, V.

SOLVA, Dyfed, 51°52′·00N, 05°12′·00W, Zone 0 (GMT), Admty chart 1478. HW −0450 on Dover, +0012 on Milford Haven, HW height −1·3m on Milford Haven; ML 3·2m; Duration 0555. Good shelter for small boats that can take the ground. Beware Black Rock in centre of entrance (E side entrance recommended) and stone spit at Trwyn Caws on W just inside entrance. Strong S winds make entrance difficult. There are nine visitors buoys painted red and some drying moorings available. Anchor behind the rock in approx 3m. Small craft can go up to the quay. Facilities very limited; stores available in village. FW on quay. Hr Mr St. Davids 721373, M, CH, Access HW∓3; **Solva Boat Owners Assn.** ☎ St Davids 721209.

ST BRIDES BAY, Dyfed, 51°48′·00N, 05°10′·00W, Zone 0 (GMT), Admty chart 1478. HW (Little Haven) − 0450 on Dover, +0010 on Milford Haven; HW height −1·3m on Milford Haven; ML 3·2m; Duration 0555. Many good anchorages, especially between Little Haven and Borough Head in S or E winds or between Solva and Dinas Fawry in N or E winds, but in W winds boats should shelter in Solva (see above) or Skomer (see below). For approaches from the N or S see 10·11·5. Keep clear of Research Area in the middle of the bay, marked by buoys. Facilities: (Little Haven) CH, V, R, Bar, FW (cans).

SKOMER, Dyfed, 51°44′·00N, 05°17′·00W, Zone 0 (GMT), Admty charts 2878, 1478. HW −0455 Dover, −0005 on Milford Haven; HW height −0·4m (Sp), −0·1m (Np) on Milford Haven. The island is a nature reserve (fee payable to Warden on landing); anchorage in North Haven or South Haven; in both cases keep close to W shore entering, and land on The Neck (E side). Landing in S Haven is discouraged. Keep at least 100m off coastline 1st Sept-28th Feb to avoid disturbing seals and between 1st Mar-31st July to avoid disturbing nesting sea birds. Do not anchor in N Haven but pick up buoys provided. For Jack Sound see 10·11·5. There are no lights or marks and no facilities.

SAUNDERSFOOT, Dyfed, 51°43′·00N, 04°42′·00W, Zone 0 (GMT), Admty chart 1482 1076. HW −0510 on Dover, −0013 on Milford Haven. HW height +1·4m on Milford Haven; ML 4·4m; Duration 0605. A half-tide harbour with good shelter with S to SW winds there may be a surge and with E winds it may be rough. On approach, beware buoys marking restricted area (power boats, etc) between Coppett Hall Pt and Perry's Pt. Alongside berths are sometimes available (see Hr Mr) as are moorings in the middle. Light on pierhead Fl R 5s 6m 7M on stone cupola VHF, Hr Mr 16; 11. Facilities: EC Wed; Hr Mr ☎ 812094, CH, FW (on SW wall), Slip; **Jones and Teague** ☎ 813429, ME; **Vox Leisure** ☎ Hr Mr, BH; **Town** V, R, Bar, ⊠, Ⓑ, ⇌.

CARMARTHEN, Dyfed, 51°51′·00N, 04°18′·00W, Zone 0 (GMT), Admty chart 1076. HW −0455 on Dover, +0010 on Milford Haven; HW height −4·6m on Milford Haven. R Towy dries out, except for river water. Beware Carmarthen Bar off mouth of Rivers Towy and Taf. Local knowledge or a pilot are essential. Channel into rivers changes frequently and is not buoyed. Access HW∓2. There are six electric cables crossing between the mouth and the railway bridge in Carmarthen, min clearance 15m. Visitors berths at R Towy YC at Ferryside (9M below Carmarthen), access HW∓3 (liable to dry). Facilities: **Carmarthen** normal facilities of a market town; **Tawe Works** ☎ 236601, Gas; **River Towy YC** (Ferryside) ☎ Ferryside 366, Bar, FW, M; **Town** Normal facilities Ⓑ, Bar, ⊠, V, ⇌, ✈ (Swansea).

PORTHCAWL, Mid Glamorgan, 51°24′·00N, 03°42′·00W; Zone 0 (GMT). Admty charts 1169, 1165. HW −0505 on Dover; 0005 on Milford Haven; HW height +2·6m on Milford Haven; ML 5·3m. See 10·11·17. A small tidal harbour protected by breakwater running SE from Porthcawl Pt. Beware rock ledge (dries) to W of breakwater. At end of breakwater Porthcawl Lt Ho, W 6-sided tower with B base; F WRG 10m 6/4M; vis G302°-036°, W036°-082°, R082°-122°. In line 094° with Saint Hilary radio mast leads through Shord channel. Tidal streams can reach 6kn at springs off end of breakwater. Anchor approx 3ca SSE of Lt Ho. Facilities: EC Wed; Hr Mr 2756, 3 visitors moorings (HW∓2); **Porthcawl Marine** ☎ 4785, CH; **Porthcawl Harbour Boating Club** ☎ 2342; **Town** V, R, Bar, P and D (cans), ⊠, Ⓑ, ⇌ (Bridgend), ✈ (Cardiff).

MINOR HARBOURS AND ANCHORAGES *Continued*

NEWPORT, Gwent, 51°33'·00N, 02°59'·00W, Zone 0 (GMT), Admty charts 1176, 1152. HW −0425 on Dover, −0015 on Avonmouth, HW height −1·0m on Avonmouth; ML 6·0m; Duration 0620. See 10·11·19. A commercial port controlled by Associated British Ports (☎ 65411) but a safe sheltered port for yachts. Enter R Usk over bar (approx 0·5m) E of West Usk buoy and follow buoyed and lit channel to South Lock entrance; turn NE, yacht moorings on S side between power station pier and YC. W Usk buoy QR Bell, East Usk Lt Ho Fl (2) WRG 10s 11m 15/11M, W284°−290°, R290°−017°, W017°−037°, G037°−115°, W115°−120°. Ldg Lts 057°, both FG. Alexandra Dock, S lock W pier head 2 FR (vert) 9/7m 6M. E pier head 2 FG (vert) 9/7m 6M. VHF Ch 16; 09 11 (HW −4 to HW +4). Facilities: EC Thurs; # ☎ 273709 **Beechwood Marine** ☎ 277955, CH, El, ME, Sh; **Leeway Leisure** ☎ 276611, CH, El, ME, Sh; **Aquascan** ☎ 841117, Ⓔ; **Town** All facilities.

WESTON-SUPER-MARE, Avon, 51°21'·00N, 02°59'·00W, Zone 0 (GMT), Admty charts 1152, 1176. HW −0435 on Dover, −0025 on Avonmouth; HW height −1·1m on Avonmouth; ML 6·1m; Duration 0655. See 10·11·22. Good shelter except in S winds in Knightstone Harbour (dries) at N end of bay. Causeway at entrance marked by Bn. Access HW∓2. Grand pierhead 2 FG (vert) 6/5m. Alternative anchorage in good weather in R Axe (dries), entry HW∓2. Facilities: EC Mon, **Passey and Porter** ☎ 628281; CH, El, ME, Sh, Slip; **Uphill Boat Services** ☎ 418617; CH, El, D, FW, Slip, BH (10 ton), ME, Sh; **Weston Bay YC** ☎ 620772; FW, Bar, VHF Ch **80 Town** Bar, Ⓑ; D, FW, P, ✉, R, ⇌, V.

WATCHET, Somerset, 51°11'00N, 03°20'·00W, Zone 0 (GMT), Admty charts 1160, 1152. HW −0455 on Dover, −0043 on Avonmouth; HW height −1·7m on Avonmouth; ML 6·2m; Duration 0655. See 10·11·22. Good shelter but harbour dries; there is approx 6m in entrance at MHWS. Available approx HW∓2. Yachts should berth on W breakwater. Beware tidal streams round W pier head. Rocks and mud dry 0·5M to seaward. W breakwater head FG 9m 9M. E pier head 2 FR (vert) 3M. VHF Ch 16; 14 12 (HW−2 to HW+2). On W breakwater head B ball (Fl G at night) and on E pier 2 FR (vert) = at least 2·4m on flood or 3m on ebb. Facilities: EC Wed; Hr Mr ☎ 3430; # ☎ 31214, FW, D, P, Slip, CH, V, R, Bar; **Watchet Boat Owners Assn.**

MINEHEAD, Somerset, 51°13'·00N, 03°28'·00W, Zone 0 (GMT), Admty charts 1160, 1165. HW −0450 on Dover, −0040 on Avonmouth; HW height −2·6m (Sp), −1·9m (Np) on Avonmouth; ML 5·7m. There is no bar; access HW∓2. Small harbour formed by pier curving E and then SE, over which seas break in gales at MHWS. Best approach from N or NW; beware The Gables, shingle bank (dries 3·3m) about ¾M ENE of pier. Berth alongside pier. A sewer outfall runs from a position 2ca S of pierhead to 1¾ca NNE of it, passing ½ca E of pierhead. Outer portion is protected by rock covering, rising to 2·8m above sea bed. Outer end marked by stbd-hand Bn QG 6m 7M. Harbour gets very crowded. Pierhead Lt Fl(2)G 5s 4M; vis 127°-262°. Facilities: EC Wed; Hr Mr ☎ 702566; **Tarr and Foy** ☎ 702029, Gas; **Pier** FW, Slip; **Town** normal facilities, Bar, D, El, Gas, ME, P, R, Sh, V, ✉, Ⓑ, ⇌ (Taunton or Barnstaple), ✈ (Exeter).

PORLOCK WEIR, Somerset, 51°13'·00N, 03°38'·00W, Zone 0 (GMT), Admty charts 1160, 1165. HW −0500 on Dover, −0050 on Avonmouth; HW height −2·6m on Avonmouth; ML 5·6m; Duration 0655. See 10·11·22. Shelter very good once in harbour but entrance difficult. Channel between pebble bank to NW and wooden wall to SE approx 15m wide. There is a small pool just inside entrance for shallow draft boats − others dry out inside harbour. There are no lights. Hr Mr ☎ 862106. Facilities: very limited; FW and stores on quay; **Porlock Weir SC** ☎ 862028.

WATERMOUTH, Devon, 51°13'·00N, 04°05'·00W, Zone 0 (GMT), Admty chart 1165. HW −0525 on Dover, −0020 on Milford Haven; HW height +2·0m on Milford Haven; ML 4·9m; Duration 0625. Good shelter, except from NW winds, but harbour dries. Entrance identified by white CG cottage above Rillage Pt. SW gales cause heavy surge in harbour. Access HW∓3 at sp, outside breakwater only at np. Visitors buoys distinguished by Y handles on R buoys. Facilities: M, D (cans), FW (cans), Slip; **Watermouth Caves** ☎ 62504, Gas; **Watermouth YC** ☎ 65048, Bar.

LUNDY ISLAND, Devon, 51°11'·00N, 04°40'·00W, Zone 0 (GMT), Admty chart 1164. HW −0530 on Dover, −0030 on Milford Haven; HW height +0·9m on Milford Haven; ML 4·3m; Duration 0605. See 10·11·24. Shelter good if correct side of island is selected according to the wind. In winds from NW to SSW anchor N of SE point of island. In winds from E to N some shelter can be obtained on W side of the island but holding ground is poor. Jenny's Cove on W side is safe so long as there is no W ground swell. The high land (145m) gives considerable shelter. Waters round the island are a Marine Nature Reserve. Near N Pt, Lt Fl (2) 20s 50m 24M; vis 009°−285°. On SE Pt, Lt Fl 5s 53m 24M; vis 170°−073°; RC. Facilities: Landing place by the anchorage in the SW corner; **Lundy Co Landmark Trust** ☎ Woolacombe 870870, CH, Gas, bar and hotel.

BUDE, Cornwall, 50°50'·00N, 04°33'·00W, Zone 0 (GMT), Admty chart 1156. HW −0540 on Dover, −0040 on Milford Haven; HW height +0·7m on Milford Haven; Duration 0605. See 10·11·24. Limited shelter; Hr dries − available for average yacht HW∓2. Provided prior arrangements have been made, yachts can pass lock and berth in canal (approx 5 m over CD required). Locking fees are high (£50; £75 outside working hours; £100 Sundays), and gates will only open if there is no sea running. Ldg marks, front W spar with Y diamond topmark, rear W flagstaff, in line at 075°. Continue on this line until inner ldg marks in line at 131°, front W pile with Y triangular topmark, rear W spar with Y triangular topmark. There are no lights. VHF Ch 16; 12 (when vessel expected). Facilities: EC Thurs; Hr Mr ☎ 353111; very limited facilities; **N.E. Truscott** ☎ 352423, Gas; **Town** Ⓑ, Bar, ✉, R. V.

NEWQUAY, Cornwall, 50°25'·00N, 05°05'·00W, Zone 0 (GMT), Admty charts 1168, 1149. HW −0604 on Dover, −0100 on Milford Haven; HW height +0·1m on Milford Haven; ML 3·7m; see 10·11·25. Entrance to harbour between two walls, rather narrow. Beware Old Dane Rk and Listrey Rk outside harbour towards Towan Hd. Swells cause a surge in the harbour. Enter HW∓2 but not in strong onshore winds. Hr dries; berth as directed by Hr Mr. Lts − North Pier 2 FG (vert) 2M, South Pier 2 FR (vert) 2M. VHF Ch 16 14. Facilities: EC Wed (winter only); Hr Mr ☎ 872809, FW, Slip, D, V, R, Bar; **H. N. Bennett** ☎ 875900, Gas, Gaz; **J. B. Marine** ☎ 878185, CH. (Shallow draft boats can take the ground in Gannel Creek, close S of Newquay, but only in settled weather. Beware causeway bridge about half way up the creek.).

HAYLE, Cornwall, 50°11'·00N, 05°25'·00W, Zone 0 (GMT), Admty charts 1168, 1149. HW −0605 on Dover, −0100 on Milford Haven; HW height −0·4m on Milford Haven; ML 3·6m; Duration 0555. Shelter is very good but dangerous sea breaks on bar in strong on-shore winds; harbour dries. Approx 5m at entrance at MHWS. The harbour is divided by long arm (approx 300m) stretching almost to Ldg Lts which should be left to W. Beware training bank W of entrance channel marked by perches. Lts in line 180°, front FW 17m 4M, rear FW 23m 4M. E arm of harbour leads to Hayle, the W arm to Lelant Quay. Hayle E pierhead 2 FG (vert), W pierhead 2 FR (vert). (Note: Hayle is closed to commercial traffic. Small craft may cross the bar in good weather within 1h of HW. Charted aids do not necessarily indicate best water). Facilities: EC Thurs; Ⓑ, Bar, FW, ⇌, R, V, P and D (cans).

ST IVES, Cornwall, 50°13'·00N, 05°28'·00W, Zone 0 (GMT), Admty charts 1168, 1149. HW −0605 on Dover, −0100 on Milford Haven; HW height −0·4m on Milford Haven; ML 3·6m; Duration 0555. See 10·11·25. Shelter is good except in on-shore winds when heavy swell builds up. 9 visitors moorings available. Harbour dries but has approx 4·5m at MHWS. Alternative anchorage between the harbour and Porthminster Pt to S in 3m. Beware Hoe Rock off St Ives Hd coming from NW, and The Carracks off Porthminster Pt coming from SE. Keep E of G conical buoy about 1½ ca ENE of Smeaton's pierhead. Lights, E pier head (Smeatons pier) 2 FG (vert) 8m 5M. W pier head 2 FR (vert) 5m 3M. VHF Ch 16. Facilities: EC Thurs; Hr Mr ☎ Penzance 795018; six visitor moorings; **Fisherman's Co-op** ☎ Penzance 796276, Gas, Gaz; **Smeaton's Pier** FW; **Town** Ⓑ, ◫, Bar, FW, P (in cans), ✉, R, ⇌, V.

Area 12

South Ireland
Loop Head to Malahide

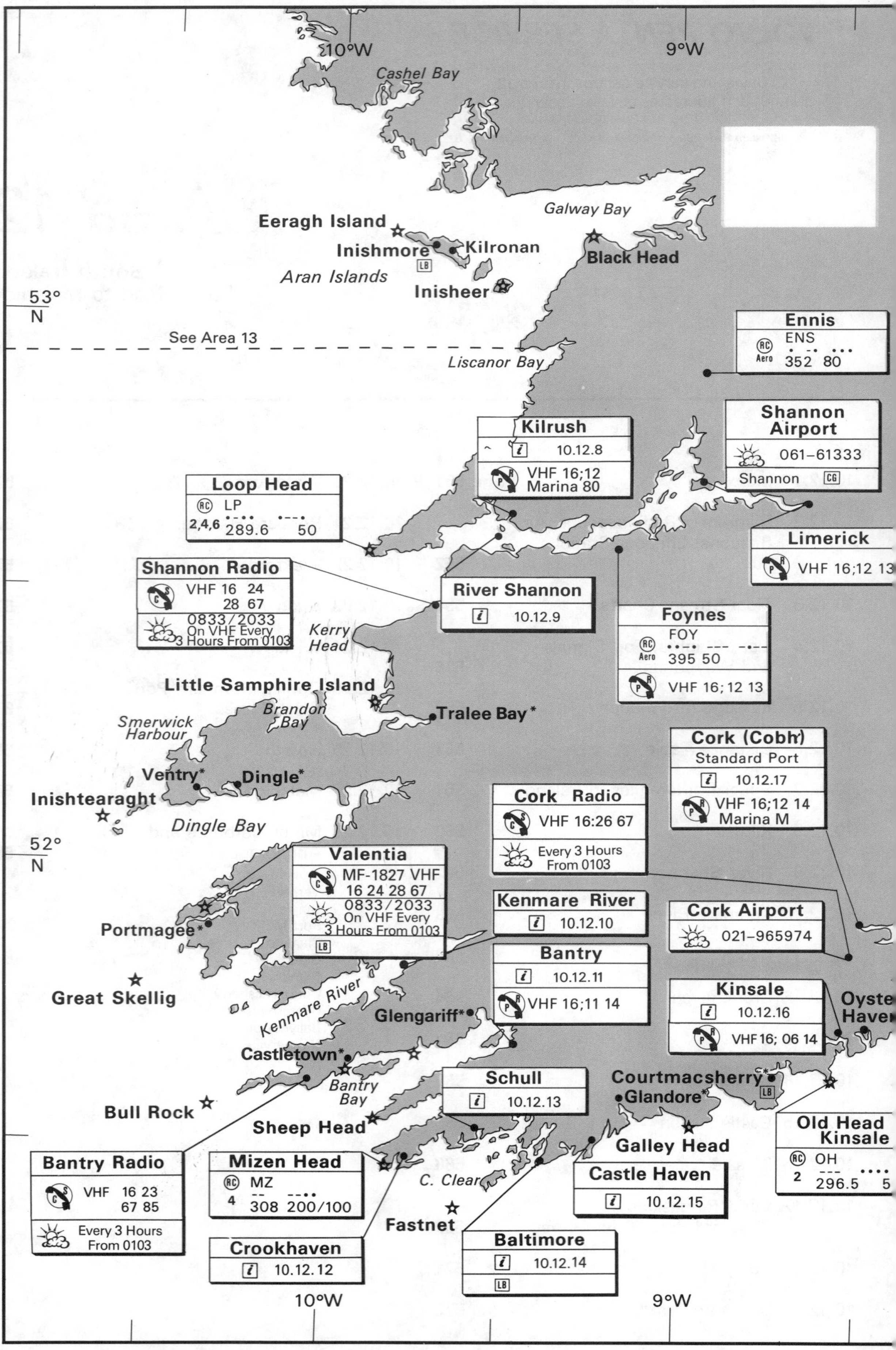
10°W
9°W
Cashel Bay
Galway Bay
Eeragh Island
Inishmore
Kilronan
Aran Islands
Inisheer
Black Head
53° N
See Area 13
Liscanor Bay
Ennis
ENS
Aero
352 80
Shannon Airport
061–61333
Shannon
CG
Kilrush
10.12.8
VHF 16;12
Marina 80
Loop Head
LP
2,4,6
289.6 50
Limerick
VHF 16;12 13
Shannon Radio
VHF 16 24
28 67
0833/2033
On VHF Every
3 Hours From 0103
River Shannon
10.12.9
Foynes
FOY
Aero
395 50
VHF 16; 12 13
Kerry Head
Little Samphire Island
Brandon Bay
Tralee Bay*
Smerwick Harbour
Ventry*
Dingle*
Inishtearaght
Dingle Bay
Cork (Cobh)
Standard Port
10.12.17
VHF 16;12 14
Marina M
Cork Radio
VHF 16:26 67
Every 3 Hours
From 0103
52° N
Valentia
MF-1827 VHF
16 24 28 67
0833/2033
On VHF Every
3 Hours From 0103
LB
Portmagee*
Kenmare River
10.12.10
Cork Airport
021–965974
Bantry
10.12.11
VHF 16;11 14
Great Skellig
Kenmare River
Glengariff*
Kinsale
10.12.16
VHF 16; 06 14
Oyster Haven
Castletown*
Bantry Bay
Bull Rock
Sheep Head
Schull
10.12.13
Courtmacsherry*
Glandore*
LB
Galley Head
Old Head Kinsale
OH
2
296.5
Bantry Radio
VHF 16 23
67 85
Every 3 Hours
From 0103
Mizen Head
MZ
4
308 200/100
C. Clear
Castle Haven
10.12.15
Fastnet
Crookhaven
10.12.12
Baltimore
10.12.14
LB
10°W
9°W

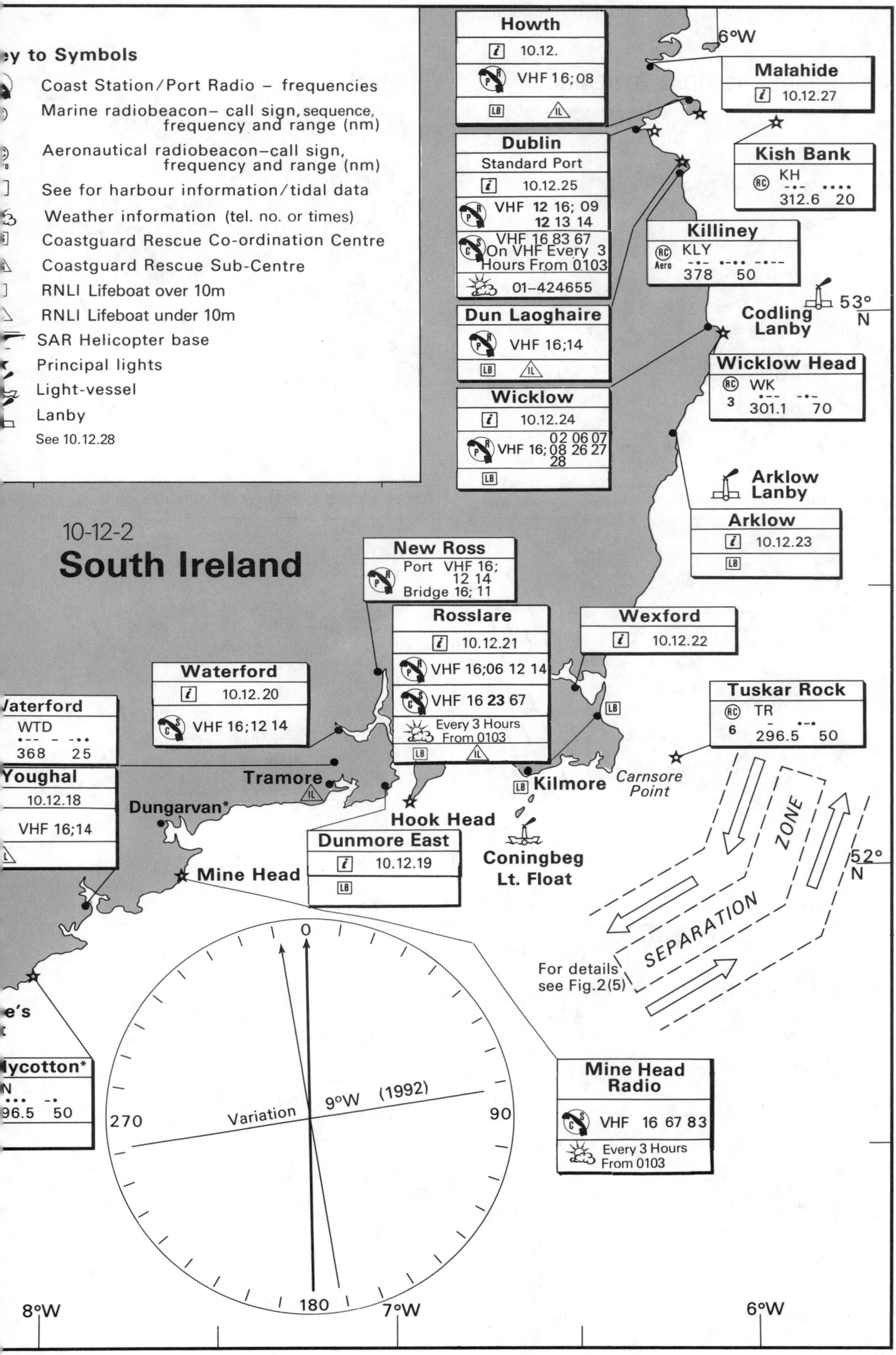
Key to Symbols
Coast Station/Port Radio – frequencies
Marine radiobeacon– call sign, sequence, frequency and range (nm)
Aeronautical radiobeacon–call sign, frequency and range (nm)
See for harbour information/tidal data
Weather information (tel. no. or times)
Coastguard Rescue Co-ordination Centre
Coastguard Rescue Sub-Centre
RNLI Lifeboat over 10m
RNLI Lifeboat under 10m
SAR Helicopter base
Principal lights
Light-vessel
Lanby
See 10.12.28
10-12-2
South Ireland
Howth
10.12.
VHF 16;08
LB
IL
6°W
Malahide
10.12.27
Dublin
Standard Port
10.12.25
VHF 12 16; 09 12 13 14
VHF 16 83 67 On VHF Every 3 Hours From 0103
01–424655
Kish Bank
KH
312.6 20
Killiney
KLY
Aero
378 50
Dun Laoghaire
VHF 16;14
Codling Lanby
53° N
Wicklow Head
WK
3
301.1 70
Wicklow
10.12.24
VHF 16; 02 06 07 08 26 27 28
Arklow Lanby
Arklow
10.12.23
New Ross
Port VHF 16; 12 14
Bridge 16; 11
Rosslare
10.12.21
VHF 16;06 12 14
VHF 16 23 67
Every 3 Hours From 0103
Wexford
10.12.22
Waterford
10.12.20
VHF 16;12 14
Waterford
WTD
368 25
Tuskar Rock
TR
6
296.5 50
Youghal
10.12.18
VHF 16;14
Tramore
Dungarvan*
Kilmore
Carnsore Point
Hook Head
Dunmore East
10.12.19
Coningbeg Lt. Float
Mine Head
52° N
ZONE
SEPARATION
For details see Fig.2(5)
Mine Head Radio
VHF 16 67 83
Every 3 Hours From 0103
e's
ycotton*
N
96.5 50
0
90
180
270
Variation 9°W (1992)
8°W
7°W
6°W

10.12.3 AREA 12 TIDAL STREAMS

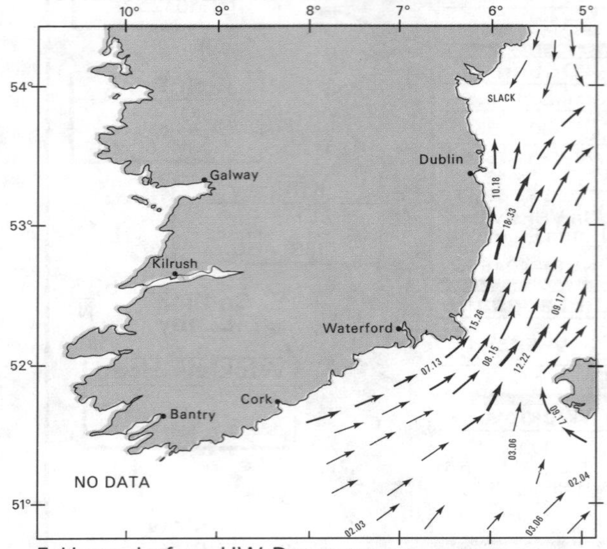
10°
9°
8°
7°
6°
5°
54°
53°
52°
51°
SLACK
Dublin
Galway
Kilrush
Waterford
Cork
Bantry
NO DATA
10.18
18.33
15.26
09.17
07.13
08.15
12.22
03.06
02.04
02.03

5 Hours before HW Dover (0530 before HW Dublin)

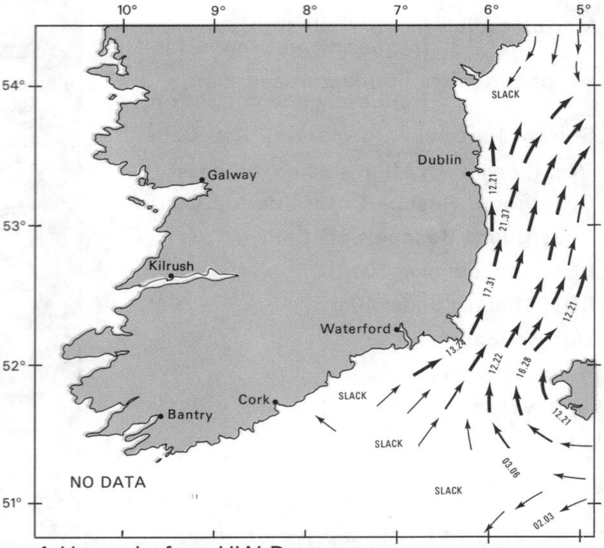
10°
9°
8°
7°
6°
5°
54°
53°
52°
51°
SLACK
Dublin
Galway
Kilrush
Waterford
Cork
Bantry
NO DATA
12.21
21.37
17.31
13.23
12.22
16.28
12.21
03.06
02.03

4 Hours before HW Dover (0430 before HW Dublin)

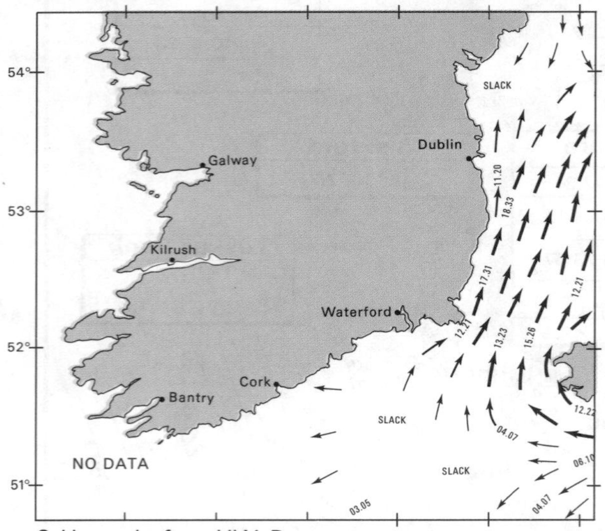
54°
53°
52°
51°
SLACK
Dublin
Galway
Kilrush
Waterford
Cork
Bantry
NO DATA
11.20
18.33
17.31
12.21
13.23
15.26
12.22
04.07
06.10
03.05

3 Hours before HW Dover (0330 before HW Dublin)

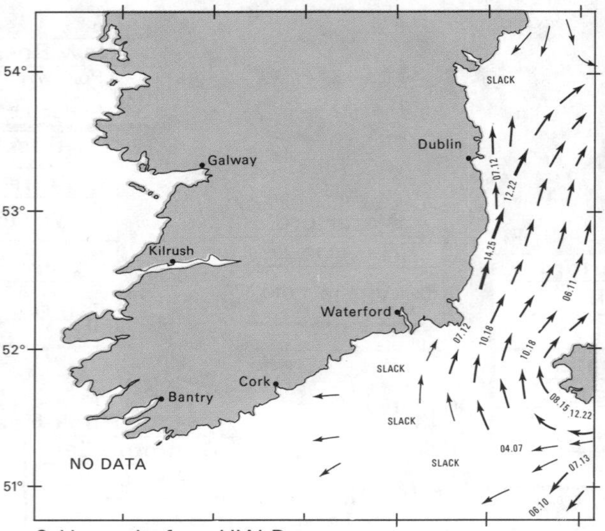
54°
53°
52°
51°
SLACK
Dublin
Galway
Kilrush
Waterford
Cork
Bantry
NO DATA
07.12
12.22
14.25
06.11
10.18
08.15
12.22
04.07
07.13
06.10

2 Hours before HW Dover (0230 before HW Dublin)

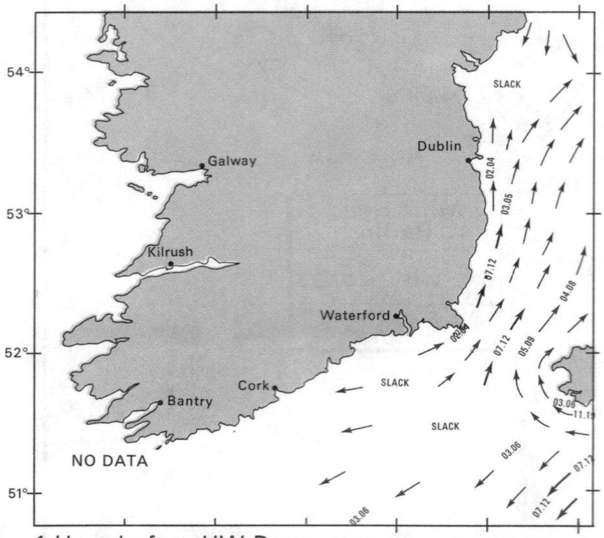
54°
53°
52°
51°
SLACK
Dublin
Galway
Kilrush
Waterford
Cork
Bantry
NO DATA
02.04
03.05
07.12
04.08
05.09
03.06
03.06

1 Hour before HW Dover (0130 before HW Dublin)

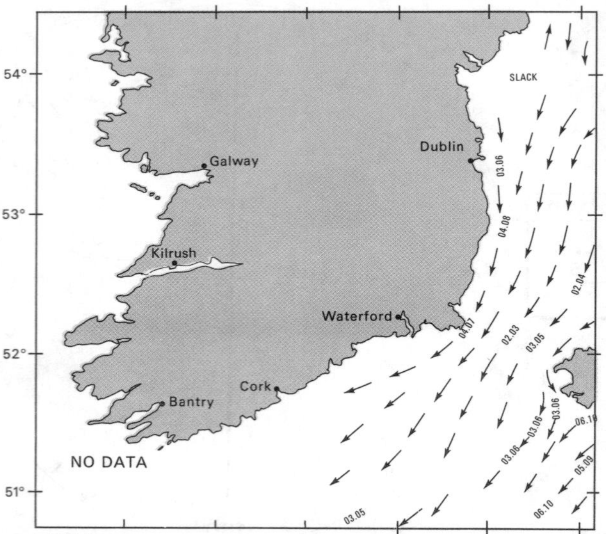
54°
53°
52°
51°
SLACK
Dublin
Galway
Kilrush
Waterford
Cork
Bantry
NO DATA
03.06
04.08
02.04
02.03
03.05
05.09
06.10
03.05

HW Dover (0030 before HW Dublin)

Northward 10.13.3 South Irish Sea 10.11.3

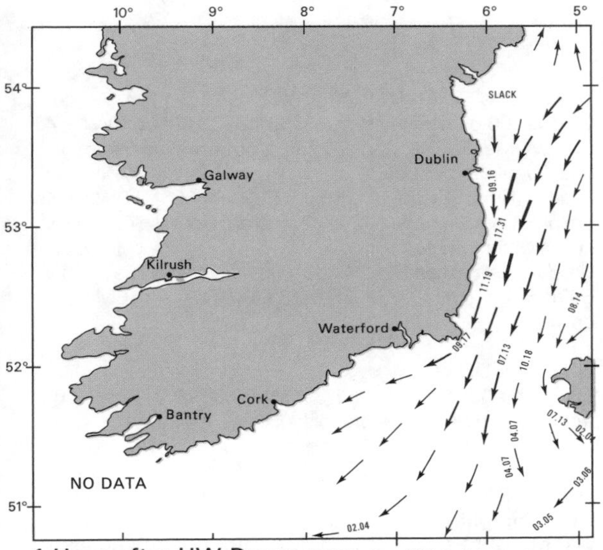
10°
9°
8°
7°
6°
5°
54°
53°
52°
51°
SLACK
Dublin
Galway
Kilrush
Waterford
Cork
Bantry
NO DATA
09.16
17.31
11.19
08.17
07.13
10.18
08.14
04.07
07.13
03.04
03.06
03.05
02.04

1 Hour after HW Dover (0030 after HW Dublin)

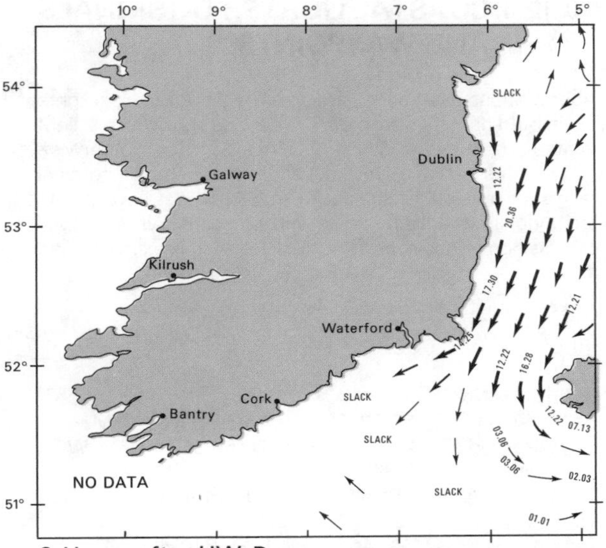
10°
9°
8°
7°
6°
5°
54°
53°
52°
51°
SLACK
Dublin
Galway
Kilrush
Waterford
Cork
Bantry
NO DATA
12.22
20.38
17.30
14.25
12.21
12.22
16.28
12.22
07.13
03.06
02.03
01.01

2 Hours after HW Dover (0130 after HW Dublin)

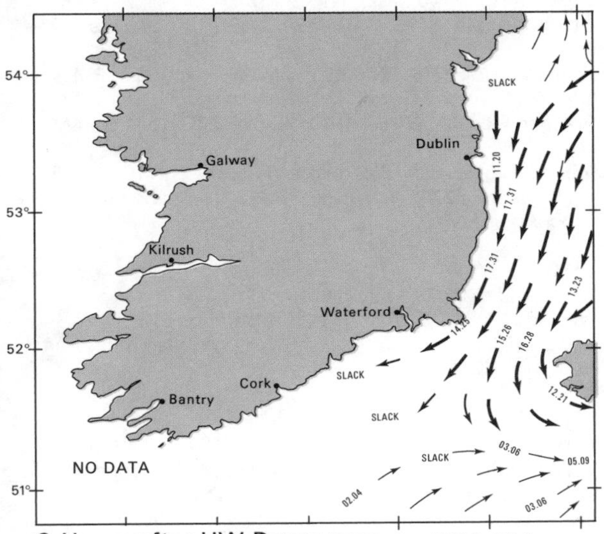
54°
53°
52°
51°
SLACK
Dublin
Galway
Kilrush
Waterford
Cork
Bantry
NO DATA
11.20
17.31
13.23
14.25
15.26
18.28
12.21
03.06
05.09
02.04
03.06

3 Hours after HW Dover (0230 after HW Dublin)

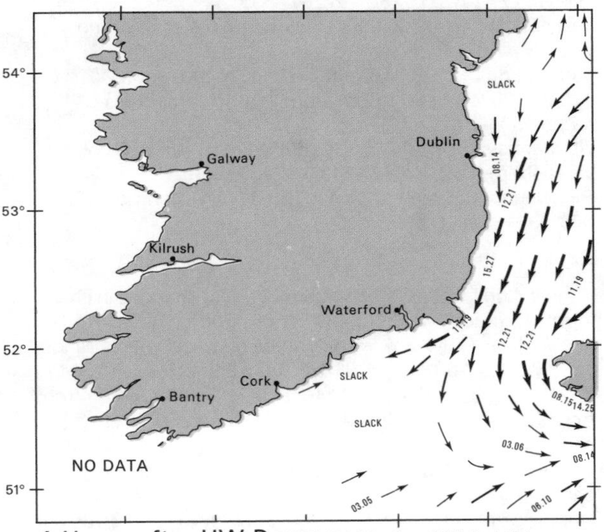
54°
53°
52°
51°
SLACK
Dublin
Galway
Kilrush
Waterford
Cork
Bantry
NO DATA
08.14
12.21
15.27
11.19
12.21
08.15
14.25
03.06
08.14
03.05
06.10

4 Hours after HW Dover (0330 after HW Dublin)

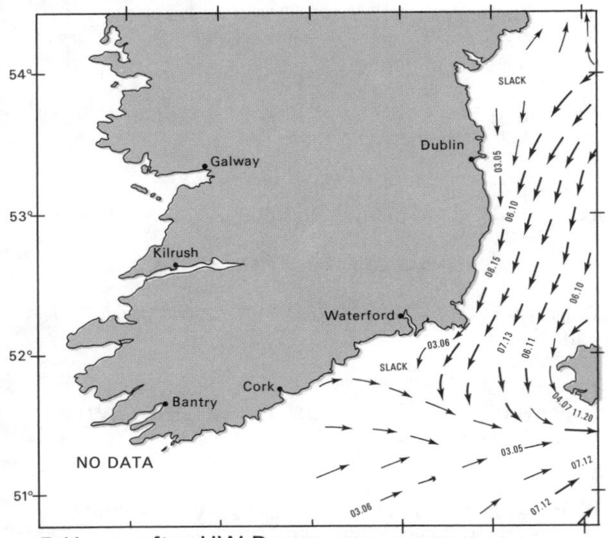
54°
53°
52°
51°
SLACK
Dublin
Galway
Kilrush
Waterford
Cork
Bantry
NO DATA
03.05
06.10
08.15
03.06
07.13
06.11
06.10
04.07
11.20
03.05
07.12
03.06

5 Hours after HW Dover (0430 after HW Dublin)

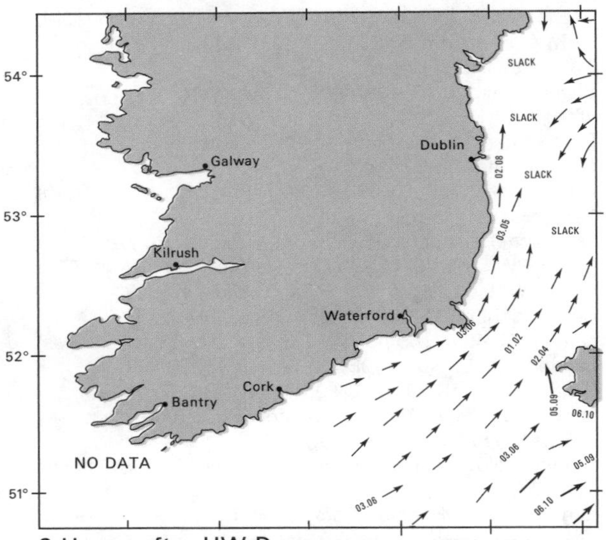
54°
53°
52°
51°
SLACK
Dublin
Galway
Kilrush
Waterford
Cork
Bantry
NO DATA
02.08
03.05
03.06
01.02
02.04
05.09
06.10
03.06
05.09
06.10

6 Hours after HW Dover (0530 after HW Dublin)

10.12.4 COASTAL LIGHTS, FOG SIGNALS AND WAYPOINTS

Abbreviations used below are given in 1.4.1. Principal lights are in **bold** print, places in CAPITALS, and light-vessels, light floats and Lanbys in *CAPITAL ITALICS*. Unless otherwise stated lights are white. m—elevation in metres; M—nominal range in n. miles. Fog signals are in *italics*. Useful waypoints are underlined – use those on land with care. All geographical positions should be assumed to be approximate. See 4.2.2.

IRELAND—WEST COAST

RIVER SHANNON
Ballybunnion Lt By 52°32'·50N 09°46'·92W VQ; NCM.
Kilcredaun Hd 52°34'·78N 09°42'·58W Fl 6s 41m 13M; W Tr; obsc within 1M 224°-247°.
Scattery Is Rineana Pt 52°36'·33N 09°31'·05W Fl (2) 7·5s 15m 10M; W Tr; vis 208°-092° (H24).
Tarbert Is N Pt Iso WR 4s 18m W14M, R10M; W ● Tr; vis W069°-277°, R277°-287°, W287°-339°.
Jetty 52°35'·4N 09°22'·5W 2 FG (vert) 3M at SW and NE ends.
Tarbert Ldg Lts 128.3°. Front Iso 2s 13m 3M; ▲ on W Tr; vis 123·2°-133·2°. Rear, 400m from front, Iso 5s 18m 3M; G stripe on W Bn.
Garraunbaun Pt Fl (3) WR 10s 16m W8M, R5M; W ■ column, vis R shore-072°, W072°-242°, R242°-shore.
Rinealon Pt, Rinalan Fl 2·5s 4m 7M; B col, W bands; vis 234°-088°.

FOYNES
W chan Ldg Lts 108·6° (may be moved for changes in chan). Front, Barneen Pt 52°36'·9N 09°06'·5W Iso WRG 4s 3m W4M, R3M, G3M; B ▲ with W stripe on W col with B bands; vis W273·2°-038·2°, R038·2°-094·2°, G094·2°-104·2°, W104·2°-108·2°, R108·2°-114·2°. Rear, E Jetty, 540m from front Oc 4s 16m 10M; B ▲ with W stripe on W col with B bands.
Colleen Pt No. 3, 52°36'·9N 09°06'·9W QG 2m 2M; W col, B bands.
Hunts (Weir) Pt No. 4, 52°37'·0N 09°07'·0W VQ (4) R 10s 2m 2M; W col, B bands.
Beeves Rk 52°39'·0N 09°01'·3W Fl WR 5s 12m W12M, R9M; vis W064·5°-091°, R091°-238°, W238°-265°, W(unintens) 265°-064·5°.
Shannon Airport 52°41'·7N 08°55'·6W Aero Al Fl WG 7·5s 40m.
Dernish Is Pier Hd, 2 FR (vert) 4m 2M each end.
E Breakwater Hd QR 3m 1M.
Conor Rock 52°40'·9N 08°54'·2W Fl R 4s 6m 6M; W Tr; vis 228°-093°.
N Channel Ldg Lts 093°. Front, Tradree Rk 52°41'·0N 08°49'·9W Fl R 2s 6m 5M; W Trs; vis 246°-110°. Rear 0·65M from front Iso 6s 14m 5M; W Tr, R bands; vis 327°-190°.
Bird Rock 52°40'·9N 08°50'·2W QG 6m 5M; W Tr.
Grass Is 52°40'·4N 08°48'·5W Fl G 2s 6m 4M; W col, B bands.
Laheen's Rk 52°40'·3N 08°48'·1W QR 4m 5M.
S side Spilling Rk 52°40'·0N 08°47'·1W Fl G 5s 5m 5M.
N side, Ldg Lts 061°. Front, Crawford Rock 490m from rear, Fl R 3s 6m 5M.
Crawford No. 2, Common rear, 52°40'·8N 08°44'·8W Iso 6s 10m 5M.
Ldg Lts 302·1°. Flagstaff Rock, 670m from rear, Fl R 2s 7m 5M.
The Whelps 52°40'·6N 08°45'·1W Fl G 3s 5m 5M; W pile.
Ldg Lts 106·5°. Meelick Rk, front 52°40'·2N 08°42'·3W Iso 4s 6m 3M. Meelick No. 2, rear 275m from front Iso 6s 9m 5M; both W pile structures.
Ldg Lts 146°, Braemar Pt, front 52°39'·1N 08°41'·9W Iso 4s 5m 5M. Rear Braemar No. 2, 122m from front Iso 6s 6m 4M; both W pile structures.
N side Clonmacken Pt 52°39'·5N 08°40'·6W Fl R 3s 7m 4M.
E side Spillane's Tr 52°39'·3N 08°39'·8W Fl 3s 11m 6M; turret on Tr.

LIMERICK DOCK
Lts in line 098·5°. Front 52°39'·5N 08°38'·8W. Rear 100m from front; both F; R ◆ on cols; occas.
N Wharf Hd 2 FR (vert) 10m; occas.

TRALEE BAY
Little Samphire Is 52°16'·23N 09°52'·80W Fl WRG 5s 27m **W16M**, R13M; G13M; Bu ● Tr; vis R262°-275°, R280°-090°, G090°-140°, W140°-152°, R152°-172°.
Gt Samphire Is 52°16'·1N 09°52'·2W QR 15m 3M; vis 242°-097°.
Fenit Pier Hd 52°16'·2N 09°51'·5W 2 FR (vert) 12m 3M; vis 148°-058°.
Brandon Pier Hd 52°16'·0N 10°09'·6W 2 FG (vert) 5m 4M.

Inishtearaght, W end Blasket Islands 52°04'·60N 10°39'·60W Fl (2) 20s 84m **27M**; W Tr; vis 318°-221° also shown by day in poor visibility.

DINGLE
NE side of ent Fl G 3s 20m 6M.
Pier Hd 52°08'·3N 10°16'·5W 2 FR (vert) 4m 2M.
Ldg Lts 182°. Front 52°07'·4N 10°16'·6W, rear 100m from front, both Oc 3s.

VALENTIA
Fort (Cromwell) Pt 51°56'·00N 10°19'·25W Fl WR 2s 16m **W17M**, **R15M**; W Tr; vis R102°-304°, W304°-351°; obsc from seaward by Doulus Hd when brg more than 180°.
FR Lts on radio masts on Geokaun hill 1·25M WSW.
Ldg Lts 141°. Front Oc WRG 4s 25m W11M, R8M, G8M; W ▲ Tr, R stripe; vis G134°-140°, W140°-142°, R142°-148°. Rear 122m from front Oc 4s 43m 5M; vis 133°-233° synchronised with front.

Skelligs Rk 51°46'·10N 10°32'·43W Fl (3) 10s 53m **27M**; W Tr; vis 262°-115°; part obsc within 6M 110°-115°.

DARRYNANE
Ldg Lts 034°. Front 51°45'·9N 10°09'·2W Oc3s 10m 4M. Rear Oc 3s 16m 4M.
Ballycrovane Hbr 51°42'·6N 09° 57'·5W Fl R 3s.

Bull Rock 51°35'·47N 10°18'·05W Fl 15s 83m **23M**; W Tr; vis 220°-186°.

BANTRY BAY
Sheep Hd 51°32'·57N 09°51'·00W Fl(3) WR 15s 83m **W18M**, **R15M**; W bldg; vis R007°-017°, W017°-212°.

BEREHAVEN
W ent, **Ardnakinna Pt** Fl (2) WR 10s 62m **W17M**, R14M; W ● Tr; vis R319°-348°, W348°-066°, R066°-shore.

FR on radio mast 3·45M 295°.
Castletown Dir Lt 024°. 51°38'·80N 09°54'·30W Dir Oc WRG 5s 4m W14M, R11M, G11M; W hut, R stripe; vis G020·5°-024°, W024°-024·5°, R024·5°-027·5°.

CASTLETOWN BERE
Perch Rk QG 4m 1M; G col.
Ldg Lts 010°. Front 51°39'·1N 09°54'·4W Oc 3s 4m 1M; W col, R stripe; vis 005°-015°. Rear 80m from front Oc 3s 7m 1M; W with R stripe; vis 005°-015°.

Roancarrigmore 51°39'·17N 09°44'·80W Fl WR 3s 18m **W18M**, R14M; W ● Tr, B band; vis W312°-050°, R050°-122°, R(unintens) 122°-242°, R242°-312°. Reserve Lt W 10M, R6M obsc 140°-220°.

WHIDDY ISLAND
W clearing Lt Oc 2s 22m 3M; vis 073°-106°.
SW dolphin QY 10m 2M; *Horn 20s.*
NE dolphin QY 10m 2M.

Mizen Hd 51°26'·97N 09°49'·18W Iso 4s 52m **16M**; vis 313°-133°; RC; Racon.

CROOKHAVEN
Rock Island Pt 51°28'·55N 09°42'·23W L Fl WR 8s 20m W13M, R11M; W Tr; vis W over Long Island B to 281°, R281°-340°; inside harbour R281°-348°, W348° towards N shore.

IRELAND—SOUTH COAST

Fastnet, W end 51°23'·33N 09°36'·13W Fl 5s 49m **28M**; Gy Tr; *Horn (4) 60s.*

Copper Pt Long Island, E end 51°30'·22N 09°32'·02W Q(3) 10s 16m 8M; W ● Tr.

SCHULL
Ldg Lts 346° Front 51°31'·6N 09°32'·5W Oc 5s 5m 11M, W mast. Rear 91m from front Oc 5s 8m 11M; W mast.

BALTIMORE
Barrack Pt 51°28'·33N 09°23'·65W Fl(2) WR 6s 40m W6M, R3M; vis R168°-294°, W294°-038°.

CASTLE HAVEN
Reen Pt 51°30'·9N 09°10'·5W Fl WRG 10s 9m W5M, R3M, G3M; W Tr; vis G shore-338°, W338°-001°, R001°-shore.

Galley Hd summit 51°31'·82N 08°57'·13W Fl(5) 20s 53m **28M**; W Tr; vis 256°-065°.

COURTMACSHERRY
Wood Pt 51°38'·3N 08°41'·0W Fl (2) WR 5s 15m 5M; vis W315°-332°, R332°-315°.
Old Hd of Kinsale, S point 51°36'·23N 08°31'·80W Fl (2) 10s 72m **25M**; B Tr, two W bands; RC; *Horn (3) 45s.*

KINSALE
Bulman Lt By 51°40'·10N 08°29'·70W Q (6) + LFl 15s; SCM.
Charles's Fort Fl WRG 5s 18m W9M, R6M, G6M; vis G348°-358°, W358°-004°, R004°-168° shown throughout 24 hrs.
Marina, each end 2 FG (vert) 2m.

CORK
Outer Hbr Rk Lt By E1 51°47'·50N 08°15'62W Fl R 2·5s; PHM.
Chicago Knoll Lt By E2 51°47'·66N 08°15'·50W Fl G 5s; SHM.
The Sound Lt By E4 51°47'·91N 08°15'·72W Q; NCM.
Roche's Pt 51°47'·56N 08°15'·24W Oc WR 20s 30m **W20M, R16M**; vis Rshore-292°, W292°-016°, R016°-033°, W(unintens) 033°-159°, R159°-shore; *Dia 30s.*
White Bay Ldg Lts 034·6°. Front Oc R 5s 11m 5M; W hut. Rear 113m from front Oc R 5s 21m 5M; W hut; synchronised with front.
Fort Davis Ldg Lts 354·1°. Front Oc 5s 29m 10M; Or ■ on Tr. Rear. Dognose Landing Quay, 203m from front Oc 5s 37m 10M; Or ■ , synchronised with front.
Curraghbinney Ldg Lts 252°. Front 51°48'·6N 08°17'·6W F 10m 3M; W ◆ on col. Rear, 61m from front, F 15m 3M; white ◆ on col; vis 229·5°-274·5°.
Crosshaven Marina 2 FR (vert) at NE and NW corners.
Whitegate Marine Terminal, Jetty 2 FG (vert) at S and N Hds.
East Ferry Marina E Passage, 2 FR (vert) at N and S ends.
Spit Bank Pile 51°50'·70N 08°16'·41W Iso WR 4s 10m W10M, R7M; W house on R piles; vis R087°-196°, W196°-221°, R221°-358°.

Ballycotton 51°49'·50N 07 59'·00W Fl WR 10s 59m **W22M, R18M**; B Tr, within W walls, B lantern; vis W238°-063°, R063°-238°; RC; *Horn (4) 90s.*

YOUGHAL
W side of ent 51°56'·55N 07°50'·49W Fl WR 2·5s 24m W12M, R9M; W Tr; vis W183°-273°, R273°-295°, W295°-307°, R307°-351°, W351°-003°.

Mine Hd 51°59'·57N 07°35'·60W Fl (4) 20s 87m **28M**; W Tr, B band; vis 228°-shore.

Ballinacourty Pt 52°04'·67N 07°33'·10W Fl (2) WRG 10s 16m W12M, R9M, G9M; W Tr; vis G245°-274°, W274°-302°, R302°-325°, W325°-117°.

12

DUNGARVAN
Ballinacourty Ldg Lts 083°. Front F 9m 2M; W col, B bands. Rear 46m from front F 12m 2M; W col, B bands.
Esplanade Ldg Lts 297·5°. Front and Rear FR 8m 2M.

WATERFORD
Hook Hd 52°07'·40N 06°55'·72W Fl 3s 46m **24M**; W Tr, two B bands; Racon; *Horn (2) 45s.*
Dunmore East, E Pier Hd L Fl WR 8s 13m W12M, R9M; Gy Tr, W lantern; vis W225°-310°, R310°-004°.
E Breakwater extn 52°08'·96N 06°59'·32W Fl R 2s 6m 4M; vis 000°-310°.
West Wharf Fl G 2s 6m 4M; vis 165°-246°.
Duncannon Dir Lt 357°. **Front** 52°13'·2N 06°56'·2W Dir Oc WRG 4s 13m W11M, R8M, G8M;; W Tr, R stripe on fort; vis G353°-356·7°, W356·7°-357·2°, R357·2°-001°. Same structure. Oc WR 4s 13m W9M, R7M; same Tr; vis R119°-149°, W149°-172°.
Middle Bar Lt By 52°11'·83N 06°56'·48W Fl R 5s; PHM.
Duncannon Spit Lt By 52°12'·67N 06°56'·00W Fl(2) G 5s; SHM.

Passage Pt 52°14'·23N 06°57'·70W Fl WR 5s 7m W6M, R5M; R pile structure; vis W shore-127°, R127°-302°.
Cheek Pt 52°16'·1N 06°59'·3W Q WR 6m 5M; W mast; vis W007°-289°, R289°-007°.
Sheagh 52°16'·3N 06°59'·4W Fl R 3s 29m 3M; Gy Tr; vis 090°-318°.
Kilmokea 52°16'·4N 06°58'·9W Fl 5s.
Power station jetty, 4 in No. 2 FG (vert) 3M.
Railway Bridge 8 FR; tfc sigs.

Snowhill Pt Ldg Lts 255°. Front Fl WR 2·5s 5m 3M; vis W222°-020°, R020°-057°, W057°-107°. Rear, Flour Mill, 0·4M from front Q 12m 5M.
Queen's chan Ldg Lts 098°. Front QR 8m 5M; B Tr, W band; vis 030°-210°. Rear 550m from front Q 15m 5M; W mast.
Giles Quay 52°15'·4N 07°04'·2W Fl 3s 9m; vis 255°-086°.
Cove 52°15'·0N 07°05'·1W Fl WRG 6s 6m 2M; W Tr; vis R111°-161°, G161°-234°, W234°-111°.
Smelting House Pt 52°15'·1N 07°05'·2W Q 8m 3M; W mast.
Ballycar 52°15'·0N 07°05'·4W Fl RG 3s 5m; vis G127°-212°, R212°-284°.

CONINGBEG Lt F 52°02'·38N 06°39'·45W Fl(3) 30s 12m **24M**; R hull, and Tr, lantern amidships; *Horn (3) 60s.* Racon.
Kilmore, Breakwater Hd Q RG 6m 5M; vis R269°-354°, G354°-003°, R003°-077°.
Carna Pier Hd 52°11'·89N 06°20'·80W Fl R 3s 6m 4M.

IRELAND—EAST COAST

Tuskar 52°12'·15N 06°12'·40W Q(2) 7·5s 33m **27M**; W Tr; RC; Racon; *Horn (4) 45s.*

ROSSLARE
Pier Hd 52°15'·41N 06°20'·22W L Fl WRG 5s 15m W13M, R10M, G10M; R Tr; vis G098°-188°, W188°-208°, R208°-246°, G246°-283°, W283°-286°, R286°-320°.
Ldg Lts 124°. Front 52°15'·3N 06°20'·1W. Rear 67m from front. Both FR 2M; Y ◆ ; vis 079°-169°.
New Ferry Pier Hd 52°15'·3N 06°20'·2W Q 10m 3M.
Ldg Lts 146°. Front 52°15'·2N 06°20'·1W, rear 110m from front, both Oc 3s 11/13m 3M, synchronised.

ARKLOW LANBY 52°39'·50N 05°58'·10W Fl(2) 12s 12m **16M**; tubular structure on By; Racon; *Horn Mo(A) 30s* .
Arklow Hd Pier Hd 52°46'·7N 06°08'·4W Oc R 10s 9m 9M.

ARKLOW
S Pier Hd 52°47'·59N 06°08'·16W Fl WR 6s 10m 13M; Tr; vis R shore-223°, W223°-350°; R350°-shore.
N Pier Hd L Fl G 7s 7m 10M; vis shore-287°.

Wicklow Hd 52°57'·93N 05°59'·83W Fl (3) 15s 37m **26M**; W Tr; RC.

WICKLOW
E Pier Hd 52°58'·98N 06°02'·01W Fl WR 5s 11m 6M; W Tr, R base and cupola; vis R136°-293°, W293°-136°.
W Pier Hd Fl G 1·5s 5m 6M.

CODLING LANBY 53°03'·02N 05°40'·70W Fl 4s 12m **15M**; tubular structure on By; Racon; *Horn 20s.*

Kish Bank 53°18'·68N 05°55'·38W Fl(2) 30s 29m **28M**; W Tr, R band, helicopter platform; RC; Racon; *Horn (2) 30s.*

DUBLIN BAY
Muglins 53°16'·53N 06°04'·52W Fl 5s 14m 8M; W conical Tr, R band.

DUN LAOGHAIRE
E Breakwater Hd 53°18'·13N 06°07'·55W Fl (2) 15s 16m **22M**; Tr, W lantern; *Dia 30s or Bell (1) 6s.*
W Breakwater Hd Fl(3) G 7·5s 11m 7M; stone Tr, W lantern; vis 188°-062°.
Car Ferry Terminal Hd 53°17'·31N 06°07'·73W Q WR 6s 3M; vis R030°-131°, W131°-030°; QY traffic signal 80m SW.

Rosbeg E Lt By 53°19'·99N 06°04'·35W Q(3) 10s; ECM.
Rosbeg S Lt By 53°20'·00N 06°04'·35W Q(6) + LFl 15s; SCM.
Bennett Bank Lt By 53°20'·16N 05°55'·07W Q (6) + LFl 15s; SCM; *Horn (3) 30s.*

PORT OF DUBLIN.
Great S Wall Hd, **Poolbeg** 53°20'·52N 06°09'·02W Oc(2) R 20s 20m **15M**; R ● Tr; *Horn (2) 60s.*
N Bull Wall Hd, **N Bull** Fl (3) G 10s 15m **15M**; G ● Tr; *Bell (4) 30s.*
N Bank Oc G 8s 10m **16M**; G ■ Tr on piles; *Bell (3) 20s.*
53°20'·4N 06°11'·3W Aero 2 QR (vert) 205/85m 11M; 3 FR (vert) Lts mark intermediate heights on chimney.

BEN OF HOWTH
Baily 53°21'·67N 06°03'·10W Fl 20s 41m **27M**; Tr; *Dia 60s.*

HOWTH
Howth Lt By 53°23'·72N 06°03'·53W FlG 5s; SHM.
Rowan Rks Lt By 53°23'·87N 06°03'·20W Q(3) 10s; ECM.
E Pier Hd Fl(2) WR 7·5s 13m **W17M**, R 13M; W Tr; vis W256°-295°, R295°-256°.
W Pier Hd Fl G 3s 7m 6M.
Marina Pier 2 FR (vert) 6m.

Dublin Airport 53°25'·7N 06°14'·7W Aero Al Fl WG 4s 95m.

Rockabill 53°35'·80N 06°00'·30W Fl WR 12s 45m **W23M**, **R19M**; W Tr, B band; vis W178°-329°, R329°-178°; *Horn (4)60s.* Also shown by day when fog signal is operating.

10.12.5 PASSAGE INFORMATION

IRELAND – WEST COAST

This coast gives wonderful cruising, but is exposed to the Atlantic and any swell offshore, but this diminishes mid-sum. In bad weather however the sea breaks dangerously on shoals with quite substantial depths. There is usually a refuge close by, but if caught out in deteriorating weather and poor vis, a stranger may need to make an offing until conditions improve, so a stout yacht and good crew are required. Tidal streams are weak, except round headlands.

There are few Lts, and inshore navigation is not wise after dark. Coastal navigation is feasible at night in good visibility, and fog is less frequent than in Irish Sea. A good watch must be kept for drift nets off the coast, and for lobster pots in inshore waters.

Stores, fuel and water are not readily available. Even in mid-sum a yacht may meet at least one gale in a two-week cruise. Listen regularly to the Radio Telefis Eireann forecasts, as described in Table 7(2).

For all Irish waters the Sailing Directions published by the Irish Cruising Club are strongly recommended, and particularly on the W coast, where other information is scant.

The stretch of coast from Black Hd to Loop Hd has no safe anchs, and no Lts S of Inisheer. Take care not to be set inshore, although there are few offlying dangers except in Liscanor Bay and near Mutton Is.

RIVER SHANNON (charts 1819, 1547, 1548, 1549, 1540)

R. Shannon is the longest river in Ireland, running 100M from Lough Allen to Limerick and thence, in the tidal section, 50M from Limerick dock to its mouth between Loop Hd and Kerry Hd. Loop Hd (Lt, RC) marks the N side of Shannon est, and should be passed 0·3M off. Here the stream runs SW from HW Galway +0300, and NE from HW Galway –0300. In the lower reaches, as far as the junction with R Fergus about 15M below Limerick, the tides and streams are those of a deep-water inlet, with roughly equal durations of rise and fall, and equal rates of flood and ebb streams. In the entrance the flood stream begins at HW Galway –0555, and the ebb at HW Galway +0015. Above the junction with R Fergus the tidal characteristics become more like those of most rivers: the flood stream is stronger than the ebb, but it runs for a shorter time. In the Shannon the stream is much affected by the wind: S and W winds increase the rate and duration of the flood stream, and reduce the ebb. Strong N or E winds have the opposite effect. Prolonged or heavy rain increases the rate and duration of the ebb.

Off Kilcredaun Pt the ebb runs at 4 kn at sp, and in strong winds between S and NW it forms a bad race. This can be mostly avoided by keeping near the N shore, which is free from offlying dangers, and thereby avoiding the worst of the tide. When leaving the Shannon in strong W winds, aim to pass Kilcredaun Pt at slack water, and again keep near the N shore.

In the estuary and lower reaches of the Shannon (10.12.9) there are several anchs available for yachts on passage up or down the coast. In N winds there is anch SE of Querrin Pt (chart 1547), 4·5M further up river on N shore. Off Kilrush (10.12.8) there are anchs E of Scattery Is and N of Hog Is. (Note that there are overfalls 0·75M S of Scattery Is with W winds and ebb tide).

LOOP HEAD TO DINGLE BAY (charts 2254)

There is no Lt from Loop Hd to Inishtearaght, apart from Little Samphire Is in Tralee B, where Fenit hbr (10.12.28) provides the only secure refuge along this coast.

There is an anch, but exposed to N winds and to swell, on the W side of Brandon B. From here the scenery is spectacular to Smerwick hbr, entered between the Duncapple Is and the E Sister. It is sheltered except from NW or N winds.

Sybil Pt has steep cliffs, and offlying rks extend 0·35M. There is a race in W or NW winds with N-going tide, and often a nasty sea between Sybil Pt and Blasket Sound.

The Blasket Is are very exposed, with strong tides and overfalls, but worth a visit in settled weather (chart 2790). Gt Blasket and Inishvickillane each have anch and landing on their NE side. Inishtearaght is the most W Is (Lt), but further W lie Tearaght Rks, and 3M SSW are Little Foze and Gt Foze Rks. Extensive rks and shoals form the W side of Blasket Sound; this is the most convenient N-S route, 1M wide, and easy in daylight and reasonable weather with fair wind or tide. The N-going stream starts at HW Galway +0430, and the S-going at HW Galway –0155, with sp rate 3 kn. Wild Bank (or Three Fathom Pinnacle), a shallow patch with overfalls, lies 2·5M SSW of Slea Hd. 3M SW of Wild Bank is Barrack Rk, with breakers in strong winds.

Dingle Bay (chart 2789) is wide and deep, with few dangers round its shores. The best anchs are at Ventry, Dingle and Portmagee – see 10.12.28.

DINGLE BAY TO MIZZEN HEAD (chart 2423)

The SW end of Puffin Is is steep-to, but the sound to the E is rky and not recommended. Rough water is met between Bray Hd and Bolus Hd with fresh onshore winds or swell. Great Skellig (lit) is 6M, and Little Skellig 5M WSW of Puffin Is. Lemon Rk lies between Puffin Is and Little Skellig. Here the stream turns N at HW Cobh +0500, and S at HW Cobh –0110. There is a Rk 0·3M SW of Great Skellig. When very calm it is possible to go alongside at Blind Man's Cove on NE side of Great Skellig, where there are interesting ruins.

Ballinskelligs Bay has an anch N of Horse Is, which has two rks close off E end. Centre of B is a prohib anch (cables). Darrynane is an attractive, sheltered hbr N of Lamb Hd. The entrance has Ldg Lts and marks, but is narrow and dangerous in bad weather.

Great Hog (or Scariff) Is has a rk close N, and a reef extending 0·2M W. Little Hog (or Deenish) Is is rky 0·1M to NE. Moylaun Is lies 1·5M E of Deenish, and has a rk 10·15M SW of it. Two Headed Is, off Lamb Hd, is steep-to. Kenmare R (chart 2495 & 10.12.10) has attractive hbrs and anchs, but its shores are rky, with no Lts. The best places are Sneem, Kilmakilloge and Ardgroom.

Dursey Is is steep-to except for rks 0·75M NE and 0·15M SW of Dursey Hd. Bull Rk (Lt, fog sig) and two rks W of it lie 2·5M WNW of Dursey Hd. Cow Rk is midway between Bull Rk and Dursey Hd, with clear water each side. Calf and Heifer Rks are 0·75M SW of Dursey Hd, where there is often broken water. 2M W of The Bull the stream turns NW at HW Cobh +0150, and SE at HW Cobh –0420. Dursey Sound (chart 2495) is a good short cut, but the stream runs 4 kn at sp. W-going starts at HW Cobh +0135, and E-going at HW Cobh –0450. A rk lies almost awash in mid-chan at the narrows, where there are also cables 24m above MHWS. Hold very close to the Is shore. Beware wind changes in the sound, and broken water at N entrance.

Keep 0·3M off Crow Is to clear dangers. Off Blackball Hd at entrance to Bantry B (10.12.11) there can be a nasty race, particularly on W-going stream against the wind. Bantry B (charts 1838, 1840) has excellent Hbrs – notably Castletown, and Glengariff (see 10.12.28). There are few dangers offshore, except around Bere and Whiddy Is.

12

Sheep Hd (Lt) separates Bantry from Dunmanus B (chart 2552) which has three Hrs – Dunmanus, Kitchen Cove and Dunbeacon. Carbery, Cold and Furze Is lie in middle of B, and it is best to keep N of them. Three Castle Hd at S end of bay has rks 0·1M W, and sea can break on S Bullig 0·4M off Hd.

MIZEN HD TO OLD HD OF KINSALE (charts 2424)

From Mizen Hd to Cork are many natural hbrs. Only the best are mentioned here. Offshore the stream seldom exceeds 1·5kn, but it is stronger off headlands causing races and overfalls with wind against tide. Prolonged W winds increase the rate/duration of the E-going stream, and strong E winds have a similar effect on the W-going stream.

Off Mizen Hd the W-going stream starts at HW Cobh +0120, and the E-going at HW Cobh –0500. The sp rate is 4 kn, which with wind against tide forms a dangerous race, sometimes extending to Three Castle Hd or Brow Hd, with broken water right to the shore.

Crookhaven (10.12.12) is a well sheltered hbr, accessible at all states of tide, entered between Rock Is Lt Ho and Alderman Rks, ENE of Streek Hd. Anch off the village. The passage from here to Schull (10.12.13) can be made inside Long Is.

Fastnet Rk (Lt, fog sig) is nearly 4M WSW of C Clear. There is one rk 0·25M NE of Fastnet. Long Is B can be reached from here or through Gascanane Sound, between C Clear Is and Sherkin Is. Carrigmore Rks lie in the middle of this chan, with Gascanane Rk 0·1M W of them. The chan between Carrigmore Rks and Badger Is is best. If bound for Crookhaven, beware Bullig Reef, N of C Clear Is.

10M E of Baltimore (10.12.14) is Castle Haven (10.12.15), a sheltered and attractive hbr, entered between Reen Pt (Lt) and Battery Pt. On passage Toe Hd has foul ground 0·05M S, and 0·75M S is a group of rks called the Stags.

Sailing E to Glandore, pass outside or inside High Is and Low Is, but if inside beware Belly Rk (awash) about 0·3M S of Rabbit Is. Good anch off Glandore (10.12.28), or off Union Hall.

Keep at least 0·5M off Galley Hd to clear Dhulic Rk, and further off in fresh winds. Clonakilty B has little to offer. Offshore the W-going stream makes at HW Cobh +0200, and the E-going at HW Cobh –0420, sp rates 1·5 kn.

Rks extend 0·02M from Seven Hds, and beware Cotton Rk and Shoonta Rk close to the E. In middle of Courtmacsherry B are several dangers – from W to E Horse Rk, Black Tom, Barrel Rk and Blueboy, with a patch called Inner Barrels further inshore. These must be avoided going to or from Courtmacsherry, a rather shallow hbr with a bar which breaks in strong S or SE winds. See 10.12.28.

OLD HD OF KINSALE TO TUSKAR RK (chart 2049)

Old Head of Kinsale (Lt, fog sig, RC) is quite steep-to, but a race extends 1M to SW on W-going stream, and to SE on E-going stream. There is an inshore Pass in light weather, but in strong winds keep 2M off.
0·5M S of Hangman Pt at entrance to Kinsale (10.12.16) is Bulman Rk. The Sovereigns are large rks off Oyster Haven – a good hbr, clear but for Harbour Rk in mid-chan off Ferry Pt which must be passed on its W side. See 10.12.28.

Daunt Rk is 0·7M SE of Robert's Hd. Little Sovereign on with Reanies Hd 241° leads inshore of it. Ringabella B offers temp anch in good weather, near entrance to Cork (10.12.17).

From Cork to Ballycotton keep 0·3M off as far as Power Hd, and then at least 0·5M off for dangers including Smiths Rks 1·5M WSW of Ballycotton Is (Lt, fog sig, RC). Sound Rk lies between Ballycotton Is and Small Is. Ballycotton Hbr (10.12.28) is small and crowded, but usually there is sheltered anch outside. N side of Ballycotton B is foul 0·5M offshore.

Pass 0·1M S of Capel Is. The sound is not recommended. For Youghal see 10.12.18. To the E, there is a submerged rk 0·05M SE of Ram Hd. Here the W-going stream starts at HW Cobh +0230, and the E-going at HW Cobh –0215, sp rates 1·5 kn. Mine Hd (Lt) has two dangerous rks, The Rogue over 0·25M E and The Longship 1M SW.

Helvick is a small sheltered hbr on S side of Dungarvan B (10.12.28) and is approached along S shore, S of Helvick Rk, N of which other dangers exist towards Ballinacourty Pt. From here to Tramore there are few offlying rks, until Falskirt – a dangerous rk off Swines Pt in W approach to Dunmore East (10.12.19 & chart 2046). Beware salmon nets.

From a point 1M S of Hook Hd (avoiding the overfalls known as Tower Race, which extend about 1M S of the Hd at times), there are no obstructions on a direct course for Saltee Sound (chart 2740). Jackeen Rk is 1M NW of the S end of North Saltee, and Sebber Bridge extends 0·75M N from the NE point of South Saltee, so care is needed through the sound, where the stream runs 3·5 kn at sp. There are several rks round the Saltees, including the Bohurs to the E of the sound. From N of Long Bohur steer to pass N of Black Rk, before altering course eastward to pass 0·2M off Carnsore Pt, and thence to Greenore Pt. Watch for lobster pots in this area. In settled weather the little hbr of Kilmore Quay (mostly dries) is available, but there are rks and shoals in the approaches.

There can be a dangerous race off Carnsore Pt. In bad weather or in poor vis, pass S of Coningbeg Lt F, the Barrels and Tuskar Rk (Lt). Dangerous rks lie up to 0·65M SSW and 0·2M NW of Tuskar Rk. Avoid the TSS; see Fig. 2(8).

TUSKAR ROCK TO LAMBAY ISLAND (charts 1787, 1468)

From Carnsore Pt to Dublin (10.12.25) the shallow offshore banks cause dangerous overfalls and dictate the route. This is not a good cruising area, but for passage making it is sheltered from the W winds. Tidal streams run mainly N and S, but the N-going flood sets across the banks on the inside, and the S-going ebb sets across them on the outside.

From Tuskar or Greenore Pt there is the choice of going inside Lucifer and Blackwater Banks, or seawards to fetch the Arklow Lanby. Again, from here either the inshore or seaward passage can be taken. Approaching Dublin B, yachts normally use Dalkey Sound, but with a foul tide or light wind it is better to use Muglins Sound. Muglins (Lt) is steep-to except for a rk about 0·1M WSW of the Lt. Beware Leac Buidhe (dries) 0·1M E of Clare Rk.

Kish Bank and Burford Bank lie offshore in the approaches to Dublin B, and Rosbeg Bank lies on the N side of it. The N-going stream begins at HW Dublin –0600, and the S-going at HW Dublin, sp rates 3 kn. The sea breaks on Burford Bank in E gales.

Ben of Howth, on N side of Dublin B, is steep-to, with no dangers more than 0·1M offshore. Ireland's Eye, a rky Is which rises steeply to a height of 99m, lies about 0·75M N of Howth (10.12.26) with reefs running SE and SW from Thulla Rk at its SE end.

For notes on crossing the Irish Sea, see 10.13.5.

10.12.6 DISTANCE TABLE

Approximate distances in nautical miles are by the most direct route while avoiding dangers and allowing for traffic separation schemes etc. Places in *italics* are in adjoining areas.

1 *Galway*	**1**																			
2 *Slyne Hd*	49	**2**																		
3 Loop Hd	55	52	**3**																	
4 Valentia	103	92	48	**4**																
5 Bantry	155	144	100	58	**5**															
6 Fastnet Rk	150	139	95	53	34	**6**														
7 Kinsale	199	188	144	102	83	49	**7**													
8 Cork	210	199	155	113	94	60	17	**8**												
9 Youghal	228	217	173	131	112	78	35	25	**9**											
10 Dunmore East	262	251	207	165	146	112	69	59	34	**10**										
11 Tuskar Rk	287	276	232	190	171	137	98	85	63	32	**11**									
12 Arklow	324	313	269	227	208	174	135	122	100	69	37	**12**								
13 Wicklow	339	328	284	242	223	189	150	137	115	84	52	15	**13**							
14 Dun Laoghaire	357	346	302	260	241	207	168	155	133	102	70	36	21	**14**						
15 *Mew Island*	309	260	312	345	326	292	253	240	218	187	155	118	107	90	**15**					
16 *Douglas*	394	345	364	322	303	269	230	217	195	164	132	102	92	80	62	**16**				
17 *South Bishop*	310	299	255	214	194	160	123	110	90	61	36	62	72	90	172	143	**17**			
18 *Lundy Island*	336	325	281	239	220	186	147	140	126	105	85	112	122	140	222	193	50	**18**		
19 *Bishop Rock*	298	287	243	201	182	148	135	136	134	140	141	175	185	215	290	260	125	110	**19**	
20 *Ouessant*	396	385	341	299	280	246	235	236	234	234	228	265	275	298	390	361	218	180	100	**20**

10.12.7 SPECIAL DIFFERENCES IN IRELAND

The Ordnance Survey map numbers refer to the Irish Ordnance Survey maps, scale 1:12670 or ½in to 1 mile, which cover the whole island, including Ulster, in 25 sheets.

Irish Customs: Yachts should preferably make their first port of call at one of the following places where there are customs posts Dublin port, Dun Laoghaire, Dunmore East, Waterford, New Ross, Dungarvan, Cobh, Cork, Crosshaven, Kinsale, Baltimore (summer only), Crookhaven, Bantry, Castletownbere, Cahirciveen, Fenit, Kilrush, Foynes, Limerick, Galway, Westport, Sligo and Killybegs.

Yachts, in fact, are permitted to make their first call anywhere and if, after the proper procedures have been gone through, no Customs Officer arrives, report to the Civil Guard station. Passports are not required by UK citizens. Fly flag Q on arrival.

Irish Coast Life Saving Service: This is staffed by volunteers who are trained in first aid and equipped with breeches buoys, cliff ladders etc and their telephone numbers are those of the Leader's residence. Where appropriate these telephone numbers are given for each port.

Irish Marine Rescue Co-ordination Centre: The centre for the whole of the Irish Republic is situated at Shannon Airport. Its telephone numbers are (061) 61219 and (061) 61969. Should these be engaged call Air Traffic Control, Shannon (061) 61233 or Cork (021) 965326 or Dublin (01) 379900. In extreme emergency dial 999. The centre can call on the RNLI, Coast Life Saving Service, Irish Army Air Corps helicopters, search aircraft, Irish naval vessels, civil aircraft, the Irish lighthouse service and the Garda Siochana. The Centre liaises with UK and France and acts as a clearing house for all messages received during the rescue operation within 100 miles of the Irish coast.

For Northern Ireland: The HM Coastguard Maritime Rescue Sub-Centre is in Bangor, Co Down, Tel. Donaghadee (0247) 883184. HM Customs have seven main places where yachtsmen should report in the event of a local Customs Officer not being available;

Larne Customs: ☎ (0232) 752511
Londonderry Customs: ☎ (0504) 262273
Kilkeel Customs: ☎ (06937) 62158
Coleraine Customs: ☎ (0265) 4803
Belfast Customs: ☎ (0232) 752511
Warrenpoint Customs: ☎ (069372) 3288
Bangor: No telephone.

Liquefied petroleum gas: In the Republic of Ireland LPG is provided by Kosan, a sister company of Calor Gas Ltd. But the bottles have different connections, and the smallest bottle is taller than the normal Calor one fitted in most yachts. Yachts visiting the Irish Republic are advised to take an ample stock of Calor. Availability of Kosan gas is indicated by symbol Kos.

Telephones: To dial the Irish Republic from the UK, dial 010 (International Exchange) followed by 353 (Irish Republic) followed by the area code (given in UK telephone books, or shown below omitting the initial 0) followed by the number. To dial UK from the Irish Republic: prefix the UK code with 03 and retain the 0 at the beginning of the UK area code, eg to call Southampton 123456 dial 03 0703 123456.

Weather: Weather messages (comprising gale warnings, 24 hr forecast for Irish coastal waters up to 30M offshore and Irish Sea) are broadcast by RTE Radio 1. For details see Table 7(2).

Radio weather bulletins on RTE Radio 1 are at:

0633	Coastal waters
1253	Coastal waters (1255 on Sun)
1825	Coastal waters
2355	Coastal waters

Note 1. There are two books of sailing directions, published by the Irish Cruising Club, one for the South and West coasts of Ireland, the other for the North and East coasts. These are highly recommended.

Note 2. For further information regarding the Republic of Ireland, write to Irish Yachting Association, 3 Park Rd, Dun Laoghaire, Co Dublin ☎ 800239 or to Irish Tourist Board, 150 New Bond Street, London W1Y 0AQ (☎ 071 493 3201).

Note 3. Currency in Republic of Ireland is the Punt (£IR) divided into 100p.

12

KILRUSH 10-12-8

Clare

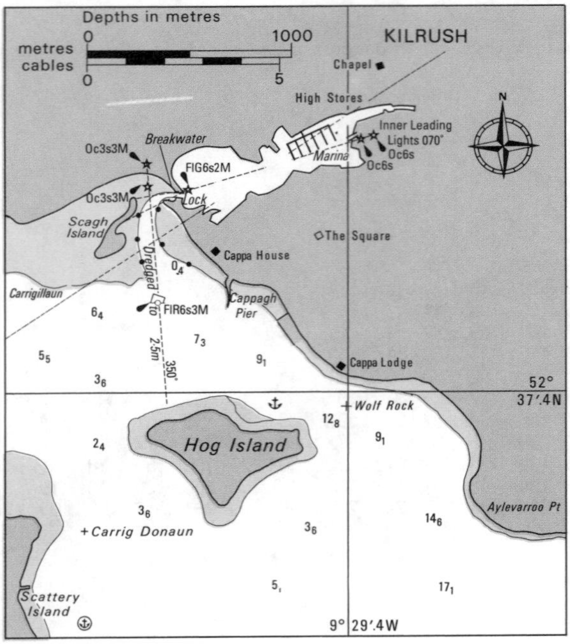
Depths in metres
metres
cables
0
1000
0
5
KILRUSH
Chapel
High Stores
Inner Leading Lights 070°
Oc6s
Oc6s
Marina
Breakwater
Oc3s3M
FlG6s2M
Oc3s3M
Lock
Scagh Island
The Square
Cappa House
Dredged to 2·5m
350°
Carrigillaun
FlR6s3M
Cappagh Pier
Cappa Lodge
52°
37′.4N
Wolf Rock
Hog Island
Aylevarroo Pt
Carrig Donaun
Scattery Island
9° 29′.4W

CHARTS

Admiralty 1547, 1819; Irish OS 17

TIDES

−0555 Dover; ML 2·6; Duration 0610; Zone 0 (GMT).

Standard Port GALWAY (⟶)

Times				Height (metres)			
HW		LW		MHWS	MHWN	MLWN	MLWS
1000	0500	0000	0600	5·1	3·9	2·0	0·6
2200	1700	1200	1800				
Differences KILRUSH							
−0006	+0027	+0057	−0016	−0·1	−0·2	−0·3	−0·1

SHELTER

The deep water harbour is Cappa, well sheltered except in SE winds. Pier is in constant use by Shannon pilot boats and tugs. Excellent shelter in Kilrush Marina (access H24).

NAVIGATION

Waypoint 52°37′·00N 09°32′·10W, 235°/055° from/to Watch House Point, 1·5M. See also 10·12·9. Coming between Hog Is and mainland, beware Wolf Rock. Approaching between Scattery Is and mainland, beware Baurnahard Spit and Carrigillaun.

LIGHTS AND MARKS

Ldg Lts as shown on chartlet. R port hand buoy Fl R 6s at entrance to channel to marina. Sectored Lt at lock gate Fl G 3s 2M.

RADIO TELEPHONE

VHF Ch 16; 12. Other stations: Foynes Ch 16; 12 13 (occas). Limerick Ch 16; 12 13 (office hours). Marina Ch **80** M.

TELEPHONE (065)

Hr Mr 51327; MRCC Limerick 61219; Coast Life Saving Service 51004; # Limerick 45327; Weather Shannon 61333; Police 17; Dr. 51275

FACILITIES

EC Thursday; **Kilrush Creek Marina** (250 + 50 visitors) ☎ 52072, Slip, BH (45 ton), AC, C (1 ton), CH, FW, Gas, Gaz, Kos, V, D, ME, Sh, El, P, ⊡, Bar, R, Access H24; **Cappa** ☎ 51027, Slip, M, L, FW, CH, AB; **George Brew** ☎ 51028, Kos; **Town** P, D, El, CH, AB, V, R, Bar. ✉; Ⓑ; ⇌ (bus to Limerick); ✈ (Shannon). **Note 1:** Car ferry across Shannon from Tarbert to Killimer (4M upstream of Kilrush).

RIVER SHANNON 10-12-9

CHARTS

Admiralty 1819, 1547, 1548, 1549, 1540. Upper reaches 5080, 5078.

TIDES

HW at	HW Galway	HW Dover
Kilbaha	−0015	+0605
Carrigaholt	−0015	+0605
Tarbert	+0035	−0530
Foynes	+0050	−0515
Limerick	+0130	−0435

SHELTER

The Shannon Estuary is 50M long, from Loop Head to Limerick. Between Kilconly and Kilcredaun Pts in the W and the entrance to R Fergus there are many sheltered anchorages protected from all but E winds. The most convenient for boats on passage N or S is Carrigaholt Bay which gives good shelter from W winds. Kilbaha Bay, 3M inside Loop Head, is sheltered in winds from W to NE but holding is poor and it is exposed to swell. The best anchorage in the estuary is at Foynes on the S bank opposite R Fergus. Above this point the river narrows and becomes shallower although there is a minimum of 2m at LWS. Yachts may proceed up to Limerick Dock but this has all the drawbacks of a commercial port — frequent shifting of berth, dirt and someone constantly on watch.

NAVIGATION

Waypoint 52°33′·50N 09°43′·00W, 236°/056° from/to Tail of Beal Bar buoy, 1·7M. For notes on entrance and tidal streams see 10·12·5. The ebb can reach 4 kn. Yachtsmen intending to visit the Shannon are advised to obtain the Irish Coast Pilot and also the Irish Cruising Club's *Sailing Directions for the South and West Coasts of Ireland*. It is the longest navigable river in the UK or Ireland and is controlled by the Limerick Harbour Commissioners. Pilots can be taken from Cappagh Pier to Limerick and from Limerick Dock to Killaloe. The channel is marked by buoys, beacons and perches. There are six large locks on the upper reaches (above Portumna) and all

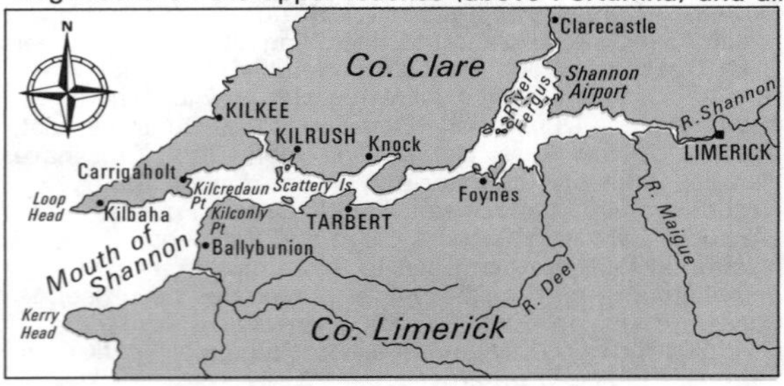
N
Clarecastle
Co. Clare
Shannon Airport
R. Fergus
R. Shannon
LIMERICK
KILKEE
KILRUSH
Knock
Carrigaholt
Kilcredaun Pt
Scattery Is
Foynes
Loop Head
Kilbaha
Kilconly Pt
TARBERT
Mouth of Shannon
Ballybunion
R. Maigue
R. Deel
Kerry Head
Co. Limerick

are manned (toll). Above Lough Ree the ideal draught is less than a metre (1½m with careful navigation). The river is slow with many lakes; Lough Derg is 24M long and Lough Ree is 16M long. Between them at Shannon Harbour, a canal runs across to Dublin, the Grand Canal with 46 locks; max length 18·6m, beam 3·9m, height 2·74m, draught 1m. The Shannon bridges have a clearance of 4·6m except the swing bridge at Portumna which has 2·4m when closed. Lifting spans at Termonbarry and Rooskey are manned during daylight hours and are controlled by traffic lights. There is little commercial traffic.

LIGHTS AND MARKS

Principal lights are shown in 10·12·4

FACILITIES

Fuel, water and stores are obtainable at many villages.

KILBAHA V, FW, D (cans) at Hehir's Pub, P, ✉; Bus to Limerick (Sat).

CARRIGAHOLT V, P, ✉, R (summer).

KILRUSH and CAPPA — see 10·12·8. Pilot Stn ☎ 51027.

TARBERT V, P, ✉; Bus to Limerick.

FOYNES V, D, FW, ✉, R; Bus to Limerick. **Foynes YC** ☎ Foynes 90, Slip, Bar.

Ballina (Logh Derg) Marina with all facilities.

LIMERICK **J & G Boyd** ☎ 44366, Kos; **Shannon Yacht Fitters** ☎ Portumna 41105, Sh, ME, El; **Peter Lawless** ☎ Limerick 51567, CH, arrangement for pilot, ME, El, Sh; **Limerick Harbour Commission** ☎ (661) 315377.

KENMARE RIVER 10-12-10

Kerry

CHARTS
Admiralty 2495; Imray C56; Irish OS 21/24

TIDES
+0515 Dover; ML Dunkerron 2·2; West Cove 2·0
Duration Dunkerron 0620; West Cove 0610
Zone 0 (GMT).

Standard Port COBH (RINGASKIDDY) (⟶)

Times				Height (metres)			
HW		LW		MHWS	MHWN	MLWN	MLWS
0500	1100	0500	1100	4·2	3·3	1·4	0·5
1700	2300	1700	2300				
Differences WEST COVE							
−0113	−0033	−0049	−0129	−0·6	−0·5	−0·1	0·0
DUNKERRON HARBOUR							
−0117	−0027	−0050	−0140	−0·2	−0·3	+0·1	0·0
BALLYCROVANE HARBOUR (Coulagh Bay)							
−0116	−0036	−0053	−0133	−0·6	−0·5	−0·1	0·0

SHELTER
SNEEM HARBOUR entered between Sherky Is and Rossdohan Is; anchor NE of Gainish Is. Considerable swell passes each side of Sherky Is making the anchorage uncomfortable at times.
KENMARE Good shelter. Berth on quay on N side of river, just below town.
ORMOND HARBOUR gives good shelter but beware rock 2½ca ENE of Hog Is.
KILMAKILLOGE HARBOUR is a safe anchorage for small boats against all winds. Entering keep W of Spanish Is. Space is restricted by a number of shoals. Anchor 1ca SW of Carrigwee; S of Eseadawer Pt or in Collorus Hr.
ARDGROOM HARBOUR affords excellent shelter but has a hazardous entrance over a rocky bar. Power is needed. Anchor in Reenvade ½ca E of pier.
CLEANDERRY HARBOUR Entrance NE of Illaunbweeheen (Yellow Is) is only 7m wide. SW of the Is, entrance is rocky. Anchor ENE of inner harbour.
BALLYCROVANE HARBOUR in Coulagh Bay is a good anchorage but exposed to W winds. N and E shores are foul. Anchor ½ca NE of Bird Is.
GARNISH BAY is only good in settled weather and wind in W. Anchor either W of the Carrigduff concrete beacon or 1ca S of Bn.
There are many other anchorages including West Cove, Coongar Hr, Blackwater R, Dunkerron Hr, Kenmare, Lehid Hr, Darrynane Hr.

NAVIGATION
Waypoint 51°41′·40N 10°10′·00W 103°/283° from/to Reenmore Point 3·65M. Three deepwater channels from N; between Scarriff Is and Deenish Is which is clear; between Deenish Is and Moylaun Is which has shallow rocky patches; between Moylaun Is and Two Headed Is which is clear and 4½ca wide. From SW approach from NW of The Bull thence NW of Dursey Is. Above Maiden Rock keep NW of Lackeen Rks. Beware salmon nets between June and September.

LIGHTS AND MARKS
Bull Rk Lt – Fl 15s 83m 31M.
Ballycrovane Hr Lt – Fl R 3s.
Kilmakilloge Hr – Ldg Lts 041°, both Iso Y 8s.
Kenmare (on Fadda Is) – 2 white piles mark in line astern max depth to the quay.
Old Watch Tower on Dursey Is (conspic) 250m.
Eagle Hill (Cod's Head) – 216m.
Conspic hotel NE side of Sneem Hr Ent.
Ardgroom Hr – two W beacons (front on Black Rk, rear ashore) leads 099° through bar.

RADIO TELEPHONE
None.

TELEPHONE (064)
MRCC (061) 61219; Coast Life-Saving Service (Waterville) 4320; ⌗ Bantry 50061; Ⓗ 41088.

FACILITIES
SNEEM L (Hotel Parknasilla, Oysterbed House pier or near town). **Town** (2M from Hr), Bar, ✉, Slip, V, Kos.
KENMARE Kenmare Bay Hotel ☎ 41300, V, R, Bar. **Town** ✉, Ⓗ, Ⓑ, ⥂ (Killarney), ✈ (Cork or Killarney).
KILMAKILLOGE HARBOUR **Bunaw Pier**, L, AB, V, Bar, D, Kos, ✉.
ARDGROOM HARBOUR Supplies available at Ardgroom (2M SSE of quay), D, Kos.

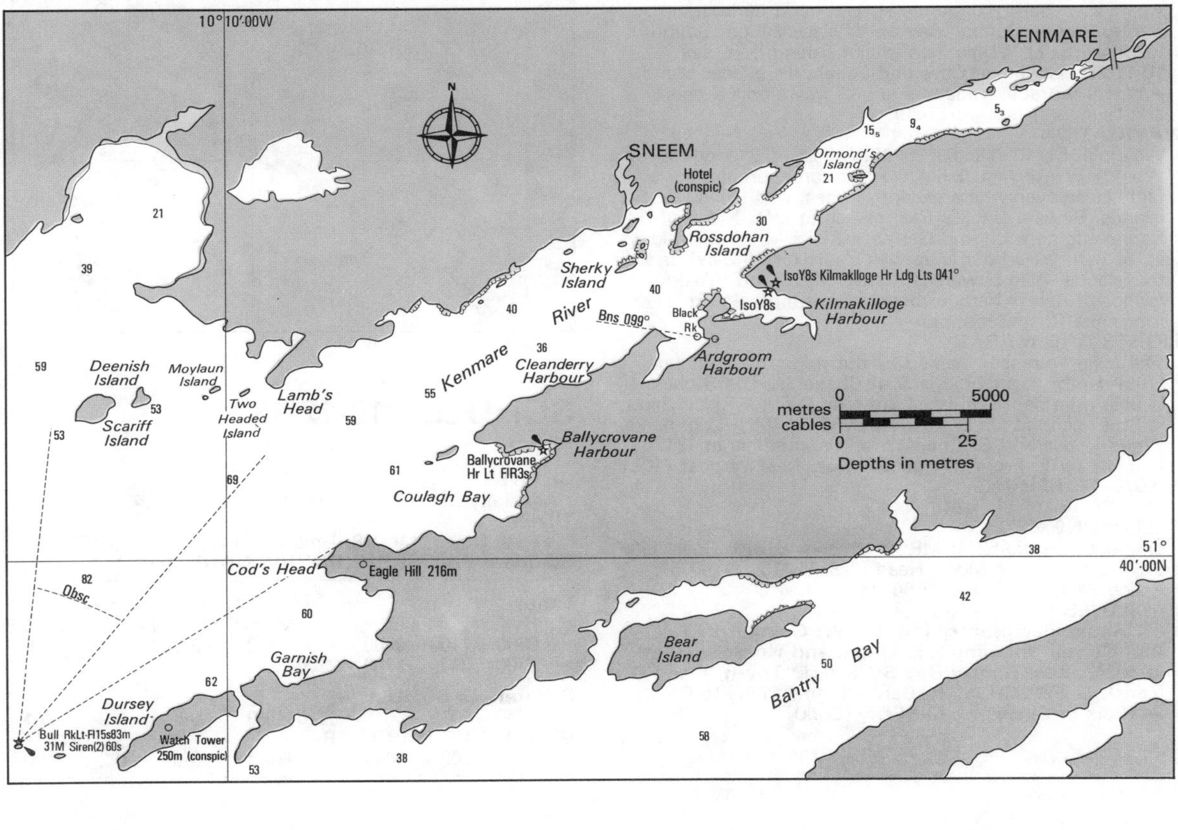
10°10′·00W
KENMARE
N
SNEEM
Hotel (conspic)
Ormond's Island
Rossdohan Island
Sherky Island
IsoY8s Kilmakilloge Hr Ldg Lts 041°
IsoY8s
Kilmakilloge Harbour
Black Rk
Bns 099°
Kenmare River
Cleanderry Harbour
Ardgroom Harbour
Deenish Island
Moylaun Island
Two Headed Island
Lamb's Head
Scariff Island
Ballycrovane Harbour
Ballycrovane Hr Lt FlR3s
Coulagh Bay
metres 0 5000
cables 0 25
Depths in metres
51° 40′·00N
Cod's Head
Eagle Hill 216m
Obsc
Garnish Bay
Bear Island
Bantry Bay
Dursey Island
Bull RkLt-Fl15s83m 31M Siren(2)60s
Watch Tower 250m (conspic)

BANTRY 10-12-11
Cork

CHARTS
Admiralty 1838, 1840, 2552; Imray C56; Irish OS 24

TIDES
+0600 Dover; ML 1·8; Duration 0610; Zone 0 (GMT).

Standard Port COBH (RINGASKIDDY) (⟶)

Times				Height (metres)			
HW		LW		MHWS	MHWN	MLWN	MLWS
0500	1100	0500	1100	4·2	3·3	1·4	0·5
1700	2300	1700	2300				
Differences BANTRY							
−0045	−0025	−0040	−0105	−0·7	−0·7	−0·1	0·0
FENIT PIER (Tralee Bay)							
−0057	−0017	−0029	−0109	+0·5	+0·2	+0·3	+0·1
DINGLE HARBOUR							
−0111	−0041	−0049	−0119	−0·3	−0·4	0·0	0·0

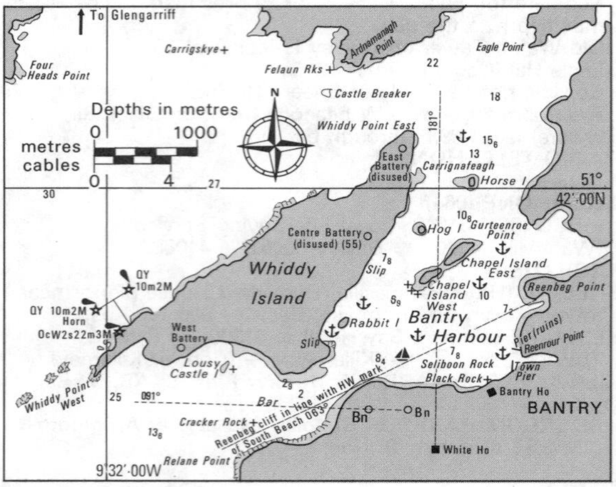

To Glengarriff
Carrigskye
Four Heads Point
Felaun Rks
Ardnamanagh Point
Eagle Point
Castle Breaker
Depths in metres
metres
cables
0
1000
0
4
Whiddy Point East
East Battery (disused)
Carrignafeagh
Horse I
51° 42'·00N
Centre Battery (disused) (55)
Hog I
Gurteenroe Point
Whiddy Island
Chapel Island East
Chapel Island West
Reenbeg Point
QY 10m2M
QY 10m2M
Horn
OcW2s22m3M
West Battery
Rabbit I
Bantry Harbour
Pier (ruins)
Reenrour Point
Lousy Castle
Seliboon Rock
Black Rock
Town Pier
Whiddy Point West
Bar
Bantry Ho
BANTRY
Cracker Rock
Reenbeg cliff in line with HW mark of South Beach 063°
Bn
White Ho
Relane Point
9°32'·00W

SHELTER
Apart from Bantry there are several good harbours in Bantry Bay — Dunboy Bay on W side of Piper Sound (exposed to E), Castletown (major fishing port, see 10·12·28), Lawrence Cove and Lonehort on Bear Island, Adrigole (attractive anchorage half way along N shore), and Glengariff (see 10·12·28).

NAVIGATION
Waypoint 51°40'·00N 09°36'·00W, 253°/073° from/to Whiddy Point West, 2·5M. Yachts can approach the shore fairly close everywhere except off Bear and Whiddy Islands. Beware Ducalia Rks, awash at LW, 1 M E of Roancarrigmore Lt, and Gerranes Rks 1 M W of Whiddy Is. In Bantry Harbour keep well clear (1½ to 2 ca) of all the islands. Also beware of Carrignafeagh off Whiddy Island. In Bantry harbour beware unlit mussel rafts all round the Chapel Islands.

LIGHTS AND MARKS
The main entrance, marked by buoys, is the N channel (10m depth) to anchorage S of Chapel Is. The S channel is unlit (min depth on bar 1·7m over Cracker Rk). Whiddy Is Lt is sectored Oc W 2s 22m 3M 073°-106°. Ldg marks, White House and S. Chapel Island ruin in line at 181°. Ldg line 091°, Front RW post FW Lt, Rear W post FR Lt.

RADIO TELEPHONE
VHF Ch 16; 14 11 (H24).

TELEPHONE (027)
Lifeboat Valentia 6214; MRCC Limerick 61219; Coast Life-Saving Service – Mizen Head (028) 35115; ⌗ 50061; Police 50045; Dr 50404; Ⓗ 50133.

FACILITIES
EC Wednesday; **Bantry Pier** L, FW; **Glengarriff** FW, V, Bar; **Carroll Shipping** ME; **Donal and Noreen Casey** ☎ 50342, Kos; **Bantry Bay SC** Slip, L; **Town**, P and D (cans), L, FW, CH, V, R, Bar. ✉; Ⓑ; ⇄ (bus to Cork); ✈ (Cork or Shannon); Car Ferry (Cork).

CROOKHAVEN 10-12-12
Cork

CHARTS
Admiralty 2184; Imray C56; Irish OS 24

TIDES
+0550 Dover; ML 1·8; Duration 0610; Zone 0 (GMT).

Standard Port COBH (RINGASKIDDY) (⟶)

Times				Height (metres)			
HW		LW		MHWS	MHWN	MLWN	MLWS
0500	1100	0500	1100	4·2	3·3	1·4	0·5
1700	2300	1700	2300				
Differences CROOKHAVEN							
−0057	−0033	−0048	−0112	−0·8	−0·6	−0·4	−0·1

SHELTER
Excellent shelter. Anchorages opposite village in middle of bay in 3m; N of W point of Rock Is; to the E of Granny Is. The last two are a long way from the village.

NAVIGATION
Waypoint 51°28'·50N 09°40'·50W, 094°/274° from/to Lt Ho on Sheemon Pt, 1M. Entrance between Sheemon Pt and Black Horse Rocks (3·5 ca ESE) on which is an N cardinal beacon. From S, keep 1 ca E of Alderman Rocks and 0·5 ca off Black Horse Rks Bn. Passage between Streek Hd and Alderman Rks is not advised. Inside the bay the shores are steep to.

LIGHTS AND MARKS
Lt Ho on Rock Is (conspic W tower) L Fl WR 8s 20m 13/11M. Outside Hr, W over Long Is Bay – 281°, R281°-340°; Inside Hr R281°-348°, W348°-N shore.

RADIO TELEPHONE
None.

TELEPHONE (028)
MRCC (061) 6 12 19; Coast Life Saving Service Goleen 3 51 17; ⌗ Bantry 5 00 61; Dr 3 51 48.

FACILITIES
Marconi Guest House ☎ 35168, Sh, ME; **Village** V, Kos, Ⓑ (Bantry); ✉; ⇄(Cork); ✈ (Cork).

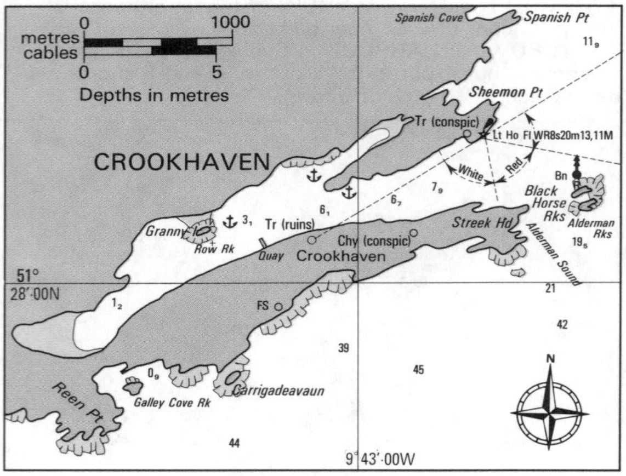

metres
cables
0
1000
0
5
Depths in metres
Spanish Cove
Spanish Pt
Sheemon Pt
Tr (conspic)
Lt Ho Fl WR8s20m13,11M
White
Red
CROOKHAVEN
Bn
Black Horse Rks
Alderman Rks
Streek Hd
Alderman Sound
Granny I
Row Rk
Tr (ruins)
Quay
Chy (conspic)
Crookhaven
51° 28'·00N
FS
Reen Pt
Galley Cove Rk
Carrigadeavaun
9°43'·00W

SCHULL 10-12-13
Cork

CHARTS
Admiralty 2129, 2184; Imray C56; Irish OS 24

TIDES
+0610 Dover; ML 1·8; Duration 0610; Zone 0 (GMT).

Standard Port COBH (RINGASKIDDY) (⟶)

Times				Height (metres)			
HW		LW		MHWS	MHWN	MLWN	MLWS
0500	1100	0500	1100	4·2	3·3	1·4	0·5
1700	2300	1700	2300				
Differences SCHULL							
−0040	−0015	−0015	−0110	−0·9	−0·6	−0·2	−0·1
DUNMANUS HARBOUR							
−0107	−0031	−0044	−0120	−0·7	−0·6	−0·2	0·0

SCHULL *Continued*

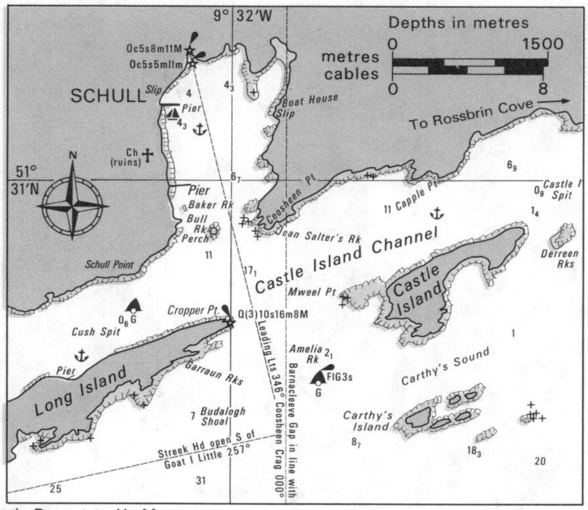
9° 32′W
Depths in metres
metres 0 1500
cables 0 8
Oc5s8m11M
Oc5s5m11m
SCHULL
Slip
Pier
Boat House Slip
To Rossbrin Cove
Ch (ruins)
51° 31′N
Pier
Baker Rk
Bull Rk Perch
Coosheen Pt
Capple Pt
Castle I Spit
Joan Salter's Rk
Castle Island Channel
Derreen Rks
Schull Point
Castle Island
Mweel Pt
Cropper Pt
Q(3)10s16m8M
Cush Spit
Amelia Rk
FlG3s
Carthy's Sound
Long Island
Garraun Rks
Budalogh Shoal
Carthy's Island
Leading Lts 346° Coosheen Crag 000°
Barnacleeve Gap in line with
Streek Hd open S of Goat I Little 257°

▲ Report to Hr Mr

SHELTER

Good shelter except in strong S winds — in these winds, best shelter is behind Long Island. Schull Harbour is available at all times. Anchor SE of pier, clear of fairway.

NAVIGATION

Waypoint 51°29′·60N 09°31′·60W, 166°/346° from/to front Ldg Lt 346°, 2·1M. Entering between Schull Pt on the W and Coosheen Pt on E, beware Bull Rock in middle of channel, marked by a R iron perch.

LIGHTS AND MARKS

Leading lights NE of village in line at 346°, both Oc 5s. The pier is normally lit by street lights all night.

RADIO TELEPHONE

None.

TELEPHONE (028)

Hr Mr 2 81 36; MRCC Limerick 6 12 19; Coast Life Saving Service 3 51 17; ⁂ Bantry 5 00 61; Police 2 81 11; Dr 2 83 11; Ⓗ Bantry 5 01 33.

FACILITIES

EC Tuesday; **Schull Pier** Slip, M, D, L, FW, AC, AB; **Sailing Club** ☎ 2 82 86; **J. O'Reilly** ☎ 2 81 36, Kos; **Rossbrin BY** ☎ 3 73 52, M, Sh, Slip; **Simon Nelson** ☎ 2 85 54, CH.
Village P, ME, El, Sh, CH, V, R, Bar. ✉; Ⓑ; ⇌ (bus to Cork); ✈ (Cork); Car Ferry (Cork)

BALTIMORE 10-12-14

Cork

CHARTS

Admiralty 3725, 2129; Imray C56; Irish OS 24

TIDES

−0605 Dover; ML 2·1; Duration 0610; Zone 0 (GMT)

Standard Port COBH (RINGASKIDDY) (⟶)

Times				Height (metres)			
HW		LW		MHWS	MHWN	MLWN	MLWS
0500	1100	0500	1100	4·2	3·3	1·4	0·5
1700	2300	1700	2300				
Differences BALTIMORE							
−0025	−0005	−0010	−0050	−0·5	−0·3	+0·1	+0·1
CLONAKILTY BAY							
−0033	−0011	−0019	−0041	−0·3	−0·2	No data	

SHELTER

Excellent shelter and harbour is always available. Anchor N or W of New Pier, or in Church Strand Bay past lifeboat slip in 2-3m. In strong W winds off ruined abbey on Sherkin I. (off chartlet), clear of ferry.

NAVIGATION

Waypoint 51°27′·80N 09°23′·42W, 180°/000° from/to Loo Rock buoy, 0·62M. On entering beware Loo Rock to starboard, marked by a buoy with Lt and Radar reflector. Beware Lousy Rocks and Wallis Rocks in the middle of the harbour. Harbour can be entered from the N but this is tricky and not recommended.

LIGHTS AND MARKS

Entrance easily identified by conspic W Tr called Lot's Wife on Beacon Pt and W Lt Ho on Barrack Pt. Barrack Pt Lt is unreliable.

RADIO TELEPHONE

Call: *Baltimore Harbour Radio* VHF Ch 16 09.

TELEPHONE (028)

Hr Mr 20184; MRCC Limerick 61219; Coast Life Saving Service 20125; ⁂ Bantry 50061; Police 41358; Dr 21488; Ⓗ 21677.

FACILITIES

EC None; **New Pier** Slip, AB; **K. Cotter** ☎ 20106, D, CH, V, Gas, Gaz, Kos, FW; **M. Casey** Bar, P; **H. Skinner** ☎ 20114, Slip, Sh; **Old Pier** FW; **R. Bushe** ☎ 20125, ACA; **T. O'Driscoll** ☎ 20344, ME. **Glenans Irish Sailing Club** ☎ 61.14.82. **Village** P, Bar. ✉; ⇌ (bus to Cork); ✈ (Cork).

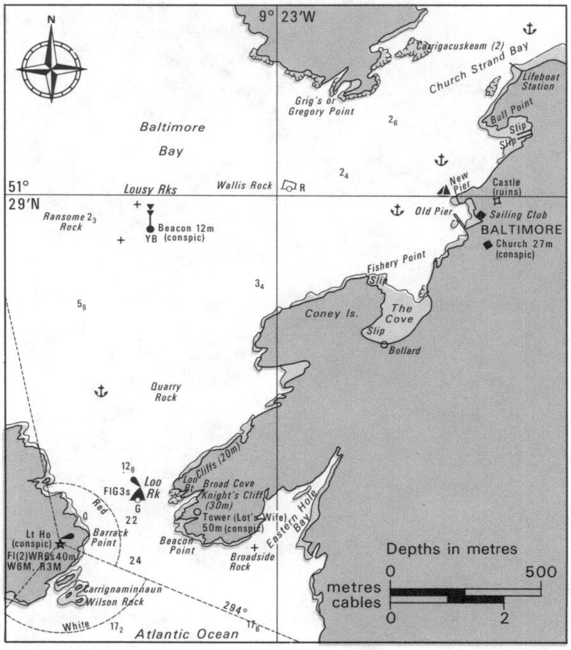
9° 23′W
Carrigacuskeam (2)
Church Strand Bay
Lifeboat Station
Grig's or Gregory Point
Bull Point
Slip
Baltimore Bay
51° 29′N
Lousy Rks
Wallis Rock
New Pier
Castle (ruins)
Ransome Rock
Beacon 12m YB (conspic)
Old Pier
Sailing Club
BALTIMORE
Church 27m (conspic)
Fishery Point
Coney Is.
The Cove
Bollard
Quarry Rock
Cliffs (20m)
Loo Rk
FlG3s
Broad Cove
Knight's Cliff (30m)
Tower (Lot's Wife) 50m (conspic)
Barrack Point
Beacon Point
Eastern Hole Bay
Broadside Rock
Lt Ho (conspic)
Fl(2)WR6s40m W6M, R3M
Red
Carrignaminnaun
Wilson Rock
White
Atlantic Ocean
294°
Depths in metres
metres 0 500
cables 0 2

CASTLE HAVEN 10-12-15

Cork

CHARTS

Admiralty 2129, 2092; Imray C56; Irish OS 24

TIDES

+0605 Dover; ML 2·2; Duration 0605; Zone 0 (GMT)

Standard Port COBH (RINGASKIDDY) (⟶)

Times				Height (metres)			
HW		LW		MHWS	MHWN	MLWN	MLWS
0500	1100	0500	1100	4·2	3·3	1·4	0·5
1700	2300	1700	2300				
Differences CASTLETOWNSHEND							
−0020	−0030	−0020	−0050	−0·4	−0·3	0·0	+0·2

CASTLE HAVEN *Continued*

SHELTER

Excellent anchorage protected from all weathers and available at all tides, day and night, although the outer part of harbour is subject to swell in S winds. Anchor in midstream SE of the slip at Castletownshend, N of Cat Island, or further upstream as shown on chartlet.

NAVIGATION

Waypoint 51°29′·00N 09°10′·00W, 171°/351° from/to Reen Point Lt, 2M. Enter between Horse I. and Skiddy I. both of which have foul ground all round. Black Rk lies off the SE side of Horse I. and is steep-to along its S side. On the other side of Horse I. is Flea Sound, a narrow boat passage, obstructed by rocks. Colonel Rk (0·5m) lies close to the E shore, 2ca N of Reen Pt. A submarine cable runs E/W across the harbour from the slip close N of Reen Pier to the slip at Castletownshend.

LIGHTS AND MARKS

Reen Point Lt, Fl WRG 10s 9m 5/3M; W Tr; vis G shore-338°, W338°-001°, R001°-shore. A ruined Tr stands on E end of Horse I.

RADIO TELEPHONE

None.

TELEPHONE (028)

MRCC (061) 61219; Coast Life Saving Service 36247; ⌗ Bantry 50061; Dr 21488; Ⓗ 21677.

FACILITIES

Reen Pier L, FW; **SC** ☎ 36100; **Castletownshend Village** Slip, Bar, R, V, FW, ✉, Ⓑ (Skibbereen), ⇄ (Cork), ✈ (Cork).

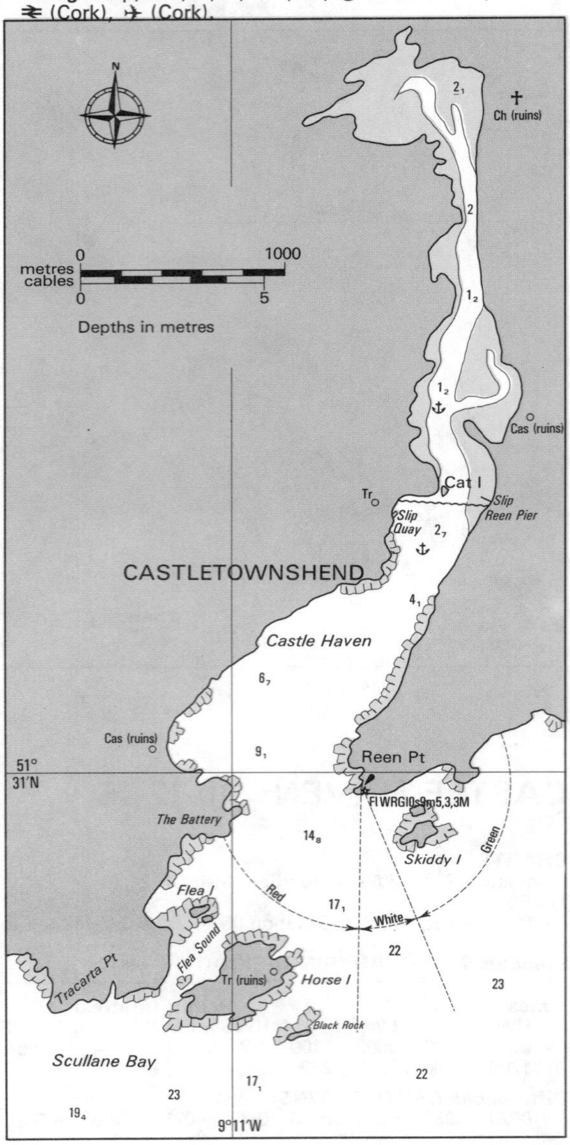

Ch (ruins)
metres
cables
1000
Depths in metres
Cas (ruins)
Cat I
Tr
Slip
Quay
Slip
Reen Pier
CASTLETOWNSHEND
Castle Haven
Cas (ruins)
51°
31′N
Reen Pt
Fl WRG10s9m5,3,3M
The Battery
Skiddy I
Green
Red
White
Flea I
Flea Sound
Tr (ruins)
Horse I
Tracarta Pt
Black Rock
Scullane Bay
9°11′W

KINSALE 10-12-16

Cork

CHARTS

Admiralty 2053, 1765; Imray C56; Irish OS 25

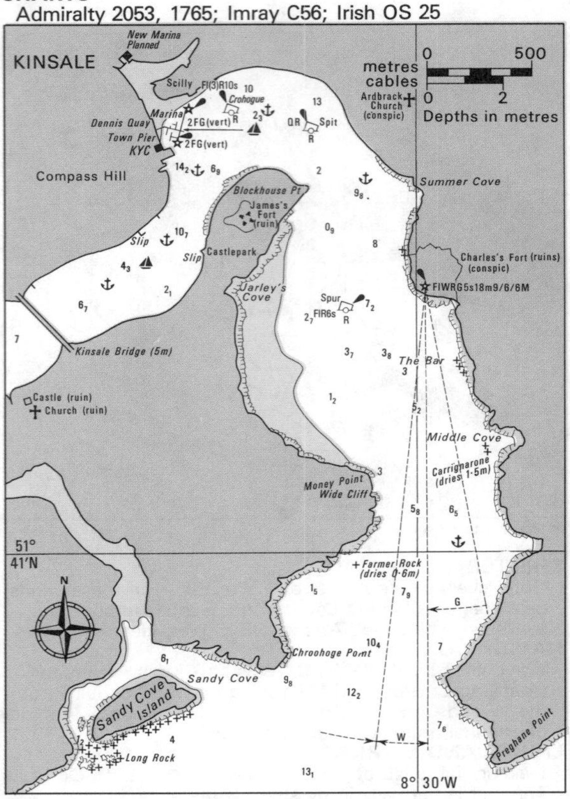

New Marina Planned
KINSALE
Scilly
Fl(3)R10s
Crohogue
Marina
Dennis Quay
Town Pier
KYC
2FG(vert)
QR
Spit
Ardbrack Church (conspic)
metres
cables
500
Depths in metres
Compass Hill
Summer Cove
Blockhouse Pt
James's Fort (ruin)
Castlepark
Slip
Jarley's Cove
Charles's Fort (ruins) (conspic)
FlWRG5s18m9/6/6M
Spur
FlR6s
Kinsale Bridge (5m)
The Bar
Castle (ruin)
Church (ruin)
Middle Cove
Carrignarone (dries 1·5m)
Money Point
Wide Cliff
51°
41′N
Farmer Rock (dries 0·6m)
Chroohoge Point
Sandy Cove
Sandy Cove Island
Long Rock
Preghane Point
8° 30′W

TIDES

−0600 Dover; ML 2·2; Duration 0600; Zone 0 (GMT)

Standard Port COBH (RINGASKIDDY) (⟶)

Times				Height (metres)			
HW		LW		MHWS	MHWN	MLWN	MLWS
0500	1100	0500	1100	4·2	3·3	1·4	0·5
1700	2300	1700	2300				
Differences KINSALE							
−0019	−0005	−0009	−0023	−0·1	−0·1	+0·1	0·0

SHELTER

Excellent sheltered harbour except in very strong SE winds. Accessible in all weathers, at all tides, day and night. Anchorage SW of James Fort between moorings and bridge. Moorings at Kinsale YC.

NAVIGATION

Waypoint 51°40′·00N 08°30′·00W, 181°/001° from/to Charles's Fort Lt, 1·7M. Bulman Rock off Hangman Pt marked by S cardinal buoy. Also beware Farmer Rock ¾ ca off shore on W bank and Carrignarone on E bank opposite Money Pt.

LIGHTS AND MARKS

Charles's Fort Fl WRG 5s; 18m 9/6M vis G348°-358°, W358°-004°, R004°-168°. Port-hand Lt buoys mark chan.

RADIO TELEPHONE

VHF Ch 16; 06 14. Kinsale YC Ch **16** M.

TELEPHONE (021)

Hr Mr 772503; MRCC Limerick 61219; Coast Life Saving Service 772133; ⌗ 772271; Police 772302; Dr 772253, 772133; Ⓗ Cork 546400.

FACILITIES

EC Thursday; **Kinsale Marina** ☎ 772196, FW, AC, D, P, AB; **Pier** ☎ 772503, Slip, M, P (cans), D, L, FW, ME, El, Sh, AB, V, R, Bar; **Kinsale YC** ☎ 772196, Slip, M, P, D, L, FW, C, R, Bar; **Kinsale Marine Services** ☎ 772611, D, M, CH, Gas, Gaz; **Kilmacsimon BY** ☎ 775134, Slip, ME, Sh, C, D, El; **McWilliam Sails** ☎ 831505, SM; (Several excellent restaurants — the gourmet centre of Ireland).

Town P, D, V, R, Bar. ✉; Ⓑ; ⇄ (bus to Cork); ✈ (Cork).

CORK (COBH) 10-12-17

Cork

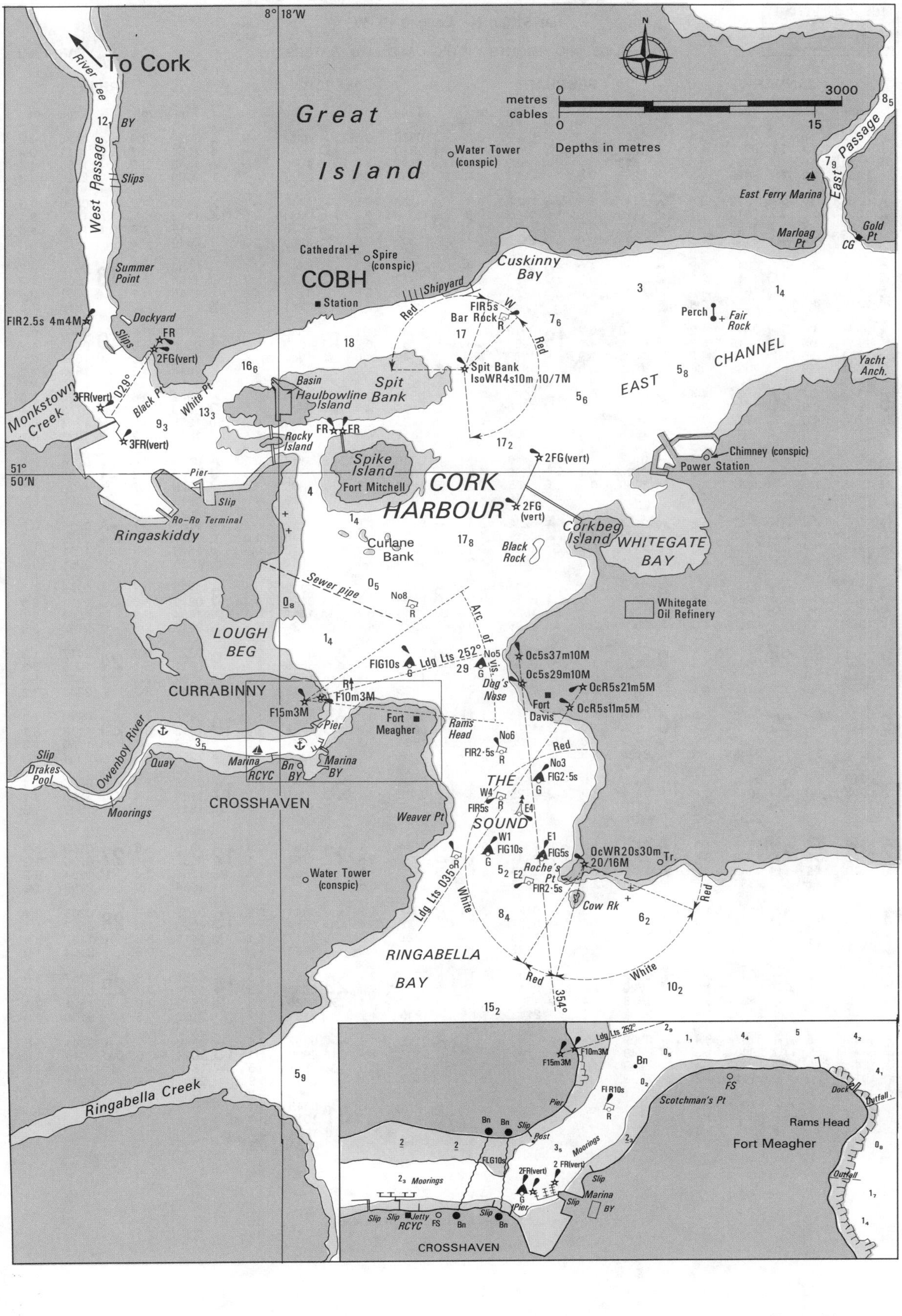
8° 18'W
To Cork
River Lee
West Passage
BY
Slips
Summer Point
Dockyard
Slips
FlR2.5s 4m4M
FR
2FG(vert)
3FR(vert)
029°
3FR(vert)
Monkstown Creek
Black Pt
White Pt
Great Island
Water Tower (conspic)
metres
cables
0
3000
15
Depths in metres
East Passage
East Ferry Marina
Marloag Pt
Gold Pt
CG
Cathedral
Spire (conspic)
COBH
Station
Shipyard
Cuskinny Bay
Red
W
Red
FlR5s
Bar Rock
R
Perch
Fair Rock
Yacht Anch.
Basin
Haulbowline Island
Spit Bank
Spit Bank
IsoWR4s10m 10/7M
EAST CHANNEL
Rocky Island
FR
FR
Spike Island
Fort Mitchell
2FG(vert)
Chimney (conspic)
Power Station
51° 50'N
Pier
Slip
Ro-Ro Terminal
Ringaskiddy
CORK HARBOUR
2FG (vert)
Corkbeg Island
WHITEGATE BAY
Curlane Bank
Black Rock
Sewer pipe
No8
R
Whitegate Oil Refinery
LOUGH BEG
Arc of vis
FlG10s
G
Ldg Lts 252°
No5
G
Oc5s37m10M
Oc5s29m10M
Dog's Nose
OcR5s21m5M
OcR5s11m5M
Fort Davis
CURRABINNY
R
F10m3M
F15m3M
Pier
Fort Meagher
Rams Head
No6
FlR2·5s
R
Red
No3
FlG2·5s
G
Owenboy River
Slip
Drakes Pool
Quay
Marina
RCYC
Bn
BY
Marina
BY
CROSSHAVEN
Moorings
THE SOUND
W4
FlR5s
R
E4
Weaver Pt
W1
FlG10s
G
E1
FlG5s
OcWR20s30m 20/16M
Tr.
Roche's Pt
E2
FlR2·5s
Water Tower (conspic)
Ldg Lts 035°
White
Cow Rk
Red
RINGABELLA BAY
Red
354°
White
Ringabella Creek
Ldg Lts 252°
F15m3M
F10m3M
Bn
Fl R10s
R
FS
Scotchman's Pt
Dock
Outfall
Rams Head
Fort Meagher
Pier
Bn
Bn
Slip
Post
Moorings
FLG10s
2FR(vert)
2 FR(vert)
G
Moorings
Slip
Marina
Slip
BY
Outfall
Slip
Slip
Jetty
RCYC
FS
Bn
Slip
Pier
Bn
CROSSHAVEN

TIME ZONE UT(GMT)

For Summer Time add ONE hour in non-shaded areas

IRELAND, SOUTH COAST – RINGASKIDDY

Lat 51°50′ N Long 8°19′ W

TIMES AND HEIGHTS OF HIGH AND LOW WATERS

YEAR **1992**

JANUARY

Day	Time	m	Day	Time	m
1 W	0227 0911 1458 2139	3·6 1·1 3·6 1·1	16 Th	0117 0757 1354 2029	3·5 1·3 3·6 1·2
2 Th	0325 1007 1552 2230	3·7 1·1 3·7 1·0	17 F	0232 0910 1505 2141	3·7 1·1 3·7 1·0
3 F	0417 1055 1638 2313	3·9 1·0 3·8 1·0	18 Sa	0341 1017 1610 2244	3·9 0·9 4·0 0·8
4 Sa ●	0502 1136 1720 2351	4·0 1·0 3·9 0·9	19 Su ○	0441 1115 1706 2339	4·2 0·7 4·2 0·6
5 Su	0543 1211 1758	4·1 0·9 4·0	20 M	0534 1208 1757	4·4 0·5 4·3
6 M	0025 0619 1243 1834	0·8 4·1 0·9 4·0	21 Tu	0029 0622 1257 1843	0·4 4·5 0·4 4·4
7 Tu	0057 0653 1314 1906	0·8 4·1 0·9 4·0	22 W	0117 0709 1344 1928	0·3 4·5 0·3 4·4
8 W	0130 0726 1345 1937	0·8 4·0 0·9 3·9	23 Th	0204 0754 1430 2013	0·3 4·5 0·4 4·3
9 Th	0201 0757 1418 2008	0·8 4·0 0·9 3·9	24 F	0249 0839 1517 2057	0·4 4·3 0·5 4·1
10 F	0234 0829 1451 2042	0·9 3·9 1·0 3·8	25 Sa	0335 0924 1603 2145	0·5 4·1 0·7 3·9
11 Sa	0310 0905 1528 2121	1·0 3·8 1·0 3·7	26 Su ☾	0424 1013 1654 2237	0·8 3·8 1·0 3·7
12 Su	0349 0948 1610 2206	1·0 3·8 1·1 3·6	27 M	0518 1108 1749 2336	1·0 3·6 1·2 3·5
13 M ☽	0435 1035 1701 2301	1·2 3·6 1·2 3·5	28 Tu	0617 1210 1852	1·2 3·4 1·3
14 Tu	0533 1134 1803	1·3 3·6 1·3	29 W	0043 0727 1320 2002	3·4 1·3 3·3 1·3
15 W	0005 0641 1242 1913	3·5 1·3 3·5 1·3	30 Th	0157 0840 1430 2111	3·4 1·3 3·4 1·2
			31 F	0304 0945 1532 2210	3·5 1·2 3·5 1·1

FEBRUARY

Day	Time	m	Day	Time	m
1 Sa	0400 1037 1623 2257	3·7 1·1 3·7 0·9	16 Su	0327 1002 1559 2228	3·8 0·9 3·9 0·7
2 Su	0447 1119 1705 2334	3·9 0·9 3·8 0·8	17 M	0430 1102 1655 2323	4·1 0·6 4·2 0·4
3 M ●	0527 1154 1743	4·0 0·8 3·9	18 Tu ○	0520 1153 1743	4·4 0·3 4·4
4 Tu	0008 0601 1225 1815	0·7 4·1 0·8 4·0	19 W	0012 0607 1239 1827	0·2 4·5 0·2 4·5
5 W	0039 0632 1253 1843	0·7 4·1 0·7 4·0	20 Th	0057 0650 1323 1907	0·1 4·5 0·2 4·5
6 Th	0107 0700 1320 1912	0·7 4·1 0·7 4·0	21 F	0140 0730 1405 1948	0·1 4·5 0·3 4·3
7 F	0134 0728 1348 1938	0·7 4·1 0·7 4·0	22 Sa	0222 0811 1446 2027	0·3 4·3 0·5 4·2
8 Sa	0204 0757 1418 2008	0·7 4·0 0·8 3·9	23 Su	0304 0850 1528 2108	0·5 4·0 0·7 3·9
9 Su	0234 0829 1450 2043	0·8 4·0 0·9 3·9	24 M	0346 0934 1612 2156	0·8 3·8 1·0 3·7
10 M	0310 0905 1529 2124	0·9 3·9 1·0 3·8	25 Tu ☾	0434 1023 1702 2252	1·1 3·5 1·2 3·4
11 Tu ☽	0355 0952 1619 2216	1·0 3·7 1·1 3·6	26 W	0530 1125 1803	1·3 3·2 1·4
12 W	0454 1049 1725 2323	1·2 3·5 1·3 3·5	27 Th	0001 0641 1239 1917	3·2 1·4 3·1 1·4
13 Th	0605 1203 1841	1·3 3·4 1·3	28 F	0121 0801 1359 2037	3·2 1·4 3·2 1·3
14 F	0043 0726 1326 2002	3·4 1·3 3·4 1·2	29 Sa	0237 0915 1507 2142	3·3 1·3 3·4 1·1
15 Sa	0209 0849 1449 2122	3·5 1·1 3·6 1·0			

MARCH

Day	Time	m	Day	Time	m
1 Su	0336 1010 1559 2231	3·6 1·1 3·6 0·9	16 M	0312 0948 1542 2212	3·8 0·8 3·9 0·6
2 M	0423 1052 1641 2309	3·8 0·9 3·8 0·8	17 Tu	0412 1044 1635 2305	4·1 0·5 4·1 0·3
3 Tu	0501 1127 1716 2343	3·9 0·8 3·9 0·6	18 W ○	0502 1133 1722 2351	4·3 0·3 4·3 0·2
4 W ●	0534 1157 1749	4·1 0·7 4·0	19 Th	0546 1217 1804	4·5 0·2 4·4
5 Th	0011 0604 1225 1815	0·6 4·1 0·6 4·1	20 F	0034 0625 1256 1842	0·1 4·5 0·2 4·4
6 F	0039 0631 1252 1842	0·6 4·1 0·6 4·1	21 Sa	0114 0703 1335 1920	0·2 4·4 0·4 4·3
7 Sa	0107 0657 1319 1909	0·6 4·1 0·6 4·1	22 Su	0152 0740 1413 1957	0·4 4·2 0·6 4·1
8 Su	0135 0726 1348 1938	0·6 4·1 0·7 4·1	23 M	0232 0816 1451 2034	0·6 4·0 0·8 3·9
9 M	0208 0757 1422 2013	0·7 4·1 0·8 4·0	24 Tu	0311 0856 1532 2118	0·9 3·7 1·0 3·6
10 Tu	0246 0834 1504 2056	0·8 3·9 0·9 3·9	25 W	0356 0942 1621 2213	1·1 3·4 1·2 3·4
11 W	0334 0922 1557 2150	1·0 3·7 1·1 3·7	26 Th ☾	0451 1041 1720 2320	1·3 3·2 1·4 3·2
12 Th ☽	0434 1024 1705 2301	1·1 3·5 1·2 3·5	27 F	0557 1156 1832	1·4 3·1 1·4
13 F	0547 1142 1822	1·3 3·4 1·3	28 Sa	0041 0714 1317 1952	3·2 1·4 3·1 1·3
14 Sa	0025 0709 1310 1945	3·4 1·2 3·4 1·2	29 Su	0155 0830 1426 2101	3·3 1·3 3·3 1·1
15 Su	0155 0834 1434 2107	3·5 1·1 3·6 0·9	30 M	0257 0929 1521 2153	3·5 1·1 3·5 0·9
			31 Tu	0345 1014 1604 2234	3·7 0·9 3·7 0·8

APRIL

Day	Time	m	Day	Time	m
1 W	0424 1051 1642 2309	3·9 0·7 3·9 0·7	16 Th	0438 1111 1658 2329	4·2 0·4 4·3 0·3
2 Th	0459 1123 1715 2340	4·0 0·7 4·0 0·6	17 F ○	0520 1153 1739	4·3 0·3 4·3
3 F ●	0530 1154 1746	4·1 0·6 4·1	18 Sa	0010 0601 1231 1818	0·3 4·3 0·4 4·3
4 Sa	0011 0600 1224 1814	0·6 4·2 0·6 4·2	19 Su	0049 0638 1309 1855	0·4 4·2 0·5 4·2
5 Su	0042 0629 1255 1843	0·6 4·2 0·6 4·2	20 M	0126 0713 1344 1931	0·5 4·1 0·7 4·1
6 M	0114 0700 1328 1917	0·6 4·2 0·7 4·2	21 Tu	0204 0748 1420 2008	0·7 3·9 0·8 3·9
7 Tu	0151 0737 1408 1955	0·7 4·1 0·8 4·1	22 W	0242 0826 1501 2051	0·9 3·7 1·0 3·7
8 W	0233 0819 1454 2043	0·8 4·0 0·9 3·9	23 Th	0325 0911 1549 2142	1·1 3·5 1·1 3·5
9 Th	0327 0911 1552 2142	0·9 3·7 1·0 3·7	24 F ☾	0417 1006 1645 2244	1·3 3·3 1·3 3·3
10 F ☽	0428 1016 1658 2254	1·1 3·5 1·1 3·5	25 Sa	0518 1113 1750 2354	1·3 3·1 1·3 3·2
11 Sa	0539 1133 1812	1·2 3·4 1·1	26 Su	0625 1225 1902	1·4 3·1 1·3
12 Su	0015 0657 1256 1934	3·5 1·1 3·4 1·0	27 M	0103 0735 1334 2008	3·3 1·3 3·2 1·2
13 M	0138 0820 1416 2050	3·6 1·0 3·6 0·8	28 Tu	0205 0837 1432 2104	3·4 1·1 3·4 1·0
14 Tu	0251 0928 1519 2152	3·8 0·7 3·9 0·5	29 W	0257 0928 1521 2150	3·6 1·0 3·6 0·9
15 W	0349 1023 1612 2244	4·1 0·5 4·1 0·3	30 Th	0341 1010 1603 2231	3·8 0·8 3·8 0·7

Chart Datum: 0.13 metres above Ordnance Datum (Dublin)

TIME ZONE **UT(GMT)**

For Summer Time add ONE hour in non-shaded areas

IRELAND, SOUTH COAST – RINGASKIDDY

Lat 51°50′ N Long 8°19′ W

TIMES AND HEIGHTS OF HIGH AND LOW WATERS

YEAR **1992**

MAY

Day	Time	m	Day	Time	m
1 F	0421 1048 1641 2309	4·0 0·7 4·0 0·6	16 Sa ○	0458 1130 1718 2351	4·1 0·5 4·2 0·5
2 Sa ●	0458 1125 1716 2346	4·1 0·7 4·1 0·6	17 Su	0539 1210 1758	4·1 0·6 4·2
3 Su	0533 1201 1751	4·2 0·6 4·2	18 M	0029 0617 1246 1836	0·6 4·1 0·6 4·1
4 M	0022 0608 1238 1828	0·6 4·2 0·6 4·2	19 Tu	0106 0653 1323 1913	0·7 4·0 0·7 4·0
5 Tu	0102 0646 1319 1907	0·6 4·2 0·6 4·2	20 W	0142 0730 1359 1951	0·8 3·8 0·8 3·9
6 W	0145 0727 1404 1951	0·6 4·1 0·7 4·1	21 Th	0220 0806 1439 2032	0·9 3·7 0·9 3·7
7 Th	0232 0815 1454 2042	0·7 4·0 0·8 4·0	22 F	0301 0849 1522 2117	1·0 3·5 1·0 3·6
8 F	0327 0910 1550 2142	0·8 3·8 0·9 3·8	23 Sa	0346 0936 1612 2209	1·1 3·4 1·1 3·4
9 Sa ☽	0426 1013 1654 2249	0·9 3·6 0·9 3·6	24 Su ☾	0438 1031 1706 2306	1·2 3·3 1·2 3·3
10 Su	0533 1125 1804	1·0 3·5 1·0	25 M	0536 1133 1808	1·2 3·2 1·2
11 M	0003 0646 1239 1919	3·6 1·0 3·5 0·9	26 Tu	0007 0636 1236 1910	3·3 1·2 3·3 1·2
12 Tu	0117 0801 1351 2029	3·6 0·9 3·6 0·7	27 W	0107 0738 1337 2011	3·4 1·2 3·4 1·1
13 W	0225 0905 1453 2131	3·8 0·7 3·8 0·6	28 Th	0205 0834 1433 2105	3·5 1·1 3·5 1·0
14 Th	0324 1000 1548 2223	3·9 0·6 4·0 0·5	29 F	0257 0927 1522 2155	3·7 0·9 3·7 0·9
15 F	0413 1048 1634 2309	4·1 0·5 4·1 0·5	30 Sa	0345 1014 1609 2240	3·8 0·8 3·9 0·7
			31 Su	0430 1059 1652 2325	4·0 0·7 4·1 0·6

JUNE

Day	Time	m	Day	Time	m
1 M ●	0513 1144 1736	4·1 0·6 4·2	16 Tu	0017 0604 1234 1825	0·7 3·9 0·7 4·0
2 Tu	0010 0556 1229 1819	0·5 4·2 0·6 4·3	17 W	0053 0641 1309 1902	0·7 3·9 0·7 4·0
3 W	0055 0641 1316 1903	0·5 4·2 0·5 4·3	18 Th	0128 0716 1342 1937	0·8 3·8 0·7 3·9
4 Th	0142 0726 1404 1951	0·5 4·2 0·5 4·2	19 F	0202 0751 1418 2012	0·8 3·8 0·8 3·8
5 F	0232 0815 1454 2042	0·5 4·1 0·6 4·1	20 Sa	0237 0826 1456 2050	0·9 3·7 0·9 3·7
6 Sa	0325 0908 1548 2138	0·6 3·9 0·6 4·0	21 Su	0315 0905 1536 2131	0·9 3·6 0·9 3·6
7 Su ☽	0421 1006 1647 2238	0·7 3·8 0·7 3·8	22 M	0356 0949 1621 2217	1·0 3·5 1·0 3·5
8 M	0522 1108 1749 2343	0·8 3·6 0·8 3·7	23 Tu ☾	0444 1040 1712 2311	1·1 3·4 1·1 3·4
9 Tu	0627 1215 1856	0·9 3·6 0·8	24 W	0536 1136 1810	1·2 3·3 1·2
10 W	0050 0735 1323 2005	3·6 0·9 3·6 0·8	25 Th	0008 0636 1238 1913	3·4 1·2 3·3 1·2
11 Th	0158 0840 1427 2110	3·7 0·8 3·7 0·8	26 F	0110 0740 1342 2018	3·4 1·2 3·4 1·1
12 F	0258 0939 1525 2204	3·7 0·8 3·8 0·7	27 Sa	0213 0844 1446 2119	3·5 1·1 3·6 1·0
13 Sa	0353 1030 1616 2254	3·8 0·7 3·9 0·7	28 Su	0312 0945 1543 2217	3·7 0·9 3·8 0·8
14 Su	0441 1115 1702 2337	3·9 0·7 4·0 0·7	29 M	0409 1041 1635 2309	3·9 0·8 4·0 0·6
15 M ○	0525 1156 1746	3·9 0·7 4·1	30 Tu ●	0459 1132 1726	4·1 0·6 4·2

JULY

Day	Time	m	Day	Time	m
1 W	0000 0549 1221 1814	0·5 4·2 0·4 4·4	16 Th	0041 0628 1255 1848	0·7 3·9 0·7 4·0
2 Th	0049 0635 1309 1900	0·4 4·3 0·3 4·4	17 F	0112 0700 1326 1919	0·7 3·9 0·7 4·0
3 F	0137 0721 1357 1947	0·3 4·3 0·3 4·4	18 Sa	0141 0731 1355 1949	0·7 3·9 0·7 3·9
4 Sa	0225 0808 1446 2034	0·3 4·2 0·3 4·3	19 Su	0211 0801 1426 2019	0·8 3·8 0·8 3·9
5 Su	0314 0857 1535 2124	0·4 4·1 0·4 4·1	20 M	0242 0833 1500 2053	0·8 3·8 0·8 3·8
6 M	0406 0948 1628 2217	0·6 3·9 0·6 3·9	21 Tu	0317 0908 1538 2131	0·9 3·7 1·0 3·7
7 Tu ☽	0459 1044 1725 2316	0·7 3·7 0·8 3·7	22 W ☾	0355 0950 1621 2217	1·0 3·6 1·1 3·5
8 W	0600 1146 1828	0·9 3·6 0·9	23 Th	0444 1041 1716 2312	1·1 3·5 1·2 3·4
9 Th	0021 0704 1252 1937	3·5 1·0 3·5 1·0	24 F	0543 1143 1822	1·2 3·4 1·3
10 F	0130 0813 1402 2047	3·5 1·0 3·5 1·0	25 Sa	0019 0652 1256 1935	3·4 1·3 3·4 1·3
11 Sa	0237 0918 1507 2150	3·5 1·0 3·6 0·9	26 Su	0133 0808 1412 2050	3·4 1·2 3·5 1·1
12 Su	0336 1014 1603 2242	3·6 0·9 3·8 0·9	27 M	0247 0921 1522 2157	3·6 1·1 3·7 0·9
13 M	0428 1104 1652 2327	3·7 0·8 3·9 0·8	28 Tu	0353 1024 1623 2257	3·8 0·8 4·0 0·6
14 Tu ○	0513 1144 1734	3·8 0·7 4·0	29 W ●	0449 1119 1716 2349	4·1 0·5 4·3 0·4
15 W	0007 0553 1222 1814	0·7 3·9 0·7 4·0	30 Th	0539 1210 1804	4·3 0·3 4·5
			31 F	0036 0625 1256 1849	0·2 4·4 0·2 4·5

AUGUST

Day	Time	m	Day	Time	m
1 Sa	0123 0710 1342 1933	0·2 4·4 0·1 4·5	16 Su	0114 0706 1328 1920	0·7 4·0 0·7 4·1
2 Su	0209 0752 1427 2016	0·2 4·4 0·2 4·4	17 M	0141 0731 1357 1947	0·7 4·0 0·7 4·0
3 M	0254 0837 1514 2101	0·4 4·2 0·4 4·2	18 Tu	0209 0759 1427 2016	0·8 3·9 0·8 3·9
4 Tu	0341 0922 1603 2149	0·6 4·0 0·6 3·9	19 W	0240 0830 1501 2051	0·9 3·9 1·0 3·8
5 W ☽	0430 1013 1655 2244	0·8 3·8 0·9 3·6	20 Th	0318 0910 1545 2134	1·0 3·8 1·1 3·7
6 Th	0525 1112 1754 2346	1·0 3·6 1·1 3·4	21 F ☾	0404 0957 1640 2228	1·2 3·6 1·2 3·5
7 F	0628 1221 1904	1·2 3·4 1·2	22 Sa	0506 1101 1747 2339	1·3 3·5 1·4 3·4
8 Sa	0059 0741 1337 2023	3·3 1·3 3·4 1·3	23 Su	0619 1219 1904	1·4 3·4 1·4
9 Su	0216 0856 1450 2134	3·3 1·2 3·5 1·2	24 M	0102 0740 1345 2026	3·3 1·3 3·5 1·2
10 M	0322 0959 1549 2228	3·5 1·1 3·7 1·0	25 Tu	0226 0900 1505 2141	3·5 1·1 3·7 1·0
11 Tu	0414 1048 1638 2313	3·6 0·9 3·9 0·8	26 W	0338 1007 1609 2241	3·8 0·8 4·1 0·6
12 W	0458 1129 1719 2350	3·8 0·7 4·0 0·7	27 Th	0435 1102 1701 2332	4·1 0·5 4·4 0·4
13 Th ○	0536 1204 1754	3·9 0·7 4·1	28 F ●	0523 1151 1747	4·4 0·3 4·5
14 F	0021 0610 1235 1827	0·7 4·0 0·6 4·1	29 Sa	0018 0607 1238 1829	0·2 4·5 0·1 4·6
15 Sa	0049 0639 1302 1855	0·7 4·0 0·6 4·1	30 Su	0103 0649 1321 1912	0·2 4·6 0·1 4·6
			31 M	0145 0730 1404 1952	0·3 4·5 0·3 4·4

12

Chart Datum: 0.13 metres above Ordnance Datum (Dublin)

IRELAND, SOUTH COAST – RINGASKIDDY

TIME ZONE UT(GMT)
For Summer Time add ONE hour in non-shaded areas

Lat 51°50′ N Long 8°19′ W

TIMES AND HEIGHTS OF HIGH AND LOW WATERS

YEAR **1992**

SEPTEMBER

Day	Time	m	Time	m	Time	m	Time	m
1 Tu	0227	0·4	0811	4·3	1447	0·5	2033	4·2
2 W	0311	0·7	0853	4·1	1532	0·8	2117	3·9
3 Th ☽	0357	0·9	0939	3·8	1621	1·0	2206	3·6
4 F	0448	1·2	1035	3·5	1719	1·3	2308	3·3
5 Sa	0550	1·4	1146	3·4	1828	1·5		
6 Su	0024	3·2	0704	1·4	1306	3·3	1951	1·5
7 M	0147	3·2	0826	1·4	1425	3·4	2107	1·3
8 Tu	0257	3·4	0932	1·2	1525	3·6	2203	1·1
9 W	0349	3·6	1023	1·0	1612	3·9	2247	0·9
10 Th	0433	3·8	1102	0·8	1651	4·0	2322	0·8
11 F	0509	4·0	1137	0·7	1726	4·1	2353	0·7
12 Sa ○	0542	4·1	1207	0·7	1757	4·2		
13 Su	0019	0·7	0610	4·1	1234	0·7	1824	4·2
14 M	0045	0·7	0636	4·1	1300	0·7	1850	4·2
15 Tu	0112	0·8	0702	4·1	1328	0·8	1916	4·1
16 W	0141	0·8	0730	4·1	1359	0·9	1945	4·1
17 Th	0213	0·9	0801	4·0	1436	1·0	2020	4·0
18 F	0251	1·1	0840	3·9	1519	1·1	2103	3·8
19 Sa ☾	0341	1·2	0929	3·7	1617	1·3	2200	3·6
20 Su	0444	1·4	1037	3·6	1725	1·4	2313	3·4
21 M	0557	1·4	1157	3·5	1842	1·4		
22 Tu	0039	3·4	0717	1·3	1323	3·6	2005	1·3
23 W	0205	3·6	0837	1·1	1443	3·8	2119	1·0
24 Th	0317	3·9	0946	0·8	1546	4·1	2220	0·7
25 F	0413	4·2	1041	0·5	1638	4·4	2311	0·5
26 Sa ●	0501	4·4	1129	0·3	1723	4·6	2356	0·3
27 Su	0544	4·5	1214	0·3	1805	4·6		
28 M	0038	0·3	0625	4·6	1256	0·3	1846	4·5
29 Tu	0119	0·4	0704	4·5	1337	0·5	1924	4·4
30 W	0159	0·6	0742	4·3	1419	0·7	2004	4·2

OCTOBER

Day	Time	m	Time	m	Time	m	Time	m
1 Th	0240	0·8	0823	4·1	1503	0·9	2044	3·9
2 F	0325	1·1	0908	3·9	1549	1·2	2132	3·6
3 Sa ☽	0414	1·3	1003	3·6	1644	1·4	2231	3·4
4 Su	0513	1·4	1109	3·4	1750	1·5	2343	3·2
5 M	0624	1·5	1227	3·3	1906	1·5		
6 Tu	0103	3·2	0741	1·4	1341	3·4	2022	1·4
7 W	0213	3·4	0850	1·3	1443	3·6	2121	1·2
8 Th	0310	3·6	0943	1·1	1532	3·8	2207	1·0
9 F	0355	3·8	1026	0·9	1613	4·0	2244	0·9
10 Sa	0433	4·0	1102	0·8	1649	4·1	2318	0·8
11 Su ○	0508	4·1	1133	0·8	1722	4·2	2347	0·8
12 M	0539	4·2	1204	0·8	1753	4·3		
13 Tu	0017	0·8	0608	4·2	1234	0·8	1821	4·3
14 W	0046	0·8	0636	4·2	1306	0·9	1852	4·2
15 Th	0119	0·9	0707	4·2	1341	0·9	1924	4·2
16 F	0155	1·0	0742	4·2	1420	1·0	2002	4·1
17 Sa	0239	1·1	0826	4·0	1508	1·2	2049	3·9
18 Su	0331	1·2	0918	3·9	1606	1·3	2148	3·7
19 M ☾	0431	1·3	1024	3·7	1711	1·4	2259	3·5
20 Tu	0542	1·3	1140	3·6	1824	1·3		
21 W	0018	3·5	0657	1·3	1300	3·7	1944	1·2
22 Th	0138	3·6	0815	1·1	1415	3·9	2056	1·0
23 F	0247	3·9	0921	0·8	1518	4·1	2155	0·8
24 Sa	0345	4·2	1017	0·6	1612	4·3	2245	0·6
25 Su ●	0434	4·4	1106	0·5	1658	4·4	2332	0·5
26 M	0519	4·5	1150	0·5	1740	4·5		
27 Tu	0014	0·5	0600	4·5	1232	0·5	1821	4·4
28 W	0053	0·6	0641	4·4	1313	0·7	1900	4·3
29 Th	0134	0·8	0720	4·3	1354	0·8	1938	4·1
30 F	0213	0·9	0801	4·1	1436	1·0	2018	3·9
31 Sa	0257	1·1	0844	3·9	1521	1·2	2103	3·7

NOVEMBER

Day	Time	m	Time	m	Time	m	Time	m
1 Su	0343	1·2	0934	3·7	1613	1·4	2157	3·5
2 M ☽	0438	1·4	1033	3·5	1711	1·5	2301	3·3
3 Tu	0540	1·4	1139	3·4	1815	1·5		
4 W	0010	3·3	0649	1·4	1246	3·4	1924	1·4
5 Th	0117	3·4	0755	1·3	1348	3·6	2026	1·3
6 F	0218	3·5	0853	1·2	1442	3·7	2117	1·2
7 Sa	0308	3·7	0941	1·1	1528	3·9	2200	1·1
8 Su	0352	3·9	1023	1·0	1610	4·0	2240	1·0
9 M	0431	4·1	1059	0·9	1648	4·2	2315	0·9
10 Tu ○	0508	4·2	1136	0·9	1723	4·2	2351	0·9
11 W	0543	4·3	1212	0·9	1758	4·3		
12 Th	0027	0·9	0618	4·3	1249	0·9	1834	4·3
13 F	0106	0·9	0655	4·3	1330	0·9	1912	4·2
14 Sa	0147	0·9	0734	4·2	1413	1·0	1954	4·1
15 Su	0233	1·0	0820	4·1	1503	1·0	2043	4·0
16 M	0324	1·0	0914	4·0	1557	1·1	2141	3·8
17 Tu ☾	0421	1·1	1014	3·9	1658	1·2	2245	3·7
18 W	0526	1·1	1122	3·8	1805	1·2	2356	3·7
19 Th	0635	1·1	1234	3·8	1917	1·2		
20 F	0107	3·7	0748	1·1	1344	3·9	2027	1·0
21 Sa	0216	3·9	0854	0·9	1449	4·0	2129	0·9
22 Su	0317	4·0	0953	0·8	1545	4·1	2223	0·8
23 M	0409	4·2	1045	0·7	1634	4·2	2309	0·7
24 Tu ●	0457	4·3	1132	0·7	1719	4·3	2353	0·7
25 W	0542	4·4	1214	0·7	1801	4·2		
26 Th	0034	0·8	0622	4·3	1255	0·8	1842	4·2
27 F	0113	0·8	0703	4·2	1335	0·9	1920	4·1
28 Sa	0152	0·9	0742	4·1	1415	1·0	1958	3·9
29 Su	0233	1·0	0823	4·0	1456	1·1	2039	3·8
30 M	0315	1·1	0907	3·8	1539	1·2	2125	3·6

DECEMBER

Day	Time	m	Time	m	Time	m	Time	m
1 Tu	0402	1·2	0956	3·7	1627	1·3	2216	3·5
2 W ☽	0454	1·3	1049	3·5	1720	1·4	2313	3·4
3 Th	0551	1·4	1147	3·5	1819	1·4		
4 F	0015	3·4	0652	1·4	1248	3·5	1920	1·4
5 Sa	0117	3·5	0752	1·3	1345	3·6	2019	1·3
6 Su	0216	3·6	0849	1·3	1440	3·7	2112	1·2
7 M	0308	3·7	0939	1·2	1529	3·9	2200	1·1
8 Tu	0356	3·9	1027	1·0	1616	4·0	2245	1·0
9 W ○	0440	4·1	1111	0·9	1659	4·1	2329	0·9
10 Th	0522	4·2	1153	0·8	1740	4·2		
11 F	0012	0·8	0603	4·3	1236	0·8	1822	4·3
12 Sa	0055	0·7	0645	4·4	1321	0·7	1904	4·3
13 Su	0140	0·7	0728	4·4	1406	0·7	1948	4·2
14 M	0226	0·7	0813	4·3	1454	0·8	2036	4·1
15 Tu	0315	0·8	0904	4·2	1546	0·9	2128	4·0
16 W ☾	0409	0·8	0959	4·0	1641	1·0	2226	3·9
17 Th	0505	0·9	1058	3·9	1742	1·1	2329	3·7
18 F	0610	1·0	1204	3·8	1848	1·1		
19 Sa	0036	3·7	0719	1·1	1313	3·7	1958	1·1
20 Su	0145	3·7	0827	1·0	1420	3·8	2104	1·0
21 M	0251	3·8	0932	1·0	1522	3·9	2202	1·0
22 Tu	0349	4·0	1028	0·9	1617	4·0	2254	0·9
23 W	0441	4·1	1118	0·9	1705	4·0	2339	0·8
24 Th ●	0527	4·2	1201	0·8	1749	4·1		
25 F	0019	0·8	0611	4·2	1242	0·8	1828	4·1
26 Sa	0057	0·8	0649	4·2	1319	0·9	1904	4·0
27 Su	0134	0·8	0726	4·1	1354	0·9	1940	4·0
28 M	0209	0·8	0801	4·0	1427	1·0	2013	3·9
29 Tu	0244	0·9	0837	3·9	1503	1·0	2050	3·8
30 W	0321	1·0	0915	3·8	1541	1·1	2131	3·6
31 Th	0402	1·1	0957	3·7	1623	1·2	2217	3·5

Chart Datum: 0.13 metres above Ordnance Datum (Dublin)

CORK *continued*

CHARTS
Admiralty 1773, 1777, 1765; Imray C56, C57; Irish OS 25

TIDES
−0523 Dover; ML 2·3; Duration 0555; Zone 0 (GMT)

Standard Port COBH (RINGASKIDDY) (⟶)

Times				Height (metres)			
HW		LW		MHWS	MHWN	MLWN	MLWS
0500	1100	0500	1100	4·2	3·3	1·4	0·5
1700	2300	1700	2300				
Differences CORK							
+0020	+0020	+0020	+0020	+0·3	+0·1	0·0	0·0

NOTE: Cobh is a Standard Port — Times and heights of tides for the year are given below.

SHELTER
Very good shelter under all conditions. Cork itself is largely a commercial port, but berths are available; before proceeding up river contact Port Operations. The main yachting centre is at Crosshaven in Owenboy River, where there are two marinas (Crosshaven Boatyard and Royal Cork YC) and anchorages further upstream, in particular in Drake's Pool. There is also a marina at East Ferry on the E side of Great Island.

NAVIGATION
Waypoint 51°46'·00N 08°15'·30W, 174°/354° from/to front Ldg Lt 354°, 2·8M. There are no navigational dangers for yachtsmen. It is one of the safest harbours to enter in the world. Harbour is deep and well marked. Tidal streams run about 1½ kn in entrance at springs, but more between the forts. Entrance to Owenboy River carries a minimum of 2m at LWS, and the channel is buoyed. There are numerous other channel buoys N of No 8 buoy.

TELEPHONE (021)
Hr Mr 273125; MRCC Limerick (061) 61219; Port Operation & Information Stn. 811380; Coast Life Saving Service (Crosshaven) 831448; # 271322; Weather 964600; Police (Crosshaven) 831222; Dr 831716 (Crosshaven) or 811546 (Cobh); ⊞ 546400.

FACILITIES
Royal Cork YC Marina ☎ 831023, AC, ⊡, V, FW, Bar, R; **Crosshaven BY Marina** (100+20 visitors) ☎ 831161, AC, BH (25 ton), C, M, Ⓔ, (1·5 ton), CH, D, El, FW, Gas, Gaz, ME, P, Sh, Slip; **East Ferry Marina** (60+12 visitors) ☎ 811342, D, AC, FW; **Salve Engineering** ☎ 831145, BY, FW, L, M, ME, D, Slip; **McWilliam Sailmakers** ☎ 831504, SM; **Union Chandlery** ☎ 271643, ACA, CH; **Glen Marine** ☎ 841163, BY, CH; **Rider Services** ☎ 841176, Ⓔ; **Irish Marine Electronics** ☎ 894155, Ⓔ; **Crosshaven Village** Bar, Dr, L, ✉, R, V, ⊡, YC; **Cork City** ACA, Bar, CH, ⊡, V, Ⓑ; ✉; Ferry Port; ⇶; ✈.

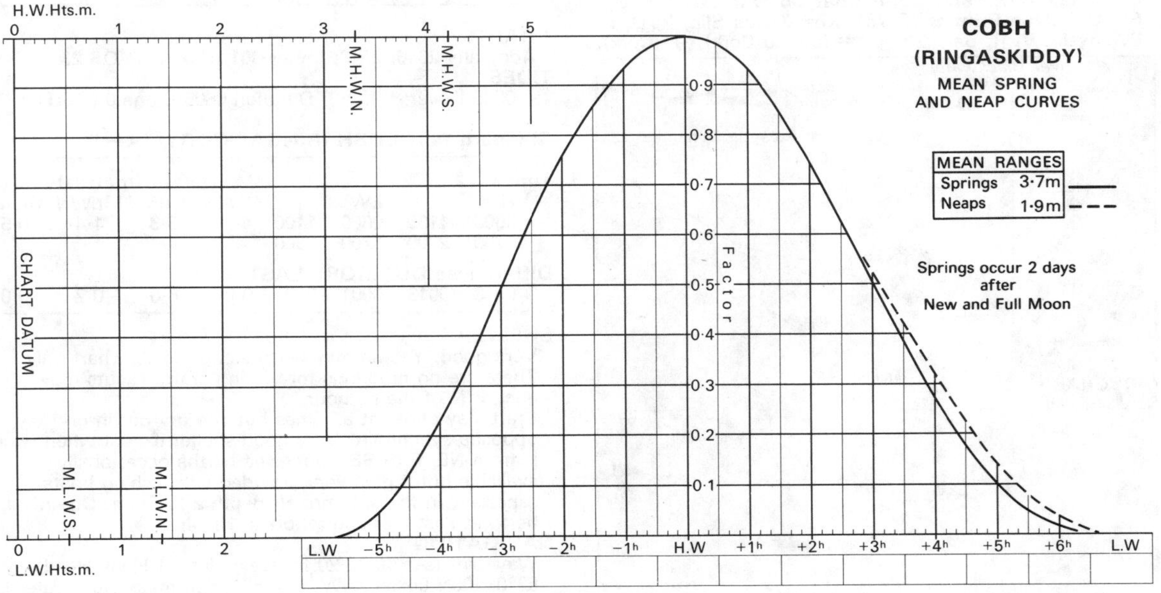
H.W.Hts.m.
0 1 2 3 4 5
M.H.W.N.
M.H.W.S.
CHART DATUM
M.L.W.S.
M.L.W.N.
0 1 2
L.W.Hts.m.
0·9 0·8 0·7 0·6 0·5 0·4 0·3 0·2 0·1
Factor
L.W −5h −4h −3h −2h −1h H.W +1h +2h +3h +4h +5h +6h L.W
COBH
(RINGASKIDDY)
MEAN SPRING AND NEAP CURVES
MEAN RANGES
Springs 3·7m
Neaps 1·9m
Springs occur 2 days after New and Full Moon

LIGHTS AND MARKS
The hammer-head water tower S of Crosshaven is a very conspic mark, 24·5m high.
Ldg Lts, two sets, both below Fort Davis on E shore;
(1) Lts Oc 5s, front 29m 10M, rear 37m 10M lead E of Harbour Rocks.
(2) Lts Oc R 5s, front 11m 5M, rear 21m 5M lead W of Harbour Rocks.
FW leading lights with W diamond day marks in line 252° lead to Crosshaven, but not easy to see.

RADIO TELEPHONE
Call: *Cork Harbour Radio* VHF Ch 16; 12 14 (H24); Crosshaven Marina Ch M (Mon-Fri: 0830-1700 LT). Royal Cork YC Marina Ch M (0900-2300 LT). East Ferry Marina Ch M.

YOUGHAL 10-12-18
Cork

CHARTS
Admiralty 2071, 2049; Imray C57; Irish OS 22

TIDES
−0545 Dover; ML 2·3; Duration 0555; Zone 0 (GMT).

YOUGHAL *continued*

Standard Port COBH (RINGASKIDDY) (⟵)

Times				Height (metres)			
HW		LW		MHWS	MHWN	MLWN	MLWS
0500	1100	0500	1100	4·2	3·3	1·4	0·5
1700	2300	1700	2300				
Differences YOUGHAL							
0000	+0010	+0010	0000	−0·2	−0·2	−0·2	−0·2
BALLYCOTTON							
−0011	+0001	+0003	−0009	0·0	0·0	−0·1	0·0
DUNGARVAN HARBOUR							
+0004	+0012	+0007	−0001	0·0	+0·1	−0·2	0·0

SHELTER
Good, but strong SE to S by W winds cause a swell inside the harbour. Good anchorages off Mall Dock, opposite the most northerly warehouse or N of Ferry Point.

NAVIGATION
East Bar waypoint 51°55'·60N 07°48'·00W, 122°/302° from/to Fl WR 2·5s Lt, 1·8M. Beware Blackball Ledge and Bar Rocks outside harbour entrance in R sector of lighthouse Lt. Do not attempt entry in rough seas. Beware salmon nets in entrance and bay during season; also mussel banks off town quays.

LIGHTS AND MARKS
A 15m white tower on W side of entrance shows Lt Fl WR 2·5s, 24m 12/9M, W 183°-273°, R 273°-295°, W 295°- 307°, R 307°-351°, W 351°-003°, the W sectors leading over the bars. Convent Tr in line with edge of Town Hall at 178° keeps clear of Red Bank to N.

RADIO TELEPHONE
VHF Ch 16; 14.

TELEPHONE (024)
Hr Mr 92365; MRCC Limerick 61219; Coast Life Saving Service 93252; # Cork 21322; Police 2200; Dr 72253.

FACILITIES
EC Wednesday; **Ferry Point Boat Co** ☎ 94232, ME, El, Sh, CH; **Alan Prim** ☎ 932781, Kos; **Town** Slip, P, D, L, FW (well), V, R, Bar; ✉; Ⓑ; ⇌ (bus to Cork); ✈ (Cork).

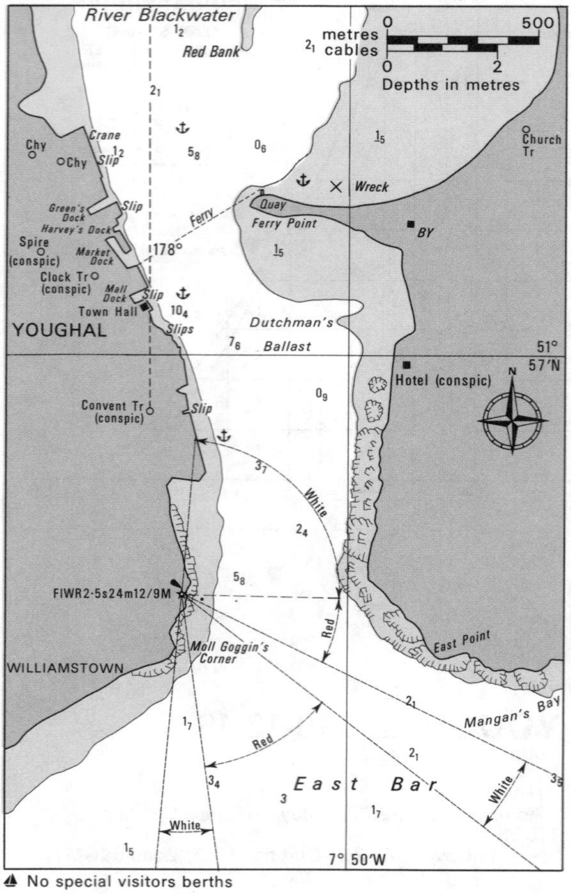
River Blackwater
Red Bank
metres
cables
Depths in metres
Church Tr
Crane
Chy
Slip
Wreck
Quay
Ferry Point
Ferry
Green's Dock
Harvey's Dock
Spire (conspic)
Market Dock
178°
BY
Clock Tr (conspic)
Mall Dock
Town Hall
Slips
YOUGHAL
Dutchman's Ballast
Hotel (conspic)
Convent Tr (conspic)
White
FlWR2·5s24m12/9M
Red
East Point
Moll Goggin's Corner
WILLIAMSTOWN
Mangan's Bay
East Bar
7° 50'W
51° 57'N

▲ No special visitors berths

DUNMORE EAST 10-12-19

Waterford

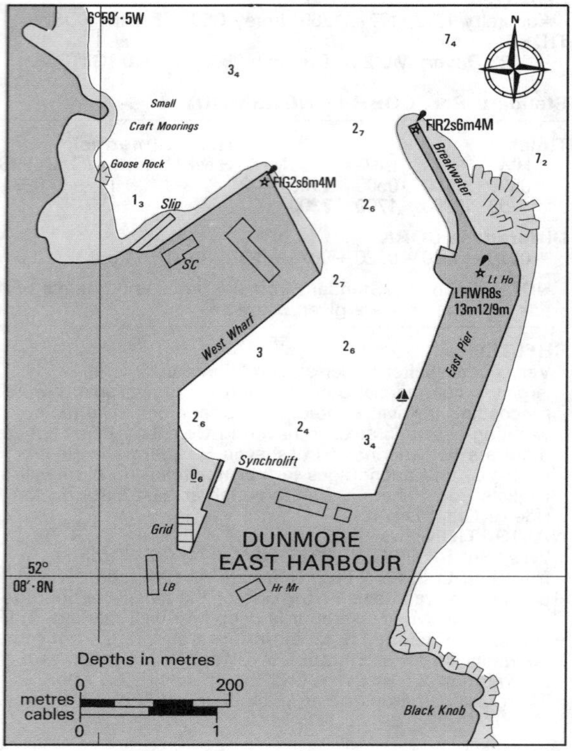
6°59'·5W
Small Craft Moorings
Goose Rock
Slip
FlG2s6m4M
FlR2s6m4M
Breakwater
SC
Lt Ho
LFlWR8s 13m12/9m
West Wharf
East Pier
Synchrolift
Grid
DUNMORE EAST HARBOUR
52° 08'·8N
LB
Hr Mr
Depths in metres
metres
cables
Black Knob

CHARTS
Admiralty 2046, 2049; Imray C61, C57; Irish OS 23

TIDES
−0535 Dover; ML 2·3; Duration 0605; Zone 0 (GMT).

Standard Port COBH (RINGASKIDDY) (⟵)

Times				Height (metres)			
HW		LW		MHWS	MHWN	MLWN	MLWS
0500	1100	0500	1100	4·2	3·3	1·4	0·5
1700	2300	1700	2300				
Differences DUNMORE EAST							
+0013	+0013	+0001	+0001	0·0	0·0	−0·2	0·0

SHELTER
Very good. Yachts may berth alongside W wharf only. There are no moorings for visiting craft. Yachts may anchor N of the harbour.
Craft stay afloat at all times but can dry out in grid opposite synchrolift. Very good shelter except when wind is from NE, E to SE. Alongside berths occasionally available but it gets very crowded with fishing boats especially in the autumn. Hr depth 2 to 3·4m. On arrival, berth at East Pier and report to Hr Mr.

NAVIGATION
Waypoint (see 10·12·20 for waypoint off Hook Head) 52°08'·00N 06°58'·00W, 137°/317° from/to breakwater Lt, 1·2M. There are no navigational dangers. Enter harbour under power, if available. Approaching by night from E, give Hook Head a wide berth (½M); when clear of Hook Head alter course for Dunmore East in R sector of breakwater Lt. From W, steer for Hook Head until in R sector and then alter course to N.

LIGHTS AND MARKS
East Pier Lt Ho L Fl WR8s 13m 12/9M, W225°-310°, R310°-004°. E Breakwater head Fl R2s 6m 4M, vis 000°-310°. W wharf Fl G 2s 6m 4M, vis 165°-246°.

RADIO TELEPHONE
VHF Ch 16; 14 (Pilot Station).

TELEPHONE (051)
Hr Mr 83166; CG Cork 26552; Pilot 83119; MRCC Limerick (061) 61219; # 75391; Coast Life Saving Service 83115; Dr 83194.

DUNMORE EAST *Continued*

FACILITIES
Harbour ☎ 83166, BH (230 ton), D, FW (on East Pier); **Waterford Harbour SC** ☎ 83389, R, Bar; **Dunmore East Garage** ☎ 83200, Kos; **Dunmore East Fishermans Co-operative Society** ☎ 83307, CH; **Dunmore Marine Supply Co** ☎ 83165, CH; **Village** Bar, D, P (cans), Slip, R, V, Ⓑ; ✉; ≷ (Waterford); ✈ (Dublin).

WATERFORD 10-12-20

Waterford

CHARTS
Admiralty 2046, 2049; Imray C57; Irish OS 23

TIDES
−0520 Dover; ML 2·4; Duration 0605; Zone 0 (GMT).

Standard Port COBH (RINGASKIDDY) (⟵)

Times				Height (metres)			
HW		LW		MHWS	MHWN	MLWN	MLWS
0500	1100	0500	1100	4·2	3·3	1·4	0·5
1700	2300	1700	2300				
Differences WATERFORD							
+0057	+0057	+0046	+0046	+0·4	+0·3	−0·1	−0·1
CARNSORE POINT							
+0029	+0019	−0002	+0008	−1·1	−1·0	No data	

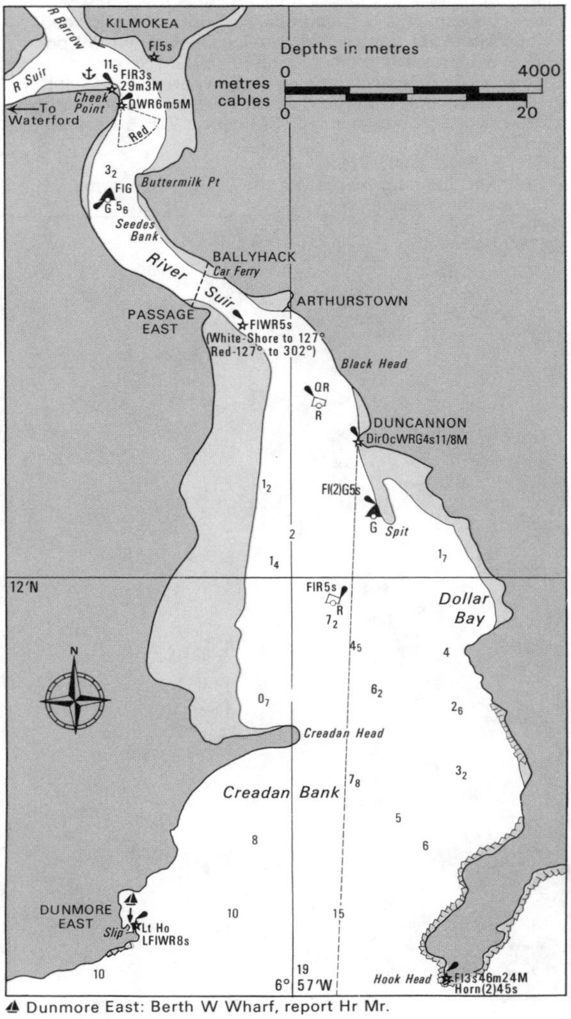
KILMOKEA
R Barrow
R Suir
⟵To Waterford
Cheek Point
FlR3s 29m3M
QWR6m5M
FI5s
Red
Depths in metres
metres
cables
Buttermilk Pt
FlG
Seedes Bank
River Suir
BALLYHACK
Car Ferry
ARTHURSTOWN
PASSAGE EAST
FlWR5s
(White-Shore to 127° Red-127° to 302°)
Black Head
QR
DUNCANNON
DirOcWRG4s11/8M
Fl(2)G5s
Spit
12′N
FlR5s
Dollar Bay
Creadan Head
Creadan Bank
DUNMORE EAST
Slip
Lt Ho
LFlWR8s
6° 57′W
Hook Head
Fl3s46m24M
Horn(2)45s

▲ Dunmore East: Berth W Wharf, report Hr Mr.

SHELTER
Very good and there are many excellent anchorages; off the quays just W of Cheek Pt; W of Little Is on S side of main river about 1½M E of Waterford; in Barrow R on E side just S of New Ross; in Barrow R on the N side of the E/W stretch about 2M S of New Ross.

NAVIGATION
Waypoint 52°06′·50N 07°56′·60W, 182°/002° from/to front Ldg Lt 002°, 6·7M. Beware of Falskirt Rock (2 ca off Swine Head) and Brecaun reef (20 ca NE of Hook Head). Give Tower Race, extending 1M to S of Hook Head, a wide berth.

LIGHTS AND MARKS
Hook Head Fl 3s 46m 24M; W Tr, two B bands. Dunmore East LFl WR 8s 13m 12/9M; vis W225°-310°, R310°-004°. Duncannon Dir Lt Oc WRG 4s 11/8M, G353°-356¾°, W356¾°-357¼°, R 357¼°-001°. Do not confuse Waterford entrance with Tramore Bay.

RADIO TELEPHONE
New Ross VHF Ch 16; 12 14 (H24).

TELEPHONE (051)
Hr Mr 74499; CG Cork 26552; MRCC Limerick 61219; # 75391; Police 74888; Dr 83194; Ⓗ 75429.

FACILITIES
EC Thursday; **Carrolls BY (Ballyhack)** ME, El, Sh, C; **Town** AB, M, FW, P, D, Gaz, V, R, Bar, ≷; ✈
Note: a marina is planned for Arthurstown.

ROSSLARE HARBOUR 10-12-21

Dublin

CHARTS
Admiralty 1772, 1787; Imray C61; Irish OS 23

TIDES
−0510 Dover; ML 1·1; Duration 0640; Zone 0 (GMT)

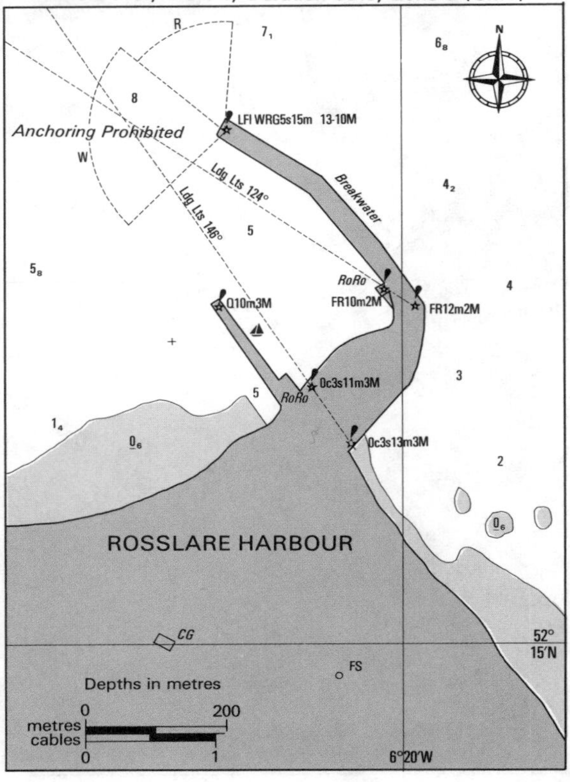
R
Anchoring Prohibited
W
LFl WRG5s15m 13-10M
Breakwater
Ldg Lts 124°
Ldg Lts 146°
RoRo
FR10m2M
FR12m2M
Q10m3M
Oc3s11m3M
RoRo
Oc3s13m3M
ROSSLARE HARBOUR
CG
FS
Depths in metres
metres
cables
52° 15′N
6°20′W

12

ROSSLARE *continued*

Standard Port DUBLIN (NORTH WALL) (⟶)

Times				Height (metres)			
HW		LW		MHWS	MHWN	MLWN	MLWS
0000	0700	0000	0500	4·1	3·4	1·5	0·5
1200	1900	1200	1700				
Differences ROSSLARE HARBOUR							
−0440	−0710	−0710	−0440	−2·2	−2·0	−0·7	−0·3

SHELTER

An artificial harbour and busy ferry port which is a useful stopping place. Yachts can anchor in the shelter of the breakwater or go alongside No 1 berth West Pier. Often uncomfortable in winds WNW to NE and dangerous with even moderate winds WNW to NNE.

NAVIGATION

Waypoint 52°14'·60N 06°15'·00W, 105°/285° from/to breakwater Lt, 3·3M. Main approach channel is South Shear. From S, beware Splaugh Rock off Greenore Point, and overfalls here and further S over The Baillies. South Shear runs S of Holdens Bed, a shallow bank with changeable depths, and the tide sets across the channel. Approach from N through North Shear. If wind shifts to dangerous sector leave immediately, through South Shear.

LIGHTS AND MARKS

Two sets of Ldg Lts, 146° both Oc 3s 10/11m, 3M and 124° both FR 10/12m 2M. Lt on the end of breakwater L Fl WRG 5s 15m 13/10M, showing R320°-286° over foul ground from Greenore Pt; W283°-286° over South Shear; G246°-283° over section of Holden's Bed with min depth 5·8m; R208°-246° over N section of Holden's Bed; W188°-208° over North Shear; G098°-188° over South Bay.

RADIO TELEPHONE

Call: *Rosslare Harbour Radio* VHF Ch 16; 06 12 14 (H24).

TELEPHONE (053)

Hr Mr 33114; MRCC Limerick 61219; Life Boat Lookout Stn 33205; # 33116; Police 22333; Dr 31154; Ⓗ Wexford 22233.

FACILITIES

EC Thursday; **Pier** ☎ 33114, M, P, D, L, FW, ME, C; **Rosslare Ship Repairers** ☎ 33194, ME, Sh, El, Slip, C; **J. Devereaux** ☎ 33104, Kos; **Town** V, R, Bar, ✉; Ⓑ; ⇌; ✈ (Dublin).

WEXFORD 10-12-22

Wexford

CHARTS

Admiralty 1772, 1787; Imray C61; Irish OS 23

TIDES

−0450 Dover; ML 1·3; Duration 0630; Zone 0 (GMT)

Standard Port DUBLIN (NORTH WALL) (⟶)

Times				Height (metres)			
HW		LW		MHWS	MHWN	MLWN	MLWS
0000	0700	0000	0500	4·1	3·4	1·5	0·5
1200	1900	1200	1700				
Differences WEXFORD							
−0350	−0720	−0725	−0325	−2·4	−2·0	−1·0	−0·3
TUSKAR ROCK							
−0457	−0627	−0601	−0517	−1·5	−1·4	No data	

SHELTER

Safe sheltered anchorage off town quays but difficult entrance which should not be attempted in strong winds from E to S when seas break on the bar.

NAVIGATION

Waypoint 52°20'·00N 06°18'·00W, 107°/287° from/to FS on The Raven Point, 2·7M (channel shifts). Bar partly dries and it's position changes. Harbour Board has ceased to function so buoys are not maintained. During summer head in between G local buoys. After 3rd R buoy, N of ruins (awash at HW) head 325°. About ¼M off, keep along shore for approx 1M. Having passed two W posts, head SW towards conspic factory tower, SE end of town. Turn in when 1ca off training wall. There are no pilots but local knowledge is very advisable — try Rosslare harbour for knowledgeable local. (J. Sherwood 22875 or night 22731).

LIGHTS AND MARKS

No lights. Leading marks (local). Dayglo buoys mark the channel in summer.

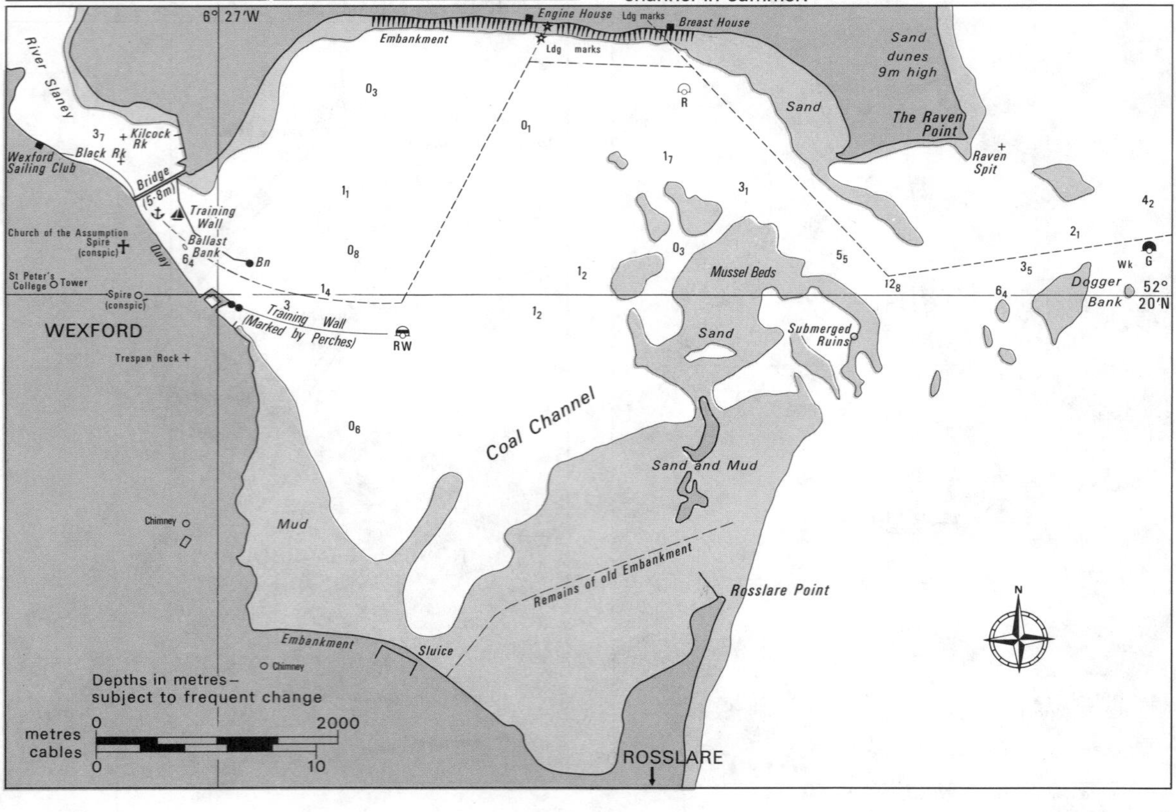
6° 27'W
Engine House
Ldg marks
Breast House
Embankment
Ldg marks
Sand dunes 9m high
River Slaney
Sand
The Raven Point
Raven Spit
Kilcock Rk
Black Rk
Wexford Sailing Club
Bridge
(5·8m)
Training Wall
Church of the Assumption Spire (conspic)
Ballast Bank
Bn
Quay
St Peter's College Tower
Spire (conspic)
Training Wall (Marked by Perches)
RW
R
Mussel Beds
Wk
G
Dogger Bank
52° 20'N
WEXFORD
Trespan Rock
Sand
Submerged Ruins
Coal Channel
Sand and Mud
Chimney
Mud
Remains of old Embankment
Rosslare Point
Embankment
Sluice
Chimney
N
Depths in metres – subject to frequent change
0
2000
metres
cables
0
10
ROSSLARE

WEXFORD *continued*

RADIO TELEPHONE
None.
TELEPHONE (053)
Hr Mr 33114; MRCC Limerick 61219; # 33116; Police 22333; Dr 31154; Ⓗ 42233.
FACILITIES
EC Thursday; **Wexford Quays** Slip, P, D, L, FW, ME, El, CH, AB, V; **Wexford Harbour Boat Club** ☎ 22039, Slip, C (5 ton), Bar; **Barrow Valley Marine** ☎ 21902, CH; **Town** ✉; Ⓑ; ⇌; ✈ (Waterford).

ARKLOW 10-12-23

Wicklow

CHARTS
Admiralty 633, 1468; Imray C61; Irish OS 19
TIDES
−0150 Dover; ML 1·3; Duration 0640; Zone 0 (GMT).

Standard Port DUBLIN (NORTH WALL) (⟶)

Times				Height (metres)			
HW		LW		MHWS	MHWN	MLWN	MLWS
0000	0700	0000	0500	4·1	3·4	1·5	0·5
1200	1900	1200	1700				
Differences ARKLOW							
−0215	−0255	−0245	−0225	−2·4	−2·0	−0·3	+0·1

SHELTER
Good shelter except in strong SE winds, when seas break across the entrance. Entrance is difficult without power. Once in dock, shelter is perfect (3m). Temporary anchorage 1M S of piers in 4m during SE winds off Roadstone Jetty (Oc R 10s 9m 9M). 2 ca S of jetty a breakwater extends ENE for 3 ca (QY). Best anchorage between jetty and breakwater.
NAVIGATION
Waypoint 52°47′·60N 06°07′·50W, 090°/270° from/to entrance, 0·40M. No navigational dangers. The entrance to the dock is only 13·5m wide. Due to obstructions it is dangerous to proceed up river of dock entrance without local knowledge.
LIGHTS AND MARKS
There are no leading lights or marks. The only two lights are on the piers. North pier LFl G 7s 7m 10M. South pier

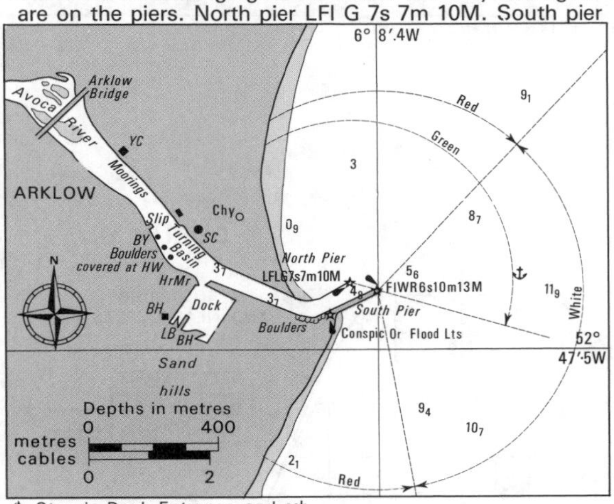
6° 8′.4W
Arklow Bridge
Avoca River
YC
Moorings
ARKLOW
ChY
Slip
Turning Basin
SC
BY
Boulders covered at HW
HrMr
Dock
BH
LB
BH
North Pier
LFlG7s7m10M
FlWR6s10m13M
South Pier
Boulders
Conspic Or Flood Lts
Red
Green
White
Red
52° 47′.5W
Sand hills
Depths in metres
metres
cables
0
400
0
2

⚠ Stop in Dock Entrance and ask

Fl WR 6s 10m 13M; R shore-223°, W223°-350°, R350°-shore.
RADIO TELEPHONE
VHF Ch 16 (office hours).
TELEPHONE (0402)
Hr Mr 32426; MRCC Limerick 61219; RNLI 32001; Coast Life Saving Service 32430; # 32497; Police 2101; Dr 32421.
FACILITIES
EC Wednesday; **Tyrrell's Yard** ☎ 32001, Slip, L, FW, ME, El Sh, C (5 ton mobile), AB; **Dock** ☎ 32426, Slip, M, D, L, FW, ME, El, C (1 ton) CH, AB; **Jack Fitzgerald** ☎ 32152, El; **J. Annelsey** Kos; **Town** CH, V, R, P and D (cans), Bar, ✉; Ⓑ; ⇌; ✈ (Dublin).

WICKLOW 10-12-24

Wicklow

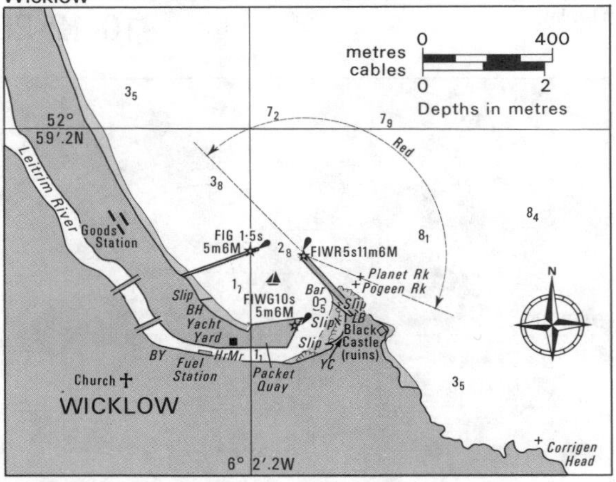
metres
cables
0
400
0
2
Depths in metres
52° 59′.2N
Leitrim River
Goods Station
FlG 1·5s 5m6M
FlWR5s11m6M
Red
Planet Rk
Pogeen Rk
Bar
Slip
LB
Black Castle (ruins)
FlWG10s 5m6M
Slip
BH
Yacht Yard
BY
Fuel Station
HrMr
Packet Quay
YC
Church
WICKLOW
Corrigen Head
6° 2′.2W

CHARTS
Admiralty 633, 1468; Imray C61; Irish OS 16
TIDES
−0010 Dover; ML 1·5; Duration 0640; Zone 0 (GMT)

Standard Port DUBLIN (NORTH WALL) (⟶)

Times				Height (metres)			
HW		LW		MHWS	MHWN	MLWN	MLWS
0000	0700	0000	0500	4·1	3·4	1·5	0·5
1200	1900	1200	1700				
Differences WICKLOW							
−0035	−0047	−0044	−0038	−1·4	−1·1	−0·6	0·0

SHELTER
Very safe, and always accessible. Outer harbour is open to NE winds which cause a swell. Inner harbour (river) gives excellent shelter. Berthing on W pier is not recommended. Moorings in N of harbour belong to YC. Beware anchoring in harbour due to heavy chain on the bottom.
NAVIGATION
Waypoint 52°59′·20N 06°01′·80W, 040°/220° from/to entrance, 0·27M. Entry presents no difficulty so long as one keeps in the R sector of the Lt on E Pier. This avoids Planet Rock and Pogeen Rock. Depth over bar 0·5m. There is a rock 5m NNW of Packet Quay off the point; keep at least 10m off at LWS.
LIGHTS AND MARKS
There are no leading marks or lights. The only lights are those shown on the chartlet on East Pier, West Pier and Packet Quay.
RADIO TELEPHONE
VHF Ch 16; 02 06 07 08 26 27 28 (when vessel expected).
TELEPHONE (0404)
Hr Mr 67455; MRCC Limerick (061) 61219; Coast Life Saving Service 67310; # 67222; Police 67107; Dr 67381.
FACILITIES
EC Thursday; **East Pier** L, AB; **South Quay** Slip, P, D, L, FW, AB; **Wicklow Marine Services** ☎ 68408, M, ME, El, Sh, C, AB; **Neil Watson** ☎ 67492, Slip, BH (16 ton), M, FW, ME, El, Sh, C, CH, AB; **Wicklow SC** ☎ 67526, M, L, FW, Bar; **J. P. Hopkins** ☎ 67413, Kos, Gaz; **Town** CH, V, R, Bar. ✉; Ⓑ; ⇌; ✈ (Dublin).

DUBLIN/DUN LAOGHAIRE

(Dublin)

10-12-25

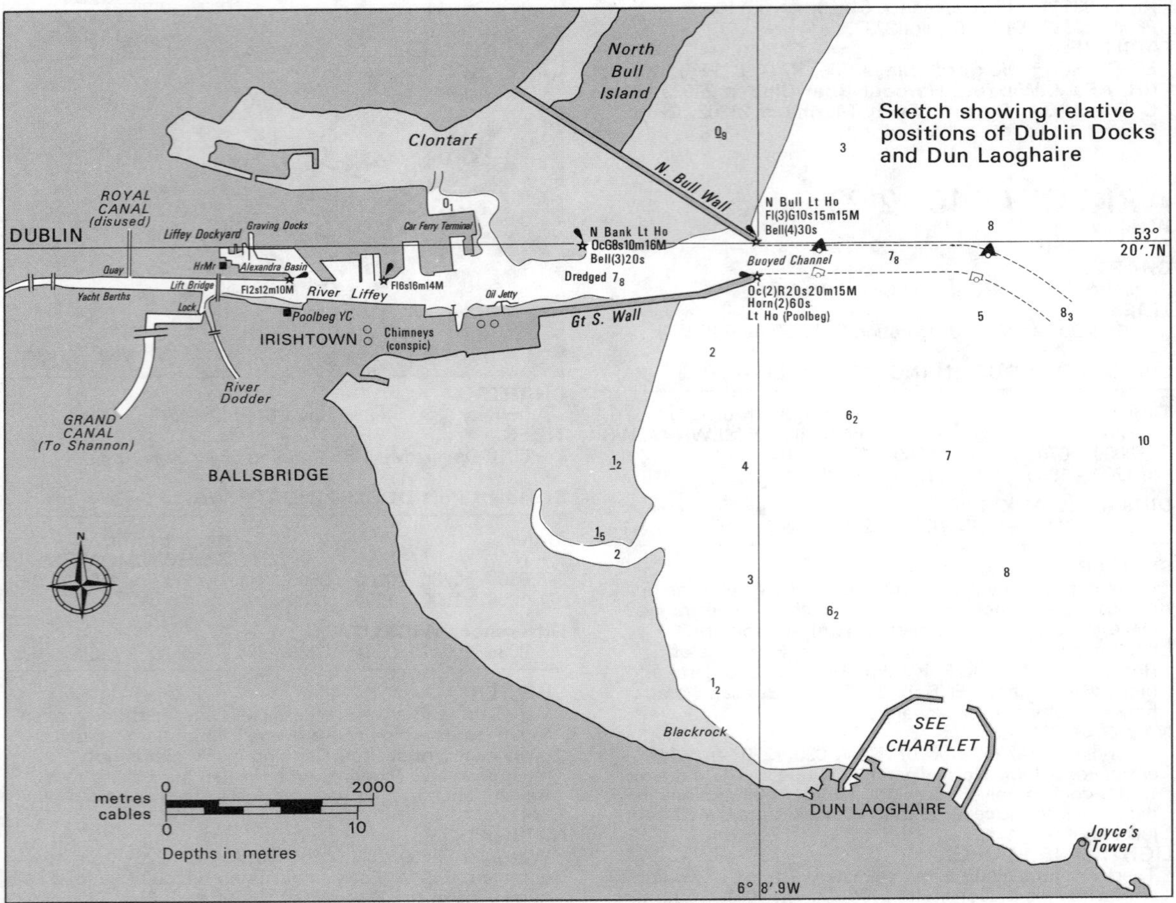
North Bull Island
Sketch showing relative positions of Dublin Docks and Dun Laoghaire
Clontarf
N. Bull Wall
ROYAL CANAL (disused)
DUBLIN
Liffey Dockyard
Graving Docks
Car Ferry Terminal
N Bull Lt Ho Fl(3)G10s15m15M Bell(4)30s
N Bank Lt Ho OcG8s10m16M Bell(3)20s
Buoyed Channel
Alexandra Basin
HrMr
Quay
Yacht Berths
Lift Bridge
Lock
Fl2s12m10M
Fl6s16m14M
River Liffey
Oil Jetty
Dredged 7.8
Oc(2)R20s20m15M Horn(2)60s Lt Ho (Poolbeg)
Poolbeg YC
Gt S. Wall
IRISHTOWN
Chimneys (conspic)
River Dodder
GRAND CANAL (To Shannon)
BALLSBRIDGE
Blackrock
SEE CHARTLET
DUN LAOGHAIRE
Joyce's Tower
53° 20'.7N
6° 8'.9W
metres 0 2000
cables 0 10
Depths in metres

▲ Call Hailing Station verbally (conspic) on N side of Dock area or on Ch 12, Dublin Port Radio

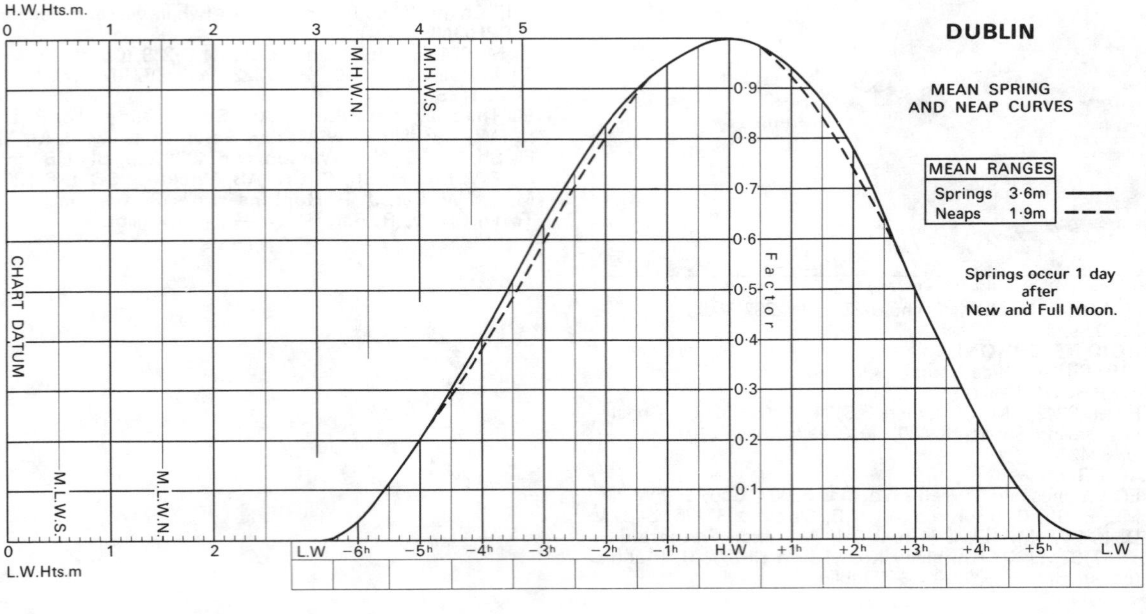
H.W.Hts.m.
0 1 2 3 4 5
M.H.W.N.
M.H.W.S.
CHART DATUM
M.L.W.S.
M.L.W.N.
L.W.Hts.m
Factor
0·9
0·8
0·7
0·6
0·5
0·4
0·3
0·2
0·1
L.W −6h −5h −4h −3h −2h −1h H.W +1h +2h +3h +4h +5h L.W
DUBLIN
MEAN SPRING AND NEAP CURVES
MEAN RANGES
Springs 3·6m
Neaps 1·9m
Springs occur 1 day after New and Full Moon.

DUBLIN/DUN LAOGHAIRE *continued*

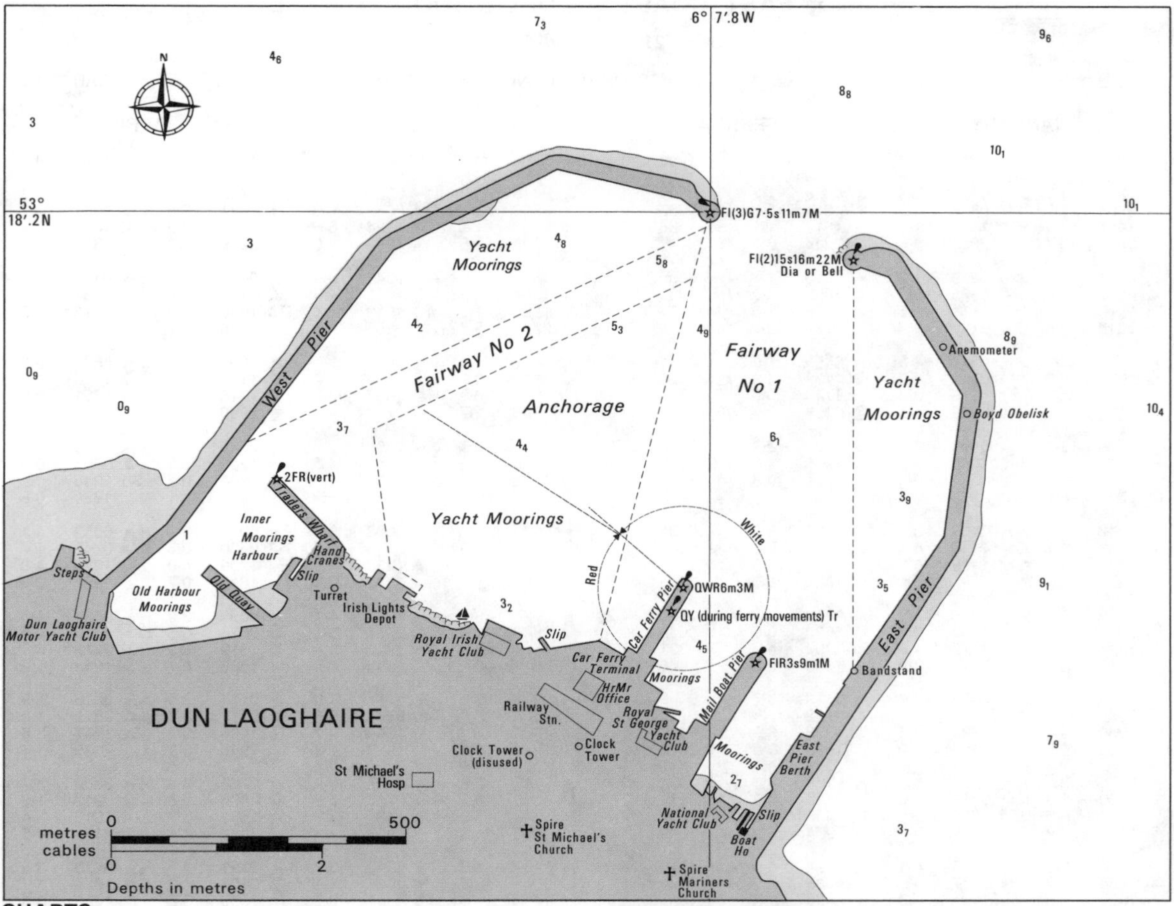
6° 7'.8W
53°
18'.2N
N
Yacht Moorings
Fairway No 2
Anchorage
Fairway No 1
Yacht Moorings
West Pier
East Pier
Fl(3)G7·5s11m7M
Fl(2)15s16m22M
Dia or Bell
Anemometer
Boyd Obelisk
2FR(vert)
Traders Wharf
Inner Moorings Harbour
Hand Cranes
Slip
Steps
Old Harbour Moorings
Old Quay
Turret
Irish Lights Depot
Dun Laoghaire Motor Yacht Club
Yacht Moorings
Royal Irish Yacht Club
Slip
Red
White
Car Ferry Pier
QWR6m3M
QY (during ferry movements) Tr
Car Ferry Terminal
Moorings
HrMr Office
Mail Boat Pier
FlR3s9m1M
Bandstand
Railway Stn.
Royal St George Yacht Club
Moorings
East Pier Berth
DUN LAOGHAIRE
Clock Tower (disused)
Clock Tower
St Michael's Hosp
National Yacht Club
Slip
Boat Ho
Spire St Michael's Church
Spire Mariners Church
metres 0 500
cables 0 2
Depths in metres

12

CHARTS
Admiralty 1447, 1415, 1468; Imray C61, C62; Irish OS 16

TIDES
Dun Laoghaire +0042 Dover; ML 2·4; Duration 0640; Zone 0 (GMT).

Standard Port DUBLIN (NORTH WALL) (⟶)

Times				Height (metres)			
HW		LW		MHWS	MHWN	MLWN	MLWS
0000	0700	0000	0500	4·1	3·4	1·5	0·5
1200	1900	1200	1700				
Differences DUBLIN BAR							
−0006	−0001	−0002	−0003	0·0	0·0	0·0	+0·1
DUN LAOGHAIRE							
−0006	−0001	−0002	−0003	0·0	0·0	0·0	+0·1

NOTE: Dublin is a Standard Port and times and heights of tides for the year are given below.
Since Dun Laoghaire is the principal yachting centre for Dublin, the following all refer to Dun Laoghaire.

SHELTER
The harbour is always available but is open to NE swell and anchor holding ground is poor. In these conditions yachts should proceed to Dublin or Howth unless YCs can provide sheltered moorings.

NAVIGATION
Waypoint 53°18'·40N 06°07'·00W, 060°/240° from/to entrance, 0·47M. Keep clear of the many coasters and ferries. Warning — do not anchor in areas marked 'moorings' or in fairways. Beware — the drying rocks approx 10m from the East Pierhead right in the entrance.

LIGHTS AND MARKS
There are no leading lights or marks. There are lights on both pierheads as shown, on Mail Boat Pierhead and on Trader's Wharf. Light on Car Ferry Pier has R sector to cover moorings, so anchor in W sector outside fairways.

RADIO TELEPHONE
VHF Call *Harbour Office Dun Laoghaire* Ch 16; 14. YCs Ch M. Dublin (Call *Dublin Port Radio*) Ch **12** 16; 09 **12** 13 14 (H24). Dublin lifting bridge (call *Eastlink*) Ch 12 13; Dublin Radio Ch 16 67 **83** (H24). Poolbeg YC Ch 12, 16.

TELEPHONE (01)
Hr Mr 801130, Dublin 748772; MRCC Limerick 61219; Coast Life Saving Service 809641 or 376497; # 801321; Weather 424655; Local weather (Dublin Bay) 1199; Police (Dublin) 778141, (Dun Laoghaire) 801285; Dr 859244; Ⓗ 806901.

FACILITIES
National YC ☎ 805725, Slip, M, L, C (4 ton), FW, D, R, Bar; **Royal St. George YC** ☎ 801811, Slip, M, D, L, FW, C (5 ton), R, Bar; **Royal Irish YC** ☎ 809452, Slip, M, D, L, FW, C (5 ton), R, Bar; **Dun Laoghaire Motor YC** ☎ 801371, Slip, FW, AB, Bar; **Poolbeg YC** ☎ 604681, M, Slip, AB, Bar, FW; **Cross Berth (Traders Wharf)** FW, C (5 ton), AB; **Downer International Sails (Dun Laoghaire)** ☎ 804286, SM; **B. J. Marine** ☎ 719605, CH, Sh; **All Weather Marine** ☎ 713305 CH; **Western Marine** ☎ 800321, CH, ME; **Windmill Leisure & Marine** ☎ 772008, CH, ACA; **Dinghy Supplies** ☎ 322312, CH; **Watson and Jameson** ☎ 326466, SM; **H. Pilsworth** ☎ 822023 ME; **E. Brunker** ☎ 342590, Ⓔ; **Apex Electrical** ☎ 541066, El; **Viking Marine** ☎ 806654, CH, Gas; **Town** P, D, ME, El, Sh, CH, V, R, Bar. ✉; Ⓑ; ⇌; ✈ (Dublin).

IRELAND, EAST COAST – DUBLIN (NORTH WALL)

Lat 53°21′ N Long 6°13′ W

TIME ZONE UT(GMT)
For Summer Time add ONE hour in non-shaded areas

TIMES AND HEIGHTS OF HIGH AND LOW WATERS

YEAR **1992**

JANUARY

Day	Time	m	Day	Time	m
1 W	0220 0904 1456 2129	1·3 3·7 1·4 3·7	16 Th	0117 0806 1351 2032	1·3 3·5 1·3 3·7
2 Th	0311 0952 1545 2219	1·3 3·8 1·2 3·8	17 F	0219 0905 1451 2131	1·2 3·8 1·0 3·9
3 F	0355 1034 1628 2259	1·2 4·0 1·1 3·8	18 Sa	0315 0959 1546 2226	1·0 4·0 0·7 4·1
4 Sa ●	0434 1112 1706 2337	1·1 4·1 1·0 3·8	19 Su ○	0406 1048 1637 2316	0·8 4·3 0·5 4·2
5 Su	0512 1147 1743	1·0 4·1 0·9	20 M	0452 1136 1726	0·7 4·5 0·3
6 M	0012 0549 1222 1817	3·8 1·0 4·1 0·9	21 Tu	0005 0539 1222 1812	4·3 0·6 4·6 0·2
7 Tu	0046 0624 1256 1853	3·7 0·9 4·1 0·9	22 W	0052 0624 1309 1900	4·2 0·6 4·6 0·2
8 W	0120 0700 1330 1928	3·7 1·0 4·0 0·9	23 Th	0138 0710 1355 1948	4·1 0·6 4·5 0·4
9 Th	0154 0735 1405 2002	3·6 1·0 3·9 1·0	24 F	0225 0757 1444 2036	4·0 0·8 4·3 0·6
10 F	0230 0811 1444 2037	3·6 1·1 3·8 1·1	25 Sa	0314 0846 1536 2128	3·8 1·0 4·1 0·9
11 Sa	0311 0849 1528 2117	3·5 1·3 3·6 1·2	26 Su ☾	0406 0942 1637 2226	3·6 1·3 3·9 1·2
12 Su	0357 0934 1617 2203	3·4 1·4 3·5 1·3	27 M	0508 1047 1746 2330	3·5 1·5 3·7 1·5
13 M ☽	0451 1027 1712 2301	3·3 1·5 3·5 1·4	28 Tu	0617 1203 1859	3·4 1·6 3·5
14 Tu	0553 1132 1817	3·3 1·6 3·5	29 W	0042 0727 1327 2009	1·6 3·5 1·6 3·5
15 W	0008 0702 1242 1926	1·4 3·4 1·5 3·6	30 Th	0152 0833 1437 2112	1·6 3·6 1·5 3·6
			31 F	0250 0929 1531 2204	1·5 3·8 1·3 3·6

FEBRUARY

Day	Time	m	Day	Time	m
1 Sa	0338 1017 1613 2248	1·3 3·9 1·1 3·7	16 Su	0305 0946 1538 2217	1·1 4·0 0·7 4·1
2 Su	0419 1058 1649 2323	1·1 4·0 1·0 3·7	17 M	0356 1037 1627 2306	0·8 4·3 0·4 4·2
3 M ●	0455 1133 1723 2356	1·0 4·0 0·9 3·7	18 Tu ○	0441 1123 1712 2350	0·6 4·5 0·2 4·3
4 Tu	0529 1205 1754	0·9 4·0 0·8	19 W	0525 1207 1756	0·5 4·6 0·2
5 W	0025 0601 1235 1825	3·7 0·8 4·0 0·8	20 Th	0031 0605 1249 1839	4·2 0·5 4·6 0·2
6 Th	0052 0632 1302 1853	3·7 0·8 4·0 0·8	21 F	0110 0648 1331 1920	4·2 0·5 4·5 0·4
7 F	0119 0702 1333 1923	3·7 0·8 3·9 0·8	22 Sa	0149 0728 1415 2004	4·0 0·7 4·3 0·7
8 Sa	0151 0733 1408 1954	3·7 0·9 3·8 0·9	23 Su	0232 0813 1504 2049	3·9 0·9 4·1 1·0
9 Su	0229 0808 1450 2032	3·6 1·0 3·8 1·0	24 M	0319 0904 1600 2141	3·7 1·1 3·8 1·3
10 M	0314 0850 1539 2117	3·5 1·1 3·7 1·2	25 Tu ☾	0416 1007 1711 2244	3·5 1·4 3·5 1·6
11 Tu ☽	0406 0942 1637 2214	3·4 1·3 3·6 1·3	26 W	0527 1125 1828	3·4 1·6 3·4
12 W	0509 1049 1746 2330	3·3 1·4 3·5 1·5	27 Th	0001 0646 1256 1944	1·8 3·4 1·6 3·4
13 Th	0627 1214 1904	3·4 1·4 3·5	28 F	0123 0801 1415 2051	1·7 3·5 1·5 3·4
14 F	0055 0744 1334 2018	1·5 3·5 1·3 3·7	29 Sa	0229 0905 1510 2146	1·5 3·7 1·3 3·5
15 Sa	0206 0850 1442 2121	1·3 3·7 1·0 3·9			

MARCH

Day	Time	m	Day	Time	m
1 Su	0318 0956 1550 2228	1·3 3·8 1·1 3·6	16 M	0253 0932 1524 2206	1·1 4·0 0·6 4·0
2 M	0357 1037 1626 2302	1·1 3·9 1·0 3·7	17 Tu	0342 1023 1612 2251	0·8 4·3 0·4 4·1
3 Tu	0433 1111 1657 2332	1·0 3·9 0·9 3·7	18 W ○	0426 1108 1655 2332	0·7 4·4 0·3 4·2
4 W ●	0505 1140 1725 2357	0·9 3·9 0·8 3·8	19 Th	0506 1149 1736	0·5 4·5 0·3
5 Th	0533 1207 1751	0·8 3·9 0·7	20 F	0008 0546 1228 1815	4·2 0·5 4·5 0·4
6 F	0021 0600 1232 1818	3·8 0·7 3·9 0·7	21 Sa	0042 0625 1307 1853	4·1 0·5 4·4 0·6
7 Sa	0048 0628 1303 1846	3·8 0·7 3·9 0·7	22 Su	0117 0704 1349 1933	4·0 0·6 4·2 0·8
8 Su	0119 0700 1340 1920	3·8 0·7 3·9 0·8	23 M	0157 0748 1436 2015	3·9 0·8 3·9 1·1
9 M	0157 0737 1422 2001	3·8 0·8 3·8 0·9	24 Tu	0242 0837 1531 2104	3·8 1·1 3·7 1·4
10 Tu	0242 0822 1514 2047	3·7 1·0 3·7 1·1	25 W	0335 0938 1638 2206	3·6 1·3 3·4 1·6
11 W	0335 0917 1616 2148	3·5 1·1 3·6 1·4	26 Th ☾	0445 1054 1757 2325	3·4 1·5 3·3 1·8
12 Th ☽	0442 1030 1730 2312	3·4 1·3 3·5 1·5	27 F	0610 1219 1912	3·4 1·5 3·3
13 F	0607 1203 1853	3·4 1·3 3·5	28 Sa	0046 0726 1337 2020	1·7 3·4 1·4 3·4
14 Sa	0041 0727 1323 2008	1·5 3·5 1·1 3·6	29 Su	0157 0832 1434 2117	1·6 3·5 1·3 3·5
15 Su	0154 0834 1429 2111	1·3 3·8 0·9 3·8	30 M	0247 0925 1517 2159	1·4 3·6 1·1 3·6
			31 Tu	0328 1006 1550 2233	1·2 3·7 1·0 3·6

APRIL

Day	Time	m	Day	Time	m
1 W	0403 1041 1621 2259	1·0 3·8 0·9 3·7	16 Th	0406 1051 1634 2312	0·7 4·3 0·4 4·1
2 Th	0433 1109 1648 2325	0·9 3·8 0·8 3·7	17 F ○	0447 1132 1713 2346	0·6 4·3 0·5 4·1
3 F ●	0501 1136 1715 2350	0·8 3·9 0·7 3·8	18 Sa	0526 1210 1751	0·6 4·3 0·6
4 Sa	0529 1205 1744	0·7 3·9 0·7	19 Su	0018 0605 1248 1829	4·1 0·6 4·2 0·8
5 Su	0019 0600 1239 1817	3·9 0·6 4·0 0·7	20 M	0052 0646 1328 1907	4·1 0·7 4·0 0·9
6 M	0055 0636 1319 1856	3·9 0·6 3·9 0·7	21 Tu	0131 0730 1415 1949	4·0 0·8 3·8 1·2
7 Tu	0135 0719 1406 1940	3·9 0·7 3·9 0·9	22 W	0216 0819 1507 2039	3·9 1·0 3·6 1·4
8 W	0223 0808 1501 2030	3·8 0·8 3·7 1·1	23 Th	0308 0917 1610 2138	3·7 1·2 3·4 1·5
9 Th	0321 0908 1606 2136	3·7 1·0 3·6 1·3	24 F ☾	0413 1024 1720 2248	3·5 1·3 3·3 1·7
10 F ☽	0431 1028 1723 2301	3·6 1·1 3·5 1·5	25 Sa	0529 1136 1831	3·4 1·4 3·2
11 Sa	0553 1151 1842	3·5 1·1 3·5	26 Su	0000 0642 1243 1935	1·7 3·4 1·4 3·3
12 Su	0022 0709 1307 1954	1·5 3·6 1·0 3·6	27 M	0107 0747 1342 2030	1·6 3·4 1·3 3·4
13 M	0133 0816 1411 2056	1·3 3·8 0·8 3·8	28 Tu	0202 0842 1429 2117	1·4 3·4 1·2 3·4
14 Tu	0232 0914 1505 2149	1·1 4·0 0·6 3·9	29 W	0247 0925 1507 2152	1·3 3·5 1·1 3·5
15 W	0321 1004 1552 2234	0·9 4·2 0·5 4·0	30 Th	0324 1002 1539 2223	1·1 3·6 1·0 3·6

Chart Datum: 0.20 metres below Ordnance Datum (Dublin)

TIME ZONE UT(GMT)

For Summer Time add ONE hour in non-shaded areas

IRELAND, EAST COAST – DUBLIN (NORTH WALL)

Lat 53°21′ N Long 6°13′ W

TIMES AND HEIGHTS OF HIGH AND LOW WATERS

YEAR **1992**

MAY

Day	Time	m	Day	Time	m
1 F	0356	1·0	16 Sa	0430	0·8
	1034	3·7		1115	4·1
	1610	0·9		1654	0·7
	2252	3·7		○ 2327	4·0
2 Sa	0427	0·9	17 Su	0512	0·8
	1106	3·8		1154	4·0
	1641	0·8		1732	0·8
	● 2323	3·9			
3 Su	0501	0·7	18 M	0001	4·0
	1143	3·9		0553	0·8
	1716	0·7		1234	4·0
				1810	0·9
4 M	0000	4·0	19 Tu	0036	4·0
	0539	0·6		0634	0·8
	1224	4·0		1314	3·9
	1756	0·7		1849	1·0
5 Tu	0039	4·0	20 W	0114	4·0
	0621	0·5		0717	0·9
	1309	4·0		1358	3·7
	1839	0·7		1931	1·1
6 W	0124	4·0	21 Th	0158	3·9
	0709	0·6		0804	1·0
	1359	3·9		1446	3·6
	1927	0·9		2018	1·2
7 Th	0216	4·0	22 F	0247	3·8
	0804	0·7		0856	1·1
	1456	3·8		1539	3·4
	2022	1·0		2110	1·4
8 F	0314	3·9	23 Sa	0341	3·6
	0908	0·8		0950	1·2
	1600	3·7		1637	3·3
	2128	1·2		2207	1·5
9 Sa	0420	3·8	24 Su	0441	3·4
	1020	0·9		1049	1·3
	1711	3·6		1739	3·2
	☽ 2242	1·4		☾ 2309	1·5
10 Su	0533	3·7	25 M	0547	3·3
	1133	0·9		1147	1·3
	1822	3·5		1838	3·2
	2354	1·4			
11 M	0645	3·8	26 Tu	0010	1·5
	1242	0·9		0649	3·3
	1931	3·6		1242	1·3
				1934	3·3
12 Tu	0103	1·3	27 W	0104	1·5
	0751	3·8		0745	3·3
	1345	0·8		1333	1·2
	2033	3·7		2023	3·3
13 W	0205	1·2	28 Th	0155	1·4
	0851	4·0		0834	3·4
	1440	0·7		1418	1·2
	2127	3·8		2105	3·4
14 Th	0258	1·0	29 F	0239	1·3
	0945	4·0		0918	3·5
	1528	0·7		1457	1·1
	2212	3·9		2143	3·6
15 F	0346	0·9	30 Sa	0318	1·1
	1033	4·1		1000	3·6
	1613	0·7		1535	0·9
	2252	4·0		2221	3·7
			31 Su	0357	0·9
				1042	3·8
				1614	0·8
				2301	3·9

JUNE

Day	Time	m	Day	Time	m
1 M	0440	0·7	16 Tu	0543	0·9
	1126	3·9		1221	3·8
	1655	0·7		1754	0·9
	● 2343	4·0			
2 Tu	0523	0·5	17 W	0027	4·1
	1211	4·0		0622	0·8
	1740	0·7		1300	3·8
				1832	0·9
3 W	0028	4·2	18 Th	0103	4·0
	0611	0·4		0703	0·8
	1300	4·0		1340	3·7
	1827	0·7		1913	1·0
4 Th	0116	4·2	19 F	0142	4·0
	0703	0·4		0744	0·9
	1352	4·0		1420	3·6
	1917	0·8		1954	1·0
5 F	0206	4·2	20 Sa	0222	3·9
	0758	0·4		0826	0·9
	1447	3·9		1503	3·5
	2012	0·9		2037	1·1
6 Sa	0301	4·1	21 Su	0305	3·7
	0857	0·5		0911	1·0
	1545	3·8		1548	3·4
	2111	1·1		2124	1·3
7 Su	0402	4·0	22 M	0350	3·5
	1000	0·7		0957	1·1
	1648	3·6		1637	3·3
	☽ 2216	1·2		2213	1·4
8 M	0506	3·9	23 Tu	0440	3·4
	1105	0·8		1047	1·2
	1754	3·6		1729	3·2
	2322	1·3		☾ 2306	1·5
9 Tu	0615	3·8	24 W	0536	3·3
	1210	0·9		1140	1·3
	1900	3·6		1825	3·2
10 W	0029	1·3	25 Th	0003	1·5
	0723	3·8		0636	3·3
	1314	0·9		1235	1·3
	2002	3·6		1923	3·3
11 Th	0135	1·3	26 F	0100	1·5
	0826	3·8		0738	3·3
	1412	1·0		1328	1·3
	2100	3·7		2016	3·4
12 F	0237	1·2	27 Sa	0155	1·4
	0925	3·8		0837	3·4
	1505	1·0		1419	1·2
	2149	3·8		2107	3·5
13 Sa	0331	1·1	28 Su	0247	1·2
	1016	3·9		0931	3·6
	1552	1·0		1508	1·1
	2234	3·9		2155	3·7
14 Su	0419	1·0	29 M	0336	0·9
	1102	3·9		1023	3·8
	1635	1·0		1555	0·9
	2313	4·0		2241	4·0
15 M	0502	0·9	30 Tu	0426	0·7
	1143	3·8		1112	3·9
	1715	0·9		1641	0·8
	○ 2350	4·0		● 2327	4·2

JULY

Day	Time	m	Day	Time	m
1 W	0513	0·5	16 Th	0012	4·1
	1200	4·1		0607	0·8
	1727	0·7		1242	3·7
				1814	0·9
2 Th	0015	4·3	17 F	0048	4·1
	0603	0·3		0642	0·8
	1249	4·1		1316	3·7
	1815	0·6		1849	0·9
3 F	0102	4·4	18 Sa	0120	4·0
	0652	0·2		0716	0·8
	1338	4·1		1348	3·7
	1903	0·6		1924	0·9
4 Sa	0151	4·4	19 Su	0152	3·9
	0744	0·3		0751	0·9
	1427	4·0		1423	3·6
	1954	0·7		2001	1·0
5 Su	0242	4·3	20 M	0227	3·8
	0837	0·4		0826	0·9
	1521	3·9		1500	3·5
	2046	0·9		2036	1·1
6 M	0335	4·2	21 Tu	0307	3·7
	0932	0·6		0903	1·0
	1616	3·7		1542	3·4
	2143	1·1		2117	1·2
7 Tu	0434	4·0	22 W	0350	3·5
	1033	0·8		0945	1·2
	1716	3·6		1628	3·4
	☽ 2245	1·3		☾ 2204	1·4
8 W	0540	3·8	23 Th	0441	3·4
	1134	1·0		1035	1·3
	1821	3·5		1723	3·3
	2354	1·4		2302	1·5
9 Th	0652	3·7	24 F	0542	3·3
	1241	1·2		1139	1·4
	1927	3·5		1827	3·3
10 F	0107	1·5	25 Sa	0012	1·5
	0801	3·6		0652	3·3
	1345	1·3		1248	1·4
	2030	3·6		1934	3·4
11 Sa	0219	1·4	26 Su	0121	1·4
	0907	3·6		0806	3·4
	1443	1·2		1354	1·3
	2128	3·7		2037	3·6
12 Su	0319	1·3	27 M	0226	1·2
	1004	3·7		0911	3·6
	1534	1·2		1450	1·2
	2217	3·9		2134	3·8
13 M	0409	1·1	28 Tu	0322	0·9
	1052	3·7		1007	3·8
	1619	1·1		1542	1·0
	2259	4·0		2224	4·0
14 Tu	0452	1·0	29 W	0414	0·6
	1132	3·7		1059	4·0
	1659	1·0		1630	0·8
	○ 2337	4·0		● 2312	4·3
15 W	0530	0·9	30 Th	0502	0·3
	1208	3·7		1147	4·1
	1737	0·9		1715	0·6
				2358	4·5
			31 F	0550	0·2
				1232	4·2
				1800	0·5

AUGUST

Day	Time	m	Day	Time	m
1 Sa	0043	4·6	16 Su	0052	4·0
	0635	0·1		0642	0·8
	1317	4·2		1314	3·7
	1843	0·5		1852	0·8
2 Su	0128	4·6	17 M	0119	3·9
	0723	0·2		0712	0·8
	1402	4·1		1344	3·7
	1930	0·6		1923	0·9
3 M	0216	4·5	18 Tu	0151	3·9
	0811	0·4		0741	0·9
	1449	4·0		1419	3·7
	2018	0·8		1955	1·0
4 Tu	0305	4·3	19 W	0230	3·8
	0900	0·7		0815	1·0
	1538	3·8		1500	3·6
	2111	1·0		2033	1·1
5 W	0400	4·0	20 Th	0314	3·7
	0956	1·0		0857	1·1
	1634	3·7		1548	3·5
	☽ 2212	1·3		2121	1·3
6 Th	0506	3·7	21 F	0406	3·5
	1058	1·3		0948	1·3
	1739	3·6		1642	3·4
	2323	1·5		☾ 2221	1·4
7 F	0622	3·5	22 Sa	0508	3·4
	1207	1·5		1057	1·5
	1849	3·5		1749	3·4
				2342	1·5
8 Sa	0045	1·6	23 Su	0625	3·4
	0738	3·5		1222	1·5
	1320	1·5		1904	3·4
	1959	3·6			
9 Su	0205	1·5	24 M	0103	1·4
	0853	3·5		0747	3·5
	1425	1·5		1337	1·4
	2105	3·7		2015	3·6
10 M	0308	1·3	25 Tu	0212	1·1
	0955	3·5		0857	3·7
	1517	1·3		1437	1·2
	2200	3·9		2115	3·9
11 Tu	0357	1·2	26 W	0310	0·8
	1041	3·6		0955	3·9
	1602	1·2		1529	1·0
	2244	4·0		2207	4·1
12 W	0437	1·0	27 Th	0400	0·5
	1119	3·7		1045	4·1
	1641	1·0		1616	0·7
	2320	4·0		2255	4·4
13 Th	0512	0·9	28 F	0447	0·3
	1150	3·7		1130	4·2
	1716	0·9		1658	0·6
	○ 2353	4·1		● 2339	4·5
14 F	0543	0·8	29 Sa	0532	0·2
	1219	3·7		1212	4·3
	1750	0·8		1740	0·5
15 Sa	0024	4·0	30 Su	0022	4·6
	0612	0·8		0614	0·2
	1248	3·7		1253	4·3
	1821	0·8		1822	0·5
			31 M	0104	4·6
				0657	0·3
				1333	4·2
				1906	0·5

Chart Datum: 0.20 metres below Ordnance Datum (Dublin)

IRELAND, EAST COAST – DUBLIN (NORTH WALL)

TIME ZONE UT(GMT)
For Summer Time add ONE hour in non-shaded areas

Lat 53°21′ N Long 6°13′ W

TIMES AND HEIGHTS OF HIGH AND LOW WATERS

YEAR **1992**

SEPTEMBER

Day	Time	m	Day	Time	m
1 Tu	0149 0741 1415 1951	4·5 0·5 4·1 0·7	16 W	0121 0704 1347 1924	3·9 0·8 3·8 0·9
2 W	0236 0827 1501 2042	4·2 0·8 3·9 1·0	17 Th	0201 0741 1427 2005	3·8 1·0 3·7 1·0
3 Th ☽	0329 0919 1553 2142	3·9 1·2 3·8 1·3	18 F	0247 0825 1517 2054	3·7 1·1 3·6 1·2
4 F	0435 1021 1658 2258	3·6 1·5 3·6 1·5	19 Sa ☾	0343 0918 1616 2159	3·6 1·4 3·5 1·3
5 Sa	0556 1136 1814	3·4 1·7 3·5	20 Su	0451 1033 1726 2327	3·4 1·6 3·5 1·4
6 Su	0025 0717 1255 1928	1·6 3·3 1·7 3·6	21 M	0612 1204 1843	3·4 1·6 3·5
7 M	0148 0836 1404 2039	1·5 3·4 1·6 3·7	22 Tu	0049 0734 1320 1955	1·2 3·5 1·5 3·7
8 Tu	0250 0936 1457 2136	1·3 3·5 1·4 3·8	23 W	0157 0842 1422 2056	1·0 3·7 1·2 4·0
9 W	0336 1023 1541 2220	1·1 3·6 1·2 3·9	24 Th	0254 0939 1512 2149	0·7 3·9 1·0 4·2
10 Th	0413 1058 1617 2255	1·0 3·7 1·1 4·0	25 F	0343 1027 1557 2235	0·5 4·1 0·8 4·4
11 F	0444 1125 1651 2326	0·9 3·7 0·9 4·0	26 Sa ●	0428 1111 1641 2319	0·3 4·2 0·6 4·5
12 Sa ○	0512 1150 1722 2354	0·9 3·8 0·9 4·0	27 Su	0511 1150 1722	0·3 4·3 0·5
13 Su	0540 1215 1751	0·8 3·8 0·8	28 M	0001 0551 1227 1803	4·6 0·3 4·3 0·5
14 M	0019 0605 1241 1819	4·0 0·8 3·8 0·8	29 Tu	0042 0632 1304 1845	4·5 0·5 4·2 0·6
15 Tu	0048 0634 1310 1849	3·9 0·8 3·8 0·8	30 W	0124 0713 1344 1930	4·3 0·7 4·1 0·8

OCTOBER

Day	Time	m	Day	Time	m
1 Th	0212 0757 1429 2019	4·1 1·0 4·0 1·0	16 F	0142 0717 1406 1947	3·9 1·0 3·9 0·9
2 F	0304 0847 1519 2119	3·8 1·3 3·8 1·3	17 Sa	0233 0804 1458 2042	3·7 1·1 3·8 1·1
3 Sa ☽	0410 0948 1623 2234	3·5 1·6 3·7 1·5	18 Su	0332 0901 1559 2153	3·6 1·4 3·7 1·2
4 Su	0529 1104 1739 2357	3·4 1·8 3·6 1·5	19 M ☾	0442 1019 1709 2315	3·5 1·5 3·6 1·2
5 M	0649 1222 1853	3·3 1·8 3·6	20 Tu	0601 1144 1825	3·5 1·6 3·7
6 Tu	0114 0805 1334 2002	1·4 3·4 1·7 3·6	21 W	0031 0717 1257 1934	1·1 3·6 1·5 3·8
7 W	0216 0905 1429 2100	1·3 3·5 1·5 3·7	22 Th	0137 0823 1359 2036	0·9 3·7 1·3 4·0
8 Th	0303 0950 1512 2146	1·2 3·6 1·3 3·8	23 F	0233 0918 1453 2129	0·7 3·9 1·1 4·2
9 F	0339 1026 1549 2223	1·1 3·7 1·1 3·8	24 Sa	0322 1007 1539 2217	0·5 4·1 0·9 4·4
10 Sa	0410 1054 1621 2254	1·0 3·7 1·0 3·9	25 Su ●	0407 1049 1623 2302	0·5 4·2 0·7 4·4
11 Su ○	0437 1118 1651 2322	0·9 3·8 0·9 3·9	26 M	0449 1129 1705 2343	0·5 4·2 0·6 4·4
12 M	0505 1143 1720 2350	0·9 3·9 0·9 3·9	27 Tu	0530 1204 1747	0·5 4·3 0·6
13 Tu	0532 1211 1751	0·8 3·9 0·8	28 W	0024 0610 1241 1829	4·3 0·7 4·3 0·7
14 W	0021 0601 1243 1824	3·9 0·8 4·0 0·8	29 Th	0106 0650 1320 1914	4·2 0·9 4·2 0·8
15 Th	0059 0636 1321 1903	3·9 0·8 3·9 0·8	30 F	0152 0734 1404 2004	4·0 1·1 4·1 1·0
			31 Sa	0243 0822 1454 2101	3·7 1·4 3·9 1·2

NOVEMBER

Day	Time	m	Day	Time	m
1 Su	0345 0919 1553 2206	3·5 1·6 3·8 1·4	16 M	0324 0850 1545 2142	3·7 1·3 3·9 0·9
2 M ☽	0454 1027 1702 2316	3·3 1·7 3·6 1·4	17 Tu ☾	0430 1000 1651 2254	3·6 1·4 3·9 1·0
3 Tu	0607 1139 1812	3·3 1·7 3·5	18 W	0542 1116 1801	3·6 1·5 3·9
4 W	0025 0717 1248 1919	1·4 3·3 1·7 3·5	19 Th	0003 0653 1227 1910	1·0 3·6 1·4 3·9
5 Th	0127 0818 1347 2016	1·4 3·4 1·6 3·6	20 F	0109 0758 1333 2012	0·9 3·7 1·3 4·0
6 F	0216 0905 1434 2104	1·3 3·5 1·4 3·6	21 Sa	0208 0854 1432 2110	0·8 3·9 1·2 4·1
7 Sa	0256 0945 1514 2143	1·2 3·6 1·3 3·7	22 Su	0300 0945 1522 2200	0·7 4·0 1·0 4·2
8 Su	0331 1016 1549 2219	1·1 3·7 1·1 3·8	23 M	0346 1030 1610 2248	0·7 4·1 0·9 4·2
9 M	0402 1044 1621 2251	1·0 3·8 1·0 3·8	24 Tu ●	0431 1111 1654 2330	0·7 4·2 0·8 4·2
10 Tu ○	0431 1113 1654 2325	0·9 3·9 0·9 3·9	25 W	0512 1147 1736	0·8 4·2 0·8
11 W	0502 1146 1727	0·9 4·0 0·8	26 Th	0011 0553 1224 1819	4·1 0·9 4·3 0·8
12 Th	0003 0539 1224 1807	4·0 0·8 4·1 0·7	27 F	0052 0632 1303 1902	4·0 1·0 4·2 0·9
13 F	0045 0618 1306 1849	4·0 0·8 4·1 0·7	28 Sa	0135 0714 1344 1948	3·9 1·1 4·1 1·0
14 Sa	0131 0702 1352 1938	3·9 0·9 4·1 0·8	29 Su	0222 0759 1430 2036	3·7 1·2 4·0 1·1
15 Su	0223 0751 1444 2036	3·8 1·1 4·0 0·8	30 M	0312 0849 1522 2129	3·5 1·4 3·8 1·2

DECEMBER

Day	Time	m	Day	Time	m
1 Tu	0410 0945 1619 2227	3·4 1·5 3·7 1·3	16 W ☾	0406 0935 1627 2224	3·7 1·2 4·0 0·9
2 W ☽	0513 1047 1722 2326	3·3 1·6 3·5 1·4	17 Th	0512 1042 1733 2330	3·6 1·4 3·9 1·0
3 Th	0617 1150 1825	3·3 1·7 3·4	18 F	0621 1153 1843	3·6 1·4 3·9
4 F	0025 0719 1250 1924	1·4 3·3 1·6 3·4	19 Sa	0038 0727 1304 1949	1·0 3·7 1·4 3·9
5 Sa	0120 0812 1345 2016	1·4 3·4 1·5 3·5	20 Su	0141 0829 1411 2051	1·0 3·8 1·3 4·0
6 Su	0208 0857 1433 2103	1·3 3·5 1·4 3·6	21 M	0239 0924 1510 2148	1·0 3·9 1·2 4·0
7 M	0250 0936 1514 2143	1·2 3·6 1·3 3·7	22 Tu	0329 1013 1600 2237	1·0 4·0 1·0 4·0
8 Tu	0328 1012 1553 2224	1·1 3·8 1·1 3·8	23 W	0416 1055 1645 2322	1·0 4·1 0·9 4·0
9 W ○	0404 1048 1631 2305	1·0 3·9 0·9 3·9	24 Th ●	0458 1134 1727	0·9 4·2 0·9
10 Th	0441 1126 1711 2347	0·9 4·1 0·7 4·0	25 F	0001 0537 1211 1807	4·0 0·9 4·2 0·8
11 F	0522 1207 1753	0·8 4·2 0·6	26 Sa	0039 0617 1248 1846	3·9 0·9 4·2 0·8
12 Sa	0032 0604 1252 1839	4·0 0·8 4·3 0·5	27 Su	0116 0655 1326 1926	3·8 1·0 4·1 0·9
13 Su	0120 0649 1338 1928	4·0 0·8 4·3 0·5	28 M	0155 0734 1405 2006	3·7 1·1 4·0 1·0
14 M	0211 0738 1430 2022	3·9 0·9 4·2 0·6	29 Tu	0236 0815 1447 2049	3·6 1·2 3·9 1·1
15 Tu	0307 0833 1525 2121	3·8 1·1 4·1 0·7	30 W	0321 0900 1534 2134	3·5 1·3 3·7 1·2
			31 Th	0410 0950 1624 2224	3·4 1·5 3·5 1·4

Chart Datum: 0.20 metres below Ordnance Datum (Dublin)

HOWTH 10-12-26

Dublin

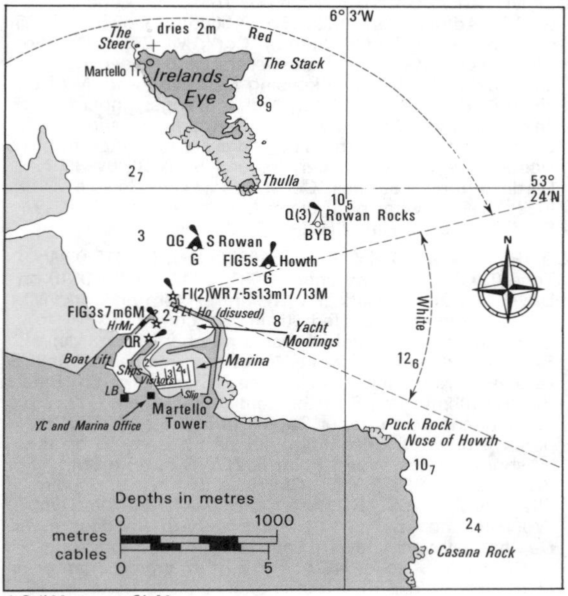
6°3'W
The Steer
dries 2m
Red
The Stack
Martello Tr
Irelands Eye
8_9
2_7
Thulla
53° 24'N
10_5
Q(3) Rowan Rocks
BYB
3
QG S Rowan
G
FlG5s Howth
G
Fl(2)WR7·5s13m17/13M
FlG3s7m6M
2_7
Lt Ho (disused)
HrMr
QR
8
Yacht Moorings
White
12_6
Boat Lift
Slips
Visitors
Marina
Slip
LB
Martello Tower
YC and Marina Office
Puck Rock
Nose of Howth
10_7
Depths in metres
0 1000
metres
cables
0 5
2_4
Casana Rock
N

Call Marina on Ch M

CHARTS
Admiralty 1415, 1468; Imray C61, C62; Irish OS 16

TIDES
+0025 Dover; ML 2·4; Duration 0625; Zone 0 (GMT)

Standard Port DUBLIN (NORTH WALL) (←)

Times				Height (metres)			
HW		LW		MHWS	MHWN	MLWN	MLWS
0000	0700	0000	0500	4·1	3·4	1·5	0·5
1200	1900	1200	1700				
Differences HOWTH							
−0005	−0015	−0005	+0005	0·0	0·0	−0·3	0·0

SHELTER
Good shelter, and available at all tides and in almost any conditions. No entry to trawler dock for pleasure craft. Marina dredged to 3m.

NAVIGATION
Waypoint Howth stbd-hand buoy, FlG 5s, 53°23'·72N 06°03'·53W, 071°/251° from/to breakwater Lt, 0·30M. Beware Casana Rk on the E side of the Ben of Howth. Also beware Puck Rk on the NE corner, and a rock about 50m off Puck Rk which dries. A mile N is Ireland's Eye with rocks running out SE and SW from Thulla, their ends marked by Rowan Rocks and South Rowan buoys. The best approach is S of Ireland's Eye. Between the Nose and the harbour, watch out for lobster pots. Beware rocks off both pierheads. Keep strictly to marked channel up to marina.

LIGHTS AND MARKS
E Pierhead Lt — Fl(2) WR 7·5s 13m 17/13M; W 256°-295°, R elsewhere. W sector leads safely to NE corner of harbour.

RADIO TELEPHONE
Hr Mr VHF Ch 16; 08. Marina Ch M 16.

TELEPHONE (01)
Hr Mr 322252; MRCC Limerick (061) 61219; # 746571; Police 322806; Dr 323191; ⊞ 377755

FACILITIES
EC Saturday. **Howth YC Marina** (220) ☎ 392777, FW, D, Slip, C (7 ton), AC; **Howth YC** ☎ 322141, R (392100), Bar; **W Pier** D, FW; **Waton and Jameson** ☎ 326466, SM; **E. Brunker** ☎ 342590, Ⓔ; **M. Hunt** ☎ 390268, Kos; **Summit Stores** ☎ 322136, Kos; **Fish Dock** ☎ 322252 D; **Dinghy Supplies** ☎ 322312, CH; **Town** P and D (cans), ✉; Ⓑ; ≠ (Dublin); ✈ (Dublin).

MALAHIDE 10-12-27

Dublin

CHARTS
Admiralty 1468, 633; Imray C61, C62; Irish OS 13, 16

TIDES
+0030 Dover; ML 2·4; Duration 0615; Zone 0 (GMT)

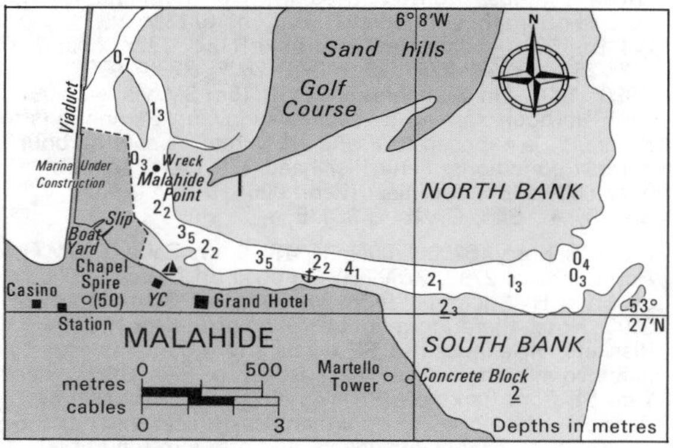
6°8'W
N
Sand hills
Golf Course
Viaduct
0_7
1_3
Marina Under Construction
0_3
Wreck
Malahide Point
2_2
NORTH BANK
Slip
Boat Yard
3_5
2_2
3_5
2_2
4_1
2_1
1_3
0_4
0_3
Chapel Spire (50)
Casino
YC
Grand Hotel
Station
53° 27'N
2_3
MALAHIDE
SOUTH BANK
0 500
metres
cables
0 3
Martello Tower
Concrete Block
2
Depths in metres

Standard Port DUBLIN (NORTH WALL) (←)

Times				Height (metres)			
HW		LW		MHWS	MHWN	MLWN	MLWS
0000	0700	0000	0500	4·1	3·4	1·5	0·5
1200	1900	1200	1700				
Differences MALAHIDE							
−0019	−0013	+0014	+0006	+0·1	+0·1	0·0	0·0
RIVER BOYNE BAR							
−0025	−0015	+0110	0000	+0·4	+0·3	No data	
DUNANY POINT							
−0028	−0018	−0008	−0006	+0·7	+0·9	No data	
DUNDALK – SOLDIERS POINT							
−0010	−0010	0000	+0045	+1·0	+0·8	+0·1	−0·1

SHELTER
A safe anchorage for yachts of up to 2m draught. Entry possible after half flood.

NAVIGATION
Waypoint 53°27'·20N 06°06'·00W, 085°/265° from/to Grand Hotel, 1·6M. The bar off the entrance is 0·3m in depth and there are sandbanks on either side. Do not attempt entry in thick weather or after dark, or in strong onshore winds. The flood stream reaches 3 kn sp, and the ebb 3½ kn. Beware wreck of trawler off the shipyard.

LIGHTS AND MARKS
During the summer only, the S bank is marked with a R buoy, the N bank with a G buoy by the bar. (Laid and altered as necessary by the Malahide YC). There are no navigational Lts. The entry bearing was 267° (1986). A RW mid-channel buoy 0·6M up stream from bar buoys.

RADIO TELEPHONE
Malahide YC. Call *Yacht Base* Ch M (occas).

TELEPHONE (01)
MRCC Limerick 61219; # Dublin 746571; Police 450216; Dr 451953; ⊞ 377755

FACILITIES
Malahide YC ☎ 453372, Slip, C; **Malahide Hardware** ☎ 450944, Kos; **Malahide Marine** ☎ 451059, BY; **Town** ▢, ✉; Ⓑ; ≠; ✈ (Dublin).

MINOR HARBOURS AND ANCHORAGES 10-12-28

TRALEE BAY, Kerry, 52°16′·00N, 09°52′·00W, Zone 0 (GMT), Admty chart 2739. HW −0612 on Dover; −0037 on Cork (Ringaskiddy); HW height +0·4m on Cork (Ringaskiddy); ML 2·6m; Duration 0605. See 10·12·11. Entering the bay from W, pass 3M N of Magharee Is. Lt on Little Samphire Is Fl WRG 5s 17m 16/13M, W140°-152° (leading clear into bay) R152°-172°, obsc 172°-262°, R262°-275°, obsc 275°-280°, R280°-090°, G090°-140°. On Samphire Is Lt QR 15m 3M vis 242°-097°. Fenit Harbour, formed by causeway joining Samphire Is to mainland, is exposed to E and NE winds. A safe harbour in most conditions. Fenit Pier head 2FR (vert) 12m 3M, obsc 058°-148°. Facilities: (Fenit 066) Hr. Mr. 36103; V, Bar, R, ⊠, Slip, C, # ☎ 36115.

VENTRY, Kerry, 52°06′·00N, 10°19′·00W, Zone 0 (GMT), Admty charts 2790, 2789. HW +0540 on Dover, −0056 on Cork; HW height −0·3m on Cork; ML 2·1m; Duration 0605. Note: there are magnetic anomalies near the Blaskets. Hr exposed to SE winds and mountains cause fierce squalls from W. Beware Reenvare Rks which extend 1 ca SE from Parkmore Pt; also NE shore 0·5M NW of Paddock Pt a ridge 3m on which seas break, extends 2·5 ca offshore. Anchor off beach in approx 4m (church bearing W, the village NE) or in 3m S side of bay. There are no lights. Facilities: L, P, Slip, V, Kos.

DINGLE, Kerry, 52°07′·00N, 10°15′·00W, Zone 0 (GMT), Admty charts 2790, 2789. HW +0540 on Dover, −0056 on Cork; HW height −0·3m on Cork; ML 2·1m; Duration 0605. See 10·12·11. Landlocked harbour giving excellent shelter. A busy fishing port. Beware Crow Rk (dries 3·7m) 0·8M SW of Reenbeg Pt, running 3 ca off shore; also the rocky ledge extending half way across entrance at Black Pt. Anchor 1M S of pier, W of dredged channel; or, for small craft, 1 ca SSW of pier in 1·5m. Lights: Tr on E side of ent Fl G 3s 20m 6M; Pier head FR 4m 2M; Ldg Lts 182° front and rear Oc W 3s, 100m apart, leading down dredged channel. E side of S end of channel, G cone buoy. Facilities: Coast Life Saving Service (066) 51278; **Pier** D, FW; **Town** Bar, P, ⊠, R, V, Kos.

PORTMAGEE, Kerry, 51°53′·00N, 10°21′·00W, Zone 0 (GMT), Admty chart 2125. HW +0550 on Dover, −0120 sp −0040 np on Cork; HW height −0·4m on Cork; ML 2·3m; Duration 0610. A good safe anchorage but entrance dangerous in heavy seas. There are no hidden dangers but navigation from Reencaragh Pt up to the pier and bridge needs to be very accurate. Anchor off the pier in approx 6m and beware of strong tides; going alongside pier is not recommended. Bridge opens on request − ring Hr Mr ☎ 6101. Facilities: limited to stores in the village, Kos.

CASTLETOWN, (Bearhaven), Cork, 51°39′·00N, 09°54′·00W, Zone 0 (GMT), Admty chart 1840. HW +0605 on Dover, −0035 on Cork; HW height −0·6m on Cork; ML 1·9m; Duration 0610. Good shelter; entrance chan only 50m wide abreast Came Pt. Anchor to E of Ldg line NW of Dinish I in 3/5m. Perch Rk in ent. chan. marked by Bn with QG Lt. Ldg Lts 010°, both Oc W 3s, 80m apart, 4/7m 1M, vis 005°−015°. There is also a Dir Oc WRG 5s 4m 14/11M with W sector 024°−024·5°. Beware Walter Scott Rk (2·7m) 2 ca S of Dinish I, marked by S Card Lt Buoy Q(6) + LFl 15s; also Carrigaglos (0·6m high) 1·5 ca from SW point of Dinish I. VHF Ch 16; 08. Facilities: FW (on pier and on quay); Synchrolift on Dinish I; Hr Mr on quay, ☎ 70220; **Town** El, ME, Sh, D and P at garage, Bar, Ⓑ, ⊠, V, R, Kos.

GLENGARIFF, Cork, 51°44′·00N, 09°33′·00W, Zone 0 (GMT), Admty chart 1838. HW +0600 on Dover, −0030 on Cork; HW height −0·4m on Cork; ML 2·0m; Duration 0610. Excellent anchorage; ent. between Big Pt and Gun Pt. Keep well to E of Illnacullen and small I to E of it. Chan to W of I is strewn with rks and has power line overhead. Beware Tinker Rks by Big Pt; Yellow Rks S of Illnacullen; Ship I with rks all round in W of ent., E of Illnacullen. Anchor; S of Bark I in 7m; in centre of Hr. in 8/10m. Facilities: **Eccles Hotel** ☎ 63003, Bar, FW, R; **Town** Bar, D, P, ⊠, R, V, Kos.

GLANDORE, Cork 51°33′·00N, 09°07′·00W, Zone 0 (GMT), Admty chart 2092. HW +0605 on Dover, −0025 on Cork; HW height −0·3m on Cork; ML 2·0m; Duration 0605. Excellent shelter. Safest entrance between Adam I and Goat's Head thence keeping E of Eve I and W of the chain of Rks, Outer Danger, Middle Danger, Inner Danger and Sunk Rk. Anchor between Glandore pier and Coosaneigh Pt in approx 3m. There are no lights, but The Dangers are marked by perches and Sunk Rk by BY N Cardinal buoy. Facilities: Coast Life Saving Service (028) 33115; FW at both piers; **Unionhall** Bar, D, P, ⊠, R, V. **Glandore** Bar, CH, ⊠, R, V, Kos.

COURTMACSHERRY, Cork, 51°38′·00N, 08°41′·00W; Zone 0 (GMT), Admty charts 2081, 2092. HW −0610 on Dover, −0012 on Cork; HW height −0·4m on Cork; ML 2·0m; Duration 0545. Harbour in NW corner of Courtmacsherry Bay which has a number of hazards; Barrel Rk (dries 2·6m) in centre of bay, marked by unlit S cardinal perch; sunken rocks 2 ca NE of the perch; Blue Boy Rk (0·2m) 4 ca E of the perch; Black Tom (2·3m) 6 ca W of the perch; Inner Barrels (0·5m) 5 ca NW of the perch; Horse Rk (dries 3·6m) 4½ ca off Barry Pt on the W shore. Lights: Wood Point Fl(2) WR 5s 15m 5M, W315°-332°, R332°-315°. Old Head of Kinsale, S point, Fl(2) 10s 72m 25M; RC. Enter over bar (2·3m) between Wood Pt and Coolmain Pt into estuary of Argideen River. Depths may vary. Beware seas break on bar in strong S or SE winds. Anchor NE of Ferry Pt in approx 2·5m or N of the pier. Weed may foul anchor; best to moor with anchors up and down stream. Facilities: Coast Life Saving Service (053) 29637. **Courtmacsherry Hotel** ☎ 46198, Bar, R, P, V; **Quay** FW, D; **Village** V, ⊠.

OYSTER HAVEN, Cork, 51°41′·00N, 08°27′·00W, Zone 0 (GMT), Admty charts 2053, 1765. HW −0600 on Dover, −0018 on Cork; ML 2·2m; Duration 0600. Good shelter but subject to swell in S winds. Enter 0·5M N of Big Sovereign, a steep islet divided into two. Keep to S of Little Sovereign on E side of entrance. There is foul ground off Ballymacus Pt on W side, and off Kinure Pt on E side. Pass W of Harbour Rock (0·9m) off Ferry Pt, the only danger within harbour. Anchor NNW of Ferry Pt or up N arm of harbour off the W shore. Weed in higher reaches may foul anchor. No lights, marks or radio telephone. Coast Life Saving Service (021) 770711. Facilities at Kinsale. See 10·12·16.

BALLYCOTTON, Cork, 51°50′·00N, 08°01′·00W, Zone 0 (GMT), Admty chart 2424. HW −0555 on Dover, +0006 on Cork; HW height 0·0m on Cork; ML 2·3m; Duration 0550. See 10·12·18. Small Hr. at W end of bay; suffers from scend in strong SE winds. Numerous fishing boats alongside piers, but yachts should go alongside and not anchor in harbour. Good anchorage in offshore winds in 6m NE of breakwater, protected by Ballycotton I. Ballycotton Lt Fl WR 10s 59m 22/18M, B Tr in W walls, on Ballycotton I; W238°−063°, R063°−238°; RC: Dia(4) 90s. Facilities: FW on pier. **Village** Bar, ⊠, R, V, LB, Kos.

DUNGARVAN, Waterford, 52°05′·00N, 07°34′·00W, Zone 0 (GMT), Admty chart 2017. HW −0540 on Dover, +0008 on Cork; HW height +0·1m on Cork; ML 2·3m; Duration 0600. See 10·12·18. A large bay, the W side of which dries. Across the entrance there are Carrickapane Rk, Helvick Rk and The Gainers, all marked. Yachts can anchor off Helvick Hr. in approx 4m, or pass up to Dungarvan Town Hr. Beware salmon nets. Channel from Ballynacourty Pt marked by buoys. Ballynacourty Pt Lt Fl(2) WRG 10s 16m 12/9M, G245°-274°, W274°-302°, R302°-325°, W325°-117°. Ballynacourty Ldg Lts 083°, both FW 9/12m 2M on W columns with B bands, 46m apart; Esplanade Ldg Lts 298°, both FR 8/9m 2M. Facilities: EC Thurs; AB, Bar, Ⓑ, D (from garage), P (on quay), ⊠, R, V, Kos.

Area 13

North Ireland
Carlingford Lough to Galway

13

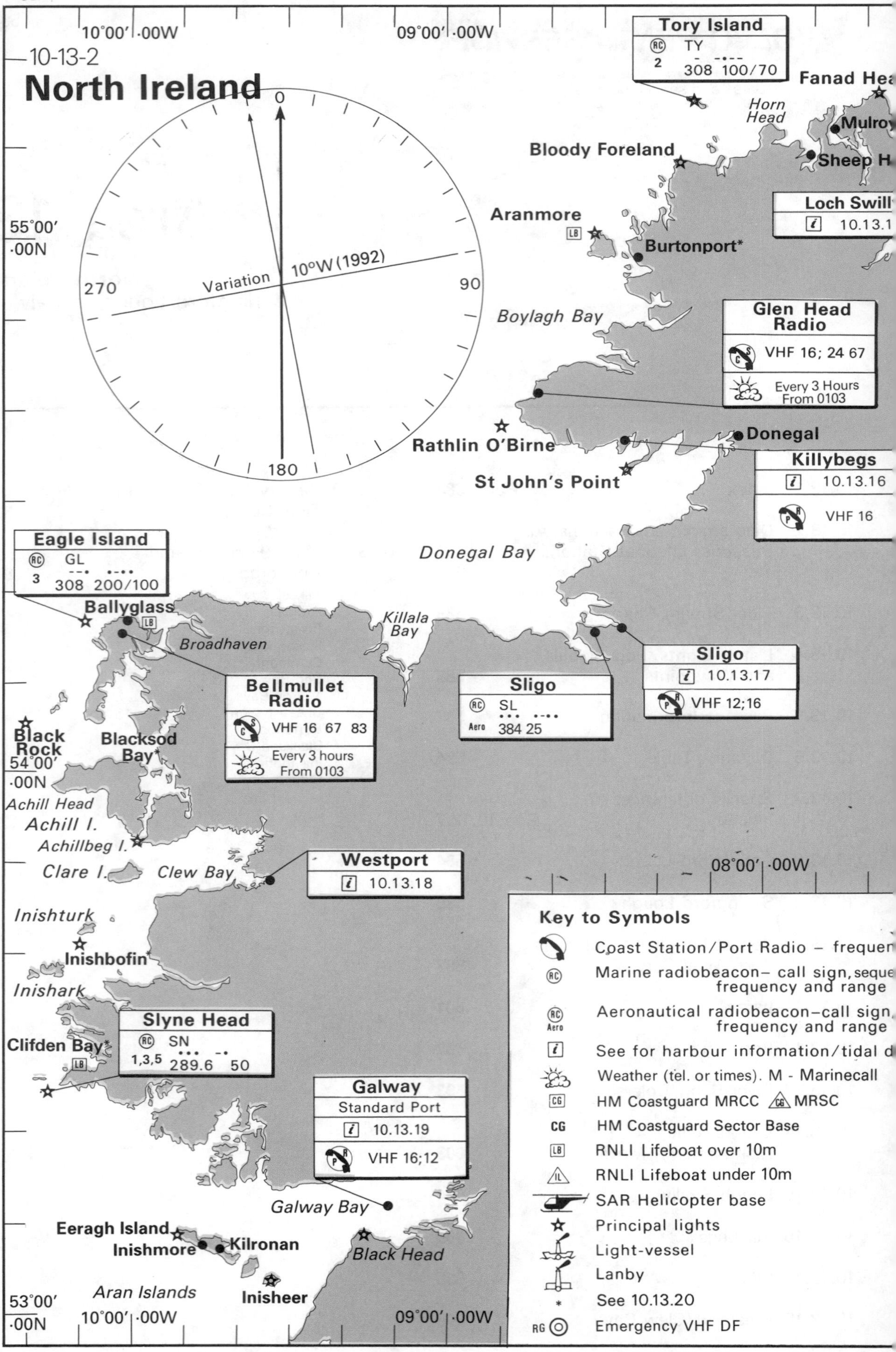
10-13-2
North Ireland
10°00′·00W
09°00′·00W
08°00′·00W
55°00′·00N
54°00′·00N
53°00′·00N
0
90
180
270
Variation 10°W (1992)
Tory Island
RC TY
2 308 100/70
Fanad Hea
Horn Head
Mulroy
Sheep H
Bloody Foreland
Loch Swill
10.13.1
Aranmore
LB
Burtonport*
Boylagh Bay
Glen Head Radio
VHF 16; 24 67
Every 3 Hours From 0103
Rathlin O'Birne
Donegal
Killybegs
10.13.16
VHF 16
St John's Point
Donegal Bay
Eagle Island
RC GL
3 308 200/100
Ballyglass
LB
Broadhaven
Killala Bay
Bellmullet Radio
VHF 16 67 83
Every 3 hours From 0103
Sligo
RC SL
Aero 384 25
Sligo
10.13.17
VHF 12;16
Black Rock
Blacksod Bay*
Achill Head
Achill I.
Achillbeg I.
Clare I.
Clew Bay
Westport
10.13.18
Inishturk
Inishbofin*
Inishark
Slyne Head
RC SN
1,3,5 289.6 50
Clifden Bay*
LB
Galway
Standard Port
10.13.19
VHF 16;12
Galway Bay
Eeragh Island
Inishmore
Kilronan
Black Head
Aran Islands
Inisheer
Key to Symbols
Coast Station/Port Radio – frequen
Marine radiobeacon– call sign, seque frequency and range
Aeronautical radiobeacon–call sign, frequency and range
See for harbour information/tidal d
Weather (tel. or times). M - Marinecall
HM Coastguard MRCC MRSC
HM Coastguard Sector Base
RNLI Lifeboat over 10m
RNLI Lifeboat under 10m
SAR Helicopter base
Principal lights
Light-vessel
Lanby
See 10.13.20
Emergency VHF DF

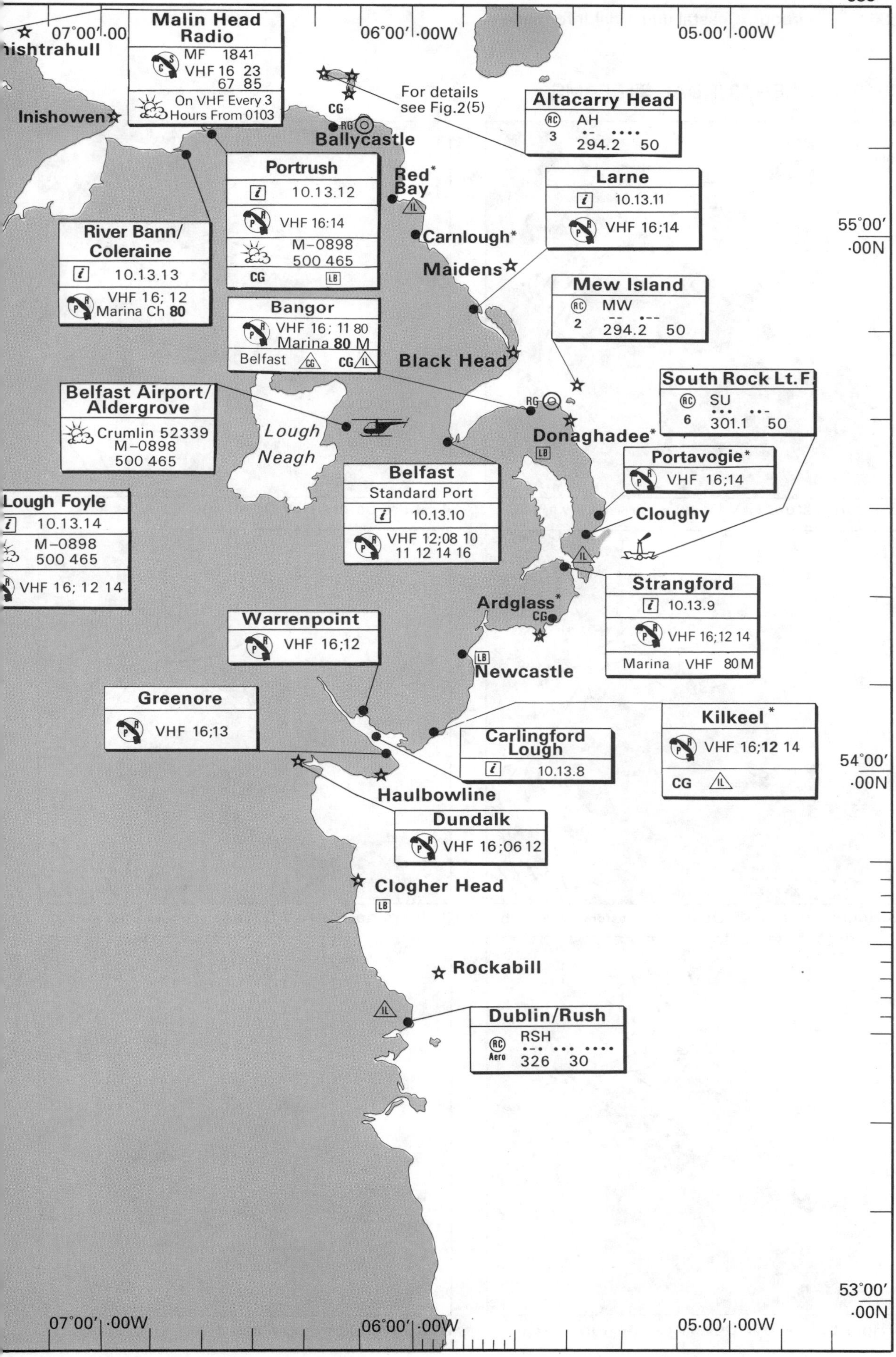

07°00'·00
06°00'·00W
05·00'·00W
55°00'·00N
54°00'·00N
53°00'·00N
07°00'·00W
06°00'·00W
05·00'·00W
Inishtrahull
Malin Head Radio
MF 1841
VHF 16 23 67 85
On VHF Every 3 Hours From 0103
Inishowen
CG
Ballycastle
For details see Fig.2(5)
Altacarry Head
AH
3
294.2 50
Portrush
10.13.12
VHF 16:14
M–0898 500 465
CG
LB
Red Bay*
Carnlough*
Maidens
Larne
10.13.11
VHF 16;14
River Bann/ Coleraine
10.13.13
VHF 16; 12
Marina Ch 80
Bangor
VHF 16; 11 80
Marina 80 M
Belfast
CG
Mew Island
MW
2
294.2 50
Black Head
South Rock Lt.F.
SU
6
301.1 50
Belfast Airport/ Aldergrove
Crumlin 52339
M–0898
500 465
Lough Neagh
RG
Donaghadee*
LB
Portavogie*
VHF 16;14
Belfast
Standard Port
10.13.10
VHF 12;08 10 11 12 14 16
Cloughy
Lough Foyle
10.13.14
M–0898
500 465
VHF 16; 12 14
Strangford
10.13.9
VHF 16;12 14
Marina VHF 80M
Ardglass*
CG
Warrenpoint
VHF 16;12
Newcastle
Greenore
VHF 16;13
Kilkeel*
VHF 16;12 14
CG
Carlingford Lough
10.13.8
Haulbowline
Dundalk
VHF 16;06 12
Clogher Head
LB
Rockabill
Dublin/Rush
RSH
Aero
326 30

10.13.3 AREA 13 TIDAL STREAMS

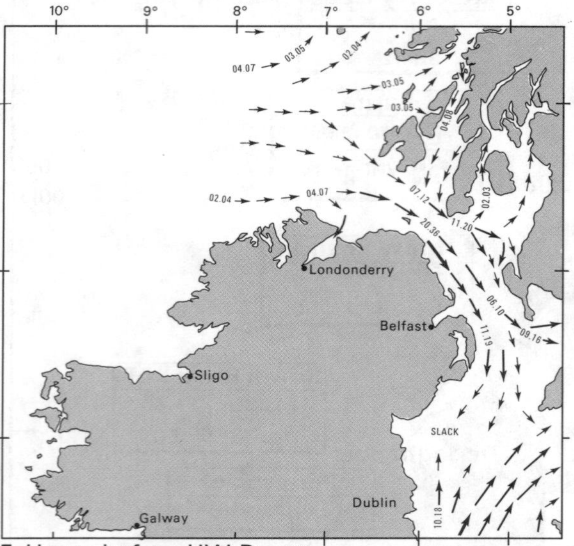
Londonderry
Belfast
Sligo
SLACK
Dublin
Galway

5 Hours before HW Dover (0450 before HW Belfast)

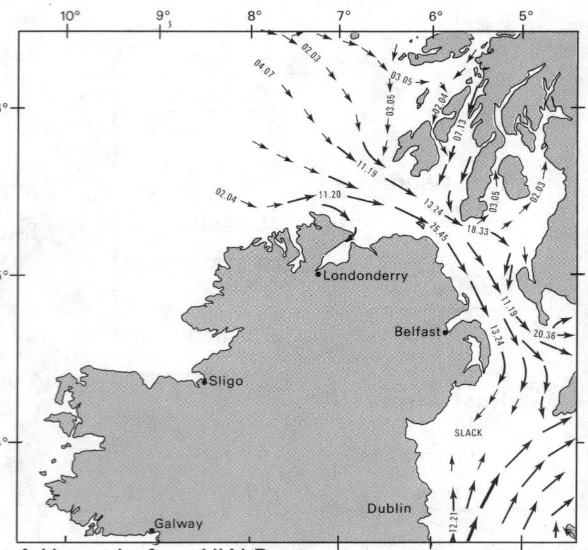
Londonderry
Belfast
Sligo
SLACK
Dublin
Galway

4 Hours before HW Dover (0350 before HW Belfast)

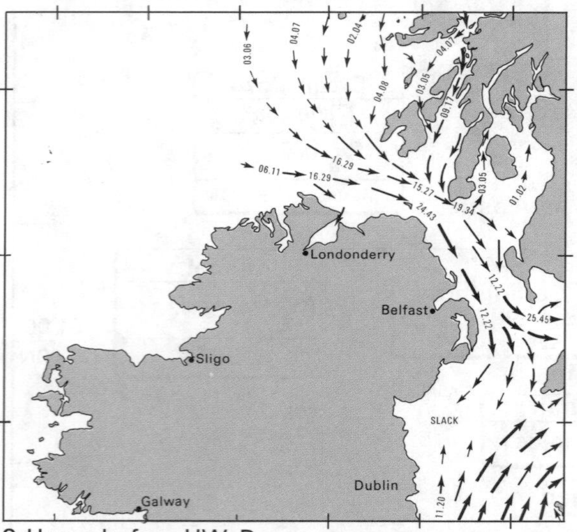
Londonderry
Belfast
Sligo
SLACK
Dublin
Galway

3 Hours before HW Dover (0250 before HW Belfast)

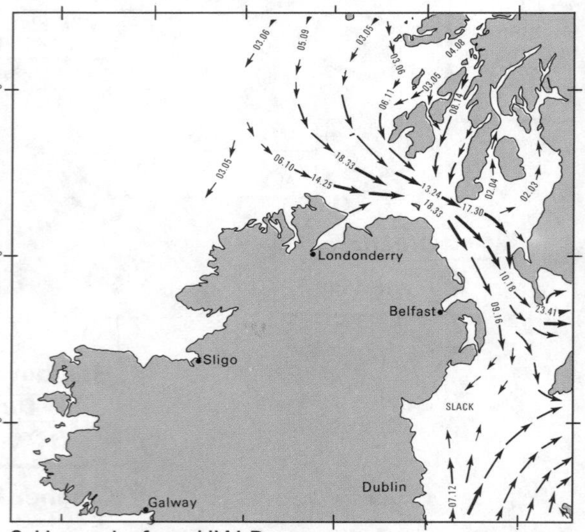
Londonderry
Belfast
Sligo
SLACK
Dublin
Galway

2 Hours before HW Dover (0150 before HW Belfast)

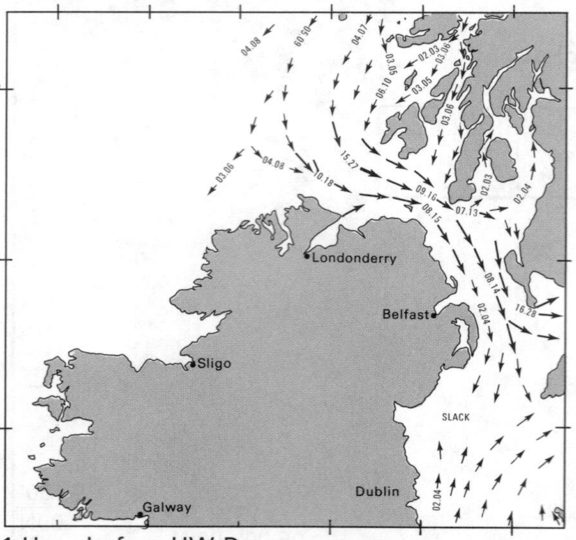
Londonderry
Belfast
Sligo
SLACK
Dublin
Galway

1 Hour before HW Dover (0050 before HW Belfast)

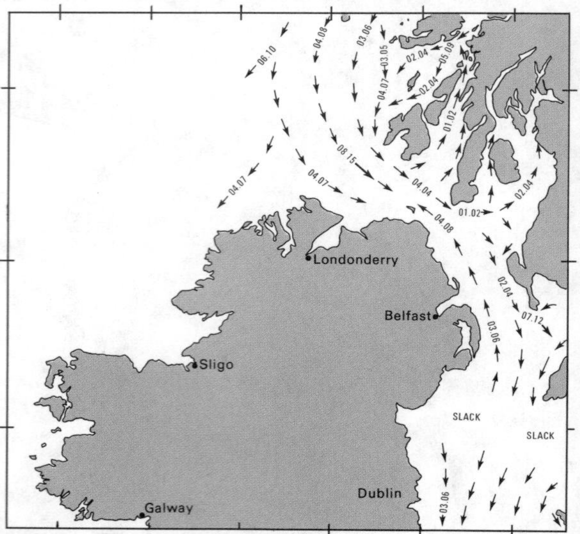
Londonderry
Belfast
Sligo
SLACK
SLACK
Dublin
Galway

HW Dover (0010 after HW Belfast)

Southward 10.12.3 North Irish Sea 10.10.3 SW Scotland 10.9.3

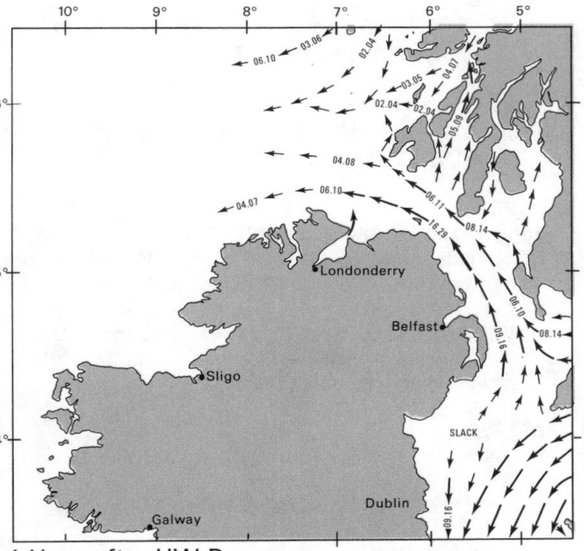
10°
9°
8°
7°
6°
5°
56°
55°
54°
Londonderry
Belfast
Sligo
Dublin
Galway
SLACK

1 Hour after HW Dover (0110 after HW Belfast)

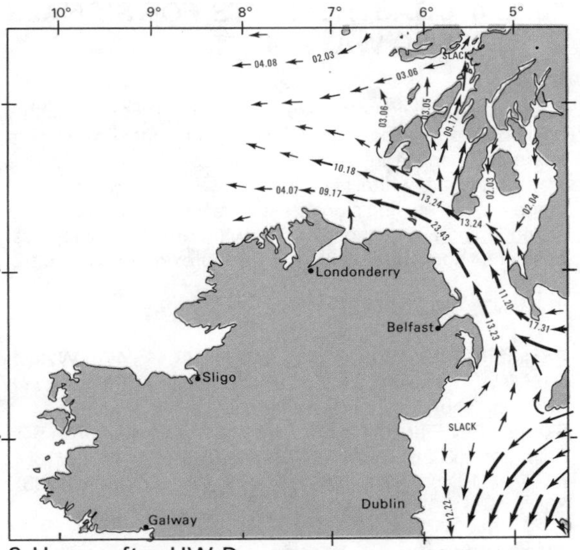
10°
9°
8°
7°
6°
5°
56°
55°
54°
SLACK
Londonderry
Belfast
Sligo
Dublin
Galway
SLACK

2 Hours after HW Dover (0210 after HW Belfast)

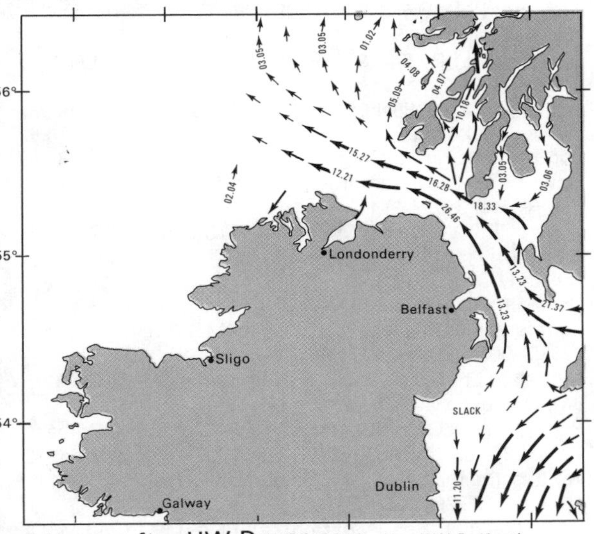
56°
55°
54°
Londonderry
Belfast
Sligo
Dublin
Galway
SLACK

3 Hours after HW Dover (0310 after HW Belfast)

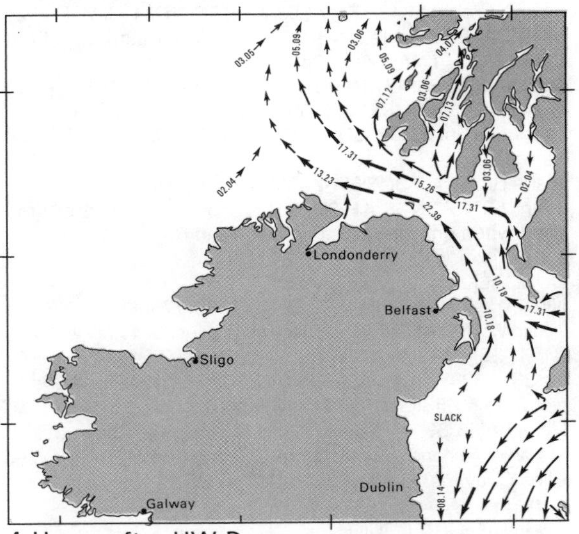
56°
55°
54°
Londonderry
Belfast
Sligo
Dublin
Galway
SLACK

4 Hours after HW Dover (0410 after HW Belfast)

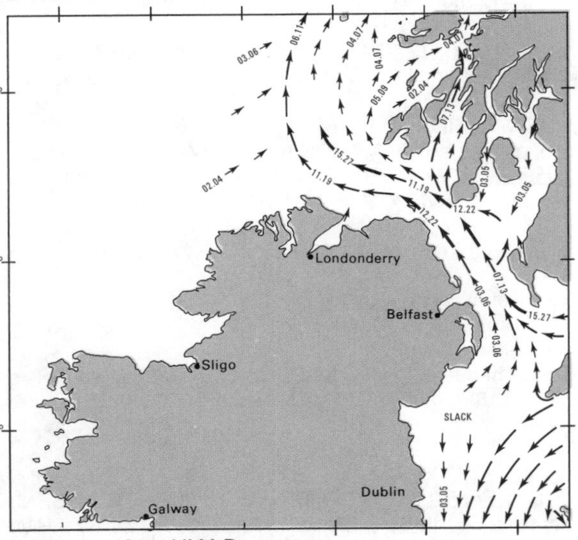
56°
55°
54°
Londonderry
Belfast
Sligo
Dublin
Galway
SLACK

5 Hours after HW Dover (0510 after HW Belfast)

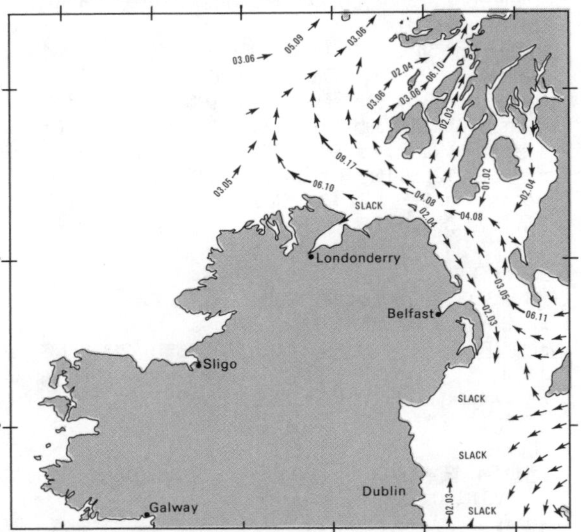
56°
55°
54°
SLACK
Londonderry
Belfast
Sligo
Dublin
Galway
SLACK
SLACK
SLACK

6 Hours after HW Dover (0610 after HW Belfast)

10.13.4 COASTAL LIGHTS, FOG SIGNALS AND WAYPOINTS

Abbreviations used below are given in 1.4.1. Principal lights are in **bold** print, places in CAPITALS, and light-vessels, light floats and Lanbys in *CAPITAL ITALICS.* Unless otherwise stated lights are white. m—elevation in metres; M—nominal range in n. miles. Fog signals are in *italics*. Useful waypoints are underlined – use those on land with care. All geographical positions should be assumed to be approximate. See 4.2.2.

IRELAND—EAST COAST

Rockabill 53°35'·80N 06°00'·30W Fl WR 12s 45m **W23M, R19M**; W Tr, B band; vis W178°-329°, R329°-178°; *Horn (4) 60s.* Also shown by day when fog signal is operating.
Skerries Bay Pier Hd Oc R 6s 7m 7M; W col; vis 103°-154°.
Balbriggan 53°36'·7N 06°10'·7W Fl(3) WRG 20s 12m W13M, R10M, G10M; W Tr; vis G159°-193°, W193°-288°, R288°-305°.

DROGHEDA.
Lts in line about 248°. **Front** 53°43'·13N 06°14'·82W Oc 12s 8m **15M**; Tr, W lantern; vis 203°-293°. **Rear** 85m from front Oc 12s 12m **17M**; Tr; vis 246°-252°.
North Light 53°43'·4N 06°15'·2W Fl R 4s 7m **15M**; Tr, W lantern; vis 282°-288°; tfc sigs.
Drogheda Bar 53°43'·3N 06°13'·7W Fl (3) R 5s 6m 3M; R col; Ra refl.
Aleria Bn 53°43'·3N 06°14'·2W QG 11m 3M; G Bn.
Lyons 53°43'·2N 06°41'·2W Fl R 2s. Above this Pt Lts on stbd hand when ent are G, and on port hand R.

DUNDALK.
N training wall Hd, **Pile Lt** 53°58'·50N 06°17'·68W Fl WR 15s 10m **W21M, R18M**; W house on R piles; vis W124°-151°, R151°-284°, W284°-313°, R313°-124°. Oc G 5s 8m; same Tr; vis 331°-334°; Fog Det Lt, VQ 7m, vis 358°; *Horn (3) 60s.*
No. 2 Bn 53°58'·3N 06°17'·8W Fl (2) R 5s 4m 3M; 2 in R ■.
No. 8 Bn 53°59'·4N 06°19'·0W Fl R 3s; R pile. Above this Pt Lts on stbd hand when ent are QG, and on port hand QR.
Giles Quay Pier Hd 53°59'·1N 06°14'·3W Fl G 3s; occas.

CARLINGFORD LOUGH.
Hellyhunter Lt By 54°00'·34N 06°01'·99W Q (6) + LFl 15s; SCM; *Horn(2) 20s.*
Haulbowline 54°01'·19N 06°04'·68W Fl (3) 10s 32m **19M**; Gy Tr; reserve Lt 15M; Fog Det Lt, VQ 26m; vis 330°.
Turning Lt FR 21m 9M; same Tr; vis 196°-208°; *Horn 30s.*
Ldg Lts 310° Vidal Bank, Front 54°01'·8N 06°05'·4W Oc 3s 7m 11M; R ▲ on Tr; vis 295°-325°. Rear, Green Is 457m from front Oc 3s 12m 11M; R ▼ on Tr; vis 295°-325°.
Greenore Pier Fl R 7·5s 10m 5M.
Carlingford Quay Hd Fl 3s 5m 2M.

NEWRY RIVER.
Ldg Lts 310·4°. Front 54°06'·4N 06°16'·5W. Rear 274m from front. Both Iso 4s 5/15m 2M; stone cols.
Warren Pt Breakwater Hd 54°05'·78N 06°15'·20W Fl G 3s 6m 3M.
Deep water quay Fl G 5s 5m 3M; R post.

KILKEEL.
Pier Hd 54°03'·45N 05°59'·27W Fl WR 2s 8m 8M; vis R296°-313°, W313°-017°.
Meeney's Pier FlG 3s 6m 2M.

ANNALONG.
E Breakwater Hd Oc WRG 5s 8m 9M; Tr; vis G204°-249°, W249°-309°, R309°-024°.

DUNDRUM BAY.
St John's Pt 54°13'·58N 05°39'·23W Q (2) 7·5s 37m **23M**; B ● Tr, Y bands. **Auxiliary Lt** Fl WR 3s 14m **W15M**, R11M; same Tr, vis W064°-078°, R078°-shore; H24 when fog sig operating; *Horn (2) 60s.*
FR on W side of chan outside hbr and 3 FR on W side of chan inside hbr when local vessels expected. FR on flagstaffs S and E of ent when firing takes place.

ARDGLASS.
Inner Pier Hd Iso WRG 4s 10m W8M, R7M, G5M; Tr; vis G shore-310°, W310°-318°, R318°-shore.
Outer Pier Hd 54 15.6N°5 36.0W Fl R 3s 10m 5M.

STRANGFORD LOUGH.
Strangford Lt By 54°18'·61N 05° 28'·63W LFl 10s; SWM; *Whis.*
Bar Pladdy Lt By 54°19'·33N 05°30'·45W Q (6) + LFl 15s; SCM.
Angus Rk 54°19'·83N 05°31'·45W Fl R 5s 15m 6M shown throughout 24 hrs.
Ldg Lts 341°. Front, Dogtail Pt, Oc (4) 10s 2m 5M. Rear, Gowland Rk 0·8M from front, Oc (2) 10s 6m 5M.
Salt Rk Fl R 3s 8m 3M.
Swan Is Fl (2) WR 6s 5m; W col; vis W115°-334°, R334°-115°.
S Pladdy Fl (3) 10s.
N Pladdy Q.
Church Pt Fl (4) R 10s; Bn.
Portaferry Pier Hd Oc WR 10s 9m W9M, R6M; Or mast; vis W335°-005°, R005°-017°, W017°-128°.
North Ldg Lts 181·5°. Rear, 70m from front, Oc R 10s 12m 6M; Or mast; vis 178°-185°.
Pier Hd N front Oc WRG 10s 8m W9M, R6M, G6M; Or mast; vis G173°-180°, W180°-183°, R183°-190° (common front); E Front, same mast, Oc WRG 5s 6m; vis R190°-244°, G244°-252°, W252°-260°, R260°-294°.
E Ldg Lts 256°, Rear 46m from front Oc R 5s 10m 6M; Or mast; vis 250°-264°.

SOUTH ROCK Lt F 54°24'·47N 05°21'·92W Fl(3) R 30s 12m **20M**; R hull and Lt Tr, W Mast; RC; Racon; *Horn (3) 45s.*

PORTAVOGIE.
Plough Rk Lt By 54°27'·37N 05°25'·07W QR; PHM; *Bell.*
S Pier Hd 54°27'·44N 05°26'·08W, Iso WRG 5s 9m 9M; ■ Tr; vis G shore-258°, W258°-275°, R275°-348°.

Skulmartin Lt By 54°31'·83N 05°24'·85W L Fl 10s; SWM; *Whis.*
Ballywalter Breakwater Hd 54°32'·67N 05°28'·75W Fl WRG 1·5s 5m 9M; vis G240°-267°, W267°-277°, R277°-314°. Unreliable.
Donaghadee, S Pier Hd 54°38'·70N 05°31'·81W Iso WR 4s 17m **W18M**, R14M; W Tr; vis W shore-326°, R326°-shore; *Siren 12s.*

Governor Rks Lt By 54°39'·36N 05°31'·94W Fl R 3s; PHM.
Deputy Reefs Lt By 54°39'·50N 05°31'·90W Fl G 2s; SHM.
Foreland Spit Lt By 54°39'·63N 05°32'·25W Fl R 6s; PHM.

BELFAST LOUGH.
Mew Is NE end 54°41'·92N 05°30'·75W Fl (4) 30s 37m **30M**; B Tr, W band; RC; *Dia (4) 30s.*
Briggs Lt By 54°41'·18N 05°35'·67W Fl (2) R 10s; PHM.

BANGOR.
N Pier Hd 54°40'·02N 05°40'·30W Iso R 12s 9m14M.
Dir Lt 105°. Dir F WRG 12M; vis G093°-104·8°, W104·8°-105·2°, R105·2°-117°.
Belfast No. 1 Chan Lt By 54°41'·67N 05°46'·30W I QG; SHM; *Bell.*
Cloghan Jetty Lt By 54°44'·12N 05°41'·52W FlG 3s; SHM.
Cloghan Jetty N end Fl G 3s 2M; G post; *Horn 15s.*
S end Fl G 3s 2M; G post.
Kilroot power station intake 54°43'·2N 05°45'·9W Oc G 4s; 2 QR on chy 500m N.
Kilroot Pt. Jetty Hd Oc G 10s 6m 9M; G Tr.

CARRICKFERGUS.
E Pier Hd Fl G 7·5s 5m 4M; G col; vis 050°-255°.
W Pier Hd Fl R 7·5s 5m 4M; R col; vis 068°-256°.
Marina E Breakwater Hd 54°42'·71N 05°48'·63W QG 8m 3M; G ● pillar.
W Breakwater QR 7m 3M; R ● pillar; vis 125°-065°.

Black Hd 54°46'·00N 05°41'·27W Fl 3s 45m **27M**; W 8-sided Tr.
N Hunter Rk Lt By 54°53'·04N 05°45'·06W Q; NCM.
S Hunter Rk Lt By 54°52'·68N 05°45'·22W Q (6) + L Fl 15s; SCM; *Horn(3) 30s.*

LARNE.
Barr Pt 54°51'·5N 05°46'·7W; *Dia 30s.*
Chaine Tr 54°51'·27N 05°47'·82W Iso WR 5s 23m 11M; Gy Tr; vis W230°-240°, R240°-shore.
Ferris Pt 54°51'·08N 05°47'·34W Iso WRG 10s 18m **W17M**, R13M, G13M; lantern on ■ W Tr; vis W345°-119°, G119°-154°, W154°-201°, R201°-223°.
Entrance Ldg Lts 184°. Front 54°49'·6N 05°47'·7W Oc 4s 6m 12M; W ◆ with R stripe on R pile structure; vis 179°-189°. Rear 610m from front Oc 4s 14m 12M; W ◆ with R stripe on R ● Tr; synchronised with front, vis 179°-189°.

Maidens 54°55'·73N 05°43'·60W Fl (3) 20s 29m **23M**; W Tr, B band. Auxiliary Lt Fl R 5s 15m 8M; same Tr; vis 142°-182° over Russel and Highland Rks.

Carnlough Hbr N Pier 54°59'·6N 05°59'·2W Fl G 3s 4m 5M; W col, B bands.
S Pier Fl R 3s 6m 5M; W col, B bands.
Red Bay Pier 55°03'·9N 06°03'·1W Fl 3s 10m 5M.

RATHLIN ISLAND.
Rue Pt 55°15'·53N 06°11'·40W Fl (2) 5s 16m 14M; W 8-sided Tr, B bands.
Altacarry Hd **Rathlin E** 55°18'·07N 06°10'·20W Fl (4) 20s 74m **26M**; W Tr, B band; vis 110°-006° and 036°-058°; RC.
Rathlin W 0·5M NE of Bull Pt 55°18'·05N 06°16'·75W Fl R 5s 62m **22M**; W Tr, lantern at base; vis 015°-225°; H24 when fog sig operating; *Horn (4) 60s.*
Manor House Pier 55°17'·5N 06°11'·6W Fl (2) R 6s 5m 4M.

IRELAND—NORTH COAST

Ballycastle Pier Hd 55°12'·5N 06°14'·3W L Fl WR 9s 6m 5M; vis R110°-212°, W212°-000°.

PORTRUSH.
N Pier Hd Fl R 3s 6m 3M; vis 220°-160°.
S Pier Hd Fl G 3s 6m 3M; vis 220°-100°.
Portstewart Pt 55°11'·3N 06°43'·2W Oc R 10s 21m 5M; R ■ hut; vis 040°-220°.

COLERAINE.
River Bann, Ldg Lts 165°. Front 55°09'·9N 06°46'·2W Oc 5s 6m 2M; W Tr. Rear 245m from front Oc 5s 14m 2M; W ■ Tr. R. marked by Fl G on stbd hand, and Fl R on port.
W Pier Fl G 5s 2M; Gy mast.
E Pier Hd Fl R 5s 6m 2M; W Tr.
Ballyaghran 55°09'·9N 06°45'·9W Fl (2) R 5s; ■ on R Bn.

Lough Foyle Lt By 55°15'·30N 06°52'·50W L Fl 10s; SWM; *Whis.*
Tuns Lt By 55°14'·01N 06°53'·38W Fl R 3s; PHM.
Inishowen 55°13'·56N 06°55'·70W Fl (2) WRG 10s 28m **W18M**, R14M, G14M; W Tr, 2 B bands; vis G197°-211°, W211°-249°, R249°-000°; *Horn (2) 30s.* Fog Det Lt VQ 16m.

LOUGH FOYLE.
Warren Pt 55°12'·58N 06°57'·06W Fl 1.5s 9m 10M; W ● Tr, G abutment. G; vis 232°-061°.
Magilligan Pt 55°11'·74N 06°57'·97W QR 7m 4M; R structure.
McKinney's Bank 55°10'·92N 07°00'·50W Fl R 5s 6m 4M; R pile structure.
Moville 55°11'·00N 07° 02'·06W Fl WR 2·5s 11m 4M; W house on G piles vis W240°-064°, R064°-240°.
Above this point the chal to R.Foyle is marked by Lts Fl G, when entering, on stbd hand, and Fl R on port hand. G Lts are shown from W structures on G or B piles; R Lts from W structures on R piles.
Kilderry 55°04'·09N 07°13'·95W Fl G 2s 6m 6M; W structure on B piles.
Muff 55°03'·63N 07°14'·21W Fl G 2s 5m 3M; G structure.
Coneyburrow 55°03'·32N 07°14'·42W Fl G 2·5s 5m 3M; G mast on G piles.
Faughan 55°03'·12N 07°14'·42W Fl R 4s 8m 3M; W lantern on R piles.
Culmore Pt 55°02'·78N 07°15'·20W Q 6m 5M; G ● Tr on B base.
Culmore Bay 55°02'·72N 07°15'·65W Fl G 5s 4m 2M; W lantern on G piles.
Lisahally 55°02'·52N 07°05'·72W QR 2M; PHM Lt Bn; R refl.
Ballynagard 55°02'·28N 07°16'·37W Fl 3s 6m 3M; W lantern on G ● house.
Otter Bank 55°01'·95N 07°16'·65W Fl R 4s 4m 3M; W structure on R ● Tr.
Brook Hall 55°01'·70N 07°17'·07W QG 4m 3M; W structure on G base.
Mountjoy 55°01'·25N 07°17'·49W QR 5m 3M; W lantern on R piles.
Inishtrahull 55°25'·85N 07°14'·60W Fl (3) 15s 59m **25M**; W Tr; Racon.

LOUGH SWILLY.
Fanad Hd 55°16'·58N 07°37'·85W Fl (5) WR 20s 39m **W18M**, R14M; W Tr; vis R100°-110°, W110°-313°, R313°-345°, W345°-100°. FR on radio mast 3·08M 200°.
Swilly More Lt By 55°15'·15N 07°35'·73W Fl G 3s; SHM.
Dunree 55°11'·85N 07°33'·20W Fl (2) WR 5s 46m W12M, R9M; vis R320°-328°, W328°-183°, R183°-196°.
Buncrana Pier near Hd Iso WR 4s 8m W14M, R11M; vis R shore-052° over Inch spit, W052°-139°, R139°-shore over White Strand Rk.

13

Rathmullan Pier Hd Fl G 3s 5M; vis 206°-345°.

MULROY LOUGH.
Limeburner By 55°18'·54N 07°48'·36W Q Fl; NCM; *Whis.*
Ravedy Is 55°15'·1N 07°46'·7W Fl 3s 9m 3M; Tr; vis 177°-357°.
Dundooan Rks 55°13'N 07° 48'W QG 4m 1M; G Tr.
Crannoge Pt 55°12'N 07°48'W Fl G 5s 5m 2M; G Tr.

IRELAND—WEST COAST

SHEEPHAVEN.
Downies Bay Pier Hd Fl R 3s 5m 2M; vis 283° through N till obsc by Downies Pt.
Portnablahy Ldg Lts 125·3°. Front 55°10'·8N 07°55'·6W Oc 6s 7m 2M; B col, W bands. Rear, 81m from front, Oc 6s 12m 2M; B col, W bands.

Tory Is NW Pt 55°16'·35N 08°14'·92W Fl (4) 30s 40m **30M**; B Tr, W band; vis 302°-277°; RC; *Horn 60s.*

Inishbofin Pier Fl 8s 3m 3M; part obsc.
Ballyness Hbr. Ldg Lts 119·5°. Front 55°09'·0N 08°06'·9W Iso 4s 25m 1M. Rear, 61m from front, Iso 4s 26m 1M.
Bloody Foreland 55°09'·5N 08°17'·0W Fl WG 7·5s 14m W6M, G4M; vis W062°-232°, G232°-062°.
Glassagh. Ldg Lts 137·4°. Front 55°06'·8N 08°18'·9W Oc 8s 12m 3M. Rear 46m from front Oc 8s 17m 3M, synchronised with front.
Inishsirrer, NW end 55°07'·4N 08°20'·9W Fl 3·7s 20m 4M; W ■ Tr vis 083°-263°.

BUNBEG.
Gola Is Ldg Lts 171·2°. Front 55°05'·1N 08°21'·0W Oc 3s 9m 2M; W Bn, B band. Rear, 86m from front, Oc 3s 13m 2M; B Bn, W band; synchronised with front.
Bo Is E Pt 55°04'·8N 08°20'·1W Fl G 3s 3m; G Bn.
Inishinny No. 1 55°04'·5N 08°19'·8W QG 3m 1M; ■ col with steps.
Carrickbullog No. 2 QR; R ■ Tr.
Inishcoole No. 4 QR 4m 1M; R ■ col on base, with steps; Neon.
Yellow Rks No. 6 QR 3m 1M; ■ col with steps; Neon.
Magheralosk No. 5 QG 4m 1M; G ■ col with steps.

Cruit Is. Owey Sound Ldg Lts 068·3°. Front Oc 10s. Rear, 107m from front, Oc 10s (TE 1983).
Rinnalea Pt 55°02'·5N 08°23'·7W Fl 7·5s 19m 9M; ■ Tr; vis 132°-167°.
Mullaghdoo Ldg Lts 184·3°, Front 55°02'·4N 08°21'·6W Iso 8s 19m 2M; W mast. Rear, 358m from front Iso 8s 29m 2M; W mast (TE 1983).

Aranmore, Rinrawros Pt 55°00'·9N 08°33'·6W Fl (2) 20s 71m **29M**; W Tr; obsc by land about 234°-007° and about 013°. Auxiliary Lt Fl R 3s 61m 13M, same Tr; vis 203°-234°.

NORTH SOUND OF ARAN.
Ldg Lts 186°. Front 54°58'·9N 08°29'·2W Oc 8s 8m 3M; B Bn, W band. Rear 395m from front Oc 8s 17m 3M; B Bn.
Ballagh Rks 54°59'·97N 08°28'·80W Fl 2·5s 13m 5M; W structure, B band.
Black Rks 54°59'·4N 08°29'·6W Fl R 3s 3m 1M; R col.

RUTLAND NORTH CHANNEL.
Inishcoo Ldg Lts 119°. Front 54°59'·1N 08°27'·7W Iso 6s 6m 1M; W Bn, B band. Rear 248m from front Iso 6s 11m 1M; B Bn, Y band.
Carrickatine No. 2 54°59'·2N 08°28'·0W QR 6m 1M; R Bn with steps; Neon.
Rutland Is Ldg Lts 138.6°. Front 54°58'·9N 08°27'·6W Oc 6s 8m 1M; W Bn, B band. Rear 330m from front Oc 6s 14m 1M; B Bn, Y band.
Inishcoo No. 4 QR 3m 1M; R Bn.
Nancy's Rk No. 1 QG 3m 1M; G Bn.
No. 6 QR 3m 1M; R Bn.

BURTONPORT.
Ldg Lts 068°. Front 54°58'·9N 08°26'·4W FG 17m 1M; grey Bn, W band. Rear 355m from front FG 23m 1M; grey Bn, Y band.

SOUTH SOUND OF ARAN.
Illancrone Is 54°56'·28N 08°28'·53W Fl 5s 7m 6M; W ■ Tr.
Wyon Pt 54°56'·50N 08°27'·50W Fl (2) WRG 10s 8m W6M, R3M; W ■ Tr; vis G shore-021°, W021°-042°, R042°-121°, W121°-150°, R 150°-shore.
Turk Rks 54°57'·30N 08°28'·15W Fl G 5s 6m 2M; G ■ Tr.
Aileen Reef 54°58'·2N 08°28'·8W QR 6m 1M. R ■ Bn.
Carrickbealatroha, Upper 54°58'·64N 08°28'·58W Fl 5s 3m 2M; W ■ brickwork Tr.

RUTLAND SOUTH CHANNEL.
Corren's Rk 54°58'·12N 08°26'·68W Fl R 3s 4m 2M; R ■ Tr.
Teige's Rk 54°58'·61N 08°26'·75W Fl 3s 4m 2M; W ● Tr, ■ base.
Dawros Hd 54°49'·6N 08°33'·6W L Fl 10s 39m 4M; W ■ col.

Rathlin O'Birne. W side 54°39'·77N 08°49'·90W Fl WR 20s 35m **W22M, R18M**; W Tr; vis R195°-307°, W307°-195°.

Teelin Hbr 54°37'·32N 08°37'·72W Fl R 10s; R structure.

Donegal Bay, St John's Pt 54°34'·15N 08°27'·60W Fl 6s 30m 14M; W Tr.
Bullockmore Lt By 54°33'·98N 08°30'·06W Qk Fl (9) 15s; WCM.

KILLYBEGS.
Rotten Is 54°36'·87N 08°26'·39W Fl WR 4s 20m **W15M**, R11M; W Tr; vis W255°-008°, R008°-039°, W039°-208°.
Ldg Lts 338°. Pier, Front Oc R 8s 5m 2M. Rear 65m from front Oc R 8s 7m 2M. Both Y ◆, on buildings.
W Pier Hd 2 FR (vert).

SLIGO.
Wheat Rk Lt By 54°18'·82N 08°39'·03W Q (6) + LFl 15s; SCM.
Blackrock 54°18'·47N 08°37'·00W Fl 5s 24m 13M; W Tr, B band. Auxiliary Lt Fl R 3s 12m 5M; same Tr; vis 107°-130° over Wheat and Seal rks.
Lower Rosses, N of Pt (Cullaun Bwee) 54°19'·72N 08°34'·37W Fl (2) WRG 10s 8m W10M, R8M, G8M; W hut on piles; vis G over Bungar bank-066°, W066°-070°, R070° over Drumcliff bar shown H24.
Ldg Lts 125°. Front Metal Man 54°18'·22N 08°34'·50W Fl 4s 3m 7M. Rear Oyster Is, 365m from front Oc 4s 13m 10M. Both shown H24.

KILLALA.
Inishcrone Pier Root Fl WRG 1·5s 8m 2M; vis W098°-116°, G116°-136°, R136°-187°.
Ldg Lts 230°. Rinnaun Pt, Front 54°13'·5N 09°12'·2W Oc 10s 7m 5M■ Tr. Rear 150m from front Oc 10s 12m 5M; ■ Tr.

Dir Lt 215°, Inch Is, 54°13'·3N 09°12'·3W Fl WRG 2s 6m 3M; ■ Tr; vis G205°-213°, W213°-217°, R217°-225°.
Ldg Lts 196°. Kilroe, Front 54°12'·6N 09°12'·2W Oc 4s 5m 2M; ■ Tr. Rear 120m from front Oc 4s 10m 2M; ■ Tr.
Ldg Lts 236°. Pier, Front Iso 2s 5m 2M; W ◆ on Tr. Rear, 200m from front, Iso 2s 7m 2M; W ◆ on pole.
Killala Bay. Bone Rk, NE end 54°15'·8N 09°11'·2W Q 7m; NCM.

Broadhaven, Gubacashel Pt 54°16'·05N 09°53'·28W Iso WR 4s 27m W12M, R9M; W Tr; vis W shore (S side of bay)-355°, R355°-shore.
Ballyglass 54°15'·3N 09°53'·4W Fl G 3s.

Eagle Is, W end 54°16'·98N 10°05'·52W Fl (3) 10s 67m **26M**; W Tr; RC. Shown H24.

Black Rock 54°04'·0N 10°19'·2W Fl WR 12s 86m **W22M, R16M**; W Tr; vis W276°-212°, R212°-276°.

Blacksod PierRoot 54°05'·90N 10°03'·63W Fl (2) WR 7·5s 13m W12M, R9M; W Tr on dwelling; vis R189°-210°, W210°-018°.
Pier Hd 54°05'·9N 10°03'·6W 2 FR(vert) 6m 3M.
Achill Is Ridge Pt. 54°01'·8N 09°58'·5W Fl 5s 21m 5M.

ACHILL SOUND.
Innish Biggle QR; R Bn.
Carrigeenfushta Fl G 3s; G Bn.
Achill Sound 53°56'·0N 09°55'·4W QG; G Bn.
Ldg Lts 330° Whitestone, Front and rear both Oc 4s; W ◆, B stripe.
Saulia Pier 53°57'·1N 09°55'·5W Fl G 3s 12m.
53°52'·1N 09°56'·5W Fl R 2s 5m; R ■ Tr.
Carrigin-a-tShrutha 53°52'·3N 09°56'·7W Q (2) R 5s; R Bn.

CLEW BAY.
Achillbeg Is S Pt 53°51'·48N 09°56'·80W Fl WR 5s 56m **W18M, R18M, R15M**; W ● Tr on ■ building; vis R262°-281°, W281°-342°, R342°-060°, W060°-092°, R(intens) 092°-099°, W099°-118°.
Clare Is E pier Fl R 3s 5m 3M.
Cloghcormick By 53°50'·54N 09°43'·27W (unlit); WCM.

WESTPORT BAY.
Dorinish Lt By 53°49'·46N 09°40'·61W Fl G 3s; SHM.
Inishgort S Pt 53°49'·58N 09°40'·17W L Fl 10s 11m 10M; W Tr. Shown H24.
Westport approach 53°47'·97N 09°34'·30W Fl 3s; G box on conical Bn.
Roonagh Quay Ldg Lts 144°, both Iso 10s 9/15m.

INISHBOFIN.
Inishlyon Lyon Hd 53°36'·7N 10°09'·6W Fl WR 7·5s 13m W7M, R4M; W post; vis W036°-058°, R058°-184°, W184°-325°, R325°-036°.
Gun Rk Fl (2) 6s 8m 4M; W col; vis 296°-253°.

Cleggan Pt 52°34'·5N 10°07'·7W Fl (3) WRG 15s 20m W6M, R3M, G3M; W col on W hut; vis W shore-091°, R091°-124°, G124°-221°.

Slyne Hd, N Tr, Illaunamid 53°23'·97N 10°14'·00W Fl (2) 15s 35m **28M**; B Tr; RC.
Inishnee 53°22'·7N 09°54'·4W Fl (2) WRG 10s 9m W5M, R3M, G3M; W col on W ■ base; vis G314°-017°, W017°-030°, R030°-080°, W080°-194°.

Croaghnakeela Is 53°19'·4N 09°58'·3W Fl 3·7s 7m 5M; W col; vis 034°-045°, 218°-286°, 311°-325°.

GALWAY BAY.
Eeragh, Rock Is 53°08'·90N 09°51'·78W Fl 15s 35m **23M**; W Tr, two B bands; vis 297°-262°.
Straw Is 53°07'·05N 09°37'·80W Fl 2) 5s 11m **17M**; W Tr.
Ldg Lts 192°. Front 53°06'·3N 09°39'·7W Oc 5s 6m 3M; W col on W ■ base; vis 142°-197°. Rear 43m from front Oc 5s 8m 2M; W col on W ■ base; vis 142°-197°.
Kilronan Pier Hd Fl WG 1·5s 5m 3M; W col; vis G240°-326°, W326°-000°.
Kiggaul Bay Fl WR 3s 5m W5M, R3M; vis W329°-359°, R359°-059°, part obsc by W shore of bay.

CASHLA BAY.
Ent W side Fl (3) WR 10s 8m W6M, R3M; W col on concrete structure; vis W216°-000°, R000°-069°.
Rossaveel Pier Ldg Lts 116° Front Oc 3s 4m; W mast. Rear 90m from front Oc 3s 8m; W mast.
Spiddle Pier Hd Fl WRG 7·5s 11m W6M, R4M, G4M; Y col; vis G102°-282°, W282°-024°, R024°-066°.
Lion Pt Dir Lt 53°15'·83N 09°33'·97W Dir Iso WRG 4s 6m W8M, R6M, G6M; W ■ Tr on col; vis G357·5°-008·5°, W008·5°-011·5°, R011·5°-017·5°.

GALWAY.
Mutton Is Lt By 53°15'05N 09°02'·88W Fl (2)R 6s; PHM.
Leverets 53°15'·32N 09°01'·87W Q WRG 9m 10M; B ● Tr, W bands; vis G015°-058°, W058°-065°, R065°-103°, G103°-143·5°, W143·5°-146·5°, R146·5°-015°.
Rinmore 53°16'·1N 09°02'·0W Iso WRG 4s 7m 5M; W ■ Tr; vis G359°-008°, W008°-018°, R018°-027°.
Approach chan Ldg Lts 325°. Front 53°16'·1N 09°02'·8W Fl R 1·5s 12m 7M; R ◆, Y diagonal stripes on mast; vis 315°-345°. Rear 310m from front Oc R 10s 19m 7M; R ◆, Y diagonal stripes on framework Tr; vis 315°-345°.
Nimmo's Pier Hd 53°15'·99N 09°02'·77W Iso Y 6s 7m 6M.

Black Hd 53°09'·25N 09°15'·78W Fl WR 5s 20m W11M, R8M, W ■ Tr; vis 045°-268°, R268°-276°.

10.13.5 PASSAGE INFORMATION

CROSSING THE IRISH SEA

Passages across the Irish Sea can range from the fairly long haul from Land's End to Cork (140M), to the relatively short hop from Mull of Kintyre to Torr Pt (11M). But such distances are deceptive, because the average cruising yacht needs to depart from and arrive at a reasonably secure hbr; also in the North chan strong tidal streams can cause heavy overfalls: so each passage needs to be treated on its merits.

Many yachts use the Land's End/Cork route on their way to (and from) the delightful cruising ground along the S coast of Ireland (see 10.12.5). Penzance Bay, or one of the Scilly Is anchs, make a convenient place from which to leave, with good Lts and Round Is radiobeacon to take departure. Although the Celtic Sea is exposed to the Atlantic, there are no dangers on pass and the tidal streams are weak. A landfall between Ballycotton and Old Hd of Kinsale (both have good Lts and radiobeacons) presents no offlying dangers, and in poor vis decreasing soundings indicate approach to land. There is likelihood, outward bound under sail, that the boat will be on the wind – a possible benefit on the return passage. If however the wind serves, and if it is intended to cruise along the southern coast, a landfall at the Fastnet with arrival at (say) Baltimore will place the yacht more to windward, with little extra dist

From Land's End the other likely destination is Dun Laoghaire. A stop at (say) Milford Haven enables the skipper to select the best time for passing the Bishops and Smalls (see 10.11.5), and roughly divides the total passage into two equal parts. From S Bishop onwards there are the options of making the short crossing to Tuskar Rk and going N inside the banks (theoretically a good idea in strong W winds), or of keeping to seaward. But in bad weather the area off Tuskar is best avoided; apart from the Traffic Scheme, the tide is strong at sp and the sea can be very rough.

The ferry route Holyhead/Dun Laoghaire is another typical crossing, and is relatively straightforward with easy landfalls either end. The tide runs hard round Anglesey at sp, so departure just before slack water minimises the set N or S. Beware also the TSS off The Skerries (see Fig 2(5)).

The Isle of Man (IOM) (see 10.10.5) is a good centre for cruising in the Irish Sea, and its hbrs provide convenient staging points whether bound N/S or E/W.

Between Scotland and Northern Ireland there are several possible routes, but much depends on weather and tide. Time of departure must take full advantage of the stream, and avoid tide races and overfalls (see 10.9.5). Conditions can change quickly, so a flexible plan is needed.

LAMBAY ISLAND TO FAIR HEAD (charts 44, 2093, 2198)

In general this coast is fairly steep-to except in larger Bs, particularly Dundalk. Streams offshore run up to 2·5kn as far as Rockabill, but are weaker further N until approaching Belfast Lough.

Lambay Is is private, and steep-to except on W side, where there can be overfalls. Skerries Is (Colt, Shenicks and St Patrick's) are 1M E and SE of Red Is, to E of Skerries hbr. Colt Is and Shenicks Is are connected to shore at LW. Pass between them and St Patrick's Is, but the latter has off-liers 0·3M to S. Rockabill, two steep-to rks with Lt Ho, is 2·5M E of St Patrick's Is. Going NE from Carlingford (10.13.8), after rounding Hellyhunter By there are no real offshore dangers until Strangford Lough (10.13.9). For Kilkeel and Ardglass see 10.13.20.

N from Strangford keep 0·5M off Ballyquintin Pt. 3M to NE are Butter Pladdy Rks; keep to E of these. 2M further N is South Rk, with disused Lt Ho, part of cluster of rks to be avoided in poor vis or bad weather by closing South Rk Lt F. In good weather pass inshore of South Rk, and between it and North Rk (chart 2156).

There are three routes for Belfast Lough (10.13.10). E of Mew Is is Ram Race (to the N on the ebb, and the S on the flood). Copeland Sound, between Mew Is and Copeland Is, is passable but not recommended. Donaghadee Sound is buoyed and a good short cut for yachts: the stream runs SSE from HW Belfast +0530 and NW from HW Belfast –0030, and can attain 4·5kn. An eddy extends S to Ballyferris Pt, and about 1M offshore. For Donaghadee see 10.13.20 and chart 3709.

N from Belfast Lough, Black Hd is straightforward. Pass E of Muck Is, which is steep-to. Hunter Rk, 2·5M off Larne, is marked by Bys. Further offshore are the Maidens, two dangerous groups of rks extending 2M N and S; E Maiden in the S group is lit.

The very small hbr of Carnlough (10.13.20) provides shelter for small yachts, but should not be approached in strong onshore winds. There is anch here in offshore winds, and also in Red B (10.13.20) 5M further N. Either can provide a useful anch on passage to or from the Western Is. There is temp anch in good weather in Cushendun B, 5M NW of Garron Pt. Fair Hd is a bold headland, steep-to all round, and marks the NE corner of Ireland.

FAIR HEAD TO BLOODY FORELAND (chart 2723)

This is a good cruising area, under the lee of land in SW wind, but very exposed to NW or N. Beware fishing boats and nets in many places and the N Chan TSS (see Fig 2(5)).

A fair tide is essential through Rathlin Sound where the stream runs 6 kn at sp, and causes dangerous overfalls. The main stream runs NW from HW Galway –0600 for five hrs, and SE from HW Galway +0100 for four hrs. A W-going eddy runs from Fair Hd close inshore towards Carrickmannanon Rk from HW Galway +0100, and an E-going eddy runs from HW Galway –0500 to –0100. The worst overfalls in the chan are from HW Galway –0500 to –0300, and it is best to enter W-bound at the end of this period, on the last of favourable tide. Keep seaward of Carrickmannanon Rk and Sheep Is. A hbr has been built in Church Bay, on the W side of Rathlin Is.

Proceeding to Portrush (10.13.12), use Skerries Sound in good weather. For Lough Foyle use either the main chan W of The Tuns, or S chan passing 0·2M N of Magilligan Pt and allowing for set towards The Tuns on the ebb (up to 3·5 kn).

Torr Rks, Inishtrahull and Garvan Is's lie N and E of Malin Hd. Inishtrahull is lit and is about 1M long, with rks extending N about 0·3M into Torr Sound. Inishtrahull Sound, between Inishtrahull and Garvan Is's is exposed, and tidal stream up to 4 kn at sp can cause a dangerous sea with no warning. Stream also sets hard through Garvan Is's, S of which Garvan Sound can be passed safely in daylight avoiding two sunken rks – one 0·15M NE of Rossnabartan, and the other 0·5M NW. The main stream runs W for only 3 hrs, from HW Galway –0500 to –0200; otherwise it runs E. W of Malin Hd a W-going eddy starts at HW Galway +0400, and an E-going one at HW Galway –0300. In bad weather it is best to pass at least 3M N of Torr Rks.

From Malin Hd to Dunaff Hd, at ent to Lough Swilly (10.13.15), keep 0·5M offshore. Trawbreaga Lough gives shelter, but is shallow, and sea can break on bar: only approach when no swell, and at half flood. Ent to Lough Swilly is clear except for Swilly Rks off the W shore, SSE of Fanad Hd.

W from Lough Swilly the coast is very foul. Beware Limeburner Rk 3M N of Melmore Hd. Mulroy B 10.13.20. has good anchs but needs accurate pilotage, as in *Irish Cruising Club Sailing Directions*.

Between Mulroy B and Sheephaven there is inshore pass S of Frenchman Rk, and between Guill Rks and Carnabollion, safe in good weather. Otherwise keep 1M offshore. Sheephaven B (10.13.20) has good anchs except in strong NW or N winds, and is easy to enter between Rinnaflagla Pt and Horn Hd. Beware Wherryman Rks, which dry, 0·1M off E shore.

Between Horn Hd and Bloody Foreland (chart 2572) are three low Is's – Inishbofin, Inishdooey and Inishbeg. The first is almost part of the mainland, but there is a temp anch on S side. 6M offshore is Tory Is (Lt, fog sig, RC) with rks for 0·5M on SW side. Temp anch in good weather in Camusmore B. In Tory Sound the stream runs W from HW Galway +0230, and E from HW Galway –0530, sp rates 2 kn.

BLOODY FORELAND TO EAGLE ISLAND (chart 2725)

For all Irish waters the Sailing Directions published by the *Irish Cruising Club* are strongly recommended, and particularly on the W coast, where other information is scant.

Off Bloody Foreland there is often heavy swell. The coast and islands S to Aranmore give good cruising. Offlying dangers are Buniver and Brinlack shoals, which can break; Bullogconnell 1M NW of Gola Is; and Stag Rks 2M NNW of Owey Is. Anchs include Bunbeg and Gweedore hbr (chart 1883), and Cruit B which is easier access. Behind Aranmore are several good anchs. Use N ent, since S one is shallow (chart 2792). Rutland N Chan is main appr to Burtonport (10.13.20).

Boylagh B has shoals and rks N of Roaninish Is. Connell Rk is 1M N of Church Pool – a good anch, best approached from Dawros Hd 4·5M to W. There is temp anch (but not in W or NW winds) just E of Rinmeasa Pt, on S side of Glen B. Rathlin O'Birne has steps E side. Anch SE of them 0·07M offshore. The sound is 0·5M wide; keep Is side to avoid rks off Malin Beg Hd.

In Donegal B (chart 2702) beware uncharted rks W of Teelin, a good natural hbr but exposed to S and W. Killybegs (10.13.16) has better shelter and is always accessible. Good shelter with fair access in Donegal hbr (chart 2715). Moderate anch at Mullaghmore in good weather with winds from SE through S to NW. Inishmurray is worth a visit in good weather: anch off S side. There are shoals close E and NE of the Is, and rks 1·5M to N. Keep well clear of coast S to Sligo (10.13.17) in onshore winds, and watch for lobster pots.

Killala B has temp anch 1M S of Kilcummin Pt, on W side. Proceeding to Killala beware St Patrick's Rks. Ent has Ldg Lts and marks, but bar is dangerous in strong NE winds.

The coast W to Broadhaven is inhospitable. Only Belderg and Portacloy give a little shelter. Stag Rks are steep-to. Broadhaven (chart 2703) is good anch and refuge, but in N/NW gales sea can break in ent. In approaches beware Slugga Rk on E side with off-lier, and Monastery Rk on S side.

EAGLE ISLAND TO SLYNE HEAD (chart 2420)

The coast from Eagle Is to Slyne Hd has many inlets, some sheltered. Streams are weak offshore. There are few Lts. Keep 0·5M off Erris Hd, and further in bad weather. Unless calm, keep seaward of Eagle Is (Lt, RC) where there is race to N. Frenchport (chart 2703) is good temp anch except in strong W winds. Inishkea Is (chart 2704) can be visited in good weather: anch N or S of Rusheen Is. The sound off Mullett Peninsula is clear, but for Pluddany Rks 0·6M E of Inishkea N.

Blacksod B (chart 2704) has easy ent, but in W gales beware breakers 1M SE of Duvillaunmore. From N, in good weather, there is chan between Duvillaunbeg and Gaghty Is. Black Rk (Lt) has rks up to 1·25M SW, but entry at night is possible. See 10.13.20.

Rough water is likely off Achil Hd. Achill Sound (chart 2667) is obstructed by cables 11m high at swing bridge. Anchs each end of Sound, but the stream runs strongly.

Clare Is has Two Fathom Rk 1·5M off NW coast, and Deace's Rk 0·5M to the N. In Clew B both Newport and Westport (see chart 2057 and 10.13.18) need detailed pilotage instructions. S of Clare Is beware Meemore Shoal 1·5M W of Roonagh Hd. 2M further W is the isolated rk Mweelaun. The offshore Is Coher, Bullybeg, Inishturk (with anch on E side) and Inishdalla have few hidden dangers, but the coast to the E must be given a berth of 1·5M even in calm weather, while in strong winds breakers extend much further seaward.

Killary B (chart 2706) and Little Killary both have good anchs in magnificent scenery. Consult sailing directions, and only approach in reasonable weather and good vis.

Ballynakill (chart 2706), easily entered either side of Freaghillaun South, has excellent shelter. Beware Mullaghadrina and Ship Rk in N chan. Anch in Fahy, Derryinver or Barnaderg B. Rks and breakers exist E of Inishbofin and S of Inishshark: see chart 2707 for clearing lines. Carrickmahoga is dangerous rk between Inishbofin and Cleggan. Lecky Rks lie 1M SSE of Davillaun. There is anch on S side of Inishbofin (Lt), but difficult in strong SW wind or swell (10.13.20).

Cleggan B is moderate anch, exposed to NW but easy access. High Is sound can be used, but not Friar Is Sound or Aughrus Passage. Clifden B (chart 2708) has offlying dangers with breakers: enter 0·3M S of Seal Rks Bn and anch between Drinagh Pt and Larner's Rk. See 10.13.20.

Slyne Hd (Lt and RC) marks SW end of Rks and Is's stretching 2M WSW from coast. Here the stream turns N at HW Galway –0320, and S at HW Galway +0300. It runs 3 kn at sp, and in bad weather causes a dangerous race. The sea may break on Barret Shoal, 3M NW of Slyne Hd.

SLYNE HEAD TO GALWAY (chart 2173)

The Connemara coast (charts 2709, 2096) and Aran Is's (chart 3339) give excellent cruising in good vis. But there are many rks, and few navigational marks. Between Slyne Hd and Roundstone B are many offlying dangers. Further E the better hbrs are Roundstone B, Cashel B, Killeany Bay, Greatman B and Cashla B. Kilronan on Inishmore is only reasonable hbr in Aran Is's, but is exposed in E winds. Cruising coastwise keep well offshore of Skird Rks.

Normal approach to Galway B is through N Sound or S Sound. N Sound is 3M wide between Eagle Rk and other dangers off Lettermullan shore, and banks on S side which break in strong winds. S Sound is wider, with no dangers except Finnis Rk 0·5M SE of Inisheer. The other chans are Gregory Sound, 1M wide between Inishmore and Inishmaan, and Foul Sound between Inishmaan and Inisheer. The latter has one danger – Pipe Rk and the reef inshore of it, extending 0·3M NW of Inisheer.

The N side of Galway B is exposed, with no shelter. Galway (10.13.19) is a commercial port, and New hbr (chart 1984) is a more pleasant anch.

10.13.6 DISTANCE TABLE

Approximate distances in nautical miles are by the most direct route while avoiding dangers and allowing for traffic separation schemes etc. Places in *italics* are in adjoining areas.

1 *Dun Laoghaire*	**1**																			
2 *Pt of Ayre*	93	**2**																		
3 *Mull of Galloway*	93	21	**3**																	
4 *Barra Hd*	238	184	163	**4**																
5 Rockabill	20	75	73	218	**5**															
6 Carlingford	50	70	60	203	30	**6**														
7 Strangford	71	44	34	175	51	36	**7**													
8 Mew Island	92	43	23	146	72	57	29	**8**												
9 Bangor	96	48	29	149	76	61	34	6	**9**											
10 Larne	108	59	37	135	88	73	45	16	16	**10**										
11 Altacarry Hd	135	85	64	104	117	102	74	45	45	31	**11**									
12 Portrush	150	98	79	103	130	115	87	58	58	48	19	**12**								
13 Londonderry	177	127	106	120	157	142	114	85	85	75	45	30	**13**							
14 Rathmullan	200	149	128	105	181	166	138	109	109	96	65	51	65	**14**						
15 Tory Island	209	156	135	95	189	174	146	117	117	105	74	61	74	35	**15**					
16 Killybegs	267	214	193	153	247	232	204	175	175	163	132	119	132	93	58	**16**				
17 Sligo	281	228	207	167	261	246	218	189	189	177	146	133	146	107	72	30	**17**			
18 Eagle Island	297	244	223	183	277	262	234	205	205	193	162	149	162	123	88	62	59	**18**		
19 Slyne Hd	352	299	278	238	332	317	289	260	260	248	217	204	217	178	143	117	114	55	**19**	
20 Galway	348	348	327	287	381	366	338	309	309	297	266	253	266	227	192	166	163	104	49	**20**

CARLINGFORD LOUGH

Louth/Down

10-13-8

CHARTS

Admiralty 2800, 44; Imray C62; Irish OS 9

TIDES

Cranfield Point +0025 and Warrenpoint +0035 Dover; ML 2·9; Duration Cranfield Point 0615, Warrenpoint 0540; Zone 0 (GMT).

Standard Port DUBLIN (NORTH WALL) (←)

Times				Height (metres)			
HW		LW		MHWS	MHWN	MLWN	MLWS
0000	0700	0000	0500	4·1	3·4	1·5	0·5
1200	1900	1200	1700				
Differences CRANFIELD POINT							
−0027	−0011	+0017	−0007	+0·7	+0·9	+0·3	+0·2
WARRENPOINT							
−0020	−0010	+0040	+0040	+1·0	+0·9	+0·1	+0·2

Note: NE coast is Ulster, SW coast the Republic of Ireland.

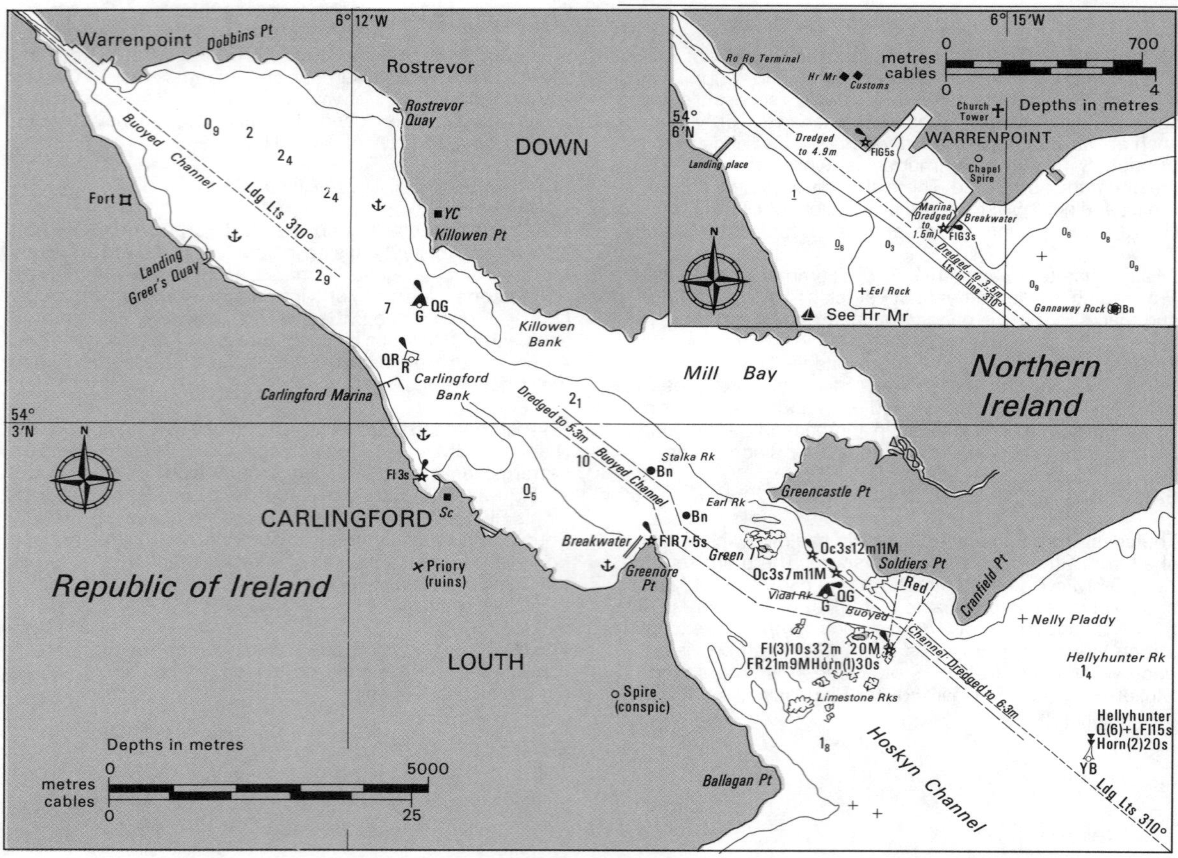

Warrenpoint
Dobbins Pt
6° 12'W
Rostrevor
Rostrevor Quay
DOWN
Buoyed Channel
Ldg Lts 310°
Fort
Landing
Greer's Quay
YC
Killowen Pt
QG
Killowen Bank
QR
Carlingford Bank
Carlingford Marina
Mill Bay
Northern Ireland
54° 3'N
Dredged to 5.3m
Buoyed Channel
Stalka Rk
Bn
Fl 3s
Greencastle Pt
Earl Rk
CARLINGFORD
Sc
Breakwater
FlR7·5s
Oc3s12m11M
Green I
Oc3s7m11M
Soldiers Pt
Greenore Pt
Priory (ruins)
Republic of Ireland
Vidal Rk
Red I
Buoyed
Channel Dredged to 6.3m
Cranfield Pt
Nelly Pladdy
Fl(3)10s32m 20M
FR21m9M Horn(1)30s
LOUTH
Hellyhunter Rk
Limestone Rks
Spire (conspic)
Hellyhunter
Q(6)+LFl15s
Horn(2)20s
YB
Depths in metres
metres
cables
0
5000
25
Ballagan Pt
Hoskyn Channel
Ldg Lts 310°
6° 15'W
Ro Ro Terminal
Hr Mr
Customs
700
4
Church Tower
Depths in metres
54° 6'N
Dredged to 4.9m
FlG5s
WARRENPOINT
Landing place
Chapel Spire
Marina (Dredged to 1.5m)
Breakwater
FlG3s
Dredged to 3.5m
Lts in line 310°
Eel Rock
Gannaway Rock
See Hr Mr

CARLINGFORD LOUGH *continued*

SHELTER
Good shelter. Anchorages at Greenore between quay and breakwater; off Greer's Quay; between Killowen Pt and Rostrevor; N of Carlingford Hr. Alongside berth at pier in Hr (dries).
NAVIGATION
Waypoint 54°00'·23N 06°02'·20W, 130°/310° from/to front Ldg Lt 310°, 2·4M. The lough becomes choppy in S winds and with on-shore winds the bar becomes impassable. Beware sudden squalls and waterspouts. Tides run up to 5 kn off Greenore. Drying rocks and shoals extend nearly across the entrance. The main channel is Carlingford Cut, about 3 ca SW of Cranfield Point, and passing 2 ca N of Haulbowline Lt Ho.
LIGHTS AND MARKS
Haulbowline Fl(3) 10s 32m 20M; granite Tr. Turning Lt FR 21m 9M; same Tr; vis 196°-208°; Horn 30s. Ldg Lts 310° both Oc 3s 7/12m 11M; G houses on piles, vis 295°-325°. Greenore Pier FIR 7·5s 10m 5M. Newry River Ldg Lts 310° both Iso 4s 5/15m 2M, stone columns.
RADIO TELEPHONE
Warrenpoint VHF Ch 16; 12 (H24). Greenore (call: *Ferry Greenore*) Ch 16; 13 (H24). Other stations: Dundalk Ch 16; 06 12.
TELEPHONE (Carlingford 042; Newry 0693)
Hr Mr Warrenpoint 73381; MRCC Limerick 61219 or (0247) 883184; # (0232) 752511; Irish # Dundalk 34114; Marinecall 0898 500 465; Police (Carlingford) 73102 (Warrenpoint) 722222; Dr Dundalk 31470; ⊞ Newry 65511, Dundalk 34701
FACILITIES
EC, Warrenpoint Wednesday. **Carlingford Marina** (50), AC, D, FW, P, Slip; **Harbour** Slip; **Carlingford YC** ☎ 38604, Bar, M, V, FW. **Dundalk SC** FW, Slip; **Greenore Pt** FW; **Warrenpoint** FW, P, D, AB; **D.A. Stukins** ☎ 72322, ME, El, Sh; **T. McArdle** ☎ 73100 Kos; **P. A. McGill** ☎ 73278, Gas.
✉ (Warrenpoint, Rostrevor, Carlingford); Ⓑ (Dundalk, Warrenpoint); ⇌ (Dundalk, Newry); ✈ (Dublin).

STRANGFORD LOUGH 10-13-9

Co. Down

CHARTS
Admiralty 2159, 2156; Imray C62; Irish OS 5, 9
TIDES
Killard Pt. 0000, Strangford Quay +0200 Dover; ML 2·0; Duration 0610; Zone 0 (GMT).

Standard Port BELFAST (⟶)

Times				Height (metres)			
HW		LW		MHWS	MHWN	MLWN	MLWS
0100	0700	0000	0600	3·5	3·0	1·1	0·4
1300	1900	1200	1800				
Differences STRANGFORD							
+0147	+0157	+0148	+0208	+0·1	+0·1	−0·2	0·0
KILLYLEAGH							
+0157	+0207	+0211	+0231	+0·3	+0·3	No data	
KILKEEL							
+0010	+0010	0000	0000	+1·8	+1·4	+0·8	+0·3

SHELTER
Excellent — largest inlet on E coast. Good anchorages in the Narrows at Cross Roads, Strangford Creek, Audley Roads and in Ballyhenry Bay. Berthing at piers in Strangford or Portaferry dependent on state of tide. Good anchorages up the lough in Quoile, Ringhaddy Sound and Whiterock. Some visitors moorings available.
NAVIGATION
Waypoint Strangford Fairway buoy, LFl 10s, Whis, 54°18'·62N 05°28'·62W, 126°/306° from/to Angus Rock Lt, 2·05M. Beware overfalls in the SE approaches and at the bar, which can be dangerous when ebb from narrows is running against strong SSW to E winds. Tidal flow in narrows, and hence the overfalls, relates to HW Strangford Quay (+0200 Dover) not to HW Killard Pt. During flood the bar presents no special problem but for preference enter when tide in the narrows is slack or on the young flood. Visitors should use the East Channel. Strong tidal streams flow through the Narrows, up to 7 kn at springs. Beware St Patricks Rk, Bar Pladdy and Pladdy Lug and whirlpool at Routen Wheel. Beware car ferry between Strangford and Portaferry. Up the lough, beware drying patches, known as pladdies and often un-marked. Swan Is, seen as grassy mound at HW, is edged with rocks and a reef extends 32m E ending at W Bn (Fl (2) WR 6s).
LIGHTS AND MARKS
Entrance identified by Strangford Fairway (safe water) buoy, W Tr on Angus Rk, Pladdy Lug Bn (W) and St Patrick's Rk perch. Leading marks to clear St Quintin Rks are perch on St Patrick's Rks and obelisk in line at 224°. Leading marks to Cross Roads anchorage are stone Bns in line at 260°, difficult to see due to trees.

Bar Pladdy Buoy	Q (6) + one long ev 15s
Angus Rk	Fl R 5s (on Tower)
Dogtail Pt	Oc (4) 10s Ldg Lts 341°
Salt Rk Bn	Fl R 3s
Gowland Rk Bn	Oc (2) 10s Ldg Lts 341°
Swan Is Bn	Fl (2) WR 6s
SW outlier (S Pladdy)	Fl (3) 10s
N outlier (N Pladdy)	Q
Church Pt Bn	Fl (4) R 10s
Portaferry Quay	Oc WR 10s
Ballyhenry Is Bn	Q G
Limestone Rk	Q R

RADIO TELEPHONE
Killyleagh Port VHF Ch 16; 12 (occas). *Strangford Harbour Port* Ch 16; 12 14 (Mon–Fri 0900–1700 LT) . In Strangford Lough most YCs and Seaquip Ch **80** M.
TELEPHONE Strangford (039 686)
Strangford Port 637; MRSC (0247) 883184; # (0232) 752511; Marinecall 0898 500 465; Police Downpatrick 615011; Medical Clinic (Downpatrick) 612971; Casualty (Downpatrick) 613311.
FACILITIES
STRANGFORD M, L, FW, CH, AB, V, R, Bar, ✉; **Seaquip** ☎ 303, D (cans), El, Ⓔ, Sh, CH; **Milligan** ☎ 233, Gas, Gaz.
PORTAFERRY M, P and D (cans), V, R, Bar, ✉, Ⓑ, L, LB, Gas, Gaz.
KILLYLEAGH M, P and D (cans), L, C (mobile), CH, V, R, Ⓑ, Bar, ✉, YC; **Seaboard Sailing Centre** ☎ (Killyleagh) 828511; **East Down YC** ☎ (Killyleagh) 828375; **Maguire** ☎ Killyleagh (828439), Gas, Gaz, Kos.
SKETRICK ISLAND R, Bar, L.
KIRCUBBIN **Maxwell Bros** ☎ (Kircubbin) 211, Gas.
Note: A marina is planned near Killyleagh.

STRANGFORD LOUGH *continued*

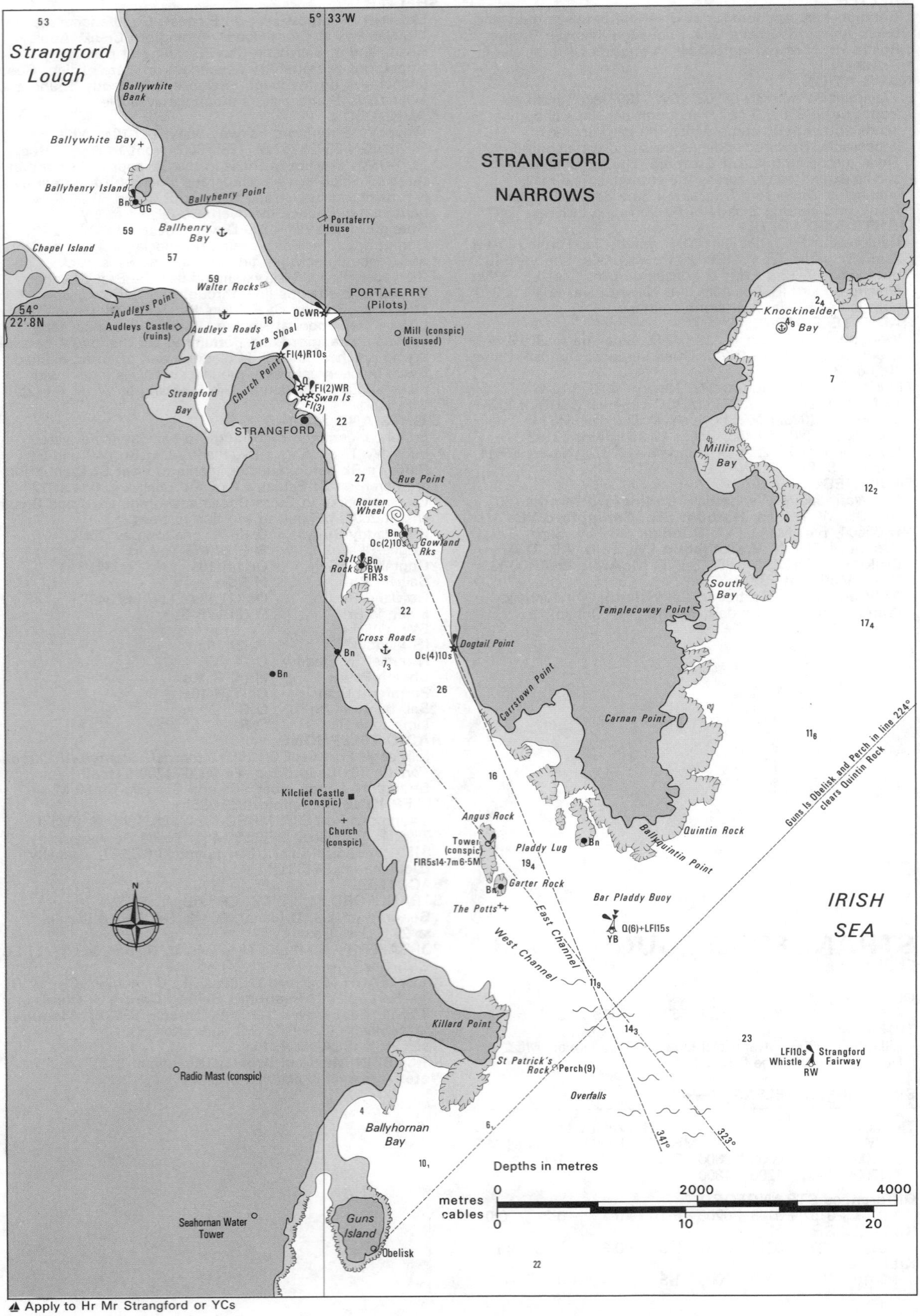
Strangford Lough
5° 33'W
Ballywhite Bank
Ballywhite Bay
STRANGFORD NARROWS
Ballyhenry Island
Bn
QG
Ballyhenry Point
Portaferry House
Ballhenry Bay
Chapel Island
Walter Rocks
PORTAFERRY (Pilots)
54° 22'.8N
Audleys Point
Audleys Castle (ruins)
Audleys Roads
OcWR
Zara Shoal
Mill (conspic) (disused)
Knockinelder Bay
Fl(4)R10s
Church Point
Strangford Bay
Fl(2)WR
Swan Is
Fl(3)
STRANGFORD
Millin Bay
Rue Point
Routen Wheel
Bn
Oc(2)10s
Gowland Rks
Salt Rock
Bn
BW
FlR3s
South Bay
Templecowey Point
Cross Roads
Oc(4)10s
Dogtail Point
Bn
Carrstown Point
Carnan Point
Guns Is Obelisk and Perch in line 224° clears Quintin Rock
Kilclief Castle (conspic)
Church (conspic)
Angus Rock
Tower (conspic)
FlR5s14-7m6-5M
Pladdy Lug
Quintin Rock
Ballyquintin Point
Garter Rock
The Potts
Bar Pladdy Buoy
Q(6)+LFl15s
YB
IRISH SEA
East Channel
West Channel
Killard Point
St Patrick's Rock
Perch(9)
Overfalls
LFl10s Whistle
Strangford Fairway
RW
Radio Mast (conspic)
Ballyhornan Bay
341°
323°
Depths in metres
metres 0 2000 4000
cables 0 10 20
Seahornan Water Tower
Guns Island
Obelisk

▲ Apply to Hr Mr Strangford or YCs

BELFAST LOUGH 10-13-10

County Down and County Antrim

CHARTS
Admiralty 1753, 2198; Imray C62, C64; Irish OS 5

TIDES
+0007 Dover; ML 2·0; Duration 0620; Zone 0 (GMT).

Standard Port BELFAST (→)

Times				Height (metres)			
HW		LW		MHWS	MHWN	MLWN	MLWS
0100	0700	0000	0600	3·5	3·0	1·1	0·4
1300	1900	1200	1800				
Differences DONAGHADEE							
+0020	+0020	+0023	+0023	+0·5	+0·4	0·0	+0·1
PORTAVOGIE							
+0010	+0020	+0010	+0020	+1·2	+0·9	+0·3	+0·2
CARRICKFERGUS							
+0005	+0005	+0005	+0005	−0·3	−0·3	−0·2	−0·1
SOUTH ROCK							
+0023	+0023	+0025	+0025	+1·0	+0·8	+0·1	+0·1

NOTE: Belfast is a Standard Port and tidal predictions for every day of the year are given below. Belfast is a commercial port and main sailing centres in Belfast Lough are Bangor, Cultra and Carrickfergus.

SHELTER
Belfast — excellent.
Cultra — good.
Ballyholme Bay — good in offshore winds.
SSE of Carrickfergus Pier — good except in E winds.
Carrickfergus — very good in marina.
Bangor — exposed to N winds; good for small boats.

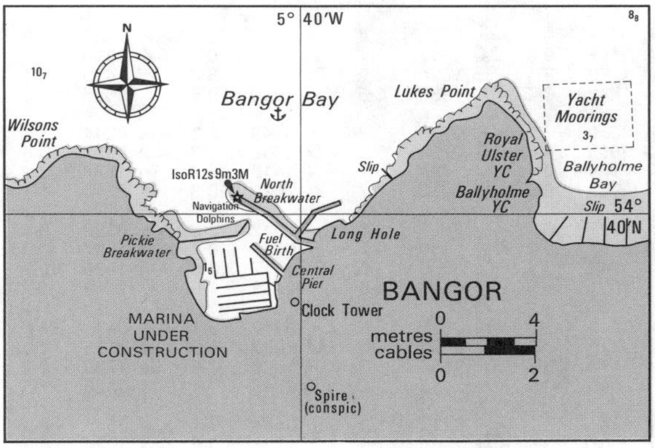

N
5° 40′W
8_8
10_7
Bangor Bay
Lukes Point
Yacht Moorings
3_7
Wilsons Point
Royal Ulster YC
Ballyholme Bay
Slip
IsoR12s9m3M
North Breakwater
Navigation Dolphins
Ballyholme YC
Slip 54°
40′N
Long Hole
Pickie Breakwater
Fuel Birth
1_5
Central Pier
BANGOR
Clock Tower
MARINA UNDER CONSTRUCTION
0 4
metres
cables
0 2
Spire (conspic)

NAVIGATION
Waypoint Bangor 54°41′·00N 05°40′·00W, 010°/190° from/to breakwater Lt, 1·0M. Rounding Orlock Pt beware Briggs Rks extending ¾ M offshore. The Lough is well marked. Beware Carrickfergus Bank extends 15 ca SSW from the harbour, and from Carrickfergus E to Kilroot Pt there is a sand bank drying up to 4 ca from shore.

LIGHTS AND MARKS
Channel up to Belfast is well marked by buoys and beacons. Once the pile beacons are reached it is dangerous to leave the channel. Tie up where directed by the Berthing Master at the Hailing House.
Carrickfergus entry signal — when sufficient water to enter — Square flag hoisted by day or extra R light on West Pierhead by night.

RADIO TELEPHONE
Call: *Belfast Harbour Radio* (at Clarendon Dock) VHF Ch 12; 08 11 **12** 14 16 (H24).
Bangor Ch 16; 11 (when vessel expected).
Carrickfergus Ch 16; 12 14 (HW−3 to HW+1, when vessel expected). Copelands Marina, Royal Northern Ireland YC and Carrickfergus Marina, Ch **16**; 11 (H24) 80.
Bangor Marina Ch M **80**.

TELEPHONE (0232)
Hr Mr Belfast 234422, Bangor (0247) 472596; MRSC (0247) 883184; ⌗ 752511; Weather: Crumlin 22339, Marinecall 0898 500 465; Police Belfast 58411, Carrickfergus 62021, Bangor 464444; Dr 454444.

FACILITIES
EC Belfast Wednesday; Bangor Thursday.
BELFAST (0232)**Harbour** ☎ 38506, Slip, P, D, L, FW, ME, El, Sh, C (up to 20 ton), CH, AB; **James Tedford** ☎ 226763, SM, Gas, ACA, CH; **J. McCready** CH; **Town** P, CH, V, R, Bar; ✉; Ⓑ; ⇌; ✈.
HOLYWOOD (023 17)**McCready** (Sailboat) ☎ Holywood 2888, ME, El, Sh, CH; **Royal North of Ireland YC, Cultra** ☎ Holywood 2041, Slip, M, P (½ M), D, L, FW, AB, R, Bar; **Town** P, CH, V, R, Bar; ✉; Ⓑ; ⇌; ✈ (Belfast).
BANGOR (0247) **Bangor Marina** (350 + 40 visitors) ☎ 453297; FW, AC, ◙ CH, BH (40 ton), ME, El, Sh, Gas, Gaz, Slip, C, SM, V, P, D, Ⓔ; **R Ulster YC** ☎ 270568, R, Bar; **Down Diving & Marina** ☎ 450831, Diving; **Hamilton** ☎ 461013, Gas; **Bangor Shipyard** ☎ 270939, ME, El, Sh, Slip, CH; **Munster Simms Engineering** ☎ 270531, ME, El, Sh; **Ballyholme YC** ☎ 462467, M, L; **Bangor Marine Services** ☎ 469916, ME; **Town** M, L, ME, El, Sh, CH, V, R, Bar; ✉; Ⓑ; ⇌; ✈ (Belfast).

13

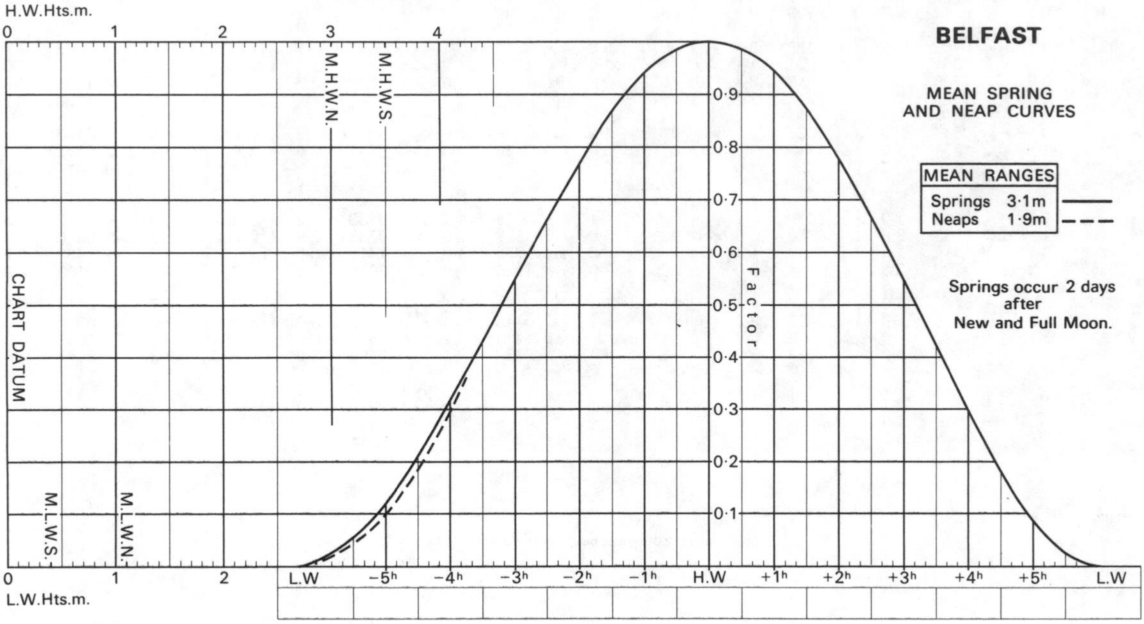

H.W.Hts.m.
0 1 2 3 4
M.H.W.N.
M.H.W.S.
BELFAST
MEAN SPRING AND NEAP CURVES
MEAN RANGES
Springs 3·1m
Neaps 1·9m
Springs occur 2 days after New and Full Moon.
0·9 0·8 0·7 0·6 0·5 0·4 0·3 0·2 0·1
Factor
CHART DATUM
M.L.W.S.
M.L.W.N.
0 1 2
L.W.Hts.m.
L.W −5h −4h −3h −2h −1h H.W +1h +2h +3h +4h +5h L.W

IRELAND, EAST COAST – BELFAST

Lat 54°36′ N Long 5°55′ W

TIMES AND HEIGHTS OF HIGH AND LOW WATERS

YEAR **1992**

TIME ZONE **UT(GMT)**

For Summer Time add ONE hour in non-shaded areas

JANUARY

Day	Time	m	Day	Time	m
1 W	0206	0·8	16 Th	0104	1·0
	0825	3·1		0717	3·1
	1440	0·8		1335	1·1
	2043	3·2		1947	3·1
2 Th	0258	0·9	17 F	0213	1·0
	0912	3·2		0825	3·2
	1531	0·8		1444	0·9
	2134	3·2		2056	3·2
3 F	0345	0·9	18 Sa	0315	0·8
	0956	3·3		0924	3·4
	1616	0·7		1543	0·7
	2219	3·2		2157	3·3
4 Sa	0424	0·8	19 Su	0410	0·7
	1037	3·4		1017	3·6
	1657	0·7		1637	0·5
●	2258	3·2	○	2252	3·4
5 Su	0501	0·8	20 M	0501	0·6
	1113	3·5		1108	3·7
	1733	0·6		1726	0·3
	2334	3·2		2343	3·4
6 M	0533	0·8	21 Tu	0549	0·5
	1147	3·5		1156	3·8
	1807	0·6		1812	0·1
7 Tu	0008	3·2	22 W	0031	3·4
	0604	0·8		0634	0·4
	1219	3·5		1242	3·9
	1838	0·6		1859	0·1
8 W	0041	3·2	23 Th	0117	3·3
	0635	0·8		0720	0·4
	1252	3·5		1328	3·8
	1910	0·6		1945	0·1
9 Th	0114	3·2	24 F	0204	3·2
	0710	0·7		0806	0·5
	1324	3·5		1416	3·7
	1945	0·6		2033	0·3
10 F	0149	3·2	25 Sa	0251	3·1
	0747	0·8		0854	0·6
	1359	3·5		1508	3·5
	2023	0·7		2122	0·5
11 Sa	0229	3·2	26 Su	0343	3·0
	0827	0·8		0949	0·8
	1439	3·4		1603	3·4
	2105	0·7	☾	2219	0·7
12 Su	0312	3·1	27 M	0442	2·9
	0914	0·9		1051	0·9
	1524	3·3		1706	3·2
	2153	0·8		2323	0·9
13 M	0402	3·1	28 Tu	0547	2·9
	1006	1·1		1204	1·0
	1616	3·2		1814	3·0
☽	2248	0·9			
14 Tu	0459	3·0	29 W	0034	1·0
	1108	1·2		0653	2·9
	1719	3·1		1317	1·0
	2353	1·0		1920	3·0
15 W	0607	3·0	30 Th	0142	1·0
	1219	1·2		0754	3·0
	1831	3·1		1422	0·9
				2022	3·0
			31 F	0240	1·0
				0849	3·1
				1515	0·8
				2115	3·0

FEBRUARY

Day	Time	m	Day	Time	m
1 Sa	0328	0·9	16 Su	0303	0·9
	0936	3·2		0908	3·4
	1602	0·7		1529	0·6
	2202	3·0		2149	3·2
2 Su	0409	0·9	17 M	0357	0·7
	1019	3·3		1002	3·6
	1641	0·6		1621	0·4
	2242	3·1		2242	3·4
3 M	0444	0·8	18 Tu	0445	0·5
	1057	3·4		1051	3·7
	1716	0·5		1708	0·2
●	2316	3·1	○	2329	3·4
4 Tu	0515	0·7	19 W	0530	0·4
	1129	3·4		1137	3·8
	1746	0·5		1753	0·1
	2347	3·2			
5 W	0543	0·6	20 Th	0012	3·4
	1158	3·4		0614	0·4
	1814	0·5		1222	3·9
				1835	0·1
6 Th	0017	3·2	21 F	0053	3·4
	0612	0·6		0656	0·4
	1227	3·5		1306	3·8
	1843	0·5		1919	0·2
7 F	0046	3·2	22 Sa	0134	3·3
	0645	0·6		0738	0·4
	1256	3·5		1351	3·7
	1914	0·5		2001	0·4
8 Sa	0119	3·3	23 Su	0216	3·2
	0720	0·6		0822	0·6
	1330	3·5		1439	3·5
	1949	0·5		2046	0·6
9 Su	0155	3·3	24 M	0303	3·1
	0758	0·7		0911	0·7
	1408	3·4		1531	3·3
	2029	0·6		2136	0·8
10 M	0236	3·2	25 Tu	0355	3·0
	0840	0·8		1010	0·9
	1451	3·3		1631	3·1
	2115	0·8	☾	2237	1·1
11 Tu	0324	3·1	26 W	0458	2·9
	0931	0·9		1125	1·0
	1543	3·2		1740	2·9
☽	2209	0·9		2353	1·2
12 W	0420	3·1	27 Th	0610	2·8
	1031	1·1		1246	1·0
	1648	3·1		1852	2·8
	2316	1·1			
13 Th	0530	3·0	28 F	0110	1·2
	1149	1·2		0719	2·9
	1808	3·0		1357	0·9
				1957	2·8
14 F	0039	1·2	29 Sa	0213	1·1
	0650	3·0		0819	3·0
	1316	1·1		1453	0·8
	1934	3·0		2053	2·9
15 Sa	0158	1·1			
	0805	3·2			
	1430	0·9			
	2049	3·1			

MARCH

Day	Time	m	Day	Time	m
1 Su	0304	1·0	16 M	0247	0·9
	0910	3·1		0847	3·3
	1538	0·7		1511	0·5
	2139	2·9		2135	3·2
2 M	0345	0·9	17 Tu	0339	0·7
	0955	3·2		0942	3·5
	1617	0·6		1600	0·3
	2219	3·0		2224	3·3
3 Tu	0419	0·7	18 W	0426	0·5
	1031	3·2		1030	3·7
	1649	0·5		1645	0·2
	2252	3·1	○	2308	3·4
4 W	0449	0·6	19 Th	0508	0·4
	1104	3·3		1116	3·8
	1718	0·5		1729	0·1
●	2322	3·1		2347	3·5
5 Th	0519	0·6	20 F	0550	0·3
	1132	3·3		1158	3·8
	1746	0·4		1810	0·2
	2349	3·2			
6 F	0549	0·5	21 Sa	0025	3·4
	1158	3·4		0631	0·4
	1814	0·4		1242	3·7
				1849	0·3
7 Sa	0018	3·3	22 Su	0103	3·4
	0619	0·5		0712	0·4
	1229	3·4		1324	3·6
	1845	0·4		1930	0·5
8 Su	0050	3·3	23 M	0142	3·3
	0655	0·5		0754	0·5
	1303	3·4		1411	3·4
	1920	0·5		2012	0·7
9 M	0127	3·3	24 Tu	0226	3·2
	0733	0·6		0840	0·7
	1342	3·4		1500	3·2
	2001	0·6		2058	1·0
10 Tu	0208	3·3	25 W	0315	3·1
	0816	0·7		0935	0·9
	1429	3·3		1557	3·0
	2046	0·8		2153	1·2
11 W	0257	3·2	26 Th	0414	3·0
	0907	0·8		1045	1·0
	1524	3·1		1705	2·8
	2142	1·0	☾	2305	1·3
12 Th	0356	3·1	27 F	0523	2·9
	1010	1·0		1207	1·0
	1633	3·0		1815	2·7
☽	2254	1·1			
13 F	0508	3·0	28 Sa	0025	1·3
	1133	1·0		0635	2·8
	1758	2·9		1319	1·0
				1921	2·7
14 Sa	0025	1·2	29 Su	0133	1·2
	0629	3·0		0738	2·9
	1303	1·0		1415	0·8
	1926	2·9		2018	2·8
15 Su	0144	1·1	30 M	0226	1·0
	0745	3·2		0833	3·0
	1413	0·7		1501	0·7
	2037	3·1		2105	2·9
			31 Tu	0308	0·9
				0918	3·0
				1539	0·6
				2145	3·0

APRIL

Day	Time	m	Day	Time	m
1 W	0345	0·8	16 Th	0403	0·5
	0957	3·1		1007	3·6
	1614	0·5		1621	0·3
	2219	3·0		2242	3·4
2 Th	0419	0·7	17 F	0445	0·4
	1030	3·2		1054	3·7
	1645	0·5		1704	0·3
	2251	3·1	○	2322	3·4
3 F	0451	0·6	18 Sa	0527	0·4
	1101	3·2		1136	3·6
	1715	0·4		1743	0·4
●	2320	3·2		2358	3·5
4 Sa	0522	0·5	19 Su	0608	0·4
	1132	3·3		1218	3·6
	1746	0·4		1822	0·5
	2351	3·3			
5 Su	0557	0·5	20 M	0036	3·5
	1205	3·3		0648	0·5
	1819	0·4		1302	3·4
				1902	0·7
6 M	0027	3·3	21 Tu	0114	3·4
	0634	0·4		0730	0·6
	1243	3·3		1345	3·3
	1857	0·5		1942	0·8
7 Tu	0106	3·3	22 W	0157	3·3
	0716	0·5		0815	0·7
	1327	3·3		1433	3·1
	1940	0·6		2025	1·0
8 W	0149	3·3	23 Th	0244	3·2
	0802	0·6		0907	0·8
	1418	3·2		1527	2·9
	2029	0·8		2115	1·1
9 Th	0242	3·2	24 F	0338	3·1
	0857	0·7		1007	0·9
	1517	3·0		1626	2·8
	2129	1·0	☾	2216	1·2
10 F	0342	3·1	25 Sa	0438	3·0
	1003	0·8		1116	1·0
	1628	2·9		1730	2·7
☽	2245	1·1		2326	1·3
11 Sa	0454	3·1	26 Su	0543	2·9
	1125	0·8		1224	0·9
	1754	2·8		1834	2·7
12 Su	0012	1·1	27 M	0035	1·2
	0611	3·1		0646	2·9
	1246	0·7		1321	0·9
	1914	2·9		1930	2·7
13 M	0126	1·0	28 Tu	0133	1·1
	0723	3·2		0742	2·9
	1352	0·6		1411	0·8
	2020	3·0		2019	2·8
14 Tu	0225	0·8	29 W	0222	1·0
	0825	3·3		0830	2·9
	1447	0·4		1453	0·7
	2115	3·2		2103	2·9
15 W	0317	0·7	30 Th	0304	0·9
	0918	3·5		0914	3·0
	1536	0·3		1532	0·6
	2202	3·3		2141	3·0

Chart Datum: 2.01 metres below Ordnance Datum (Belfast)

IRELAND, EAST COAST – BELFAST

Lat 54°36′ N Long 5°55′ W

TIME ZONE UT(GMT)
For Summer Time add ONE hour in non-shaded areas

TIMES AND HEIGHTS OF HIGH AND LOW WATERS

YEAR **1992**

MAY

Day	Time	m	Day	Time	m
1 F	0343 0952 1609 2217	0·7 3·1 0·5 3·2	16 Sa ○	0427 1033 1641 2258	0·5 3·5 0·5 3·4
2 Sa ●	0421 1030 1645 2252	0·6 3·2 0·5 3·3	17 Su	0509 1118 1722 2336	0·5 3·4 0·6 3·5
3 Su	0459 1108 1722 2329	0·5 3·2 0·5 3·3	18 M	0550 1200 1800	0·5 3·4 0·7
4 M	0539 1149 1801	0·4 3·3 0·5	19 Tu	0014 0631 1241 1838	3·5 0·5 3·3 0·8
5 Tu	0008 0621 1232 1843	3·4 0·4 3·2 0·5	20 W	0053 0712 1323 1916	3·5 0·6 3·2 0·9
6 W	0052 0707 1320 1930	3·4 0·4 3·2 0·6	21 Th	0133 0754 1406 1957	3·4 0·7 3·1 1·0
7 Th	0141 0758 1413 2023	3·4 0·4 3·1 0·8	22 F	0216 0839 1453 2042	3·3 0·7 2·9 1·0
8 F	0234 0854 1515 2125	3·3 0·5 3·0 0·9	23 Sa	0301 0928 1543 2132	3·2 0·8 2·9 1·1
9 Sa ☽	0335 1000 1627 2238	3·2 0·6 2·9 1·0	24 Su ☾	0352 1023 1638 2228	3·1 0·9 2·8 1·2
10 Su	0441 1113 1744 2354	3·2 0·6 2·8 1·0	25 M	0447 1119 1734 2329	3·0 0·9 2·8 1·2
11 M	0551 1224 1855	3·2 0·5 2·9	26 Tu	0543 1217 1831	2·9 0·9 2·8
12 Tu	0102 0659 1327 1957	0·9 3·2 0·5 3·0	27 W	0031 0641 1312 1926	1·1 2·9 0·8 2·9
13 W	0201 0759 1422 2050	0·8 3·3 0·4 3·1	28 Th	0128 0735 1402 2015	1·1 2·9 0·8 3·0
14 Th	0253 0856 1512 2136	0·7 3·4 0·4 3·3	29 F	0220 0827 1450 2101	1·0 3·0 0·7 3·1
15 F	0342 0946 1559 2219	0·6 3·5 0·5 3·4	30 Sa	0310 0917 1535 2146	0·8 3·1 0·6 3·2
			31 Su	0356 1003 1620 2228	0·7 3·1 0·6 3·3

JUNE

Day	Time	m	Day	Time	m
1 M ●	0441 1051 1704 2312	0·5 3·2 0·5 3·4	16 Tu	0537 1143 1742 2356	0·5 3·2 0·8 3·5
2 Tu	0527 1137 1749 2357	0·4 3·2 0·5 3·5	17 W	0615 1222 1817	0·6 3·2 0·8
3 W	0614 1227 1835	0·3 3·2 0·5	18 Th	0032 0652 1300 1852	3·5 0·6 3·1 0·8
4 Th	0043 0702 1317 1924	3·5 0·3 3·2 0·6	19 F	0109 0730 1338 1928	3·5 0·6 3·1 0·9
5 F	0133 0754 1411 2018	3·5 0·3 3·1 0·6	20 Sa	0147 0808 1418 2008	3·4 0·6 3·0 0·9
6 Sa	0226 0849 1510 2117	3·5 0·3 3·0 0·7	21 Su	0226 0849 1500 2051	3·3 0·7 3·0 0·9
7 Su ☽	0324 0948 1614 2220	3·4 0·3 2·9 0·8	22 M	0308 0934 1545 2139	3·2 0·8 2·9 1·0
8 M	0424 1051 1722 2327	3·3 0·4 2·9 0·8	23 Tu ☾	0353 1021 1635 2233	3·1 0·8 2·9 1·1
9 Tu	0529 1157 1828	3·3 0·5 2·9	24 W	0445 1116 1732 2332	3·1 0·9 2·9 1·1
10 W	0034 0634 1300 1928	0·8 3·3 0·5 3·0	25 Th	0543 1214 1829	3·0 0·9 2·9
11 Th	0135 0737 1358 2023	0·8 3·3 0·6 3·1	26 F	0036 0645 1314 1928	1·1 3·0 0·9 3·0
12 F	0232 0834 1451 2112	0·7 3·3 0·6 3·2	27 Sa	0140 0747 1412 2025	1·0 3·0 0·8 3·1
13 Sa	0324 0928 1539 2157	0·6 3·3 0·7 3·3	28 Su	0240 0847 1508 2118	0·9 3·1 0·8 3·2
14 Su	0412 1017 1624 2238	0·6 3·3 0·7 3·4	29 M	0335 0945 1600 2209	0·7 3·1 0·7 3·4
15 M ○	0455 1101 1704 2318	0·6 3·3 0·7 3·4	30 Tu ●	0427 1037 1649 2258	0·5 3·2 0·6 3·5

JULY

Day	Time	m	Day	Time	m
1 W	0516 1129 1737 2344	0·4 3·2 0·5 3·6	16 Th	0557 1200 1756	0·5 3·1 0·8
2 Th	0604 1218 1825	0·2 3·3 0·5	17 F	0010 0629 1234 1827	3·5 0·5 3·1 0·7
3 F	0032 0652 1309 1913	3·7 0·1 3·2 0·5	18 Sa	0042 0700 1306 1859	3·5 0·5 3·1 0·7
4 Sa	0121 0741 1359 2004	3·7 0·1 3·2 0·5	19 Su	0114 0734 1340 1935	3·4 0·6 3·1 0·7
5 Su	0211 0832 1451 2056	3·6 0·2 3·1 0·6	20 M	0148 0809 1418 2015	3·4 0·6 3·1 0·8
6 M	0304 0925 1549 2153	3·5 0·3 3·0 0·7	21 Tu	0226 0849 1458 2057	3·3 0·7 3·1 0·9
7 Tu ☽	0402 1023 1649 2255	3·4 0·4 2·9 0·8	22 W ☾	0308 0934 1545 2146	3·3 0·8 3·1 1·0
8 W	0504 1125 1754	3·3 0·6 2·9	23 Th	0357 1024 1638 2242	3·2 0·9 3·0 1·1
9 Th	0004 0610 1231 1857	0·8 3·2 0·7 3·0	24 F	0455 1123 1740 2350	3·1 1·0 3·0 1·2
10 F	0112 0714 1335 1955	0·8 3·1 0·8 3·0	25 Sa	0604 1232 1848	3·0 1·0 3·0
11 Sa	0213 0816 1433 2049	0·8 3·1 0·8 3·1	26 Su	0106 0717 1342 1954	1·1 3·0 1·0 3·1
12 Su	0310 0912 1524 2136	0·7 3·1 0·8 3·2	27 M	0216 0827 1446 2056	1·0 3·1 0·9 3·3
13 M	0359 1002 1609 2220	0·6 3·1 0·8 3·3	28 Tu	0317 0929 1543 2149	0·7 3·2 0·8 3·4
14 Tu ○	0442 1045 1648 2259	0·6 3·1 0·8 3·4	29 W ●	0410 1024 1634 2240	0·5 3·2 0·6 3·6
15 W	0522 1125 1723 2336	0·5 3·1 0·8 3·5	30 Th	0459 1115 1722 2327	0·3 3·3 0·5 3·7
			31 F	0547 1203 1808	0·1 3·3 0·4

AUGUST

Day	Time	m	Day	Time	m
1 Sa	0014 0632 1249 1853	3·8 0·0 3·3 0·4	16 Su	0012 0628 1232 1829	3·4 0·5 3·2 0·6
2 Su	0102 0719 1335 1940	3·8 0·1 3·3 0·4	17 M	0042 0659 1303 1903	3·4 0·5 3·3 0·6
3 M	0149 0805 1423 2027	3·7 0·2 3·2 0·5	18 Tu	0113 0733 1338 1940	3·4 0·6 3·3 0·7
4 Tu	0240 0854 1514 2121	3·6 0·3 3·1 0·7	19 W	0151 0811 1419 2022	3·4 0·6 3·3 0·8
5 W ☽	0335 0948 1612 2221	3·4 0·6 3·0 0·8	20 Th	0232 0853 1504 2108	3·3 0·8 3·2 0·9
6 Th	0435 1049 1715 2333	3·2 0·8 2·9 0·9	21 F ☾	0322 0942 1557 2204	3·2 0·9 3·1 1·1
7 F	0544 1201 1822	3·1 0·9 2·9	22 Sa	0421 1044 1701 2316	3·1 1·1 3·1 1·2
8 Sa	0048 0653 1313 1926	0·9 3·0 1·0 3·0	23 Su	0534 1200 1814	3·0 1·2 3·1
9 Su	0157 0758 1415 2023	0·9 3·0 1·0 3·1	24 M	0039 0656 1320 1927	1·1 3·0 1·1 3·2
10 M	0254 0856 1507 2114	0·8 3·0 0·9 3·2	25 Tu	0155 0811 1427 2032	0·9 3·1 1·0 3·3
11 Tu	0343 0943 1550 2159	0·7 3·0 0·9 3·3	26 W	0257 0914 1524 2128	0·7 3·2 0·8 3·5
12 W	0424 1026 1628 2238	0·6 3·1 0·8 3·4	27 Th	0350 1007 1614 2219	0·4 3·3 0·6 3·7
13 Th ○	0501 1102 1701 2313	0·5 3·1 0·8 3·4	28 F ●	0438 1057 1701 2306	0·2 3·4 0·5 3·8
14 F	0532 1134 1729 2344	0·5 3·1 0·7 3·4	29 Sa	0523 1140 1744 2351	0·1 3·4 0·4 3·9
15 Sa	0600 1203 1758	0·5 3·2 0·7	30 Su	0607 1224 1828	0·1 3·4 0·4
			31 M	0036 0650 1306 1913	3·9 0·2 3·4 0·4

Chart Datum: 2.01 metres below Ordnance Datum (Belfast)

TIME ZONE UT(GMT)
For Summer Time add ONE hour in non-shaded areas

IRELAND, EAST COAST – BELFAST

Lat 54°36′ N Long 5°55′ W

TIMES AND HEIGHTS OF HIGH AND LOW WATERS

YEAR **1992**

SEPTEMBER

Date	Day	Time	m	Date	Day	Time	m
1	Tu	0123 0735 1349 1958	3·8 0·3 3·3 0·5	16	W	0043 0659 1307 1912	3·4 0·6 3·4 0·7
2	W	0212 0820 1437 2049	3·6 0·5 3·2 0·7	17	Th	0121 0737 1347 1954	3·4 0·7 3·4 0·7
3	Th ☽	0305 0911 1531 2146	3·4 0·8 3·1 0·9	18	F	0205 0820 1433 2042	3·3 0·8 3·3 0·9
4	F	0407 1012 1634 2301	3·1 1·0 3·0 1·0	19	Sa ☾	0256 0911 1528 2139	3·2 1·0 3·2 1·0
5	Sa	0518 1127 1744	3·0 1·2 2·9	20	Su	0359 1016 1633 2254	3·0 1·2 3·1 1·1
6	Su	0022 0629 1246 1853	1·0 2·9 1·2 3·0	21	M	0516 1139 1749	2·9 1·2 3·1
7	M	0133 0735 1351 1955	0·9 2·9 1·1 3·0	22	Tu	0019 0641 1302 1903	1·0 3·0 1·2 3·2
8	Tu	0230 0832 1442 2047	0·8 2·9 1·0 3·1	23	W	0134 0755 1408 2008	0·9 3·1 1·0 3·4
9	W	0318 0919 1525 2132	0·7 3·0 0·9 3·2	24	Th	0234 0856 1503 2104	0·6 3·2 0·8 3·6
10	Th	0357 0959 1600 2212	0·6 3·0 0·8 3·3	25	F	0327 0948 1552 2156	0·4 3·4 0·6 3·7
11	F	0431 1034 1633 2244	0·6 3·1 0·7 3·3	26	Sa ●	0414 1033 1638 2242	0·3 3·5 0·5 3·8
12	Sa ○	0501 1104 1702 2313	0·5 3·2 0·7 3·4	27	Su	0458 1115 1722 2327	0·2 3·5 0·4 3·9
13	Su	0529 1132 1730 2342	0·5 3·2 0·6 3·4	28	M	0542 1156 1804	0·2 3·5 0·4
14	M	0556 1200 1801	0·5 3·3 0·6	29	Tu	0012 0624 1236 1846	3·8 0·3 3·5 0·5
15	Tu	0010 0625 1232 1835	3·4 0·5 3·4 0·6	30	W	0059 0706 1319 1931	3·7 0·5 3·5 0·6

OCTOBER

Date	Day	Time	m	Date	Day	Time	m
1	Th	0147 0749 1404 2020	3·5 0·7 3·3 0·7	16	F	0102 0714 1326 1937	3·3 0·7 3·4 0·7
2	F	0239 0837 1456 2117	3·3 1·0 3·2 0·9	17	Sa	0148 0759 1413 2027	3·2 0·8 3·4 0·8
3	Sa ☽	0338 0934 1555 2226	3·1 1·2 3·1 1·0	18	Su	0242 0854 1510 2128	3·1 1·0 3·3 0·9
4	Su	0445 1044 1704 2346	2·9 1·3 3·0 1·0	19	M ☾	0346 1002 1614 2241	3·0 1·2 3·2 0·9
5	M	0556 1204 1812	2·8 1·3 3·0	20	Tu	0504 1122 1727	2·9 1·2 3·2
6	Tu	0057 0702 1312 1916	1·0 2·8 1·3 3·0	21	W	0001 0625 1241 1839	0·9 3·0 1·1 3·3
7	W	0155 0758 1405 2011	0·9 2·9 1·1 3·1	22	Th	0112 0737 1345 1944	0·7 3·1 1·0 3·4
8	Th	0242 0846 1449 2057	0·8 2·9 1·0 3·2	23	F	0211 0834 1442 2042	0·6 3·2 0·8 3·6
9	F	0321 0925 1527 2138	0·7 3·0 0·9 3·2	24	Sa	0303 0925 1531 2134	0·4 3·4 0·7 3·7
10	Sa	0356 1000 1600 2212	0·6 3·1 0·8 3·3	25	Su ●	0350 1010 1616 2221	0·4 3·5 0·6 3·8
11	Su ○	0427 1033 1633 2242	0·6 3·2 0·7 3·3	26	M	0435 1052 1701 2308	0·4 3·6 0·5 3·8
12	M	0457 1102 1704 2312	0·6 3·3 0·6 3·3	27	Tu	0518 1132 1743 2353	0·4 3·6 0·5 3·7
13	Tu	0526 1132 1736 2344	0·5 3·4 0·6 3·4	28	W	0600 1212 1827	0·6 3·6 0·5
14	W	0558 1205 1812	0·6 3·4 0·6	29	Th	0038 0641 1253 1910	3·6 0·7 3·6 0·6
15	Th	0019 0634 1243 1852	3·4 0·6 3·5 0·6	30	F	0124 0723 1337 1957	3·4 0·9 3·5 0·7
				31	Sa	0212 0808 1425 2049	3·2 1·0 3·4 0·9

NOVEMBER

Date	Day	Time	m	Date	Day	Time	m
1	Su	0307 0857 1518 2149	3·0 1·2 3·2 1·0	16	M	0234 0846 1457 2119	3·1 0·9 3·4 0·6
2	M ☽	0406 0956 1619 2257	2·9 1·3 3·1 1·0	17	Tu ☾	0338 0950 1559 2227	3·0 1·0 3·4 0·7
3	Tu	0511 1105 1723	2·8 1·4 3·0	18	W	0449 1104 1706 2339	2·9 1·1 3·3 0·7
4	W	0004 0614 1214 1827	1·0 2·8 1·3 3·0	19	Th	0605 1217 1815	3·0 1·1 3·4
5	Th	0103 0712 1313 1923	1·0 2·8 1·2 3·0	20	F	0046 0714 1321 1921	0·7 3·1 1·0 3·4
6	F	0154 0801 1404 2013	0·9 2·9 1·1 3·1	21	Sa	0147 0813 1419 2020	0·6 3·2 0·8 3·5
7	Sa	0237 0846 1447 2057	0·8 3·0 1·0 3·1	22	Su	0242 0905 1511 2115	0·6 3·3 0·7 3·6
8	Su	0317 0924 1527 2136	0·7 3·1 0·9 3·2	23	M	0331 0950 1600 2206	0·5 3·5 0·6 3·6
9	M	0352 1000 1604 2213	0·7 3·3 0·8 3·2	24	Tu ●	0417 1034 1645 2252	0·6 3·6 0·6 3·6
10	Tu ○	0427 1035 1641 2248	0·6 3·4 0·7 3·3	25	W	0501 1115 1729 2337	0·6 3·6 0·6 3·5
11	W	0502 1111 1719 2326	0·6 3·4 0·6 3·3	26	Th	0542 1156 1812	0·7 3·6 0·6
12	Th	0539 1147 1758	0·6 3·5 0·6	27	F	0021 0621 1235 1855	3·5 0·8 3·6 0·6
13	F	0007 0618 1228 1842	3·3 0·6 3·5 0·5	28	Sa	0104 0700 1316 1937	3·3 0·9 3·6 0·7
14	Sa	0050 0702 1313 1928	3·3 0·7 3·5 0·5	29	Su	0148 0741 1358 2022	3·2 1·0 3·5 0·8
15	Su	0140 0749 1402 2020	3·2 0·8 3·5 0·6	30	M	0233 0823 1444 2110	3·1 1·1 3·4 0·9

DECEMBER

Date	Day	Time	m	Date	Day	Time	m
1	Tu	0322 0911 1534 2202	3·0 1·2 3·2 1·0	16	W ☾	0324 0934 1542 2206	3·0 0·8 3·5 0·5
2	W ☽	0416 1004 1627 2259	2·9 1·2 3·1 1·0	17	Th	0428 1038 1645 2312	3·0 0·9 3·4 0·6
3	Th	0513 1105 1725 2358	2·8 1·3 3·0 1·0	18	F	0539 1149 1753	3·0 1·0 3·3
4	F	0611 1208 1824	2·9 1·3 3·0	19	Sa	0019 0648 1257 1900	0·7 3·0 0·9 3·3
5	Sa	0055 0707 1309 1921	1·0 2·9 1·2 3·0	20	Su	0124 0751 1401 2005	0·7 3·1 0·9 3·4
6	Su	0147 0759 1404 2013	0·9 3·0 1·1 3·1	21	M	0223 0846 1458 2103	0·7 3·2 0·8 3·4
7	M	0234 0847 1454 2103	0·9 3·1 1·0 3·1	22	Tu	0317 0935 1549 2155	0·7 3·4 0·7 3·4
8	Tu	0319 0931 1541 2148	0·8 3·3 0·8 3·2	23	W	0404 1020 1637 2242	0·7 3·5 0·6 3·4
9	W ○	0403 1013 1624 2231	0·7 3·4 0·7 3·3	24	Th ●	0448 1102 1719 2326	0·8 3·6 0·6 3·4
10	Th	0444 1054 1706 2315	0·6 3·5 0·6 3·3	25	F	0527 1140 1800	0·8 3·6 0·6
11	F	0526 1134 1750	0·6 3·6 0·5	26	Sa	0005 0604 1218 1838	3·3 0·8 3·6 0·6
12	Sa	0000 0610 1218 1835	3·3 0·6 3·6 0·4	27	Su	0043 0639 1255 1914	3·3 0·8 3·6 0·6
13	Su	0045 0655 1303 1923	3·3 0·6 3·6 0·3	28	M	0120 0714 1331 1951	3·2 0·9 3·5 0·7
14	M	0133 0742 1352 2012	3·2 0·6 3·6 0·3	29	Tu	0158 0751 1409 2030	3·1 0·9 3·5 0·7
15	Tu	0226 0836 1444 2107	3·1 0·7 3·6 0·4	30	W	0239 0832 1450 2112	3·1 1·0 3·4 0·8
				31	Th	0322 0917 1534 2159	3·0 1·0 3·2 0·9

Chart Datum: 2.01 metres below Ordnance Datum (Belfast)

BELFAST LOUGH *continued*

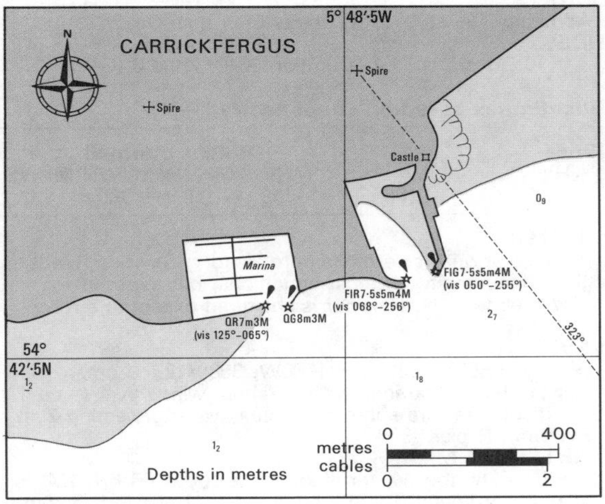
5° 48'·5W
CARRICKFERGUS
N
Spire
Spire
Castle
Marina
QR7m3M
(vis 125°-065°)
QG8m3M
FIR7·5s5m4M
(vis 068°-256°)
FIG7·5s5m4M
(vis 050°-255°)
323°
54°
42'·5N
metres
cables
0
400
0
2
Depths in metres

DONAGHADEE (0247) Hr Mr 882377 **Copelands Marina** ☎ 882184, D, FW, C (20 ton); **County Hardware** ☎ 883300, Gas. **Town** V, R, Bar, ✉; Ⓑ; ≷ (Bangor); ✈ (Belfast).

GROOMSPORT (0247) Hr Mr ☎ Bangor 464733, M, Slip, FW; **Cockle Island Boat Club**, Slip, M, FW, L, R. **Murphy's** ☎ 337, Gas. **Town** ✉ (Bangor); Ⓑ (Bangor); ≷ (Bangor); ✈ (Belfast).

CARRICKFERGUS. (096 03) Easily recognised by conspic castle to E of commercial port. Marina depths 1·9m to 2·4m. **Carrickfergus Marina** (270+30 visitors) ☎ 453297, AC, BH (10½ ton), CH, D, El, FW, Sh; **Carrickfergus S.C.** ☎ 51402, M, L, FW, C, AB; **Caters Carrick** ☎ 51919 CH, Gas, Rigging; **W.W. Marine** ☎ 69895 ME, El, Sh; **Belfast Lough Marine Electronics** ☎ 65565, El, Ⓔ; **Town** V, R,Ⓑ; ✉; ≷; ✈ (Belfast).

LARNE 10-13-11

Antrim

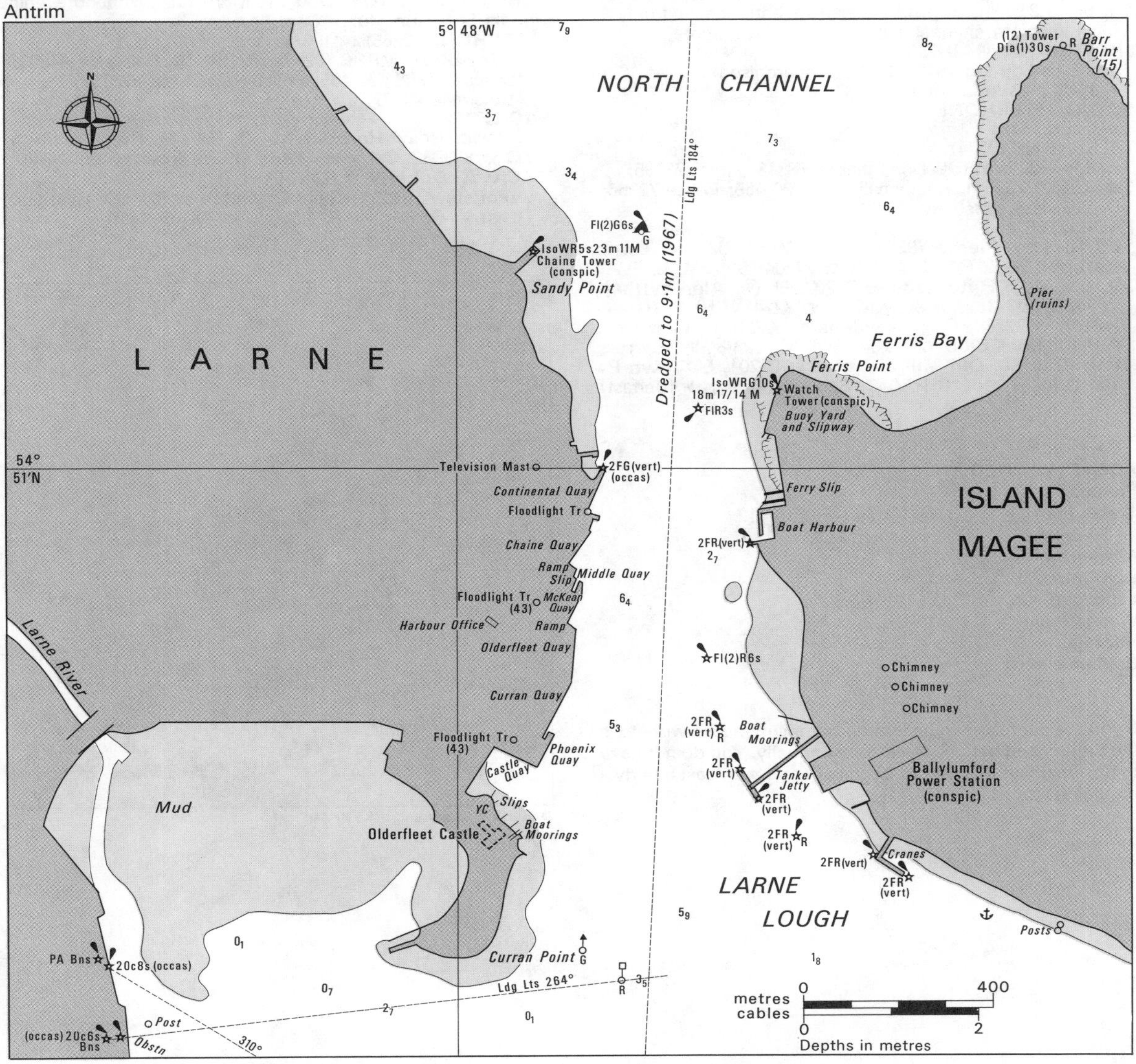
5° 48'W
NORTH CHANNEL
(12) Tower
Dia(1)30s
Barr Point (15)
Ldg Lts 184°
Dredged to 9·1m (1967)
Fl(2)G6s
IsoWR5s23m11M
Chaine Tower
(conspic)
Sandy Point
Pier (ruins)
Ferris Bay
Ferris Point
IsoWRG10s
18m 17/14 M
Watch Tower (conspic)
FIR3s
Buoy Yard and Slipway
L A R N E
54°
51'N
Television Mast
2FG(vert)
(occas)
Continental Quay
Floodlight Tr
Chaine Quay
Ramp
Slip
Middle Quay
Floodlight Tr
(43)
McKean Quay
Harbour Office
Ramp
Olderfleet Quay
Curran Quay
Floodlight Tr
(43)
Phoenix Quay
Castle Quay
Slips
YC
Boat Moorings
Olderfleet Castle
Ferry Slip
Boat Harbour
2FR(vert)
ISLAND
MAGEE
Fl(2)R6s
Chimney
Chimney
Chimney
2FR (vert)
Boat Moorings
Tanker Jetty
Ballylumford
Power Station
(conspic)
Cranes
2FR(vert)
LARNE
LOUGH
Posts
Larne River
Mud
PA Bns
2Oc8s (occas)
(occas) 2Oc6s
Bns
Post
Obstn
310°
Curran Point
Ldg Lts 264°
metres
cables
0
400
0
2
Depths in metres

13

LARNE *continued*

CHARTS
Admiralty 1237, 2198; Imray C62, C64; Irish OS 5
TIDES
0000 Dover; ML 1·6; Duration 0620; Zone 0 (GMT).

Standard Port BELFAST (⟵)

Times				Height (metres)			
HW		LW		MHWS	MHWN	MLWN	MLWS
0100	0700	0000	0600	3·5	3·0	1·1	0·4
1300	1900	1200	1800				
Differences LARNE							
+0005	0000	+0010	−0005	−0·7	−0·5	−0·3	0·0
RED BAY							
+0022	−0010	+0007	−0017	−1·9	−1·5	−0·8	−0·2

SHELTER
Secure shelter in Larne Lough. Anchorage S of Ballylumford Power Stn. Harbour can be entered day or night in any conditions. W side is commercial until Curran Pt where there are two YCs with moorings.
NAVIGATION
Waypoint 54°51′·70N 05°47′·47W, 004°/184° from/to front Ldg Lt 004°, 2·1M. Beware Hunter Rock 2M NE of harbour entrance. N.B. Abnormal magnetic variation exists near Hunter Rock and between it and the mainland. Larne is a busy commercial port. Tide in the entrance runs at up to 3½ kn. Beyond the narrow entrance, the only recommended channel is close along the E shore.
LIGHTS AND MARKS
Entrance Ldg Lts 184°, Oc 4s, synchronised and vis 179°-189°; W diamonds with R stripes.
RADIO TELEPHONE
VHF Ch 16 14.
TELEPHONE (0574)
Hr Mr 79221; MRSC Donaghadee 883184; Pilot 73785; ⌗ (0232) 752511; Marinecall 0898 500 465; Police 72266; Dr 75331; Ⓗ (Casualty) 75431.
FACILITIES
EC Tuesday; **Pier** ☎ 79221, M, L, FW, C (32 ton); **Larne Harbour** M, L, FW; **E.A. BC** ☎ 77204, Slip, M, L, FW, V, Bar; **A.C. Hutcheson** ☎ 73207, El, Ⓔ; **Alan Lyttle** ☎ 72850, D; **Curran Saw Mills** ☎ 72241, CH; **T. R. Fulton** ☎ 72288, Gas; **Howdens** ☎ 60222, D; **East Antrim Boat Club** ☎ 77204, Slip, M, L, V, FW, Bar; **Rea Bros** Sh; **Old Mill Electrics** ☎ 83201, El; **Town** P and D (delivered), CH, V, R, Bar, ✉; Ⓑ; ⇌; ✈ (Belfast).

PORTRUSH 10-13-12
Antrim

CHARTS
Admiralty 49, 2499, 2798; Imray C64; Irish OS 2
TIDES
−0410 Dover; ML 1·1; Duration 0610; Zone 0 (GMT).

Tidal figures based on Londonderry (⟶)

Times		Height (metres)			
HW	LW	MHWS	MHWN	MLWN	MLWS
−0105	−0105	−0·8	−0·6	−0·2	0·0

SHELTER
Anchorage on E side of Ramore Head in Skerries Roads gives good shelter in most conditions, but exposed to sea/swell from N. Harbour is sheltered except in strong NW-N winds.
NAVIGATION
Waypoint 55°13′·00N 06°41′·00W, 308°/128° from/to N Pier Lt, 1·1M. Entrance with on-shore winds over force 4 is difficult. Beware submerged breakwater projecting 20m SW from N pier.
LIGHTS AND MARKS
Ldg Lts 028° (occas, for lifeboat use) both FR 6/8 1M; R triangles on metal Bn and metal mast. N pier Fl R 3s 6m 3M; vis 220°-160°. S pier Fl G 3s 6m 3M; vis 220°-100°. Fixed Bu Lt on CG look-out, Ramore Hd.
RADIO TELEPHONE
VHF Ch 16; 14 (0900-1730 LT, Mon–Fri. Extended evening hours Sat–Sun, June–Sept.)
TELEPHONE (0265)
Hr Mr 822307; MRSC (0247) 883184; ⌗ Coleraine 44803; Marinecall 0898 500 465; Police 822721; Dr 823767; Ⓗ Coleraine 44177.
FACILITIES
EC Wednesday; **Harbour** AB, D, FW, M, Slip; **Portrush YC** ☎ 823932, Bar, FW; **Todd Chart Agency** ☎ 824176, ACA; **A. Doherty** ☎ 824735, El, Ⓔ; **C. Trolan** ☎ Portstewart 2221, Gas; **J. Mullan** ☎ 822209, Gas, Gaz; **Town** V, R, Bar, ▢, P, ✉; Ⓑ; ⇌; ✈ (Belfast).

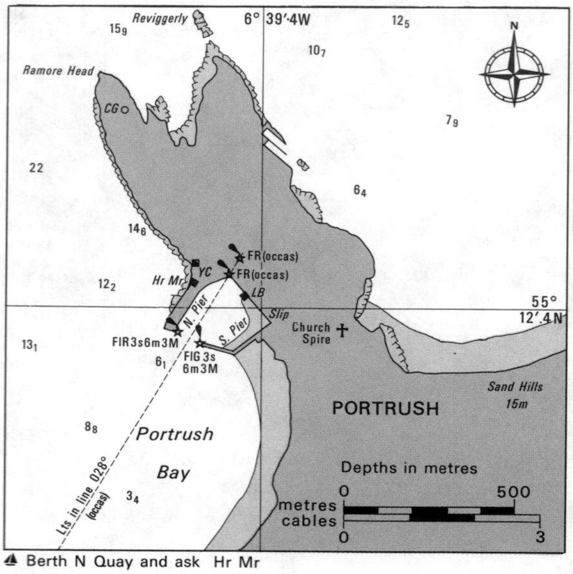
Revigglerly
6° 39′·4W
Ramore Head
CG
N
Hr Mr
YC
FR(occas)
FR(occas)
LB
Slip
N. Pier
S. Pier
FlR3s6m3M
FlG 3s 6m3M
Church Spire
55° 12′·4N
PORTRUSH
Sand Hills 15m
Portrush Bay
Lts in line 028° (occas)
Depths in metres
0 500
metres
cables
0 3

⚓ Berth N Quay and ask Hr Mr

RIVER BANN 10-13-13

Londonderry/Antrim

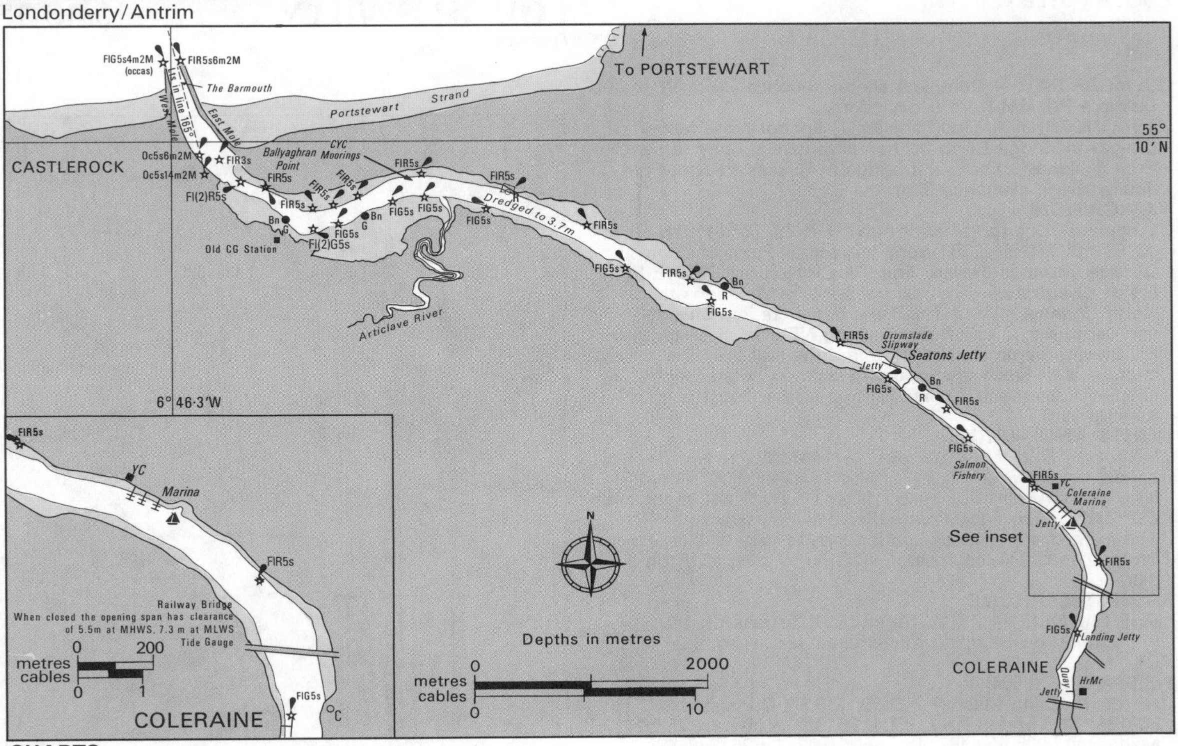
To PORTSTEWART
FlG5s4m2M (occas)
FlR5s6m2M
Lts in line 165°
The Barmouth
Portstewart Strand
West Mole
East Mole
55° 10′N
CASTLEROCK
Oc5s6m2M
Oc5s14m2M
FlR3s
Ballyaghran Point
CYC Moorings
FlR5s
Fl(2)R5s
FlG5s
Bn
G
Old CG Station
Fl(2)G5s
Dredged to 3.7m
Articlave River
Drumslade Slipway
Seatons Jetty
Jetty
R
Salmon Fishery
YC
Coleraine Marina
See inset
Landing Jetty
COLERAINE
Quay
HrMr
6° 46·3′W
Marina
Railway Bridge
When closed the opening span has clearance of 5.5m at MHWS, 7.3 m at MLWS
Tide Gauge
metres
cables
Depths in metres
N

CHARTS
Admiralty 2499, 2798, 2723; Imray C64; Irish OS 2

TIDES
−0345 Dover (Coleraine); ML 1·1; Duration 0540; Zone 0 (GMT).

Tidal figures based on Londonderry (⟶)

Times		Height (metres)			
HW	LW	MHWS	MHWN	MLWN	MLWS
−0117	−0050	−0·6	−0·4	−0·3	−0·1

SHELTER
The Mouth, known as The Barmouth, is between two moles, running 2 ca N from the beaches. Once inside shelter is good. Do not attempt entry in strong on-shore winds or when waves breaking across the entrance. If in doubt call Coleraine Harbour Radio (Ch 16, 12) or ring Coleraine 42012. Anchor upstream of old CG Station, or go up to Drumslade Slipway or Coleraine Marina, 3½M & 4½M from entrance on NE bank.

NAVIGATION
Waypoint 55°11′·00N, 06°47′·07W, 022°/202° from/to Barmouth entrance breakwaters, 1M. Approach from E of N to bring Ldg Lts into line at Mole ends. The sand bar is constantly moving but has a dredged depth of approx 3·5m. Beware salmon nets across the width of the river during the salmon fishing season at 2M or 4M from entrance. Also beware commercial traffic.

LIGHTS AND MARKS
Ldg Lts 165°, front Oc 5s 6m 2M on W metal tower; rear Oc 5s 14m 2M.

RADIO TELEPHONE
VHF Ch 12 (Mon-Fri: 0900-1700 LT). Coleraine Marina Ch **80** M.

TELEPHONE (0265)
Hr Mr 42012; # Coleraine 44803; MRSC Donaghadee 883184; Rly Bridge 42403; Marinecall 0898 500 465; Police (Portrush) 44122; Ⓗ 44177; Dr 44831.

FACILITIES
COLERAINE EC Thursday. **Coleraine (Borough Council) Marina** (45+15 visitors), ☎ 44768, Slip, D, FW, R, BH (15 ton), AC; **Coleraine Boat Centre** ☎ 52525, CH; **Coleraine YC** ☎ 44503, Bar M; **Seaton Sail & Power (Drumslade Slipway)** ☎ 832086, Slip, CH; **Calor Kosangas Gas Centre** ☎ 57057, Gas, Kos; **Alan Doherty** ☎ 824735, El, Ⓔ. **Coleraine Harbour** ☎ 42012, BH (35 ton) **Town** P, D, V, R, ✉; Ⓑ; ⇌; ✈ (Belfast).

LOUGH FOYLE 10-13-14

Londonderry/Donegal

CHARTS
Admiralty 2499, 2798, 2723; Imray C64; Irish OS 2

TIDES
Culmore Point −0025 Londonderry
Moville (−0055 Londonderry
(−0300 Dover
(−0400 Belfast
Warren Point −0400 Dover
Londonderry −0300 Dover
ML 1·5; Duration 0615; Zone 0 (GMT)

Standard Port GALWAY (⟶)

Times				Height (metres)			
HW		LW		MHWS	MHWN	MLWN	MLWS
0200	0900	0200	0800	5·1	3·9	2·0	0·6
1400	2100	1400	2000				
Differences LONDONDERRY							
+0254	+0319	+0322	+0321	−2·4	−1·8	−0·8	−0·1

SHELTER
The SE side of the Lough is low lying and shallow. The NW rises steeply and has a number of village harbours between the entrance and Londonderry (often referred to as Derry).
GREENCASTLE — a busy fishing harbour, safe in NNW to WSW winds. Anchor off or go alongside fishing boats.
MOVILLE — the pier is close to the village and has 1·5m at the end (shops closed all day Wed).
CARRICKARORY — has a good pier/quay, the end 25m of which has a depth of 2m. Good shelter with winds NNW to SW.

LOUGH FOYLE *continued*

CULMORE BAY — Complete shelter (anchor 1½ca W of Culmore Pt). 4M from Londonderry.
LONDONDERRY — Good shelter — anchor close below Craigavon Bridge Berth on non-commercial quay (down from Guildhall). There is a bridge at Rosses Pt about 2M downstream, clearance 32m.

NAVIGATION
Waypoint Tuns (port-hand) buoy, FlR 3s, 55°14′·01N 06°53′·38W, 055°/235° from/to Warren Point Lt, 2·5M. Outside entrance beware The Tuns which run 3M NE from E side of entrance. The main channel ¾M wide is the North Channel NW of The Tuns but there is a channel, min depth 4m, 3 ca off shore along NE side of Magilligan Pt. Beware commercial traffic; in June and July the channel is at times obstructed by salmon nets at night. N channel tides reach 3½ kn, and up in the river the ebb runs up to 6 kn.

LIGHTS AND MARKS
Inishowen Fl(2) WRG 10s 28m 18/14M; W Tr, two B bands; vis G197°-211°, W211°-249°, R249°-000°; Horn(2) 30s. Warren Point Fl 1·5s 9m 10M; W Tr, G abutment; vis 232°-061°. Magilligan Point QR 7m 4M; R structure.
The main channel up to Londonderry is very well lit. Foyle Bridge centre FW each side; VQG on W pier; VQR on E pier.

RADIO TELEPHONE
VHF Ch 16; 12 14 (H24). Safety and Distress Ch 16; Information on Shipping movements and navigation Ch 14.

TELEPHONE (0504)
Hr Mr (Berthing Master) 263680; MRSC Donaghadee 883184; ⌗ Londonderry (0504) 261937 or Belfast 752511; Marinecall 0898 500 465; Police 261893; Dr 264868; Ⓗ 45171.

FACILITIES (Londonderry)
EC Thursday; **Harbour Office** ☎ 263680, M, FW, C (10 ton mobile), AB; **8 & 9 Sheds** M, FW, C (2 x 1½ ton elec), AB; **7 Shed** M, FW, AB; **14/15 Berth** M, FW, AB; **Dolphins** M, FW, El, AB; **NR Quay** P, D, ME, El; **Prehen Boat Club** ☎ 43405; **Town** P, D, ME, El, CH, V, R, Bar. ✉; Ⓑ; ⇌; ✈.

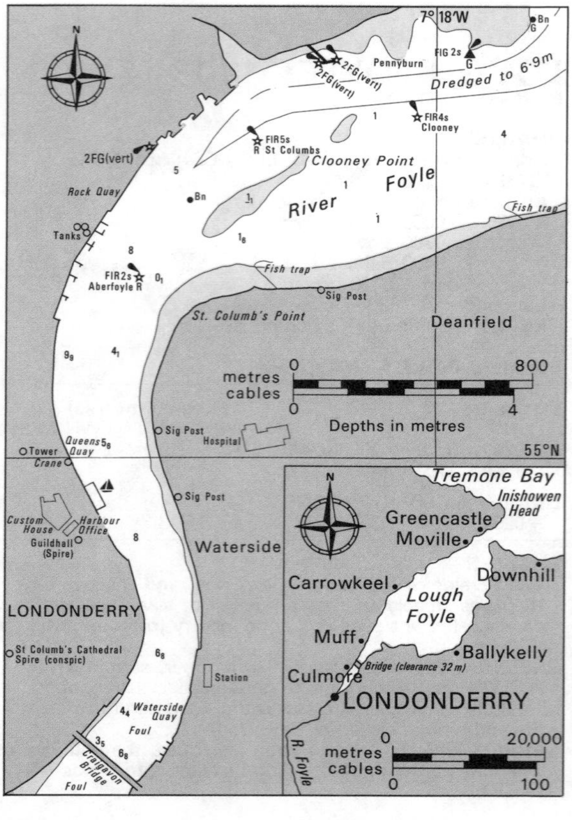

7°18′W
Bn G
FlG 2s G
Pennyburn
2FG(vert)
Dredged to 6·9m
FlR4s Clooney
FlR5s R St Columbs
Clooney Point
River Foyle
2FG(vert)
Rock Quay
Bn
Fish trap
Tanks
FlR2s Aberfoyle R
Fish trap
Sig Post
St. Columb's Point
Deanfield
metres
cables
0
800
4
Depths in metres
Sig Post
Hospital
Queens Quay
Tower
Crane
55°N
Sig Post
Custom House
Harbour Office
Guildhall (Spire)
Waterside
LONDONDERRY
St Columb's Cathedral Spire (conspic)
Station
Waterside Quay
Foul
Craigavon Bridge
Foul
Tremone Bay
Inishowen Head
Greencastle
Moville
Downhill
Carrowkeel
Lough Foyle
Muff
Ballykelly
Bridge (clearance 32 m)
Culmore
LONDONDERRY
R. Foyle
0
20,000
100

LOUGH SWILLY 10-13-15

Donegal

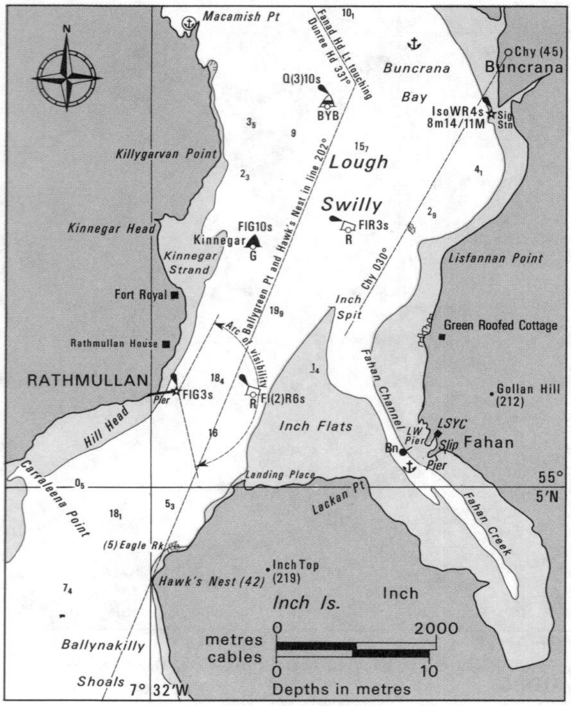

Macamish Pt
Fanad Hd Lt touching Dunree Hd 331°
Buncrana Bay
Buncrana
Chy (45)
Q(3)10s
BYB
IsoWR4s 8m14/11M
Sig Stn
Killygarvan Point
Lough Swilly
FlR3s R
Kinnegar Head
FlG10s
Kinnegar
G
Kinnegar Strand
Ballygreen Pt and Hawk's Nest in line 202°
Chy 030°
Lisfannan Point
Fort Royal
Inch Spit
Green Roofed Cottage
Rathmullan House
Arc of visibility
Fahan Channel
Gollan Hill (212)
RATHMULLAN
Pier
FlG3s
Fl(2)R6s
R
Hill Head
Inch Flats
LSYC
LW Pier
Slip
Fahan
Pier
Carraleena Point
Landing Place
Lackan Pt
55° 5′N
(5) Eagle Rk
Fahan Creek
Inch Top (219)
Hawk's Nest (42)
Inch Is.
Inch
metres
cables
0
2000
10
Ballynakilly
Shoals
7° 32′W
Depths in metres

CHARTS
Admiralty 2697; Irish OS 1

TIDES
−0500 Dover; ML 2·5; Duration 0605; Zone 0 (GMT)

Standard Port GALWAY (⟶)

Times				Height (metres)			
HW		LW		MHWS	MHWN	MLWN	MLWS
0200	0900	0200	0800	5·1	3·9	2·0	0·6
1400	2100	1400	2000				
Differences RATHMULLAN							
+0125	+0050	+0126	+0118	−0·8	−0·7	−0·1	−0·1
FANAD HEAD							
+0115	+0040	+0125	+0120	−1·1	−0·9	−0·5	−0·1
MULROY BAY BAR							
+0108	+0052	+0102	+0118	−1·2	−1·0	No data	
SHEEP HAVEN (DOWNIES BAY)							
+0057	+0043	+0053	+0107	−1·1	−0·9	No data	

SHELTER
Entrance easy in all weathers but swell can render anchorages below Inch Island uncomfortable. Anchorages — Port Salon Bay when wind not in E, but liable to swell (off chartlet to NW); Fahan Creek E of Inch Is entered at HW; W of Macamish Pt sheltered from SE to N through W; Rathmullan Road S of pier off town.

NAVIGATION
Lough Swilly waypoint 55°17′·50N 07°34′·50W, 352°/172° from/to Dunree Head Lt, 5·7M. Six lit lateral buoys and one lit cardinal buoy mark main channel. Beware Swilly More Rks, Kinnegar Spit, Colpagh rks off E shore, Kinnegar Strand, Inch Flats and fish farms.

LIGHTS AND MARKS
Leading lines into Lough Swilly
(1) Fanad Hd Lt touching Dunree Head at 331°.
(2) Ballygreen Pt and Hawk's Nest in line at 202°.

RADIO TELEPHONE
None.

TELEPHONE (074)
Hr Mr 58177; MRSC Limerick 61219; ⌗ 21935; Police 58113; Dr 58135.

LOUGH SWILLY *continued*

FACILITIES
RATHMULLAN EC Wednesday; **Pier** AB, AC, C (5 ton), FW, L, M, Slip; **E. Toomey** ☎ 58125, CH; **Rathmullan House Hotel** ☎ 58117, M, L, R, Bar; **Fort Royal Hotel** ☎ 58100, M, L, R, Bar; **Town** D and P (cans), Kos, Bar, R, V, ✉; Ⓑ; ⇌ (bus to Londonderry); ✈ (Londonderry).
RAMELTON **Quay** AB, L; **Town** Bar, P and D (cans), FW, Kos, R, V, ✉.
FAHAN Slip, FW, L, M (ask YC), R; **Lough Swilly YC** ☎ Fahan 6 01 89, Bar; **Bradley's Garage** (1M SE), Kos, V, P and D (cans).

KILLYBEGS 10-13-16
Donegal

CHARTS
Admiralty 2792, 2702; Irish OS 3
TIDES
−0520 Dover; ML 2·2; Duration 0620; Zone 0 (GMT).

Standard Port GALWAY (⟶)

Times				Height (metres)			
HW		LW		MHWS	MHWN	MLWN	MLWS
0600	1100	0000	0700	5·1	3·9	2·0	0·6
1800	2300	1200	1900				
Differences KILLYBEGS							
+0040	+0050	+0055	+0035	−1·0	−0·9	−0·5	0·0
BURTONPORT							
+0042	+0055	+0115	+0055	−1·2	−1·0	−0·6	−0·1
DONEGAL HARBOUR (SALTHILL QUAY)							
+0038	+0050	+0052	+0104	−1·2	−0·9	No data	
MULLAGHMORE							
+0036	+0048	+0047	+0059	−1·4	−1·0	−0·4	−0·2

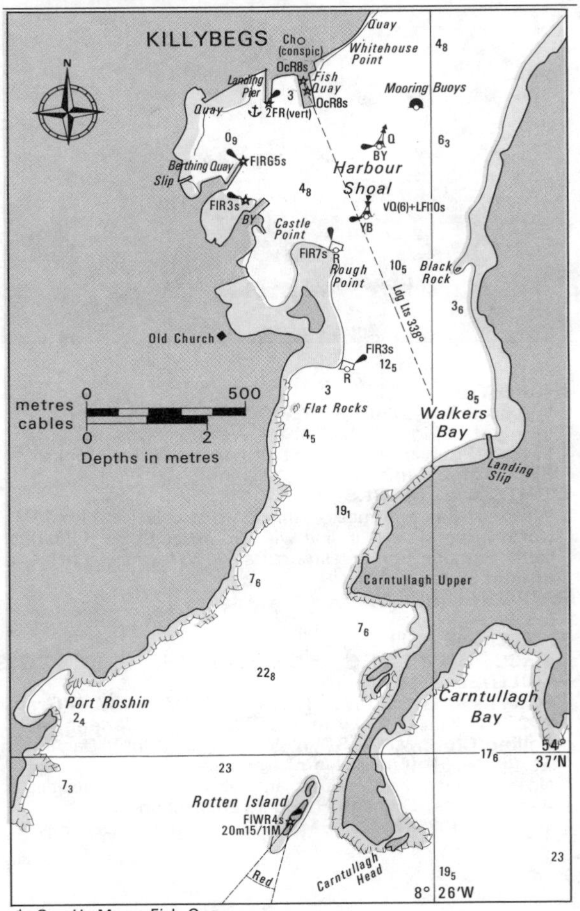
KILLYBEGS
Cho (conspic)
Quay
Whitehouse Point
Landing Pier
OcR8s
Fish Quay
OcR8s
2FR(vert)
Mooring Buoys
Quay
BY
Q
Berthing Quay
FlRG5s
Slip
Harbour Shoal
FlR3s
BY
VQ(6)+LFl10s
YB
Castle Point
FlR7s
R
Rough Point
Black Rock
Ldg Lts 338°
Old Church
FlR3s
R
metres
cables
0
500
2
Depths in metres
Flat Rocks
Walkers Bay
Landing Slip
Carntullagh Upper
Port Roshin
Carntullagh Bay
54°
37′N
Rotten Island
FlWR4s
20m15/11M
Red
Carntullagh Head
8°
26′W
⚠ See Hr Mr on Fish Quay

SHELTER
A secure harbour although SSW winds cause a little swell. Accessible in all weathers day and night.
NAVIGATION
Waypoint 54°36′·00N 08°27′·00W, 202°/022° from/to Rotten Island Lt, 0·94M. Beware of Fintragh. Note that Manister Rock is covered at HW and dries at LW.
LIGHTS AND MARKS
Keep mid channel until off Rough Pt then follow the leading lights into harbour by Fish Quay. Ldg Lts 338°, both Oc R 8s.
RADIO TELEPHONE
VHF Ch 16.
TELEPHONE (073)
Hr Mr 31032; MRCC Limerick 61219; # 31070; Police 31002; Dr 31181 (Home) 31148 (Surgery).
FACILITIES
EC Wednesday; **Landing Pier** ☎ 31032, Slip, M, D, P, FW, L, ME, El, CH, AB, V, R, Bar; **Berthing Quay** Slip, M, D, AB; **Mooney Boats** ☎ 31152, Sh, C (12 ton), ME, El, Sh; **Gallaher Bros** ☎ 31004, Kos; **Barry Electronics** ☎ 31215, Ⓔ.
Town ✉; Ⓑ; ⇌ (bus to Sligo); ✈ (Strandhill).

SLIGO 10-13-17
Sligo

CHARTS
Admiralty 2852, 2767; Irish OS 7
TIDES
−0511 Dover; ML 2·3; Duration 0620; Zone 0 (GMT).

Standard Port GALWAY (⟶)

Times				Height (metres)			
HW		LW		MHWS	MHWN	MLWN	MLWS
0600	1100	0000	0700	5·1	3·9	2·0	0·6
1800	2300	1200	1900				
Differences SLIGO HARBOUR (Oyster Is)							
+0043	+0055	+0042	+0054	−1·0	−0·9	−0·5	−0·1
KILLALA BAY (INISHCRONE)							
+0035	+0055	+0030	+0050	−1·3	−1·2	−0·7	−0·2
BROADHAVEN							
+0040	+0050	+0040	+0050	−1·4	−1·1	−0·4	−0·1
BLACKSOD QUAY							
+0025	+0035	+0040	+0040	−1·2	−1·0	−0·6	−0·2
BLACKSOD BAY (BULL'S MOUTH)							
+0101	+0057	+0109	+0105	−1·5	−1·0	−0·6	−0·1

SHELTER
The lower harbour is fairly exposed but Sligo town is 5M from open sea and gives good shelter.
NAVIGATION
Waypoint 54°18′·62N 08°39′·00W, 248°/068° from/to Cullaun Bwee Lt, 3·0M. The passage between Oyster Island and Coney Island is marked 'Dangerous'. Pass N of Oyster Is leaving Blennick Rks to Port. Passage up to Sligo town between training walls. Some perches are in bad repair. Pilots at Raghley Head and Rosses Pt. Channel up to quays dredged to 2·4m.
LIGHTS AND MARKS
Ldg Lts into harbour 125°, lead to Metal Man Rocks. Channel lights up the harbour are under repair.
RADIO TELEPHONE
Pilots VHF Ch 16; 14.
TELEPHONE (071)
Harbour Office 61197; MRCC Limerick 61219; # 61064; Police 42031; Dr 42886.
FACILITIES
EC Monday, all day; **Deepwater Pier** P and D (in cans), L, FW, ME, El, Sh, C (15 ton), CH, AB; **Ballast Quay** ☎ 61197, M, L, FW, ME, El, C, CH, AB; **Rodney Lomax** ☎ 66124, Slip, ME, El, Sh; **Sligo YC** ☎ 77168, M, FW, Bar, Slip; **Sligo Bedding Centre** ☎ 2303, Kos.
Town V, R, Bar. ✉; Ⓑ; ⇌; ✈ (Strandhill).

SLIGO HARBOUR *continued*

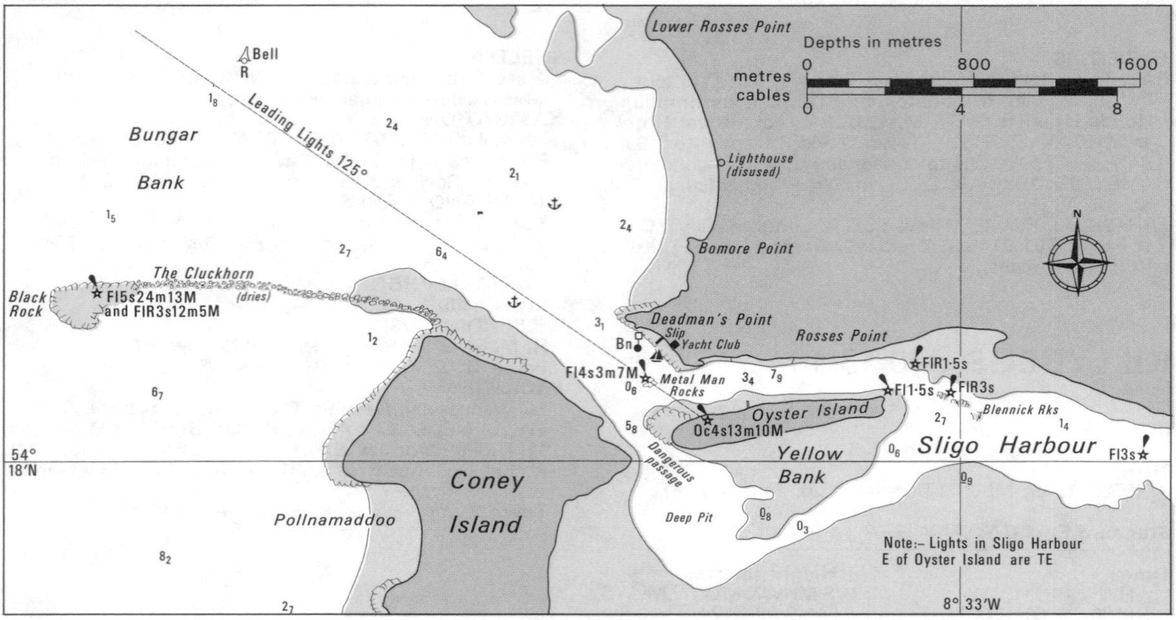
Lower Rosses Point
Depths in metres
0
800
1600
metres
cables
0
4
8
Bell
R
Leading Lights 125°
Bungar
Bank
Lighthouse (disused)
Bomore Point
The Cluckhorn
(dries)
Black Rock
Fl5s24m13M and FlR3s12m5M
Deadman's Point
Slip
Yacht Club
Rosses Point
Bn
FlR1·5s
Fl4s3m7M
Metal Man Rocks
Fl1·5s
FlR3s
Blennick Rks
Oyster Island
Oc4s13m10M
Sligo Harbour
Fl3s
Dangerous passage
Yellow
Bank
54°
18'N
Coney
Island
Pollnamaddoo
Deep Pit
Note:– Lights in Sligo Harbour E of Oyster Island are TE
8° 33'W

WESTPORT (CLEW BAY)

Mayo

10-13-18

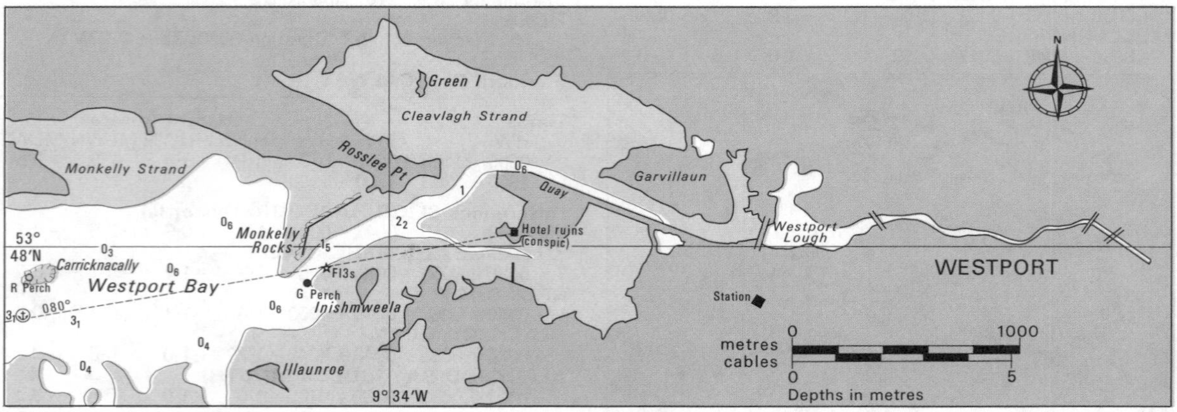
Green I
Cleavlagh Strand
Rosslee Pt
Monkelly Strand
Garvillaun
Quay
Hotel ruins (conspic)
Westport Lough
53°
48'N
Monkelly Rocks
Carricknacally
R Perch
Westport Bay
Fl3s
G Perch
080°
Inishmweela
WESTPORT
Station
metres
cables
0
1000
5
Illaunroe
Depths in metres
9° 34'W

CHARTS
Admiralty 2057, 2667; Irish OS 10 and 11

TIDES
−0545 Dover; ML 2·5; Duration 0610; Zone 0 (GMT)

Standard Port GALWAY (⟶)

Times				Height (metres)			
HW		LW		MHWS	MHWN	MLWN	MLWS
0600	1100	0000	0700	5·1	3·9	2·0	0·6
1800	2300	1200	1900				
Differences INISHRAHER							
+0030	+0012	+0058	+0026	−0·6	−0·5	−0·3	−0·1
CLARE ISLAND							
+0019	+0013	+0029	+0023	−1·0	−0·7	−0·4	−0·1
KILLARY HARBOUR							
+0021	+0015	+0035	+0029	−1·0	−0·8	−0·4	−0·1
CLIFDEN BAY							
+0005	+0005	+0016	+0016	−0·7	−0·5	No data	

SHELTER
Westport Bay affords secure anchorage amongst the islands and is available at all states of tide.

NAVIGATION
Waypoint 53°49′·20N 09°42′·10W, 251°/071° from/to Inishgort Lt Ho, 1·2M. Pilot for Westport lives on Inishlyre. Beware of the Spit and Mondelly (or Monkelly) Rks which are unmarked.

LIGHTS AND MARKS
Westport Bay entrance — Inishgort Lt L Fl 10s 11m 10M. North of hotel ruins in line with South of Lt Bn (Fl 3s) at 080°. Passage from Westport Bay to Westport, 5 miles, is marked by Bns.

RADIO TELEPHONE
None.

TELEPHONE (098)
MRCC (061) 61219; # 25230; Police 25555; Ⓗ (094) 21733

FACILITIES
EC Wednesday; **Quays** M, L, AB, V, R, Bar; **M O'Grady** ☎ 25072, Kos. **T.P. Lynn** ☎ 25230 El, Ⓔ; **Glénans Irish Sailing Club; Mayo SC** ☎ 26260 L, C (3 ton), Bar; **Town** ✉; Ⓑ; ≹; ✈ (Enniskillen or Knock).
Note:– Between Westport and Galway, repair facilities at **Aster Boats,** Drimagh Harbour, Errislannan ☎ Clifden (095) 21323. See 10·13·20 under Clifden Bay.

GALWAY BAY 10-13-19

Galway

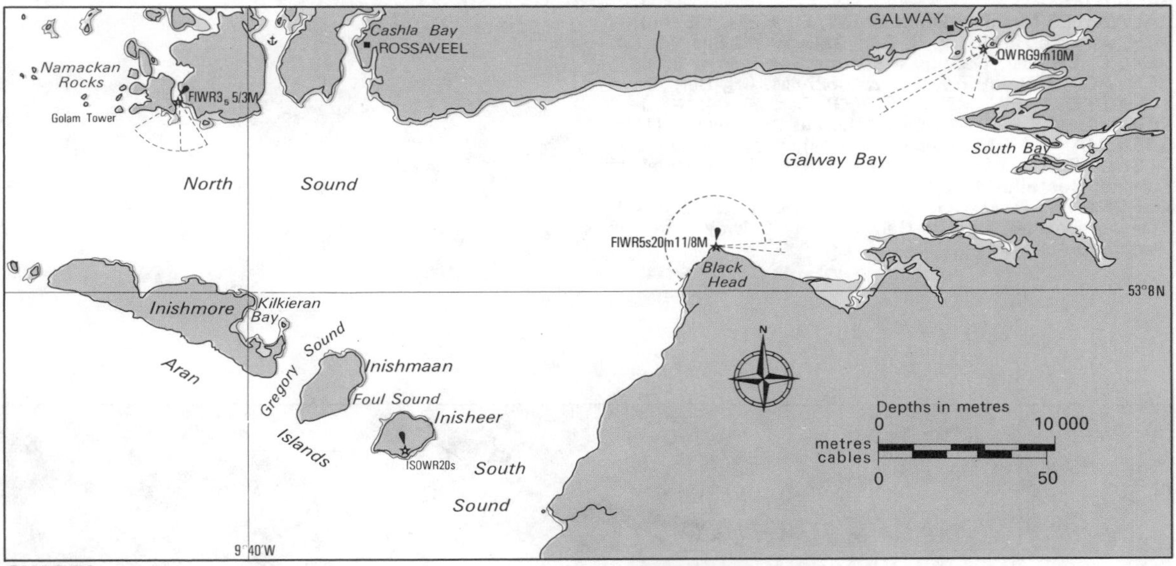
GALWAY
Cashla Bay
ROSSAVEEL
QWRG9m10M
Namackan Rocks
FlWR3s 5/3M
Golam Tower
South Bay
Galway Bay
North
Sound
FlWR5s20m11/8M
Black Head
53°8N
Inishmore
Kilkieran Bay
Gregory Sound
Aran
Islands
Inishmaan
Foul Sound
Inisheer
IsoWR20s
South
Sound
Depths in metres
0
10 000
metres
cables
0
50
9°40'W

CHARTS
Admiralty 1903, 1984, 3339, 2173; Irish OS 14

TIDES
−0555 Dover; ML 2·9; Duration 0620; Zone 0 (GMT).

Standard Port GALWAY (⟶)

Times				Height (metres)			
HW		LW		MHWS	MHWN	MLWN	MLWS
0600	1100	0000	0700	5·1	3·9	2·0	0·6
1800	2300	1200	1900				
Differences KILKIERAN COVE							
+0005	+0005	+0016	+0016	−0·3	−0·2	−0·1	0·0
INISHBOFIN HARBOUR							
+0013	+0009	+0021	+0017	−1·0	−0·8	−0·4	−0·1
KILLEANY BAY (Aran Islands)							
−0008	−0008	+0003	+0003	−0·4	−0·3	−0·2	−0·1
LISCANNOR							
−0003	−0007	+0006	+0002	−0·4	−0·3	No data	

NOTE: Galway is a Standard Port and tidal information for each day of the year are given below.

SHELTER
Galway Bay is sheltered from large swells by Aran Islands, but seas get up in the 20M from Aran Is to Galway. There are numerous anchorages in Galway Bay, but the principal ones are:
KIGGAUL BAY. Easy entrance, day or night, anchor close to Lt (Fl 3s WR 5/3M) to W or NW. Depth 3 to 4m; exposed to S and SE winds.
GREATMAN BAY. Beware English Rk (dries 1·2m), Keeraun Shoal (breaks in heavy weather), Arkeena Rk, Trabaan Rk, Rin Rks and Chapel Rks. Anchor off Natawny Quay or go alongside at Maumeen Quay.
CASHLA BAY. Easiest harbour on this coast; enter in any weather. Anchor off Clashnacally pier.
There is no safe harbour from Cashla to Galway (20M).
GALWAY HARBOUR gives very good protection, being sheltered from SW by Mutton Is. Dock gates open HW−2 to HW. Enter inner dock and secure in SW corner of basin. New Harbour (home of Galway Bay SC) is nearest safe anchorage to Galway.
CREEKS E of Black Head have rocks and shallows but give excellent shelter. Ballyvaghan Bay, Aughinish Bay, South Bay, and Kinvarra Bay are the main ones.
MUTTON ISLAND. (52°48′·6N, 09° 31′·5W) Anchorage about 1 to 1½ ca off SE end of Is, called Tobacco Cove, in approx 3m, sheltered except from S.
ARAN ISLANDS. The only reasonable shelter is in Killeany Bay in Inishmore. Anchor S of Kilronan pier. Alternatively, anchor off Trawmore Strand or in good weather at Portmurvy.

NAVIGATION
Galway Waypoint 53°14′·80N 09°03′·40W, 241°/061° from/to Leverets Lt, 1·1M.
Approaches:
North Sound between Inishmore and mainland, 4½M wide, is easiest but beware Brocklinmore Bank in heavy weather.
Gregory Sound between Inishmore and Inishmaan, is free of dangers but give Straw Is a berth of 2 to 3 ca.
Foul Sound between Inishmaan and Inisheer; only danger is Pipe Rk (dries) at end of reef extending 3 ca from NW end of Inisheer.
South Sound between Inisheer and mainland. Only danger Finnis Rk (dries 0·4m) 4½ca SE of E point of Inisheer (marked by E cardinal Lt buoy Q(3) 10s). Approaching from S, beware Kilstiffin Rks off Liscannor Bay.
In Galway it is dangerous to lie in the 'Layby' (a dredged cut E of pier extending from dock gates) when wind is S or SE. When wind is strong from these points, seas sweep round the pierhead.

LIGHTS AND MARKS
Kiggaul Bay Lt Fl.WR 3s 5/3M.
Cashla Bay Killeen Pt Fl(3) WR 10s 6/3M; Lion Pt Dir (010°) Iso WRG 4s 8/6M.
Galway Leverets Q WRG 9m 10M; B Tr W bands; vis G015°-058°, W058°-065°, R065°-103°, G103°-143°, W143°-146°, R146°-015°. Ldg Lts 325° Front Fl R 1·5s, Rear Oc R 10s; both R diamonds with Y diagonal stripes on masts vis 315°-345°.
Black Head Lt Fl WR 5s 20m 11/8M, R sector covering Illanloo Rk (268°-293°).
Aran Islands Inishmore Rock Is Fl 15s 35m 23M
Straw Is Fl(2) 5s 11m 17M
Inisheer Iso WR 20s 34m 20/16M (R sector covers Finnis Rk) R269°-245°, W245°-231°, obsc 231°-115°, W115°-269°.

RADIO TELEPHONE
Call *Harbour Master Galway* VHF Ch 16; 12 (HW−2½ to HW+1).

TELEPHONE (091)
Hr Mr 61874; Coast Life-Saving Service (099) 61107; MRCC Limerick (061) 61219; Harbour Office 61874; ⌗ 62539; Police 63161; Dr 62453.

GALWAY BAY *continued*

FACILITIES

GALWAY EC Monday; **Dock** L, FW, El, ME, C (35 ton), CH, AB (see Hr Mr), V, R, Bar; **Galway YC** Slip, M, L, FW, C, CH, Bar; **Galway Maritime Services ☎** 66568, CH, ACA; **Galway Bay SC ☎** 94527, M, CH, Bar; **Town** Slip, P, D, L, FW, ME, El, C, V, R, Bar, ✉; Ⓑ; ⇌; ✈.
KIGGAUL BAY Bar (no phone), shop at Lettermullen (1M).
GREATMAN BAY Maumeen V, P (1M), Bar.
CASHLA BAY No facilities. **Carraroe** (1M) Shop, Hotel, phone; **Costelloe** (1½M), Hotel, ✉, Garage.
KILRONAN V, D, FW, Good shelter but very crowded with fishing boats ✉, Ferry to Galway; ✈ to Galway from airstrip on beach.

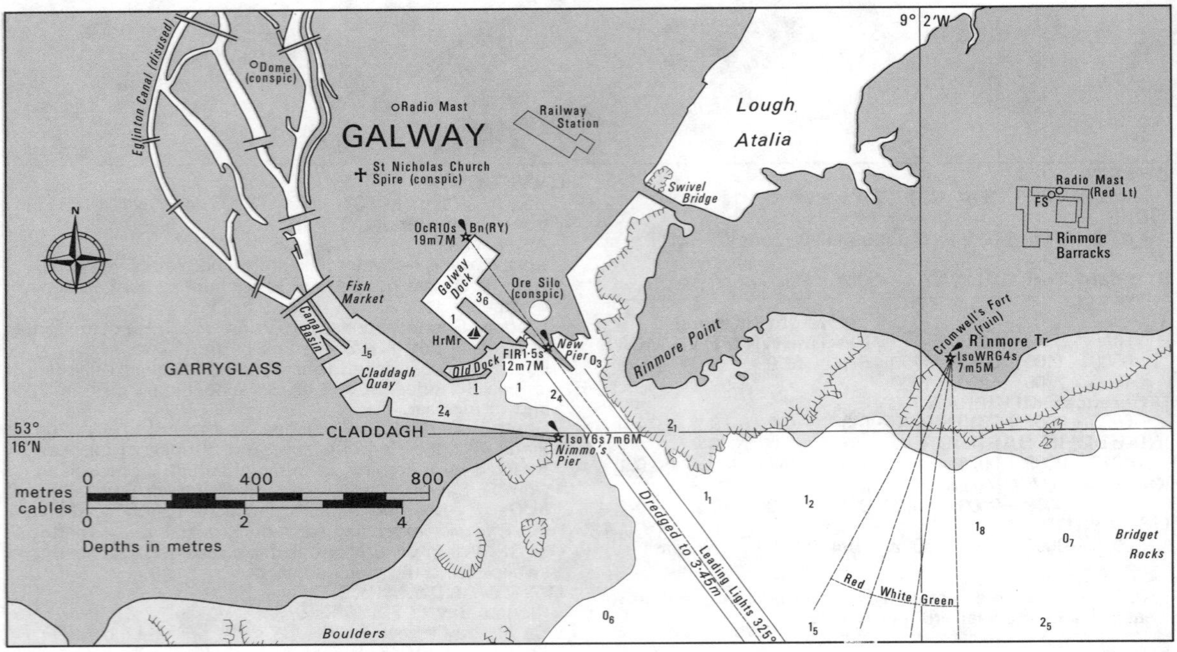
GALWAY
Eglinton Canal (disused)
Dome (conspic)
Radio Mast
Railway Station
Lough Atalia
St Nicholas Church Spire (conspic)
Swivel Bridge
Radio Mast (Red Lt)
FS
Rinmore Barracks
OcR10s Bn(RY) 19m7M
Galway Dock
Ore Silo (conspic)
Fish Market
Canal Basin
HrMr
New Pier
FlR1·5s 12m7M
Old Dock
Claddagh Quay
Rinmore Point
Cromwell's Fort (ruin)
Rinmore Tr IsoWRG4s 7m5M
GARRYGLASS
53° 16′N
CLADDAGH
IsoY6s7m6M
Nimmo's Pier
9° 2′W
metres
cables
0 400 800
0 2 4
Depths in metres
Dredged to 3·45m
Leading Lights 325°
Red White Green
Bridget Rocks
Boulders

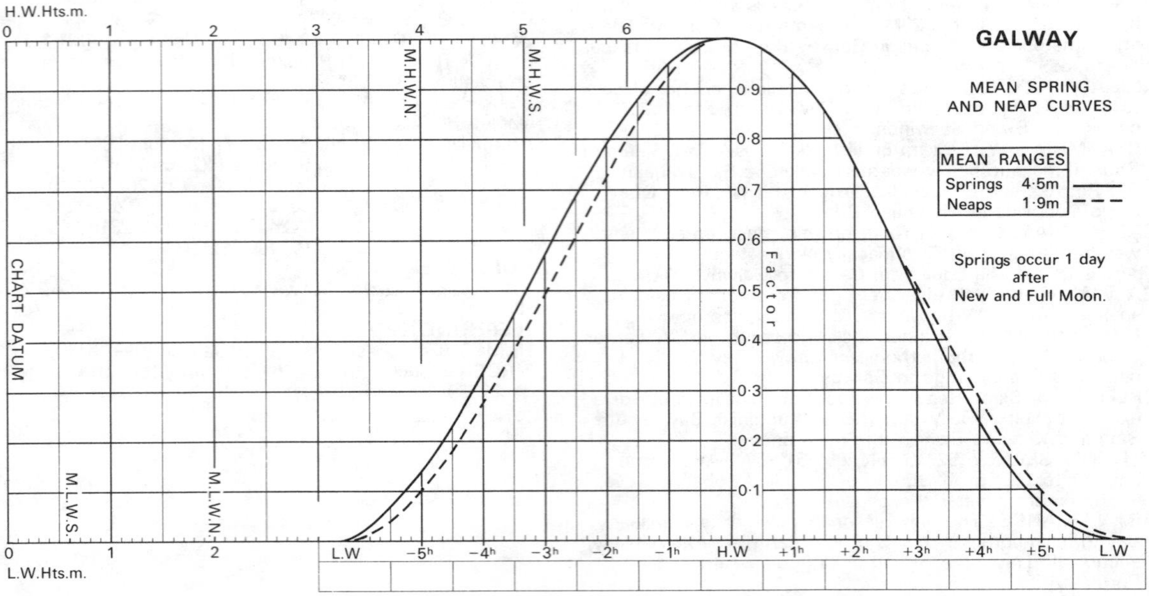
GALWAY
MEAN SPRING AND NEAP CURVES
MEAN RANGES
Springs 4·5m
Neaps 1·9m
Springs occur 1 day after New and Full Moon.
H.W.Hts.m.
0 1 2 3 4 5 6
M.H.W.N.
M.H.W.S.
CHART DATUM
M.L.W.S.
M.L.W.N.
L.W.Hts.m.
Factor
0·9 0·8 0·7 0·6 0·5 0·4 0·3 0·2 0·1
L.W −5h −4h −3h −2h −1h H.W +1h +2h +3h +4h +5h L.W

TIME ZONE UT(GMT)

For Summer Time add ONE hour in non-shaded areas

IRELAND, WEST COAST - GALWAY

Lat 53°16′ N Long 9°03′ W

TIMES AND HEIGHTS OF HIGH AND LOW WATERS

YEAR **1992**

JANUARY

Day	Time	m	Day	Time	m
1 W	0216	4·4	16 Th	0120	4·1
	0827	1·8		0740	1·8
	1449	4·2		1355	4·2
	2049	1·8		2002	1·7
2 Th	0307	4·5	17 F	0226	4·4
	0918	1·6		0844	1·5
	1538	4·4		1458	4·5
	2135	1·7		2101	1·4
3 F	0352	4·7	18 Sa	0321	4·7
	1003	1·4		0939	1·0
	1623	4·5		1553	4·8
	2217	1·5		2153	1·1
4 Sa ●	0433	4·8	19 Su ○	0413	5·1
	1044	1·2		1028	0·6
	1702	4·6		1644	5·1
	2255	1·4		2241	0·7
5 Su	0512	4·9	20 M	0501	5·4
	1122	1·1		1115	0·3
	1740	4·6		1732	5·3
	2333	1·3		2326	0·5
6 M	0550	5·0	21 Tu	0547	5·6
	1157	1·0		1158	0·1
	1817	4·7		1817	5·4
7 Tu	0008	1·2	22 W	0010	0·4
	0627	4·9		0632	5·6
	1232	1·0		1242	0·2
	1853	4·7		1902	5·3
8 W	0042	1·3	23 Th	0053	0·5
	0702	4·9		0719	5·5
	1306	1·0		1324	0·3
	1927	4·6		1947	5·2
9 Th	0117	1·3	24 F	0137	0·7
	0735	4·8		0804	5·2
	1340	1·1		1409	0·7
	2001	4·5		2032	4·9
10 F	0152	1·4	25 Sa	0223	1·0
	0811	4·6		0850	4·9
	1415	1·3		1456	1·1
	2036	4·4		2119	4·6
11 Sa	0229	1·6	26 Su ☾	0312	1·4
	0849	4·5		0942	4·5
	1453	1·4		1548	1·5
	2114	4·2		2213	4·3
12 Su	0310	1·8	27 M	0410	1·7
	0929	4·3		1041	4·1
	1535	1·6		1649	1·9
	2159	4·1		2316	4·0
13 M ☽	0400	2·0	28 Tu	0525	2·0
	1019	4·1		1200	3·8
	1627	1·8		1812	2·1
	2254	4·0			
14 Tu	0504	2·1	29 W	0036	3·9
	1123	4·0		0700	2·1
	1734	1·9		1330	3·8
				1938	2·1
15 W	0005	4·0	30 Th	0154	4·0
	0624	2·0		0819	1·9
	1241	4·0		1443	3·9
	1850	1·9		2043	2·0
			31 F	0254	4·1
				0914	1·7
				1534	4·1
				2129	1·7

FEBRUARY

Day	Time	m	Day	Time	m
1 Sa	0342	4·4	16 Su	0311	4·6
	0956	1·4		0931	0·9
	1616	4·3		1545	4·7
	2209	1·5		2145	0·9
2 Su	0421	4·6	17 M	0402	5·0
	1033	1·2		1016	0·4
	1652	4·5		1633	5·0
	2245	1·2		2228	0·5
3 M ●	0459	4·7	18 Tu ○	0448	5·3
	1106	0·9		1058	0·1
	1726	4·6		1716	5·3
	2318	1·0		2311	0·2
4 Tu	0533	4·9	19 W	0532	5·5
	1139	0·8		1139	0·1
	1758	4·7		1758	5·4
	2350	0·9		2351	0·1
5 W	0607	4·9	20 Th	0614	5·6
	1210	0·7		1219	0·0
	1829	4·7		1839	5·4
6 Th	0021	0·9	21 F	0031	0·2
	0638	4·9		0656	5·5
	1239	0·7		1259	0·2
	1900	4·7		1920	5·2
7 F	0050	0·9	22 Sa	0112	0·4
	0710	4·9		0740	5·2
	1309	0·8		1340	0·6
	1930	4·6		2002	4·9
8 Sa	0123	1·0	23 Su	0155	0·8
	0742	4·7		0823	4·8
	1340	0·9		1422	1·0
	2002	4·5		2047	4·6
9 Su	0155	1·2	24 M	0240	1·2
	0816	4·6		0910	4·4
	1413	1·1		1510	1·5
	2036	4·4		2135	4·2
10 M	0232	1·4	25 Tu ☾	0332	1·6
	0856	4·4		1004	3·9
	1453	1·4		1607	2·0
	2117	4·2		2233	3·8
11 Tu ☽	0317	1·6	26 W	0442	2·0
	0942	4·1		1119	3·6
	1542	1·6		1733	2·2
	2207	4·0		2353	3·6
12 W	0416	1·9	27 Th	0628	2·1
	1044	3·9		1306	3·5
	1648	1·9		1920	2·2
	2318	3·8			
13 Th	0543	2·0	28 F	0128	3·7
	1208	3·8		0801	2·0
	1819	2·0		1429	3·7
				2027	2·0
14 F	0048	3·9	29 Sa	0237	3·9
	0721	1·8		0856	1·7
	1338	4·0		1519	3·9
	1948	1·8		2114	1·7
15 Sa	0209	4·2			
	0834	1·4			
	1450	4·3			
	2053	1·4			

MARCH

Day	Time	m	Day	Time	m
1 Su	0324	4·1	16 M	0256	4·5
	0936	1·4		0912	0·7
	1557	4·2		1528	4·7
	2150	1·4		2127	0·8
2 M	0403	4·4	17 Tu	0343	4·9
	1012	1·1		0956	0·3
	1631	4·4		1613	5·0
	2224	1·1		2209	0·4
3 Tu	0437	4·6	18 W ○	0428	5·2
	1042	0·8		1035	0·1
	1702	4·6		1654	5·2
	2255	0·9		2249	0·2
4 W ●	0509	4·8	19 Th	0511	5·4
	1112	0·6		1115	0·0
	1732	4·7		1734	5·3
	2325	0·7		2329	0·1
5 Th	0540	4·9	20 F	0551	5·4
	1140	0·5		1153	0·0
	1801	4·8		1814	5·3
	2353	0·6			
6 F	0611	4·9	21 Sa	0008	0·2
	1208	0·5		0634	5·3
	1829	4·8		1232	0·3
				1855	5·1
7 Sa	0022	0·6	22 Su	0048	0·4
	0642	4·9		0714	5·0
	1238	0·6		1312	0·7
	1859	4·8		1935	4·9
8 Su	0053	0·7	23 M	0130	0·7
	0714	4·8		0758	4·7
	1309	0·7		1352	1·1
	1931	4·7		2018	4·5
9 M	0127	0·9	24 Tu	0213	1·2
	0749	4·6		0843	4·2
	1342	1·0		1437	1·6
	2006	4·5		2103	4·2
10 Tu	0205	1·1	25 W	0304	1·6
	0830	4·4		0935	3·9
	1423	1·3		1531	2·0
	2047	4·3		2156	3·8
11 W	0250	1·4	26 Th ☾	0409	1·9
	0919	4·1		1041	3·5
	1512	1·6		1651	2·3
	2139	4·0		2308	3·6
12 Th ☽	0352	1·7	27 F	0543	2·1
	1023	3·9		1221	3·4
	1623	1·9		1836	2·3
	2251	3·8			
13 F	0523	1·8	28 Sa	0042	3·6
	1151	3·8		0717	2·0
	1804	2·0		1354	3·6
				1951	2·1
14 Sa	0028	3·8	29 Su	0159	3·7
	0707	1·6		0818	1·7
	1327	3·9		1447	3·8
	1937	1·7		2042	1·8
15 Su	0154	4·1	30 M	0251	4·0
	0820	1·2		0901	1·4
	1437	4·3		1527	4·1
	2039	1·3		2119	1·4
			31 Tu	0331	4·2
				0936	1·1
				1600	4·3
				2153	1·1

APRIL

Day	Time	m	Day	Time	m
1 W	0406	4·4	16 Th	0404	5·0
	1009	0·9		1010	0·3
	1630	4·5		1630	5·1
	2224	0·9		2226	0·4
2 Th	0438	4·6	17 F ○	0447	5·2
	1038	0·7		1049	0·3
	1659	4·7		1709	5·2
	2254	0·7		2306	0·3
3 F ●	0509	4·8	18 Sa	0529	5·2
	1106	0·6		1127	0·4
	1727	4·8		1749	5·2
	2323	0·6		2346	0·4
4 Sa	0542	4·9	19 Su	0611	5·0
	1136	0·6		1207	0·6
	1757	4·9		1829	5·1
	2356	0·5			
5 Su	0614	4·9	20 M	0027	0·6
	1208	0·6		0653	4·8
	1829	4·9		1246	0·9
				1910	4·9
6 M	0028	0·6	21 Tu	0109	0·9
	0650	4·8		0735	4·5
	1242	0·8		1327	1·3
	1904	4·8		1952	4·6
7 Tu	0106	0·8	22 W	0154	1·2
	0730	4·7		0820	4·2
	1320	1·0		1412	1·6
	1944	4·6		2036	4·3
8 W	0148	1·0	23 Th	0243	1·5
	0815	4·5		0910	3·9
	1405	1·3		1504	2·0
	2030	4·4		2125	4·0
9 Th	0239	1·3	24 F ☾	0341	1·8
	0908	4·2		1007	3·7
	1500	1·6		1610	2·2
	2127	4·1		2226	3·8
10 F ☽	0345	1·5	25 Sa	0454	1·9
	1014	4·0		1122	3·5
	1613	1·9		1734	2·2
	2238	3·9		2342	3·7
11 Sa	0513	1·6	26 Su	0614	1·9
	1139	3·9		1250	3·6
	1749	1·9		1855	2·1
12 Su	0008	3·9	27 M	0100	3·7
	0646	1·5		0720	1·8
	1307	4·0		1355	3·8
	1914	1·7		1954	1·9
13 M	0131	4·2	28 Tu	0201	3·9
	0754	1·1		0812	1·6
	1413	4·3		1442	4·0
	2015	1·3		2039	1·6
14 Tu	0232	4·5	29 W	0247	4·1
	0846	0·8		0851	1·3
	1504	4·7		1518	4·2
	2103	0·9		2115	1·3
15 W	0321	4·8	30 Th	0325	4·3
	0929	0·5		0927	1·1
	1548	4·9		1552	4·4
	2145	0·6		2149	1·1

Chart Datum: 0.20 metres below Ordnance Datum (Dublin)

IRELAND, WEST COAST – GALWAY

Lat 53°16′ N Long 9°03′ W

TIME ZONE UT(GMT)

For Summer Time add ONE hour in non-shaded areas

TIMES AND HEIGHTS OF HIGH AND LOW WATERS

YEAR **1992**

MAY

Day	Time	m	Day	Time	m
1 F	0402 1000 1623 2223	4·5 0·9 4·6 0·9	16 Sa ○	0427 1026 1647 2248	4·8 0·8 5·0 0·7
2 Sa ●	0437 1033 1654 2255	4·7 0·8 4·8 0·7	17 Su	0511 1106 1727 2329	4·8 0·8 5·0 0·7
3 Su	0512 1108 1729 2332	4·8 0·7 4·9 0·6	18 M	0553 1147 1808	4·8 1·0 5·0
4 M	0551 1144 1805	4·9 0·7 5·0	19 Tu	0011 0635 1227 1849	0·8 4·6 1·1 4·8
5 Tu	0010 0632 1224 1846	0·6 4·9 0·8 4·9	20 W	0053 0719 1309 1931	1·0 4·5 1·4 4·6
6 W	0052 0717 1307 1931	0·7 4·8 1·0 4·8	21 Th	0137 0802 1351 2013	1·2 4·3 1·6 4·4
7 Th	0140 0806 1357 2022	0·9 4·6 1·3 4·6	22 F	0222 0847 1439 2058	1·4 4·1 1·8 4·2
8 F	0234 0901 1454 2119	1·1 4·4 1·5 4·4	23 Sa	0311 0935 1532 2148	1·6 3·9 2·0 4·0
9 Sa ☽	0339 1006 1603 2227	1·3 4·2 1·7 4·2	24 Su ☾	0406 1030 1634 2244	1·7 3·8 2·1 3·8
10 Su	0455 1119 1723 2344	1·4 4·1 1·8 4·1	25 M	0506 1134 1744 2349	1·8 3·7 2·1 3·8
11 M	0612 1236 1842	1·4 4·2 1·6	26 Tu	0610 1245 1852	1·8 3·8 2·0
12 Tu	0100 0720 1342 1945	4·2 1·2 4·4 1·4	27 W	0056 0709 1342 1947	3·8 1·7 3·9 1·8
13 W	0204 0815 1436 2037	4·4 1·0 4·6 1·1	28 Th	0152 0759 1429 2032	4·0 1·5 4·1 1·6
14 Th	0256 0901 1522 2122	4·6 0·9 4·8 0·9	29 F	0242 0843 1508 2114	4·2 1·3 4·3 1·3
15 F	0342 0945 1604 2206	4·7 0·8 4·9 0·7	30 Sa	0325 0924 1546 2153	4·4 1·2 4·6 1·0
			31 Su	0407 1004 1624 2233	4·6 1·0 4·8 0·8

JUNE

Day	Time	m	Day	Time	m
1 M ●	0449 1045 1705 2315	4·8 0·9 5·0 0·6	16 Tu	0540 1132 1751 2358	4·6 1·1 4·9 0·9
2 Tu	0534 1127 1749 2358	4·9 0·8 5·1 0·5	17 W	0621 1211 1831	4·5 1·2 4·8
3 W	0619 1212 1834	4·9 0·8 5·1	18 Th	0039 0702 1252 1912	0·9 4·5 1·3 4·7
4 Th	0045 0709 1259 1923	0·5 4·9 0·9 5·0	19 F	0119 0741 1331 1951	1·0 4·4 1·4 4·6
5 F	0134 0758 1349 2013	0·7 4·8 1·1 4·9	20 Sa	0158 0820 1411 2030	1·1 4·2 1·5 4·4
6 Sa	0227 0851 1443 2108	0·8 4·6 1·3 4·7	21 Su	0237 0901 1454 2111	1·3 4·1 1·7 4·2
7 Su ☽	0324 0948 1543 2207	1·0 4·4 1·5 4·4	22 M	0319 0943 1541 2156	1·5 4·0 1·8 4·0
8 M	0427 1051 1651 2315	1·2 4·3 1·6 4·3	23 Tu ☾	0407 1031 1635 2247	1·6 3·9 2·0 3·9
9 Tu	0534 1201 1805	1·4 4·2 1·6	24 W	0501 1129 1740 2349	1·7 3·8 2·0 3·8
10 W	0028 0643 1309 1914	4·2 1·4 4·3 1·6	25 Th	0601 1234 1848	1·7 3·8 1·9
11 Th	0135 0745 1408 2013	4·2 1·4 4·4 1·4	26 F	0056 0704 1335 1949	3·8 1·7 4·0 1·7
12 F	0234 0837 1458 2105	4·3 1·3 4·6 1·2	27 Sa	0159 0802 1429 2043	4·0 1·6 4·2 1·4
13 Sa	0325 0925 1545 2152	4·4 1·2 4·7 1·1	28 Su	0254 0856 1517 2131	4·2 1·4 4·5 1·1
14 Su	0413 1009 1628 2235	4·5 1·2 4·8 0·9	29 M	0345 0943 1603 2219	4·5 1·1 4·8 0·8
15 M ○	0457 1051 1709 2318	4·6 1·2 4·9 0·9	30 Tu ●	0434 1030 1649 2304	4·7 0·9 5·0 0·5

JULY

Day	Time	m	Day	Time	m
1 W	0522 1116 1736 2349	4·9 0·7 5·2 0·3	16 Th	0604 1154 1812	4·5 1·0 4·8
2 Th	0608 1201 1824	5·1 0·6 5·3	17 F	0019 0641 1231 1849	0·8 4·5 1·0 4·8
3 F	0035 0656 1248 1912	0·3 5·1 0·6 5·3	18 Sa	0053 0716 1306 1924	0·8 4·5 1·1 4·7
4 Sa	0121 0744 1334 1959	0·3 5·0 0·7 5·1	19 Su	0127 0751 1340 1959	0·9 4·4 1·2 4·5
5 Su	0209 0832 1423 2050	0·5 4·8 0·9 4·9	20 M	0201 0825 1416 2034	1·0 4·3 1·4 4·4
6 M	0258 0924 1517 2143	0·8 4·6 1·2 4·6	21 Tu	0237 0901 1456 2114	1·2 4·1 1·6 4·2
7 Tu ☽	0353 1019 1617 2244	1·1 4·4 1·5 4·3	22 W ☾	0317 0941 1541 2159	1·4 4·0 1·8 4·0
8 W	0457 1123 1729 2356	1·4 4·2 1·7 4·0	23 Th	0403 1030 1638 2257	1·6 3·9 1·9 3·8
9 Th	0610 1235 1848	1·6 4·1 1·7	24 F	0504 1133 1753	1·8 3·8 2·0
10 F	0113 0721 1344 1959	4·0 1·7 4·2 1·6	25 Sa	0010 0618 1249 1913	3·7 1·8 3·8 1·8
11 Sa	0222 0823 1442 2057	4·0 1·7 4·3 1·4	26 Su	0127 0733 1358 2022	3·9 1·7 4·1 1·5
12 Su	0318 0915 1531 2145	4·1 1·5 4·5 1·2	27 M	0234 0837 1457 2118	4·1 1·4 4·4 1·1
13 M	0404 1000 1614 2227	4·3 1·4 4·6 1·0	28 Tu	0331 0931 1548 2206	4·4 1·1 4·8 0·6
14 Tu ○	0448 1040 1657 2306	4·4 1·2 4·7 0·9	29 W ●	0421 1019 1635 2251	4·8 0·7 5·1 0·3
15 W	0527 1119 1734 2344	4·5 1·1 4·8 0·8	30 Th	0508 1102 1722 2334	5·0 0·5 5·4 0·0
			31 F	0553 1146 1807	5·2 0·3 5·5

AUGUST

Day	Time	m	Day	Time	m
1 Sa	0017 0638 1229 1853	0·0 5·3 0·3 5·4	16 Su	0024 0646 1236 1855	0·6 4·6 0·9 4·8
2 Su	0100 0721 1313 1938	0·1 5·2 0·4 5·3	17 M	0053 0717 1307 1927	0·7 4·6 1·0 4·6
3 M	0144 0806 1358 2026	0·3 5·0 0·7 4·9	18 Tu	0124 0748 1340 2001	0·9 4·4 1·2 4·5
4 Tu	0229 0854 1447 2115	0·7 4·7 1·1 4·6	19 W	0157 0822 1415 2037	1·1 4·3 1·4 4·3
5 W ☽	0319 0946 1543 2213	1·2 4·4 1·5 4·2	20 Th	0233 0900 1457 2122	1·3 4·1 1·6 4·0
6 Th	0420 1048 1655 2326	1·6 4·1 1·8 3·8	21 F ☾	0318 0946 1553 2219	1·6 3·9 1·9 3·8
7 F	0539 1204 1829	1·9 3·9 1·9	22 Sa	0420 1051 1713 2337	1·9 3·8 2·0 3·7
8 Sa	0057 0709 1326 1954	3·7 2·0 3·9 1·8	23 Su	0546 1215 1852	2·0 3·8 1·8
9 Su	0216 0818 1429 2051	3·8 1·9 4·1 1·6	24 M	0106 0716 1337 2008	3·8 1·8 4·1 1·4
10 M	0312 0908 1519 2136	4·0 1·7 4·3 1·3	25 Tu	0220 0823 1442 2104	4·1 1·5 4·5 1·0
11 Tu	0356 0949 1602 2214	4·2 1·4 4·5 1·1	26 W	0317 0917 1532 2150	4·5 1·0 4·9 0·5
12 W	0433 1026 1640 2248	4·4 1·2 4·7 0·8	27 Th	0404 1002 1619 2233	4·9 0·6 5·3 0·1
13 Th ○	0508 1059 1715 2322	4·5 1·0 4·8 0·7	28 F ●	0449 1044 1704 2313	5·2 0·3 5·5 –0·1
14 F	0542 1133 1749 2353	4·6 0·9 4·8 0·6	29 Sa	0532 1125 1747 2353	5·4 0·1 5·6 –0·1
15 Sa	0614 1204 1822	4·6 0·8 4·8	30 Su	0614 1207 1831	5·4 0·1 5·5
			31 M	0034 0656 1248 1914	0·0 5·3 0·3 5·3

Chart Datum: 0.20 metres below Ordnance Datum (Dublin)

TIME ZONE UT(GMT)
For Summer Time add ONE hour in non-shaded areas

IRELAND, WEST COAST – GALWAY

Lat 53°16′ N Long 9°03′ W

TIMES AND HEIGHTS OF HIGH AND LOW WATERS

YEAR **1992**

SEPTEMBER

Day	Time	m	Day	Time	m
1 Tu	0116 0740 1331 1959	0·4 5·0 0·7 4·9	16 W	0049 0713 1309 1930	0·9 4·7 1·1 4·6
2 W	0159 0825 1419 2049	0·9 4·7 1·1 4·5	17 Th	0123 0747 1345 2009	1·1 4·5 1·3 4·4
3 Th	0247 0915 1514 ☽ 2145	1·4 4·4 1·5 4·1	18 F	0201 0827 1429 2056	1·4 4·3 1·6 4·2
4 F	0346 1014 1626 2259	1·8 4·0 1·9 3·7	19 Sa	0247 0917 1527 ☾ 2156	1·7 4·1 1·8 3·9
5 Sa	0511 1133 1811	2·2 3·8 2·0	20 Su	0353 1024 1654 2318	2·0 3·9 2·0 3·8
6 Su	0042 0655 1304 1941	3·6 2·2 3·8 1·9	21 M	0526 1151 1836	2·1 3·9 1·8
7 M	0206 0804 1412 2034	3·8 2·0 4·0 1·6	22 Tu	0052 0700 1319 1949	3·9 1·9 4·2 1·4
8 Tu	0257 0850 1500 2115	4·0 1·7 4·2 1·4	23 W	0205 0806 1422 2043	4·3 1·5 4·6 0·9
9 W	0336 0928 1539 2149	4·2 1·5 4·5 1·1	24 Th	0258 0857 1512 2127	4·7 1·0 5·0 0·5
10 Th	0410 1002 1616 2221	4·4 1·2 4·7 0·9	25 F	0343 0941 1557 2209	5·0 0·6 5·3 0·2
11 F	0442 1034 1648 2252	4·6 1·0 4·8 0·7	26 Sa	0426 1021 1641 ● 2248	5·3 0·3 5·5 0·0
12 Sa	0513 1106 1720 ○ 2322	4·7 0·8 4·9 0·6	27 Su	0508 1102 1723 2327	5·5 0·2 5·6 0·1
13 Su	0543 1136 1753 2350	4·8 0·8 4·9 0·6	28 M	0549 1143 1807	5·5 0·2 5·5
14 M	0612 1205 1824	4·8 0·8 4·9	29 Tu	0007 0631 1225 1850	0·3 5·4 0·4 5·2
15 Tu	0019 0642 1236 1856	0·7 4·7 0·9 4·8	30 W	0048 0713 1309 1935	0·7 5·1 0·8 4·9

OCTOBER

Day	Time	m	Day	Time	m
1 Th	0131 0758 1355 2025	1·1 4·8 1·2 4·5	16 F	0057 0721 1326 1951	1·2 4·8 1·3 4·6
2 F	0218 0846 1449 2119	1·6 4·4 1·6 4·1	17 Sa	0140 0806 1413 2042	1·5 4·6 1·5 4·3
3 Sa	0315 0943 1557 ☽ 2228	2·0 4·1 2·0 3·8	18 Su	0232 0900 1517 2145	1·8 4·3 1·7 4·1
4 Su	0434 1057 1733	2·3 3·9 2·1	19 M	0339 1007 1638 ☾ 2304	2·0 4·2 1·8 4·0
5 M	0005 0617 1225 1902	3·7 2·3 3·9 2·0	20 Tu	0508 1130 1810	2·1 4·2 1·7
6 Tu	0134 0728 1337 1958	3·8 2·2 4·0 1·8	21 W	0031 0635 1253 1921	4·2 1·9 4·4 1·4
7 W	0226 0819 1429 2040	4·0 1·9 4·2 1·5	22 Th	0141 0741 1358 2015	4·5 1·6 4·7 1·0
8 Th	0305 0858 1508 2117	4·2 1·6 4·4 1·3	23 F	0234 0833 1449 2101	4·8 1·2 5·0 0·7
9 F	0339 0934 1545 2149	4·5 1·3 4·6 1·1	24 Sa	0319 0918 1535 2143	5·1 0·8 5·3 0·5
10 Sa	0412 1006 1619 2219	4·7 1·1 4·8 0·9	25 Su	0402 1000 1620 ● 2224	5·4 0·6 5·4 0·4
11 Su	0441 1037 1649 ○ 2248	4·8 1·0 4·9 0·8	26 M	0444 1041 1702 2304	5·5 0·5 5·4 0·5
12 M	0511 1106 1722 2318	4·9 0·9 4·9 0·8	27 Tu	0525 1123 1746 2344	5·5 0·5 5·3 0·7
13 Tu	0540 1137 1754 2349	5·0 0·9 4·9 0·9	28 W	0607 1205 1831	5·4 0·7 5·1
14 W	0610 1210 1829	5·0 0·9 4·9	29 Th	0025 0649 1249 1916	1·0 5·2 1·0 4·8
15 Th	0021 0643 1245 1907	1·0 4·9 1·1 4·7	30 F	0107 0734 1335 2004	1·4 4·9 1·3 4·5
			31 Sa	0154 0820 1427 2056	1·8 4·6 1·7 4·2

NOVEMBER

Day	Time	m	Day	Time	m
1 Su	0247 0912 1528 2155	2·1 4·3 1·9 3·9	16 M	0223 0849 1507 2132	1·7 4·7 1·5 4·4
2 M	0353 1013 1640 ☽ 2308	2·3 4·1 2·1 3·8	17 Tu	0327 0952 1617 ☾ 2241	1·9 4·5 1·6 4·3
3 Tu	0513 1126 1757	2·4 4·0 2·1	18 W	0441 1104 1733 2357	2·0 4·4 1·6 4·4
4 W	0032 0634 1241 1903	3·8 2·3 4·0 2·0	19 Th	0600 1221 1845	1·9 4·5 1·5
5 Th	0138 0734 1341 1954	4·0 2·1 4·1 1·8	20 F	0109 0710 1328 1944	4·5 1·7 4·6 1·3
6 F	0225 0820 1429 2034	4·2 1·9 4·3 1·6	21 Sa	0206 0808 1426 2034	4·8 1·4 4·8 1·1
7 Sa	0303 0900 1508 2111	4·5 1·6 4·5 1·4	22 Su	0256 0857 1515 2119	5·0 1·2 5·0 1·0
8 Su	0336 0935 1545 2143	4·7 1·4 4·7 1·2	23 M	0341 0942 1602 2203	5·2 1·0 5·1 0·9
9 M	0407 1007 1620 2216	4·8 1·2 4·8 1·1	24 Tu	0423 1026 1647 ● 2245	5·3 0·8 5·2 0·9
10 Tu	0438 1040 1654 ○ 2249	5·0 1·0 4·9 1·0	25 W	0506 1109 1732 2327	5·4 0·8 5·1 1·0
11 W	0511 1115 1732 2325	5·1 1·0 5·0 1·0	26 Th	0549 1153 1815	5·3 0·9 5·0
12 Th	0546 1151 1811	5·1 0·9 5·0	27 F	0008 0631 1236 1900	1·2 5·2 1·0 4·8
13 F	0001 0624 1231 1853	1·1 5·1 1·0 4·9	28 Sa	0050 0714 1320 1944	1·4 5·0 1·3 4·6
14 Sa	0043 0707 1316 1940	1·3 5·0 1·1 4·8	29 Su	0134 0758 1406 2030	1·7 4·8 1·5 4·4
15 Su	0130 0755 1408 2033	1·5 4·9 1·3 4·6	30 M	0220 0843 1454 2118	1·9 4·5 1·7 4·2

DECEMBER

Day	Time	m	Day	Time	m
1 Tu	0312 0932 1548 2213	2·1 4·3 1·9 4·0	16 W	0307 0932 1548 ☾ 2213	1·5 4·8 1·3 4·6
2 W	0412 1027 1647 ☽ 2315	2·3 4·1 2·0 3·9	17 Th	0409 1034 1654 2319	1·7 4·5 1·5 4·4
3 Th	0520 1130 1750	2·3 4·0 2·0	18 F	0520 1146 1805	1·8 4·4 1·6
4 F	0027 0632 1238 1852	4·0 2·3 4·0 2·0	19 Sa	0031 0638 1300 1914	4·4 1·8 4·4 1·6
5 Sa	0128 0733 1338 1945	4·1 2·1 4·1 1·8	20 Su	0138 0745 1406 2013	4·6 1·7 4·5 1·5
6 Su	0218 0820 1427 2030	4·3 1·9 4·3 1·7	21 M	0234 0843 1503 2105	4·7 1·5 4·6 1·4
7 M	0258 0903 1511 2111	4·5 1·7 4·5 1·5	22 Tu	0324 0932 1553 2152	4·9 1·3 4·7 1·3
8 Tu	0335 0942 1553 2150	4·7 1·4 4·7 1·3	23 W	0410 1019 1638 2234	5·1 1·1 4·8 1·2
9 W	0410 1020 1633 ○ 2228	4·9 1·2 4·9 1·2	24 Th	0452 1101 1722 ● 2316	5·2 1·0 4·9 1·2
10 Th	0448 1059 1715 2309	5·1 1·0 5·0 1·1	25 F	0534 1143 1804 2356	5·2 0·9 4·9 1·2
11 F	0529 1140 1758 2351	5·2 0·8 5·1 1·0	26 Sa	0615 1222 1845	5·1 0·9 4·8
12 Sa	0611 1224 1843	5·3 0·8 5·1	27 Su	0035 0656 1302 1924	1·3 5·1 1·0 4·7
13 Su	0035 0657 1309 1931	1·1 5·3 0·8 5·0	28 M	0114 0735 1341 2004	1·4 4·9 1·2 4·5
14 M	0121 0745 1358 2020	1·2 5·2 0·9 4·9	29 Tu	0154 0815 1420 2043	1·5 4·7 1·4 4·4
15 Tu	0212 0837 1450 2114	1·3 5·0 1·1 4·7	30 W	0234 0854 1500 2124	1·7 4·5 1·6 4·2
			31 Th	0318 0936 1545 2209	1·9 4·3 1·8 4·0

Chart Datum: 0.20 metres below Ordnance Datum (Dublin)

MINOR HARBOURS AND ANCHORAGES 10-13-20

KILKEEL, Down, 54°04′·00N, 05°59′·00W, Zone 0 (GMT), Admty charts 2800, 44. HW +0015 on Dover, +0025 on Belfast; HW height +1·6m on Belfast; ML 2·9m; Duration 0620. See 10·13·9. Shelter is complete in inner basin, but it becomes very crowded. Depth off quays approx 1m. There are drying banks both sides of entrance channel and SE gales cause sand bank right across entrance. This is removed by dredging or is slowly washed away in E winds. CG stn is conspic mark for entering, red brick with W flagstaff to W of entrance. Secure in inner basin and see Hr Mr. Breakwater Lt is Fl WR 2s 8m 8M, R296°–313°, W313°–017°, storm signals. Meeney's pier Fl G 3s. VHF Ch 16 **12** 14 (Mon-Fri: 0900–2000). Facilities: EC Thurs; Hr Mr ☎ 62287 FW on quay; **Shipyard** (between fish market and dock) El, ME, Sh, Slip; **Town** (¾M) Bar, ⊠, R, V, Gas.

ARDGLASS, Down, 54°16′·00N, 05°36′·00W, Zone 0 (GMT), Admty charts 633, 2093. HW +0025 on Dover, +0015 on Belfast; HW height +1·7m on Belfast; ML 3·0m; Duration 0620. A rocky bay partly sheltered by breakwater with quays on inside. Further up hr on SW side is old tidal dock giving excellent shelter. Safe harbour except in strong winds from E to S. Yachts should consult Hr Mr who will allocate berth or anchorage clear of fishing vessels. Yachts can go alongside E wall of inner hr. VHF Ch 16 14 12. Lts on inner pier head E of Tidal Dock, Iso WRG 4s 10m 8/5M G shore–310°, W310°–318°, R318°–shore. Breakwater Fl R 3s 10m 5M. Facilities: Hr Mr ☎ (0396) 841291; FW (on quay); **Town** P and D nearby; Bar, ⊠, R, V, Gas.

PORTAVOGIE, Down, 54°27′·00N, 05°26′·00W, Zone 0 (GMT), Admty chart 2156. HW +0016 on Dover, +0015 on Belfast; HW height +1·1m on Belfast; ML 2·6m; Duration 0620. See 10·13·10. Good shelter; harbour very full of fishing boats. Beware Plough Rks to S, and McCammon Rks to N of ent. Keep in W sector of Lt on Outer Breakwater Iso WRG 5s 12m 9M G shore-258°, W258°-275°, R275°-348°. Inner Breakwater 2 FG (vert) 6m 4M. About 3 ca NE of Plough Rk is a R can buoy, Bell, Fl(2) R 10s. VHF Ch 16; 14 12 (Mon-Fri: 0900–2000 LT). Facilities: EC Thurs; Hr Mr ☎ 71470; Slip, FW (on central quay) Sh, ME, El; **Town** CH, D, P, ⊠, R, Gas, V. No licenced premises.

DONAGHADEE, Down, 54°38′·00N, 05°32′·00W, Zone 0 (GMT), Admty charts 3709, 1753. HW +0025 on Dover, +0020 on Belfast; HW height +0·5m on Belfast; ML 2·2m; Duration 0615. See 10·13·10. Hr is small and very full; scend often sets in. Best berth alongside SE quay. Depth in harbour approx 3m. Beware ledge with less than 2m extends 1·5 ca ENE from S pier head. Alternatively go to the Marina 3 ca S of hr., excellent shelter and facilities but tricky entrance (pilots available). South Pier Lt, Iso WR 4s 17m 18/14M W shore–326°, R326°–shore. No lights on marina. Facilities: Hr Mr ☎ 882377; **Copeland's Marina** ☎ 882184 Access HW∓4; all facilities. **Town** Bar, D, Gas, FW, P, ⊠, R, V.

CARNLOUGH HARBOUR, Antrim, 54°59′·00N, 05°58′·00W, Zone 0 (GMT), Admty chart 2198. HW +0006 on Dover, +0005 on Belfast; HW height −1·6m on Belfast; ML 0·9m; Duration 0625. Small Hr accommodating yachts & small fishing boats, visitors welcome. Good shelter except in SE gales. Entrance dredged annually in May to 1·6m, harbour 2·0m. Entrance difficult in strong onshore winds. Beware rocks which cover at HW on either side of entrance. N pier Lt, Fl G 3s; S Pier Fl R 3s. VHF Ch 16 (occas.). Facilities: EC Wed, Hr Mr ☎ (0574) 84486; **Quay** AB, AC (see Hr Mr), FW, L, Slip; **Town** Bar, P and D (cans), Gas, Gaz, ⊠, R, V.

RED BAY, Antrim, 55°04′·00N, 06°03′·00W, Zone 0 (GMT), Admty chart 2199. HW +0006 on Dover, +0022 sp −0010 np on Belfast; HW height −1·7m on Belfast; ML 0·9m; Duration 0625. See 10·13·11. Good anchorage but open to N and E winds. Beware rks and two ruined piers W of Garron Pt. In S and E winds anchor 2 ca off W stone arch near head of bay in approx 3·5m; in N or W winds anchor S of small pier in 2/5m 0·5M NE of Waterfoot village. Facilities: **Cushendall** (1M N of pier) Bar, D, P, ⊠, R, V, Gas.

MULROY BAY, Donegal, 55°15′·00N, 07°47′·00W, Zone 0 (GMT), Admty chart 2699; HW (bar) −0455 on Dover, +0100 on Galway; HW height −1·1m on Galway. Beware Limeburner Rk, (marked by buoy) 2½M N of ent and the bar which is dangerous in swell or onshore winds. Channel runs between Black Rks and Sessiagh Rks thence through First, Second and Third Narrows (with strong tides) to Broad Water. HW at the head of the lough is 2¼ hrs later than at the bar. Anchorages: Close SW of Ravedy Is (Fl 3s); Fanny's Bay (2m), excellent; Rosnakill Bay (3·5m) in SE side; Cranford Bay; Milford Port (3 to 4m). Beware electric cable 6m, over Moross channel, barring North Water to high masted boats. Facilities: **Milford Port** AB, FW, V; **Fanny's Bay** ⊠, Shop at Downings village (1M), hotel at Rosepenna (¾M).

SHEEP HAVEN, Donegal, 55°11′·00N, 07°51′·00W, Zone 0 (GMT), Admty chart 2699. HW −0515 on Dover, +0050 on Galway; HW height −1·0m on Galway. See 10·13·15. Bay is 4M wide with numerous anchorages, easily accessible in daylight, but exposed to N winds. Beware rocks for 3ca off Rinnafaghla Pt; also Wherryman Rocks, which dry, 1ca off E shore 2¼M S of Rinnafaghla Pt. Anchor in Downies (or Downings) Bay to SW of pier; in Pollcormick Inlet close W in 3m; in Ards Bay for excellent shelter, but beware the bar in strong winds. Lights: Portnablahy Ldg Lts 125°, both Oc 6s 7/12m 2M; Downies pier head Fl R 3s 5m 2M. Facilities: (Downies) EC Wed, V, FW, P(cans, 300m), R, Bar; (Portnablahy Bay) V, P (cans), R, Bar.

BURTONPORT, Donegal, 54°59′·00N, 08°26′·00W, Zone 0 (GMT), Admty charts 2792, 1879. HW −0525 on Dover, +0050 on Galway; HW height −0·9m on Galway; ML 2·2m; Duration 0605. See 10·13·16. Normal ent. via North Channel. Hr very full. Berth on local boat on pier or go to Rutland Hr or Aran I. Ent. safe in all weathers except NW gales. N Channel Ldg Lts 119° on Inishcoo, Front Iso 6s 6m 1M. Rear, 248m from front, Iso 6s 11m 1M. Rutland I Ldg Lts 138° Front Oc 6s 8m 1M. Rear, 330m from front, Oc 6s 14m 1M. Burtonport Ldg Lts 068°, Front FG, 17m 1M, rear, 355m from front, FG 23m 1M. Facilities: D (just inside pier), FW (root of pier), P (0·5M inland), **Village** Bar, ⊠, R, V, Kos.

BLACKSOD BAY, Mayo, 54°06′·00N, 10°04′·00W, Zone 0 (GMT), Admty chart 2704. HW −0525 on Dover, +0030 on Galway; HW height −1·1m on Galway; ML 2·2m; Duration 0610. See 10·13·17. Safe anchorage with no hidden dangers, accessible by day or night. Beware Rk which dries 3·5 ca SSE of Ardmore Pt. Good anchorages at Elly Bay (1·8m); NW of Blacksod Quay (3m); Saleen Bay; Elly Hr; N of Claggan Pt. Blacksod Pier root Lt, Fl(2) WR 7·5s 13m 12/9M, R189°–210°, W210°–018°. Blacksod pier head Lt 2 FR (vert) 6m 3M. There are no facilities but normal supplies can be obtained at Belmullet 2·5M N of Claggan Pt.

INISHBOFIN, Mayo, 53°37′·00N, 10°13′·00W, Zone 0 (GMT) Admty charts 2707, 1820. HW−0555 on Dover, −0010 on Galway. HW height − 0·9m on Galway; ML 1·9m. See 10·13·19. Very secure harbour once through narrow entrance. Ldg line, 2 conspic W Trs at 032°. Lt on Gun Rock Fl (2) 6s 8 m 4M; vis 296°–253°. Facilities: FW, R, Bar, V, Hotel, ☎ (095) 45803

CLIFDEN BAY, Galway, 53°29′·00N, 10°01′·00W, Zone 0 (GMT), Admty charts 2708, 1820. HW −0600 on Dover, +0005 on Galway; HW height −0·6m on Galway; ML 2·3m; Duration 0610. See 10·13·18. It is essential to identify the high W beacon on Carrickarana Rks, 2·8M SW of Fishing Pt before entering. Ldg Marks 080° W Bn on Fishing Pt in line with Clifden Castle. Beware bar at ent by Fishing Pt and another SE of creek going up to Clifden; also Doolick Rks, Coghan Rks and Rks off Errislannon Pt. Anchor between Larner Rks and Drinagh Pt, dry out alongside Clifden Quay or anchor beyond Yellow Slate Rks in 3·4m in Ardbear Bay. Keep clear of fish farming cages. Facilities: EC Thurs;
A. O'Connell ☎ 21332, El, FW, M, ME, Sh, Slip; **Aster Boats** ☎ 21332 Slip, L, FW, D, AB, C, CH, M, ME, El, Sh; **Town** Bar, Ⓑ, CH, D, P, ⊠, R, V, Kos, FW, V, R, Dr, Ⓗ.

Area 14

South Biscay
Spanish border to River Loire

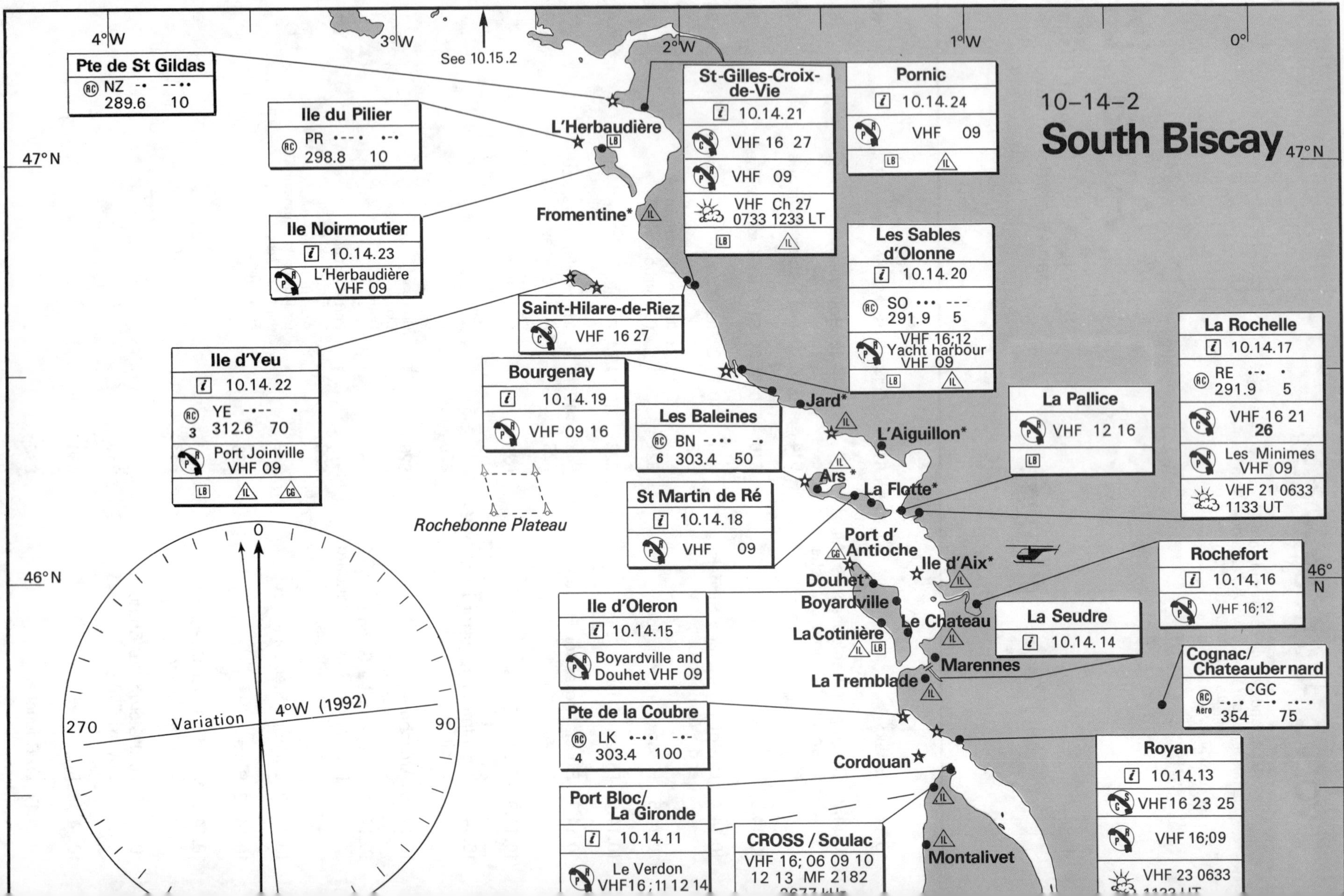
10–14–2
South Biscay
47°N
46°N
4°W
3°W
2°W
1°W
0°
See 10.15.2
Pte de St Gildas
NZ 289.6 10
Ile du Pilier
PR 298.8 10
Ile Noirmoutier
10.14.23
L'Herbaudière VHF 09
Ile d'Yeu
10.14.22
YE 3 312.6 70
Port Joinville VHF 09
St-Gilles-Croix-de-Vie
10.14.21
VHF 16 27
VHF 09
VHF Ch 27 0733 1233 LT
Pornic
10.14.24
VHF 09
Les Sables d'Olonne
10.14.20
SO 291.9 5
VHF 16;12 Yacht harbour VHF 09
Saint-Hilare-de-Riez
VHF 16 27
Bourgenay
10.14.19
VHF 09 16
Les Baleines
BN 6 303.4 50
St Martin de Ré
10.14.18
VHF 09
La Pallice
VHF 12 16
La Rochelle
10.14.17
RE 291.9 5
VHF 16 21 26
Les Minimes VHF 09
VHF 21 0633 1133 UT
Rochefort
10.14.16
VHF 16;12
La Seudre
10.14.14
Cognac/ Chateaubernard
CGC
Aero 354 75
Ile d'Oleron
10.14.15
Boyardville and Douhet VHF 09
Pte de la Coubre
LK 4 303.4 100
Port Bloc/ La Gironde
10.14.11
Le Verdon VHF16; 11 12 14
CROSS / Soulac
VHF 16; 06 09 10 12 13 MF 2182
Royan
10.14.13
VHF16 23 25
VHF 16;09
VHF 23 0633
L'Herbaudière
Fromentine*
Jard*
L'Aiguillon*
Ars*
La Flotte*
Port d' Antioche
Ile d'Aix*
Douhet*
Boyardville
Le Chateau
La Cotinière
Marennes
La Tremblade
Cordouan
Montalivet
Rochebonne Plateau
0
90
270
Variation
4°W (1992)

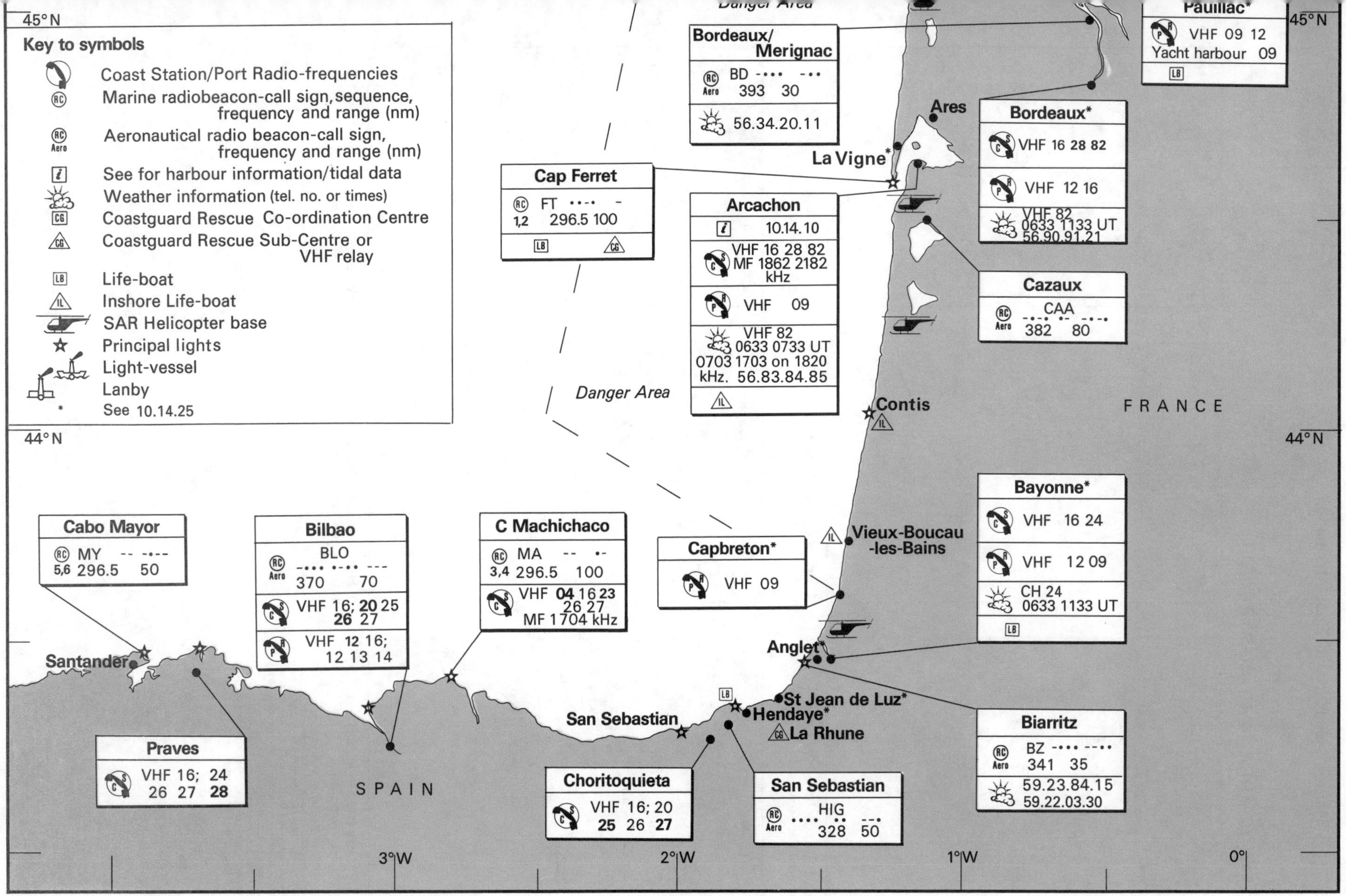
45°N
44°N
3°W
2°W
1°W
0°
Key to symbols
Coast Station/Port Radio-frequencies
Marine radiobeacon-call sign, sequence, frequency and range (nm)
Aeronautical radio beacon-call sign, frequency and range (nm)
See for harbour information/tidal data
Weather information (tel. no. or times)
Coastguard Rescue Co-ordination Centre
Coastguard Rescue Sub-Centre or VHF relay
Life-boat
Inshore Life-boat
SAR Helicopter base
Principal lights
Light-vessel
Lanby
* See 10.14.25
Danger Area
Danger Area
Pauillac*
VHF 09 12
Yacht harbour 09
Bordeaux/ Merignac
BD 393 30
56.34.20.11
Bordeaux*
VHF 16 28 82
VHF 12 16
VHF 82 0633 1133 UT 56.90.91.21
Ares
La Vigne*
Cap Ferret
FT 1,2 296.5 100
Arcachon
10.14.10
VHF 16 28 82 MF 1862 2182 kHz
VHF 09
VHF 82 0633 0733 UT 0703 1703 on 1820 kHz. 56.83.84.85
Cazaux
CAA 382 80
Contis
FRANCE
Bayonne*
VHF 16 24
VHF 12 09
CH 24 0633 1133 UT
Vieux-Boucau -les-Bains
Capbreton*
VHF 09
Anglet*
St Jean de Luz*
Hendaye*
La Rhune
Biarritz
BZ 341 35
59.23.84.15 59.22.03.30
San Sebastian
San Sebastian
HIG 328 50
Choritoquieta
VHF 16; 20 25 26 27
C Machichaco
MA 3,4 296.5 100
VHF 04 16 23 26 27 MF 1704 kHz
Bilbao
BLO 370 70
VHF 16; 20 25 26 27
VHF 12 16; 12 13 14
Cabo Mayor
MY 5,6 296.5 50
Santander
Praves
VHF 16; 24 26 27 28
SPAIN

10.14.3 AREA 14 TIDAL STREAMS

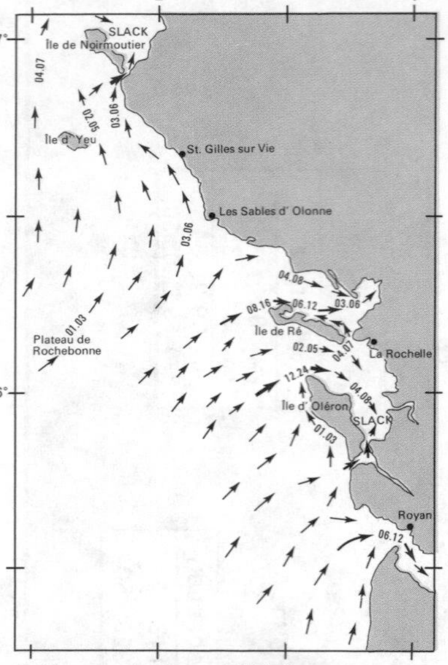
2°
1°
47°
46°
SLACK
Île de Noirmoutier
Île d' Yeu
St. Gilles sur Vie
Les Sables d' Olonne
Plateau de Rochebonne
Île de Ré
La Rochelle
Île d' Oléron
SLACK
Royan

5 Hours before HW Brest
(0010 after HW Dover)

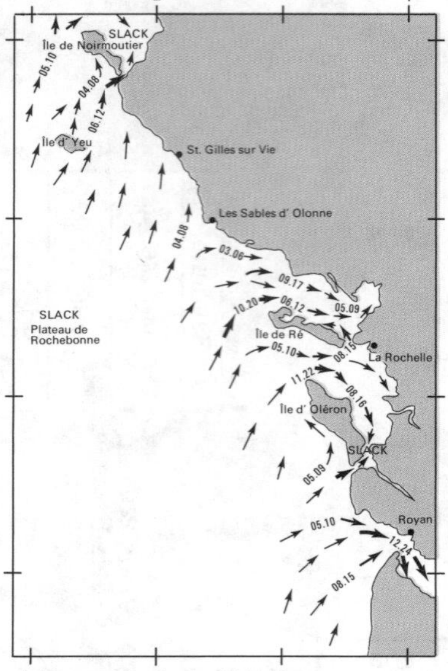
2°
1°
47°
46°
SLACK
Île de Noirmoutier
Île d' Yeu
St. Gilles sur Vie
Les Sables d' Olonne
SLACK
Plateau de Rochebonne
Île de Ré
La Rochelle
Île d' Oléron
SLACK
Royan

4 Hours before HW Brest
(0110 after HW Dover)

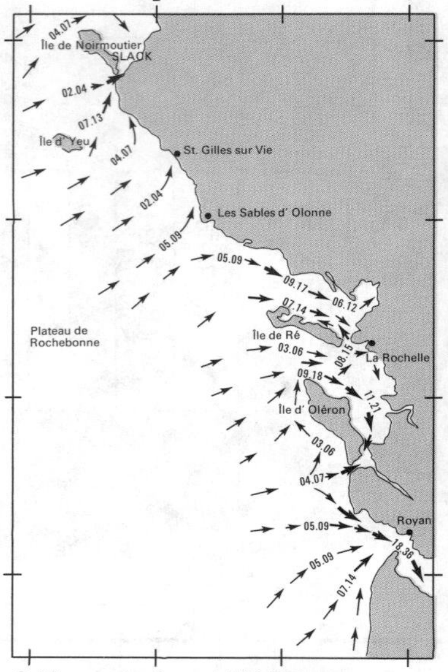
2°
1°
47°
46°
Île de Noirmoutier
SLACK
Île d' Yeu
St. Gilles sur Vie
Les Sables d' Olonne
Plateau de Rochebonne
Île de Ré
La Rochelle
Île d' Oléron
Royan

3 Hours before HW Brest
(0210 after HW Dover)

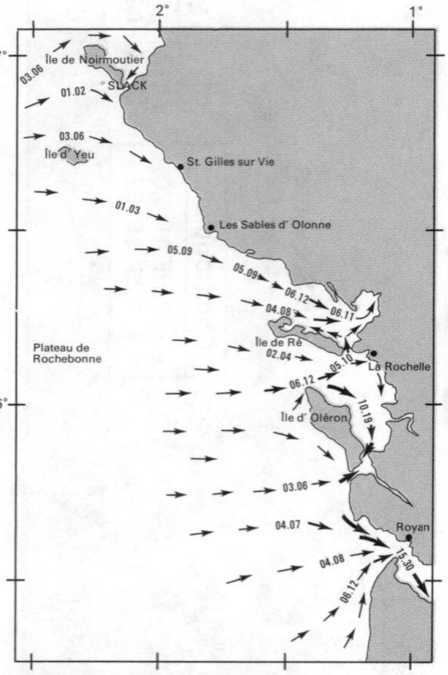
2°
1°
47°
46°
Île de Noirmoutier
SLACK
Île d' Yeu
St. Gilles sur Vie
Les Sables d' Olonne
Plateau de Rochebonne
Île de Ré
La Rochelle
Île d' Oléron
Royan

2 Hours before HW Brest
(0310 after HW Dover)

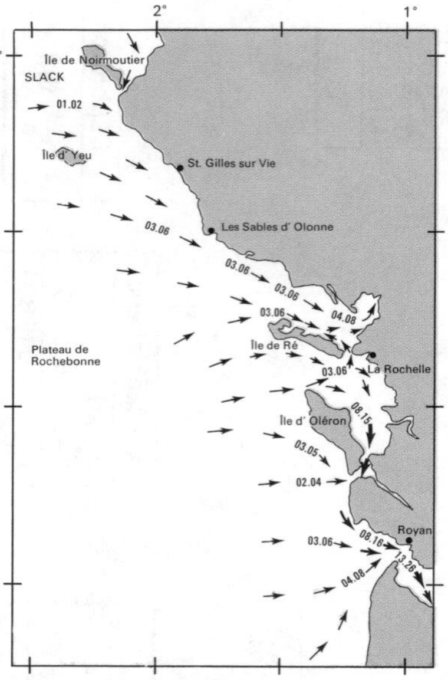
2°
1°
47°
46°
Île de Noirmoutier
SLACK
Île d' Yeu
St. Gilles sur Vie
Les Sables d' Olonne
Plateau de Rochebonne
Île de Ré
La Rochelle
Île d' Oléron
Royan

1 Hour before HW Brest
(0410 after HW Dover)

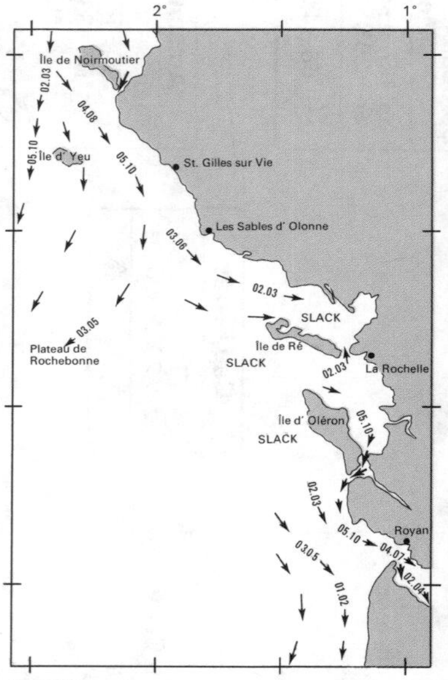
2°
1°
47°
46°
Île de Noirmoutier
Île d' Yeu
St. Gilles sur Vie
Les Sables d' Olonne
SLACK
Plateau de Rochebonne
Île de Ré
SLACK
La Rochelle
Île d' Oléron
SLACK
Royan

HW Brest
(0510 after HW Dover)

CAUTION:- Due to the very strong rates of the tidal streams in some of the areas, many eddies may occur. Where possible some indication of these eddies has been included. In many areas there is either insufficient information or the eddies are unstable.
Generally tidal streams are weak offshore and strong winds have a very great effect on the rate and direction of the tidal streams.

Northward 10.15.3

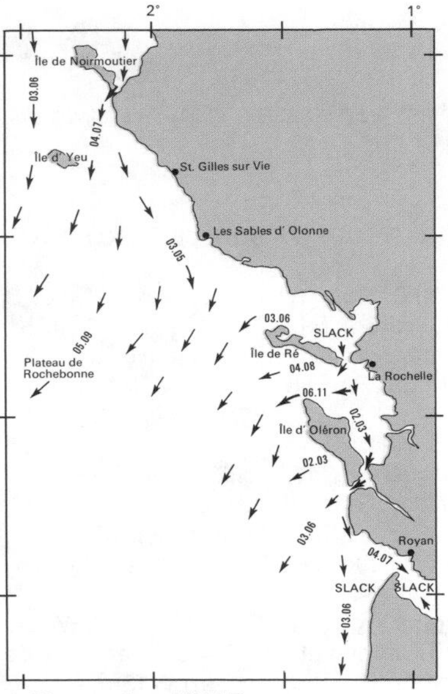
2°
1°
47°
46°
Île de Noirmoutier
Île d' Yeu
St. Gilles sur Vie
Les Sables d' Olonne
Plateau de Rochebonne
SLACK
Île de Ré
La Rochelle
Île d' Oléron
Royan
SLACK
SLACK

1 Hour after HW Brest
(0610 after HW Dover)

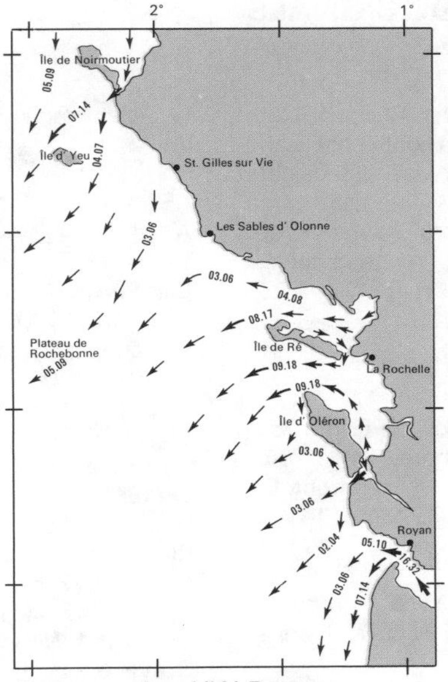
2°
1°
47°
46°
Île de Noirmoutier
Île d' Yeu
St. Gilles sur Vie
Les Sables d' Olonne
Plateau de Rochebonne
Île de Ré
La Rochelle
Île d' Oléron
Royan

2 Hours after HW Brest
(0515 before HW Dover)

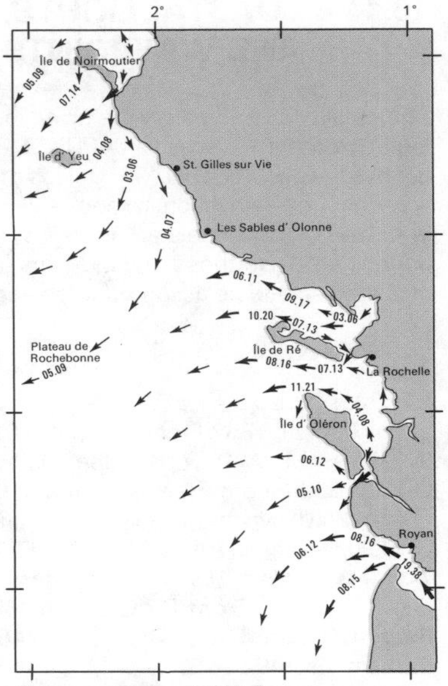
2°
1°
47°
46°
Île de Noirmoutier
Île d' Yeu
St. Gilles sur Vie
Les Sables d' Olonne
Plateau de Rochebonne
Île de Ré
La Rochelle
Île d' Oléron
Royan

3 Hours after HW Brest
(0415 before HW Dover)

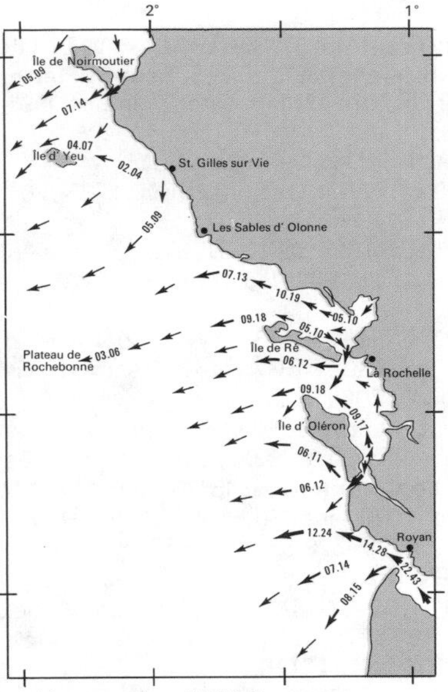
2°
1°
47°
46°
Île de Noirmoutier
Île d' Yeu
St. Gilles sur Vie
Les Sables d' Olonne
Plateau de Rochebonne
Île de Ré
La Rochelle
Île d' Oléron
Royan

4 Hours after HW Brest
(0315 before HW Dover)

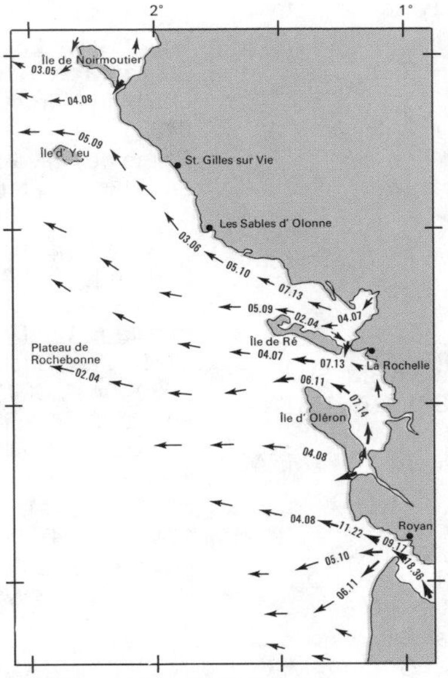
2°
1°
47°
46°
Île de Noirmoutier
Île d' Yeu
St. Gilles sur Vie
Les Sables d' Olonne
Plateau de Rochebonne
Île de Ré
La Rochelle
Île d' Oléron
Royan

5 Hours after HW Brest
(0215 before HW Dover)

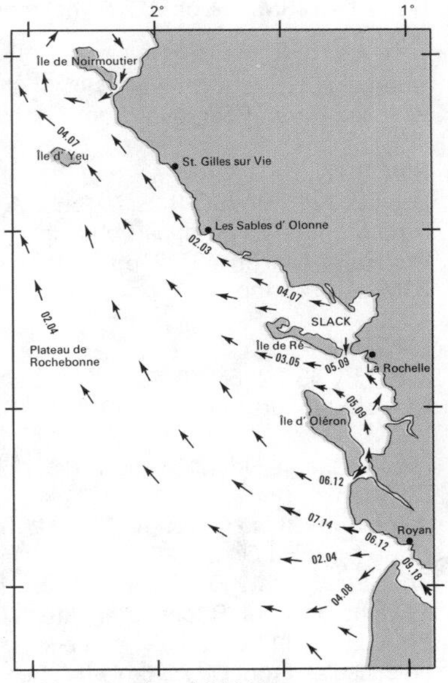
2°
1°
47°
46°
Île de Noirmoutier
Île d' Yeu
St. Gilles sur Vie
Les Sables d' Olonne
Plateau de Rochebonne
SLACK
Île de Ré
La Rochelle
Île d' Oléron
Royan

6 Hours after HW Brest
(0115 before HW Dover)

10.14.4 COASTAL LIGHTS, FOG SIGNALS AND WAYPOINTS

Abbreviations used below are given in 1.4.1. Principal lights are in **bold** print, places in CAPITALS, and light-vessels and Lanbys in *CAPITAL ITALICS*. Unless otherwise stated lights are white. m—elevation in metres; M—nominal range in n. miles. Fog signals are in *italics*. Useful waypoints are underlined – use those on land with care. All geographical positions should be assumed to be approximate. See 4.2.2.

FRANCE—WEST COAST

ST JEAN DE LUZ.
Socoa Ldg Lts 138°. Front 43°23'·8N 01°41'·1W Q WR 36m W12M, R8M; W ■ Tr, B stripe; vis W shore-264°, R264°-282°, W282°-shore. Rear **Bordagain**, 0·77M from front, Dir Q 67m **20M**; synchronised with front; intens 134·5°-141·5°.
Digue des Criquas Hd 43°23'·92N 01°40'·59W Iso G 4s 11m 7M; G ■ Tr; *Horn 15s.*
Ldg Lts 150·7°, **Front** Dir QG 18m **16M**; W ■ Tr, R stripe. **Rear**, 410m from front, Dir QG 27m **16M**; W ■ Tr, G stripe. Both intens 149·5°-152°.
Ste Barbe Ldg Lts 101°. **Front** Dir Oc (3+1) R 12s 30m **18M**; W ▲; intens 095°-107°. **Rear**, 340m from front, Dir Oc (3+1) R 12s 47m **18M**; B ▲ on W Tr; synchronised with front; intens 095°-107°.

Guethary Ldg Lts 133°. Front 43°25'·6N 01°36'·5W QR 11m; W mast, R top. Rear, 66m from front, QR 33m; W Tr.

BIARRITZ.
Ldg Lts 174°. Both Fl R 2s 7/19m 2M.
Aero Mo (L) 7·5s 80m; part obsc (occas).
Pte Saint-Martin 43°29'·69N 01°33'·17W Fl (2) 10s 73m **29M**; W Tr, B top.

L'ADOUR.
BA Lt By 43°32'·66N 01°32'·68W L Fl 10s 8m 8M; SWM.
Digue exterieure Sud 43°31'·60N 01°31'·68W, Q (9) 15s 8M; WCM.
Digue du large Hd 43°31'·96N 01°31'·92W QR 11m 7M; W Tr, R top.
Jetée Sud Hd Iso G 4s 9m 7M; W ■ Tr, G top.
Jetée Nord Hd Oc (2) R 6s 12m 8M; W pylon, R top.
Boucau Ldg Lts 090°. Front Dir Q 9m 14M. Rear Dir Q 15m 14M; both W Trs, R tops, both intens 086·5°-093·5°.
Ent Ldg Lts 111·5° (moved as necessary and lit when chan practicable). Front Dir FG 6m 14M. Rear Dir FG 10m 14M; W Tr, G bands; both intens 109°-114°.
Digue Nord Hd Fl (2) R 6s 9m 6M; W Tr, R top; vis 296°-091°.
Training wall root (Marina ent) Fl G 2s 5m 3M; W Tr, G top.
From Port d'Anglet to Bayonne Ldg Lts 322·5°, Front QR 15m 7M; vis 188°-098°, Rear Iso R 4s 23m; intens 311°-331°.
La Forme de Radoub Ldg Lts 205° 43°30'·58N 01°29'·73W both Dir FG 17/24m **16M**; both intens 203·5°-206·5°.
Blancpignon Ldg Lts 345° both FG 17/23m 6/10M Vis 237°-093°; intens 338·5°-351·5°.
Pont de l'Aveugle QG 8m 8M; W col, G top; vis 094°-004°.

CAPBRETON.
Estacade Sud Iso G 4s 7m 11M; Gy Tr; vis 335°-245°.
Digue Nord Hd Fl(2) R 6s 13m 10M; W ● Tr, R top; *Horn 30s.*
Contis 44°05'·7N 01°19'·2W Fl (4) 25s 50m **23M**; W ● Tr, B diagonal stripes.
ZDS By 44°28'·00N 01°19'·30W Fl (3) Y 12s 8m 7M; Y By.
Emissaire By 44°30'·5N 01°17'·6W Fl (2) 6s 8m 5M; IDM; Ra refl.
La Salie wharf Hd 44°30'·9N 01°15'·6W Q (9) 15s 19m 10M; WCM.

ARCACHON.
ATT-ARC Lt By 44°34'·70N 01°17'·96W L Fl 10s; SWB; *Whis.*
Cap Ferret 44°38'·83N 01°15'·02W Fl R 5s 53m **27M**; W ● Tr, R top; RC. Oc (3) 12s 46m 14M; same Tr; vis 045°-135°.
Arcachon W Breakwater Hd QG 6M; G mast.
Hourtin 45°08'·5N 01°09'·7W Fl 5s 55m **23M;** R ■ Tr.

LA GIRONDE, PASSE SUD.
Cordouan 45°35'·25N 01°10'·34W Oc (2+1) WRG 12s 60m **22/18M**; W conical Tr, dark Gy band and top; vis W014°-126°, G126°-178·5°, W178·5°-250°, W(unintens)250°-267°, R(unintens)267°-294·5°, R294·5°-014°; obsc in est when brg more than 285°.
Ldg Lts 063°. **St Nicolas Front** 45°33'·80N 01°04'·93W Dir QG 22m **17M**; W ■ Tr; intens 061·5°-064·5°. **Rear Pte de Grave**, 0·84M from front, Oc WRG 4s 26m **W19M**, R15M, G15M; W ■ Tr, B corners and top; vis W(unintens) 033°-054°, W054°-233·5°, R233·5°-303°, W303°-312°, G312°-330°, W330°- 341°, W(unintens) 341°-025°.
Ldg Lts 041°, **Le Chay Front**, 45°37'·35N 01°02'·40W Dir QR 33m **18M**; W Tr, R top; intens 039·5°-042·5. **Rear St Pierre**, 0·97M from front, Dir QR 61m **18M**; R water Tr; intens 039°-043°.
Pointe de Grave Jetée Nord, Hd Q 6m 2M; NCM.
Spur 45°34'·38N 01°03'·57W Iso G 4s 5m 2M; vis 173°-020°.

LA GIRONDE, GRANDE PASSE DE L'OUEST.
BXA Lt By 45°37'·60N 01°28'·60W Iso 4s 8m 8M; R&W By; Ra refl; Racon; *Whis.*
Pte de la Coubre 45°41'·87N 01°13'·93W Fl (2) 10s 64m **28M**; W l Tr, R top; RC; Sig Stn. F RG 42m 12M; same Tr; vis R030°-043°, G043°-060°, R060°-110°.
Ldg Lts 081·5°. **Front, La Palmyre**, 1·1M from rear, Dir Oc 4s 21m **22M**; W mast on dolphin; intens 080·5°-082.5°; Q (2) 5s 10m 3M; same structure. **Common rear** 45°39'·8N 01°07'·2W Dir Q 57m **27M**; W radar Tr; intens 080·5°-082·5°. Dir FR 57m **17M**; same Tr; intens 325·5°-328·5°.
Ldg Lts 327°. **Terre-Nègre**, Front, 1·1M from rear, Oc (3) WRG 12s 39m **W18M**, R14M, G14M; W Tr, R top on W side; vis R304°-319°, W319°-327°, G327°-000°, W000°-004°, G004°-097°, W097°-104°, R104°-116°.

LA SEUDRE.
Pont de la Seudre QW 20m 10M each side, vis 054°-234° and 234°-054°.
Pte de Mus de Loup Oc G 4s 8m 6M; G&W col, W to seaward; vis 118°-147°.

ÎLE D'OLÉRON.
St Trojan-les-Bains Fl G 4s 8m; Viaduct d'Oleron marked by F 1·1M ENE.
Le Château d'Oléron Ldg Lts 319°. Front QR 11m 7M; R line on W Tr; vis 191°-087°. Rear, 240m from front, QR 24m 7M; W Tr, R top; synchronised with front.
Tourelle Juliar Q (3) WG 10s 12m W11M; G8M; ECM; vis W147°-336°, G336°-147°.
La Pérrotine Oc (2) R 6s 8m 7M; W Tr, R top; obsc by Pte des Saumonards when brg less than 150°.
Rocher d'Antioche 46°04'·00N 01°23'·70W Q 20m 11M; NCM.

ATT Maumusson Lt By 45°47'·00N 01°17'·80W L Fl 10s; SWM.
S Denis d' Oléron Jetée Hd 46°02'·16N 01°21'·97W Fl (2) G 6s 4m 5M; on G pole.
Pte de Chassiron 46°02'·80N 01°24'·60W Fl 10s 50m **28M**; W ● Tr, B bands; part obsc 297°-351°; Sig Stn.

LA COTINIERE.
Dir Lt 048°. Dir Oc WRG 4s 13m W9M, R7M, G7M; W stripe with B border on W col; vis G033°-046°, W046°-050°, R050°-063°.
Ent Ldg Lts 339°. Front Dir Oc (2) 6s 6m 13M; W Tr, R top; vis 329°-349°; Horn *(2) 20s* (HW-3 to HW+3). Rear, 425m from front, Dir Oc (2) 6s 14m 12M; W Tr, R bands; synchronised with front; intens 329°-349°.
Grande Jetée elbow Oc R 4s 11m 8M; W Tr, R top.
Digue Sud Hd Iso G 4s 9m 7M; W Tr, G top.

LA CHARENTE.
Ile d'Aix 46°00'·67N 01°10'·60W Fl WR 5s 24m **W24M**, **R20M**; two W ● Trs, one for Lt, one to screen R sector; vis R103°-118°, W118°-103°.
Ldg Lts 115°. Front, **Fort de la Pointe** 45°58'·0N 01°04'·3W Dir QR 8m **19M**; W ■ Tr, R top; intens 113°-117°. **Rear**, 600m from front, Dir QR 21m **20M**; W ■ Tr, R top; intens 113°-117°. QR 21m 8M; same Tr; vis 322°-067° over Port-des-Barques anchorage.
Port Nord de Fouras Pier Hd 45°59'·88N 01°05'·75W Oc (3+1) WG 12s 9m W11M, G8M; W&G Tr; vis G084°-127°, W127°-084°.

ÎLE DE RÉ.
Lt By PA 46°05'·7N 01°42'·4W Iso 4s 8m 7M; SWM; *Whis*; Ra refl.
Chanchardon 46°09'·72N 01°28'·45W Fl WR 4s 15m W11M, R9M; B 8-sided Tr, W base; vis R118°-290°, W290°-118°.
Chauveau 46°08'·09N 01°16'·33W Oc (2+1) WR 12s 23m **W15M**, R11M; W ● Tr, R top; vis W057°-094°, R094°-104°, W104°-342°, R342°-057°.
Pte de Sablanceaux 46°09'·82N 01°15'·08W Q Vi 7m 1M; W mast and hut, G top.
Rivedoux-Plage Ldg Lts 200°. Front QG 6m 6M; W Tr, G top. Rear, 100m from front, QG 9m 7M; W and G chequered col; synchronised with front.
La Flotte 46°11'·3N 01°19'·3W Fl WG 4s 10m W12M, G9M; W● Tr, G top; vis G130°-205°, W205°-220°, G220°-257°; *Horn(3) 30s* (by day HW-2 to HW+2). Moiré effect Dir Lt 212·5°.

St MARTIN DE RÉ.
Breakwater West Hd 46°12'·57N 01°21'·82W Fl R 2·5s 7m 4M; W post, R top.
46°12'·5N 01°21'·9W on ramparts E of ent Oc (2) WR 6s 18m W10M, R7M; W Tr, R top; vis W shore-245°, R245°-281°, W281°-shore.
Mole Hd Iso G 4s 10m 6M; W tripod, G top; obsc by Pte de Loix when brg less than 124°.
Le Fier d'Ars Ldg Lts 265°. Front 46°14'·0N 01°28'·8W Iso 4s 5m 11M; ■ on W hut; vis 141°-025°. Rear, 370m from front, Dir Iso G 4s 13m **15M**; G ■ on dwelling; synchronised with front, intens 263°-267°.

ARS-EN-RÉ.
Ldg Lts 232°. Front 46°12'·8N 01°30'·5W Q 5m 9M; W hut, R lantern. Rear, 370m from front, Q 13m 11M; B stripe on W framework Tr, G top; vis 142°-322°.
Les Baleines 46°14'·70N 01°33'·60W Fl (4) 15s 53m **27M**; Gy 8-sided Tr, R lantern; RC.
Les Baleineaux 46°15'·85N 01°35.20W Oc (2) 6s 23m 11M; pink Tr, R top.

LA ROCHELLE.
Chauveau Lt By 46°06'·62N 01°15'·98W VQ (6) + L Fl 10s; SCM; *Whis.*
Roche du Sud Lt By 46°06'·43N 01°15'·15W Q (9) 15s; WCM.
Le Lavardin 46°08'·15N 01°14'·45W Fl (2) WG 6s 14m W11M, G8M; B Tr, R band; vis G160°-169°, W169°-160°; IDM.
Tour Richelieu 46°08'·95N 01°10'·27W Fl (4) R 12s 10m 9M; R Tr; RC; *Siren (4) 60s* (HW-1 to HW+1).
Ldg Lts 059°. Front 46°09'·4N 01°09'·1W Dir Q 15m 14M; R ●Tr, W bands; intens 056°-062°; by day Fl 4s. Rear, 235m from front, Q 25m 14M; W 8-sided Tr, G top; synchronised with front, vis 350°-125°, obsc 061°-065° by St Nicolas Tr; by day Fl 4s.

LA PALLICE.
Mole d'Escale Hd, 46°09'·42N 01°14'·43W Dir Lt 016°. Dir Q WRG 33m W14M, R13M, G13M; Gy Tr; vis G009°-014·7°, W014·7°-017·3°, R017·3°-031°. Sig Stn.
Môle SE corner Oc (2) R 6s 7m 6M; W framework Tr, R top.
Avant Port Jetée Nord Hd Oc (2) R 6s 10m 7M; Gy● Tr, R top; vis 234°-144°, unintens 164°-184°.

PERTUIS BRETON, NORTH SHORE.
Port du Plomb W mole 46°12'·4N 01°12'·1W Fl R 4s 9m 7M; W col, R top.
Sèvre Niortaise ent, Port du Pavé de Charron 46°18'·1N 01°08'·0W Fl G 4s 9m 7M; W col, G top.
La Tranche-sur-Mer Pier Hd 46°20'·7N 01°25'·5W Fl (2) R 6s 6m 6M; R col.
Pte du Grouin-du-Cou 46°20'·68N 01°27'·80W Fl WRG 5s 29m **W20M**, **R16M**, **G16M**; W 8-sided Tr, B top; vis R034°-061°, W061°-117°, G117°-138°, W138°-034°.

PLATEAU DE ROCHEBONNE.
Rochebonne NW Lt By 46°12'·9N 02°31'·9W Q (9) 15s 8m 7M; WCM; *Whis*; Ra refl.
Rochebonne SW Lt By 46°10'·1N 02°27'·0W Fl (2) R 6s 9m 3M; ■ on R By; Ra refl.
Rochebonne SE Lt By 46°09'·2N 02°21'·2W Q (3) 10s 8m 8M; ECM; *Bell*; Ra refl.
Rochebonne NE Lt By 46°12'·7N 02°25'·0W Iso G 4s 8m 5M; ▲ on G By; Ra refl.

BOURGENAY.
Ldg Lts 040°. Front 46°26'·4N 01°40'·5W QG 8M. Rear QG 8M.
Digue W Hd Fl R 4s 9M.
Roches du Joanne Lt By 46°25'·35N 01°41'·90W L Fl 10s; SWM.

LES SABLES D'OLONNE.
Nouch Sud Lt By 46°28'·63N 01°47'·43W Q (6) + L Fl 15s; SCM.

PASSE DU SW.
Ldg Lts 033°. **Front** 46°29'·5N 01°46'·3W Iso R 4s 14m **16M**; mast; H24. **Rear**, 330m from front, Iso R 4s 33m **16M**; W ■ Tr; H24.
Ldg Lts 320°, Jetée des Sables Hd Front 46°29'·45N 01°47'·52W QG 11m 8M; W Tr, G top. Rear, Tour de la Chaume Oc (2+1) 12s 33m 13M; large Gy ■ Tr, W turret; RC.
Ldg Lts 327°, Front FR 6m 11M; R line on W hut. Rear, 65m from front, FR 9m 11M; R line on W Tr; intens 324°-330°.

14

Jetée St Nicolas, Hd UQ (2) R 1s 16m 10M; W Tr, R top; vis 143°-094°.

L'Armandèche Fl (2+1) 15s 42m **24M**; W 6-sided Tr, R top; vis 295°-130°.

LA PETITE BARGE Lt By 46°28'·9N 01°50'·6W Q (6) + L Fl 15s 8m 7M; SCM; *Whis*; Ra refl.

Les Barges 46°29'·7N 01°50'·4W Fl (2) R 10s 25m **17M**; Gy Tr, helicopter platform; vis 265°-205°.

St GILLES-CROIX-DE-VIE.

Pill'Hours Lt By 46°41'·1N 01°58'·2W Q (6) + L Fl 15s; SCM; *Bell*.

Ldg Lts 043·5°. Front Dir Oc (3+1) R 12s 7m **13M**; W ■ Tr, R top; intens 033·5°-053·5°. **Rear**, 260m from front, Dir Oc (3+1) R 12s 28m **13M**; W ■ Tr, R top; synchronised with front; intens 033·5°-053·5°.

Jetée de Boisvinet Fl (2) WR 6s 8m W10M, R7M; R col; vis R045°-225°, W225°-045°.

Pte de Grosse Terre Fl (4) WR 12s 25m W17M, R13M; W truncated conical Tr; vis W290°-125°, R125°-145°.

St Jean de Monts Jetty Hd 46°47'·1N 02°05'·1W Q (2) R 5s 10m 3M; W mast, R top.

ILE D'YEU.

Pte des Corbeaux 46°41'·4N 02°17'·1W Fl (2+1) R 15s 25m **20M**; W ■ Tr, R top; obsc 083°-143°.

PORT JOINVILLE.

Jetty NW Hd Oc (3) WG 12s 6m W11M, G9M; W 8-sided Tr, G top; vis G shore-150°, W150°-232°, G232°-279°, W279°-285°, G285°-shore; *Horn(3) 30s*.

Les Chiens Perrins 46°43'·6N 02°24'·6W Q (9) WG 15s 16m W8M, G4M; WCM; vis G330°-350°, W350°-200°.

Pte du But Horn *60s*. TD 1987.

Petite Foule 46°43'·1N 02°22'·9W Fl 5s 56m **24M**; W ■ Tr, G lantern; RC.

La Meule 46°41'·7N 02°20'·6W Oc WRG 4s 9m W9M, R6M, G5M; Gy ■ col, R top; vis G007·5°-018°, W018°-027·5°, R027·5°-041·5°.

FROMENTINE.

Pte de Notre Dame-de-Monts 46°53'·3N 02°08'·5W Dir Oc (2) WRG 6s 21m W13M, R10M, G10M; W Tr, B top; vis G000°-043°, W043°-063°, R063°-073°, W073°-094°, G094°-113°, W113°-116°, R116°-175°, G175°-196°, R196°-230°.

Bridge, each side on centre span Iso 4s 32m **18M**; H24.

Tourelle Milieu 46°53'·6N 02°09'·6W Fl (4) R 12s 6m 5M; R ■ on Tr.

ILE DE NOIRMOUTIER.

Passage du Gois, E shore Fl R 4s 6m 6M; R hut; vis 038°-218°.

E turning Pt Fl 2s 5m 6M; Gy pyramid structure.

W turning Pt Fl 2s 5m 3M; Gy pyramid structure.

Bassotière Fl G 2s 7m 2M; W tripod, G lantern; vis 180°-000°.

Noirmoutier Jetty Hd Oc (2) R 6s 6m 7M; W col, R top.

Pte des Dames 47°00'·7N 02°13'·3W Oc (3) WRG 12s 34m **W19M**, **R15M**, **G15M**; W ■ Tr; vis G016·5°-057°, R057°-124°, G124°-165°, W165°-191°, R191°-267°, W267°-357°, R357°-016·5°.

Pierre Moine 47°03'·43N 02°12'·30W Fl (2) 6s 14m 9M; IDM.

Basse du Martroger 47°02'·65N 02°17'·05W Dir Q WRG 10m W9M, R6M, G6M; NCM; vis G033°-055°, W055°-060°, R060°-095°, G095°-124°, W124°-153°, R153°-201°, W201°-240°, R240°-033°; NCM.

Port de l'Herbaudière Jetée Ouest Hd Oc (2+1) WG 12s 9m W10M, G7M; W col and hut, G top; vis W187·5°-190°, G190°-187·5°.

Jetée Est Hd Fl 2) R 6s 8m 4M; R tripod.

Ile du Pilier 47°02'·62N 02°21'·53W Fl (3) 20s 33m **29M**; Gy ▲ Tr. Auxiliary Lt QR 10m 11M, same Tr; vis 321°-034; RC.

Pte de Devin 46°59'·1N 02°17'·6W Oc (4) WRG 12s 10m W11M, R8M, G8M; W col and hut, G top; vis G314°-028°, W028°-035°, R035°-134°.

BAIE DE BOURGNEUF.

Bec de l'Époids 46°56'·4N 02°04'·5W Dir Iso WRG 4s 6m W12M, R9M, G9M; W n Tr, R top; vis G106°-113·5°, R113·5°-122°, G122°-157·5°, W157·5°-158·5°, R158·5°-171·5°, W171·5°-176°.

Étier des Brochets 46°59'·9N 02°01'·9W Oc (2+1) WRG 12s 8m W10M, R7M, G7M; G Tr, W band; vis G071°-091°, W091°-102·5°, R102·5°-116·5°, W116·5°-119·5°, R119·5°-164·5°.

Le Collet 47°01'·8N 01°59'·0W Oc (2) WR 6s 7m W9M, R6M; vis W shore-093°, R093°-shore.

Ldg Lts 118° both QG 4/12m 6M; W ■ G stripe, on W pylon.

La Bernerie-en-Retz Jetty Hd 47°04'·6N 02°02'·4W Fl R 2s 3m 2M; W structure, R top.

PORNIC.

Yacht Hbr Digue Ouest SW elbow Fl (2+1) 7s 4m 3M.

Hd 46°06'·53N 02°06'·61W Fl (2) R 6s 4m 4M; B col, T top.

Jetée Est Hd Fl G 2·5s 4m 2M; B col, G top.

Pte de Noëveillard Oc (3+1) WRG 12s 22m W13M, R9M, G9M; W ■ Tr, G top, W dwelling; vis G shore-051°, W051°-079°, R079°-shore.

Pte de Gourmalon Breakwater Hd Fl (2) G 6s 4m 8M; W mast, G top.

Pte de St-Gildas 47°08'·10N 02°14'·67W Q WRG 23m **W15M**, R12M, G10M; framework Tr on W house; vis R264°-308°, G308°-078°, W078°-088°, R088°-174°, W174°-180°, G180°-264°; RC.

10.14.5 PASSAGE INFORMATION

For general notes on French waters see 10.14.7. Further passage information appears in 10.15.5. A glossary of French terms used on charts or in sailing directions is given in 10.14.8.

Larger scale French charts are often more suitable for inshore waters. *The Bay of Biscay Pilot* is recommended, as are *South Biscay Pilot* and *North Biscay Pilot* (Adlard Coles Nautical) and *French Pilot Volume 4* (Adlard Coles Nautical).

BAY OF BISCAY (chart 1104)

Despite its reputation, weather in B of Biscay is no worse than in English chan, and the S part generally enjoys a warmer and more settled climate. Bigger seas and longer swells from the Atlantic may be met. Although W winds mostly prevail, NE winds are often experienced with anticyclones over the continent. In summer the wind is seldom from SE or S. Often the wind varies in speed and direction from day to day. Gales may be expected once a month in summer. S of La Gironde, sea and land breezes are well developed in summer months. Coastal rainfall is moderate, increasing in the SE corner, where thunder is more frequent. Sea fog may be met from May to October, but is less common in winter.

The general direction of the surface current in summer is SE, towards the SE corner of B of Biscay, where it swings W along N coast of Spain. Rate and direction much depend on wind. With W gales in winter, the current runs E along N coast of Spain, sometimes at 3kn or more. When crossing B of Biscay, allow for a likely set to the E, particularly after strong W winds. Tidal streams are weak offshore, but can be strong in estuaries and channels, and around headlands. It is wise to study the prevailing current and stream from fish floats etc.

BAIE DE FONTARABIE (chart 1343, 1102)

Known to the Spanish as Rada de Higuer, this lies on the border of Spain and France, and is entered between Cabo Higuer (a bare, rugged cape with Lt Ho, connected by drying reefs to Isla Amuitz, 24m high) and Pte Ste Anne 1·75M ESE. Les Briquets (dry) lie 1M N of Pte Ste Anne. In strong W winds pass to W of Banc Chicharvel in ent to Bay.

In the middle of the roadstead is a neutral area, marked by Bns and shown on chart. Outside this area the boundary line (approximately 01°46'·2W) runs N from a white pyramid on the S shore, about 1M SW of Pte Ste Anne. Ria Fuenterrabia is entered between breakwaters in SW corner of the Bay, giving access to Hendaye-Plage (see 10.14.25). Entry should not be attempted with strong onshore winds or heavy swell.

POINTE SAINT ANNE TO R. L'ADOUR (charts 1343, 1102)

In bad weather the sea breaks on Plateau de St Jean de Luz, a chain of rky shoals lying 1-4M offshore along this coast, which as far as Pte St Martin has mostly a sandy beach and rky cliffs, with mountains inland.

St Jean de Luz (chart 1343 and 10.14.25) may be approached through four passes. Passe d'Illarguita (between Illarguita and Belhara Perdun) is recommended in bad weather: follow the 138° transit (Le Socoa in line with Bordagain) until the Ste Barbe Ldg Lts (101°) are in line, and thence by Passe de l'Ouest on the 151° transit of the St Jean de Luz Ldg Lts. There are facilities at Anglet and Bayonne (10.14.25). N of Pte St Martin the coast changes to sand dunes. The sea breaks over Loutrou shoal in strong W winds. At L'Adour ent the flood runs E and SE, sp rate 2-4 kn; the ebb runs W, sp rate 3-5 kn.

L'ADOUR TO LA GIRONDE (charts 1102, 2664)

Apart from the entrance to Arcachon (10.14.10), this is a featureless coast bordered by sand dunes and fir trees, with no shelter from W winds. 5M offshore a current usually sets N at about 0·5 kn, particularly with a S wind: in winter this may be stronger after W winds. Within 1M of the coast there may be a counter-current setting S.

A submerged canyon, the Fosse (or Gouf) de Capbreton, runs at right angles to and within 2M of the coast. In strong W winds a dangerous sea develops along the N and S sides of this. A firing area lies offshore, bounded to the S by a line 295° from Capbreton Bn, and to the N by a line 245° from Pte de la Négade Bn, and extending to 02°25'W. The inshore limit is 3M off, but connected to the shore at three places, two between Biscarosse and Pte d'Arcachon, and one at Hourtin. The area is divided into 31S and 31N, which are S and N of a clear chan 8M wide running 270° from Arcachon. 31S and 31N are further divided into areas indicated by distance from coast. Thus, 31S 27·45 means the S section, 27-45M offshore. Areas in use are bcst by Bordeaux-Arcachon Radio at 0803 and 1803 (zone –0100). Sectors 31S 12·27 and 31N 12·27 are used on working days from 0800-1800 (zone –0100).

LA GIRONDE – APPROACHES (chart 2910)

La Gironde est is formed by the R. Garonne and the R. Dordogne, which join at Bec d'Ambes, 38M above Pte de Grave. BXA Lt By is moored about 11M WSW of Pte de la Coubre, off which lies Banc de la Mauvaise, the S end of which dr. Cordouan Lt Ho is on a large rky bank in the middle of the estuaries. Grande Passe de l'Ouest starts about 4M E of BXA By and is dredged through Grand Banc – the outer bar of La Gironde. Enter to seaward of Bys Nos 1 and 2, and keep in buoyed chan with Ldg Lts. Off Terre-Nègre Lt the SE-going stream begins at HW –0500 (sp rate 1·5 kn), and the NW-going at HW +0130 (sp rate 2·5 kn).

Passe Sud, a lesser chan, is entered 5·5M W of Pte de la Négade, and runs NE past Pte de Grave. There are two sets of Ldg Lts; the second lead over Platin de Grave, but it is better to pass NW of this shoal. Both entrance chans are dangerous in strong onshore winds, due to breakers and also the mascaret (bore) on the outgoing stream. Westerly swell breaks on La Mauvaise and around Cordouan, and sandbanks shift constantly. In places tidal stream runs 4 kn or more, and with wind against tide a dangerous sea can build up.

14

ILE D'OLERON (charts 2748, 2746, 2663)

From Pte de l'Epinette 13M N to Pte de Chassiron, the W coast is bounded by drying rks and shoals. In bad weather the sea breaks 4 or 5M offshore, where tidal streams are weak, sp rate 1 kn, starting NW at +0300 HW Pte de Grave and SE at –0505 HW Pte de Grave, but often overcome by current due to prevailing wind. The rate however increases towards Pte de Gatseau, where Pertuis de Maumusson separates the Island from mainland. Its ent is marked by By (SWM) about 2·75M W of Pte d'Arvert. Banc des Mattes and Banc de Gatseau, both of which dry in places, lie S and N of the chan, and are joined by a sand bar which usually has a depth of about 1·5m. Depth and position vary, and Bys are moved accordingly. Any swell forms breakers, and the chan is very dangerous then or in even moderately strong W winds, especially on the ebb (sp rate 3·5 kn). In good weather and with no swell, enter about HW–1.

Coureau d'Oleron, joined by R. La Seudre (10.14.14) near its S end, leads between ledges and oyster beds, and constantly changes, with Bys moved to conform. It is crossed by a bridge, clearance 15m, about 2M SE of Le Chateau (10.14.15): chan (prohib anch) is marked by boards at road level, ▲ W&G to be left to stbd, ■ R&W to be left to port, illuminated at night. S-going stream starts –0230 HW Pte de Grave, N-going at

+0500 HW Pte de Grave, sp rates 2 kn. Just N of bridge is Fort du Chapus, connected to mainland by causeway.

The N end of Coureau d'Oleron leads into Grande Rade, where good anch is found except in fresh NW winds. At N end of Grande Rade is entrance to R. La Charente (10.14.16). From the N, Grande Rade is entered from Pertuis d'Antioche through Passage de l'Est close to Île d'Aix (10.14.25) or Passage de l'Ouest, which run each side of La Longe du Boyard – an extensive sandbank on which stands a fort.

PERTUIS D'ANTIOCHE (chart 2746)

A By (SWM) is moored in W approach to Pertuis d'Antioche which runs between Ile d'Oleron and Ile de Ré, giving access to Rochefort (10.14.16) and La Rochelle (10.14.17). Its shores are low. Off Pte de Chassiron (Lt Ho, Sig Stn) reefs extend 0·5M W, 1·5M N to Rocher d'Antioche (lit), and 1·5M E, and there is often a nasty sea. Île de Ré forms the N shore, and its coast is fringed by rky ledges extending 2·5M SE from Pte de Chanchardon (Lt) and nearly 1M from Pte de Chauveau (marked by Bn and Lt Tr).

Plateau de Rochebonne, with depths of less than 4m, is a large rky plateau 35-40M W of Île de Ré, marked by Bys. It is steep-to on all sides, and the sea breaks dangerously on it.

PERTUIS BRETON (chart 2641)

Pertuis Breton is entered between Pte des Baleines (Île de Ré) and Pte du Grouin du Cou (both lit). It gives access to the hbrs on N shore of Île de Ré, to L'Aiguillon (10.14.25) and Marans on the mainland shore, and provides (except in NW winds) a sheltered route to La Pallice and La Rochelle, through Coureau de la Pallice. Beware rky ledges (dry) extending 2·5M NW from Les Baleines. There are shallows and drying areas all along the N coast of Île de Ré. Near St Martin and La Flotte there are extensive fisheries, with seaward limits marked by Bys (SPMs).

On N shore, Pte du Grouin du Crou has steep cliffs: with fresh NW winds against NW-going stream a bad sea builds on the bank which extends 8M W. 1M S of the Pt is Roche de l'Aunis (depth 0·3m). From the point sand dunes run 8M ESE to the entrance to Rivière Le Lay, which is fronted by a bar (dries 1m), dangerous in bad weather. The chan to L'Aiguillon (10.14.25) is marked by Bns and Bys. 4M further E is entrance to Anse de l'Aiguillon, in which are extensive mussel beds.

BAIE DE BOURGNEUF (charts 3216, 2646)

B de Bourgneuf is entered between Pte de l'Herbaudière, the NW extremity of Ile de Noirmoutier, and Pte de St Gildas about 7M NNE. The S entrance through Goulet de Fromentine is obstructed by a causeway, Route du Gois, which dries 3m. The Bay is sheltered except in W winds, which can raise a heavy sea with the ebb stream. There are good anchs but the S and E sides of the B are encumbered with shoals, rks and oyster or mussel fisheries.

From the S, beware Chaussée des Boeufs, marked by Bys, extending 3·5M W and 7·5M SW of Ile de Noirmoutier. Some of these dry, and the tide sets on to them. Chenal de la Grise (chart 3216) between Ile du Pilier and Pte de l'Herbaudière has 2·7m in the W sector of Basse du Martroger Lt, and gives access to L'Herbaudière marina (10.14.23). If proceeding E to Pornic (10.14.24), pass N of Basse du Martroger, and beware Roches des Pères about 1M ENE.

From the N (chart 3216) the approach is simple, but beware La Couronnée, dries 1·8m and marked by Bys, on a rky bank about 2M WSW of Pte de St Gildas. 2M S of Pte de St Gildas, Banc de Kerouars extends 3M in an E/W direction with depths of 1m, where the sea breaks.

From westward, approach Pornic in the W sector of Pte de Noveillard Lt – S of Banc de Kerouars and N of Notre Dame Bn Tr, which lies 2M SW of Pornic and marks end of a line of rks extending WNW from La Bernerie. Pierre du Chenal is an isolated rk about 1M SSE of Notre Dame. Within the B are Noirmoutier (10.14.23) and minor drying hbrs – Bec de l'Epoids, Port des Brochets, Le Collet and La Bernerie-en-Retz – with a good anch at Pte des Dames.

10.14.6 DISTANCE TABLE

Approximate distances in nautical miles are by the most direct route while avoiding dangers and allowing for traffic separation schemes etc. Places in *italics* are in adjoining areas.

1 *Pointe du Raz*	**1**																			
2 *Le Palais (Belle Ile)*	81	**2**																		
3 Pornic	125	45	**3**																	
4 Port Joinville (Ile d'Yeu)	126	50	30	**4**																
5 St-Gilles-Croix-de-Vie	141	64	40	18	**5**															
6 Les Sables d'Olonne	156	79	55	31	20	**6**														
7 St Martin (Ile de Ré)	177	105	75	55	44	27	**7**													
8 La Rochelle	186	110	92	66	51	36	12	**8**												
9 Pointe de Chassiron	185	107	84	58	46	32	17	13	**9**											
10 Royan	224	146	115	97	85	71	56	52	39	**10**										
11 Bordeaux	278	200	169	151	139	125	110	106	93	54	**11**									
12 Castets (canal lock)	308	230	199	181	169	155	140	136	123	84	30	**12**								
13 Cap Ferret (Arcachon)	253	185	160	138	130	113	102	98	85	68	118	152	**13**							
14 Capbreton	298	235	215	192	186	171	162	158	145	124	174	208	58	**14**						
15 Bayonne	307	242	223	200	195	178	149	166	153	132	182	216	70	12	**15**					
16 St Jean de Luz	310	250	230	206	200	186	153	174	161	136	186	220	76	19	16	**16**				
17 *San Sebastian*	307	249	233	210	204	191	159	178	165	142	192	226	85	31	29	17	**17**			
18 *Santander*	280	239	241	212	210	201	190	198	185	173	223	257	130	104	102	95	83	**18**		
19 *La Coruna*	321	334	357	335	340	342	365	354	341	348	398	432	327	315	317	314	298	223	**19**	
20 *Cabo Finisterre*	369	385	408	386	391	393	416	405	392	399	449	483	378	366	368	365	349	274	59	**20**

SPECIAL NOTES FOR FRENCH AREAS (Areas 14, 15, 16, 18 and 19) 10-14-7

There are certain differences in the harbour information where French ports are concerned. Instead of 'County' the 'Department' is given. It should also be remembered that the Time Zone for France is − 0100 (i.e. 1300 Standard Time in France is 1200 GMT), daylight saving schemes not having been taken into account (see 9.1.2.)

For special information about passports, visas, triptyques, carnets, Permis de Circulation, etc. see the relevant sections in earlier chapters or, for greater detail apply to the French Government Tourist Office, 178 Piccadilly, London, W1V 0AL. Tel. 071-499-6911.

AFFAIRES MARITIMES

In every French port there is a representative of the central government, L'Administration Maritime, known as Affaires Maritimes. This organisation watches over all maritime activities and helps them develop harmoniously − commercial, fishing, pleasure, etc. All information about navigation and any other maritime problems can be supplied by the local representative. If in doubt whom to consult, the Affaires Maritimes is the best place to start. Their headquarters is at

Bureau de la Plaisance − 3 Place Fonteroy, 75007 Paris.
Tel: (1) 45.67.55.05

and the telephone number of their local representative is given under each port.

CHARTS

Two French chart numbers are given; SHOM are those issued by the 'Service Hydrographique et Oceanographique de la Marine', the Hydrographic Service of the French Navy; also ECM 'Éditions Cartographiques Maritimes', which are charts for sea and river navigation (Carte-Guide de navigation maritime et fluviale).

The letters SHOM after entries in the 'Facilities' indicates an agent for SHOM charts.

SIGNALS

There are standard sets of signals for Traffic, Storm Warnings, Distress and Tidal, and these apply in all French ports unless otherwise stated.

Traffic Signals

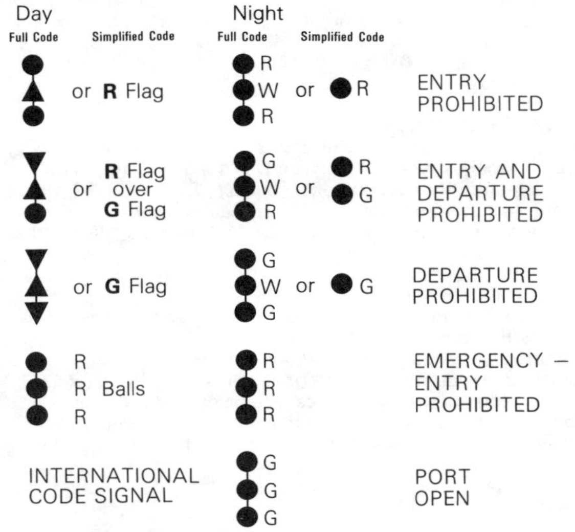
Day
Full Code
Simplified Code
Night
Full Code
Simplified Code
or R Flag
R
W
R
or
R
ENTRY PROHIBITED
or
R Flag over G Flag
G
W
R
or
R
G
ENTRY AND DEPARTURE PROHIBITED
or G Flag
G
W
G
or
G
DEPARTURE PROHIBITED
R
R Balls
R
R
R
R
EMERGENCY − ENTRY PROHIBITED
INTERNATIONAL CODE SIGNAL
G
G
G
PORT OPEN

A Black Flag displayed indicates a shipping casualty in the area.

Flag 'P' is sometimes displayed to indicate that lock or dock gates are open.

Distress Signals (from Lighthouse) or Danger Signals

Most isolated French lighthouses have radiotelephones, but the following signals may be displayed:

A ball above or below a square flag	−	Require immediate assistance
A black flag at the masthead	−	Shipwreck in vicinity of lighthouse

Storm Signals (International System)

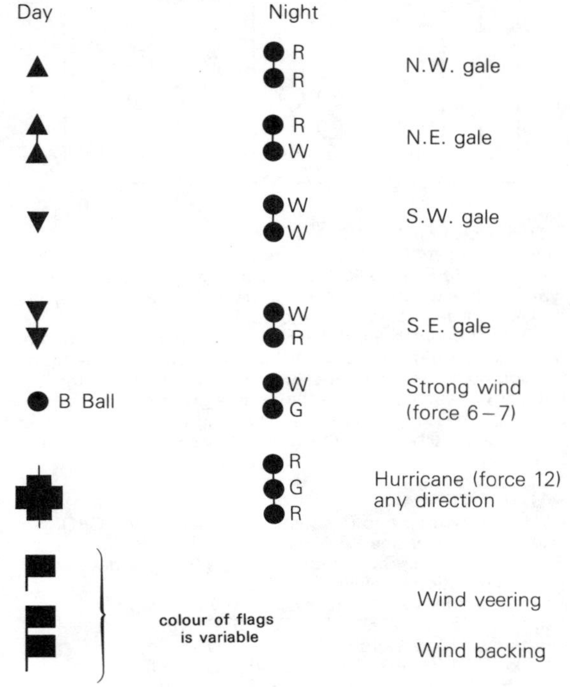
Day
Night
R
R
N.W. gale
R
W
N.E. gale
W
W
S.W. gale
W
R
S.E. gale
B Ball
W
G
Strong wind (force 6−7)
R
G
R
Hurricane (force 12) any direction
colour of flags is variable
Wind veering
Wind backing

In France, flashing white lights, by day only, indicate wind over Force 6, as follows: − Quick flashing − within three hours; Interrupted quick flashing − within six hours.

Tidal Signals

There are two sets of signals, one showing the state of the tide and the other showing the depth of water.

State of the tide is shown by: −

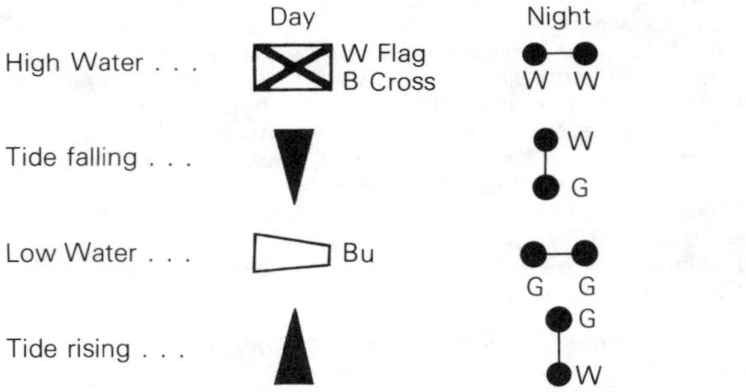
Day
Night
High Water . . .
W Flag
B Cross
W W
Tide falling . . .
W
G
Low Water . . .
Bu
G G
Tide rising . . .
G
W

The depth of water signals show the depth above Chart Datum and to ascertain the figure the various shapes have to be added together;

by day: a cone point down = 0.2 m, a cylinder = 1.0 m, a ball = 5.0 m.

by night: G light = 0.2 m, R light = 1.0 m, W light = 5.0 m.

The three different shapes are shown horizontally, with cones to the left of cylinders and balls to the right, viewed from seaward. Lights are disposed similarly.

The following examples will help to explain.

BY DAY

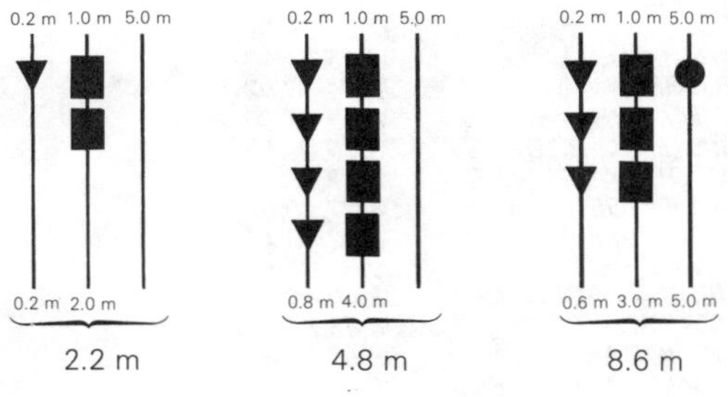
0.2 m 1.0 m 5.0 m
0.2 m 2.0 m
2.2 m
0.2 m 1.0 m 5.0 m
0.8 m 4.0 m
4.8 m
0.2 m 1.0 m 5.0 m
0.6 m 3.0 m 5.0 m
8.6 m

SPECIAL NOTES FOR FRENCH AREAS *continued*

BY NIGHT

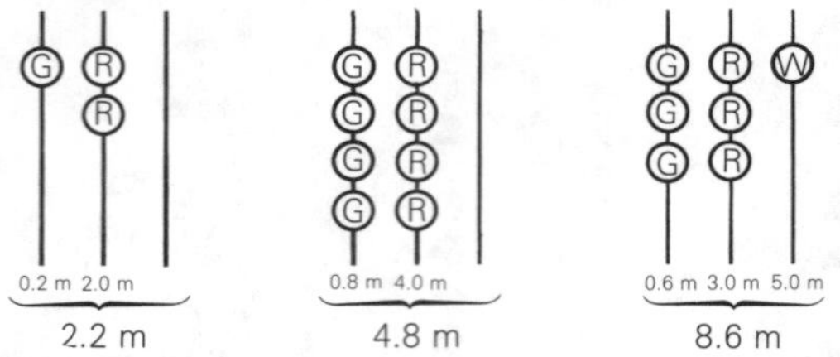
G
R
W
0.2 m 2.0 m
2.2 m
0.8 m 4.0 m
4.8 m
0.6 m 3.0 m 5.0 m
8.6 m

TIDAL COEFFICIENTS

The French use tidal coefficients which vary from 45 at mean neaps (Morte Eau) to 95 at mean springs (Vive Eau), but which with exceptional tides can be as little as 20 or as much as 120. For an average tide the coefficient is 70. The coefficients, which are published in France for every tide of the year, therefore indicate the size of each tide. The ratio of the coefficients of different tides equals the ratio of their ranges. For example, from the figures given above it can be seen that the range of the largest spring tide (coefficient 120) is six times the range of the smallest neap tide (coefficient 20).

SAFETY AT SEA

Control of Search and Rescue is exercised by the CROSS organisation (Centres Régionaux Operationnels de Surveillance et de Sauvetage) available 24 hrs a day.
The organisation is divided as follows:-
Spanish border to Pointe du Raz: CROSS Etel, Tel. 97.55.35.35, (2182 kHz and VHF Ch 16).
Pointe du Raz to Mont St Michel: CROSS Corsen, Tel. 98.89.31.31, (2182 kHz and VHF Ch 11 16).
Mont St Michel to Antifer: CROSS Jobourg, Tel. 33.52.72.13, (2182 kHz and VHF Ch 11 16).
Antifer to Belgian border: CROSS Gris Nez; Tel. 21.87.21.87, (2182kHz and VHF Ch 16 69).
Note: CROSS Soulac, near Pointe du Grave, is a subsidiary station of CROSS Etel, Tel. 56.59.82.00, (2182 kHz and VHF Ch 16, 0600-2100).
Besides the Search and Rescue function CROSS will provide urgent up-to-date navigational information such as buoys adrift, lights not working etc.
The following CROSS VHF relay stations keep watch on Ch 16; La Rhune (near Spanish border), Cap Ferret, Chassiron (Ile de Oléron), Ile d'Yeu, Belle Ile and Penmarc'h.
CROSS can be contacted by radiotelephone, by telephone, through coast radio stations, via the semaphore system (French Navy on Ch 16) as shown below, or via the National Gendarmerie or Affaires Maritimes.
Naval 'Semaphore' stations keep watch on Ch 16 (working channel Ch 10) or by telephone as follows:
For information broadcasts by VTS centres and Associated Communications centres see Chapter 2.

SEMAPHORE	*TELEPHONE*
● *SOCOA*	*59.47.18.54*
CAP FERRET	*56.60.60.03*
POINTE-DE-GRAVE	*56.09.60.03*
LA COUBRE	*46.22.41.73*
ILE D'AIX	*46.88.66.07*
CHASSIRON (Oléron)	*46.47.85.43*
LES BALEINES (Ré)	*46.29.42.06*
ST-SAUVEUR (Yeu)	*51.58.31.01*
● *CHEMOULIN*	*40.91.99.00*
PIRIAC-SUR-MER	*40.23.59.87*
ST-JULIEN	*97.50.09.35*
TALUT (Belle-Ile)	*97.31.85.07*
TAILLEFER (Belle-Ile)	*97.31.83.18*
BEG MELEN (Groix) (PEN MEN)	*97.05.80.13*
ETEL	*97.55.35.59*
● *PORT-LOUIS*	*97.85.52.10*
BEG MEIL	*98.94.98.92*
● *PENMARCH*	*98.58.61.00*
● *POINTE-DU-RAZ*	*98.70.66.57*
CAP-DE-LA-CHEVRE	*98.27.09.55*
TOULINGUET	*98.27.90.02*
● *MINOU (Vigie)*	*98.22.10.43*
● *ST-MATHIEU*	*98.89.01.59*
OUESSANT CREACH	*98.48.80.49.*
● *OUESSANT STIFF*	*98.48.81.50*
● *BRIGNOGAN*	*98.83.50.84*
● *ST QUAY-PORTRIEUX*	*96.70.42.18*
BATZ	*98.61.76.06*
● *PLOUMANACH*	*96.23.21.50*
BREHAT	*96.20.00.12*
ST-CAST	*96.41.85.30*
LE GROUIN	*99.89.60.12*
LE ROC	*33.50.05.85*
CARTERET	*33.53.85.08*
LA HAGUE	*33.52.71.87*
● *LE HOMET*	*33.92.60.08*
LEVY	*33.54.31.17*
● *BARFLEUR*	*33.54.04.37*
ST-VAAST	*33.54.44.50*
● *PORT-EN-BESSIN*	*31.21.81.51*
VILLERVILLE	*31.88.11.13*
● *LA HEVE*	*35.46.07.81*
FECAMP	*35.28.00.91*
DIEPPE	*35.84.23.82*
AULT	*22.60.47.33*
BOULOGNE	*21.31.32.10*
● *DUNKERQUE*	*20.66.86.18*

● H24. Remainder sunrise to sunset.

Whereas in UK, lifeboats should be contacted only through HM Coastguard, in France, although the lifeboat service comes under the CROSS organisation, it is encouraged to contact the lifeboat stations (Societe Nationale de Sauvetage en Mer, SNSM) direct. Where appropriate, therefore, the telephone numbers of local SNSMs are given.

MEDICAL

Telephone numbers of doctors and/or hospitals are given for each port. There is also the Services d'Aide Médicale Urgente (SAMU), which liaises closely with CROSS, which can be contacted as follows: –

PYRÉNÉES-ATLANTIQUE (Bayonne)	59.63.33.33
LANDES (Mont-de-Marsan)	58.75.44.44
GIRONDE (Bordeaux)	56.96.70.70
CHARENTE-MARITIME (La Rochelle)	46.27.15.15
VENDEE (La Roche-sur-Yon)	51.62.62.15
LOIRE-ATLANTIQUE (Nantes)	40.48.35.35
MORBIHAN (Vannes)	97.54.22.11
FINISTERE (Brest)	98.46.11.33
CÔTES-DU-NORD (Saint Brieuc)	96.94.40.15
CALVADOS (Caen)	31.44.88.88
SEINE-MARITIME (Le Havre)	35.21.11.00
SOMME (Amiens)	22.44.33.33
PAS-DE-CALAIS (Arras)	21.71.51.51
NORD (Lille)	20.54.22.22

PUBLIC HOLIDAYS

New Year's Day, Easter Sunday and Monday, Labour Day (1 May), Ascension Day, Armistice Day 1945 (8 May), Whit Sunday and Monday, National (Bastille) Day (14 July), Feast of the Assumption (15 August), All Saints' Day (1 November), Remembrance Day (11 November), Christmas Day.

METEO (Weather)

The BQR (Bulletin Quotidien des Renseignements) is a daily information bulletin displayed in Harbour Masters' Offices and in yacht clubs, and is very informative.

Telephone numbers of the principal coastal Bureaux Meteorologiques (Met. Offices) are given in 7.2.4. This also shows numbers for Repondeurs Automatiques (recorded messages) which are sufficiently detailed for short coastal passages.

For details of weather information from French radio stations see – Table 7 (5).

TELEPHONES

To telephone France from UK, dial 010 33 followed by the number. For all exchanges outside Paris, area codes have been added on to individual numbers. All numbers therefore have eight digits. From inside France, dial the eight figures shown in the Almanac. From UK dial 010 33 followed by the eight digit number shown. There are two sorts of ringing tone: one consists of three second bursts of tone separated by three seconds silence; the other consists of one and a half second bursts of tone followed by three and a half seconds silence. Engaged is similar to that in UK. Number unobtainable is indicated by a recorded announcement. A rapid series of pips indicates your call is being connected. For Police dial 17. For Fire or Hospital dial 18.
To telephone UK from France dial 19; wait for the second dialling tone then dial 44 followed by the area dialling code (omitting the first 0) and then the number.

SPECIAL NOTES FOR FRENCH AREAS *continued*

Phonecards for public telephones may be bought at the PTT or at some cafés and tabacs. Cheap rates are from 2130 to 0800 Mon-Sat; and all day Sun.

Note 1.
See 2.5.3 regarding French Customs regulations.

Note 2.
Speed under power is limited in France to 5 kn. when within 300 m of the shore.

Note 3.
There are strict penalties for infringing the International Regulations for Prevention of Collision at Sea and for French yachts not carrying the correct documentation or safety equipment.

Note 4.
The following abbreviations are used in telephone numbers:

Capitaine du Port	Hr Mr
Affaires Maritimes	Aff Mar
Centre régional opérationnel de surveillance et sauvetage	CROSS
Societe Nationale de Sauvetage en Mer (Lifeboats)	SNSM
Meteorologie/Weather	Meteo
Meteo Repondeur Automatique	Auto

Note 5.
Foreign vessels over 25m must get permission to navigate or anchor in French internal waters and keep watch on Ch 16 or other nominated frequency.

FRENCH GLOSSARY OF TERMS 10-14-8

Accalmie	lull
Accastillage	chandlery (CH)
Accostage	alongside berth, mooring (AB)
Alt	Alternating
Amer	landmark
Anse	bay
Arrière	port/inner harbour
Assechage	drying berth
Avant port	outer harbour
Avis de coup de vent	GALE WARNING
Babord	port (side).
Baie	shoal
Balise	beacon (Bn)
Basse mer	low water (LW)
Basse pression	low pressure
B,b	White (W)
Belle	smooth (sea).
Béton	concrete
Bl	blue (Bu)
Bouée	buoy
Brise	breeze
Brise-lames	breakwater
Brouillard	fog
Bruine	drizzle
Brume	mist
Bureau de Poste	post office
Cale	slipway (slip)
Canal	canal, channel
Canon	explosive
Canot de Sauvetage	lifeboat (LB)
Carré	square
Chantier naval	boatyard (BY)
Charpente	framework tower
Chaussée	bank
Chenal	channel
Cloche	bell
Clocher	steeple
Colonne	column
Cone, conique	cone, conical
Constructeur	shipwright (Sh)
Corne de brume	foghorn
Coup de vent	gale
Couvert	overcast
A damier	chequered
Darse	basin
Demi-congé des magasins	early closing (EC)
Derive	aground
Dique	breakwater, mole
Douane	customs (#)
Duc d'Albe	dolphin
É,é	flashing (Fl)
...É	group quick flashing
Eau potable	fresh water (FW)
Écluse	lock
Él,él	long flashing
Epave	wreck
Escalier du quai	landing (L)
Essence	petrol (P)
Est	east (E)
Etale	slack water
Éteint	extinguished
Élévateur	boat hoist (BH)
Falaise	cliff
Fer	metal
Feu	light
Feu flottant	light-vessel float
Fixé	fixed
Fix É	fixed and flashing
Fleuve	river
Fort	strong (wind)
Forte	rough
Fraise	fresh
Gare	railway station (⇌)
Garde-Côtiere	coastguard (CG)
Gas-oil	diesel
Golfe	gulf
Goulet	narrows
Grain	squall
Grand frais	near gale
Grève	sandy beach
Gris	grey
Grue	crane (C)
Houle	swell
Île	island
Indicatif	call sign
Ingénieur	engineer
Iso	isophase
Jaune,J	yellow (Y)
Jetée	jetty
Laverie	launderette ▣
Maconnerie	stone
Maison	house
Marché	food supplies, market (V)
Marée	tide
Mât	mast, flagstaff
Mo	morse code (Mo)
Morte eau	neaps (Np)
Mouillage	anchorage (⚓)
Moulin	mill
Neige et pluie	sleet
Noeuds	knots (Kn)
Noir	black
Nord	north (N)
Naugeux	cloudy
Occ	occulting (Oc)
...Occ	group occulting(2)
Occasionnel	occasional
Orage	thunderstorm
Org	orange (Or)
Ouest	west (W)
Passe	channel
Pertuis	strait
Petrole	paraffin
Phare	lighthouse (Lt Ho)
Pierre	stone
Pleine mer	high water (HW)
Pluie	rain
Pointe	point
Pont	bridge
Port de plaisance	yacht harbour, marina
Poteau	post
Presqu'ile	peninsula
Prevision	forecast
Quai	quay
R,r	red
Rade	roadsted
Radiophone	radiobeacon
Rafale	gust
Raie	stripe
Recif	reef
Remous	overfalls
Rivière	river
Roche(r)	rock
Sable	sand

SPECIAL NOTES FOR FRENCH AREAS *continued*

Scint,sc	quick flashing (Q)
Scint,rapide	very quick flashing
Scint, dis	interrupted quick flashing
Sifflet	whistle
Signeaux de Mouvement de navire	traffic signals
Sirène	siren
Station de pilotage	pilot station
Sud	south (S)
Tempête	storm
Temporaire	temporary
Tour, tourelle	tower (Tr)
Triang	triangular
Tribord	starboard (Stbd)
Trompette	reed (horn)
V,v	green (G)
Vente fraise	strong breeze
Ville	town
Vio	violet (Vi)
Vitesse	rate (tide)
Vive eau	springs (sp)
Voilier	sailmaker (SM)
Voy	topmark
Zone interdite	prohibited area

TIDAL INFORMATION FOR NORTH COAST OF SPAIN 10-14-9

Standard Port POINTE DE GRAVE (⟶)

Times				Height (metres)			
HW		LW		MHWS	MHWN	MLWN	MLWS
0000	0600	0500	1200	5·3	4·3	2·1	1·0
1200	1800	1700	2400				
Differences CORUNA							
−0110	−0050	−0030	−0100	−1·5	−1·5	−0·6	−0·5
ORTIGUEIRA							
−0020	0000	+0020	−0010	−1·2	−1·1	−0·6	−0·4
LUARCA							
+0010	−0015	+0025	−0015	−1·1	−1·0	−0·5	−0·3
GIJON							
−0005	−0030	+0010	−0030	−1·3	−1·2	−0·6	−0·4
SANTANDER							
−0020	−0100	0000	−0050	−0·8	−0·8	−0·2	−0·2
BILBAO							
−0125	−0045	−0035	−0055	−1·1	−0·9	−0·5	−0·2
LEQUEITO							
−0115	−0035	−0025	−0045	−1·1	−0·9	−0·5	−0·2
SAN SEBASTIAN							
−0110	−0030	−0020	−0040	−1·1	−0·9	−0·5	−0·2

ARCACHON 10-14-10

Gironde

CHARTS

Admiralty 2664; SHOM 6766, 7070; ECM 255, 1024.

TIDES

+0620 Dover; ML 2·2; Zone −0100

Standard Port POINTE DE GRAVE (⟶)

Times				Height (metres)			
HW		LW		MHWS	MHWN	MLWN	MLWS
0000	0600	0500	1200	5·3	4·3	2·1	1·0
1200	1800	1700	2400				
Differences ARCACHON							
+0005	+0030	+0015	+0040	−1·1	−1·1	−1·0	−0·8
ST JEAN DE LUZ (SOCOA)							
−0050	−0045	−0025	−0040	−1·0	−1·0	−0·5	−0·5
L'ADOUR (BOUCAU)							
−0035	−0030	−0010	−0030	−1·0	−0·9	−0·3	−0·2
CAP FERRET							
−0015	0000	+0005	+0015	−1·2	−1·0	−0·7	−0·6

SHELTER

Good shelter in marina in Bassin d'Arcachon. Entry impossible at night or in strong winds from SW to N. Max length 15m. Besides the Port d'Arcachon there are numerous other small drying harbours round the basin. On the West, La Vigne, Le Canon, Piquey and Claouey; on the South La Teste and Gujan; on the NE Port de Lège, Ares, Andernos, Port de Fontaine Vielle, Lanton (Cassy) and Audenge.

NAVIGATION

Waypoint ATT/ARC (safe water buoy), LFl 10s, Whis, 44°34'·70N, approx 173°/353° from/to Nos 1 and 2 channel buoys, 2·6M. Beware shifting sand banks in entrance channel, the sea breaks on these banks in any wind but the entrance channel can be seen through the breakers. With a strong on-shore wind the bar is impassable from HW+1 until LW, and it is best to wait until LW+3. Buoys are adjusted each spring but channel can change later. Latest information from Service de la Marine Gironde at Arcachon 56.82.32.97 or at Bordeaux 56.83.03.00. Average depth over bar is 4·5m. Beware firing ranges to seaward and S of Arcachon. See 10.14.5.

LIGHTS AND MARKS

Cap Ferret Fl R 5s 53m 27M and Oc (3) 12s vis 045°-135°. Arcachon harbour W breakwater QG, E breakwater QR. Port de la Vigne Iso R 4s 7m 4M. La Salie Q (9) 15s 19m 10M.

RADIO TELEPHONE

VHF Ch 09.

TELEPHONE (56)

Hr Mr 56.83.22.44; Aff Mar 56.83.03.00; # 56.83.05.89; SNSM 56.83.22.44; CROSS 56.09.82.00; Auto 56·83·84·85; Police 56.83.04.63; Dr 56.83.04.72; Ⓗ 56.83.39.50; Brit Consul 56.52.28.35.

FACILITIES

Marina (2243+57 visitors), FW, AC, Slip, C (20 ton), BH (45 ton), D, Access HW∓3; **Station Elf** ☎ 56.83.29.72, P, D; **Y C d'Arcachon** ☎ 56.83.22.11, P, D, FW, Slip, Bar, R; **Arcachon Plaisance** ☎ 56.83.31.31, P, D, L, FW, ME, Ⓔ, El, Sh, CH; **Arcachon Shipchandler** ☎ 56.83.23.69 CH, ME, El, Sh, Ⓔ; **Nautic Service** ☎ 56.83.84.10, ME, El, Sh, CH; **Service Nautique** ☎ 56.83.27.45, SHOM; **Voiles Assistance** ☎ 56.83.58.55, SM; **N Jetty** ☎ 56.83.22.44, Slip, L, FW, C (10 ton), AB; **Town** AB, V, R, Gaz, ✉; Ⓑ; ⇌; ✈ (Bordeaux).
Ferry UK — Roscoff—Plymouth; St Malo—Portsmouth.

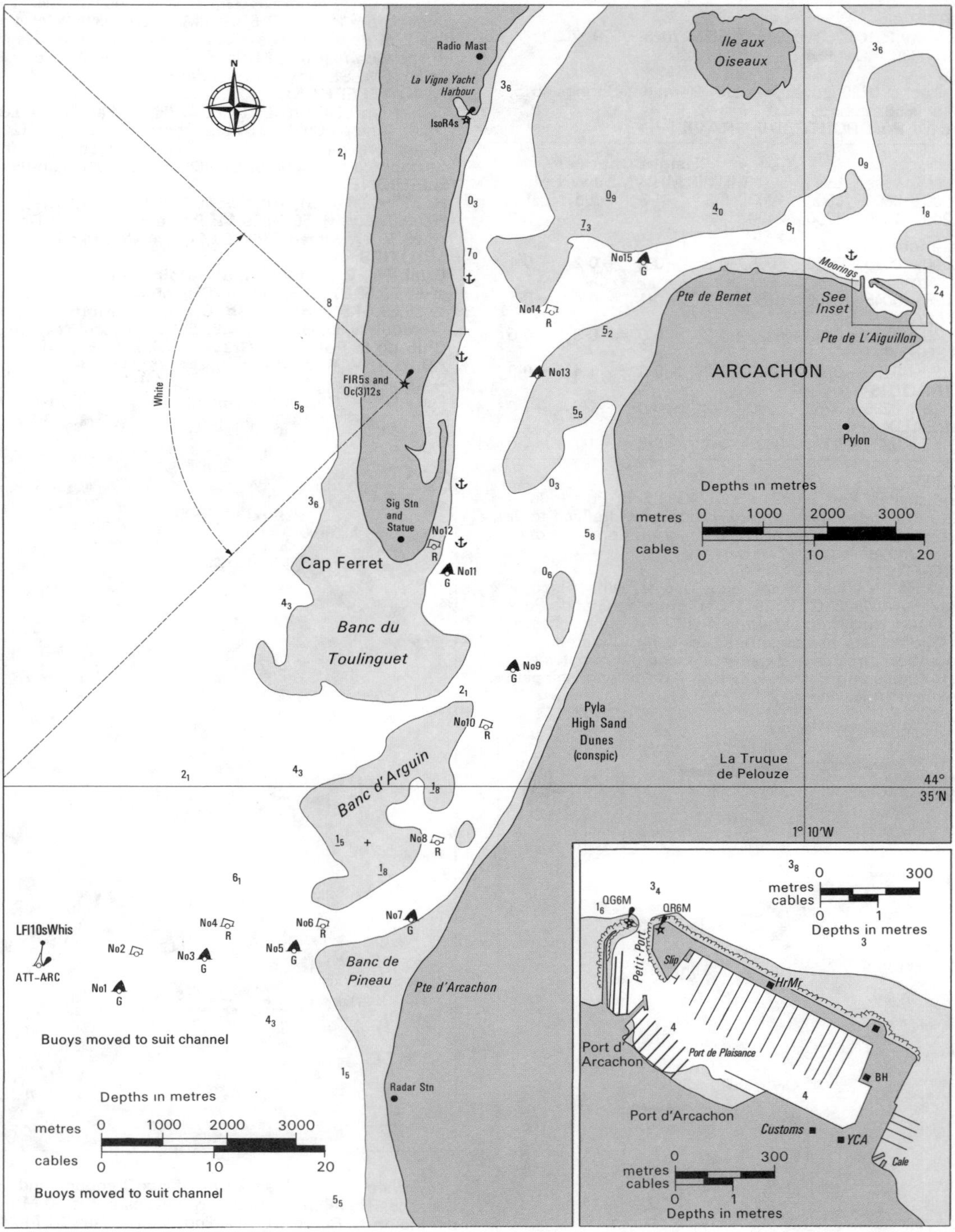
N
Radio Mast
La Vigne Yacht Harbour
IsoR4s
Ile aux Oiseaux
Moorings
See Inset
Pte de Bernet
Pte de L'Aiguillon
ARCACHON
Pylon
No15 G
No14 R
No13
FIR5s and Oc(3)12s
White
Sig Stn and Statue
No12 R
No11 G
Cap Ferret
Banc du Toulinguet
No9 G
No10 R
Pyla High Sand Dunes (conspic)
La Truque de Pelouze
44° 35'N
1° 10'W
Banc d'Arguin
No8 R
No7 G
No6 R
No5 G
No4 R
No3 G
No2
No1 G
LFl10sWhis
ATT-ARC
Banc de Pineau
Pte d'Arcachon
Radar Stn
Buoys moved to suit channel
Depths in metres
metres 0 1000 2000 3000
cables 0 10 20
Buoys moved to suit channel
QG6M
QR6M
Petit-Port
Slip
HrMr
Port d' Arcachon
Port de Plaisance
BH
Port d'Arcachon
Customs
YCA
Cale
metres 0 300
cables 0 1
Depths in metres

PORT BLOC/ LA GIRONDE 10-14-11

Gironde

CHARTS
Admiralty 2910, 2664, 2916; SHOM 7028, 7029, 7030, 6335, 6336; ECM 554

TIDES
(Pauillac) +0720 Dover; ML 3·0; Duration: Springs 0615; Neaps 0655; Zone −0100

Standard Port POINTE DE GRAVE (⟶)

Times				Height (metres)			
HW		LW		MHWS	MHWN	MLWN	MLWS
0000	0600	0500	1200	5·3	4·3	2·1	1·0
1200	1800	1700	2400				
Differences ROYAN							
0000	−0020	−0010	−0005	−0·2	−0·2	−0·2	−0·1
LAMENA							
+0035	+0045	+0100	+0130	+0·2	+0·1	−0·4	−0·3
PAUILLAC							
+0045	+0110	+0140	+0220	+0·2	0·0	−0·8	−0·5
LA REUILLE							
+0120	+0155	+0230	+0320	−0·2	−0·4	−1·4	−0·9
LE MARQUIS							
+0130	+0205	+0250	+0340	−0·2	−0·4	−1·6	−1·0
BORDEAUX							
+0155	+0235	+0330	+0425	−0·1	−0·3	−1·7	−1·0

SHELTER
Good shelter. Port Bloc is 4 ca (740m) S of Pointe de Grave at the entrance to the Gironde. It is dredged to 3m. Yachts use the W side of the harbour on pontoons or moor between buoys.

NAVIGATION
Waypoint BXA (safe water) buoy, Iso 4s, Whis, Racon, 45°37′·60N 01°28′·60W, 261°/081° from/to Grande Passe de l'Ouest Nos 1 and 2 buoys, 4·8M. The approaches to the Gironde can be dangerous see 10.14.5. There are very strong tidal streams and currents encountered between the entrance and Pointe de Grave. Also beware shipping entering and leaving.

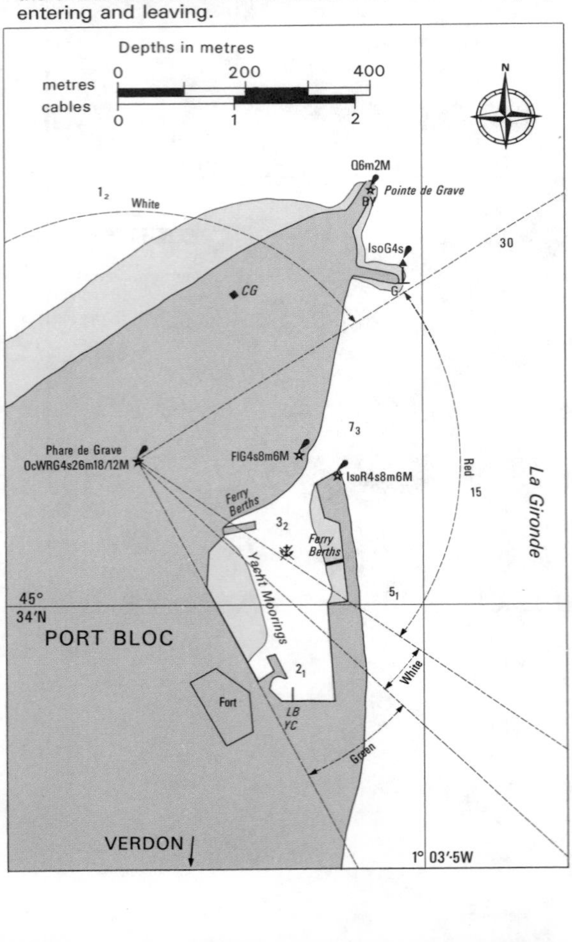

Depths in metres
metres
cables
0
200
400
0
1
2
N
Q6m2M
Pointe de Grave
BY
White
IsoG4s
G
30
CG
Phare de Grave
OcWRG4s26m18/12M
FlG4s8m6M
IsoR4s8m6M
Ferry Berths
Ferry Berths
Yacht Moorings
Red
15
La Gironde
White
Green
45°
34′N
PORT BLOC
Fort
LB
YC
VERDON
1° 03′·5W

LIGHTS AND MARKS
Ldg Lts 041°. Front QR 33m 18M, intens 039°-043°. Rear, 0·97M from front, QR 61m 18M, intens 039°-043°. Ldg line E of Pointe de Grave 327° astern with Tèrre Negre Lt in line with rear of La Palmyre, FR. Lts on NW jetty Fl G 4s 8m 6M, SE jetty Iso R 4s 8m 6M.

RADIO TELEPHONE
Le Verdon VHF Ch 16; 11 12 14 (H24). Pauillac Ch 09 12 (H24). Ambès Ch 12 (H24). Bordeaux Ch 16; 12 (H24). Water level reports on Ch 71. Reports on sea state from Semaphore (La Coubre) Ch 16; 06 12. Marina Ch 09.

TELEPHONE (56)
Hr Mr 56.09.63.91; Aff Mar 56.09.60.23; CROSS 56.09.82.00; # 56.09.65.14; Police 56.09.60.13; Dr 56.09.60.37; Meteo 56.34.20.11; Brit Consul 56.52.28.35.

FACILITIES
Quai FW, C (10 ton); **Nautic Pointe de Grave** ☎ 56.59.63.27; ME, El, Sh, CH; **Médoc Loisirs** (Verdon) ☎ 56.59.64.91, ME, El, Sh, CH; **La Boutique du Marin** (Verdon) ☎ 56.59.63.75, ME, El, CH; **Moto Yachting Club de la Pointe de Grave** ☎ 56.09.61.58; **Town** P, D, AB, Gaz, V, R, ✉ (Verdon); Ⓑ (Verdon); ⇄; ✈ (Bordeaux);
Ferry UK — Roscoff—Plymouth; St Malo—Portsmouth.

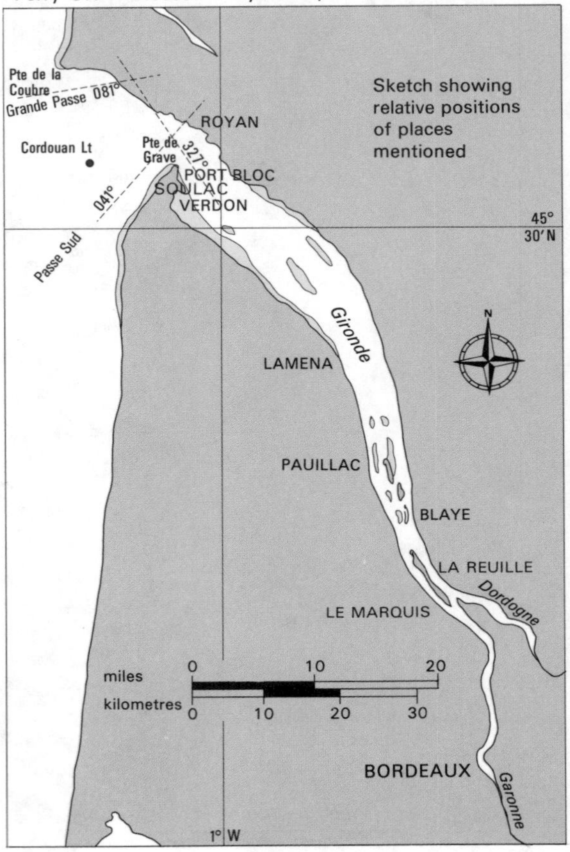

Pte de la Coubre
Grande Passe 081°
Cordouan Lt
Pte de Grave
327°
ROYAN
PORT BLOC
SOULAC
VERDON
041°
Passe Sud
Sketch showing relative positions of places mentioned
45°
30′N
Gironde
N
LAMENA
PAUILLAC
BLAYE
LA REUILLE
Dordogne
LE MARQUIS
miles
kilometres
0
10
20
0
10
20
30
BORDEAUX
Garonne
1° W

La Gironde is the estuary of the rivers Dordogne and Garonne. There are a number of havens in the 50 M from the mouth to Bordeaux including Pauillac (see 10.14.24), Lamarque and Blaye. In Bordeaux there is a marina opposite Lormont, just after passing under the first bridge (see 10.14.25). About 27 M up the Garonne from Bordeaux, at Castets, there is the first lock into the Canal Lateral à la Garonne which leads into the Canal du Midi. In the Garonne at springs, the flood stream starts with a small bore and then runs at about 3 kn, while the ebb runs at 5 kn. In the other rivers the spring rate does not exceed 3 kn on the flood and 4 kn, on the ebb.
NOTE: A major marina is due to be built at Verdon.

TIME ZONE -0100
(French Standard Time)
Subtract 1 hour for GMT
For French Summer Time add ONE hour in non-shaded areas

FRANCE, WEST COAST - POINTE DE GRAVE

LAT 45°34'N LONG 1°04'W

TIMES AND HEIGHTS OF HIGH AND LOW WATERS

YEAR **1992**

JANUARY

Day	Time	m	Day	Time	m
1 W	0247 0827 1512 2048	4.5 1.8 4.5 1.8	**16** TH	0133 0717 1408 1952	4.4 1.9 4.5 1.9
2 TH	0333 0921 1556 2138	4.6 1.7 4.6 1.7	**17** F	0237 0825 1510 2056	4.7 1.6 4.7 1.6
3 F	0413 1008 1633 2221	4.8 1.5 4.7 1.6	**18** SA	0334 0927 1606 2155	5.0 1.3 5.0 1.3
4 SA	0448 1049 1708 ● 2259	4.9 1.4 4.8 1.5	**19** SU	0427 1023 1658 ○ 2248	5.3 1.0 5.2 1.1
5 SU	0521 1125 1740 2333	5.0 1.4 4.9 1.5	**20** M	0517 1114 1747 2337	5.6 0.8 5.4 0.9
6 M	0552 1158 1811	5.0 1.3 4.9	**21** TU	0604 1202 1833	5.7 0.7 5.4
7 TU	0005 0623 1229 1841	1.4 5.0 1.3 4.9	**22** W	0023 0651 1248 1918	0.8 5.7 0.7 5.4
8 W	0037 0652 1301 1912	1.4 5.0 1.4 4.8	**23** TH	0107 0736 1331 2001	0.8 5.6 0.8 5.2
9 TH	0109 0723 1333 1944	1.5 4.9 1.4 4.7	**24** F	0151 0820 1415 2042	0.9 5.3 1.0 5.0
10 F	0143 0756 1408 2019	1.5 4.8 1.6 4.6	**25** SA	0235 0904 1500 2125	1.2 5.0 1.3 4.7
11 SA	0220 0833 1445 2101	1.6 4.7 1.7 4.5	**26** SU	0323 0954 1549 ☾ 2215	1.5 4.6 1.7 4.4
12 SU	0301 0917 1529 2153	1.8 4.5 1.9 4.3	**27** M	0419 1059 1648 2333	1.8 4.3 2.0 4.1
13 M	0350 1019 1622 ☽ 2302	1.9 4.3 2.0 4.2	**28** TU	0530 1233 1800	2.1 4.1 2.2
14 TU	0451 1136 1728	2.0 4.2 2.1	**29** W	0114 0650 1355 1917	4.1 2.1 4.1 2.2
15 W	0020 0603 1256 1841	4.3 2.0 4.3 2.1	**30** TH	0225 0804 1454 2024	4.2 2.0 4.3 2.1
			31 F	0316 0902 1539 2117	4.5 1.8 4.4 1.9

FEBRUARY

Day	Time	m	Day	Time	m
1 SA	0356 0948 1615 2201	4.7 1.6 4.6 1.7	**16** SU	0319 0911 1553 2140	5.0 1.3 5.0 1.3
2 SU	0430 1026 1647 2237	4.9 1.5 4.8 1.5	**17** M	0412 1007 1644 2232	5.4 1.0 5.3 1.0
3 M	0501 1101 1718 ● 2310	5.0 1.3 4.9 1.4	**18** TU	0501 1057 1730 ○ 2319	5.6 0.7 5.5 0.8
4 TU	0530 1132 1747 2342	5.1 1.2 5.0 1.3	**19** W	0546 1142 1813	5.8 0.6 5.5
5 W	0559 1203 1816	5.2 1.2 5.0	**20** TH	0003 0629 1225 1853	0.6 5.7 0.6 5.5
6 TH	0013 0626 1234 1844	1.2 5.2 1.2 5.0	**21** F	0045 0710 1306 1930	0.7 5.6 0.8 5.3
7 F	0044 0654 1305 1912	1.2 5.1 1.2 5.0	**22** SA	0125 0749 1346 2004	0.8 5.3 1.0 5.0
8 SA	0116 0723 1336 1943	1.3 5.0 1.4 4.9	**23** SU	0206 0827 1427 2038	1.1 5.0 1.3 4.7
9 SU	0149 0752 1410 2019	1.4 4.9 1.5 4.7	**24** M	0250 0909 1512 2117	1.4 4.6 1.7 4.4
10 M	0227 0834 1449 2103	1.5 4.7 1.7 4.5	**25** TU	0341 1005 1605 ☾ 2215	1.8 4.2 2.1 4.1
11 TU	0311 0926 1537 ☽ 2205	1.7 4.4 1.9 4.3	**26** W	0448 1143 1715	2.2 3.9 2.4
12 W	0407 1049 1640 2334	1.9 4.2 2.1 4.2	**27** TH	0023 0614 1321 1839	3.9 2.3 3.9 2.4
13 TH	0521 1225 1800	2.0 4.2 2.2	**28** F	0153 0735 1425 1954	4.1 2.2 4.1 2.3
14 F	0104 0647 1347 1925	4.4 1.9 4.4 2.0	**29** SA	0249 0834 1511 2050	4.3 1.9 4.3 2.0
15 SA	0217 0806 1455 2039	4.7 1.7 4.7 1.7			

MARCH

Day	Time	m	Day	Time	m
1 SU	0330 0919 1548 2133	4.6 1.7 4.6 1.8	**16** M	0302 0854 1536 2122	5.0 1.3 5.0 1.3
2 M	0404 0956 1620 2210	4.8 1.5 4.8 1.5	**17** TU	0355 0947 1625 2212	5.3 1.0 5.3 1.0
3 TU	0434 1030 1650 2244	5.0 1.3 5.0 1.3	**18** W	0442 1035 1709 ○ 2258	5.5 0.8 5.4 0.7
4 W	0504 1103 1720 ● 2316	5.1 1.2 5.1 1.2	**19** TH	0525 1119 1749 2341	5.6 0.7 5.5 0.6
5 TH	0532 1135 1749 2348	5.2 1.1 5.1 1.1	**20** F	0606 1201 1827	5.6 0.7 5.4
6 F	0600 1206 1817	5.2 1.1 5.1	**21** SA	0022 0644 1241 1901	0.7 5.4 0.9 5.3
7 SA	0020 0627 1238 1846	1.1 5.2 1.1 5.1	**22** SU	0101 0721 1319 1933	0.9 5.2 1.1 5.0
8 SU	0051 0656 1309 1916	1.1 5.1 1.2 5.0	**23** M	0140 0758 1358 2005	1.1 4.8 1.4 4.7
9 M	0125 0727 1343 1951	1.2 4.9 1.4 4.9	**24** TU	0221 0838 1439 2043	1.5 4.5 1.8 4.4
10 TU	0202 0808 1422 2035	1.3 4.7 1.6 4.7	**25** W	0308 0930 1528 2135	1.8 4.1 2.1 4.1
11 W	0245 0900 1509 2138	1.5 4.4 1.8 4.4	**26** TH	0410 1053 1632 ☾ 2317	2.1 3.9 2.4 3.9
12 TH	0341 1031 1612 ☽ 2310	1.8 4.2 2.1 4.3	**27** F	0532 1231 1753	2.3 3.9 2.4
13 F	0457 1209 1737	2.0 4.2 2.2	**28** SA	0104 0653 1340 1910	4.0 2.2 4.0 2.3
14 SA	0044 0630 1332 1909	4.4 1.9 4.4 2.0	**29** SU	0208 0754 1431 2010	4.2 2.0 4.3 2.1
15 SU	0200 0751 1440 2023	4.7 1.6 4.7 1.7	**30** M	0253 0840 1512 2057	4.5 1.7 4.5 1.8
			31 TU	0330 0920 1547 2136	4.7 1.5 4.7 1.5

APRIL

Day	Time	m	Day	Time	m
1 W	0403 0957 1620 2213	4.9 1.3 4.9 1.3	**16** TH	0422 1012 1646 2236	5.3 0.9 5.3 0.8
2 TH	0434 1032 1651 2248	5.0 1.2 5.1 1.1	**17** F	0504 1056 1726 ○ 2320	5.4 0.9 5.3 0.8
3 F	0505 1106 1723 ● 2322	5.1 1.1 5.1 1.0	**18** SA	0544 1137 1802	5.3 0.9 5.2
4 SA	0536 1140 1754 2356	5.1 1.1 5.2 1.0	**19** SU	0000 0623 1217 1837	0.8 5.2 1.1 5.1
5 SU	0607 1214 1826	5.1 1.1 5.1	**20** M	0040 0659 1255 1910	1.0 4.9 1.3 4.9
6 M	0031 0640 1248 1900	1.0 5.0 1.2 5.1	**21** TU	0118 0736 1333 1944	1.2 4.7 1.5 4.7
7 TU	0107 0717 1324 1939	1.1 4.9 1.4 4.9	**22** W	0158 0817 1412 2024	1.5 4.4 1.8 4.5
8 W	0146 0804 1406 2029	1.2 4.6 1.6 4.7	**23** TH	0242 0906 1457 2113	1.8 4.2 2.0 4.2
9 TH	0232 0908 1457 2136	1.5 4.4 1.8 4.5	**24** F	0336 1010 1553 ☾ 2226	2.0 4.0 2.2 4.1
10 F	0331 1031 1603 ☽ 2301	1.7 4.2 2.0 4.4	**25** SA	0444 1130 1703 2359	2.2 3.9 2.3 4.0
11 SA	0450 1158 1729	1.9 4.2 2.1	**26** SU	0558 1244 1816	2.1 4.0 2.3
12 SU	0027 0619 1316 1854	4.5 1.8 4.4 1.9	**27** M	0112 0702 1342 1921	4.1 2.0 4.2 2.1
13 M	0141 0733 1421 2004	4.7 1.6 4.7 1.6	**28** TU	0206 0754 1429 2013	4.3 1.8 4.4 1.9
14 TU	0243 0833 1516 2100	5.0 1.3 4.9 1.3	**29** W	0249 0839 1509 2058	4.5 1.6 4.6 1.6
15 W	0335 0924 1603 2150	5.2 1.0 5.1 1.0	**30** TH	0327 0920 1546 2139	4.7 1.4 4.8 1.4

Chart Datum: 2.93 metres below Lallemand System (Mean Sea level, Marseilles)

TIME ZONE -0100
(French Standard Time)
Subtract 1 hour for GMT
For French Summer Time add ONE hour in non-shaded areas

FRANCE, WEST COAST - POINTE DE GRAVE

LAT 45°34'N LONG 1°04'W

TIMES AND HEIGHTS OF HIGH AND LOW WATERS

YEAR 1992

MAY

Day	Time	m	Day	Time	m
1 F	0402 0959 1622 2219	4.9 1.3 5.0 1.2	16 SA	0446 1035 1705 ○ 2302	5.0 1.1 5.1 1.0
2 SA	0438 1037 1658 ● 2257	5.0 1.2 5.1 1.0	17 SU	0526 1117 1743 2343	5.0 1.2 5.1 1.1
3 SU	0514 1115 1735 2336	5.0 1.1 5.2 1.0	18 M	0605 1156 1818	4.9 1.2 5.0
4 M	0552 1154 1813	5.0 1.1 5.2	19 TU	0023 0642 1234 1852	1.1 4.8 1.4 4.9
5 TU	0015 0633 1233 1854	1.0 5.0 1.2 5.1	20 W	0101 0718 1310 1927	1.3 4.6 1.5 4.8
6 W	0056 0719 1314 1940	1.0 4.8 1.3 5.0	21 TH	0138 0756 1348 2006	1.5 4.5 1.7 4.6
7 TH	0140 0812 1400 2034	1.2 4.6 1.5 4.8	22 F	0218 0839 1428 2050	1.6 4.3 1.8 4.4
8 F	0230 0915 1455 2138	1.4 4.5 1.7 4.7	23 SA	0302 0929 1515 2143	1.8 4.2 2.0 4.3
9 SA	0330 1027 1600 ☽ 2251	1.6 4.4 1.8 4.6	24 SU	0355 1029 1611 ☾ 2249	1.9 4.1 2.1 4.1
10 SU	0442 1141 1716	1.7 4.4 1.9	25 M	0457 1137 1717	2.0 4.1 2.2
11 M	0006 0559 1253 1832	4.6 1.7 4.5 1.8	26 TU	0002 0601 1242 1823	4.1 2.0 4.1 2.1
12 TU	0117 0708 1357 1939	4.7 1.5 4.6 1.6	27 W	0106 0701 1338 1923	4.2 1.9 4.3 1.9
13 W	0220 0808 1453 2037	4.8 1.4 4.8 1.3	28 TH	0200 0754 1426 2016	4.3 1.7 4.5 1.7
14 TH	0315 0901 1542 2129	4.9 1.2 4.9 1.2	29 F	0246 0841 1510 2104	4.5 1.6 4.7 1.5
15 F	0402 0949 1625 2217	5.0 1.1 5.0 1.1	30 SA	0330 0926 1552 2149	4.7 1.4 4.9 1.3
			31 SU	0413 1010 1635 2233	4.8 1.3 5.1 1.1

JUNE

Day	Time	m	Day	Time	m
1 M	0457 1054 1718 ● 2318	5.0 1.2 5.2 1.0	16 TU	0548 1138 1801	4.8 1.4 5.0
2 TU	0542 1138 1803	5.0 1.1 5.3	17 W	0006 0623 1214 1834	1.2 4.7 1.4 4.9
3 W	0003 0629 1223 1850	0.9 5.0 1.1 5.3	18 TH	0041 0656 1248 1907	1.3 4.7 1.4 4.9
4 TH	0049 0719 1308 1939	0.9 4.9 1.2 5.2	19 F	0116 0730 1323 1941	1.4 4.6 1.5 4.8
5 F	0136 0812 1357 2032	1.0 4.8 1.3 5.1	20 SA	0150 0806 1359 2019	1.5 4.5 1.6 4.6
6 SA	0226 0908 1449 2129	1.2 4.7 1.4 4.9	21 SU	0228 0847 1438 2100	1.6 4.4 1.7 4.5
7 SU	0321 1009 1547 ☽ 2231	1.3 4.6 1.6 4.7	22 M	0309 0933 1524 2150	1.7 4.3 1.9 4.3
8 M	0422 1114 1652 2339	1.5 4.5 1.7 4.6	23 TU	0358 1029 1618 ☾ 2249	1.9 4.2 2.0 4.2
9 TU	0528 1223 1802	1.6 4.4 1.7	24 W	0455 1133 1720 2357	2.0 4.1 2.1 4.2
10 W	0050 0637 1331 1912	4.6 1.6 4.5 1.6	25 TH	0559 1239 1827	2.0 4.2 2.0
11 TH	0158 0740 1431 2014	4.6 1.6 4.6 1.5	26 F	0104 0702 1340 1930	4.2 1.9 4.4 1.9
12 F	0256 0838 1523 2111	4.6 1.5 4.7 1.4	27 SA	0205 0800 1435 2027	4.4 1.8 4.6 1.6
13 SA	0347 0930 1608 2201	4.7 1.4 4.8 1.3	28 SU	0300 0854 1525 2121	4.6 1.6 4.8 1.4
14 SU	0431 1017 1648 2247	4.7 1.4 4.9 1.2	29 M	0351 0945 1614 2212	4.8 1.4 5.1 1.1
15 M	0511 1059 1726 ○ 2328	4.8 1.3 4.9 1.2	30 TU	0442 1035 1703 ● 2302	4.9 1.2 5.3 0.9

JULY

Day	Time	m	Day	Time	m
1 W	0531 1124 1751 2351	5.1 1.0 5.4 0.8	16 TH	0559 1152 1811	4.8 1.3 5.0
2 TH	0621 1212 1840	5.1 1.0 5.5	17 F	0017 0629 1224 1840	1.2 4.8 1.3 5.0
3 F	0039 0710 1258 1928	0.8 5.1 0.9 5.4	18 SA	0048 0659 1256 1911	1.3 4.8 1.3 4.9
4 SA	0125 0759 1344 2018	0.8 5.1 1.0 5.3	19 SU	0120 0731 1329 1942	1.3 4.7 1.4 4.8
5 SU	0212 0848 1432 2109	1.0 4.9 1.2 5.1	20 M	0153 0805 1404 2017	1.4 4.6 1.5 4.7
6 M	0300 0940 1524 2203	1.2 4.7 1.3 4.8	21 TU	0229 0843 1442 2057	1.6 4.5 1.7 4.5
7 TU	0353 1037 1622 ☽ 2306	1.4 4.5 1.6 4.6	22 W	0309 0930 1527 ☾ 2149	1.7 4.3 1.8 4.3
8 W	0454 1146 1730	1.6 4.3 1.8	23 TH	0357 1030 1623 2257	1.9 4.2 2.0 4.2
9 TH	0021 0602 1304 1844	4.4 1.8 4.3 1.8	24 F	0457 1144 1731	2.0 4.2 2.1
10 F	0138 0713 1413 1954	4.3 1.8 4.4 1.8	25 SA	0017 0608 1259 1846	4.1 2.1 4.3 2.0
11 SA	0242 0817 1509 2055	4.4 1.8 4.5 1.6	26 SU	0131 0720 1405 1955	4.3 1.9 4.5 1.7
12 SU	0334 0913 1555 2147	4.5 1.7 4.7 1.5	27 M	0236 0825 1503 2057	4.5 1.7 4.8 1.4
13 M	0416 1000 1633 2231	4.6 1.5 4.8 1.4	28 TU	0333 0924 1556 2154	4.8 1.4 5.1 1.1
14 TU	0453 1042 1708 ○ 2310	4.7 1.5 4.9 1.3	29 W	0427 1018 1647 ● 2246	5.0 1.1 5.4 0.9
15 W	0527 1118 1740 2345	4.7 1.4 5.0 1.3	30 TH	0517 1109 1736 2336	5.2 0.9 5.6 0.7
			31 F	0606 1156 1823	5.3 0.8 5.7

AUGUST

Day	Time	m	Day	Time	m
1 SA	0022 0652 1241 1910	0.6 5.3 0.7 5.6	16 SU	0019 0629 1229 1839	1.2 4.9 1.2 5.0
2 SU	0106 0736 1325 1955	0.7 5.2 0.8 5.4	17 M	0050 0658 1300 1907	1.2 4.9 1.3 4.9
3 M	0150 0820 1409 2042	0.9 5.0 1.0 5.1	18 TU	0121 0728 1333 1937	1.3 4.8 1.4 4.8
4 TU	0234 0905 1456 2132	1.1 4.8 1.3 4.8	19 W	0154 0802 1408 2012	1.5 4.7 1.5 4.6
5 W	0323 0955 1550 ☽ 2232	1.4 4.5 1.6 4.4	20 TH	0230 0843 1449 2101	1.7 4.5 1.7 4.4
6 TH	0419 1102 1657 2354	1.8 4.2 1.9 4.2	21 F	0314 0940 1540 ☾ 2215	1.9 4.3 1.9 4.2
7 F	0528 1237 1818	2.0 4.1 2.0	22 SA	0410 1103 1648 2348	2.1 4.2 2.1 4.1
8 SA	0121 0646 1357 1936	4.1 2.1 4.2 2.0	23 SU	0525 1230 1812	2.1 4.3 2.0
9 SU	0227 0757 1455 2039	4.2 2.0 4.4 1.8	24 M	0111 0649 1344 1933	4.3 2.0 4.6 1.8
10 M	0317 0854 1538 2128	4.4 1.8 4.6 1.6	25 TU	0219 0804 1445 2040	4.5 1.8 4.9 1.4
11 TU	0357 0941 1614 2209	4.5 1.7 4.8 1.5	26 W	0318 0907 1540 2137	4.8 1.4 5.2 1.1
12 W	0430 1020 1645 2245	4.7 1.5 5.0 1.3	27 TH	0411 1001 1630 2228	5.1 1.1 5.5 0.8
13 TH	0502 1055 1715 ○ 2318	4.8 1.4 5.1 1.2	28 F	0500 1051 1718 ● 2316	5.3 0.8 5.7 0.7
14 F	0531 1127 1744 2349	4.9 1.3 5.1 1.2	29 SA	0545 1136 1803	5.4 0.7 5.7
15 SA	0600 1158 1812	4.9 1.2 5.1	30 SU	0000 0629 1220 1847	0.6 5.4 0.6 5.6
			31 M	0043 0710 1302 1930	0.7 5.3 0.8 5.4

Chart Datum: 2.93 metres below Lallemand System (Mean Sea level, Marseilles)

TIME ZONE -0100
(French Standard Time)
Subtract 1 hour for GMT
For French Summer Time add ONE hour in non-shaded areas

FRANCE, WEST COAST - POINTE DE GRAVE

LAT 45°34'N LONG 1°04'W

TIMES AND HEIGHTS OF HIGH AND LOW WATERS

YEAR **1992**

SEPTEMBER

Day	Time	m	Day	Time	m
1 TU	0125	0.9	16 W	0053	1.3
	0750	5.1		0659	4.9
	1345	1.0		1307	1.3
	2014	5.1		1907	4.8
2 W	0208	1.2	17 TH	0126	1.5
	0830	4.8		0732	4.8
	1430	1.3		1342	1.5
	2101	4.7		1945	4.6
3 TH	0253	1.6	18 F	0202	1.7
	0916	4.5		0814	4.6
	1521	1.7		1423	1.6
	☽ 2200	4.3		2035	4.4
4 F	0347	1.9	19 SA	0246	1.9
	1020	4.2		0913	4.4
	1627	2.0		1514	1.9
	2328	4.0		☾ 2159	4.2
5 SA	0454	2.2	20 SU	0343	2.1
	1208	4.0		1042	4.3
	1752	2.2		1623	2.0
				2336	4.1
6 SU	0058	4.0	21 M	0501	2.2
	0616	2.3		1212	4.4
	1334	4.2		1753	2.0
	1914	2.1			
7 M	0203	4.1	22 TU	0057	4.3
	0732	2.2		0631	2.1
	1431	4.4		1326	4.6
	2016	1.9		1917	1.8
8 TU	0252	4.3	23 W	0204	4.6
	0830	2.0		0748	1.8
	1514	4.6		1429	5.0
	2102	1.7		2023	1.4
9 W	0330	4.5	24 TH	0301	4.9
	0915	1.7		0849	1.4
	1548	4.8		1523	5.3
	2141	1.5		2117	1.1
10 TH	0403	4.7	25 F	0353	5.2
	0954	1.5		0942	1.0
	1619	5.0		1612	5.5
	2216	1.3		2207	0.9
11 F	0434	4.9	26 SA	0440	5.4
	1028	1.4		1031	0.8
	1648	5.1		1658	5.7
	2248	1.2		● 2254	0.7
12 SA	0504	5.0	27 SU	0524	5.5
	1100	1.2		1116	0.7
	1716	5.1		1742	5.6
	○ 2320	1.2		2338	0.7
13 SU	0533	5.0	28 M	0606	5.4
	1132	1.2		1159	0.7
	1744	5.1		1825	5.5
	2351	1.2			
14 M	0602	5.0	29 TU	0020	0.9
	1203	1.2		0646	5.3
	1811	5.1		1242	0.8
				1907	5.3
15 TU	0022	1.2	30 W	0102	1.1
	0630	5.0		0724	5.1
	1235	1.2		1324	1.1
	1839	5.0		1950	4.9

OCTOBER

Day	Time	m	Day	Time	m
1 TH	0144	1.4	16 F	0107	1.5
	0803	4.8		0719	4.8
	1407	1.4		1326	1.4
	2036	4.6		1939	4.6
2 F	0228	1.7	17 SA	0146	1.7
	0847	4.5		0806	4.7
	1457	1.8		1410	1.6
	2133	4.2		2038	4.4
3 SA	0318	2.0	18 SU	0232	1.9
	0948	4.2		0910	4.5
	1559	2.1		1503	1.8
	☽ 2254	4.0		2159	4.2
4 SU	0422	2.3	19 M	0332	2.0
	1125	4.1		1032	4.4
	1718	2.3		1613	2.0
				☾ 2325	4.2
5 M	0019	4.0	20 TU	0449	2.1
	0539	2.4		1155	4.5
	1253	4.1		1739	1.9
	1838	2.2			
6 TU	0125	4.1	21 W	0041	4.4
	0655	2.3		0615	2.0
	1354	4.3		1308	4.7
	1940	2.0		1859	1.7
7 W	0215	4.3	22 TH	0146	4.7
	0755	2.1		0729	1.7
	1439	4.5		1410	5.0
	2027	1.8		2002	1.4
8 TH	0256	4.5	23 F	0243	4.9
	0842	1.8		0829	1.4
	1517	4.7		1505	5.2
	2107	1.6		2056	1.2
9 F	0332	4.7	24 SA	0334	5.1
	0922	1.6		0922	1.1
	1549	4.9		1555	5.4
	2143	1.4		2146	1.0
10 SA	0405	4.9	25 SU	0420	5.3
	0959	1.4		1011	0.9
	1620	5.0		1641	5.5
	2218	1.3		● 2233	0.9
11 SU	0437	5.0	26 M	0504	5.4
	1033	1.3		1057	0.8
	1650	5.1		1725	5.4
	○ 2252	1.2		2317	0.9
12 M	0508	5.1	27 TU	0545	5.3
	1107	1.2		1141	0.9
	1720	5.1		1807	5.3
	2325	1.2			
13 TU	0539	5.1	28 W	0000	1.0
	1140	1.2		0625	5.2
	1750	5.0		1224	1.0
	2358	1.3		1849	5.1
14 W	0610	5.0	29 TH	0041	1.2
	1214	1.2		0703	5.0
	1821	4.9		1306	1.2
				1930	4.8
15 TH	0032	1.4	30 F	0122	1.5
	0642	5.0		0742	4.8
	1249	1.3		1349	1.5
	1856	4.8		2013	4.5
			31 SA	0205	1.7
				0824	4.6
				1435	1.8
				2103	4.3

NOVEMBER

Day	Time	m	Day	Time	m
1 SU	0251	2.0	16 M	0228	1.7
	0917	4.3		0908	4.7
	1529	2.0		1459	1.6
	2206	4.1		2151	4.4
2 M	0345	2.2	17 TU	0326	1.8
	1030	4.2		1018	4.6
	1633	2.2		1604	1.8
	☽ 2322	4.0		☾ 2305	4.4
3 TU	0451	2.3	18 W	0436	1.9
	1154	4.1		1132	4.6
	1743	2.2		1718	1.8
4 W	0032	4.1	19 TH	0017	4.5
	0602	2.3		0552	1.9
	1302	4.2		1244	4.7
	1848	2.1		1832	1.7
5 TH	0130	4.2	20 F	0124	4.6
	0706	2.1		0704	1.7
	1356	4.4		1350	4.9
	1942	1.9		1937	1.5
6 F	0218	4.4	21 SA	0224	4.8
	0800	1.9		0807	1.5
	1440	4.6		1448	5.0
	2028	1.7		2034	1.4
7 SA	0259	4.6	22 SU	0316	5.0
	0846	1.7		0903	1.3
	1518	4.7		1540	5.1
	2109	1.5		2126	1.2
8 SU	0335	4.8	23 M	0404	5.1
	0926	1.5		0955	1.1
	1552	4.9		1627	5.2
	2147	1.4		2215	1.2
9 M	0410	4.9	24 TU	0448	5.2
	1005	1.4		1042	1.1
	1626	5.0		1711	5.2
	2224	1.3		● 2300	1.2
10 TU	0444	5.0	25 W	0529	5.2
	1042	1.2		1128	1.1
	1700	5.0		1753	5.1
	○ 2301	1.3		2343	1.2
11 W	0519	5.1	26 TH	0609	5.1
	1120	1.2		1210	1.1
	1736	5.0		1832	5.0
	2338	1.3			
12 TH	0556	5.1	27 F	0024	1.3
	1158	1.2		0646	5.0
	1813	4.9		1251	1.3
				1910	4.8
13 F	0016	1.4	28 SA	0103	1.5
	0634	5.1		0722	4.9
	1237	1.2		1330	1.4
	1855	4.8		1947	4.6
14 SA	0055	1.4	29 SU	0141	1.6
	0717	5.0		0759	4.7
	1318	1.3		1410	1.6
	1943	4.7		2028	4.5
15 SU	0138	1.6	30 M	0221	1.8
	0807	4.9		0842	4.5
	1405	1.5		1453	1.8
	2042	4.5		2114	4.3

DECEMBER

Day	Time	m	Day	Time	m
1 TU	0305	2.0	16 W	0313	1.5
	0933	4.4		0956	4.9
	1542	2.0		1544	1.5
	2212	4.2		☾ 2234	4.6
2 W	0357	2.1	17 TH	0413	1.7
	1038	4.2		1102	4.7
	1639	2.1		1648	1.7
	☽ 2321	4.1		2344	4.5
3 TH	0459	2.2	18 F	0522	1.8
	1153	4.2		1215	4.6
	1742	2.1		1758	1.8
4 F	0030	4.1	19 SA	0057	4.5
	0605	2.2		0635	1.8
	1301	4.2		1329	4.6
	1845	2.1		1908	1.7
5 SA	0130	4.3	20 SU	0205	4.6
	0708	2.1		0745	1.7
	1356	4.3		1434	4.7
	1941	1.9		2012	1.6
6 SU	0220	4.5	21 M	0303	4.8
	0803	1.9		0847	1.5
	1442	4.5		1529	4.8
	2030	1.8		2109	1.5
7 M	0303	4.6	22 TU	0352	4.9
	0851	1.7		0942	1.4
	1523	4.7		1617	4.9
	2115	1.6		2200	1.4
8 TU	0343	4.8	23 W	0436	5.0
	0936	1.5		1031	1.2
	1603	4.8		1659	5.0
	2158	1.5		2246	1.3
9 W	0422	5.0	24 TH	0516	5.1
	1019	1.3		1115	1.2
	1643	5.0		1738	5.0
	○ 2240	1.3		● 2328	1.3
10 TH	0502	5.2	25 F	0553	5.1
	1101	1.2		1155	1.2
	1724	5.0		1814	5.0
	2322	1.3			
11 F	0543	5.3	26 SA	0006	1.3
	1144	1.1		0626	5.1
	1807	5.1		1232	1.2
				1846	4.9
12 SA	0004	1.2	27 SU	0041	1.4
	0627	5.3		0658	5.0
	1228	1.1		1306	1.3
	1852	5.0		1918	4.8
13 SU	0047	1.2	28 M	0115	1.5
	0712	5.3		0730	4.9
	1312	1.1		1340	1.4
	1941	5.0		1951	4.7
14 M	0132	1.3	29 TU	0149	1.6
	0802	5.2		0804	4.8
	1359	1.2		1415	1.6
	2033	4.8		2027	4.6
15 TU	0220	1.4	30 W	0226	1.7
	0856	5.0		0842	4.6
	1449	1.4		1453	1.8
	2130	4.7		2109	4.4
			31 TH	0307	1.9
				0927	4.4
				1538	1.9
				2200	4.2

Chart Datum: 2.93 metres below Lallemand System (Mean Sea level, Marseilles)

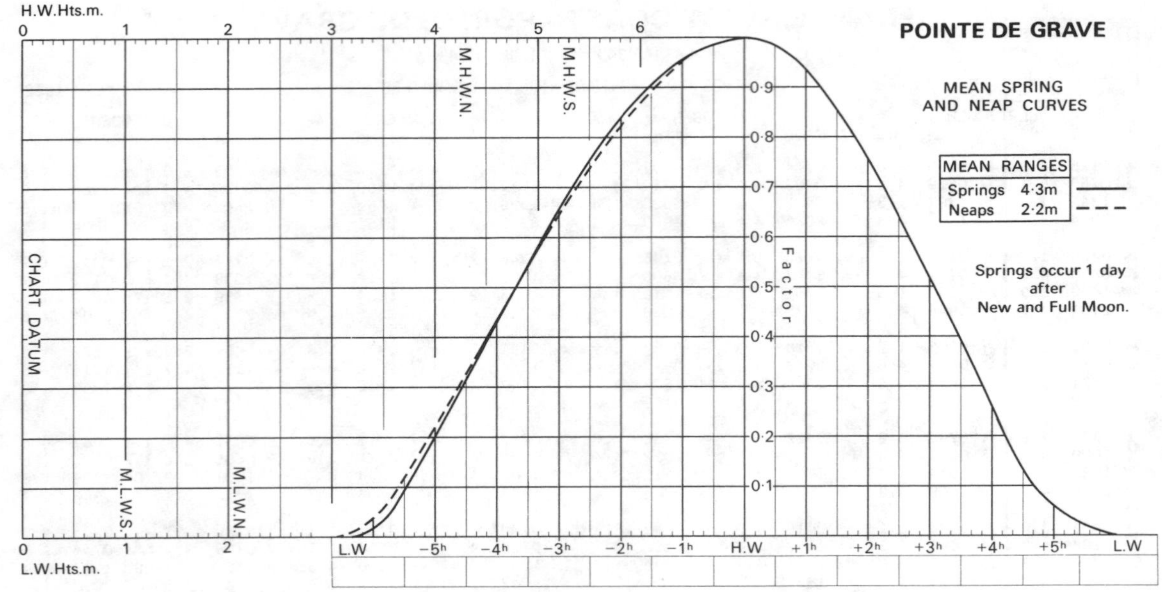
H.W.Hts.m.
0 1 2 3 4 5 6
M.H.W.N.
M.H.W.S.
CHART DATUM
M.L.W.S.
M.L.W.N.
0 1 2
L.W.Hts.m.
L.W -5h -4h -3h -2h -1h H.W +1h +2h +3h +4h +5h L.W
0·9 0·8 0·7 0·6 0·5 0·4 0·3 0·2 0·1
Factor
POINTE DE GRAVE
MEAN SPRING AND NEAP CURVES
MEAN RANGES
Springs 4·3m
Neaps 2·2m
Springs occur 1 day after New and Full Moon.

CANAL CONNECTIONS 10-14-12

The Canal Latéral à la Garonne and the Canal du Midi provide a popular route to the Mediterranean, despite the large number of locks to be negotiated. If necessary the transit can be done in about a week, but this is not recommended.

Masts can be unstepped at Royan, Pauillac or Bordeaux. Leave Bordeaux at LW Pointe de Grave for the passage up river to the first lock at Castets-en-Dorthe. If necessary a tow can usually be arranged.

Plenty of stout fenders (for example car tyres in strong canvas bags) are needed. Commercial traffic and boats bound west have right of way. On the Canal Latéral à la Garonne most of the locks are automatic. On the Canal du Midi there are many hire cruisers in the summer months. Fuel is available alongside at Agen, Castelnaudary and Port de la Robine, and at other places by can. Food and water are readily obtained along the route. Further information from Service de la Navigation de Toulouse, 2 Port St Etienne, Toulouse. Tel. 61.80.79.91.

Canal	From	To	Km/ Locks	Min Depth (m)	Min Height (m)
Lateral à la Garonne	Castets	Toulouse	193/ 53	2·2	3·5
Du Midi	Toulouse	Sete	240/ 65	1·8	3·0
De la Nouvelle	Salleles	Port la Nouvelle	37/ 14	1·8	3·1

Notes: Max length 30m. Max beam 5·5m.
Headroom of 3·0m is to top of arch. Over a width of 4m, clearance is about 2·50m. Speed limit 8 km/hour (about 4½ kn), but 3 km/hour over aquaducts and under bridges.

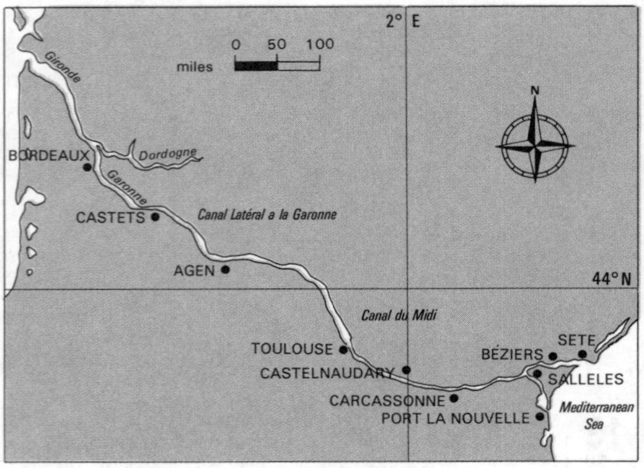
2° E
0 50 100
miles
N
Gironde
BORDEAUX
Dordogne
Garonne
CASTETS
Canal Latéral a la Garonne
AGEN
44° N
Canal du Midi
TOULOUSE
CASTELNAUDARY
CARCASSONNE
PORT LA NOUVELLE
BÉZIERS
SETE
SALLELES
Mediterranean Sea

ROYAN 10-14-13

Charente Maritime

CHARTS
Admiralty 2910, 2916, 2664; SHOM 7028, 7070; ECM 553

TIDES
+0530 Dover; ML 3·0; Duration 0615 Springs, 0655 Neaps; Zone −0100

Standard Port POINTE DE GRAVE (⟵)

Times				Height (metres)			
HW		LW		MHWS	MHWN	MLWN	MLWS
0000	0600	0500	1200	5·3	4·3	2·1	1·0
1200	1800	1700	2400				
Differences ROYAN							
0000	−0020	−0010	−0005	−0·2	−0·2	−0·2	−0·1

SHELTER
Good shelter and easy access day and night except with strong winds from the W or NW. The entrance channel is dredged to 1·0m. Yachts use N basin. A good port of call for Canal du Midi with crane for masts.

NAVIGATION
Waypoint No 12 (port-hand) buoy, OcR 4s, 45°36'·45N 01°03'·00W, 237°/057° from/to Jetée Sud Lt, 1·1M. The approaches to La Gironde can be dangerous – see 10.14.5 and 10.14.11. The sandbanks off Royan shift and buoys are consequently altered. Give the Mauvaise bank and shoals round Cordouan a wide berth. Off harbour entrance, there is an eddy, running S at about 1 kn on the flood and 3 kn on the ebb. Beware ferries.

LIGHTS AND MARKS
La Coubre light – Fl (2) W 10s 64m 28M RC, also FRG 42m 12/10M R030°-043°, G043°-060°, R060°-110°. Channel buoyed past Courdouan Lt Oc(2+1) WRG 12s 60m 22/18M, W014°-126°, G126°-178·5°, W178·5°-250°, W (unintens) 250°-267°, R (unintens) 267°-294·5°, R294·5°-014°. Obscured in estuary when bearing over 285°.

RADIO TELEPHONE
VHF Ch 16 09(in season 0800–2000; out of season 0900–1800 LT). Le Verdon Ch 16; 11 12 14.

TELEPHONE (46)
Hr Mr 46.38.72.22; Aff Mar 46.38.32.75; CROSS 56.09.82.00; SNSM 46.38.75.79; ⋕ 46.38.51.27; Meteo 56.34.20.11; Police 46.38.34.22; Dr 46.05.68.69; Ⓗ 46.38.01.77; Brit Consul 56.52.28.35.

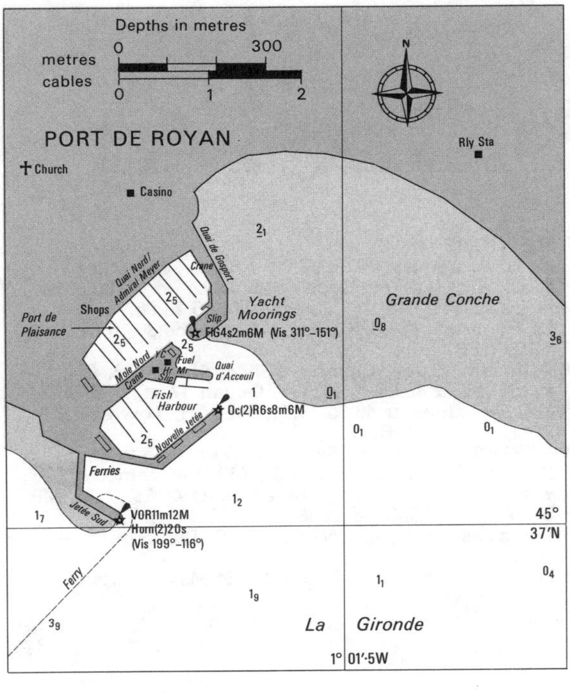

Depths in metres
metres
cables
0
300
0
1
2
N
PORT DE ROYAN
Church
Casino
Rly Sta
Quai de Gasport
Quai Nord/Admiral Meyer
Crane
Yacht Moorings
Grande Conche
Port de Plaisance
Shops
Slip
FlG4s2m6M (Vis 311°–151°)
Mole Nord
YC
Hr Mr
Fuel
Slip
Quai d'Acceuil
Crane
Fish Harbour
Nouvelle Jetée
Oc(2)R6s8m6M
Ferries
Jetée Sud
VQR11m12M
Horn(2)20s
(Vis 199°–116°)
45°
37'N
Ferry
La Gironde
1° 01'·5W

FACILITIES
Marina (570 + 60 visitors) Slip, P, D, FW, ME, AC, El, Sh, C (6 ton), BH (26 ton); **Les Regates de Royan** ☎ 46.38.59.64; **Quai Nord** P, D; **Quai Sud** P, D, C (4.5 ton); **Loca Marine** ☎ 46.38.45.99 ME, El, Sh, CH, Ⓔ; **Winckel** (la Voilerie) ☎ 46.38.36.95, SM, CH, Ⓔ; **Royan Marine Service** ☎ 46.38.54.00, CH, SHOM; **Evasion Maritime 17** ☎ 46.05.06.44, Sh, ME, El, Ⓔ, CH; **Meneau Marine** ☎ 46.39.81.27, ME. **Town** Slip, P, D, FW, V, R, Bar, Gaz, ✉; Ⓑ; ⇌; ✈ (Bordeaux).
Ferry UK – Roscoff–Plymouth, St Malo–Portsmouth.

AGENTS WANTED
Ploumanac'h
Trébeurden
Le Touquet
Norderney
Dornumersiel
Langeoog
Wangerooge
Hooksiel
Bremerhaven

If you are interested in becoming our agent please write to the Editors and get your free copy annually. You do not have to be a resident in a port to be the agent but at least a fairly regular visitor.

SEUDRE RIVER 10-14-14

Charente Maritime

CHARTS
Admiralty 2663; SHOM 6912, 6335; ECM 552

TIDES
+0545 Dover; ML 3·5; Duration Springs 0545, Neaps 0700; Zone −0100

Standard Port POINTE DE GRAVE (⟵)

Times				Height (metres)			
HW		LW		MHWS	MHWN	MLWN	MLWS
0000	0600	0500	1200	5·3	4·3	2·1	1·0
1200	1800	1700	2400				
Differences LA CAYENNE							
−0015	−0035	−0020	0000	+0·5	+0·3	+0·3	+0·1

SHELTER
La Seudre is navigable to lock at Riberou. There are secure anchorages at La Cayenne, La Grève (½M upstream), and off entrance to Chenal de la Tremblade; or yachts can lock into the basin near Marennes, 2M from the river.

SEUDRE RIVER *continued*

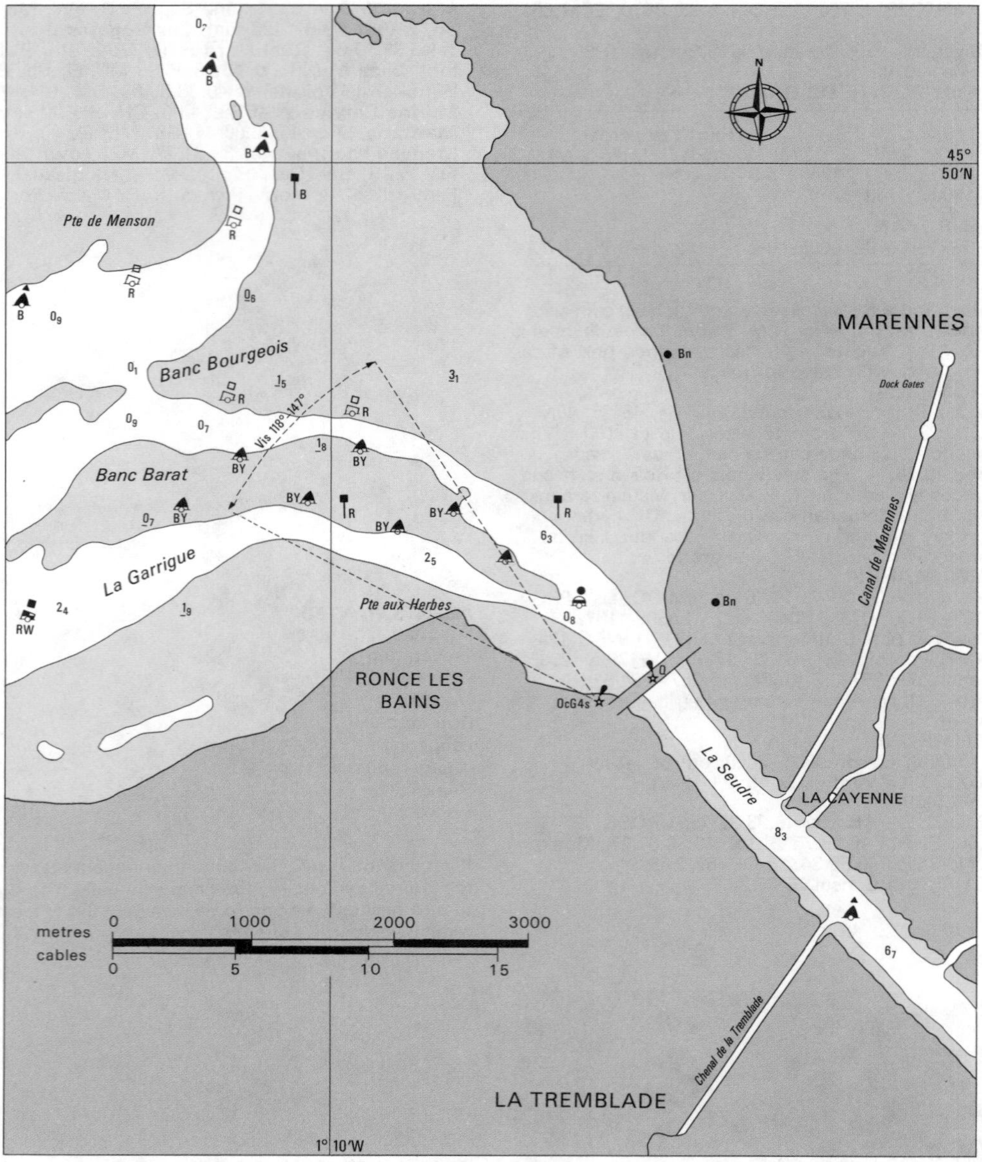

N
45° 50′N
Pte de Menson
Banc Bourgeois
Banc Barat
La Garrigue
Vis 118°-147°
Pte aux Herbes
MARENNES
Dock Gates
Canal de Marennes
RONCE LES BAINS
OcG4s
Q
La Seudre
LA CAYENNE
LA TREMBLADE
Chenal de la Tremblade
metres 0 1000 2000 3000
cables 0 5 10 15
1° 10′W

NAVIGATION

Waypoint Pertuis de Maumusson (safe water) buoy, Whis, 45°47′·70N 01°17′·85W, 260°/080° from/to Pte de Gatseau, 2·7M. Pertuis de Maumusson can be used only in good weather, at about HW−1, see 10.14.5. In even moderate weather it is extremely dangerous, particularly with out-going stream or any swell. It is advisable to approach La Seudre from N, through Coreau d'Oleron, and thence through Chenal de la Soumaille (dries about 0·7m). Chenal de la Garrigue carries slightly more water. Both are marked by Bns and buoys. Beware oyster beds. Pont de Seudre has clearance of 18m. An overhead cable (16m) spans Canal de Marennes.

LIGHTS AND MARKS

There are no leading lights or marks. Lights: Pte de Mus de Loup Oc G 4s 8m 6M vis 118°-147°. On bridge between piers 6 and 7; downstream Q 20m 10M vis 054°-234°; upstream Q 20m 10M vis 234°-054°. Channel is marked by W boards.

RADIO TELEPHONE

VHF Ch 09.

TELEPHONE (46)

Hr Mr (Marennes) 46.85.02.68; Aff Mar, Marennes 46.85.14.33, La Tremblade 46.36.00.22; # 46.36.03.03; Police 46.85.00.19; Dr Marennes 46.85.23.06, La Tremblade 46.36.16.35; Brit Consul 56.36.16.35.

FACILITIES

MARENNES **Quay (Claude)** ☎ 46.85.15.11, ME, CH; **Paraveau** ☎ 46.85.10.77, Sh; **Ocean 17** ☎ 46.85.36.27, ME, CH; **Quay** ☎ 46.85.15.11, ME, CH; **Town** Slip, M, P, D, L, FW, V, R, Bar.

LA TREMBLADE **Quay** Slip, P, D, FW, C (5 ton); **Bernard Frères** ☎ 46.36.09.00, ME, Sh; **Jamain** ☎ 46.36.01.50 SM, CH; **Boulanger** ☎ 46.36.01.34, ME, Sh; **Atlantic Garage** ☎ 46.36.00.67, ME; **Town** Slip, P, D, L, FW, Gaz, V, R, Bar, ✉; Ⓑ; ⇄; ✈ (La Rochelle).

Ferry UK — Roscoff—Plymouth; St Malo—Portsmouth.

ILE D'OLÉRON 10-14-15

Charente Maritime

CHARTS
Admiralty 2748, 2746, 2663; SHOM 6912, 6913, 6914, 6335, 6334; ECM 552

TIDES
+0545 Dover; ML 3·8; Duration 0540; Zone −0100

Standard Port POINTE DE GRAVE (⟵)

Times				Height (metres)			
HW		LW		MHWS	MHWN	MLWN	MLWS
0000	0600	0500	1200	5·3	4·3	2·1	1·0
1200	1800	1700	2400				
Differences ROCHEFORT							
+0015	−0020	+0045	+0120	+1·1	+0·8	+0·1	+0·4

There are two harbours, Le Chateau d'Oléron and Boyardville. A third on W coast, La Cotiniere, suffers almost constantly from Atlantic swells.

SHELTER
LE CHATEAU: Good shelter, but very full of oyster boats which use inner harbour. Yachts lie on quay SW side (dries 3m) – check with Hr Mr. Access ∓3.
BOYARDVILLE: Good anchorage, sheltered from S and W, in 3m (sand) ½M N of La Perrotine Lt. Landing jetty inshore. Good shelter alongside quays (dry) on N side of harbour. Access HW∓2. Boyardville yacht harbour, non-tidal, entered through automatic gates which open when height of tide is 2·4m. (Approx HW∓2½).

NAVIGATION
Waypoint Pertuis d'Antioche PA (safe water) buoy, Iso 4s, Whis, 46°05'·55N 01°42'·60W, 283°/103° from/to Pte de Chassiron Lt, 13M.

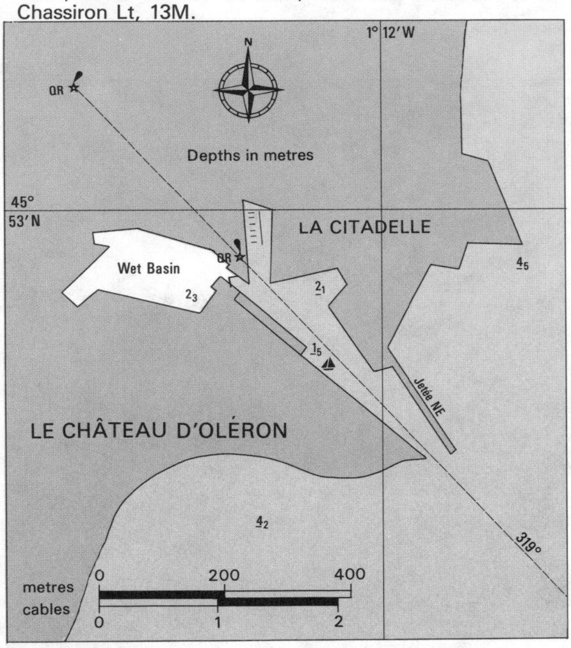

1° 12'W
N
QR
Depths in metres
45° 53'N
LA CITADELLE
Wet Basin
QR
2₃
2₁
4₅
1₅
Jetée NE
LE CHÂTEAU D'OLÉRON
4₂
319°
metres
cables
0
200
400
0
1
2

LE CHATEAU: Bridge to mainland lies 2M S, 15m clearance under spans 20-24, channel marked by boards – W&G to stbd, W&R to port, illuminated at night. Beware Grande Mortanne, a drying ledge, marked by Bns. From N, beware Rocher du Doux (dries) and Rocher Juliar (dries). Mortanne Sud Bn marks entrance to channel (depth 0·8m) indicated by Ldg Lts.
BOYARDVILLE: Bar dries 2m and extends 3 ca (560m) E of breakwater head. Inside bar the channel mostly dries. Beware ferries.

LIGHTS AND MARKS
LE CHATEAU: Ldg Lts 319°, Both QR 11/24m 7M; W Tr with R top; synchronised. Tourelle Juliar Q(3) WG 10s 12m 11/8M; E cardinal mark; vis W147°-336°, G336°-147°.
BOYARDVILLE: Breakwater head Oc(2) R 6s 8m 6M; W Tr with R top; obsc by Pte des Saumonards when brg less than 150°.

RADIO TELEPHONE
Boyardville VHF Ch 09.

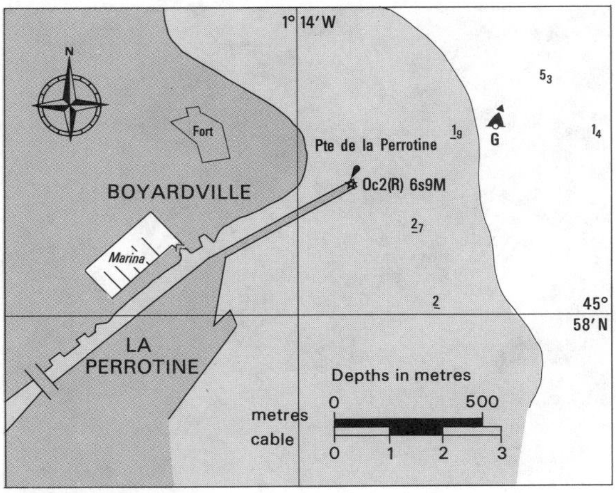

1° 14'W
N
Fort
BOYARDVILLE
Pte de la Perrotine
Oc2(R) 6s9M
5₃
1₉
G
1₄
2₇
Marina
2
45° 58'N
LA PERROTINE
Depths in metres
metres
cable
0
500
0
1
2
3

TELEPHONE (46)
Hr Mr (Le Chateau) 46.47.00.01; Hr Mr (Boyardville) 46.47.23.71; Hr Mr Douhet 46.76.71.13 # 46.47.62.53; Aff Mar 46.47.60.01; CROSS 56.09.82.00; Meteo 46.41.29.14; Auto 46.50.62.32; Police 46.47.61.77; Dr 46.47.60.68; Brit Consul 56.52.28.35.

FACILITIES
LE CHATEAU **Jetty**, Slip, L, FW, C (2.5 ton); **Blondel** ☎ 46.47.61.89, ME, El; **Sorlut Marine** ☎ 46.47.54.08, ME, El, Ⓔ, Sh, CH; **Oléron-Motors-Cycles** ☎ 46.47.62.78, ME, El, CH; **Dubois** ☎ 46.47.62.57, ME, Sh, El, CH; **Magasin 2000** ☎ 46.47.61.43, CH;
BOYARDVILLE **Marina** (150+50 visitors) ☎ 46.47.01.36, AC, FW, C (7 ton), Slip; **Môle chenal de la Perrotine** P, D; **Sodinautic** ☎ 46.47.25.65, ME, Sh, CH; **Marine Oléron** ☎ 46.47.01.36, ME, El, Sh, CH; **Barbaud** ☎ 46.47.01.10, ME.
Ferry UK — Roscoff—Plymouth, St Malo—Portsmouth

ROCHEFORT 10-14-16

Charente Maritime

CHARTS
Admiralty 2748, 2746; SHOM 4333, 6334; ECM 552

TIDES
+0610 Dover; Zone −0100

Standard Port POINTE DE GRAVE (⟵)

Times				Height (metres)			
HW		LW		MHWS	MHWN	MLWN	MLWS
0000	0600	0500	1200	5·3	4·3	2·1	1·0
1200	1800	1700	2400				
Differences ROCHEFORT							
+0015	−0020	+0045	+0120	+1·1	+0·8	+0·1	+0·4
ILE D'AIX							
−0005	−0035	−0025	−0015	+0·9	+0·7	+0·4	0·0

SHELTER
Rochefort is on N bank of Charente, about 10M from the mouth. Entry advised on late flood, as bar breaks on ebb. Anchor out of channel at Martrou or Soubise, or enter Port de Plaisance in Basin No1 (access HW∓1), first basin on W bank: pontoon on N side of entrance for waiting. No 3 Basin, 2½ ca (400m) N, is for commercial craft only. The river is navigable to Tonnay-Charente.

NAVIGATION
Waypoint Les Palles N cardinal buoy, Q, 45°59'·58N 01°09'·53W, 293°/113° from/to front Ldg Lt 115°, 4·0M. Stream in river runs about 2 kn (4 kn in narrows), and at springs there is a bore. Beware wreck just S of first Ldg Line (115°). When WSW of Fouras pick up second (Port-des-Barques) Ldg Line (135°). The bar at Fouras carries about 0·5m. From Port-des-Barques follow the alignment of lettered pairs of Bns. There is a lifting bridge at Martrou, with moorings above and below it.

14

ROCHEFORT *continued*

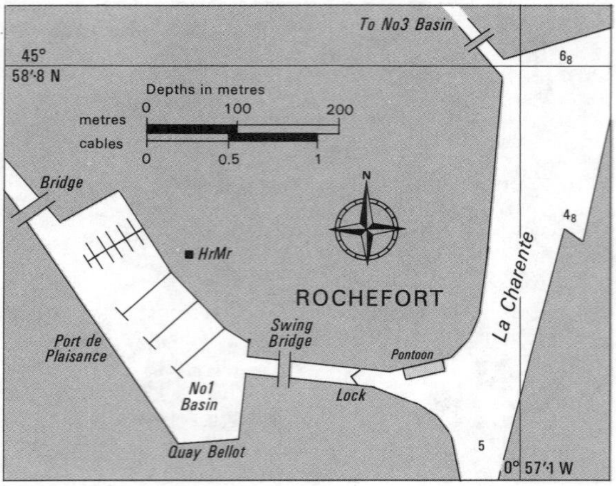
To No3 Basin
45°
58'8 N
Depths in metres
metres
cables
0 100 200
0 0.5 1
Bridge
HrMr
ROCHEFORT
La Charente
Swing Bridge
Port de Plaisance
No1 Basin
Pontoon
Lock
Quay Bellot
0° 57'1 W

LIGHTS AND MARKS
Ile d'Aix Fl WR 5s 24m 24/20M; twin W Trs with R tops; vis R103°-118°, W118°-103°. Ldg Lts 115°, both QR; W square Trs with R tops; intens 113°-117°. Port Sud de Fouras, pierhead, Fl WR 4s 6m, 9/6M; vis R117°-177°, W177°-117°. Port-des-Barques Ldg Lts 135°, both Iso G 4s; W square Trs; synchronised and intens 125°-145°.

RADIO TELEPHONE
VHF Ch 09 16. Yacht harbour CH 09 (HW∓1).

TELEPHONE (46)
Hr Mr 46.84.30.30; Aff Mar 46.84.22.67; CROSS 56.09.82.00; ⌗ 46.99.03.90; Meteo 46.41.29.14; Police 46.87.38.10; Dr 46.99.61.11; Brit Consul 56.52.28.35.

FACILITIES
Marina (180+20 visitors) ☎ 46.84.30.30, FW, ME, El, Sh, AC, C (30 ton); **Port Neuf** Slip, FW; **Club Nautique Rochefortais** ☎ 46.87.34.61 Slip; **Rochefort Marine** ☎ 46.87.52.08, ME, El, Ⓔ, Sh, CH; **Town** P, D, V, Gaz, R, Bar, ✉; Ⓑ; ⇌; ✈ (La Rochelle).
Ferry UK — Roscoff—Plymouth; St Malo—Portsmouth.

LA ROCHELLE 10-14-17

Charente Maritime

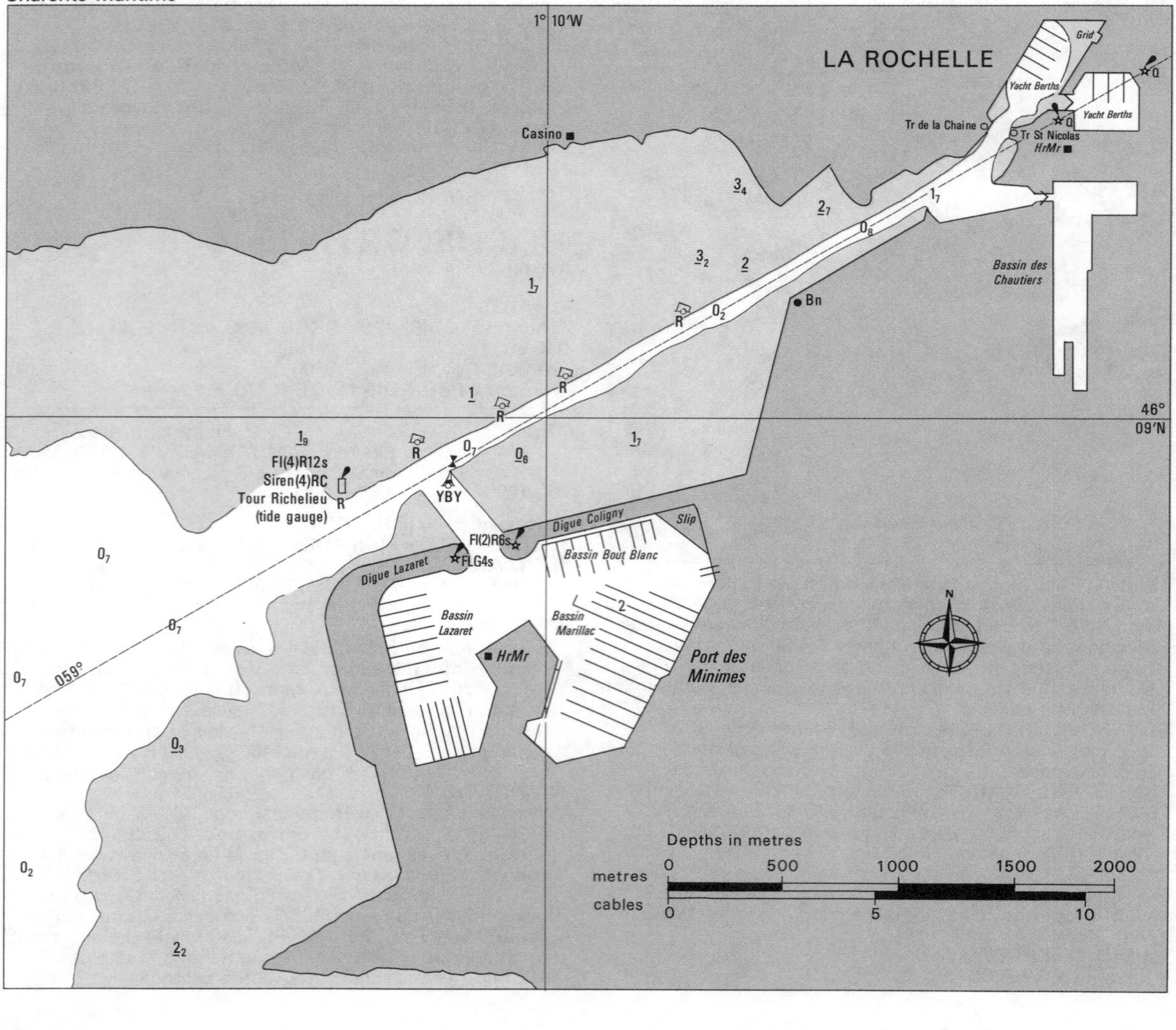
LA ROCHELLE
1° 10'W
Grid
Yacht Berths
Tr de la Chaine
Tr St Nicolas
HrMr
Casino
Bn
Bassin des Chautiers
46° 09'N
Fl(4)R12s
Siren(4)RC
Tour Richelieu
(tide gauge)
YBY
Fl(2)R6s
FlG4s
Digue Lazaret
Digue Coligny
Slip
Bassin Bout Blanc
Bassin Lazaret
Bassin Marillac
Port des Minimes
059°
Depths in metres
metres
cables
0 500 1000 1500 2000
0 5 10

LA ROCHELLE *continued*

CHARTS
Admiralty 2743, 2746, 2641; SHOM 6468, 6333; ECM 551, 1022

TIDES
+0515 Dover; ML 3·6; Zone −0100

Standard Port POINTE DE GRAVE (←)

Times				Height (metres)			
HW		LW		MHWS	MHWN	MLWN	MLWS
0000	0600	0500	1200	5·3	4·3	2·1	1·0
1200	1800	1700	2400				
Differences LA ROCHELLE							
+0005	−0035	−0020	−0015	+0·8	+0·6	+0·4	0·0
LA PALLICE							
+0005	−0035	−0020	−0015	+0·8	+0·6	+0·4	0·0

NOTE: La Pallice is the commercial port of La Rochelle and yachts are not welcome there, nor are any facilities provided. La Rochelle has two ports for yachts, La Rochelle-Ville and the Port des Minimes (a large marina).

SHELTER
La Rochelle-Ville harbour, in the old town, is entered between the two towers of St Nicolas and La Chaine. It has an outer basin (tidal), and an inner basin (non-tidal with depth of 3m) on the E side which is entered by a gate (open HW−2 to HW+½). In outer basin (100 berths), the first pontoon is reserved for fishing boats. Port des Minimes is a marina with a depth of 2m (max length 14m). All the above give excellent shelter. There is a water bus from Minimes to the town.

NAVIGATION
Waypoint Chauveau S cardinal buoy, VQ(6)+LFl 10s, Whis, 46°06'·63N 01°15'·98W, 240°/060° from/to Tour Richelieu, 4·6M. Approach from about 1M S of Le Lavardin Lt Tr on Ldg Line 059°. Drying rocks off Pte des Minimes (SW of marina) extend ¼M offshore. Tour Richelieu marks S extremity of rocks extending from N shore. Least depth in channel 0·2m. Just past Tour Richelieu (tide gauge for channel), entrance to Port des Minimes is marked by W cardinal buoy, and buoys mark NE side of channel to marina. For La Rochelle-Ville keep on 059° Ldg Line in channel marked by buoys on N side, least depth 0·2m.

LIGHTS AND MARKS
Ldg Lts 059°. Front Q 15m 14M (Fl 4s by day); R round Tr, W bands. Rear Q 25m 14M (Fl 4s by day); W octagonal Tr, G top; synchronised with front, obsc 061°-065° by St Nicolas Tr. Le Lavardin Fl(2) WG 6s 14m 11/8M; B Tr, R band; vis G160°-169°, W169°-160°. Tourelle Richelieu Fl(4)R 12s 10m 9M; R Tr; RC; Siren(4) 60s. Port des Minimes W Mole head FlG 4s, E Mole head Fl(2)R 6s.

RADIO TELEPHONE
La Pallice VHF Ch 12 16 (HW−2 to HW+1). Port des Minimes Ch 09 (H24).

TELEPHONE (46)
Port des Minimes Hr Mr 46.44.41.20, La Rochelle-Ville Hr Mr 46.41.68.73, Aff Mar 46.41.43.91, CROSS 56.09.82.00; # 46.42.64.64; Meteo 46.41.29.14; Auto 46.50.62.32; Police 46.34.67.55; Dr 46.42.19.22; Ⓗ 46.27.33.33; Brit Consul 56.52.28.35.

FACILITIES
PORT DES MINIMES **Marina** (2,800+250 visitors pontoons 14 and 15), ☎ 46.44.69.,86, Gaz, AC, Slip, C (10 ton), P, D, FW, BH (15 ton), R: (also control berths in wet dock in town); **Société des Regates Rochellaises** ☎ 46.44.62.44; **Atlantic Loisirs** ☎ 46.44.21.35, ME, Sh, CH, Ⓔ;**Atlanticoque** ☎ 46.41.39.26, ME, El, Sh, **Label Bleu** ☎ 46.45.10.54, ME, El, Sh, Ⓔ, CH; **Comptoir Maritime Rochelais** ☎ 46.44.34.97, ME, Sh, SHOM, El, Ⓔ, CH; **Fabre Marine** ☎ 46.41.33.25, El; **Proust** ☎ 46.44.13.66, ME, El, Sh, CH; **Pochon** ☎ 46.41.30.53, Ⓔ; **Accastillage Diffusion** ☎ 46.45.49.49, ME, El, Ⓔ, Sh, CH, SHOM; **Chantier Pinta** ☎ 46.44.40.70, ME, El, Sh; **La Rochelle Boat Centre** ☎ 46.45.42.72. ME, El, Sh, CH, Ⓔ; **Voile Système** ☎ 46.41.83.52, SM;

LA ROCHELLE-VILLE **Quay** Slip, FW, C (10 ton), SM, ME, Sh, CH; **Outer Basin** (100) ☎ 46.41.32.05 (3.8m) Access HW−2 to HW+½; **Town** P, D, V, Gaz, R, Bar, ✉; Ⓑ, ⇌; ✈.
Ferry to the Ile de Ré; internal air services from Laleu airport (2½km N of port).
Ferry UK — Roscoff—Plymouth; St Malo—Portsmouth.
Note: Bridge under construction between Pte de La Repentie (on mainland) and Pte de Sablanceaux (on Ile de Ré). Passage to/from Rade de La Pallice must be made N-bound between piles Nos 13 and 14, and S-bound between piles Nos 11 and 12. The passages are buoyed.

14

ST MARTIN, Ile de Ré 10-14-18

Charente Maritime

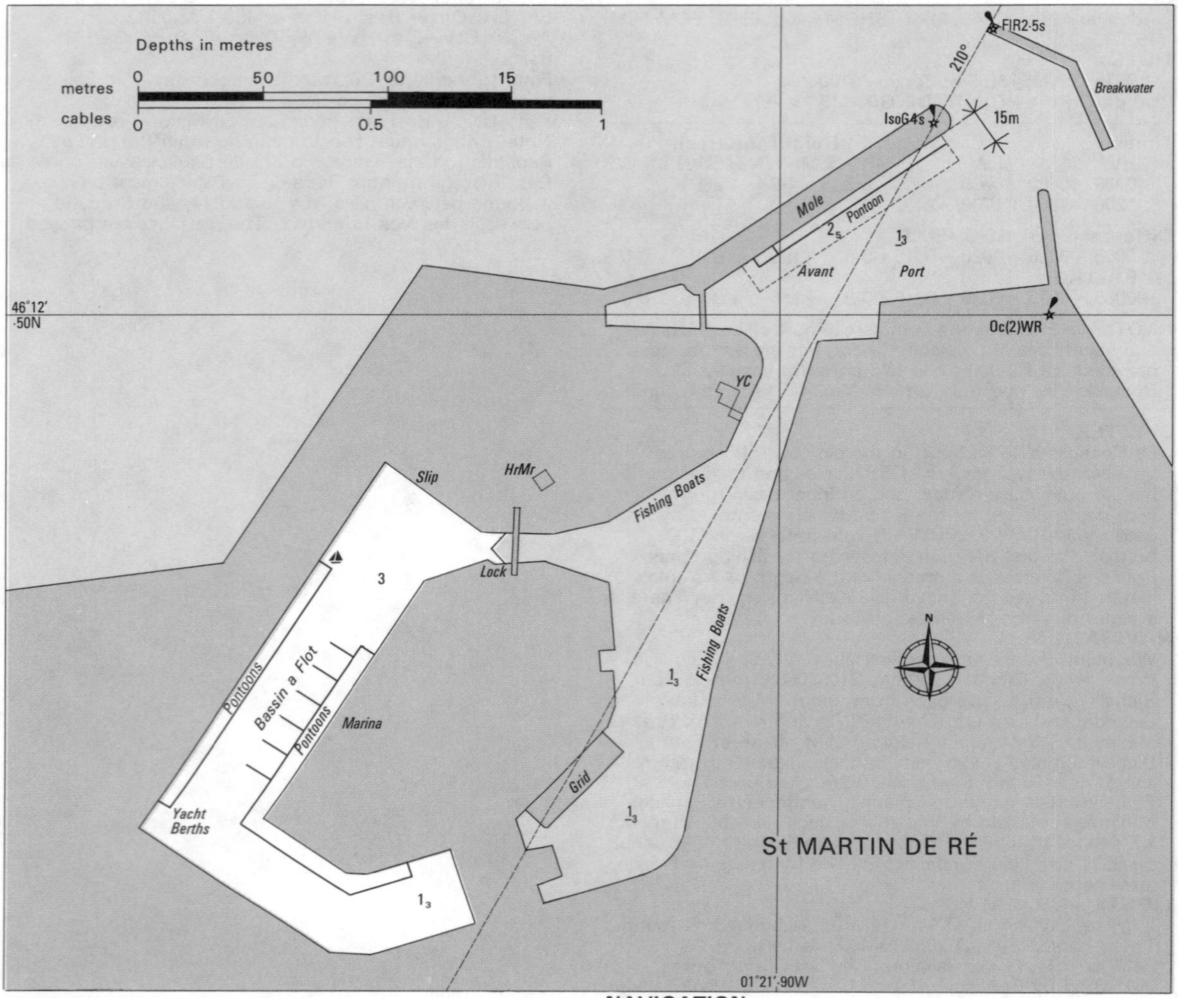
Depths in metres
metres
0
50
100
15
cables
0
0.5
1
FlR2·5s
210°
Breakwater
IsoG4s
15m
Mole
Pontoon
2₅
1₃
Avant
Port
46°12'
·50N
Oc(2)WR
YC
Slip
HrMr
Fishing Boats
Lock
3
Pontoons
Bassin a Flot
Pontoons
Marina
1₃
Fishing Boats
N
Grid
1₃
Yacht Berths
St MARTIN DE RÉ
1₃
01°21'·90W

CHARTS

Admiralty 2641, 2746; SHOM 6668, 6521; ECM 551

TIDES

+0535 Dover; ML 3·4; Zone −0100

Standard Port POINTE DE GRAVE (⟵)

Times				Height (metres)			
HW		LW		MHWS	MHWN	MLWN	MLWS
0000	0600	0500	1200	5·3	4·3	2·1	1·0
1200	1800	1700	2400				
Differences ST. MARTIN, Ile de Ré							
−0025	−0045	−0005	−0005	+0·8	+0·4	+0·1	−0·3

SHELTER

Approach channel dries 1·2m; access HW−3 to HW+1. Avant port protected by mole on W side, and break water to NE. This leads to drying basin where fishing boats lie. Wet dock (with marina) entered by gates which open about HW−1 to HW+1, with sill 0·8m above CD Complete shelter in wet dock (depth 3m), but often very crowded. Berthing instructions from Hr Mr. 15 m wide area inside NW mole dredged to 2·5m and pontoon provided. Four W mooring buoys for yachts awaiting this tide provided off entrance.

NAVIGATION

Waypoint Rocha N cardinal buoy, Q, 46°14'·75N 01°20'·80W, 020°/200° from/to St Martin mole head, 2·4M. Time arrival for dock gates opening. From the NW, pass N and E of Le Rocha, a rocky bank running 2½M ENE from Pte du Grouin. Approach with church Tr in transit with mole head Lt (202°). From SE, pass well N of Le Couronneau N cardinal Bn, about ¾M NE of entrance, marking a drying ledge in R sector of St Martin Lt (245°-281°).

LIGHTS AND MARKS

Ldg Line, church and Lt Ho in line 210°. NW of entrance Iso G 4s 10m 7M obscured by Pte de Loix when bearing less than 124°. SE of entrance, Oc(2)WR 6s 18m 10/7M W shore-245°, R245°-281°, W281°-shore.

RADIO TELEPHONE

VHF Ch 09 (0800-1900 LT in summer season).

TELEPHONE (46)

Hr Mr 46.09.26.69; Aff Mar 46.09.68.89; # 46.09.21.78; Meteo 46.41.29.14; Auto 46.50.62.32; CROSS 56.09.82.00; Police 46.09.21.17; Dr 46.09.20.08; Ⓗ 46.09.20.01; Brit Consul 56.52.28.35.

FACILITIES

Marina (135+50 visitors), P, D, FW, ME, El, Sh; **Garage du Port** ☎ 46.09.20.41, ME; **YC St Martin** ☎ 46.09.22.07; **Chantiers Naval** ☎ 46.09.21.06, ME, El, Ⓔ, Sh, CH, SHOM; **Quay** FW, C (4 ton); **Ré-Multiservices** ☎ 46.09.40.74, ME, El, Sh, CH. **Town** P, D, V, Gaz, R, Bar, ✉; Ⓑ; ⇌ (La Rochelle); ✈ (La Rochelle).

Ferry UK – Roscoff-Plymouth; St Malo-Portsmouth.

BOURGENAY 10-14-19

Vendee

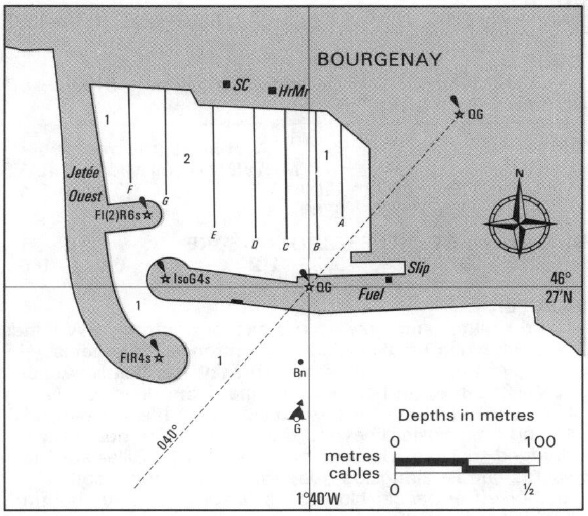
BOURGENAY
SC
HrMr
QG
1
2
1
Jetée
Ouest
F
G
Fl(2)R6s
E
D
C
B
A
N
Slip
IsoG4s
QG
Fuel
46°
27'N
1
FlR4s
1
Bn
G
040°
Depths in metres
0
100
metres
cables
0
½
1°40'W

CHARTS
Admiralty 2641; SHOM 6522; ECM 1022

TIDES
+0600 Dover; ML 3·1; Duration 0640; Zone −0100

Standard Port BREST (⟶)

Times				Height (metres)			
HW		LW		MHWS	MHWN	MLWN	MLWS
0500	1100	0500	1100	7·5	5·9	3·0	1·4
1700	2300	1700	2300				
Differences BOURGENAY							
−0030	+0015	−0035	−0030	−2·2	−1·7	−0·9	−0·6

SHELTER
Good shelter in the marina. In bad weather, especially with SW winds, a big swell can break at the entrance.

NAVIGATION
Waypoint 46°25′·40N, 01°41′·60W, 220°/040° from/to pierhead, 1·3M. Entrance channel leads 040° from safe water Lt Buoy to seaward of Roches de Joanne (which are dangerous in bad weather). Beware shallow patch to W of entrance, marked by stbd-hand Bn.

LIGHTS AND MARKS
Ldg Lts 040°, both QG 8M; G panels. Digue Ouest head Fl R 4s 9M; R structure. Mole E head Iso G 4s 5M; not vis to seaward. Breakwater elbow Fl (2) R 6s 5M, not vis to seaward.

RADIO TELEPHONE
VHF Ch 09 16 (office hours; in summer 0800-2100 LT).

TELEPHONE (51)
Hr Mr 51.22.20.36; Port Office 51.22.20.36; SNSM 51.22.20.36; CROSS 97.55.35.35; Auto 51.62.45.99; # 51.32.02.33; Aff Mar 51.21.01.80; Police 51.33.20.07; Dr 51.90.62.68; Ⓗ 51.21.86.33; Brit Consul 56.52.28.35.

FACILITIES
Marina (410+100 visitors) ☎ 51.22.20.36, Slip, FW, AC, C (15 ton), **Fuel Point** P, D; **Atlantica** ☎ 51.22.29.54 Ch; **Nauticea** ☎ 51.22.28.46 CH; **Super 2000** Gaz; **Bourgenay Nautique** ☎ 51.22.24.36, SM; **Association Nautique de Bourgenay** ☎ 51.22.27.11; **Town** R, ◙, C (15 ton), V, Bar, ✉; Ⓑ; ⥂ (Les Sables d'Olonne); ✈ (La Lande, Chateau d'Olonne).
Ferry UK — Roscoff—Plymouth; St. Malo—Portsmouth.

LES SABLES D'OLONNE 10-14-20

Vendee

CHARTS
Admiralty 3640, 2663; SHOM 6551, 6522, 6523; ECM 1022

TIDES
+0530 Dover; ML 3·1; Duration 0640; Zone −0100

Standard Port BREST (⟶)

Times				Height (metres)			
HW		LW		MHWS	MHWN	MLWN	MLWS
0500	1100	0500	1100	7·5	5·9	3·0	1·4
1700	2300	1700	2300				
Differences LES SABLES D'OLONNE							
−0030	+0015	−0035	−0030	−2·2	−1·7	−0·9	−0·6

SHELTER
Available at all states of tide, and entry is good except in winds from SE to SW when approaches get rough. There are two main channels — the navigation controlled (SW) channel with La Potence Lt bearing 033°, which leads into E channel on Ldg Line 320°. In bad weather use the E channel. Sailing is forbidden in the access channel to harbour. Visitors marina pontoons A, C, E and F. Access to basin forbidden to yachts. Access to Port Olona Marina H24. There are also 110 berths in harbour for yachts on passage.

NAVIGATION
Waypoint Nouch Sud S cardinal buoy, Q(6)+LFl 15s, 46°28′·63N 01°47′·43W, 220°/040° from/to front Ldg Lt 033°, 1·2M. To the W, beware Les Barges d'Olonne, extending 3M W from Pte de Aiguille. Le Noura and Le Nouch are two isolated rocks on shallow patches SSE of Jetée St Nicolas. Further SE, Barre Marine breaks, even in moderate weather. A buoyed wreck (dries) lies off harbour entrance, to E of 320° Ldg Line. From port to marina, dredged channel (2m) is on W side.

LIGHTS AND MARKS
SW passage Ldg Lts 033°. Front Iso R 4s 14m 16M. Rear, 330m from front, Iso R 4s 33m 16M; (both H24).
E passage Ldg Lts 320°. Front QG 11m 8M. Rear, 465m from front, Oc (2+1) 12s 33m 13M; RC. Port signals St Nicolas jetty head UQ(2)R 1s 16m 10M vis 094°-043°; Horn(2) 30s.

RADIO TELEPHONE
Port VHF Ch 16 12; 12 (HW−2 to HW+2). Marina Ch 09 16 (0600-2400 LT in season; 0800-2000 LT out of season and occasionally outside these times).

TELEPHONE (51)
Hr Mr Port de Plaisance 51.32.51.16; Aff Mar 51.21.01.80; CROSS 97.55.35.35; Meteo 51.36.10.78; Auto 51.62.45.99; # 51.32.02.33; SNSM 51.21.20.55; Police 51.32.69.91; Dr 51.95.14.47; Ⓗ 51.21.06.33; Brit Consul 56.52.28.35.

FACILITIES
Port Olona Marina (800+50 visitors), ☎ 51.32.51.16, Slip, P, D, FW, ME, El, AC, Sh, BH (27 ton), Access H24; **Plaisance 85** ☎ 51.95.07.38, ME, El, Sh, CH, BH (27 ton), Ⓔ; **Heriaud** ☎ 51.21.06.88, ME, El, Sh, CH; **Parisot Marine** ☎ 51.32.59.97, ME, CH; **Sablais Nautique** ☎ 51.32.62.16, ME, CH, El, Ⓔ, Sh, SHOM; **Voilerie Olane** ☎ 51.21.12.92 SM; **A. Masson** ☎ 51.32.01.07 Ⓔ; **Voilerie Tarot** ☎ 51.21.22.87 SM; **La Jeune Marine** ☎ 51.32.30.24 ME, El, CH, Divers, Ⓔ; **Espace Mer** ☎ 51.21.14.64 ME, El; **Compagnie Radio Marine** ☎ 51.32.07.73, Ⓔ, El; **Town** P, D, V, Gaz, R, Bar, ✉; Ⓑ; ⥂; ✈.
Ferry UK — Roscoff—Plymouth; St Malo—Portsmouth.

LA SABLES D'OLONNE *continued*

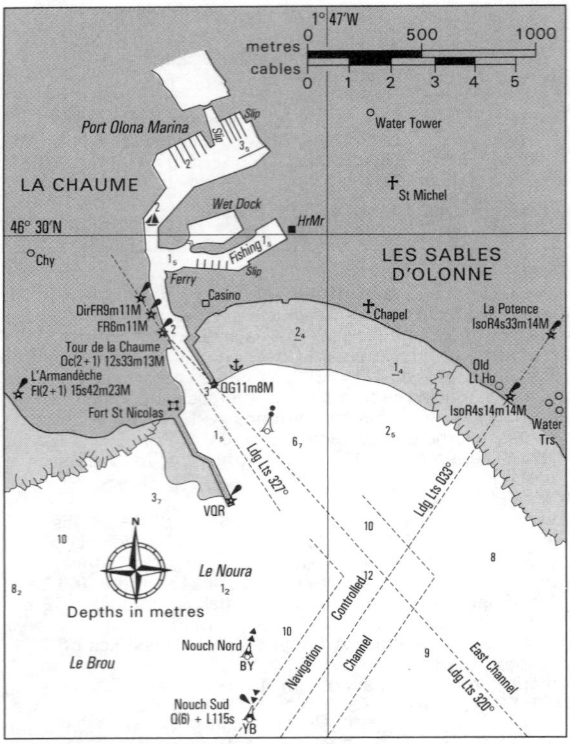
1° 47'W
0 500 1000
metres
cables
0 1 2 3 4 5
Port Olona Marina
Slip
Water Tower
LA CHAUME
St Michel
Wet Dock
HrMr
46° 30'N
Chy
Fishing
Slip
Ferry
LES SABLES D'OLONNE
Casino
Chapel
La Potence IsoR4s33m14M
DirFR9m11M
FR6m11M
Tour de la Chaume Oc(2+1) 12s33m13M
L'Armandèche Fl(2+1) 15s42m23M
QG11m8M
Old Lt Ho
Fort St Nicolas
IsoR4s14m14M
Water Trs
Ldg Lts 327°
Ldg Lts 033°
VQR
Le Noura
Depths in metres
Controlled
Navigation
Channel
East Channel
Ldg Lts 320°
Nouch Nord
BY
Le Brou
Nouch Sud Q(6) + L115s
YB

ST GILLES-CROIX-DE-VIE 10-14-2

Vendee

CHARTS

Admiralty 3640, 2663; SHOM 6613, 6853, 6523; ECM 1022, 549

TIDES

+0500 Dover; ML 3·1; Duration 0600; Zone −0100

Standard Port BREST (⟶)

Times				Height (metres)			
HW		LW		MHWS	MHWN	MLWN	MLWS
0500	1100	0500	1100	7·5	5·9	3·0	1·4
1700	2300	1700	2300				
Differences ST GILLES-CROIX-DE-VIE							
−0030	−0015	−0030	−0035	−2·2	−1·7	−0·9	−0·6

SHELTER

Good shelter, and easy access except in strong SW winds or swell when breakers form off entrance. Channel is dredged, but very shallow near breakwater heads. Access HW−2 to HW. In harbour, channel 1·5m deep. On N bank lie: – small yacht basin inside Grand Môle; two tidal fishing boat basins; beyond them the marina nominally dredged to 1·5m. Up river on E bank at St-Gilles-sur-Vie yachts can lie alongside quay (dries). In good weather anchor off entrance, close SE of leading line. Anchoring prohibited in channel.

NAVIGATION

Waypoint Pill'Hours S cardinal buoy, Q(6)+LFl 15s, Bell, 46°41'·10N 01°58'·33W, 233°/053° from/to Jetée de la Garenne Lt, 0·90M. Landmarks are Pte de Grosse-Terre (rocky headland) with Lt Ho, the rear Ldg Lt structure, two spires, and water towers round town. Beware Rocher Pill'Hours and drying reefs extending 1 ca (180m) SE. Tide runs strongly in entrance, particularly on ebb.

LIGHTS AND MARKS

Ldg Lts at 043°. Both Oc(3+1)R 12s 7/28m 13M; intens 033·5°-053·5° synchronized. Pointe de Grosse Terre Fl(4)WR 12s 25m 17/13M; vis W290°-125°, R125°-145°. SE Mole head QWG 8m 9/6M vis: G045°-335°, W335°-045°, Reed 20s. NW Mole head Fl(2)WR 6s 8m 10/7M; R045°-225°, W225°-045°.

RADIO TELEPHONE

VHF Ch 09 (season 0600-2200; out of season 0800-1200, 1400-1800 LT).

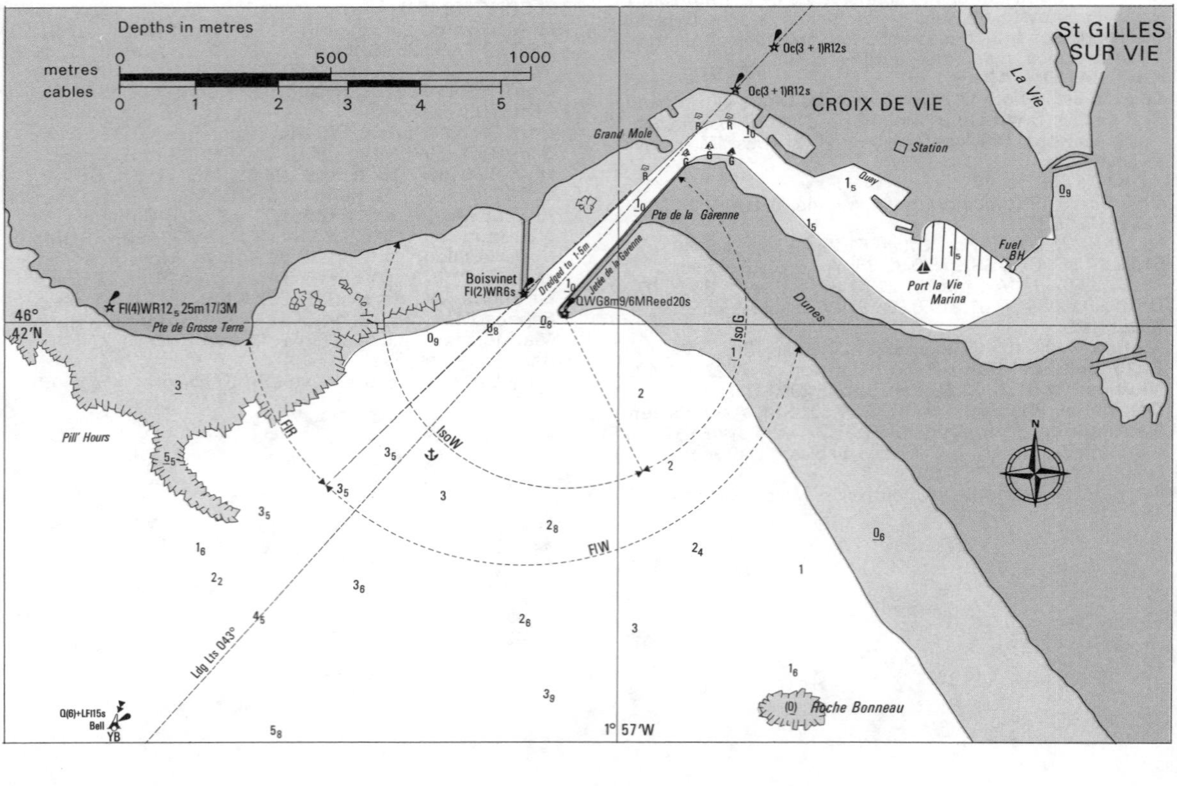
Depths in metres
0 500 1000
metres
cables
0 1 2 3 4 5
Oc(3+1)R12s
Oc(3+1)R12s
St GILLES SUR VIE
La Vie
CROIX DE VIE
Grand Mole
Station
Quay
Pte de la Garenne
Fuel BH
Port la Vie Marina
Boisvinet Fl(2)WR6s
Dredged to 1.5m
Jetée de la Garenne
QWG8m9/6MReed20s
Dunes
Fl(4)WR12s25m17/3M
46° 42'N
Pte de Grosse Terre
Iso G
Pill' Hours
FlR
IsoW
FlW
Ldg Lts 043°
Q(6)+LFl15s Bell
YB
1° 57'W
Roche Bonneau

ST GILLES-CROIX-DE-VIE *continued*

TELEPHONE (51)
Hr Mr Port de Plaisance 51.55.30.83; Aff Mar 51.55.10.58; # 51.55.10.58; CROSS 97.55.35.35; SNSM 51.55.01.19; Meteo 51.36.10.78; Auto 51.62.45.99; Police 51.55.01.19; Dr 51.55.11.93; Brit Consul 40.63.16.02.

FACILITIES
Port la Vie Marina (750+60 visitors) ☎ 51.55.30.83, Bar, CH, Gaz, R, SM, V, BH (26 ton), P, D, FW, ME, El, AC, Slip (Access H24); **Quay** Slip, FW, C (6 ton); **Force 5** ☎ 51.55.83.57 ME, El, Sh, CH; **Ship Shop** ☎ 51.54.24.14 ME, El, Ⓔ, Sh, CH; **Massif Marine** ☎ 51.55.45.17, ME, El, Ⓔ, Sh, CH, C (15 ton); **Cooperative Maritime des Marins-Pecheurs** ☎ 51.55.31.39, CH, SHOM; **Meca Marine** ☎ 51.55.42.93, ME, El, Sh, CH; **CN de Havre de Vie** ☎ 51.55.87.91; **BM Sails** ☎ 51.55.50.48, SM; **Transnav** ☎ 51.55.31.60, Ⓔ;
Town V, Gaz, R, Bar, ✉; Ⓑ; ⇌. There is a ferry to Ile d'Yeu.
Ferry UK — Roscoff—Plymouth; St Malo—Portsmouth.

ILE D'YEU 10-14-22
Vendee

CHARTS
Admiralty 3640, 2663; SHOM 6613, 6890, 6853; ECM 549

TIDES
+0550 Dover; ML 3·1; Duration 0600; Zone −0100

Standard Port BREST (⟶)

Times				Height (metres)			
HW		LW		MHWS	MHWN	MLWN	MLWS
0500	1100	0500	1100	7·5	5·9	3·0	1·4
1700	2300	1700	2300				
Differences PORT JOINVILLE (Ile d'Yeu)							
−0035	−0010	−0035	−0035	−2·2	−1·8	−0·9	−0·6

Although Port de la Meule is a fine weather small port (dries) on the S coast all information following refers to Port Joinville unless otherwise stated.

SHELTER
Swell runs in the entrance in winds from N to NE but shelter is good once in the marina in the NE part of the harbour. Marina gets very crowded mid-season. Yachts can anchor fore and aft (rafted together) between Gare Maritime and the ice factory, leaving room for commercial traffic to west. There is a mooring buoy SW of the ledge for yachts to use, in cluster moorings. Yachts can enter the wet basin Access HW∓1½, where there are no pontoons. Control lights R & G, just S of lock.

NAVIGATION
Waypoint Basse Mayence N cardinal buoy, 46°44′·65N 02°19′·10W, 055°/235° from/to breakwater Lt, 1·4M. Harbour gets very full in summer. Approach with care at LW. Beware Basse du Bouet 3ca (500m) NW, La Sablaire shoal to the E and rocks along the coast both sides of harbour entrance. Anchoring in outer harbour is prohibited. In the main harbour a forbidden zone is marked by R&W paint. At night keep in W sector of Dir Q WRG Lt.

LIGHTS AND MARKS
There is a conspic water tower behind the town; NW jetty head Oc(3)WG 12s 9m 11/9M; G shore-150°, W150°-232°, G232°-279°, W279°-285°, G285°-shore. Horn (3) 30s; tidal signals. Quai de Canada Ldg Lts 219°, Front QR 11m 6M; pylon; Rear (85m from front) QR 16m 6M; mast, both vis 169°-269°. Quai de Canada head Iso G 4s 7m 6M unintens 337°-067°. Galiote jetty root Fl(2)R 5s 1M.

RADIO TELEPHONE
Yacht Harbour VHF Ch 16 09 (office hours).

TELEPHONE (51)
Hr Mr 51.58.38.11; Harbour Office 51.58.51.10; Aff Mar 51.58.35.39; # 51.58.37.88, CROSS 97.55.35.35; Meteo 51.36.10.78; Auto 51.62.45.99; SNSM 51.58.35.39; Police 51.58.30.05; Dr 51.58.31.70; Ⓗ 51.68.30.23; Brit Consul 40.63.16.02.

FACILITIES
Marina (100+40 visitors), FW, AB, P, D, ME, El, Sh; **2nd Tidal Basin** ☎ 51.58.38.11, Slip, L, FW, C (5 ton); **Berlivet** ☎ 51.58.33.11, CH; **CN Ile d'Yeu** ☎ 51.58.31.50; **Comptoir Nautique** ☎ 51.58.73.40 ME, El, Sh, CH; **Oya Nautique** ☎ 51.58.73.40, ME, El, CH; **Poiraud** ☎ 51.58.50.69, ME; **Radio Maritime** ☎ 51.58.32.83, Ⓔ; **M. Naud Gilbert** ☎ 51.58.71.44, Gaz; **Town** V, Gaz, R, Bar, ✉; Ⓑ; ⇌ (St-Gilles-Croix-de-Vie); ✈ (Nantes). Flights to Nantes and (summers only) to Les Sables d'Olonne. (Airfield 2M westward).
Ferry UK — Roscoff—Plymouth; St Malo—Portsmouth.
Note: There are no cash telephones — Phone-cards available from PTT or at some tabacs and cafés.

14

ILE D'YEU *continued*

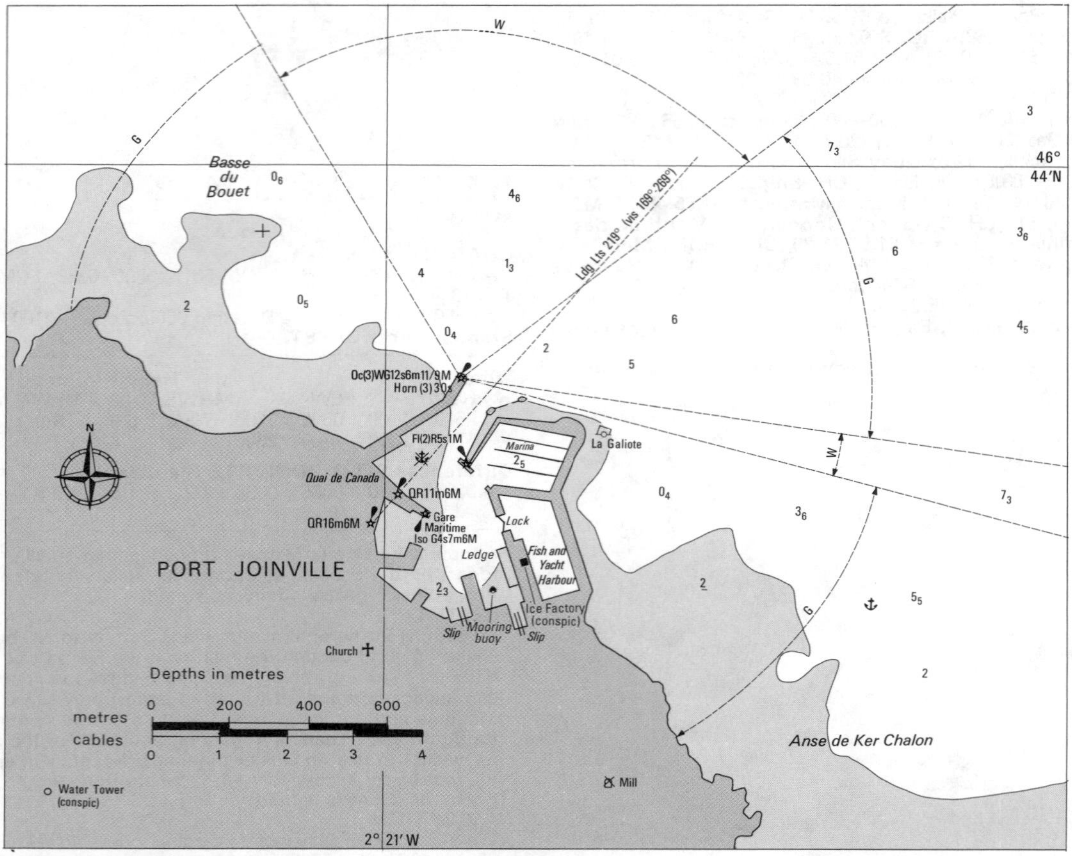
W
G
Basse du Bouet
46° 44′N
Ldg Lts 219° (vis 169°-269°)
Oc(3)WG12s6m11/9M Horn (3) 30s
Fl(2)R5s1M
Marina
La Galiote
Quai de Canada
QR11m6M
Gare Maritime Iso G4s7m6M
QR16m6M
Lock
Ledge
Fish and Yacht Harbour
PORT JOINVILLE
Slip
Mooring buoy
Ice Factory (conspic)
Church
Depths in metres
metres 0 200 400 600
cables 0 1 2 3 4
Water Tower (conspic)
Mill
Anse de Ker Chalon
2° 21′ W

ILE DE NOIRMOUTIER 10-14-23

Vendee

CHARTS
Admiralty 3216, 2646; SHOM 5039; ECM 549

TIDES
+0500 Dover; ML 2·8; Zone −0100

Standard Port BREST (→)

Times				Height (metres)			
HW		LW		MHWS	MHWN	MLWN	MLWS
0500	1100	0500	1100	7·5	5·9	3·0	1·4
1700	2300	1700	2300				
Differences BOIS DE LA CHAISE							
−0030	−0020	0000	−0005	−2·1	−1·9	−1·4	−1·0
FROMENTINE							
−0025	−0020	−0005	+0015	−2·2	−1·9	−1·3	−0·9

SHELTER
Anchor in Bois de la Chaise, exposed to N and E winds. Good shelter alongside in Noirmoutier-en-l'Ile but harbour dries 1·8m-2·4m, access HW∓1. L'Herbaudière comprises fishing harbour (W side) and marina (E side), dredged 2m-3m with good shelter. Visitors report to Pontoon F.

NAVIGATION
Waypoint Baie de Bourgneuf SN3 (safe water) buoy, LFl 10s, 47°06′·00N 02°21′·50W, 318°/138° from/to Basse du Martroger Lt Bn, 4·5M. Chaussée des Boeufs extends 3½M W and 6M SW of island, which is fringed by rocks and banks on N and E sides. W sector (187·5°-190°) of L'Herbaudière West breakwater Lt leads into entrance channel, dredged to 1·3m and passing close W of two 0·8m patches. W breakwater obscures vessels leaving. For Noirmoutier-en-l'Ile, a long channel marked by beacons leads through rocks. La Vendette is one of the highest parts of rocky ledges, E of entrance to Noirmoutier-en-l'Ile.
For Fosse de Fromentine see 10.14.25.

LIGHTS AND MARKS
Noirmoutier jetty Oc(2)R 6s 6m 7M; L'Herbaudière E jetty Fl(2)R 6s 8m 5M; W jetty Oc(2+1)WG 12s 9m 10/7M; W187·5°-190°, G elsewhere.

RADIO TELEPHONE
L'Herbaudière VHF Ch 09. (Hr Mr in working hours).

TELEPHONE (51)
Hr Mr (L'Herbaudière) 51.39.05.05; Aff Mar 51.39.01.64; SNSM 51.39.33.90; CROSS 97.55.35.35; Meteo 40.84.80.19; Auto 40.04.15.15; # 51.39.06.80; Police 51.39.04.36; Dr 51.39.05.64; Brit Consul 40.63.16.02.

FACILITIES
L'HERBAUDIÈRE. **Marina** (442+50 visitors), ☎ 51.39.05.05, P, D, AC, C (25 ton), Slip, FW, ME, V, SM, ⊡, R, Gas, Gaz, Bar (July, Aug), Sh, SC; **Quay** P, D, Bar, R, Gaz, ME, Sh, SM, V; **Gendron Plaisance** ☎ 51.39.18.69, ME, C, El, Ⓔ, Sh, CH; **Gendron Yvon** ☎ 51.39.12.06, ME; **Massif Marine** ☎ 51.39.05.86, ME, C, El, Ⓔ, Sh, CH, Gaz; **Voilerie Burgaud** ☎ 51.39.23.89, SM; **Voilerie Simonin** ☎ 51.39.41.87, SM.
NOIRMOUTIER. **Quay** FW, C (4 ton); **Nautique 85** ☎ 51.39.05.78, ME, El, Ⓔ, Sh, CH; **Quincaillerie de la Mer** ☎ 51.39.47.67, CH; **Voilerie Burgaud** ☎ 51.39.12.66, SM.
Town P, D, V, Gaz, R, Bar, ⊡, ✉; Ⓑ; ⇌ (ferry to Pornic, bus to Nantes); ✈ (Nantes).
Ferry UK — Roscoff—Plymouth; St Malo—Portsmouth.

ILE DE NOIRMOUTIER *continued*

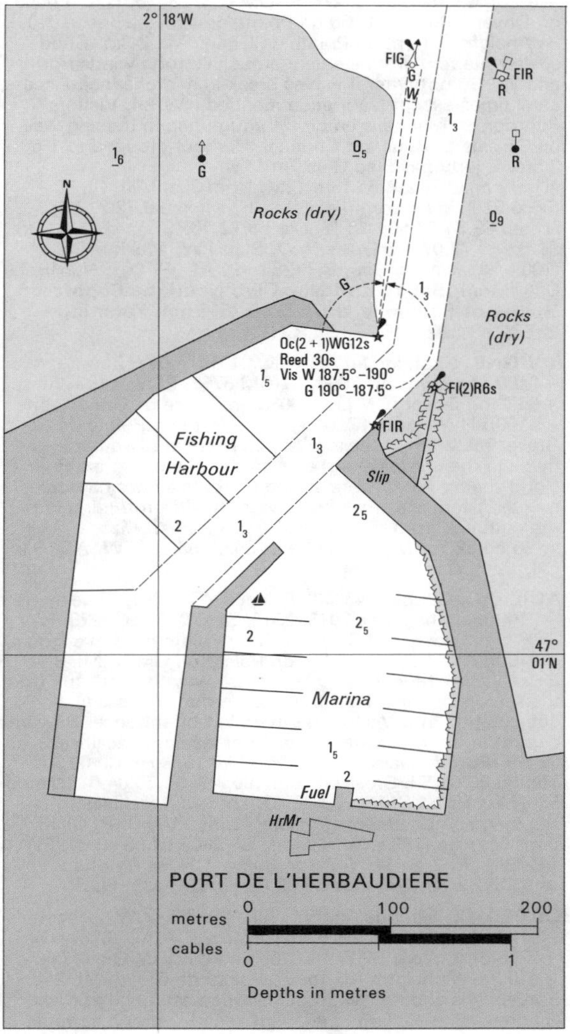
2° 18'W
FlG
G
W
FlR
R
Rocks (dry)
Rocks (dry)
Oc(2 + 1)WG12s
Reed 30s
Vis W 187·5°–190°
G 190°–187·5°
Fl(2)R6s
FlR
Fishing Harbour
Slip
Marina
Fuel
HrMr
47° 01'N
PORT DE L'HERBAUDIERE
metres
cables
Depths in metres

PORNIC 10-14-24

Loire Atlantique

CHARTS
Admiralty 3216, 2646; SHOM 5039, 6854, 6825; ECM 549

TIDES
+0515 Dover; ML 2·9; Duration 0540; Zone −0100

Standard Port BREST (⟶)

Times				Height (metres)			
HW		LW		MHWS	MHWN	MLWN	MLWS
0500	1100	0500	1100	7·5	5·9	3·0	1·4
1700	2300	1700	2300				
Differences PORNIC							
−0035	−0015	+0005	+0005	−2·1	−1·9	−1·4	−1·1

SHELTER
Very good shelter in the large Pornic-Noëveilland marina, P1, P2 and P3 pontoons reserved for visitors. Old harbour dries (1·8m); access HW∓2½. Entry dangerous in strong winds from SE to W. Marina Access HW∓5.

NAVIGATION
Waypoint Notre Dame Bn, isolated danger mark, 47°05'·49N 02°08'·20W, 227°/047° from/to jetty head, 1·5M. Beware Banc de Kerouars in N of bay; all other hazards are well marked. There is an exit to the S (possible HW∓1 near springs) but a drying causeway joins Ile de Noirmoutier to the mainland. The S end of bay is devoted to oyster beds, and there are many obstructions.

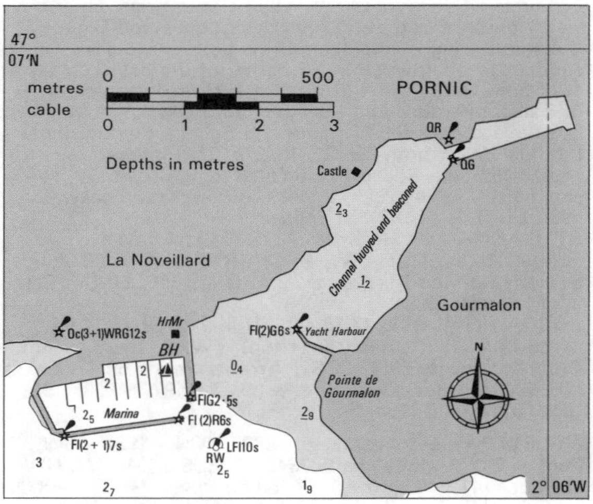
47° 07'N
metres
cable
Depths in metres
PORNIC
QR
QG
Castle
Channel buoyed and beaconed
La Noveillard
Gourmalon
Oc(3+1)WRG12s
HrMr
BH
Fl(2)G6s
Yacht Harbour
Pointe de Gourmalon
FlG2·5s
Marina
Fl(2)R6s
Fl(2 + 1)7s
LFl10s
RW
2° 06'W

LIGHTS AND MARKS
Marina SW elbow Fl(2+1) 7s 4m 3M; SW jetty head Fl(2)R 6s 4m 4M; E jetty head FlG 2·5s 4m 2M; Pointe de Noëveilland Oc(3+1)WRG 12s 22m 13/9M; G shore-051°, W051°-079°, R079°-shore. Entry signals (simplified).

RADIO TELEPHONE
VHF Ch 09 (H24).

TELEPHONE (40)
Hr Mr 40.82.01,51; Aff Mar 40.82.01.69; # 40.82.03.17; SNSM 40.82.01.54; Auto 40.04.15.15; CROSS 97.55.35.35; Police 40.82.00.29; Dr 40.82.01.80; Brit Consul 40.63.16.02.

FACILITIES
Port-la-Noëveillard Marina (750+165 visitors) ☎ 40.82.01.51, P, D (on pontoon), FW, ME, AC, El, Sh, BH (20 ton), C (6 ton) CH; **CN de Pornic** ☎ 40.82.42.26; **Pornic Nautic** ☎ 40.82.04.64, ME, El, Ⓔ, Sh, CH; **MEP** ☎ 40.82.52.60 ME, El, Sh, Ⓔ; **Copart Nautique** ☎ 40.82.12.10 ME, El, Sh, CH, Ⓔ, CH; **Town** V, Gaz, R, Bar, ✉; Ⓑ; ⇌; ✈ (Nantes).
Ferry UK — Roscoff—Plymouth; St Malo—Portsmouth.

MINOR HARBOURS AND ANCHORAGES 10.14.25

HENDAYE, Pyrénées Atlantique, 43°22′·00N, 01°47′·00W, Zone −0100; Admty charts 1343, 2665, SHOM 6556, 6558. HW +0450 on Dover (GMT), −0030 on Pointe de Grave (zone −0100). HW height −1·1m on Pointe de Grave, ML 2·3m. Hendaye lies on the French bank of the Rio Bidasoa, the other bank being Fuenterrabia in Spain. Access to river HW∓3. Beware Les Briquets lying to the E of the bay. Lt Ho on W end of bay, Cabo Higuer, Fl(2) 60s 63m 23M. River ent breakwater heads, East L Fl R 10s 7m 8M, West FG 9m 4M. River dredged to 2m. Yacht anchorage 1 ca (185m) SW of landing place at Hendaye Plage in 3·5m, or in about 3m off Roca Punta at root of W breakwater, or S of Hendaye quay. Much of bay dries. Facilities: Hr Mr ☎ 59.20.16.97; ⋕ ☎ 59.20.01.98; Aff Mar 59.55.06.68; **Quay** C (20 ton), D, FW; **Club Maritime Hendaye** ☎ 59.20.03.02, VHF Ch 09, P, C (20 ton); **Jabin** ☎ 59.20.08.96, ME, CH; **Comption Marina Basque** ☎ 59.20.22.14 CH, Ⓔ; **Town** V, R, Bar, ✉; Ⓑ; ≹; ✈.

ST JEAN-DE-LUZ, Pyrénées Atlantique, 43°23′·00N, 01°40′·00W, Zone −0100; Admty chart 1343, SHOM 6526, 6558. HW +0435 on Dover (GMT), −0045 on Pointe de Grave (zone −0100); HW height −1·0m on Pointe de Grave; ML 2·5m. There are two harbours, St Jean-de-Luz on SE of bay and Socoa to the W of the bay. Approaching from N, keep W of Les Esquilletac, a rock ½M off Pointe St Barbe. The bay can be entered at all times except in strong NW winds, and good anchorage found in approx 4m. There is a small yacht harbour in SW corner of St Jean-de-Luz. Socoa harbour dries. Enter bay via W passage between Digue des Criquas and Digue d'Artha. Sailing is forbidden in the port. Beware a submerged obstruction in SE corner of the bay. Ldg Lts at 101° both Oc(3+1)R 12s 30/47m 18M lead in from W, S of Belhara Perdun. Ldg Lts 138° Front QWR 12/8M, Rear Q 20M lead between Illarguita and Belhara Perdun. Inner Ldg Lts 158·7° both Dir QG 18/27m 16M intens 149·7°-152°. Le Socoa Lt Ho QWR 36m 12/8M, W shore-264°, R264°-282°, W282°-264°. Socoa breakwater head Iso G 4s 11m 7M. Facilities:
ST JEAN-DE-LUZ Hr Mr ☎ 59.26.26.81; Aff Mar ☎ 59.47.14.55; **Quay** FW, P, C; **CRM** ☎ 59.47.05.85 Ⓔ; **Stream Service Marine** ☎ 59.47.05.85 ME, El, Sh, CH, Ⓔ, Meteo 59.23.84.15.
SOCOA Hr Mr ☎ 59.47.18.44; Aff Mar ☎ 59.47.14.55; ⋕ ☎ 59.47.18.61; **Jetty** C (1 ton), FW, P, D, AC; **Yacht Club Basque** ☎ 59.47.26.81; **Arrantzalat** ☎ 59.47.02.02, ME, CH; **Larmanou-Marine** ☎ 59.47.99.97, ME, El, Sh, CH: **Town** V, R, Bar, ✉; Ⓑ; ≹.

ANGLET, Pyrénées Atlantique, 43°32′·00N, 01°31′·00W, Zone −0100; Admty charts 1343, 2665, SHOM 6571. HW at Boucau (1½M up river) +0450 on Dover (GMT), −0035 on Pointe de Grave (zone −0100); HW height −1·0m on Pointe de Grave; ML 2·6m. Access good except in strong winds from SW to NW when entry may be impracticable. Tidal stream is strong, up to 5 kn on ebb at springs. The marina is on the S side ¾M from ent to R Adour. There are yacht moorings W of marina ent. Pointe St Martin Fl(2) 10s 73m 29M is approx 2½M SSW of ent. BA buoy (safe water mark) L Fl 10s is moored 9 ca (1650m) NW of breakwater head which has QR Lt. Ldg Lts 090°, both Q intens 087°-093°, W Trs with R tops. N jetty head Oc(2)R 6s 12m 8M. S jetty head Iso G 4s 9m 7M. Inner Ldg Lts approx 111°, both FG moved as necessary. Traffic signals (full code, see 10.14.7) shown from Tr S of entrance. Marina VHF Ch 09. Facilities: Hr Mr ☎ 59.63.05.45; Aff Mar and ⋕ at Bayonne; Meteo 59.23.84.15; **Marina** (390+10 visitors), ☎ 59.63.05.45; P, D, FW, ME, El, AC, C (1·3 ton), BH (13 ton), Slip, Sh; **YC Adour Atlantique** ☎ 59.63.16.22, **Nivadour Nautique** ☎ 59.63.16.85, ME, El, Sh, CH, Ⓔ.

BAYONNE, Pyrénées Atlantique, 43°30′·00N, 01°29′·00W, Zone −0100; Admty chart 1343, SHOM 6536, 6557/8. Details of tides, entry lights etc are as shown under Anglet above. Bayonne is 3M upstream from Anglet, the channel being well marked with Ldg Lts, buoys and beacons. There are numerous commercial wharves. Yachts berth on S bank below the bridge near town hall where R Nive joins the R Adour. VHF Ch 09 12 (H24); Facilities: Hr Mr ☎ 59.63.11.57; Aff Mar ☎ 59.55.06.68; ⋕ ☎ 59.59.08.29; **Port** C (30 ton), Slip, FW, P, D; **Club Nautique de Bayonne**; **Sorin** ☎ 59.59.16.87, CH, SHOM.

CAPBRETON, Landes, 43°39′·00N, 01°26′·00W, Zone −0100; Admty chart 2665, SHOM 6557, 6586. HW +0450 on Dover (GMT), −0030 on Pointe de Grave (zone −0100); HW height −1·1m on Pointe de Grave, ML 2·3m. Good shelter, narrow entrance dangerous in strong winds from N and W. Do not enter if waves break in mid-channel. Access at all times except LW; recommended HW∓4. Visitors Pontoon B. Marina is entered through gap in training wall on SE side of Boucaret Channel. Harbour dredged to 1·5 to 2·5m. S jetty head Iso G 4s 7m 11M.
N jetty head Fl(2)R 6s 13m 12M, Horn 30s. VHF Ch 09 (0600-2200 in season). Facilities: Hr Mr ☎ 58.72.21.23; Meteo 89.24.58.80; Aff Mar ☎ 58.72.10.43; ⋕ ☎ 58.72.07.47; **Quay** P, D, Slip, FW; **Marina** (700+70 visitors), Slip, BH (28 ton), AC, P, D, FW, ME, El, C (1.5 ton), Sh; **YC Landais**; **Club Nautique Capbreton-Hossegor-Seignone** ☎ 58.72.05.25; **Erick Yachting** ☎ 58.72.14.32, ME, El, Sh, CH, Ⓔ.

LA VIGNE, Gironde, 44°40′·00N, 01°14′·00W; Zone −0100. Admty chart 2664, SHOM 6766, ECM 255. HW +0620 on Dover (GMT); +0030 on Pointe de Grave (zone −0100); HW height (Cap Ferret) −1·1m on Pointe de Grave; ML 2·3m. Access HW∓2. There are two perches marking the entrance and a Lt on the SW point, Iso R 4s. Good shelter but beware strong currents across harbour mouth. There is a small breakwater (unlit) protruding into the entrance from the NE side. Facilities: Aff Mar ☎ 56.60.52.76, **Marina** (268) ☎ 56.60.85.80, FW, AC, Slip, CH, C, P, D.

PAUILLAC, Gironde, 45°12′·00N, 00°45′·00W, Zone −0100; Admty charts 2916, 2910; SHOM 7029, 7028; HW +0620 on Dover (GMT), +0045 on Pointe de Grave (zone −0100); HW height +0·2m on Pointe de Grave; ML 3·0m. Excellent shelter in marina about half way to Bordeaux from the sea on W bank, 25M from Le Verdon. Access at all tides (depth 3m). Visitors berth on left of entrance. Beware current in the river when entering or leaving. Facilities: Hr Mr (Port de Plaisance) ☎ 56.59.12.16, VHF Ch 09 Aff Mar 56.59.01.58; Cross 56.09.82.00; ⋕ 56.59.04.01; Meteo 56.34.20.11; SNSM 56.09.82.00. There are facilities for stepping and un-stepping masts; **Quay** FW, D, P, C (15 ton); **Marina** (185+15 visitors), ☎ 56.59.04.53, P, D, FW, AC, Slip, ME, El, Sh; fuel (on quay); **CN de Pauillac** ☎ 56.59.12.58; **Guiet** ☎ 56.59.02.66, CH, ME, El, Sh.

BORDEAUX, Gironde, 44°50′·00N, 00°34′·00W, Zone −0100; Admty chart 2916, SHOM 7029, 7030, 7028. HW +0715 on Dover (GMT), +0155 on Pointe de Grave (zone −0100); HW height −0·1m on Pointe de Grave; ML 2·4m. Bordeaux is about 55M up the Gironde estuary and River Garonne. Beware large merchant vessels, strong currents (up to 5 kn when river in spate) and large bits of flotsam. Point du Jour marina is 2M from Bordeaux, on W bank just S of suspension bridge (Pont d'Aquitaine, clearance 51m), with visitors berths and crane for masts. Moorings may be available just upstream. No 1 Basin, 1½M above bridge, access HW−2 to HW+½, may be dirty; crane available. Or go alongside wharves between No 1 Basin and Pont de Pierre, but stream is strong. The channel up to Bordeaux is well marked and lit. VHF Ch 12. Facilities: Hr Mr ☎ 56.90.58.00; Aff Mar ☎ 56.52.26.23; ⋕ ☎ 56.44.47.10; Meteo 56.90.91.21; **Sport Nautique de la Gironde** ☎ 56.50.84.14; **Cercle de la Voile de Bordeaux**; **Agence Nautique du Sud Ouest** ☎ 56.91.23.83, ME, El, Sh, CH; **Le Compas** ☎ 56.50.60.02, ME, El, Sh, CH, Ⓔ; **Poitevin-Duault** ☎ 56.52.55.50, CH, Ⓔ, SHOM; **Quay** Slip, C (5 ton).

BLAYE, Charente Maritime, 45°07′·00N, 00°40′·00W, Zone −0100, Admty chart 2916, SHOM 7029, 7028. HW +0175 on Dover (GMT), +0145 on Pointe de Grave (zone −0100); HW height −0·3m on Pointe de Grave; ML 2·4m. Good shelter; access good except in winds S to SW. Entrance to NE of Ile du Paté, marked by Lt Fl G on S bank. Max stay 24 hours. VHF Ch 12 (H24). Facilities: Hr Mr ☎ 57.42.13.49; ⋕ ☎ 57.42.01.11. **Quay** FW, AC, P, D, C (25 ton), Slip, Access HW∓2½; **Auxemerry** ☎ 57.42.13.43, ME; **A. Moulinier** ☎ 57.42.11.94, ME.

MINOR HARBOURS *continued*

DOUHET, Ile d'Oleron, Charente Maritime, 46°00′·00N, 01°20′·00W, Zone −0100; Admty chart 2746, SHOM 6334. HW +0545 on Dover (GMT) −0020 on Pointe de Grave (zone −0100); HW height +0.8m on Pointe de Grave; ML 3.7m. In the NE part of the island, access approx HW∓4. There are no lights. Beware rocks E and W of ent channel. Yacht harbour in wet dock, 1.5m. Max length 7m. Facilities: Hr Mr 46.76.71.13, Auto 46.41.11.11; Aff Mar and # – Le Chateau; Marina (350) FW, AC Slip Access HW∓2½; **Geron** ☎ 46.76.53.96 ME, El, Ⓔ, Sh, CH; **Quay** FW, AB, Slip. Correspondence with Hr Mr Boyardville.

ILE D'AIX, Charente Maritime, 46°01′·00N, 01°10′·00W, Zone −0100; Admty charts 2746, 2748, SHOM 6914, 6334. HW +0545 on Dover (GMT), −0020 on Pointe de Grave (zone −0100); HW height +0·8m on Pointe de Grave; ML 3·7m. Only a fine weather anchorage; anchor or pick up a buoy off the landing jetty at St Catherine's Point, the most southerly tip of the island. Lt on the point is FlWR 5s 24m 24/20M. Mooring available E of St Catherine's Pt (shallow), four W buoys to West of St Catherine's Pt (deeper) and another four SE of the point. Facilities: C (1·5 ton), Slip, AB (SE jetty), shop and restaurant.

PORT D'ANTIOCHE (Port St Denis), Ile d'Oleron, 46°02′·00N, 01°22′·00W zone−0100. Admty charts 2746, 2748. SHOM 6334, 6914. HW+0545 on Dover (GMT); as for Rochefort (zone−0100). HW height +1·0m on Pointe de Grave. ML 3·8m. Easy entrance. Conspic mark – tower of St Denis; keep at 260°. Light 2FR (west) on jetty. VHF Ch 09. Depth in basin 1·5m. Capacity 600 plus 50 for visitors. Hr Mr 46.47.97.97. (0800–2000) in season. Port de Plaisance ☎ 46.47.24.68, Slip, FW, AC. Yacht Club de l'Ocean ☎ 46.47.93.64, open all year. **Barbancon** ☎ 46.47.86.80 ME.

LA FLOTTE, Ile de Ré, Charente Maritime, 46°11′·00N, 01°19′·00W, Zone −0100; Admty charts 2641, 2746, SHOM 6668, 6521. HW +0535 on Dover (GMT), −0025 on Pointe de Grave (zone −0100); HW height +0·6m on Pointe de Grave; ML 3·4m. La Flotte lies 2M SE of St Martin (see 10.14.17). From NW keep clear of Le Couronneau; from E, keep N of Bn off Pointe des Barres. Approach with La Flotte Lt Ho (W Tr with G top) bearing 215° in W sector. La Flotte Lt Fl WG 4s 10m 12/9M; vis G130°-205°, W205°-220°, G220°-257°, Horn (3)30s by day HW−2 to HW+2. Avant port is sheltered by mole and dries (2·4m); inner harbour dries (2·7m). Access HW∓3. There is an anchorage off La Flotte in 3m, sheltered from S and W. Facilities: Visitors use North Jetty; Hr Mr on Quai Senac Ouest; Aff Mar and # at St Martin; **Quay** Slip, FW; **Cercle Nautique de la Flotte-en-Ré** (CNLF) (open July-15 Sept); **Chauffour** ☎ 46.09.60.25, ME.

ARS-EN-RÉ, Ile de Ré, Charente Maritime, 46°12′·00N, 01°31′·00W, Zone −0100; Admty chart 2641, SHOM 6521, 6334 HW +0540 on Dover (GMT), −0045 on Pointe de Grave (zone −0100); HW height +0·6m; ML 3·4m. Port d'Ars is at the head of a creek in the SW corner of the bay Mer du Fier, the entrance obstructed by rocks which dry. Channel through Mer du Fier marked by buoys and bns; Access HW∓3. There are two quays (dry) and a wet dock with sill gate, 2·9m above CD. Ldg Lts to Fiers d'Ars 265°, Front Iso 4s 5m 11M W square on hut; vis 141°-025°. Rear 370m from front, Dir Iso G 4s 13m 15m, G square Tr on dwelling (synchronised with front and intens 264°-266°). Port d'Ars Ldg Lts 232°, front Q 5m 9M, W rectangle with R lantern, rear 370m from front, Q 13m 11M, B rectangle on W framework Tr, G top; vis 142°-322°. There is an anchorage close S of Pte du Fier with min depth of 2·4m; most of the bay dries. VHF Ch 09. Facilities: Hr Mr ☎ 46.29.40.19, Aff Mar and # at St Martin (see 10.14.18); SNSM ☎ 46.29.41.49; **Cercle Nautique d'Ars-en-Ré** ☎ 46.29.41.13 (open Apl to Nov); **Blanchard** ☎ 46.29.40.43, ME, El, Sh; **Blondeau Marine** ☎ 46.29.40.39, ME; **Jetties** Slip, FW, C (6 ton).

L'AIGUILLON-LA-FAUTE-SUR-MER, Vendée, 46°20′·00N, 01°18′·00W, Zone −0100; Admty charts 2641, 2663, SHOM 6521. HW +0535 on Dover (GMT), −0030 on Pointe de Grave (zone −0100); HW height +0·6m on Pointe de Grave; ML 3·4m. Shelter good except in strong winds from W or S; entry only safe in fine weather with off-shore winds. Access HW∓2½. Beware mussel bed timber piers which cover at HW. Also beware oyster beds. The area is very flat and, being shallow, waves build up quickly in any wind. The bar to seaward dries and is dangerous in bad weather. Entrance can be identified by a hill, La Dive, opposite side of entrance to Pointe d'Arcay, with a conspic transformer on it. Enter with transformer bearing 033°. Anchor in R Lay or go alongside on YC pontoons, (40). Facilities: Hr Mr ☎ 51.56.45.02 Aff Mar ☎ 51.56.45.35; CROSS 56.09.82.00; Dr ☎ 51.56.46.17; **Club Nautique Aiguillonais et Fautais** (CNAF) open July-Sept; ☎ 51.56.44.42; **Groisard-Hériaud** ☎ 51.97.08.73 ME; **Co-operative Maritimes** ☎ 51.56.44.89, CH.

JARD-SUR-MER, Vendee, 46°24′·00N, 01°35′·00W, Zone −0100; Admty charts 2641, 2663, SHOM 6522. HW +0600 on Dover (GMT), −0010 on Brest (zone −0100); HW height −2·0m on Brest; ML 3·1m; Duration 0640. White daymarks 4 ca (740m) E of harbour lead 038° between Roches de l'Islatte (dry) and Roches de la Brunette (dry), marked by buoys. Then pick up 293° transit of RW marks on W side of harbour, leading to entrance. There are no lights. Facilities: Hr Mr ☎ 51.33.40.17; # ☎ 51.95.11.33; **Jetty** FW, C (5 ton); **Jard Marine** ☎ 51.33.46.84, CH; **Morineau** ☎ 51.33.42.05 Divers.

FROMENTINE, Vendée, 46°54′·00N, 02°08′·00W, Zone −0100; Admty chart 2646, SHOM 5039, 6853. HW +0550 on Dover (GMT), −0025 on Brest (zone −0100); HW height −2·1m on Brest; ML 2·9m; Duration 0540. Do not approach from Baie de Bourgneuf as there is a road causeway which dries 3m, connecting Ile de Noirmoutier with the mainland. Enter through Goulet de Fromentine, under the bridge (clearance 27m). The channel is marked by buoys, moved as necessary but it is very shallow, so dangerous in bad weather. The ebb stream runs at more than 5 kn at springs. Do not attempt night entry. Anchor W of pier. Coming from N, beware Les Boeufs. Tourelle Milieu lies on the N side of Le Goulet de Fromentine, Fl(4)R 12s 6m 5M, R Tr. Pointe de Notre Dames-de-Monts Lt Oc(2)WRG 6s 21m 13/10M, G000°-043°, W043°-063°, R063°-073°, W073°-094°, G094°-113°, W113°-116°, R116°-175°, G175°-196°, R196°-230°. Fromentine light-buoy (safe water mark) 46°53′.1N, 2°11′.5W Fl 10s Bell is about 1.5M WSW of Pointe du Notre Dames-de-Monts. Bridge W end Iso W 4s 32m 18M; E end Iso W 4s 32m 18M. Facilities: Aff Mar at Noirmoutier; # at Beauvois-sur-Mer; **Quay** Slip, C (3 ton), FW; **Cercle Nautique de Fromentine-Barfatre** (CNFB); **Marine Motoculture** ☎ 51.68.53.77, ME, El, Sh, CH;

Area 15

South Brittany
River Loire to Camaret

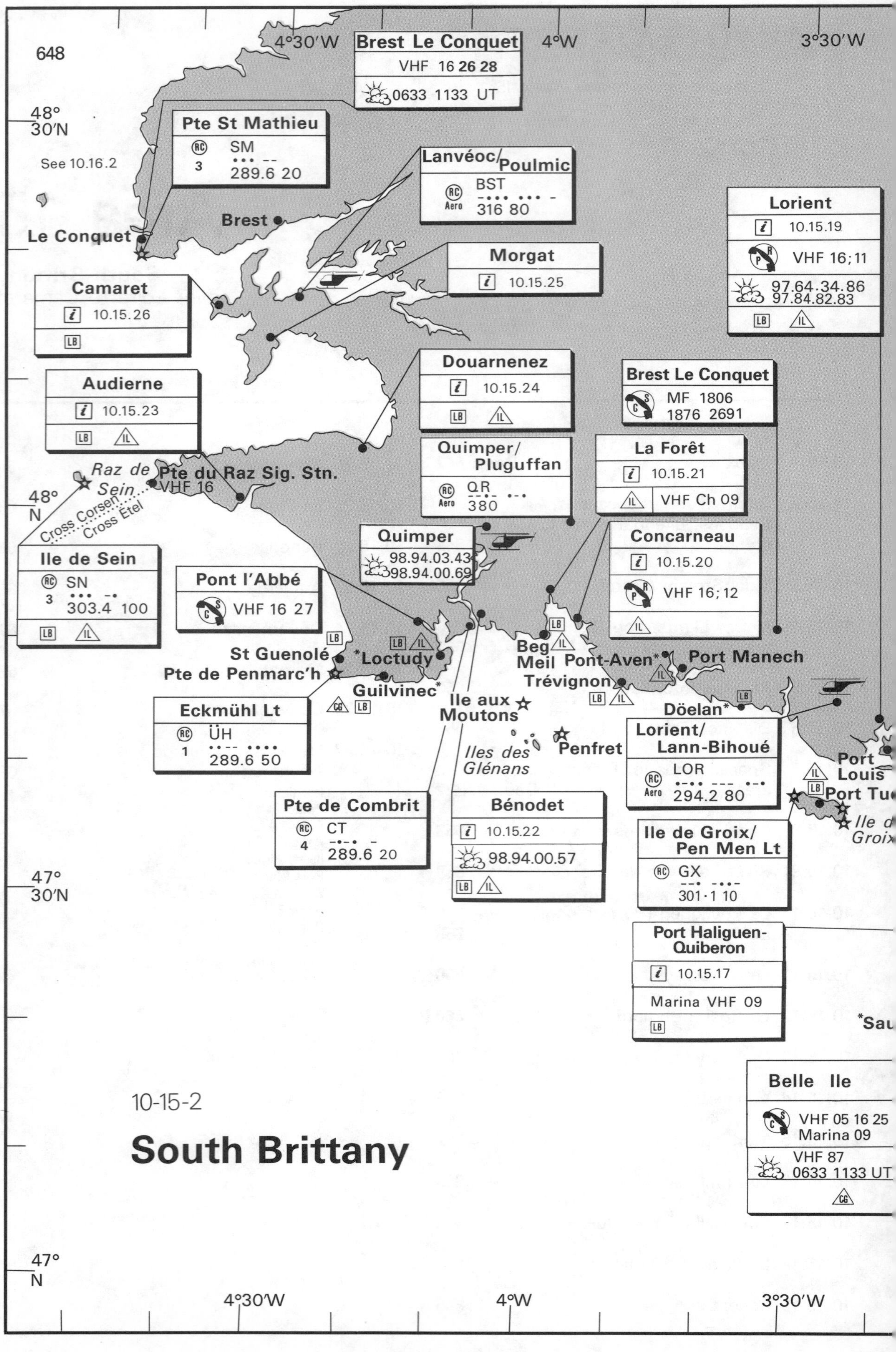

4°30′W
4°W
3°30′W
48° 30′N
48° N
47° 30′N
47° N
See 10.16.2
Brest Le Conquet
VHF 16 26 28
0633 1133 UT
Pte St Mathieu
RC 3
SM
289.6 20
Lanvéoc/Poulmic
RC Aero
BST
316 80
Brest
Le Conquet
Morgat
10.15.25
Camaret
10.15.26
LB
Audierne
10.15.23
LB IL
Douarnenez
10.15.24
LB IL
Brest Le Conquet
MF 1806
1876 2691
Lorient
10.15.19
VHF 16; 11
97.64.34.86
97.84.82.83
LB IL
Quimper/Pluguffan
RC Aero
QR
380
La Forêt
10.15.21
IL VHF Ch 09
Raz de Sein
Pte du Raz Sig. Stn.
VHF 16
Cross Corsen
Cross Etel
Quimper
98.94.03.43
98.94.00.69
Concarneau
10.15.20
VHF 16; 12
IL
Ile de Sein
RC 3
SN
303.4 100
LB IL
Pont l'Abbé
VHF 16 27
St Guenolé
*Loctudy
Pte de Penmarc'h
Guilvinec*
CG LB
Beg Meil
Pont-Aven*
Port Manech
Trévignon
Ile aux Moutons
Döelan*
Eckmühl Lt
RC 1
ÜH
289.6 50
Iles des Glénans
Penfret
Lorient/Lann-Bihoué
RC Aero
LOR
294.2 80
Port Louis
Port Tu
Ile d
Groix
Pte de Combrit
RC 4
CT
289.6 20
Bénodet
10.15.22
98.94.00.57
LB IL
Ile de Groix/Pen Men Lt
RC
GX
301·1 10
Port Haliguen-Quiberon
10.15.17
Marina VHF 09
LB
*Sau
Belle Ile
VHF 05 16 25
Marina 09
VHF 87
0633 1133 UT
CG

10-15-2

South Brittany

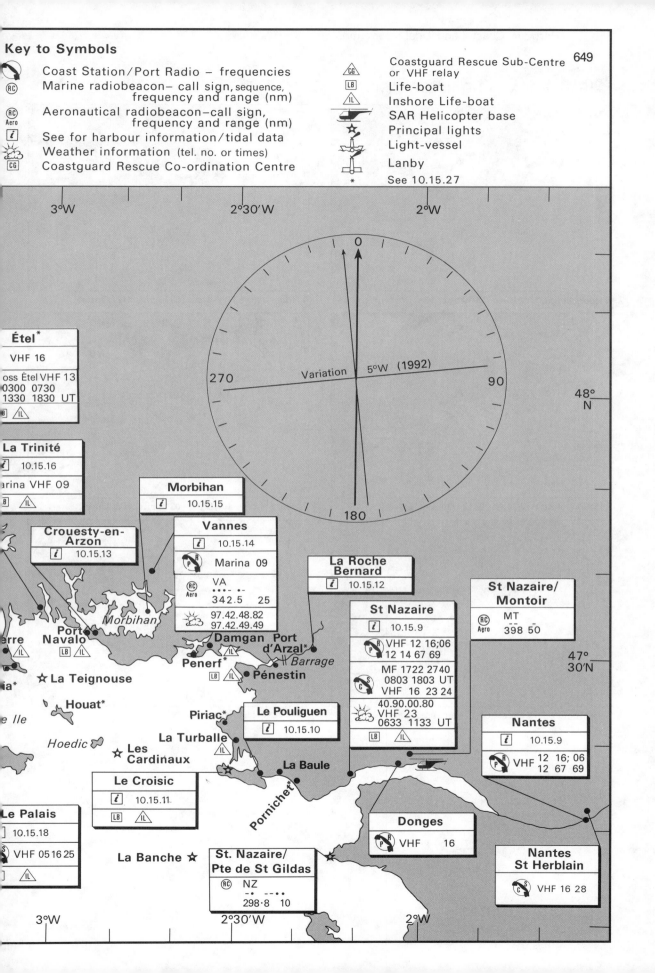

Key to Symbols

- Coast Station/Port Radio – frequencies
- (RC) Marine radiobeacon– call sign, sequence, frequency and range (nm)
- (RC) Aero Aeronautical radiobeacon–call sign, frequency and range (nm)
- [i] See for harbour information/tidal data
- Weather information (tel. no. or times)
- [CG] Coastguard Rescue Co-ordination Centre
- CG Coastguard Rescue Sub-Centre or VHF relay
- [LB] Life-boat
- IL Inshore Life-boat
- SAR Helicopter base
- ☆ Principal lights
- Light-vessel
- Lanby
- * See 10.15.27

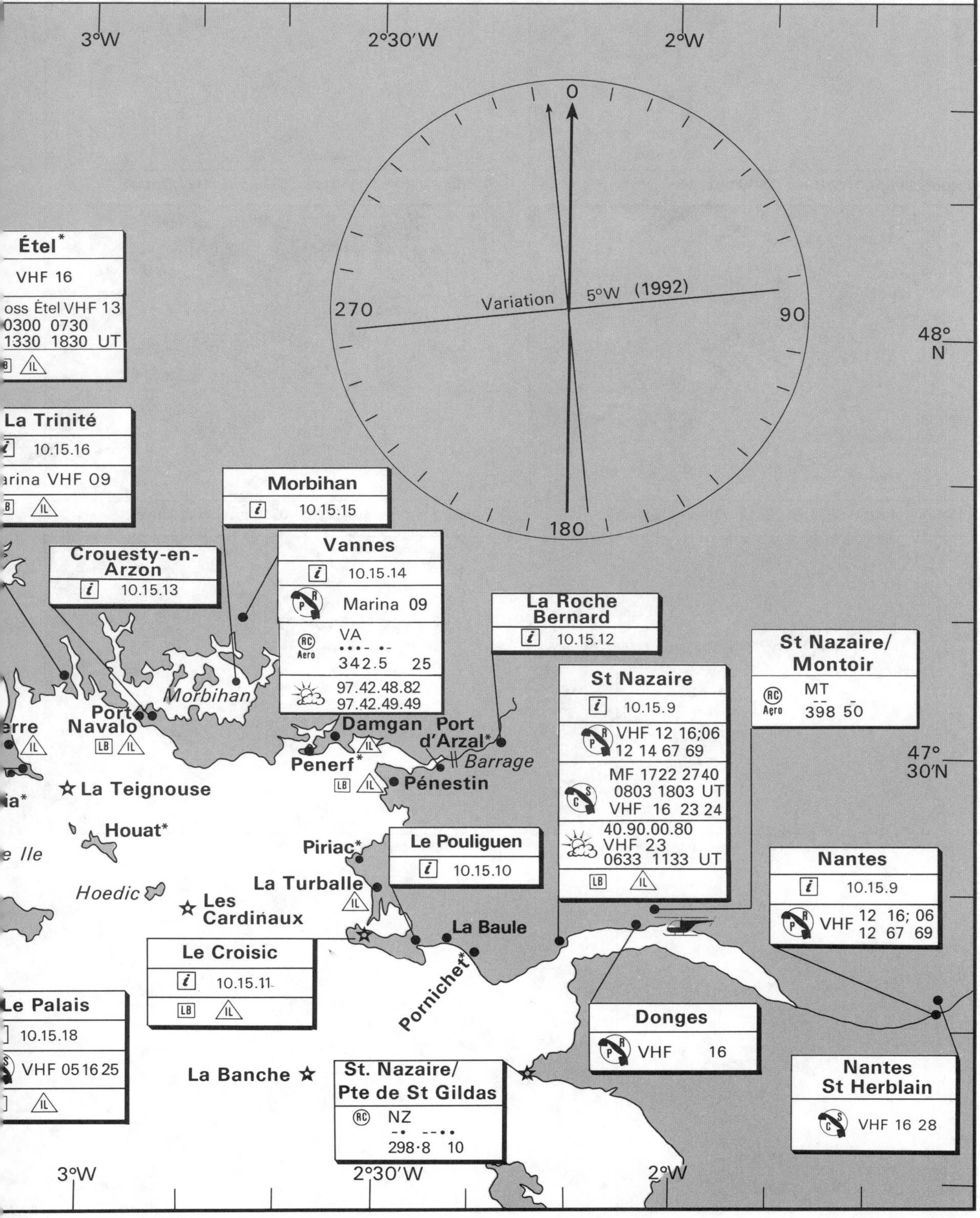

3°W
2°30′W
2°W
48° N
47° 30′N
0
90
180
270
Variation 5°W (1992)
Étel*
VHF 16
oss Étel VHF 13
0300 0730
1330 1830 UT
La Trinité
10.15.16
arina VHF 09
Morbihan
10.15.15
Crouesty-en-Arzon
10.15.13
Vannes
10.15.14
Marina 09
VA
342.5 25
97.42.48.82
97.42.49.49
La Roche Bernard
10.15.12
St Nazaire/Montoir
MT
398 50
St Nazaire
10.15.9
VHF 12 16;06
12 14 67 69
MF 1722 2740
0803 1803 UT
VHF 16 23 24
40.90.00.80
VHF 23
0633 1133 UT
Nantes
10.15.9
VHF 12 16; 06
12 67 69
Morbihan
Port Navalo
Damgan
Port d'Arzal*
Barrage
Penerf*
Pénestin
La Teignouse
Houat*
Hoedic
Les Cardinaux
Piriac*
La Turballe
Le Pouliguen
10.15.10
La Baule
Pornichet*
Le Croisic
10.15.11
Le Palais
10.15.18
VHF 05 16 25
La Banche
St. Nazaire/Pte de St Gildas
NZ
298·8 10
Donges
VHF 16
Nantes St Herblain
VHF 16 28

10.15.3 AREA 15 TIDAL STREAMS

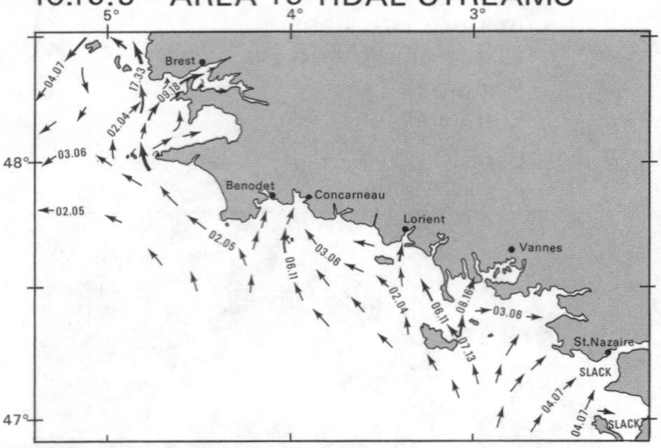
5°
4°
3°
48°
47°
Brest
Benodet
Concarneau
Lorient
Vannes
St.Nazaire
SLACK

5 Hours before HW Brest (0010 after HW Dover)

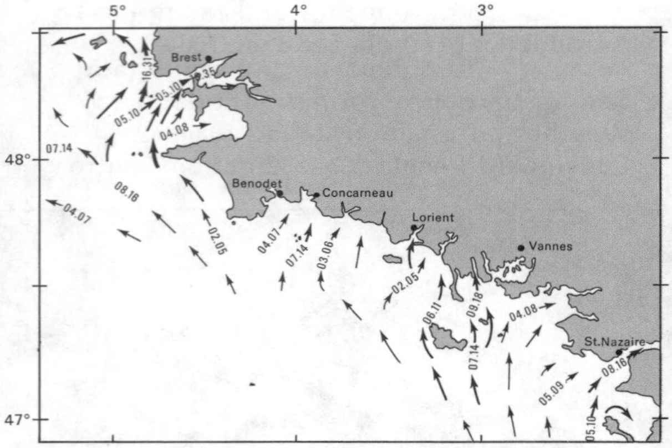
5°
4°
3°
48°
47°
Brest
Benodet
Concarneau
Lorient
Vannes
St.Nazaire

4 Hours before HW Brest (0110 after HW Dover)

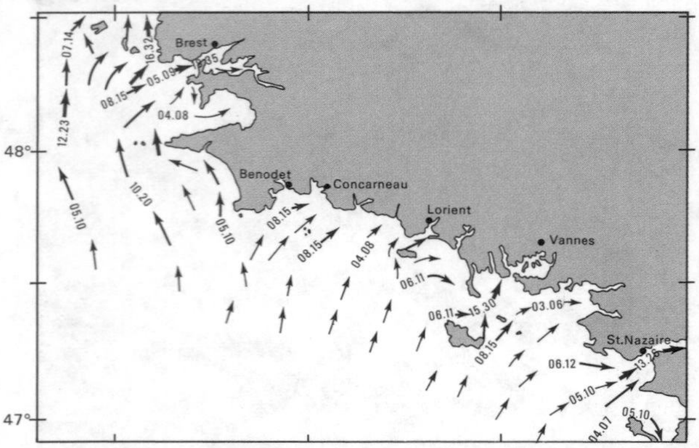
48°
47°
Brest
Benodet
Concarneau
Lorient
Vannes
St.Nazaire

3 Hours before HW Brest (0210 after HW Dover)

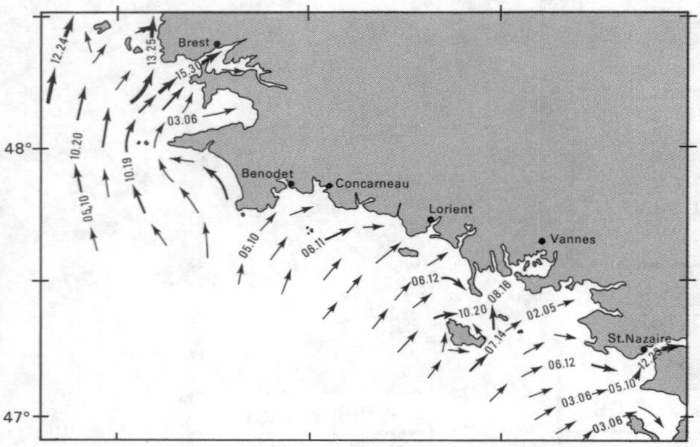
48°
47°
Brest
Benodet
Concarneau
Lorient
Vannes
St.Nazaire

2 Hours before HW Brest (0310 after HW Dover)

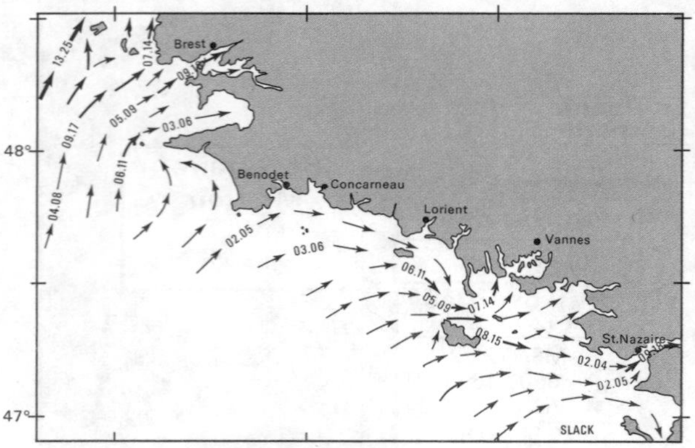
48°
47°
Brest
Benodet
Concarneau
Lorient
Vannes
St.Nazaire
SLACK

1 Hour before HW Brest (0410 after HW Dover)

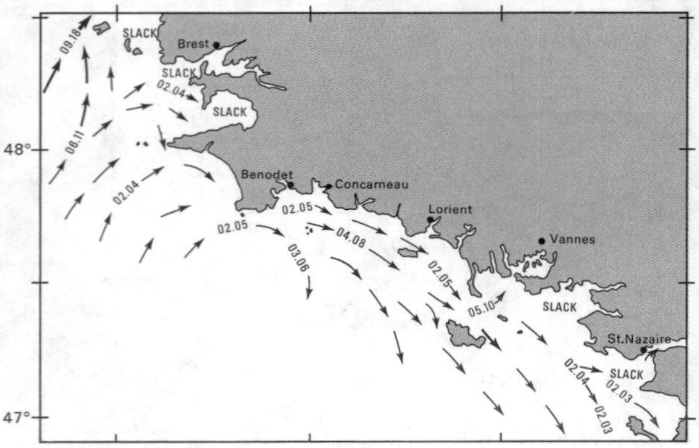
48°
47°
SLACK
Brest
Benodet
Concarneau
Lorient
Vannes
St.Nazaire

HW Brest (0510 after HW Dover)

Northward 10.16.3 Southward 10.14.3

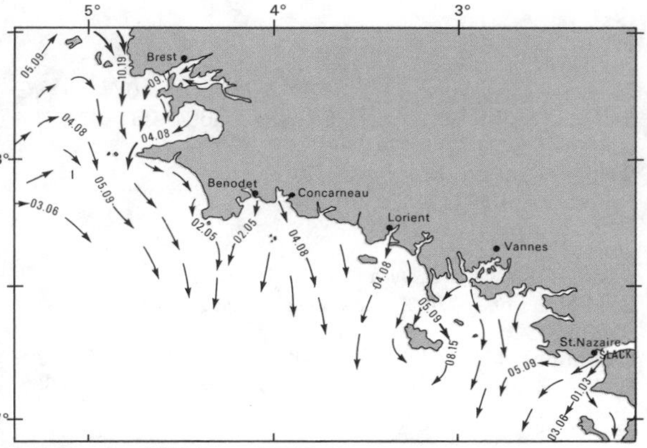
5°
4°
3°
48°
47°
Brest
Benodet
Concarneau
Lorient
Vannes
St.Nazaire
SLACK
1 Hour after HW Brest (0610 after HW Dover)

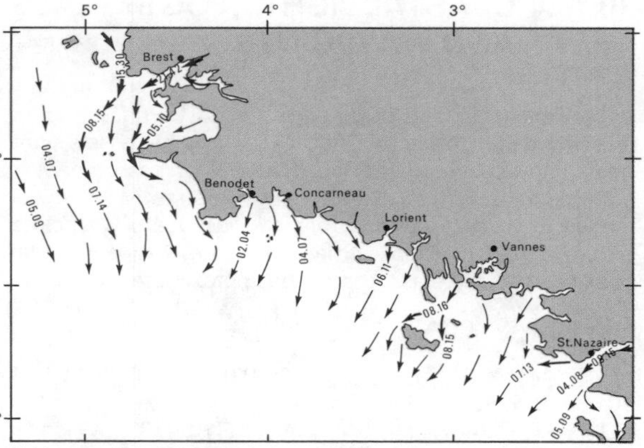
5°
4°
3°
48°
47°
Brest
Benodet
Concarneau
Lorient
Vannes
St.Nazaire
2 Hours after HW Brest (0515 before HW Dover)

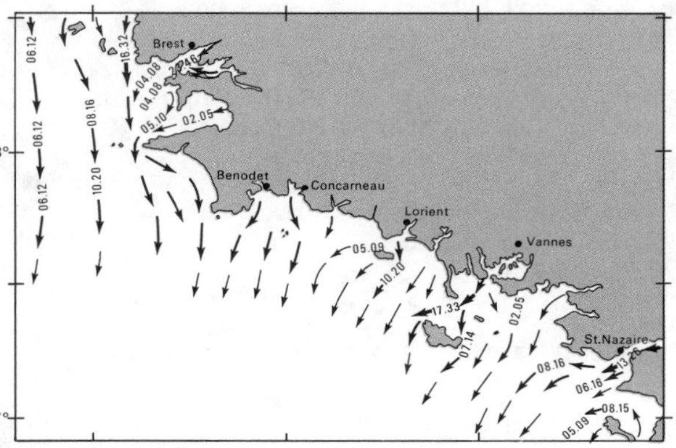
48°
47°
Brest
Benodet
Concarneau
Lorient
Vannes
St.Nazaire
3 Hours after HW Brest (0415 before HW Dover)

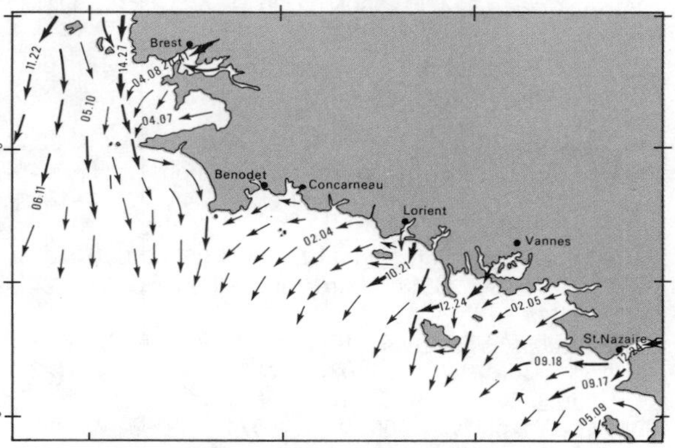
48°
47°
Brest
Benodet
Concarneau
Lorient
Vannes
St.Nazaire
4 Hours after HW Brest (0315 before HW Dover)

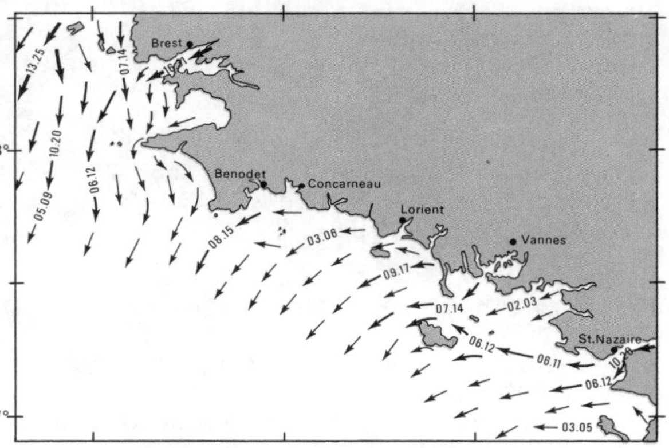
48°
47°
Brest
Benodet
Concarneau
Lorient
Vannes
St.Nazaire
5 Hours after HW Brest (0215 before HW Dover)

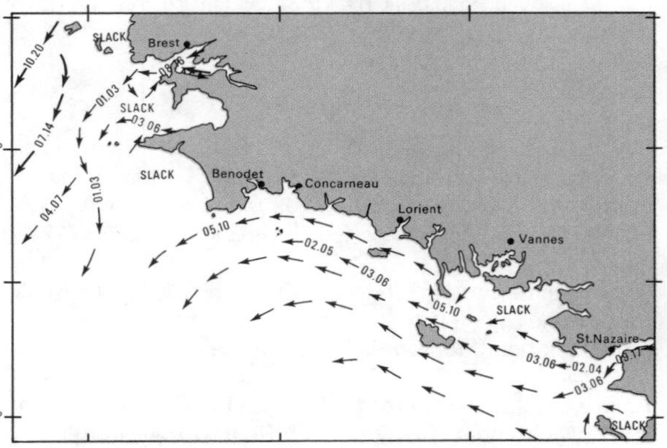
48°
47°
Brest
SLACK
Benodet
Concarneau
Lorient
Vannes
St.Nazaire
6 Hours after HW Brest (0115 before HW Dover)

10.15.4 COASTAL LIGHTS, FOG SIGNALS AND WAYPOINTS

Abbreviations used below are given in 1.4.1. Principal lights are in **bold** print, places in CAPITALS, and light-vessels, light floats and Lanbys in *CAPITAL ITALICS*. Unless otherwise stated lights are white. m—elevation in metres; M—nominal range in n. miles. Fog signals are in *italics*. Useful waypoints are underlined – use those on land with care. All geographical positions should be assumed to be approximate. See 4.2.2.

FRANCE—W COAST

LOIRE APPROACH Lt By SN1 47°00'05N 02°39'·95W L Fl 10s 8m 8M; SWM; *Whis*; Racon.
LOIRE APPROACH Lt By SN2 47°02'·15N 02°33'·45W Iso 4s 8m 5M; SWM; Ra refl.
NW BANCHE Lt By 47°12'·90N 02°30'·95W Q 8m 8M; NCM; *Bell*; Ra refl.
LA COURONNEE Lt By 47°07'·67N 02°20'·00W QG 8m 6M; SHM; Ra refl; Racon.

Pte de Saint Gildas 47°08'·10N 02°14'·67W Q WRG 23m **W11M**, R6M, G6M; framework Tr on W house; vis R264°-308°, G308°-078°, W078°-088°, R088°-174°, W174°-180°, G180°-264°. RC.
P. de La Gravette Jetty Hd 47°09'·80N 02°12'·60W Fl (3) WG 12s 7m W8M, G5M; W structure, G top; vis G224°-124°, W124°-224°.
P. de Comberge S Jetty 47°10'·60N 02°09'·95W Oc WG 4s 7m W9M, G5M; W Tr, G top; vis W123°-140°, G140°-123°.
Le Pointeau 47°14'·05N 02°10'·90W Fl WG 4s 4m W10M, G6M; G&W ● hut; vis G050°-074°, W074°-149°, G149°-345°, W345°-050°.
Les Morées 47°15'·05N 02°12'·95W Oc (2) WR 6s 12m W9M, R6M; G Tr; vis W058°-224°, R300°-058°.
Point de Minden W Mole Fl G 2s 5m 2M.

DONGES.
SW dolphin 47°18'·1N 02°05'·0W Fl G 4s 12m 7M; Gy col.
NE dolphin (close ENE) Iso G 4s 12m 6M; G col.
Paimboeuf Mole Hd 47°17'·4N 02°02'·0W Oc (3) WG 12s 9m **W16M**, G11M; W ● Tr, G top; vis G shore-123°, W123°-shore.
Île du Petit Carnet 47°17'·3N 02°00'·3W Fl G 2·5s 8m 6M; W framework Tr, G top.
From Paimboeuf to Nantes Lts on S side are G, and N Red.

Portcé Ldg Lts 025°. **Front** 47°14'·6N 02°15'·4W Dir Q 6m **23M**; W col; intens 024.7°-026.2°. **Rear**, 0·75M from front, 47°15'·3N 02°14'·9W Q 36m **27M**; W Tr; intens 024·7°-026·2° (H24).
Pointe d'Aiguillon 47°14'·60N 02°15'·70W Oc (4) WR 12s 27m **W15M**, R11M; W Tr; vis W233°-293°, W297°-300°, R300°-327°, W327°-023°, W027°-089°.
Villèz-Martin Jetty Hd, 47°15'·3N 02°13'·7W Fl (2) 6s 10m 12M; W Tr, R top.

SAINT-NAZAIRE.
W Jetty Oc (4) R 12s 11m 10M; W Tr, R top.
East Jetty Oc (4) G 12s 11m 11M; W Tr, G top.
Old Mole Hd Oc (2+1) 12s 18m 12M; W Tr, R top; vis 153·5°-063·5°; weather signals.
Le Grand Charpentier 47°12'·90N 02°19'·05W Q WRG 22m W14M, R10M, G10M; Gy Tr, G lantern; vis G020°-049°, W049°-111°, R111°-310°, W310°-020°; helicopter platform; sig stn 1·5M NE.

PORNICHET.
La Baule S Breakwater Hd 47°15'·55N 02°21'·10W Iso WG 4s 11m W12M, G9M; W Tr, G top; vis G084°-081°, W081°-084°.
S Hd Fl G 2s 3m 2M.
N Breakwater Hd Fl R 2s 3m 2M.

LE POULIGUEN.
S Jetty QR 13m 9M; W col; vis 171°-081°.
Les Petits Impairs Fl (2) G 6s 6m 6M; G ▲, on Tr; vis outside B. 298°-034°.
La Banche 47°10'·70N 02°28'·00W Fl (2+1) WR 15s 22m **W17M**, R12M; B Tr, W bands; vis R266°-280°, W280°-266°.

LE CROISIC.
Jetée de Tréhic Hd 47°18'·5N 02°31'·4W Iso WG 4s 12m W13M, G10M; Gy Tr, G top; vis G042°-093°, W093°-137°, G137°-345°; F Bu Fog Det Lt.
Ldg Lts 156°. **Front** 47°18'·0N 02°31'·0W Dir Oc (2+1) 12s 10m **18M**; Or topmark on W Tr. **Rear, 116m from f**ront, Dir Oc (2+1) 12s 14m **18M**; Or topmark on W Tr, G top; synchronised with front, both intens 154°-158°.
Ldg Lts 174° both QG 5/8m 11M; vis 170·5°-177·5° on Y ■, G & W structure; both intens 170·5°-177·5°.
Ldg Lts 134·5° both Dir QR 6/10m 11M; intens 125·5°-143·5°; RW pylons.
Le Grand Mabon 47°18'·1N 02°31'·0W Fl R 2·5s 6m 5M, R pedestal.
Le Four 47°17'·9N 02°38'·0W Fl 5s 23m **19M**; W Tr, B stripes, G top.

ILE DE HOEDIC.
Port de l'Argol Breakwater Hd 47°20'·7N 02°52'·5W Fl WG 4s 10m W9M, G6M; W Tr, G top; vis W143°-163°, G163°-183°, W183°-203°, G203°-143°.
Les Grands Cardinaux 47°19'·3N 02°50'·1W Fl (4) 15s 28m 13M; R and W Tr.

ILE DE HOUAT.
Port de Saint-Gildas Môle Nord 47°23'·5N 02°57'·4W Oc (2) WG 6s 8m W8M, G5M; W Tr, G top; vis W168°-198°, G198°-210°, W210°-240°, G240°-168°.

LA TURBALLE.
Ldg Lts 006·5° both Dir F Vi 11/19m 3M, both intens 004°-009°.
Jetée de Garlahy Fl (4) WR 12s 13m W10M, R7M; W pylon, R top; vis R060°-315°, W315°-060°.
Digue Tourlandroux Fl G 4s 7m 6M; W pedestal, G top; *Siren 10 min.*

PIRIAC-SUR-MER.
Pipeline 47°22'·1N 02°32'·8W Oc (2+1) WRG 12s 14m W12M, R9M, G9M; W ■, R stripe on R Tr; vis G300°-036°, W036°-068°, R068°-120°.
Inner Mole Hd 47°22'·9N 02°32'·7W Oc (2) WRG 6s 8m W10M, R7M, G6M; W col; vis R066°-185°, W185°-201°, G201°-224°; Siren 120s.
Breakwater Hds Fl G 4s and Fl R 4s 5m 5M.
Mesquer, Jetty Hd 47°25'·3N 02°28'·1W Oc (3+1) WRG 12s 7m W12M, R8M, G7M; W col and bldg; vis W067°-072°, R072°-102°, W102°-118°, R118°-293°, W293°-325°, G325°-067°.

Île Dumet 47°24'·7N 02°37'·2W Fl (2+1) WRG 15s 14m W8M, R6M, G6M; W col, G top on fort; vis G090°-272°, W272°-285°, R285°-325°, W325°-090°.

Basse de Kervoyal Dir Q WR W8M, R6M; vis W269°-271°, R271°-269°; SCM on B Tr.

LA VILAINE.
Basse Bertrand 47°31'·1N 02°30'·7W Iso WG 4s 6m W9M, G6M; G Tr; vis W040°-054°, G054°-227°, W227°-234°, G234°-040°.
Penlan 47°31'·0N 02°30'·2W Oc (2) WRG 6s 26m **W15M**, R11M, G11M; W Tr, R bands; vis R292·5°-025°, G025°-052°, W052°-060°, R060°-138°, G138°-180°.
Pointe du Scal, 47°29'·7N 02°26'·8W Oc (3) G 12s 8m 6M; W ■ Tr, G top.

PÉNERF.
Le Pignon 47°30'·1N 02°38'·9W Fl (3) WR 12s 6m W9M , R6M ; R ■ on Tr; vis R028·5°-167°, W167°-175°, R175°-349·5°, W349·5°-028·5°.
Saint-Jacques-en-Sarzeau 47°29'·2N 02°'·47.4W Oc (2) R 6s 5m 6M; W 8-sided Tr, R top.

CROUESTY EN ARZON.
Ldg Lts 058°. **Front** 47°32'·6N 02°53'·9W Dir Q 10m **19M** ; framework Tr; intens 056·5°-059·5°. **Rear**, 315m from front, Dir Q 27m **19M** ; W Tr; intens 056·5°-059·5°.
N Jetty Hd Oc (2) R 6s 9m 7M; R and W ■ Tr, R top.
S jetty Hd Fl G 4s 9m 7M; G&W ■ Tr.
Port-Navalo 47°32'·90N 02°55'·12W Oc (3) WRG 12s 32m **W15M** , R11M , G11M ; W Tr and dwelling; vis W155°-220°, G317°-359°, W359°-015°, R015°-105°.
Le Grand Mouton 47°33'·8N 02°54'·8W QG 4m 3M; G tripod.
Rivière D'Auray. Le Grégan Q (6) + L Fl 15s 3m 8M .

RIVIÉRE DE CRAC'H.
Ldg Lts 347°. Front 47°34'·1N 03°00'·4W Q WRG 10m W10M, R7M, G7M; W Tr, G top; vis G321°-345°, W345°-013°·5, R013·5°-080°. **Rear**, 560m from front, Dir Q 21m **15M**; W I Tr, G top; synchronised with front, intens 337°-357°.
La Trinite-sur-Mer Dir Lt 347°. 47°35'·0N 03°01'·0W Dir Oc WRG 4s 9m W14M, R11M, G11M; W Tr; vis G345°-346°, W346°-348°, R348°-349°.

LA TRINITÉ-SUR-MER.
S Pier Hd Oc (2) WR 6s 6m W10M, R7M; W Tr, R top; vis R090°-293·5°, W293·5°-300·5°, R300·5°-329°.
Jetty Hd Iso R 4s 8m 5M; W Tr, R top.

LE PALAIS
Jetée Sud 47°20'·8N 03°09'·1W Oc (2) R 6s 11m 11M; W Tr; obsc 298°-170°.
Jetée Nord Fl (2+1) G 12s11m 7M; W Tr, G top; obsc 298°-168°.
Sauzon, Jetée QG 9m 6M; W Tr, G top; vis 194°-045°.
Pte des Poulains 47°23'·3N 03°15'·1W Fl 5s 34m **24M** ; W ■ Tr and dwelling; vis 023°-291°.

PASSAGE DE LA TEIGNOUSE.
La Teignouse 47°27'·5N 03°02'·8W Fl WR 4s 19m 15/11M; W ●Tr, R top vis W033°-039°, R039°-033° .
BASSE DU MILIEU LANBY 47°25'·9N 03°04'·2W Fl (2) G 6s 9m 5M; SHM.

PORT HALIGUEN.
Marina old Breakwater Hd Fl R 4s 10m 5M; W Tr, R top.
New Breakwater Hd 47°29'·4N 03°06'·0W Oc (2) WR 6s 10m W12M, R9M; W Tr, R top; vis W233°-240·5°, R240·5°-299°, W299°-306°, R306°-233°.

PORT MARIA.
Ldg Lts 006·5°. Front 47°28'·7N 03°07'·2W Dir QG 5m 13M; W Tr, B band. Rear, 230m from front, Dir QG 13m 13M; W Tr, B band; both intens 005°-008°.
Main light 47°28'·8N 03°07'·5W Q WRG 28m **W14M**, R10M, G10M; W Tr; vis W246°-252°, W291°-297°, G297°-340°, W340°-017°, R017°-051°, W051°-081°, G081°-098°, W098°-143°.
Brise-lames Sud Hd Oc (2) R 6s 9m 7M; W Tr, R top.
Môle Est Hd Iso G 4s 9m 7M; W Tr, G top.

Plateau des Birvideaux 47°29'·20N 03°17'·45W Fl (2) 6s 24m 9M; B Tr, R bands.
Rivière d'Étel, W side ent 47°38'·7N 03°12'·8W Oc (2) WRG 6s 13m W9M, R6M, G6M; R Tr; vis W022°-064°, R064°-123°, W123°-330°, G330°-022°; 2 FR on radio Mast 2·3M NW; FR and F on radio Mast 2·4M NW.

BELLE ILE.
Goulphar 47°18'·67N 03°13'·67W Fl (2) 10s 87m **24M**; Gy Tr.
Pointe de Kerdonis 47°18'·6N 03°03'·6W Fl (3) R 15s 35m **15M** ; W ■ Tr and dwelling; obsc by Pointes d'Arzic and de Taillefer 025°-129°.

LORIENT.
Ldg Lts Passe Sud 008·5°. Front, Fish Market 47°43'·8N 03°21'·7W Dir QR 16m 15M; R ■ on Gy Tr; intens 006°-011°. Rear, Kergroise-La Perrière 515m from front Dir QR 28m **16M;** R ■, W stripe on Gy Tr; synchronised with front; intens 006°-011°.
Ile aux Souris 47°42'·22N 03°21'·43W Dir Q WG 6m W3M, G2W; G Tr; vis W041·5°-043·5°, G043·5°-041·5°.
Ldg Lts Passe Ouest 057°. Front, Les Soeurs 47°42'·22N 03°21'·70W Dir Q 6m 13M, R Tr, W bands; vis intens 042·5°-058·5°, (4M) 058·5°-042·5°. Rear, **Port Louis** 740m from front Dir Q **18M**; W daymark, R bands on bldg. Lts intens 042·5°-058·5°, (4M) 058·5°-042·5°.
Les Trois Pierres 47°41'·58N 03°22'·40W Q RG 11m R6M, G6M; B Tr, R bands; vis G060°-196°, R196°-002°.
"L" Banc des Truics Lt By 47°40'·82N 03°24'·40W Q (9) 15s; WCM.
A2 Locqueltas Lt By 47°41'·00N 03°24'·90W Fl R 2·5s; PHM.
Bastresse Sud Lt By 47°40'·83N 03°22'·01W QG; SHM; *Bell.*
Les Errants Lt By 47°41'·16N 03°22'·29W Fl (2) R 6s; PHM.

Île Saint Michel Passe de la Citadelle Ldg Lts 016°. **Front** Dir Oc (3) G 12s 8m **16M**; W Tr, G top. **Rear**, 306m from front, Dir Oc (3) G 12s 14m **16M**; W Tr, G top; synchronised with front; both intens 014·5°-017·5°.
W side, La Jument Oc R 4s 5m 6M; R Tr; vis 182°-024°.
E side Tourelle de la Citadelle Oc G 4s 6m 6M; G Tr; vis 009°-193°.
Port-Louis Jetty Iso G 4s 7m 6M; W Tr, G top; vis 043°-301°.
W side Le Cochon Fl R 4s 5m 5M; R Tr, G band.
Kéroman, submarine base Ldg Lts 350°. **Front** Dir Oc (2) R 6s 25m **17M**. **Rear**, 91m from front, Dir Oc (2) R 6s 31m **17M**; R&W topmark on Gy pylon, R top; Lts synchronised and intens 348°-353°.
Fishing Hbr SE side of ent Fl RG 4s 7m 6M; W Tr, G top; vis G000°-235°, R235°-360°.
Kernevel Ldg Lts 217°. 47°43'·08N 03°22'·23W Front Dir QR 0m 14M; R ■ on R and W Tr; intens 215°-219°. Rear, 290m from front Dir QR 18m 14M; W■Tr, R top; synchronised with front; intens 215°-219°.
Pengarne Fl G 2·5s 3m 4M; G Tr.
Pointe de l'Espérance Dir Lt 037°. Dir Q WRG 8m W10M , R8M, G8M; W Tr, G top; vis G034·2°-036·7°, W036·7°-037·2°, R037·2°-047·2°.
Avant-port de Commerce Fl (4) WR 12s 7m W10M, R7M; W Tr, R top; vis W110°-347°, R347°-355°, W355°-035°.

ILE DE GROIX.
Pointe des Chats 47°37'·30N 03°25'·25W Fl R 5s16m **19M**; W ■ Tr and dwelling.
Pointe de la Croix Oc WR 4s 16m W12M, R9M; W pedestal, R lantern; vis W169°-336°, R336°-345°, W345°-353°.
P.Tudy Môle Est Hd 47°38'·7N 03°26'·7W Fl (2) R 6s 11m 6M; W ● Tr, R top; vis 112°-226°.
P.Tudy Môle Nord Hd Iso G 4s 12m 6M; W Tr, G top.
Pen Men 47°38'·87N 03°30'·48W Fl (4) 25s 59m **29M**; W ■ Tr, B top; vis 309°-275°; RC.

Lomener Anse de Stole Dir Lt 357·2°. 47°42'·4N 03°25'·5 Dir Q WRG 18m W10M, R8M, G8M; W Tr, R top; vis G349·2°-355·2°, W355·2°-359·2°, R359·2°-005·2°.
Kerroc'h 47°42'·0N 03°27'·7W Oc (2) WRG 6s 22m W11M, R8M, G8M; W Tr, R top; vis R096·5°-112°·5, G112·5°-132°, R132°-302°, W302°-096·5°.

DOËLAN
Ldg Lts 014°. Front 47°46'·3N 03°36'·5W Oc (3) WG 20W 12s W13M, G10M; W Tr, G band and top; vis W shore-305°, G305°-314°, W314°-shore. Rear 326m from front, QR 27m 9M; W Tr, R band and top.

MERRIEN.
47°47'·1N 03°39'·0W QR 26m 7M; W ■ Tr, R top; vis 004°-009°.

BRIGNEAU.
Mole Hd 47°46'·9N 03°40'·2W Oc (2) WRG 6s 7m W12M, R9M, G9M; W col, R top; vis G280°-329°, W329°-339°, R339°-034°.

PORT MANECH.
Pointe de Beg-ar-Vechen 47°48'·0N 03°44'·4W Oc (4) WRG 12s 38m W10M, R7M, G7M; W & R Tr; vis W(unintens) 050°-140°, W140°-296°, G296°-303°, W303°-311°, R311°-328° over Les Verres, W328°-050°; obsc by Pte de Beg-Morg when brg less than 299°.

TRÉVIGNON.
Breakwater root 47°47'·6N 03°51'·3W Oc (3+1) WRG 12s 11m W14M, R11M, G11M; W ■ Tr, G top; vis W004°-051°, G051°-085°, W085°-092°, R092°-127°, R322°-351°.
Mole Hd Fl G 4s 5m 8M; W col, G top.
Baie de Pouldohan 47°51'·0N 03°53'·7W Fl G 4s 7m 8M; W ■ Tr, G top; vis 053°-065°.

CONCARNEAU.
Ldg Lts 028·5°. Front La Croix 47°52'·22N 03°55'·00W Oc (3) 12s 14m 13M; R and W Tr; vis 006·5°-093°. **Rear Beuzec**, 1·34M from front, Dir Q 87m **23M**; Belfry; intens 026·5°-030·5°.
Lanriec QG 13m 8M; G stripe on W gable; vis 063°-078°.
La Medée Fl R 2·5s 6m 4M; R Tr.
Passage de Lanriec 47°52'·3N 03°54'·8W Oc (2) WR 6s 4m W8M, R6M; R Tr; vis R209°-354°, W354°-007°, R007°-018°; Fl R 4s and Q (6) + L Fl R 10s shown on W side, Fl G 4s and Fl (2) G 6s on E side of passage.
Le Cochon 47°51'·53N 03°55'·47W Fl (3) WRG 12s 5m W9M, R6M, G6M; G Tr; vis G048°-205°, R205°-352°, W352°-048°.
Basse du Chenal QR 6m 5M; R Tr; vis 180°- 163°.

LA FORÊT.
Cap Coz Mole Hd 47°53'·55N 03°58'·20W Fl (2) R 6s 5m6M.

Kerleven, shelter mole Hd Fl G 4s 8m 6M .
Inner Mole Hd Iso G 4s 5m 5M.

ÎLES DE GLÉNAN.
Penfret 47°43'·32N 03°57'·10W Fl R 5s 36m **21M**; W ■ Tr, R top; auxiliary Lt Dir Q 34m 12M; same Tr; vis 295°-315°.
Fort Cigogne Q (2) RG 5s 2M; vis G106°-108°, R108°-262°, G262°-268°, obsc 268°-106°; shown 1/5 to 1/10.
Île-aux-Moutons 47°46'·5N 04°01'·7W Oc (2) WRG 6s 18m **W15M**, R11M, G11M; W ■ Tr and dwelling; vis W035°-050°, G050°-063°, W063°-081°, R081°-141°, W141°-292°, R292°-035°; **auxiliary Lt** Dir Oc (2) 6s 17m **24M**; same Tr; synchronised with main Lt, intens 278·5°-283·5°.

Jaune de Glenan Lt By 47°42'·6N 03°49'·8W Q (3) 10s; ECM; *Whis*.
Jument de Glenan Lt By 47°38'·8N 04°01'·3W Q (6) + L Fl 15s 10m 8M; SCM; *Whis*; Ra refl.
Basse Perennes Lt By 47°41'·1N 04°06'·3W Q (9) 15s 8m 8M ; WCM; *Whis*; Ra refl.
Rouge de Glénan Lt By 47°45'·5N 04°03'·9W VQ (9) 10s 8m 8M ; WCM; *Whis*; Ra refl.
Beg-Meil Quay Hd 47°51'·72N 03°58'·85W Fl R 2s 6m 2M; R and W col.

BENODET.
Ldg Lts 345·5°. Front **Pte du Coq**, 336m from rear, Dir Oc (2+1) G 12s 11m **17M**; W ● Tr, G stripe; intens 345°-347°.
Common rear Pyramide Oc (2+1) 12s 48m 11M; W Tr, G top; vis 338°-016°, synchronised withfront.
Ldg Lts 000·5°. Pte de Combrit, 47°51'·92N 04°06'·70W, front 0·63M from rear, Oc (3+1) WR 12s 19m W12M , R9M; W ■ Tr, Gy corners; vis W325°-017°, R017°-325°; RC.
Pte du Toulgoet Fl R 2s 2m 2M; R mast.
Pont de Cornouaille NE side 2 FG 2M; G ▲ in W■ .
SW side 47°53'·1N 04°07'·3W 2 FR 3M; R ■ , W border.

LOCTUDY.
Pointe de Langoz S side 47°49'·94N 04°09'·48W Fl (4) WRG 12s 12m **W15M**, R11M, G11M; W Tr, R top; vis W115°-257°, G257°-284°, W284°-295°, R295°-318°, W318°-328°, R328°-025°.
Les Perdrix 47°50'·3N 04°10'·0W Fl WRG 4s 15M W11M, R8M, G8M; ▲ on B & W Tr; vis G090°-285°, W285°-295°, R295°-090°.
Karek-Saoz 47°50'·08N 04°09'·30W QR 3m 1M; R Tr.
Le Blas 47°50'·3N 04°10'·1W Fl (3) G 12s 5m 1M; G ▲ on truncated col.

LESCONIL.
Men-ar-Groas 47°47'·8N 04°12'·6W Fl (3) WRG 12s 14m W13M, R9M, G9M; W Tr, G top; vis G268°-313°, W313°-333°, R333°-050°.
E Breakwater Hd 47°47'·77N 04°12'·56W QG 5m 9M; G Tr.
S Breakwater Hd Oc R 4s 5m 8M.

GUILVINEC.
Ldg Lts 053°. Mole de Léchiagat, spur, front 47°47'·5N 04°17'·0W Q 7m 8M; W pylon; vis 233°-066°.
Rocher Le Faoute's, Middle, 210m from front Q WG 12m W14M, G11M; R ● on W pylon; vis W006°-293°, G293°-006°; synchronised with front. Rear, 0·58M from front, Dir Q 26m 8M; R ● on W pylon; vis 051·5°-054·5°; synchronised with front.
Lost Moan 47°47'·07N 04°16'·69W Fl (3) WRG 12s 8m W9M, R6M, G6M; ■ on W Tr, R top; vis R327°-014°, G014°-065°, R065°-140°, W140°-160°, R160°-268°, W268°-273°, G273°-317°, W317°-327°.
Môle de Lechiagat Hd Fl G 4s 5m 7M; W hut, G top.
Môle Ouest Hd Fl R 4s 11m 9M; W Tr, R top.

Outer Breakwater Hd Fl (2) R 6s 4m 5M; R structure.
Kérity. Men Hir 47°47'·3N 04°20'·6W Fl R 2·5s 6m 2M; R■ on Bn .
Detached Breakwater Hd Fl (2) G 6s 5m 1M .
Locarec 47°47'·3N 04°20'·3W Iso WRG 4s 11m W9M, R6M, G6M; W tank on rk; vis G063°-068°, R068°-271°, W271°-285°, R285°-298°, G298°-340°, R340°-063°.

POINTE DE PENMARC'H
Eckmühl 47°47'·95N 04°22'·35W Fl 5s 60m **24M**; Gy 8-sided Tr; RC; *Siren 60s*.
Le Menhir 47°47'·8N 04°23'·9W Fl (2) WG 6s 6m W8M, G5M; W Tr, B band; vis G135°-315°, W315°-135°.
Scoedec 47°48'·5N 04°23'·1W Fl G 2·5s 6m 3M; G Tr.

SAINT GUÉNOLÉ.
Ldg Lts 026·5°. Front 47°49'·1N 04°22'·6W QR 8m 4M ; R mast. Rear, 51m from front, QR 12m 4M; mast, R and W bands; synchronised with front.
Roches de Groumilli Ldg Lts 123°. Front FG 9m 9M; Or ● on W Tr, B bands. Rear, 300m from front, FG 13m 9M ; Or ● on W Tr, B bands.
Ldg Lts 055·4°. Front 47°48'·7N 04°22'·7W VQ 5m 2M; G and W col. Rear, 320m from front F Vi 12m 1M; G and W col; vis 040°-070°.
Pors Poulhan, W side of ent 47°59'·1N 04°28'·0W QR 14m 9M; W ■ Tr, R lantern.

AUDIERNE.
Gamelle Ouest Lt By 47°59'·53N 04°32'·76W VQ (9) 10s; WCM; *Whis*.
Passe de l'Est Ldg Lts 331°. Front Jetée de Raoulic 48°00'·60N 04°32'·37W Oc (2+1) WG 12s 11m W14M, G9M; W●Tr; vis W shore-034°, G034°-shore, but may show W037°-055°. Rear, 0·5M from front, Dir FR 44m 9M ; W 8-sided Tr, R top; intens 321°-341°.
Kergadec Dir Lt 006°. 48°01'·0N 04°32'·8W Dir Q WRG 43m W12M, R9M, G9M; same Tr as previous Lt; vis G000°-005·3°, W005·3°-006·7°, R006·7°-017°.
Jetée de Sainte-Évette Oc (2) R 6s 2m 7M; R lantern; vis 090°-270°
Pointe de Lervily 48°00'·1N 04°34'·0W Fl (2+1) WR 12s 20m W14M, R11M; W Tr, R top; vis W211°-269°, R269°-294°, W294°-087°, R087°-121°.

RAZ DE SEIN.
Le Chat 48°01'·44N 04°48'·80W Fl (2) WRG 6s 27m W9M, R6M, G6M; SCM; vis G096°-215°, W215°-230°, R230°-271°, G271°-286°, R286°-096°; Ra refl.
La Plate 48°02'·36N 04°45'·50W VQ (9) 10s 19m 8M; WCM.
La Vieille 48°02'·5N 04°45'·4W Oc (2+1) WRG 12s 33m **W17M**, R14M, G13M; Gy ■ Tr; vis W290°-298°, R298°-325°, W325°-355°, G355°-017°, W017°-035°, G035°-105°, W105°-123°, R123°-158°, W158°-205°; R Lt on radio mast 3·4M ENE; *Siren (2+1) 60s*.
Tévennec 48°04'·3N 04°47'·6W Q WR 28m W9M R6M; W ■ Tr and dwelling; vis W090°-345°, R345°-090°; Dir Lt Iso 4s 24m 12M; same Tr; intens 324°-332°.

CHAUSSÉE DE SEIN.
Île de Sein 48°02'·70N 04°51'·95W Fl (4) 25s 49m **29M**; W Tr, B top; RC.
Ar Guéveur 48°02'·0N 04°51'·4W *Dia 60s*; W Tr.
Men-Brial, 0·8M 115° from main Lt, Oc (2) WRG 6s 16m W12M, R9M, G7M; G & W Tr; vis G149°-186°, W186°-192°, R192°-221°, W221°-227°, G227°-254°.
Ar-Men 48°03'·0N° 04°59'·9W Fl (3) 20s 29m **24M**; W Tr, B top. *Siren (3) 60s*.

CHAUSSÉE DE SEIN LANBY 48°03'·80N 05°07'·70W VQ (9) 10s 9m 8M; WCM; *Whis*; Racon; Ra refl.

Pointe du Millier 48°05'·9N 04°27'·9W Oc (2) WRG 6s 34m **W16M**, R12M, G11M; W house; vis G080°-087°, W087°-113°, R113°-120°, W120°-129°, G129°-148°, W148°-251°, R251°-258°; part obsc 255·5°-081·5°.

TRÉBOUL.
Épi de Biron Hd 48°06'·1N 04°20'·4W QG 7m 6M; W col, G top.
Île Tristan 48°06'·2N 04°20'·3W Oc (3) WR 12s 35m W13M, R10M; Gy Tr, W band, B top; vis W shore-138°, R138°-153°, W153°-shore; obsc by Pte de Leidé when brg less than 111°.

DOUARNENEZ.
Bassin Nord, N Mole E Hd 48°06'·0N 04°19'·3W Iso G 4s 9m 4M; W & G pylon.
S Mole N Hd Oc (2) R 6s 6m 6M; W & R pylon.
Elbow, Môle de Rosmeur Hd Oc G 4s 6m 6M; W pylon, G top; vis 170°-097°.

BASSE VIEILLE Lt By 48°08'·40N 04°35'·58W Fl (2) 6s 8m 8M; IDM; *Whis*; Ra refl.
Basse le Bouc Lt By 48°11'·50N 04°37'·34W Q (9) 15s; WCM; *Whis*.

Pointe de Morgat 48°13'·2N 04°29'·9W Oc (4) WRG 12s 77m **W15M**, R11M, G10M; W ■ Tr, R top, W dwelling; vis W shore-281°, G281°-301°, W301°-021°, R021°-043°; obsc by Pte du Rostudel when brg more than 027°.
Morgat Mole Hd 48°13'·6N 04°29'·9W Oc (2) WR 6s 8m W9M, R6M; W & R framework Tr; vis Wshore-257°, R257°-shore.
Marina pontoons marked by Fl G 4s at E end and Fl R 4s at W end, 320m E.

BASSE DU LIS LANBY 48°13'·05N 04°44'·46W Q (6) + L Fl 15s 9m 8M; SCM; *Whis*.
La Parquette 48°15'·91N 04°44'·25W Fl RG 4s 17m R6M, G5M; W 8-sided Tr, B diagonal stripes; vis R244°-285°, G285°-244°.
Vandrée Lt By 48°15'·06N 04°48'·23W VQ (9) 10s; *Whis*, WCM.
Roc du Charles Martel Lt By 48°18'·82N 04°42'·20W QR; *Whis*; PHM.
Swansea Vale Lt By 48°18'·58N 04°39'·52W Fl (2) 6s; *Whis*; IDM.
Pointe du Toulinguet 48°16'·87N 04°37'·64W Oc (3) WR 12s 49m **W15M**, R11M; W ■ Tr on bldg; vis W shore-028°, R028°-090°, W090°-shore.

CAMARET
Môle Nord Hd 48°16'·92N 04°35'·20W Iso WG 4s 7m W12M, G8M; W pylon, G top; vis W135°-182°, G182°-027°; obsc by Pte des Capucins when brg more than 187°.
Môle Sud Hd Fl (2) R 6s 9m 5M; R pylon; obsc by Pte du Grande Gouin when brg less than 143°, and by Pointe des Capucins when brg more than 185°.

10.15.5 PASSAGE INFORMATION

BAY OF BISCAY – NORTH PART (chart 20)

In crossing the B of Biscay, allowance should be made for possible set to E. Onshore winds carry cloud which may cause mist or fog rising over land, sometimes obscuring high Lts. Swell usually comes from W or NW. In summer the sea is usually calm or slight. Wind may be changeable in speed and direction, predominantly from SW to NW in summer. Offshore the tidal stream is weak, but gets stronger in N part of B of Biscay towards English chan, and may run strongly near the coast, off headlands.

French charts are often on larger scale than Admiralty charts, and hence are more suitable for inshore waters. Yachts are recommended to carry the *B of Biscay Pilot and North Biscay Pilot* (Adlard Coles Nautical). *French Pilot Volume 4* (Adlard Coles Nautical) covers from the Gironde to the Morbihan, while *Volume 3* continues from Belle Île to the Raz de Sein. For French Glossary see 10.14.8.

La Loire R. (charts 2985, 2989) carries much commercial tfc. The est (chart 3216) is divided by two shoals, Plateau de la Banche and Plateau de la Lambarde, which lie about 10M and 6M WNW of Pte de St Gildas. Chenal du Nord runs between these two shoals on S side and the coast on N side. Chenal du Sud, the main chan, leads between Plateau de la Lambarde and Pte de St Gildas. In the apprs to St Nazaire beware Le Vert, Les Jardinets and La Truie (all dry) which lie SW of Le Pointeau. In Grande Rade the in-going stream begins at HW Brest –0500, and the out-going at HW Brest +0050, sp rates about 2·75kn.

From Chenal du Nord, B de Pouliguen (10.15.10) is entered between Pte de Penchâteau and Pte du Bec, 3M to E. In SE corner of bay is the yacht hbr of Pornichet (10.15.27). The B is part sheltered from S by rks and shoals extending SE from Pte de Penchâteau, but a heavy sea develops in strong S-SW winds. The chan through these rks runs between Basse Martineau and Les Guérandaises.

Between Pte de Penchâteau and Pte du Croisic, Basse Lovre is a rky shoal with depths of 0·9m, 0·5M offshore. Off Pte du Croisic dangers extend 1M to W and to N. Plateau du Four, a dangerous drying bank of rks, lies about 4M W and WSW of Pte du Croisic, marked by Bys and Lt Ho near N end. Off Pte du Castelli, Les Bayonelles (dry) extend 0·5M W, and Plateau de Piriac extends about 1·75M NW with depths of 3m and drying rks closer inshore. There is chan between Plateau de Piriac and Île Dumet (Lt), which is fringed by drying rks and shoals particularly on N and E sides.

In the approaches to R. La Vilaine (10.15.12) beware Basse du Bile, a rky shoal depth 0·6m, 1M W of Île du Bile; Basse de Loscolo, depth 0·6m, about 1M to N; and La Grande Accroche, an extensive shoal with depths of less than 1·8m, astride the ent. The main chan is lit and runs NW of La Grande Accroche, to the bar on N side thereof. Here the flood stream begins at HW Brest –0515, and the ebb at HW Brest +0035, sp rates 2·5 kn. In SW winds against the stream the sea breaks heavily in this area, and then the chan 0·5M off Pte du Halguen is better, but beware La Varlingue (dries).

S of Penerf (10.15.27), which provides good anch, Plateau des Mats is an extensive rky bank, drying in places, up to 1·75M offshore. Dangers extend 1M seaward of Pte de St Jacques, and 3M offshore lies Plateau de la Recherche with depths of 1·8m.

BAIE DE QUIBERON (chart 2353)

The S side of bay is enclosed by a long chain of islands, islets, rks and shoals from Presqu'ile de Quiberon to Les Grands Cardinaux 13M SE. This chain includes the attractive islands of Houat (10.15.27) and Hoëdic, well worth visiting, preferably mid-week, and through it the main chan is Passage de la Teignouse which is well marked. In this chan the NE-going (flood) stream begins at HW Brest –0610, and the SW-going at HW Brest –0005, sp rates 3·75 kn: in strong winds it is best to pass at slack water. A good alternative chan is Passage du Béniguet, NW of Houat.

B de Quiberon is an important and attractive yachting area, with major centres at Crouesty (10.15.13), the Morbihan (10.15.15), La Trinité (10.15.16), Port Haliguen (10.15.17) and Port Maria (10.15.27).

BELLE ILE TO ILE DE GROIX (charts 2353, 2352)

Apart from rks which extend 0·75M W of Pte des Poulains, and La Truie (dries) marked by Bn Tr 0·5M off the S coast, there are no dangers more than 0·25M offshore. The S coast is much indented and exposed to swell from W: in good settled weather (only) and in absence of swell there is an attractive anch in Port du Vieux Château, 1M S of Pte des Poulains – see *N Biscay Pilot*. On the NE coast lie Le Palais (10.15.18) and Sauzon (10.15.27), which dries but has good anch off and is sheltered from S and W. Off Le Palais the ESE-going (flood) stream begins at HW Brest –0610, and the WNW- going at HW Brest +0125, sp rates 1·5 kn.

6M NNW of Pte des Poulains lies Plateau des Birvideaux (Lt), a rky bank (depth 2m) on which the sea breaks in bad weather. Between here and Lorient, Etel River (10.15.27 & chart 2352) is an attractive hbr, but must only be approached in good weather and on the last of the flood. The chan over the bar is shallow and shifts; local semaphore signals indicate the best water, or when entry is impossible. See 10.15.27.

Île de Groix lies in SW approach to Lorient (10.15.19). The main offlying dangers are shoals off Pte de la Croix, Les Chats which extend 1M SE from Pte des Chats, and shoals extending 0·75M seaward off Port Loc Maria.

Port Tudy (10.15.27), on N coast, is the main hbr, and is easy of access and well sheltered except from NE. Port Loc Maria is 0·75M W of Pte des Chats. The unspoiled little hbr is open to the S, but provides an attractive anch in offshore winds, and particularly near nps.

LORIENT TO BENODET (chart 2352)

Between Pte du Talut and Pte de Trévignon sandy beaches give way to rky cliffs. Grand Cochon and Petit Cochon lie about 1M offshore 2M NW of Pte de Keroch. There are many shoals in approaches to Rivière de Bélon and L'Aven. To the W, Ile Verte lies 0·6M S of Ile de Raguénès, with foul ground another 0·2M to S; Men an Tréas, a rk which dries, is 1M WSW of Ile Verte and marked by By; Corn Vas, depth 1·8m, is 1·75M SE of Pte de Trévignon, marked by a By; Men Du, a rk 0·3m high, lies about 1·25M SE of the same pt, and is marked by a Bn. From Pte de Trévignon to Pte de Cabellou (1M S of Concarneau, 10.15.20) rks extend nearly 1·5M offshore in places. Chaussée de Beg Meil extends 0·85M SE, where Linuen rk (dries) is marked by Bn. The coast W from Beg Meil is fringed by rks, many of which dry, extending 1M offshore, and 1·75M S of Pte de Mousterlin.

Along this coast are several hbrs and anchs, but most are dangerous to approach in strong onshore winds. They include Le Pouldu (Rivière de Quimperlé); Doëlan (but most of hbr dries); Merrien (also mostly dries); Brigneau; and Rivières de Bélon and L'Aven. All are described in *North Biscay Pilot*. For Doëlan and Pont-Aven see 10.15.27.

ILES DE GLÉNAN (chart 3640, French chart 6648)

Îles de Glénan lie off ent to Benodet (10.15.22). The main Is is Penfret (Lt), well known for its Centre Nautique, at NE corner of the group which, with its offlying dangers, stretches 5M from E to W and 4M from N to S. There are Bys on SE, S and SW sides. The islands are interesting to explore, but anchs are rather exposed. Easiest approach is from N, to W side of Penfret: anch there or proceed W to La Chambre, S of Île de St Nicolas. 3·5M E of Penfret lies Basse Jaune, a shallow bank part of which dries, marked by By. Between Îles de Glénan and Benodet lie Les Pourceaux, reefs which dry, and Île aux Moutons which has dangers extending SW and NW.

BENODET TO RAZ DE SEIN (chart 2351)

Between Benodet and Raz de Sein lies Pte de Penmarc'h (Lt, fog sig, RC) off which dangers extend 3M to SE, and 1M to S, W and NW, and breaking seas occur in strong winds. The hbrs of Loctudy, Lesconil and Le Guilvinec all provide sheltered anchs. See 10.15.27.

Chausée de Sein (chart 2351) is a chain of islands, rks and shoals extending 12M W from a position 3M WSW of Pte du Raz. The outer end is marked by a Lt By, and near inner end is Île de Sein (Lt, RC). 5M W of Île de Sein is Ar-Men Tr (Lt, fog sig), 0·5M E of which is a narrow N/S chan. Île de Sein is interesting to visit in fair weather and good vis, preferably near nps. Best appr is through Chenal d'Ezaudi, with Men-Brial Lt Ho, Oc(2) WRG 6s, on with third house (W with B stripe) from left, close S of Lt Ho, at 187°. Drying rks lie each side, and tide sets across the chan. Anchor off or inside mole, but exposed to N and E. Hbr partly dries. For directions on Île de Sein and Raz de Sein see *North Biscay Pilot* (Adlard Coles Nautical).

RAZ DE SEIN (chart 798)

Raz de Sein is the chan between Le Chat Bn Tr at E end of Chaussée de Sein and the dangers extending 0·8M off Pte du Raz, the extremity of which is marked by La Plate Lt Tr. 2M N of Raz de Sein is the Plateau de Tévennec, consisting of islets, rks and shoals which extend 0·5M in all directions from the Lt Ho thereon. Other dangers on the N side of the Raz are rks and shoals extending nearly 1M W and 0·8M WSW from Pointe du Van, and Basse Jaune (dries) 1M to N. On the S side the main dangers are: Cornoc Bras, a rk with depth of 3m, 1·5M SW of La Vieille Lt Tr; Masclougreiz, rky shoals on which sea can break heavily, 1·5M S of La Vieille; and Roche Moullec 1·5M SE of La Vieille.

In the middle of Raz de Sein the NE-going (flood) stream begins at HW Brest +0550, sp rate 6·5kn; the SW-going (ebb) stream begins at HW Brest –0030, sp rate 5·5kn. There are eddies near La Vieille on both streams. In good weather, near np, and with wind and tide together, the Raz presents no difficulty, but in moderately strong winds it should be taken at slack water, which lasts for about 0·5 hour at end of flood stream. In strong winds the chan must not be used with wind against tide, when there are overfalls with a steep breaking sea.

L'IROISE (chart 798)

Entering B de Douarnenez from Raz de Sein beware Basse Jaune, an isolated rk (dries) about 1M N of Pte du Van. 4·5M to E lies Duellou Rk (4m high) 0·5M offshore, with other rks extending 1M to E. Otherwise the S shore of the B is clear of dangers more than 0·2M offshore. Approaching Douarnenez (10.15.24) beware Basse Veur and Basse Neuve. On N side of B beware group of drying rks including La Pierre-Profonde and Le Taureau close SSW of Les Verrès (rk 9m high) which lies nearly 2·5M ESE of Morgat (10.15.25).

Off C de la Chèvre various dangers, on which the sea can break, extend SW for 2·25M to Basse Vieille (dries) which is marked by Lt By. 2·5M NW of C de la Chèvre is Le Chevreau (dries), with La Chèvre 0·5M to NE of it (1·25M WSW of Pte de Dinan). 7M W of Pte de Dinan lies Basse du Lis, rky shoals with depth of 2·4m, marked by Lt By.

On the NE side of L'Iroise (chart 3427) a chain of rks extends 7M W from Pte du Toulinguet. There are several chans through these rks, of which the most convenient for Camaret (10.15.26) and for Brest (10.16.9) is the inshore one – Chenal du Toulinguet, which runs between La Louve Bn Tr (0·1M W of Pte du Toulinguet) on E side and a rk called Le Pohen on the W side. Keep in the middle of the chan, which is about 0·3M wide. Here the N-going stream begins at HW Brest –0550, and the S-going at HW Brest +0015, sp rates 2·75kn.

10.15.6 DISTANCE TABLE

Approximate distances in nautical miles are by the most direct route while avoiding dangers and allowing for traffic separation schemes etc. Places in *italics* are in adjoining areas.

	1	2	3	4	5	6	7	8	9	10	11	12	13	14	15	16	17	18	19	20
1 *Le Four*																				
2 *Brest*	25																			
3 Camaret	21	8																		
4 Morgat	32	23	16																	
5 Douarnenez	42	27	21	11																
6 Pointe du Raz	30	24	18	17	20															
7 Audierne	40	34	28	27	30	10														
8 Pte de Penmarc'h	52	46	40	39	42	22	15													
9 Benodet	70	64	58	57	60	40	33	18												
10 Concarneau	74	68	62	61	64	44	37	22	11											
11 Lorient	98	92	86	85	88	68	61	46	36	32										
12 Port Haliguen	117	111	105	104	107	87	80	65	57	53	32									
13 Le Palais	111	105	99	98	101	81	74	59	52	47	26	11								
14 La Trinité	122	116	110	109	112	92	85	70	62	58	37	8	16							
15 Crouesty	122	116	110	109	112	92	85	70	62	58	37	9	16	8						
16 Roche Bernard	146	140	134	133	136	116	109	94	86	82	61	35	40	35	30					
17 Le Croisic	136	130	124	123	126	106	99	84	76	72	51	27	27	28	23	25				
18 St Nazaire	150	144	138	137	140	120	113	98	91	87	66	42	41	45	40	43	20			
19 *Ile d'Yeu*	156	150	144	143	146	126	119	104	98	95	76	56	50	60	56	61	38	34		
20 *La Rochelle*	216	210	204	203	206	186	179	164	158	155	136	116	110	120	116	121	98	94	60	

CANAL CONNECTIONS IN BRITTANY 10-15-8

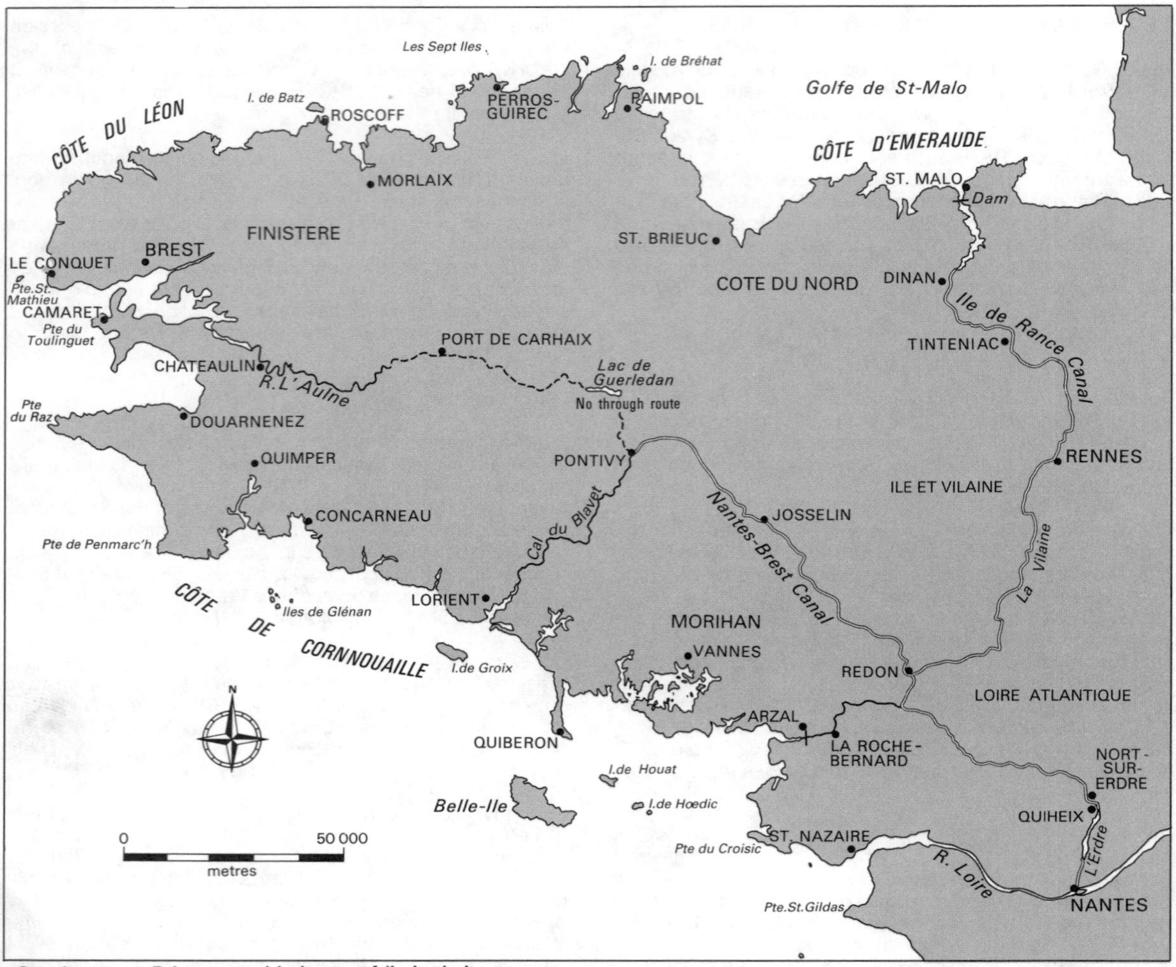
Les Sept Iles
I. de Bréhat
I. de Batz
ROSCOFF
PERROS-GUIREC
PAIMPOL
Golfe de St-Malo
CÔTE DU LÉON
CÔTE D'EMERAUDE
MORLAIX
ST. MALO
Dam
FINISTERE
ST. BRIEUC
LE CONQUET
BREST
Pte.St. Mathieu
CAMARET
Pte du Toulinguet
COTE DU NORD
DINAN
Ile de Rance Canal
TINTENIAC
PORT DE CARHAIX
CHATEAULIN
R.L'Aulne
Lac de Guerledan
No through route
Pte du Raz
DOUARNENEZ
QUIMPER
PONTIVY
RENNES
ILE ET VILAINE
Nantes-Brest Canal
JOSSELIN
CONCARNEAU
Cal du Blavet
Pte de Penmarc'h
La Vilaine
LORIENT
Iles de Glénan
CÔTE DE CORNOUAILLE
MORIHAN
VANNES
I.de Groix
REDON
LOIRE ATLANTIQUE
ARZAL
QUIBERON
LA ROCHE-BERNARD
I.de Houat
NORT-SUR-ERDRE
Belle-Ile
I.de Hœdic
QUIHEIX
0
50 000
metres
ST. NAZAIRE
Pte du Croisic
R. Loire
L'Erdre
Pte.St.Gildas
NANTES
N

Canals across Brittany enable boats of limited size to go from the Channel to the Bay of Biscay avoiding the passage around Finistere.

SUMMARY

Channel — Biscay (Ile et Rance Canal and La Vilaine)

	Length km	No of locks	Max draught m	Max air	Max length m	Max beam m	Speed limit
St MALO-ARZAL							
Rance Maritime	22.6	1	–	19	6.5	1.3	5.4
Ile de Rance Canal	84.8	48	1.1	2.5	26	4.5	4.3
La Vilaine	13·7	13	1·3	3·2/2·6 x	26	4·5	4·3

x Depending on water level.

	Length km	No of locks	Max draught m	Max air	Max length m	Max beam m	Speed limit
LORIENT-NANTES							
Canal du Blavet	70	28	1.4	2.6	26	4.6	4.3
Canal Nantes-Brest	184.3	106	–	3	26	4.6	4.3
Pontivy-Rohan			0.8				
Rohan-Josselin			1.0				
Josselin-Redon			1.4				
Redon-Quiheix			1.1				
L'Erdre	27.6	1	1.4	3.8	40	6.2	13.5
L'AULNE							
Chateaulin-Port de Carhaix	76	34	0.8	–	25	4.6	4.3

Contact: Channel—Biscay — Rennes 99.59.20.60
Redon 99.71.10.66

Nantes—Lorient (Brest) — Nantes 40.71.70.70
Hennebont 97.65.20.82
Lorient 97.21.21.54

Locks — shut in winter each Wednesday (approx first week in November to last week in March) for repairs. July and August, in order to conserve water, open on the hour only (and at half hour if traffic demands).

Channel—Biscay Assembly —Northbound—Lengager Lock. Southbound—Madeleine Lock.

For information and guide books write (with addressed envelope) to
Comité des Canaux Bretons,
Service de Documentation du Comité,
12 rue de Jemmapes,
44000 Nantes (Tel. 40.47.42.94)

RIVER LOIRE/ST NAZAIRE

Loire Atlantique

10-15-9

CHARTS

Admiralty 2985, 2989, 3216; SHOM 5992, 6261, 6260, 6493, 6797, 6854, 6825; ECM 248, 547

TIDES

St Nazaire-Dover: Springs +0445, Neaps −0540; ML 3·0; Duration: Springs 0640; Neaps 0445; Zone −0100

RIVER LOIRE/ST. NAZAIRE *continued*

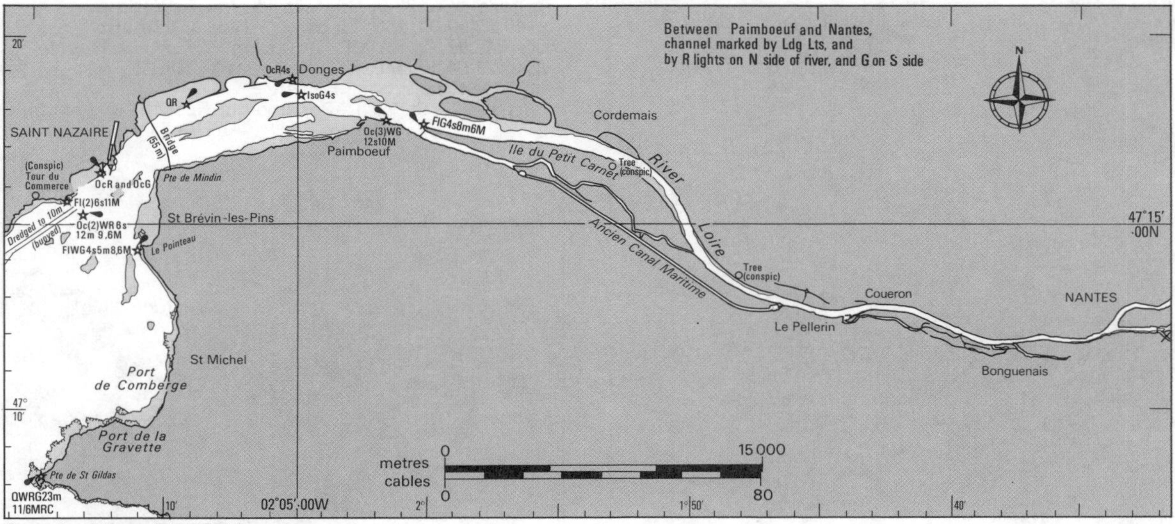
Between Paimboeuf and Nantes, channel marked by Ldg Lts, and by R lights on N side of river, and G on S side
N
20'
OcR4s
Donges
IsoG4s
QR
SAINT NAZAIRE
Bridge (55 m)
Oc(3)WG 12s10M
Paimboeuf
FlG4s8m6M
Cordemais
Ile du Petit Carnet
Tree (conspic)
River
Loire
(Conspic) Tour du Commerce
OcR and OcG
Pte de Mindin
Fl(2)6s11M
Dredged to 10m (buoyed)
Oc(2)WR6s 12m 9.6M
FlWG4s5m8.6M
St Brévin-les-Pins
Le Pointeau
Ancien Canal Maritime
Tree (conspic)
Coueron
NANTES
Le Pellerin
47°15'·00N
St Michel
Port de Comberge
Bonguenais
47° 10'
Port de la Gravette
metres
cables
0
15 000
80
Pte de St Gildas
QWRG23m 11/6MRC
10'
02°05'·00W
2°
1°50'
40'

Standard Port BREST (⟶)

Times				Height (metres)			
HW		LW		MHWS	MHWN	MLWN	MLWS
0000	0600	0000	0600	7·5	5·9	3·0	1·4
1200	1800	1200	1800				
Differences ST NAZAIRE							
+0030	−0025	−0005	−0010	−2·0	−1·7	−1·1	−0·8
NANTES (Chantenay)							
+0155	+0140	+0330	+0245	−1·8	−1·3	−1·1	+0·1

SHELTER
In strong winds from West the bar is only safe HW−3 to HW. St Nazaire is principally commercial although yachts can stop exceptionally. Yachts enter the Bassin de St Nazaire through E lock and berth at S end of Bassin Penhoët. Port Control and Hr Mr NE side of Avant Port. Anchorages in Bonne Anse and Villez Martin.

NAVIGATION
Waypoint Chenal du Sud 47°07'·95N 02°20'·00W, 205°/025° from/to front Ldg Lt 025°, 7·3M. Entrance to Loire divided by La Banche bank with well marked channels N and S. River is shallow beyond Nantes but is navigable in optimum conditions for small craft West of Angers. At Nantes the Brittany canal system can be entered through canal Saint-Felix by Malakoff Lock (see 10.15.8); also there are places reserved for visiting yachts at Trentemoult near the Bureau du Port, accessible at all times.

LIGHTS AND MARKS
Ldg Lts over bar, 025°; both Q 23/27M, intens 022°-028°.

RADIO TELEPHONE
St Nazaire Port VHF Ch 12 16; 06 12 14 67 69 (H24). Other stations: Donges VHF Ch 12 16; 12 14 67 69 (H24). Pte de Chémoulin Sig Stn Ch 16.
Nantes VHF Ch 12 16; 06 12 67 69 (H24); water level reports bcst on Ch 73 every 15 min commencing H+00.

TELEPHONE
ST NAZAIRE Hr Mr 40.00.45.20; Aff Mar 40.22.46.32; CROSS 97.55.35.35; SNSM 40.61.03.20; # 40.66.82.65; Meteo 40.90.00.80; Auto 40.90.19.19; Police 40.70.55.00; Dr 40.22.15.32; Ⓗ 40.90.60.60.
NANTES Hr Mr 40.44.20.54; Aff Mar 40.73.18.70; # 40.73.39.55; Meteo 40.84.80.19; Auto 40.04.15.15; Dr 40.47.03.19; Ⓗ 40.48.33.33; Brit Consul 40.63.16.02.

FACILITIES
ST NAZAIRE **La Société Nautique de St Nazaire** ☎ 40.70.10.47, M; **Genet-Loisirs** ☎ 40.22.44.52, M, ME, El, Sh, CH; **Quai** P, D, L, FW, C; **Perraud** ☎ 40.22.51.39, ME, El; **Burodess** ☎ 40.22.11.12; SHOM; **CRM** ☎ 40.66.25.99, Ⓔ; **Town** V, Gaz, R, Bar. ✉; Ⓑ; ⇌; Air.
NANTES **Quai** FW, C; **Librairie Beaumont** ☎ 40.48.24.21, CH, SHOM; **Ancre Marine** ☎ 40.73.86.22, ME, CH, SHOM, El, Ⓔ; **Town** all facilities; ✉; Ⓑ; ⇌; ✈.
Ferry UK — St Malo—Portsmouth; Roscoff—Plymouth.

LE POULIGUEN 10-15-10
(PORT OF LA BAULE)
Loire Atlantique

CHARTS
Admiralty 3216, 2353; SHOM 6825, 7033; ECM 547

TIDES
Dover: Springs +0435 Neaps +0530; ML 2·9; Duration: Springs 0530 Neaps 0645; Zone −0100

Standard Port BREST (⟶)

Times				Height (metres)			
HW		LW		MHWS	MHWN	MLWN	MLWS
0000	0600	0000	0600	7·5	5·9	3·0	1·4
1200	1800	1200	1800				
Differences LE POULIGUEN							
+0015	−0040	0000	−0020	−2·1	−1·8	−1·2	−0·9

SHELTER
Very good shelter, protected from all winds except SE. Approach from West between Pte de Penchateau and the Grand Charpentier. Best approach HW−1. Visitors berths (30) on Quai Rageot de la Touche.

NAVIGATION
Waypoint 47°15'·00N 02°25'·00W, 232°/052° from/to Basse Martineau buoy, 0·58M. Beware rocks extending 4 M to the Grand Charpentier Lt Ho and breakers in shallow water when wind in S. It is not advisable to enter at night. Beware strong ebb tide.

LIGHTS AND MARKS
From Basse Martineau leave La Vieille and Les Impairs as on chartlet to stbd, and two Bns off Penchateau to port. S Jetty QR 13m 9M; vis 171°-081°.

RADIO TELEPHONE
Pouliguen VHF Ch 09. Pornichet Ch 09.

TELEPHONE (40)
Hr Mr 40.60.37.40; Aff Mar 40.42.32.55; CROSS 97.55.35.35; SNSM 40.61.03.20; # 40.61.32.04; Meteo 40.90.00.80; Auto 40.90.19.19; Police 40.24.48.17; Dr Le Pouliguen 40.60.51.73; Dr La Baule 40.60.17.20; Brit Consul 40.63.16.02.

FACILITIES
Quai (Pontoons 620) ☎ 40.60.03.50, Slip, P, D, AC, L, FW, C (18 ton); **Callaghan Naval** ☎ 40.60.05.60, M, ME, Sh, CH; **Petit Breton Nautique** ☎ 40.42.10.14, M, ME, Ⓔ, El, Sh, CH; **Prat** ☎ 40.60.31.30, Sh, Divers; **Voilerie X Voiles** ☎ 40.60.47.52, SM; **Le Baule YC** ☎ 40.60.20.90 (allocates berths for visitors); **Town** V, Gaz, R, Bar. ✉ (Le Pouliguen and La Baule); Ⓑ (Le Pouliguen and La Baule); ⇌ (La Baule); ✈ (St Nazaire, La Baule).
Ferry UK — St Malo—Portsmouth; Roscoff—Plymouth.

15

LE POULIGUEN *continued*

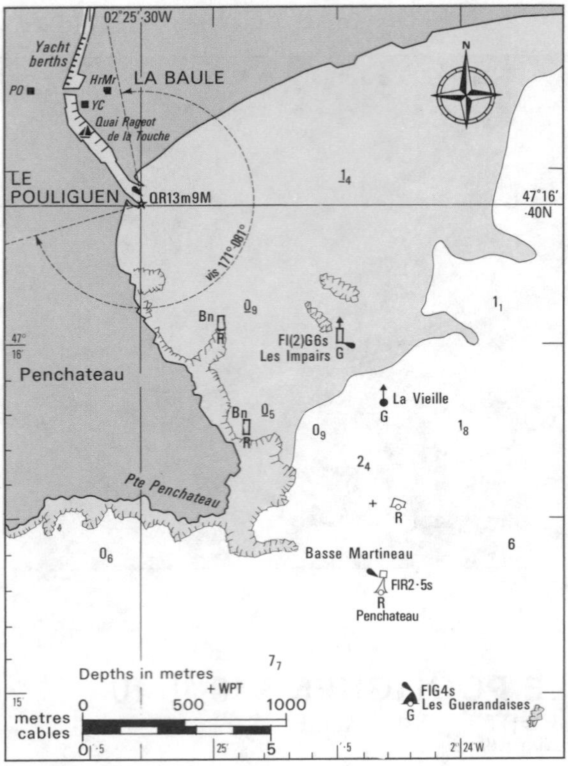

02°25'·30W
Yacht berths
HrMr
LA BAULE
PO
YC
Quai Rageot de la Touche
LE POULIGUEN
QR13m9M
47°16'·40N
vis 171°-081°
Bn
R
Fl(2)G6s
Les Impairs
G
La Vieille
G
Penchateau
Pte Penchateau
Basse Martineau
FlR2·5s
R
Penchateau
Depths in metres
+ WPT
FlG4s
Les Guerandaises
G
metres
cables
0
500
1000
2°24'W

LE CROISIC 10-15-11

Loire Atlantique

CHARTS
Admiralty 2353; SHOM 6826, 6825, 7033; ECM 546, 547

TIDES
+0450 Dover; ML 3·0; Duration 0605; Zone −0100

Standard Port BREST (⟶)

Times				Height (metres)			
HW		LW		MHWS	MHWN	MLWN	MLWS
0000	0600	0000	0600	7·5	5·9	3·0	1·4
1200	1800	1200	1800				
Differences LE CROISIC							
+0030	−0030	−0015	−0010	−2·3	−1·8	−1·1	−0·8
ILE DE HÖEDIC							
−0005	−0025	−0030	−0020	−2·3	−1·9	−1·1	−0·8

SHELTER
Safest anchorage is up Pen Bron creek. Alongside berths, called *Chambres* formed by islands called *Jonchères*, dry out. Access HW ∓ 1. Yachts use the fifth *Chambre*. A mooring may be available in Le Poul.

NAVIGATION
Waypoint 47°19'·00N 02°31'·80W, 336°/156° from/to front Ldg Lt 156°, 1·2M. At springs, tides run up to 4 kn. Safest entry then is HW−1. Beware the rocks at Hergo tower. Beware that the Tréhic Lt, which leads clear of distant dangers, will lead onto close dangers.

LIGHTS AND MARKS
Ldg Lts 156°. Front Dir Oc(2+1) 12s 10m 18M; Y topmark on W pylon. Rear Dir Oc(2+1) 12s 14m 18M; Y topmark on W pylon, G top; both intens 154°-158°, synchronized. Ldg Lts 174° both QG 5/8m 11M; G & W structures; vis 170°-177°. Ldg Lts 134° both QR. The sanatorium and hospital are conspic.

RADIO TELEPHONE
VHF Ch 16.

TELEPHONE (40)
Hr Mr 40.23.10.95; Port de Plaisance 40.23.10.95; Aff Mar 40.23.05.38; CROSS 97.55.35.35; SNSM 40.23.01.17; # 40.23.05.38; Meteo 40.90.08.80; Police 40.23.00.19; Dr 40.23.01.70; Ⓗ 40.23.01.12; Brit Consul 40.63.16.02.

FACILITIES
Marina (220+15 visitors), P, D, FW, C, ME, El, Sh; **Quai** Slip, M, FW, ME, El, Sh, C (10 ton), CH, V, R, Bar; **Bollore** ☎ 40.23.00.85, ME; **Marine Atlantique** ☎ 40.23.09.00, ME, El, Sh, Ⓔ, Divers; **Lemerie** ☎ 40.42.92.12, M, ME, El, Ⓔ, Sh, CH; **Meca Navale** ☎ 40.23.04.10, ME, El, Sh. **Town** V, Gaz, R, Bar. ✉; Ⓑ; ≉; ✈ (St Nazaire, La Baule).
Ferry UK — St Malo—Portsmouth; Roscoff—Plymouth.

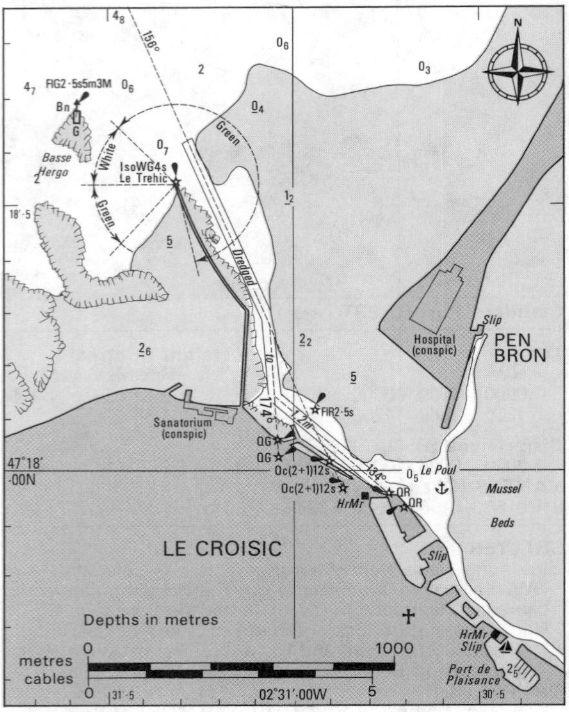

156°
FlG2·5s5m3M
Bn
G
Basse Hergo
White
Green
IsoWG4s
Le Trehic
Dredged
Hospital (conspic)
Slip
PEN BRON
FlR2·5s
Sanatorium (conspic)
QG
QG
Oc(2+1)12s
Oc(2+1)12s
HrMr
QR
QR
Le Poul
Mussel Beds
47°18'·00N
LE CROISIC
Slip
Depths in metres
HrMr
Slip
Port de Plaisance
metres
cables
0
1000
02°31'·00W

LA ROCHE BERNARD 10-15-12

Morbihan

CHARTS
Admiralty 2353; SHOM 2381, 5418, 7033; ECM 546

TIDES
+0500 Dover; ML (Pénerf) 3·1; Duration 0610; Zone −0100

Standard Port BREST (⟶)

Times				Height (metres)			
HW		LW		MHWS	MHWN	MLWN	MLWS
0000	0600	0000	0600	7·5	5·9	3·0	1·4
1200	1800	1200	1800				
Differences PÉNERF							
−0010	−0020	−0025	−0020	−2·0	−1·7	−1·0	−0·7

SHELTER
Good shelter, on S bank of La Vilaine, about 7M E of Tréhiguier. There are two marinas — Nouveau Port close to bridge (clearance 30m) and Vieux Port (or Quai de Sainte-Antoine) ¼M downstream. Anchor at Tréhiguier or at Vieille Roche while waiting for lock at Arzal (see 10.15.27).

LA ROCHE BERNARD *continued*

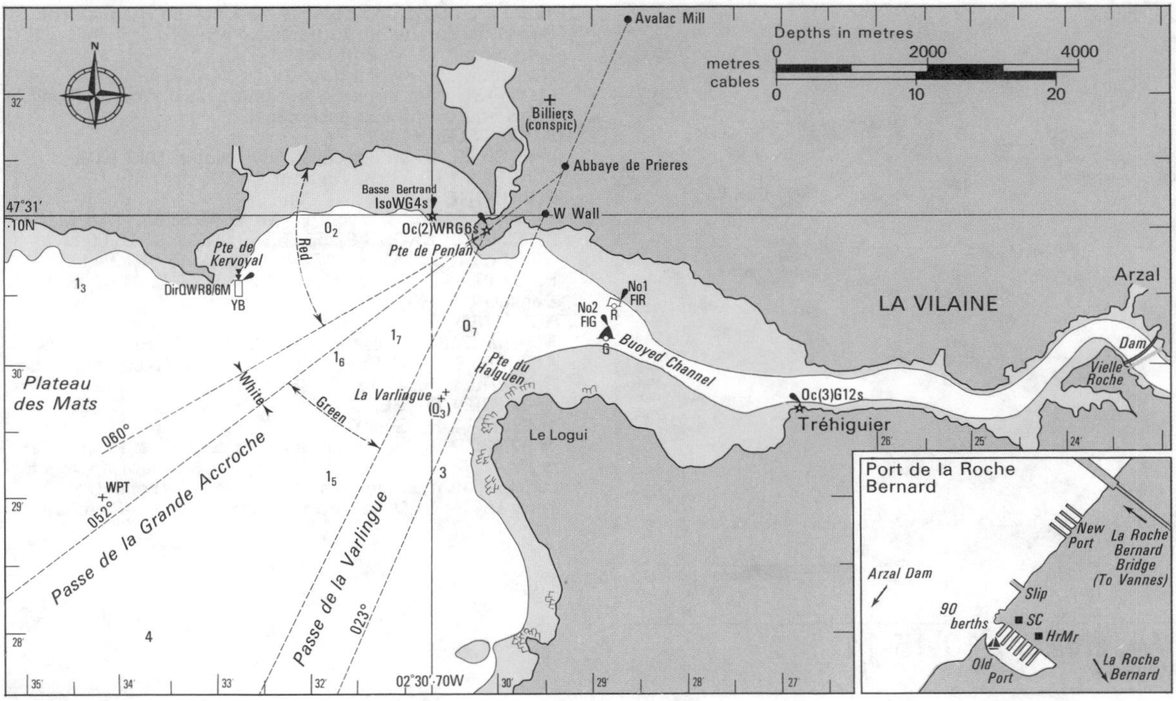
Avalac Mill
Depths in metres
metres
cables
0
2000
4000
0
10
20
Billiers (conspic)
Abbaye de Prieres
W Wall
Basse Bertrand IsoWG4s
Oc(2)WRG6s
Pte de Penlan
47°31'·10N
Pte de Kervoyal
DirQWR8/6M
YB
Red
White
Green
Plateau des Mats
060°
052°
WPT
Passe de la Grande Accroche
Passe de la Varlingue
023°
La Varlingue
Pte du Halguen
Le Logui
No1 FIR
No2 FIG
Buoyed Channel
LA VILAINE
Arzal
Dam
Vielle Roche
Oc(3)G12s
Tréhiguier
02°30'·70W
Port de la Roche Bernard
New Port
La Roche Bernard Bridge (To Vannes)
Arzal Dam
Slip
90 berths
SC
HrMr
Old Port
La Roche Bernard

NAVIGATION
La Vilaine waypoint Passe de la Grande Accroche 47°29'·00N 02°34'·28W, 234°/054° from/to Penlan Lt, 3·5M. Approach to La Vilaine has a bar (min 0·5m except for La Varlingue rocks which dry 0·3m off Pte du Halguen — beware this when sailing channel 1 below). Sea breaks on the bar in strong on-shore winds especially with low or ebb tides. Follow the line of cockle beds for deep water. The dam, Le Barrage d'Arzal, down river, has a lock which opens on the hour 0700 to 2200 (LT) in July and August; in other months 0730, 0900, 1030, 1200, 1400, 1600, 1730, 1900, 2000 LT. Yachts should keep strictly to the channel above and below the dam. Yachts with masts can reach Redon where there is a marina and access to Brittany canal system (see 10.15.8). There is a swing bridge at Pont Cran, before reaching Redon.

LIGHTS AND MARKS
There are two approaches to river entrance:
(1) Passe de la Varlingue (W wall, Abbey de Prieres and Avalac Mill in line at 023°), unlit.
(2) Passe de la Grande Accroche (Lt Ho and Abbey de Prieres in line at 052°).
Two principal lights
(1) Basse Bertrand G Tr, Iso WG 4s 6m 9/6M W040°-054°, G054°-227°, W227°-234°, G234°-040°.
(2) Penlan W Tr with R bands Oc (2) WRG 6s 26m 16/11M, R292°-025°, G025°-052°, W052°-060°, R060°-138°, G138°-180°.
Channel from Pte du Halguen to Tréhiguier marked by R and G numbered buoys.

RADIO TELEPHONE
None.

TELEPHONE (99)
Hr Mr 99.90.62.17; Aff Mar 97.41.12.43; CROSS 97.55.35.35; # (Vannes) 97.63.18.71; Auto 97.42.49.49; Police 99.90.61.06; Dr 99.90.61.25; Ⓗ 99.90.61.20; Brit Consul 40.63.16.02.

FACILITIES
Marina (New Port) (70), ☎ 99.90.65.91, FW, AC, C, CH; **Marina (Old Port)** (200), ☎ 99.90,66.77, P, D, ▣, CH, FW, Slip; **Chantier Naval de la Couronne** ☎ 99.90.66.77, M, ME, El, Ⓔ, Sh, CH. **Arvor Marine** ☎ 99.90.64.98, ME, El, Ⓔ, Sh, CH; **Town** V, Gaz, R, Bar. ✉; Ⓑ; ≹ (Pontchateau); ✈ (Nantes or Rennes). Ferry UK — St Malo—Portsmouth; Roscoff—Plymouth.

CROUESTY-EN-ARZON
Morbihan

10-15-13

CHARTS
Admiralty 2358, 2353; SHOM 6992, 7034, 7033; ECM 546

TIDES
+0505 Dover; ML 3·0; Duration 0555; Zone −0100

Standard Port BREST (⟶)

Times				Height (metres)			
HW		LW		MHWS	MHWN	MLWN	MLWS
0000	0600	0000	0600	7·5	5·9	3·0	1·4
1200	1800	1200	1800				
Differences PORT NAVALO							
+0025	−0005	−0010	−0005	−2·5	−2·0	−1·1	−0·7

SHELTER
Good shelter, protected from all winds by Quiberon peninsular. A very large marina gives added protection.

NAVIGATION
Waypoint 47°32'·12N 02°55'·00W, 238°/058° from/to front Ldg Lt, 0·85M. There are no navigational dangers, the entrance being well marked.

LIGHTS AND MARKS
Ldg Lts 058°, Front Q 10m 19M on metal tower, Rear Q 27m 19M on W column: both intens 056°-060°. Marina breakwater heads: N Oc (2) R 6s, S Fl G 4s.

RADIO TELEPHONE
VHF Ch 09.

TELEPHONE (97)
Hr Mr 97.53.73.33; Aff Mar 97.41.84.10; CROSS 97.55.35.35; Meteo 97.64.34.86; Auto 97.84.82.83; SNSM 97.41.27.40; # 97.53.25.66; Police 97.53.71.65; Dr 97.51.60.05; Dr (Arzon) 97.26.23.23; Brit Consul 40.63.16.02.

FACILITIES
Marina (1000+120 visitors) ☎ 97.53.73.33, BH (45 ton), P, D, L, FW, ME, El, Sh, Slip, CH, AB, Bar, C (3 ton); **Ateliers Maritimes du Crouesty** ☎ 97.53.71.30, M, ME, El, Ⓔ, Sh, CH; **Chantier Naval du Redo** ☎ 97.53.78.70, ME, El, Ⓔ, Sh, CH; **Diamond Sailmakers France** ☎ 97.53.78.58, SM; **Town** V, Gaz, R, Bar. ✉ (Arzon); Ⓑ (Arzon); ≹ (Vannes); ✈ (Lorient—Nantes)
Ferry UK — St Malo—Portsmouth; Roscoff—Plymouth.

CROUESTY-EN-ARZON *continued*

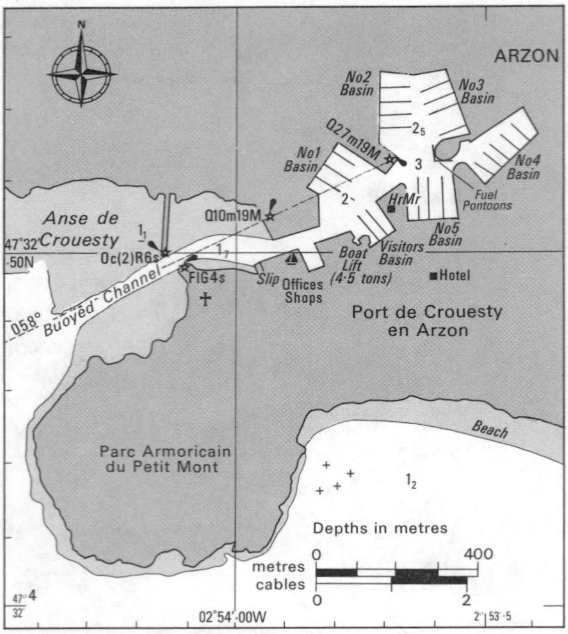
ARZON
No2 Basin
No3 Basin
027°m19M
No1 Basin
No4 Basin
HrMr
Fuel Pontoons
Anse de Crouesty
Q10m19M
47°32'·50N
Oc(2)R6s
Fl G4s
No5 Basin
Visitors Basin
Boat Lift (4·5 tons)
Hotel
Slip
Offices Shops
058° Buoyed Channel
Port de Crouesty en Arzon
Beach
Parc Armoricain du Petit Mont
Depths in metres
metres
cables
0
400
2
02°54'·00W
2°53'·5

VANNES 10-15-14

Morbihan

CHARTS
Admiralty 2358, 2353; SHOM 7034, 7033; ECM 546

TIDES
−0515 Dover; ML 2·7; Duration —; Zone −0100

Standard Port BREST (⟶)

Times				Height (metres)			
HW		LW		MHWS	MHWN	MLWN	MLWS
0000	0600	0000	0600	7·5	5·9	3·0	1·4
1200	1800	1200	1800				
Differences VANNES							
+0145	+0155	+0200	+0105	−4·1	−3·2	−2·0	−1·0

SHELTER
Very good shelter, protected from all winds. Access to the port by day only. Marina boat will meet and indicate pontoon. Lock into wet basin opens HW∓2½ (0800-2000 (LT) in season; 0830-1900 (LT) other periods). Swing bridge opens on the hour and half hour whilst lock is open. Details from Marina office. Lock sill 1·3m above CD.

NAVIGATION
Waypoint — see 10.15.15. Beware very strong streams off the Réchauds, after passing between the Ile aux Moines and the mainland — Réchauds rocks marked by two beacons to stbd. Thereafter passage to Conleau is straightforward and well marked. Passage on to Vannes only advisable near HW.

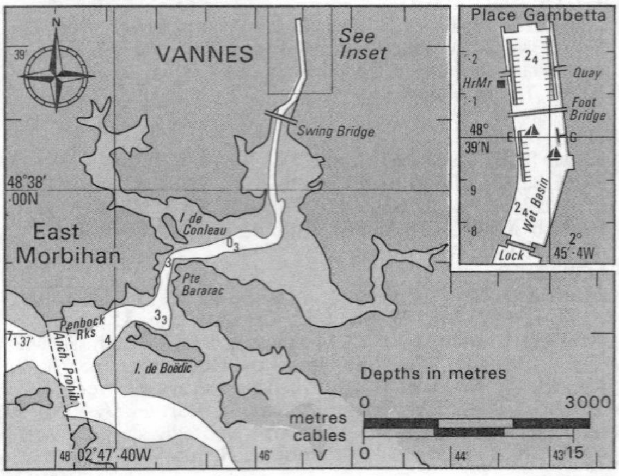
VANNES
See Inset
Swing Bridge
48°38'·00N
East Morbihan
I. de Conleau
Pte Bararac
Penbock Rks
Anch. Prohib
I. de Boëdic
Depths in metres
metres
cables
0
3000
02°47'·40W
Place Gambetta
HrMr
Quay
Foot Bridge
48°39'N
Wet Basin
Lock
2°45'·4W

LIGHTS AND MARKS
There are buoys and perches marking the channel from Pointe de Bararac up to Vannes.
G Lt over R Lt = Port closed
No lights = Port open
Lts shown from the lock, but boats must stop and wait at the S end of the approach canal.

RADIO TELEPHONE
VHF Ch 09. (Summer 0800-2100; winter 0900-1200, 1330-1800 LT). Yacht Harbour Ch 09.

TELEPHONE (97)
Hr Mr 97.54.16.08; Yacht Hr Mr ☎ 51.58.38.11Aff Mar 97.63.40.95; CROSS 97.55.35.35; SNSM 97.26.00.56; # 97.63.18.71; Meteo 97.64.34.86; Auto 97.42.49.49; Police 97.54.22.56; Dr 97.47.47.25; Ⓗ 97.42.66.42; Brit Consul 40.63.16.02.

FACILITIES
Marina (240+60 visitors), ☎ 97.54.16.08, Slip, ⊡, FW, AC, ME, Sh, C (12 ton), V, R, P and D (1400–1700); **La Corderie** ☎ 97.47.15.52, CH; **Vannes Nautique** ☎ 97.63.20.17, ME, Sh, El, Ⓔ, CH; **Voilerie Daniel** ☎ 97.47.14.41, Gas, CH, SM, SHOM; **Marin Tronics** ☎ 97.42.58.75, Ⓔ; **Quai visiteurs** Slip, FW; **Le Pennec** ☎ 97.47.32.09, P, D, ME, El, Sh (on E side of approach canal). **Town** all facilities. ✉; Ⓑ; ⇌; ✈ (Lorient).
Ferry UK — St Malo—Portsmouth; Roscoff—Plymouth.

MORBIHAN 10-15-15

Morbihan

CHARTS
Admiralty 2358, 2353; SHOM 6992, 7034, 7033; ECM 546.

TIDES
−0515 Dover; ML 3·1; Zone −0100

Standard Port BREST (⟶)

Times				Height (metres)			
HW		LW		MHWS	MHWN	MLWN	MLWS
0000	0600	0000	0600	7·5	5·9	3·0	1·4
1200	1800	1200	1800				
Differences AURAY							
+0025	−0005	+0025	−0005	−2·6	−2·0	−1·1	−0·6

SHELTER
Golfe du Morbihan is an inland sea with deep approaches and entrance. It is about 50 sq miles and thick with islands, most of which are privately owned. There are numerous anchorages, some of which are shown on the chartlet below and some are as follows (see chart 2358):
PORT NAVALO — anchor in bay but exposed to W to NW winds. All facilities.
LE ROCHER — in Auray river. Good shelter.
AURAY — anchor in middle of river (3·5m) or go alongside at St Goustan. Road bridge clearance 14m.
LARMOR BADEN — perfect anchorage to N (2 to 4m).
ILE AUX MOINES — one of the public islands. Anchor off N end, landing at Pt. de Drech or Pt. de Réchauds, or secure to yacht moorings (see Hr Mr).
ILE PIREN — good anchorage but in tidal stream.
ILE D'ARS — one of the public islands. Anchor NE of Pt de Beluré where there is a landing.
VANNES — see 10.15.14.
PORT BLANC MARINA 1¼ M WSW of Pt d'Aradon.
NOYALLO RIVER — anchor in Anse de Truscatte or between Le Passage and Ile de Pechit.
KERNES — off the Anse de Kernes in 3 to 6m.
AR GAZEK — in Ile de Jument in perfect shelter.

NAVIGATION
Waypoint 47°32'·00N 02°55'·13W, 180°/000° from/to Port-Navalo Lt, 0·90M. Beware very strong tides, max 8 kn, which run in the entrance and between some of the islands. Channels and dangers are well marked.

MORBIHAN *continued*

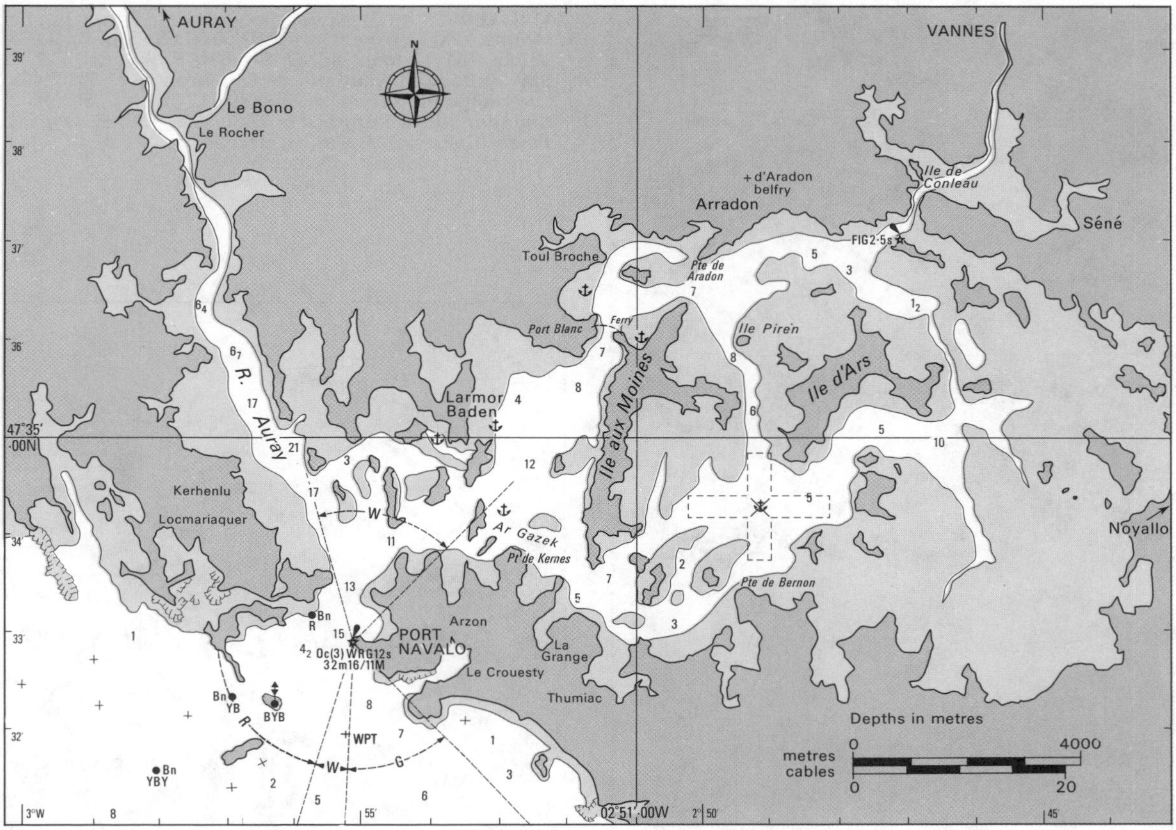
AURAY
VANNES
N
Le Bono
Le Rocher
+d'Aradon belfry
Arradon
Ile de Conleau
Séné
FlG2·5s
Toul Broche
Pte de Aradon
Port Blanc
Ferry
Ile Piren
Ile d'Ars
Ile aux Moines
R. Auray
Larmor Baden
47°35'·00N
Kerhenlu
Locmariaquer
Ar Gazek
Pt de Kernes
Pte de Bernon
Noyallo
Arzon
PORT NAVALO
Oc(3) WRG12s 32m16/11M
La Grange
Le Crouesty
Thumiac
Bn
YB
BYB
YBY
WPT
Depths in metres
metres
cables
0
4000
20
3°W
55'
02°51'·00W
2°50'
45'

TOWNS

PORT NAVALO. all facilities. # ☎ 97.41.21.53; Police 97.24.17.17.

AURAY. All facilities. Aff Mar ☎ 97.24.01.43; **Accastillage Diffusion** ☎ 97.24.18.89, ME, El, Sh, CH, SHOM; **Miran** ☎ 97.24.07.19, ME, Sh, CH; **Chatenay et Cie 'La Chateyne'** ☎ 97.24.91.52, CH.

LE BONO — Anchorage. **Boursicot** ☎ 97.57.82.57, ME.

LARMOR BADEN. Aff Mar ☎ 97.57.05.66.

ILE AUX MOINES. Bureau du Port ☎ 97.26.30.57, M, FW. Yachts can secure to moorings — see Hr Mr.

LOCMARIAQUER. Protected anchorage. **Madec** ☎ 97.24.92.56, ME.

ARRADON — good anchorage. Slip; Hr Mr 97.26.01.23; **Mechanique Marine** (Pramer) ☎ 97.26.01.16, ME.

CONLEAU — Anchorage in bight just S of village. **Le Mée (Michelet)**, ME, El, Sh.

VANNES (see 10.15.14).

SÉNÉ — **Le Gal** ☎ 97.66.96.90, ME.

ILE D'ARS — Rudevent. Visitors anchorage, slip; exposed to winds from S and E. **Toussaint Guy** ☎ 97.26.30.01, ME, El, Sh.

PORT BLANC — Hr Mr 97.57.01.00. Limited facilities.

15

LA TRINITÉ-SUR-MER

Morbihan

10-15-16

CHARTS

Admiralty 2358, 2353; SHOM 5352, 7032; ECM 546, 545

TIDES

+0455 Dover; ML 3·1; Duration 0610; Zone −0100

Standard Port BREST (⟶)

Times				Height (metres)			
HW		LW		MHWS	MHWN	MLWN	MLWS
0000	0600	0000	0600	7·5	5·9	3·0	1·4
1200	1800	1200	1800				
Differences LA TRINITÉ							
+0010	−0020	−0025	−0015	−2·1	−1·7	−0·9	−0·7

SHELTER

Very good shelter except in strong SE to S winds when the sandbank La Vanererse is covered. Anchorage in the river is forbidden. Marina boat will meet and indicate pontoon. Access day and night at all tides.

NAVIGATION

Waypoint 47°31'·90N 02°59'·63W, 167°/347° from/to front Ldg Lt 347°, 2·3M. Beware many oyster beds, marked with perches. There are no navigational dangers and the river is well marked by buoys and perches. Deepest water close to E shore. Anchoring and fishing prohibited. Speed limit 5 kn.

LIGHTS AND MARKS

Ldg Lts 347°. Front Q WRG (W345°-013°). Rear QW 21m 17M; synchronised; intens 337°-357°. Dir Lt 347° Oc WRG 4s (W346°-348°).

RADIO TELEPHONE

Marina VHF Ch 09.

TELEPHONE (97)

Hr Mr Port de Plaisance 97.55.71.49; Aff Mar 97.55.73.46; CROSS 97.55.35.35; SNSM 97.24.00.14; # 97.55.73.46; Meteo 97.64.34.86; Auto 97.84.82.83; Police 97.55.71.62; Dr 97.55.74.03; Brit Consul 40.63.16.02.

FACILITIES

Marina (900+100 visitors) ☎ 97.55.71.27, AC, P, D, FW, BH (36 ton), Gridiron; **Kervilor** ☎ 97.55.71.69, M, ME, El, CH; **Le Cuillier** ☎ 97.55.82.01, CH, SHOM; **Rioux** ☎ 97.55.72.43, ME, CH; **S.E.E.M.A.** ☎ 97.55.78.06, Ⓔ; **Technique Voile** ☎ 97.55.78.08, CH, SM; **Club Nautique** ☎ 97.55.73.48; **Town** V, Gaz, R, Bar. ✉; Ⓑ; ⇌ (Auray); ✈ (Lorient).

Ferry UK — Roscoff—Plymouth; St Malo—Portsmouth.

LA TRINITE-SUR-MER *continued*

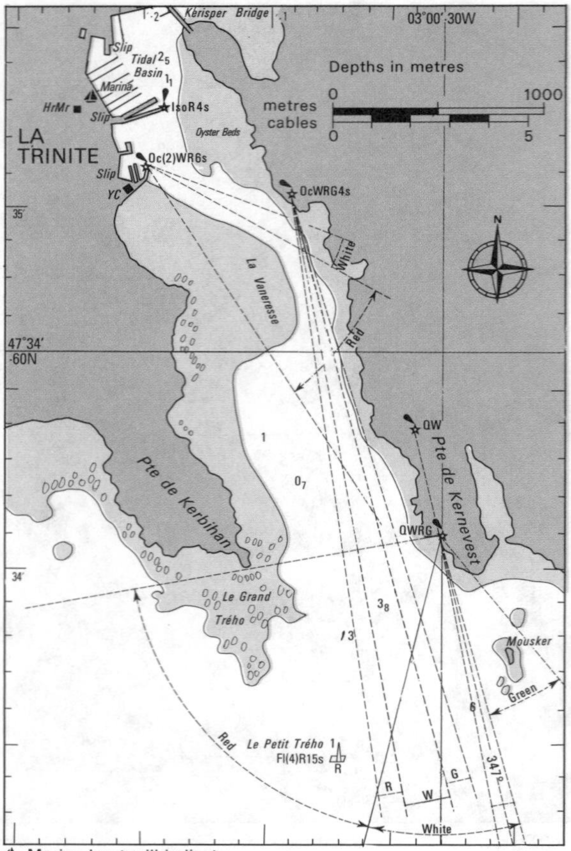
Kerisper Bridge
03°00'·30W
Depths in metres
metres
cables
0
1000
5
Slip
Tidal Basin
Marina
HrMr
Slip
IsoR4s
Oyster Beds
LA TRINITE
Oc(2)WR6s
Slip
YC
OcWRG4s
35'
White
La Vanenesse
Red
47°34'·60N
QW
Pte de Kernevest
Pte de Kerbihan
QWRG
34'
Le Grand Trého
Mousker
Green
Red
Le Petit Trého
Fl(4)R15s
R
W
G
347°
White

▲ Marina boat will indicate

FACILITIES
Marina (640 + 80 visitors) ☎ 97.50.20.56, Slip, P, D, C (2 ton), BH (13 ton), ME, El, Sh, Bar, R, AC, CH, FW, ◙, SM, V; **Société Nautique de Quiberon** ☎ 97.50.17.45; **Loc'Haliguen Marine** ☎ 97.30.40.81, CH, ME, El, Sh; **Chantier Naval Kergroix** ☎ 97.30.80.87 ME, El, Sh, CH; **Town** (Quiberon) V, Gaz, R, Bar. ✉; Ⓑ; ⇌; ✈.
Ferry UK — Roscoff—Plymouth.

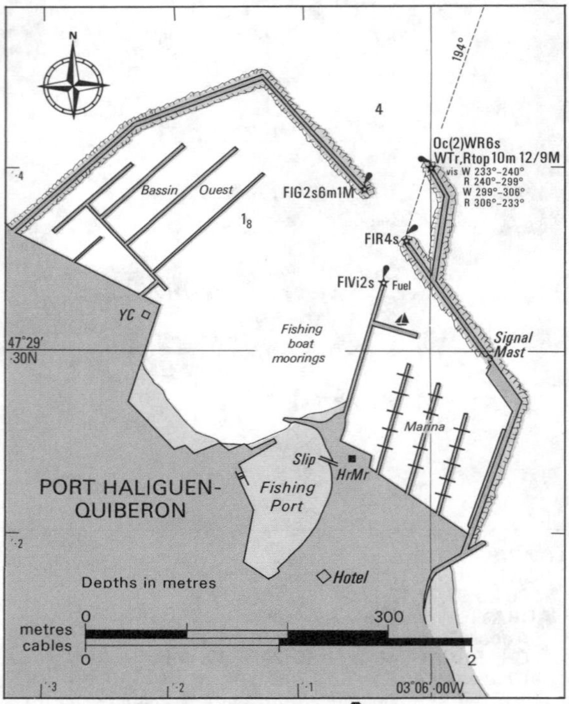
N
194°
4
Oc(2)WR6s
WTr,Rtop10m 12/9M
vis W 233°-240°
R 240°-299°
W 299°-306°
R 306°-233°
Bassin Ouest
Fl G2s6m1M
1₈
FlR4s
FlVi2s
Fuel
YC
Fishing boat moorings
47°29'·30N
Signal Mast
Marina
Slip
HrMr
PORT HALIGUEN-QUIBERON
Fishing Port
Hotel
Depths in metres
metres
cables
0
300
2
03°06'·00W

PORT HALIGUEN-QUIBERON

Morbihan

10-15-17

CHARTS
Admiralty 2353; Imray C38; SHOM 5352, 7032; ECM 545

TIDES
+0500 Dover; ML 3·0; Duration 0615; Zone −0100

Standard Port BREST (⟶)

Times				Height (metres)			
HW		LW		MHWS	MHWN	MLWN	MLWS
0000	0600	0000	0600	7·5	5·9	3·0	1·4
1200	1800	1200	1800				
Differences PORT HALIGUEN-QUIBERON							
0000	−0020	−0025	−0015	−2·3	−1·9	−1·0	−0·8

SHELTER
Good shelter but strong winds from NW to NE make it uncomfortable. Yachts usually moor stern to pontoons. Secure to visitors' pontoon and ask the Hr Mr. Access at all tides, day and night.

NAVIGATION
Waypoint 47°29'·80N 03°05'·00W, 060°/240° from/to breakwater Lt, 0·75M. Approach from E or SE. Beware shoal (1·8m) ENE of breakwater Lt in R sector 240°-299°.

LIGHTS AND MARKS
W sector 246°-252° of Port Maria Lt (Q WRG) leads N of Banc de Quiberon; W sector 299°-306° of Haliguen Lt (Oc(2)WR 6s) leads S of it.

RADIO TELEPHONE
VHF Ch 09.

TELEPHONE (97)
Hr Mr 97.50.20.56; Aff Mar 97.50.08.71; CROSS 97.55.35.35; SNSM 97.50.14.39; ⊞ 97.55.73.46; Meteo 97.64.34.86; Auto 97.84.82.83; Police 97.50.07.39; Dr 97.50.13.94 (Quiberon); Brit Consul 40.63.16.02.

LE PALAIS (BELLE ÎLE)

Morbihan

10-15-18

CHARTS
Admiralty 2353; Imray C38; SHOM 5911, 7032; ECM 545

TIDES
+0458 Dover; ML 3·0; Duration 0615; Zone −0100

Standard Port BREST (⟶)

Times				Height (metres)			
HW		LW		MHWS	MHWN	MLWN	MLWS
0000	0600	0000	0600	7·5	5·9	3·0	1·4
1200	1800	1200	1800				
Differences LE PALAIS							
−0015	−0030	−0030	−0025	−2·3	−1·9	−1·0	−0·6

SHELTER
Good shelter except during strong E winds when a marked swell builds up. Yachts can lock into the Bassin à Flot HW−1½ to HW+1 (0600-2200 LT) and thence through lifting bridge into marina. Inner harbour partly dredged. Usual berth for deep keel yachts on three lines of mooring buoys inside Mole Bourdelle. Gets very crowded in summer. As an alternative, Sauzon has space in outer harbour with approx 2m over CD (see 10.15.27).

NAVIGATION
Waypoint 47°21'·20N 03°08'·00W, 065°/245° from/to Jetée Nord Lt, 0·80M. There are no navigational dangers but beware ferries which leave and enter at high speed. Anchorage between Sauzon and Le Palais is prohibited.

LIGHTS AND MARKS
Mole Bourdelle (N) Fl (2+1) G 12s 11m 7M
Mole Bonnelle (S) Oc (2) R 6s 11m 11M.

RADIO TELEPHONE
VHF Ch 09.

LE PALAIS *continued*

TELEPHONE (97)
Harbour Office 97.31.42.90; Aff Mar 97.31.83.17; CROSS 97.55.35.35; SNSM 97.47.48.49; ⋕ 97.31.85.95; Police 97.31.80.22; Dr 97.31.40.90; Ⓗ 97.31.81.82; Brit Consul 40.63.16.02.

FACILITIES
Marina ☎ 97.52.83.17, P, D, AC, FW, ME, El, Sh, Access HW∓1; **Quai** Slip, FW, C (10 + 5 ton), AB; **Belle-Ile Plaisances** ☎ 97.31.80.23, ME, El, Sh, CH; **YC de Belle Ile** ☎ 97.31.80.46, M; **Guidal** ☎ 97.31.83.75, ME; **Marec** ☎ 97.31.83.60, M, ME, El.
Town V, Gaz, R, Bar. ✉; Ⓑ; ≹ (ferry to Quiberon); ✈.
Ferry UK — Roscoff—Plymouth.

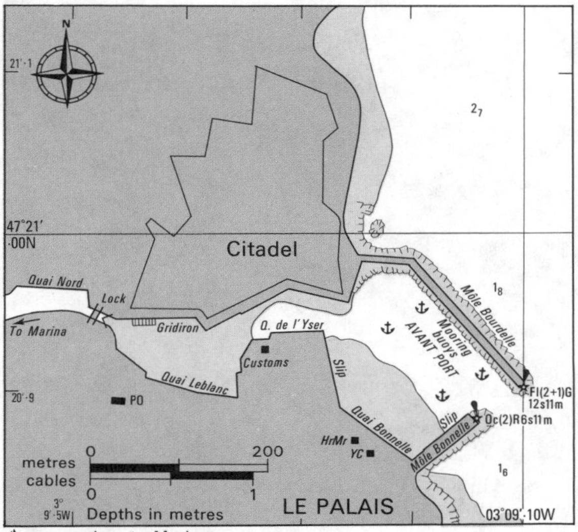

21'·1
2₇
47°21'·00N
Citadel
Quai Nord
Lock
To Marina
Gridiron
Q. de l'Yser
Customs
Quai Leblanc
Slip
Mooring buoys
AVANT PORT
Môle Bourdelle
1₈
Fl(2+1)G 12s11m
20'·9
PO
Quai Bonnelle
Slip
Oc(2)R6s11m
HrMr
YC
Môle Bonnelle
1₆
metres 0 200
cables 0 1
3° 9'·5W
Depths in metres
LE PALAIS
03°09'·10W

⏶ proceed up to Marina

LORIENT 10-15-19

Morbihan

CHARTS
Admiralty 304, 2352; Imray C38; SHOM 6470, 5912, 7031; ECM 544

TIDES
+0455 Dover; ML 3·0; Duration 0620; Zone −0100

Standard Port BREST (⟶)

Times				Height (metres)			
HW		LW		MHWS	MHWN	MLWN	MLWS
0000	0600	0000	0600	7·5	5·9	3·0	1·4
1200	1800	1200	1800				
Differences LORIENT							
+0005	−0025	−0025	−0015	−2·4	−1·9	−1·0	−0·5
PORT LOUIS							
−0010	−0025	−0020	−0020	−2·4	−1·9	−0·9	−0·5
PORT TUDY (Ile de Groix)							
−0005	−0035	−0030	−0025	−2·4	−1·9	−0·9	−0·5
PENFRET (Iles de Glenan)							
−0010	−0025	−0030	−0020	−2·5	−2·0	−1·2	−0·6

SHELTER
The Ile de Groix shelters the entrance from SW winds. Good shelter in all weathers. Anchorage N of Kernével. Lock into Marina Lorient HW∓1. Waiting berths are provided outside lock. There is excellent shelter up the Blavet River.

NAVIGATION
Waypoint Passe du Sud 47°40'·50N 03°22'·40W, 188°/008° from/to front Ldg Lt 008°, 3·35M.
Waypoint Passe de l'Ouest 47°40'·80N 03°24'·92W, 237°/057° from/to front Ldg Lt 057°, 3·0M. There are few navigational dangers entering Lorient so long as leading lines are kept to, but yachts must keep clear of shipping in the main channel. There is a secondary channel for yachts to the W of the main channel (see inset). Depths in this channel are 1m less than shown on panel.

LIGHTS AND MARKS
There are the following leading or directional lights:
(1) Passe de l'Ouest: Ldg Lts 057°. Front, Les Soeurs, Dir Q 13M; R Tr, W bands. Rear, Port Louis, 740m from front, Dir Q 18M; W daymark, R bands, on building.
(2) Ile aux Soris: Dir QWG 6m 3/2M; G Tr, W041·5°-043·5°, G043·5°-041·3°.
(3) Passe Sud: Ldg Lts 008·5°; Front, Fish Market, Dir QR 16m 15M; R square, G bands on Gy Tr; intens 006°-011°. Rear, Kergroise-La Perriere, 515m from front, Dir QR 28m **16M**; R square, W stripe on Gy Tr; intens 006°-011°.
(4) Ile Saint-Michel: Ldg Lts 016·5°. Front Dir Oc (3) G 12s 8m **16M**; W Tr, G top; intens 015°-018°. Rear, 306m from front, Dir Oc(3) G 12m 12s **16M**; W Tr, G Top; intens 015°-018°.
(5) Les Trois Pierres: QRG 11m 6/6M; B Tr, W bands G 060°-196°, R196°-002°.
(6) Kernével: Ldg Lts 217°; Front, Dir Oc(4)R 12s 10m 14M. Rear, 290m from front, Dir Oc(4)R 12s 18m 14M; W square Tr, R top; intens 215°-219°, synchronised.
(7) Pointe de l'Esperance: Dir Lt 037°: Dir Q WRG 8m 10/8M; G034·2°-036·7°, W036·7°-037·2°, R037·2°-047·2°.
(8) Pont Gueydon: Dir Lt 352°: Dir Iso WRG 4s 6m 11/9M; G168°-169·5°, W169·5°-170·5°, R170·5°-173·5°.
(9) Pointe de Keroman: Ldg Lts 350°. Front, Dir Oc (2) R 6s 25m **17M**; R house, W bands; intens 348°-353°. Rear, 91m from front, Dir Oc (2) R 6s 31m **17M**; RW Topmark on Gy pylon, R top. intens 348°-353°.

RADIO TELEPHONE
Call: *Vigie Port Louis* VHF Ch 16; 11 (H24). Marinas Ch 09 (office hours).

TELEPHONE (97)
Hr Mr Port de Plaisance 97.21.10.14; Aff Mar 97.37.16.22; CROSS 97.55.35.35; SNSM 97.64.32.42; ⋕ 97.37.29.57; Meteo 97.64.34.86; Auto 97.84.82.83; Police 97.64.27.17; Ⓗ 97.37.51.33; Brit Consul 40.63.16.02.

FACILITIES
Marina Kerneval (410+60 visitors) ☎ 97.65.48.25, P, D, FW, AC, ◙, Slip, BH (25 ton), C (100 ton), YC (☎ 97.21.14.01), Access H24; **Marina Lorient** (320+50 visitors) ☎ 97.21.10.14, P, D, FW, AC, ◙, Slip, BH (25 ton), C (100 ton); **Co-opérative Maritimes Lorient** ☎ 97.37.07.91, ME, El, Ⓔ, Sh, CH, SHOM; **Guillet** ☎ 97.37.26.76, Sh; **Intership** ☎ 97.37.00.97, ME, CH, Ⓔ, SHOM; **Lorient Marine** ☎ 97.37.34.78, M, ME, El, Ⓔ, CH, Sh; **V. V. Tonnerre** ☎ 97.37.23.55, CH, SM; **Club Nautique de Lorient** ☎ 97.84.81.30. Bar, C (1½ ton), FW, Slip; **Town** All facilities, ✉; Ⓑ; ≹; ✈.
Ferry UK — Roscoff—Plymouth.

15

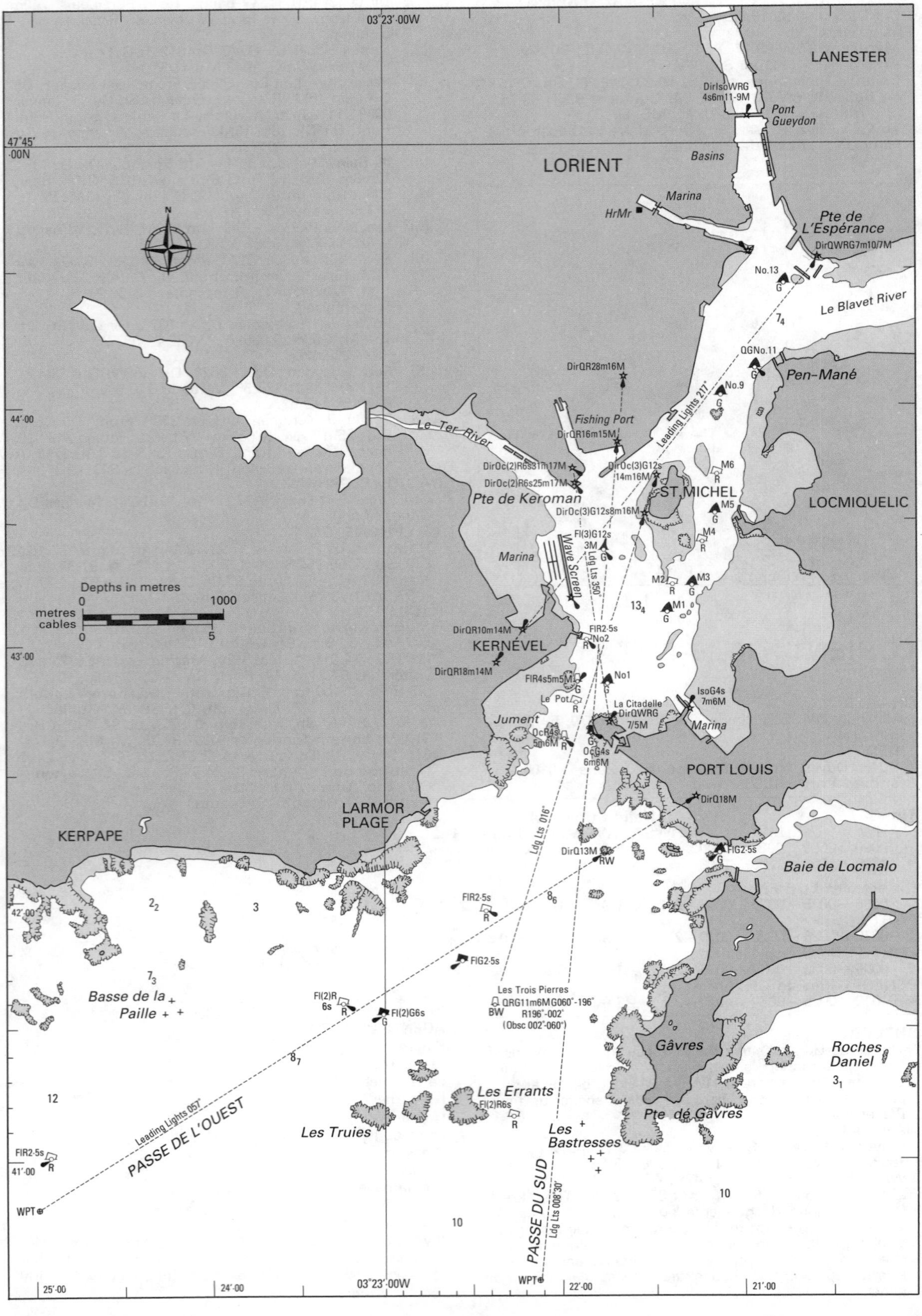
03°23'·00W
LANESTER
DirIsoWRG 4s6m11-9M
Pont Gueydon
47°45'·00N
LORIENT
Basins
Marina
HrMr
Pte de L'Espérance
DirQWRG7m10/7M
No.13
Le Blavet River
QGNo.11
Pen-Mané
DirQR28m16M
No.9
Fishing Port
DirQR16m15M
Leading Lights 217°
Le Ter River
DirOc(2)R6s31m17M
DirOc(2)R6s25m17M
DirOc(3)G12s 14m16M
M6
ST. MICHEL
Pte de Keroman
LOCMIQUELIC
DirOc(3)G12s8m16M
M5
Fl(3)G12s 3M
M4
Marina
Wave Screen
Ldg Lts 350
Depths in metres
metres 0 1000
cables 0 5
M2
M3
M1
DirQR10m14M
Fl R2·5s No2
KERNÉVEL
DirQR18m14M
FlR4s5m5M
No1
IsoG4s 7m6M
Le Pot
La Citadelle DirQWRG 7/5M
Jument
OcR4s 5m6M
OcG4s 6m6M
Marina
PORT LOUIS
DirQ18M
LARMOR PLAGE
KERPAPE
Ldg Lts 016°
DirQ13M RW
FlG2·5s
Baie de Locmalo
FlR2·5s
Fl G2·5s
Basse de la Paille
Fl(2)R 6s
Fl(2)G6s
Les Trois Pierres
QRG11m6M G060°-196° R196°-002° (Obsc 002°-060°)
BW
Gâvres
Roches Daniel
Les Errants
Fl(2)R6s
Les Truies
Leading Lights 057°
PASSE DE L'OUEST
Pte dé Gâvres
Les Bastresses
FlR2·5s
WPT
PASSE DU SUD
Ldg Lts 008°30'
WPT
25'·00
24'·00
03°23'·00W
22'·00
21'·00
44'·00
43'·00
42'·00
41'·00

CONCARNEAU 10-15-20

Finistere

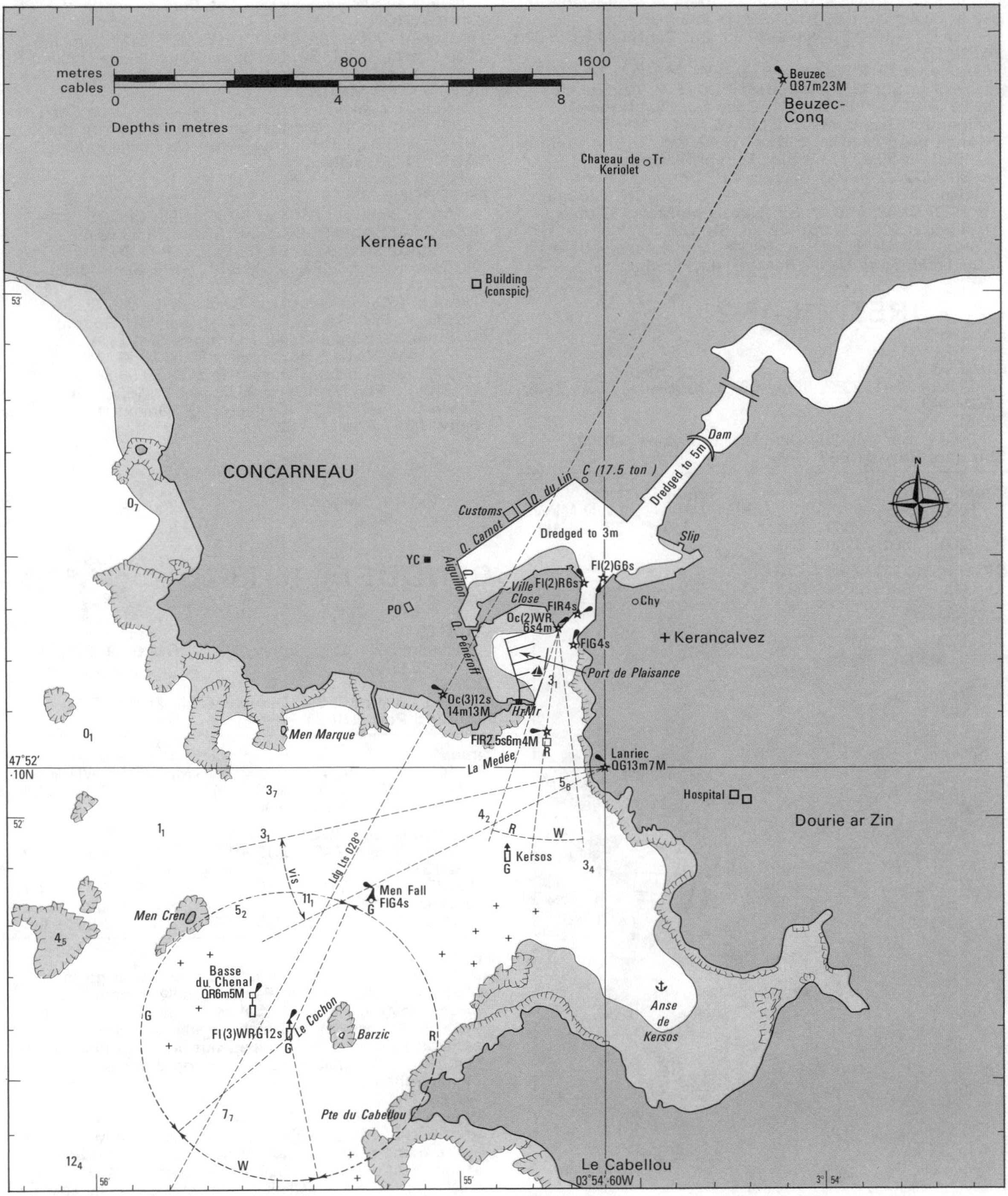
metres
cables
0
800
1600
0
4
8
Depths in metres
Beuzec
Q87m23M
Beuzec-Conq
Chateau de Keriolet
Tr
Kernéac'h
Building (conspic)
CONCARNEAU
Dam
Dredged to 5m
C (17.5 ton)
Q. du Lin
Customs
Q. Carnot
Dredged to 3m
Slip
YC
Aiguillon
Fl(2)G6s
Ville Close
Fl(2)R6s
PO
FlR4s
Chy
Oc(2)WR 6s4m
FlG4s
Kerancalvez
Q. Pénéroff
Port de Plaisance
Oc(3)12s 14m13M
HrMr
Men Marque
FlR2.5s6m4M
R
La Medée
Lanriec
QG13m7M
47°52'·10N
53'
52'
Hospital
Dourie ar Zin
Ldg Lts 028°
vis
R
W
Kersos
G
Men Fall
FlG4s
G
Men Cren
Basse du Chenal
QR6m5M
G
Fl(3)WRG12s
Le Cochon
G
Barzic
R
Anse de Kersos
Pte du Cabellou
W
Le Cabellou
03°54'·60W
56'
55'
3° 54'
N

CHARTS

Admiralty 3641, 2352; Imray C38; SHOM 6650, 7146; ECM 544

TIDES

+0455 Dover; ML 2·9; Duration 0615; Zone −0100

Standard Port BREST (⟶)

Times				Height (metres)			
HW		LW		MHWS	MHWN	MLWN	MLWS
0000	0600	0000	0600	7·5	5·9	3·0	1·4
1200	1800	1200	1800				
Differences CONCARNEAU							
−0005	−0035	−0030	−0020	−2·5	−2·0	−1·0	−0·6

SHELTER

Very good shelter in the marina which has the added protection of an anti-wash barrier but exposed to strong S winds. The inner quays are reserved for fishing boats.

NAVIGATION

Waypoint 47°50'·00N 03°56'·80W, 208°/028° from/to front Ldg Lt 028°, 2·52M. Following the leading lights, beware rocks round Men Cren and Le Cochon.

LIGHTS AND MARKS

Ldg Lts 028°, front Oc (3) 12s 14m 13M rear, 1·35M from front, Q 87m 23M. Lanriec Lt, QG 13m 7M vis 063°-078°.

RADIO TELEPHONE

VHF Ch 16; 12 (H 24). Marina Ch 09.

CONCARNEAU *continued*

TELEPHONE (98)
Hr Mr 98.97.33.80; Marina Office 98.97.57.96; Aff Mar 98.97.53.45; CROSS 97.55.35.35; 97.64.32.42; Meteo 98.94.03.43; Auto 98.94.00.69; # 98.97.01.73; Police 98.97.00.71; Ⓗ 98.50.30.30; Brit Consul 40.63.16.02.

FACILITIES
Marina (267 + 40 visitors), P, D, FW, ME, AC, El, C (17 ton), Slip, Sh; **Quay Pénéroff** P, D, FW, AB; **Barzic** ☎ 98.97.01.57, CH, SHOM; **Chantiers Nautique du Minaouet Grignallou** ☎ 98.97.46.79, M, ME, El, Sh, CH; **Concarneau Marine** ☎ 98.97.19.63, ME, El, Sh; **Voilerie Le Bras** ☎ 98.97.17.49 SM; **Techni Plaisance** ☎ 98.97.22.02 ME, El, Ⓔ, Sh, CH; **Concarneau Plaisance** ☎ 98.97.00.50, M, ME, El, Sh, CH; **Gloaguen** ☎ 98.97.04.08, ME, El, Sh; **Nautisme-Motor Club Dolliou** ☎ 98.97.12.05, ME, El, Sh, CH.
Town V, Gaz, R, Bar. ✉; Ⓑ; ⇌ (bus to Quimper); ✈ (Quimper). Ferry UK — Roscoff—Plymouth.

LA FORÊT 10-15-21

Finistere

CHARTS
Admiralty 3641, 2352; Imray C37, C38; SHOM 6650, 7146; ECM 543, 544

TIDES
+0450 Dover; ML 2·9; Duration 0615; Zone −0100
Standard Port BREST (⟶)

Times				Height (metres)			
HW		LW		MHWS	MHWN	MLWN	MLWS
0000	0600	0000	0600	7·5	5·9	3·0	1·4
1200	1800	1200	1800				
Differences CONCARNEAU							
−0005	−0035	−0030	−0020	−2·5	−2·0	−1·0	−0·6

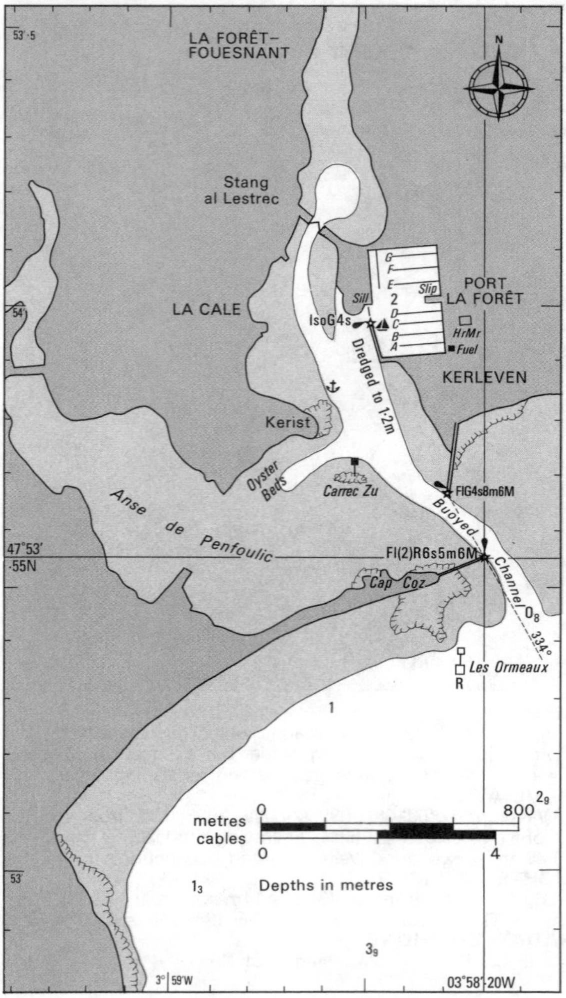

53'·5
LA FORÊT–
FOUESNANT
N
Stang
al Lestrec
LA CALE
54'
Sill
IsoG4s
Slip
PORT
LA FORÊT
HrMr
Fuel
Dredged to 1·2m
KERLEVEN
Kerist
Oyster Beds
Carrec Zu
FlG4s8m6M
Buoyed Channel
Anse de Penfoulic
47°53'
·55N
Fl(2)R6s5m6M
Cap Coz
334°
Les Ormeaux
R
metres
cables
0
800
0
4
Depths in metres
53'
3°59'W
03°58'·20W

SHELTER
Good shelter in the Port de Plaisance in all weathers. There is an anchorage inside Cap Coz.

NAVIGATION
Waypoint 47°52'·70N 03°57'·80W, 162°/342° from/to Cap-Coz Lt, 0·9M. Beware Basse Rouge 6·5ca (1200m) S of Cape Coz and Le Scoré to the SE of Cape Coz.

LIGHTS AND MARKS
Channel is marked by buoys and beacons. Cape Coz Lt is Fl (2) R 6s 5m 6M and that on the breakwater to the NNW, Fl G 4s 8m 6M. Breakwater Lts in line at 334°.

RADIO TELEPHONE
VHF Ch 09.

TELEPHONE (98)
Hr Mr 98.56.98.45; Aff Mar 98.56.01.98; CROSS 97.55.35.35; Auto 98.94.00.57; SNSM 98.56.98.45; # (Concarneau) 98.97.01.73; Police 98.56.00.11; Ⓗ (Concarneau) 98.97.10.60; Brit Consul 40.63.16.02.

FACILITIES
Marina (690 + 70 visitors) ☎ 98.56.98.45, ME, El, Sh, CH, AC, D, P, FW, Gaz, R, ⊡, SM, V, Bar, BH (16 ton), C (2 ton), Slip (multi hull); **Pontoons** SM, P, AC, D, FW, C (2.5 ton), V, Bar; **Horizons** ☎ 98.56.99.72, ME, El, Sh, CH; **Kerleven (Chantier Naval)** ☎ 98.56.96.85, M, ME, El, Sh, Ⓔ; **PLF Marine** ☎ 98.56.96.04, ME, El, Sh.
Town Gaz, ✉; Ⓑ; ⇌ (Quimper); ✈ (Quimper).
Ferry UK — Roscoff—Plymouth.

BÉNODET 10-15-22

Finistere

CHARTS
Admiralty 3641, 2352; Imray C37; SHOM 6649, 6679, 7146; ECM 543

TIDES
+0450 Dover; ML 2.7; Duration 0610; Zone −0100
Standard Port BREST (⟶)

Times				Height (metres)			
HW		LW		MHWS	MHWN	MLWN	MLWS
0000	0600	0000	0600	7.5	5.9	3.0	1.4
1200	1800	1200	1800				
Differences BÉNODET							
−0010	−0025	−0040	−0015	−2.6	−2.2	−1.3	−0.8
CORNIGUEL							
+0015	+0010	−0015	−0010	−2.6	−2.1	−1.4	−1.1
LOCTUDY							
−0010	−0030	−0030	−0025	−2.6	−2.1	−1.3	−0.9

SHELTER
Anchor in Anse du Trez in offshore winds; or go to one of two marinas; Anse de Penfoul (apply to berthing master on quay); or go to Sainte Marine marina on the W bank. Access day and night at any tide. River Odet easily navigable up to Quimper, but bridge at Poulguinan (just before city) necessitates lowering the mast, or mooring there.

NAVIGATION
Waypoint 47°51'.00N 04°06'.10W, 166°/346° from/to front Ldg Lt 346°, 1.43M. Beware Roches de Mousterlin at the E end of the bay and various rocks round Loctudy at the West end of this bay. In the centre it is clear for small craft. There is a tanker channel past the Ile aux Moutons off the West horn of the bay. Speed limit 3 kn in harbour.

LIGHTS AND MARKS
Ile-aux-Moutons Oc (2) WRG 6s 18m 15/11M and Dir Oc (2) 6s 17m 24M; intens 278°-283°. Ldg Lts 346°. Front Pte du Coq Oc (2+1) G 12s 11m 17M. Rear Oc (2+1) 12s 48m 11M; both W Trs, G tops, synchronized.

RADIO TELEPHONE
VHF Ch 09 (0800-2000 LT in season); both marinas.

TELEPHONE (98)
Hr Mr 98.57.38.72; Aff Mar 98.57.03.82; CROSS 97.55.35.35; SNSM 97.57.02.00; # 98.55.04.19; Meteo 98.94.03.43; Police 98.56.00.11; Dr 98.57.22.21; Brit Consul 40.63.16.02.

BENODET *continued*

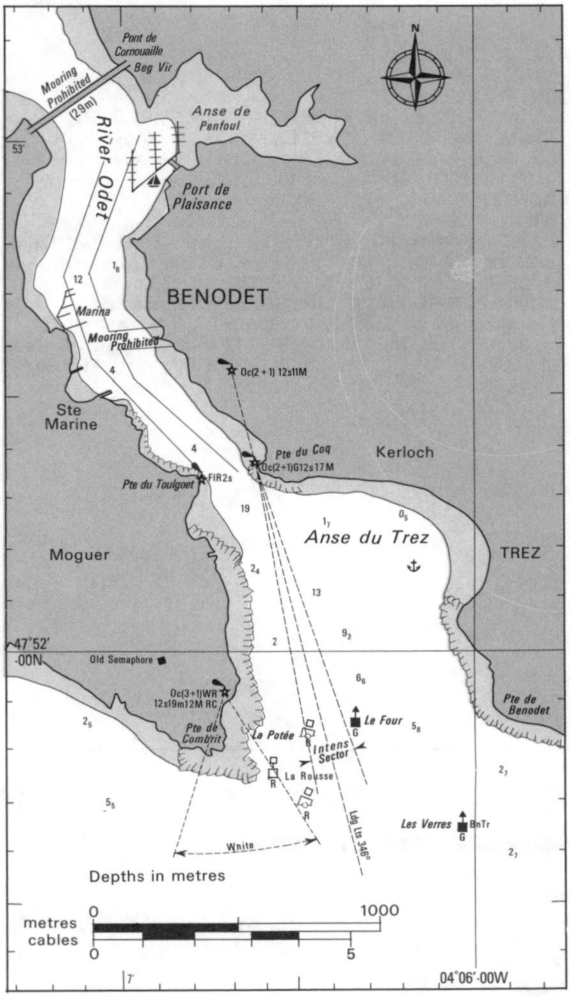
Pont de Cornouaille
Beg Vir
Mooring Prohibited
(29m)
Anse de Penfoul
River Odet
Port de Plaisance
53'
BENODET
Marina
Mooring Prohibited
Oc(2+1) 12s11M
Ste Marine
Pte du Coq
Oc(2+1)G12s17M
Kerloch
Pte du Toulgoet
FlR2s
Anse du Trez
Moguer
TREZ
47°52'·00N
Old Semaphore
Oc(3+1)WR 12s19m12M RC
Pte de Combrit
La Potée
Le Four
Intens Sector
La Rousse
Pte de Benodet
Les Verres
BnTr
White
Ldg Lts 346°
Depths in metres
metres
cables
0
1000
5
7'
04°06'·00W

FACILITIES
BENODET **Anse de Penfoul Marina** (250 + 40 visitors on pontoons; also 175 moorings + 15 for visitors) ☎ 98.57.05.78, AC, FW, ⊡, R, CH, ME, V, P, D; **Accasting 29** ☎ 98.57.20.83, M, ME, El, Ⓔ, Sh, CH; **Le Gai Matelot** ☎ 98.57.19.73, C, M, ME, El, Divers; **Town Quay** C (10 ton); **Le Bihan Voiles** ☎ 98.57.18.03, SM; **Cornouaille Nautique** ☎ 98.57.00.87, ME, El, Ⓔ, Sh, CH; **Town** All facilities, Gaz, ✉; Ⓑ; ⇄ (bus to Quimper); ✈ (Quimper).
SAINTE MARINE **Ste Marine Marina** (257 + 150 visitors) ☎ 98.51.92.11. **Village** V, R, Bar, ⊡, Ⓔ.

AUDIERNE 10-15-23

Finistere

CHARTS
Admiralty 3640, 2351; SHOM 7147, 6594, 6609; Imray C36, C37; ECM 541

TIDES
+0440 Dover; ML 3·1; Duration 0605; Zone −0100
Standard Port BREST (→)

Times				Height (metres)			
HW		LW		MHWS	MHWN	MLWN	MLWS
0000	0600	0000	0600	7·5	5·9	3·0	1·4
1200	1800	1200	1800				
Differences AUDIERNE							
−0020	−0040	−0040	−0020	−2·3	−1·9	−0·9	−0·5
LE GUILVINEC							
−0010	−0035	−0035	−0020	−2·4	−1·9	−1·0	−0·5
ILE DE SEIN							
−0010	−0010	−0010	−0015	−1·1	−0·9	−0·5	−0·3

SHELTER
River is accessible above half tides in all but strong SE-SW winds which cause breakers at the ent.. Breakwater by Ste Evette gives shelter in all but SE winds although there may be a swell there when wind is S or SW. Keep clear of slip area as vedettes enter with much verve. Visitors buoys are white and marked 'Payant-Visiteurs'.

NAVIGATION
Waypoint 47°59'·00N 04°31'·03W, 151°/331° from/to front Ldg Lt, 1·85M. Access is difficult in strong S-SW winds. There are two rock outcrops, Le Sillon de Galets to the W and La Gamelle in the middle of the bay. A good drying anchorage opposite quays (E side of river). Fishermen resent yachts on quays except in NW corner, which is foul.

LIGHTS AND MARKS
Ldg Lts at 331°, Front Oc (2+1) WG 12s 11m 14/9M, Rear FR 44m 9M. Dir Q WRG 43m 12/9M G 000°-005°, W 005°-007°, R 007°-017°. This latter Lt in line with Old Lt Ho gives Ldg line at 006°.

RADIO TELEPHONE
None. Other station Pointe du Raz Ch 16.

TELEPHONE (98)
Hr Mr 98.70.07.91; Aff Mar 98.70.03.33; CROSS 97.55.35.35; SNSM 98.70.03.31; # 98.70.70.97; Meteo 98.94.03.43; Auto 98.94.00.69; Police 98.70.04.38; Ⓗ 98.70.00.18; Brit Consul 40.63.16.02.

FACILITIES
Port de Plaisance (300) ☎ 98.70.08.47 Bar, R, CH, ME, El, Sh, FW, ⊡, V; **Poulgoazec** C (15 ton), Slip, P and D (cans); **Marine Service** ☎ 98.70.22.85, ME, El, Sh; **Bosser** ☎ 98.70.10.52, El, Ⓔ; **Club Nautique de la Baie d'Audierne** ☎ 98.70.21.69.

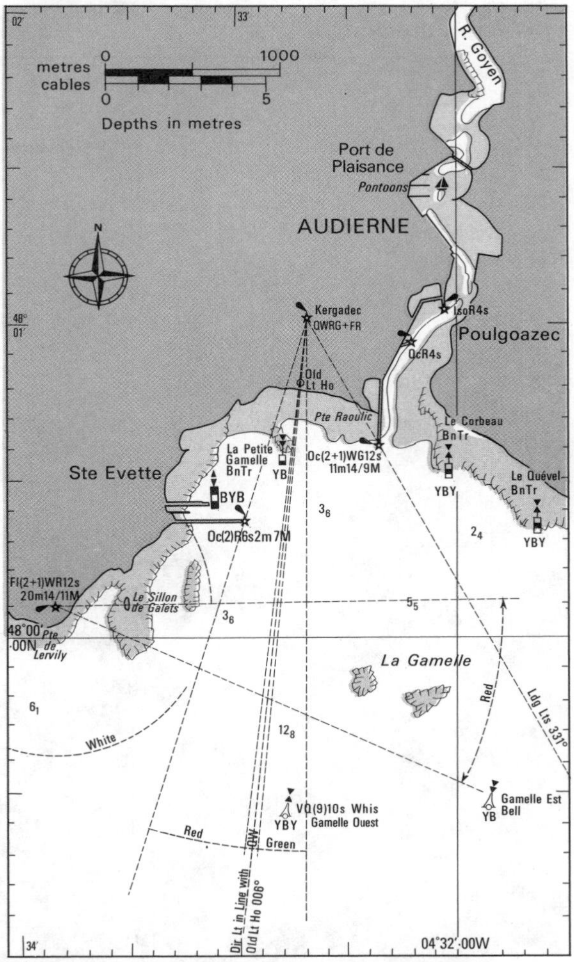
02'
33'
R. Goyen
metres
cables
0
1000
5
Depths in metres
Port de Plaisance
Pontoons
AUDIERNE
48°01'
Kergadec
QWRG+FR
IsoR4s
Poulgoazec
QcR4s
Old Lt Ho
Pte Raoulic
Le Corbeau BnTr
La Petite Gamelle BnTr
Oc(2+1)WG12s 11m14/9M
Ste Evette
BYB
Le Quével BnTr
Oc(2)R6s2m7M
YB
YBY
Fl(2+1)WR12s 20m14/11M
Le Sillon de Galets
48°00'·00N
Pte de Lervily
La Gamelle
White
Red
Ldg Lts 331°
VQ(9)10s Whis
Gamelle Ouest
Gamelle Est Bell
Green
Dir Lt in Line with Old Lt Ho 006°
34'
04°32'·00W

Town V, Gaz, R, Bar. ✉; Ⓑ; ⇄ (bus to Quimper); ✈ (Quimper).
Ferry UK — Roscoff—Plymouth.

DOUARNENEZ 10-15-24

Finistere

CHARTS
Admiralty 798; SHOM 6677, 6099; Imray C36; ECM 542.

TIDES
+0500 Dover; ML 4.2; Duration 0615; Zone −0100

Standard Port BREST (⟶)

Times				Height (metres)			
HW		LW		MHWS	MHWN	MLWN	MLWS
0000	0600	0000	0600	7.5	5.9	3.0	1.4
1200	1800	1200	1800				
Differences DOUARNENEZ							
−0015	−0010	−0015	−0020	−0.5	−0.5	−0.2	0.0

SHELTER
Very good shelter and open in all weathers and tides. Yachts are not allowed in the Fishing Harbour but can use the marina (Port de Plaisance) in Treboul, Port Rhu, further up river or Port de Rosmeur. Some visitors berths are in the marina at Quai de l'Yser. Most are in the river outside and are subject to swell from passing traffic. Access day and night at all tides.

NAVIGATION
Waypoint 48°07'.00N 04°20'.30W, 000°/180° from/to Ile Tristan Lt, 0.83M. There are three rocks to the NW of Ile Tristan, Basse Veur, Petite Basse Neuve and Basse Neuve from 3 to 9 ca (555 to 1665m). All are in the R sector of Ile Tristan Lt.

LIGHTS AND MARKS
Approx 5 M to W is Pte du Millier Lt, Oc (2) WRG 6s 34m 16/11M G 080°-087°, W 087°-113°, R 113°-120°, W 120°-129°, G 129°-148°, W 148°-251°, R 251°-258°. There are no leading lights or marks but the entrance through the Grande Passe is 158°.

RADIO TELEPHONE
VHF Ch 09 (0800−1200 and 1330−2000 LT in season).

TELEPHONE (98)
Hr Mr (Plaisance) 98.74.02.56; Aff Mar 98.92.00.91; CROSS 98.89.31.31; SNSM 98.89.63.16; # 98.92.01.45; Meteo 98.84.60.64; Auto 98.84.82.83; Police 98.92.01.22; [H] 98.92.25.00; Brit Consul 40.63.16.02.

FACILITIES
Marina (380+30 visitors) ☎ 98.92.09.99, Slip, FW, AC, P, D, C (6 ton), ME, El, Sh; **Port Rhu** AB, R, Bar; **Quai de l'Yser** P, D, L, FW, C, AB, V, R, Bar; **Bateau Baloin** ☎ 98.92.10.40, M, Sh, ME, El, CH; **Riou Louis** ☎ 98.92.15.76, ME, El, Sh; **Ste des Regates de Douarnenez** ☎ 98.92.27.28; **Yachting Fiacre** ☎ 98.92.06.28, ME, El, Sh, BH (12 ton), CH, SM; **Bideau** ☎ 98.92.05.71, Ⓔ; **Town** Slip, P, D, FW, CH, AB, Gaz, V, R, Bar. ✉; Ⓑ; ≷; ✈ (Quimper).
Ferry UK — Roscoff—Plymouth.

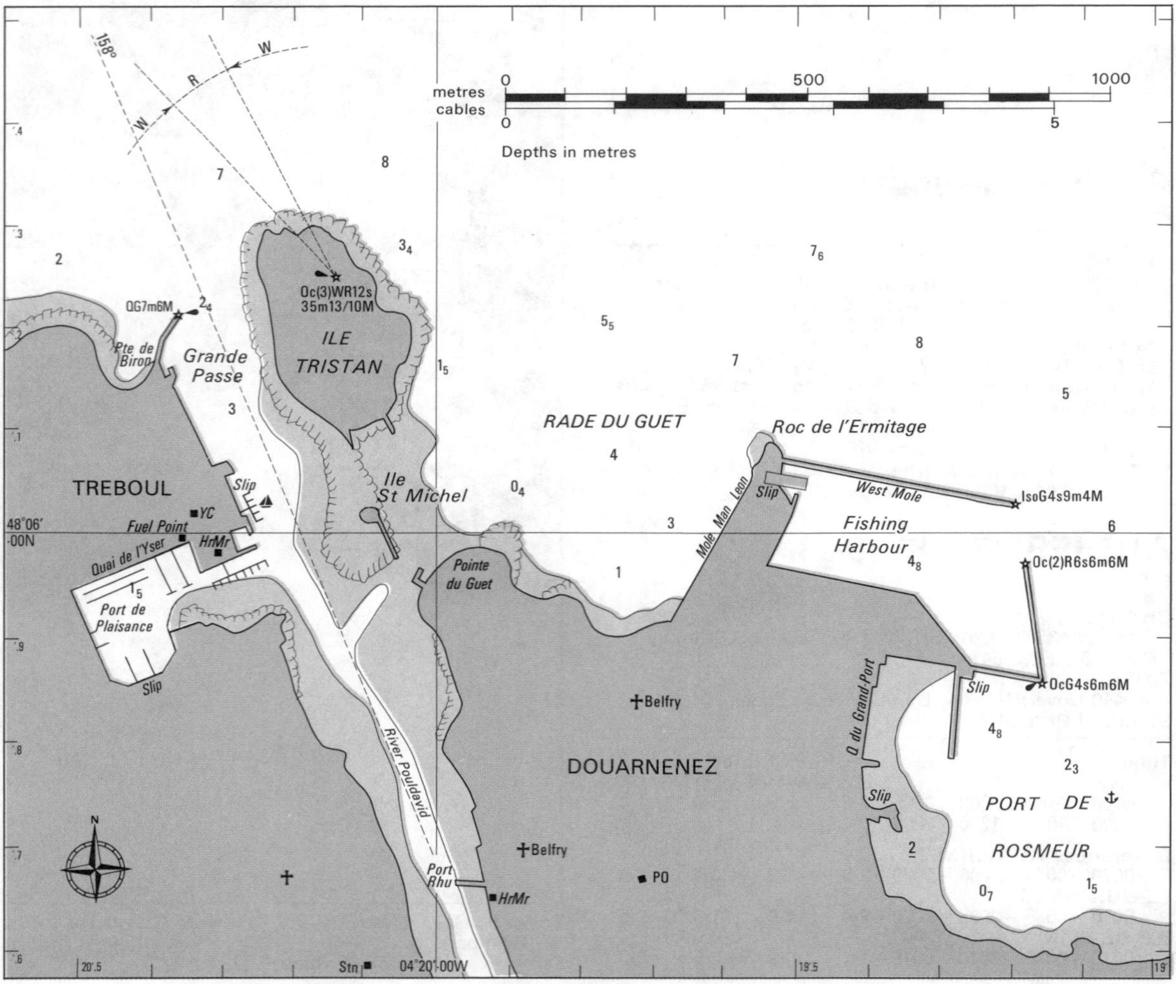

158°
W
R
W
metres
cables
0
500
1000
5
Depths in metres
Oc(3)WR12s
35m13/10M
ILE
TRISTAN
QG7m6M
Pte de Birop
Grande Passe
RADE DU GUET
Roc de l'Ermitage
Ile St Michel
TREBOUL
Slip
YC
Fuel Point
HrMr
Quai de l'Yser
Port de Plaisance
48°06'
·00N
West Mole
IsoG4s9m4M
Mole Man Leon
Fishing Harbour
Oc(2)R6s6m6M
OcG4s6m6M
Pointe du Guet
Belfry
River Pouldavid
DOUARNENEZ
Q du Grand-Port
PORT DE
ROSMEUR
Port Rhu
HrMr
PO
Stn
04°20'·00W
20'5
19'5
19'

MORGAT 10-15-25

Finistere

CHARTS
Admiralty 798; SHOM 6676, 6099; Stanford 17; Imray C36; ECM 541, 542.

TIDES
+0500 Dover; ML 4·2; Duration No data; Zone −0100

Standard Port BREST (⟶)

Times				Height (metres)			
HW		LW		MHWS	MHWN	MLWN	MLWS
0000	0600	0000	0600	7·5	5·9	3·0	1·4
1200	1800	1200	1800				
Differences MORGAT							
−0010	−0010	−0015	−0015	−0·5	−0·5	−0·2	0·0

SHELTER
The port is exposed to winds from the W and N but the marina is protected by concrete pontoons.

NAVIGATION
Waypoint 48°12′·00N 04°28′·00W, 147°/327° from/to E breakwater head, 1·9M. Few dangers in approaches. There are rocks under the cliffs S of Pte de Morgat, and Les Verres 2M ESE of entrance.

LIGHTS AND MARKS
Pointe de Morgat Lt Oc (4) WRG 12s 77m 15/10M G sector covers Les Verres.

RADIO TELEPHONE
VHF Ch 25 87 Marina 09 16.

TELEPHONE (98)
Hr Mr 98.27.01.97; Aff Mar 98.27.09.95; CROSS 98.89.31.31; Auto 98.84.82.83; SNSM 98.27.00 41; # 98.27.93.02; Police 98.27.00.22; Ⓗ 98.27.05.33; Brit Consul 40.63.16.02.

FACILITIES
Marina (425+60 visitors), ☎ 98.27.01.97, AC, FW, C (8 ton), Slip, CH, ◙, D, P, ME, Access H24; **Alemany** ☎ 98.27.01.97, Slip, M, L, FW, ME, C (6 ton), AB, V, R, Bar; **Quay by Hr Mr** P, D; **Service-Plaisance** ☎ 98.27.95.90, M, ME, El, Sh, CH, Ⓔ; **YC du Crozon-Morgat** ☎ 98.27.01.98. **Town** (Crozon), V, Gaz, R, Bar. ✉; Ⓑ; ≹; ✈ (Brest or Quimper). Ferry UK — Roscoff—Plymouth.

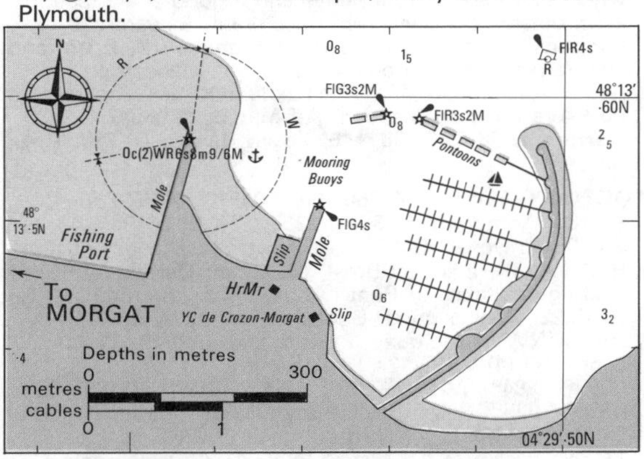

N
R
W
0₈
1₅
Fl R 4s
R
48°13′·60N
Fl G 3s 2M
0₈
Fl R 3s 2M
2₅
Oc(2)WR 6s 8m 9/6M
Mooring Buoys
Pontoons
48° 13′·5N
Fishing Port
Mole
Slip
Mole
Fl G 4s
To MORGAT
HrMr
YC de Crozon-Morgat
Slip
0₆
3₂
Depths in metres
0
300
metres
cables
1
04°29′·50N

CAMARET 10-15-26

Finistere

CHARTS
Admiralty 3427, 798; SHOM 6678, 6099; Imray C36; Stanford 17; ECM 542.

TIDES
+0500 Dover; ML 4·1; Duration 0610; Zone −0100

Standard Port BREST (⟶)

Times				Height (metres)			
HW		LW		MHWS	MHWN	MLWN	MLWS
0000	0600	0000	0600	7·5	5·9	3·0	1·4
1200	1800	1200	1800				
Differences CAMARET							
−0015	−0015	−0015	−0020	−0·5	−0·5	−0·2	−0·1

SHELTER
Harbour gives good shelter except from strong E winds, but much of it dries and there is a restricted area: see chartlet. Shelter in both marinas, Plaisance La Pointe or Plaisance Styvel, is always good.

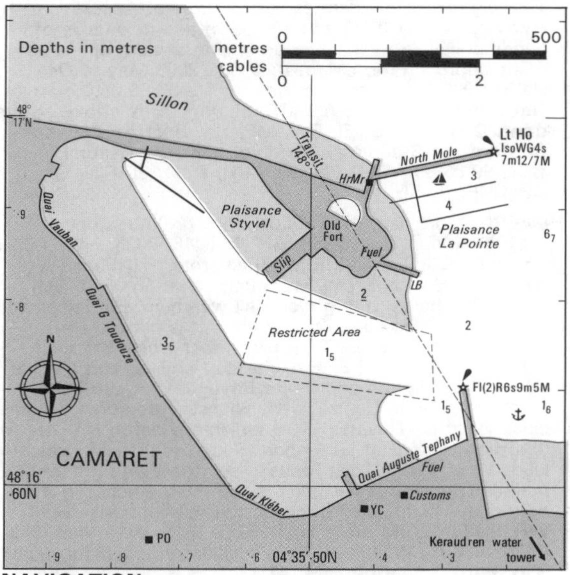

Depths in metres
metres
cables
0
500
0
2
Sillon
48° 17′N
Transit 148°
Lt Ho Iso WG 4s 7m 12/7M
North Mole
HrMr
3
4
Quai Vauban
Plaisance Styvel
Old Fort
Plaisance La Pointe
Fuel
Slip
LB
2
Quai G Toudouze
Restricted Area
2
3₅
1₅
N
Fl(2)R 6s 9m 5M
1₅
1₆
CAMARET
Quai Auguste Tephany
48°16′·60N
Fuel
Quai Kléber
Customs
YC
PO
04°35′·50N
Keraudren water tower

NAVIGATION
Waypoint 48°18′·00N 04°36′·00W, 335°/155° from/to North Mole Lt, 1·2M. Beware rocks W of Pointe du Grand Gouin. Anchoring in harbour forbidden.

LIGHTS AND MARKS
Lt Ho at end of N Mole Iso WG 4s W135°-182°, G182°-027°; Ldg line at 148° with front — top of the old fort, back — Keraudren water tower on hill behind.

RADIO TELEPHONE
None. For Ouessant Traffic see Chapter 2 Fig.2(1).

TELEPHONE (98)
Hr Mr 98.27.95.99; Bureau de Port 98.27.93.30; Aff Mar 98.27.93.28; CROSS 98.89.31.31; SNSM 98.27.94.76, # 98.27.93.02; Auto 98.84.82.83; Police 98.27.00.22; Dr 98.27.91.35; Brit Consul 40.63.16.02.

FACILITIES
Plaisance 'La Pointe (30+120 visitors), ☎ 98.27.95.99, FW, AC, C (8 ton), D, Access H24; **Plaisance 'Styvel'** (180+30 visitors), FW, AC, Access HW∓3; **Service Plaisance** ☎ 98.27.95.90, M, L, FW, ME, El, Ⓔ, Sh, CH, AB; **Boennec Frères** ☎ 98.27.90.61, ME; **Le Roy** ☎ 98.27.94.32, ME; **Quai Tephany** P, D, L, C (5 ton); **Voilerie Lastennet** ☎ 98.27.92.32, SM; **Hugot** ☎ 98.27.90.88, SHOM; **Town** V, Gaz, R, Bar. ✉; Ⓑ; ≹ (Brest); ✈ (Brest or Quimper).
Ferry UK — Roscoff—Plymouth.

MINOR HARBOURS AND ANCHORAGES 10-15-27

PORNICHET, Loire-Atlantique, 47°15′·00N, 02°20′·00W, Zone −0100, Admty chart 2989, SHOM 6797. HW +0500 on Dover (GMT), −0040 sp, +0015 np on Brest (zone −0100); HW height −1·9m on Brest; ML 2·9m; Duration 0530 sp 0645 np. Excellent shelter in artificial harbour. No navigational dangers; available at all tides (up to 3·5m draught). Lt on S breakwater head Iso WG 4s 11m 12/9M, G084°−081°, W081°−084°. S breakwater FlG 2s. N breakwater FlR 2s. VHF Ch 09. Facilities are extensive; Hr Mr ☎ 40.47.23.71. # ☎ 40.61.32.04. Meteo ☎ 40.90.08.80; Aff Mar ☎ 40.60.56.13; CROSS ☎ 97.55.35.35. **Marina** (1100+150 visitors), ☎ 40.61.03.20, AC, Slip, FW, P, D, BH (24 ton), V, R, Bar; **L'Ancre Marine** ☎ 40.61.09.37 ME, El, Ⓔ, Sh, CH SHOM; **Town** Bar, Dr, ✉, R, ≹, V.

PIRIAC, Loire-Atlantique, 47°23′·00N, 02°32′·00W, Zone −0100, Admty chart 2353, SHOM 7033. HW +0505 on Dover (GMT), −0015 on Brest (zone −0100); HW height −1·9m on Brest; ML 3·1m; Duration 0605. A small resort and fishing village with good small harbour. Available HW∓3, 30 berths for visitors, ask at Cercle Nautique ☎ 40.23.52.32 (July-Aug only). Lt Oc(2) WRG 6s 8m 10/6M, vis R066°−185°, W185°−201°, G201°−224°. Facilities: D, P on quay. **Piriac Marine Service** ☎ 40.23.50.86, CH, Ⓔ, El, ME, Sh; **Town** Bar, Dr, R, V.

15

PORT D'ARZAL, Morbihan, 47°30′·00N, 02°24′·00W, Zone −0100, Admty chart 2353, SHOM 2381, 5418, 7033. Tidal figures below dam as for St Nazaire. Access HW∓3. See 10.15.12 and 10.15.9. Keep to outside of bends going up river. Lock on N side of dam opens as boats approach (no charges); 0700−2000 May to Oct, 0800−1900 in winter. Facilities: Hr Mr 97.90.05.06; **Arzal Nautique** ☎ 97.45.03.52, ME, El, Ⓔ, Sh; **N shore above dam**. C (15 ton) D, El, FW, ME, Sh. **Port de Plaisance, Camoel** (on S shore above dam) (660+50 visitors), ☎ 99.90.05.86 AC, C (15 ton), CH, P, D, El, FW, Gas, Gaz, ME, R, Sh, V.

PENERF, Morbihan, 47°31′·00N, 02°37′·00W, Zone −0100, Admty chart 2353, SHOM 5418, 7033. HW +0515 on Dover (GMT), −0010 on Brest (zone −0100); HW height −1·9m on Brest; ML 3·0m; Duration 0610. See 10.15.12. Shelter very good in all weathers. Entrances are all difficult. Passe de l'Est has 4m but is narrow and rocky; it leads E of La Traverse, a reef which dries, marked by Bn 1¼M ENE of Pte de Penvins, and thence between Le Pignon and Petite Bayonelle to join Passe du Centre. Passe du Centre is the widest and easiest, leading close W of La Traverse, N of which the depth is 0·1m, and then close E of Le Pignon. Passe de l'Ouest, which leads W of Plateau des Passes, is shallow and not well marked. Beware oyster beds in the river. Anchor in 3·5m near quay. Light, Le Pignon, in the river entrance Fl (3) WR 12s 6m 9/6M on R Tr: R028°−167°, W167°−175°, R175°−349°, W349°−028°. Facilities: P and D (on quay), Slip. **Penerf Marine** ☎ 97.41.13.86, CH, El, ME, Sh; **Town** Bar, Dr, R, V.

ÎLE DE HOUAT, 47°24′·00N, 02°57′·00W, Zone −0100, Admty chart 2353, SHOM 7033. HW +0505 on Dover (GMT), −0017 on Brest (zone −0100); HW height −1·9m on Brest; ML 2·9m; Duration 0605. See 10.15.11 (Île de Höedic). Good shelter at Port St Gildas, towards E end of the N coast, protected by wave-break. Beware rock in the middle (1m) and rocks protruding 6m from breakwater. Anchor inside breakwater in approx 2m. S part of harbour dries. Lt on N mole Oc (2) WG 6s 8m 8/5M from W Tr with G top. W168°−198°, G198°−210°, W210°−240°, G240°−168°. Facilities very limited. Ferries to Quiberon (Port Maria) and Île de Höedic.

PORT MARIA, Morbihan, 47°28′·00N, 03°08′·00W, Zone −0100, Admty chart 2353, SHOM 5352, 7032. HW +0505 on Dover (GMT), −0010 on Brest (zone −0100); HW height −2·1m on Brest; ML 2·9m; Duration 0615. Shelter good in all winds. Access dangerous in strong winds from SE to SW. Half harbour dries. E mole reserved for ferries. Anchor in S of harbour in approx 2m. Beware rocks at base of S mole. Ldg Lts 006°, both QG intens 005°−008°. E mole head Iso G 4s 9m 6M. S end of wave-break Oc (2) R 6s 9m 8M. Main Lt Ho Q WRG 28m 15/10M, W246°−252°, W291°−297°, G297°−340°, W340°−017°, R017°−051°, W051°−081°, G081°−098°, W098°−143°. Facilities: Hr Mr and Aff Mar ☎ 97.50.08.71. # ☎ 97.50.14.81. C (6 ton), FW at E quay. **Monvoisin** ☎ 97.50.09.67 SHOM; **Ateliers Normand** ☎ 97.50.26.17 El, ME, Sh; **Town** (and at Quiberon 0.5M) Bar, R, V.

SAUZON, Belle Ile, 47°22′·00N, 03°13′·00W, Zone −0100, Admty charts 2353, SHOM 7032, ECM 545; HW +0450 on Dover (GMT), −0020 on Brest (zone −0100); HW height −2·0m on Brest; ML 3·0m; Duration 0615. Small attractive harbour which dries, 4M N of Le Palais. See 10.15.18. Good shelter except in E winds. Moorings available (17 deep water buoys) just inside E and W moles, or go into inner harbour and dry out. Main Lt QG 9m 5M. NW Jetée FlG 4s. SE Jetée FlR 4s. Facilities: FW on quay; **Société Nautique de Sauzon** ☎ 97.31.84.56. V, R, Bar in village.

RIVER ÉTEL, Morbihan, 47°39′·00N, 03°12′·00W, Zone −0100, Admty charts 2352, SHOM 7032. HW +0505 on Dover (GMT), −0020 on Brest (zone −0100); ML 2·8m; Duration 0617. Shelter excellent but approach should only be made on flood tide, by day in good weather at about HW−1½. Bar dries. There is a small marina inside the town quay. Ldg line at 042° is marked by two water towers. Hoist ensign to mast-head or call Mat Fenoux Ch 16; 12. Semaphore arms will be rotated, one turn to acknowledge and then as follows: Arrow vertical = remain on course. Arrow inclined = alter course in direction indicated. Arrow horizontal with ball over = no entry. R flag = insufficient depth at bar. Light W side of ent Oc (2) WRG 6s 13m 9/6M W022°−064°, R064°−123°, W123°−330°, G330°−022°. Anchoring prohibited within ½M of this Lt. VHF Ch 16; 13. In Etel town, anchor S of LB house SW of quay, above town (beware strong currents) or go alongside quay (end of quay reserved for ferries) or alongside in yacht harbour beyond quay. Facilities: Hr Mr ☎ 97.55.46.62; Aff Mar ☎ 97.55.90.32; Semaphore tower ☎ 97.55.35.59; Sig.Stn. ☎ 97.52.35.29; Auto ☎ 97.64.54.43; **Kenkiz Marine** ☎ 97.55.34.58. CH, El, ME, Sh; **Town** Bar, Dr, FW, R, V.

PORT TUDY, Ile de Groix, 47°39′·00N, 03°27′·00W, Zone −0100, Admty charts 2352, SHOM 7031, 5912. HW +0505 on Dover (GMT), −0035 on Brest (zone −0100); HW height −2·2m on Brest; ML 3·1m; Duration 0610. See 10.15.19. Very good shelter in marina in inner harbour. Access HW∓1½ (0600-2200). Outer harbour open to NE. Beware large unlit mooring buoys NE of entrance and rocks both sides of approach. Ldg line at 220°, spire of St Tudy church in line with W end of N jetty. Lights; E mole head Fl (2) R 6s 11m 6M vis 112°−226°. N mole head Iso G 4s 12m 6M. Facilities limited. Hr Mr ☎ 98.05.80.90; # ☎ 97.05.80.93; **Marina** (150), FW, P, D, ME, El, Sh; **An C' Hanot** ☎ 97.05.81.86 ME, El, Sh, CH; **Coopérative Maritime** ☎ 97.05.80.03, CH; **Town** V, R, Bar, ferry to Lorient.

DOËLAN, Finistere, 47°46′·00N, 03°36′·00W, Zone −0100, Admty charts 2352, SHOM 7031. HW +0450 on Dover (GMT), −0035 on Brest (zone −0100); HW height −2·2m on Brest; ML 3·1m; Duration 0607. Shelter is good except in bad onshore weather. Harbour dries. Anchorage in outer part of creek or just inside breakwater. Ldg Lts 014°, front Oc (3) WG 12s 20m 13/10M, W shore−305°, G305°−314°, W314°−shore. Rear QR 27m 9M. Facilities: Aff Mar ☎ 98.96.62.38. **Doëlan-Nautic** ☎ 98.71.50.76 CH, El, Ⓔ, ME, Sh; **Town** Bar, D, Dr, FW, P, ✉, R, V.

PONT-AVEN, Finistere, 47°49′·00N, 03°44′·00W, Zone −0100, Admty charts 2352, SHOM 7031. HW +0450 on Dover (GMT), −0030 on Brest (zone −0100). HW height −1·9m on Brest; ML 2·8m; Duration 0610. Very good shelter at Pont-Aven. Moorings in 2·5m; alongside the quay dries 2·5m. Pont-Aven is 3·6M from Port Manech where there are visitors buoys and a good anchorage in 2·5m outside the bar which dries 0·9m. Beware Les Cochons de Rousbicout to W of entrance (dry 0·3m) and Les Verres to E. The only Lt is at Port Manech on Pte Beg ar Vechen Oc (4) WRG 12s 38m 10/6M. Facilities: **YC de l'Aven** at Port Manech. Aff Mar ☎ 98.06.00.73; **Derrien** ☎ 98.06.01.35, ME; **Town** Bar, C, D, FW, P, R, Slip, V.

LOCTUDY, Finistere, 47°50′·00N, 04°10′·00W, Zone −0100, Admty charts 3641, 2352, SHOM 6649, 7146. HW +0505 on Dover (GMT), −0020 on Brest (zone −0100). HW height −2·4m on Brest; ML 2·8m; Duration 0615. (All tidal figures taken at Pont l'Abbé, 3M from entrance). See 10.15.22. Shelter good. Buoys for yachts W of Ile Tudy or anchor NW of the quay. Beware mussel beds. Lights: Langoz Fl (4) WRG 12s 12m 15/10M, W115°−257°, G257°−284°, W284°−295°, R295°−318°, W318°−328°, R328°−025°. Basse Bilien buoy (2M off entrance) VQ (3) 5s. Les Perdrix Lt on N of entrance Fl WRG 4s 15m 11/8M. Facilities: Aff Mar ☎ 98.87.41.79; **wet basin** C (10 ton), D, FW, P; **Club Nautique Loctudy** ☎ 98.87.42.84; **SO.ME.CO.** ☎ 98.87.50.00, El, ME, Sh.

LE GUILVINEC, Finistere, 47°48′·00N, 04°17′·00W, Zone −0100, Admty charts 3640, 2351, SHOM 6646, 7146. HW + 0447 on Dover (GMT), −0023 on Brest (zone −0100); HW height −2·1m on Brest; ML 3·0m. See 10.15.23. Good shelter; harbour always available (unless over 2·5m draught). Good anchorage off entrance protected by reef but keep clear of fairway. Beware Lost Moan Rks SE of entrance marked by RW Bn Tr, Fl (3) WRG 12s 8m 9/6M. Ldg Lts 053°. Front, Mole de Lechiagat Q 7m 8m; W pylon; vis 233°-066°. Middle, Rocher Le Faoute's, 210m from front QWG 12m W14M, G11M; R sphere on W pylon; vis W006°-293°, G293°-006°; synchronised with front. Rear, 0·58M from front, DirQW 26m 8M; R sphere on W pylon; vis 051·5°-054·5°; synchronised with front. VHF Ch 12. Secure to two buoys, fore and aft, marked 'Port de Plaisance' at N end of harbour. Facilities: Hr Mr ☎ 98.58.05.67; Aff Mar ☎ 98.58.13.13; #; C, D, FW, P; **Glehen** ☎ 98.58.12.00. El, ME, Sh; **Biguais** ☎ 98.58.27.43. CH. **CRM** ☎ 98.58.09.58 Ⓔ, El;

Area 16

North Brittany
Brest to Paimpol

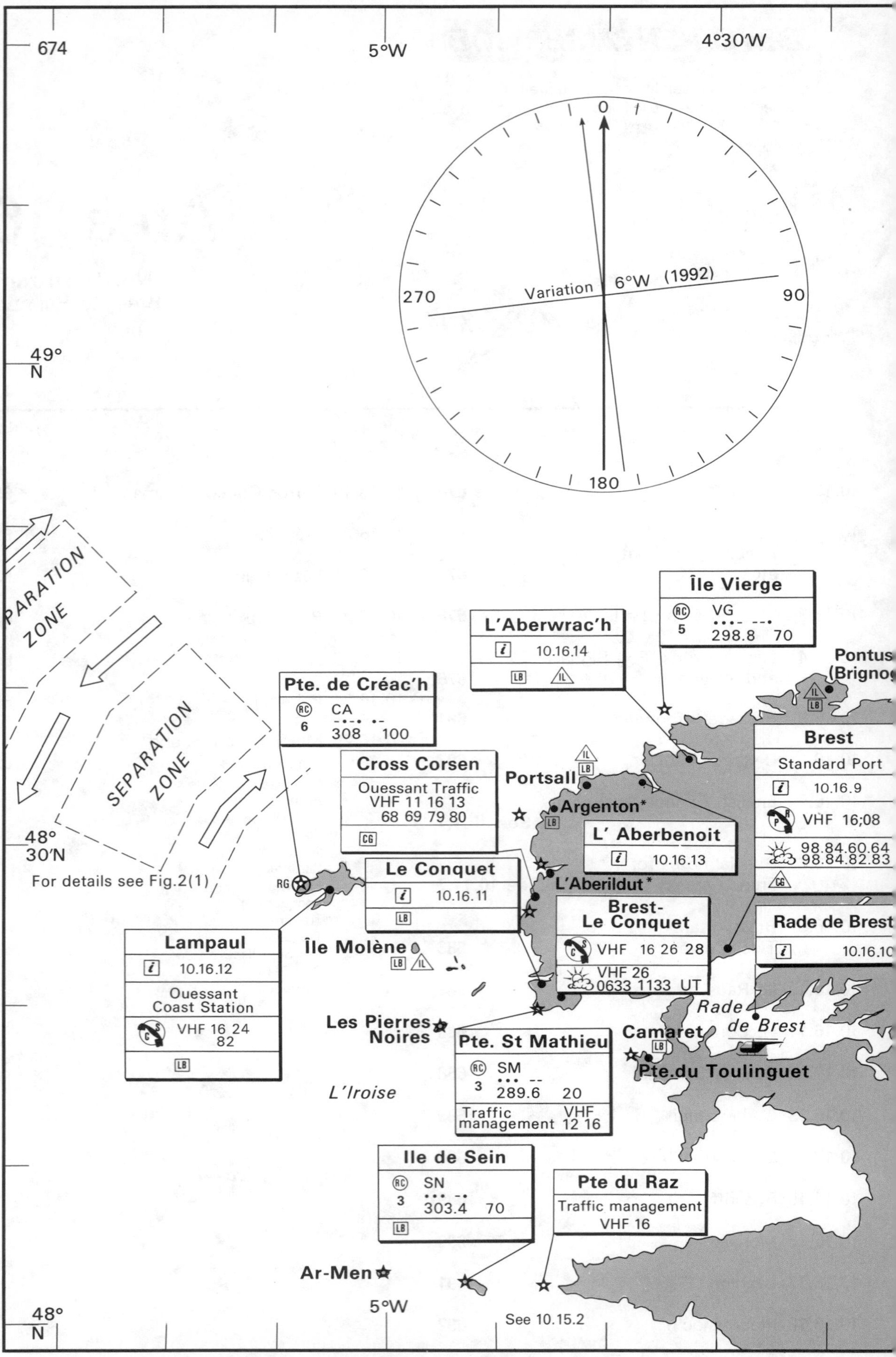
5°W
4°30'W
49° N
48° 30'N
48° N
0
90
180
270
Variation 6°W (1992)
SEPARATION ZONE
SEPARATION ZONE
For details see Fig.2(1)
Île Vierge
RC 5 VG 298.8 70
L'Aberwrac'h
10.16.14
LB IL
Pontus
(Brignog
Pte. de Créac'h
RC 6 CA 308 100
Cross Corsen
Ouessant Traffic
VHF 11 16 13
68 69 79 80
CG
Portsall
Argenton*
L' Aberbenoit
10.16.13
L'Aberildut*
Brest
Standard Port
10.16.9
VHF 16;08
98.84.60.64
98.84.82.83
CG
Le Conquet
10.16.11
LB
Brest-
Le Conquet
VHF 16 26 28
VHF 26
0633 1133 UT
Rade de Brest
10.16.10
RG
Lampaul
10.16.12
Ouessant
Coast Station
VHF 16 24
82
LB
Île Molène
LB IL
Les Pierres
Noires
Rade
de Brest
Camaret
LB
Pte.du Toulinguet
Pte. St Mathieu
RC 3 SM 289.6 20
Traffic management VHF 12 16
L'Iroise
Ile de Sein
RC 3 SN 303.4 70
LB
Pte du Raz
Traffic management
VHF 16
Ar-Men
See 10.15.2

10-16-2

North Brittany

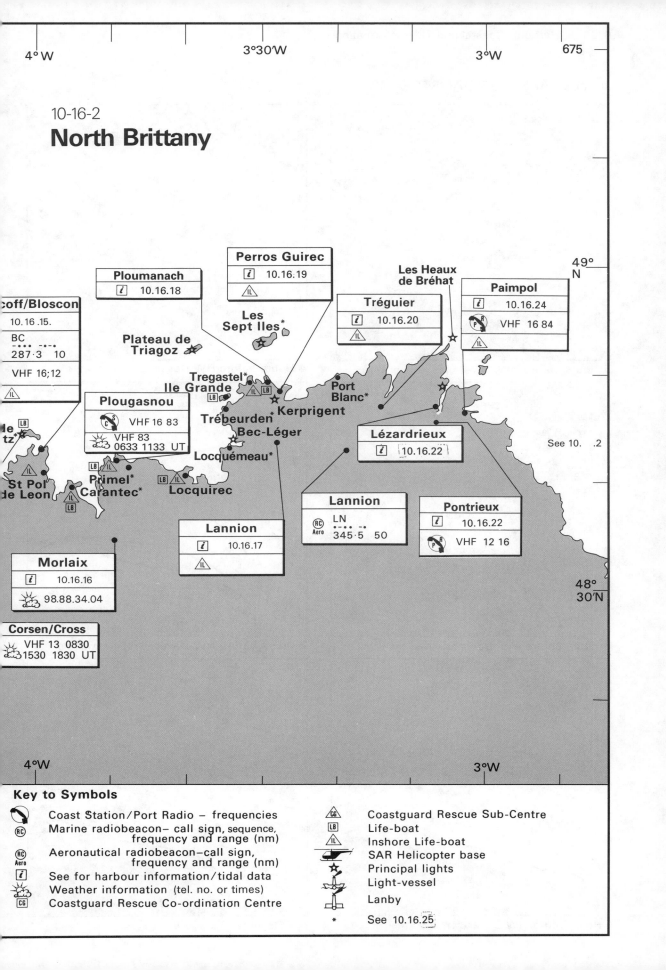

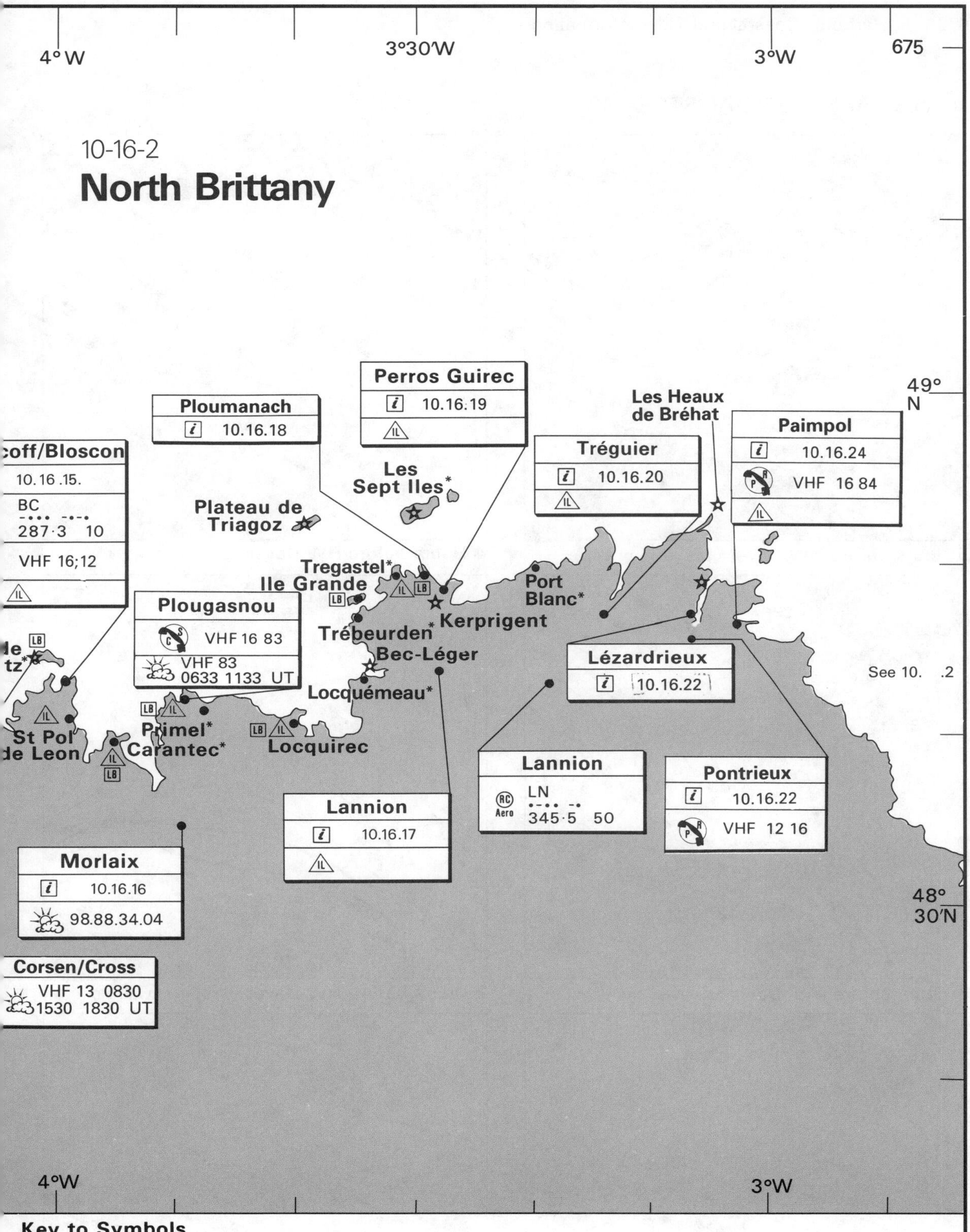
4° W
3°30'W
3°W
49° N
48° 30'N
Perros Guirec
10.16.19
Ploumanach
10.16.18
Les Heaux de Bréhat
Paimpol
10.16.24
VHF 16 84
Tréguier
10.16.20
coff/Bloscon
10.16 .15.
BC
287·3 10
VHF 16;12
Les Sept Iles*
Plateau de Triagoz
Tregastel*
Ile Grande
Port Blanc*
Plougasnou
VHF 16 83
VHF 83
0633 1133 UT
Kerprigent
Trébeurden*
Bec-Léger
Lézardrieux
10.16.22
See 10. .2
Locquémeau*
Primel*
Carantec*
Locquirec
St Pol de Leon
Lannion
LN
345·5 50
Pontrieux
10.16.22
VHF 12 16
Lannion
10.16.17
Morlaix
10.16.16
98.88.34.04
Corsen/Cross
VHF 13 0830
1530 1830 UT
4°W
3°W

Key to Symbols

Coast Station/Port Radio – frequencies
Marine radiobeacon– call sign, sequence, frequency and range (nm)
Aeronautical radiobeacon–call sign, frequency and range (nm)
See for harbour information/tidal data
Weather information (tel. no. or times)
Coastguard Rescue Co-ordination Centre
Coastguard Rescue Sub-Centre
Life-boat
Inshore Life-boat
SAR Helicopter base
Principal lights
Light-vessel
Lanby
* See 10.16.25

10.16.3 AREA 16 TIDAL STREAMS

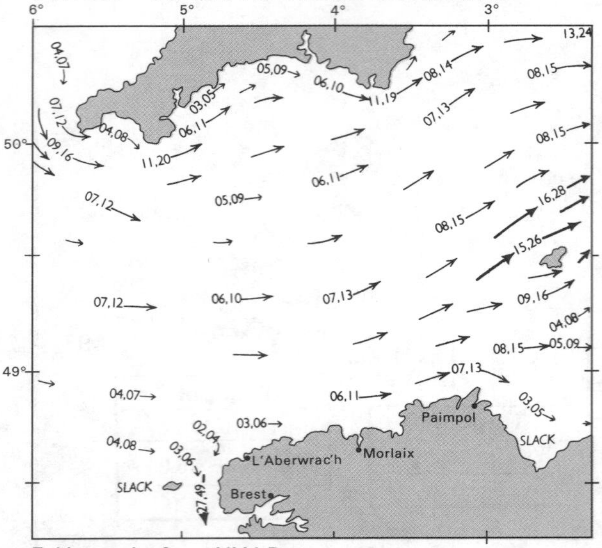
6°
5°
4°
3°
50°
49°
SLACK
Paimpol
Morlaix
L'Aberwrac'h
Brest
SLACK

5 Hours before HW Dover (0215 after HW Brest)

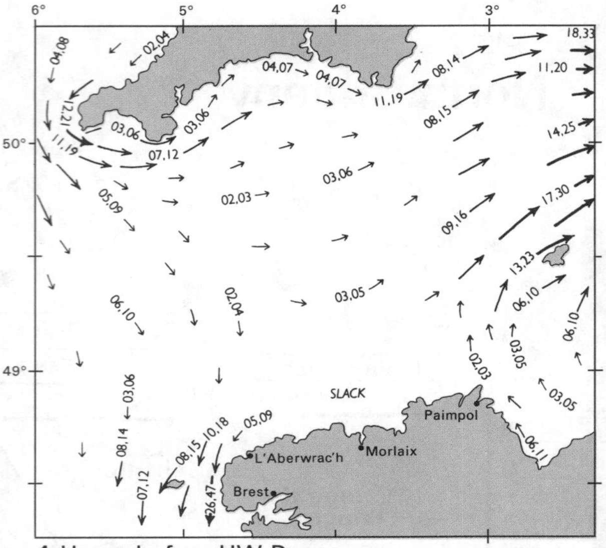
6°
5°
4°
3°
50°
49°
SLACK
Paimpol
Morlaix
L'Aberwrac'h
Brest

4 Hours before HW Dover (0315 after HW Brest)

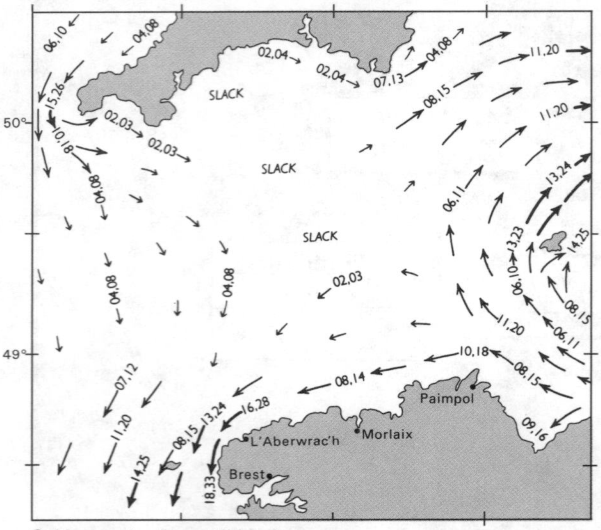
50°
49°
SLACK
SLACK
SLACK
Paimpol
Morlaix
L'Aberwrac'h
Brest

3 Hours before HW Dover (0415 after HW Brest)

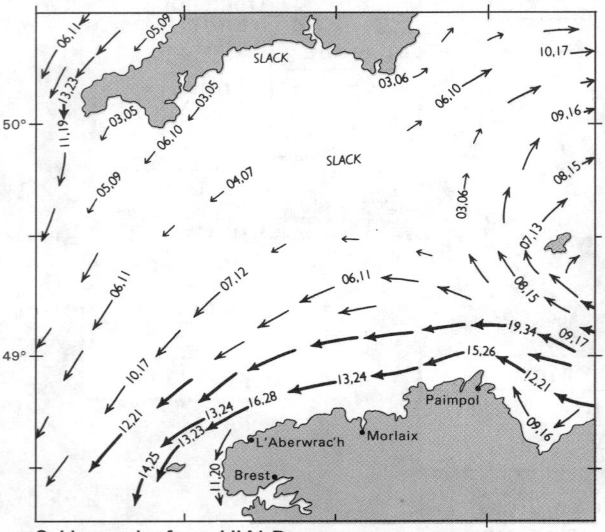
50°
49°
SLACK
SLACK
Paimpol
Morlaix
L'Aberwrac'h
Brest

2 Hours before HW Dover (0515 after HW Brest)

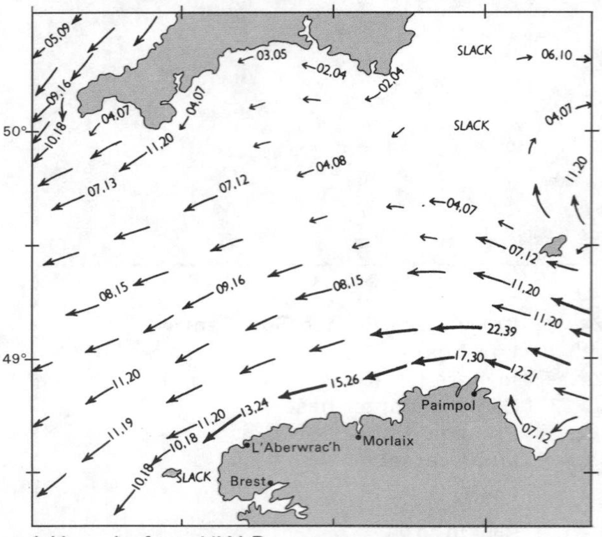
50°
49°
SLACK
SLACK
SLACK
Paimpol
Morlaix
L'Aberwrac'h
Brest

1 Hour before HW Dover (0615 after HW Brest)

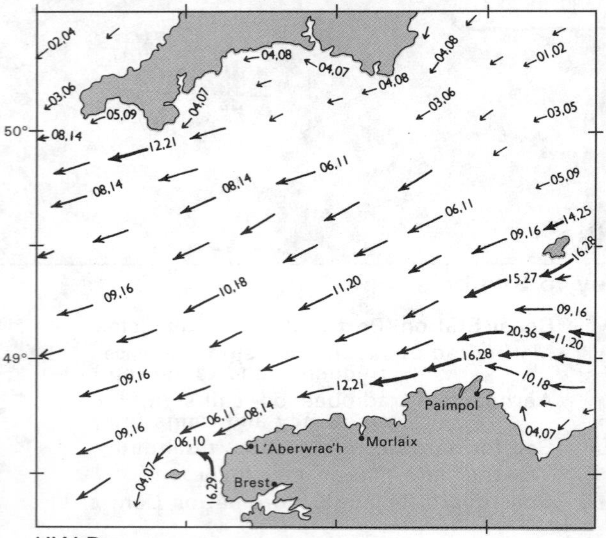
50°
49°
Paimpol
Morlaix
L'Aberwrac'h
Brest

HW Dover (0510 before HW Brest)

Southward 10.15.3. Eastward 10.18.3. Northward 10.1.3.

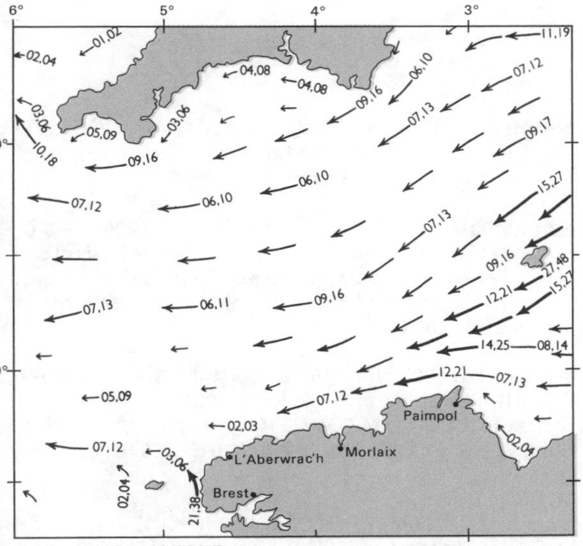
6°
5°
4°
3°
50°
49°
Paimpol
Morlaix
L'Aberwrac'h
Brest

1 Hour after HW Dover (0410 before HW Brest)

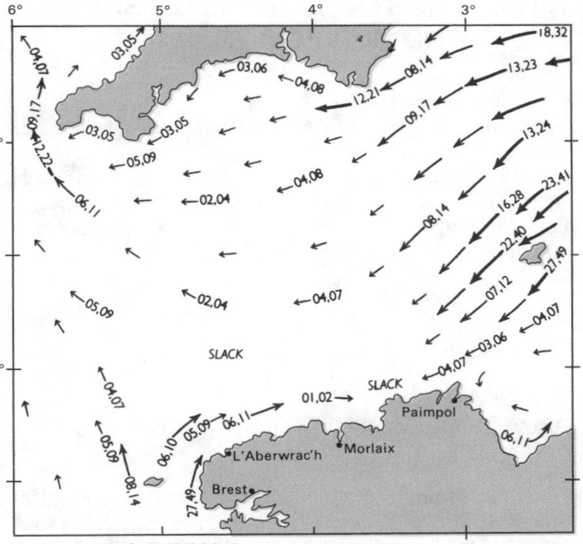
6°
5°
4°
3°
50°
49°
SLACK
SLACK
Paimpol
Morlaix
L'Aberwrac'h
Brest

2 Hours after HW Dover (0310 before HW Brest)

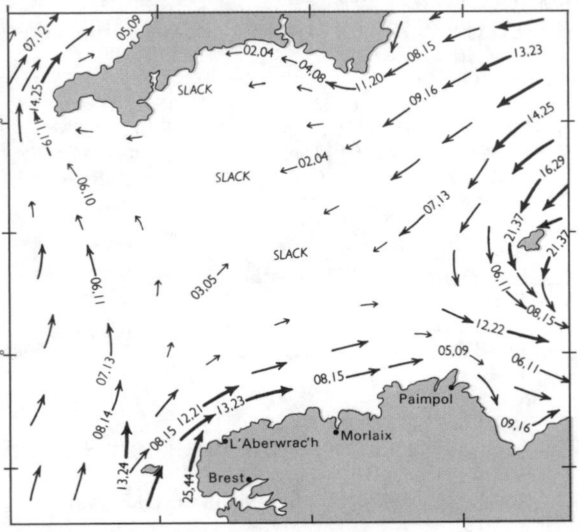
50°
49°
SLACK
SLACK
SLACK
Paimpol
Morlaix
L'Aberwrac'h
Brest

3 Hours after HW Dover (0210 before HW Brest)

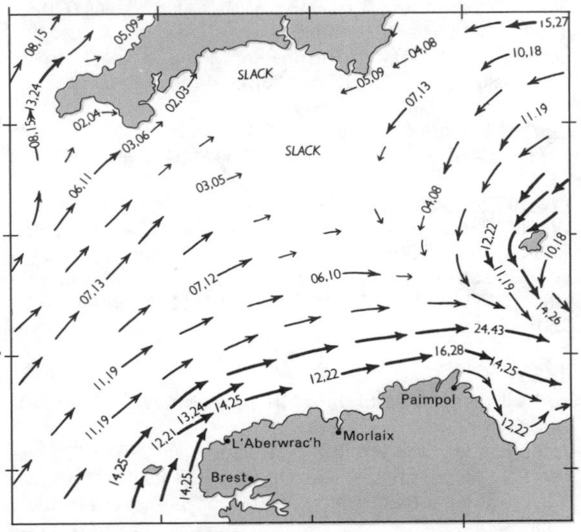
50°
49°
SLACK
SLACK
Paimpol
Morlaix
L'Aberwrac'h
Brest

4 Hours after HW Dover (0110 before HW Brest)

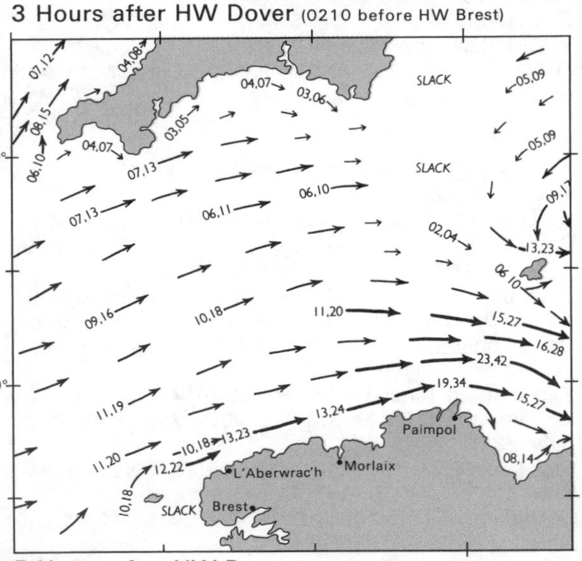
50°
49°
SLACK
SLACK
SLACK
Paimpol
Morlaix
L'Aberwrac'h
Brest

5 Hours after HW Dover (0010 before HW Brest)

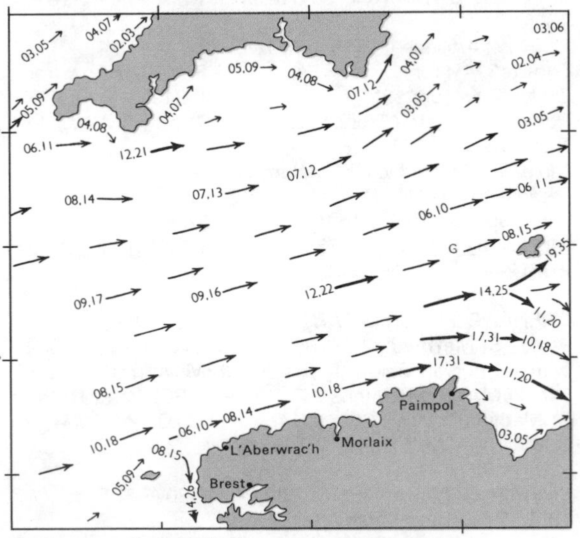
50°
49°
G
Paimpol
Morlaix
L'Aberwrac'h
Brest

6 Hours after HW Dover (0050 after HW Brest)

10.16.4 COASTAL LIGHTS, FOG SIGNALS AND WAYPOINTS

Abbreviations used below are given in 1.4.1. Principal lights are in **bold** print, places in CAPITALS, and light-vessels, light floats and Lanbys in *CAPITAL ITALICS*. Unless otherwise stated lights are white. m—elevation in metres; M—nominal range in n. miles. Fog signals are in *italics*. Useful waypoints are underlined – use those on land with care. All geographical positions should be assumed to be approximate. See 4.2.2.

FRANCE—WEST COAST

GOULET DE BREST.
Charles Martel Lt By 48°18'·90N 04°42'·10W Fl (4) R; PHM; *Whis.*

Pte du Petit-Minou 48°20'·26N 04°36'·80W Dir Q 30m **23M**; intens 065·5°-070·5°; *Horn 60s* and Fl (2) WR 6s 32m **W19M R15M**; Gy ● Tr, R top; vis R shore-252°, W252°-260°, R260°-307°, W (unintens) 307°-015°; W015°-065·5°, W 070·5°-shore. FR 1·5M and 2·7M NE.
Ldg Lts 068°. **Front** from Pte du Petit-Minou Tr, Rear from Pte du Portzic Tr, both Q 56/54m **23M**, intens 065°-071°.

Roche Mengam 48°20'·40N 04°34'·48W Fl (3) WR 12s 11m W11M, R8M; R Tr, B bands; vis R034°-054°, W054°-034°.

Pte du Portzic 48°21'·55N 04°31'·96W Oc (2) WR 12s 56m **W19M, R15M**; Gy 8-sided Tr; vis R219°-259°, W259°-338°, R338°-000°, W000°-065·5°, W070·5°-219°; vis 041°-069° in W of Goulet. Same structure, Rear, Dir Q 54m **23M**; same Tr; intens 065°-071°. Dir Q (6) + L Fl 15s 54m **24M**; intens 045°-050°.

BREST.
Port Militaire, Jetée Sud Hd QR 10m 5M; W Tr, R top; vis 094°-048°.
Jetée Est, Hd QG 10m 5M; W Tr, G top; vis 299°-163°.
Terre-pleine du Château Dir Oc (2) WRG 6s 19m W11M, R8M, G8M; on roof of bldg; vis G335°-344°, W344°-350°, R350°-014°.
La Penfeld, E side of ent, Iso G 3s 11m 7M; W pylon; vis 316°-180°.
Quai de l'Artillerie Iso R 3s 8m 7M; vis 144°-350°.
Ldg Lts 314° Front Dir Iso R 5s 9m 10M. Rear, 17m from front, Dir Iso R 5s 16m 12M; both intens 309°-319°.
Port de Commerce. E ent, S side Oc (2) R 6s 8m 5M; W pylon, R top; vis 018°-301°.
Mole de l'Est Hd Oc (2) G 6s 8m 7M.
Jetée Ouest Hd Iso R 4s 10m 7M.
Jetée Sud W Hd Fl G 4s 10m 6M; vis 022°-257°.
Moulin Blanc Lt By 48°22'·85N 04°25'·90W Fl (3) R 12s; PHM.

CHENAL DU FOUR (S PART).
Pte de St Mathieu 48°19'·85N 04°46'·17W. Ldg Lts 158·5° with Kermorvan (below) Fl 15s 56m **29M**; W Tr, R top. Dir F 54m **28M**; same Tr; intens 157·5°-159·5°; RC. 54m 291° from St Mathieu Q WRG 26m W14M, R11M, G11M; W Tr; vis G085°-107°, W107°-116°, R116°-134°.

Les Pierres Noires 48°18'·73N 04°54'·80W Fl R 5s 27m **19M**; W Tr, R top; *Siren (2) 60s.*
Les Vieux-Moines 48°19'·40N 04°46'·55W Fl R 4s 16m 5M; R 8-sided Tr; vis 280°-133°.

Lochrist 48°20'·6N 04°45'·9W Dir Oc (3) 12s 49m **22M**; W 8-sided Tr, R top; intens 135°-140°; Rear Ldg Lt 137·5° for Chenal de la Helle with Kermorvan.

Kermorvan 48°21'·80N 04°47'·30W Fl 5s 20m **22M**; W ■ Tr; obsc by Pte de St Mathieu when brg less than 341°; front Ldg Lt for Chenal de la Helle with Lochrist. Common Front Ldg Lt 158·5° with Pte de St Mathieu (above), and 007° with Trézien (below); *Reed 60s.*

Trézien Ldg Lt 007°; Rear 48°25'·4N 04°46'·8W Dir Oc (2) 6s 84m **21M**; Gy Tr, W on S side; intens 003°-011°.
Corsen 48°24'·9N 04°47'·7W Dir Q WRG 33m W12M, R8M, G8M; W hut; vis R008°-012°, W012°-015°, G015°-021°.

CONQUET.
Mole 48°21'·6N 04°47'·1W Oc G 4s 3m 6M; G mast.
La Grande Vinotière 48°22'·00N 04°48'·30W Oc R 6s 15m 5M; R 8-sided Tr.
Rouget Lt By 48°22'·00N 04°48'·80W Iso G 4s; SHM; *Whis.*

ÎLE DE MOLÈNE.
Molène môle Hd Dir Lt 191°, Dir Fl (3) WRG 12s 6m W9M, R7M, G7M; vis G183°-190°, W190°-192°, R192°-203°.
Chenal des Las Dir Lt 261°, Dir Fl (2) WRG 6s 9m W9M, R7M, G7M; same structure; vis G252·5°-259·5°, W259·5°-262·5°, R262·5°-269·5°.

CHENAL DE LA HELLE.
Les Trois-Pierres 48°24'·75N 04°56'·75W Iso WRG 4s 15m W9M, R6M, G6M; W col; vis G070°-147°, W147°-185°, R185°-191°, G191°-197°, W197°-213°, R213°-070°.
Le Faix 48°25'·80N 04°53'·82W VQ; 16m 8M; NCM; in line with Le Stiff (below) bears 293·5°.

CHENAL DU FOUR (N PART).
Les Plâtresses 48°26'·35N 04°50'·85W Fl RG 4s 17m 6M; W Tr; vis R343°-153°, G153°-333°.
La Valbelle Lt By 48°26'·55N 04°49'·90W Fl (2) R 6s 8m 5M; PHM; *Whis.*
L'Aberildut 48°28'·3N 04°45'·6W Dir Oc (2) WR 6s 12m **W25M, R20M**; W bldgs; vis W081°-085°, R085°-087°.
Le Four 48°31'·45N 04°48'·23W Fl (5) 15s 27m **18M**; Gy ● Tr; *Siren (3+2) 75s.*

OUESSANT.
OUESSANT SW LANBY 48°31'·68N 05°49'·10W Fl 4s 12m **20M**; RC; Racon.
NE Lt By 48°45'·90N 05°11'·60W L Fl 10s 9m 8M; *Whis*; Racon.

La Jument 48°25'·40N 05°07'·95W Fl (3) R 15s 36m **22M**; Gy 8-sided Tr, R Top; obsc by Ouessant 199°-241°; *Horn (3) 60s.*
Pierre-Vertes Lt By 48°22'·2N 05°04'·7W VQ (9) 10s 9m 8M; W CM; *Whis*; Ra refl.
Kéréon (Men-Tensel) 48°26'·30N 05°01'·45W Oc (2+1) WR 24s 38m **W19M, R15M**; Gy Tr; vis W019°-248°, R248°-019°; *Siren (2+1) 120s.*
Men-Korn 48°27'·95N 05°01'·22W VQ (3) WR 5s 21m W8M, R8M; ECM; vis W145°-040°, R040°-145°.
Le Stiff 48°28'·60N 05°03'·10W Fl (2) R 20s 85m **24M**; two adjoining W Trs.
Créac'h 48°27'·62N 05°07'·72W Fl (2) 10s 70m **34M**; W Tr,

B bands; obsc 247°-255°; Racon, RC; RG; *Horn (2) 120s.*
An-Ividig (Nividic) 48°26'·80N 05°08'·95W VQ (9) 10s 28m 9M; W 8-sided Tr, R bands; obsc by Ouessant 225°-290°. Helicopter platform.
Port du Stiff. Môle Est Hd 48°28'·18N 05°03'·16W Dir Q WRG 11m W10M, R7M, G7M; W Tr, G top; vis G251°-254°, W254°-264°, R264°-267°.

FRANCE—NORTH COAST

Basse de Portsall Lt By 48°36'·78N 04°46'·05W VQ (9) 10s 9m 8M; WCM; *Whis*; Ra refl.
Portsall 48°33'·9N 04°42'·3W Oc (3+1) WRG 12s 9m W16M, R13M, G13M; W col, R top; vis G058°-084°, W084°- 088°, R088°-058°.
Corn-Carhai 48°35'·2N 04°43'·9W Fl (3) 12s 19m 9M; W 8-sided Tr, B top.
Libenter Lt By 48°37'·5N 04°38'·4W Q (9) 15s 8m 8M; WCM; Ra refl; *Whis.*

L'ABERWRAC'H.
Ldg Lts 100° Front Île Wrac'h 48°36'·9N 04°34'·6W QR 20m 7M; W ■ Tr, Or top, dwelling. Rear, Lanvaon 1·63M from front Dir Q 55m 12M; W ■ Tr, Or ▲ on top; intens 090·5°-110·5°.
Breac'h Ver 48°36'·70N 04°35'·40W Fl G 2·5s 6m 3M; ▲ on Bn Tr, SHM.
Dir Lt 128°, La Palue 48°35'·9N 04°33'·9W Dir Oc (2) WRG 6s 5m W13M, R11M, G11M; vis G125·7°-127·2°, W127·2°-128·7°, R128·7°-130·2°.

Île-Vierge 48°38'·38N 04°34'·10W Fl 5s 77m **27M**; Gy Tr; vis 337°-325°; RC; *Siren 60s.*
Pontusval, Pte de Beg-Pol 48°40'·7N 04°20'·8W Oc (3) WR 12s 16m W10M, R7M; W ■ Tr, B top, W dwelling; vis W shore-056°, R056°-096°, W096°-shore. QY and FR Lts on towers 2·4M S.
Lizen Ven Ouest Lt By 48°40'·57N 04°33'·68W VQ (9) 10s 8m 8M; WCM; *Whis* .
Aman-ar-Ross Lt By 48°41'·9N 04°27'·0W Q 9m 7M; NCM; *Whis.*

PORT DE MOGUÉRIEC.
Ldg Lts 162°. Front, jetty Hd Iso WG 4s 9m W11M, G6M; W Tr, G top; vis W158°-166°, G166°-158°. Rear, 440m from front FG 22m 7M; W Col, G top; vis 142°-182°.

ÎLE DE BATZ.
48°44'·78N 04°01'·55W Fl (4) 25s 69m **23M**; Gy Tr; auxiliary Lt FR 67m 7M; same Tr; vis 024°-059°.

ROSCOFF.
Astan Lt By 48°44'·95N 03°57'·55W VQ (3) 5s 12m 8M; ECM; *Whis*; Ra refl.
Ar-Chaden 48°43'·99N 03°58'·15 W Q (6) + LFl WR 15s 14m W8M, R6M; SCM Bn Tr; vis R262°-288°, W288°-294°, R294°-326°, W326°-110°.
Men-Guen-Bras 48°43'·81N 03°57'·95W Q WRG 14m W9M, R6M, G6M; NCM Bn Tr; vis W068°-073°, R073°-197°, W197°-257°, G257°-068°.
Basse de Bloscon Lt By 48°43'·77N 03°57'·48W VQ; NCM.
Le Menk Lt Tr 48°43'·35N 03°56'·60W Q (9) WR 15s 6m 5/3M; WCM Bn Tr; vis W160°-188°.
Ldg Lts 209°. Front, NW Môle Oc (2+1) G 12s 7m 7M; W col, G top; vis 078°-318°. **Rear** 430m from front Oc (2+1) 12s 24m **15M**; Gy ■ Tr, W on NE side; vis 062°-242°.
Jetty Hd 48°44'·0N 03°59'·0W F Vi 5m 1M.

Slip 48°44'·3N 04°00'·5W VQ (6) + LFl 10s 13m 7M; SCM.

BLOSCON.
Jetty Hd 48°43'·30N 03°57'·65W Fl WG 4s 9m W10M, G7M; W Tr, G top, vis W210°-220°, G220°-210°; RC.

BAIE DE MORLAIX.
Ldg Lts 190·5°. Front, Île Noire 48°40'·39N 03°52'·58W Oc (2) WRG 6s 15m W11M, R8M, G8M; W ■ Tr, R top; vis G051°-135°, R135°-211°, W211°-051°; obsc in places. Rear (common with Île Louet 176°)
La Lande 48°38'·2N 03°53'·1W Fl 5s 85m **23M**; W ■ Tr, B top; obsc by Pte Annelouesten when brg more than 204°.
Ldg Lts 176°. Front **Île Louet** 48°40'·5N 03°53'·4W Oc (3) WG 12s 17m **W15M**; G10M; W ■ Tr, B top; vis W305°-244°, G244°-305°, vis 139°-223° from offshore, except when obsc by Is. Rear, La Lande above.

ANSE DE PRIMEL.
Ldg Lts 152°. Front FR 35m 6M; W ■, R stripe on pylon; vis 134°-168°. Rear, 202m from front FR 56m 6M; W ■, R stripe.
Jetty Hd 48°42'·82N 03°49'·53W Fl G 4s 6m 7M; W col, G top on hut.

LOCQUEMEAU.
Ldg Lts 121°. Front FR 21m 6M; W pylon, R top; vis 068°-228°. Rear, 484m from front Oc (2+1) R 12s 39m 7M; W gabled house; vis 016°-232°.

Beg-Léguer 48°44'·40N 03°32'·83W Oc (4) WRG 12s 60m W13M, R10M, G10M; W face of White house, R lantern; vis G007°-084°, W084°-098°, R098°-129°.
Les Triagoz 48°52'·35N 03°38'·73W Oc (2) WR 6s 31m **W15M**, R11M; Gy ■ Tr, R lantern; vis W010°-339°, R339°-010°; obsc in places 258°-268° by Les Sept-Îles.

LES SEPT-ÎLES.
Île-aux-Moines 48°52'·78N 03°29'·33W Fl (3) 15s 59m **24M**; Gy Tr and dwelling; obsc by Îlot Rouzic and E end of Île Bono 237°-241°, and in Baie de Lannion when brg less than 039°.

PLOUMANAC'H.
Méan-Ruz 48°50'·32N 03°28'·90W Oc WR 4s 26m W13M, R10M; pink ■ Tr; vis W226°-242°, R242°-226°; obsc by Pte de Trégastel when brg less than 080°, and part obsc by Sept-Îles 156°-207°, and by Île Tomé 264°-278°.

PERROS-GUIREC.
Passe de l'Ouest. **Kerjean** Dir Lt 143·5°. Dir Oc (2+1) WRG 12s 78m **W15M**, R13M, G13M; W Tr, B top; vis G133·7°-143·2°, W143·2°-144·8°, R144·8°-154.3°.
Passe de l'Est Ldg Lts 225°. Front **Le Colombier** Dir Oc (4) 12s 28m **18M**; W house; intens 219·5°-229·5°. Rear, **Kerprigent** 1·5M from front Dir Q 79m **22M**; W Tr; intens 221°-228°.
Jetée Est (Linkin) Hd 48°48'·26N 03°26'·23W Fl (2) G 6s 4m 7M; W pile, G top.
Môle Ouest Hd Fl (2) R 6s 4m 8M; W pile, R top.

PORT BLANC.
Le Voleur Fl WRG 4s 17m W14M, R11M, G11M; W Tr; vis G140°-148°, W148°-152°, R152°-160°.

TRÉGUIER.
La Corne 48°51'·40N 03°10'·53W Fl (3) WRG 12s 14m W11M, R8M, G8M; W Tr, R base; vis W052°-059°, R059°-173°, G173°-213°, W213°-220°, R220°-052°.

Grande Passe Ldg Lts 137°. Front, Port de la Chaîne Oc 4s 12m 12M; W house. Rear **St Antoine** 0·75M from front Dir Oc R 4s 34m **15M**; R & W house; synchronised with front, intens 134°-140°.

Les Héaux de Bréhat 48°54'·53N 03°05'·20W Oc (3) WRG 12s 48m **W17M**, R12M, G12M; Gy ● Tr; vis R227°-247°, W247°-270°, G270°-302°, W302°-227°.

LE TRIEUX RIVER (LEZARDRIEUX).
Moisie Rk Bn Tr 48°53'·85N 03°02'·22W (unlit); ECM.
Noguejou Bihan Bn 48°53'·43N 03°01'·93W (unlit); ECM.
Les Sirlots Buoy 48°52'·97N 02°59'·60W (unlit); SHM; *Whis.*
Vieille du Tréou Bn Tr 48°52'·02N 03°01'·12W (unlit); SHM.
Rocher Men-Grenn 48°51'·3N 03°03'·9W Q (9) 15s 7m 8M; WCM Bn Tr.
Ldg Lts 225°. Front **La Croix** 48°50'·25N 03°03'·25W Oc 4s 15m **19M**; two Gy ● Trs joined, W on NE side, R tops; intens 215°-235°. Rear **Bodic**, 2·1M from front Dir Q 55m **22M**; W house with G gable; intens 221°-229°.
Coatmer Ldg Lts 219°. Front 48°48'·30N 03°05'·78W F RG 16m R9M, G8M; W gable; vis R200°-250°, G250°-053°. Rear, 660m from front, FR 50m 9M; W gable; vis 197°-242°.
Les Perdrix 48°47'·77N 03°05'·83W Fl (2) WG 6s 5m W9M, G6M; G Tr; vis G165°-197°, W197°-202·5°, G202·5°-040°.
3 F Bu Lts mark marina pontoons, 750m SSW.

ILE DE BRÉHAT.
Rosédo 48°51'·5N 03°00'·3W Fl 5s 29m **20M**; W Tr; RC.
Le Paon 48°51'·95N 02°59'·17W F WRG 22m W12M, R9M, G9M; Y Tr; vis W033°-078°, G078°-181°, W181°-196°, R196°-307°, W307°-316°, R316°-348°.
Men-Joliguet 48°50'·14N 03°00'·23W Iso WRG 4s 6m W13M, R10M, G10M; WCM Bn Tr; vis R255°-279°, W279°-283°, G283°-175°.
Chenal de Ferlas, Roche Quinonec, Dir Lt 257·5°, Dir Q WRG 12m W10M, R8M, G8M; Gy Tr; vis G254°-257°, W257°-257·7°, R257·7°-260·7°.
Kermouster, Embouchure du Trieux, Dir Lt 271°, Dir Fl WRG 2s 16m W10M, R8M, G8M; W col; vis G267°-270°, W270°-272°, R272°-274°.
La Horaine 48°53'·55N 02°55'·30W Fl (3) 12s 13m 11M; Gy 8-sided Tr on B hut.

PAIMPOL.
Pte de Porz-Don Oc (2) WR 6s 13m **W15M**, R11M; W house; vis W269°-272°, R272°-279°.
Ldg Lts 264°. Jetée de Kernoa, front FR 5m 7M; W & R hut. Rear 360m from front Dir FR 12m 14M; W pylon, R top; intens 261·5°-266·5°.

L'Ost Pic 48°46'·75N 02°56'·45W Oc WR 4s 20m W11M, R8M; 2 W Trs, R tops; vis W105°-116°, R116°-221°, W221°-253°, R253°-291°, W291°-329°; obsc by islets near Bréhat when brg less than 162°.

Barnouic 49°01'·70N 02°48'·40W VQ (3) 5s 15m 9M; ECM Bn Tr, Y band, W base.

Roches Douvres 49°06'·47N 02°48'·82W Fl 5s 60m **28M**; pink Tr on dwelling with G roof; RC; RG; *Siren 60s.*

Note. For English Channel Waypoints see 10.1.7

10.16.5 PASSAGE INFORMATION

APPROACH TO BREST (Charts 798 3427)

The outer apprs lie ENE between Pte du Toulinguet to the S and Pte St. Mathieu to the N. From the W steer on the 068° transit of Petit Minhou and Portzic, both Lt Ho's on the N shore. From the SW steer NNE toward Petit Minhou to pick up the transit. The outer apprs are subject to a Traffic Management Scheme from which vessels less than 25m long are exempt, but listen on VHF Ch 8/16 and keep to stbd of whichever chan you use.

Abeam Petit Minhou Lt Ho the Goulet (Narrows) de Brest narrow to 1M wide and are divided by well-marked drying rks almost in mid stream. A course of 075° through the Passe Nord will clear Roc Mengam Lt Bn by 0·2M to stbd.

Tidal streams attain 4·5 kn in the Goulet. In Passe Sud there is a useful back-eddy close inshore which runs ENE during the ebb.

Once past Port du Portzic a buoyed chan leads ENE past the Naval & commercial hbrs to the Moulin Blanc marina (10.16.9). The Rade de Brest (10.16.10) opens to the E and S.

OUESSANT (USHANT) (chart 2694)

Ouessant is 10M off the W end of coast of France. It is rky Is, with dangers extending 0·5M to NE, 0·75M to SE, 1·5M to SW and 1M to NW (where Chaussée de Keleren is a dangerous chain of drying and submerged rks running 1M W of Île de Keleren).

Tidal streams are strong close to the Is, and in chans between it and mainland. Off Créach Pt (Lt, fog sig, RC) the stream turns NNE at HW Brest –0550, and SSW at HW Brest +0045, sp rate 5·5 kn.

Apart from Lampaul (10.16.12) the only other anch is B du Stiff which gives some shelter in moderate winds between S and NW: beware the rk awash about 0·35M SSW of the rk with IDM in middle of B.

Ouessant is something of a barrier between W and N coasts of France, but in fair weather and with reasonable vis the pilotage in the chans between it and the mainland is not very demanding. They are well buoyed and marked, but the tide runs hard in places, causing overfalls when against wind of over force 5. The route outside Ouessant has little to commend it: unless bound to or from Spain or Portugal it adds much to the distance, it is exposed to sea and swell, and the traffic scheme – see Fig.2(1) – restricts the free passage of yachts. In thick weather this is an unhealthy area, and it is prudent to stay in harbour until the vis improves.

There are three main chans between the island and mainland. The inshore one, Chenal du Four, is most direct and most popular. Chenal de la Helle, partly used for access to Île Moléne, is not so direct but better in bad weather. Passage du Fromveur, immediately SE of Ouessant, is easiest but can become extremely rough.

CHENAL DU FOUR (Chart 2694)

The tide runs strongest at S end of Chenal du Four, entered 1M W of Pte St Mathieu, with Kermorvan and Trézien Ldg Lts on at 007°. Here the N-going stream begins at HW Brest –0550 and reaches 5·5 kn at sp. The S-going stream starts at HW Brest +0015, reaching 4·75 kn. Further N, off Pte de Corsen, the stream is weaker, less than 3 kn at sp. Bound homeward, or along the N coast of France, enter the S end of Chenal du Four at LW Brest: then the strongest tide off Kermorvan will be avoided, since it runs at about HW Brest –0300, while full use can be made of the NE stream past Île Vierge.

Compared to larger vessels, there are several routes for a yacht through Chenal du Four. The following can be used day or night, if necessary from By to By if marks are obscured. The 007° transit above is followed until the Q WRG St Mathieu Lt is abeam (in G sector). Then alter to make good 325° (Le Faix Tr on with Grande Courleau Bn) for about 1M until La Grande Vinotière and Pte de Corsen Lts are in transit at 009°. At this point steer to make good 005° to pass between La Grande Vinotière and Roche du Rouget By which are 1·25M away. Aim to pass 0·1M W of La Grande Vinotière, and continue on this course until the transit of Kermorvan and Pte St Mathieu is picked up at 158°. Then alter to port to follow this stern transit. There are Bys marking chan if difficult to follow the marks (or powerful Lts) astern. Do not confuse St Mathieu with Lochrist; the latter is rear Ldg Lt for outer part of Chenal de la Helle. Follow the 158° transit until Le Four is abeam, although in fact open water is reached once past L'Aberildut.

Coming S, the reverse procedure is followed. It may be difficult to identify the Kermorvan/St Mathieu 158° transit, but assuming moderate vis locate Le Four Tr E of the approach, and then Les Plâtresses slightly W of the transit, and only 5M from Kermorvan.

CHENAL DE LA HELLE (Chart 2694)

For Chenal de la Helle from S, follow the above route until Trézien is in transit with Corsen, bearing 050°. At this point pick up transit of Le Faix Tr with Stiff (NE corner of Ouessant) at 293°. Follow this transit for 2M until Kermorvan comes on with Lochrist astern at 138°. Take this stern transit out into open water, passing 0·6M NE of Le Faix. From the N, if difficult to see the 138° Ldg marks, the positions of Les Plâtresses to E of Ldg Line, and of Le Faix Tr and La Helle rk (12m elevation, and 0·7M W of Le Faix) to the W of it, will help locate them. At N end of Chenal de la Helle the ENE stream starts at HW Brest –0520 (sp rate 2·75 kn), and the SW stream at HW Brest –0045 (sp rate 3·75 kn).

In fair weather access to Moléne is easy from Chenal de la Helle. The key transit is Les Trois Pierres on with North Mill at 215°, picked up 0·5M W of La Helle Rk. North Mill may be obsc by Tr of Les Trois Pierres: as the latter is approached alter to stbd to skirt it at 0·1M. When 0·1M W of Les Trois Pierres, alter to 190° to pass close E of Bazou Real Bn Tr, which brings South Mill over the bow and in line with white patch on mole. Do not borrow to port, where there are rks, and anch about 0·1M N of mole.

Passage du Fromveur is 1M wide, between Ouessant and the dangers round Kéréon Lt Tr. But the stream runs 7 kn at sp, and with wind against tide the chan can be very dangerous. In good conditions it is safe and convenient with a fair tide.

LE FOUR TO ILE DE BATZ (Charts 3668, 3669)

Proceeding NE from Le Four, and E towards Roscoff (10.16.15) there are many off-lying dangers, in places 3M offshore. Swell may break on shoals even further to seaward. The tide runs strongly, and in poor vis or bad weather it is a coast to avoid. 1M W of Le Four the E-going stream begins at HW Brest –0545, sp rate 3·5 kn; the W-going stream begins at HW Brest +0100, sp rate 4 kn. Off Le Libenter, at N side of L'Aberwrac'h entrance the E-going stream starts at HW Brest –0500, sp rate 3·75 kn, and the W-going stream at HW Brest +0110. But in good conditions this is an admirable cruising ground with delightful Hrs such as L'Aberildut, Argenton, and Portsall (10.16.25), L'Aberbenoit (10.16.13), L'Aberwrac'h (10.16.14), Coréjou, Pontusval (10.16.25), and Mogueriec.

E of Le Four is an inshore Pass leading to Portsall, and thence to L'Aberwrac'h Ent. This is convenient and sheltered, but must only be used by day and in good conditions. Chart 1432 or French chart 5772 and full pilotage directions, as in *North Brittany Pilot*, are needed. N of L'Aberwrac'h is Île Vierge Lt Ho, the tallest in the world, and a conspic landmark.

In daylight and above half tide there is a useful short cut to Roscoff through the Canal de l'Île de Batz, between the Is and the mainland at half tide or above. See chart 2745 or French chart 5828. Coming from the W, steer just N of Basse Plate Bn Tr, with Le Loup (a rk withW patch at N end) in transit with St Barbe (a W pyramid beyond Roscoff hbr) brg 106°. This transit leads to L'Oignon NCM, where course is altered to 083° for Pen ar Cleguer at S end of Île de Batz. Short of this point, when Per Roch NCM bears 45° on stbd bow, alter course to leave it 0·5M to stbd. When Per Roch is passed, alter course slightly to stbd to leave An Oan SCM to port, and steer for the vi Bn at end of the conspic Roscoff ferry pier. Pass 30m N of this Bn, and at this point alter to 095° which leads to Ar Chaden. For Ile de Batz see 10.16.25.

Approaching from NE, leave Basse Astan ECM to stbd steering with Men Guen Bras (lit) in transit with Chapelle St Barbe 213° to round Ar Chaden either to enter Roscoff or transit W through Canal de L'Ile de Batz.

N of Île de Batz the E-going stream begins at HW Brest –0435, and the W-going stream at HW Brest +0105, sp rates both 3·75 kn.

MORLAIX TO LES SEPT ILES (Chart 3669)

The B de Morlaix (10.16.16 and chart 2745) is well endowed with drying rks and shoal Gd, all marked. Careful pilotage and adequate vis are needed to negotiate any of the 3 chans which are narrow in parts. The Grand Chenal passes close E of Île Rickard with Île Louet and La Lande (both lit) in transit 176°; abeam Calhic Bn Tr alter to port to transit between Chateau du Taureau (conspic) and Île Louet. Continue SSE to enter the Morlaix R.

Sailing E from Roscoff, Bloscon or Morlaix pass inside or outside Plateau de la Méloine; the former is obvious choice if bound for Lannion (10.16.17). The radome NE of Trébeurden (10.16.25). is conspic.

Plateau des Triagoz has offlying dangers WSW and NE of the Lt, where the sea breaks heavily. Here the stream turns ENE at HW Brest –0325, and WSW at HW Brest +0245, sp rates both 3·75 kn.

Les Sept Îles consist of four main Is and several Is, through which the tide runs strongly. Île aux Moines is lit, and there is an open anch between it and Île de Bono, which is a bird sanctuary.

PLOUMANAC'H TO PAIMPOL (Chart 3670)

Between Ploumanac'h (10.16.18) and Perros-Guirec (10.16.19) there is a nice anch in Anse Trestraou, sheltered from S and W winds.

A useful inshore Pass, avoiding detour round Les Heaux, is Passage de la Gaine between Tréguier River (10.16.20) and Lézardrieux (10.16.21). It should only be used by day, and in good vis. Front Ldg mark is Men Noblance Bn Tr (W, with B stripe). The rear mark (in transit at 242°) is less conspic, and is a W mark with vertical B stripe on a wall just below the skyline, to right of Plougrescant church (conspic). This mark is easier to see from W end of transit, than from Les Heaux. However, there are three Bns which mark the SE side of Basses des Heaux, and should be passed close on required side. If the pass is made at above half tide it presents no problem in fair weather. From the E end of Passe de la Gaine the chan de La Moisie leads SSE into the Grand Chenal to Lézardrieux

Le Ferlas chan (chart 3673) runs S of Île de Brehat (10.16.23), and is useful if entering or leaving Trieux R from or to the E. It is well marked and not difficult, but there are unmarked rks in chan almost awash at or near LW, so is best tackled at half tide. If proceeding SE from the E end of La Ferlas chan keep to seaward of the three ECMs off L'Ost-Pic.

La Horaine (lit) marks NE part of rks extending seawards from Île de Brehat, but there are rky patches 0·5M N and E, and also up to 2M SE, of the Lt Ho.

NNE of Île de Brehat are Plateau de Barnouic (lit) and Plateau des Roches Douvres (Lt, fog sig, RC), both with drying and submerged rks, to be avoided particularly in poor vis.

10.16.6 DISTANCE TABLE

Approximate distances in nautical miles are by the most direct route while avoiding dangers and allowing for traffic separation schemes etc. Places in *italics* are in adjoining areas.

1 *Le Palais*	**1**																			
2 *Pointe du Raz*	81	**2**																		
3 Brest	105	24	**3**																	
4 Pointe St Mathieu	99	18	13	**4**																
5 Le Four	111	30	25	12	**5**															
6 L'Aberwrac'h	127	46	41	28	15	**6**														
7 Ile Vierge	124	43	38	25	13	6	**7**													
8 Roscoff	152	71	66	53	41	34	28	**8**												
9 Morlaix	163	82	77	64	52	45	39	12	**9**											
10 Les Sept Iles	171	90	85	72	60	53	47	21	26	**10**										
11 Perros Guirec	175	94	89	76	64	57	51	25	30	5	**11**									
12 Tréguier	191	110	105	92	80	73	61	41	46	20	20	**12**								
13 Lézardrieux	199	118	113	100	88	81	75	49	54	28	28	22	**13**							
14 *Roches Douvres*	200	119	114	101	89	82	76	50	55	29	31	26	22	**14**						
15 *St Malo*	233	152	147	134	122	115	109	83	88	62	62	54	49	42	**15**					
16 *Les Hanois*	216	135	130	117	105	98	92	66	71	45	48	45	42	20	56	**16**				
17 *Casquets*	231	150	145	132	120	113	107	89	94	68	71	68	65	43	70	23	**17**			
18 *Bishop Rock*	212	131	127	114	102	109	105	119	131	129	134	150	155	148	187	147	160	**18**		
19 *Eddystone*	214	133	128	115	103	99	93	88	98	84	89	96	109	86	128	74	79	89	**19**	
20 *Portland Bill*	264	183	178	165	153	146	140	125	129	108	115	1130	113	87	118	67	48	162	73	**20**

BREST 10-16-9

Finistere

CHARTS
Admiralty 3428, 3427, 798; SHOM 6542, 6426; ECM 542; Stanford 17; Imray C36

TIDES
Dover +0520; ML 4·4; Duration 0605; Zone −0100

NOTE: Brest is a Standard Port and the tidal predictions for each day of the year are given below.

SHELTER
Excellent shelter in Brest, and in many anchorages round the Rade du Brest (50 sq miles). Yachts should not use the Port du Commerce but the Port de Plaisance in the Anse du Moulin Blanc. Access at any tide day or night.

NAVIGATION
Waypoint 48°18'·30N 04°44'·00W, 248°/068° from/to front Ldg Lt 068° (Pte du Petit Minou), 5·3M.
Moulin Blanc port-hand buoy, Fl(3)R 12s, 48°22'·85N 04°25'·90W, 207°/027° from/to MB1 and MB2 channel buoys, 0·55M. There are two forbidden areas — the Port Militaire in Brest and the zone round the Ile Longue. Fast tidal streams run in the Goulet de Brest. Brest is a busy commercial, naval and fishing port.

LIGHTS AND MARKS
Approaches marked by Lts at Pte St Mathieu, Pte du Petit Minou and Pte du Portzic. Marina 2 M E of the Port de Commerce, marked by buoys.

RADIO TELEPHONE
Call: *Brest Port* (at Pointe du Petit Minou) VHF Ch 08 16 (controls approaches to Brest). Moulin Blanc Marina Ch 09 16 (H24).
Saint Mathieu Ch 16; 12 is part of Ouessant traffic management system, for vessels proceeding in Chenal de la Helle or Chenal du Four. In an emergency or poor visibility radar assistance can be provided for small craft transiting the Chenel du Four. PC Rade (Tour César) Ch 08 16. All vessels entering keep watch on Ch 16.

TELEPHONE (98)
Hr Mr Brest 98.44.13.44; Moulin Blanc 98.02.20.02; Aff Mar 98.80.62.25; CROSS 98.89.31.31; # 98.44.35.20; Meteo 98.84.60.64; Auto 98.94.82.83; Dr 98.44.38.70; Police 98.22.83.90; (H) 98.22.33.33; Brit Consul 99.46.26.64.

FACILITIES (MOULIN BLANC)
Moulin Blanc Marina (1100+100 visitors), ☎ 98.02.20.02, Slip, P (in cans), D, FW, ME, El, Sh, BH (14 and 35 ton), AC, Bar, Gaz, R, ⊡, SM, V, C (3 and 12 ton), CH, Access H24; **Quai** Slip, P, D, C, CH; **Société des Régates de Brest** ☎ 98.02.53.36 R, all facilities; **Occase Mer** ☎ 98.42.03.01, Sh, CH, ME; **Comptoirs Maritime** ☎ 98.02.30.04, CH, ME, El, (E), Sh; **Service Plaisance** ☎ 98.02.60.07, ME, El, Sh, CH, (E), SHOM; **Voiles Océan** ☎ 98.80.28.32, CH, SM; **Accastilage Diffusion** ☎ 98.42.03.57 ME, El, (E), Sh, CH; **Jet Marine** ☎ 48.41.80.25, ME, Sh; **S.E.N.** ☎ 98.42.10.35, CH, El, (E), ER.

FACILITIES (BREST)
Amor Moteurs ☎ 98.43.04.18, ME; **Berra Marine Services** ☎ 98.44.44.91, CH, SM; **Chantier Nautique de Keralliou** ☎ 98.40.38.57, ME, El, Sh, (E); **EPSHOM** ☎ 98.22.10.80, SHOM. **Town** all facilities, Gaz, ✉, (B), ⇌, ✈.
Ferry UK. Roscoff—Plymouth.

RADE DE BREST 10-16-10

Finistere

CHARTS
Admiralty 3427, 3428; SHOM 6542, 6426 6427; Stanford 17; Imray C36

The Rade de Brest provides a sheltered cruising ground, useful in bad weather, with many attractive anchorages. Beyond Pont Albert-Louppe (28m) it is possible to explore L'Elorn (or R de Landerneau) for about 6M. There is a good anchorage at Le Passage, ½M above the bridge. The port of Landerneau dries.

L'Aulne (or R de Chateaulin) is a lovely river with steep and wooded banks. Near the mouth of the estuary, on the N shore, is a good anchorage in Anse de l'Auberlach. Other anchorages near Landévennec, below Térénez bridge (27m), and also 1½M above the bridge. At Port Launay, 14M above Landévennec, there is a lock, open HW−2 to shortly after HW, leading into a basin where yachts can lie afloat.

Three small rivers run into the Aulne from the N — R Daoulas, R de l'Hôpital and R du Faou. They mostly dry, but provide sheltered berths for boats which can take the ground.

Along the S side of Rade de Brest are various naval installations, with prohibited anchorage around Ile Longue. There are however anchorages at Le Fret, on SE side of Ile Longue, and also at Roscanvel on E side of the Quelern peninsula.

In most of the bays in Rade de Brest the tidal streams are weak, but in the main rivers they can attain 2 kn or more at springs.

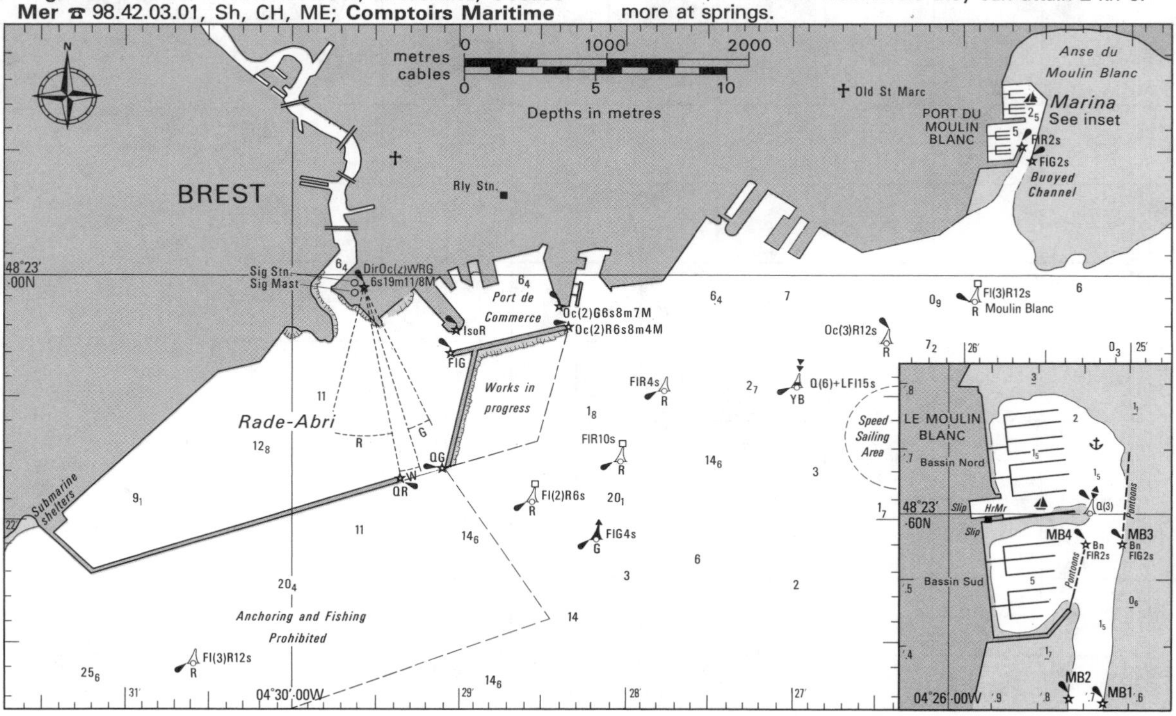

metres
cables
Depths in metres
BREST
Rly Stn.
Old St Marc
Anse du Moulin Blanc
PORT DU MOULIN BLANC
Marina See inset
FIR2s
FIG2s
Buoyed Channel
Sig Stn.
Sig Mast
DirOc(2)WRG 6s19m11/8M
Port de Commerce
Oc(2)G6s8m7M
Oc(2)R6s8m4M
IsoR
FIG
Works in progress
Rade-Abri
QG
QR
Submarine shelters
Fl(3)R12s
Moulin Blanc
Oc(3)R12s
FIR4s
Q(6)+LFI15s
YB
FIR10s
Fl(2)R6s
FIG4s
Speed Sailing Area
Anchoring and Fishing Prohibited
Fl(3)R12s
04°30'·00W
48°23'·00N
LE MOULIN BLANC
Bassin Nord
Bassin Sud
HrMr
Slip
Pontoons
MB4
MB3
MB2
MB1
Bn FIR2s
Bn FIG2s
Q(3)
48°23'·60N
04°26'·00W

RADE DE BREST *continued*

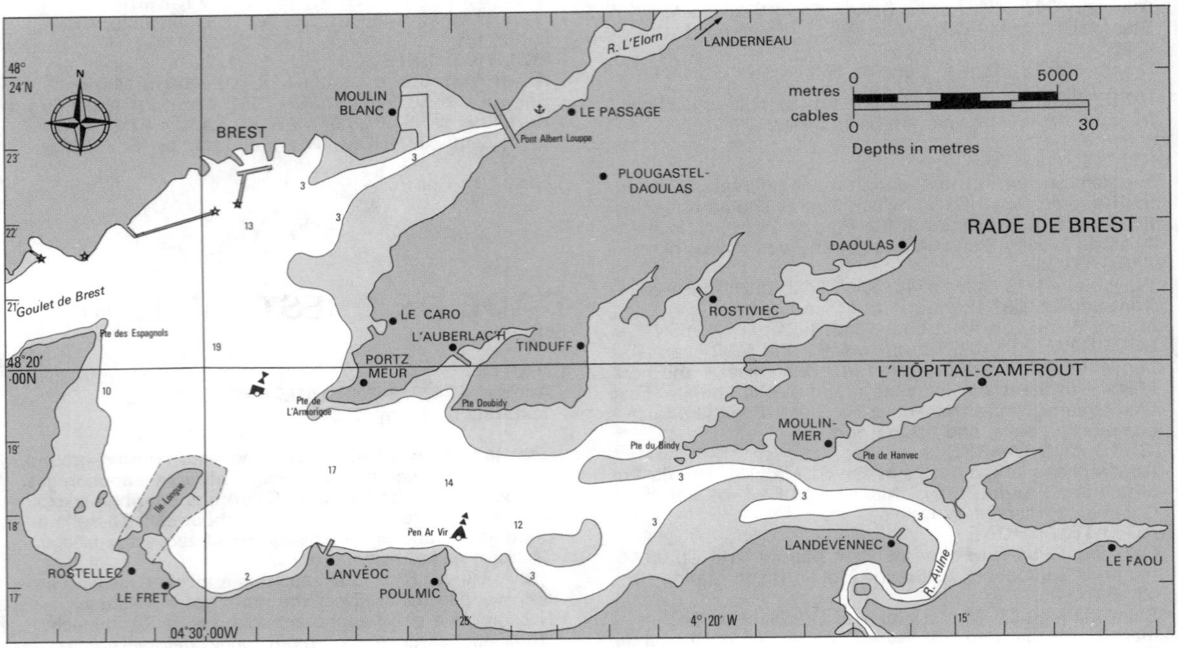
R. L'Elorn
LANDERNEAU
MOULIN BLANC
LE PASSAGE
BREST
Pont Albert Louppe
metres
cables
0
5000
30
Depths in metres
PLOUGASTEL-DAOULAS
RADE DE BREST
DAOULAS
Goulet de Brest
ROSTIVIEC
LE CARO
Pte des Espagnols
L'AUBERLAC'H
TINDUFF
48°20'·00N
PORTZ MEUR
L' HÔPITAL-CAMFROUT
Pte de L'Armorique
Pte Doubidy
MOULIN-MER
Pte du Bindy
Pte de Hanvec
Ile Longue
Pen Ar Vir
LANDÉVÉNNEC
LE FAOU
R. Aulne
ROSTELLEC
LE FRET
LANVÉOC
POULMIC
04°30'·00W
4°20' W

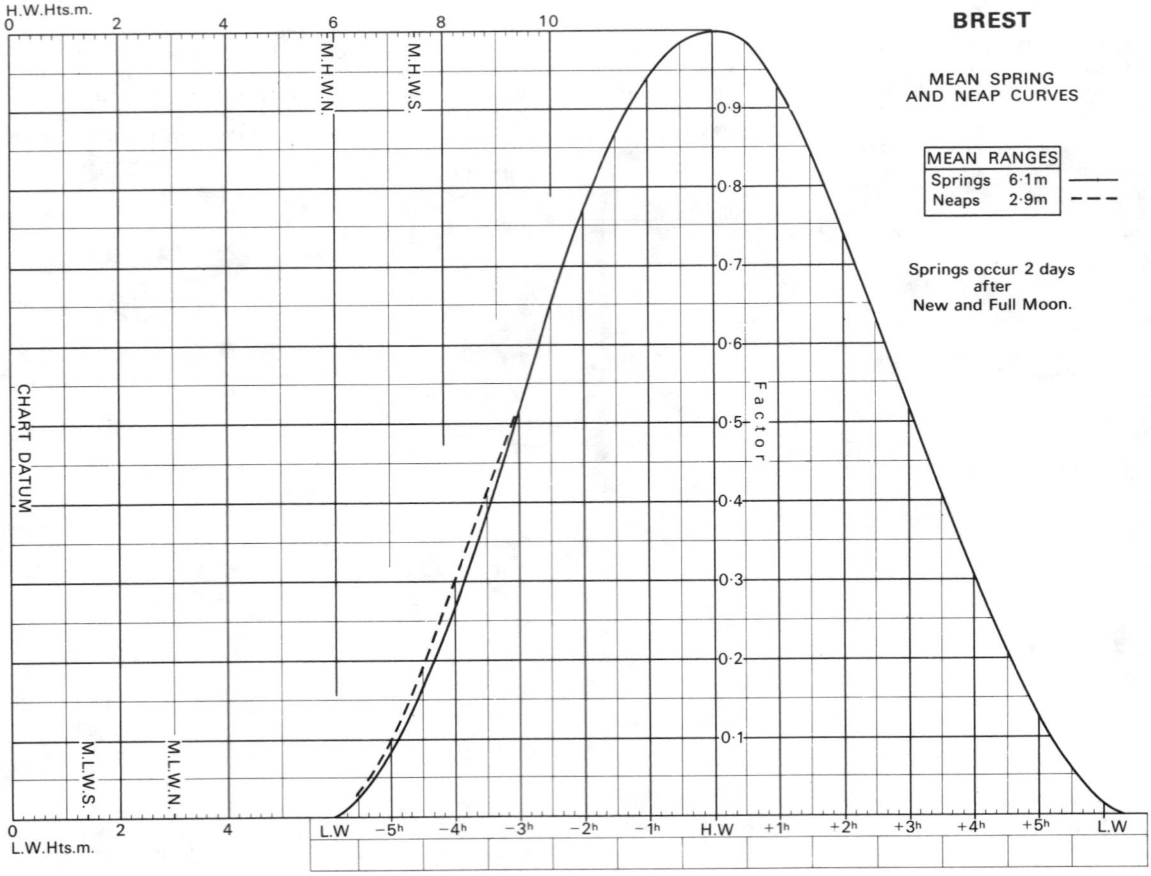
BREST
MEAN SPRING AND NEAP CURVES
MEAN RANGES
Springs 6·1m
Neaps 2·9m
Springs occur 2 days after New and Full Moon.
H.W.Hts.m.
M.H.W.N.
M.H.W.S.
CHART DATUM
Factor
M.L.W.S.
M.L.W.N.
L.W.Hts.m.
L.W -5h -4h -3h -2h -1h H.W +1h +2h +3h +4h +5h L.W

TIME ZONE -0100
(French Standard Time)
Subtract 1 hour for GMT
For French Summer Time add ONE hour in non-shaded areas

FRANCE, WEST COAST - BREST

LAT 48°23'N LONG 4°29'W

TIMES AND HEIGHTS OF HIGH AND LOW WATERS

YEAR **1992**

JANUARY

Day	Time	m	Day	Time	m
1 W	0212 0835 1442 2103	6.1 2.7 6.1 2.7	16 TH	0100 0728 1339 2004	6.0 2.8 6.1 2.7
2 TH	0309 0930 1534 2154	6.3 2.5 6.3 2.5	17 F	0214 0839 1447 2110	6.3 2.4 6.4 2.3
3 F	0357 1016 1619 2237	6.6 2.3 6.5 2.3	18 SA	0318 0940 1546 2208	6.7 2.0 6.8 1.8
4 SA	0439 1056 1657 ● 2314	6.8 2.1 6.6 2.2	19 SU	0413 1034 1639 ○ 2259	7.2 1.5 7.2 1.4
5 SU	0515 1132 1733 2349	6.9 2.0 6.7 2.1	20 M	0504 1124 1728 2348	7.6 1.1 7.5 1.1
6 M	0550 1206 1806	7.0 1.9 6.8	21 TU	0552 1211 1815	7.9 0.8 7.7
7 TU	0023 0623 1239 1839	2.0 7.0 1.9 6.8	22 W	0034 0638 1257 1900	1.0 8.0 0.8 7.6
8 W	0055 0655 1311 1911	2.0 7.0 1.9 6.7	23 TH	0120 0722 1342 1943	1.0 7.9 1.0 7.4
9 TH	0128 0727 1345 1943	2.1 6.9 2.0 6.6	24 F	0203 0803 1425 2025	1.3 7.5 1.4 7.1
10 F	0202 0800 1419 2017	2.2 6.7 2.2 6.4	25 SA	0247 0846 1510 2108	1.7 7.1 1.9 6.6
11 SA	0238 0835 1457 2055	2.3 6.5 2.4 6.3	26 SU	0333 0932 1558 ☾ 2158	2.2 6.5 2.4 6.2
12 SU	0318 0915 1540 2139	2.5 6.3 2.6 6.1	27 M	0425 1026 1655 2300	2.7 6.0 2.9 5.8
13 M	0404 1004 1632 ☽ 2234	2.7 6.1 2.8 5.9	28 TU	0529 1137 1808	3.0 5.7 3.2
14 TU	0502 1107 1735 2343	2.9 5.9 3.0 5.9	29 W	0019 0650 1302 1932	5.6 3.2 5.6 3.2
15 W	0612 1221 1850	2.9 5.9 2.9	30 TH	0145 0811 1422 2046	5.7 3.1 5.7 3.0
			31 F	0254 0916 1522 2142	6.0 2.8 5.9 2.7

FEBRUARY

Day	Time	m	Day	Time	m
1 SA	0346 1004 1607 2225	6.3 2.5 6.2 2.4	16 SU	0307 0930 1536 2157	6.6 1.9 6.7 1.7
2 SU	0426 1043 1644 2301	6.6 2.1 6.5 2.1	17 M	0403 1023 1627 2247	7.2 1.3 7.2 1.2
3 M	0501 1117 1717 ● 2333	6.8 1.9 6.7 1.9	18 TU	0451 1110 1713 ○ 2332	7.7 0.9 7.6 0.8
4 TU	0533 1149 1748	7.0 1.7 6.9	19 W	0535 1154 1756	8.0 0.6 7.8
5 W	0004 0603 1219 1818	1.8 7.2 1.6 7.0	20 TH	0015 0617 1235 1838	0.7 8.1 0.6 7.8
6 TH	0034 0633 1248 1848	1.7 7.2 1.6 7.0	21 F	0056 0658 1315 1916	0.8 7.9 0.8 7.6
7 F	0103 0703 1318 1917	1.7 7.2 1.6 6.9	22 SA	0135 0735 1355 1955	1.1 7.6 1.3 7.2
8 SA	0134 0731 1349 1947	1.8 7.0 1.8 6.8	23 SU	0215 0814 1435 2033	1.6 7.0 1.8 6.7
9 SU	0206 0803 1423 2021	1.9 6.8 2.0 6.6	24 M	0256 0854 1518 2116	2.1 6.4 2.4 6.1
10 M	0241 0839 1501 2058	2.2 6.5 2.3 6.3	25 TU	0342 0942 1610 ☾ 2211	2.7 5.9 3.0 5.7
11 TU	0323 0921 1548 ☽ 2148	2.5 6.2 2.7 6.0	26 W	0442 1048 1721 2332	3.1 5.4 3.3 5.4
12 W	0416 1018 1650 2256	2.8 5.8 3.0 5.8	27 TH	0607 1222 1856	3.3 5.3 3.4
13 TH	0529 1140 1813	3.0 5.7 3.1	28 F	0112 0742 1356 2022	5.5 3.2 5.4 3.2
14 F	0027 0700 1315 1944	5.8 2.9 5.8 2.8	29 SA	0232 0854 1501 2121	5.7 2.9 5.7 2.8
15 SA	0157 0824 1435 2059	6.1 2.5 6.2 2.3			

MARCH

Day	Time	m	Day	Time	m
1 SU	0325 0943 1546 2203	6.1 2.5 6.1 2.4	16 M	0254 0915 1521 2141	6.7 1.8 6.8 1.6
2 M	0404 1021 1621 2237	6.5 2.1 6.4 2.1	17 TU	0346 1006 1609 2228	7.2 1.2 7.3 1.1
3 TU	0438 1053 1653 2308	6.8 1.8 6.7 1.8	18 W	0431 1050 1652 ○ 2310	7.7 0.8 7.6 0.8
4 W	0508 1123 1722 ● 2338	7.0 1.6 7.0 1.6	19 TH	0513 1131 1733 2350	7.9 0.7 7.8 0.7
5 TH	0537 1152 1751	7.2 1.4 7.1	20 F	0552 1210 1811	8.0 0.7 7.7
6 F	0006 0605 1221 1820	1.4 7.3 1.3 7.2	21 SA	0029 0631 1248 1850	0.9 7.7 1.0 7.5
7 SA	0035 0635 1250 1850	1.4 7.3 1.4 7.1	22 SU	0107 0707 1326 1926	1.2 7.4 1.4 7.1
8 SU	0106 0704 1321 1921	1.5 7.2 1.5 7.0	23 M	0145 0745 1405 2003	1.6 6.9 1.9 6.6
9 M	0138 0736 1355 1954	1.7 6.9 1.8 6.7	24 TU	0225 0824 1446 2045	2.2 6.3 2.5 6.1
10 TU	0214 0813 1434 2033	2.0 6.6 2.2 6.4	25 W	0309 0908 1535 2136	2.7 5.8 3.0 5.7
11 W	0257 0856 1522 2123	2.4 6.2 2.6 6.0	26 TH	0405 1009 1641 ☾ 2249	3.1 5.4 3.3 5.4
12 TH	0352 0955 1627 ☽ 2235	2.7 5.8 3.0 5.7	27 F	0524 1138 1812	3.3 5.2 3.4
13 F	0510 1121 1758	3.0 5.6 3.1	28 SA	0028 0659 1314 1940	5.4 3.3 5.3 3.2
14 SA	0014 0647 1302 1933	5.8 2.9 5.7 2.8	29 SU	0151 0815 1422 2043	5.6 2.9 5.6 2.8
15 SU	0146 0812 1422 2046	6.1 2.4 6.2 2.2	30 M	0247 0906 1509 2127	6.0 2.6 6.0 2.5
			31 TU	0328 0945 1546 2203	6.4 2.2 6.4 2.1

APRIL

Day	Time	m	Day	Time	m
1 W	0403 1019 1619 2235	6.7 1.9 6.7 1.8	16 TH	0407 1025 1628 2246	7.5 1.1 7.4 1.1
2 TH	0434 1050 1650 2305	7.0 1.6 7.0 1.5	17 F	0448 1106 1708 ○ 2326	7.6 1.0 7.5 1.1
3 F	0505 1120 1720 ● 2336	7.2 1.4 7.2 1.4	18 SA	0528 1145 1747	7.6 1.1 7.5
4 SA	0536 1151 1751	7.3 1.3 7.3	19 SU	0005 0606 1224 1825	1.2 7.4 1.4 7.3
5 SU	0007 0607 1224 1824	1.3 7.3 1.4 7.3	20 M	0043 0644 1302 1904	1.5 7.1 1.7 7.0
6 M	0041 0641 1258 1859	1.4 7.2 1.5 7.1	21 TU	0121 0722 1341 1941	1.8 6.7 2.1 6.6
7 TU	0117 0717 1336 1936	1.6 6.9 1.8 6.8	22 W	0201 0800 1422 2022	2.2 6.3 2.5 6.2
8 W	0157 0758 1420 2021	1.9 6.6 2.2 6.5	23 TH	0245 0845 1510 2110	2.6 5.8 2.9 5.9
9 TH	0245 0846 1513 2116	2.3 6.2 2.6 6.1	24 F	0337 0939 1609 ☾ 2212	2.9 5.5 3.2 5.6
10 F	0346 0951 1624 ☽ 2232	2.6 5.8 2.8 5.9	25 SA	0444 1051 1723 2333	3.2 5.3 3.3 5.5
11 SA	0506 1117 1751	2.8 5.7 2.9	26 SU	0603 1214 1841	3.2 5.4 3.2
12 SU	0005 0636 1248 1917	6.0 2.6 5.9 2.5	27 M	0051 0716 1324 1947	5.6 3.0 5.6 2.9
13 M	0128 0753 1402 2024	6.3 2.2 6.3 2.1	28 TU	0153 0813 1418 2037	5.9 2.7 6.0 2.6
14 TU	0231 0852 1458 2118	6.7 1.8 6.8 1.6	29 W	0240 0858 1501 2118	6.2 2.3 6.3 2.2
15 W	0322 0942 1545 2204	7.2 1.4 7.2 1.3	30 TH	0320 0937 1538 2155	6.5 2.0 6.6 1.9

Chart Datum: 4.45 metres below Lallemand System (Mean Sea Level, Marseilles)

TIME ZONE -0100
(French Standard Time)
Subtract 1 hour for GMT
For French Summer Time add ONE hour in non-shaded areas

FRANCE, WEST COAST - BREST

LAT 48°23'N LONG 4°29'W

TIMES AND HEIGHTS OF HIGH AND LOW WATERS

YEAR **1992**

MAY

Day	Time	m	Day	Time	m
1 F	0356	6.8	16 SA	0427	7.1
	1013	1.8		1045	1.6
	1614	6.9		1648	7.2
	2231	1.6	○	2306	1.5
2 SA	0431	7.1	17 SU	0508	7.1
	1048	1.6		1126	1.6
	1649	7.2		1728	7.2
●	2306	1.5		2346	1.6
3 SU	0507	7.2	18 M	0548	7.0
	1124	1.5		1205	1.7
	1725	7.3		1807	7.1
	2343	1.4			
4 M	0544	7.2	19 TU	0025	1.7
	1202	1.5		0626	6.8
	1804	7.3		1244	1.9
				1846	6.9
5 TU	0022	1.4	20 W	0103	1.9
	0624	7.1		0704	6.6
	1242	1.6		1323	2.2
	1845	7.2		1924	6.7
6 W	0104	1.6	21 TH	0143	2.2
	0706	6.9		0743	6.3
	1326	1.8		1403	2.4
	1929	7.0		2003	6.4
7 TH	0150	1.8	22 F	0224	2.4
	0752	6.6		0824	6.0
	1416	2.1		1447	2.7
	2018	6.7		2046	6.1
8 F	0243	2.1	23 SA	0311	2.7
	0846	6.3		0910	5.8
	1513	2.4		1536	2.9
	2116	6.4		2136	5.9
9 SA	0346	2.4	24 SU	0404	2.9
	0950	6.1		1005	5.6
	1621	2.6		1633	3.0
☽	2226	6.2	☾	2236	5.8
10 SU	0459	2.5	25 M	0504	3.0
	1107	6.0		1109	5.6
	1737	2.6		1736	3.0
	2346	6.2		2343	5.7
11 M	0615	2.4	26 TU	0609	2.9
	1224	6.1		1216	5.7
	1850	2.4		1840	2.9
12 TU	0059	6.4	27 W	0047	5.9
	0724	2.2		0710	2.8
	1332	6.4		1317	5.9
	1955	2.1		1938	2.7
13 W	0202	6.7	28 TH	0144	6.1
	0824	2.0		0804	2.6
	1429	6.7		1409	6.2
	2050	1.9		2029	2.4
14 TH	0255	6.9	29 F	0233	6.3
	0915	1.7		0852	2.3
	1520	6.9		1456	6.5
	2139	1.7		2115	2.1
15 F	0343	7.0	30 SA	0318	6.6
	1002	1.6		0937	2.0
	1605	7.1		1540	6.8
	2224	1.5		2158	1.9
			31 SU	0401	6.8
				1020	1.8
				1622	7.0
				2241	1.6

JUNE

Day	Time	m	Day	Time	m
1 M	0444	7.0	16 TU	0534	6.7
	1103	1.6		1152	2.0
	1705	7.2		1753	7.0
●	2324	1.5			
2 TU	0527	7.1	17 W	0011	1.8
	1147	1.5		0612	6.7
	1750	7.3		1229	2.0
				1830	6.9
3 W	0009	1.4	18 TH	0048	1.9
	0613	7.1		0649	6.6
	1232	1.5		1306	2.1
	1836	7.3		1906	6.8
4 TH	0056	1.4	19 F	0124	2.0
	0700	7.0		0724	6.5
	1321	1.6		1343	2.2
	1924	7.2		1942	6.6
5 F	0146	1.6	20 SA	0201	2.2
	0749	6.9		0800	6.3
	1412	1.8		1420	2.4
	2014	7.0		2019	6.4
6 SA	0239	1.8	21 SU	0240	2.4
	0841	6.6		0838	6.1
	1507	2.0		1501	2.6
	2108	6.8		2059	6.2
7 SU	0336	2.0	22 M	0323	2.6
	0938	6.4		0921	6.0
	1607	2.2		1546	2.7
☽	2209	6.6		2145	6.0
8 M	0438	2.2	23 TU	0410	2.7
	1042	6.3		1010	5.8
	1710	2.4		1637	2.8
	2316	6.4	☾	2238	5.9
9 TU	0544	2.3	24 W	0505	2.8
	1150	6.2		1108	5.8
	1817	2.4		1734	2.9
				2340	5.8
10 W	0025	6.3	25 TH	0606	2.9
	0650	2.4		1212	5.8
	1257	6.2		1837	2.8
	1922	2.4			
11 TH	0130	6.4	26 F	0044	5.9
	0754	2.3		0709	2.8
	1401	6.4		1317	6.0
	2023	2.3		1940	2.7
12 F	0230	6.5	27 SA	0147	6.1
	0852	2.2		0810	2.6
	1457	6.5		1417	6.3
	2118	2.1		2039	2.4
13 SA	0323	6.6	28 SU	0245	6.3
	0943	2.1		0906	2.3
	1548	6.7		1512	6.6
	2207	2.0		2132	2.1
14 SU	0411	6.7	29 M	0337	6.6
	1030	2.0		0958	2.0
	1633	6.9		1603	7.0
	2251	1.9		2223	1.7
15 M	0454	6.7	30 TU	0427	6.9
	1112	2.0		1047	1.7
	1714	6.9		1651	7.3
○	2332	1.8	●	2311	1.4

JULY

Day	Time	m	Day	Time	m
1 W	0515	7.2	16 TH	0555	6.7
	1135	1.4		1212	1.9
	1739	7.5		1812	7.0
	2359	1.2			
2 TH	0603	7.3	17 F	0028	1.8
	1223	1.3		0629	6.7
	1827	7.6		1245	1.9
				1845	7.0
3 F	0047	1.1	18 SA	0101	1.8
	0651	7.3		0701	6.7
	1311	1.3		1317	2.0
	1914	7.6		1917	6.9
4 SA	0136	1.2	19 SU	0134	1.9
	0738	7.2		0732	6.6
	1400	1.4		1350	2.1
	2001	7.4		1949	6.7
5 SU	0224	1.4	20 M	0207	2.0
	0826	7.0		0805	6.5
	1449	1.6		1425	2.2
	2050	7.1		2023	6.5
6 M	0315	1.7	21 TU	0243	2.3
	0915	6.7		0840	6.3
	1541	2.0		1502	2.4
	2141	6.7		2059	6.3
7 TU	0408	2.1	22 W	0323	2.5
	1009	6.4		0921	6.1
	1637	2.3		1545	2.7
☽	2240	6.4	☾	2144	6.0
8 W	0507	2.4	23 TH	0410	2.7
	1112	6.1		1010	5.9
	1740	2.6		1638	2.8
	2347	6.1		2241	5.8
9 TH	0614	2.7	24 F	0509	2.9
	1223	6.0		1114	5.8
	1850	2.7		1743	3.0
				2351	5.8
10 F	0059	6.0	25 SA	0620	3.0
	0726	2.8		1230	5.8
	1336	6.0		1858	2.9
	2001	2.7			
11 SA	0210	6.0	26 SU	0110	5.9
	0833	2.7		0736	2.8
	1441	6.2		1346	6.1
	2103	2.5		2012	2.6
12 SU	0310	6.2	27 M	0221	6.1
	0931	2.5		0844	2.5
	1536	6.4		1452	6.5
	2156	2.3		2115	2.1
13 M	0400	6.4	28 TU	0321	6.6
	1019	2.3		0943	2.0
	1622	6.7		1549	7.0
	2240	2.1		2210	1.6
14 TU	0443	6.5	29 W	0414	7.0
	1100	2.1		1035	1.5
	1702	6.8		1639	7.4
○	2319	1.9	●	2259	1.2
15 W	0520	6.7	30 TH	0503	7.4
	1137	2.0		1123	1.2
	1738	6.9		1727	7.8
	2355	1.8		2346	0.9
			31 F	0550	7.6
				1209	0.9
				1813	7.9

AUGUST

Day	Time	m	Day	Time	m
1 SA	0032	0.7	16 SU	0034	1.6
	0635	7.7		0633	7.0
	1254	0.9		1248	1.7
	1857	7.9		1848	7.1
2 SU	0117	0.8	17 M	0103	1.7
	0719	7.5		0703	6.9
	1339	1.1		1318	1.8
	1940	7.7		1917	7.0
3 M	0201	1.1	18 TU	0134	1.8
	0801	7.2		0732	6.7
	1423	1.5		1350	2.0
	2023	7.3		1948	6.7
4 TU	0246	1.6	19 W	0206	2.1
	0845	6.8		0804	6.5
	1509	1.9		1424	2.2
	2108	6.7		2022	6.5
5 W	0334	2.1	20 TH	0243	2.4
	0934	6.4		0841	6.3
	1601	2.4		1504	2.5
☽	2202	6.2		2102	6.1
6 TH	0430	2.7	21 F	0328	2.7
	1033	6.0		0927	6.0
	1703	2.8		1555	2.8
	2309	5.8	☾	2156	5.8
7 F	0539	3.0	22 SA	0426	3.0
	1149	5.7		1031	5.8
	1820	3.0		1703	3.0
				2312	5.6
8 SA	0032	5.6	23 SU	0545	3.1
	0702	3.1		1157	5.7
	1315	5.8		1830	3.0
	1942	3.0			
9 SU	0154	5.7	24 M	0044	5.7
	0819	3.0		0714	2.9
	1429	6.0		1327	6.0
	2052	2.7		1954	2.6
10 M	0258	5.9	25 TU	0205	6.1
	0919	2.7		0830	2.5
	1524	6.3		1438	6.5
	2144	2.4		2101	2.1
11 TU	0347	6.2	26 W	0308	6.6
	1006	2.4		0929	1.9
	1608	6.6		1535	7.1
	2226	2.1		2155	1.5
12 W	0427	6.5	27 TH	0400	7.2
	1044	2.1		1020	1.3
	1645	6.8		1623	7.6
	2301	1.9		2243	1.0
13 TH	0502	6.7	28 F	0446	7.6
	1118	1.9		1105	0.9
	1718	7.0		1708	8.0
○	2334	1.7	●	2327	0.6
14 F	0533	6.9	29 SA	0530	7.9
	1149	1.8		1149	0.7
	1748	7.1		1751	8.1
15 SA	0004	1.6	30 SU	0010	0.6
	0603	6.9		0612	7.9
	1219	1.7		1231	0.7
	1818	7.1		1833	8.0
			31 M	0052	0.8
				0654	7.7
				1312	1.0
				1914	7.7

Chart Datum: 4.45 metres below Lallemand System (Mean Sea Level, Marseilles)

FRANCE, WEST COAST - BREST

LAT 48°23'N LONG 4°29'W

TIME ZONE **-0100**
(French Standard Time)
Subtract 1 hour for GMT
For French Summer Time add ONE hour in non-shaded areas

TIMES AND HEIGHTS OF HIGH AND LOW WATERS

YEAR **1992**

SEPTEMBER

Day	Time	m	Day	Time	m
1 TU	0133 0733 1354 1954	1.2 7.3 1.5 7.2	16 W	0103 0703 1319 1918	1.7 7.0 1.8 6.9
2 W	0215 0815 1437 2037	1.7 6.8 2.0 6.6	17 TH	0136 0735 1354 1954	2.0 6.7 2.1 6.6
3 TH	0301 0900 1526 ☽ 2127	2.3 6.3 2.6 6.0	18 F	0214 0813 1435 2035	2.3 6.4 2.5 6.2
4 F	0355 0957 1627 2233	2.9 5.9 3.0 5.6	19 SA	0300 0900 1528 ☾ 2131	2.7 6.1 2.8 5.8
5 SA	0506 1116 1750	3.3 5.6 3.3	20 SU	0402 1007 1641 2251	3.0 5.8 3.0 5.6
6 SU	0004 0637 1251 1921	5.4 3.3 5.6 3.2	21 M	0527 1140 1814	3.1 5.8 3.0
7 M	0135 0800 1410 2033	5.5 3.1 5.9 2.9	22 TU	0029 0659 1313 1939	5.8 2.9 6.1 2.5
8 TU	0240 0900 1505 2123	5.9 2.8 6.2 2.5	23 W	0150 0814 1422 2044	6.2 2.4 6.7 2.0
9 W	0326 0944 1546 2202	6.2 2.4 6.5 2.2	24 TH	0250 0911 1516 2136	6.8 1.8 7.2 1.4
10 TH	0403 1019 1620 2236	6.5 2.1 6.8 1.9	25 F	0340 0959 1602 2221	7.3 1.2 7.7 0.9
11 F	0435 1051 1651 2306	6.8 1.8 7.1 1.7	26 SA	0424 1043 1646 ● 2304	7.7 0.9 8.0 0.7
12 SA	0505 1120 1720 ○ 2335	7.0 1.7 7.2 1.5	27 SU	0506 1125 1727 2345	7.9 0.7 8.1 0.7
13 SU	0534 1149 1748	7.1 1.6 7.3	28 M	0547 1205 1808	7.9 0.9 7.9
14 M	0003 0603 1218 1817	1.5 7.2 1.6 7.2	29 TU	0026 0628 1246 1848	1.0 7.7 1.2 7.6
15 TU	0033 0632 1248 1847	1.6 7.1 1.7 7.1	30 W	0106 0707 1327 1928	1.4 7.3 1.6 7.1

OCTOBER

Day	Time	m	Day	Time	m
1 TH	0147 0748 1409 2009	1.9 6.8 2.1 6.5	16 F	0115 0716 1335 1935	2.0 6.9 2.1 6.6
2 F	0232 0832 1456 2057	2.5 6.3 2.7 6.0	17 SA	0157 0758 1420 2022	2.3 6.6 2.4 6.3
3 SA	0324 0926 1556 ☽ 2200	3.0 5.9 3.1 5.5	18 SU	0247 0849 1517 2120	2.7 6.3 2.7 6.0
4 SU	0432 1040 1715 2327	3.3 5.6 3.3 5.4	19 M	0352 0958 1632 ☾ 2241	2.9 6.0 2.9 5.8
5 M	0601 1215 1845	3.4 5.6 3.2	20 TU	0515 1126 1759	3.0 6.0 2.8
6 TU	0058 0725 1335 1958	5.5 3.2 5.8 3.0	21 W	0011 0640 1251 1918	6.0 2.7 6.3 2.4
7 W	0205 0825 1430 2049	5.8 2.9 6.1 2.6	22 TH	0127 0751 1358 2020	6.4 2.3 6.8 1.9
8 TH	0252 0910 1512 2129	6.2 2.5 6.5 2.3	23 F	0226 0847 1452 2112	6.9 1.8 7.2 1.5
9 F	0330 0946 1546 2202	6.5 2.2 6.8 2.0	24 SA	0316 0935 1539 2158	7.3 1.4 7.6 1.2
10 SA	0402 1018 1618 2233	6.8 1.9 7.0 1.8	25 SU	0401 1020 1622 ● 2241	7.6 1.1 7.8 1.1
11 SU	0433 1049 1648 ○ 2304	7.1 1.7 7.2 1.6	26 M	0444 1102 1704 2323	7.8 1.1 7.8 1.1
12 M	0503 1119 1718 2334	7.2 1.6 7.3 1.5	27 TU	0525 1143 1745	7.7 1.2 7.6
13 TU	0534 1150 1749	7.3 1.5 7.3	28 W	0004 0606 1224 1826	1.3 7.6 1.4 7.3
14 W	0005 0605 1222 1822	1.6 7.3 1.6 7.2	29 TH	0044 0646 1305 1906	1.7 7.2 1.8 6.9
15 TH	0039 0639 1256 1857	1.7 7.1 1.8 6.9	30 F	0125 0727 1347 1947	2.1 6.9 2.2 6.5
			31 SA	0209 0809 1432 2032	2.5 6.4 2.6 6.0

NOVEMBER

Day	Time	m	Day	Time	m
1 SU	0258 0858 1525 2127	2.9 6.1 3.0 5.7	16 M	0242 0845 1512 2115	2.4 6.6 2.4 6.2
2 M	0357 1000 1632 ☽ 2238	3.2 5.8 3.2 5.5	17 TU	0345 0949 1620 ☾ 2225	2.6 6.4 2.6 6.1
3 TU	0509 1118 1749 2358	3.3 5.7 3.2 5.5	18 W	0457 1105 1734 2343	2.7 6.3 2.6 6.2
4 W	0626 1236 1901	3.3 5.8 3.1	19 TH	0612 1221 1847	2.6 6.5 2.4
5 TH	0109 0732 1338 1959	5.8 3.0 6.0 2.8	20 F	0055 0720 1328 1951	6.4 2.3 6.7 2.2
6 F	0203 0823 1426 2044	6.1 2.7 6.3 2.5	21 SA	0158 0820 1426 2047	6.7 2.1 6.9 1.9
7 SA	0247 0905 1506 2123	6.4 2.4 6.6 2.2	22 SU	0252 0912 1517 2137	7.0 1.8 7.2 1.7
8 SU	0325 0941 1542 2159	6.7 2.1 6.9 2.0	23 M	0341 1000 1604 2223	7.3 1.6 7.3 1.6
9 M	0400 1016 1617 2234	7.0 1.9 7.1 1.8	24 TU	0426 1045 1648 ● 2307	7.4 1.5 7.3 1.6
10 TU	0434 1051 1652 ○ 2308	7.2 1.7 7.2 1.7	25 W	0509 1128 1730 2348	7.4 1.5 7.3 1.7
11 W	0509 1126 1727 2344	7.3 1.6 7.2 1.7	26 TH	0550 1209 1811	7.4 1.6 7.1
12 TH	0546 1203 1805	7.3 1.6 7.2	27 F	0029 0631 1249 1851	1.9 7.2 1.8 6.8
13 F	0022 0624 1243 1845	1.8 7.3 1.7 7.0	28 SA	0109 0710 1329 1930	2.1 7.0 2.1 6.6
14 SA	0104 0705 1326 1928	1.9 7.1 1.9 6.8	29 SU	0149 0749 1410 2010	2.4 6.7 2.4 6.3
15 SU	0150 0752 1415 2017	2.2 6.8 2.2 6.5	30 M	0232 0831 1455 2054	2.7 6.4 2.7 6.0

DECEMBER

Day	Time	m	Day	Time	m
1 TU	0319 0919 1545 2146	2.9 6.1 2.9 5.8	16 W	0329 0931 1559 ☾ 2201	2.2 6.8 2.2 6.4
2 W	0413 1015 1643 ☽ 2247	3.1 5.9 3.1 5.7	17 TH	0430 1034 1702 2308	2.4 6.5 2.4 6.3
3 TH	0515 1120 1748 2354	3.2 5.8 3.1 5.7	18 F	0536 1143 1811	2.5 6.4 2.5
4 F	0621 1228 1852	3.1 5.9 3.0	19 SA	0019 0646 1254 1920	6.3 2.6 6.4 2.5
5 SA	0058 0722 1328 1950	5.9 3.0 6.0 2.8	20 SU	0129 0753 1402 2025	6.4 2.4 6.5 2.4
6 SU	0155 0816 1420 2040	6.1 2.7 6.3 2.6	21 M	0232 0854 1501 2122	6.6 2.3 6.6 2.2
7 M	0244 0903 1506 2125	6.4 2.4 6.5 2.3	22 TU	0328 0948 1553 2212	6.8 2.1 6.8 2.1
8 TU	0328 0946 1549 2207	6.7 2.1 6.8 2.1	23 W	0416 1035 1638 2257	7.0 1.9 6.9 1.9
9 W	0409 1028 1630 ○ 2248	7.0 1.9 7.0 1.8	24 TH	0500 1118 1720 ● 2338	7.2 1.8 7.0 1.9
10 TH	0450 1109 1711 2330	7.3 1.6 7.2 1.7	25 F	0540 1157 1759	7.2 1.7 7.0
11 F	0532 1151 1753	7.4 1.5 7.2	26 SA	0016 0617 1234 1836	1.9 7.2 1.8 6.9
12 SA	0012 0615 1234 1837	1.6 7.5 1.5 7.2	27 SU	0053 0654 1311 1910	2.0 7.1 1.9 6.7
13 SU	0057 0700 1320 1923	1.6 7.4 1.5 7.1	28 M	0128 0728 1346 1945	2.1 6.9 2.1 6.6
14 M	0144 0746 1409 2010	1.8 7.2 1.7 6.9	29 TU	0204 0802 1423 2021	2.3 6.7 2.3 6.3
15 TU	0235 0836 1501 2102	2.0 7.0 1.9 6.6	30 W	0242 0840 1502 2059	2.5 6.4 2.5 6.1
			31 TH	0323 0921 1545 2144	2.7 6.2 2.8 5.9

Chart Datum: 4.45 metres below Lallemand System (Mean Sea Level, Marseilles)

LE CONQUET 10-16-11

Finistere

CHARTS
Admiralty 3345, 2694; SHOM 5159, 7122, 5287; ECM 540; Stanford 17; Imray C36

TIDES
Dover +0535; ML 4·3; Duration 0600; Zone −0100

Standard Port BREST (⟵)

Times				Height (metres)			
HW		LW		MHWS	MHWN	MLWN	MLWS
0000	0600	0000	0600	7·5	5·9	3·0	1·4
1200	1800	1200	1800				
Differences LE CONQUET							
0000	0000	+0010	0000	−0·3	−0·3	−0·1	0·0

SHELTER
Good shelter except in strong winds from the W. Anchor inside the mole, Pierre Glissant. Yachts can go further up harbour but it dries. Six visitors buoys on N side of harbour.

NAVIGATION
Waypoint 48°21′·50N 04°48′·50W, 263°/083° from/to Mole Pierre Glissante Lt, 1·0M. Coming from the NW, beware the Grande Vinotière rocks. Also note strong cross streams in the Chenal du Four.

LIGHTS AND MARKS
Leading line — Lt on end of mole, Pierre Glissant, Oc G 4s in line with spire of Le Conquet church at 095°. Tr beacon and end of Mole St Christophe in line at 079°.

RADIO TELEPHONE
St Mathieu Sig Stn (call: *St Mathieu*) VHF Ch 16 for Chenal du Four and Chenal de la Helle (see 10.16.12).

TELEPHONE (98)
Hr Mr 98.89.00.05; Aff Mar 98.89.00.05; Meteo 98.84.60.64; CROSS 98.89.31.31; SNSM 98.89.02.07; Police 98.89.00.13; Dr 98.89.01.86; Brit Consul 99.46.26.64.

FACILITIES
Bay Slip, M, L; **Garage Tanniou** ☎ 98.89.00.29, ME, El; **Coopérative Maritime** ☎ 98.89.01.85, CH; **Plasti-Bois** ☎ 98.89.11.73 ME; **Town** P, D, FW, ME, El, V, Gaz, R, Bar. ✉; Ⓑ; ⇌ (bus to Brest); ✈ (Brest).
Ferry UK — Roscoff—Plymouth.

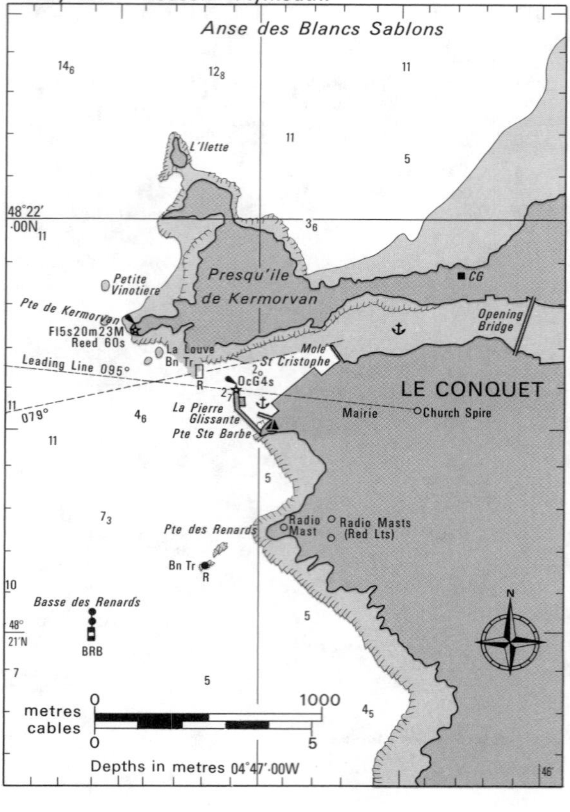

Anse des Blancs Sablons
L'Ilette
48°22′·00N
Presqu'ile de Kermorvan
Petite Vinotière
Pte de Kermorvan
Fl5s20m23M Reed 60s
CG
Opening Bridge
La Louve
Bn Tr
Mole St Christophe
Leading Line 095°
079°
OcG4s
La Pierre Glissante
Pte Ste Barbe
LE CONQUET
Mairie
Church Spire
Pte des Renards
Radio Mast
Radio Masts (Red Lts)
Bn Tr
Basse des Renards
BRB
48° 21′N
metres
cables
0
1000
5
Depths in metres 04°47′·00W

LAMPAUL (ILE D'OUESSANT/ USHANT) 10-16-12

Finistere

CHARTS
Admiralty 2694; SHOM 7123, 5287; ECM 540; Stanford 17; Imray C36

TIDES
Dover +0522; ML 4·4; Duration 0555; Zone −0100

Standard Port BREST (⟵)

Times				Height (metres)			
HW		LW		MHWS	MHWN	MLWN	MLWS
0000	0600	0000	0600	7·5	5·9	3·0	1·4
1200	1800	1200	1800				
Differences BAIE DE LAMPAUL							
0000	+0005	−0005	−0005	0·0	−0·1	0·0	+0·1
ILE MOLENE							
+0010	+0010	+0015	+0015	0·0	+0·1	−0·1	−0·2

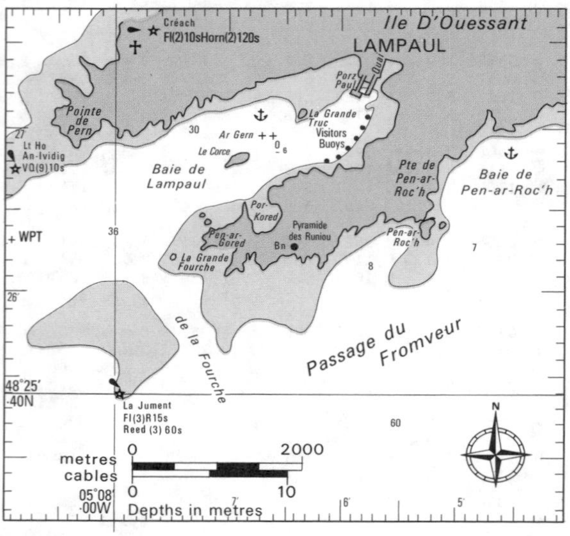

Créach
Fl(2)10sHorn(2)120s
Ile D'Ouessant
LAMPAUL
Porz Paul
Quai
Pointe de Pern
Lt Ho An-Ividig VQ(9)10s
Ar Gern
Le Corce
La Grande Truc
Visitors Buoys
Baie de Lampaul
Pte de Pen-ar-Roc'h
Baie de Pen-ar-Roc'h
WPT
Por Kored
Pyramide des Runiou
Pen-ar-Gored
La Grande Fourche
Pen-ar-Roc'h
de la Fourche
Passage du Fromveur
48°25′·40N
La Jument Fl(3)R15s Reed (3) 60s
metres
cables
0
2000
10
05°08′·00W
Depths in metres

SHELTER
Lampaul Bay is open to strong SW winds and is not recommended except in settled weather. There is normally no room for visitors in the small harbour to E of piers; entrance 15 m wide.

NAVIGATION
Waypoint 48°26′·30N 05°09′·00W, 250°/070° from/to Le Corce Rk, 1·4M. Bring Le Stiff Lt Ho 055° open N of Le Corce, which may be passed on either side; Bn Trs mark Me-ar-Blanh and Kargroe Rks further inshore. Beware ferries whch use the T shaped new quay. Ferries also use the Chenal de la Fourche but this should be attempted with great caution.

LIGHTS AND MARKS
La Jument Fl (3) R 15s 36m 22M; grey 8-sided Tr, R top; obsc 199°-241°; Horn (3) 60s. An-Ividig (Nividic) VQ(9) 10s 28m 9M; W 8-sided Tr, R bands; obsc 225°-290°; helicopter platform. Creac'h Fl (2) 10s 70m 34M; W Tr, B bands; obsc 247°-255°; Horn (2) 120s; RC; Racon.

RADIO TELEPHONE
None.

TELEPHONE (98)
Hr Mr 98.89 20 05; Aff Mar 94.48.80.27; CROSS 98.89.31.31; Meteo 98.84.60.64; SNSM 98.89.70.04; Police 98.68.10.39; Dr 98.89.92.70; Brit Consul 99.46.26.64.

FACILITIES
There are few facilities in Lampaul; L, AB, FW, P and D (in cans), Slip. **Town** Gaz, ✉; Ⓑ; ⇌ (ferry to Brest); ✈.
Ferry UK — Roscoff—Plymouth.

L'ABERBENOIT 10-16-13

Finistere

CHARTS
Admiralty 1432; SHOM 7094, 7150; ECM 539; Stanford 17; Imray C35

TIDES
Dover +0535; ML 4·7; Duration 0555; Zone −0100

Standard Port BREST (⟵)

Times				Height (metres)			
HW		LW		MHWS	MHWN	MLWN	MLWS
0000	0600	0000	0600	7·5	5·9	3·0	1·4
1200	1800	1200	1800				
Differences L'ABERBENOIT							
+0020	+0020	+0035	+0035	+0·6	+0·5	+0·1	−0·2

SHELTER
Good shelter, but do not enter at night or in strong WNW winds; best near LW when dangers can be seen. River navigable to bridge at Treglonou. Anchor as shown on chartlet, where there are also six visitors buoys.

NAVIGATION
Waypoint 48°37'·10N 04°39'·00W, 332°/152° from/to Ile Guénioc, 1·15M. Beware Plateau de Rusven (buoyed) close NW of Ile Guénioc, and other dangers to NE and SW. From 2ca (370m) W of Ile Guénioc steer to pass close W of Poul Orvil port-hand Bn, and thence to La Jument off Ile Garo.

LIGHTS AND MARKS
There are no Lts. As alternative to route above, La Jument de Garo on with Le Chien 143° avoids most dangers, but leads close to Men Renéat (rk 1m high).

RADIO TELEPHONE
None.

TELEPHONE (98)
Hr Mr none; CROSS 98.89.31.31; # 98.04.90.27; Meteo 98.84.60.64; Police (Landéda) 98.04.00.18; Dr 98.04.91.96; Brit Consul 99.46.26.64.

FACILITIES
Le Passage Slip, M, L, FW; **Treglonou** Slip; **Chantier Naval des Abers** ☎ 98.89.86.55, Sh, ME, El, M; **Town** Gaz, ✉ (Ploudalmezeau); Ⓑ (Ploudalmezeau); ⇌ (bus to Brest); ✈ (Brest). Ferry UK — Roscoff—Plymouth.

La Jument
Ile Garo
La Vieille
Pierre Noaz
143°
Anse de Broennou
04°36'·00W
BROENNOU
Corn ar Gazel
Tr Le Chien
CG
PENAR CREAC'H
PRAT-AR-COUM
Chapel
Chapel (ruins)
48°34'·50N
Oyster Beds
Pier
Le Passage
Aberbenoit
Depths in metres
metres
cables
ST PABU

L'ABERWRAC'H 10-16-14

Finistere

CHARTS
Admiralty 1432; SHOM 7094, 7150; ECM 539, 540; Stanford 17; Imray C35

TIDES
Dover +0547; ML 4·5; Duration 0600; Zone −0100

Standard Port BREST (⟵)

Times				Height (metres)			
HW		LW		MHWS	MHWN	MLWN	MLWS
0000	0600	0000	0600	7·5	5·9	3·0	1·4
1200	1800	1200	1800				
Differences ABERWRAC'H, FORT CÉZON							
+0020	+0030	+0035	+0020	+0·5	+0·2	−0·1	−0·3

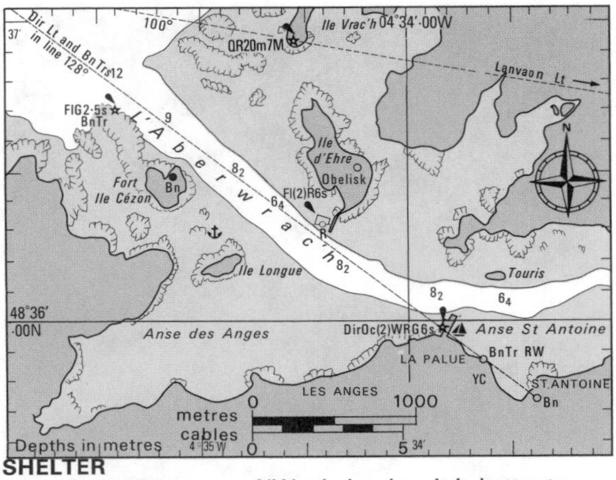
100°
Dir Lt and BnTrs in line 128°
Ile Vrac'h
04°34'·00W
QR20m7M
Lanvaon Lt
FlG2·5s
BnTr
L'Aberwrac'h
Ile d'Ehre
Obelisk
Fl(2)R6s
Fort Ile Cézon
Bn
Ile Longue
Touris
48°36'·00N
Anse des Anges
DirOc(2)WRG6s
Anse St Antoine
LA PALUE
BnTr RW
YC
ST.ANTOINE
LES ANGES
metres
cables
Depths in metres

SHELTER
Good except in strong NW winds when it is better to proceed up river to Paluden (to E, off chartlet) where there are fore and aft moorings for visitors and a jetty. Max length 10 m. Vessels at these moorings may collide at slack water or when wind and tide conflict. If anchoring, beware oyster beds. Free water taxi in summer.

NAVIGATION
Waypoint Grand Chenal 48°37'·40N 04°38'·40W, 280°/100° from/to front Ldg Lt 100°, 2·6M. W cardinal Lt buoy (Whis), 2·6M WxN from Ile Vrac'h, marks Le Libenter shoal. Also beware Basse Trousquennou to S. There are two channels to inner Ldg line 128° (1) From W and best for strangers. Grand Chenal running S of Libenter, Grand Pot de Beurre and Petit Pot de Beurre. (2) From N, Chenal de la Malouine, only by day and in good weather. Transit Petit Pot de Beurre on Pain Sucre (Ile de Croix). Great precision is required.

LIGHTS AND MARKS
For the Grand Chenal the first pair of Ldg Lts at 100° are Ile Vrac'h (QR) and Lanvaon (Dir Q, 1·63M to the rear). Then Dir Oc(2) WRG 6s 128° takes one to the jetty at La Palue. There are no lights further up river.

RADIO TELEPHONE
VHF Ch 09 16 (0700-2100 LT).

TELEPHONE (98)
Hr Mr 98.04.91.62; Aff Mar 98.04.90.13; CROSS 98.89.31.31; SNSM 98.04.81.30; # 98.04.90.27; Meteo 98.84.60.64; Police 98.04.00.18; Ⓗ 98.46.11.33; Dr 98.04.91.87; Brit Consul 99.46.26.64.

FACILITIES
Pontoons (80, some visitors) ☎ 98.04.91.62, M, AC, D, BH (12 ton), FW, ME, El, CH, AB; **Y.C. des Abers** ☎ 98.04.92.60, Bar; **Tech' Marine** ☎ 98.04.99.36 ME, El, Sh, CH, Ⓔ; **Slipway** Slip, M, D, L, FW, ME, El, Sh, C (3 ton mobile), CH, AB, V, R, Bar; **Town** P, V, Gaz, R, ⊡, P, Bar. ✉; Ⓑ (Lannilis); ⇌ (bus to Brest); ✈ (Brest). Ferry UK — Roscoff—Plymouth.

ROSCOFF 10-16-15

Finistere

CHARTS
Admiralty 2745, 3669; SHOM 7095, 7151; ECM 538; Stanford 17; Imray C35

TIDES
Dover −0605; ML 5·2; Duration 0600; Zone −0100

Standard Port BREST (⟵)

Times				Height (metres)			
HW		LW		MHWS	MHWN	MLWN	MLWS
0000	0600	0000	0600	7·5	5·9	3·0	1·4
1200	1800	1200	1800				
Differences ROSCOFF							
+0055	+0105	+0115	+0050	+1·4	+1·1	+0·4	−0·1
ILE DE BATZ							
+0045	+0100	+0105	+0050	+1·4	+1·1	+0·5	0·0

ROSCOFF *continued*

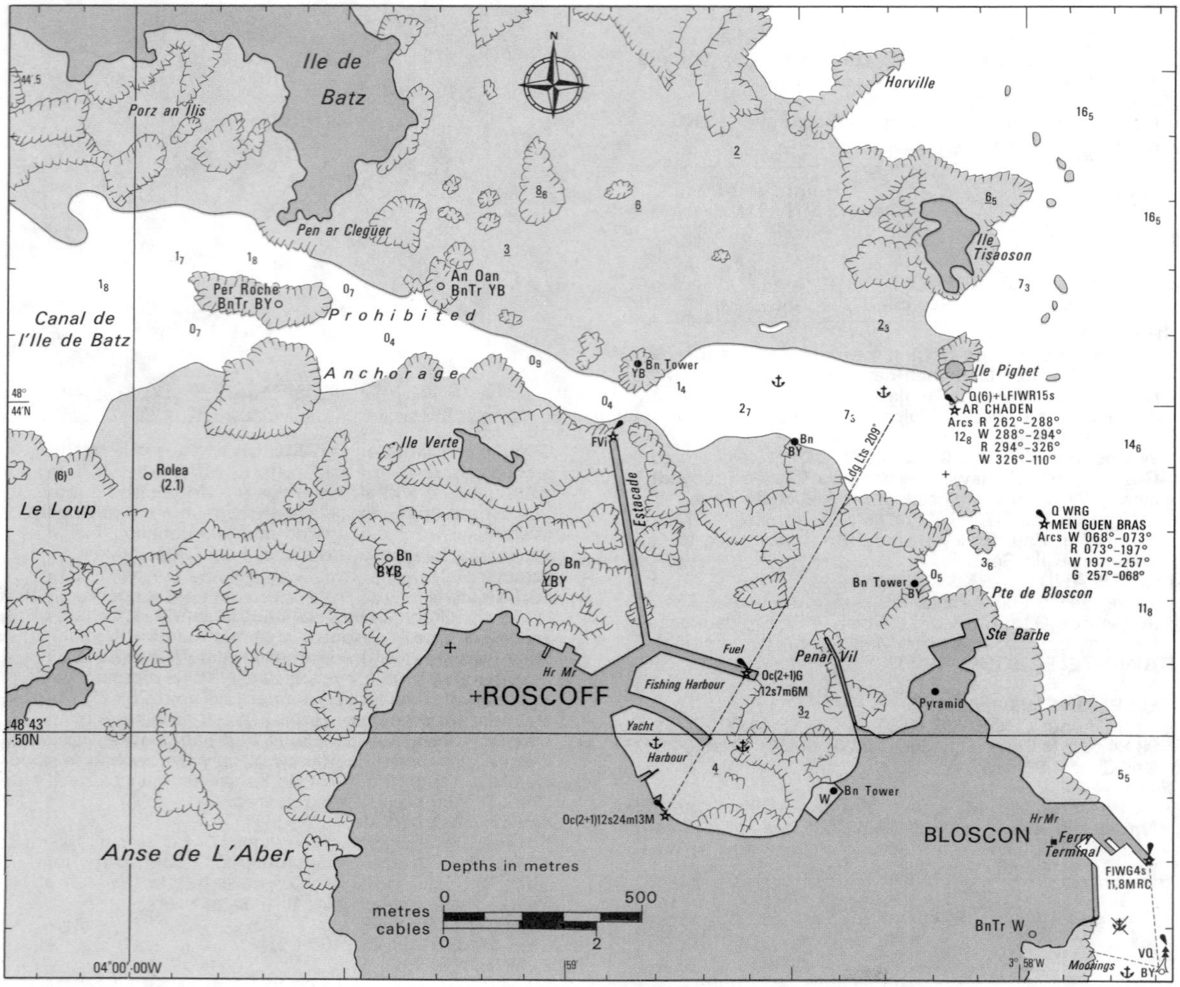
Ile de Batz
Porz an Ilis
Pen ar Cleguer
Per Roche BnTr BY
An Oan BnTr YB
Canal de l'Ile de Batz
Prohibited
Anchorage
Bn Tower YB
Horville
Ile Tisaoson
Ile Pighet
Q(6)+LFIWR15s
AR CHADEN
Arcs R 262°-288°
W 288°-294°
R 294°-326°
W 326°-110°
Ile Verte
Rolea (2.1)
Le Loup
Estacade
Ldg Lts 209°
Q WRG
MEN GUEN BRAS
Arcs W 068°-073°
R 073°-197°
W 197°-257°
G 257°-068°
Pte de Bloscon
Ste Barbe
Penar Vil
Pyramid
Fuel
Hr Mr
Fishing Harbour
Oc(2+1)G 12s7m6M
+ROSCOFF
Yacht Harbour
Bn Tower
Oc(2+1)12s24m13M
Anse de L'Aber
Depths in metres
metres
cables
BLOSCON
Ferry Terminal
FIWG4s 11,8M RC
BnTr W
Moorings
04°00'·00W
3°58'W
48°43'·50N

SHELTER
Good shelter in Roscoff (dries) except with strong winds from N and E. Berth on inner side of jetty in Yacht Harbour or secure to visitors buoy in SW corner. Access HW∓2. A sill is under construction (1988) to maintain deep water in the harbour. Entry to ferry harbour at Bloscon is forbidden without Capitaine du Port's permission. Yachts moor or anchor to the S and well clear of ferry jetty.

NAVIGATION
Waypoint 48°46'·00N 03°55'·80W, 033°/213° from/to Men Guen Bras Lt, 2·6M. The entrance to Roscoff is difficult due to the numerous large rocks in the area. Yachtsmen are advised to enter near high tide. The channels are well marked and must be kept to. Bloscon is easier to approach.

LIGHTS AND MARKS
Ile de Batz Lt Ho (conspic) Fl(4) 25s 69m 23M. Off Roscoff are Ar Chaden Q(6)+LFlWR 15s, S cardinal mark, and Men-Guen-Bras Q WRG, N cardinal mark. Ldg Lts 209°. Front on NW mole Oc(2+1)G 12s. Rear Oc(2+1) 12s. Bloscon jetty head FlWG 4s; W sector 206°-216° shows correct approach.

RADIO TELEPHONE
VHF Ch 16; 12. May-Aug 0700-1200, 1300-2200 LT. Sept-Apr 0800-1200, 1400-1800 LT.

TELEPHONE (98)
Hr Mr (Port de Plaisance) 98.69.76.37; Hr Mr (Roscoff) 98.61.27.84; Harbour Office (Port de Plaisance) 98.69.76.37; Aff Mar 98.69.70.15; CROSS 98.89.31.31; SNSM 98.61.27.84; # (Roscoff) 98.69.19.67; # (Bloscon) 98.61.27.86; Auto 98.88.34.04; Police 98.69.00.48; Ⓗ 98.88.40.22; Dr 98.69.71.18; Brit Consul 99.46.26.64.

FACILITIES
Vieux Port (220+30 visitors) ☎ 98.69.76.37, FW, AC, ME, BY; **Quai Neuf** Reserved for fishing vessels, C (5 ton); **Harbour** M; **Chautier Naval Yvin** ☎ 98.61.27.97, ME, El, Sh, SM; **Mechanique Marine** ☎ 98.61.24.87, ME; **Centre Nautique de Roscoff** ☎ 98.69.72.79; **Club Nautique de Roscoff** ☎ 98.69.72.79, Bar; **Chantier Naval Le Coz** ☎ 98.69.13.83 ME, El, Sh, CH; **Le Got** ☎ 98.69.71.86, BY. **Town** P, D, ME, El, Sh, CH, Gaz, V, R, Bar. ✉; Ⓑ; ⇌; ✈ (Morlaix).
Ferry UK — Plymouth.

MORLAIX 10-16-16

Finistere

CHARTS
Admiralty 2745, 3669; SHOM 7095, 7151; ECM 538; Stanford 17; Imray C34, C35

TIDES
Dover −0610; ML 5·2; Duration 0610; Zone −0100

Standard Port BREST (⟵)

Times				Height (metres)			
HW		LW		MHWS	MHWN	MLWN	MLWS
0000	0600	0000	0600	7·5	5·9	3·0	1·4
1200	1800	1200	1800				
Differences MORLAIX (CHÂTEAU DU TAUREAU)							
+0100	+0115	+0115	+0050	+1·5	+1·1	+0·5	−0·1

MORLAIX *continued*

SHELTER

Good shelter in the bay and in Dourduff although the latter dries. Yachts can proceed up to Morlaix town and enter the lock into the Bassin à Flot where there is a marina and shelter is complete. Beware a movable pontoon connects E and W banks, opposite YC, acting as a footbridge. Lock opens HW−1½ and HW+1 during daytime. Waiting moorings off 'Pen a Lann' (5M downstream).

NAVIGATION

Waypoint Grand Chenal 48°43'·00N 03°53'·50W, 356°/176° from/to Ile Louet Lt, 2·5M. Morlaix Bay is divided by the Ile de Callot on E side of which lies Morlaix River. There are three entrances and all have rocky dangers

(1) Grand Chenal E of Ricard Is (shallower but lit 176°).
(2) Chenal Ouest, W of Ricard Is. Big ship channel, not lit.
(3) Chenal de Tréguier (190° and best at night), almost dries at LW.

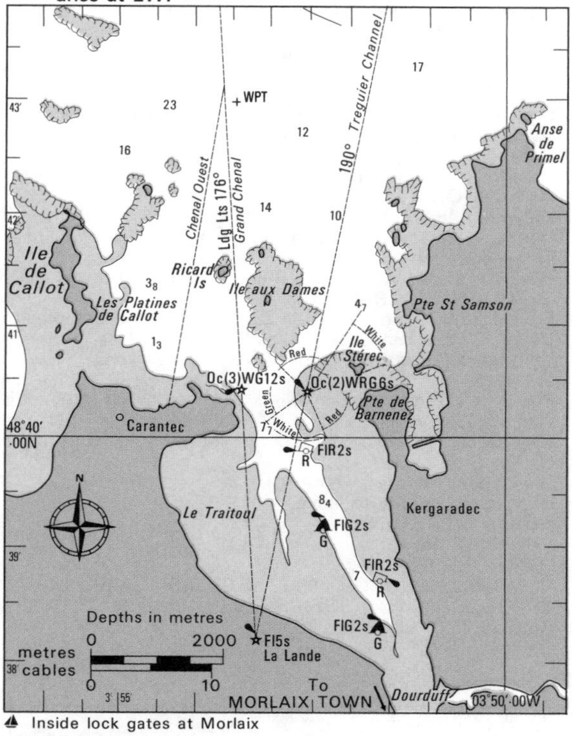
WPT
190° Treguier Channel
Chenal Ouest
Ldg Lts 176°
Grand Chenal
Anse de Primel
Ile de Callot
Ricard Is
Ile aux Dames
Les Platines de Callot
Pte St Samson
Ile Stérec
Oc(3)WG12s
Oc(2)WRG6s
Pte de Barnenez
Carantec
FIR2s
Le Traitoul
FIG2s
Kergaradec
Depths in metres
metres
cables
FI5s La Lande
To MORLAIX TOWN
Dourduff
03°50'·00W
48°40'·00N

▲ Inside lock gates at Morlaix

LIGHTS AND MARKS

Grand Chenal Lts in line 176° (Ile Louet and La Lande). Treguier Chenal Lts in line 190° (Ile Noire and La Lande). River up to Morlaix town 3M above Dourduff is buoyed but unlit..

RADIO TELEPHONE

VHF Ch 09 16.

TELEPHONE (98)

Hr Mr 98.62.13.14; Lock 98.88.54.92; Aff Mar 98.62.10.47; CROSS 98.89.31.31; SNSM 98.88.00.76; # 98.88.06.31; Auto 98.88.34.04; Police 98.88.58.13; Ⓗ 98.88.40.22; Brit Consul 99.46.26.64.

FACILITIES

Marina (100+60 visitors) ☎ 98.62.13.14, AC, FW, C (8 ton), (Access HW−1½ HW and HW+1); **Rio L** ☎ 98.88.13.54, Sh, ME, El; **YC de Morlaix** ☎ 98.62.08.51, Slip, M, P, D, L, FW, ME, El, Sh, CH, AB; **Loisirs Nautique** ☎ 98.88.27.30, ME, CH, Sh, SM, Ⓔ, El; **Cap Mer** ☎ 98.88.25.85, CH, Ⓔ; **Jegou Ritz** ☎ 98.88.04.15, SHOM; **Société Morlaisienne de la Mer** ☎ 98.62.19.21, CH, ME; **Town** P, D, V, Gaz, R, Bar. ✉; Ⓑ; ≹; ✈.
Ferry UK — Roscoff—Plymouth.

LANNION (Léguer River)

Côtes du Nord

10-16-17

CHARTS

Admiralty 3669, 2668; SHOM 7124, 967; ECM 538; Stanford 17; Imray C34

TIDES

Dover −0605; ML 5·3; Duration —; Zone −0100

Standard Port BREST (←)

Times				Height (metres)			
HW		LW		MHWS	MHWN	MLWN	MLWS
0000	0600	0000	0600	7·5	5·9	3·0	1·4
1200	1800	1200	1800				
Differences TRÉBEURDEN							
+0105	+0110	+0120	+0100	+1·6	+1·3	+0·5	−0·1

SHELTER

Good shelter except in strong winds from NW to W. Anchor in estuary or in river by Guiodel. There are drying berths at Lannion.

NAVIGATION

Waypoint 48°46'·65N 03°42'·20W, 302°/121° from/to front Locquemeau Ldg Lt 122°, 6M. There are non-drying pools off Le Yaudet and Le Beguen. Beware sandbank N and NE of Pt de Dourvin, running about 2 ca (370m), which dries. Pass up the channel near to the Trs; this is impossible at very low water especially with strong NW winds which cause sea to break on the bar.

LIGHTS AND MARKS

The large radome 3·5 M NNE of entrance is conspic landmark. Lt on Pt Beg-Léguer Oc (4) WRG 12s 60m 13/10M; vis W084°-098°, R098°-129°, G007°-084°. Channel to Lannion is narrow and marked by towers and beacons.

RADIO TELEPHONE

None.

TELEPHONE (96)

Hr Mr 96.37.06.52; Aff Mar 96.37.06.52; CROSS 98.89.31.31; SNSM 96.23.52.07; # 96.37.45.32; Auto 98.88.34.04; Police 96.37.03.78; Dr 96.37.42.52; Brit Consul 99.46.26.64.

FACILITIES

Quai de Loguivy Slip, L, FW, C (1 ton mobile), AB; **Coopérative Maritime** ☎ 96.37.03.18, CH; **Lesbleiz** ☎ 96.48.35.01, M, ME, El, Sh, SHOM, Ⓔ, CH; **Town** M, CH, V, Gaz, R, Bar. ✉; Ⓑ; ≹; ✈ (Morlaix, Lannion).
Ferry UK — Roscoff—Plymouth.

16

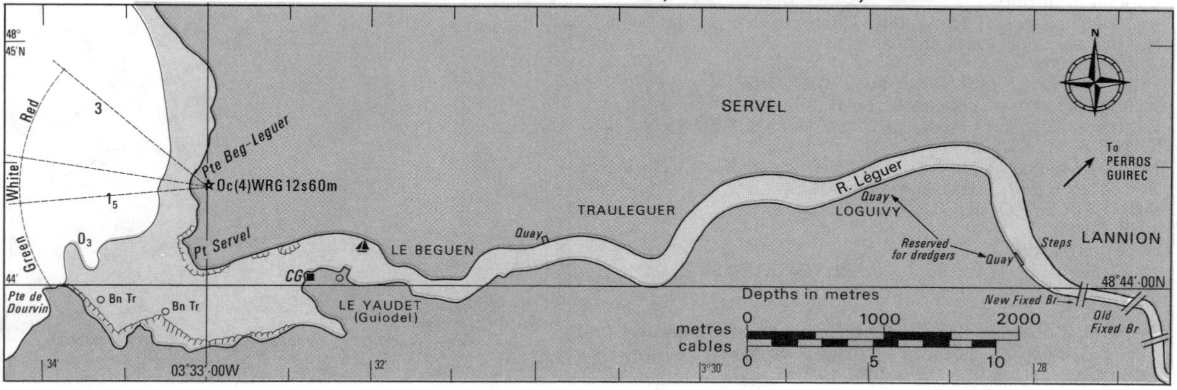
SERVEL
Pte Beg-Leguer
Oc(4)WRG12s60m
Red
White
Green
Pt Servel
LE BEGUEN
TRAULEGUER
R. Léguer
Quay LOGUIVY
Reserved for dredgers
Quay
Steps
LANNION
To PERROS GUIREC
Pte de Dourvin
Bn Tr
LE YAUDET (Guiodel)
Depths in metres
metres
cables
New Fixed Br
Old Fixed Br
48°44'·00N
03°33'·00W

PLOUMANAC'H 10-16-18

Côtes du Nord

CHARTS
Admiralty 3669, 3670; SHOM 5950, 967; ECM 537, 538; Stanford 17; Imray C34

TIDES
Dover −0550; ML 4·9; Duration 0605; Zone −0100

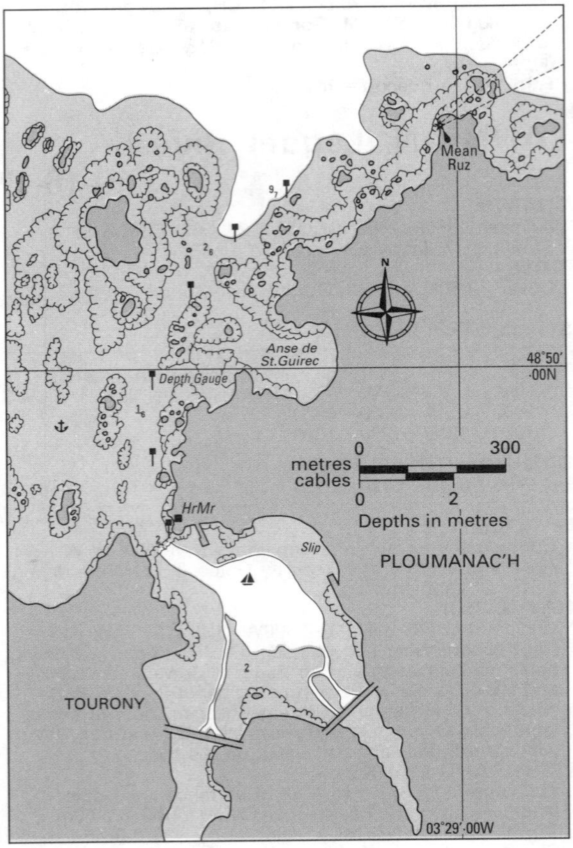

Mean Ruz
Anse de St.Guirec
48°50'·00N
Depth Gauge
N
metres
cables
0
300
0
2
Depths in metres
HrMr
Slip
PLOUMANAC'H
TOURONY
03°29'·00W

Standard Port ST MALO (⟶)

Times				Height (metres)			
HW		LW		MHWS	MHWN	MLWN	MLWS
0100	0800	0200	0700	12·2	9·2	4·4	1·5
1300	2000	1400	1900				
Differences PLOUMANAC'H							
−0034	−0039	−0130	−0050	−3·2	−2·1	−1·0	−0·4

SHELTER
Shelter is good, moored fore and aft alongside dumbell fender buoys. Channel is well marked but unlit. Entry is difficult in strong NW winds. A sill, 2·25m above CD maintains at least 1·5m within. There are tide gauges on the last two port hand stakes.

NAVIGATION
Waypoint 48°51'·50N 03°29'·00W, 008°/188°, 1·25M from/to entrance between Mean Ruz Lt Ho to E and Ch Coztaeres (conspic) to W. Les Sept Iles are 2·5M to N.

LIGHTS AND MARKS
Iles aux Moines Lt Ho Fl(3) 15s to N; Mean Ruz Lt Ho Oc WR 4s to E with adjacent sig stn (conspic).

RADIO TELEPHONE
VHF Ch 09.

TELEPHONE (96)
Hr Mr 96.91.14.31 (or 96.23.37.82); SNSM 98.23.20.16; Auto 96.20.01.92.

FACILITIES
Port de Plaisance (230 + 12 visitors); **Quai Bellevue** FW, AC, Slip; **YC Societe Nautique de Perros Guirec.**
Ferry UK — Roscoff—Plymouth.

PERROS-GUIREC 10-16-19

Côtes du Nord

CHARTS
Admiralty 3672, 3670, 2668; SHOM 974, 967; ECM 537, 538; Stanford 17; Imray C34

TIDES
Dover −0550; ML 5·1; Duration 0605; Zone −0100

Standard Port ST MALO (⟶) (Note 9.1.2 last para)

Times				Height (metres)			
HW		LW		MHWS	MHWN	MLWN	MLWS
0100	0800	0200	0700	12·2	9·2	4·4	1·5
1300	2000	1400	1900				
Differences PERROS-GUIREC							
−0034	−0044	−0130	−0050	−2·8	−1·9	−0·9	−0·2
PLOUMANAC'H							
−0034	−0039	−0130	−0050	−3·2	−2·1	−1·0	−0·4

SHELTER
Anchorage off Pointe du Chateau gives good shelter but exposed to NE winds. Drying moorings 1 ca E of Jetee du Linkin. Shelter in the marina is very good. Access, via a narrow gate (6m wide), varies from HW−2 to HW+1½ @ Springs to HW−1 to HW @ Neaps; contact Hr Mr for exact times. Caution: at small Neap tides the gate may be shut for up to 4 days. Gate opening depends on water levels equalising over a sill 7m above CD (there is no lock). Sill is marked by R & W poles. No anchoring allowed in non-tidal basin.

NAVIGATION
Waypoint 48°52'·40N 03°20'·00W, 045°/225° from/to front Ldg Lt 225° (Le Colombier), 6·4M. Beware Ile Tomé in the entrance to Anse de Perros. Rocks extend 7 ca (1300m) off the W side and 6 ca (1110m) E of the N side.

LIGHTS AND MARKS
From E of Ile Tomé, Ldg Lts 225° — Front Le Colombier Dir Oc (4) 12s 28m 18M, intens 220°-230°. Rear Kerprigent (1·5M from front) Q 79m 22M, intens 221°-228°.
Passe de l'Ouest. Kerjean Dir Lt 144° Oc (2+1) WRG 12s 78m 15/13M vis G134°-143°, W143°-144°, R144°-154°.
Gate signals (flags by day Lts by night).
G over R = closed
G = open, priority to enter
R = open, priority to leave.

RADIO TELEPHONE
VHF Ch 09 16.

TELEPHONE (96)
Hr Mr 96.23.37.82; Gate 96.23.19.03; Aff Mar 96.23.13.78; CROSS 98.89.31.31; SNSM 96.23.20.16; # 96.23.18.12; Auto 96.20.01.92; Police 96.23.20.17; Dr 96.23.20.01; Brit Consul 99.46.26.64.

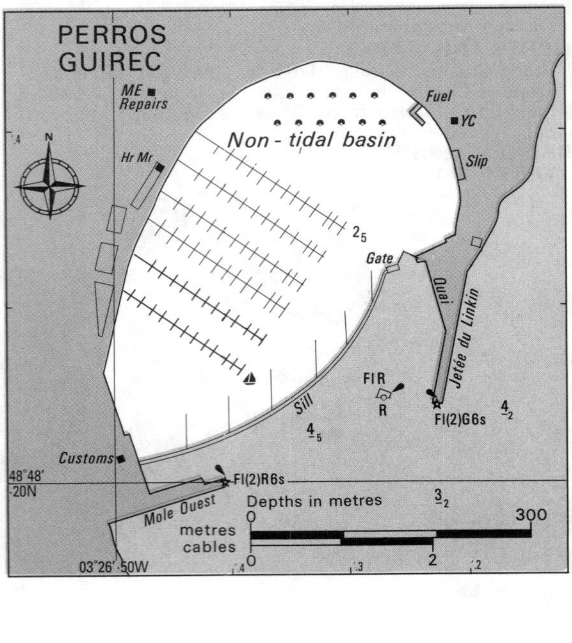

PERROS GUIREC
ME Repairs
Fuel
YC
N
Non - tidal basin
Hr Mr
Slip
Gate
Quai
Jetée du Linkin
Sill
FI R
R
Fl(2)G6s
Customs
Fl(2)R6s
48°48'·20N
Mole Ouest
Depths in metres
metres
cables
0
300
0
2
03°26'·50W

FACILITIES
Marina (600+50 visitors) ☎ 96.23.19.03, P, D, FW, ME, AC, El, Sh, C (7 ton), CH, V, R, SM, Gas, Gaz, Kos, ◎, Bar; **Le Locat Marine** ☎ 96.23.05.08, ME, El, Ⓔ, Sh, CH; **Ponant Loisirs** ☎ 96.23.18.38, ME, El, Ⓔ, Sh, CH, SHOM; **Ship Marine** ☎ 96.91.11.88, D, P, CH, ME, El, Ⓔ Sh; **PMP Marine** ☎ 96.91.16.07 ME, El, Ⓔ, Sh, CH; **Town** P, FW, CH, V, Gaz, R, Bar. ✉; Ⓑ; ≹ (Lannion); ✈ (Morlaix/Lannion).
Booking for pontoons and moorings — at Town Hall ☎ 96.23.22.64;

TRÉGUIER 10-16-20

Côtes du Nord

CHARTS
Admiralty 3672, 3670, 2668; SHOM 973, 972, 967; ECM 537, 538; Stanford 17; Imray C34
TIDES
Dover −0540; ML 5·5; Duration 0600; Zone −0100

Standard Port ST MALO (⟶) (Note 9.1.2 last para)

Times				Height (metres)			
HW		LW		MHWS	MHWN	MLWN	MLWS
0100	0800	0200	0700	12·2	9·2	4·4	1·5
1300	2000	1400	1900				
Differences TRÉGUIER							
−0038	−0032	−0130	−0035	−2·4	−1·7	−1·1	−0·4

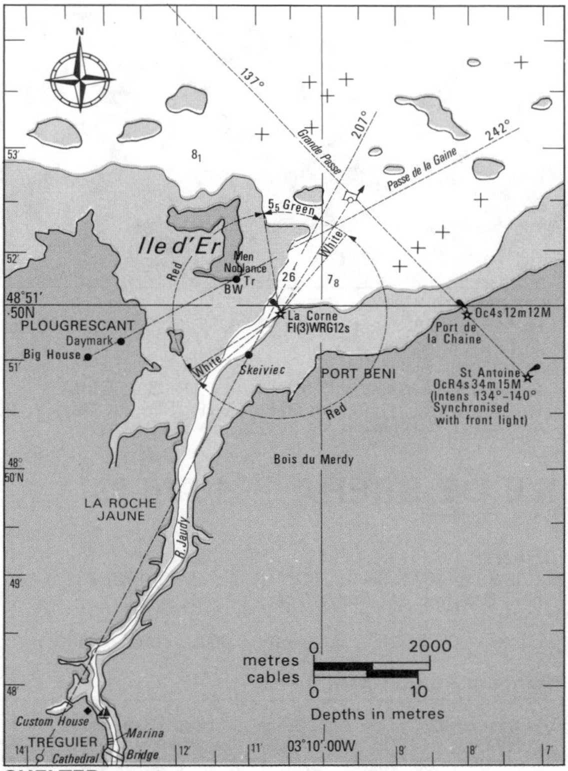

137°
207°
242°
Grande Passe
Passe de la Gaine
Ile d'Er
Green
White
Red
Men Noblance Tr BW
La Corne Fl(3)WRG12s
Oc4s12m12M
Port de la Chaine
48°51'·50N
PLOUGRESCANT Daymark
Big House
Skeiviec
PORT BENI
St Antoine OcR4s34m15M (Intens 134°-140° Synchronised with front light)
Bois du Merdy
LA ROCHE JAUNE
R. Jaudy
metres
cables
Depths in metres
Custom House
TRÉGUIER
Cathedral
Marina
Bridge
03°10'·00W

SHELTER
Good shelter can be found from most winds; SW of La Corne Lt Tr, exposed to NE to NW; off Roche Jaune village; up in Tréguier by the quay; by Palamos, 1M N of marina by No 10 buoy.
NAVIGATION
Waypoint 48°55'·00N 03°12'·80W, 317°/137° from/to front Ldg Lt 137°, 5M·
There are three entrance channels:
(1) Grande Passe. Well marked, but strong tidal streams across the channel.
(2) Passe de la Gaine. Navigable with care by day in good visibility.
(3) Passe du Nord-Est. Dangerous with winds from W and NW as sea breaks across the channel.
Speed limit 6kns above La Roche Jaune.

LIGHTS AND MARKS
Important marks are Men Noblance Bn Tr (BW) on SE corner of Ile d'Er, Skeiviec Bn Tr (W), and La Corne Lt Tr (WR) Fl(3) WRG 12s. Leading marks:
(1) For Grande Passe. Port de la Chaine and St Antoine Lts at 137°.
(2) For Passe de la Gaine. Men Noblance and Plougrescant daymark (W with B vert stripe) at 242°.
(3) For approach to La Corne. Tréguier cathedral spire and Skeiviec (from SW of La Jument) at 207°.
RADIO TELEPHONE
Tréguier Marina Ch 09.
TELEPHONE (96)
Hr Mr 96.92.42.37; Aff Mar 96.92.30.38; CROSS 96.54.11.11; # 96.92.31.44; Auto 96.20.01.92; Police 96.92.30.33; Dr 96.92.32.14; Ⓗ 96.92.30.72; Brit Consul 99.46.26.64.
FACILITIES
EC Sunday; **Marina** (200+130 visitors), ☎ 96.92.42.37, Slip, FW, ME, C (8 ton), CH, AC, Bar, Gaz; **Station Service** ☎ 96.92.30.52, P and D (cans); **Jetties** M, L, FW, ME, El, Sh, CH, AB; **Marina Sports** ☎ 96.92.47.60, M, ME, Sh, CH; **Co-Per Marine** ☎ 96.92.35.72, M. CH; **Club Nautique du Tregor** ☎ 96.92.42.37, excellent facilities, open all year.
Town P, FW, CH, V, Gaz, R, Bar. ✉; Ⓑ; ≹ (bus to Paimpol); ✈ (St Brieuc, Lannion).
Ferry UK — Roscoff—Plymouth.

LÉZARDRIEUX 10-16-21

Côtes du Nord

CHARTS
Admiralty 3673, 3670, 2668; SHOM 2845, 882, 832; ECM 537; Stanford 17, 16; Imray C34
TIDES
Dover −0510; ML 5·6; Duration 0610; Zone −0100

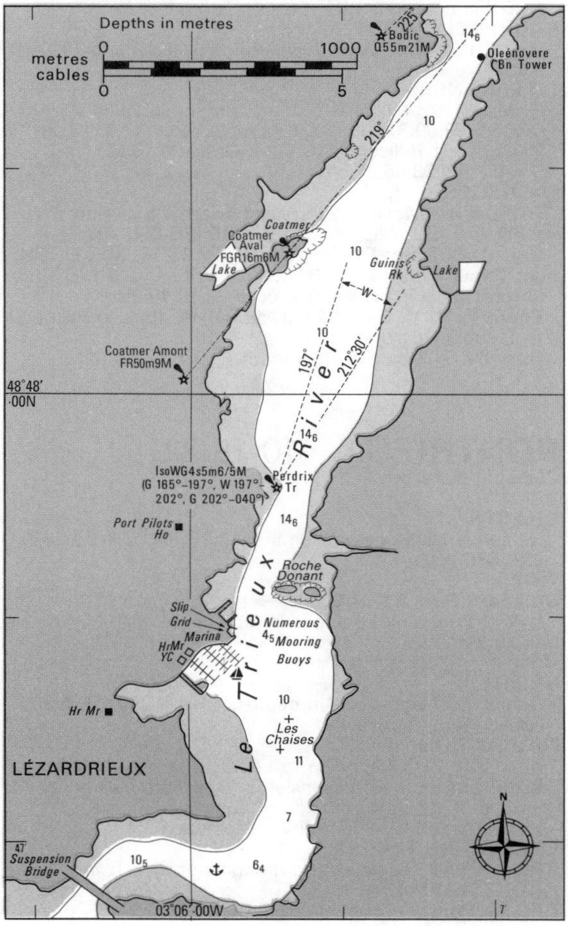

Depths in metres
metres
cables
Bodic Q55m21M
225°
Oleénovere Bn Tower
219°
Coatmer
Coatmer Aval FGR16m6M
Lake
Guinis Rk
Coatmer Amont FR50m9M
197°
212°30'
48°48'·00N
Le Trieux River
IsoWG4s5m6/5M (G 165°-197°, W 197°-202°, G 202°-040°)
Perdrix Tr
Port Pilots Ho
Roche Donant
Slip
Grid
Marina
HrMr YC
Numerous Mooring Buoys
Hr Mr
Les Chaises
LÉZARDRIEUX
Suspension Bridge
03°06'·00W

Standard Port ST MALO (⟶)

Times				Height (metres)			
HW		LW		MHWS	MHWN	MLWN	MLWS
0100	0800	0200	0700	12·2	9·2	4·4	1·5
1300	2000	1400	1900				
Differences LÉZARDRIEUX							
−0008	−0006	−0050	−0015	−2·0	−1·6	−0·9	−0·5

SHELTER

Very good in all weathers. Harbour and marina can be entered at all tides day or night. Beware strong cross currents off river entrance. Multi-hulls and boats over 12·5 m are not welcome at pontoons, so should moor on visitors buoys in front of marina. Yachts can proceed up river (bridge clearance 18m) to Pontrieux, about 12 km beyond Lézardrieux, (10.16.22).

NAVIGATION

Waypoint 48°55′·00N 02°56′·20W, 045°/225° from/to front Ldg Lt 225° (La Croix), 6·7M. Outlying dangers are Barnouic Rks and Roches Douvres. There are three entrance channels, Moisie channel, Grand Chenal which is recommended for strangers and the Ferlas Channel from the E.

LIGHTS AND MARKS

(1) Moisie channel — Amer du Rosédo W pyramid in line with St Michael's chapel at 160°.
(2) Grand Chenal Lts in line at 225°.
Front — La Croix Oc 4s 15m 19M; two Trs joined, W on NE side with R tops. Intens 215°-235°.
Rear — Bodic (2·1 M from front) Q 55m 22M (intens 221°-229°).
(3) Ferlas channel.
W sector of Joliguet Lt Ho
W sector of Loguivy
W sector of Ile à Bois lead to Coatmer line
(4) Coatmer Ldg Lts 219°. Front F RG 16m 9/9M; vis R200°-250°, G250°-053°. Rear, 660m from front, FR 50m 9M.

3 marina pontoons have FBu Lts at end of each.

RADIO TELEPHONE

VHF Ch 09 (0800-2000 July Aug: 0800-1200 and 1400-1800 rest of year LT).

TELEPHONE (96)

Hr Mr 96.20.14.22; Aff Mar at Paimpol 96.20.84.30; CROSS 98.89.31.31; # at Paimpol 96.20.81.87; Auto 96.20.01.92; Police 96.20.10.17; Dr 96.20.10.30; Brit Consul 99.46.26.64.

FACILITIES

EC Sunday; **Marina** (230, vacant berths for visitors), ☎ 96.20.14.22, Slip, P, D, FW, ME, El, CH, AC, Bar, Gaz, R, SM, Sh; **Ruffloc'h** ☎ 96.22.13.16, ME, El, CH, Ⓔ; **Trieux Marine** ☎ 96.20.14.71, ME, CH, Sh, C (6 ton), Divers; **YC de Trieux** ☎ 96.20.10.39.
Town P, D, V, Gaz, R, Bar. ✉; Ⓑ; ⇌ (bus to Paimpol); ✈ (Lannion/St Brieuc).
Ferry UK — Roscoff—Plymouth.

PONTRIEUX 10-16-22

Côtes du Nord

CHARTS

Nil above Lezardrieux; Admiralty 3673 and SHOM 2845, 537, 970 below

TIDES

Standard Port ST MALO (⟶)

HW at Pontrieux Lock occurs at HW ST MALO. See also 10.16.21

SHELTER

Complete shelter in 2-4m depth alongise Quay (E bank), approx 1km above lock.

NAVIGATION

See 10.16.21 for appr up to Lezardrieux. Not before mid-flood, proceed via suspension bridge (18m clearance) 6M up-river, keeping to outside of bends. Lock opens HW−1½ to HW+1. Waiting By close E.

LIGHTS AND MARKS

River is unlit (beware sand dredgers at night); few marks.

RADIO TELEPHONE

Écluse/Port de Pontrieux VHF Ch 12 16.

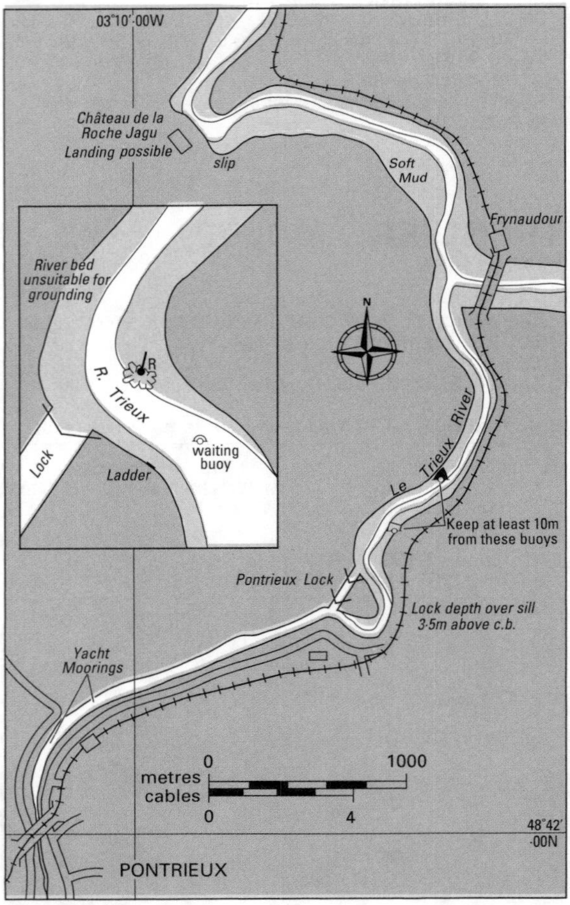
03°10′·00W
Château de la Roche Jagu Landing possible
slip
Soft Mud
Frynaudour
River bed unsuitable for grounding
R. Trieux
R
waiting buoy
Lock
Ladder
N
Le Trieux River
Keep at least 10m from these buoys
Pontrieux Lock
Lock depth over sill 3·5m above c.b.
Yacht Moorings
metres
cables
0
1000
0
4
48°42′·00N
PONTRIEUX

TELEPHONE

Hr Mr 96.95.64.66; Lock 96.95.60.70; SNSM 92.20.00.45. Auto 96.20.01.92.

FACILITIES

Quay 100 (AB), FW, C (6 ton), AC, R, Bar; **Club Nautique** Bar, R; **Town** Bar, FW, R, Slip, V, Gaz, P, D, Ⓑ, ✉, ⊡, ⇌ Paimpol/Guingamp, ✈ St Brieux.

ILE DE BRÉHAT 10-16-23

Côtes du Nord

CHARTS

Admiralty 3673, 3670, 2668; SHOM 2845, 882, 832; ECM 537; Stanford 16; Imray C34

TIDES

Dover −0525; ML 5·8; Duration 0605; Zone −0100

Standard Port ST MALO (⟶)

Times				Height (metres)			
HW		LW		MHWS	MHWN	MLWN	MLWS
0100	0800	0200	0700	12·2	9·2	4·4	1·5
1300	2000	1400	1900				
Differences ILE DE BRÉHAT							
−0014	−0004	−0055	−0035	−1·7	−1·2	−0·7	−0·3

SHELTER

Possible anchorages are

Port Clos — busy main harbour; good shelter; harbour dries. No alongside berths.

Port de la Corderie — good shelter for all except W winds. Well out of strong tides; harbour dries.

La Chambre in SE. Anchor in upper reaches just N of the 'No anchoring' area, close to the town of Le Bourg. (Note there are no cars allowed on the island.)

ILE DE BRÉHAT *continued*

Guerzido in the Chenal de Ferlas, is good holding ground, partly out of the strong tides. Anchor E of Men Allan and close to the buoys of the boat barrier.

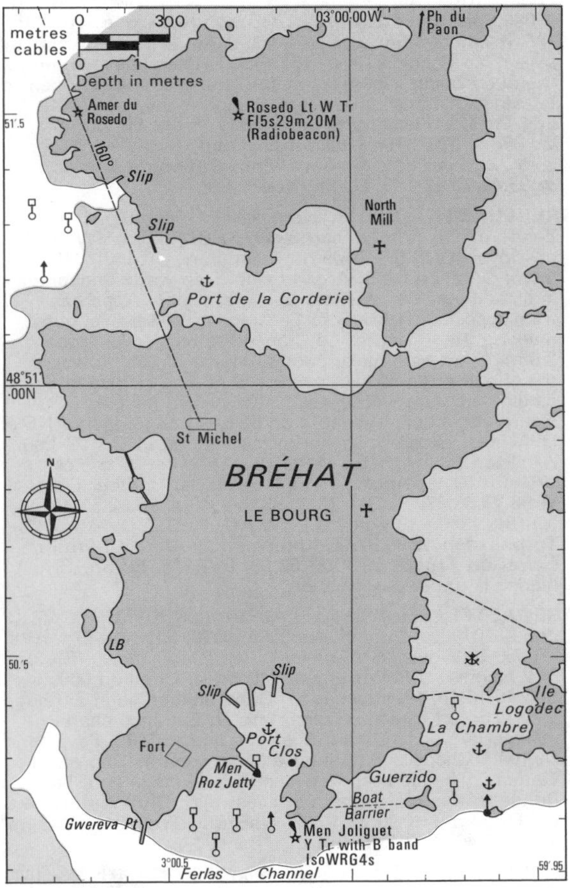
metres
cables
0
300
0
1
Depth in metres
03°00·00W
Ph du Paon
Amer du Rosedo
Rosedo Lt W Tr
Fl5s29m20M
(Radiobeacon)
51'.5
160°
Slip
Slip
North Mill
Port de la Corderie
48°51'
·00N
St Michel
BRÉHAT
LE BOURG
LB
50'.5
Slip
Slip
Port Clos
Fort
Men Roz Jetty
Ile Logodec
La Chambre
Guerzido
Boat Barrier
Gwereva Pt
Men Joliguet
Y Tr with B band
IsoWRG4s
3°00'.5
Ferlas Channel
59'.95

NAVIGATION
Waypoint Ferlas channel 48°49'·45N 02°55'·00W, 098°/278° from/to La Croix Lt, 5·5M. See also 10.16.21. On approach, beware the Barnouic and Roches Douvres (12 and 17 M NNE) and La Horaine, Men March and Ringue Bras closer in. There is a prohibited anchorage SW of Port Clos, between Brehat and the mainland.

LIGHTS AND MARKS
There are three principal lights on Ile de Bréhat:
(1) In the N, Phare du Paon F WRG 22m 12/9M; Y Tr; vis W033°-078°, G078°-181°, W181°-196°, R196°-307°, W307°-316°, R316°-348°.
(2) In NW part, Rosédo Fl 5s 29m 20M; W Tr and G gallery; RC.
(3) In the S, on E side of Port Clos entrance, Men-Joliguet Iso WRG 4s 6m 13/10M, Y Tr with B band; vis R255°-279°, W279°-283°, G283°-175°.

RADIO TELEPHONE
None.

TELEPHONE (96)
Hr Mr none; CROSS 98.89.31.31; SNSM 96.20.00.14; Auto 96.20.01.92; # 96.20.81.87; Police 96.20.80.17; Dr 96.20.00.99; Brit Consul 99.46.26.64.

FACILITIES
Club Nautique de Bréhat ☎ 96.20.00.69, M, FW, Bar; **Mervel** ☎ 96.20.01.39, ME; **Harbours** Slip, M, FW; **Village** V, Gaz, Bar. ✉; Ⓑ (Paimpol); ≹ (ferry to Pointe de l'Arcouest, bus to Paimpol); ✈ (St Brieuc).
Ferry UK — Roscoff—Plymouth.

PAIMPOL 10-16-24

Côtes du Nord

CHARTS
Admiralty 3673, 2668, 3670; SHOM 3670, 832; ECM 537; Stanford 16; Imray C34

TIDES
Dover −0525; ML 5·5; Duration 0600; Zone −0100

Standard Port ST MALO (⟶) (Note 9.1.2 last para)

Times				Height (metres)			
HW		LW		MHWS	MHWN	MLWN	MLWS
0100	0800	0200	0700	12·2	9·2	4·4	1·5
1300	2000	1400	1900				
Differences PAIMPOL							
−0009	−0006	−0040	−0010	−1·7	−1·4	−1·2	−0·9

SHELTER
There is good shelter in Paimpol from all winds but the whole Anse de Paimpol dries. Lock opens HW−1½ to HW springs, HW−1 to HW neaps, (when sufficient height of tide, 8m). Visitors' berths at Pontoon A, as available.

NAVIGATION
Waypoint 48°47'·40N 02°51'·50W, 090°/270° from/to Pte de Porz-Don Lt, 6·6M. There are rocks which dry very close to the leading lines. The Anse de Paimpol is divided by rocks (El Paimpol and El Bras) down the centre.

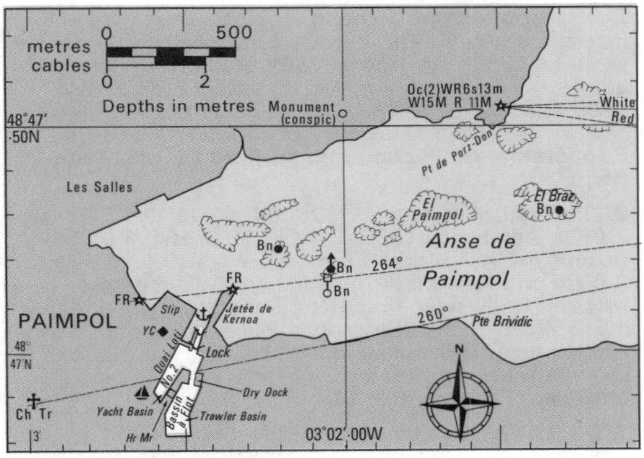
metres
cables
0
500
0
2
Depths in metres
Monument (conspic)
Oc(2)WR6s13m
W15M R 11M
White
Red
48°47'
·50N
Pt de Porz-Don
Les Salles
El Paimpol
El Bras
Bn
Anse de Paimpol
264°
260°
Pte Brividic
FR
FR
Slip
Jetée de Kernoa
PAIMPOL
YC
Lock
Quai Loti
No 2
Dry Dock
Trawler Basin
Yacht Basin
Bassin à Flot
Hr Mr
Ch Tr
48°47'N
03°02'·00W

LIGHTS AND MARKS
Leading marks — Paimpol church tower and the top of Pt Brividic 260°. Second leading Lts 5/12m Jetée de Kernoa and Paimpol front (both FR) 264°. Pointe de Porz-Don Lt Oc (2) WR 6s 13m 15/11M; vis W269°-272°, R272°-279°

RADIO TELEPHONE
VHF Ch 09 (0800-1200 LT and lock opening hours).

TELEPHONE (96)
Hr Mr 96.20.47.67; Port de Plaisance 96.20.47.65; Aff Mar 96.20.84.30; CROSS 98.89.31.31; # 96.20.81.87; Auto 96.20.01.92; Police 96.20.80.17; Ⓗ 96.20.86.02; Dr 96.20.80.04; Brit Consul 99.46.26.64.

FACILITIES
Bassin No 2 (marina 260+10 visitors), FW, AB, D, P, ME, El, C (6 ton, 3 ton); **Quai de Kernoa** P, ME; **Quai neuf** Slip, M, FW, AB; **Dauphin** ☎ 96.20.81.38, Sh, CH, SHOM; **Despretz** ☎ 96.20.82.00, M, ME, Sh, CH; **Le Lionnaise Marine** ☎ 96.20.85.18, ME, El, Sh, CH; **MEE** ☎ 96.20.74.47, Ⓔ; **Town** P, D, CH, V, Gaz, R, Bar. ✉; Ⓑ; ≹; ✈ (St Brieuc).
Ferry UK — Roscoff—Plymouth.

MINOR HARBOURS AND ANCHORAGES 10-16-25

L'ABERILDUT, Finistere, 48°28'·00N, 04°45'·00W, Zone −0100, Admty charts 3345, 2694; SHOM 7122. HW +0520 on Dover (GMT), +0007 on Brest (zone −0100). From N beware Les Liniou Rks 2M S of Le Four Lt (Fl(5)15s). Good shelter but exposed to W winds and harbour partly dries. Beware strong cross tides in approach. For Chenal du Four see 10.16.5. Aberildut Lt Dir Oc(2) WR 6s, vis W081°-085°, R085°-087°. Ldg marks Brélès spire and Lanildut spire at 079° lead into fairway between rks which dry, marked by Bn Trs. Facilities: several slips, village shop; **Cariou** ☎ 98.04.30.44, ME. **Hélies Marine** ☎ 98.04.39.16 Sh, ME, El, CH, M.

ARGENTON, Finistere, 48°31'·00N, 04°46'·00W, Zone −0100, Admty charts 3347, 2694, SHOM 7122, 5287. HW +0535 on Dover (GMT), +0020 on Brest (zone −0100); HW height +0·5m on Brest; ML 4·6m; Duration 0600. Small drying Hr giving good shelter except in W winds when a swell comes up the bay into the Hr. Access HW∓3. Approach is well marked. Beware strong E−W tides. Anchorage in deep water off Hr ent. 10 visitors moorings. There are no lights. Facilities: FW, P on quay; **SC** ☎ 98.89.54.04; **Town** Bar, R, V.

PORTSALL, Finistere, 48°33'·00N, 04°42'·00W, Zone −0100, Admty charts 1432, 3688, SHOM 7094, 7150. HW +0535 on Dover (GMT), +0020 on Brest (zone −0100); HW height +0·5m on Brest; ML 4·4m; Duration 0600. Small drying harbour at head of bay. Access HW∓3. Good shelter except in strong N winds. Entrance to bay marked by two Bn Trs. Beware numerous rocks lying off-shore for about 2M. Anchor to W of ent. or go alongside quay in Hr. Facilities: Aff.Mar. ☎ 98.80.62.25; SNSM ☎ 98.48.65.92; Dr ☎ 98.48.10.46. **Quay** C (0.5 ton), D, FW, P, Slip; **Club Nautique** (CNPK) ☎ 98.48.63.10. **Coopérative de Pêcheurs** ☎ 98.48.63.26, CH; **Town** Bar, ✉, R, V.

PONTUSVAL, Finistere, 48°40'·00N, 04°19'·00W, Zone −0100, Admty chart 3668, SHOM 7150. HW +0605 on Dover (GMT), +0055 on Brest (zone −0100); HW height +0·7m on Brest; ML 4·7m Duration 0600. Entrance between An Neudenn Bn Tr to E and three white topped rks to W. Hr, port of Brignogan-Plage, is open to N winds and is often full of fishing boats. Ldg line into Hr, Bn on shore in line with church steeple at 178°. Entry at night forbidden. Facilities: Bar, FW, R, V.

ILE DE BATZ, Finistere, 48°44'·00N, 04°00'·00W, Zone −0100, Admty charts 2745, 3669; SHOM 7095 HW +0610 Dover (GMT), +0055 on Brest (zone −0100) HW height +1·3m on Brest. For Canal de l'Ile de Batz see 10.16.15. Porz-Kernoc'h gives good shelter but dries. E slip is reserved for ferries. Anchor in E or W parts of the channel depending on wind, but holding ground poor. Anchorage prohibited in area W of Roscoff landing slip. Ile de Batz Lt Fl(4) 25s. Facilities: there are a few shops.

CARENTEC, Finistere, 48°40'·00N, 03°55'·00W, Zone −0100, Admty chart 2745, SHOM 7095. HW +0610 on Dover (GMT), +0105 on Brest (zone −0100); HW height +1·2m on Brest; ML 5·0m; Duration 0605. Approach as for Morlaix, (10.16.16) but pass W of Ile Callot. La Penzé Rivière is narrow and tortuous. Yachts can dry out in shelter off Penpoul on the W shore. The anchorage off Carentec is exposed, especially to NW; landing stage dries about 4·6m. Further S the river is not marked but shelter is better SW of Pte de Lingos, or off the old ferry slipways which provide landing places. Beyond the bridge (15m) the river is navigable on the tide for 3M to Penzé. No lights. Facilities: Aff.Mar. ☎ 98.67.03.80; **Centre Nautique Carantec-Henvic** ☎ 98.67.01.12; **Elies** ☎ 98.67.03.61. El, ME, Sh, M; **Marine Service** ☎ 98.67.00.04; Ⓔ, CH; **Comptoirs Maritime** ☎ 98.67.01.85, CH, P, D; **Lebras** ☎ 98.67.04.50, ME, El, Sh; **Town** Ⓑ, Bar, ✉, R, V.

PRIMEL, Finistere, 48°42'·00N, 03°50'·00W, Zone −0100, Admty charts 2745, 3669, SHOM 7095, 7151. HW −0610 on Dover (GMT), +0100 on Brest (zone −0100); HW height +0·9m on Brest; ML 4·8m; Duration 0600. Good deep anchorage well protected; seas break across ent in strong winds. Beware rks off Pte de Primel to E of ent. and Le Zamegues to W. Ldg Lts 152°, front FR 35m 6M; vis 134°−168°, rear, 202m from front, FR 56m 6M; both have framework Tr with W square with R vert stripe. Jetty head Lt Fl G 4s 6m 7M. Anchor in channel in 2 to 9m or go alongside quay (1m). VHF Ch 09 16 (summer). Facilities: Bar, C (12 ton), FW, R. Slip, V; **Rolland Marine** ☎ 98.72.32.76. CH, El, ME, Sh, Ⓔ.

LOCQUEMEAU, Côtes du Nord, 48°43'·00N, 03°34'·00W, Zone −0100, Admty charts 3669, 2668, SHOM 7124. HW −0600 on Dover (GMT), +0110 on Brest (zone −0100); HW height +1·5m on Brest; ML 5·3m. A small drying Hr by ent. to Lannion River. (10.16.17). There are two quays, the outer being accessible at LW, but this quay is open to W winds. Yachts can dry out at inner quay, on S side. Ldg Lts 122°, leading to outer quay, Front FR 21m 6M; vis 068°−228°. Rear 484m from front, Oc (2+1) R 12s 39m 7M. Facilities: **Ateliers Mecaniques de Lannion** ☎ 96.48.72.32 ME, El, Sh; **Town** Bar.

TREBEURDEN, Côtes du Nord, 48°46'·00N, 03°35'·00W; Zone −0100; Admty chart 3669; SHOM 6056. HW −0605 on Dover (GMT), +0105 on Brest (zone −0100); ML 5·3m; Duration 0605. A good safe deep water anchorage in settled weather. Visitors buoys available. Approach from a position 1·5M S of Le Crapaud W cardinal buoy, marking the W end of Le Crapaud (a reef which dries 3·9m). From here make good a course of 065° towards the N end of Ile Milliau, to pass S of Ar Goureudeg S cardinal Lt Buoy VQ(6) + LFl 10s. When past Ar Goureudeg buoy, alter to E and SE, so as to anchor NE of Ile Milliau. Excellent shelter in the marina. LDG LTS Lan Kerellec. Sector LT Iso WRG 4s − keep in W sector. VHF Ch 09 16. Access HW±4. Facilities: Harbour Office ☎ 96.23.66.93; SNSM 96.23.53.82, # ☎ 96.92.31.44; **Marina** (340+10 visitors), FW, AC, P, D; **YC de Trébeurden** ☎ 96.37.00.40 (open July-Aug); **Chantier Naval du Trégor** ☎ 96.23.52.09, BY, ME, El, Sh, CH. A marina is under construction.

TRÉGASTEL, Côtes du Nord, 48°50'·00N, 03°31'·00W, Zone −0100, Admty charts 3669, 3670, SHOM 967. HW −0550 on Dover (GMT), +0005 on Brest (zone −0100); HW height −1·8m on Brest; ML 5·1m; Duration 0605. See 10.16.18. (Ploumanac'h). Good anchorage in 2m but very exposed to winds from W to N. Entrance channel marked by port and stbd Bns. Ldg line at 149°, Pavilion in line with Chapelle St Anne leads between Ile Dhu and Le Taureau. Thence keep between Bns round to S of Ile Ronde to the anchorage. Facilities: Slip; **Club Nautique de Tregastel** ☎ 96.23.45.05; **Neptune Tregastel Marine** ☎ 96.23.46.13 CH. **Town** Bar, Bank, ✉, R, V.

LES SEPT ILES, Côtes du Nord, 48° 52'·80N, 03°29'·50W. Zone −0100. Admty charts 3669, 3670; SHOM 967. HW−0550 on Dover (GMT), +0005 on Brest (zone−0100). HW height −1·8m on Brest. ML 5·2m. All seven islands are a bird sanctuary. Main anchorage between Île aux Moines and Ile Bono. Landing on latter is prohibited. Anchor due E of jetty; below the Old Fort or close to S side of Ile Bono. Lighthouse on Île aux Moines, Grey Tr, Fl (3) 15s 59m 24M, obsc 237°−241° and in Baie de Lannion when bearing less than 039°. There are no facilities.

PORT BLANC, Côtes du Nord, 48°50'·00N, 03°19'·00W, Zone −0100, Admty charts 3672, 3670, SHOM 974, 967. HW −0545 on Dover (GMT), −0040 on St Malo (zone −0100); HW height −2·0m on St Malo; ML 5·3m; Duration 0600. Good natural Hr but exposed to winds between NW and NNE. Ldg marks in line at 150°, Moulin de la Comtesse and Le Voleur Lt; Le Voleur, Fl WRG 4s 17m 14/11M, G140°−148°, W148°−152°, R152°−160°. Yachts can anchor off or dry out alongside quays (known as Port Bago). Facilities: AB, FW on quay, Slip; **Gelgon Nautisme** ☎ 96.92.67.00. CH, El, ME, Sh; **Town** Bar, R, V.

Area 17

Channel Islands
Alderney to Jersey

17

10-17-2

Channel Islands

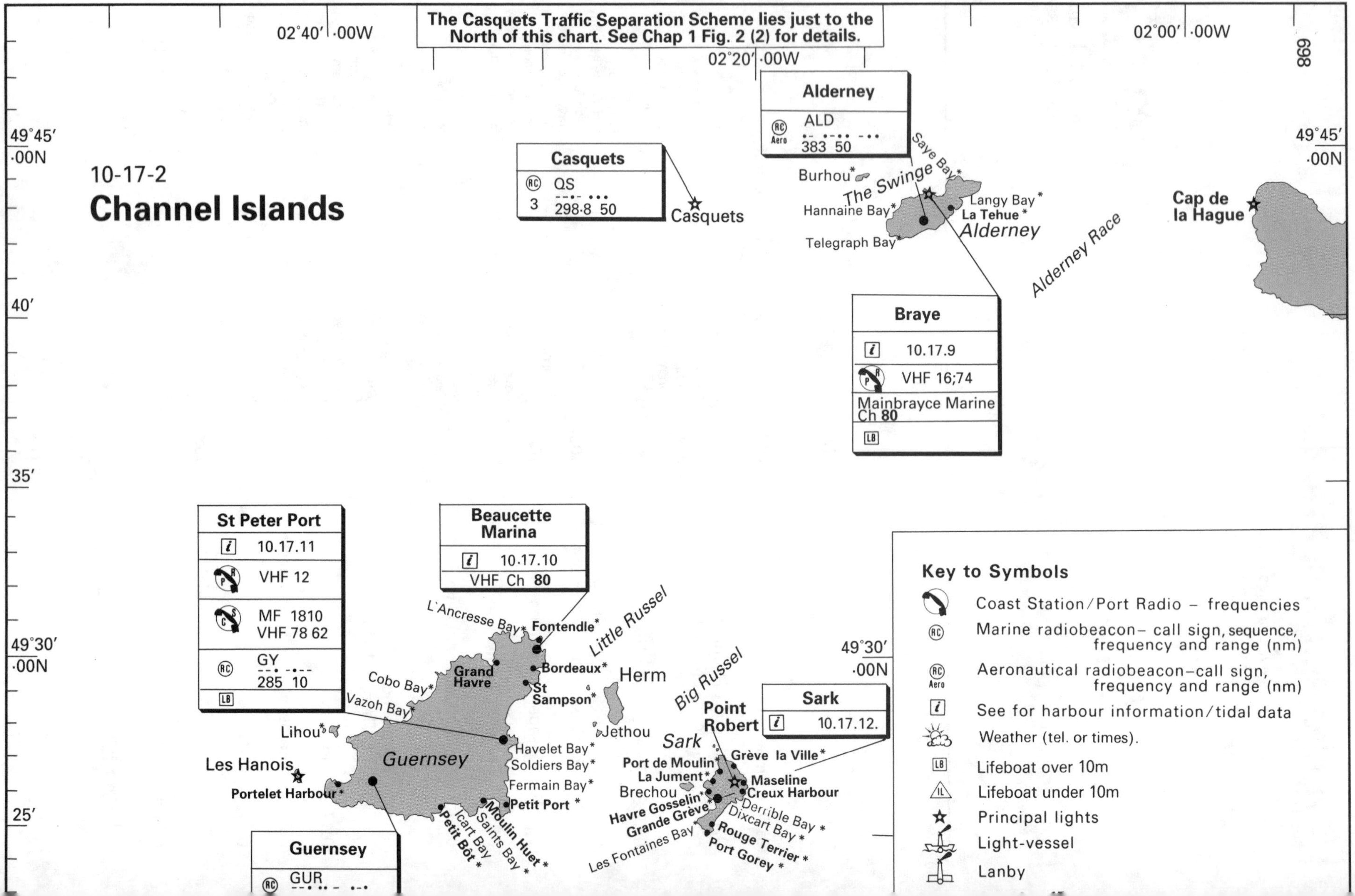
The Casquets Traffic Separation Scheme lies just to the North of this chart. See Chap 1 Fig. 2 (2) for details.
02°40′·00W
02°20′·00W
02°00′·00W
49°45′·00N
40′
35′
49°30′·00N
25′
Casquets
QS
3
298·8 50
Casquets
Alderney
ALD
Aero
383 50
Burhou*
The Swinge
Saye Bay*
Hannaine Bay*
Langy Bay*
La Tehue*
Alderney
Telegraph Bay*
Alderney Race
Cap de la Hague
Braye
10.17.9
VHF 16;74
Mainbrayce Marine Ch 80
LB
St Peter Port
10.17.11
VHF 12
MF 1810
VHF 78 62
GY
285 10
LB
Beaucette Marina
10.17.10
VHF Ch 80
L'Ancresse Bay*
Fontendle*
Little Russel
Grand Havre
Bordeaux*
Herm
Cobo Bay*
St Sampson*
Vazoh Bay*
Jethou
Lihou*
Guernsey
Havelet Bay*
Soldiers Bay*
Fermain Bay*
Petit Port*
Les Hanois
Portelet Harbour*
Icart Bay
Petit Bôt*
Saints Bay*
Moulin Huet*
Guernsey
GUR
Big Russel
Point Robert
Sark
Sark
10.17.12.
Port de Moulin*
La Jument*
Brechou
Havre Gosselin*
Grande Grève
Les Fontaines Bay
Grève la Ville*
Maseline
Creux Harbour
Derrible Bay*
Dixcart Bay*
Rouge Terrier*
Port Gorey*
Key to Symbols
Coast Station/Port Radio – frequencies
Marine radiobeacon– call sign, sequence, frequency and range (nm)
Aeronautical radiobeacon–call sign, frequency and range (nm)
See for harbour information/tidal data
Weather (tel. or times).
Lifeboat over 10m
Lifeboat under 10m
Principal lights
Light-vessel
Lanby

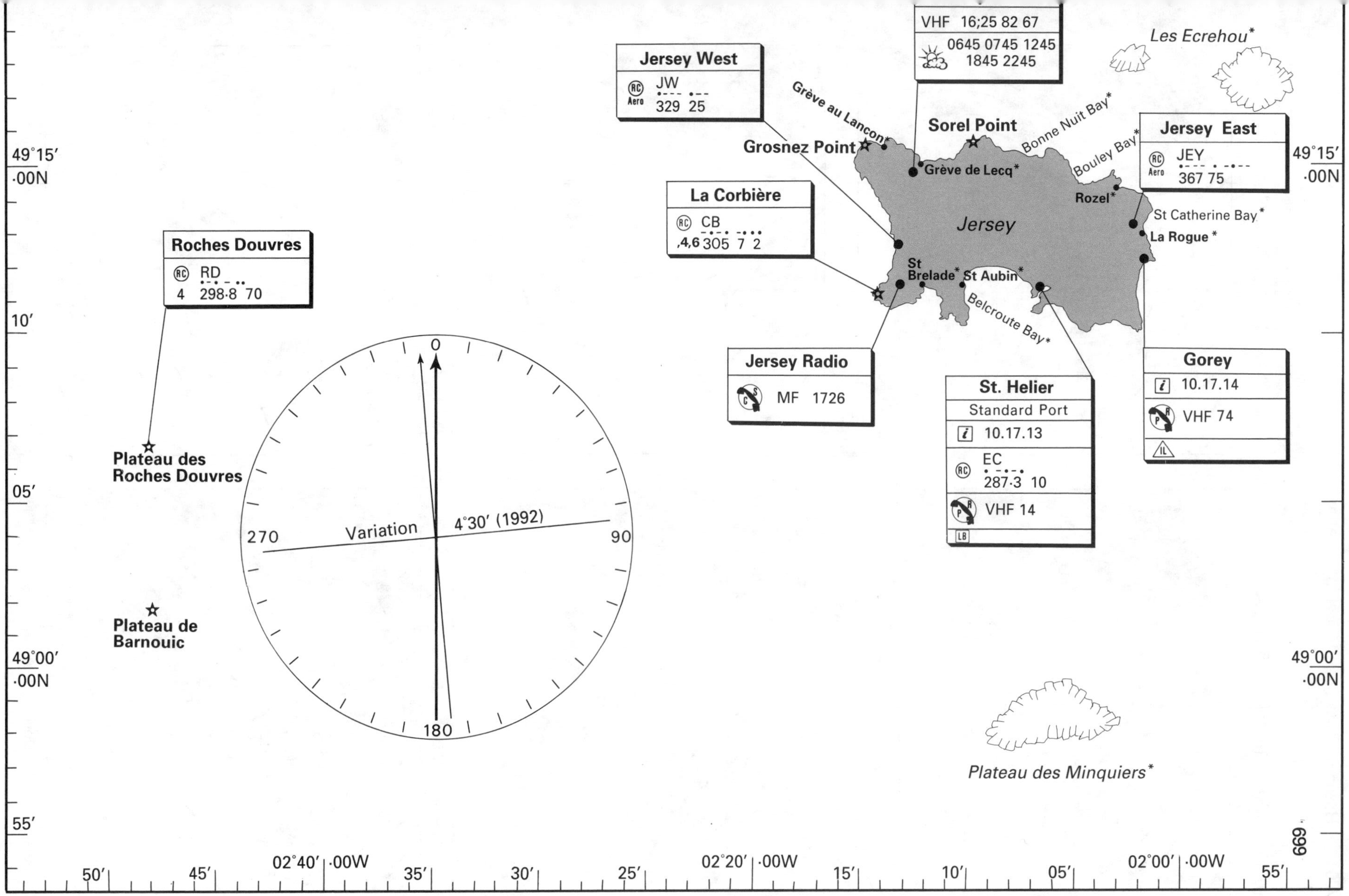

Roches Douvres
RD
4 298·8 70
Plateau des Roches Douvres
Plateau de Barnouic
Jersey West
JW
329 25
La Corbière
CB
,4,6 305 7 2
Grosnez Point
Grève au Lancon*
VHF 16;25 82 67
0645 0745 1245
1845 2245
Sorel Point
Grève de Lecq*
Bonne Nuit Bay*
Bouley Bay*
Rozel*
Jersey
Jersey East
JEY
367 75
Les Ecrehou*
St Catherine Bay*
La Rogue*
St Brelade*
St Aubin*
Belcroute Bay*
Jersey Radio
MF 1726
St. Helier
Standard Port
10.17.13
EC
287·3 10
VHF 14
LB
Gorey
10.17.14
VHF 74
IL
Plateau des Minquiers*
Variation
4°30′ (1992)
0
90
180
270
49°15′ ·00N
10′
05′
49°00′ ·00N
55′
50′
45′
02°40′ ·00W
35′
30′
25′
02°20′ ·00W
15′
10′
05′
02°00′ ·00W
55′

Notes:
1. Due to very strong tidal stream rates, eddies may occur. Where possible some indication of these has been shown, but in many areas there is either insufficient information or the eddies are unstable.
2. For details of tidal streams round Alderney, see NP 264 part 2.

10.17.3 AREA 17 TIDAL STREAMS

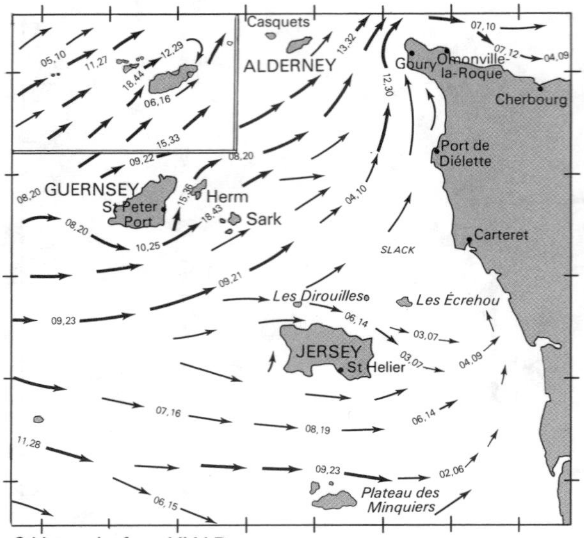
Casquets
ALDERNEY
Goury
Omonville-la-Roque
Cherbourg
Port de Diélette
GUERNSEY
St Peter Port
Herm
Sark
Carteret
SLACK
Les Dirouilles
Les Écrehou
JERSEY
St Helier
Plateau des Minquiers

6 Hours before HW Dover (0100 before HW St. Helier)

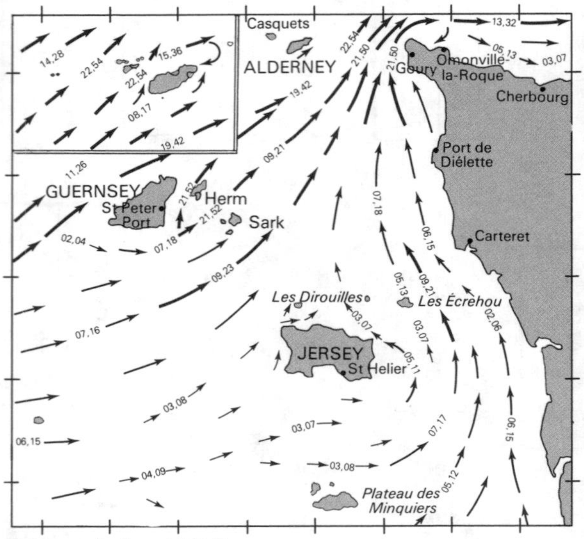
Casquets
ALDERNEY
Goury
Omonville-la-Roque
Cherbourg
Port de Diélette
GUERNSEY
St Peter Port
Herm
Sark
Carteret
Les Dirouilles
Les Écrehou
JERSEY
St Helier
Plateau des Minquiers

5 Hours before HW Dover (HW St. Helier)

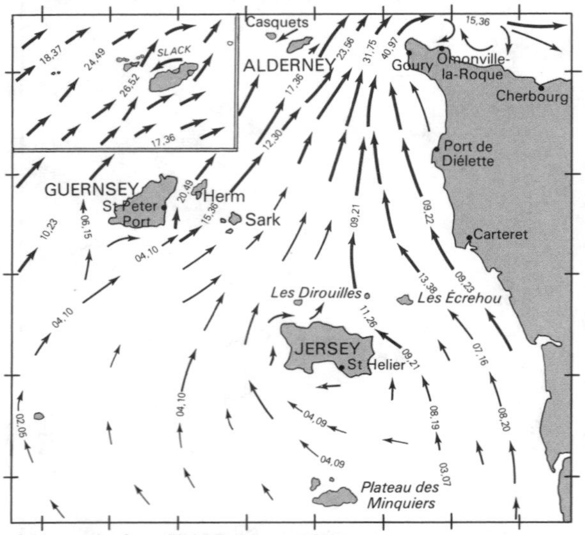
Casquets
SLACK
ALDERNEY
Goury
Omonville-la-Roque
Cherbourg
Port de Diélette
GUERNSEY
St Peter Port
Herm
Sark
Carteret
Les Dirouilles
Les Écrehou
JERSEY
St Helier
Plateau des Minquiers

4 Hours before HW Dover (0100 after HW St. Helier)

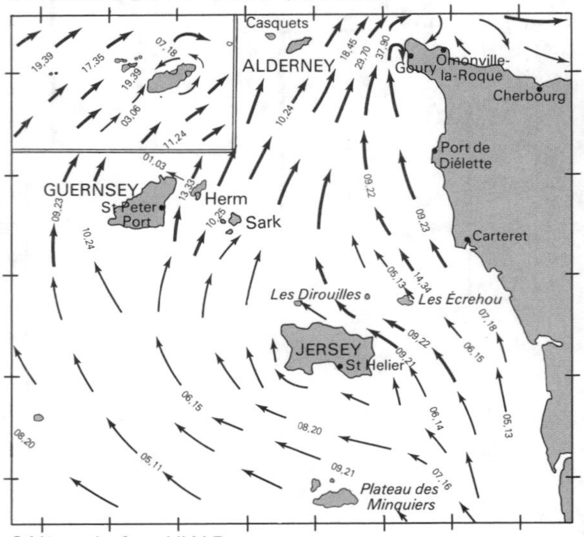
Casquets
ALDERNEY
Goury
Omonville-la-Roque
Cherbourg
Port de Diélette
GUERNSEY
St Peter Port
Herm
Sark
Carteret
Les Dirouilles
Les Écrehou
JERSEY
St Helier
Plateau des Minquiers

3 Hours before HW Dover (0200 after HW St. Helier)

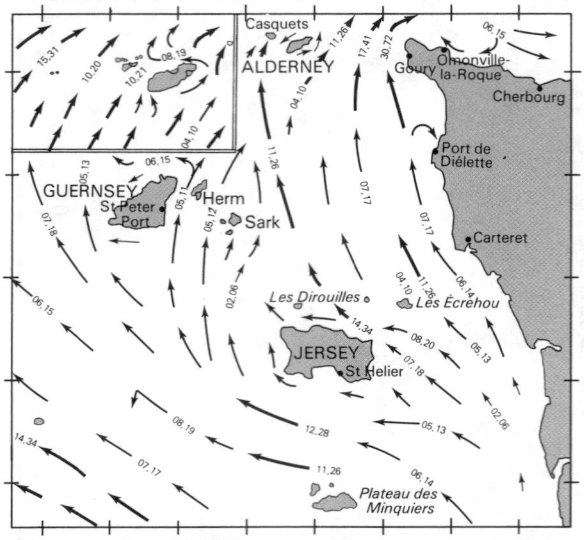
Casquets
ALDERNEY
Goury
Omonville-la-Roque
Cherbourg
Port de Diélette
GUERNSEY
St Peter Port
Herm
Sark
Carteret
Les Dirouilles
Les Écrehou
JERSEY
St Helier
Plateau des Minquiers

2 Hours before HW Dover (0300 after HW St. Helier)

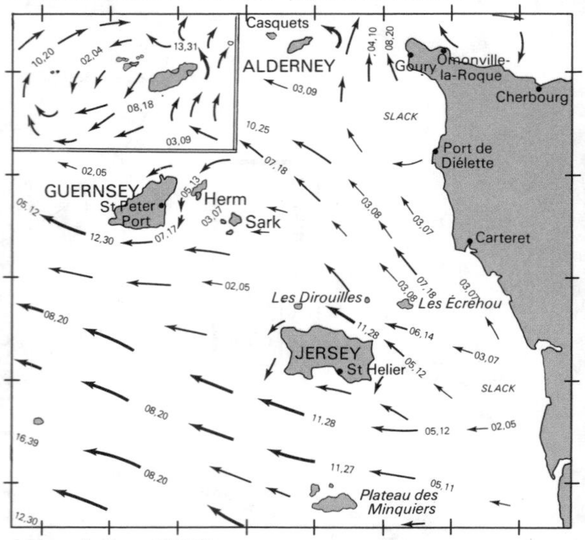
Casquets
ALDERNEY
Goury
Omonville-la-Roque
SLACK
Cherbourg
Port de Diélette
GUERNSEY
St Peter Port
Herm
Sark
Carteret
Les Dirouilles
Les Écrehou
JERSEY
St Helier
SLACK
Plateau des Minquiers

1 Hour before HW Dover (0400 after HW St. Helier)

Northward 10.2.3. Westward 10.16.3. Southward 10.18.3. Isle of Wight 10.2.29. Portland 10.2.10.

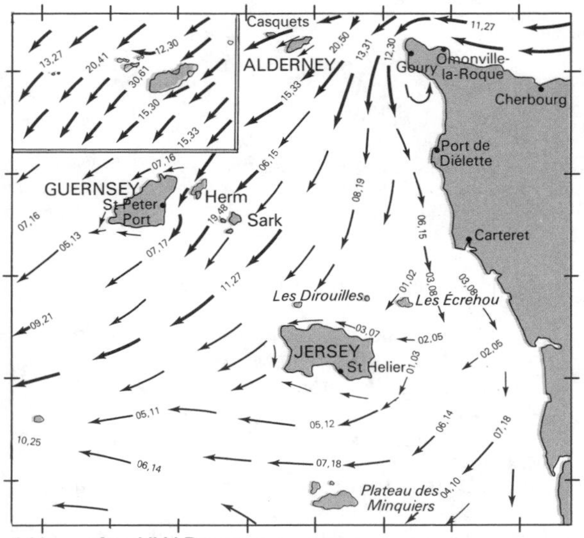
Casquets
ALDERNEY
Goury
Omonville-la-Roque
Cherbourg
Port de Diélette
GUERNSEY
St Peter Port
Herm
Sark
Carteret
Les Dirouilles
Les Écrehou
JERSEY
St Helier
Plateau des Minquiers

1 Hour after HW Dover (0600 after HW St. Helier)

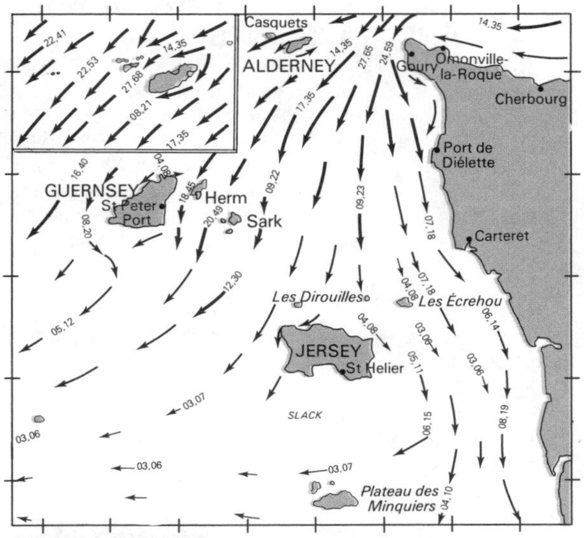
Casquets
ALDERNEY
Goury
Omonville-la-Roque
Cherbourg
Port de Diélette
GUERNSEY
St Peter Port
Herm
Sark
Carteret
Les Dirouilles
Les Écrehou
JERSEY
St Helier
SLACK
Plateau des Minquiers

2 Hours after HW Dover (0530 before HW St. Helier)

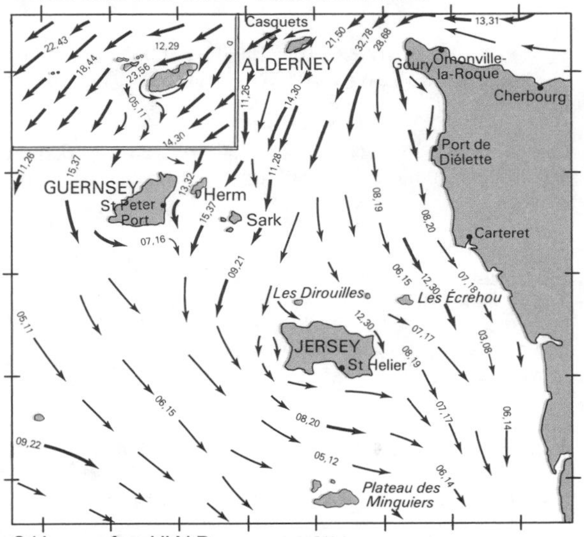
Casquets
ALDERNEY
Goury
Omonville-la-Roque
Cherbourg
Port de Diélette
GUERNSEY
St Peter Port
Herm
Sark
Carteret
Les Dirouilles
Les Écrehou
JERSEY
St Helier
Plateau des Minquiers

3 Hours after HW Dover (0430 before HW St. Helier)

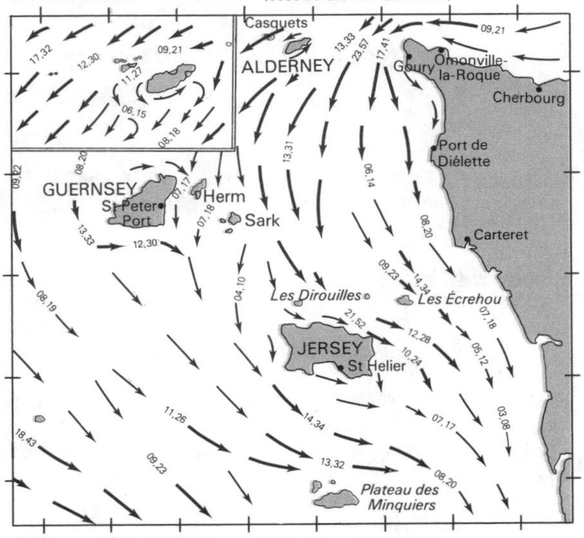
Casquets
ALDERNEY
Goury
Omonville-la-Roque
Cherbourg
Port de Diélette
GUERNSEY
St Peter Port
Herm
Sark
Carteret
Les Dirouilles
Les Écrehou
JERSEY
St Helier
Plateau des Minquiers

4 Hours after HW Dover (0330 before HW St. Helier)

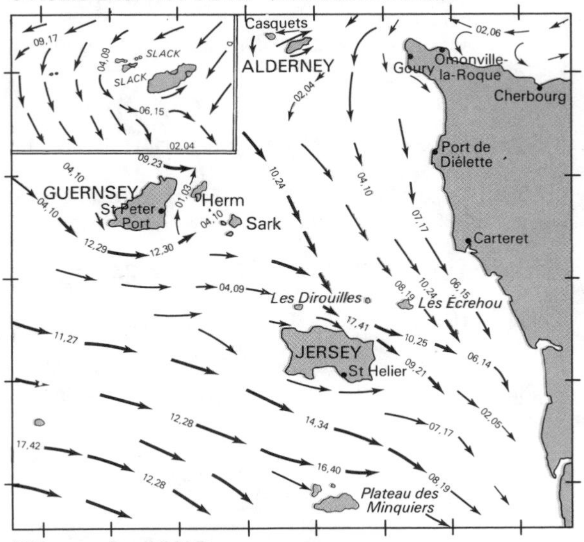
Casquets
ALDERNEY
SLACK
SLACK
Goury
Omonville-la-Roque
Cherbourg
Port de Diélette
GUERNSEY
St Peter Port
Herm
Sark
Carteret
Les Dirouilles
Les Écrehou
JERSEY
St Helier
Plateau des Minquiers

5 Hours after HW Dover (0230 before HW St. Helier)

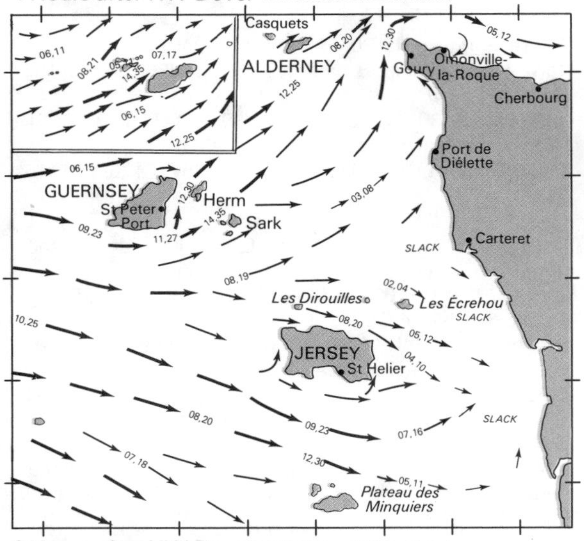
Casquets
ALDERNEY
Goury
Omonville-la-Roque
Cherbourg
Port de Diélette
GUERNSEY
St Peter Port
Herm
Sark
SLACK
Carteret
Les Dirouilles
Les Écrehou
SLACK
JERSEY
St Helier
SLACK
Plateau des Minquiers

6 Hours after HW Dover (0130 before HW St. Helier)

10.17.4 COASTAL LIGHTS, FOG SIGNALS AND WAYPOINTS

Abbreviations used below are given in 1.4.1. Principal lights are in **bold** print, places in CAPITALS, and light-vessels, light floats and Lanbys in *CAPITAL ITALICS*. Unless otherwise stated lights are white. m—elevation in metres; M—nominal range in n. miles. Fog signals are in *italics*. Useful waypoints are underlined – use those on land with care. All geographical positions should be assumed to be approximate. See 4.2.2.

OFFSHORE AIDS

CHANNEL LT V 49°54'·42N 02°53'·67W Fl 15s 12m **25M**; R hull with Lt Tr amidships; RC; Racon; *Horn (1) 20s*.
E. CHANNEL LT BY 49°58'·67N 02°28'·87W Fl Y 5s; X on Y HFP By; Racon; *Horn (2) 30s*.
EC 1 Lt By 50°05'·90N 01°48'·35W Fl Y 2·5s; X on Y HFP By; Racon; *Whis*.
EC 2 Lt By 50°12'·10N 01°12'·40W Fl (4)Y 15s; X on Y HFP By; Racon; *Whis*.
EC 3 Lt By 50°18'·30N 00°36'·10W Fl Y 5s; X on Y HFP By; Racon; *Whis*.

Roches Gautier Lt By 49°00'·05N 02°52'·95W VQ(9) 10s; WCM; *Whis*.

CHANNEL ISLANDS

Casquets 49°43'·38N 02°22'·55W Fl (5) 30s 37m **25M**; W Tr, the highest and NW of three; RC; Racon; *Horn (2) 60s*.

ALDERNEY.
Alderney (Quenard Pt.) 49°43'·81N 02°09'·77W Fl (4) 15s 37m **18M**; W I Tr, B band; vis 085°-027°; *Siren (4) 60s*.
Château à l'Étoc Pt 49°44'·00N 02°10'·55W Iso WR 4s 20m W10M, R7M; W col; vis R071·1°-111·1°, W111·1°-151·1°; in line 111·1° with main Lt.
Braye Harbour 49°43'·46N 02°11'·83W Ldg Lts 215°. **Front**, elbow of old pier Q 8m **17M**; vis 210°-220°. **Rear** 335m from front Iso 10s 17m **18M**; vis 210°-220°. Both metal posts on W cols.
Quay Head FY.

LITTLE RUSSEL CHANNEL

Platte Fougère 49°30'·88N 02°29'·05W Fl WR 10s 15m **16M**; W 8-sided Tr, B band; vis W155°-085°, R085°-155°; Racon; *Horn 45s*.
Tautenay 49°30'·17N 02°26'·74W Q (3) WR 6s 7m W7M, R6M; B and W Bn; vis W050°-215°, R215°-050°.
Petite Canupe Lt Bn 49°30'·25N 02°29'·05W Qk (6) + L Fl 15s; SCM.

Roustel 49°29'·28N 02°28'·71W Q 8m 7M; B and W chequered Tr, G lantern.
Platte 49°29'·15N 02°29'·50W Fl WR 3s 6m W7M, R5M; G Tr; vis R024°-219°, W219°-024°.
Brehon 49°28'·34N 02°29'·20W Iso 4s 19m 9M; Bn on● Tr.

GUERNSEY

BEAUCETTE MARINA.
Ldg Lts 276°. Front FR 49°30'·25N 02°30'·13W; W board with R stripe. Rear 185m from front FR; R board with W stripe.

ST SAMPSON.
Crocq Pier FR 11m 5M; R col; vis 250°-340°; tfc signals.
N Pier Hd FG 3m 5M; vis 230°-340°.
Ldg Lts 286°. Front S Pier Hd 49°28'·97N 02°30'·66W FR 3m 5M; vis 230°-340°. Rear, 390m from front FG 13m; clock Tr. 2 FR (vert) on chimneys 300m N.

ST PETER PORT.
Reffée Lt By 49°27'·80N 02°31'·18W VQ (6) + LFl 10s; SCM.
Ldg Lts 220°. **Front**, Castle Breakwater Hd 49°27'·36N 02°31'·34W Al WR 10s 14m **16M**; dark● Tr, W on NE side; vis 187°-007°; RC; *Horn 15s*. Rear Belvedere Oc 10s 61m 14M; W ■ with Y stripe on W Tr; vis 179°-269°.
White Rock Pier Hd 49°27'·43N 02°31'·60W Oc G 5s 11m 14M; ● stone Tr; intens 174°-354°.
S Pier Hd Oc R 5s 10m 14M; W framework Tr, R lantern.
Queen Elizabeth II Marina 49°27'·79N 02°31'·78W. Dir Lt 270° Dir Oc WRG 10s 5m 6M; vis G258°-268°, W268°-272°, R272°-282°.

St Martin's Pt 49°25'·37N 02°31'·61W Fl (3) WR 10s 15m 14M; flat-roofed, W bldg; vis R185°-191°, W191°-011°, R011°-081°. Horn *(3) 30s*.

Les Hanois 49°26'·16N 02°42'·02W Q (2) 5s 33m **23M**; grey ●Tr, B lantern, helicopter platform; vis 294°-237°; 4 FR on masts 1·27M ESE; *Horn (2) 60s*.

BIG RUSSEL.
Noire Pute 49°28'·27N 02°24'·93W Fl (2) WR 15s 8m 6M; vis W220°-040°, R040°-220°. Destroyed (T).
Fourquies Lt By 49°27'·34N 02°26'·47W Q; NCM.
Lower Heads Lt By 49°25'·91N 02°28'·48W Q (6) + LFl 15s; SCM; *Bell*.

HERM.
Alligande 49°27'·91N 02°28'·69W Fl 3) G 5s; Or A on B mast; shown 1/4-1/11; Ra refl.
Épec Bn 49°28'·04N 02°27'·81W Fl G 3s; B E on G mast; shown 1/4-1/11.
Vermerette Bn 49°28'·18N 02°27'·67W Fl (2) Y 5s; Or V on Bn; shown 1/4-1/11.
Percée Pass, Gate Rock 49°27'·94N 02°27'·44W Q (9)15s; WCM Bn.

SARK.
Courbée du Nez 49°27'·15N 02°22'·08W Fl (4) WR 15s 14m 8M; vis W057°-230°, R230°-057°.
Pt Robert 49°26'·25N 02°20'·67W Fl 15s 65m **28M**; W 8-sided Tr; vis 138°-353°; *Horn (2) 60s*.

Blanchard Lt By 49°25'·42N 02°17'·35W Q (3) 10s; ECM; *Bell*.
Monument (100) 49°25'·78N 02°22'·35W and Sark Mill (116) in line 070° (both unlit).

Desormes Lt By 49°19'·00N 02°17'·90W Q (9) 15s; WCM.

JERSEY.

<u>Grosnez Pt</u> 49°15'·55N 02°14'·75W Fl (2) WR 15s 50m **W19M**, **R17M**; W hut; vis W081°-188°, R188°-241°.
<u>La Corbière</u> 49°10'·85N 02°14'·90W Iso WR 10s 36m **W18M**, **R16M**; ● stone Tr; vis W shore-294°, R294°-328°, W328°-148°, R148°-shore; RC; *Horn Mo (C) 60s.*

WESTERN PASSAGE.
Ldg Lts 082°. <u>Front La Gréve d'Azette</u> 49°10'·21N 02°05'·00W Oc 5s 23m 14M; vis 034°-129°. Rear, Mont Ubé 1M from front Oc R 5s 46m 12M; vis 250°-095°; Racon.
Noirmont Pt 49°09'·97N 02°09'·94W Fl (4) 12s 18m 13M; B Tr, W band.
<u>Passage Rk Lt By</u> 49°09'·59N 02°12'·18W VQ Fl; NCM.
<u>Les Fours Lt By</u> 49°09'·65N 02°10'·08W Q Fl G; SHM.
<u>Ruaudière Rk Lt By</u> 49°09'·80N 02°08'·51W Fl G 3s; SHM; *Bell.*

SAINT AUBIN HARBOUR.
North Pier Hd 49°11'·28N 02°09'·94W Iso R 4s 12m 10M; and Dir Lt 252° Dir F WRG 5m, vis G246°-251°, W251°-253°, R253°-258°.
Fort Pier Hd Fl (2) Y 5s 8m 1M.

ST HELIER.
Small Roads Ldg Lts 022·7°. Front, Albert Pier 49°10'·81N 02°06'·78W Oc G 5s 8m 11M; W bracket and lantern on sea wall. Rear, esplanade 576m from front Oc R 5s 20m 12M; R stripe on W framework Tr; synchronised with front.
<u>Platte Rock</u> 49°10'·22N 02°07'·27W Fl R 1·5s 6m 5M; R framework Tr.
Ldg Lts 078°. Front FG. Rear, 90m from front, FG; both W cols.
Victoria Pier Hd *Bell;* in reply to vessels' fog signals; tfc signals.

<u>Demie de Pas</u> 49°09'·07N 02°06'·05W Mo(D) WR 12s 11m W14M, R10M; B Tr, Y top; vis R130°-303°, W303°-130°; Racon; *Horn (3) 60s.*
<u>Canger Rock Lt By</u> 49°07'·41N 02°00'·30W Q (9) 15s; WCM.
<u>Frouquier Aubert Lt By</u> 49°06'·14N 01°58'·78W Q (6) + LFl 15s; SSM.
<u>Violet Lt By</u> 49°07'·87N 01°57'·05W LFl 10s; SWM.

GOREY.
Ldg Lts 298°. Front, Pier Hd 49°11'·86N 02°01'·25W Oc RG 5s 8m 12M; W framework Tr; vis R304°-352°, G352°-304°. Rear 490m from front Oc R 5s 24m 8M.

ST CATHERINE BAY.
<u>Verclut breakwater Hd</u> 49°13'·39N 02°00'·57W Fl 1·5s 18m 13M; framework Tr.

ROZEL BAY
Dir Lt 245° 49°14'·27N 02°02'·68W Dir F WRG 11m 5M; vis G240°-244°, W244°-246°, R246°-250°.

BONNE NUIT BAY.
Ldg Lts 223°. Front Pier Hd 49°15'·17N 02°07'·08W FG 7m 6M. Rear, 170m from front FG 34m 6M.

<u>Sorel Pt</u> 49°15'·64N 02°09'·45W L Fl WR 7·5s 50m **15M**; B and W chequered ●Tr; vis W095°-112°, R112°-173°, W173°-230°, R230°-269°, W269°-273°.

PLATEAU DES MINQUIERS.
<u>NW Minquiers Lt By</u> 48°59'·70N 02°20'·50W Q; NCM; *Bell.*
<u>Demi de Vascelin By</u> 49°00'·08N 02°05'·10W; SHM; (unlit).
<u>N Minquiers Lt By</u> 49°01'·70N 02°00'·50W Q; NCM.
<u>NE Minquiers Lt By</u> 49°00'·90N 01°55'·20W VQ (3) 5s; ECM; *Bell.*
<u>SW Minquiers Lt By</u> 48°54'·40N 02°19'·30W Q (9) 15s; WCM; *Whis.*
<u>S Minquiers Lt By</u> 48°53'·15N 02°10'·00W Q (6) + LFl 15s; SCM.
<u>SE Minquiers Lt By</u> 48°53'·50N 02°00'·00W Q (3) 10s; ECM; *Bell.*

Note. For English Channel Waypoints see 10.1.7

10.17.5 PASSAGE INFORMATION

Sailing Directions for this popular cruising area are listed in Chapter 15 (15.5.5) of *The Macmillan & Silk Cut Yachtsman's Handbook*. Particular features are a rugged shoreline with sandy bays, numerous offlying rks, strong tidal streams, and a big range of tide. It is important to have large scale charts, and to use recognised leading marks (of which there are plenty) when entering or leaving many of the hbrs and anchs.

Neap tides are best, particularly for a first visit, and tidal streams need to be worked carefully. Boats which can take the ground have an advantage for exploring the quieter hbrs. Be careful to avoid lobster pots, and oyster beds.

CHANNEL ISLANDS – GENERAL (10.17.8 and chart 2669)

For detailed instructions, refer to sailing directions. In the following paragraphs brief mention is made only of some of the most important navigational features.

Apart from the main hbrs described in 10.17.9 – 10.17.14, there are many delightful minor hbrs & anchs. 10.17.15. In the very nature of islands a lee can usually be found somewhere.

Approaching the islands from N, note the Traffic Separation Scheme off the Casquets – see Fig. 2(2); soundings of Hurd Deep can help navigation. Seen from the W, Guernsey slopes down from S to N, and Jersey from N to S. Individually and collectively the islands are fringed by many rky dangers: there is considerable range of tide (most in Jersey, and least in Alderney), and the streams run very hard through the chans and around headlands; strong W winds cause a heavy sea, usually worst from local HW –0300 to local HW +0300. In bad vis it is prudent to stay in hbr.

Tidal streams are rotatory anti-clockwise, particularly in open water and in wider chans. The E-going (flood) stream is of less duration than the W-going, but is stronger. The islands lie across the main direction of the streams, so eddies are common along the shores.

THE CASQUETS AND ALDERNEY (chart 60)

Casquets Lt Ho (Lt, fog sig, RC) is on the largest Is of this group of rks 5·5M W of Alderney (10.17.9). Off-lying dangers extend 0·4M W and WSW (The Ledge and Noire Roque) and 0·4M E (Pte Colotte). The tide runs very hard round and between these various obstructions. A shallow bank, on which are situated Fourquie and l'Equet rks (dry), lies from 0·5M to 1M E of Casquets, and should not be approached. 3·5M E of Casquets is Ortac rk (24m). Ortac chan runs N/S 0·5M W of Ortac: here the stream begins to run NE at HW St Helier –0230, and SW at HW St Helier +0355, with sp rates 7 kn. Ortac chan should not be used in bad weather, when there are very heavy overfalls in this area. In the approaches to Casquets, overfalls may also be met over Eight-fathom Ledge (0·85M W of Casquets), Casquets SW bank, Casquets SSW bank, and Casquets SSE bank.

The Swinge lies between Burhou with its bordering rks, and the NW coast of Alderney. It can be a dangerous chan, and should only be used in reasonable vis and fair weather. The tide runs very hard, and in strong or gale force winds from S or W there are very heavy overfalls on the SW- going stream between Ortac and Les Etacs (off W end of Alderney). In strong E winds, on the NE-going stream, overfalls occur between Burhou and Braye breakwater. These overfalls can mostly be avoided by choosing the best time and route (see below), but due to the uneven bottom and strong tides broken water may be met even in calm conditions.

The NE-going stream begins at HW St Helier –0245, and the SW stream at HW St Helier +0340, sp rates 7 or 8 kn. On the NE-going stream, beware the very strong northerly set in vicinity of Ortac.

On N side of the Swinge the main dangers are Boues des Kaines, almost awash at LW about 0·75M ESE of Ortac, and North Rk 0·25M SE of Burhou. On S side of the Swinge beware Pierre au Vraic (dries) almost in the fairway 1·75M S of Ortac, Barsier Rk (dries) 0·35M NNW of Fort Clonque, and Corbet Rk with outliers 0·5M N of Fort Clonque.

Heading NE, avoid the worst overfalls in W-going tide by keeping near SE side of chan. Great Nannel in transit with E end of Burhou clears Pierre au Vraic to the E, but passes close W of Les Etacs. On this transit when Roque Tourgis fort is abeam, alter slightly to stbd to pass 0·1M NW of Corbet Rk.

The best time to pass SW through the Swinge is when the NE-going stream slackens at about HW St Helier +0400, when the reverse route to that described above should be followed. But after HW St Helier +0500 keep close to Burhou and Ortac, avoiding North Rk and Boues des Kaines, to clear the worst of the overfalls.

Burhou, Saye B, Corblet B, Longy B, La Tchue, Telegraph B and Hannaine B, (10.17.15) all provide anchs and a degree of shelter under different conditions.

THE ALDERNEY RACE (chart 3653)

The Alderney Race, so called due to very strong tidal streams, runs NE/SW between Alderney and C de la Hague. The fairway, approx 4M wide, is bounded by Race Rk and Alderney S Banks to the NW, and to the SE by rky banks 4M WSW of C de la Hague, Milieu and Banc de la Schôle (least depth 2·7m). These dangers which cause breaking seas and heavy overfalls should be carefully avoided. In bad weather and strong wind-against-tide conditions the seas break in all parts of the Race and passage is not recommended. Conditions are exacerbated at sp tides.

In mid-chan the NE going stream starts at HW St Helier -0210 (HW Dover +0530) and the SW stream at HW St Helier +0430 (HW Dover), sp rates both 5·5 kn. The times at which stream turns do not vary much for various places, but the rates do; for example, 1M W of C de la Hague the sp rates are 7 or 8 kn.

To obtain optimum conditions, timing is of the essence. As a rule of thumb the Race should be entered at about slack water so as to avoid the peak tidal stream with attendant overfalls/seas.

Thus, bound SW, arrrive at around HW St Helier +0430 (HW Dover) off C de la Hague when the stream will be slack, whilst just starting to run SW off Alderney. A yacht leaving Cherbourg at HW Dover -0300 will achieve the above timing by utilising the inshore W-going tidal eddy.

Conversely, NE bound, the Race can be entered N of Banc de la Schôle at about slack water (HW St Helier +0400) by leaving St Peter Port at approx HW St Helier +0030 with last of fair tide. An earlier departure will achieve a faster passage, but possibly less favourable conditions in the Race. On the NE stream the worst overfalls are on the French side.

APPROACHES TO GUERNSEY (charts 808, 3654)

The Little Russel between Guernsey and Herm (chart 808) gives the most convenient access to/from N for Beaucette Marina (10.17.10) and St Peter Port (10.17.11). But it needs care, due to rks which fringe the chan and appr, and the strong tide which also sets across the ent. The Big Russel is wider and easier. Doyle Passage, which runs on a line 146°/326° off Doyle Point, can be used with local knowledge by day.

In mid chan, S of Platte and NW of Brehon, the NE-going stream begins at HW St Helier –0250, and the SW stream at HW St Helier +0325, sp rates both 5·25 kn which can cause a very steep sea with wind against tide.

With Lts on Platte Fougère, Tautenay, Roustel, Platte and Bréhon, plus the Ldg Lts (220°) for St Peter Port, the Little Russel can be navigated day or night in reasonable vis, even at LW.

In bad weather or in poor vis it is better to approach St Peter Port from the S via the Big Russel or, round St Martin's Pt, which is the natural route when coming from S or W. In onshore winds keep well clear of the W coast of Guernsey, where in bad weather the sea breaks on dangers up to 4M from land .

The minor hbrs and anchs (10.17.15) on the E coast include Bordeaux, St Sampson, Havelet B, Soldiers B and Fermain B. On the S coast Moulin Huet B and Icart B provide good anch in N & E winds. Portelet hbr and Lihou Is on the W coast and Grande Havrè, L'Ancresse and Fontenelle B on the N coast also provide shelter.

HERM AND JETHOU (Charts 807, 808).

Herm and Jethou (10.17.15) can be approached from the Little Russel via any of 7 passages which require reasonable vis and care with tidal streams. The appr from the Big Russel is more open and leads easily to anchs at Belvoir Bay and Shell Bay.

SARK (Chart 808)

Whatever the wind direction, there is usually a sheltered anch in the lee of the Is; on the NW coast Port a La Jument and Port du Moulin (10.17.15) in Banquette B provide some shelter from the S and E. La Grève de la Ville, La Maseline and Creux hbr (10.17.12) have landing places with different degrees of protection on the E coast. Derrible B, Dixcart B and Rouge Terrier (10.17.15) are anchs on the SE coast. Port Gorey, Les Fontaines B, La Grande Grève and Havre Gosselin are all on the W coast.

JERSEY (charts 3655, 1136, 1137, 1138)

To N and NE of Jersey, Les Pierres de Lecq, Les Dirouilles and Les Ecrehou are groups of drying rks, 2-4M offshore. Coming from N, a convenient landfall is Desormes W CM Lt By, 4M NNW of Grosnez Pt. Keep 0·75M clear of La Corbière Lt, SE of which begins the Western Passage (buoyed) leading E past Noirmont Pt towards St Helier.

In St Ouen B on the W coast there are no good anchorages except to the NW of La Rocco Tr which is sheltered from offshore winds. On the S coast St Brelade B and St Aubin (10.17.15) to the W of St Helier provide different degrees of shelter.

Around the SE point of Jersey runs the Violet channel (chart 1138). Although buoyed it is not easy, and should be avoided in bad weather or poor vis. There are dangers to seaward of this chan.

Les Minquiers (10.17.15) also have an exposed anch which should only be approached with extreme caution and in good weather.

10.17.6 DISTANCE TABLE

Approximate distances in nautical miles are by the most direct route while avoiding dangers and allowing for Traffic Separation Schemes, etc. Places in *italics* are in adjoining areas.

1. *Le Four*	**1**																			
2. *Ile de Batz*	37	**2**																		
3. *Roches Douvres*	89	52	**3**																	
4. *Lezardrieux*	88	49	22	**4**																
5. *St Quay-Portrieux*	100	63	28	21	**5**															
6. Casquets	120	90	43	65	71	**6**														
7. Alderney (Braye)	133	96	46	68	73	8	**7**													
8. Beaucette	118	78	29	52	55	15	19	**8**												
9. St Peter Port	114	74	25	48	51	18	23	4	**9**											
10. Les Hanois	105	67	20	42	48	23	29	14	10	**10**										
11. Sark (Creux)	121	82	27	38	51	18	22	11	10	16	**11**									
12. St Helier	119	82	30	47	44	43	46	33	29	32	24	**12**								
13. *St Malo*	122	83	42	49	35	70	73	58	54	56	52	39	**13**							
14. *Granville*	134	97	51	54	54	63	66	59	55	58	50	30	23	**14**						
15. *Carteret*	132	95	44	68	64	32	28	34	31	37	23	26	38	38	**15**					
16. *Cap de la Hague*	139	102	50	74	74	17	9	25	28	35	23	45	73	61	23	**16**				
17. *Cherbourg*	153	116	64	88	88	31	23	39	42	49	37	59	87	75	37	14	**17**			
18. *Start Point*	113	90	76	95	103	57	67	66	70	61	72	93	117	120	89	77	91	**18**		
19. *Portland Bill*	153	125	87	113	115	48	49	62	66	67	66	91	118	111	75	52	62	49	**19**	
20. *Needles*	178	149	108	132	132	64	62	78	82	86	82	103	131	119	81	59	61	84	35	**20**

SPECIAL NOTES FOR THE CHANNEL ISLANDS

10-17-8

The Channel Islands (Jersey, Guernsey, Alderney, Sark and other small islands) lie, not in the Channel, but in the Bay of St. Malo. Alderney is part of the Bailiwick of Guernsey and the States of Alderney have seats in the States of Guernsey. Brecqhou belongs to Sark which in turn with Herm and Jethou are part of Guernsey. Although the eastern ends of Jersey (15 miles) and Alderney (8½ miles) are close to France, the Channel Islands have never been French. They were part of Normandy and became British with William of Normandy, William the Conqueror in 1066. The French call them the Iles Anglo-Normandes (Jersey, Guernsey, Aurigny and Sercq).

The Islands are British but are not part of the United Kingdom. They are self governing and have their own customs regulations and laws. No special documentation is needed for British yachts entering Channel Island ports but they will be subject to customs formalities on return to U.K. Yachts going to France need the normal documentation (passports etc.) and British yachts returning to the Channel Islands from France, must, like all French yachts, wear the Q flag. (It is advisable to do so when arriving from U.K., but not mandatory, except in Alderney). All Channel Islands have a reciprocal medical arrangement with U.K.

Customs and Immigration clearance formalities are carried out at St. Helier and Gorey (Jersey), St Peter Port, St Sampson and Beaucette (Guernsey) and Braye (Alderney). Unlike U.K., there are no coastguards but lifeboats are stationed at St Helier, St Catherines (Jersey), St Peter Port (Guernsey) and Braye (Alderney). Sea Rescue operations are directed by the Harbourmasters of Jersey (for the Southern Area) and Guernsey (for the Northern Area), via Jersey Radio and St Peter Port Radio respectively. Major incidents have additional co-ordination via CROSSMA Joburg and Falmouth Coastguard MRCCs.

The main problems around the Channel Islands are steep seas which get up very quickly, overfalls, fog and thick weather and the very large tidal range.

CURRENCY

Currency is interchangeable, with UK currency except in coin. Using channel island notes on return to UK is not always popular! Postage stamps, issued by Jersey, Guernsey and Alderney must be used in the appropriate island. There is only one class of post and it is cheaper than UK.

TELEPHONES

All channel islands are linked to the UK telephone system. The codes are Alderney 0481, Guernsey 0481, Sark 048 183, Jersey 0534.

COURTESY FLAGS

Further to 6.4.6, many yachts fly a courtesy flag in channel island ports as a mark of politeness but it not de rigeur. The local flags are:-

Jersey White flag with red diagonal cross, with the Jersey Royal Arms (three lions passant with gold crown above) in the canton.

Guernsey Red ensign with Duke William's cross in the fly. Vessels owned by Guernsey residents may wear this ensign.

Sark The English (St George's) flag with the Normandy arms in the canton.

Alderndey The English (St George's) flag and in the centre a green disc charged with a gold lion.

Herm The English (St George's) flag, and in the canton the Arms of Herm (three cowled monks on a gold diagonal stripe between blue triangles containing a silver dolphin).

CARS

Cars can be hired in Jersey, Guernsey and Alderney. All cars are forbidden in Sark.

ANIMALS

The rules regarding animals are as strict as they are in UK. Landing of animals is permitted only from boats from UK, Ireland, Isle of Man or other channel islands but not if the boat has visited France. Unless express permission is granted by a Revenue Officer, no vessel may lie alongside a pontoon or quay with an animal on board.

BRAYE 10-17-9

Alderney (Channel Islands)

CHARTS
Admiralty 2845, 60, 3653, 2669, SHOM 6934, 828, ECM 1014; Stanford 16; Imray C33A

TIDES
−0400 Dover; ML 3·6; Duration 0545; Zone 0 (GMT).

Standard Port ST HELIER (⟶)

Times				Height (metres)			
HW		LW		MHWS	MHWN	MLWN	MLWS
0300	0900	0200	0900	11·1	8·1	4·1	1·3
1500	2100	1400	2100				
Differences BRAYE							
+0050	+0040	+0025	+0105	−4·8	−3·4	−1·5	−0·5

SHELTER
Good shelter in Braye (Alderney) Harbour except in strong N and NE winds. There are 80 visitors' yellow mooring buoys in the western part of the harbour and the area near Fort Albert. Anchorage in harbour is good, but keep clear of the jetty because of steamer traffic. Landing on Admiralty Pier is forbidden. The old derelict length of pier extending in NE direction has been removed. There is a FY Lt on end of remaining quay, as shown. Harbour speed limit 4 kn.

NAVIGATION
Waypoint 49°44′·32N 02°10′·90W, 035°/215° from/to front Ldg Lt 215°, 1·05M. The principal dangers are the strong tidal streams, but the N coast of Alderney is covered with detached rocks. The safest approach is from the NE. Beware the Swinge and Alderney Race (see 10.17.5). In harbour entrance, beware the breakwater submerged extension.

LIGHTS AND MARKS
Clearing line for the Nannels:
N side of Fort Albert and end of Admiralty Pier 115°.
Ldg Lts 215° lead into harbour. Front Q 8m 17M vis 210°-220° Rear Iso 10s 17m 18M vis 210°-220°
Daymarks — St Anne's church spire in line with W beacon on Douglas Quay at 210°
There is a sector Lt at Çhateau à l'Etoc Pt E of the harbour, Iso WR 4s; vis R071°-111°, W111°-151°. This is in line 111° with the Quenard Pt Lt Ho Fl (4) 15s.
Lt buoys QR and QG mark fairway.

RADIO TELEPHONE
Call: *Alderney Radio* VHF Ch 16; 74 (Nov-Mar 0800-1700, Apl, May and mid Sept to end Oct 0800-1800; June to mid Sept 0800-2200: all LT). Outside these hours call St Peter Port. Mainbrayce Marine Ch **80** 37 (Apl-mid Sept: 0800-2000 LT). For Casquets traffic scheme see Cherbourg (10.18.19).

TELEPHONE (0481)
Hr Mr 822620; ⩩ 822620; Marinecall 0898 500 457; Police 822731; Dr 822077; Ⓗ 822822.

FACILITIES
EC Wednesday; **Marine Engine Services** ☎ 823586, ME, El, Sh; **Mainbrayce** ☎ 822772, Slip, D, FW, ME, El, Ⓔ, Gas, SM, ACA, Sh, CH, P, D (inner harbour HW∓2); (For Water Taxi service, call Mainbrayce on Ch 16 **80** 37); **Harbour** M, FW, C, ⊡; **Jetty** FW; **Sapper Slip** Slip, FW; **Alderney SC** ☎ 822758, Bar; **Riduna Garage** ☎ 822919, P, D (cans), Gaz, Gas, Kos. **Blanchard's Building Supplies** ☎ 822722 P and D (cans), Gas; **Town** V, R, ⊡, Bar. ✉; Ⓑ; ✈ — to Guernsey, Jersey, Hurn, Southampton or Cherbourg
Ferry UK — via Guernsey—Weymouth/Poole (Direct to Torquay, Tuesdays mid-June—early Sept).

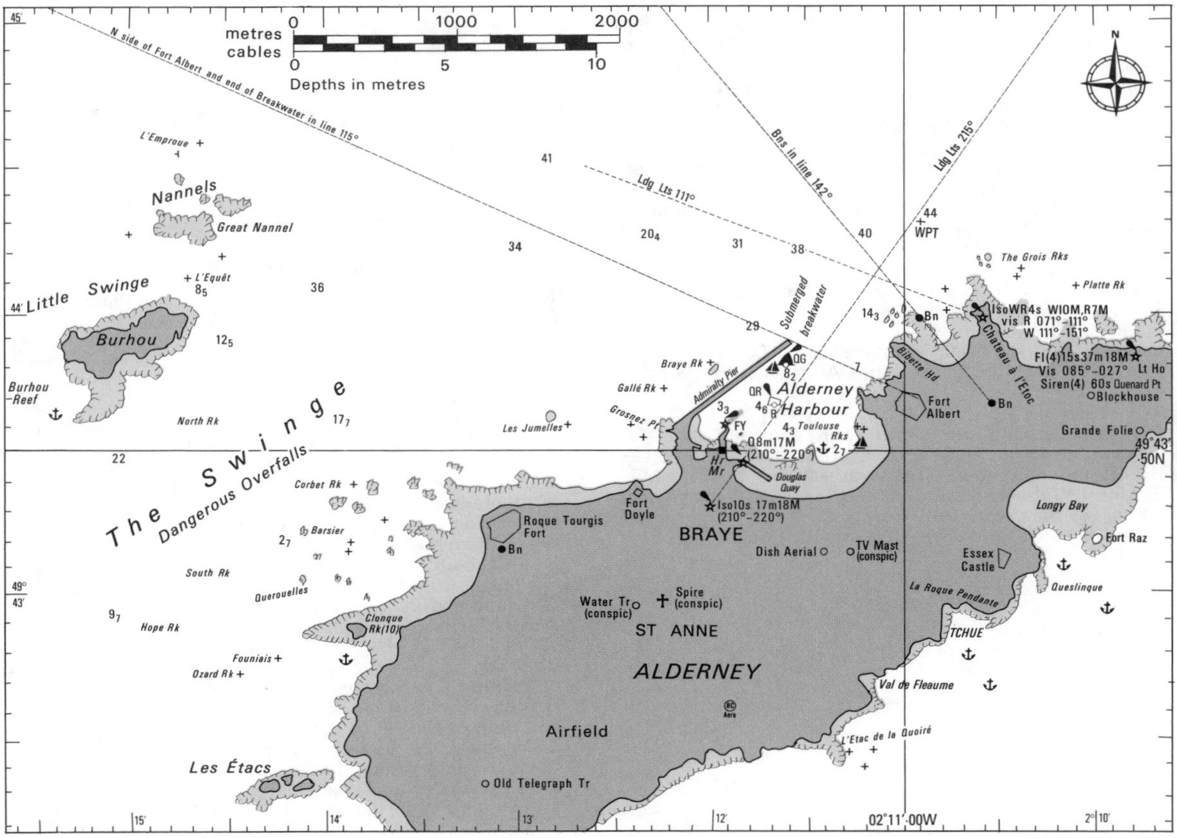

metres
cables
0 1000 2000
0 5 10
Depths in metres
N side of Fort Albert and end of Breakwater in line 115°
Bns in line 142°
Ldg Lts 215°
Ldg Lts 111°
L'Emproue
Nannels
Great Nannel
Little Swinge
Burhou
Burhou Reef
L'Equêt
North Rk
The Swinge
Dangerous Overfalls
Corbet Rk
Barsier
South Rk
Querouelles
Hope Rk
Founiais
Ozard Rk
Clonque Rk(10)
Les Étacs
Les Jumelles
Braye Rk
Gallé Rk
Grosnez Pt
Admiralty Pier
Submerged breakwater
QG
QR
FY
Alderney Harbour
Toulouse Rks
Q8m17M (210°-220°)
Iso10s 17m18M (210°-220°)
Douglas Quay
Hr Mr
Fort Doyle
Roque Tourgis Fort
Bn
BRAYE
Dish Aerial
TV Mast (conspic)
Water Tr (conspic)
Spire (conspic)
ST ANNE
ALDERNEY
Airfield
Old Telegraph Tr
44 WPT
The Grois Rks
Platte Rk
IsoWR4s WlOM,R7M vis R 071°-111° W 111°-151°
Fl(4)15s37m18M Vis 085°-027° Lt Ho Siren(4) 60s Quenard Pt
Blockhouse
Château à l'Etoc
Bibette Hd
Fort Albert
Grande Folie
Longy Bay
Fort Raz
Essex Castle
La Roque Pendante
Queslinque
TCHUE
Val de Fleaume
L'Etac de la Quoiré
49°43'·50N
02°11'·00W
45'
44'
49° 43'
15'
14'
13'
12'
2°10'

BEAUCETTE 10-17-10

Guernsey (Channel Islands)

CHARTS
Admiralty 808, 807, 3654; SHOM 6903, 6904, 3155; ECM 1014; Stanford 16; Imray C33A

TIDES
−0450 Dover; ML 5·0; Duration 0550; Zone 0 (GMT)

NOTE: To ascertain the depth of water over the sill at the Channel Island Yacht Marina at Beaucette
1. Note the predicted *Height* of HW at St Peter Port for the day.
2. Note the *Time* of LW for the day.
3. On following table, select the line corresponding to the predicted Height of HW. The seven columns at the right of the table show the depth of water over the sill at hourly intervals either side of LW.

Predicted height of HW at St Peter Port	Depth of Water over the Sill in metres (sill dries 2·1m)						
HW metres	L.W.	∓1hr	∓2hr	∓3hr	∓4hr	∓5hr	∓6hr
9·75	—	—	0·30	2·74	5·18	6·79	7·62
9·44	—	—	0·15	2·74	5·03	6·55	7·31
9·14	—	—	0·60	2·74	4·87	6·31	7·01
8·83	—	—	0·76	2·74	4·72	6·03	6·70
8·53	—	—	0·91	2·74	4·57	5·79	6·40
8·22	—	—	1·06	2·74	4·42	5·54	6·09
7·92	—	0·18	1·21	2·74	4·26	5·27	5·79
7·61	—	0·42	1·37	2·74	4·11	5·03	5·48
7·31	0·30	0·70	1·52	2·74	3·96	4·78	5·18
7·00	0·60	0·94	1·67	2·74	3·81	4·51	4·87
6·70	0·91	1·21	1·82	2·74	3·65	4·27	4·57
6·39	1·21	1·46	1·98	2·74	3·50	4·02	4·27
6·09	1·52	1·70	2·13	2·74	3·35	3·75	3·96

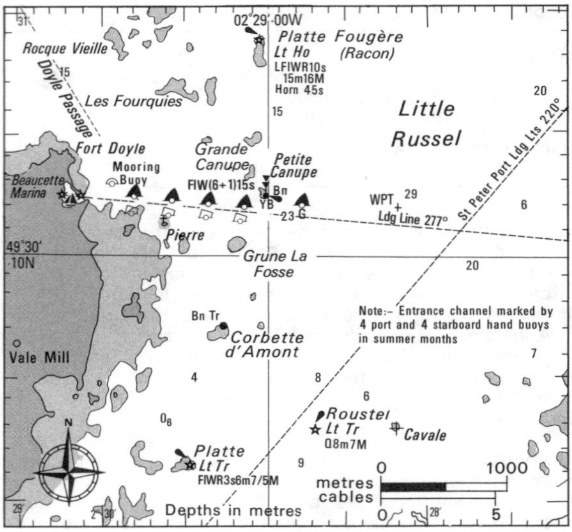

02°29'·00W
Rocque Vieille
Doyle Passage
Platte Fougère
Lt Ho
(Racon)
LFlWR10s
15m16M
Horn 45s
Les Fourquies
Little
Russel
St Peter Port Ldg Lts 220°
Fort Doyle
Mooring
Buoy
Grande
Canupe
Petite
Canupe
Fl W(6+1)15s
Bn
YB
Beaucette
Marina
WPT
Ldg Line 277°
Pierre
49°30'
·10N
Grune La
Fosse
Bn Tr
Corbette
d'Amont
Note:– Entrance channel marked by
4 port and 4 starboard hand buoys
in summer months
Vale Mill
Roustel
Lt Tr
Q8m7M
Cavale
Platte
Lt Tr
FlWR3s6m7/5M
metres
cables
0
1000
5
Depths in metres

SHELTER
Excellent shelter but entry restricted as above, and not advised in strong onshore winds or heavy swell. Secure to mooring buoy (see chartlet) while waiting. Space inside is very limited.

NAVIGATION
Waypoint 49°30'·15N 02°28'·50W, 096°/276° from/to entrance, 1·1M. Approach either from N or S along Little Russel until between Platte Fougère Lt Ho (W with B band, 25m) and Roustel Lt Tr (BW checked). Half way between, pick up the leading marks, but beware the Petit Canupe Rks (buoyed) to the N. Running in, there are rocks and drying areas to the S. Entrance channel buoyed with R and G buoys. The entrance is very narrow indeed.

LIGHTS AND MARKS
Ldg Lts 277°. Front FR; R stripe on W background at N side of entrance. Rear FR; W stripe on R background, on roof of building, with windsock.

RADIO TELEPHONE
VHF Ch 16; **80** 37. Other station: St Sampson Ch 16; 12 (H24).

TELEPHONE (0481)
Hr Mr 45000; # 45000; Marinecall 0898 500 457; Police 25111; Dr 25211 (St Johns Ambulance St Peter Port).

FACILITIES
EC Thursday; **Channel Island Yacht Marina** (200+50 visitors), ☎ 45000, D, FW, C, AC, Gas, Gaz, V, R, ⊡, BH (30 ton), Slip, Bar; **Greenway Marine** ☎ 47471 ME, El, **John Webster Marine** ☎ 48879 Marine Management, ✉; Ⓑ (St Sampson); ✈ (Guernsey).
Ferry UK — St Peter Port—Weymouth/Poole.

ST PETER PORT 10-17-11

Guernsey (Channel Islands)

CHARTS
Admiralty 3140, 808, 807, 3654, 807; SHOM 6903, 6904, 3155; ECM 1014; Stanford 16; Imray C33A

TIDES
−0439 Dover; ML 5·0; Duration 0550; Zone 0 (GMT)

NOTE: St Peter Port is a Standard Port and times and heights of HW and LW for each day of the year are shown below.

SHELTER
Good shelter especially in the Victoria Marina which has a sill 4·4 m above CD. Access approx HW∓3. Approach via buoyed channel along S side of harbour. Marina waiting pontoon and some visitors' moorings to E of marina entrance. Local boat moorings occupy centre of harbour, but there is also a fairway to N of them. Albert Dock Marina and Queen Elizabeth II Marina are for local boats only. Alternative anchorages in Guernsey are Havelet Bay, Icart Pt, Fermain Bay, St Sampsons (see 10.17.15) and Bordeaux. Customs/immigration at St Peter Port, St Sampson and Beaucette.

NAVIGATION
Waypoint 49°27'·88N 02°30'·70W, 040°/220° from/to front Ldg Lt 220°, 0·68M. Offlying dangers, big tidal range and strong tidal streams demand careful navigation. Easiest approach from N via Big Russel between Herm and Sark passing S of Lower Heads Lt buoy: slightly more direct, the Little Russel which needs care — see 10.17.5. Coming round W and S of Guernsey, give Les Hanois a wide berth. Beware ferries and shipping. Speed limits are 4 kns to the W of the jetty and 6 kns from jetty to the pier head.

ST. PETER PORT *continued*

LIGHTS AND MARKS
Ldg Lts: Front Castle Breakwater head Al WR 10s 14m 16M (vis 187°-007°) Horn 15s: Rear Belvedere Oc 10s 61m 14M in line at 220°.
On White Rock Pierhead
FR (vis from seaward) – No entry
FR (vis from landward) – No exit
On SW corner of New Pier
FR (vis from landward) – No exit
These signals do not apply to small boats, less than 15m LOA, under power and keeping clear of the fairways.

RADIO TELEPHONE
Call: *Port Control* VHF Ch **12** 78 (H24). Messages may be sent through St Peter Port Radio – See 6.3.15.

TELEPHONE (0481)
Hr Mr 720229; Signal Station (CG) 20085; # 26911; Marina Office 25987; Marinecall 0898 500 457; Police 25111; Dr 25211 (St John's Ambulance).

FACILITIES
EC Thursday; **Victoria Marina** (280, all visitors) ☎ 25987, Slip, FW, AC, ⊡, R, Max stay 14 days (Access HW∓3 sill maintains level CD+4·2m); **North Pier** ☎ 20085, C (32 ton 20 ton 7 ton), AB; **Jetty Harbour Office** ☎ 20229, AB; **Castle Pier** P, D; **Marquand Bros.** ☎ 20962, CH, Gas, Gaz; **Navigation and Marine Suppliers** ☎ 25838, CH, ACA; **G. Scott** ☎ 28989, SM; **Herm Seaway Marine** ☎ 26829, ME, El, Gas, Gaz; **Seaward Marine** ☎ 45353, ME, El, BY, CH; **John Webster (Marine Management)** ☎ 27030; **Royal Channel Islands YC** ☎ 25500; Bar, **Guernsey YC** ☎ 22838; **Auto Electrical & Diesel Service** ☎ 26811, El; **Boatwork+** ☎ 26071, Ⓔ, CH, ME, El, ACA; **Greenway Marine** ☎ 45805 ME, El; **Town** P, D, V, CH, R, ⊡, Bar. ✉; Ⓑ; ≢ (ferry to Weymouth, Poole, Cherbourg, St. Malo); Hydrofoil to Sark, Weymouth, Jersey, St Malo; ✈ (Guernsey Airport). Ferry UK—Weymouth/Poole.

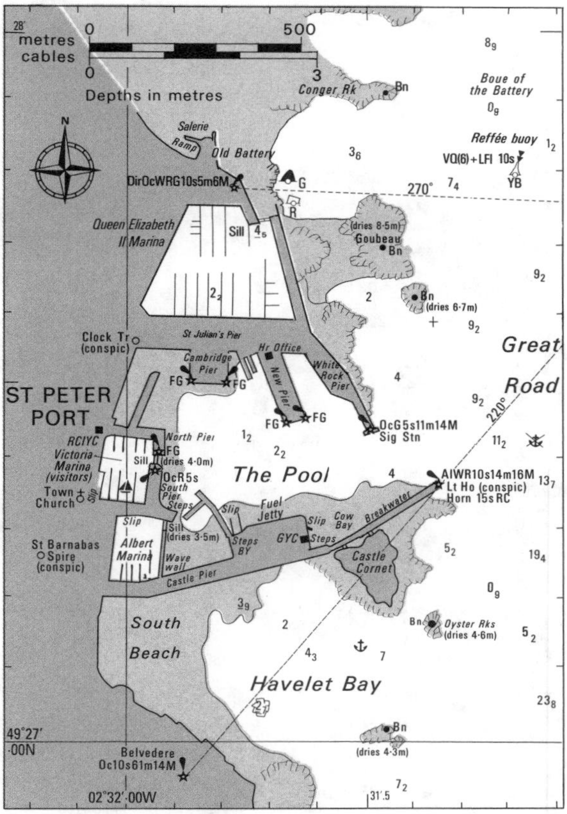
metres
cables
Depths in metres
Conger Rk
Boue of the Battery
Salerie Ramp
Old Battery
Reffée buoy
VQ(6)+LFl 10s
YB
DirOcWRG10s5m6M
270°
Queen Elizabeth II Marina
Sill
Goubeau
Bn
Clock Tr (conspic)
St Julian's Pier
Hr Office
Cambridge Pier
New Pier
White Rock Pier
Great Road
220°
ST PETER PORT
RCIYC
Victoria Marina (visitors)
Town Church
North Pier
OcR5s
South Pier
The Pool
OcG5s11m14M
Sig Stn
AlWR10s14m16M
Lt Ho (conspic)
Horn 15s RC
Fuel Jetty
GYC
Steps
Cow Bay
Breakwater
Castle Cornet
Albert Marina
Wave wall
Castle Pier
St Barnabas Spire (conspic)
South Beach
Oyster Rks (dries 4·6m)
Havelet Bay
49°27'·00N
Belvedere Oc10s61m14M
02°32'·00W
31'·5

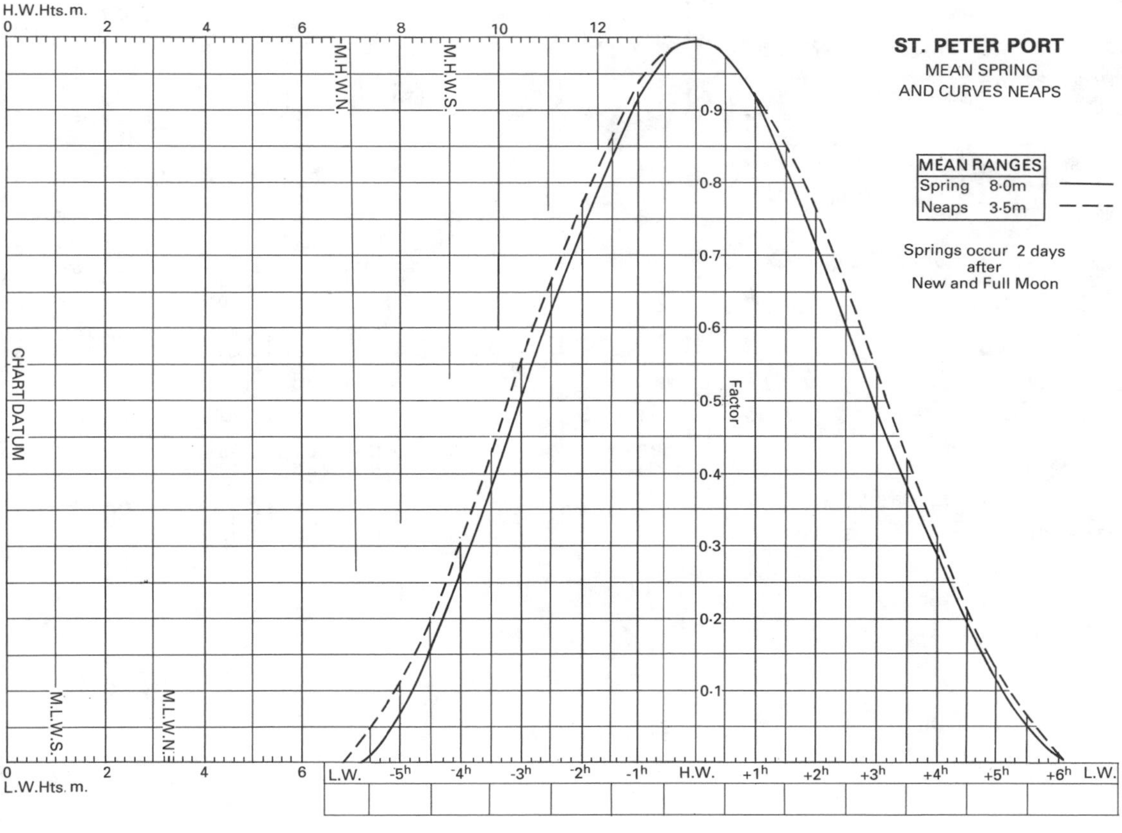
H.W.Hts.m.
M.H.W.N.
M.H.W.S.
CHART DATUM
Factor
M.L.W.S.
M.L.W.N.
L.W.Hts.m.
L.W. -5h -4h -3h -2h -1h H.W. +1h +2h +3h +4h +5h +6h L.W.
ST. PETER PORT
MEAN SPRING AND CURVES NEAPS
MEAN RANGES
Spring 8·0m
Neaps 3·5m
Springs occur 2 days after New and Full Moon

CHANNEL ISLANDS – ST. PETER PORT

Lat 49°27′ N Long 2°31′ W

TIME ZONE UT(GMT)
For Summer Time add ONE hour in non-shaded areas

TIMES AND HEIGHTS OF HIGH AND LOW WATERS

YEAR **1992**

JANUARY

Day	Time	m	Day	Time	m
1 W	0325 1004 1556 2231	7·3 3·1 7·3 3·0	16 Th	0215 0903 1504 2141	7·0 3·4 7·0 3·1
2 Th	0425 1100 1652 2322	7·6 2·7 7·5 2·7	17 F	0341 1027 1625 2256	7·4 2·8 7·5 2·5
3 F	0515 1147 1741	7·9 2·4 7·8	18 Sa	0450 1133 1727 2354	8·0 2·0 8·1 1·8
4 Sa	0003 0600 1228 ● 1825	2·3 8·1 2·0 8·0	19 Su ○	0548 1228 1822	8·6 1·3 8·7
5 Su	0042 0642 1306 1905	2·1 8·4 1·7 8·2	20 M	0046 0642 1315 1912	1·1 9·2 0·7 9·2
6 M	0118 0722 1340 1943	1·9 8·5 1·6 8·2	21 Tu	0133 0730 1401 1959	0·7 9·5 0·4 9·4
7 Tu	0151 0758 1412 2017	1·8 8·5 1·6 8·2	22 W	0218 0815 1445 2044	0·5 9·6 0·3 9·3
8 W	0222 0831 1442 2049	1·9 8·3 1·7 8·0	23 Th	0303 0859 1527 2126	0·7 9·5 0·6 9·1
9 Th	0252 0902 1512 2119	2·0 8·2 1·9 7·9	24 F	0344 0941 1608 2207	1·0 9·1 1·1 8·7
10 F	0321 0930 1539 2148	2·2 8·0 2·1 7·7	25 Sa	0426 1023 1650 2248	1·6 8·6 1·8 8·1
11 Sa	0350 0959 1611 2218	2·5 7·8 2·4 7·5	26 Su	0508 1103 1733 ☾ 2331	2·2 8·0 2·5 7·6
12 Su	0425 1032 1650 2255	2·8 7·5 2·7 7·3	27 M	0555 1150 1823	2·8 7·4 3·1
13 M	0508 1114 1740 ☽ 2341	3·1 7·3 3·0 7·1	28 Tu	0022 0650 1247 1924	7·1 3·4 6·9 3·6
14 Tu	0608 1211 1848	3·3 7·0 3·3	29 W	0129 0800 1407 2041	6·8 3·7 6·6 3·8
15 W	0049 0729 1330 2013	6·9 3·5 6·8 3·3	30 Th	0250 0926 1531 2201	6·8 3·6 6·7 3·6
			31 F	0403 1040 1636 2303	7·0 3·2 7·1 3·1

FEBRUARY

Day	Time	m	Day	Time	m
1 Sa	0500 1133 1727 2350	7·5 2·6 7·5 2·5	16 Su	0442 1123 1720 2346	7·8 1·9 8·1 1·6
2 Su	0545 1215 1809	7·9 2·1 7·9	17 M	0539 1216 1811	8·6 1·0 8·8
3 M	0030 0626 1252 ● 1849	2·0 8·3 1·6 8·3	18 Tu	0036 0629 1303 ○ 1859	0·8 9·3 0·3 9·3
4 Tu	0105 0704 1325 1924	1·6 8·6 1·3 8·5	19 W	0120 0715 1346 1943	0·3 9·7 0·0 9·6
5 W	0136 0738 1356 1958	1·4 8·7 1·2 8·5	20 Th	0203 0759 1426 2023	0·1 9·8 0·0 9·5
6 Th	0205 0812 1424 2028	1·4 8·7 1·3 8·4	21 F	0242 0839 1505 2103	0·3 9·6 0·4 9·3
7 F	0234 0841 1449 2055	1·5 8·5 1·4 8·3	22 Sa	0321 0919 1542 2140	0·7 9·2 1·0 8·8
8 Sa	0300 0908 1515 2120	1·7 8·4 1·7 8·1	23 Su	0357 0955 1616 2215	1·4 8·6 1·7 8·2
9 Su	0325 0933 1543 2148	2·0 8·1 2·0 7·9	24 M	0433 1031 1653 2252	2·1 7·9 2·5 7·6
10 M	0354 1003 1616 2221	2·3 7·9 2·3 7·7	25 Tu	0512 1110 1733 ☾ 2333	2·8 7·3 3·2 7·0
11 Tu	0433 1040 1701 ☽ 2303	2·7 7·5 2·8 7·4	26 W	0601 1157 1828	3·4 6·7 3·8
12 W	0529 1130 1806	3·1 7·1 3·2	27 Th	0035 0709 1322 1948	6·5 3·9 6·3 4·1
13 Th	0003 0650 1250 1936	7·0 3·5 6·6 3·5	28 F	0215 0842 1508 2127	6·4 3·9 6·4 3·9
14 F	0141 0834 1449 2119	6·7 3·4 6·7 3·2	29 Sa	0341 1015 1617 2243	6·7 3·5 6·8 3·3
15 Sa	0328 1014 1617 2244	7·1 2·8 7·3 2·5			

MARCH

Day	Time	m	Day	Time	m
1 Su	0439 1113 1705 2333	7·2 2·8 7·4 2·6	16 M	0428 1109 1702 2331	7·8 1·7 8·1 1·5
2 M	0523 1154 1745	7·8 2·1 7·9	17 Tu	0522 1200 1752	8·6 0·9 8·8
3 Tu	0010 0603 1230 1822	2·0 8·3 1·5 8·3	18 W	0019 0610 1243 ○ 1837	0·7 9·2 0·3 9·3
4 W	0045 0640 1302 ● 1857	1·5 8·7 1·1 8·6	19 Th	0102 0654 1325 1919	0·2 9·6 0·0 9·5
5 Th	0115 0713 1332 1930	1·2 8·9 1·0 8·7	20 F	0141 0737 1403 1959	0·1 9·6 0·1 9·5
6 F	0144 0745 1400 2000	1·1 8·9 1·0 8·7	21 Sa	0219 0816 1438 2037	0·3 9·4 0·6 9·2
7 Sa	0212 0815 1425 2028	1·2 8·8 1·2 8·6	22 Su	0256 0854 1512 2112	0·8 9·0 1·2 8·7
8 Su	0238 0844 1452 2055	1·4 8·6 1·5 8·5	23 M	0328 0929 1544 2144	1·4 8·4 1·9 8·1
9 M	0305 0910 1521 2123	1·7 8·4 1·8 8·2	24 Tu	0401 1001 1618 2217	2·1 7·8 2·6 7·5
10 Tu	0336 0941 1556 2158	2·1 8·0 2·2 7·9	25 W	0437 1036 1655 2254	2·8 7·1 3·2 7·0
11 W	0418 1020 1643 2240	2·5 7·6 2·7 7·5	26 Th	0523 1120 1747 ☾ 2347	3·4 6·6 3·8 6·5
12 Th	0515 1111 1751 ☽ 2341	2·9 7·0 3·2 6·9	27 F	0627 1238 1859	3·8 6·2 4·1
13 F	0635 1238 1921	3·3 6·5 3·5	28 Sa	0129 0753 1427 2039	6·3 3·9 6·2 4·0
14 Sa	0129 0820 1443 2105	6·7 3·3 6·7 3·2	29 Su	0303 0931 1539 2205	6·5 3·6 6·7 3·5
15 Su	0317 1000 1604 2231	7·1 2·7 7·3 2·4	30 M	0403 1037 1629 2300	7·0 2·9 7·2 2·8
			31 Tu	0449 1122 1709 2340	7·6 2·2 7·8 2·1

APRIL

Day	Time	m	Day	Time	m
1 W	0529 1158 1748	8·1 1·7 8·3	16 Th	0544 1219 1810	8·9 0·6 9·0
2 Th	0015 0606 1232 1824	1·6 8·5 1·3 8·6	17 F	0038 0629 1300 ○ 1851	0·5 9·2 0·5 9·2
3 F	0048 0642 1303 ● 1857	1·3 8·8 1·1 8·8	18 Sa	0118 0712 1337 1933	0·4 9·2 0·6 9·1
4 Sa	0119 0716 1333 1930	1·1 8·9 1·0 8·9	19 Su	0154 0752 1412 2009	0·6 9·0 1·0 8·9
5 Su	0150 0749 1404 2002	1·1 8·9 1·2 8·8	20 M	0229 0830 1445 2045	1·0 8·6 1·5 8·5
6 M	0221 0820 1435 2034	1·3 8·7 1·4 8·7	21 Tu	0304 0905 1517 2117	1·6 8·1 2·0 8·0
7 Tu	0254 0854 1510 2108	1·6 8·4 1·8 8·4	22 W	0336 0939 1550 2151	2·1 7·6 2·6 7·5
8 W	0329 0930 1550 2147	1·9 8·1 2·2 8·0	23 Th	0413 1013 1626 2227	2·7 7·1 3·1 7·0
9 Th	0416 1014 1642 2234	2·3 7·6 2·7 7·5	24 F	0455 1055 1715 ☾ 2315	3·1 6·7 3·5 6·6
10 F	0516 1113 1749 ☽ 2341	2·7 7·0 3·1 7·1	25 Sa	0551 1157 1816	3·5 6·3 3·8
11 Sa	0633 1243 1913	3·0 6·7 3·2	26 Su	0032 0702 1326 1935	6·4 3·7 6·3 3·9
12 Su	0121 0806 1425 2048	6·9 3·0 6·9 3·0	27 M	0202 0824 1442 2102	6·5 3·5 6·6 3·6
13 M	0253 0937 1539 2208	7·2 2·5 7·5 2·3	28 Tu	0308 0938 1538 2210	6·8 3·1 7·0 3·1
14 Tu	0401 1044 1636 2309	7·9 1·7 8·1 1·5	29 W	0401 1034 1625 2259	7·3 2·6 7·5 2·5
15 W	0455 1136 1724 2355	8·5 1·1 8·7 0·9	30 Th	0446 1117 1707 2340	7·8 2·1 8·0 2·0

Chart Datum: 5.06 metres below Ordnance Datum (Local)

TIME ZONE UT(GMT)
For Summer Time add ONE hour in non-shaded areas

CHANNEL ISLANDS – ST. PETER PORT

Lat 49°27′ N Long 2°31′ W

TIMES AND HEIGHTS OF HIGH AND LOW WATERS

YEAR **1992**

MAY

Day	Time	m	Day	Time	m
1 F	0527 1156 1747	8·3 1·6 8·4	16 Sa ○	0014 0603 1235 1825	1·2 8·6 1·2 8·7
2 Sa ●	0018 0607 1233 1824	1·6 8·6 1·3 8·7	17 Su	0055 0647 1312 1906	1·0 8·6 1·2 8·7
3 Su	0055 0647 1309 1902	1·3 8·8 1·2 8·9	18 M	0132 0730 1349 1945	1·1 8·5 1·4 8·6
4 M	0130 0726 1346 1940	1·2 8·8 1·2 8·9	19 Tu	0208 0809 1422 2023	1·3 8·3 1·7 8·3
5 Tu	0208 0805 1424 2019	1·2 8·7 1·4 8·8	20 W	0243 0845 1456 2059	1·7 7·9 2·1 8·0
6 W	0248 0845 1505 2101	1·4 8·5 1·7 8·5	21 Th	0317 0922 1529 2133	2·0 7·6 2·5 7·6
7 Th	0331 0930 1553 2146	1·7 8·2 2·0 8·2	22 F	0353 0957 1604 2208	2·4 7·2 2·8 7·3
8 F	0422 1020 1644 2238	2·0 7·7 2·4 7·8	23 Sa	0430 1034 1644 2250	2·8 6·9 3·1 7·0
9 Sa ☽	0519 1120 1748 2343	2·3 7·3 2·7 7·4	24 Su ☾	0516 1120 1733 2340	3·0 6·7 3·4 6·7
10 Su	0627 1235 1900	2·6 7·1 2·9	25 M	0610 1217 1833	3·2 6·6 3·5
11 M	0102 0743 1355 2020	7·2 2·6 7·2 2·7	26 Tu	0046 0712 1326 1945	6·6 3·3 6·6 3·5
12 Tu	0219 0905 1504 2137	7·4 2·4 7·5 2·4	27 W	0156 0822 1430 2059	6·7 3·2 6·8 3·3
13 W	0327 1013 1603 2238	7·7 2·0 7·9 1·9	28 Th	0300 0931 1528 2205	7·0 2·9 7·2 2·9
14 Th	0425 1106 1655 2330	8·1 1·6 8·3 1·5	29 F	0356 1028 1620 2259	7·4 2·5 7·7 2·4
15 F	0516 1153 1741	8·4 1·3 8·6	30 Sa	0446 1119 1708 2347	7·9 2·1 8·1 1·9
			31 Su	0534 1205 1755	8·3 1·7 8·5

JUNE

Day	Time	m	Day	Time	m
1 M ●	0032 0622 1249 1842	1·5 8·6 1·4 8·8	16 Tu	0113 0712 1329 1929	1·5 8·2 1·7 8·4
2 Tu	0115 0709 1333 1927	1·2 8·8 1·2 9·0	17 W	0151 0752 1404 2008	1·5 8·1 1·8 8·3
3 W	0200 0756 1417 2012	1·1 8·8 1·2 9·0	18 Th	0226 0830 1438 2044	1·6 8·0 1·9 8·1
4 Th	0243 0842 1503 2058	1·1 8·7 1·3 8·8	19 F	0300 0905 1510 2117	1·8 7·8 2·1 7·9
5 F	0331 0930 1551 2146	1·2 8·5 1·6 8·6	20 Sa	0331 0939 1542 2150	2·0 7·5 2·4 7·6
6 Sa	0419 1020 1642 2236	1·5 8·1 1·9 8·2	21 Su	0404 1010 1615 2223	2·3 7·3 2·6 7·4
7 Su ☽	0512 1114 1737 2333	1·8 7·8 2·2 7·8	22 M	0439 1044 1653 2258	2·6 7·1 2·9 7·1
8 M	0611 1213 1838	2·1 7·5 2·5	23 Tu ☾	0520 1123 1739 2343	2·8 7·0 3·1 7·0
9 Tu	0033 0715 1318 1946	7·6 2·4 7·4 2·7	24 W	0611 1214 1837	3·0 6·8 3·3
10 W	0142 0825 1425 2058	7·4 2·5 7·4 2·6	25 Th	0040 0712 1316 1948	6·8 3·2 6·8 3·4
11 Th	0250 0934 1527 2204	7·4 2·5 7·6 2·4	26 F	0152 0825 1427 2107	6·8 3·1 7·0 3·2
12 F	0354 1035 1625 2302	7·6 2·3 7·8 2·1	27 Sa	0305 0941 1536 2221	7·1 2·9 7·4 2·8
13 Sa	0450 1126 1716 2352	7·8 2·1 8·1 1·8	28 Su	0413 1047 1639 2322	7·5 2·5 7·8 2·2
14 Su	0542 1212 1803	8·0 1·9 8·2	29 M	0512 1143 1734	8·0 1·9 8·4
15 M ○	0035 0628 1252 1847	1·6 8·1 1·7 8·4	30 Tu ●	0015 0607 1235 1828	1·6 8·4 1·4 8·8

JULY

Day	Time	m	Day	Time	m
1 W	0105 0659 1322 1916	1·1 8·8 1·0 9·1	16 Th	0134 0734 1347 1949	1·4 8·2 1·6 8·4
2 Th	0150 0749 1410 2005	0·7 9·0 0·8 9·3	17 F	0207 0810 1418 2023	1·4 8·2 1·6 8·4
3 F	0236 0837 1456 2052	0·6 9·1 0·8 9·2	18 Sa	0238 0844 1448 2056	1·5 8·1 1·8 8·2
4 Sa	0322 0922 1542 2137	0·7 8·9 1·0 9·0	19 Su	0307 0913 1515 2124	1·7 7·9 2·0 8·0
5 Su	0407 1007 1628 2223	1·0 8·6 1·4 8·6	20 M	0334 0941 1544 2153	1·9 7·7 2·2 7·8
6 M	0455 1054 1717 2310	1·4 8·2 1·9 8·2	21 Tu	0403 1007 1615 2221	2·2 7·5 2·5 7·5
7 Tu ☽	0545 1143 1810	2·0 7·8 2·4	22 W ☾	0436 1038 1654 2257	2·5 7·4 2·8 7·3
8 W	0002 0641 1239 1909	7·7 2·5 7·4 2·8	23 Th	0520 1119 1745 2343	2·8 7·2 3·2 7·0
9 Th	0103 0742 1343 2017	7·3 2·9 7·2 3·0	24 F	0618 1215 1855	3·1 6·9 3·4
10 F	0213 0853 1454 2131	7·1 3·1 7·1 3·0	25 Sa	0053 0734 1335 2022	6·7 3·3 6·8 3·4
11 Sa	0328 1005 1600 2240	7·1 3·0 7·3 2·8	26 Su	0226 0902 1507 2151	6·8 3·2 7·1 3·0
12 Su	0432 1104 1657 2334	7·3 2·7 7·6 2·4	27 M	0354 1024 1622 2304	7·2 2·7 7·6 2·3
13 M	0526 1154 1747	7·6 2·3 7·9	28 Tu	0501 1129 1723	7·8 2·0 8·3
14 Tu ○	0019 0613 1236 1831	1·9 7·9 2·0 8·2	29 W ●	0002 0557 1222 1817	1·5 8·5 1·3 8·9
15 W	0059 0654 1312 1911	1·6 8·1 1·7 8·4	30 Th	0052 0649 1311 1906	0·8 9·0 0·7 9·4
			31 F	0139 0736 1357 1953	0·3 9·3 0·4 9·6

AUGUST

Day	Time	m	Day	Time	m
1 Sa	0222 0820 1441 2037	0·2 9·4 0·4 9·6	16 Su	0211 0816 1422 2030	1·2 8·5 1·5 8·5
2 Su	0305 0905 1524 2120	0·3 9·3 0·6 9·3	17 M	0238 0844 1448 2056	1·4 8·3 1·7 8·3
3 M	0347 0947 1606 2201	0·7 8·9 1·1 8·8	18 Tu	0304 0909 1514 2120	1·7 8·1 2·0 8·1
4 Tu	0430 1028 1650 2244	1·4 8·4 1·8 8·2	19 W	0329 0934 1543 2148	2·0 7·9 2·3 7·8
5 W ☽	0515 1111 1736 2328	2·1 7·8 2·4 7·6	20 Th	0401 1001 1618 2221	2·4 7·7 2·7 7·5
6 Th	0602 1159 1831	2·8 7·3 3·0	21 F ☾	0442 1040 1707 2304	2·8 7·4 3·1 7·1
7 F	0024 0702 1303 1938	7·0 3·3 6·9 3·5	22 Sa	0540 1133 1820	3·2 7·0 3·4
8 Sa	0141 0815 1426 2100	6·7 3·6 6·8 3·5	23 Su	0013 0702 1258 1955	6·7 3·5 6·7 3·5
9 Su	0310 0940 1542 2220	6·7 3·5 7·0 3·2	24 M	0207 0839 1451 2134	6·6 3·4 6·9 3·1
10 M	0420 1048 1642 2319	7·0 3·1 7·4 2·6	25 Tu	0345 1010 1611 2251	7·1 2·8 7·6 2·2
11 Tu	0511 1138 1729	7·4 2·6 7·9	26 W	0450 1117 1709 2349	7·9 1·9 8·4 1·3
12 W	0002 0554 1218 1811	2·1 7·9 2·0 8·3	27 Th	0544 1209 1802	8·6 1·1 9·1
13 Th ○	0039 0634 1253 1850	1·6 8·2 1·6 8·6	28 F ●	0037 0631 1255 1849	0·5 9·2 0·4 9·6
14 F	0112 0711 1325 1926	1·3 8·4 1·4 8·7	29 Sa	0120 0716 1337 1933	0·1 9·6 0·1 9·8
15 Sa	0143 0744 1356 1959	1·2 8·5 1·3 8·7	30 Su	0203 0759 1419 2016	0·0 9·7 0·2 9·7
			31 M	0242 0841 1500 2056	0·3 9·4 0·6 9·4

Chart Datum: 5.06 metres below Ordnance Datum (Local)

CHANNEL ISLANDS – ST. PETER PORT

Lat 49°27′ N Long 2°31′ W

TIME ZONE UT(GMT)
For Summer Time add ONE hour in non-shaded areas

TIMES AND HEIGHTS OF HIGH AND LOW WATERS

YEAR **1992**

SEPTEMBER

Date	Time	m	Date	Time	m
1 Tu	0321 0919 1539 2136	0·8 9·0 1·2 8·8	16 W	0235 0838 1448 2054	1·6 8·4 1·9 8·3
2 W	0400 0958 1619 2214	1·6 8·4 1·9 8·1	17 Th	0304 0905 1518 2122	2·0 8·2 2·2 8·0
3 Th ☽	0440 1036 1702 2257	2·4 7·8 2·6 7·4	18 F	0335 0936 1554 2157	2·4 7·9 2·6 7·6
4 F	0524 1120 1754 2347	3·1 7·2 3·3 6·8	19 Sa ☾	0419 1015 1648 2243	2·9 7·5 3·1 7·1
5 Sa	0621 1223 1902	3·7 6·7 3·8	20 Su	0522 1111 1803 2357	3·3 7·1 3·4 6·6
6 Su	0112 0739 1359 2029	6·4 4·0 6·5 3·9	21 M	0646 1243 1939	3·6 6·7 3·4
7 M	0253 0913 1524 2158	6·5 3·9 6·8 3·5	22 Tu	0200 0825 1437 2119	6·6 3·4 7·0 3·0
8 Tu	0400 1027 1620 2257	6·9 3·4 7·3 2·8	23 W	0331 0953 1554 2234	7·2 2·7 7·7 2·1
9 W	0447 1117 1705 2338	7·4 2·7 7·8 2·2	24 Th	0432 1059 1650 2330	8·0 1·8 8·5 1·2
10 Th	0527 1154 1744	7·9 2·1 8·3	25 F	0522 1150 1739	8·7 1·0 9·2
11 F	0014 0604 1229 1821	1·6 8·4 1·6 8·7	26 Sa ●	0015 0607 1235 1826	0·6 9·3 0·5 9·6
12 Sa ○	0045 0640 1259 1856	1·3 8·6 1·3 8·9	27 Su	0057 0651 1315 1909	0·2 9·6 0·2 9·7
13 Su	0115 0712 1327 1930	1·1 8·8 1·2 8·9	28 M	0137 0733 1356 1952	0·3 9·6 0·4 9·6
14 M	0143 0744 1356 1959	1·2 8·7 1·3 8·8	29 Tu	0217 0813 1434 2032	0·6 9·4 0·8 9·2
15 Tu	0210 0812 1422 2027	1·4 8·6 1·6 8·6	30 W	0254 0851 1512 2109	1·2 8·9 1·4 8·6

OCTOBER

Date	Time	m	Date	Time	m
1 Th	0329 0927 1550 2147	1·9 8·3 2·1 8·0	16 F	0246 0845 1507 2106	2·0 8·4 2·2 8·1
2 F	0407 1003 1630 2225	2·6 7·7 2·8 7·3	17 Sa	0325 0920 1549 2147	2·4 8·1 2·5 7·7
3 Sa ☽	0450 1044 1719 2315	3·3 7·1 3·4 6·7	18 Su	0413 1006 1644 2240	2·9 7·7 2·9 7·2
4 Su	0544 1143 1824	3·9 6·6 3·9	19 M ☾	0516 1106 1758 2357	3·2 7·2 3·2 6·8
5 M	0035 0657 1319 1949	6·3 4·2 6·4 4·0	20 Tu	0635 1235 1925	3·4 6·9 3·2
6 Tu	0216 0831 1447 2117	6·4 4·1 6·7 3·6	21 W	0142 0807 1413 2055	6·9 3·3 7·2 2·8
7 W	0324 0950 1545 2219	6·8 3·6 7·2 3·0	22 Th	0304 0930 1527 2208	7·4 2·7 7·8 2·2
8 Th	0411 1041 1630 2303	7·3 2·9 7·7 2·4	23 F	0404 1035 1625 2304	8·0 2·0 8·4 1·5
9 F	0452 1122 1709 2339	7·9 2·3 8·2 1·9	24 Sa	0455 1126 1715 2352	8·6 1·3 8·9 1·0
10 Sa	0529 1156 1747	8·3 1·8 8·6	25 Su ●	0541 1212 1802	9·1 0·8 9·3
11 Su ○	0013 0604 1229 1824	1·5 8·7 1·5 8·8	26 M	0033 0625 1253 1846	0·7 9·3 0·6 9·4
12 M	0043 0639 1300 1857	1·3 8·8 1·4 8·9	27 Tu	0112 0706 1332 1929	0·8 9·3 0·8 9·2
13 Tu	0113 0711 1330 1930	1·3 8·9 1·4 8·9	28 W	0151 0747 1411 2008	1·1 9·1 1·1 8·9
14 W	0144 0741 1401 2000	1·5 8·8 1·6 8·7	29 Th	0228 0825 1448 2046	1·5 8·7 1·6 8·4
15 Th	0214 0812 1432 2032	1·7 8·6 1·8 8·4	30 F	0304 0902 1524 2124	2·1 8·3 2·2 7·8
			31 Sa	0339 0939 1603 2201	2·7 7·7 2·8 7·3

NOVEMBER

Date	Time	m	Date	Time	m
1 Su	0419 1017 1648 2248	3·3 7·2 3·3 6·8	16 M	0411 1006 1643 2243	2·6 8·0 2·5 7·5
2 M ☽	0507 1107 1744 2350	3·7 6·8 3·7 6·5	17 Tu ☾	0511 1104 1748 2351	2·9 7·6 2·8 7·2
3 Tu	0608 1220 1853	4·0 6·5 3·8	18 W	0620 1216 1902	3·1 7·3 2·9
4 W	0113 0727 1345 2011	6·4 4·0 6·6 3·7	19 Th	0112 0738 1337 2021	7·2 3·1 7·4 2·8
5 Th	0226 0848 1453 2121	6·7 3·8 6·9 3·3	20 F	0226 0856 1451 2136	7·4 2·8 7·6 2·4
6 F	0321 0951 1543 2215	7·1 3·3 7·4 2·8	21 Sa	0331 1005 1554 2235	7·8 2·3 8·0 2·0
7 Sa	0407 1040 1629 2258	7·6 2·8 7·8 2·4	22 Su	0426 1100 1647 2326	8·3 1·8 8·4 1·6
8 Su	0447 1120 1709 2336	8·1 2·3 8·3 2·0	23 M	0516 1149 1738	8·6 1·4 8·7
9 M	0527 1158 1748	8·5 1·9 8·6	24 Tu ●	0010 0602 1232 1825	1·4 8·9 1·2 8·8
10 Tu ○	0013 0604 1235 1826	1·7 8·7 1·6 8·8	25 W	0050 0644 1312 1908	1·4 8·9 1·2 8·8
11 W	0048 0642 1309 1905	1·5 8·9 1·5 8·8	26 Th	0129 0727 1351 1951	1·5 8·8 1·4 8·6
12 Th	0123 0718 1346 1943	1·6 8·9 1·5 8·8	27 F	0207 0806 1428 2030	1·8 8·6 1·7 8·2
13 F	0201 0756 1424 2020	1·7 8·8 1·7 8·6	28 Sa	0242 0844 1504 2108	2·1 8·3 2·1 7·9
14 Sa	0239 0835 1504 2103	1·9 8·7 1·9 8·3	29 Su	0317 0920 1539 2146	2·5 7·9 2·5 7·5
15 Su	0322 0917 1550 2150	2·2 8·4 2·2 7·9	30 M	0353 0958 1618 2224	2·9 7·5 2·9 7·2

DECEMBER

Date	Time	m	Date	Time	m
1 Tu	0432 1037 1701 2307	3·3 7·2 3·2 6·9	16 W ☾	0458 1054 1729 2331	2·3 8·1 2·3 7·7
2 W ☽	0519 1126 1752	3·6 6·9 3·4	17 Th	0556 1151 1831	2·7 7·7 2·6
3 Th	0000 0617 1226 1853	6·7 3·8 6·7 3·6	18 F	0033 0703 1258 1941	7·4 2·9 7·5 2·8
4 F	0106 0725 1336 2004	6·7 3·8 6·7 3·5	19 Sa	0143 0817 1413 2056	7·4 3·0 7·4 2·8
5 Sa	0212 0839 1442 2110	6·9 3·6 7·0 3·3	20 Su	0254 0931 1522 2205	7·5 2·8 7·5 2·6
6 Su	0311 0946 1539 2210	7·2 3·3 7·3 2·9	21 M	0358 1037 1626 2303	7·8 2·4 7·8 2·3
7 M	0403 1041 1630 2300	7·6 2·8 7·8 2·5	22 Tu	0454 1130 1722 2352	8·1 2·0 8·1 2·0
8 Tu	0450 1129 1717 2346	8·1 2·3 8·2 2·1	23 W	0544 1216 1810	8·4 1·7 8·3
9 W ○	0537 1213 1803	8·5 1·9 8·5	24 Th ●	0036 0629 1259 1854	1·8 8·6 1·5 8·4
10 Th	0029 0621 1255 1847	1·7 8·8 1·5 8·8	25 F	0113 0712 1337 1936	1·7 8·6 1·4 8·4
11 F	0109 0704 1336 1933	1·5 9·0 1·3 8·9	26 Sa	0151 0752 1412 2015	1·7 8·6 1·5 8·3
12 Sa	0151 0747 1418 2016	1·5 9·1 1·3 8·8	27 Su	0225 0830 1446 2052	1·8 8·4 1·7 8·1
13 Su	0235 0831 1501 2101	1·5 9·0 1·4 8·7	28 M	0257 0905 1518 2126	2·1 8·2 2·0 7·8
14 M	0320 0916 1546 2148	1·7 8·8 1·6 8·4	29 Tu	0328 0937 1549 2157	2·4 7·9 2·3 7·6
15 Tu	0407 1003 1635 2236	2·0 8·5 1·9 8·0	30 W	0358 1008 1621 2228	2·7 7·6 2·6 7·3
			31 Th	0433 1041 1658 2303	3·0 7·3 2·9 7·1

Chart Datum: 5.06 metres below Ordnance Datum (Local)

SARK 10-17-12

Sark (Channel Islands)

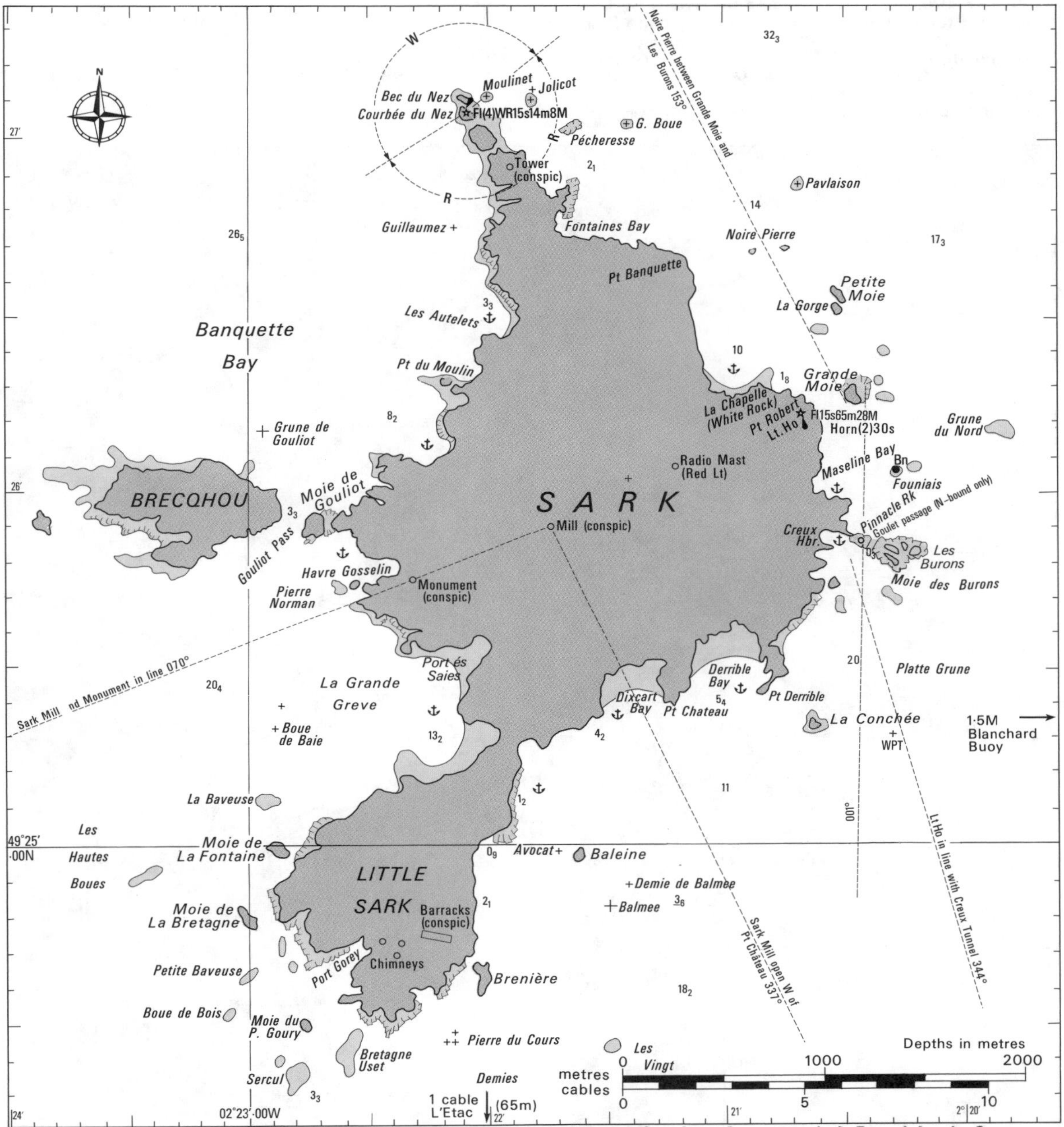
N
W
R
R
Moulinet
Jolicot
Bec du Nez
Courbée du Nez
Fl(4)WR15s14m8M
G. Boue
Pécheresse
Tower (conspic)
Noire Pierre between Grande Moie and Les Burons 153°
Pavlaison
Guillaumez
Fontaines Bay
Noire Pierre
Pt Banquette
Petite Moie
La Gorge
Les Autelets
Banquette Bay
Pt du Moulin
Grande Moie
La Chapelle (White Rock)
Pt Robert Lt Ho
Fl15s65m28M Horn(2)30s
Grune du Nord
Grune de Gouliot
Radio Mast (Red Lt)
Maseline Bay
Bn
Founiais
BRECQHOU
Moie de Gouliot
S A R K
Pinnacle Rk
Goulet passage (N-bound only)
Mill (conspic)
Creux Hbr.
Les Burons
Gouliot Pass
Havre Gosselin
Pierre Norman
Monument (conspic)
Moie des Burons
Sark Mill and Monument in line 070°
Platte Grune
Port és Saies
La Grande Greve
Derrible Bay
Pt Derrible
Dixcart Bay
Pt Chateau
Boue de Baie
La Conchée
WPT
1·5M Blanchard Buoy
La Baveuse
Les Hautes Boues
Moie de La Fontaine
LITTLE SARK
Avocat
Baleine
Demie de Balmée
Balmee
Moie de La Bretagne
Barracks (conspic)
Chimneys
Port Gorey
Petite Baveuse
Brenière
Sark Mill open W of Pt Château 337°
Lt Ho in line with Creux Tunnel 344°
Boue de Bois
Moie du P. Goury
Pierre du Cours
Les Vingt
Bretagne Uset
Sercul
Demies
1 cable L'Etac (65m)
Depths in metres
metres
cables
02°23'·00W
49°25'·00N

CHARTS

Admiralty 808, 3654; SHOM 6904, 3155; ECM 1014; Stanford 16; Imray C33A

TIDES

−0450 Dover; ML 4·9; Duration 0550; Zone 0 (GMT).

Standard Port ST HELIER (⟶)

Times				Height (metres)			
HW		LW		MHWS	MHWN	MLWN	MLWS
0300	0900	0200	0900	11·1	8·1	4·1	1·3
1500	2100	1400	2100				
Differences SARK (MASELINE PIER)							
+0005	+0015	+0005	+0010	−2·1	−1·5	−0·6	−0·3

SHELTER

Many sheltered anchorages, shown on chartlet, depending on wind direction. Main harbours are Creux (dries) and Maseline. Goulet passage for N-bound traffic only. Berthing at jetties prohibited when steamers due, and always when boat is unattended. Remaining in Creux harbour for longer than it takes to disembark passengers, is forbidden without prior permission of the Hr Mr (or call the Tourist office, call sign Tango Oscar, on Ch 74).

NAVIGATION

Creux waypoint 49°25′·30N 02°20′·30W, 164°/344° from/to entrance, 0·57M. Beware large tidal range and strong tidal streams. There are numerous rocks all round Sark but the centres of the bays are clear of dangers for the most part. Sark is not a comfortable place to lie except in settled weather. Beware numerous lobster pots.

LIGHTS AND MARKS

From S, Pinnacle Rock on with E side of Grand Moie at 001°; or W patch on Creux Hr pierhead in line with Pt Robert Lt Ho at 350°. Point Robert Fl 15s 65m 28M; W 8-sided Tr; vis 138°-353°; Horn(2) 30s.

RADIO TELEPHONE

None.

TELEPHONE (0481 83)

Lighthouse Keeper 2021; # 2021; Marinecall 0898 500 457; Police (Guernsey) 25111; Dr 2045.

SARK *continued*

FACILITIES

EC Thursday and Saturday — Winter only; **Harbour (east)** ☎ 2025, Slip, M, L, FW, C (1 ton), AB; **Maseline Jetty** ☎ 2070, M, C (3 ton); **Landing (west)** M, L; **Gallery Stores** ☎ 2078, Gas, Gaz, Kos; **Village** P and D (cans), V, R, Bar. ✉; Ⓑ; ⇌ (ferry to Guernsey-Weymouth, Poole, St Malo or Granville); ✈ (Guernsey).
Ferry UK — Guernsey (St. Peter Port)—Weymouth/Poole.
Hydrofoil — Guernsey, Alderney, Jersey, St Malo, Weymouth.

ST HELIER 10-17-13

Jersey (Channel Islands)

CHARTS

Admiralty 3278, 1137, 3655; SHOM 6938, 5232, 826; ECM 1014; Stanford 16; Imray C33B

TIDES

−0455 Dover; ML 6·5; Duration 0545; Zone 0 (GMT)

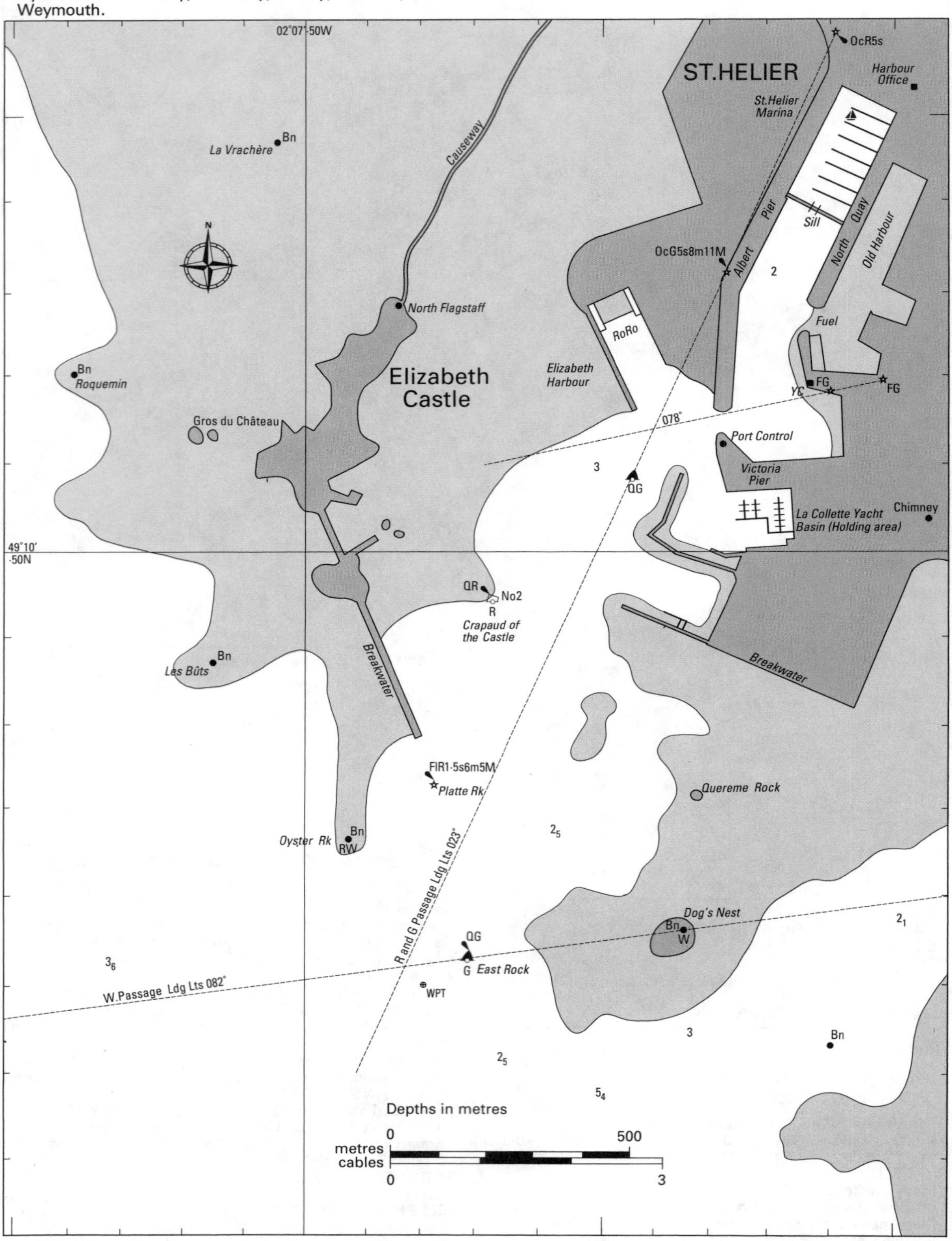
02°07'·50W
49°10'·50N
ST.HELIER
OcR5s
Harbour Office
St.Helier Marina
Albert Pier
Sill
North Quay
Old Harbour
OcG5s8m11M
2
Fuel
RoRo
Elizabeth Harbour
FG
YC
FG
078°
Port Control
3
QG
Victoria Pier
La Collette Yacht Basin (Holding area)
Chimney
Breakwater
Causeway
La Vrachère
Bn
North Flagstaff
Elizabeth Castle
Bn
Roquemin
Gros du Château
QR
No2
R
Crapaud of the Castle
Bn
Les Bûts
Breakwater
FlR1·5s6m5M
Platte Rk
Quereme Rock
Bn
Oyster Rk
RW
R and G Passage Ldg Lts 023°
2₅
Dog's Nest
Bn
W
2₁
QG
G East Rock
3₆
W.Passage Ldg Lts 082°
WPT
3
Bn
2₅
5₄
Depths in metres
metres
cables
0
500
0
3

Standard Port ST HELIER (⟶)

Times				Height (metres)			
HW		LW		MHWS	MHWN	MLWN	MLWS
0300	0900	0200	0900	11·1	8·1	4·1	1·3
1500	2100	1400	2100				
Differences LES MINQUIERS							
+0007	0000	−0008	+0013	+0·5	+0·8	−0·1	+0·1
LES ECREHOU							
+0004	+0012	+0010	+0020	−0·2	+0·3	−0·3	0·0

NOTE: St Helier is a Standard Port and the tidal predictions for each day of the year are shown below.

SHELTER
Excellent shelter in marina and good in La Collette. For St Aubin's Bay see 10.17.15. Anchoring prohibited in St Helier Roads due to shipping and fish storage boxes.

NAVIGATION
Waypoint 49°10′·01N 02°07′·30W, 203°/023° from/to front Ldg Lt 023°, 0·87M. Note the very large tidal range, and many offlying rks. Four main channels are Western Passage, Danger Rk Passage, Red and Green Passage, and South Passage. In Western Passage beware race off Noirmont Pt. Entering harbour note Oyster Rks (RW Bn) to West of Red and Green Passage, and Dog's Nest Rks (W Bn with globe topmark) to E. Speed limit 10 kn N of Platte Rk, and 5 kn N of La Collette. Ldg Lts difficult to see against town lights.

LIGHTS AND MARKS
Western Passage Ldg Lts and Dog's Nest Bn 082° lead N of Les Fours and Ruaudière Lt Buoys, to position close to East Rk Lt Buoy, where course is altered to 023° on the Red and Green Passage Ldg Line (Front Oc G 5s. Rear Oc R 5s, synchronised). Port-hand buoy beyond Platte Rk (Fl R 1·5s) marks channel. Main harbour Ldg Lts 078°, both FG on W columns. Bell at Victoria Pierhead is rung in answer to vessel's fog signals.

Entry Signals (Port Control Stn and Marina)

FG or Fl G Lt at Port Control Stn. — Vessels may enter but not leave
FR or Fl R Lt at Port Control Stn. — Vessels may leave but not enter
R and G Lts together at Port Control Stn. — No vessel may enter or leave

QY Lts on NW and NE of Port Control Stn indicate power driven craft of under 25m length may enter or leave against the signals displayed (keeping to stbd at entrance). Marina sill fixed (CD+5m) and hinged flap which lifts 1·4m over sill to maintain 5·0m.
Sill lights as above.

RADIO TELEPHONE
Call: *St Helier Port Control* VHF Ch 14 (H24). Messages can be routed through Jersey Radio, the Coast Radio Station, VHF Ch 16; 25 82 (H24). Weather forecasts on Ch 25, 82 at 0645, 1245, 1845 and 2245 GMT. No marina VHF. Contact Port Control if necessary.

TELEPHONE (0534)
Hr Mr 34451; Marina Office 79549; ⌗ 30232 and 73561; Duty Forecaster 0077007; Recorded weather forecast 0077002; Marinecall 0898 500 457; Police 69996; Dr 35742 and 53178; Ⓗ 59000.

FACILITIES
EC Thursday; **St Helier Marina** (180+200 visitors), ☎ 79549, Grid, CH, ME, El, Sh, FW, V, AC, Gas, Gaz, Kos, (visitors area — fingers E, F, & G. Vessels over 12m use N. side of finger A); Access HW∓3; **Marina Shop** ☎ 36955, CH, V, Gas, Gaz; **La Collette Yacht Basin** ☎ 69147; (holding area when marina is inaccessible and a few visitors berths for up to 24 hours), FW, AC, BH (18 ton) slip. **Harbours Department** ☎ 34451, FW, C (various, max 32 ton), Slip, Grids, BH (18 ton), AC. **St Helier Yacht Club** ☎ 32229, R, Bar; **South Pier Shipyard** ☎ 31907, P, D, ME, El, Ⓔ, Sh, CH, ACA, Gas. **Battricks Boatyard** ☎ 43412, Sh, CH. **Bernard Amy** ☎ 42071, SM, CH, Sh. **D.K. Collins** ☎ 32415, ME, El. **Raffray** ☎ 23151, ME. **Fox Marine Services** ☎ 21312, ME, El. **Jersey Marine Electronics** ☎ 21603, El, Ⓔ. **Bill Keating** ☎ 33977, ME, El. **Channel Islands Yacht Services** ☎ 42071, ME, SM, Ⓔ, CH, Gas. **Iron Stores Marine** ☎ 77755, CH. **Town** P, D, CH, V, R, Bar. ✉; Ⓑ; ⇌ (ferry to Poole, St Malo, Granville), ✈ (Jersey Airport).
Ro Ro Ferry — Poole, Guernsey, St Malo.
Hydrofoil — Weymouth, Guernsey, Sark, St Malo, (Mar-Nov).
Ferries — St Malo, Granville, Guernsey, Sark, Saint Quay — Portrieux.

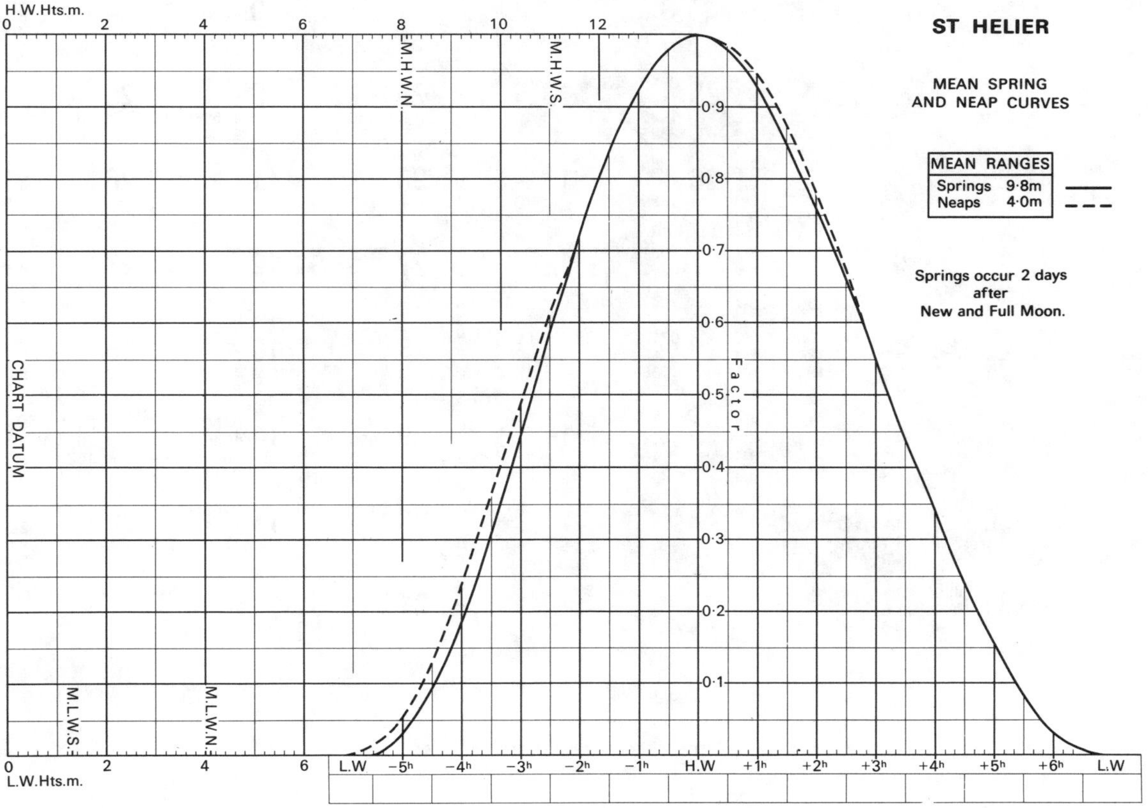
H.W.Hts.m.
0 2 4 6 8 10 12
M.H.W.N.
M.H.W.S.
CHART DATUM
Factor
0·9 0·8 0·7 0·6 0·5 0·4 0·3 0·2 0·1
M.L.W.S.
M.L.W.N.
0 2 4 6
L.W.Hts.m.
L.W -5h -4h -3h -2h -1h H.W +1h +2h +3h +4h +5h +6h L.W
ST HELIER
MEAN SPRING AND NEAP CURVES
MEAN RANGES
Springs 9·8m
Neaps 4·0m
Springs occur 2 days after New and Full Moon.

CHANNEL ISLANDS – ST. HELIER

Lat 49°11′ N Long 2°07′ W

TIMES AND HEIGHTS OF HIGH AND LOW WATERS

YEAR **1992**

TIME ZONE UT(GMT)
For Summer Time add ONE hour in non-shaded areas

JANUARY

Date	Day	Time	m	Time	m	Time	m	Time	m
1	W	0325	8·9	1003	3·6	1555	8·9	2231	3·5
2	Th	0423	9·2	1102	3·3	1649	9·2	2325	3·2
3	F	0511	9·6	1151	2·8	1736	9·6		
4	Sa ●	0008	2·8	0554	10·0	1234	2·4	1818	9·9
5	Su	0049	2·5	0634	10·3	1313	2·1	1856	10·1
6	M	0126	2·3	0712	10·4	1348	2·0	1933	10·1
7	Tu	0159	2·2	0747	10·4	1420	2·0	2006	10·0
8	W	0230	2·3	0819	10·2	1450	2·1	2037	9·8
9	Th	0300	2·4	0850	10·0	1519	2·3	2107	9·6
10	F	0328	2·7	0918	9·7	1546	2·6	2136	9·4
11	Sa	0356	3·0	0948	9·5	1617	2·9	2207	9·2
12	Su	0430	3·3	1021	9·2	1654	3·2	2245	8·9
13	M ☽	0512	3·6	1105	8·9	1743	3·5	2334	8·6
14	Tu	0610	3·9	1205	8·5	1848	3·8		
15	W	0045	8·4	0728	4·1	1328	8·3	2011	3·9
16	Th	0215	8·5	0901	3·9	1504	8·5	2139	3·6
17	F	0341	9·0	1027	3·3	1623	9·2	2257	3·0
18	Sa	0448	9·8	1136	2·5	1723	10·0	2358	2·2
19	Su ○	0543	10·6	1234	1·6	1815	10·7		
20	M	0053	1·4	0634	11·3	1323	0·9	1903	11·3
21	Tu	0141	1·0	0720	11·8	1409	0·6	1948	11·6
22	W	0226	0·8	0804	11·9	1453	0·6	2032	11·5
23	Th	0310	0·9	0847	11·7	1534	0·9	2114	11·2
24	F	0350	1·3	0929	11·2	1614	1·4	2156	10·6
25	Sa	0431	1·9	1012	10·5	1654	2·2	2238	10·0
26	Su ☾	0512	2·7	1054	9·8	1736	3·0	2323	9·3
27	M	0557	3·4	1143	9·0	1824	3·7		
28	Tu	0017	8·6	0650	4·0	1243	8·3	1923	4·2
29	W	0127	8·2	0759	4·3	1406	8·0	2039	4·4
30	Th	0250	8·2	0924	4·3	1531	8·1	2200	4·2
31	F	0402	8·6	1040	3·8	1634	8·6	2305	3·7

FEBRUARY

Date	Day	Time	m	Time	m	Time	m	Time	m
1	Sa	0457	9·1	1136	3·1	1723	9·2	2354	3·0
2	Su	0540	9·7	1221	2·5	1803	9·7		
3	M ●	0036	2·4	0619	10·2	1259	2·0	1841	10·1
4	Tu	0112	2·0	0655	10·6	1333	1·6	1914	10·4
5	W	0144	1·8	0728	10·7	1404	1·5	1947	10·5
6	Th	0213	1·8	0801	10·7	1432	1·6	2016	10·4
7	F	0242	1·9	0829	10·5	1457	1·8	2043	10·2
8	Sa	0307	2·1	0856	10·3	1522	2·1	2108	10·0
9	Su	0332	2·4	0921	10·0	1549	2·4	2136	9·7
10	M	0400	2·8	0952	9·7	1621	2·8	2210	9·4
11	Tu ☽	0438	3·2	1030	9·2	1705	3·3	2254	9·0
12	W	0532	3·7	1122	8·6	1808	3·8	2357	8·4
13	Th	0650	4·0	1246	8·0	1935	4·1		
14	F	0140	8·1	0832	4·0	1449	8·1	2117	3·8
15	Sa	0328	8·6	1013	3·4	1616	8·9	2245	3·0
16	Su	0440	9·6	1126	2·3	1716	9·9	2350	2·0
17	M	0534	10·6	1222	1·3	1805	10·8		
18	Tu ○	0042	1·1	0622	11·4	1310	0·6	1850	11·5
19	W	0128	0·5	0706	12·0	1354	0·2	1933	11·8
20	Th	0211	0·3	0748	12·1	1434	0·2	2012	11·8
21	F	0250	0·5	0827	11·9	1512	0·6	2051	11·4
22	Sa	0328	1·0	0907	11·3	1548	1·3	2128	10·8
23	Su	0403	1·7	0943	10·6	1621	2·1	2204	10·0
24	M	0438	2·5	1020	9·7	1657	3·0	2242	9·2
25	Tu ☾	0516	3·3	1101	8·8	1736	3·8	2325	8·5
26	W	0603	4·0	1151	8·0	1829	4·4		
27	Th	0031	7·9	0709	4·5	1320	7·5	1947	4·7
28	F	0215	7·7	0840	4·6	1508	7·7	2125	4·6
29	Sa	0341	8·1	1014	4·1	1616	8·3	2244	3·9

MARCH

Date	Day	Time	m	Time	m	Time	m	Time	m
1	Su	0437	8·8	1115	3·3	1702	9·0	2336	3·1
2	M	0519	9·5	1158	2·5	1740	9·7		
3	Tu	0015	2·4	0557	10·2	1236	1·9	1815	10·2
4	W ●	0052	1·8	0632	10·6	1309	1·5	1849	10·6
5	Th	0123	1·5	0704	10·9	1340	1·3	1920	10·8
6	F	0152	1·4	0735	11·0	1408	1·3	1949	10·7
7	Sa	0220	1·5	0804	10·8	1433	1·5	2016	10·6
8	Su	0246	1·8	0832	10·6	1500	1·8	2043	10·4
9	M	0312	2·1	0858	10·3	1528	2·2	2111	10·1
10	Tu	0343	2·5	0929	9·9	1602	2·7	2146	9·7
11	W	0423	3·0	1009	9·3	1648	3·2	2230	9·1
12	Th ☽	0518	3·5	1102	8·5	1753	3·8	2334	8·4
13	F	0636	3·9	1234	7·9	1920	4·0		
14	Sa	0127	8·1	0818	3·9	1443	8·0	2103	3·8
15	Su	0317	8·6	0959	3·2	1603	8·9	2231	2·9
16	M	0426	9·6	1111	2·1	1659	10·0	2334	1·8
17	Tu	0518	10·6	1205	1·2	1747	10·9		
18	W ○	0025	1·0	0604	11·4	1250	0·5	1829	11·5
19	Th	0109	0·4	0646	11·8	1333	0·2	1910	11·8
20	F	0149	0·3	0727	11·9	1411	0·3	1948	11·7
21	Sa	0227	0·5	0805	11·6	1446	0·8	2025	11·3
22	Su	0303	1·0	0842	11·1	1519	1·5	2100	10·7
23	M	0335	1·7	0917	10·3	1550	2·3	2132	9·9
24	Tu	0407	2·5	0950	9·5	1623	3·1	2206	9·2
25	W	0442	3·3	1026	8·7	1659	3·8	2244	8·5
26	Th ☾	0526	3·9	1112	7·9	1749	4·4	2340	7·8
27	F	0628	4·4	1234	7·4	1859	4·8		
28	Sa	0127	7·5	0752	4·6	1427	7·5	2037	4·7
29	Su	0303	7·9	0929	4·2	1539	8·1	2204	4·1
30	M	0402	8·5	1037	3·5	1627	8·8	2302	3·3
31	Tu	0447	9·3	1125	2·7	1706	9·5	2344	2·6

APRIL

Date	Day	Time	m	Time	m	Time	m	Time	m
1	W	0525	10·0	1203	2·1	1743	10·1		
2	Th	0021	2·0	0600	10·5	1238	1·6	1817	10·6
3	F ●	0055	1·6	0634	10·8	1310	1·4	1849	10·8
4	Sa	0127	1·4	0707	11·0	1341	1·3	1920	10·9
5	Su	0158	1·5	0738	10·9	1412	1·5	1951	10·9
6	M	0229	1·6	0809	10·7	1443	1·8	2022	10·6
7	Tu	0301	1·9	0842	10·4	1517	2·2	2056	10·3
8	W	0336	2·3	0918	9·9	1556	2·6	2135	9·8
9	Th	0421	2·8	1003	9·3	1647	3·2	2224	9·2
10	F ☽	0519	3·2	1104	8·6	1751	3·6	2334	8·6
11	Sa	0634	3·6	1239	8·1	1913	3·8		
12	Su	0119	8·3	0804	3·5	1425	8·3	2046	3·5
13	M	0253	8·8	0935	2·9	1539	9·1	2207	2·8
14	Tu	0400	9·6	1045	2·1	1634	9·9	2311	1·9
15	W	0452	10·4	1140	1·4	1720	10·7		
16	Th	0000	1·2	0539	11·0	1225	0·9	1804	11·2
17	F ○	0045	0·8	0622	11·3	1307	0·7	1843	11·4
18	Sa	0126	0·7	0703	11·4	1345	0·9	1923	11·3
19	Su	0202	0·9	0741	11·1	1420	1·3	1958	10·9
20	M	0237	1·3	0818	10·6	1453	1·8	2033	10·4
21	Tu	0311	1·9	0853	10·0	1524	2·5	2105	9·8
22	W	0343	2·6	0927	9·3	1556	3·1	2139	9·2
23	Th	0419	3·2	1002	8·6	1631	3·7	2216	8·6
24	F ☾	0459	3·7	1045	8·1	1718	4·1	2306	8·0
25	Sa	0553	4·1	1151	7·6	1817	4·5		
26	Su	0027	7·7	0702	4·3	1324	7·5	1934	4·5
27	M	0201	7·8	0822	4·1	1442	7·9	2100	4·2
28	Tu	0308	8·3	0936	3·7	1538	8·5	2209	3·6
29	W	0400	8·9	1034	3·1	1623	9·2	2301	3·0
30	Th	0444	9·5	1119	2·5	1704	9·8	2344	2·4

Chart Datum: 5.88 metres below Ordnance Datum (Local)

TIME ZONE UT(GMT)

For Summer Time add ONE hour in non-shaded areas

CHANNEL ISLANDS – ST. HELIER

Lat 49°11′ N Long 2°07′ W

TIMES AND HEIGHTS OF HIGH AND LOW WATERS

YEAR **1992**

MAY

Day	Time	m	Time	m	Time	m	Time	m
1 F	0523	10·1	1201	2·0	1742	10·3		
2 Sa ●	0024	1·9	0601	10·6	1239	1·7	1817	10·7
3 Su	0102	1·7	0639	10·8	1316	1·5	1853	10·9
4 M	0138	1·5	0716	10·9	1354	1·6	1930	11·0
5 Tu	0216	1·6	0754	10·8	1432	1·8	2008	10·8
6 W	0256	1·8	0833	10·5	1512	2·1	2049	10·5
7 Th	0338	2·1	0918	10·0	1559	2·4	2134	10·0
8 F	0427	2·4	1009	9·4	1649	2·9	2228	9·5
9 Sa ☽	0522	2·8	1112	8·9	1750	3·2	2336	9·0
10 Su	0628	3·1	1231	8·6	1900	3·4		
11 M	0059	8·8	0742	3·1	1354	8·7	2018	3·3
12 Tu	0219	9·0	0903	2·9	1504	9·1	2135	2·9
13 W	0327	9·4	1012	2·4	1602	9·7	2238	2·3
14 Th	0423	9·9	1108	2·0	1652	10·2	2333	1·8
15 F	0512	10·3	1157	1·6	1736	10·5		
16 Sa ○	0019	1·5	0557	10·6	1241	1·5	1818	10·7
17 Su	0102	1·3	0639	10·6	1320	1·6	1857	10·7
18 M	0140	1·4	0720	10·5	1357	1·8	1935	10·5
19 Tu	0216	1·7	0758	10·1	1430	2·1	2012	10·2
20 W	0251	2·0	0833	9·7	1503	2·5	2047	9·7
21 Th	0324	2·5	0910	9·2	1536	2·9	2121	9·3
22 F	0359	2·9	0945	8·8	1610	3·3	2157	8·8
23 Sa	0435	3·3	1024	8·4	1649	3·7	2240	8·4
24 Su ☾	0519	3·6	1112	8·1	1736	4·0	2333	8·1
25 M	0611	3·8	1212	7·9	1834	4·1		
26 Tu	0042	8·0	0712	3·9	1324	8·0	1944	4·1
27 W	0155	8·1	0820	3·8	1430	8·3	2057	3·9
28 Th	0300	8·5	0929	3·5	1528	8·8	2204	3·4
29 F	0355	9·1	1028	3·0	1619	9·4	2301	2·9
30 Sa	0444	9·6	1122	2·5	1705	10·0	2351	2·3
31 Su	0530	10·1	1210	2·1	1750	10·5		

JUNE

Day	Time	m	Time	m	Time	m	Time	m
1 M ●	0038	1·9	0615	10·6	1256	1·7	1834	10·9
2 Tu	0123	1·5	0700	10·8	1341	1·6	1917	11·1
3 W	0208	1·4	0745	10·8	1425	1·6	2001	11·1
4 Th	0251	1·4	0830	10·7	1510	1·7	2046	10·9
5 F	0338	1·5	0918	10·4	1557	2·0	2134	10·5
6 Sa	0424	1·8	1009	10·0	1647	2·3	2226	10·1
7 Su ☽	0516	2·2	1105	9·5	1740	2·7	2325	9·6
8 M	0612	2·6	1207	9·2	1839	3·0		
9 Tu	0029	9·2	0714	2·9	1316	9·0	1945	3·2
10 W	0141	9·0	0823	3·0	1425	9·0	2056	3·1
11 Th	0250	9·1	0932	3·0	1527	9·2	2203	2·9
12 F	0353	9·3	1035	2·8	1623	9·5	2304	2·6
13 Sa	0448	9·6	1129	2·5	1712	9·9	2356	2·2
14 Su	0537	9·8	1217	2·3	1757	10·1		
15 M ○	0041	2·0	0621	10·0	1259	2·1	1839	10·3
16 Tu	0121	1·8	0703	10·0	1337	2·1	1919	10·3
17 W	0159	1·8	0741	9·9	1412	2·2	1957	10·1
18 Th	0234	2·0	0818	9·8	1446	2·3	2032	9·9
19 F	0307	2·2	0853	9·5	1517	2·6	2105	9·6
20 Sa	0338	2·5	0927	9·2	1548	2·9	2138	9·3
21 Su	0410	2·8	0959	8·9	1620	3·1	2212	9·0
22 M	0444	3·0	1034	8·6	1657	3·4	2249	8·7
23 Tu ☾	0523	3·3	1115	8·4	1742	3·7	2336	8·4
24 W	0612	3·6	1208	8·3	1838	3·9		
25 Th	0036	8·3	0712	3·7	1314	8·3	1947	4·0
26 F	0151	8·3	0823	3·7	1427	8·5	2105	3·8
27 Sa	0305	8·6	0939	3·4	1536	9·0	2221	3·3
28 Su	0412	9·1	1048	2·9	1637	9·6	2325	2·6
29 M	0509	9·8	1147	2·3	1730	10·3		
30 Tu ●	0021	2·0	0601	10·4	1241	1·8	1821	10·9

JULY

Day	Time	m	Time	m	Time	m	Time	m
1 W	0112	1·4	0650	10·8	1330	1·3	1907	11·3
2 Th	0158	1·0	0738	11·1	1418	1·1	1954	11·5
3 F	0244	0·8	0825	11·2	1503	1·1	2040	11·4
4 Sa	0329	0·9	0910	11·0	1548	1·3	2125	11·1
5 Su	0413	1·3	0956	10·6	1633	1·8	2212	10·6
6 M	0459	1·8	1044	10·1	1720	2·3	2301	10·0
7 Tu ☽	0547	2·4	1136	9·5	1811	2·8	2356	9·4
8 W	0641	3·0	1235	9·0	1909	3·3		
9 Th	0100	8·8	0741	3·4	1342	8·7	2015	3·6
10 F	0213	8·6	0851	3·6	1454	8·7	2129	3·6
11 Sa	0328	8·6	1004	3·5	1559	8·9	2240	3·3
12 Su	0430	8·9	1106	3·2	1654	9·3	2337	2·8
13 M	0522	9·3	1158	2·8	1742	9·7		
14 Tu ○	0025	2·4	0607	9·6	1242	2·4	1824	10·1
15 W	0106	2·0	0646	9·9	1320	2·1	1902	10·3
16 Th	0142	1·8	0724	10·1	1355	2·0	1938	10·4
17 F	0215	1·7	0759	10·1	1426	2·0	2012	10·3
18 Sa	0246	1·8	0832	9·9	1456	2·1	2044	10·1
19 Su	0314	2·0	0901	9·7	1522	2·4	2112	9·8
20 M	0341	2·3	0929	9·4	1550	2·7	2141	9·5
21 Tu	0409	2·6	0956	9·2	1620	3·0	2210	9·2
22 W ☾	0441	3·0	1028	9·0	1658	3·4	2247	8·9
23 Th	0523	3·3	1111	8·7	1747	3·7	2336	8·5
24 F	0619	3·7	1210	8·4	1855	4·0		
25 Sa	0049	8·2	0733	3·9	1333	8·3	2020	4·0
26 Su	0226	8·2	0900	3·8	1507	8·6	2150	3·6
27 M	0353	8·7	1024	3·2	1621	9·3	2306	2·7
28 Tu	0458	9·6	1132	2·4	1719	10·2		
29 W ●	0007	1·8	0551	10·4	1228	1·6	1810	11·0
30 Th	0059	1·1	0641	11·1	1319	1·0	1857	11·6
31 F	0147	0·5	0726	11·5	1405	0·6	1942	11·9

AUGUST

Day	Time	m	Time	m	Time	m	Time	m
1 Sa	0230	0·4	0809	11·7	1449	0·6	2025	11·9
2 Su	0312	0·5	0853	11·5	1531	0·9	2108	11·5
3 M	0353	1·0	0935	11·0	1612	1·5	2150	10·9
4 Tu	0435	1·7	1017	10·3	1654	2·2	2234	10·1
5 W ☽	0518	2·5	1102	9·6	1739	2·9	2320	9·3
6 Th	0604	3·3	1153	8·9	1832	3·6		
7 F	0019	8·5	0702	3·9	1300	8·3	1937	4·0
8 Sa	0140	8·0	0813	4·3	1426	8·2	2058	4·1
9 Su	0310	8·1	0938	4·2	1542	8·5	2220	3·8
10 M	0419	8·5	1049	3·7	1640	9·0	2322	3·1
11 Tu	0508	9·1	1142	3·1	1725	9·6		
12 W	0007	2·5	0549	9·6	1224	2·5	1805	10·1
13 Th ○	0046	2·0	0627	10·1	1300	2·0	1842	10·5
14 F	0120	1·6	0702	10·4	1333	1·7	1916	10·7
15 Sa	0151	1·5	0734	10·5	1404	1·7	1948	10·7
16 Su	0219	1·5	0805	10·4	1430	1·8	2018	10·5
17 M	0246	1·8	0832	10·2	1456	2·1	2044	10·2
18 Tu	0311	2·1	0857	9·9	1521	2·4	2108	9·9
19 W	0336	2·4	0922	9·7	1549	2·8	2136	9·6
20 Th	0407	2·8	0950	9·4	1623	3·2	2210	9·2
21 F ☾	0447	3·3	1030	9·0	1711	3·6	2255	8·6
22 Sa	0543	3·7	1125	8·5	1821	4·0		
23 Su	0007	8·1	0702	4·1	1255	8·1	1954	4·1
24 M	0206	7·9	0837	4·0	1451	8·4	2132	3·6
25 Tu	0345	8·6	1009	3·3	1610	9·3	2252	2·7
26 W	0448	9·6	1119	2·3	1706	10·3	2353	1·6
27 Th	0539	10·6	1214	1·4	1756	11·3		
28 F ●	0043	0·8	0624	11·4	1302	0·7	1841	11·9
29 Sa	0128	0·3	0707	11·9	1345	0·3	1923	12·2
30 Su	0211	0·2	0748	11·9	1427	0·4	2005	12·1
31 M	0250	0·5	0829	11·7	1507	0·8	2044	11·6

Chart Datum: 5.88 metres below Ordnance Datum (Local)

CHANNEL ISLANDS – ST. HELIER

TIME ZONE UT(GMT)
For Summer Time add ONE hour in non-shaded areas

Lat 49°11′ N Long 2°07′ W

TIMES AND HEIGHTS OF HIGH AND LOW WATERS

YEAR **1992**

SEPTEMBER

Date	Day	Time	m	Time	m	Time	m	Time	m
1	Tu	0328	1·1	0907	11·1	1546	1·5	2124	10·9
2	W	0406	1·9	0946	10·4	1624	2·3	2203	10·0
3	Th ☽	0445	2·8	1026	9·5	1706	3·1	2247	9·1
4	F	0527	3·7	1112	8·7	1756	3·9	2340	8·2
5	Sa	0622	4·3	1218	8·0	1902	4·4		
6	Su	0109	7·7	0738	4·7	1358	7·8	2027	4·5
7	M	0253	7·8	0911	4·5	1524	8·2	2157	4·1
8	Tu	0359	8·3	1027	3·9	1619	8·9	2258	3·3
9	W	0445	9·0	1119	3·2	1702	9·6	2342	2·6
10	Th	0523	9·7	1158	2·5	1739	10·2		
11	F	0019	2·0	0558	10·3	1235	2·0	1814	10·7
12	Sa ○	0052	1·6	0632	10·6	1306	1·7	1848	10·9
13	Su	0123	1·4	0703	10·8	1335	1·6	1920	11·0
14	M	0151	1·5	0734	10·8	1404	1·7	1948	10·8
15	Tu	0218	1·7	0801	10·6	1430	1·9	2015	10·5
16	W	0243	2·0	0826	10·3	1456	2·3	2042	10·2
17	Th	0311	2·4	0853	10·0	1525	2·7	2110	9·8
18	F	0342	2·9	0924	9·7	1600	3·1	2145	9·3
19	Sa ☾	0424	3·4	1004	9·2	1652	3·6	2233	8·6
20	Su	0525	3·9	1102	8·6	1805	4·0	2351	8·0
21	M	0646	4·2	1239	8·1	1938	4·0		
22	Tu	0159	8·0	0823	4·0	1437	8·5	2117	3·5
23	W	0331	8·8	0952	3·2	1553	9·4	2234	2·5
24	Th	0430	9·8	1101	2·2	1648	10·4	2333	1·6
25	F	0518	10·8	1154	1·3	1734	11·3		
26	Sa ●	0021	0·8	0601	11·5	1241	0·7	1819	11·9
27	Su	0104	0·5	0643	11·9	1323	0·4	1900	12·1
28	M	0145	0·5	0723	11·9	1404	0·6	1941	11·9
29	Tu	0225	0·8	0802	11·6	1442	1·0	2020	11·3
30	W	0301	1·5	0839	11·0	1519	1·7	2057	10·6

OCTOBER

Date	Day	Time	m	Time	m	Time	m	Time	m
1	Th	0336	2·3	0915	10·2	1556	2·5	2135	9·7
2	F	0413	3·1	0952	9·4	1635	3·3	2214	8·9
3	Sa ☽	0454	3·9	1034	8·6	1722	4·0	2306	8·1
4	Su	0546	4·5	1136	8·0	1825	4·5		
5	M	0031	7·6	0657	4·8	1317	7·7	1948	4·6
6	Tu	0216	7·7	0829	4·7	1447	8·1	2115	4·2
7	W	0324	8·2	0949	4·2	1545	8·7	2219	3·6
8	Th	0410	8·9	1042	3·4	1628	9·4	2305	2·9
9	F	0449	9·6	1125	2·8	1706	10·1	2343	2·3
10	Sa	0525	10·2	1201	2·2	1742	10·6		
11	Su ○	0018	1·9	0558	10·7	1235	1·9	1817	10·9
12	M	0050	1·7	0631	10·9	1307	1·7	1849	11·0
13	Tu	0121	1·6	0702	11·0	1338	1·8	1920	10·9
14	W	0152	1·8	0731	10·9	1409	1·9	1949	10·7
15	Th	0222	2·1	0801	10·6	1440	2·2	2020	10·4
16	F	0254	2·5	0833	10·3	1514	2·6	2054	9·9
17	Sa	0332	2·9	0908	9·9	1555	3·0	2135	9·4
18	Su	0419	3·4	0955	9·4	1649	3·5	2230	8·7
19	M ☾	0519	3·8	1057	8·8	1800	3·8	2351	8·2
20	Tu	0636	4·0	1231	8·4	1924	3·8		
21	W	0141	8·3	0805	3·8	1413	8·7	2053	3·3
22	Th	0304	9·0	0928	3·2	1527	9·5	2207	2·6
23	F	0403	9·8	1035	2·4	1623	10·3	2306	1·8
24	Sa	0452	10·6	1129	1·6	1711	11·0	2356	1·3
25	Su ●	0536	11·2	1217	1·1	1756	11·4		
26	M	0039	1·0	0618	11·5	1300	0·9	1838	11·6
27	Tu	0120	1·1	0657	11·5	1340	1·0	1919	11·4
28	W	0159	1·4	0737	11·3	1419	1·4	1957	10·9
29	Th	0236	1·9	0813	10·8	1456	2·0	2034	10·3
30	F	0311	2·6	0850	10·1	1531	2·6	2112	9·6
31	Sa	0346	3·2	0927	9·5	1609	3·3	2150	8·9

NOVEMBER

Date	Day	Time	m	Time	m	Time	m	Time	m
1	Su	0424	3·8	1006	8·8	1652	3·8	2238	8·3
2	M ☽	0511	4·3	1058	8·2	1746	4·3	2343	7·9
3	Tu	0610	4·7	1215	7·9	1853	4·5		
4	W	0110	7·8	0726	4·7	1344	8·0	2009	4·3
5	Th	0226	8·1	0846	4·4	1453	8·4	2119	3·9
6	F	0321	8·7	0950	3·9	1543	9·0	2214	3·4
7	Sa	0406	9·3	1041	3·3	1627	9·6	2259	2·8
8	Su	0445	9·9	1123	2·7	1706	10·1	2340	2·4
9	M	0523	10·4	1203	2·3	1743	10·6		
10	Tu ○	0018	2·1	0558	10·7	1241	2·0	1819	10·8
11	W	0055	1·9	0634	11·0	1317	1·9	1856	10·9
12	Th	0131	1·9	0709	11·0	1354	1·9	1933	10·8
13	F	0209	2·1	0745	10·9	1432	2·1	2009	10·5
14	Sa	0247	2·3	0823	10·6	1511	2·3	2051	10·2
15	Su	0329	2·7	0905	10·3	1556	2·6	2138	9·7
16	M	0417	3·1	0955	9·8	1648	3·0	2233	9·2
17	Tu ☾	0515	3·4	1055	9·3	1750	3·3	2344	8·8
18	W	0621	3·6	1211	8·9	1902	3·4		
19	Th	0109	8·7	0737	3·6	1335	9·0	2019	3·3
20	F	0226	9·1	0854	3·3	1451	9·3	2134	2·9
21	Sa	0331	9·6	1004	2·8	1553	9·9	2235	2·4
22	Su	0424	10·2	1102	2·2	1645	10·4	2329	2·0
23	M	0512	10·6	1153	1·8	1733	10·7		
24	Tu ●	0015	1·8	0556	10·9	1238	1·5	1818	10·8
25	W	0057	1·7	0636	11·0	1320	1·5	1859	10·8
26	Th	0137	1·8	0717	10·9	1359	1·7	1940	10·5
27	F	0215	2·1	0755	10·6	1436	2·0	2018	10·1
28	Sa	0250	2·6	0832	10·2	1511	2·5	2056	9·6
29	Su	0324	3·0	0908	9·7	1546	2·9	2134	9·2
30	M	0359	3·4	0946	9·2	1623	3·4	2213	8·7

DECEMBER

Date	Day	Time	m	Time	m	Time	m	Time	m
1	Tu	0437	3·8	1027	8·7	1705	3·8	2258	8·3
2	W ☽	0522	4·2	1118	8·3	1754	4·0	2354	8·1
3	Th	0618	4·4	1221	8·1	1853	4·2		
4	F	0103	8·1	0724	4·5	1334	8·1	2002	4·1
5	Sa	0211	8·3	0837	4·3	1442	8·5	2108	3·9
6	Su	0311	8·7	0945	3·9	1539	8·9	2209	3·4
7	M	0402	9·3	1042	3·3	1628	9·5	2302	3·0
8	Tu	0448	9·9	1132	2·8	1713	10·0	2350	2·5
9	W ○	0532	10·4	1218	2·3	1757	10·5		
10	Th	0035	2·1	0614	10·8	1302	1·9	1839	10·8
11	F	0117	1·9	0655	11·1	1344	1·7	1923	10·9
12	Sa	0159	1·8	0737	11·2	1426	1·6	2005	10·9
13	Su	0243	1·9	0819	11·1	1508	1·7	2049	10·6
14	M	0327	2·1	0904	10·8	1552	2·0	2136	10·3
15	Tu	0413	2·4	0952	10·4	1640	2·3	2226	9·8
16	W ☾	0502	2·8	1044	9·9	1732	2·7	2323	9·4
17	Th	0558	3·2	1144	9·4	1832	3·1		
18	F	0029	9·1	0703	3·4	1255	9·1	1940	3·3
19	Sa	0142	9·0	0815	3·5	1412	9·0	2054	3·3
20	Su	0254	9·1	0929	3·3	1522	9·2	2204	3·1
21	M	0357	9·5	1037	2·9	1624	9·5	2305	2·8
22	Tu	0451	9·9	1133	2·5	1718	9·9	2356	2·4
23	W	0539	10·3	1222	2·1	1804	10·2		
24	Th ●	0042	2·2	0622	10·5	1306	1·9	1846	10·3
25	F	0121	2·1	0703	10·6	1345	1·8	1926	10·3
26	Sa	0159	2·1	0741	10·6	1420	1·9	2004	10·2
27	Su	0233	2·2	0818	10·4	1454	2·1	2040	9·9
28	M	0304	2·5	0853	10·0	1525	2·4	2114	9·6
29	Tu	0335	2·8	0925	9·6	1555	2·8	2145	9·2
30	W	0404	3·2	0957	9·3	1626	3·1	2217	8·9
31	Th	0438	3·5	1031	8·9	1702	3·5	2254	8·6

Chart Datum: 5.88 metres below Ordnance Datum (Local)

GOREY 10-17-14

Jersey (Channel Islands)

CHARTS
Admiralty 1138, 3655; SHOM 6939, 826, 5232; ECM 1014; Stanford 16; Imray C33A

TIDES
−0454 Dover; ML 6·1; Duration 0545; Zone 0 (GMT)

Standard Port ST HELIER (⟵)

Times				Height (metres)			
HW		LW		MHWS	MHWN	MLWN	MLWS
0300	0900	0200	0900	11·1	8·1	4·1	1·3
1500	2100	1400	2100				
Differences ST. CATHERINE'S BAY							
0000	+0010	+0010	+0010	0·0	−0·1	0·0	+0·1

SHELTER
Good shelter in the harbour which dries out completely. Access HW $\mp$3. Good anchorage in Gorey Roads and in St Catherine's Bay to the N of Gorey, except in S to SE winds; deep water.

NAVIGATION
Waypoint 49°10′·50N 01°57′·33W, 118°/298° from/to front Ldg Lt 298°, 2·9M. Beware the very large tidal range. On approaching harbour, keep well outside all local beacons until the leading marks are picked up. Beware Banc du Chateau 1M offshore to N of Ldg Line and Azicot Rk (dries 2·2m) just S of Ldg Line 2 ca from ent.

LIGHTS AND MARKS
(1) Ldg Lts 298°. Front Gorey pier Oc RG 5s 8m 12M; W framework Tr; vis R304°-352°, G352°-304°. Rear, 490m from front, OcR 5s 24m 8M; W square with R border.
(2) Gorey pier Lt on with church spire 304° leads over Road Rk (3·3m), and Azicot Rk.
(3) Gorey pier Lt on with Fort William 250° leads close to Pacquet Rk (0·6m).

RADIO TELEPHONE
Gorey Harbour Ch 74 (HW−3 to HW+3 summer only).

TELEPHONE (0534)
Hr Mr 53616; ⌗ 30232; Marinecall 0898 500 457; Dr Contact Hr Mr.

FACILITIES
EC Thursday; **Jetty** FW; **Gorey Yacht Services** ☎ 53958, M, P, D, ME, El, Sh, Gas, CH; **Pier** ☎ 53616, M, P, D, L, FW, C (7 ton), AB.
Town P, CH, V, R, Bar. ✉; Ⓑ; Ferry to Portbail, Carteret. Bus to St. Helier.

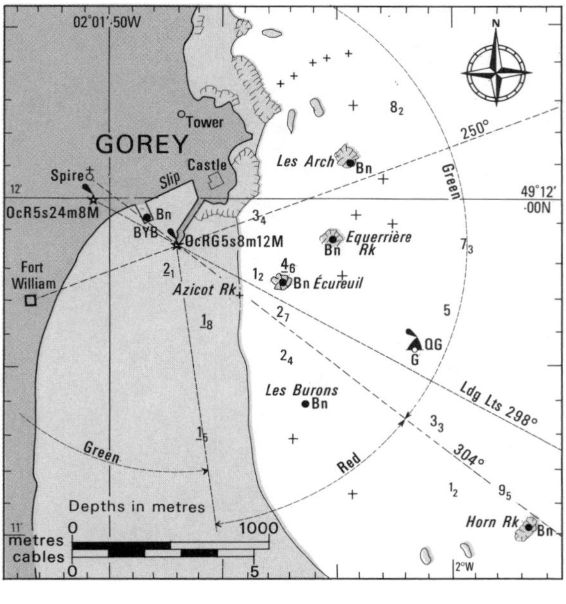

02°01'·50W
GOREY
Tower
Castle
Slip
Spire
12'
OcR5s24m8M
Bn
BYB
OcRG5s8m12M
Fort William
Azicot Rk
Les Arch
Bn
250°
Green
49°12'·00N
Equerrière Rk
Bn Écureuil
QG
G
Les Burons
Bn
Ldg Lts 298°
Red
304°
Green
Horn Rk
Bn
Depths in metres
11'
metres
cables
0
1000
5
2°W

MINOR HARBOURS AND ANCHORAGES 10.17.15

ALDERNEY
There are a number of anchorages, all picturesque but only safe in off-shore winds. Zone 0 (GMT) Admty charts 60,3653, HW −0410 on Dover (GMT). Tides see 10.17.9. Anchorages in a clockwise direction from BRAYE:
SAYE BAYE, Small sandy bay adjacent to Braye.
CORBLET BAY, A clear bay in NE corner of the island.
LONGY BAY, Wide sandy bay with good holding in sand. Restaurant nearby.
LA TCHUE, Good holding in small bay surrounded by cliffs.
TELEGRAPH BAY, Pleasant sandy bay in SW corner of the island.
HANNAINE BAY, A good place to wait for the tide.
PLATTE SALINE BAY, Good shelter from E winds.
BURHOU, Anchor in bay in SW of the islands, below half tide.
None of these anchorages provide any facilities.

GUERNSEY
Zone O (GMT) Admty charts 807, 3654: HW-0450m Dover (GMT). Tides see 10.17.11.
Anchorages, in a clockwise direction from St. Peter Port.
HAVELET BAY, Just S of St. Peter Port harbour. Crowded in summer.
SOLDIERS BAY, Quiet anchorage, sandy bottom, no facilities.
FERMAIN BAY, Popular with tourists, ferry to St. Peter Port. Good shelter from SW/NW. Cafe.
PETIT PORT BAY.
MOULIN HUET BAY.
SAINTS BAY.
PETIT BOT BAY.
} All tourist attractions with usual amenities. S coast bays with sandy bottoms. (Last is part of Icart Bay)
PORTELET HARBOUR, Anchor/sandy bottom. Beware of fish farm. Stone Quay (dries) but not advisable to dry out alongside. Facilities:- Hotel, cafe/toilets. Bus to St. Peter Port.
LIHOU ISLAND, Privately owned island, but visitors are welcome. Anchor off NE corner.
VAZON BAY, Large sandy beach with long surf line. Beware surfers and bathers. Facilities:- Hotel/Timeshare complex, bus to St. Peter Port.
COBO BAY, Sandy beach with many local moorings. Facilities:- Hotel, bar, D, L, P, ✉, R, V. Bus to St. Peter Port.
GRANDE HAVRE, Very popular, many local moorings. Anchor to W of Hommet de Greve. Stone slip; very busy in summer; lying alongside not recommended. Facilities:- Hotel/Bar bus to St. Peter Port.
L'ANCRESSE BAY, Sandy bay with good shelter from S/SW.
FONTENELLE BAY, Good shelter but many rocks.
BORDEAUX HARBOUR, Small drying harbour full of local moorings. Facilities:- Cafe. Bus to St. Peter Port.
ST. SAMPSON HARBOUR, Harbour dries. Guernsey's second harbour and very commercial. Official port of entry. Good shelter but the disadvantages of a commercial port. Lt on Crocq pier head. FR 11m 5M; vis 250° — 340°, and traffic signals. N pier head FG 3m 5M; vis 230° — 340°. Ldg Lts 286°, Front on S pier head FR 3m 5M; vis 230° — 340°; Rear, 390m from front, on clocktower, FG 13m. VHF Ch 12 (H24). Facilities:- See Hr Mr for AB, C, FW. No facilities for yachts.
Marine and General ☎ 45808, Slip, ME, El, Sh, C. Bus to St Peter Port.
Note:- JETHOU, CREVICHON, GRANDE FAUCONNIERE are private and landing is forbidden.

HERM ISLAND
Herm harbour has Ldg Lts, (occas) both FW at 078°. Hr. used by local ferries above half tide. Very congested in summer. Facilities:- Hotel/bar Hr Mr ☎ 22377. Alternatively use Rosaire steps to the S; or anchor in the bight to W. of Rosaire steps. Other anchorages are on the E. coast in Belvoir bay and Shell beach bay.

SARK
There are a number of anchorages around the island, all safe in settled weather and off-shore winds. There are no lights in any of these anchorages. Zone O (GMT); Admty chart 808; HW −0450 on Dover (GMT); Tides see 10.17.12. Anchorages in a clock-wise direction from Creux Harbour:

MINOR HARBOURS AND ANCHORAGES *continued*

LES LACHES, (outside Creux harbour) Anchor E of white patch on pier head.
DERRIBLE BAY, Good shelter and good holding in sand
DIXCART BAY, Sandy and sheltered with two hotels. Good holding ground.
ROUGE TERRIER, (in Little Sark) Sandy with cliff path to hotel.
CLOUET BAY, (Good departure point for l'Etac). Low water anchorage. Unpleasant swell at HW.
PORT GOURY, Remains of quay exists but anchor in bay.
LES FONTAINES BAY, SW facing small bay.
LA GRANDE GREVE, Big sandy bay with small drying rock in centre. Exposed to SW winds. Pub at cliff top.
HAVRE GOSSELIN, Is a safe small anchorage, exposed to SW winds. Crowded in summer.
PORT À LA JOUMENT, Shingle bay with good holding.
PORT DU MOULIN, Shingle bay.
LES FONTAINES BAY, Exposed to NE winds.
GREVE DE LA VILLE, Sand and shingle close into stone steps with access to village at cliff top.

JERSEY
Zone O (GMT); Admty charts 1136, 1137, 1138; HW −0455 on Dover (GMT); for tides see 10.17.13. There are numerous anchorages around the island and the following are the main ones going clockwise from St. Helier.
ST. AUBIN, Good quiet anchorage in bay with off-shore winds, or yachts can go alongside N quay and dry. Ent to N of St. Aubin Fort (on S) in W sector of Lt. N pier head Iso R 4s 12m 10M and Dir Lt 252°, Dir F WRG 5m, G246° −251°, W251°−253°, R253°−258°. St. Aubin Fort pier head F1 (2) Y 5s 8m 1M. Facilities:- FW on N quay, Slip C (1 and 5 ton), Grid; **Royal Channel Islands** YC, ☎ 41023 Bar, R, M, Slip; **Battricks** ☎ 43412, BY, Gas; **Jacksons Yacht Services** ☎ 43819. CH, El, ME, Sh; **St. Aubin** BY ☎ 45499 ME, El, Sh, CH; **Paddock** ME, Sh; **Town** Bar, D, FW, ⊡, P, R, V, buses to St. Helier.
BELCROUTE BAY, Bay on E of Noirmont Pt — steep to, deep water, excellent shelter from W to SW winds; landing by dingy.
ST. BRELADE BAY, Small stone pier in NW corner, local moorings in Bouilly Port. Good shelter from N and W. A very popular sandy tourist beach with various hotels. A quiet anchorage can be found in Beau Port.
GREVE AU LANCON, A wide sandy bay E of Grosnez Pt which covers at high tide. Suitable for day visits on calm days. Exposed to swell.
GREVE de LECQ, Ldg line, Round tower, W, in line with W house with grey roof at 202°. Ruins extend E from present pier. Pub, and bus to St. Helier. Exposed to swell.
BONNE NUIT BAY, Ldg Lts. 223° (FG). Harbour dries; sand and shingle. Many local boat moorings. Hotel.
BOULEY BAY, Good anchorage. Rocky bottom close to pier. Local boat moorings. Hotel.
ROZEL BAY, Dir Lt 245° FWRG, W sector leads between pier heads and Bn. Harbour dries with sand and shingle. Local boat moorings. Shops and pubs, bus to St. Helier.
ST. CATHERINE, Many local moorings to S of breakwater. F1 1·5s 13M. Landing on slip at root of breakwater. Dinghy Sailing Club RNLI ILB, Station, Cafe.
LA ROQUE, Small pier, local boat moorings, sandy beach. Not suitable for visitors without good local knowledge. No facilities.
LES ECREHOU, 5M NE of Rozel, has about a dozen cottages. Arrive at about ½ tide ebbing. Anchor WSW 0·2M off Marmotiere (with FS and houses); other islands are Maitre Ile (one house), Blanche and 5 other small islands. Beware of strong and eddying tidal streams 4 to 8 kts. Without local knowledge, a detailed pilotage book is essential.
PLATEAU des MINQUIERS, About 12M S of Jersey (Chart 3656). Approach from Demi de Vascelin Buoy. Safe in settled weather and light winds. Maitresse Ile has about a dozen cottages. Beware of strong and eddying tidal streams. Land at the slipway NW of the States mooring buoy. Without local knowledge, a detailed pilotage book is essential.

Area 18

North France
St. Quay-Portrieux – Pointe de Barfleur

18

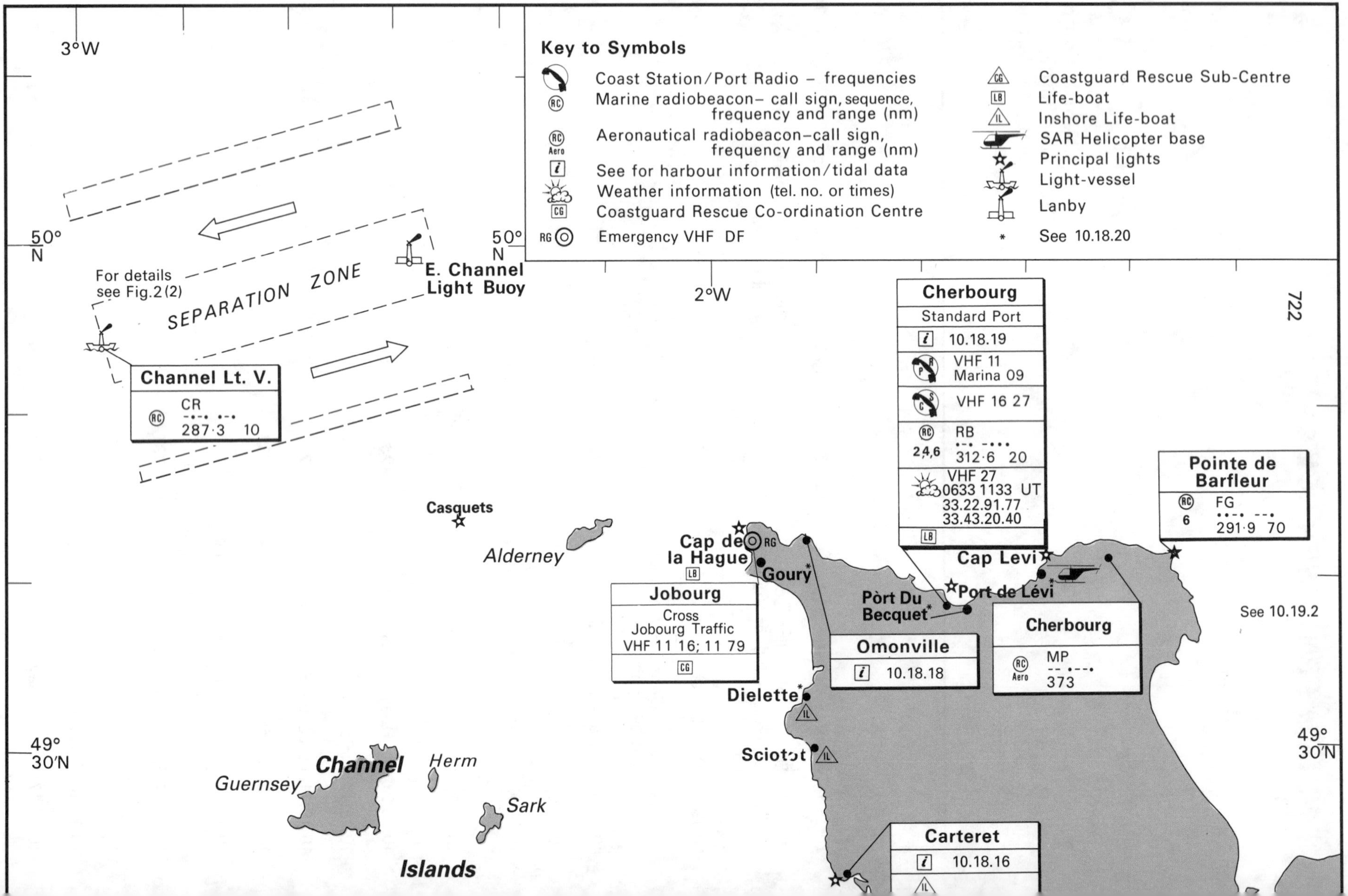
Key to Symbols
Coast Station/Port Radio – frequencies
Marine radiobeacon– call sign, sequence, frequency and range (nm)
Aeronautical radiobeacon–call sign, frequency and range (nm)
See for harbour information/tidal data
Weather information (tel. no. or times)
Coastguard Rescue Co-ordination Centre
Emergency VHF DF
Coastguard Rescue Sub-Centre
Life-boat
Inshore Life-boat
SAR Helicopter base
Principal lights
Light-vessel
Lanby
* See 10.18.20
3°W
2°W
50° N
49° 30′N
For details see Fig.2(2)
SEPARATION ZONE
E. Channel Light Buoy
Channel Lt. V.
CR
287·3 10
Casquets
Alderney
Cap de la Hague
Jobourg
Cross
Jobourg Traffic
VHF 11 16; 11 79
Goury
Dielette
Sciotot
Pòrt Du Becquet
Omonville
10.18.18
Cherbourg
Standard Port
10.18.19
VHF 11
Marina 09
VHF 16 27
RB
2,4,6
312·6 20
VHF 27
0633 1133 UT
33.22.91.77
33.43.20.40
Cap Levi
Port de Lévi
Cherbourg
MP
373
Pointe de Barfleur
FG
6
291·9 70
See 10.19.2
Carteret
10.18.16
Guernsey
Channel
Herm
Sark
Islands

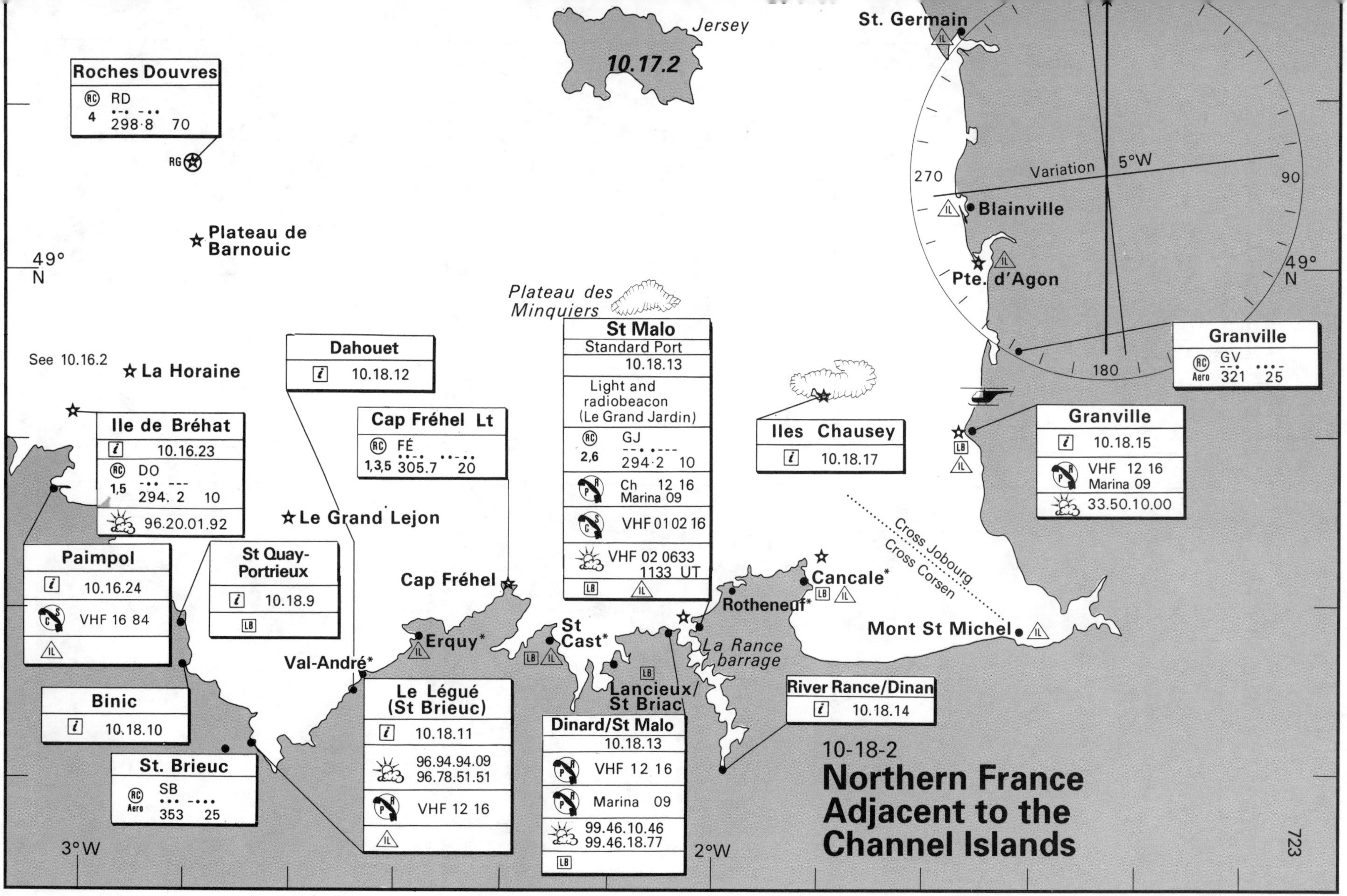

10-18-2
Northern France Adjacent to the Channel Islands
Jersey
10.17.2
St. Germain
Blainville
Pte. d'Agon
Variation 5°W
270
90
180
49° N
49° N
3°W
2°W
Roches Douvres
RD
4
298·8 70
RG
Plateau de Barnouic
See 10.16.2
La Horaine
Ile de Bréhat
10.16.23
DO
1,5
294. 2 10
96.20.01.92
Paimpol
10.16.24
VHF 16 84
St Quay-Portrieux
10.18.9
Binic
10.18.10
St. Brieuc
SB
Aero
353 25
Dahouet
10.18.12
Cap Fréhel Lt
FÉ
1,3,5
305.7 20
Le Grand Lejon
Cap Fréhel
Erquy*
Val-André*
Le Légué (St Brieuc)
10.18.11
96.94.94.09
96.78.51.51
VHF 12 16
Plateau des Minquiers
St Malo
Standard Port
10.18.13
Light and radiobeacon (Le Grand Jardin)
GJ
2,6
294·2 10
Ch 12 16
Marina 09
VHF 01 02 16
VHF 02 0633
1133 UT
St Cast*
Lancieux/St Briac
Dinard/St Malo
10.18.13
VHF 12 16
Marina 09
99.46.10.46
99.46.18.77
Rotheneuf*
La Rance barrage
River Rance/Dinan
10.18.14
Cancale*
Mont St Michel
Cross Jobourg
Cross Corsen
Iles Chausey
10.18.17
Granville
10.18.15
VHF 12 16
Marina 09
33.50.10.00
Granville
GV
Aero
321 25

Notes:
1. Due to very strong tidal stream rates, eddies may occur. Where possible some indication of these has been shown, but in many areas there is either insufficient information or the eddies are unstable.
2. For details of tidal streams round Alderney, see NP 264 part 2.

10.18.3. AREA 18 TIDAL STREAMS

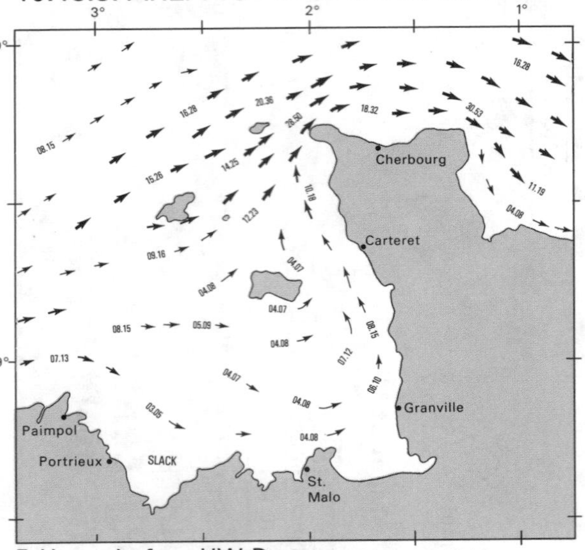
3°
2°
1°
50°
49°
Cherbourg
Carteret
Granville
Paimpol
Portrieux
SLACK
St. Malo

5 Hours before HW Dover (0030 before St.Malo)

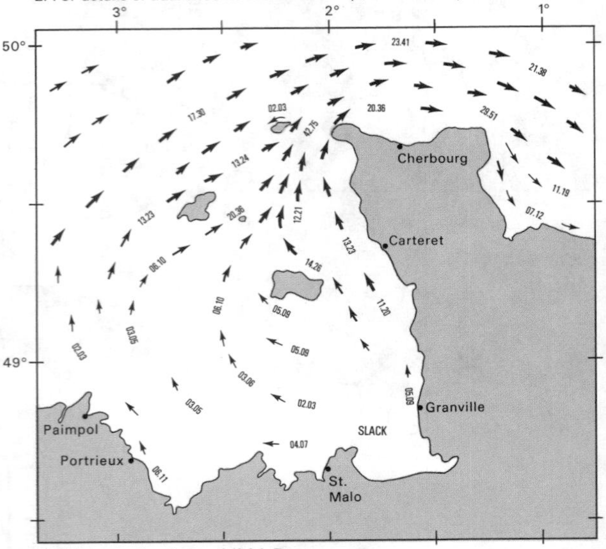
3°
2°
1°
50°
49°
Cherbourg
Carteret
Granville
Paimpol
Portrieux
SLACK
St. Malo

4 Hours before HW Dover (0030 after St.Malo)

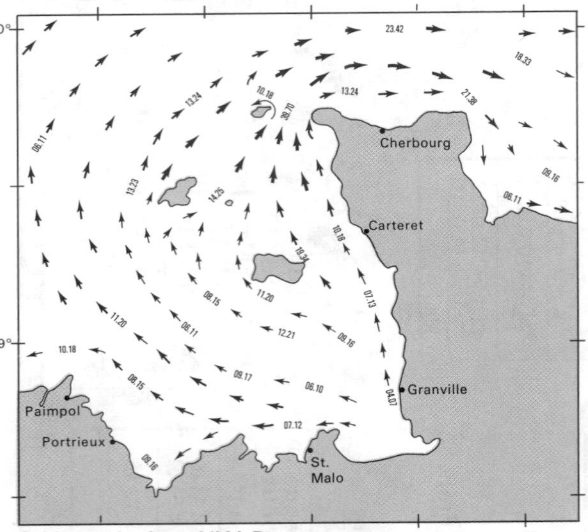
50°
49°
Cherbourg
Carteret
Granville
Paimpol
Portrieux
St. Malo

3 Hours before HW Dover (0130 after St.Malo)

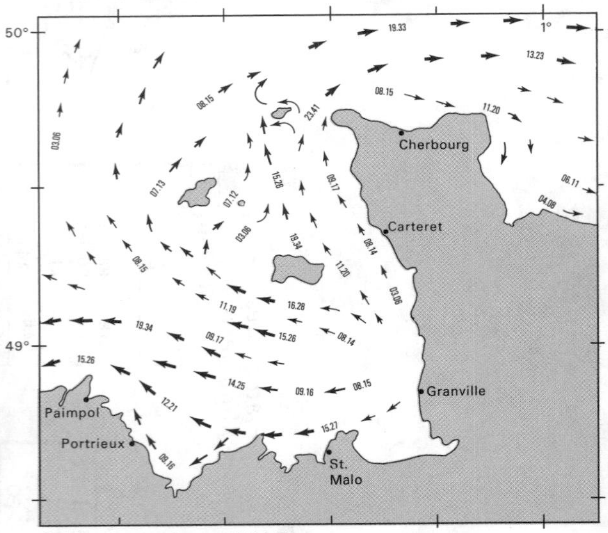
50°
1°
49°
Cherbourg
Carteret
Granville
Paimpol
Portrieux
St. Malo

2 Hours before HW Dover (0230 after St.Malo)

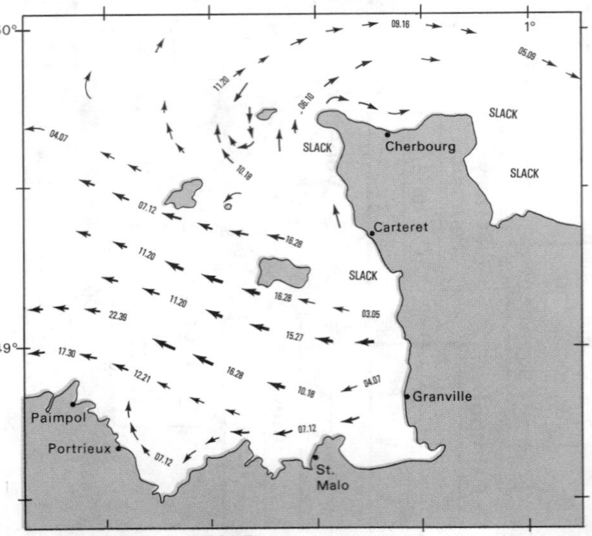
50°
1°
49°
SLACK
Cherbourg
SLACK
Carteret
SLACK
Granville
Paimpol
Portrieux
St. Malo

1 Hour before HW Dover (0330 after St.Malo)

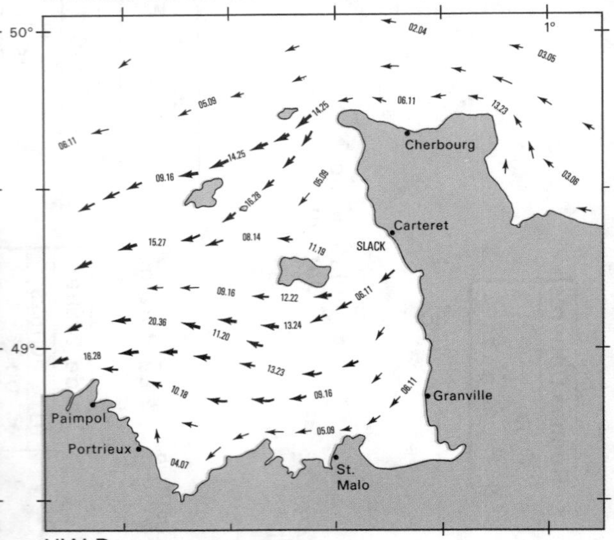
50°
1°
49°
Cherbourg
Carteret
SLACK
Granville
Paimpol
Portrieux
St. Malo

HW Dover (0430 after St.Malo)

Westward 10.16.3. Eastward 10.19.3. Northward 10.2.3. Isle of Wight 10.2.29. Portland 10.2.10.

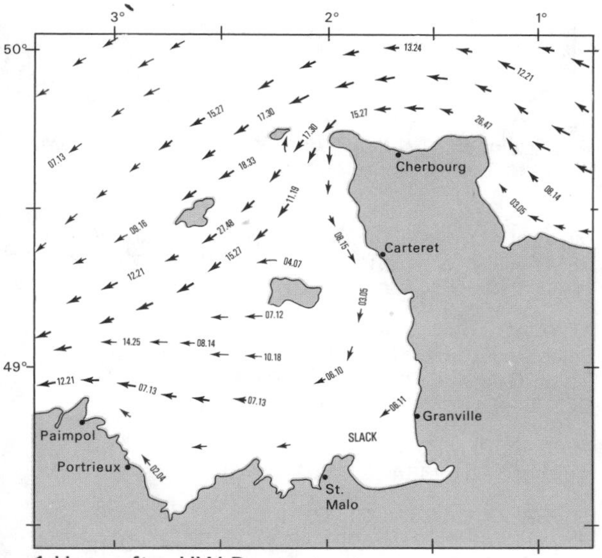
3°
2°
1°
50°
49°
Cherbourg
Carteret
Granville
Paimpol
Portrieux
St. Malo
SLACK

1 Hour after HW Dover (0530 after St.Malo)

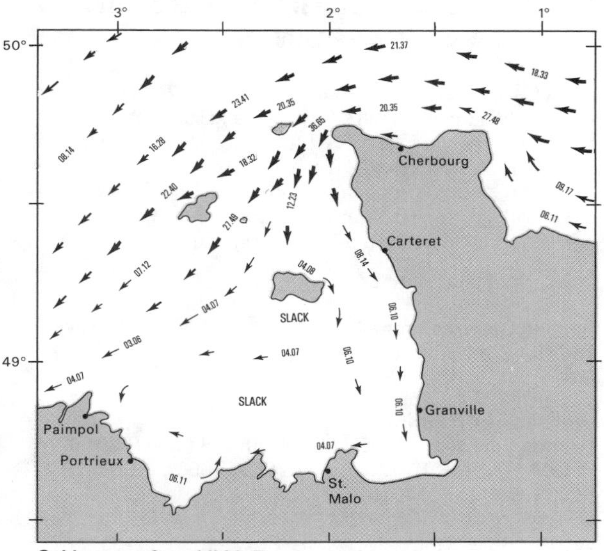
3°
2°
1°
50°
49°
Cherbourg
Carteret
Granville
Paimpol
Portrieux
St. Malo
SLACK
SLACK

2 Hours after HW Dover (0600 before St.Malo)

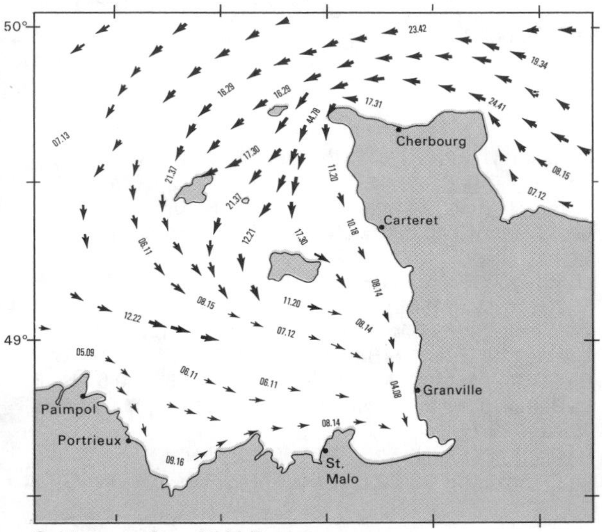
50°
49°
Cherbourg
Carteret
Granville
Paimpol
Portrieux
St. Malo

3 Hours after HW Dover (0500 before St.Malo)

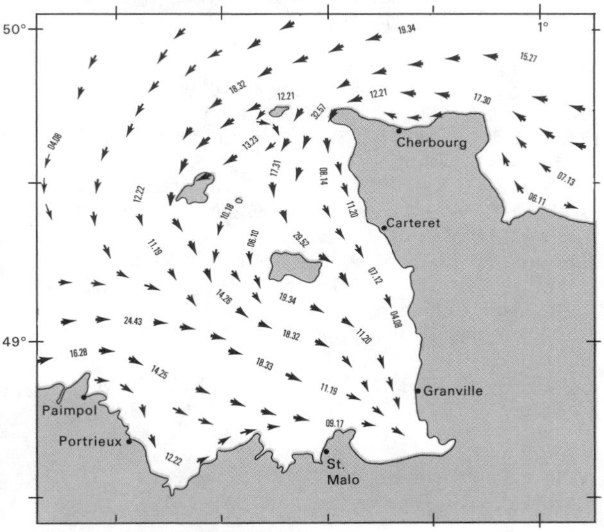
50°
49°
1°
Cherbourg
Carteret
Granville
Paimpol
Portrieux
St. Malo

4 Hours after HW Dover (0400 before St.Malo)

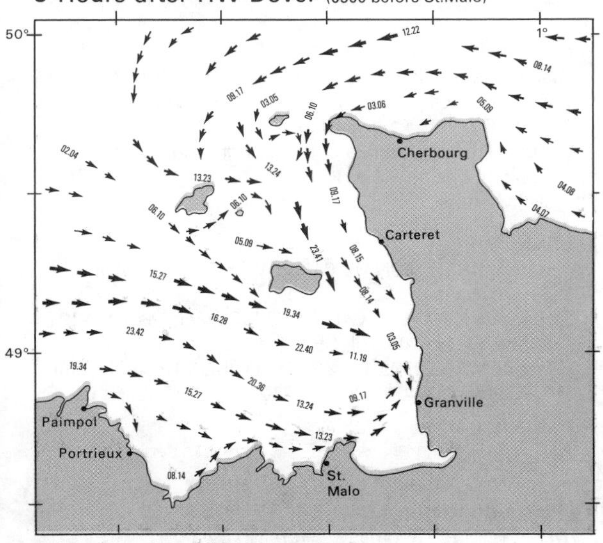
50°
49°
1°
Cherbourg
Carteret
Granville
Paimpol
Portrieux
St. Malo

5 Hours after HW Dover (0300 before St.Malo)

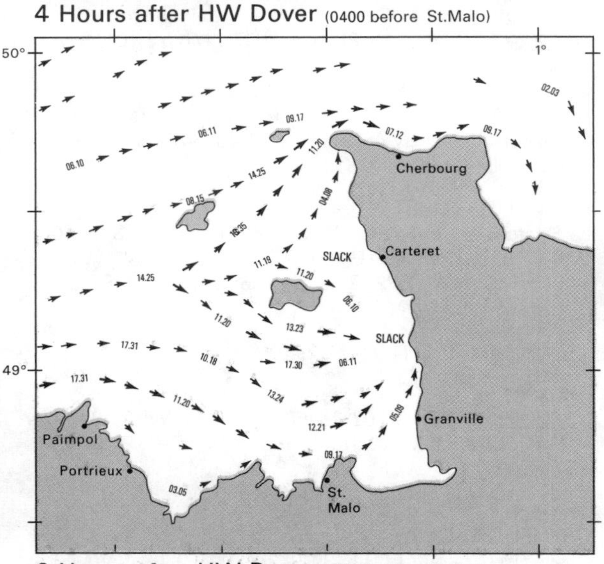
50°
49°
1°
Cherbourg
Carteret
Granville
Paimpol
Portrieux
St. Malo
SLACK
SLACK

6 Hours after HW Dover (0200 before St.Malo)

10.18.4 COASTAL LIGHTS, FOG SIGNALS AND WAYPOINTS

Abbreviations used below are given in 1.4.1. Principal lights are in **bold** print, places in CAPITALS, and light-vessels, light floats and Lanbys in *CAPITAL ITALICS*. Unless otherwise stated lights are white. m—elevation in metres; M—nominal range in n. miles. Fog signals are in *italics*. Useful waypoints are underlined – use those on land with care. All geographical positions should be assumed to be approximate. See 4.2.2.

FRANCE—NORTH COAST

Roches Douvres (from Area 16) 49°06'·47N 02°48'·82W F 15s 60m **28M**; pink Tr on dwelling with G roof; RC; RG; *Siren 60s.*

BAIE DE SAINT BRIEUC.
Grande Lejon 48°44'·95N 02°39'·90W Fl (5) WR 20s 17m **W18M**, R14M; R Tr, W bands; vis R015°-058°, W058°-283°, R283°-350°, W350°-015°.
Le Rohein 48°38'·88N 02°37'·68W VQ (9) WRG 10s 13m W10M, R8M, G8M; WCM; vis R072°-105°, W105°-180°, G180°-193°, W193°-237°, G237°-282°, W282°-301°. G301°-330°, W330°-072°.

SAINT-QUAY-PORTRIEUX.
Île Harbour Roches de Saint-Quay 48°40'·05N 02°48'°42W Oc (2) WRG 6s 16m W11M, R8M, G8M; W Tr and dwelling, R top; vis R011°-133°, G133°-270°, R270°-306°, G306°-358°, W358°-011°.
Herfleux Dir Lt 130° 48°39'·13N 02°47'·87W Dir Fl (2) WRG 6s W8M, R6M, G6M; vis G115°-125°, W125°-135°, R135°-145°; SCM Bn Tr; .
Elbow 43°39'·0N 02°49'·1W Dir Iso WRG 4s **W15M**, R11M, G11M; vis 159°-179°, G179°-316°, W316°-320·5°, R320·5°-159°; Reserve Lt ranges 12/9M.
NE Môle Hd 48°38'·9N 02°48'·9W Fl (3) G 12s 2M; G Tr.
SE Môle Hd Fl (3) R 12s; R Tr.
Caffa Lt By 48°37'·89N 02°43'·00W Q (3) 10s; ECM.
La Roselière Lt By 48°37'·51N 02°46'·31W VQ (9) 10s; WCM.

BINIC.
Môle de Penthièvre Hd 48°36'·13N 02°48'·84W Oc (3) 12s 12m 12M; W Tr, G gallery; unintens 020°-110°.

LE LÉGUÉ (St BRIEUC).
Le Légué Lt By 48°34'·38N 02°41'·07N Mo (A) 10s; SWM; *Whis.*
Pointe à l'Aigle 48°32'·15N 02°43'·05W QG 13m 8M; ▲ on G & W Tr; vis 160°-070°.
Custom House Jetty 48°31'·96N 02°43'·34W Iso G 4s 6m 7M, W cols, G top.

PORT DE DAHOUET.
La Petite-Muette 48°34'·91N 02°34'·21W Fl WRG 4s 10m W9M, R6M, G6M; ▲ on G and W Tr; vis G055°-114°, W114°-146°, R146°-196°. Fl (2) G 6s; vis 156°-286° 240m SE.

PLÉNEUF-VAL-ANDRÉ.
Jetty Hd 48°35'·89N 02°33'·24W

ERQUY.
S Môle Hd 48°38'·13N 02°28'·60W Oc (2+1) WRG 12s 11m W11M, R9M, G9M; W Tr, R top; vis R055°-081°, W081°-094°, G094°-111°, W111°-120°, R120°-134°.
Inner Jetty Hd Fl R 2·5s 10m 3M; R and W Tr.

CHENEL D'ERQUY.
Basses du Courant Lt By 48°39'·29N 02°29'·08W VQ (6) + LFl 10s; SCM.
Les Justières Lt By 48°40'·66N 02°26'·43W Q(6) + L Fl 15s; SCM.
Cap Fréhel 48°41'·10N 02°19'·07W Fl (2) 10s 85m **29M**; Brown ■ Tr, G lantern; *Horn (2) 60s*; RC.

ST CAST.
Môle Hd 48°38'·47N 02°14'·50W Iso WG 4s 11m W11M, G8M; G and W structure; vis W204°-217°, G217°-233°, W233°-245°, G245°-204°.

ST BRIAC.
Embouchure du Fremur. Dir Lt 125° 48°37'·1N 02°08'·2W Dir Iso WRG 4s 20m W14M, R11M, G11M; W mast on hut, vis G121·5°-124·5°, W124·5°-125·5°, R125·5°-129.5°.

APPROACHES TO ST MALO.
Banchenou Lt By 48°40'·52N 02°11'·42W Fl (5) G 20s; SHM.

CHENAL DE LA GRANDE PORTE
No 2 Lt By 48°47'·27N 02°07'·48W Fl (3) R 12s; PHM; *Whis.*
No. 1 Lt By 48°40'·24N 02°05'·97W Fl G 4s; SHM; *Whis.*
Le Sou Lt By 48°40'·14'N 02°05'·22W VQ (3) 5s; ECM.
Ldg Lts 089·1°. Front Rear **Rochebonne** 4·2M from front 48°40'·32N 01°58'·61W FR 40m **24M**; Gy n Tr, R top; intens 088·2°-089·7°.

CHENAL DE LA PETITE PORTE.
Lt By 48°41'·42N 02°07'·21W L Fl; SWM; *Whis.*
Bassee NE Lt By 48°42'·51N 02°09'·34W Q; NCM; *Bell.*
Fairway Lt By 48°41'·42N 02°07'·21W LFl 10s; SWM; *Whis.*
Les Courtis 48°40'·52N 02°05'·72W Fl (3) G 12s 14m 9M.
Brunel Lt By 48°40'·88N 02°05'·26W Q (9) 15s; WCM; *Bell.*
Ldg Lts 130°. Front **Le Grand Jardin** 48°40'·27N 02°04'·90W Fl (2) R 10s 24m **15M**; Gy Tr, R top; RC. Rear **La Ballue**, 0·9M from front Dir FG 69m **25M**; Gy ■ Tr; intens 128·2°-129·7°.
Ldg Lts 129°. Front **Les Bas-Sablons** 48°38'·22N 02°01'·23W Dir FG 20m **16M**; W ■ Tr, B top; intens 127·5°-130·5°. Rear **La Ballue**, 0·9M from front Dir FG 69m **25M**; Gy ■ Tr; intens 128·2°-129·7°.
Basse du Buron No.12 Lt By Fl R 10s; PHM.
Le Buron 48°39'·38N 02°03'·60W Fl (2) G 6s 15m 9M; G Tr.

ST MALO.
Môle des Noires Hd 48°38'·58N 02°01'·85W Fl R 5s 11m 13M; W Tr, R top; obsc 155°-159°, 171°-178°, and when brg more than 192°; *Horn(2) 20s.*
Ecluse du Naye Ldg Lts 071°. Front 48°38'·64N 02°01'·46W FR 6m 3M; W O, purple border, over lock gate. Rear 580m from front FR 23m 8M; vis 030°-120°.
F Vi Lts in line 071° marks S limits of dredged chan.
Bas-Sablons Marina Môle Hd 48°38'·48N 02°01'·63W Fl G 4s 7m 5M; Gy mast.

LA RANCE.
La Jument 48°37'·50N 02°01'·68W Fl (5) G 20s 4M; G Tr, SHM.
Tidal barrage NW wall Fl G 4s 6m 5M, G pylon, vis 191°-291°.
NE dolphin Fl (2) R 6s 5M, SE.
La Plate 48°40'·83N 02°01'·83W VQ WRG 11m W9M, R6M, G6M; NCM; vis W140°-203°, R203°-210°, W210°-225°, G225°-140°.

ROTHENEUF.
Entrance Bn 48°41'·42N 01°57'·61W; SHM; (unlit).
La Pierre-de-Herpin 48°43'·83N 01°48'·83W Oc (2) 6s 20m **17M**; W Tr, B top and base; *Siren Mo (N) 60s.*

CANCALE.
Jetty 48°40'·16N 01°51'·04W Oc (3) G 12s 12m 7M; W pylon, G top, G hut; obsc when brg less than 223°.

GRANVILLE.
Pointe du Roc 48°50'·11N 01°36'·70W Fl (4) 15s 49m **23M**; Gy Tr, R top.
Le Loup 48°49'·63N 01°36'·17W Fl (2) 6s 8m 11M; IDM, R refl.
Hérel. Marina 48°49'·96N 01°35'·82W Fl R 4s 12m 8M; W ● Tr, R top; *Horn (2) 40s.*
Jetée Est, Hd Iso G 4s 11m 6M; W pylon, G top on hut.
Jetée Ouest, Hd Iso R 4s 12m 6M; R pylon.
La Tourelle Fourchie *Horn (4) 60s.*
La Fourchie 48°50'·21N 01°36'·92W; R Tr; *Horn (4) 60s.*
Le Videcoq Lt By 48°49'·70N 01°42'·02W VQ (9) 10s; WCM.

ÎLES CHAUSEY.
Grande Île 48 52'·25N 01°49'·27W Fl 5s 39m **23M**; Gy ■ Tr; *Horn 30s.*
La Crabière Est 48°52'·58N 01°49'·30W Oc WRG 4s 5m W9M, R6M, G6M; B Tr, Y top; vis W079°-291°, G291°-329°, W329°-335°, R335°-079°.
Anvers Lt By 48°53'·90N 01°40'·84W Q (3) 10s; ECM.
Le Pignon 48°53'·55N 01°43'·30 W Oc (2) WR 6s 10m W11M, R8M; B Tr, Y band; vis R005°-150°, W150°-005°.

PASSAGE DE LA DÉROUTE.
SW Minquiers Lt By 48°54'·40N 02°19'·30W Q (9) 15s; SCM; *Whis.*
S Minquiers Lt By 48°53'·13N 02°10'·13W Q (6) + LFl 15s; SCM.
SE Minquiers Lt By 48°53'·50N 02°00'·00W Q (3) 10s; ECM; *Bell.*
NE Minquiers Lt By 49°00'·91N 01°55'·20W VQ (3) 5s; ECM; *Bell.*
Les Ardentes Lt By 48°57'·84N 01°51'·53W Q (3) 10s; ECM.
Basse le Marié Lt By 49°01'·89N 01°48'·76W Q (9) 15s; WCM.
Bas. Jourdan Lt By 49°06'·90N 01°44'·07W Q (3) 10s; ECM; *Whis.*
Écrévière Lt By 49°15'·32N 01°52'·07W Q (6) + LFl 15s; SCM; *Bell.*

REGNÉVILLE.
La Catheue Lt By 48°57'·95N 01°41'·00W Q (6) + L Fl 15s; SCM.
Pte d'Agon 49°00'·25N 01°34'·60W Oc (2) WR 6s 12m W10M, R7M; W Tr, R top, W dwelling; vis R063°-110°, W110°-063°.
Dir Lt 028° 49°00'·77N 01°33'·28W Dir Oc WRG 4s 9m W9M, R7M, G7M; House; vis G024°-027°, W027°-029°, R029°-033°.
Le Sénéquet 49°05'·54N 01°39'·65W Fl (3) WR 12s 18m W13M, R10M; W Tr; vis R083°-116°, W116°-083°.

PORTBAIL.
Ldg Lts 042°. Front La Caillourie 49°19'·79N 01°42'·40W Q 14m 11M; W pylon, R top. Rear 870m from front Q 20m 9M; belfry. Training wall Hd Q (2) R 5s 5m 2M; W mast, R top.

CARTERET.
Cap de Carteret 49°22'·46N 01°48'·35W Fl (2+1) 15s 81m **26M**; Gy Tr, G top; *Horn (3) 60s.*
Trois-Grunes Lt By 49°21'·88N 01°55'·12W Q (9) 15s; WCM.
Jetée Ouest, Hd 49°22'·20N 01°47'·40W Oc R 4s 6m 8M; W col, R top. Training wall Hd Fl (2) G 5s; W mast, G top.

DIÉLETTE.
Flamanville Lt By 49°36'·42N 01°53'·93W Q (9) 15s; WCM.
Ldg Lts 125·5°. Front, Jetée Ouest 49°33'·23N 01°51'·73W Oc WRG 4s 12m W8M, R6M, G6M; W Tr, G top; vis G shore-072°, W072°-138°, R138°-206°, G206°-shore. Rear 460m from front Dir FR 23m 11M; intens 121°-130°.
La Foraine 49°42'·95N 01°58'·75W; WCM; *Whis;* (occasionally submerged).

Cap de la Hague (Gros du Raz) 49°43'·37N 01 57'·19W Fl 5s 48m **23M**; Gy Tr, W top; *Horn 30s.*
La Plate 49°44'·03N 01°55'·64W Fl (2+1) WR 12s 11m W9M, R6M; Y 8-sided Tr, with B top; vis W115°-272°, R272°-115°.
Basse Bréfort Lt By 49°43'·70N 01°51'·05W VQ 8m 8M; NCM; *Whis.*

OMONVILLE, LA ROGUE.
49°42'·33N 01°50'·10W Iso WRG 4s 13m W11M, R8M, G8M; W pylon; vis G180°-252°, W252°-262°, R262°-287°.

CHERBOURG.
PASSE DE L'OUEST.
CH1 Lt By 49°43'·30N 01°42'·10W L Fl 10s 8m ; SWM; *Whis,* Ra refl.
Passe de l'Ouest Ldg Lts 140·5° and 142°. **Front**, Jetée du Homet Dir Q (2 hor) 5m **15M**; W ▲ on parapet at root of jetty; 63m apart; intens 138°-144°. Rear, Gare Maritime 0·98M from front Dir Q 35m **21M**; Gy framework with W ▲ on building; intens 140°-142·5°.
Fort de l'Ouest 49°40'·50N 01°38'·87W Fl (3) WR 15s 19m **W24M**, **R20M**; Gy Tr, R top, on fort; vis W122°-355°, R355°-122°; RC; *Reed (3) 60s.*
Digue de Querqueville, Hd Oc(3) WG 12s 8m W11M, G8M; W col, G top; vis W120°-290°, G290°-120°.
Le Tenarde Lt By 49°48'·78N 01°37'·67W VQ; NCM.
Ldg Lts 124·5°. Front Jetée du Homet Hd (E end) 49°39'·53N 01°36'·88W FG 10m 9M; W pylon, G top on blockhouse; Ree*d (2+1) 60s.* Rear Terre-plein de Mielles 0·75M from front Iso G 4s 16m 12M; W col, B bands; intens 114·5°-134·5°.
Fort Central VQ (6) + LFl 10s 5m 8M; vis 322°-032°.

PASSE EST.
Fort des Flamands 49°39'·16N 01°35'·53W Dir Q WRG 13m W12M, R10M, G10M; vis G173·5°-176°, W176°-183°, R183°-193°.
Fort de l'Est 49°40'·33N 01°35'·93W Iso WG 4s 19m W13M, G10M; W pylon, G top; vis W008°-229°, G229°-008°.
La Truite Lt By 49°40'·39N 01°35'·39W Fl (4) R 15s; PHM.
Forte Île Pelée Oc (2) WR 6s 19m W11M, R8M; W and R pedestal on fort; vis W055°-120°, R120°-055°.
Gare Maritime NW corner QR 6m 8M; W col, R lantern.
Marina Môle Hd 49°38'·93N 01°37'·07W Oc (2) G 6s 7m 6M; G pylon.
Jetée Ouest Hd Iso G 4s 4m 2M; W pylon, G top.

LE BECQUET.
Ldg Lts 186·5°. **Front** 49°39'·3N 01°32'·8W Dir Oc (2+1) 12s 8m **16M**; W 8-sided Tr; intens 183·5°-190.5°. Rear 50m from front, Dir Oc (2+1) R 12s 13m 11M; W 8-sided Tr, R top; synchronised with front, intens 183·5°-190·5°.

PORT DE LÉVI.
Cap Lévi 49°41'·80N 01°28'·40W Fl R 5s 36m **22M**; Gy n Tr, W top.
Port de Lévi 49°41'·30N 01°28'·27W F WRG 7m W11M, R8M, G8M; vis G050°-109°, R109°-140°, W140°-184°.
La Pierre Noire Lt By 49°43'·57N 01°28'·98W Q (9) 15s 8m 9M; WCM.
Basse du Renier Lt By 49°44'·90N 01°22'·00W VQ 8m 8M; NCM; *Whis.*

Note. For English Channel Waypoints see 10.1.7

18

10.18.5 PASSAGE INFORMATION

The French coastline from St Quay-Portrieux to St Malo is characterised by deep bays (often drying), a few rugged headlands and many offlying rks. From St Malo E to Mont St Michel and N to C de Flamanville the coast changes to extensive offshore shoals, sand dunes studded with rks and a series of drying hbrs. Continuing N to C de la Hague and E to C Lévi the coast is cleaner with few dangers extending more than 1M offshore; but between C Lévi and Pte de Barfleur rky shoals extend up to 2·5M seaward.

The sea areas around this coast, including the Channel Islands, are dominated by powerful tidal streams with an anti-clockwise rotational pattern and a very large tidal range. Between Alderney and C de la Hague and across the top of the Cherbourg Peninsular the main English Channel tidal streams are rectilinear E/W. Neap tides are best, particularly for a first visit, and tidal streams need to be worked carefully. Boats which can take the ground have an advantage for exploring the quieter hbrs. Be careful to avoid lobster pots, and oyster & mussel beds in some rivers and bays.

For French Glossary see 10.14.8. The whole area is covered by charts 2669 and 1106.

L'OST PIC TO ST MALO (charts 3674, 3659)

The Plateaux des Roches Douvres (Lt, fog sig, RC) and de Barnouic lie to the N of the B de St Brieuc and should be avoided. Local magnetic anomalies are reported. The E going stream begins at about HW St Malo -0400 and the W-going at about HW St Malo +0100 with Sp rates exceeding 4 kn.

To seaward of B de St Brieuc is Grand Léjon (Lt), a rky shoal 9M NE of St Quay-Portrieux. Rks extend 0·25M W and 0·8M NNE of the Lt Ho. Petit Léjon (dries) lies 3·5M SSE of Lt Ho. B de St Brieuc is flanked by two rky shoals: on the W side, Roches de St Quay and offlying patches extend 4M E from St Quay-Portrieux (10.18.9) which can only be approached from NW or SE; on the E side the Plateau du Rohein, at W end of long ridge, is 6M W of C d'Erquy. Between these two shoals is a chan 3M wide leading to the hbrs of Binic (10.18.10), Le Légué (10.18.11), Dahouet (10.18.12), Val André and Erquy (10.18.20). On the E side of theB, Chenal d'Erquy runs in a WSW/ENE direction about 0·3M off C d'Erquy and inshore of the various rky patches close to seaward. There are several rky shoals within the B itself, some extending nearly 2M from shore. Erquy is a pleasant, drying hbr, but often crowded with fishing boats.

From C d'Erquy to C Fréhel there are no worthwhile hbrs. But between C Fréhel and St Malo (10.18.13) there is St Cast hbr (10.18.20) , and anchs in B de la Fresnaie, B de l'Arguenon, and S of Île Agot in the apprs to the drying hbr of St Briac. Beware Le Vieux-Banc (dries) 6M ENE of C Fréhel. Here the E-going stream begins at HW St Helier –0555, and the W-going at HW St Helier –0015, sp rates 2·5kn. There are W-going eddies very close inshore on the E-going stream.

In the apprs to St Malo (chart 2700) are many islets, rks and shoals, between which are several chans that can be used in good vis. Tidal streams reach 4 kn at sp, and can set across chans. Chenal de la Grande Porte and Chenal de la Petite Porte are the easiest routes and are well marked. With sufficient rise of tide, and good vis, Chenal du Décollé, Chenal de la Grande Conchée, Chenal des Petis Pointus or Chenal de la Bigne can be used, but they all pass over or near to drying patches.

By passing through the lock at W end of the R Rance barrage (10.18.14) it is possible to cruise up river to Dinan, via the lock at Châtelier (French chart 4233). At Dinan is ent to Canal d'Ille et Rance (see 10.15.8).

ST MALO TO CAP DE LA HAGUE (charts 3659, 3656, 3655, 3653)

4M E of St Malo is the large drying hbr of Rothéneuf (10.18.20 and chart 2700), with anch off in good weather. Proceeding E, beware many dangers off Pte du Grouin, marked by La Pierre-de-Herpin (Lt, fog sig) 4M S of which is the drying hbr of Cancale (10.18.20), with many oyster beds. There is a fair weather anch SE of Île des Rimains. To E of Cancale is the drying expanse of B du Mont St Michel (10.18.20).

The W coast of the Cherbourg peninsula is exposed to the W, and is mostly rky, shallow and inhospitable. Granville (10.18.15) is the only hbr where a yacht can lie afloat. The two main chans to/from the Alderney Race are Passage de la Déroute and Déroute de Terre. The former passes W of Îles Chausey (10.18.16), SE and E of Les Minquiers and Les Ardentes, between Chaussée de Boeufs and Plateau de l'Arconie, between Basses de Taillepied and Les Écrehou, and W of Plateau des Trois Grunes. Parts of this chan are not well marked, and it is advisable not to use it at night.

Déroute de Terre leads between Pte du Roc (off Granville) and Îles Chausey, between Le Sénéquet Lt Tr and Les Boeufs, between Basses de Portbail and Bancs Félés, and E of Plateau des Trois Grunes. For detailed directions see Channel Pilot. The S end of this chan, E of Îles Chausey, is very shallow, and along much of this coast as far N as Carteret there is little depth of water, so that a nasty sea can build up. There are drying hbrs at Portbail (10.18.20), Carteret (10.18.16), Dielette (10.18.20) and Goury (10.18.20); these are more readily accessible if visited whilst cruising from S to N. 5M S of C de la Hague beware Les Huquets de Jobourg, an extensive bank of drying and submerged rks , and Les Huquets de Vauville (dry) close SE of them. The Jobourg radar surveillance station (CROSSMA) and atomic energy station Chy (R Lts) are conspic about 3-4M SE of Gros du Raz (Lt, fog sig), off C de la Hague.

THE ALDERNEY RACE (chart 3653)

The Alderney Race, so called due to very strong tidal streams, runs NE/SW between Alderney and C de la Hague. The fairway, approx 4M wide, is bounded by Race Rk and Alderney S Banks to the NW, and to the SE by rky banks 4M WSW of C de la Hague, Milieu and Banc de la Schôle (least depth 2·7m). These dangers which cause breaking seas and heavy overfalls should be carefully avoided. In bad weather and strong wind-against-tide conditions the seas break in all parts of the Race and passage is not recommended. Conditions are exacerbated at sp tides.

In mid-chan the NE going stream starts at HW St Helier -0210 (HW Dover +0530) and the SW stream at HW St Helier +0430 (HW Dover), sp rates both 5·5 kn. The times at which stream turns do not vary much for various places, but the rates do;

for example, 1M W of C de la Hague the sp rates are 7 or 8 kn.

To obtain optimum conditions, timing is of the essence. As a rule of thumb the Race should be entered at about slack water so as to avoid the peak tidal stream with attendant overfalls/seas.

Thus, bound SW, arrrive at around HW St Helier +0430 (HW Dover) off C de la Hague when the stream will be slack, whilst just starting to run SW off Alderney. A yacht leaving Cherbour at HW Dover -0300 will achieve the above timing by utilising the inshore W-going tidal eddy.

Conversely, NE bound, the Race can be entered N of Banc de la Schôle at about slack water (HW St Helier +0400) by leaving St Peter Port at approx HW St Helier +0030 with last of fair tide. An earlier departure will achieve a faster passage, but possibly less favourable conditions in the Race. On the NE stream the worst overfalls are on the French side.

CAP DE LA HAGUE TO POINTE DE BARFLEUR (chart 1106)

The N coast of the Cherbourg peninsula runs for 26M, mostly bordered by rks which extend 1M offshore between C de la Hague and Pte de Jardeheu, and 2·5M offshore from C Lévi to Pte de Barfleur. Tidal streams reach 5 kn at sp, and raise a steep sea with wind against tide. Between C de la Hague and Cherbourg (10.18.19) an eddy runs W close inshore during the last of the E-going stream.

There is anch in Anse de St Martin, about 2M E of C de la Hague, exposed to N, but useful while awaiting tide for Alderney Race, as alternative to Omonville (10.18.18).
Off Cherbourg (10.18.19) the stream is E-going from about HW-0430 and W-going from HW+0230. E of Cherbourg Port de Becquet and Port Lévi are two small drying hbrs (10.18.20). Off C Lévi a race develops with wind against tide, and extends nearly 2M to N. Pte de Barfleur has dangers up to 2M offshore, and a race in which the sea breaks heavily, extending 3-4M NE and E from Lt Ho: in bad weather, particularly with winds from NW or SE against the tide, it is necessary to keep at least 6M to seaward to avoid the worst effects.

The inshore passage between C Lévi and Pte de Barfleur is not recommended without local knowledge except in good weather and visibility when the transits shown on chart 1106 can be used. Tidal streams run strongly with considerable local variations.

10.18.6 DISTANCE TABLE

Approximate distances in nautical miles are by the most direct route while avoiding dangers and allowing for Traffic Separation Schemes, etc. Places in *italics* are in adjoining areas.

1. *Roches Douvres*	**1**																			
2. *Lézardrieux*	22	**2**																		
3. *St Peter Port*	25	48	**3**																	
4. *St Helier*	30	47	29	**4**																
5. St Quay - Portrieux	28	21	51	44	**5**															
6. Dahouet	33	29	52	41	11	**6**														
7. St Malo	42	49	54	39	35	29	**7**													
8. Granville	51	54	55	30	54	45	23	**8**												
9. Iles Chausey	43	53	54	25	47	37	17	9	**9**											
10. Carteret	44	68	31	26	64	60	50	38	33	**10**										
11. Cap de la Hague	50	74	28	45	74	74	73	61	55	23	**11**									
12. Cherbourg	64	88	42	59	88	88	87	75	69	37	14	**12**								
13. *Le Havre*	134	158	112	129	158	158	157	145	139	107	84	70	**13**							
14. *Cap Griz Nez*	208	232	186	203	232	232	231	219	213	181	158	147	108	**14**						
15. *Start Point*	76	95	70	93	103	109	117	120	111	89	77	91	156	210	**15**					
16. *Portland Bill*	87	113	66	91	115	118	118	111	102	75	52	62	118	161	49	**16**				
17. *Needles*	108	132	82	103	132	133	131	119	114	81	59	61	98	126	84	35	**17**			
18. *Nab Tower*	120	144	98	115	144	144	143	131	125	93	70	66	85	101	110	60	27	**18**		
19. *Brighton*	147	171	125	142	171	171	170	158	152	120	97	90	87	69	142	94	62	35	**19**	
20. *Royal Sovereign*	154	184	138	155	184	184	183	171	165	133	110	102	82	47	163	114	82	54	22	**20**

18

SAINT QUAY-PORTRIEUX

Côtes d'Armor

10-18-9

CHARTS
Admiralty 3672, 3674, 2669; SHOM 5725, 833; ECM 536; Stanford 16; Imray C33B, C34

TIDES
−0520 Dover; ML 6·4; Duration 0550; Zone −0100

Standard Port ST-MALO (⟶)

Times				Height (metres)			
HW		LW		MHWS	MHWN	MLWN	MLWS
0805	0120	0749	0256	12·2	9·2	4·4	1·5
2005	1320	1949	1456				
Differences ST QUAY-PORTRIEUX							
−0005	−0006	−0021	−0032	−0·8	−0·6	−0·3	−0·1

SHELTER
There is reasonable shelter in the harbour but in winds from SE to N, a surge occurs. Anchorage in the Rade de Portrieux is good but affected by winds from N to SE. Harbour dries. Max stay three days in season. There is excellent shelter in the marina.

NAVIGATION
Waypoint 48°41′·00N 02°49′·70W, 347°/167° from/to Moulières de Portrieux E cardinal Bn, 1·7M. Portrieux lies inside the Roches de St Quay the channel between being about ½ M wide. N end of the Roches de St Quay is the Ile Harbour Lt Ho. Beware the Moulières de Portrieux.

LIGHTS AND MARKS
To NE lie the rocky Ile Harbour and to the E Rochers Déan. Ile Harbour Lt Oc WRG 6s 16m 11/8M vis W080°-133°, G133°-270° and 306°-011°, R011°-080°. On Rochers Déan, Herflux Dir Lt Fl (2) WRG 6s 8/6M vis G115°-125°, W125°-135°, R135°-145°.

RADIO TELEPHONE
VHF Ch 09 (0830-1230; 1330-1830 LT. H24 in season).

TELEPHONE (96)
Old Hr Mr 96.70.95.31; New Hr Mr 96.70.49.51; Aff Mar 96.70.42.27; CROSS 98.89.31.31; SNSM 96.70.52.04; # 96.33.33.03; Meteo 99.46.10.46; Auto 99.46.18.77; Police 96.70.61.24; Dr 96.70.41.31; Brit Consul 99.46.26.64.

FACILITIES
Marina (900+100 visitors) ☎ 96.70.49.51, BH, AC, C (5 ton), D, P, FW; **Harbour** (500+8 visitors) – Max 3 days in July/Aug. Slip, M, P, D, L, FW, Sh, C (1.5 ton), ME, El, Sh, CH, AB, R, Bar; **Cercle de la Voile de Portrieux** ☎ 96.70.41.76, M, FW, C (1 ton), Bar; **Mathurin Cras** ☎ 96.70.57.83, ME, El, C (5 ton), Sh, Ⓔ, CH; **Town** V, Gaz, R, Bar. ✉; Ⓑ; ⇌ (bus to St Brieuc); ✈ (St Brieuc–Armor).
Ferry UK – St Malo–Portsmouth.

AGENTS WANTED
Ploumanac'h
Trébeurden
Le Touquet
Norderney
Dornumersiel
Langeoog
Wangerooge
Hooksiel
Bremerhaven

If you are interested in becoming our agent please write to the Editors and get your free copy annually. You do not have to be a resident in a port to be the agent but at least a fairly regular visitor.

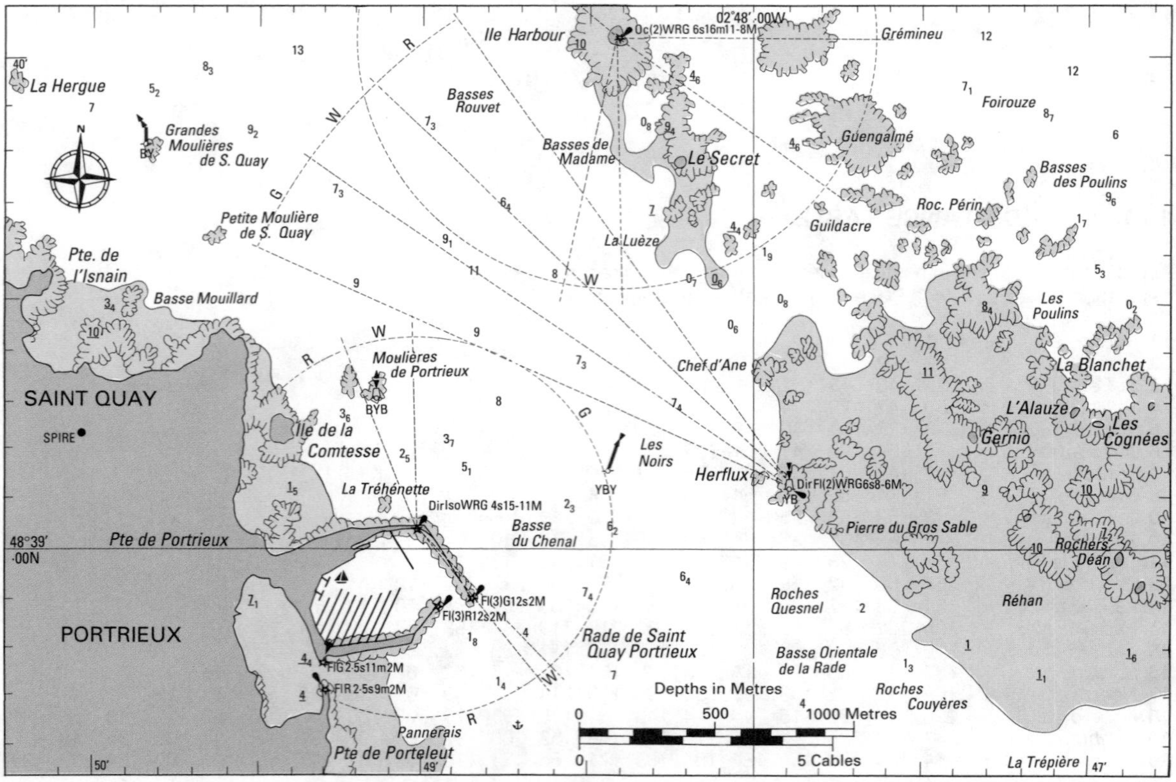
Ile Harbour
Oc(2)WRG 6s16m11-8M
02°48′·00W
Grémineu
La Hergue
Grandes Moulières de S. Quay
Petite Moulière de S. Quay
Pte. de l'Isnain
Basse Mouillard
SAINT QUAY
SPIRE
Ile de la Comtesse
Moulières de Portrieux
BYB
La Tréhénette
DirIsoWRG 4s15-11M
Basse du Chenal
Pte de Portrieux
48°39′·00N
PORTRIEUX
FlG 2·5s11m2M
FlR 2·5s9m2M
Fl(3)G12s2M
Fl(3)R12s2M
Pannerais
Pte de Porteleut
Rade de Saint Quay Portrieux
Basses Rouvet
Basses de Madame
Le Secret
La Luèze
Chef d'Ane
Les Noirs
YBY
Herflux
DirFl(2)WRG6s8-6M
YB
Pierre du Gros Sable
Guengalmé
Foirouze
Basses des Poulins
Roc. Périn
Guildacre
Les Poulins
La Blanchet
L'Alauze
Les Cognées
Gernio
Rochers Déan
Réhan
Roches Quesnel
Basse Orientale de la Rade
Roches Couyères
La Trépière
Depths in Metres
0 500 1000 Metres
0 5 Cables
50′
49′
47′
40′

BINIC 10-18-10

Côtes du Nord

CHARTS
Admiralty 3674, 2669; SHOM 5725, 833; ECM 536; Stanford 16; Imray C33B

TIDES
−0525 Dover; ML 5·6; Duration 0550; Zone −0100

Standard Port ST-MALO (⟶)

Times				Height (metres)			
HW		LW		MHWS	MHWN	MLWN	MLWS
0805	0120	0749	0256	12·2	9·2	4·4	1·5
2005	1320	1949	1456				
Differences BINIC							
−0002	−0004	−0018	−0029	−0·8	−0·5	−0·3	−0·1

SHELTER
Good shelter especially in Bassin à Flot (yacht harbour). Gate opens in working hours when tide reaches 9·5m (not near neaps). Access to Avant Port HW∓3 easy, day or night, except in E winds.

NAVIGATION
Waypoint 48°37'·00N 02°42'·00W, 078°/258° from/to entrance, 4·7M. Best approach from E, from Baie de St Brieuc (see 10.18.5) keeping E of Caffa W cardinal buoy, from which entrance is 246°; or from N through Rade de Portrieux. Entrance between moles, dries 4·2m.

LIGHTS AND MARKS
N mole head Oc(3) 12s 12m 12M; W Tr, G gallery. Gate and sliding bridge signals on mast N of gate:

By day	— St Andrew's Cross, B on W flag	— Gate open
By night	— W and R Lts (hor)	No entry
	— W and G Lts (hor)	No exit
	— R and G Lts (hor)	No movements

RADIO TELEPHONE
VHF Ch 09.

TELEPHONE (96)
Hr Mr 96.73.61.86; Aff Mar 96.73.61.86; CROSS 98.89.31.31; # 96.42.61.84; Meteo 99.46.10.46; Auto 99.46.18.77; Police 96.70.61.24; Dr 96.42.61.05; Brit Consul 99.46.26.64.

FACILITIES
Basin Slip, FW, AC, C (20 ton), Slip, AB; **Jean Bart Marine** ☎ 96.73.75.28, CH, SHOM; **Marinarmor** ☎ 96.73.60.55, CH, ME, El, (E), Sh, SM; **Club Nautique de Binic** ☎ 96.73.82.72; **Town** P, V, Gaz, R, Bar. ✉; (B); ⇌ (bus to St Brieuc); ✈ (St Brieuc). Ferry UK — St Malo—Portsmouth.

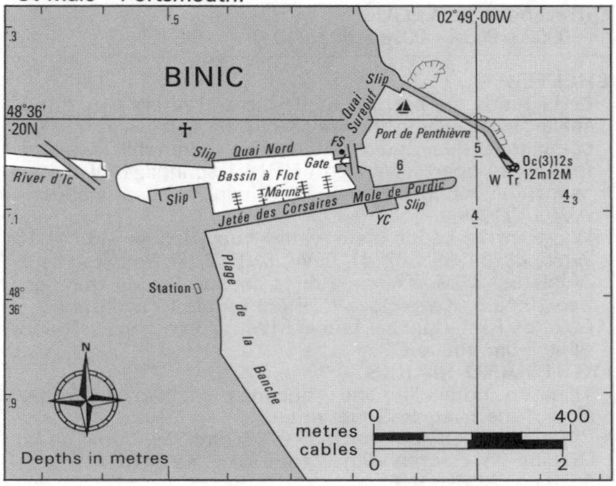

BINIC
02°49'·00W
48°36'·20N
Quai Surcouf
Slip
Port de Penthièvre
Quai Nord
Gate
Bassin à Flot
Marina
Jetée des Corsaires
Mole de Pordic
YC
River d'Ic
Station
Plage de la Banche
Oc(3)12s 12m12M
W Tr
metres
cables
0
400
2
Depths in metres

LE LÉGUÉ (ST BRIEUC) 10-18-11

Côtes du Nord

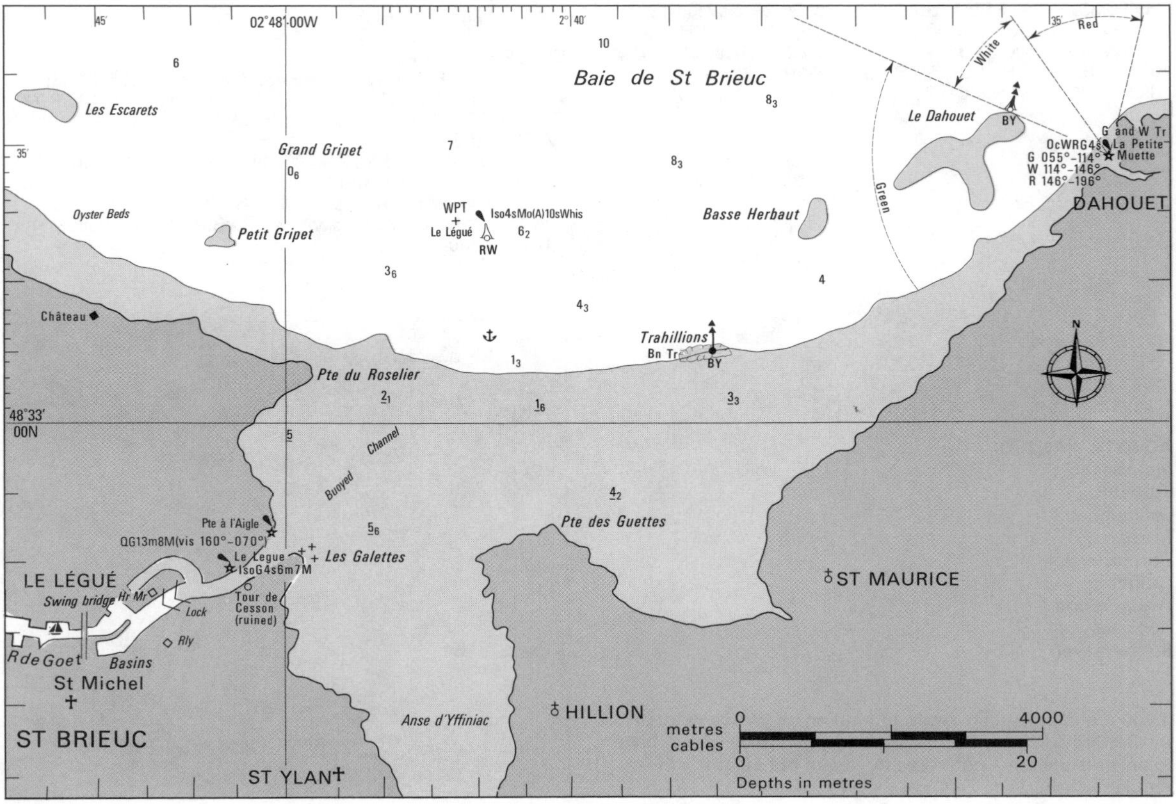

02°48'·00W
2°40'
35'
45'
48°33'00N
Baie de St Brieuc
Les Escarets
Grand Gripet
Petit Gripet
Oyster Beds
Château
WPT
Le Légué
Iso4sMo(A)10sWhis
RW
Le Dahouet
BY
Basse Herbaut
White
Red
Green
OcWRG4s
G 055°-114°
W 114°-146°
R 146°-196°
G and W Tr
La Petite Muette
DAHOUET
Trahillions
Bn Tr
Pte du Roselier
Buoyed Channel
Pte à l'Aigle
QG13m8M(vis 160°-070°)
Le Legue
IsoG4s6m7M
Les Galettes
Tour de Cesson (ruined)
LE LÉGUÉ
Swing bridge
Hr Mr
Lock
Rly
R de Goet
Basins
St Michel
ST BRIEUC
Pte des Guettes
ST MAURICE
HILLION
Anse d'Yffiniac
ST YLAN
metres
cables
0
4000
20
Depths in metres

18

LE LÉGUÉ/ST BRIEUC *continued*

CHARTS
Admiralty 3674, 2669; SHOM 5725, 833; ECM 536; Stanford 16; Imray C34, C33B
TIDES
−0520 Dover; ML 5·6; Duration 0550; Zone −0100

Standard Port ST-MALO (⟶)

Times				Height (metres)			
HW		LW		MHWS	MHWN	MLWN	MLWS
0805	0120	0749	0256	12·2	9·2	4·4	1·5
2005	1320	1949	1456				
Differences LE LÉGUÉ							
−0002	−0004	−0018	−0029	−0·8	−0·5	−0·3	−0·1

SHELTER
Le Légué is the port for St Brieuc and offers very good shelter especially in the wet basin. Le Quai Gilette is a commercial quay but yachts can lie there whilst waiting for lock to open (HW−2 to HW+1 springs; HW ∓1 neaps). Yachts use Bassin No 2 (min 3m) near viaduct.
NAVIGATION
Waypoint Le Légué (safe water) buoy, Iso 4s Mo (A) 10s Whis, 48°34′·39N 02°41′·09W, 030°/210° from/to Pte à l'Aigle Lt, 2·6M. The area dries beyond Pte du Roselier. See 10.18.5. Keep close to Pte à l'Aigle to avoid the Galettes Rks. Channel buoyed (with some gaps). The lock sill is 5·0m above CD.
LIGHTS AND MARKS
There are no leading lines, but there are two Lts on the N side of the river de Gouet ent.
Pte à l'Aigle QG 8M vis 160°-070° 13m 7M. Jetée de la Douane (W column with G top) Iso G 4s 6m 7M.
RADIO TELEPHONE
Call: *Légué Port* VHF Ch 12 16 (occas).
TELEPHONE (96)
Hr Mr 96.33.35.41; Aff Mar 96.61.22.61; CROSS 98.89.31.31; Meteo 99.46.10.46; Auto 99.46.18.77; SNSM 96.88.35.47; # 96.33.33.03; Police 96.94.52.25; Dr St Brieuc 96.61.49.07; Brit Consul 99.46.26.64.
FACILITIES
Quai (120+15 visitors), AB, C (30 ton); **22 Voiles** ☎ 96.33.14.04, SM; **Inter-Nautic** ☎ 96.33.28.71, ME, Sh, Ⓔ, El, CH; **Lecoq** ☎ 96.33.16.68, Sh, ME, El, CH; **Travadon** ☎ 96.33.38.54, ME. **Town (St Brieuc)** P, D, FW, ME, El, CH, Gaz, V, R, Bar, ✉; Ⓑ; ⇌; ✈.
Ferry UK — St Malo—Portsmouth.

AGENTS WANTED
Ploumanac'h
Trébeurden
Le Touquet
Norderney
Dornumersiel
Langeoog
Wangerooge
Hooksiel
Bremerhaven

If you are interested in becoming our agent please write to the Editors and get your free copy annually. You do not have to be a resident in a port to be the agent but at least a fairly regular visitor.

DAHOUET 10-18-12
Cotes du Nord

CHARTS
Admiralty 2668, 2669, 3674; SHOM 833, 6966; ECM 536; Stanford 16; Imray C33B, C34
TIDES
−0520 Dover; ML 6·1; Duration 0550; Zone −0100

Standard Port ST-MALO (⟶)

Times				Height (metres)			
HW		LW		MHWS	MHWN	MLWN	MLWS
0805	0120	0749	0256	12·2	9·2	4·4	1·5
2005	1320	1949	1456				
Differences DAHOUET							
−0007	−0005	−0009	−0035	−0·9	−0·5	−0·5	−0·2
ERQUY							
−0005	−0004	−0013	−0028	−0·8	−0·5	−0·3	−0·1

SHELTER
Good except in strong NW winds. Outer basin (fishing vessels) dries (Access HW∓2). Marina, min depth 3m, accessible over sill 5·5m above CD.
NAVIGATION
Waypoint 48°36′·85N 02°37′·70W, 310°/130° 3M from/to La Petite Muette Lt Tr.
LIGHTS AND MARKS
Approach channel is marked and there is a Lt Tr, La Petite Muette, Fl WRG 4s 10m 9/6M G055°-114°, W114°-146°, R146°-196°. 240m SE of La Petite Muette Fl (2) G 6s, vis 156°-286°.
RADIO TELEPHONE
None.
TELEPHONE (96)
Hr Mr 96.72.83.20; Meteo 99.46.10.46; # 96.33.13.83; Aff Mar 96.61.22.61; Cross 98.89.31.31; Auto 99.46.18.77. Ⓗ 96.45.23.28; Brit Consul 99.46.26.64.
FACILITIES
Marina (396) ☎ 96.72.95.46, FW, AC, BH (10 ton), Slip, C (6 ton), P, D; **Bouguet** ☎ 96.72.97.00, CH, El, ME, Sh; **YC du Val-André** ☎ 96.72.21.68; **Dahouet Garage** ☎ 96.72.95.46, ME; **Town**, V, R, Bar, ⇌(Lamballe), ✈ (St. Brieuc).
Ferry UK — St. Malo—Portsmouth.

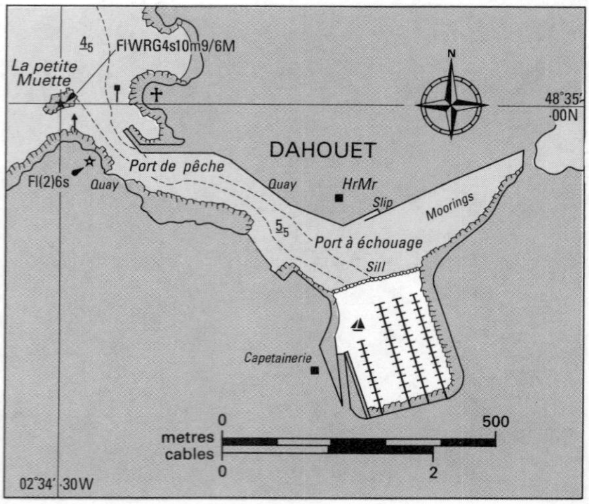

FlWRG4s10m9/6M
La petite Muette
N
48°35′·00N
DAHOUET
Port de pêche
Fl(2)6s
Quay
Quay
HrMr
Slip
Moorings
Port à échouage
Sill
Capetainerie
0
500
metres
cables
0
2
02°34′·30W

ST MALO/DINARD 10-18-13

Ille et Vilaine

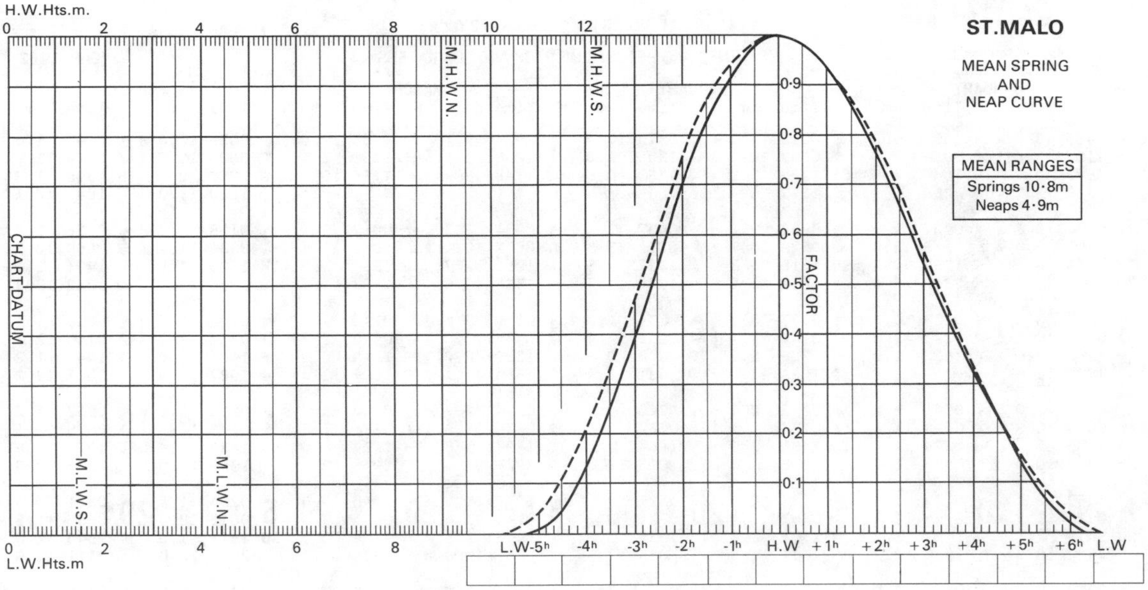
H.W.Hts.m.
0 2 4 6 8 10 12
M.H.W.N.
M.H.W.S.
CHART DATUM
M.L.W.S.
M.L.W.N.
FACTOR
0·9 0·8 0·7 0·6 0·5 0·4 0·3 0·2 0·1
0 2 4 6 8
L.W.Hts.m
L.W-5h -4h -3h -2h -1h H.W +1h +2h +3h +4h +5h +6h L.W
ST.MALO
MEAN SPRING AND NEAP CURVE
MEAN RANGES
Springs 10·8m
Neaps 4·9m

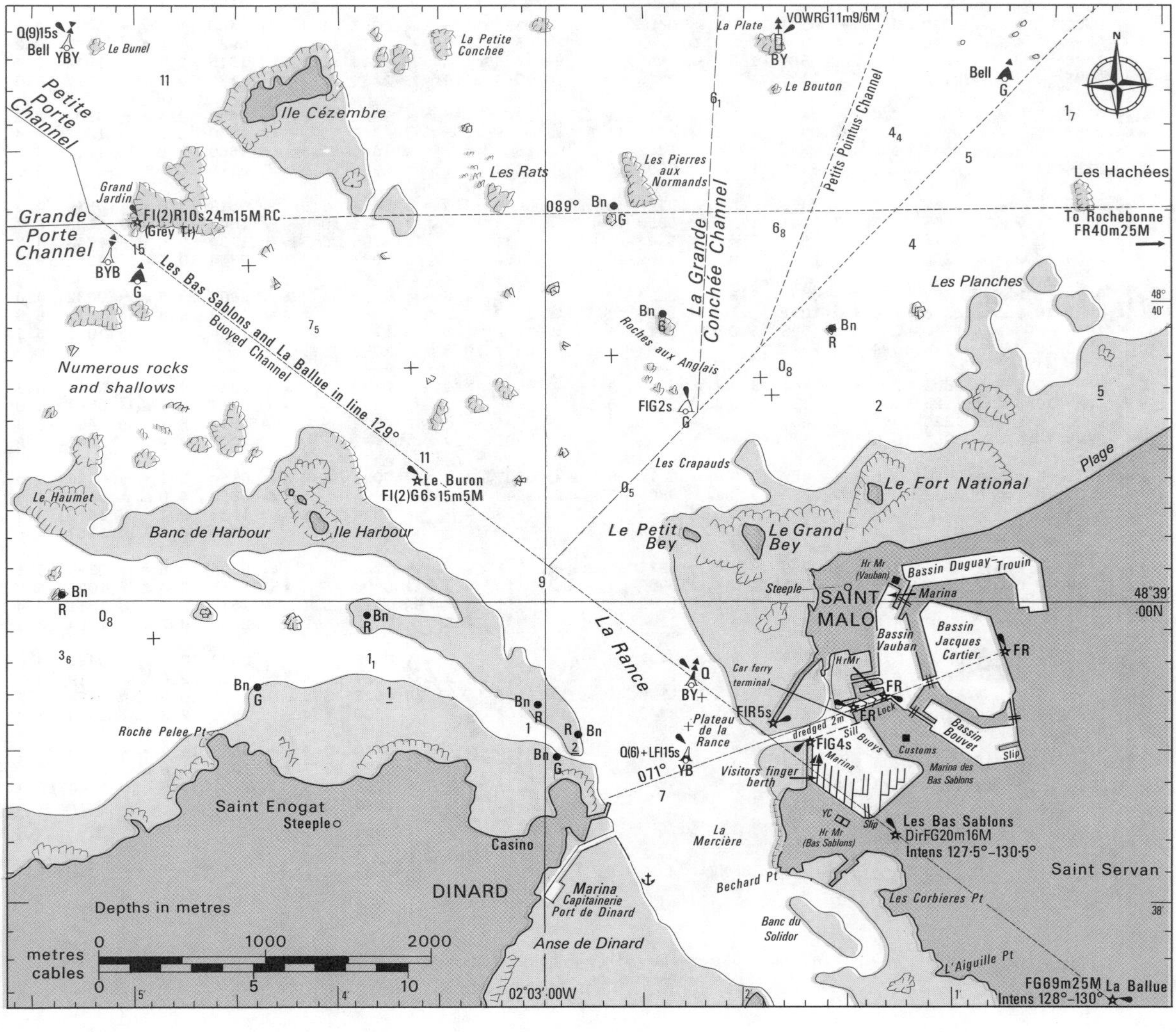
Q(9)15s Bell YBY
Le Bunel
La Petite Conchee
La Plate
VQWRG11m9/6M
BY
Le Bouton
Bell G
Ile Cézembre
Petite Porte Channel
Grand Jardin
Fl(2)R10s24m15M RC
(Grey Tr)
Grande Porte Channel
BYB
G
Les Rats
Les Pierres aux Normands
089°
Bn G
La Grande Conchée Channel
Petits Pointus Channel
Les Hachées
To Rochebonne FR40m25M
Les Planches
Les Bas Sablons and La Ballue in line 129° Buoyed Channel
Numerous rocks and shallows
Roches aux Anglais
Bn G
Bn R
Fl G2s G
Les Crapauds
Le Buron Fl(2)G6s15m5M
Le Haumet
Banc de Harbour
Ile Harbour
Le Petit Bey
Le Grand Bey
Le Fort National
Plage
Hr Mr (Vauban)
Bassin Duguay-Trouin
Steeple
SAINT MALO
Marina
Bassin Vauban
Bassin Jacques Cartier
FR
La Rance
Q BY
Car ferry terminal
Fl R5s
FR
Lock
Bassin Bouvet
Customs
Slip
Plateau de la Rance
dredged 2m
Sill
Buoys
Fl G4s
Marina
Marina des Bas Sablons
Q(6)+LFl15s YB
071°
Visitors finger berth
Roche Pelee Pt
Bn G
Bn R
Bn G
Saint Enogat Steeple
Casino
DINARD
YC
Hr Mr (Bas Sablons)
Slip
Les Bas Sablons DirFG20m16M Intens 127·5°-130·5°
La Mercière
Saint Servan
Bechard Pt
Marina Capitainerie Port de Dinard
Les Corbieres Pt
Banc du Solidor
Anse de Dinard
L'Aiguille Pt
FG69m25M La Ballue Intens 128°-130°
Depths in metres
metres 0 1000 2000
cables 0 5 10
02°03'·00W
48°39'·00N
48° 40'
38'

18

FRANCE, NORTH COAST - ST. MALO

TIME ZONE -0100
(French Standard Time)
Subtract 1 hour for GMT
For French Summer Time add ONE hour in non-shaded areas

LAT 48°38'N LONG 2°02'W

TIMES AND HEIGHTS OF HIGH AND LOW WATERS

YEAR 1992

JANUARY

Day	Time	m	Day	Time	m
1 W	0415	9.7	16 TH	0303	9.3
	1102	3.8		0956	4.0
	1643	9.7		1546	9.5
	2335	3.7		2235	3.7
2 TH	0514	10.1	17 F	0421	9.9
	1202	3.4		1115	3.3
	1739	10.1		1659	10.2
				2348	2.9
3 F	0029	3.3	18 SA	0526	10.7
	0602	10.6		1223	2.4
	1252	3.0		1802	11.0
	1826	10.4			
4 SA	0113	3.0	19 SU	0051	2.2
	0644	10.9		0623	11.6
	1335	2.7		1324	1.6
	● 1907	10.7		○ 1856	11.7
5 SU	0152	2.7	20 M	0149	1.5
	0721	11.2		0715	12.3
	1413	2.5		1421	1.0
	1942	10.9		1946	12.2
6 M	0227	2.6	21 TU	0242	1.0
	0755	11.3		0803	12.7
	1447	2.3		1512	0.6
	2015	11.0		2032	12.5
7 TU	0300	2.5	22 W	0330	0.8
	0826	11.4		0848	12.9
	1520	2.3		1557	0.5
	2045	11.1		2115	12.5
8 W	0331	2.5	23 TH	0413	0.9
	0857	11.3		0929	12.7
	1550	2.3		1639	0.8
	2115	11.0		2155	12.2
9 TH	0400	2.6	24 F	0452	1.3
	0927	11.2		1008	12.3
	1620	2.5		1716	1.4
	2145	10.9		2232	11.6
10 F	0429	2.8	25 SA	0528	1.9
	0957	10.9		1046	11.6
	1649	2.8		1750	2.2
	2216	10.6		2309	10.9
11 SA	0458	3.1	26 SU	0603	2.7
	1029	10.6		1125	10.7
	1720	3.1		1826	3.1
	2249	10.2		☾ 2351	10.0
12 SU	0531	3.5	27 M	0644	3.5
	1104	10.1		1212	9.7
	1756	3.5		1910	3.9
	2328	9.8			
13 M ☽	0613	3.9	28 TU	0047	9.2
	1149	9.6		0739	4.3
	1843	3.9		1321	8.9
				2014	4.6
14 TU	0020	9.4	29 W	0215	8.7
	0709	4.2		0901	4.7
	1252	9.2		1501	8.5
	1946	4.2		2148	4.8
15 W	0135	9.1	30 TH	0352	8.9
	0826	4.3		1034	4.5
	1419	9.1		1629	8.9
	2110	4.1		2313	4.3
			31 F	0500	9.4
				1145	3.9
				1729	9.5

FEBRUARY

Day	Time	m	Day	Time	m
1 SA	0013	3.7	16 SU	0516	10.4
	0549	10.1		1208	2.5
	1236	3.2		1753	10.8
	1813	10.1			
2 SU	0058	3.1	17 M	0037	2.1
	0629	10.7		0612	11.5
	1319	2.7		1311	1.5
	1851	10.6		1844	11.7
3 M	0137	2.7	18 TU	0135	1.3
	0704	11.1		0702	12.4
	1356	2.3		1406	0.7
	● 1924	11.0		○ 1931	12.4
4 TU	0212	2.3	19 W	0226	0.7
	0737	11.4		0747	12.9
	1430	2.0		1454	0.3
	1955	11.3		2013	12.8
5 W	0243	2.1	20 TH	0311	0.4
	0807	11.7		0829	13.1
	1501	1.8		1536	0.2
	2024	11.5		2053	12.8
6 TH	0313	1.9	21 F	0351	0.5
	0836	11.8		0908	13.0
	1531	1.7		1614	0.6
	2052	11.6		2129	12.5
7 F	0341	1.9	22 SA	0426	0.9
	0904	11.8		0943	12.4
	1559	1.8		1646	1.2
	2121	11.5		2203	11.8
8 SA	0409	2.0	23 SU	0457	1.6
	0932	11.6		1017	11.6
	1627	2.0		1715	2.1
	2149	11.3		2235	11.0
9 SU	0436	2.4	24 M	0526	2.6
	1001	11.2		1050	10.6
	1655	2.4		1743	3.1
	2219	10.9		2309	10.1
10 M	0506	2.8	25 TU	0559	3.5
	1032	10.6		1128	9.5
	1725	3.0		1817	4.1
	2252	10.3		☾ 2353	9.1
11 TU	0541	3.4	26 W	0645	4.4
	1110	10.0		1223	8.5
	1805	3.6		1911	4.9
	☽ 2334	9.7			
12 W	0629	3.9	27 TH	0117	8.3
	1203	9.3		0803	5.1
	1902	4.1		1420	7.9
				2056	5.3
13 TH	0039	9.1	28 F	0321	8.2
	0741	4.3		0957	4.9
	1331	8.8		1609	8.3
	2029	4.4		2244	4.9
14 F	0223	8.9	29 SA	0437	8.9
	0924	4.2		1117	4.2
	1526	8.9		1708	9.1
	2210	4.0		2346	4.0
15 SA	0404	9.4			
	1056	3.5			
	1651	9.8			
	2331	3.1			

MARCH

Day	Time	m	Day	Time	m
1 SU	0524	9.7	16 M	0458	10.4
	1208	3.4		1151	2.4
	1748	9.9		1734	10.8
2 M	0031	3.3	17 TU	0017	2.1
	0602	10.4		0552	11.5
	1250	2.7		1250	1.5
	1823	10.6		1823	11.7
3 TU	0109	2.6	18 W	0113	1.3
	0637	11.0		0640	12.3
	1328	2.2		1343	0.8
	1856	11.1		○ 1907	12.4
4 W	0144	2.2	19 TH	0202	0.7
	0710	11.5		0724	12.8
	1402	1.8		1429	0.5
	● 1927	11.5		1948	12.7
5 TH	0217	1.8	20 F	0246	0.5
	0741	11.8		0805	12.9
	1435	1.5		1509	0.5
	1957	11.8		2026	12.7
6 F	0247	1.6	21 SA	0324	0.6
	0810	12.0		0842	12.7
	1505	1.4		1544	0.9
	2026	11.9		2102	12.3
7 SA	0318	1.5	22 SU	0357	1.1
	0839	12.0		0917	12.1
	1535	1.4		1614	1.5
	2054	11.9		2134	11.7
8 SU	0347	1.6	23 M	0426	1.8
	0908	11.8		0949	11.3
	1603	1.7		1641	2.3
	2124	11.7		2205	10.9
9 M	0416	2.0	24 TU	0454	2.6
	0938	11.4		1021	10.4
	1631	2.2		1706	3.3
	2154	11.3		2237	10.0
10 TU	0446	2.5	25 W	0524	3.6
	1010	10.8		1055	9.4
	1702	2.8		1736	4.2
	2227	10.6		2315	9.1
11 W	0520	3.1	26 TH ☾	0603	4.4
	1048	10.1		1142	8.4
	1741	3.5		1822	5.0
	2309	9.9			
12 TH ☽	0607	3.8	27 F	0023	8.2
	1140	9.2		0709	5.1
	1838	4.2		1324	7.8
				1955	5.5
13 F	0013	9.1	28 SA	0224	8.0
	0719	4.3		0900	5.1
	1311	8.6		1518	8.1
	2007	4.5		2153	5.2
14 SA	0202	8.8	29 SU	0348	8.5
	0904	4.3		1027	4.5
	1515	8.8		1623	8.8
	2152	4.1		2300	4.4
15 SU	0348	9.4	30 M	0440	9.3
	1039	3.5		1123	3.7
	1637	9.8		1706	9.6
	2313	3.2		2348	3.5
			31 TU	0522	10.1
				1209	3.0
				1744	10.4

APRIL

Day	Time	m	Day	Time	m
1 W	0029	2.8	16 TH	0047	1.6
	0600	10.8		0614	11.9
	1250	2.4		1316	1.3
	1820	11.0		1841	12.1
2 TH	0108	2.3	17 F	0136	1.2
	0636	11.4		0659	12.2
	1328	1.9		1401	1.1
	1854	11.5		○ 1922	12.3
3 F	0144	1.8	18 SA	0219	1.1
	0710	11.7		0740	12.3
	1404	1.6		1441	1.2
	● 1927	11.8		2001	12.2
4 SA	0220	1.6	19 SU	0257	1.2
	0743	11.9		0819	12.1
	1438	1.4		1515	1.5
	1959	12.0		2037	12.0
5 SU	0254	1.5	20 M	0331	1.6
	0815	12.0		0855	11.6
	1511	1.5		1546	2.0
	2031	12.0		2111	11.5
6 M	0327	1.6	21 TU	0402	2.1
	0848	11.8		0928	11.0
	1543	1.7		1614	2.7
	2103	11.8		2143	10.8
7 TU	0400	1.9	22 W	0431	2.8
	0923	11.4		1002	10.2
	1615	2.2		1642	3.4
	2138	11.4		2217	10.0
8 W	0434	2.4	23 TH	0502	3.6
	1000	10.8		1037	9.4
	1650	2.8		1712	4.2
	2216	10.7		2255	9.3
9 TH	0513	3.0	24 F	0539	4.3
	1043	10.1		1123	8.7
	1734	3.5		1753	4.8
	2304	10.0		☾ 2351	8.6
10 F ☽	0604	3.6	25 SA	0632	4.8
	1143	9.3		1233	8.3
	1834	4.1		1902	5.2
11 SA	0014	9.3	26 SU	0114	8.3
	0717	4.1		0754	5.0
	1314	8.9		1401	8.3
	2001	4.4		2042	5.2
12 SU	0154	9.1	27 M	0236	8.6
	0852	4.0		0920	4.6
	1458	9.1		1515	8.7
	2134	4.0		2157	4.6
13 M	0325	9.6	28 TU	0340	9.1
	1018	3.4		1025	4.0
	1612	9.9		1611	9.4
	2250	3.2		2254	3.9
14 TU	0432	10.5	29 W	0431	9.8
	1127	2.5		1119	3.3
	1708	10.8		1657	10.2
	2352	2.3		2343	3.2
15 W	0526	11.3	30 TH	0516	10.5
	1225	1.8		1207	2.7
	1757	11.6		1740	10.8

Chart Datum: 6.60 metres below Lellemand System (Mean Sea Level, Marseilles).

TIME ZONE -0100
(French Standard Time)
Subtract 1 hour for GMT
For French Summer Time add
ONE hour in non-shaded areas

FRANCE, NORTH COAST - ST. MALO

LAT 48°38′N LONG 2°02′W

TIMES AND HEIGHTS OF HIGH AND LOW WATERS

YEAR **1992**

MAY

Day	Time	m	Day	Time	m
1 F	0028 0559 1251 1820	2.6 11.1 2.2 11.3	16 SA ○	0111 0637 1336 1900	1.9 11.5 1.9 11.7
2 SA ●	0112 0639 1333 1858	2.1 11.4 1.9 11.7	17 SU	0155 0721 1417 1941	1.8 11.5 2.0 11.7
3 SU	0154 0718 1414 1935	1.8 11.7 1.7 11.9	18 M	0235 0802 1453 2019	1.9 11.4 2.1 11.6
4 M	0234 0757 1452 2013	1.6 11.8 1.7 12.0	19 TU	0311 0840 1526 2055	2.1 11.1 2.4 11.3
5 TU	0314 0836 1531 2052	1.7 11.7 1.9 11.8	20 W	0345 0916 1558 2130	2.4 10.8 2.8 10.8
6 W	0353 0918 1610 2133	1.9 11.4 2.2 11.5	21 TH	0418 0951 1629 2205	2.8 10.3 3.3 10.3
7 TH	0434 1002 1652 2219	2.3 10.9 2.7 10.9	22 F	0451 1026 1701 2241	3.3 9.8 3.9 9.8
8 F	0520 1052 1740 2312	2.8 10.3 3.3 10.3	23 SA	0525 1106 1737 2324	3.8 9.3 4.3 9.3
9 SA ☽	0613 1152 1840	3.3 9.7 3.8	24 SU ☾	0606 1153 1826	4.2 9.0 4.7
10 SU	0018 0719 1307 1953	9.9 3.6 9.4 3.9	25 M	0018 0701 1253 1932	9.0 4.4 8.8 4.8
11 M	0136 0834 1428 2110	9.7 3.6 9.6 3.7	26 TU	0124 0809 1402 2046	8.9 4.4 8.9 4.6
12 TU	0253 0949 1539 2221	9.9 3.3 10.1 3.2	27 W	0232 0920 1509 2154	9.1 4.2 9.3 4.1
13 W	0400 1057 1638 2324	10.4 2.8 10.7 2.7	28 TH	0335 1024 1608 2254	9.6 3.7 9.9 3.6
14 TH	0457 1157 1729	10.9 2.4 11.2	29 F	0432 1122 1700 2349	10.1 3.2 10.5 3.0
15 F	0020 0549 1250 1816	2.2 11.3 2.1 11.6	30 SA	0523 1216 1748	10.6 2.7 11.1
			31 SU	0041 0612 1306 1833	2.5 11.1 2.3 11.5

JUNE

Day	Time	m	Day	Time	m
1 M ●	0131 0659 1354 1918	2.0 11.4 2.0 11.8	16 TU	0220 0750 1438 2006	2.3 11.0 2.5 11.4
2 TU	0219 0745 1441 2003	1.8 11.7 1.8 12.0	17 W	0258 0828 1513 2041	2.3 11.0 2.6 11.3
3 W	0307 0831 1526 2048	1.6 11.7 1.8 12.0	18 TH	0333 0902 1546 2115	2.4 10.9 2.7 11.1
4 TH	0353 0918 1611 2134	1.6 11.6 1.9 11.8	19 F	0406 0935 1617 2147	2.6 10.7 3.0 10.8
5 F	0439 1004 1657 2221	1.8 11.3 2.3 11.5	20 SA	0437 1007 1648 2220	2.9 10.4 3.3 10.4
6 SA	0526 1053 1744 2310	2.2 10.9 2.7 11.0	21 SU	0508 1040 1719 2254	3.2 10.1 3.6 10.1
7 SU ☽	0615 1144 1836	2.6 10.5 3.1	22 M	0541 1116 1754 2333	3.6 9.8 4.0 9.7
8 M	0004 0708 1243 1934	10.6 3.0 10.1 3.4	23 TU ☾	0620 1159 1839	3.9 9.4 4.2
9 TU	0106 0807 1351 2039	10.2 3.3 9.9 3.5	24 W	0022 0710 1255 1939	9.4 4.1 9.2 4.4
10 W	0216 0915 1502 2148	10.0 3.4 10.0 3.5	25 TH	0126 0814 1405 2053	9.2 4.2 9.2 4.3
11 TH	0327 1025 1608 2256	10.1 3.3 10.3 3.2	26 F	0239 0928 1517 2207	9.3 4.1 9.5 4.0
12 F	0432 1130 1707 2356	10.3 3.1 10.6 2.9	27 SA	0350 1039 1623 2314	9.6 3.6 10.0 3.4
13 SA	0530 1227 1759	10.6 2.8 11.0	28 SU	0453 1143 1721	10.1 3.1 10.7
14 SU	0050 0622 1316 1846	2.6 10.8 2.6 11.2	29 M	0014 0551 1242 1815	2.7 10.7 2.5 11.3
15 M ○	0138 0709 1359 1928	2.4 10.9 2.5 11.4	30 TU ●	0112 0645 1338 1906	2.1 11.3 2.0 11.8

JULY

Day	Time	m	Day	Time	m
1 W	0207 0736 1431 1954	1.6 11.7 1.6 12.2	16 TH	0241 0810 1456 2022	2.3 11.1 2.4 11.5
2 TH	0300 0825 1520 2041	1.3 12.0 1.4 12.5	17 F	0315 0841 1528 2052	2.2 11.2 2.4 11.5
3 F	0349 0911 1607 2127	1.1 12.1 1.3 12.4	18 SA	0345 0910 1557 2121	2.2 11.2 2.4 11.3
4 SA	0435 0956 1651 2210	1.1 12.0 1.5 12.2	19 SU	0415 0939 1625 2151	2.4 11.0 2.6 11.1
5 SU	0518 1039 1734 2254	1.4 11.6 1.9 11.7	20 M	0443 1008 1652 2220	2.6 10.8 3.0 10.7
6 M	0600 1122 1817 2339	2.0 11.1 2.5 11.1	21 TU	0511 1039 1722 2252	3.0 10.4 3.4 10.2
7 TU ☽	0644 1210 1905	2.6 10.5 3.1	22 W ☾	0543 1113 1758 2331	3.4 10.0 3.8 9.7
8 W	0031 0734 1308 2003	10.4 3.3 9.9 3.6	23 TH	0623 1157 1847	3.8 9.5 4.2
9 TH	0137 0836 1422 2114	9.8 3.8 9.6 3.9	24 F	0025 0718 1301 1956	9.2 4.2 9.2 4.5
10 F	0256 0952 1542 2230	9.5 4.0 9.7 3.8	25 SA	0143 0835 1427 2124	9.0 4.4 9.1 4.3
11 SA	0414 1106 1652 2338	9.6 3.8 10.0 3.4	26 SU	0313 1001 1551 2244	9.2 4.1 9.6 3.7
12 SU	0520 1209 1748	10.0 3.4 10.5	27 M	0431 1116 1701 2352	9.7 3.4 10.3 2.8
13 M	0035 0613 1301 1834	3.0 10.4 3.0 10.9	28 TU	0536 1222 1800	10.5 2.6 11.2
14 TU ○	0123 0657 1344 1914	2.7 10.7 2.7 11.2	29 W ●	0054 0632 1322 1852	2.0 11.3 1.8 12.0
15 W	0205 0736 1422 1950	2.4 10.9 2.5 11.4	30 TH	0153 0723 1416 1941	1.3 12.0 1.2 12.6
			31 F	0246 0810 1506 2026	0.8 12.4 0.8 13.0

AUGUST

Day	Time	m	Day	Time	m
1 SA	0334 0854 1552 2109	0.6 12.6 0.7 13.0	16 SU	0317 0839 1529 2051	1.9 11.5 2.0 11.7
2 SU	0418 0935 1633 2150	0.6 12.5 1.0 12.7	17 M	0345 0907 1556 2119	2.0 11.5 2.2 11.5
3 M	0457 1014 1711 2229	1.1 12.0 1.5 12.0	18 TU	0412 0935 1623 2147	2.2 11.3 2.5 11.1
4 TU	0534 1052 1748 2308	1.8 11.4 2.3 11.2	19 W	0439 1003 1651 2216	2.6 10.9 2.9 10.6
5 W ☽	0611 1134 1829 2354	2.7 10.6 3.1 10.2	20 TH	0507 1034 1723 2250	3.1 10.4 3.5 10.0
6 TH	0653 1225 1922	3.6 9.7 3.9	21 F ☾	0543 1112 1806 2338	3.7 9.8 4.1 9.3
7 F	0056 0753 1343 2038	9.3 4.3 9.1 4.4	22 SA	0634 1209 1912	4.3 9.2 4.5
8 SA	0228 0920 1522 2208	8.8 4.6 9.0 4.4	23 SU	0056 0753 1343 2048	8.8 4.6 8.9 4.5
9 SU	0402 1047 1639 2322	9.0 4.3 9.5 3.8	24 M	0247 0933 1528 2221	8.8 4.3 9.3 3.8
10 M	0509 1152 1733	9.5 3.8 10.2	25 TU	0416 1055 1644 2333	9.5 3.5 10.2 2.8
11 TU	0017 0557 1241 1815	3.2 10.1 3.2 10.8	26 W	0520 1202 1742	10.5 2.5 11.2
12 W	0102 0636 1322 1851	2.7 10.6 2.7 11.2	27 TH	0035 0614 1301 1833	1.9 11.5 1.7 12.2
13 TH ○	0141 0711 1358 1924	2.4 11.0 2.4 11.5	28 F ●	0132 0702 1356 1920	1.1 12.2 1.0 12.9
14 F	0215 0742 1430 1955	2.1 11.3 2.2 11.7	29 SA	0224 0747 1444 2004	0.6 12.7 0.6 13.2
15 SA	0247 0811 1500 2024	2.0 11.5 2.0 11.8	30 SU	0310 0829 1528 2045	0.4 12.9 0.5 13.1
			31 M	0351 0908 1606 2124	0.6 12.7 0.9 12.7

Chart Datum: 6.60 metres below Lellemand System (Mean Sea Level, Marseilles).

FRANCE, NORTH COAST - ST. MALO

TIME ZONE -0100
(French Standard Time)
Subtract 1 hour for GMT
For French Summer Time add ONE hour in non-shaded areas

LAT 48°38′N LONG 2°02′W

TIMES AND HEIGHTS OF HIGH AND LOW WATERS

YEAR 1992

SEPTEMBER

Day	Time	m	Time	m	Time	m	Time	m
1 TU	0428	1.2	0945	12.1	1641	1.5	2200	11.9
2 W	0500	2.0	1020	11.4	1714	2.4	2237	11.0
3 TH ☽	0532	3.0	1058	10.4	1750	3.4	2317	9.9
4 F	0609	4.0	1145	9.5	1838	4.3		
5 SA	0015	8.9	0704	4.8	1304	8.7	1957	4.9
6 SU	0159	8.3	0844	5.2	1457	8.6	2143	4.9
7 M	0344	8.5	1024	4.8	1616	9.1	2258	4.2
8 TU	0447	9.2	1126	4.1	1706	9.9	2349	3.5
9 W	0529	10.0	1211	3.4	1745	10.5		
10 TH	0030	2.9	0604	10.6	1250	2.8	1819	11.1
11 F	0107	2.4	0637	11.1	1325	2.4	1852	11.5
12 SA ○	0142	2.1	0708	11.5	1357	2.1	1923	11.8
13 SU	0214	1.9	0738	11.7	1428	1.9	1952	11.9
14 M	0244	1.8	0806	11.8	1458	1.9	2020	11.9
15 TU	0314	1.8	0835	11.8	1527	2.0	2049	11.7
16 W	0342	2.1	0903	11.6	1556	2.3	2118	11.3
17 TH	0410	2.5	0932	11.2	1625	2.7	2148	10.8
18 F	0439	3.0	1004	10.6	1657	3.3	2223	10.1
19 SA ☾	0515	3.7	1043	10.0	1741	4.0	2312	9.3
20 SU	0607	4.3	1141	9.2	1846	4.5		
21 M	0033	8.7	0729	4.7	1321	8.9	2025	4.5
22 TU	0232	8.8	0912	4.4	1508	9.3	2201	3.8
23 W	0358	9.6	1035	3.5	1622	10.3	2313	2.8
24 TH	0459	10.6	1140	2.5	1719	11.3		
25 F	0013	1.8	0549	11.6	1238	1.6	1808	12.2
26 SA ●	0108	1.1	0636	12.3	1330	1.0	1854	12.8
27 SU	0158	0.7	0720	12.7	1418	0.7	1938	13.0
28 M	0242	0.7	0801	12.8	1500	0.8	2019	12.9
29 TU	0322	1.0	0840	12.5	1538	1.2	2057	12.4
30 W	0356	1.6	0916	12.0	1611	1.8	2133	11.6

OCTOBER

Day	Time	m	Time	m	Time	m	Time	m
1 TH	0427	2.4	0951	11.2	1643	2.7	2209	10.7
2 F	0456	3.3	1027	10.3	1716	3.6	2247	9.6
3 SA ☽	0529	4.2	1111	9.3	1759	4.5	2341	8.7
4 SU	0617	5.0	1223	8.5	1908	5.1		
5 M	0117	8.1	0752	5.5	1410	8.3	2055	5.2
6 TU	0301	8.3	0940	5.2	1532	8.8	2214	4.6
7 W	0405	9.0	1044	4.4	1623	9.5	2307	3.8
8 TH	0447	9.7	1129	3.7	1704	10.2	2350	3.1
9 F	0523	10.5	1209	3.0	1740	10.9		
10 SA	0029.	2.6	0558	11.0	1247	2.5	1815	11.4
11 SU ○	0106	2.2	0632	11.5	1323	2.2	1849	11.7
12 M	0141	2.0	0705	11.7	1357	2.0	1922	11.9
13 TU	0214	1.9	0736	11.9	1431	1.9	1953	11.9
14 W	0247	1.9	0807	11.9	1504	2.0	2025	11.7
15 TH	0318	2.1	0839	11.7	1536	2.2	2058	11.4
16 F	0350	2.5	0913	11.4	1610	2.7	2134	10.8
17 SA	0424	3.0	0950	10.8	1647	3.2	2215	10.2
18 SU	0505	3.7	1035	10.1	1734	3.8	2309	9.4
19 M ☾	0600	4.3	1138	9.5	1840	4.3		
20 TU	0032	9.0	0719	4.6	1310	9.2	2010	4.3
21 W	0214	9.1	0852	4.3	1444	9.6	2139	3.7
22 TH	0333	9.8	1011	3.5	1554	10.4	2249	2.9
23 F	0432	10.7	1116	2.6	1651	11.3	2349	2.1
24 SA	0523	11.5	1213	1.9	1742	12.0		
25 SU ●	0043	1.5	0609	12.1	1305	1.4	1829	12.4
26 M	0132	1.3	0654	12.4	1352	1.2	1914	12.5
27 TU	0216	1.3	0735	12.4	1435	1.3	1956	12.3
28 W	0255	1.6	0815	12.2	1513	1.6	2035	11.9
29 TH	0329	2.1	0853	11.7	1548	2.2	2113	11.2
30 F	0401	2.7	0929	11.0	1620	2.9	2149	10.5
31 SA	0431	3.5	1006	10.3	1654	3.6	2228	9.6

NOVEMBER

Day	Time	m	Time	m	Time	m	Time	m
1 SU	0503	4.2	1047	9.5	1731	4.3	2314	8.9
2 M ☽	0544	4.9	1142	8.8	1824	4.9		
3 TU	0020	8.4	0650	5.3	1259	8.5	1943	5.1
4 W	0144	8.3	0825	5.3	1420	8.6	2106	4.8
5 TH	0257	8.8	0941	4.8	1523	9.2	2210	4.2
6 F	0352	9.4	1037	4.1	1613	9.8	2302	3.6
7 SA	0437	10.1	1125	3.4	1658	10.5	2348	3.0
8 SU	0519	10.8	1209	2.9	1739	11.0		
9 M	0030	2.5	0558	11.3	1251	2.4	1819	11.4
10 TU ○	0110	2.2	0636	11.6	1331	2.2	1856	11.6
11 W	0149	2.1	0712	11.8	1410	2.0	1934	11.7
12 TH	0227	2.1	0748	11.9	1449	2.0	2011	11.6
13 F	0304	2.2	0826	11.8	1528	2.2	2051	11.4
14 SA	0342	2.5	0906	11.5	1607	2.5	2133	11.0
15 SU	0423	2.9	0949	11.1	1651	2.9	2220	10.5
16 M	0509	3.4	1039	10.5	1740	3.3	2315	9.9
17 TU ☾	0603	3.8	1138	10.0	1840	3.7		
18 W	0023	9.5	0710	4.1	1251	9.8	1951	3.8
19 TH	0144	9.5	0826	4.0	1411	9.9	2108	3.6
20 F	0300	9.9	0942	3.6	1523	10.3	2221	3.1
21 SA	0403	10.5	1049	3.0	1624	10.9	2324	2.6
22 SU	0457	11.1	1149	2.4	1719	11.3		
23 M	0020	2.2	0547	11.6	1243	2.0	1810	11.7
24 TU ●	0110	2.0	0634	11.9	1332	1.8	1857	11.8
25 W	0155	1.9	0718	11.9	1416	1.8	1941	11.7
26 TH	0235	2.1	0759	11.8	1456	2.0	2022	11.4
27 F	0311	2.3	0838	11.5	1533	2.3	2100	11.1
28 SA	0345	2.8	0914	11.1	1607	2.7	2136	10.6
29 SU	0417	3.2	0950	10.6	1640	3.3	2211	10.1
30 M	0448	3.8	1026	10.0	1713	3.8	2248	9.5

DECEMBER

Day	Time	m	Time	m	Time	m	Time	m
1 TU	0522	4.3	1105	9.5	1750	4.2	2331	9.1
2 W ☽	0604	4.7	1154	9.1	1839	4.6		
3 TH	0026	8.8	0703	4.9	1256	8.9	1944	4.7
4 F	0135	8.8	0818	4.9	1408	9.0	2057	4.5
5 SA	0246	9.1	0931	4.5	1516	9.4	2205	4.1
6 SU	0348	9.6	1035	4.0	1614	9.9	2304	3.5
7 M	0441	10.3	1131	3.3	1706	10.4	2356	3.0
8 TU	0528	10.9	1221	2.8	1753	10.9		
9 W ○	0044	2.6	0612	11.3	1309	2.3	1838	11.3
10 TH	0130	2.2	0655	11.7	1355	2.0	1922	11.6
11 F	0215	2.0	0738	11.9	1441	1.8	2005	11.7
12 SA	0259	1.9	0821	12.0	1526	1.8	2049	11.7
13 SU	0343	2.0	0904	12.0	1611	1.9	2133	11.5
14 M	0427	2.2	0949	11.7	1655	2.1	2219	11.1
15 TU	0512	2.6	1036	11.3	1741	2.5	2307	10.7
16 W ☾	0559	3.0	1126	10.8	1829	2.9		
17 TH	0001	10.2	0652	3.4	1223	10.3	1925	3.3
18 F	0105	9.9	0754	3.7	1332	10.0	2031	3.6
19 SA	0220	9.8	0907	3.7	1448	9.9	2147	3.6
20 SU	0333	10.0	1022	3.4	1600	10.2	2259	3.3
21 M	0438	10.5	1130	3.0	1704	10.5		
22 TU	0002	2.9	0534	10.9	1229	2.6	1800	10.9
23 W	0056	2.6	0624	11.3	1320	2.3	1849	11.1
24 TH ●	0142	2.4	0708	11.5	1405	2.1	1932	11.3
25 F	0223	2.3	0749	11.6	1445	2.1	2011	11.3
26 SA	0300	2.3	0825	11.6	1521	2.2	2046	11.2
27 SU	0333	2.5	0859	11.4	1553	2.3	2118	11.0
28 M	0404	2.7	0930	11.1	1624	2.6	2149	10.7
29 TU	0432	3.0	1001	10.7	1652	3.0	2219	10.3
30 W	0459	3.4	1032	10.3	1720	3.4	2251	9.9
31 TH	0529	3.8	1106	9.8	1753	3.8	2329	9.5

Chart Datum: 6.60 metres below Lellemand System (Mean Sea Level, Marseilles).

ST MALO/DINARD *continued*

CHARTS
Admiralty 2700, 3659; SHOM 5645, 844; ECM 535; Stanford 16; Imray C33B

TIDES
−0506 Dover; ML 6·8; Duration 0535; Zone −0100

Standard Port ST-MALO (⟶)

Times				Height (metres)			
HW		LW		MHWS	MHWN	MLWN	MLWS
0805	0120	0749	0256	12·2	9·2	4·4	1·5
2005	1320	1949	1456				
Differences ERQUY							
−0005	−0004	−0013	−0028	−0·8	−0·5	−0·3	−0·1
SAINT CAST							
−0002	0000	−0006	−0018	−0·1	−0·1	0·0	0·0
CANCALE							
+0005	+0002	+0012	+0012	+1·3	+1·1	+0·8	+0·6

Saint-Malo is a Standard Port and the tidal predictions for each day of the year are given below.

SHELTER
Excellent shelter in Bassin Vauban or Bassin Duguay-Trouin, min depth 6m. Lock opens HW−2½ to HW+1½. Also good shelter in Port des Bas Sablons Marina entered over sill 2m above CD. There is a yacht anchorage at Dinard.

NAVIGATION
Waypoint Fairway (safe water) buoy, LFl, Whis, 48°41′·42N 02°07′·20W, 307°/127° from/to Grand Jardin Lt, 1·9M. There are numerous dangerous rocks round the entrance channel and there are strong tidal streams. There are three principal entrance channels, Grande Porte channel, Petite Porte channel and the Grande Conchée channel. Care needs to be exercised on all three. Lights at night are very good for the first two. Speed limit in basins is 3 kn. Anchoring in basins is forbidden.

LIGHTS AND MARKS
Chenal de la Grande Porte; Outer Ldg Lts at 089° are:
Front — Le Grand Jardin Fl (2) R 10s 24m 15M grey Tr.
Rear — Rochebonne (off chartlet) 4·2M from Front, FR 40m 24M leads into Chenal de la Petite Porte.
Leading Lts (Les Bas Sablons Dir FG 20m 16M in front and La Ballue Dir FG 69m 25M at rear) at 129° lead in from the Grand Jardin Lt Ho.
La Plate Lt VQ WRG, 11m 9/6M W140°-203°, R203°-210°, W210°-225°, G225°-140°.
St Malo Lock signals

G
W } No entry to lock without instructions
G

G
G } Boats may enter lock
G

R
R } No entry. Keep 200m from gates
R

A Y Lt alongside the top Lt shows that all gates are open but instructions are the same.

2 R Lts over G Lt — all movements prohibited except departure of large ships
Port des Bas Sablons — there is a sill and the depth over the sill is shown on a neon indicator; white figures indicate metres, red figures indicate decimetres and zero indicates 'No entry'.
Ldg Lts into basin, 2 FR, at 071°.
Les Bas Sablons Marina Lt Fl G 4s.

RADIO TELEPHONE
Call: *St Malo Port* or *Grand Jardin* VHF Ch 12 (H24). Bas Sablons Marina, St Servan Ch 09. Port Vauban Ch 09.

TELEPHONE
ST MALO Hr Mr 99.81.62.86; Hr Mr (Sablons) 99.81.71.34; Hr Mr (Vauban) 99.56.51.91; Aff Mar 99.56.87.00; CROSS 98.89.31.31; SNSM 98.89.31.31; # 99.81.65.90; Meteo 99.46.10.46; Auto 99.46.18.77; Police 99.81.52.30; Ⓗ 99.56.56.19; Brit Consul 99.46.26.64
DINARD Hr Mr 99.46.65.55; # 99.46.12.42; Meteo 99.46.10.46; Auto 99.46.18.77; Ⓗ 99.46.18.68.

FACILITIES
ST MALO: **Marina des Bas-Sablons** (1216+60 visitors, visitors Pontoon A) ☎ 99.81.71.34, (sill 2m above CD), Slip, P and D (at Pontoon 1), AC, BH (10 ton), FW, CH, Gaz, R, YC, Bar; **Port Vauban** ☎ 99.56.51.91, FW, C (1 ton), AC; **Chantier Naval de la Ville Audrain** ☎ 99.56.48.06, El, Ⓔ, ME, CH, Sh; **Chantier Labbé** ☎ 99.56.31.72, ME, El, C, Sh, CH; **Chantier Naval de la Plaisance** ☎ 99.82.62.97, M, ME, El, Sh, CH; **Chatelais et le Gall** ☎ 99.56.14.67, ME,El, Sh, CH; **Richard** ☎ 99.81.63.81, SM, CH; **Armor Voile** ☎ 99.81.49.30, SM; **Société Nautique de la Baie de Saint-Malo** ☎ 99.40.84.42, Bar (visitors welcome); **F. Lessard** ☎ 99.56.13.61, P, D; **Librairie Marine** ☎ 99.40.91.73, Nautical Books, SHOM; **Town** Slip, P, Gaz, D, ME, El, Sh, C, V, R, Bar, ✉; Ⓑ; ⇌; ✈ (Dinard); Ferry UK—Portsmouth; or Jersey.

DINARD: **Port de Dinard** ☎ 99.46.65.55, Slip, M, P, D, L, FW, AB; **Kerbrat Daniel** ☎ 99.46.49.82 ME, El, Ⓔ, Sh, M; **YC de Dinard** ☎ 99.46.14,32, Bar; **G. L. Voile** ☎ 99.46.48,99, SM; **Town** P, D, ME, El, CH, V, Gaz, R, Bar; ✉; Ⓑ; ⇌; ✈.

RIVER RANCE/DINAN 10-18-14

Ille-et-Vilaine

CHARTS
Admiralty 2700, 3659; SHOM 4233, 5645, 844; Stanford 16; Imray C33B

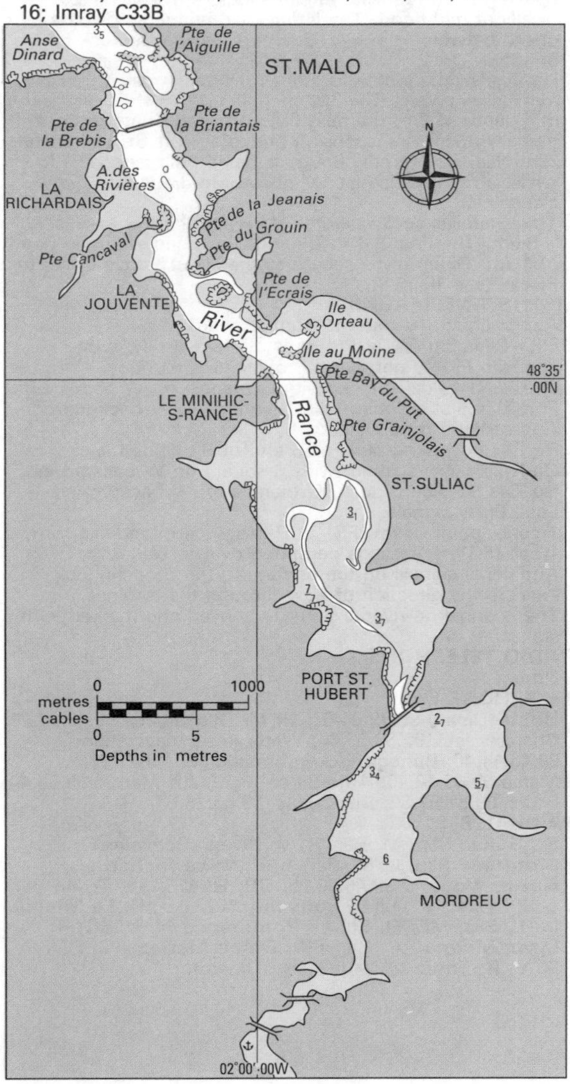
Anse Dinard
Pte de l'Aiguille
ST.MALO
Pte de la Briantais
Pte de la Brebis
A.des Rivières
LA RICHARDAIS
Pte de la Jeanais
Pte du Grouin
Pte Cancaval
LA JOUVENTE
Pte de l'Ecrais
Ile Orteau
River
Ile au Moine
Pte Bay du Put
48°35'·00N
LE MINIHIC-S-RANCE
Rance
Pte Grainjolais
ST.SULIAC
PORT ST. HUBERT
0 1000
metres
cables
0 5
Depths in metres
MORDREUC
02°00'·00W
N

18

RIVER RANCE *continued*

TIDES
Standard Port St.—MALO (⟵) Zone −0100
Water levels up-river from the Rance Hydro-electric tidal barrage are artifically maintained by sluice gates; from 0700 to 2100LT 4m above CD is guaranteed, whilst from 0800 to 2000LT, during a specified 4 hour period, 8·5m above CD will be maintained. Outside these hours levels may, exceptionally, drop by as much as 1·4m in 10 minutes. A French language pahmphlet, issued by Électricité de France available from Hr Mr at St. Malo and St. Servan, is essential for a detailed understanding of the barrage and water level schedule which is also published daily in *Ouest-France*.

SHELTER
Good shelter up-river dependent on wind direction. The principal anchorages/moorings on the E. bank are at St. Suliac and Mordreuc, and on the W. bank at La Richardais, La Jouvente, Le Minihic and La Pommeraie. There is a marina at Lyvet (above the Chatelier lock) and complete shelter at Dinan.

NAVIGATION
From St. Malo/Dinard approach the lock at the W end of the barrage between a Prohibited Area marked by port-hand buoys and wire cables and the Pointe de La Jument to starboard. Waiting dolphins either side of the lock. Lock opening by day on the hour, every hour provided the level is at least 4m above CD; from 2030 to 0430LT opening is on request. yachts should arrive at H−20, ideally at mid-flood. The lifting road-bridge across the lock opens between H & H+15. Boats leaving the lock have priority.
Up-river of the lock a further Prohibited Area to port is marked as above. The 3M channel up to St. Suliac has min depth of 2m; the next 6M up to the Chatelier Lock partially dries. A suspension bridge at Port St. Hubert has 23m clearance (a new bridge is being built alongside it), whilst a railway viaduct 1M above Mordreuc has 19m clearance.
The Chatelier Lock operates HJ when there is at least CD +8·5m. The final 3M to Dinan is canalised with min depth of 1·7m. Dinan gives access to the Ille et Rance Canal to Biscay (see 10-15-8).

LIGHTS AND MARKS
Approaching the barrage from seaward:
Fl(5) G20s 6m 4M at Pte de la Jument Bn Tr; with opposite Fl R4s port-hand Prohibited Area buoy
Fl G4s NW side of lock, with G triangle on W background
Fl R(2)6s first dolphin, with R square on W background
Approaching from Dinan:
Oc R4s port-hand buoy at S end of Prohibited Area
Oc R(2)6s last dolphin, with R square on W background
Iso G4s SE side of lock, G triangle on W background
Lock Entry signals:
1 cone, point down (FR) = Passage permitted sea to river
1 ball (FG) = Passage permitted river to sea
Additional signals on the barrage to the E of the lock indicate the direction of flow through the turbines.
The channel up-river is partially buoyed and marked with stakes.

RADIO TELEPHONE
None.

TELEPHONE (96)
Hr Mr (Dinan) 96.39.04.67; Hr Mr (Richardais) 99.46.24.20; Chatelier lock 96.39.55.66; Water levels/navigation 99.46.14.46; Barrage/lock information 99.46.21.87; Meteo 99.46.10.46; Auto 99.46.18.77; Aff Mar 96.39.56.44; Police 99.81.52.30; Brit Consul 99.46.26.64.

FACILITIES
St. Suliac Slip, M, Bar, R, V, Divers (Convoimer): **Mordreuc** Slip, L, M, Bar, R, P, V; **La Richardais: Naviga Voile** ☎ 99.46.99.25, CH, El, ME, Sh; **Town** Bar, D, P, ✉, R, V, Ⓑ; **La Jouvente** AB, Bar, R; **Le Minihic** M, L, Slip, ME, El, Sh; **La Pommeraie** M, L, SC, R; **Lyvet Marina** AC, Bar, FW; **Dinan Marina** AC, FW, P, D, V, R; **Town** ✉, Ⓑ, ≹, ✈ (Dinard).

GRANVILLE 10-18-15

Manche

CHARTS
Admiralty 3672, 3656, 3659; SHOM 5897, 824; ECM 535; Stanford 16; Imray C33B

TIDES
−0510 Dover; ML 7·2; Duration 0525; Zone −0100

Standard Port St.—MALO (⟵)

Times				Height (metres)			
HW		LW		MHWS	MHWN	MLWN	MLWS
0805	0120	0749	0256	12·2	9·2	4·4	1·5
2005	1320	1949	1456				
Differences GRANVILLE							
+0003	+0006	+0007	+0022	+0·7	+0·5	+0·2	−0·1

SHELTER
Shelter is good in the marina, Port de Hérel. Approach is rough in strong W winds. The old harbour is only for commercial and fishing vessels: yachts use the marina. Enter and leave under power. Access HW−2½ to HW+3½. Speed limit 4 kn; 2 kn between pontoons.

NAVIGATION
Waypoint 48°49′·40N 01°37′·00W, 235°/055° from/to Digue Principale Lt (FlR 4s), 0·95M. From W, Le Videcoq rks (dry 0·8m) lie 3¼M W of Pte du Roc, marked by W cardinal whis buoy. Beware rks off Pte du Roc and La Fourchie Bn, and Banc de Tombelaine 1M SSW of Le Loup Lt Tr.

LIGHTS AND MARKS
Port de Hérel marina is a half-tide harbour and depths at the entrance are shown by illuminated figures. W numbers are metres, Or numbers decimetres. Zero means no entry. Ldg Lts as on chartlet. 5 F Bu Lts mark the sill.

RADIO TELEPHONE
VHF Ch 12 16 (HW−1½ to HW+1). Marina Ch 09.

TELEPHONE (33)
Hr Mr 33.50.00.59; Hr Mr (Hérel) 33.50.20.06; Aff Mar 33.50.00.59; CROSS 33.52.72.13; SNSM 33.61.26.51; ⋕ 33.50.19.90; Meteo 33.22.91.77; Auto 33.50.10.00; Police 33.50.01.00; Dr 33.50.00.07; Hosp 33.90.74.75; Brit Consul 33.44.20.13.

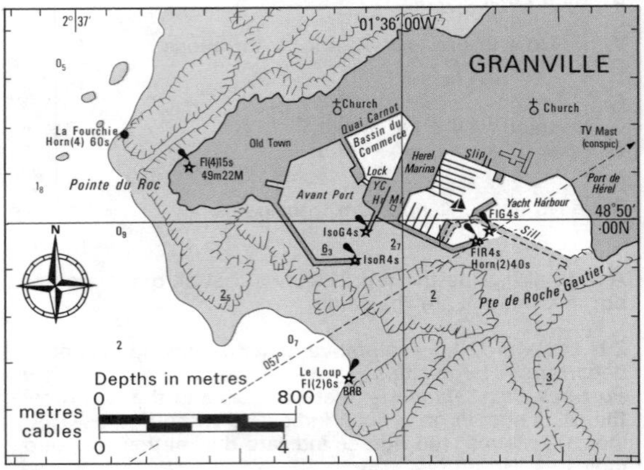

GRANVILLE
2°37′
01°36′00W
48°50′·00N
Church
Church
Quai Carnot
Bassin du Commerce
La Fourchie Horn(4) 60s
Old Town
Fl(4)15s 49m22M
Pointe du Roc
Lock
YC
Hr Mr
Avant Port
Herel Marina
Slip
TV Mast (conspic)
Port de Hérel
Yacht Harbour
FlG4s
Sill
IsoG4s
IsoR4s
FlR4s Horn(2)40s
Pte de Roche Gautier
057°
Le Loup Fl(2)6s
N
Depths in metres
metres 0 800
cables 0 4

FACILITIES
Hérel Marina (850+150 visitors) ☎ 33.50.20.06, Slip, P, D, FW, ME, AC, BH (12 ton), C (10 ton), CH, Gaz, R, ⊡, V, Bar, SM, El, Sh; **YC de Granville** ☎ 33.50.04.25, L, M, BH, D, P, CH, ⊡, Slip FW, AB, Bar; **Comptoir Maritime** ☎ 33.50.18.71, CH; **Granville Plaisance** ☎ 33.50.23.82, ME, El, Ⓔ, M, Sh, CH; **Lecoulant Marine** ☎ 33.50.20.34, M, ME, El, Ⓔ, Sh, CH; **La Marine** ☎ 33.50.71.31, SHOM; **Voiles Mora** ☎ 33.50.38.69, SM; **Town** P, D, ME, V, Gaz, R, Bar. ✉; Ⓑ; ≹; ✈ (Dinard).
Ferry UK via Jersey or Cherbourg—Weymouth/Poole.

CARTERET 10-18-16

Manche

CHARTS
Admiralty 3655, 2669; SHOM 827; ECM 535; Stanford 16; Imray C33A

TIDES
−0440 Dover; ML 6·3; Duration 0545; Zone −0100

Standard Port St.—MALO (⟵)

Times				Height (metres)			
HW		LW		MHWS	MHWN	MLWN	MLWS
0805	0120	0749	0256	12·2	9·2	4·4	1·5
2005	1320	1949	1456				
Differences CARTERET							
+0027	+0025	+0025	+0018	−1·0	−0·7	−0·3	0·0

SHELTER
Shelter good but harbour dries completely — entry only possible at HW∓2. Exposed to winds from W and SW which make entrance rough. There are no safe anchorages off shore. It dries ½ M to seaward. Bar at right angles to pier-head rises up to 3m and 15m long. The Petit Port provides the best shelter but is only suitable for shallow draught yachts able to take the bottom. Bar forms after NW winds but is removed by local sand company.

NAVIGATION
Waypoint 49°21′·00N 01°52′·25W, 250°/070° from/to Jetée Ouest Lt, 3·5M. From N keep well off shore on approach to avoid rocks 1 M N of Cap de Carteret extending about 1M from coast. From W, about 4 M off shore, beware Trois Grune Rks (dry 1·6m) marked by W cardinal Lt Buoy.

LIGHTS AND MARKS
Cap de Carteret Fl (2+1) 15s 81m 26M; grey Tr, G top; Horn (3) 60s. Training wall, head Fl (2) G 5s; in line with lifeboat house leads 007°. Jetée Ouest, head Oc R 4s 6m 8M; W column, R top.

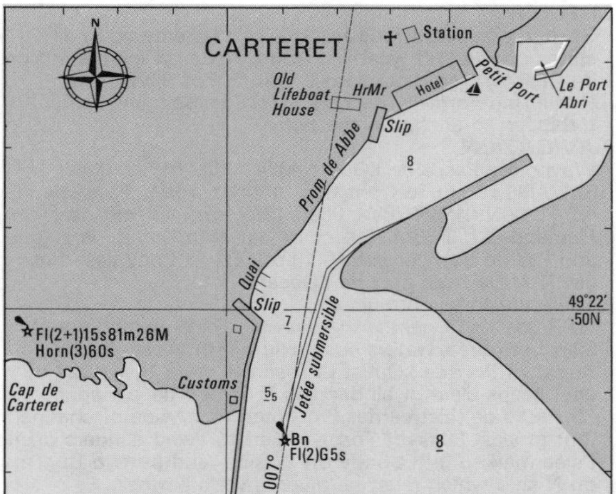

CARTERET
Station
Old Lifeboat House
HrMr
Hotel
Petit Port
Le Port Abri
Slip
Prom de Abbe
Quai
Jetée submersible
Customs
Cap de Carteret
Fl(2+1)15s81m26M
Horn(3)60s
Bn Fl(2)G5s
OcR4s Bn
007°
49°22′·50N
01°47′·40W
metres
cables
0
700
3

RADIO TELEPHONE
VHF Ch 16 64 (remotely controlled from Boulogne).

TELEPHONE (33)
Hr Mr 33.44.00.13; CROSS 33.52.72.13; # 33.04.90.08; Meteo 33.22.91.77; Auto 33.43.20.40; Police 33.53.80.17; H (Valognes) 33.40.14.39; Brit Consul 33.44.20.13.

FACILITIES
West Jetty Slip, FW, AB, R, Bar; **Cercle Nautique de Barneville-Carteret** ☎ 33.53.88.29, Slip, M, Bar; **Port de Plaisance** ☎ 33.04.70.84, AB; **Garage Tollemer** ☎ 33.53.85.62, ME, P and D (cans). **Town** V, Gaz, R, Bar, ✉; Ⓑ (Barneville); ⇄ (Valognes); ✈ (Cherbourg). Ferry UK — Cherbourg—Portsmouth; Weymouth (summer only).
Note: 5M to S, Portbail is a safe harbour although choppy in E winds. See 10.18.20.
Note: A marina is planned.

ILES CHAUSEY 10-18-17

Manche

CHARTS
Admiralty 3656, 3659; SHOM 7134, 824, 4599; ECM 534; Stanford 16; Imray C33B

TIDES
−0500 Dover; ML 7·5; Duration 0530; Zone −0100

Standard Port St.—MALO (⟵)

Times				Height (metres)			
HW		LW		MHWS	MHWN	MLWN	MLWS
0805	0120	0749	0256	12·2	9·2	4·4	1·5
2005	1320	1949	1456				
Differences ILES CHAUSEY (Grande Ile)							
+0008	+0010	+0011	+0014	+0·8	+0·7	+0·5	+0·5

SHELTER
Shelter good except in strong NW or SE winds. When anchoring remember the big tidal range. Visitors buoys are provided for mooring fore and aft.

NAVIGATION
Waypoint 48°51′·50N 01°48′·48W, 152°/332° from/to La Crabière Est Lt, 1·2M. Although very large range of tide (see above), tidal streams are not excessive. The most direct route into Sound of Chausey is from the S, but beware rocks extending from Pte de la Tour. Alternative route from N with sufficient height of tide but refer to detailed sailing directions for transits to be followed. Local knowledge is needed. Dangerous wreck reported N of La Petite Entrée (off chartlet).
Note:— Yachts may not visit the Iles Chausey without having first made official entry elsewhere, such as Granville.
Harbour gets very crowded in summer weekends.

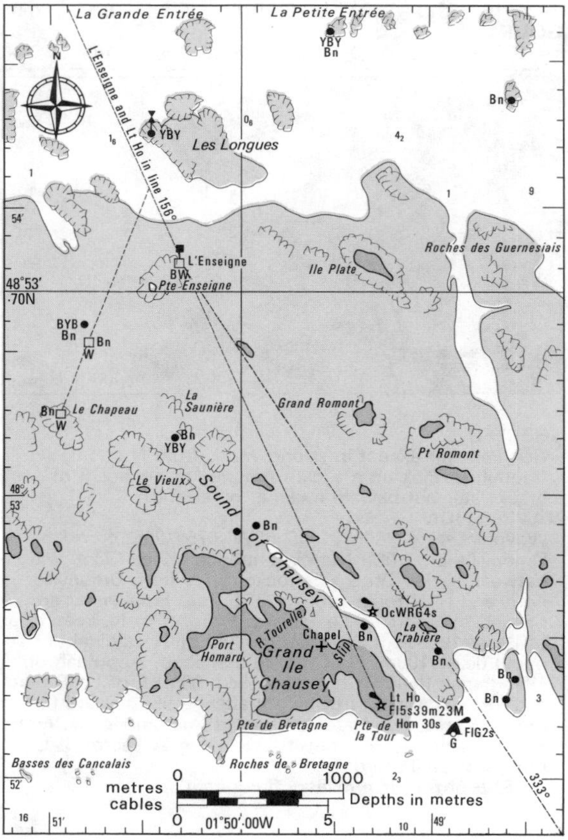

La Grande Entrée
La Petite Entrée
YBY Bn
Bn
YBY
Les Longues
L'Enseigne and Lt Ho in line 156°
Roches des Guernesiais
Ile Plate
L'Enseigne
BW
Pte Enseigne
48°53′·70N
BYB Bn
Bn W
Bn Le Chapeau W
La Saunière
Grand Romont
Pt Romont
Bn YBY
Le Vieux
Sound of Chausey
Bn
OcWRG4s
La Crabière
Bn
Chapel
R Tourelle
Port Homard
Grand Ile Chausey
Slip
Lt Ho Fl5s39m23M Horn 30s
FlG2s G
Pte de Bretagne
Pte de la Tour
Basses des Cancalais
Roches de Bretagne
metres
cables
0
1000
5
Depths in metres
01°50′·00W
333°

ILES CHAUSEY *continued*

LIGHTS AND MARKS
Grande Ile, Pte de la Tour Fl 5s 39m 23M; Horn 30s. La Crabière Est Oc WRG 4s 5m 9/6M; B pylon, Y top; vis W079°-291°, G291°-329°, W329°-335°, R335°-079°.
From N, L'Enseigne Bn Tr (19m) in line with Pte de la Tour Lt Ho leads 156°. From S, La Crabière in line with L'Enseigne leads 333°.
Note:— The island is private property.

RADIO TELEPHONE
None.

TELEPHONE (33)
Police 33.52.72.02.

FACILITIES
R. Tourelle L; **Town** FW, Gaz, V, R, Bar.
✉ (Granville); Ⓑ (Granville); ⇄ (Granville); ✈ (Dinard).
Ferry UK via Granville and Jersey—Weymouth/Poole.

OMONVILLE-la-ROGUE 10-18-18
Manche

CHARTS
Admiralty 1106, 2669; SHOM 5631, 5636, 6737; ECM 528; Stanford 16, 7; Imray C33A

TIDES
−0330 Dover; ML 3·8; Duration 0545; Zone −0100

Standard Port CHERBOURG (⟶)

Times				Height (metres)			
HW		LW		MHWS	MHWN	MLWN	MLWS
0300	1000	0400	1000	6·3	5·0	2·5	1·1
1500	2200	1600	2200				
Differences OMONVILLE							
−0015	−0010	−0020	−0025	−0·1	0·0	+0·1	0·0
GOURY							
−0100	−0045	−0110	−0120	+1·6	+1·5	+1·0	+0·1

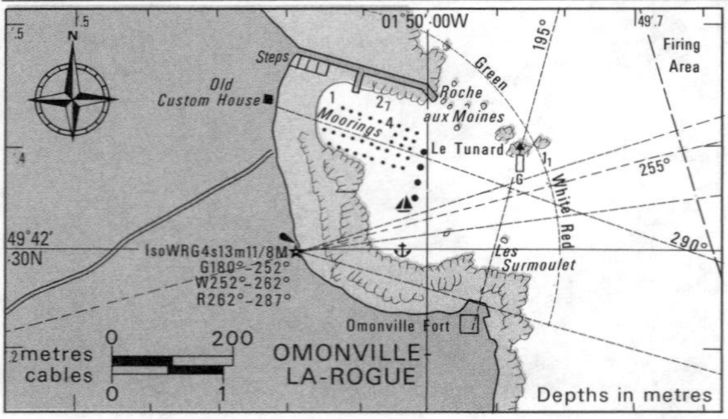
01°50'·00W
49'·7
Firing Area
Steps
Old Custom House
Moorings
Green
Roche aux Moines
Le Tunard
G
195°
255°
290°
White
Red
49°42'·30N
IsoWRG4s13m11/8M
G180°-252°
W252°-262°
R262°-287°
Les Surmoulet
Omonville Fort
metres
cables
0
200
0
1
OMONVILLE-LA-ROGUE
Depths in metres

SHELTER
Good shelter except in strong winds from N to SE through E. Pick up a vacant mooring or anchor S of breakwater but beware rocks at outer end.

NAVIGATION
Waypoint 49°42'·50N 01°48'·60W, 075°/255° from/to Omonville Lt, 1·0M. Narrow entrance, ½ ca (93m) wide, between rocks. On S side rocks run N from Omonville Fort, and to N rocks running ESE from breakwater are marked by G Bn Tr, Le Tunard. From W or N, keep clear of Basse Bréfort (depth 1m, marked by N cardinal Lt buoy) 6ca (1100m) N of Pte de Jardeheu. Approach on 195° transit (below), but pass ½ca (93m) E of Le Tunard and into W sector of Lt before altering 95° to stbd for mooring area, heading 290° for old Custom House. From E, approach on 255° transit (below), in W sector of Lt, until S of Le Tunard.
To ENE of port is a military firing area.

LIGHTS AND MARKS
Omonville Lt Iso WRG 4s 13m 11/8M on W framework Tr with R top; vis G180°-252°, W252°-262°, R262°-287°. Lt in transit with church steeple, 650m beyond, leads 255° S of Le Tunard. Le Tunard Bn Tr in line with centre of Omonville Fort leads 195°, but pass ½ca (93m) E of Le Tunard.

RADIO TELEPHONE
None. For Casquets traffic scheme see Cherbourg (10.18.19).

TELEPHONE (33)
Hr Mr Cherbourg 33.53.05.60; Aff Mar Cherbourg 33.53.21.76; ⌗ Cherbourg 33.53.05.60; CROSS 33.52.72.13; 33.52.71.33; Meteo 33.22.91.77; Auto 33.43.20.40; Police 33.52.72.02; Dr 33.53.08.69; Brit Consul 33.44.20.13.

FACILITIES
Jetty M, L, FW, AB, V, R, Bar; **Village** V, Gaz, R, Bar.
✉ (Beaumont Hague); Ⓑ (Beaumont Hague); ⇄ (bus to Cherbourg); ✈ (Cherbourg).
Ferry UK — Cherbourg—Portsmouth; Weymouth (summer only).

CHERBOURG 10-18-19
Manche

CHARTS
Admiralty 2602, 1106; SHOM 7086, 7092, 6737; ECM 528; Stanford 16, 7; Imray C32, C33A

TIDES
−0308 Dover; ML 3·8; Duration 0535; Zone −0100

Cherbourg is a Standard Port and tidal predictions for every day of the year are given below.

SHELTER
Shelter is excellent and harbour can be entered in all states of tide and weather. Good shelter in marina in Port de Chantereyne. Lock into Bassin à Flot (HW−1 to HW+1) is normally for commercial vessels only. It is forbidden to anchor in the port.

NAVIGATION
Waypoints Passe de l'Ouest 49°41'·10N 01°39'·80W, 321°/141° from/to front Ldg Lt 141°, 1·9M. Passe de l'Est 49°41'·00N 01°35'·70W, 000°/180° from/to Fort des Flamands Lt, 1·85M. For coast between Cap de la Hague and Pte de Barfleur see 10.18.5. CH1 Lt buoy lies about 3M N × W from Fort de l'Ouest.
There are three entrances:
(1) Passe de l'Ouest is the easiest. Rocks extend about 80m from breakwaters each side. From West, the W sector of Fort de l'Ouest Lt (bearing more than 122° by day) keeps clear of all dangers E of Cap de la Hague.
(2) Passe de l'Est carries 6m. Keep to W side of channel (but at least 80m off Fort de l'Est) to avoid dangers off Ile Pelée marked by Lt buoy on W side, and by two Bn Trs on N side which must be given a wide berth.
(3) Passe Cabart Danneville is a shallow channel ½ca (93m) wide through Digue de l'Est, near the shore. Not recommended except in good conditions and near HW.

LIGHTS AND MARKS
There are three powerful Lts near Cherbourg. To the W Cap de la Hague, Fl 5s 48m 23M; to the E Cap Levi, Fl R 5s 36m 22M, and Pte de Barfleur, Fl(2) 10s 72m 29M. For details see 10.17.4 and 10.18.4.
Fort de l'Ouest Lt, at W end of Digue Centrale, Fl(3)WR 15s 19m 24/20M; vis W122°-355°, R355°-122°; RC; Reed(3) 60s.
Passe de l'Ouest Ldg Lts 140°30'. Gare Maritime Lt (Q 35m 21M) in line with centre of 2Q(hor) 5m 15M at base of Digue du Homet.
Grande Rade Ldg Lts 124°. Front FG 10m 9M; W pylon, G top, on blockhouse; Reed(2+1) 60s. Rear, 0·75M from front, Iso G 4s 16m 12M; W column, B bands, W top; intens 114°-134°.
Passe de l'Est is indicated by W sector (176°-183°) of Dir Q WRG Lt 13m 12/10M at Fort des Flamands.

CHERBOURG *continued*

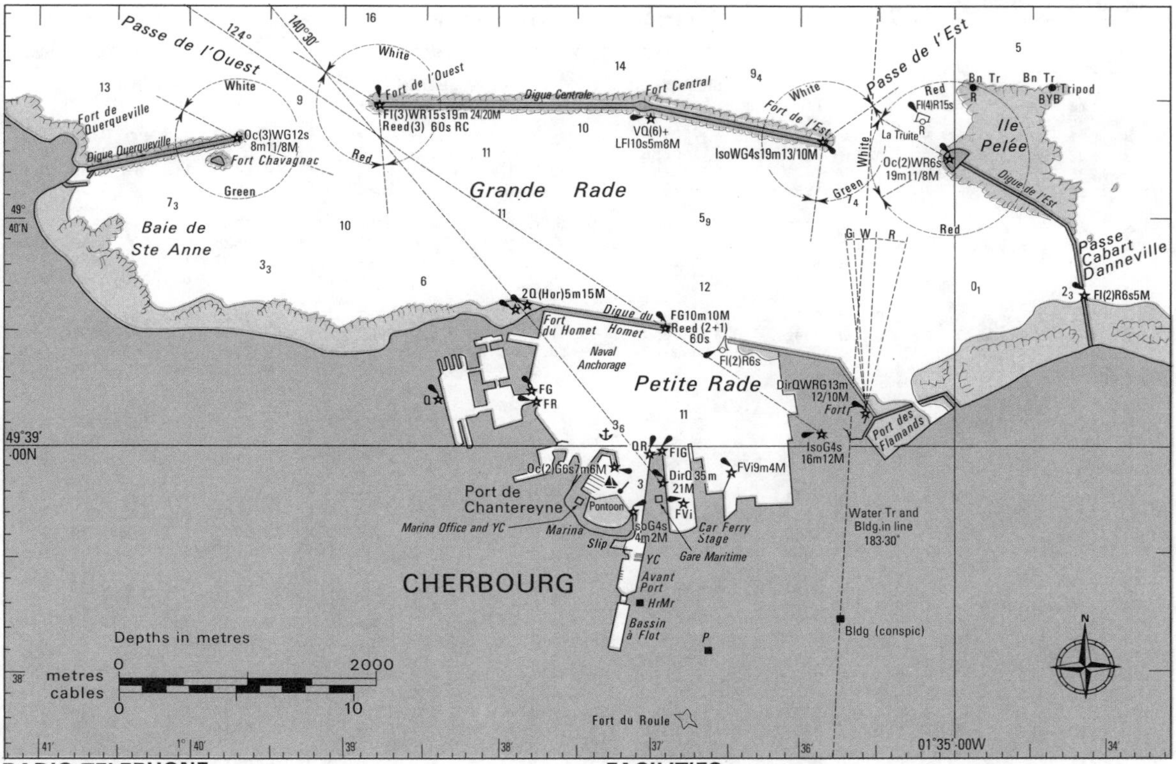

Passe de l'Ouest
124°
140°30'
White
Fort de l'Ouest
Digue Centrale
Fort Central
Fort de l'Est
Passe de l'Est
Fort de Querqueville
Digue Querqueville
Oc(3)WG12s 8m11/8M
Fort Chavagnac
Green
Red
Fl(3)WR15s19m 24/20M Reed(3) 60s RC
VQ(6)+ LFl10s5m8M
IsoWG4s19m13/10M
Grande Rade
Baie de Ste Anne
Bn Tr
Bn Tr
Tripod
BYB
Fl(4)R15s
La Truite
Ile Pelée
Oc(2)WR6s 19m11/8M
Digue de l'Est
Passe Cabart Danneville
Fl(2)R6s5M
2Q(Hor)5m15M
Digue du Homet
Fort du Homet
FG10m10M Reed(2+1) 60s
Fl(2)R6s
Naval Anchorage
Petite Rade
DirQWRG13m 12/10M
Fort
Port des Flamands
FG
FR
Q
IsoG4s 16m12M
QR
FIG
Oc(2)G6s7m6M
DirQ 35m 21M
FVi9m4M
FVi
Port de Chantereyne
Pontoon
Marina Office and YC
Marina
Slip
IsoG4s 4m2M
Car Ferry Stage
Gare Maritime
YC
Avant Port
HrMr
Bassin à Flot
CHERBOURG
Water Tr and Bldg.in line 183·30°
Bldg (conspic)
Depths in metres
metres
cables
0
2000
10
Fort du Roule
N
49° 40'N
49°39' ·00N
38'
41'
1° 40'
39'
38'
37'
36'
01°35'·00W
34'

RADIO TELEPHONE
Marina Ch 09. (0800-2000 LT).
Call: *COM Cherbourg* VHF Ch 16 (H24). Casquets traffic scheme, Ship Movement Report System (MAREP), call *Jobourg Traffic* (near Cap de la Hague) Ch **11**; 16 11 79 (H24). Information broadcasts in English and French on Ch 11 at H+20 and H+50, also at H+05 and H+35 when visibility is less than 2M.

TELEPHONE (33)
Hr Mr 33.44.00.13; Hr Mr (Port de Plaisance) 33.53.75.16; Aff Mar 33.44.00.13; CROSS 33.52.72.13; # 33.44.16.00; Marina 33.53.79.65; Meteo 33.22.91.77; Auto 33.43.20.40; Police 33.44.21.24; (H) 33.52.61.45; Dr 33.53.05.68; Brit Consul 33.44.20.13.

FACILITIES
Marina (670+130 visitors), Slip, P, D, FW, ME, El, Sh, BH (27 ton), CH; Access H24; **Quay Capitainerce** ☎ 33.53.75.16, P, D (0800-2000), Access HW∓3; **YC de Cherbourg** ☎ 33.53.02.83, FW, Bar; **Aries Cherbourg** ☎ 33.94.15.50 ME, El, (E), Sh, CH, M: **Legrand** ☎ 33.53.27.34 ME, El, (E), Sh, M, SM, CH; **Cotentin Marine** ☎ 33.53.07.30, ME, El, Sh, CH; **Cherbourg Général Yachting** ☎ 33.53.63.73, ME, El, (E), SM, CH; **Nordie** ☎ 33.53.02.67, V; **Daily Tanker** D; **Nicollet** ☎ 33.53.11.74, SHOM; **Serelle** ☎ 33.43.70.11, ME, El, (E), Sh. **Town** P, D, Gaz, V, R, Bar. ✉; (B); ≠; ✈.
Ferry UK—Portsmouth; Weymouth (summer only).

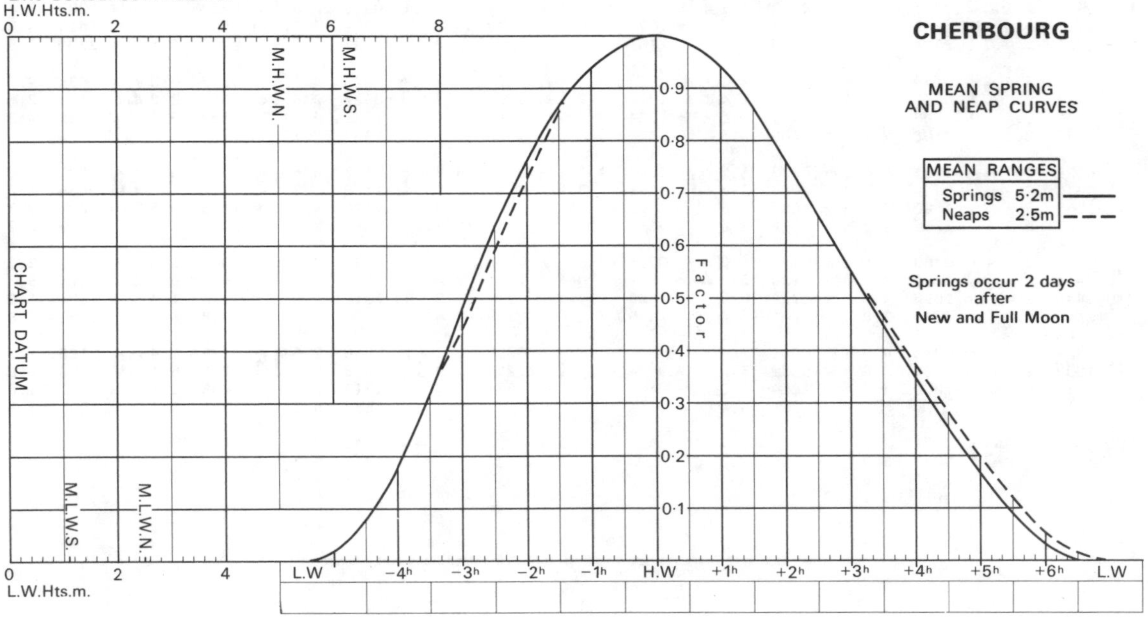

H.W.Hts.m.
0
2
4
6
8
M.H.W.N.
M.H.W.S.
CHART DATUM
M.L.W.S.
M.L.W.N.
L.W.Hts.m.
0·9
0·8
0·7
0·6
0·5
0·4
0·3
0·2
0·1
Factor
L.W
−4h
−3h
−2h
−1h
H.W
+1h
+2h
+3h
+4h
+5h
+6h
L.W
CHERBOURG
MEAN SPRING AND NEAP CURVES
MEAN RANGES
Springs 5·2m
Neaps 2·5m
Springs occur 2 days after New and Full Moon

18

TIME ZONE -0100
(French Standard Time)
Subtract 1 hour for GMT
For French Summer Time add ONE hour in non-shaded areas

FRANCE, NORTH COAST - CHERBOURG

LAT 49°39'N LONG 1°38'W

TIMES AND HEIGHTS OF HIGH AND LOW WATERS

YEAR **1992**

JANUARY

Day	Time	m	Day	Time	m
1 W	0022 0602 1255 1834	2.4 5.3 2.3 5.2	16 TH	0453 1153 1735	5.1 2.4 5.2
2 TH	0121 0658 1349 1929	2.3 5.5 2.1 5.4	17 F	0022 0606 1303 1845	2.2 5.5 2.0 5.5
3 F	0210 0744 1434 2013	2.1 5.7 1.9 5.6	18 SA	0128 0708 1405 1944	1.9 5.9 1.5 5.9
4 SA	0252 0825 1514 ● 2051	1.9 5.9 1.7 5.8	19 SU	0227 0803 1501 ○ 2038	1.5 6.3 1.1 6.3
5 SU	0330 0901 1551 2126	1.8 6.0 1.5 5.9	20 M	0320 0855 1552 2129	1.2 6.6 0.7 6.5
6 M	0407 0936 1625 2158	1.7 6.1 1.5 5.9	21 TU	0410 0944 1639 2217	0.9 6.8 0.6 6.6
7 TU	0439 1008 1657 2229	1.7 6.1 1.4 5.9	22 W	0458 1032 1724 2303	0.8 6.8 0.5 6.6
8 W	0511 1039 1729 2300	1.7 6.0 1.5 5.8	23 TH	0542 1116 1808 2345	0.9 6.7 0.7 6.4
9 TH	0542 1111 1800 2331	1.8 5.9 1.6 5.7	24 F	0626 1158 1850	1.1 6.5 1.0
10 F	0613 1143 1831	1.9 5.8 1.7	25 SA	0025 0708 1237 1931	6.1 1.5 6.1 1.5
11 SA	0004 0647 1217 1906	5.6 2.1 5.6 1.9	26 SU	0105 0751 1319 ☾ 2014	5.7 1.9 5.6 2.0
12 SU	0040 0726 1255 1947	5.4 2.2 5.4 2.1	27 M	0149 0840 1408 2106	5.3 2.3 5.1 2.5
13 M	0122 0813 1343 ☽ 2037	5.2 2.4 5.1 2.3	28 TU	0247 0944 1520 2219	5.0 2.7 4.8 2.8
14 TU	0217 0914 1448 2144	5.1 2.6 5.0 2.5	29 W	0409 1109 1656 2348	4.8 2.8 4.7 2.8
15 W	0329 1032 1611 2304	5.0 2.6 5.0 2.5	30 TH	0534 1231 1820	4.9 2.6 4.9
			31 F	0101 0640 1333 1917	2.6 5.2 2.3 5.2

FEBRUARY

Day	Time	m	Day	Time	m
1 SA	0156 0729 1421 1959	2.3 5.5 2.0 5.5	16 SU	0116 0656 1353 1935	2.0 5.8 1.5 5.9
2 SU	0239 0810 1500 2036	2.0 5.8 1.7 5.7	17 M	0216 0753 1447 2028	1.5 6.2 1.0 6.3
3 M	0316 0846 1535 ● 2109	1.8 6.0 1.5 5.9	18 TU	0309 0844 1537 ○ 2116	1.0 6.6 0.6 6.6
4 TU	0350 0919 1607 2140	1.6 6.1 1.3 6.0	19 W	0356 0932 1623 2201	0.8 6.9 0.4 6.7
5 W	0421 0950 1637 2209	1.5 6.2 1.2 6.0	20 TH	0441 1015 1705 2242	0.6 6.9 0.4 6.7
6 TH	0451 1020 1707 2237	1.4 6.2 1.2 6.0	21 F	0522 1056 1744 2319	0.7 6.8 0.6 6.5
7 F	0520 1050 1736 2307	1.4 6.2 1.2 6.0	22 SA	0600 1133 1820 2353	0.9 6.5 1.0 6.2
8 SA	0550 1120 1805 2336	1.5 6.0 1.4 5.8	23 SU	0637 1207 1856	1.3 6.1 1.5
9 SU	0621 1149 1836	1.6 5.8 1.6	24 M	0026 0714 1242 1932	5.8 1.8 5.6 2.0
10 M	0006 0655 1221 1913	5.7 1.9 5.6 1.9	25 TU	0102 0756 1324 ☾ 2016	5.4 2.2 5.0 2.6
11 TU	0040 0737 1301 ☽ 1958	5.4 2.1 5.3 2.2	26 W	0152 0851 1430 2123	4.9 2.7 4.6 3.0
12 W	0127 0832 1401 2100	5.2 2.4 5.0 2.5	27 TH	0318 1018 1624 2311	4.6 2.9 4.4 3.0
13 TH	0238 0949 1536 2228	5.0 2.6 4.8 2.6	28 F	0503 1159 1801	4.7 2.7 4.7
14 F	0421 1124 1719	4.9 2.4 5.0	29 SA	0038 0617 1308 1856	2.8 5.0 2.4 5.0
15 SA	0001 0550 1254 1835	2.4 5.3 2.0 5.4			

MARCH

Day	Time	m	Day	Time	m
1 SU	0135 0706 1357 1935	2.4 5.3 2.0 5.4	16 M	0102 0642 1336 1920	1.9 5.7 1.4 5.9
2 M	0218 0746 1436 2010	2.0 5.7 1.7 5.7	17 TU	0200 0737 1429 2010	1.4 6.2 0.9 6.3
3 TU	0253 0822 1510 2043	1.7 5.9 1.4 5.9	18 W	0251 0827 1517 ○ 2055	1.0 6.6 0.6 6.6
4 W	0326 0856 1541 ● 2114	1.5 6.1 1.2 6.0	19 TH	0337 0912 1600 2137	0.7 6.8 0.5 6.7
5 TH	0357 0927 1611 2144	1.3 6.2 1.1 6.1	20 F	0418 0953 1640 2215	0.6 6.8 0.6 6.6
6 F	0426 0957 1641 2212	1.2 6.3 1.0 6.2	21 SA	0457 1031 1716 2250	0.7 6.6 0.8 6.5
7 SA	0456 1027 1710 2241	1.2 6.3 1.1 6.1	22 SU	0533 1106 1750 2322	0.9 6.3 1.2 6.2
8 SU	0526 1058 1740 2311	1.2 6.2 1.2 6.0	23 M	0608 1139 1824 2353	1.3 5.9 1.6 5.8
9 M	0558 1128 1812 2340	1.4 5.9 1.4 5.8	24 TU	0643 1213 1858	1.7 5.5 2.1
10 TU	0633 1201 1848	1.6 5.7 1.8	25 W	0027 0722 1252 1940	5.4 2.1 5.0 2.6
11 W	0015 0714 1242 1935	5.6 1.9 5.3 2.2	26 TH	0112 0812 1352 ☾ 2041	5.0 2.6 4.6 3.0
12 TH	0102 0809 1344 ☽ 2039	5.2 2.3 4.9 2.5	27 F	0229 0929 1541 2234	4.6 2.8 4.4 3.1
13 F	0215 0928 1525 2210	4.9 2.5 4.8 2.7	28 SA	0417 1110 1718 2355	4.6 2.8 4.6 2.8
14 SA	0405 1107 1712 2348	4.9 2.4 5.0 2.4	29 SU	0535 1224 1816	4.8 2.5 4.9
15 SU	0537 1235 1824	5.2 1.9 5.4	30 M	0056 0628 1317 1858	2.5 5.1 2.1 5.3
			31 TU	0141 0711 1358 1935	2.1 5.5 1.8 5.6

APRIL

Day	Time	m	Day	Time	m
1 W	0219 0750 1434 2010	1.8 5.8 1.5 5.9	16 TH	0229 0804 1453 2030	1.1 6.4 0.9 6.4
2 TH	0254 0826 1507 2043	1.5 6.0 1.2 6.1	17 F	0314 0849 1535 ○ 2110	0.9 6.5 0.8 6.5
3 F	0326 0900 1540 ● 2115	1.3 6.2 1.1 6.2	18 SA	0355 0930 1613 2147	0.9 6.5 0.9 6.4
4 SA	0359 0932 1613 2146	1.1 6.3 1.0 6.3	19 SU	0433 1007 1649 2222	0.9 6.3 1.1 6.3
5 SU	0432 1005 1645 2218	1.1 6.3 1.1 6.2	20 M	0509 1043 1724 2255	1.1 6.1 1.4 6.1
6 M	0506 1040 1719 2251	1.1 6.2 1.2 6.1	21 TU	0543 1117 1758 2328	1.3 5.8 1.8 5.8
7 TU	0541 1115 1754 2326	1.2 6.0 1.4 5.9	22 W	0619 1153 1834	1.7 5.4 2.1
8 W	0619 1154 1835	1.5 5.7 1.8	23 TH	0004 0657 1232 1915	5.4 2.0 5.1 2.5
9 TH	0007 0705 1242 1926	5.7 1.8 5.3 2.2	24 F	0048 0744 1325 ☾ 2010	5.1 2.4 4.8 2.8
10 F	0059 0803 1348 ☽ 2035	5.3 2.1 5.0 2.5	25 SA	0149 0847 1445 2128	4.8 2.6 4.6 3.0
11 SA	0213 0922 1525 2205	5.0 2.3 4.9 2.5	26 SU	0316 1008 1613 2300	4.6 2.7 4.6 2.9
12 SU	0353 1053 1657 2333	5.0 2.2 5.1 2.3	27 M	0435 1123 1719	4.7 2.5 4.8
13 M	0517 1212 1803	5.3 1.8 5.5	28 TU	0000 0535 1221 1809	2.6 5.0 2.2 5.2
14 TU	0042 0621 1313 1858	1.9 5.7 1.4 5.9	29 W	0052 0625 1309 1851	2.2 5.3 1.9 5.5
15 W	0139 0715 1406 1946	1.4 6.1 1.1 6.2	30 TH	0136 0709 1351 1931	1.9 5.6 1.6 5.8

Chart Datum: 3.70 metres below Lallemand System (Mean Sea Level, Marseilles)

TIME ZONE -0100
(French Standard Time)
Subtract 1 hour for GMT
For French Summer Time add ONE hour in non-shaded areas

FRANCE, NORTH COAST - CHERBOURG

LAT 49°39'N LONG 1°38'W

TIMES AND HEIGHTS OF HIGH AND LOW WATERS

YEAR **1992**

MAY

Day	Time	m	Day	Time	m
1	0217	1.6	16	0251	1.3
	0750	5.8		0827	6.1
F	1430	1.4	SA	1510	1.3
	2008	6.0	○	2046	6.2
2	0254	1.4	17	0333	1.2
	0830	6.0		0910	6.1
SA	1508	1.2	SU	1550	1.3
●	2045	6.2		2124	6.2
3	0332	1.2	18	0412	1.2
	0908	6.2		0948	6.0
SU	1546	1.1	M	1627	1.4
	2121	6.3		2200	6.1
4	0411	1.1	19	0449	1.3
	0946	6.2		1025	5.9
M	1624	1.2	TU	1703	1.6
	2159	6.3		2235	6.0
5	0450	1.0	20	0525	1.4
	1026	6.2		1101	5.7
TU	1704	1.3	W	1739	1.8
	2238	6.2		2311	5.8
6	0530	1.1	21	0601	1.6
	1108	6.0		1137	5.5
W	1746	1.5	TH	1816	2.1
	2320	6.0		2348	5.6
7	0614	1.3	22	0639	1.9
	1154	5.8		1215	5.3
TH	1832	1.7	F	1855	2.3
8	0007	5.8	23	0028	5.3
	0705	1.6		0720	2.1
F	1246	5.5	SA	1259	5.0
	1928	2.0		1941	2.5
9	0102	5.5	24	0115	5.0
	0804	1.8		0809	2.3
SA	1351	5.2	SU	1352	4.8
☽	2035	2.3	☾	2038	2.7
10	0211	5.3	25	0214	4.9
	0915	2.0		0907	2.4
SU	1511	5.1	M	1457	4.8
	2153	2.3		2145	2.7
11	0332	5.2	26	0322	4.8
	1032	1.9		1013	2.4
M	1629	5.3	TU	1605	4.8
	2308	2.2		2253	2.6
12	0447	5.4	27	0428	4.9
	1144	1.8		1117	2.3
TU	1733	5.5	W	1707	5.0
				2354	2.4
13	0015	1.9	28	0529	5.1
	0552	5.6		1214	2.1
W	1245	1.6	TH	1801	5.3
	1829	5.8			
14	0113	1.6	29	0048	2.1
	0649	5.8		0624	5.3
TH	1339	1.4	F	1306	1.9
	1919	6.0		1849	5.6
15	0205	1.4	30	0137	1.8
	0741	6.0		0714	5.6
F	1427	1.3	SA	1354	1.6
	2005	6.1		1934	5.9
			31	0223	1.5
				0801	5.8
			SU	1440	1.4
				2018	6.1

JUNE

Day	Time	m	Day	Time	m
1	0309	1.3	16	0356	1.4
	0847	6.0		0934	5.8
M	1525	1.3	TU	1612	1.6
●	2101	6.2		2144	6.0
2	0354	1.1	17	0434	1.4
	0932	6.2		1010	5.8
TU	1609	1.2	W	1648	1.7
	2145	6.3		2220	6.0
3	0439	1.0	18	0510	1.4
	1017	6.2		1045	5.7
W	1655	1.2	TH	1723	1.8
	2230	6.3		2255	5.9
4	0525	1.0	19	0545	1.5
	1104	6.1		1119	5.6
TH	1742	1.3	F	1758	1.9
	2317	6.2		2330	5.7
5	0613	1.0	20	0619	1.6
	1152	6.0		1153	5.5
F	1832	1.5	SA	1833	2.0
6	0006	6.1	21	0005	5.5
	0703	1.2		0654	1.8
SA	1244	5.8	SU	1229	5.3
	1926	1.7		1910	2.2
7	0058	5.8	22	0043	5.3
	0758	1.5		0732	2.0
SU	1340	5.5	M	1309	5.1
☽	2025	1.9		1953	2.4
8	0156	5.6	23	0125	5.1
	0857	1.7		0815	2.2
M	1443	5.4	TU	1355	5.0
	2129	2.1	☾	2044	2.5
9	0302	5.4	24	0217	5.0
	1003	1.9		0909	2.3
TU	1551	5.3	W	1452	4.9
	2237	2.1		2147	2.6
10	0411	5.3	25	0320	4.9
	1111	1.9		1012	2.4
W	1658	5.4	TH	1558	5.0
	2345	2.1		2256	2.5
11	0520	5.3	26	0430	4.9
	1215	1.9		1121	2.3
TH	1759	5.5	F	1707	5.1
12	0047	1.9	27	0003	2.3
	0624	5.5		0540	5.1
F	1313	1.8	SA	1225	2.1
	1854	5.7		1810	5.4
13	0143	1.8	28	0103	2.0
	0722	5.6		0643	5.4
SA	1405	1.8	SU	1323	1.9
	1943	5.8		1905	5.7
14	0232	1.6	29	0158	1.6
	0812	5.7		0739	5.7
SU	1451	1.7	M	1417	1.6
	2027	5.9		1957	6.0
15	0316	1.5	30	0250	1.3
	0856	5.8		0830	6.0
M	1532	1.6	TU	1509	1.3
○	2107	6.0	●	2046	6.3

JULY

Day	Time	m	Day	Time	m
1	0340	1.0	16	0418	1.4
	0920	6.2		0954	5.8
W	1558	1.2	TH	1634	1.6
	2134	6.4		2203	6.0
2	0429	0.8	17	0452	1.3
	1009	6.3		1026	5.8
TH	1647	1.1	F	1704	1.6
	2223	6.5		2235	6.0
3	0517	0.7	18	0523	1.4
	1057	6.3		1056	5.8
F	1735	1.1	SA	1735	1.7
	2310	6.5		2306	5.9
4	0604	0.7	19	0553	1.4
	1144	6.3		1126	5.7
SA	1823	1.2	SU	1805	1.8
	2358	6.4		2337	5.8
5	0651	0.9	20	0623	1.6
	1230	6.1		1156	5.6
SU	1912	1.4	M	1837	1.9
6	0044	6.1	21	0009	5.6
	0739	1.2		0655	1.8
M	1317	5.8	TU	1229	5.4
	2002	1.7		1912	2.1
7	0132	5.8	22	0044	5.4
	0830	1.6		0731	2.0
TU	1408	5.5	W	1306	5.2
☽	2058	2.0	☾	1955	2.3
8	0227	5.4	23	0126	5.1
	0927	2.0		0816	2.2
W	1508	5.3	TH	1353	5.1
	2202	2.2		2050	2.5
9	0333	5.1	24	0222	4.9
	1033	2.2		0915	2.5
TH	1618	5.2	F	1456	4.9
	2314	2.3		2203	2.6
10	0451	5.0	25	0338	4.8
	1146	2.3		1033	2.5
F	1731	5.2	SA	1619	5.0
				2324	2.5
11	0024	2.2	26	0507	4.9
	0607	5.1		1153	2.4
SA	1252	2.3	SU	1740	5.2
	1835	5.4			
12	0126	2.0	27	0037	2.1
	0711	5.3		0622	5.2
SU	1349	2.1	M	1301	2.0
	1929	5.6		1845	5.6
13	0219	1.8	28	0140	1.7
	0802	5.5		0722	5.7
M	1437	1.9	TU	1401	1.7
	2014	5.8		1941	6.0
14	0303	1.6	29	0237	1.2
	0844	5.7		0817	6.0
TU	1519	1.8	W	1455	1.3
○	2054	5.9	●	2033	6.4
15	0342	1.5	30	0328	0.9
	0921	5.8		0908	6.3
W	1557	1.7	TH	1546	1.0
	2130	6.0		2123	6.6
			31	0417	0.6
				0957	6.5
			F	1634	0.8
				2211	6.8

AUGUST

Day	Time	m	Day	Time	m
1	0503	0.5	16	0456	1.3
	1042	6.6		1028	6.0
SA	1720	0.8	SU	1708	1.5
	2256	6.8		2239	6.1
2	0547	0.5	17	0524	1.3
	1126	6.5		1055	5.9
SU	1804	0.9	M	1736	1.6
	2340	6.6		2308	6.0
3	0630	0.8	18	0552	1.4
	1207	6.3		1123	5.8
M	1848	1.2	TU	1805	1.7
				2337	5.8
4	0021	6.2	19	0621	1.6
	0712	1.2		1152	5.7
TU	1247	5.9	W	1838	1.9
	1932	1.6			
5	0103	5.8	20	0008	5.5
	0756	1.7		0654	1.9
W	1329	5.6	TH	1224	5.4
☽	2022	2.1		1916	2.2
6	0150	5.3	21	0045	5.2
	0847	2.2		0736	2.2
TH	1422	5.2	F	1306	5.2
	2123	2.4	☾	2007	2.5
7	0256	4.9	22	0138	4.9
	0955	2.6		0832	2.5
F	1539	4.9	SA	1409	4.9
	2243	2.6		2120	2.6
8	0428	4.7	23	0302	4.7
	1120	2.7		0955	2.7
SA	1707	4.9	SU	1543	4.9
				2254	2.6
9	0005	2.5	24	0448	4.8
	0559	4.8		1130	2.5
SU	1236	2.6	M	1720	5.1
	1821	5.2			
10	0112	2.2	25	0018	2.2
	0703	5.1		0608	5.2
M	1336	2.3	TU	1246	2.1
	1915	5.5		1829	5.6
11	0204	1.9	26	0126	1.6
	0748	5.4		0708	5.7
TU	1423	2.0	W	1346	1.6
	1958	5.8		1925	6.1
12	0246	1.7	27	0220	1.1
	0826	5.7		0801	6.2
W	1502	1.8	TH	1440	1.2
	2035	6.0		2017	6.5
13	0323	1.5	28	0310	0.7
	0859	5.9		0851	6.5
TH	1537	1.6	F	1529	0.9
○	2109	6.1	●	2106	6.8
14	0356	1.3	29	0357	0.5
	0931	5.9		0937	6.7
F	1610	1.5	SA	1615	0.7
	2141	6.2		2152	6.9
15	0427	1.3	30	0441	0.4
	1000	6.0		1020	6.7
SA	1639	1.5	SU	1658	0.7
	2211	6.2		2235	6.9
			31	0522	0.6
				1100	6.6
			M	1739	0.8
				2315	6.6

Chart Datum: 3.70 metres below Lallemand System (Mean Sea Level, Marseilles)

TIME ZONE -0100
(French Standard Time)
Subtract 1 hour for GMT
For French Summer Time add ONE hour in non-shaded areas

FRANCE, NORTH COAST - CHERBOURG

LAT 49°39′N LONG 1°38′W

TIMES AND HEIGHTS OF HIGH AND LOW WATERS

YEAR **1992**

SEPTEMBER

Day	Time	m	Day	Time	m
1 TU	0602 1137 1819 2353	0.9 6.4 1.2 6.2	16 W	0522 1052 1738 2310	1.4 6.0 1.6 5.9
2 W	0640 1213 1859	1.4 6.0 1.6	17 TH	0552 1121 1811 2342	1.6 5.8 1.8 5.6
3 TH	0031 0720 1250 ☽ 1944	5.7 1.9 5.6 2.1	18 F	0626 1154 1849	1.9 5.6 2.1
4 F	0115 0806 1339 2042	5.2 2.5 5.1 2.6	19 SA	0020 0709 1237 ☾ 1940	5.3 2.3 5.3 2.4
5 SA	0220 0914 1458 2209	4.7 2.9 4.8 2.8	20 SU	0117 0807 1343 2055	5.0 2.6 5.0 2.6
6 SU	0406 1054 1642 2342	4.6 3.0 4.8 2.7	21 M	0248 0935 1524 2234	4.8 2.8 4.9 2.5
7 M	0544 1216 1759	4.7 2.8 5.0	22 TU	0437 1114 1702	4.9 2.6 5.2
8 TU	0049 0642 1314 1851	2.4 5.1 2.4 5.4	23 W	0007 0552 1229 1810	2.1 5.4 2.1 5.7
9 W	0139 0722 1359 1932	2.0 5.4 2.0 5.7	24 TH	0105 0649 1328 1906	1.6 5.8 1.6 6.2
10 TH	0219 0757 1437 2008	1.7 5.7 1.8 6.0	25 F	0158 0740 1420 1956	1.1 6.3 1.1 6.6
11 F	0255 0830 1510 2042	1.5 5.9 1.6 6.1	26 SA	0247 0827 1507 ● 2044	0.8 6.6 0.8 6.8
12 SA	0326 0901 1542 ○ 2113	1.3 6.1 1.5 6.2	27 SU	0333 0911 1552 2128	0.6 6.7 0.7 6.9
13 SU	0356 0930 1610 2142	1.3 6.1 1.4 6.2	28 M	0415 0952 1633 2210	0.6 6.7 0.7 6.8
14 M	0425 0957 1639 2210	1.2 6.1 1.4 6.2	29 TU	0455 1030 1713 2249	0.8 6.6 0.9 6.5
15 TU	0454 1024 1708 2240	1.3 6.1 1.4 6.1	30 W	0533 1106 1751 2326	1.2 6.3 1.3 6.1

OCTOBER

Day	Time	m	Day	Time	m
1 TH	0610 1140 1829	1.6 6.0 1.7	16 F	0532 1103 1754 2330	1.7 6.0 1.7 5.7
2 F	0003 0647 1217 1910	5.6 2.1 5.6 2.2	17 SA	0610 1141 1836	2.0 5.7 1.9
3 SA	0046 0731 1304 ☽ 2003	5.2 2.6 5.1 2.6	18 SU	0015 0657 1230 1930	5.4 2.3 5.4 2.2
4 SU	0147 0834 1417 2124	4.8 3.0 4.8 2.9	19 M	0115 0759 1337 ☾ 2043	5.1 2.6 5.2 2.4
5 M	0328 1017 1559 2300	4.6 3.1 4.7 2.8	20 TU	0242 0924 1508 2215	4.9 2.7 5.1 2.4
6 TU	0503 1139 1718	4.7 2.9 4.9	21 W	0418 1055 1638 2342	5.1 2.5 5.3 2.0
7 W	0010 0601 1238 1813	2.5 5.0 2.5 5.3	22 TH	0529 1207 1746	5.5 2.1 5.7
8 TH	0101 0643 1324 1855	2.2 5.4 2.2 5.6	23 F	0040 0625 1305 1842	1.6 5.9 1.6 6.1
9 F	0142 0719 1402 1933	1.9 5.7 1.9 5.9	24 SA	0134 0715 1357 1933	1.2 6.3 1.3 6.5
10 SA	0218 0754 1436 2009	1.6 5.9 1.7 6.1	25 SU	0223 0802 1445 ● 2020	1.0 6.5 1.0 6.6
11 SU	0251 0827 1509 ○ 2042	1.4 6.1 1.5 6.2	26 M	0308 0845 1529 2105	0.9 6.6 0.9 6.6
12 M	0323 0857 1540 2113	1.3 6.2 1.4 6.3	27 TU	0350 0925 1610 2146	1.0 6.6 1.0 6.5
13 TU	0355 0926 1612 2145	1.3 6.2 1.3 6.2	28 W	0430 1002 1649 2225	1.2 6.5 1.1 6.3
14 W	0426 0957 1645 2217	1.3 6.2 1.4 6.2	29 TH	0507 1038 1727 2302	1.4 6.3 1.4 6.0
15 TH	0458 1028 1718 2252	1.5 6.1 1.5 6.0	30 F	0544 1114 1804 2340	1.8 6.0 1.7 5.6
			31 SA	0622 1152 1844	2.2 5.6 2.1

NOVEMBER

Day	Time	m	Day	Time	m
1 SU	0022 0704 1237 1931	5.3 2.6 5.3 2.5	16 M	0014 0655 1229 1928	5.6 2.1 5.7 1.9
2 M	0115 0757 1336 ☽ 2033	4.9 2.9 4.9 2.7	17 TU	0113 0756 1330 ☾ 2033	5.4 2.4 5.4 2.1
3 TU	0230 0913 1457 2154	4.7 3.1 4.8 2.8	18 W	0226 0909 1446 2150	5.2 2.5 5.3 2.2
4 W	0355 1042 1616 2310	4.7 3.0 4.8 2.7	19 TH	0347 1027 1606 2310	5.3 2.4 5.4 2.0
5 TH	0502 1146 1719	4.9 2.7 5.1	20 F	0457 1139 1715	5.5 2.1 5.6
6 F	0009 0553 1238 1809	2.4 5.2 2.4 5.4	21 SA	0013 0556 1241 1816	1.8 5.8 1.8 5.9
7 SA	0056 0635 1321 1853	2.1 5.5 2.1 5.6	22 SU	0109 0649 1335 1911	1.6 6.1 1.5 6.1
8 SU	0137 0714 1401 1933	1.9 5.8 1.8 5.9	23 M	0201 0737 1425 2001	1.4 6.3 1.3 6.2
9 M	0214 0751 1437 2011	1.7 6.0 1.6 6.1	24 TU	0247 0822 1510 ● 2046	1.3 6.4 1.2 6.3
10 TU	0251 0826 1513 ○ 2047	1.5 6.2 1.4 6.2	25 W	0329 0903 1552 2128	1.4 6.4 1.2 6.2
11 W	0328 0900 1550 2124	1.4 6.3 1.3 6.2	26 TH	0410 0941 1631 2207	1.5 6.4 1.3 6.1
12 TH	0404 0936 1627 2201	1.4 6.3 1.3 6.2	27 F	0448 1019 1709 2244	1.6 6.2 1.4 6.0
13 F	0442 1013 1706 2242	1.5 6.3 1.3 6.1	28 SA	0525 1056 1746 2322	1.8 6.0 1.6 5.7
14 SA	0521 1053 1747 2325	1.6 6.1 1.5 5.9	29 SU	0602 1133 1823	2.1 5.8 1.9
15 SU	0605 1138 1833	1.9 5.9 1.7	30 M	0000 0641 1212 1903	5.5 2.3 5.5 2.2

DECEMBER

Day	Time	m	Day	Time	m
1 TU	0042 0724 1257 1948	5.2 2.6 5.2 2.4	16 W	0102 0745 1316 ☾ 2016	5.7 1.9 5.8 1.8
2 W	0132 0815 1351 ☽ 2043	5.0 2.8 5.0 2.6	17 TH	0200 0845 1417 2119	5.5 2.2 5.5 2.0
3 TH	0233 0919 1457 2149	4.8 2.9 4.9 2.7	18 F	0308 0953 1528 2230	5.4 2.3 5.4 2.1
4 F	0342 1031 1607 2258	4.9 2.9 4.9 2.6	19 SA	0419 1106 1643 2343	5.4 2.3 5.4 2.1
5 SA	0447 1139 1711	5.0 2.7 5.1	20 SU	0526 1216 1753	5.5 2.1 5.5
6 SU	0000 0544 1238 1808	2.4 5.3 2.4 5.3	21 M	0047 0626 1317 1855	2.0 5.7 1.9 5.7
7 M	0052 0633 1324 1858	2.2 5.6 2.1 5.6	22 TU	0143 0720 1410 1949	1.8 5.9 1.7 5.8
8 TU	0139 0717 1407 1943	1.9 5.8 1.7 5.9	23 W	0232 0807 1457 2035	1.7 6.1 1.5 6.0
9 W	0223 0759 1450 ○ 2026	1.7 6.1 1.5 6.1	24 TH	0316 0849 1539 ● 2116	1.6 6.2 1.4 6.0
10 TH	0306 0840 1533 2108	1.5 6.3 1.3 6.2	25 F	0357 0928 1618 2153	1.6 6.2 1.3 6.0
11 F	0349 0921 1616 2151	1.4 6.4 1.1 6.3	26 SA	0435 1004 1654 2228	1.6 6.2 1.4 6.0
12 SA	0432 1004 1659 2235	1.4 6.4 1.1 6.2	27 SU	0510 1039 1729 2302	1.7 6.1 1.5 5.9
13 SU	0516 1048 1744 2321	1.4 6.4 1.1 6.1	28 M	0544 1114 1802 2336	1.8 6.0 1.6 5.7
14 M	0603 1134 1830	1.5 6.3 1.3	29 TU	0617 1147 1835	2.0 5.8 1.8
15 TU	0010 0652 1223 1920	5.9 1.7 6.0 1.5	30 W	0009 0651 1221 1910	5.5 2.2 5.5 2.0
			31 TH	0044 0729 1259 1949	5.3 2.4 5.3 2.3

Chart Datum: 3.70 metres below Lallemand System (Mean Sea Level, Marseilles)

MINOR HARBOURS AND ANCHORAGES 10-18-20

VAL-ANDRÉ, Côtes du Nord, 48°36′·00N, 02°33′·00W, Zone −0100, Admty charts 3674, 2669, SHOM 833. HW −0520 on Dover (GMT), −0006 on St.-Malo (zone −0100); HW height −0·7m on St.-Malo; ML 6·1m; Duration 0550. A small drying harbour exposed to S and SW winds. Beware Verdelet coming from E and Platier des Trois Têtes from W. Yachts can go alongside the quay, ask YC for mooring off Le Piegu or anchor off. Hr accessible HW∓3. Facilities: Hr Mr ☎ 96.72.83.20, FW, Slip; **YC du Val-André** ☎ 96.72.21.68. Bar, R; **Troalen** ☎ 96.72.20.20. CH, El, ME, Sh; **Town** Bar, R, V.

ERQUY, Côtes du Nord, 48°38′·00N, 02°28′·00W, Zone −0100, Admty charts 3672, 3674, 2669, SHOM 833, 5724. HW −0515 on Dover (GMT), −0005 on St.-Malo (zone −0100); HW height −0·7m on St.-Malo; ML 6·1m; Duration 0550. See 10.18.13. Sheltered from E, but exposed to SW or W winds. Hr dries and is usually full of fishing boats. Beware Plateau des Portes d'Erquy (dry) about 2M to West. Coming from S, beware of rks off Pte de la Houssaye. Lt on mole-head Oc(2+1) WRG 12s 11m 11/6M R055°−081°, W081°−094°, G094°−111°, W111°−120°, R120°−134°. Inner jetty, head Fl R 2.5s 10m 3M. Facilities: Hr Mr and # ☎ 96.72.19.32; **Quay** C (1 ton), D, FW, P; **Cercle de la Voile d'Erquy** ☎ 96.72.32.40; **Régina Plaisance** ☎ 96.72.13.70. CH, El, ME, Sh; **Town** Bar, R, V.

SAINT-CAST, Côtes du Nord, 48°38′·00N, 02°15′·00W, Zone −0100, Admty charts 3659, 2669, SHOM 5646, 844. HW −0515 on Dover (GMT), −0001 on St.-Malo (zone −0100); HW height −0·1m on St.-Malo; ML 6·3m; Duration 0550. See 10.18.13. Good shelter from S through W to NW, and moorings are available in 1·8m. Beware Les Bourdinots (dry 2m) with E cardinal buoy ¾M NE of Pte de Saint-Cast, and La Feuillâtre (marked by Bn) and Bec Rond off harbour. Mole-head Lt Iso WG 4s 11m 11/8M, W204°−217°, G217°−233°, W233°−245°, G245°−204°. Facilities: Hr Mr ☎ 96.41.88.34. SNSM ☎ 96.41.88.34. Signal Tr 99.41.85.30; **YC de Saint-Cast** ☎ 96.41.91.77. **La Maison Blanche** ☎ 96.41.81.40. CH, El, ME, Sh; **L.M.B. Marine** ☎ 96.41.80.23. CH, El, ME, Sh; **Town** Ⓑ; Bar, D, P, ✉, R, V.

ROTHENEUF, Ille-et-Vilaine, 48°42′·00N, 01°56′·00W, Zone −0100, Admty charts 2700, 3659, SHOM 5644, 844. HW −0510 on Dover (GMT), HW times and heights as for St.-Malo (zone −0100); ML 7·0m; Duration 0540. Complete shelter in Hr which dries completely. Anchor outside in 4m just N of spar Bn marking ent. Rocks on both sides of ent which is less than 170m wide. Safest to enter when rks uncovered. There are no lights; ldg line at 163° W side of Pte Benard and old converted windmill. Facilities: FW, Slip; **Village** Bar, D, P, R, V.

CANCALE, Ille-et-Vilaine, 48°40′·00N, 01°51′·00W, Zone −0100, Admty chart 3659, SHOM 5644, 824. HW −0510 on Dover (GMT), +0004 on St.-Malo (zone −0100); HW height +1·2m on St.-Malo; ML 7·5m; Duration 0535. See 10.18.13. A drying Hr just inside Bay of Mont St Michel, 1M SW of Point de la Chaine. Area dries to about 1M off-shore; anchor off end of Pte de la Chaine in deep water. Drying berths usually available in La Houle, the Hr in Cancale. Exposed to winds SW to SE. Jetty-head Lt Oc(3)G 12s 12m 8M, obsc when bearing less than 223°. Facilities: **Quay** C (1.5 ton) D, FW, P; **Club Nautique de Cancale** ☎ 99.89.90.22; **Froc** ☎ 99.89.61.74. El, M, ME, Sh; **Town** (famous for oysters), Ⓑ, Bar, D, P, ✉, R, V.

PORTBAIL, Manche, 49°19′·00N, 01°43′·00W, Zone −0100, Admty chart 3655, 2669, SHOM 826, 827. HW −0440 on Dover (GMT), +0026 on St.-Malo (zone −0100); HW height −0·9m on St.-Malo; ML 6·3m; Duration 0545. See 10.18.16. Good shelter. Hr dries but access HW∓½ at np, HW∓2½ at sp for a draught of 1m. Beware very strong tide over bar. Passage through sand banks buoyed to Training Wall (covers at HW) which is marked by R spar Bns. Drying harbour E of jetty – 1st line of buoys parallel to jetty for visitors; slip to W of jetty. Training Wall head Q(2)R 5s 5m 2M. Ldg Lts 042°, Front (La Caillourie) QW 14m 11M. Rear, 870m from front, QW 20m 9M. VHF Ch 09. Facilities: Hr Mr ☎ 33.04.33.48; **Quay** C (5 ton) D, FW, P; **Cercle Nautique de Portbail-Denneville** ☎ 33.04.86.15. Bar, R; **YC de Portbail** ☎ 33.04.83.48. AB, C, Slip; **Gérard** ☎ 33.04.80.07. El, ME, Sh; **Le Cornec** Sh (wood); **Fleury** Sh, ME, El; **Flambard** Sh, ME, El; **Town** Bar, Ⓑ, ✉, R, ⇌ (Valognes), V.

DIELETTE, Manche, 49°33′·30′N, 01°51′·80′W, Zone −0100. Admty chart 3653; SHOM 6059, 827. HW −0430 on Dover (GMT), +0035 on St Malo (zone −0100), HW height −2·0m on St Malo. Good Hr used by fishing boats; Hr dries; good granite jetty. Exposed to winds from SW to NW. Ldg Lts 125°30′, Front on end of Jetée Ouest, Oc WRG 4s 12m, 8/6M on W Tr with G top; G shore −072°, W072°-138°, R138°-206°, G206°-shore. Rear (460m from front) Dir FR 23m 11M, intends 121°-130° on W house with gable. Entering, keep just S of the R sector of the front Lt. A prohibited area from Dielette to C de Flamanville extends 0·5M off shore. No Hr Mr – contact the Mairie at Flamanville. Meteo 33.42.20.40. **YC de Dielette** ☎ 33.53.03.85. Facilities: FW, YC, V, Bar, R, hotel. Most facilities available at Flamanville (1.3M).

GOURY, Manche, 49°43′·00N, 01°56·70′W. Zone −0100. Admty charts 1106, 3653; SHOM 5631. HW −0410 on Dover (GMT); −0050 on Cherbourg (zone −0100). HW height +1·5m on Cherbourg. Beware severe undertow. Ldg Lts 065° Front QR 4m 7M Rear (110m from front) Q10m 12M, intens 057°-075°, lead between Charlin to Stbd and les Grois to port. Hr dries – flat sand/mud bottom. L by Jet d'Amont. Facilities: R, Bar, L. Village of Auderville (0·5M).

PORT DU BECQUET, Manche, 49°39′·30N, 01°32′·80W, Zone −0100. Admty chart 1106; SHOM 7092. Tides as 10.18.19. Shelter is good except in winds from N to E when a strong scend occurs. Secure to S of jetty (which runs E and W). Ldg Lts at 186·5°, Front Dir Oc (2+1) 12s 8m 16M, W 8-sided Tr, intens 183·5°-190·5°; Rear, 48m from front, Dir Oc (2+1) R 12s 13m 11M, synchronised, also in W 8-sided Tr. Facilities: extremely few; all facilities at Cherbourg 2·5M.

PORT DE LÉVI, Manche, 49°41′·30N, 01°28′·30W, Zone −0100. Admty chart 1106; SHOM 5609; HW −0310 on Dover (GMT), +0024 on Cherbourg (zone −0100). HW height +0·2m on Cherbourg. Shelter good except in winds SW to N. Secure to wall on NE side below W bldg. Lt is F WRG 7m 11/8M, G050°-109°, R109°-140°, W140°-184°. Keep in G sector. By day keep the Lt structure between the W marks on each side of the ent. Beware lobster pots. Facilities: None. Fermanville (1·5M) has V, R, Bar.

Area 19

North-East France
Barfleur to Dunkerque

19

10.19.2
North-East France

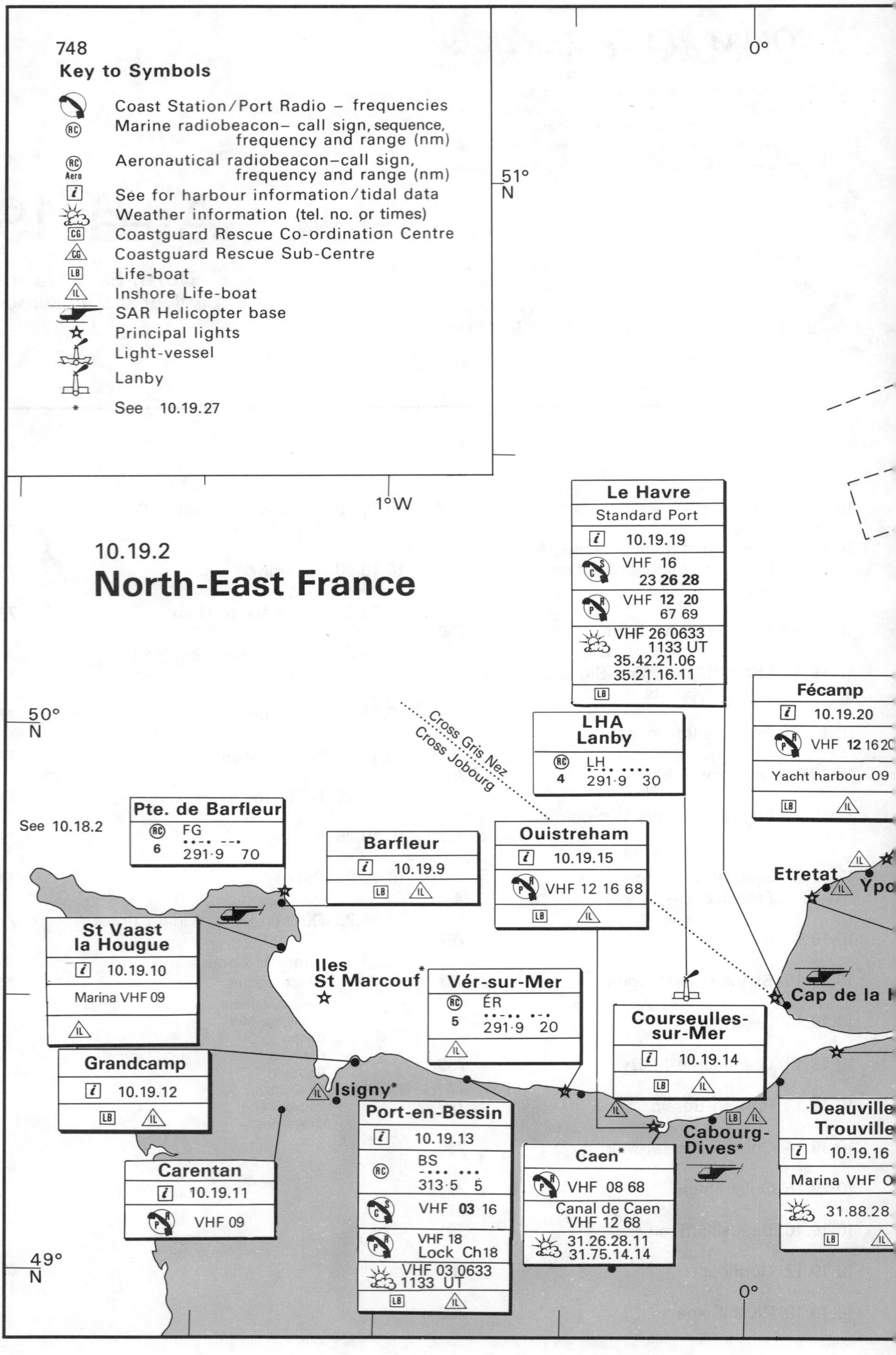
Key to Symbols
Coast Station/Port Radio – frequencies
Marine radiobeacon– call sign, sequence, frequency and range (nm)
Aeronautical radiobeacon–call sign, frequency and range (nm)
See for harbour information/tidal data
Weather information (tel. no. or times)
Coastguard Rescue Co-ordination Centre
Coastguard Rescue Sub-Centre
Life-boat
Inshore Life-boat
SAR Helicopter base
Principal lights
Light-vessel
Lanby
* See 10.19.27
0°
51° N
1°W
50° N
49° N
0°
See 10.18.2
Cross Gris Nez
Cross Jobourg
Le Havre
Standard Port
10.19.19
VHF 16 23 26 28
VHF 12 20 67 69
VHF 26 0633 1133 UT
35.42.21.06
35.21.16.11
LB
Fécamp
10.19.20
VHF 12 16 20
Yacht harbour 09
LHA Lanby
RC 4
LH
291·9 30
Pte. de Barfleur
RC 6
FG
291·9 70
Barfleur
10.19.9
Ouistreham
10.19.15
VHF 12 16 68
Etretat
Ypo
St Vaast la Hougue
10.19.10
Marina VHF 09
Iles St Marcouf*
Vér-sur-Mer
RC 5
ÉR
291·9 20
Cap de la H
Courseulles-sur-Mer
10.19.14
Grandcamp
10.19.12
Isigny*
Port-en-Bessin
10.19.13
BS
313·5 5
VHF 03 16
VHF 18
Lock Ch18
VHF 03 0633
1133 UT
Cabourg-Dives*
Caen*
VHF 08 68
Canal de Caen
VHF 12 68
31.26.28.11
31.75.14.14
Deauville
Trouville
10.19.16
Marina VHF O
31.88.28
Carentan
10.19.11
VHF 09

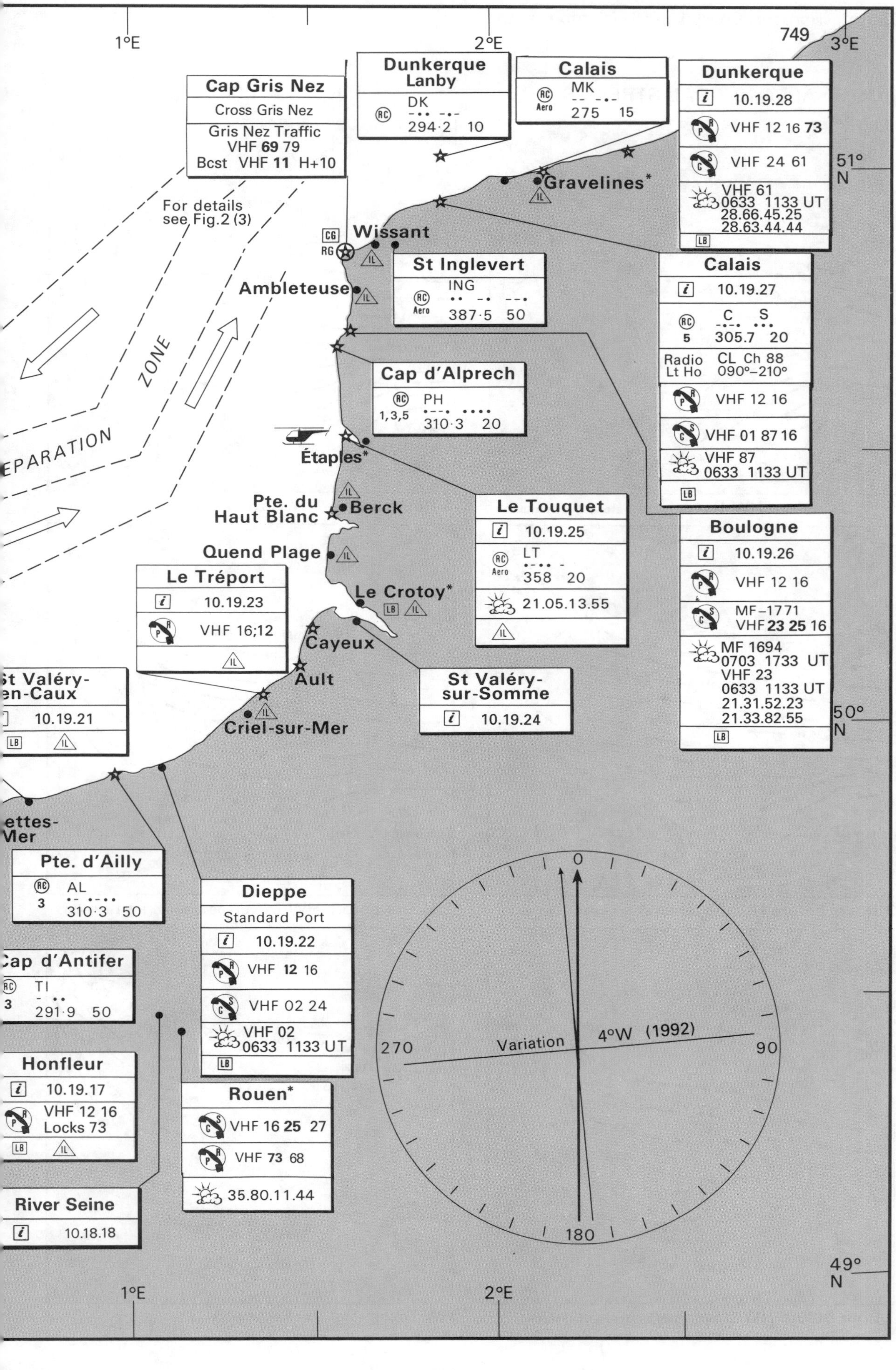
1°E
2°E
3°E
51° N
50° N
49° N
Dunkerque Lanby
DK
294·2 10
Calais
MK
Aero
275 15
Dunkerque
10.19.28
VHF 12 16 73
VHF 24 61
VHF 61
0633 1133 UT
28.66.45.25
28.63.44.44
LB
Cap Gris Nez
Cross Gris Nez
Gris Nez Traffic
VHF 69 79
Bcst VHF 11 H+10
For details see Fig.2 (3)
Gravelines*
Wissant
CG
RG
St Inglevert
ING
Aero
387·5 50
Calais
10.19.27
C S
5
305.7 20
Radio Lt Ho
CL Ch 88
090°–210°
VHF 12 16
VHF 01 87 16
VHF 87
0633 1133 UT
LB
Ambleteuse
SEPARATION
ZONE
Cap d'Alprech
PH
1,3,5
310·3 20
Étaples*
Pte. du Haut Blanc
Berck
Le Touquet
10.19.25
LT
Aero
358 20
21.05.13.55
Boulogne
10.19.26
VHF 12 16
MF–1771
VHF 23 25 16
MF 1694
0703 1733 UT
VHF 23
0633 1133 UT
21.31.52.23
21.33.82.55
LB
Quend Plage
Le Crotoy*
LB
Le Tréport
10.19.23
VHF 16;12
Cayeux
Ault
St Valéry-sur-Somme
10.19.24
St Valéry-en-Caux
10.19.21
LB
Criel-sur-Mer
Pte. d'Ailly
AL
3
310·3 50
Dieppe
Standard Port
10.19.22
VHF 12 16
VHF 02 24
VHF 02
0633 1133 UT
LB
Cap d'Antifer
TI
3
291·9 50
Honfleur
10.19.17
VHF 12 16
Locks 73
LB
Rouen*
VHF 16 25 27
VHF 73 68
35.80.11.44
River Seine
10.18.18
0
90
180
270
Variation 4°W (1992)

10.19.3 AREA 19 TIDAL STREAMS

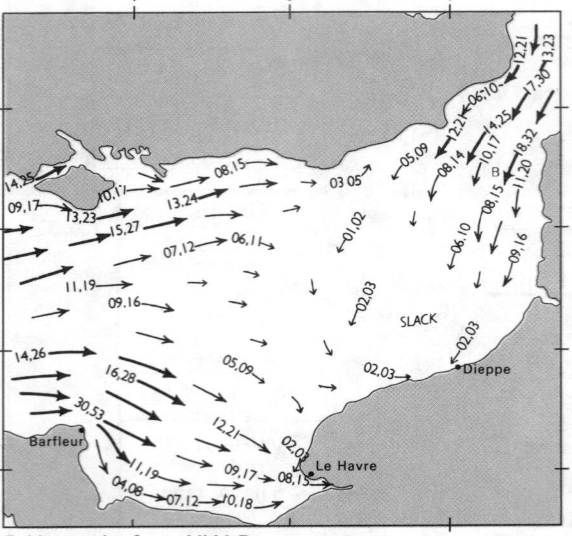

1°
0°
1°
51°
50°
14,25
09,17
13,23
10,17
15,27
13,24
08,15
07,12
06,11
11,19
09,16
03 05
05,09
01,02
12,21
08,14
14,25
10,17
08,15
06,10
17,30
18,32
11,20
09,16
06,10
12,21
13,23
B
02,03
SLACK
02,03
02,03
14,26
16,28
05,09
30,53
12,21
11,19
04,08
07,12
10,18
09,17
08,13
02,03
Barfleur
Le Havre
Dieppe

5 Hours before HW Dover (0345 before HW Le Havre)

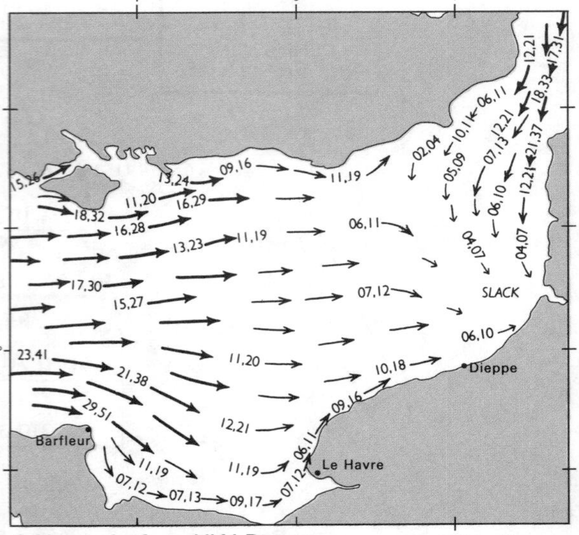

1°
0°
1°
51°
50°
15,26
18,32
13,24
09,16
11,19
02,04
10,14
06,11
12,21
17,31
11,20
16,29
16,28
13,23
11,19
06,11
05,09
07,13
12,21
18,33
21,37
12,21
06,10
04,07
04,07
17,30
15,27
07,12
SLACK
06,10
23,41
21,38
11,20
10,18
29,51
09,16
12,21
11,19
06,11
07,12
07,13
09,17
07,12
Barfleur
Le Havre
Dieppe

4 Hours before HW Dover (0245 before HW Le Havre)

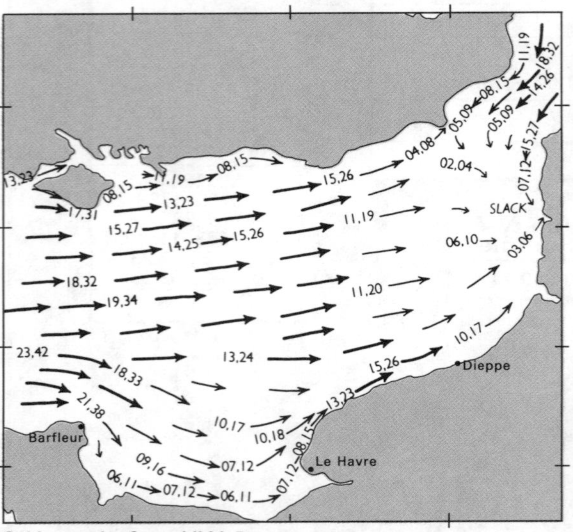

51°
50°
13,23
17,31
08,15
11,19
08,15
13,23
15,27
14,25
15,26
15,26
04,08
05,09
08,15
11,19
18,32
14,26
05,09
02,04
15,27
07,12
SLACK
11,19
06,10
03,06
18,32
19,34
11,20
10,17
23,42
18,33
13,24
15,26
21,38
13,23
10,17
10,18
08,15
09,16
07,12
06,11
07,12
06,11
07,12
Barfleur
Le Havre
Dieppe

3 Hours before HW Dover (0145 before HW Le Havre)

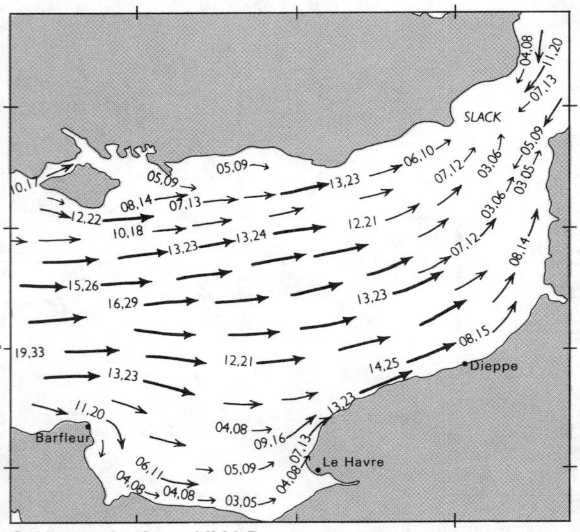

51°
50°
04,08
11,20
07,13
SLACK
05,09
10,17
05,09
06,10
07,12
03,06
12,22
08,14
07,13
13,23
03,05
10,18
13,23
13,24
12,21
03,06
07,12
15,26
13,23
08,14
16,29
19,33
12,21
14,25
08,15
13,23
11,20
13,23
04,08
09,16
07,13
06,11
05,09
04,08
04,08
03,05
04,08
Barfleur
Le Havre
Dieppe

2 Hours before HW Dover (0045 before HW Le Havre)

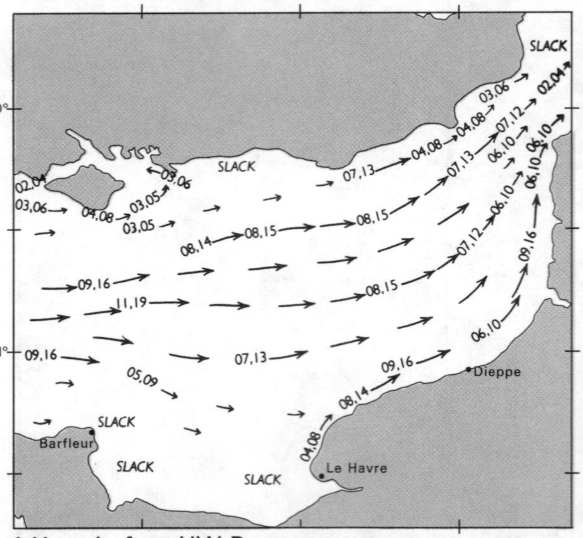

50°
51°
SLACK
03,06
02,04
02,04
SLACK
03,06
04,08
07,12
03,06
04,08
03,05
07,13
04,08
07,13
06,10
06,10
03,05
08,14
08,15
08,15
06,10
09,16
07,12
09,16
11,19
08,15
06,10
09,16
07,13
09,16
05,09
08,14
SLACK
SLACK
04,08
SLACK
Barfleur
Le Havre
Dieppe

1 Hour before HW Dover (0015 after HW Le Havre)

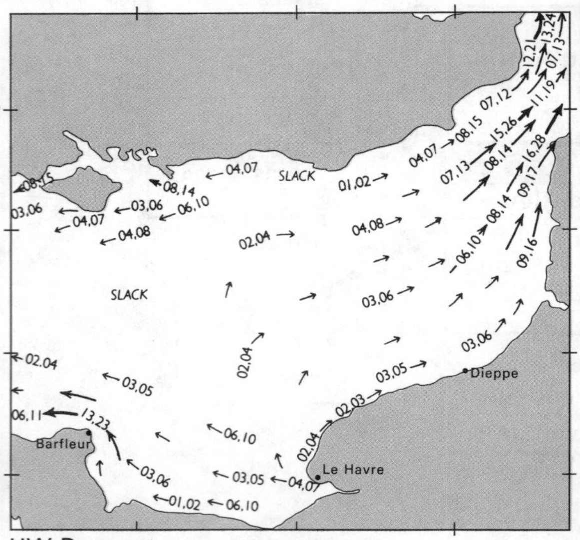

50°
51°
12,21
13,24
07,13
07,12
11,19
08,15
15,26
16,28
08,15
04,07
08,14
04,07
SLACK
01,02
07,13
08,14
03,06
06,10
03,06
04,07
04,08
02,04
04,08
06,10
08,14
09,17
SLACK
09,16
03,06
03,06
02,04
02,04
03,05
03,05
06,11
13,23
06,10
02,03
02,04
03,06
03,05
04,07
01,02
06,10
Barfleur
Le Havre
Dieppe

HW Dover (0115 after HW Le Havre)

Westward 10.18.3. North-westward 10.2.3. Northward 10.3.3. Isle of Wight 10.2.29.

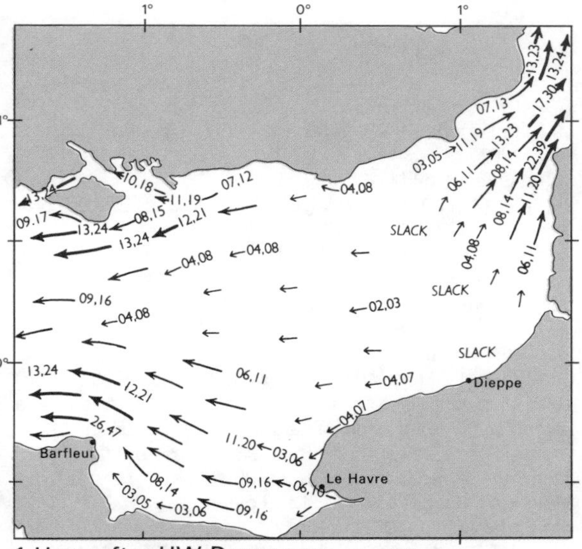
1°
0°
1°
51°
50°
SLACK
Dieppe
Barfleur
Le Havre

1 Hour after HW Dover (0215 after HW Le Havre)

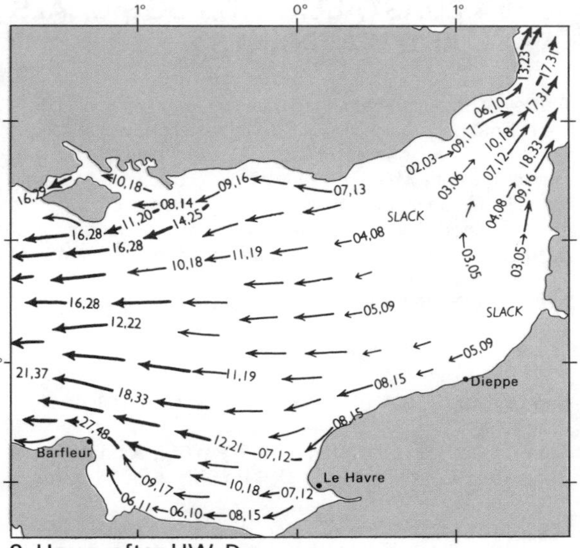
1°
0°
1°
51°
50°
SLACK
Dieppe
Barfleur
Le Havre

2 Hours after HW Dover (0315 after HW Le Havre)

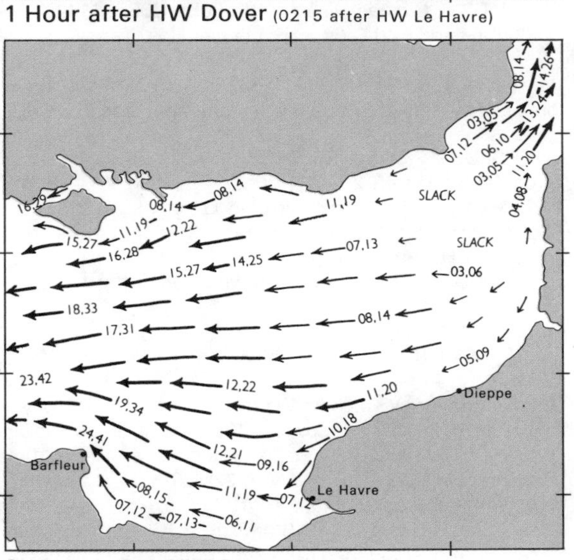
51°
50°
SLACK
Dieppe
Barfleur
Le Havre

3 Hours after HW Dover (0415 after HW Le Havre)

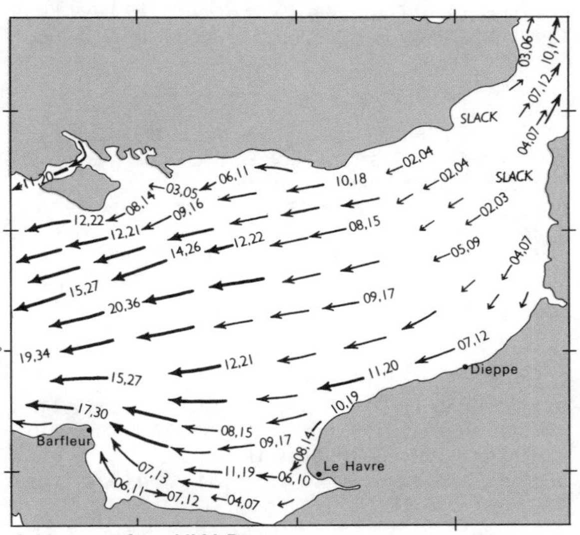
51°
50°
SLACK
Dieppe
Barfleur
Le Havre

4 Hours after HW Dover (0515 after HW Le Havre)

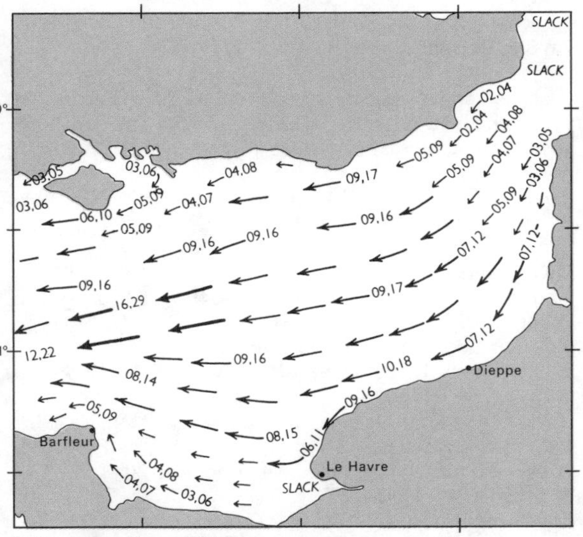
50°
51°
SLACK
Dieppe
Barfleur
Le Havre

5 Hours after HW Dover (0615 after HW Le Havre)

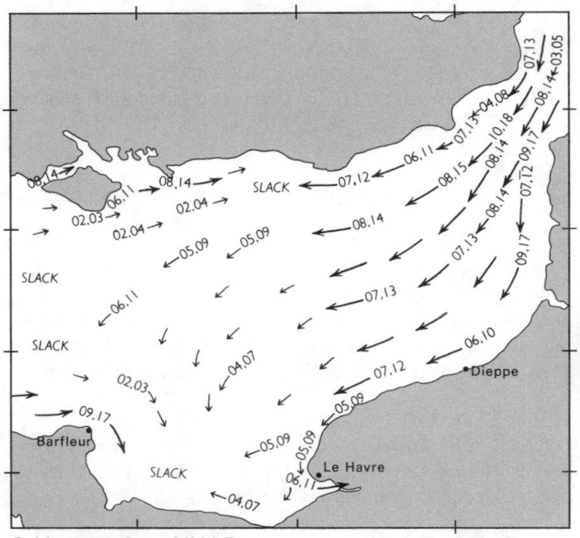
50°
51°
SLACK
Dieppe
Barfleur
Le Havre

6 Hours after HW Dover (0510 before HW Le Havre)

10.19.4 COASTAL LIGHTS, FOG SIGNALS AND WAYPOINTS

Abbreviations used below are given in 1.4.1. Principal lights are in **bold** print, places in CAPITALS, and light-vessels, light floats and Lanbys in *CAPITAL ITALICS*. Unless otherwise stated lights are white. m—elevation in metres; M—nominal range in n. miles. Fog signals are in *italics*. Useful waypoints are underlined – use those on land with care. All geographical positions should be assumed to be approximate. See 4.2.2.

Note. For English Channel Waypoints see 10.1.7

FRANCE—NORTH COAST

Cap Lévi 49°41'·80N 01°28'·30W Fl R 5s 36m **22M**; Gy ■ Tr, W top.
Anse de Vicq Ldg Lts 158°. Front FR 8m 6M; ▲ on W pylon, R top. Rear 428m from front FR 14m 6M; ▲ on W pylon, R top.
Les Équets Lt By 49°43'·68N 01°18'·28W Q 8m 4M; NCM.

Pte de Barfleur-Gatteville 49°41'·87N 01°15'·87W Fl (2) 10s 72m **29M**; Gy Tr, B top; obsc when brg less than 088°; RC; *Horn (2) 60s.*

BARFLEUR.
Ldg Lts 219·5°. Front Oc (3) 12s 7m 10M; W ■ Tr. Rear 288m from front Oc (3) 12s 13m 10M; Gy and W ■ Tr, G top; vis 085°-355°; synchronised with front.
Jetée Est Hd 49°40'·4N 01°15'·4W Oc R 4s 5m 6M; W hut, R top.
Jetée Ouest Hd Fl G 4s 8m 6M; W pylon, G top.

Pte de Saire 49°36'·44N 01°13'·75W Oc (2+1) 12s 11m 13M; W Tr, G top.

ST VAAST-LA-HOUGUE.
Jetty Hd 49°35'·25N 01°15'·35W Oc 2) WRG 6s 12m W11M, R8M; W 8 sided Tr, R top; vis R219°-237°, G237°-310°, W310°-350°, R350°-040°; *Siren Mo(N) 30s.*
NE side Breakwater Hd Iso G 4s 6m 5M; W pedestal, G top.
SW side, groyne Hd Oc(4) R 12s 6m 7M; W hut, R top.

MORSALINES.
Ldg Lts 267°. Front 49°34'·28N 01°16'·45W Oc 4s 9m 10M; W pylon, G top; obsc by Île de Tatihou when brg less than 228°. Rear 1·8M from front 49°34'·2N 01°19'·1W Oc (3+1) WRG 12s 90m W12M, R9M, G8M; W 8-sided Tr, G top; vis W 171°-316°, G316°-321°, R321°-342°, W342°-355°.

ÎLES SAINT-MARCOUF.
Île du Large 49°29'·90N 01°08'·90W VQ (3) 5s 18m 9M; Gy Tr, G top.

CARENTAN.
Cl Lt By 49°25'·50N 01°07'·08W Iso 4s; SWM.
Ldg Lts 209·5°. **Front** Oc (3) R 12s 6m **17M**; W mast, R top; intens 208·7°-211·2°. Rear 723m from front Oc (3) 12s 14m 11M; W gantry, G top; vis 120°-005°; synchronised with front.

ISIGNY-SUR-MER.
Ldg Lts 172·5°. **Front** Dir Oc (2+1) 12s 7m **18M**; intens 170·5°-174·5°. **Rear** 600m from front Dir Oc (2+1) 12s 19m **18M**; W pylon, B top; synchronised with front, intens 170·5°-174·5°.

GRANDCAMP-LES-BAINS.
La Maresquerie 49°23'·2N 01°02'·7W Oc 4s 28m 12M; vis 090°-270°. J
Jetée Ouest Hd Fl G 4s 9m 6M.
Jetée Est Hd 49°23'·50N 01°03'·00W Oc (2) R 6s 10m 9M; *Siren Mo(N) 30s.*
Perré 49°23'·4N 01°02'·5W Oc 4s 8m 12M; G pylon on W hut; vis 083°-263°.
Ldg Lts 146°, both Q 4m 7M; vis 136°-156°.

PORT-EN-BESSIN.
Ldg Lts 204°. Front 49°21'·0N 00°45'·5W Oc (3) 12s 25m 10M; W pylon; vis 069°-339°; *Siren 20s* — sounded over a sector of 90° each side of Ldg line, continuous in the W sector, interrupted in the E. Rear, 93m from front Oc (3) 12s 42m 11M; W & Gy house; synchronised with front; RC.
Môle Est Hd Oc R 4s 14m 7M; R pylon.
Môle Ouest Hd 49°21'·21N 00°45'·42W Fl WG 4s 14m W10M, G7M; G pylon; vis W114·5°-065°, G065°-114·5°.
Oc (2) R 6s and Fl 2) G 6s mark the pier Hds.

Ver 49°20'·47N 00°31'·15W Fl (3) 15s 42m **26M**; W Tr, Gy top; obsc by cliffs of St Aubin when brg more than 275°; RC.

COURSEULLES-SUR-MER.
Jetée Ouest Hd 49°20'·47N 00°27'·28W Iso WG 4s 7m W9M, G6M; brown pylon on dolphin, G top; vis W135°-235°, G235°-135°; *Horn 30s* sounded from 2 hours before to 2 hours after HW.
Jetée Est Oc (2) R 6s 9m 7M; brown pylon, R top.

OUISTREHAM.
OC Lt By 49°19'·89N 00°14'·53W Iso 4s 8m 4M; SWM; *Whis.*
Ouistreham Oc WR 4s 37m **W17M**, R 13M; W Tr, R top; vis W151°-115°, R115°-151°. Ldg Lts 185°. Front, Jetée Est Dir Oc (3+1) R 12s 10m 13M; W pylon, R top; Ra refl. Rear 610m from front Dir Oc 3+1) R 12s 30m **22M**; Tripod, R top; synchronised with front; intens 183°-187°.
Jetée Ouest Hd Iso G 4s 12m 9M; W pylon, G top, on dolphin; Ra refl; *Horn 10s*, sounded from 2·5 hours before to 3 hours after HW.
Enrochements Est Hd 49°18'·08N 00°14'·56W Oc (2) R 6s 7m 8M; W pylon, R top; Ra refl.

Canal de Caen marked by QR and OcR 4s Lts on E side, and by QG and IsoG 4s Lts on W side. Viaduc de Calix Iso 4s on upstream and downstream sides; FG on N side, FR on S side.

Dives-sur-Mer Oc (2+1) WRG 12s 6m W12M, R9M, G9M; vis G124°-154°, W154°-157°, R157°-193°.

TROUVILLE.
Trouville SW Lt By 49°22'·68N 00°02'·64E VQ (9) 10s; WCM.
W Jetty 49°22'·44N 00°04'·17E Fl WG 4s 10m W12M, G9M; B pylon on dolphin; vis W005°-176°, G176°-005°.
E Jetty Fl (4) WR 12s 8m W10M, R7M; W pylon, R top; vis W131°-175°, R175°-131°.
Ldg Lts 148°. Front Oc R 4s 11m 12M; W Tr, R top; vis 330°-150°; *Horn (2) 30s.* Rear 217m from front Oc R 4s 17m 10M; W pylon, R top; synchronised with front vis 120°-170°.
W Jetty QG 11m 9M; W Tr, G Top.
Breakwater Hd Iso G 4s 9m 5M; G mast.

HONFLEUR.
Digue du Ratier Hd 49°25'·97N 00°06'·66E VQ 8m 8M; Tank on B col; Ra refl.
Spillway 49°25'·8N 00°12'·8E VQ (9) 10s 15m 6M; WCM.
Falaise des Fonds 49°25'·5N 00°12'·9E Fl (3) WRG 12s 15m **W17M**, R13M, G13M; W ■ Tr, G top; vis G040°-080°, R080°-084°, G084°-100°, W100°-109°, R109°-162°, G162°-260°.

Digue Ouest Hd QG 10m 6M; G pylon.
Digue Est Hd Q 9m 9M; NCM; *Horn (5) 40s.*
Jetée Est Hd Oc (2) R 6s 12m 6M, W Tr, R top.
Jetée du Transit F Vi 10m 1M; W pylon, B bands.
Quay de Hornfleur W 2 FG (vert) 6m 5M, Gy mast..
E Quay 2 FG (vert) 6m 5M, Gy mast.

LA SEINE MARITIME.
La Risle, Digue Sud (Km 346·0), 49°26'·3N 00°22'·0E Iso G 4s 11m 7M; W pylon , G top; Ra refl.
Digue Nord, Tourelle Ygou, VQ R 7m 5M; R lantern on Gy tank.
Digue Sud, Épi de la Roque, QG 8m 6M; W col, G top.
Marais-Vernier Fl G 4s 8m 5M; W Col, R top.
Digue Nord, Tancarville, QR 9m 6M; W col, R top.
Aero Fl R 3s on each of 2 bridge pillars.

Cap de la Hève 49°30'·80N 00°04'·24E Fl 5s 123m **24M**; W 8-sided Tr, R top;

LE HAVRE LANBY 49°31'·67N 00°09'·80W Q (2) R 10s 10m 20M; W By, R stripes; RC; Racon.

LE HAVRE.
Digue Sud Hd 49°29'·10N 00°05'·45E VQ (3) G 2s 15m 11M; W Tr, G top.
Digue Nord Hd Fl R 5s 15m **21M**; W Tr, R top; *Horn 15s.*
Ldg Lts 107°. Front **Quai Roger Meunier** Dir F 36m **25M**; Gy Tr, G top; intens 106°-108°; (H24). Rear Qu**ai Joannes Couvert** 0·73M from front Dir F 78m **25M**; Gy Tr, G top; intens 106°-108°; (H24); Ra refl.
Ldg Lts 090°. **Front** 49°29'·5N 00°05'·8E Dir FR 21m **18M** ; W Tr, R top; intens 089°-091°. **Rear**, 620m from front, Dir FR 43m **18M**; ■ col on house; intens 089°-091° (both occas).
Yacht Hbr, Digue Augustin Normand, Q (2) G 5s 5m 2M.
Quai des Abeilles Hd Q R 9m 7M; W and R mast; *Bell (1) 2·5s.*

PORT D'ANTIFER.
Bassin de Caux, Mole Ouest Hd Fl R 4s 13m 5M; W mast, R top.
Jetée Est Hd Fl G 4s 13m 5M; W mast, G top.
Antifer 49°39'·5N 00°09'·2E Dir Oc WRG 4s 24m W14M, R13M, G13M; W pylon, G top; vis G068°-078°, W078°-088°, R088°-098°.
Jetty Hd 49°39'·8N 00°07'·1E QR 20m 9M; W Tr, R top.
Port D'Antifer Ldg Lts 127·5°. **Front** 49°38'·3N 00°09'·2E Dir Oc 4s 105m **22M**; W pylon, G top vis 127°-128°. **Rear**, 430m from front, Dir Oc 4s 124m **22M**; W mast, G top. By day both show FW Lts **33M** vis 126·5°-128·5°, occasl.

Cap d'Antifer 49°41'·07N 00°10'·00E Fl 20s 128m **29M**; Gy 8-sided Tr, G top; vis 021°-222°; RC.

YPORT.
Ldg Lts 165°. Front Oc 4s 11m, W mast, G top.
Rear 30m from front Oc 4s 14m, W pylon, G top on house.

FÉCAMP.
Jetée Nord 49°46'·00N 00°21'·87E Fl (2) 10s 15m **16M**; Gy Tr, R top; Re*ed (2) 30s*. Lts in line 085°.
Front Jetée Sud Hd, QG 14m 9M; grey Tr, G top; vis 072°-217°. Rear, Jetée Nord, root, QR 10m; R I on W mast.

SAINT VALERY-EN-CAUX.
Jetée Ouest 49°52'·45N 00°42'·50E Oc (2+1) G 12s 13m 14M; G Tr.
Jetée Est Fl (2) R 6s 8m 4M; W mast, R top.

Pointe d'Ailly 49°55'·13N 00°57'·56E Fl (3) 20s 95m **31M**; W ■ Tr, G top; RC; *Horn (3) 60s* (TD).
D1 Lt By 49°57'·10N 01°01'·26E VQ (3) 5s; ECM.

DIEPPE.
Jetée Est Hd 49°56'·22N 01°05·17E Oc (4) R 12s 19m 8M; R col.
Jetée Ouest Hd 49°56'·20N 01°05'·05E Iso WG 4s 11m W12M, G8M; W Tr, G top; vis W095°-164°, G164°-095°; *Horn 30s.*
Falaise du Pollet Q R 35m 9M; R & W structure; vis 105·5°-170·5°.
Daffodils Lt By 50°02'·50N 01°04'·15E VQ (9) 10s; W CM.

LE TRÉPORT.
Jetée Ouest Hd 50°03'·94N 01°22'·22E Fl (2) G 10s 15m **20M**; W Tr, G top; *Reed Mo(N) 30s.*
Jetée Est Oc R 4s 8m 6M; W Col, R top. Port signals Fl (5) G 500m SE.

Ault 50°06'·35N 01°27'·24E Oc (3) WR 12s 95m **W18M**, R14M, W Tr, R top; vis W040°-175°, R175°-220°.

Cayeux-sur-Mer 50°11'·75N 01°30'·70E Fl R 5s 32m **22M**; W Tr, R top.
Pte du Hourdel 50°12'·95N 01°34'·00E Oc (3) WG 12s 19m W12M, G9M; W Tr, G top; vis W053°-248°, G248°-323°; *Reed (3) 30s.*

PORT DU CROTOY.
Le Crotoy 50°12'·9N 01°37'·4E Oc (2) R 6s 19m 9M; W pylon; vis 285°-135°.
Yacht Hbr, W side Jetty Hd Fl R 2s 4m 2M.
Yacht Hbr, E side Fl G 2s 4m 2M.

SAINT VALERY-SUR-SOMME
W Hd of embankment 50°11'·5N 01°37'·6E Iso G 4s 9m 9M; W pylon, G top; vis 347°-222°.
Embankment Hd 50°12'·3N 01°35'·9E Q (3) G 6s 2m 2M; G pylon; Ra refl.
La Ferté Môle Hd 50°11'·2N 01°38'·6E Fl R 4s 9m 9M; W pylon, R top; vis 000°-250°.

Pointe du Haut-Blanc (Berck-Plage) 50°23'·90N 01°33'·75E Fl 5s 44m **23M**; Or Tr, R Brown band, W & G top.

LE TOUQUET
Pointe du Touquet 50°31'·4N 01°35'·6E Fl (2) 10s 54m **25M**; Y Tr, brown band; W and G top.

Camiers, Riviere Canche ent, N side Oc (2) WRG 6s 17m W9M, R7M, G6M; R pylon; vis G015°-090°, W090°-105°, R105°-141°.

Bassurelle Lt By 50°32'·70N 00°57'·80E Fl (4) R 15s 6M; Racon; R refl; *Whis.*

<u>Cap d'Alprech</u> 50°41'·95N 01°33'·83E Fl (3) 15s 62m **23M**; W Tr, B top; RC; FR Lts on radio mast 600m NE.

Hoverport Ldg Lts 119° both Dir FR 10/15m 14M; W cols, Gy tops; occas.

BOULOGNE.
<u>Approaches Lt By</u> 50°45'·25N 01°31'·15E VQ (6) + LFl 10s; SCM; *Whis.*
<u>Digue Sud (Carnot)</u> 50°44'·48N 01°34'·13E Fl (2+1) 15s 25m **19M**; W Tr, G top; *Horn(2+1) 60s.*
Digue Nord Hd Fl (2) R 6s 10m 6M; R Tr.
Ro Ro berth Ldg Lts 197°. Front 50°43'·7N 01°34'·1E FG 16m 8M; dolphin; vis 107°-287°. Rear, 480m from front FR 23m 13M; R mast, W band; vis 187°-207°.
Darse Sarraz-Bournet, ent E side Oc (2) R 6s 8m 6M; W pylon, R top.
Jetée Ouest Hd Iso G 4s 8m 5M; W pylon, G top.
Jetée NE Hd FR 11m 9M; R Tr.
Jetée SW, FG 17m 5M; W col, G top; *Horn 30s.*

<u>ZC1 Lt By</u> 50°44'·85N 01°27'·10E Fl (4) Y 15s; SPM.
<u>ZC2 Lt By</u> 50°53'·50N 01°31'·00E Fl (2+1) Y 15s; SPM.

<u>Cap Gris-Nez</u> 50°52'·17N 01°35'·07E Fl 5s 72m **29M**; W Tr, B top; obsc 232°-005°; RG; *Siren 60s.*

<u>Sangatte</u> 50°57'·23N 01°46'·57E Oc WG 4s 12m W8M, G6M; W pylon, B top; vis G065°-089°, W089°-152°, G152°-245°; Racon.

CALAIS.
<u>CA4 Lt By</u> 50°58'·90N 01°45'·15E VQ (9) 10s; WCM; R refl; *Whis.*
<u>Jetée Ouest Hd</u> 50°58'·30N 01°50'·48E Iso G 3s 12m 9M; (in fog Iso 3s); W Tr, G top; *Bell (1) 5s.*
Jetée Est Hd Fl (2) R 6s 12m **17M**; Gy Tr, R top; Reed(2) 40s; Ra refl. (in fog 2 Fl (2) (vert) 6s) (on request));
Calais 50°57'·7N 01°51'·2E Fl (4) 15s 59m **23M**; W 8-sided Tr, B top; vis 073°-260°; RW (on trial).

<u>SANDETTIE LT V</u> 51°09'·40N 01°47'·20E Fl 5s 12m **24M**; R hull, Lt Tr amidships; *Horn 3s;* Racon.
<u>MPC Lt By</u> 51°06'·17N 01°38'·33E Fl Y 2·5s 10m 6M; SPM.
<u>DUNKERQUE LANBY</u> 51°03'·00N 01°51'·83E Fl 3s 10m **20M**; R tubular structure on circular By; Racon.

Walde 50°59'·7N 01°54'·9E Fl (3) 12s 13m 4M; B pylon on hut.
<u>DKA Lt By</u> 51°02'·59N 01°57'·06E L Fl 10s; SWM.

GRAVELINES.
<u>Jetée Ouest</u> 51°00'·93N 02°05'·68E Fl (2) WG 6s 9m W9M, G6M; vis W317°-327°, G078°-085°, W085°-244°.
Jetée Est Fl (3) R 12s 5m 4M.

DUNKERQUE PORT OUEST.
Ldg Lts 120°. **Front** Dir FG 16m **19M**; W col, G top; intens 119°-121°. **Rear**, 600m from front, Dir FG 30m **22M**; W col, G top; intens 119°-121°. By day both show FW 28M.
Jetée du Dyck Hd 51°02'·3N 02°09'·9E Fl G 4s 24m 10M; W col, G top.
Jetée Clipon Hd Fl (4) 12s 24m 13M; W col, R top; vis 278°-243°; *Siren (4) 60s.*
Dir Lt 167° Dir Iso WRG 4s 12m 11M; vis G162°-166°, W166°-168°, 168°-172°.

DUNKERQUE.
Dunkerque 51°03'·0N 02°21'·9E Fl (2) 10s 59m **29M**; W Tr, B top.
Ldg Lts 185°. Front Dir F Vi 10m 3M; W col, R top; intens 183°-187°. Common rear Dir F Vi 24m 4M; Gy pylon; intens 183·7°-186·2°, 177·7°-180·2°.
Front Ldg Lt 179° Dir F Vi 10m 3M; W col, G top; intens 177°-181°.
Jetée Est Hd Oc(3) R 12s 11m 10M; W framework Tr, R top. *Horn (3) 30s.*
<u>Jetée Ouest</u> <u>Hd</u> 51°03'·68N 02°21'·05E Oc (2+1) WG 12s 35m **W17M**, G12M; W Tr, brown top; vis G252°-310°, W310°-252°; *Dia (2+1) 60s.*

10.19.5 PASSAGE INFORMATION

The coasts of Normandy and Picardy are convenient to hbrs along the S Coast of England – the distance from (say) Brighton to Fécamp being hardly more than an overnight passage. It should be noted however that many of the hbrs dry, so that a boat which can take the ground is an advantage. For details of traffic schemes in Dover Strait see Fig. 2(2). Notes on the English Channel and on cross channel pass appear in 10.3.5. For detailed sailing directions, refer to *Normandy hbrs and Pilotage* (Adlard Coles Nautical), which conveniently covers this area. *The Shell Pilot to the English Channel* (Faber and Faber) covers the French coast from Dunkerque to Brest, and the Channel Islands. For French glossary see 10.14.8.

POINTE DE BARFLEUR TO DEAUVILLE (chart 2613)

Raz de Barfleur (10.18.5) must be avoided in bad weather. Pte de Barfleur marks the W end of B de Seine, which stretches 53M E to C de la Hève, close NW of Le Havre. There are no obstructions on a direct course across the B, but a transhipment area for large tankers is centred about 10M ESE of Pte de Barfleur. A feature of B de Seine is the stand of tide at HW.

S from Barfleur (10.19.9) the coast runs SSE 4M to Pte de Saire, with rks and shoals up to 1·25M offshore. 2M S of Pte de Saire is St Vaast-la-Hougue (10.19.10): approach S of Île de Tatihou, but beware La Tourelle (rk which dries) 4·5M E of Is, and Le Gavendest (dries) and La Dent (dries) which lie 0·6M SE and 0·5M SSE of Is and are marked by Bys. There is a chan inshore of Île de Tatihou which can be used near HW. Anch in Grande Rade in offshore winds, exposed to E and S.

Îles St Marcouf lie 7M SE of St Vaast-la-Hougue, about 4M offshore, and consist of Île du Large (Lt) and Île de Terre about 0·25M apart. (See 10.19.29). Banc de St Marcouf with depths of 2·4m extends 2·5M NW from the Iss, and the sea breaks on this in strong N or NE winds. There is anch, rather exposed, SW of Lt Ho. Landing is possible by dinghy in the small hbr on W side of Île du Large from about local HW –0200 to HW +0200. There is a bird sanctuary on Île de Terre.

At the Hd of B du Grand Vey, about 10M S of Îles St Marcouf, are the (very) tidal hbrs of Carentan (10.19.11) and Isigny (10.19.29). Entry is only possible near HW. The Carentan chan is well buoyed and adequately lit. It trends SSW across sandbanks for about 4M, beyond which it runs between two breakwaters leading to a lock gate, and thence into canal to town of Carentan. The Isigny chan is deeper, but the hbr dries. Neither chan should be attempted in strong onshore winds.

On E side of B du Grand Vey, Roches de Grandcamp (dry) extend more than 1M offshore, N and W of Grandcamp (10.19.12), but they are flat and can be crossed from the N in normal conditions from about HW –0130 to HW +0130. Heavy kelp can give false echo soundings.

Between Pt de la Percée and Port-en-Bessin (10.19.13) a bank lies offshore, with drying ledges extending 0·3M. A race forms over this bank with wind against tide. Off Port-en-Bessin the E-going stream begins about HW Le Havre –0500, and the W-going at about HW Le Havre +0050, sp rates 1·25 kn.

From Port-en-Bessin the coast runs E 4M to C Manvieux, E of which lies the wartime hbr of Arromanches, where there is anch. Between C Manvieux and Langrune, 10M E, Plateau du Calvados lies offshore. Rocher du Calvados (dries) lies on the W part of this bank, and there are several wrecks in this area.

Roches de Ver (dry) lie near centre of Plateau du Calvados, extending 0·8M offshore about 1M W of Courseulles-sur-Mer (10.19.14). The approach to this hbr is dangerous in strong onshore winds. Les Essarts de Langrune (dry) lie E of Courseulles-sur-Mer, and extend up to 2·25M seaward off Langrune: at their E end lie Roches de Lion (dry), which reach up to 1·5M offshore in places and extend to a point 2·5M W of the hbr of Ouistreham (10.19.15). Here there is a canal to Caen (10.19.29).

6M E of Ouistreham is R. Dives, where a yacht can dry out (if there is room) alongside the jetty at Cabourg. The banks dry for 1M to seaward, and entry is only possible near HW and in reasonable conditions. See 10.19.29.

Deauville, 8M ENE of Dives, is an important yachting hbr (see 10.19.16). Beware Banc de Trouville (dries) which extends ENE from a point 2M N of entrance. The sands dry more than 0·5M offshore, and in strong winds from W or N the entrance is dangerous. In marginal conditions it is best attempted within 15 mins of HW, when the stream is slack. At other times, or in worse weather, the sea breaks between the jetties.

ESTUAIRE DE LA SEINE/LE HAVRE (chart 2146, 2990)

The Seine est is entered between Dives and Le Havre, and is encumbered by shallow and shifting banks which extend seawards to Banc de Seine, 15M W of Le Havre. With wind against tide there is a heavy sea on this bank. Here the SW-going stream begins at HW Le Havre +0400, and the NE-going at HW Le Havre –0300, sp rates 1·5 kn. Between Deauville and Le Havre the sea can be rough in W winds.

Chenal du Rouen is the main chan into R. Seine, and carries a great deal of commercial tfc. The S side of the chan is contained by Digue du Ratier, a training wall which extends E to Honfleur (10.19.17). Note that for tidal reasons Honfleur is not a useful staging port when bound up-river. For notes on R. Seine see 10.19.18, and for Rouen see 10.19.29.

Le Havre (10.19.19) is a large commercial port, as well as a yachting centre. Approaching from the NW, the most useful mark is the Le Havre Lanby 9M W of C de la Hève (Lt). The appr chan, which runs 6M WNW from the hbr ent, is well buoyed and lit. Strong W winds cause rough water over shoal patches either side of the chan. Coming from the N or NE, there is deep water close off C de la Hève, but from here steer S to join the main ent chan. Beware Banc de l'Éclat (depth 0·1m), which lies on N side of main chan and about 1·5M from hbr ent.

CAP D'ANTIFER TO Pte DU HAUT BLANC (chart 2451)

Immediately S of C d'Antifer (Lt, RC) is the large oil tanker hbr of Port d'Antifer. A breakwater extends about 1·5M seaward, and should be given a berth of about 1M, or more in heavy weather when there may be a race with wind against tide. Off C d'Antifer the NE-going stream begins about HW Le Havre –0430, and the SW-going at about HW Le Havre +0140. There are eddies close inshore E of C d'Antifer on both streams.

From C d'Antifer to Fécamp (10.19.20) drying rks extend up to 0·25M offshore. At Fécamp pierheads the E-going stream begins about HW Le Havre –0500, and the W-going at about HW Le Havre +0025, sp rates 2·75kn. Off Pte Fagnet, close NE of Fécamp, lie Les Charpentiers (rks which dry, about 1·5M offshore).

From Fécamp to St Valéry-en-Caux (10.19.21), which lies 15M ENE, the coast consists of chalk cliffs broken by valleys. There are rky ledges, extending 0·4M offshore in places. The nuclear power station at Paluel 3M W of St Valéry-en-Caux is conspic. Immediately E of St Valéry-en-Caux shallow sandbanks, Les Ridins de St Valéry, with a least depth of

0·6m, extend about 6·5M offshore. At St Valéry-en-Caux ent the E-going stream begins about HW Dieppe –0550, and the W-going stream begins about HW Dieppe –0015, sp rates 2·75 kn. E of the ent a small eddy runs W on the E-going stream.

Between St Valéry-en-Caux and Pte d'Ailly (Lt, fog sig, RC) there are drying rks 0·4M offshore in places. About 1·5M E of Pte de Sotteville a rky bank (depth 4·2m) extends about 1M NNW; a strong eddy causes a race over this bank.

From Pte d'Ailly to Dieppe (10.19.22) the coast is fringed by a bank, drying in places, up to 0·4M offshore. Off Pte d'Ailly are Roches d'Ailly, which dry and extend 0·5M: on this reef is La Galére, a rk which dries, about 0·3M N of Lt Ho. About 6M N of Pte d'Ailly, Les Ecamias are banks with depths of 11m, dangerous in a heavy sea. E of Pte d'Ailly an eddy runs W close inshore on first half of E-going stream. Off Dieppe the ENE-going stream begins about HW Dieppe –0505, and the WSW-going at about HW Dieppe +0030, sp rates 2 kn.

Between Dieppe and Le Tréport (10.19.23), 14M NE, rky banks, drying in places, extend 0·5M offshore. A prohib area extends 0·75M offshore of Penly nuclear power station and is marked by Lt Bys. There are no dangers further to seaward, nor in outer approaches to Le Tréport except Ridins du Tréport (depth 4·9m) about 3M NW of ent, which should be avoided in bad weather.

Between Le Tréport and B de Somme, Banc Franc-Marqué (depth 3·1m) lies 2M offshore, and about 3M N of Le Tréport. B de Somme, entered between Cayeux-sur-Mer and Pte de St Quentin 6M NNE, is a shallow and drying area of shifting sands. Offshore there are two shoals, Bassurelle de la Somme and Quémer, on parts of which the sea breaks in bad weather.

4·5M NW of Cayeux-sur-Mer the stream is rotatory anticlockwise. The E-going stream begins about HW Dieppe –0200, and reaches 2·5 kn at sp in a direction 070°: the W-going stream begins about HW Dieppe +0600, and reaches 1·5 kn at sp in a direction 240°. The chan, which runs close to Pte du Hourdel, is buoyed, but the whole est dries out 3M to seaward, and should not be approached in strong W or NW winds. For St Valéry-sur-Somme see 10.19.24, and for Le Crotoy see 10.19.29.

From Pte de St Quentin the coast runs 7M N to Pte du Haut Blanc, with a shallow coastal bank which dries for about 0·5M offshore.

LE TOUQUET TO DUNKERQUE (charts 2451, 1892, 323)

Le Touquet (10.19.25) lies in the Embouchure de la Canche, entered between Pte du Touquet and Pte de Lornel, and with a drying bank which extends 1M seaward of a line joining these two points. Le Touquet-Paris-Plage Lt is shown from a conspic Tr, 1M S of Pte du Touquet. Off the entrance the N-going stream begins about HW Dieppe –0335, sp rate 1·75 kn; and the S-going stream begins about HW Dieppe +0240, sp rate 1·75kn. See also Étaples (10.19.29).

In the approaches to Pas de Calais a number of shoals lie offshore – La Bassurelle, Le Vergoyer, Bassure de Baas, Le Battur, Les Ridens, and The Ridge (or Le Colbart). In bad weather, and particularly with wind against tide in most cases, the sea breaks heavily on all these shoals.

From Pte de Lornel to Boulogne (10.19.26) the coast dries up to 0·5M offshore. Beware hovercraft traffic S of the hbr (chart 438). Off Digue Carnot the N-going stream begins HW Dieppe –0130, and the S-going at HW Dieppe +0350, sp rates 1·75kn.

Between Boulogne and C Gris Nez (Lt, fog sig) the coastal bank dries about 0·4M offshore. The NE-bound traffic lane of the TSS Fig 2(2) lies only 3M off C Gris Nez. 1M NW of C Gris Nez the NE-going stream begins at HW Dieppe –0150, and the SW- going at HW Dieppe +0355, sp rates 4 kn.

In bad weather the sea breaks heavily on Ridens de Calais, 3M N of Calais (10.19.27 & chart 1352), and also on Ridens de la Rade about 1·5M NE of the hbr. Midway between Calais and Dunkerque (10.19.28) is the drying hbr of Gravelines (10.19.29) which should not be used in strong onshore winds.

Offshore lie Sandettié bank (about 14M to N), Outer Ruytingen midway between Sandettié and the coast, and the Dyck banks which extend in a NE direction for 30M from a point 5M NE of Calais. There are chans between these banks, and they are well buoyed, but great care is needed in poor vis. In general the banks are steep-to on the inshore side, and slope seaward. In bad weather the sea breaks on the shallower parts.

10.19.6 DISTANCE TABLE

Approximate distances in nautical miles are by the most direct route while avoiding dangers and allowing for traffic separation schemes etc. Places in *italics* are in adjoining areas.

	1	2	3	4	5	6	7	8	9	10	11	12	13	14	15	16	17	18	19	20
1 *Casquets*	**1**																			
2 *Cherbourg*	31	**2**																		
3 *Portland Bill*	48	62	**3**																	
4 *Needles*	64	60	35	**4**																
5 *Nab Tower*	81	66	60	27	**5**															
6 *Royal Sovereign*	124	102	114	82	54	**6**														
7 *Dover*	167	145	157	125	97	43	**7**													
8 Barfleur	48	20	70	60	62	91	138	**8**												
9 Port en Bessin	76	48	98	88	80	98	143	28	**9**											
10 Ouistreham	94	66	112	99	88	95	134	46	22	**10**										
11 Deauville	104	76	126	102	89	90	127	56	36	14	**11**									
12 Honfleur	110	82	132	107	91	91	126	62	40	24	10	**12**								
13 Rouen	179	151	201	176	160	160	195	131	109	93	79	69	**13**							
14 Le Havre	101	70	118	98	85	85	120	56	36	19	8	9	75	**14**						
15 Fécamp	111	80	120	93	75	60	95	64	52	39	32	34	100	25	**15**					
16 Dieppe	139	108	143	115	92	55	75	94	81	68	61	63	129	54	29	**16**				
17 Boulogne	167	142	160	128	100	46	25	128	125	115	108	110	176	101	76	54	**17**			
18 Cap Gris Nez	175	147	157	126	101	47	19	135	132	122	115	117	183	108	83	61	7	**18**		
19 Calais	188	160	174	142	114	60	22	148	145	135	128	130	196	121	96	74	20	13	**19**	
20 Dunkerque	210	182	196	164	136	82	43	170	167	157	150	152	218	143	118	96	42	35	22	**20**

BARFLEUR 10-19-9

Manche

CHARTS
Admiralty 1349, 1106, 2613; SHOM 7090, 5609, 6864; ECM 528; Stanford 7; Imray C32

TIDES
Dover −0208; ML 3·9; Duration 0550; Zone −0100

Standard Port CHERBOURG (⟵)

Times				Height (metres)			
HW		LW		MHWS	MHWN	MLWN	MLWS
0300	1000	0400	1000	6·3	5·0	2·5	1·1
1500	2200	1600	2200				
Differences BARFLEUR							
+0100	+0100	+0050	+0040	+0·3	+0·3	+0·1	+0·1

SHELTER
Excellent shelter although entrance difficult in E to NE winds. Harbour dries. Normally yachts lie along NW wall. Beware rocks in SE of harbour. Anchorage outside harbour is safe in off-shore winds. Access HW∓3. Moorings controlled by Capitaine du Port.

NAVIGATION
Waypoint 49°41′·30N 01°14′·21W, 039°/219° from/to front Ldg Lt, 1·35M. Beware Barfleur Race, about 3½ M E and NE of Barfleur Pt, in rough weather. There are numerous rocks between Barfleur Pt and the harbour, and also cross currents. Keep ¼ M E of La Grotte Rks (buoyed). Beware Le Hintar Rks (buoyed) and La Raie (Bn) to E of Ldg Line.

LIGHTS AND MARKS
Pte de Barfleur Fl (2) 10s 72m 29M; grey Tr, B top (conspic); Reed (2) 60s. Ldg Lts 219°30′. Front Oc (3) 12s 7m 10M; W square Tr. Rear Oc (3) 12s 13m 10M; grey and W square Tr, G top; synchronized, not easy to see by day. Jetée Est Oc R 4s 5m 6M. Jetée Ouest FlG 4s 8m 6M.

RADIO TELEPHONE
None.

TELEPHONE (33)
Hr Mr 33.54.43.61; Aff Mar 33.44.00.13; CROSS 33.52.72.13; SNSM 33.54.04.62; ⌗ 33.54.48.81; Meteo 33.22.91.77; Auto 33.43.20.40; Police 33.54.12.11; Dr 33.54.00.02; Brit Consul 33.44.20.13.

FACILITIES
NW Quay Slip, P, L, FW, AB; **Harbour** (100+45 visitors) M; **Bouly** ☎ 33.54.02.66 P, ME, El; **Chantier Bellot** ☎ 33.54.04.29, Sh; **Garage Marine** ☎ 33.54.00.23, D. **Town** P, D, Sh, CH, V, Gaz, R, Bar. ✉; Ⓑ; ⇄ (bus to Cherbourg); ✈ (Cherbourg).
Ferry UK — Cherbourg—Portsmouth/Weymouth (latter in summer only).

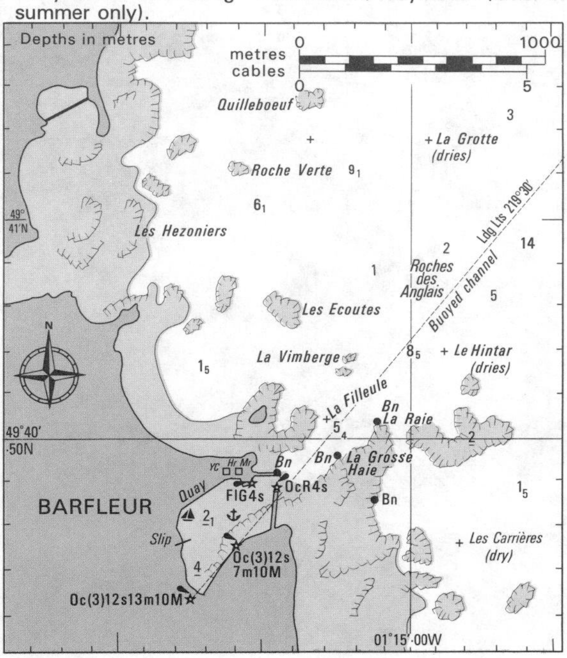

Depths in metres
metres 0 1000
cables 0 5
Quilleboeuf
La Grotte (dries)
Roche Verte
Les Hezoniers
Ldg Lts 219°30′
Roches des Anglais
Buoyed channel
Les Ecoutes
La Vimberge
Le Hintar (dries)
La Filleule
La Raie
La Grosse Haie
BARFLEUR
Quay
Slip
FlG4s
OcR4s
Oc(3)12s 7m10M
Oc(3)12s13m10M
Les Carrières (dry)
49°40′·50N
49°41′N
01°15′·00W

ST VAAST-LA-HOUGUE 10-19-10

Manche

CHARTS
Admiralty 1349, 2613; SHOM 7090, 6864; ECM 527; Stanford 2; Imray C32

TIDES
Dover −0240; ML 3·8; Duration 0530; Zone −0100

Standard Port CHERBOURG (⟵)

Times				Height (metres)			
HW		LW		MHWS	MHWN	MLWN	MLWS
0300	1000	0400	1000	6·3	5·0	2·5	1·1
1500	2200	1600	2200				
Differences ST VAAST-LA-HOUGUE							
+0105	+0055	+0120	+0100	+0·3	+0·4	−0·2	−0·2

SHELTER
The harbour is protected from all sides. If harbour full, anchorage in the approach channel is satisfactory except in strong winds from E to S. Marina lock gates open HW−2¼ to HW+3. Visitors pontoons A, B and C.

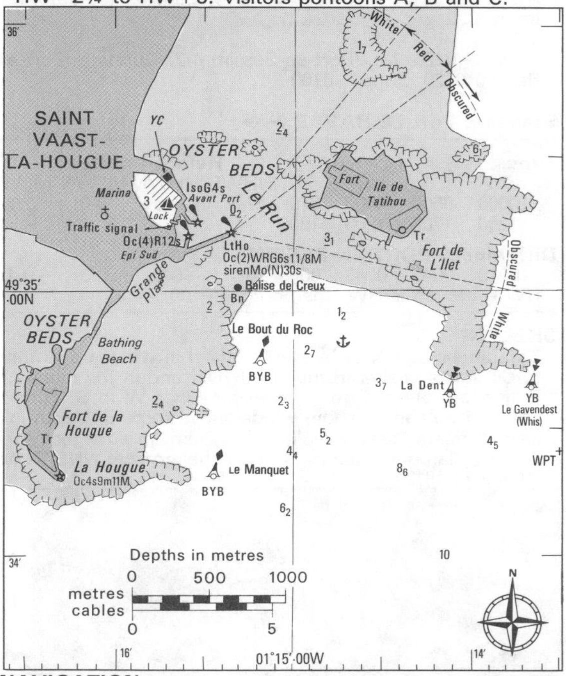

SAINT VAAST-LA-HOUGUE
White
Red
Obscured
YC
OYSTER BEDS
Le Run
Ile de Tatihou
Fort
Fort de L'Ilet
Marina
Lock
IsoG4s Avant Port
Traffic signal
Oc(4)R12s
Epi Sud
LtHo Oc(2)WRG6s11/8M sirenMo(N)30s
Balise de Creux
Grande Plage
OYSTER BEDS
Bathing Beach
Le Bout du Roc
BYB
La Dent
YB
Le Gavendest (Whis)
Fort de la Hougue
La Hougue Oc4s9m11M
Le Manquet
WPT
Depths in metres
metres 0 500 1000
cables 0 5
49°35′·00N
01°15′·00W

NAVIGATION
Waypoint 49°34′·40N 01°13′·50W, 087°/267° from/to La Hougue Lt (Oc 4s), 1·8M. Do not confuse with Lt on jetty. From waypoint head 267° until Reville Point de Saire Lt is just concealed by the Fort de l'Ilet, turn on to 346°. Head for St Vaast la Hougue jetty Lt leaving the Bout du Roc & Balise de Creux buoys to port. Watch out for cross currents.
"Le Run" approach is not recommended and should not be attempted with a boat of over 1·2m draft. The entrance is wide and well marked. Harbour gets very full in summer. Beware oyster beds.

LIGHTS AND MARKS
There are two prominent towers to indicate position—one on Ile de Tatihou and an identical one on La Hougue Pt. Prominent light structure on the end of the outer jetty, Oc (2) WRG 6s 12m 11/8M vis R219°-237°, G237°-310°, W310°-350°, R350°-040°. Siren Mo (N) 30s. Control of traffic in and out of marina by R & G lights.

RADIO TELEPHONE
VHF Ch 09.

TELEPHONE (33)
Hr Mr 33.54.48.81; Aff Mar 33.54.43.61; CROSS 33.52.72.13; SNSM 33.54.42.52; ⌗ 33.44.16.00; Meteo 33.22.91.77; Auto 33.43.20.40; Police 33.54.12.11; Dr 33.54.43.42; Brit Consul 33.44.20.13.

FACILITIES
Marina (500+150 visitors) ☎ 33.54.48.81, FW, C (25 ton), ME, El, Sh, Gaz, D, P, CH, Bar, R, ◙, V, AC, Slip; Access HW−2½ to HW+3; **Bernard** ☎ 33.54.43.47, ME.

ST VAAST-LA-HOUGUE *continued*

El, Sh, CH; **CCE Saint-Vaast** ☎ 33.54.55.08 Ⓔ; **E. Massieu** ☎ 33.54.41.00, ME, El; **Manelec** ☎ 33.54.63.82, El, Ⓔ; **Cercle Nautique de la Hougue** ☎ 33.54.55.73, Bar, R, C (3 ton), P, D, CH, FW, V; **Town** P, D, V, Gaz, R, Bar, ⊡. ✉; Ⓑ; ⇄ (bus to Valognes); ✈ (Cherbourg).
Ferry UK — Cherbourg—Portsmouth/Weymouth (summer only).

CARENTAN 10-19-11

Manche

CHARTS
Admiralty 2613; SHOM 7056, 6614; ECM 847; Stanford 1; Imray C32

TIDES
Dover −0225; ML (Port-en-Bessin) 4·2; Duration (Port-en-Bessin) 0520; Zone −0100

Standard Port LE HAVRE (⟶)

Times				Height (metres)			
HW		LW		MHWS	MHWN	MLWN	MLWS
0000	0500	0000	0700	7·9	6·6	3·0	1·2
1200	1700	1200	1900				
Differences PORT-EN-BESSIN							
−0045	−0040	−0040	−0045	−0·7	−0·6	−0·3	−0·1

HW Carentan is HW Cherbourg +0100

SHELTER
Safe anchorage N of buoyed channel in winds up to force 5. Complete shelter in the canal/river and in the marina. Entrance protected from prevailing winds W to S. Entry not advisable in on-shore winds above force 5. Depth in locked marina basin max/min 3·5/2·9m. In emergency the Iles St. Marcouf close by provide shelter from NNE, N and W see 10.19.29.

NAVIGATION
Waypoint Cl safe water buoy, Iso 4s, 49°25′·50N 01°07′·00W, 034°/214° from/to entrance to buoyed channel, 1·6M. Iles St Marcouf are a good landmark, 4·5M to N. Channel is liable to vary. All buoys have R or G reflective panels; four are lit, Fl R or G (3) 12s. Start from Cl buoy between HW−2 and HW−1½. After about 4M the channel enters between two breakwaters, marked by Bns. 3·5M further on the channel divides into three, forming a small pool. Enter the lock ahead (opens HW−2 to HW+3, traffic sigs) and proceed up the canal to marina. There are waiting pontoons on E side above and below the lock.

LIGHTS AND MARKS
Breakwaters are marked by Bns, the second of which inwards are lit port and stbd, Fl(3)R 12s and Fl(3)G 12s respectively. Ldg Lts 209°30′, Front Oc(3)R 12s 6m 17M and Rear Oc(3) 12s 14m 11M, lead through the part of the channel 1·6M inwards from the ends of the breakwaters and immediately outside (not for the buoyed channel).
Lock signals: FG = lock open, FR = lock closed.

RADIO TELEPHONE
VHF Ch 09 (0800−1800 LT and during lock opening hours.)

TELEPHONE (33)
Hr Mr 33.44.00.13; Aff Mar 33.44.00.13; # 33.44.16.00; CROSS 33.52.72.13; Meteo 33.22.91.77; Auto 33.43.20.40; Lockmaster 33.71.10.85; Police 33.42.00.17; Ⓗ 33.42.14.12; Dr 33.42.33.21; Brit Consul 33.44.20.13.

FACILITIES
Marina (550+55 visitors) ☎ 33.42.24.44 FW, AC, Slip, C (25 ton), BH (16 ton), P and D (0900-1000; 1500-1600), Access HW−2 to HW+3; **YC Croiseurs Côtiers de Carentan** ☎ 33.42.40.42, Bar; **Hardy** ☎ 33.42.02.87, ME, El, Sh, CH; **Itelec Nautic** ☎ 33.42.07.83, ME, El, Sh, CH; **Le Guen Hemidy Marine** ☎ 33.42.26.55, Sh; **G.A.M. Marine** ☎ 33.71.17.02, ME, BY, CH, El, **Town** Bar, Ⓑ, D, P; ✉, ⇄, R, V, ✈ (Cherbourg).
Ferry UK — Cherbourg—Portsmouth.

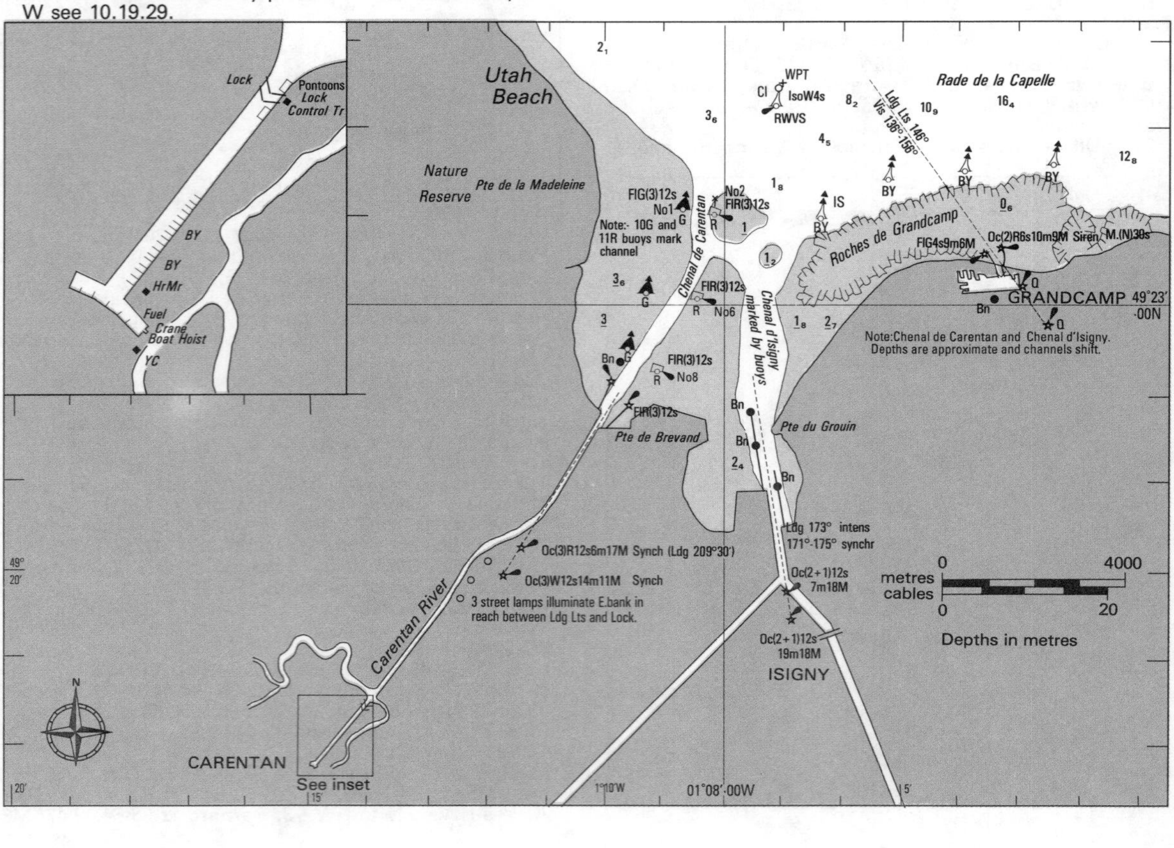

Lock
Pontoons
Lock Control Tr
BY
HrMr
Fuel
Crane
Boat Hoist
YC
Utah Beach
Nature Reserve
Pte de la Madeleine
WPT
Cl
IsoW4s
RWVS
Rade de la Capelle
Ldg Lts 146° Vis 136°-156°
Fl(3)G12s No1
No2 Fl(3)R12s
Note:- 10G and 11R buoys mark channel
Chenal de Carentan
IS
Roches de Grandcamp
Fl G4s9m6M
Oc(2)R6s10m9M
Siren M.(N)30s
GRANDCAMP
49°23′·00N
Fl(3)R12s No6
Chenal d'Isigny marked by buoys
Note:Chenal de Carentan and Chenal d'Isigny. Depths are approximate and channels shift.
Fl(3)R12s No8
Fl(3)R12s
Pte de Brevand
Pte du Grouin
Bn
Ldg 173° intens 171°-175° synchr
Oc(3)R12s6m17M Synch (Ldg 209°30′)
Oc(3)W12s14m11M Synch
3 street lamps illuminate E.bank in reach between Ldg Lts and Lock.
Oc(2+1)12s 7m18M
Oc(2+1)12s 19m18M
ISIGNY
metres 0 4000
cables 0 20
Depths in metres
Carentan River
CARENTAN
See inset
N
01°08′·00W
49° 20′

GRANDCAMP-MAISY 10-19-12

Calvados

CHARTS
Admiralty 2613; SHOM 7056; ECM 527; Stanford 1; Imray C32

TIDES
Dover −0220; ML Port-en-Bessin 4·2; Duration Port-en-Bessin 0520; Zone −0100

Standard Port LE HAVRE (⟶)

Times				Height (metres)			
HW		LW		MHWS	MHWN	MLWN	MLWS
0000	0500	0000	0700	7·9	6·6	3·0	1·2
1200	1700	1200	1900				
Differences PORT-en-BESSIN							
−0045	−0040	−0040	−0045	−0·7	−0·6	−0·3	−0·1

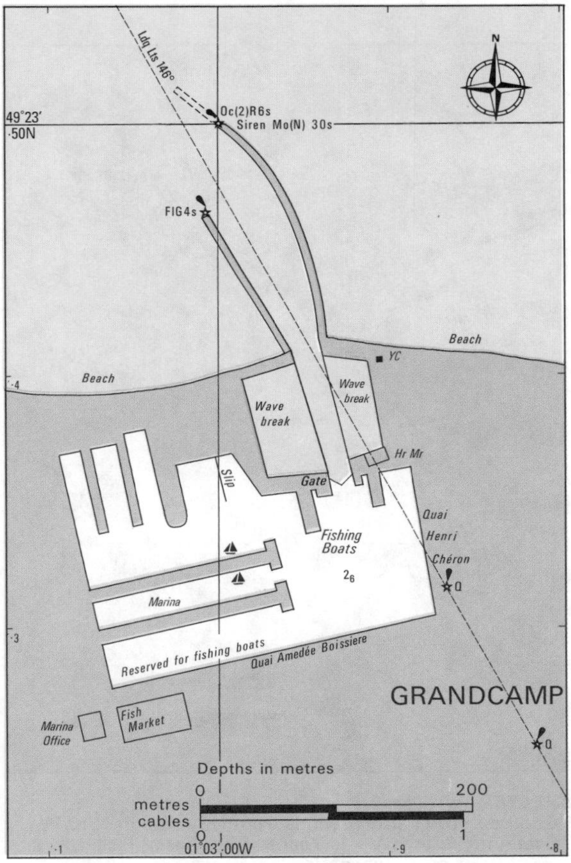
Ldg Lts 146°
N
Oc(2)R6s
Siren Mo(N) 30s
49°23'
·50N
FlG4s
Beach
YC
Beach
Wave break
Wave break
Hr Mr
Slip
Gate
Quai Henri Chéron
Fishing Boats
2₆
Q
Marina
Reserved for fishing boats
Quai Amedée Boissiere
GRANDCAMP
Marina Office
Fish Market
Q
Depths in metres
0
200
metres
cables
0
1
01°03'·00W

SHELTER
Access day and night but difficult in winds from NW to NE over force 6. Safe approach springs HW∓2, neaps HW∓1½. Wet basin, containing marina on W side, has gate which opens HW−2 to HW+2½. Visitors pontoon near gate. SW corner is very dirty.

NAVIGATION
Waypoint 49°25'·00N 01°04'·60W, 326°/146° from/to front Ldg Lt 146°, 2·0M. Large flat rocks, les Roches de Grandcamp, stretch for about 1½ M out from the harbour and dry about 1·5m. Entrance between HW∓2 is safe for most yachts.

LIGHTS AND MARKS
Line of three N cardinal buoys mark the seaward limit of Les Roches de Grandcamp, numbered 1, 3 and 5. Approach from between any of these. E pierhead Lt Oc(2) R 6s on a RW column. Ldg Lts 146°, both Q. E jetty due to be extended in 1988 as shown and Lt moved to the end.

RADIO TELEPHONE
VHF Ch 09.

TELEPHONE (31)
Hr Mr 31.22.63.16; Aff Mar 31.22.60.65; CROSS 33.52.72.13; SNSM 31.22.64.25; Meteo 31.26.28.11; Auto 31.75.14.14; Police 31.22.00.18; Dr 31.22.60.50; Brit Consul 35.42.27.47.

FACILITIES
Marina (268+25 visitors) ☎ 31.22.63.16, El, FW, BH (4 ton), Bar, V, AC; **Conin** ☎ 31.22.62.79, ME; **Galliot Marine** ☎ 31.22.61.95, CH; **Yachting 14** ☎ 31.22.67.02, ME, El, Ⓔ, Sh, CH, Gaz; **Town** Gaz, ✉; Ⓑ; ⇌ (Carentan); ✈ (Caen).
Ferry UK — Riva-Bella (Ouistreham) — Portsmouth. (May-Sept, also to Poole).

AGENTS WANTED
Ploumanac'h
Trébeurden
Le Touquet
Norderney
Dornumersiel
Langeoog
Wangerooge
Hooksiel
Bremerhaven

If you are interested in becoming our agent please write to the Editors and get your free copy annually. You do not have to be a resident in a port to be the agent but at least a fairly regular visitor.

PORT-EN-BESSIN 10-19-13

Calvados

CHARTS
Admiralty 2613; SHOM 7056, 6927; ECM 527; Stanford 1; Imray C32

TIDES
Dover −0215; ML 4·2; Duration 0520; Zone −0100

Standard Port LE HAVRE (⟶)

Times				Height (metres)			
HW		LW		MHWS	MHWN	MLWN	MLWS
0000	0500	0000	0700	7·9	6·6	3·0	1·2
1200	1700	1200	1900				
Differences PORT-EN-BESSIN							
−0045	−0040	−0040	−0045	−0·7	−0·6	−0·3	−0·1

SHELTER
Good shelter although outer harbour dries completely. There is little room for yachts. Basins accessible from HW∓2. Yachtsmen must contact Hr Mr on arrival. Yachts waiting to enter, berth on Quai de L'Epi.

PORT-EN-BESSIN *continued*

NAVIGATION
Waypoint 49°22′·00N 00°44′·90W, 024°/204° from/to front Ldg Lt 204°, 1·1M. Anchoring prohibited in outer harbour and 1ca either side of 204° transit. Busy fishing port. Yachts are admitted for short stays (up to 24 hrs). Entry is difficult with strong winds from N and NE and may become impossible. Beware submerged jetty from end of E Wharf towards Mole Ouest marked by R Bn. Keep out of G sector of Mole Ouest Lt.

LIGHTS AND MARKS
Ldg Lts 204°. Front Oc (3) 12s 25m 10M; W pylon, G top; vis 069°-339°; Siren 20s (sounded over 90° each side of leading line, continuous in W sector, interrupted in E sector). Rear Oc (3) 12s 42m 11M; W and grey house; vis 114°-294°, synchronized with front; RC.
Entry signals: FR over FG, or R flag over G flag means basins closed. Bridge has FR Lt each side, and one in the middle, lit when bridge shut. Lock opens HW∓2. Bridge opens when lock first opens and before it shuts. Between, it opens on the hour for 5 mins.

RADIO TELEPHONE
VHF Ch 18 (HW∓2) for lock opening.

TELEPHONE (31)
Hr Mr 31.21.70.49; Aff Mar 31.21.71.52; CROSS 33.52.72.13; SNSM 31.21.81.51; # 31.21.71.09; Meteo 31.26.28.11; Auto 31.75.14.14; Lock 31.21.71.77; Police 31.21.70.10; Dr 31.21.74.26; Ⓗ 31.92.29.47; Brit Consul 35.42.27.47.

FACILITIES
EC: Open every day — including Sunday in summer; **Outer Harbour** Slip, L; **Bassin II** Slip, M, L, FW, AB, C (4 ton); **Ayello** ☎ 31.21.72.24, CH; **Hutrel** ☎ 31.21.72.36, CH; **M. Marie** ☎ 31.21.74.33 El, Ⓔ; **Digne Francoise** ☎ 31.21.72.16, ME; **LK Electronique** ☎ 31.21.93.79, Ⓔ; **Gaubert** ☎ 31.21.70.53, ME, El, Sh; **Nautic Port Bois** ☎ 31.21.17.01, Sh; **CRM** ☎ 31.21.70.41, Ⓔ; **Town** P, AB, V, Gaz, R, Bar. ✉; Ⓑ; ⇌ (bus to Bayeux); ✈ (Caen).
Ferry UK — Riva Bella (Ouistreham)—Portsmouth. (May-Sept, also to Poole).

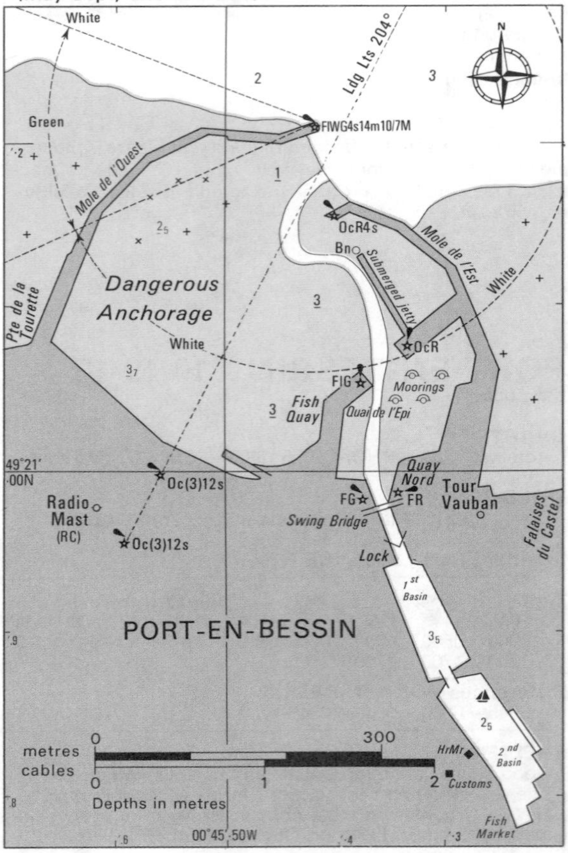
White
Ldg Lts 204°
Green
Mole de l'Ouest
FlWG4s14m10/7M
Dangerous
Anchorage
White
Pte de la Tourette
OcR4s
Bn
Submerged jetty
Mole de l'Est
White
OcR
FlG
Moorings
Fish Quay
Quai de l'Epi
Quay Nord
Tour Vauban
FG
FR
Swing Bridge
Falaises du Castel
Oc(3)12s
Radio Mast (RC)
Oc(3)12s
Lock
1st Basin
PORT-EN-BESSIN
2nd Basin
HrMr
Customs
Fish Market
metres
cables
0
300
1
2
Depths in metres
49°21′·00N
00°45′·50W

COURSEULLES-SUR-MER
Calvados

10-19-14

CHARTS
Admiralty 1349, 2613; SHOM 5598, 6927; ECM 527, 528; Stanford 1; Imray C32

TIDES
−0300 Dover; ML 3·9; Duration No data; Zone −0100

Standard Port LE HAVRE (⟶)

Times				Height (metres)			
HW		LW		MHWS	MHWN	MLWN	MLWS
0000	0500	0000	0700	7·9	6·6	3·0	1·2
1200	1700	1200	1900				
Differences COURSEULLES-SUR-MER							
−0030	No data	No data	−0020	−0·8	−1·0	−0·7	−0·3

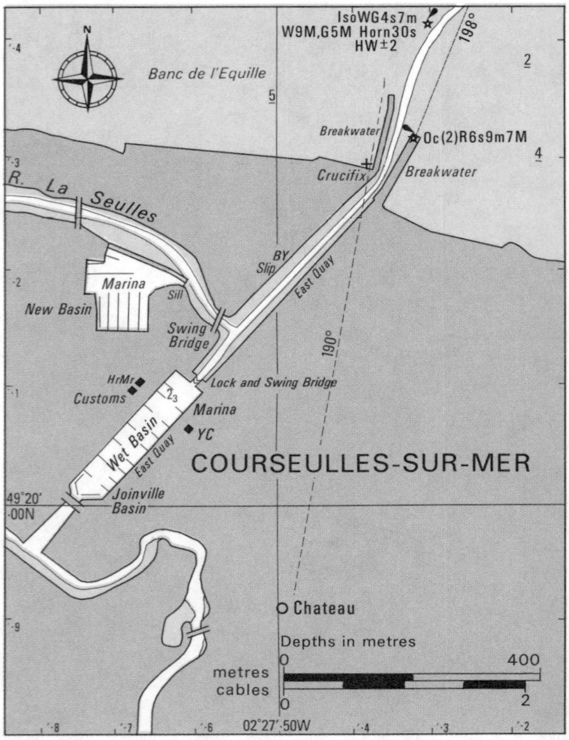
IsoWG4s7m W9M,G5M Horn30s HW±2
198°
Banc de l'Equille
Breakwater
Oc(2)R6s9m7M
Crucifix
Breakwater
R. La Seulles
Marina
New Basin
Sill
BY Slip
East Quay
Swing Bridge
190°
HrMr
Customs
Lock and Swing Bridge
Marina
YC
Wet Basin
East Quay
COURSEULLES-SUR-MER
Joinville Basin
49°20′·00N
Chateau
Depths in metres
metres
cables
0
400
2
02°27′·50W

SHELTER
Good except in strong winds from NE through N to W. Best entry is at HW−1. Yachts enter basin (lock opens HW∓2) or go to marina in New Basin.

NAVIGATION
Waypoint 49°22′·50N 00°29′·50W, 313°/133° from/to Bernières-sur-Mer church Tr, 3·7M. Plateau du Calvados extends 2M offshore. Banks dry for ⅔M. RW buoy, Iso 4s, lies 1M N by W from entrance. To S of this beware rks awash at CD and sunken breakwater on W side extending 2 ca (370m) from entrance. When harbour entrance bears 198°, alter course to that bearing.

LIGHTS AND MARKS
Large crucifix at root of W pier is a conspic mark when entering. Ldg Lts (Oc (2) R 6s on end of E jetty in line with FR at root of E jetty) in line at 198°. Day — two Ldg marks to seaward on this line. Crucifix in line with Chateau (conspic) 190°.

RADIO TELEPHONE
VHF Ch 09.

TELEPHONE (31)
Hr Mr 31.37.51.69; Lock Keeper 31.37.46.03; Aff Mar 31.37.46.19; CROSS 33.52.72.13; SNSM 31.37.45.24; #

COURSEULLES-SUR-MER *continued*

West Quai, no ☎.; Meteo 31.26.28.11; Auto 31.75.14.14; Police 31.37.46.75; Dr 31.37.45.24.26.28; Brit Consul 35.42.27.47.

FACILITIES

Marina ☎ 31.97.46.03, P, D, FW, ME, El, Sh; **Outer Harbour** ☎ 31.37.46.03, M, FW, C (8 ton), AB; **Wet Basin** Slip, P, FW, Sh, C (10 ton), CH, AB; **Chantier Naval de la Seulles** ☎ 31.37.42.34 ME, El, Ⓔ, Sh, CH, M, SM; **Chantiers Navals de la Côte de Nacre** ☎ 31.37.45.08, M, ME, El, Sh, CH; **Ste des Regates de Courseulles** ☎ 31.37.47.42, Bar.
Town P, D, V, Gaz, R, Bar. ✉; Ⓑ; ⇌ (bus to Caen); ✈ (Caen).
Ferry UK — Riva-Bella (Ouistreham) — Portsmouth. (May-Sept, also to Poole).

OUISTREHAM 10-19-15

Calvados

CHARTS

Admiralty 1349, 2613; SHOM 7055, 6928, 6927, 6614; ECM 526; Stanford 1; Imray C32

TIDES

Dover −0118; ML 4·4; Duration 0525; Zone −0100

Standard Port LE HAVRE (⟶)

Times				Height (metres)			
HW		LW		MHWS	MHWN	MLWN	MLWS
0000	0500	0000	0700	7·9	6·6	3·0	1·2
1200	1700	1200	1900				
Differences OUISTREHAM							
−0020	−0010	−0005	−0010	−0·3	−0·3	−0·3	−0·2
DIVES-SUR-MER							
−0055	No data	No data	−0115	−0·5	−0·5	−0·6	−0·4

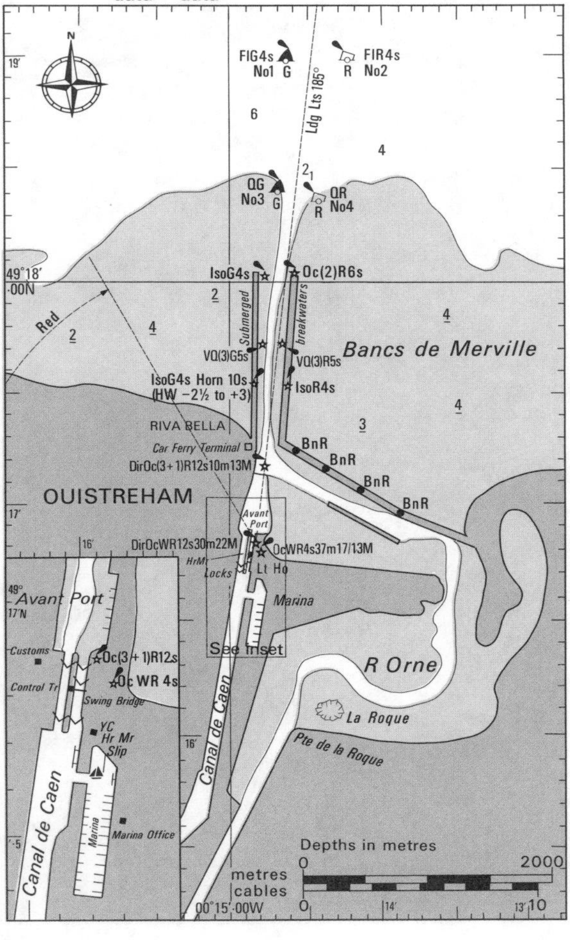
N
19'
FlG4s No1 G
FlR4s R No2
Ldg Lts 185°
QG No3 G
QR R No4
49°18'·00N
IsoG4s
Oc(2)R6s
Red
Submerged
breakwaters
VQ(3)G5s
VQ(3)R5s
Bancs de Merville
IsoG4s Horn 10s (HW −2½ to +3)
IsoR4s
RIVA BELLA
Car Ferry Terminal
DirOc(3+1)R12s10m13M
BnR
OUISTREHAM
17'
Avant Port
16'
DirOcWR12s30m22M
OcWR4s37m17/13M
HrM
Locks
Lt Ho
Marina
See Inset
R Orne
La Roque
Pte de la Roque
Canal de Caen
49° 17'N
Customs
Oc(3+1)R12s
Control Tr
Oc WR 4s
Swing Bridge
YC Hr Mr Slip
Marina Office
Depths in metres
metres
cables
00°15'·00W
14'
13'
0
2000
10

SHELTER

Very good inside locks. Temporary berths on pontoons outside, and moorings in R Orne. Enter canal by locks each side of control tower. Yachts normally use E lock. Locks open for departure HW−2 and HW+1¾; and for entry HW−1½ and HW+2¼. From 15 June−15 Sep, and at weekends and public holidays from 1 Apr−15 June and 15 Sep−31 Oct, extra openings between 0700 and 2000 local time as follows: for departure at HW−3 and HW+2¾, and for entry at HW−2½ and HW+3¼. Marina (depth 3·5m) is 1 ca (185m) inside locks on E side (Access HW∓3). Canal to Caen, 7·5 M, depth 10m to 2·5m, max speed 7 kts, overtaking prohibited. Good marina at Caen. See 10.19.29.

NAVIGATION

Waypoint OC (safe water) buoy, Iso 4s, Whis, 49°19'·90N 00°14'·57W, 005°/185° from/to front Ldg Lt 185°, 2·7M. Training walls run each side of entrance channel, marked by beacons. Beware turbulence in locks. Passage of Caen canal (four lifting bridges) is arranged at Ouistreham or Caen.

LIGHTS AND MARKS

From Ouistreham buoy (RW, Iso 4s, 3M from Lt Ho) follow Ldg Lts 185°. Main Lt Ho, conspic, W with R top, Oc WR 4s. Traffic signals (full code — see 10.14.7) shown from two panels on control tower between locks. The main signals do not apply to yachts or fishing craft, which must only enter lock when white light shows alongside lowest light of signal panel referring to lock concerned.

RADIO TELEPHONE

Call: *Ouistreham Port* VHF Ch 12 16 68 (HW−2 to HW+3). Call: *Caen Port* Ch 12 68; Ste des Regates Ch 09 (office hours).

TELEPHONE (31)

Hr Mr 31.97.14.43; Port de Plaisance/Ste des Regates 31.97.13.05; Aff Mar 31.97.18.65; CROSS 33.52.72.13; SNSM 31.97.17.47; Lock Tower 31.97.14.43; Ferry terminal 31.96.80.80; # 31.86.61.50; Meteo 31.26.28.11; Auto 31.75.14.14; Police 31.97.13.15; Dr 31.97.18.45; Brit Consul 35.42.27.47.

FACILITIES

Marina (600+65 visitors) ☎ 31.97.13.05, Slip, P, D, FW, ME, El, Sh, CH, AC, BH (8 ton), Gas, Gaz, Kos, SM, Bar; **Société des Régates de Caen-Ouistreham** ☎ 31.97.13.05, FW, ME, El, Sh, CH, V, Bar; **Nauti Plaisance** ☎ 31.97.03.08, Sh, El, Ⓔ, ME, CH; **Serra Marine** ☎ 31.97.03.60, ME, El, Ⓔ, CH, Sh, SHOM, SM; **Accastillage Diffusion** ☎ 31.96.07.75, Ⓔ, ME, El, Sh, CH, SHOM; **SNIP** ☎ 31.97.34.47, ME, El, Ⓔ, CH; **JPL Marine** ☎ 31.96.29.92, ME, El, Sh; **Normandie Voile** ☎ 31.97.06.29, SM. **Town** V, Gaz, R, Bar. ✉; Ⓑ; ⇌ (bus to Caen); ✈ (Caen).
Ferry UK — Riva-Bella (Ouistreham) — Portsmouth. (May-Sept, also to Poole).
CAEN — See 10.19.29.

DEAUVILLE/TROUVILLE 10-19-16

Calvados

CHARTS

Admiralty 1349, 2146, 2613; SHOM 6928; ECM 526; Stanford 1; Imray C32

TIDES

Dover −0130; ML 4·5; Duration 0510; Zone −0100

Standard Port LE HAVRE (⟶)

Times				Height (metres)			
HW		LW		MHWS	MHWN	MLWN	MLWS
0000	0500	0000	0700	7·9	6·6	3·0	1·2
1200	1700	1200	1900				
Differences TROUVILLE							
−0035	−0015	0000	−0010	−0·2	−0·2	−0·2	−0·1

SHELTER

Good shelter — entry to channel difficult in NW to N winds above about force 6. Excellent marina and Yacht Harbour but remainder of harbour dries. Yacht Harbour gates open HW−2 to HW+2½.

NAVIGATION

Waypoint 49°23'·10N 00°03'·68E, 330°/150° from/to front Ldg Lt 150°, 1·2M. About 2½ M from the harbour, on the transit line, there is a wreck marked by a buoy. Do not approach from E of N because of Banc de Trouville. SW

19

DEAUVILLE/TROUVILLE *continued*

Trouville buoy, W cardinal, VQ(9) 10s, lies about 1M WNW of entrance. Access from seaward about HW∓2.

LIGHTS AND MARKS
The casino is conspic building on Trouville side. Ldg Lts 148° (both Oc R 4s synchronised). Lock signals 3 FR (vert) – closed, 3 FG (vert) – passage in one direction, 2G over 1W – passage allowed in both directions.

RADIO TELEPHONE
Deauville Yacht Harbour VHF Ch 11; Port Deauville Marina VHF Ch 09.

TELEPHONE (31)
Hr Mr Marina 31.98.30.01; Hr Mr Yacht Harbour 31.88.28.71; Aff Mar 31.88.36.21; SNSM 31.88.13.07; CROSS 33.52.72.13; # 31.88.35.29; Meteo 31.26.28.11; Auto 31.75.14.14; Police 31.88.13.07; Dr 31.88.23.57; H 31.88.14.00; Brit Consul 35.42.27.47.

FACILITIES
Port Deauville (Marina) (738 + 100 visitors) ☎ 31.98.30.01, Slip, D, AC, FW, ME, El, Sh, C (6 ton), BH (50 ton), CH, R, Bar; **Yacht Harbour** (320 + 80 visitors) ☎ 31.98.50.40, Slip, C (6 ton), D, FW, AC; Access HW∓2; **Top Marine** ☎ 31.88.65.55 SM, CH; **Chantier Naval** ☎ 31.88.05.75 Slip, Sh, ME, El; **Serra Deauville** ☎ 31.98.50.92 CH; **Bassin Morny** M, P, D, L, FW, ME, El, Sh, C (6 ton), AB; **Touques Nautisme** ☎ 31.88.45.00, Slip, ME, El, Sh, P, D, C (50 ton); **Deauville YC** ☎ 31.88.38.19, L, FW, C (5 ton), AB, CH, Bar; **Callac** ☎ 31.88.55.94, ME, El, CH; **Town** P, D, FW, CH, V, Gaz, R, Bar. ✉; Ⓑ; ≠; ✈ (Deauville).
Ferry UK — Le Havre—Portsmouth or Riva-Bella (Ouistreham)—Portsmouth. (May-Sept, also to Poole).

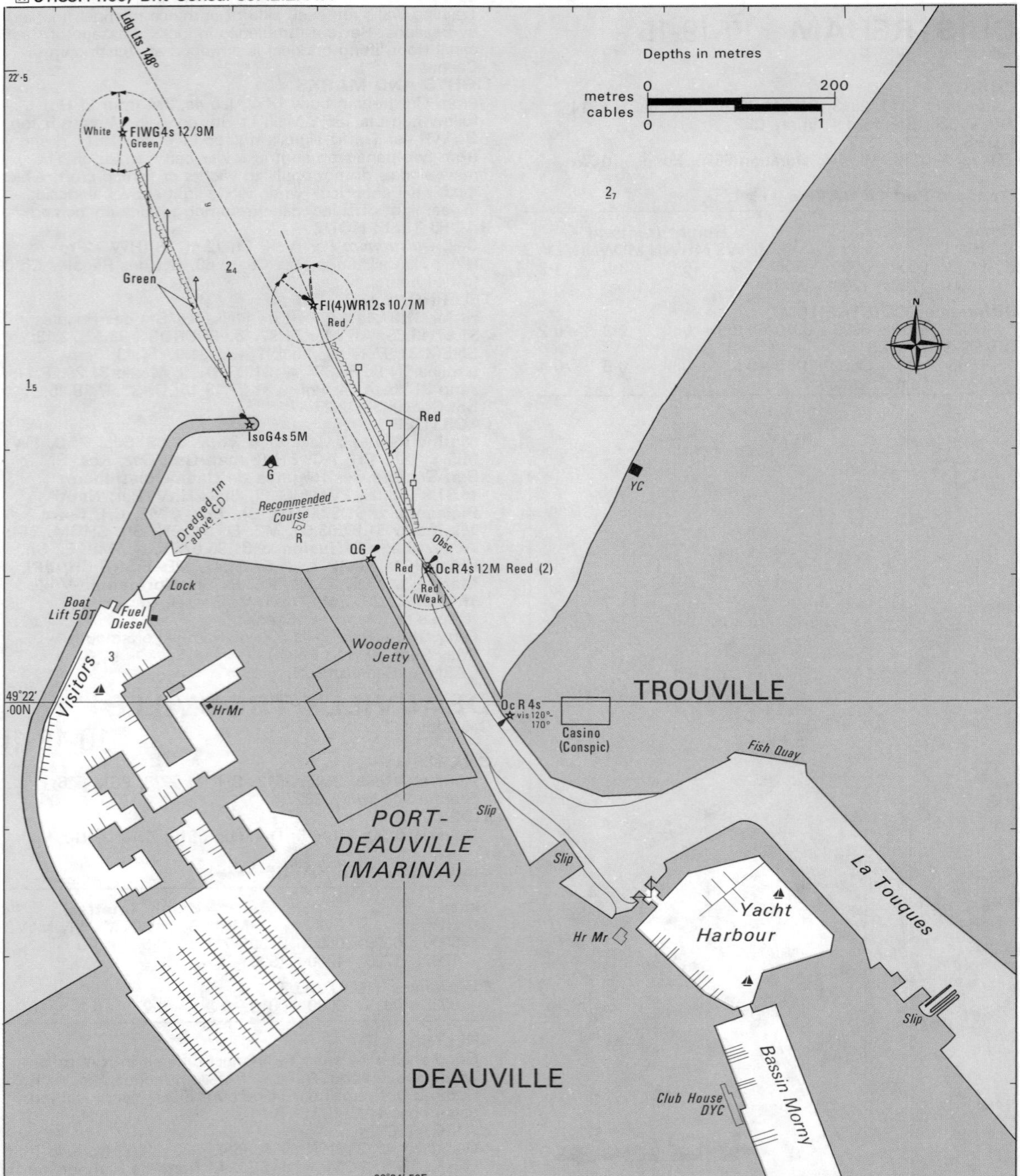

Ldg Lts 148°
Depths in metres
metres
cables
0
200
0
1
White
FlWG4s 12/9M
Green
Green
Fl(4)WR12s 10/7M
Red
Red
IsoG4s 5M
G
Dredged 1m above CD
Recommended Course
R
QG
Red
OcR4s 12M Reed (2)
Obsc.
Red (Weak)
Lock
Boat Lift 50T
Fuel Diesel
Visitors
Wooden Jetty
HrMr
YC
TROUVILLE
Oc R 4s vis 120°-170°
Casino (Conspic)
Fish Quay
Slip
Slip
PORT-DEAUVILLE (MARINA)
La Touques
Yacht Harbour
Hr Mr
Slip
DEAUVILLE
Club House DYC
Bassin Morny
22'·5
49°22'·00N
00°04'·50E
0°5'
N

HONFLEUR 10-19-17

Calvados

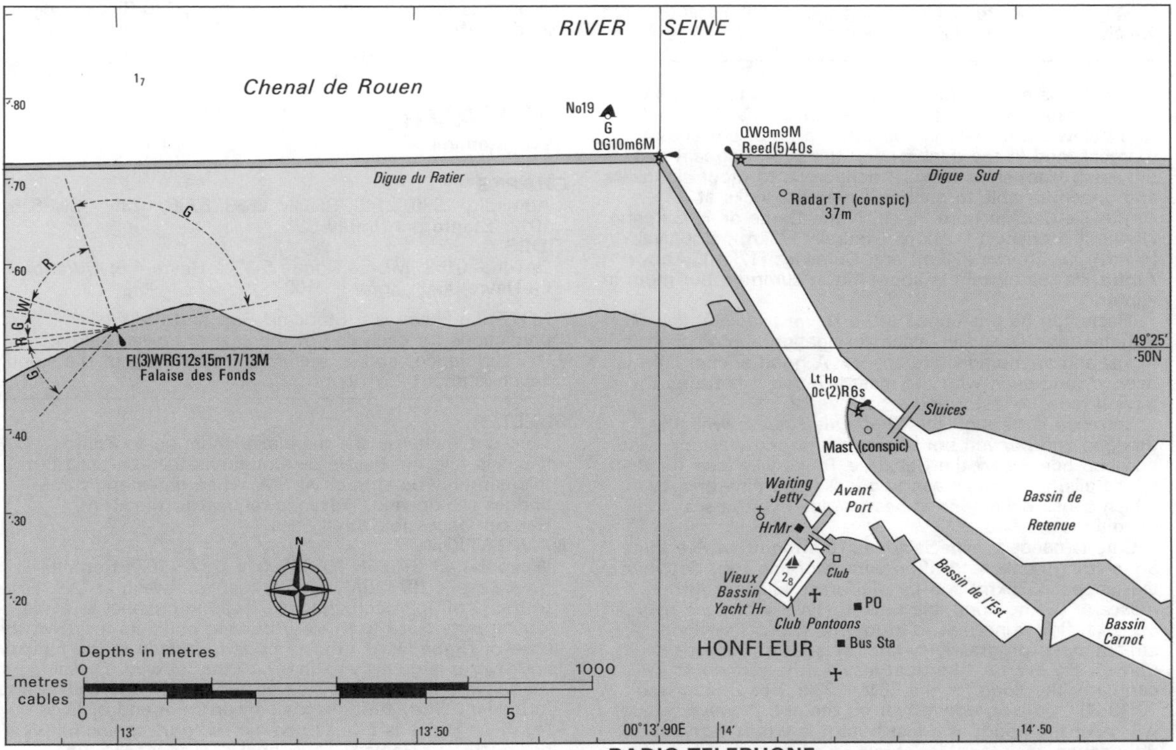
RIVER SEINE
Chenal de Rouen
No19
G
QG10m6M
QW9m9M
Reed(5)40s
Digue du Ratier
Digue Sud
Radar Tr (conspic)
37m
Fl(3)WRG12s15m17/13M
Falaise des Fonds
Lt Ho
Oc(2)R6s
Sluices
Mast (conspic)
Waiting Jetty
Avant Port
Bassin de Retenue
HrMr
Club
Vieux Bassin Yacht Hr
Club Pontoons
PO
Bus Sta
HONFLEUR
Bassin de l'Est
Bassin Carnot
Depths in metres
metres
cables
0
1000
5
13'
13'·50
00°13'·90E
14'
14'·50
49°25'·50N

CHARTS
Admiralty 2994, 2146, 2613; SHOM 6796, 6683; ECM 1012; Stanford 1; Imray C31

TIDES
−0135 Dover; ML 4·6; Duration 0540; Zone −0100

Standard Port LE HAVRE (⟶)

Times				Height (metres)			
HW		LW		MHWS	MHWN	MLWN	MLWS
0000	0500	0000	0700	7·9	6·6	3·0	1·2
1200	1700	1200	1900				
Differences HONFLEUR							
−0140	−0135	+0005	+0040	−0·1	−0·2	−0·1	+0·2

There is a stand of about 2 hours. Differences are for the beginning of the stand.

SHELTER
Shelter is very good indeed especially in the Vieux Bassin. Access HW∓1. Ask YC member when taking vacant spaces on pontoon. Visitors can use NW quay with no facilities. Larger yachts can lock into Bassin de l'Est; see Hr Mr.

NAVIGATION
Waypoint Ratier NW (stbd-hand) buoy, VQG, 49°26'·63N, 00°03'·41E, at entrance to Chenal de Rouen. Chenal de Rouen is well marked by buoys. Due to commercial shipping, yachtsmen should proceed HW∓3 between the Digue Nord, well marked by posts, and the port hand channel buoys. Entrance marked by conspic Radar tower. Access HW∓2½ but beware strong currents across entrance. Keep in mid channel approaching Avant Port. Bridge lifting & lock opening HW−1, HW, HW+1, HW+2 during day in high season and week-ends: out of season and at night HW−1, HW, HW+1. Make sure lock-keeper knows you are approaching.

LIGHTS AND MARKS
Falaise des Fonds Lt, ¾ M W of ent Fl (3) WRG 12s 15m, 17/13M, W square Tr vis G040°-080°, R080°-084°, G084°-100°, W100°-109° R109°-162°, G162°-260°
E Mole QW 9m 9M; Y metal framework Tr with B top, Reed (5) 40s. West Mole QG 10m 6M; G framework Tr.

RADIO TELEPHONE
VHF Ch 68 **73** (H24). Other stations: Honfleur Radar Ch 16; **11** 13 71 73 (H24); Tancarville Ch 11 16 (H24). Lock Ch 18. Call: *Rouen Port Capitainerie* Ch 16; 06 11 13 73 (H24); Call: *Rouen Port* Ch 11 13 73 74.

TELEPHONE (31)
Hr Mr 31.89.20.23; Lock Master 31.89.22.57; Aff Mar 31.89.20.67; CROSS 33.52.72.13; SNSM 31.89.06.02; # 31.89.12.13; Meteo 35.42.21.06; Auto 35.21.16.11; Police 31.89.21.24; Dr 31.89.07.40; Ⓗ 31.89.07.74; Brit Consul 35.42.27.47.

FACILITIES
Vieux Bassin Yacht Hr (20 visitors) ☎ 31.89.01.85, FW, C (16 ton), AB, AC; **Cercle Nautique d' Honfleur** ☎ 31.89.87.13, M; **Ateliers et Chantiers d'Honfleur** ☎ 31.89.13.71, Sh; **CRM** ☎ 31.89.05.17 Ⓔ; **Town** V, R, Bar, Gaz, ✉; Ⓑ; ≷; ✈ (Deauville).
Ferry UK — Le Havre—Portsmouth.

RIVER SEINE 10-19-18

CHARTS
Admiralty 2880, 2994, 2146, 2613; SHOM 6683, 6796, 6117; Stanford 1; Imray C31

TIDES
Zone −0100

Standard Port LE HAVRE (⟶)

Times				Height (metres)			
HW		LW		MHWS	MHWN	MLWN	MLWS
0000	0500	0000	0700	7·9	6·6	3·0	1·2
1200	1700	1200	1900				
Differences TANCARVILLE*							
−0105	−0100	+0105	+0140	−0·1	−0·1	−0·2	+1·0
QUILLEBOEUF*							
−0045	−0050	+0120	+0200	0·0	0·0	0·0	+1·4
VATTEVILLE*							
+0005	−0020	+0225	+0250	0·0	−0·1	−0·6	+2·5
CAUDEBEC*							
+0020	−0015	+0230	+0300	−0·3	−0·2	−0·7	+2·4

19

RIVER SEINE *continued*

ROUEN
+0440 +0415 +0525 +0525 −0·2 −0·1 +1·4 +3·6
*HW differences refer to the beginning of the stand, which can be up to 2½ to 3 hours.

The Seine is a beautiful river giving access to Paris and central France, and to the Mediterranean via the canals (see below). But there is constant traffic of *péniches* (barges), and in the tidal section the strong stream and the wash from ships make it dangerous to moor alongside and uncomfortable to anchor. There are locks at Amfreville (202km from Paris), Notre Dame de la Garenne (161km), Mericourt (121km), Andresy (73km), Bougival (49km), Le Chatou (44km) and Suresnes (17km). Above Amfreville the current is about 1kt in summer, but more in winter.

Masts can be unstepped at Le Havre (Société des Régates) and Deauville. Yacht navigation is prohibited at night, and anchorages are scarce. A good anchor light is needed, and even with the mast lowered it is useful to have a radar reflector and a VHF aerial.

Entrance is through the Chenal de Rouen, which is dredged and buoyed but rough in a strong westerly wind and ebb tide, or by the Canal de Tancarville (see 10.19.19 for details). The canal has two locks and nine bridges which cause delay, and is best avoided unless sea conditions are bad.

Care is needed, especially near the mouth where there are shifting banks and often early morning fog. Between Quilleboeuf (335km) and La Mailleraye (303km) the *mascaret* (Seine bore) still runs at HWS when the river is in flood. It is important to study the tides. The flood stream starts progressively later as a boat proceeds upriver. So even a 4-kn boat leaving the estuary at LW can carry the flood for the 78M (123km) to Rouen (see 10.19.29). Coming down river on the ebb however a boat will meet the flood: in a fast boat it is worth carrying on, rather than anchoring for about four hours, because the further downstream the sooner the ebb starts.

The most likely mooring places below Rouen are Quilleboeuf, Villequier, Caudebec, Le Trait and Duclair. In Rouen (a major port) yachts use the Bassin St Gervais, some way from the city centre and rather squalid, but there is also a marina on the north side of Ile Lacroix above Pont Corneille. In the non-tidal section there are alongside berths at Les Andelys, Vernon, Port Maria (near Mantes) and Les Mureaux. In Paris the Touring Club de France (Pont de la Concorde) is helpful and cheap, but noisy and uncomfortable. Fuel is available alongside at Rouen, Rolleboise, Conflans and Paris. There is a marina near the Bastille.

For detailed information see *A Cruising Guide to the Lower Seine* (Imray, Laurie, Norie and Wilson Ltd).

CANALS TO MEDITERRANEAN
The quickest route to the Mediterranean is Le Havre/Paris/ St Mammes/canal du Loing/canal du Briare/canal Latéral à la Loire/canal du Centre/Saône/Rhône, a distance of 1319km (824 miles) with 182 locks. Maximum dimensions: length 38·5m, beam 5·0m, draught 1·8m, air draught 3·5m. Further details and list of chomages (stoppages) for current year (available from March), can be obtained from French Tourist Office, 178 Piccadilly, London, W1V 0AL.

LE HAVRE 10-19-19

Seine Maritime

CHARTS
Admiralty 2990, 2146; SHOM 6683, 6796, 6736; ECM 526, 1012; Stanford 1; Imray C31

TIDES
Dover −0103; ML La Roque 5·3 Le Havre 4·6; Duration Le Havre 0543; Zone −0100

NOTE: Le Havre is a Standard Port and the tidal predictions for each day of the year are given below. HW differences above refer to the beginning of the stand which is about 2½ hours.

SHELTER
Excellent shelter in the marina. Visitors go to Pontoon O. If this is full, the Bassin du Commerce can be used but this can only be entered at HW when gates and three bridges are opened. Advance request to the Hr Mr. Harbour accessible at all tides.

NAVIGATION
Waypoint 49°31′·05N 00°04′·00W, 287°/107° from/to front Ldg Lt 107°, 7M. Shingle banks, awash at LW, lie to the N of approach channel. Keep in channel to avoid lobster pots close each side. Beware boulders inside at the base of Digue Nord. Anchoring is forbidden in the fairway and over a large area to the N of the fairway. Crossing the fairway the harbour side of buoys LH7 and LH8 is also forbidden. Obey traffic signals given from end of Digue Nord. Le Havre is a busy commercial port so yachts must not obstruct shipping. The Canal de Tancarville runs eastwards from Le Havre to the River Seine at Tancarville (see 10.19.18). To enter the canal at Le Havre proceed through the small craft lock (Écluse de la Citadelle) in the NE corner of the Arrière Port, across Bassin de la Citadelle and under a bridge into Bassin de l'Eure. Turn south, and after 400m turn east into Bassin Bellot. At the far end alter course to port under two bridges into Bassin Vétillart. From here proceed straight through Garage de Graville, Bassin de Despujois, and across the north end of Bassin de Lancement, which leads under two bridges into Canal de Tancarville.

LIGHTS AND MARKS
Ldg Lts 107° both Dir FW 36/78m 25M; grey Trs, G tops; intens 106°-108° (H24).

RADIO TELEPHONE
Call: *Havre Port* Sig Stn VHF Ch **12** 20 (or 2182 kHz). Port Operations Ch 67 69 (H24). Marina Ch 09.
Other station: Havre-Antifer Ch 14 **67** 22 (H24).

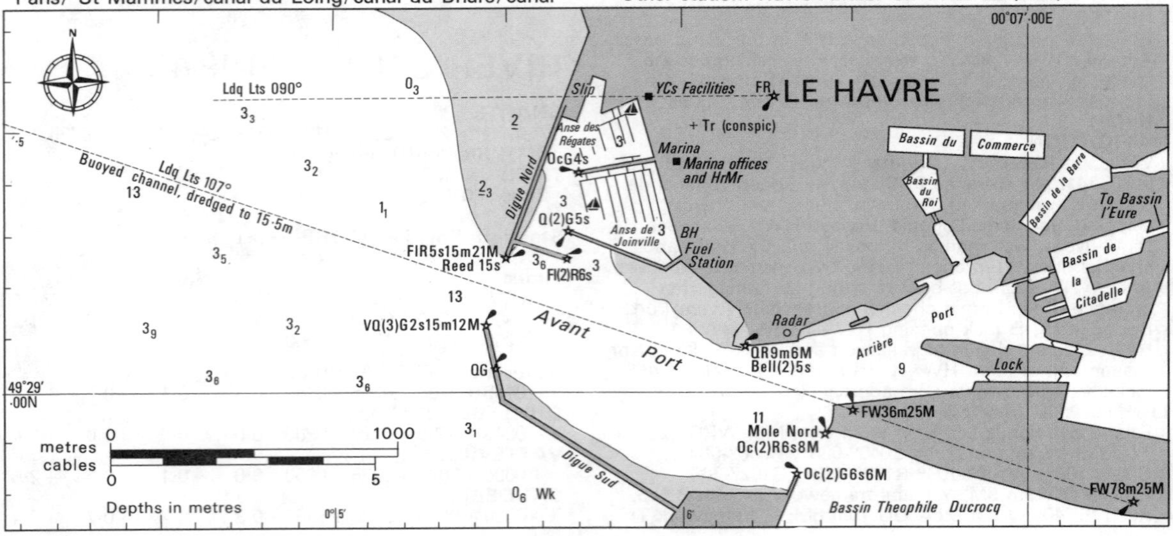

00°07′·00E
N
LE HAVRE
Ldg Lts 090°
Slip
YCs Facilities
FR
+ Tr (conspic)
Anse des Régates
Marina
Marina offices and HrMr
Bassin du
Commerce
Bassin du Roi
Bassin de la Barre
To Bassin l'Eure
Ldg Lts 107°
Buoyed channel, dredged to 15·5m
Digue Nord
OcG4s
Q(2)G5s
Anse de Joinville
BH
Fuel Station
Bassin de la Citadelle
FlR5s15m21M
Reed 15s
Fl(2)R6s
Radar
Port
Avant Port
Arrière
VQ(3)G2s15m12M
QR9m6M
Bell(2)5s
Lock
QG
49°29′ ·00N
FW36m25M
Mole Nord
Oc(2)R6s8M
Oc(2)G6s8M
Digue Sud
metres
cables
0
1000
5
Depths in metres
0°5′
Wk
FW78m25M
Bassin Theophile Ducrocq

TIME ZONE **-0100**
(French Standard Time)
Subtract 1 hour for GMT
For French Summer Time add ONE hour in non-shaded areas

FRANCE, NORTH COAST - LE HAVRE

LAT 49°29'N LONG 0°07'E

TIMES AND HEIGHTS OF HIGH AND LOW WATERS

YEAR **1992**

JANUARY

Day	Time	m	Time	m	Time	m	Time	m
1 W	0224	2.8	0808	6.9	1459	2.6	2042	6.8
2 TH	0325	2.6	0902	7.1	1555	2.4	2132	7.0
3 F	0416	2.4	0946	7.3	1642	2.1	2214	7.2
4 SA	0500	2.2	1024	7.4	1723	1.9	● 2251	7.3
5 SU	0540	2.0	1058	7.5	1801	1.7	2323	7.4
6 M	0618	1.9	1131	7.6	1838	1.6	2356	7.4
7 TU	0653	1.9	1204	7.6	1911	1.6		
8 W	0028	7.4	0725	1.9	1236	7.5	1942	1.7
9 TH	0100	7.4	0756	2.0	1308	7.5	2012	1.8
10 F	0131	7.3	0826	2.1	1341	7.3	2042	2.0
11 SA	0205	7.2	0857	2.3	1416	7.2	2113	2.2
12 SU	0241	7.0	0933	2.5	1456	6.9	2150	2.5
13 M	0324	6.8	1016	2.8	1544	6.7	☽ 2237	2.7
14 TU	0417	6.7	1112	2.9	1647	6.6	2339	2.9
15 W	0530	6.6	1224	3.0	1814	6.5		
16 TH	0059	2.9	0656	6.7	1353	2.7	1936	6.7
17 F	0229	2.6	0806	7.0	1511	2.2	2044	7.1
18 SA	0340	2.1	0906	7.4	1616	1.7	2142	7.5
19 SU	0442	1.7	1000	7.7	1717	1.2	○ 2234	7.8
20 M	0542	1.3	1051	8.0	1815	0.9	2324	8.0
21 TU	0637	1.0	1139	8.1	1906	0.6		
22 W	0011	8.1	0726	0.9	1226	8.2	1952	0.6
23 TH	0057	8.1	0810	0.9	1311	8.1	2033	0.8
24 F	0141	7.9	0849	1.2	1354	7.9	2110	1.2
25 SA	0223	7.6	0926	1.6	1437	7.5	2145	1.7
26 SU	0305	7.3	1003	2.1	1521	7.1	☾ 2221	2.3
27 M	0352	6.9	1044	2.6	1615	6.7	2307	2.8
28 TU	0453	6.6	1140	3.0	1729	6.3		
29 W	0014	3.2	0615	6.4	1300	3.2	1909	6.2
30 TH	0142	3.3	0743	6.5	1426	3.0	2026	6.4
31 F	0259	3.0	0845	6.7	1534	2.6	2119	6.7

FEBRUARY

Day	Time	m	Time	m	Time	m	Time	m
1 SA	0400	2.6	0931	7.0	1627	2.2	2159	7.0
2 SU	0448	2.2	1008	7.3	1710	1.9	2233	7.3
3 M	0528	1.9	1040	7.5	1748	1.6	● 2303	7.4
4 TU	0605	1.7	1111	7.6	1823	1.5	2334	7.5
5 W	0638	1.6	1143	7.7	1854	1.4		
6 TH	0005	7.6	0708	1.5	1215	7.7	1923	1.4
7 F	0035	7.6	0736	1.6	1246	7.7	1952	1.4
8 SA	0106	7.5	0805	1.7	1317	7.6	2020	1.6
9 SU	0138	7.4	0835	1.8	1351	7.4	2049	1.8
10 M	0210	7.2	0907	2.1	1426	7.2	2121	2.2
11 TU	0246	7.0	0942	2.4	1508	6.9	☽ 2200	2.5
12 W	0333	6.8	1028	2.7	1607	6.5	2258	2.9
13 TH	0444	6.5	1144	3.0	1743	6.4		
14 F	0022	3.1	0627	6.5	1323	2.8	1919	6.6
15 SA	0207	2.8	0749	6.8	1452	2.3	2032	7.0
16 SU	0325	2.2	0854	7.3	1603	1.7	2131	7.5
17 M	0433	1.6	0949	7.7	1708	1.1	2222	7.8
18 TU	0534	1.1	1038	8.0	1804	0.7	○ 2308	8.1
19 W	0625	0.8	1123	8.2	1851	0.4	2352	8.2
20 TH	0710	0.6	1207	8.3	1932	0.4		
21 F	0034	8.1	0749	0.7	1249	8.2	2009	0.7
22 SA	0114	8.0	0824	1.0	1329	7.9	2042	1.1
23 SU	0152	7.7	0856	1.4	1407	7.5	2111	1.7
24 M	0228	7.3	0926	2.0	1446	7.1	2140	2.3
25 TU	0307	6.9	1000	2.5	1533	6.6	☾ 2219	2.9
26 W	0401	6.5	1049	3.0	1643	6.1	2321	3.4
27 TH	0525	6.1	1207	3.4	1833	6.0		
28 F	0059	3.6	0709	6.1	1347	3.3	2001	6.2
29 SA	0230	3.2	0820	6.4	1505	2.8	2056	6.6

MARCH

Day	Time	m	Time	m	Time	m	Time	m
1 SU	0337	2.7	0907	6.8	1602	2.3	2134	6.9
2 M	0427	2.2	0942	7.1	1647	1.9	2206	7.2
3 TU	0507	1.8	1014	7.4	1726	1.6	2236	7.4
4 W	0543	1.6	1046	7.6	1800	1.4	● 2307	7.6
5 TH	0615	1.4	1118	7.7	1830	1.3	2338	7.7
6 F	0644	1.3	1150	7.8	1859	1.2		
7 SA	0009	7.7	0713	1.3	1223	7.8	1928	1.2
8 SU	0041	7.7	0744	1.3	1256	7.7	1958	1.4
9 M	0113	7.6	0815	1.5	1331	7.5	2028	1.7
10 TU	0147	7.4	0847	1.8	1408	7.2	2100	2.1
11 W	0223	7.2	0922	2.2	1452	6.8	2139	2.5
12 TH	0311	6.8	1011	2.6	1554	6.5	☽ 2238	2.9
13 F	0426	6.5	1124	2.9	1735	6.4		
14 SA	0007	3.1	0613	6.5	1306	2.7	1907	6.6
15 SU	0153	2.7	0734	6.8	1436	2.2	2018	7.1
16 M	0312	2.1	0839	7.3	1549	1.6	2115	7.5
17 TU	0419	1.5	0932	7.7	1652	1.1	2202	7.8
18 W	0517	1.0	1019	8.0	1744	0.7	○ 2246	8.0
19 TH	0605	0.8	1102	8.1	1828	0.5	2328	8.1
20 F	0647	0.7	1144	8.1	1907	0.6		
21 SA	0008	8.1	0723	0.8	1225	8.0	1941	0.9
22 SU	0046	7.9	0756	1.0	1304	7.8	2011	1.3
23 M	0122	7.7	0827	1.4	1341	7.4	2039	1.8
24 TU	0157	7.3	0855	1.9	1419	7.0	2106	2.4
25 W	0234	6.9	0926	2.4	1503	6.5	2143	2.9
26 TH	0322	6.4	1010	2.9	1606	6.1	☾ 2242	3.4
27 F	0439	6.1	1122	3.3	1744	5.9		
28 SA	0014	3.6	0618	6.0	1258	3.3	1913	6.1
29 SU	0146	3.3	0735	6.3	1417	2.9	2014	6.5
30 M	0254	2.8	0828	6.6	1518	2.4	2056	6.9
31 TU	0347	2.3	0907	7.0	1608	2.0	2130	7.2

APRIL

Day	Time	m	Time	m	Time	m	Time	m
1 W	0431	1.9	0942	7.3	1650	1.6	2203	7.4
2 TH	0510	1.6	1016	7.5	1727	1.4	2236	7.6
3 F	0544	1.4	1051	7.7	1759	1.3	● 2309	7.7
4 SA	0616	1.3	1125	7.7	1831	1.2	2342	7.7
5 SU	0649	1.2	1200	7.8	1904	1.2		
6 M	0016	7.7	0723	1.2	1237	7.7	1938	1.4
7 TU	0052	7.6	0758	1.4	1316	7.5	2012	1.6
8 W	0131	7.4	0833	1.6	1359	7.2	2047	2.0
9 TH	0213	7.2	0912	2.0	1448	6.9	2131	2.4
10 F	0306	6.9	1003	2.4	1555	6.6	☽ 2233	2.8
11 SA	0423	6.6	1118	2.6	1729	6.6		
12 SU	0003	2.9	0558	6.6	1254	2.5	1850	6.8
13 M	0136	2.5	0714	6.9	1416	2.1	1957	7.2
14 TU	0251	2.0	0817	7.3	1525	1.6	2052	7.5
15 W	0355	1.6	0910	7.6	1626	1.2	2139	7.7
16 TH	0451	1.2	0957	7.8	1717	1.0	2222	7.9
17 F	0539	1.0	1040	7.9	1759	0.9	○ 2303	7.9
18 SA	0619	0.9	1122	7.9	1837	1.0	2342	7.9
19 SU	0655	1.0	1203	7.8	1911	1.2		
20 M	0019	7.8	0729	1.2	1242	7.6	1942	1.5
21 TU	0056	7.6	0759	1.5	1320	7.3	2012	1.9
22 W	0132	7.3	0829	1.9	1358	7.0	2042	2.4
23 TH	0209	6.9	0901	2.3	1440	6.6	2118	2.8
24 F	0253	6.5	0943	2.7	1534	6.3	☾ 2212	3.2
25 SA	0354	6.2	1044	3.1	1651	6.1	2329	3.4
26 SU	0520	6.1	1203	3.1	1811	6.2		
27 M	0048	3.3	0635	6.2	1317	2.9	1916	6.4
28 TU	0156	2.9	0735	6.5	1421	2.5	2007	6.8
29 W	0254	2.5	0823	6.8	1515	2.2	2048	7.1
30 TH	0344	2.1	0905	7.1	1603	1.9	2127	7.3

Chart Datum: 4.72 metres below Lallemand System (Mean Sea Level, Marseilles)

TIME ZONE -0100
(French Standard Time)
Subtract 1 hour for GMT
For French Summer Time add ONE hour in non-shaded areas

FRANCE, NORTH COAST - LE HAVRE

LAT 49°29'N LONG 0°07'E

TIMES AND HEIGHTS OF HIGH AND LOW WATERS

YEAR **1992**

MAY

Date	Time	m	Date	Time	m
1 F	0428	1.8	16 SA	0509	1.4
	0944	7.4		1022	7.6
	1646	1.6		1729	1.4
	2203	7.5		○ 2241	7.7
2 SA	0509	1.5	17 SU	0551	1.3
	1022	7.5		1104	7.6
	1725	1.5		1808	1.5
	● 2240	7.6		2320	7.7
3 SU	0547	1.3	18 M	0628	1.3
	1101	7.6		1145	7.6
	1804	1.3		1844	1.6
	2317	7.7		2358	7.6
4 M	0627	1.2	19 TU	0704	1.4
	1140	7.7		1223	7.5
	1843	1.3		1918	1.7
	2356	7.7			
5 TU	0706	1.1	20 W	0035	7.5
	1222	7.7		0737	1.5
	1922	1.4		1302	7.3
				1951	2.0
6 W	0037	7.7	21 TH	0111	7.3
	0746	1.2		0810	1.8
	1306	7.5		1340	7.1
	2002	1.6		2025	2.3
7 TH	0121	7.5	22 F	0149	7.0
	0826	1.5		0843	2.1
	1354	7.3		1418	6.8
	2044	1.9		2101	2.6
8 F	0208	7.3	23 SA	0228	6.8
	0911	1.8		0920	2.4
	1447	7.1		1501	6.6
	2133	2.2		2144	2.9
9 SA	0304	7.1	24 SU	0313	6.5
	1006	2.1		1006	2.7
	1554	6.9		1553	6.4
	☽ 2236	2.5		☾ 2239	3.1
10 SU	0416	6.8	25 M	0412	6.3
	1116	2.3		1105	2.9
	1712	6.8		1701	6.3
	2354	2.5		2343	3.1
11 M	0535	6.8	26 TU	0524	6.3
	1233	2.2		1209	2.9
	1824	7.0		1810	6.4
12 TU	0111	2.4	27 W	0048	3.0
	0645	6.9		0633	6.4
	1346	2.0		1313	2.7
	1928	7.2		1910	6.7
13 W	0221	2.1	28 TH	0151	2.7
	0750	7.2		0731	6.7
	1453	1.8		1415	2.5
	2025	7.4		2001	6.9
14 TH	0324	1.8	29 F	0250	2.4
	0846	7.3		0823	6.9
	1553	1.6		1512	2.2
	2115	7.6		2047	7.2
15 F	0421	1.5	30 SA	0344	2.0
	0936	7.5		0910	7.2
	1645	1.5		1605	1.9
	2159	7.7		2131	7.4
			31 SU	0434	1.7
				0955	7.4
				1654	1.7
				2213	7.6

JUNE

Date	Time	m	Date	Time	m
1 M	0522	1.4	16 TU	0605	1.6
	1040	7.5		1130	7.4
	1741	1.5		1822	1.8
	● 2256	7.7		2340	7.5
2 TU	0609	1.2	17 W	0643	1.5
	1125	7.7		1207	7.4
	1828	1.4		1859	1.8
	2340	7.8			
3 W	0655	1.1	18 TH	0016	7.5
	1212	7.7		0719	1.6
	1914	1.3		1243	7.3
				1935	1.9
4 TH	0026	7.8	19 F	0051	7.4
	0742	1.1		0753	1.7
	1259	7.7		1318	7.2
	2001	1.4		2008	2.1
5 F	0114	7.7	20 SA	0126	7.2
	0828	1.2		0826	1.9
	1349	7.5		1353	7.1
	2048	1.6		2042	2.3
6 SA	0204	7.5	21 SU	0201	7.1
	0916	1.4		0858	2.1
	1442	7.4		1428	6.9
	2138	1.8		2115	2.5
7 SU	0257	7.3	22 M	0237	6.9
	1006	1.7		0932	2.3
	1540	7.2		1506	6.8
	☽ 2232	2.1		2154	2.7
8 M	0358	7.1	23 TU	0320	6.7
	1102	1.9		1012	2.5
	1644	7.0		1552	6.6
	2332	2.3		☾ 2242	2.8
9 TU	0504	6.9	24 W	0412	6.5
	1204	2.1		1103	2.7
	1749	7.0		1650	6.6
				2340	2.9
10 W	0038	2.3	25 TH	0517	6.5
	0612	6.9		1205	2.8
	1311	2.2		1800	6.6
	1855	7.1			
11 TH	0146	2.3	26 F	0046	2.9
	0722	6.9		0632	6.5
	1418	2.2		1315	2.7
	1958	7.2		1909	6.7
12 F	0251	2.1	27 SA	0159	2.6
	0826	7.0		0741	6.7
	1519	2.1		1427	2.5
	2053	7.3		2009	7.0
13 SA	0350	2.0	28 SU	0306	2.2
	0921	7.2		0840	7.0
	1614	2.0		1531	2.2
	2141	7.4		2102	7.2
14 SU	0441	1.8	29 M	0405	1.8
	1009	7.3		0934	7.3
	1701	1.9		1629	1.8
	2224	7.5		2152	7.5
15 M	0525	1.7	30 TU	0501	1.4
	1052	7.4		1024	7.5
	1743	1.8		1724	1.5
	○ 2303	7.5		● 2240	7.7

JULY

Date	Time	m	Date	Time	m
1 W	0556	1.1	16 TH	0627	1.5
	1113	7.7		1147	7.4
	1819	1.3		1844	1.7
	2328	7.9		2355	7.6
2 TH	0649	0.9	17 F	0702	1.5
	1202	7.8		1219	7.4
	1911	1.1		1917	1.7
3 F	0017	7.9	18 SA	0028	7.5
	0739	0.8		0734	1.5
	1250	7.9		1252	7.4
	2000	1.1		1948	1.8
4 SA	0105	7.9	19 SU	0101	7.5
	0826	0.8		0804	1.6
	1338	7.8		1324	7.3
	2045	1.2		2017	1.9
5 SU	0152	7.8	20 M	0132	7.3
	0910	1.0		0832	1.8
	1426	7.7		1355	7.2
	2129	1.4		2046	2.1
6 M	0240	7.6	21 TU	0205	7.2
	0953	1.4		0900	2.0
	1515	7.4		1428	7.1
	2213	1.8		2118	2.3
7 TU	0331	7.3	22 W	0242	7.0
	1037	1.8		0933	2.3
	1608	7.1		1507	6.9
	☽ 2302	2.1		☾ 2156	2.6
8 W	0428	7.0	23 TH	0325	6.7
	1128	2.2		1014	2.6
	1708	6.9		1554	6.7
				2246	2.8
9 TH	0000	2.5	24 F	0421	6.5
	0536	6.7		1109	2.9
	1232	2.6		1656	6.6
	1819	6.8		2352	3.0
10 F	0110	2.6	25 SA	0539	6.4
	0656	6.6		1223	3.0
	1344	2.7		1821	6.6
	1934	6.8			
11 SA	0222	2.5	26 SU	0117	2.8
	0813	6.7		0708	6.5
	1451	2.6		1353	2.8
	2037	7.0		1939	6.8
12 SU	0325	2.3	27 M	0238	2.4
	0912	6.9		0818	6.9
	1550	2.4		1509	2.3
	2128	7.2		2041	7.2
13 M	0420	2.1	28 TU	0345	1.9
	0959	7.1		0918	7.3
	1642	2.2		1612	1.8
	2211	7.3		2136	7.5
14 TU	0508	1.9	29 W	0447	1.4
	1039	7.3		1010	7.6
	1727	2.0		1713	1.4
	○ 2248	7.5		● 2227	7.8
15 W	0549	1.7	30 TH	0547	1.0
	1114	7.4		1100	7.9
	1807	1.8		1810	1.1
	2322	7.5		2315	8.1
			31 F	0641	0.7
				1147	8.0
				1902	0.9

AUGUST

Date	Time	m	Date	Time	m
1 SA	0002	8.2	16 SU	0002	7.7
	0728	0.5		0710	1.4
	1233	8.1		1223	7.5
	1948	0.8		1923	1.6
2 SU	0048	8.1	17 M	0033	7.6
	0811	0.6		0737	1.5
	1318	8.0		1253	7.5
	2029	0.9		1951	1.7
3 M	0133	8.0	18 TU	0104	7.5
	0851	0.9		0805	1.6
	1402	7.8		1323	7.4
	2108	1.3		2019	1.9
4 TU	0217	7.7	19 W	0136	7.3
	0928	1.3		0833	1.9
	1445	7.5		1355	7.2
	2146	1.7		2050	2.1
5 W	0301	7.3	20 TH	0211	7.1
	1005	1.9		0903	2.2
	1530	7.1		1431	7.0
	☽ 2227	2.2		2124	2.4
6 TH	0352	6.9	21 F	0251	6.8
	1048	2.5		0939	2.6
	1626	6.8		1514	6.7
	2320	2.7		☾ 2200	2.7
7 F	0501	6.5	22 SA	0345	6.5
	1150	3.0		1030	2.9
	1742	6.5		1615	6.5
				2311	3.0
8 SA	0034	3.0	23 SU	0507	6.3
	0635	6.3		1145	3.1
	1313	3.1		1749	6.4
	1913	6.5			
9 SU	0157	2.9	24 M	0046	3.0
	0801	6.5		0648	6.4
	1430	3.0		1330	3.0
	2023	6.7		1918	6.7
10 M	0307	2.6	25 TU	0219	2.5
	0900	6.7		0802	6.9
	1536	2.6		1453	2.4
	2114	7.0		2025	7.2
11 TU	0406	2.2	26 W	0329	1.8
	0944	7.0		0903	7.4
	1630	2.3		1558	1.8
	2154	7,3		2121	7.6
12 W	0454	1.9	27 TH	0433	1.3
	1020	7.3		0954	7.8
	1713	2.0		1700	1.3
	2228	7.5		2210	8.0
13 TH	0533	1.6	28 F	0532	0.8
	1051	7.4		1041	8.0
	1750	1.7		1756	0.9
	○ 2259	7.6		● 2257	8.2
14 F	0608	1.5	29 SA	0624	0.5
	1121	7.5		1127	8.2
	1824	1.6		1844	0.7
	2330	7.7		2342	8.3
15 SA	0641	1.4	30 SU	0708	0.4
	1152	7.5		1210	8.2
	1855	1.6		1927	0.7
			31 M	0026	8.2
				0748	0.6
				1253	8.1
				2006	0.9

Chart Datum: 4.72 metres below Lallemand System (Mean Sea Level, Marseilles)

TIME ZONE **-0100**
(French Standard Time)
Subtract 1 hour for GMT
For French Summer Time add ONE hour in non-shaded areas

FRANCE, NORTH COAST - LE HAVRE

LAT 49°29′N LONG 0°07′E

TIMES AND HEIGHTS OF HIGH AND LOW WATERS

YEAR **1992**

SEPTEMBER

Day	Time	m	Day	Time	m
1	0109	8.0	16	0037	7.6
	0824	1.0		0739	1.6
TU	1333	7.9	W	1254	7.5
	2041	1.3		1955	1.7
2	0150	7.7	17	0111	7.4
	0858	1.5		0809	1.9
W	1413	7.5	TH	1327	7.3
	2115	1.8		2027	2.0
3	0232	7.2	18	0148	7.1
	0930	2.1		0840	2.2
TH	1454	7.1	F	1404	7.1
	☽ 2151	2.4		2101	2.3
4	0320	6.8	19	0231	6.8
	1009	2.8		0916	2.6
F	1546	6.7	SA	1449	6.8
	2239	2.9		☾ 2141	2.7
5	0428	6.3	20	0327	6.5
	1110	3.3		1007	3.0
SA	1705	6.3	SU	1554	6.5
	2356	3.2		2249	3.0
6	0610	6.1	21	0455	6.4
	1243	3.5		1127	3.2
SU	1846	6.3	M	1733	6.5
7	0129	3.1	22	0028	2.9
	0741	6.3		0633	6.6
M	1408	3.2	TU	1316	2.9
	2001	6.5		1900	6.8
8	0243	2.7	23	0202	2.4
	0840	6.7		0745	7.0
TU	1515	2.7	W	1436	2.3
	2052	6.9		2006	7.2
9	0341	2.3	24	0312	1.8
	0920	7.0		0843	7.5
W	1606	2.2	TH	1541	1.7
	2129	7.2		2101	7.7
10	0427	1.9	25	0414	1.2
	0953	7.3		0933	7.9
TH	1647	1.9	F	1640	1.2
	2201	7.5		2150	8.0
11	0506	1.6	26	0510	0.8
	1022	7.5		1019	8.1
F	1725	1.7	SA	1734	0.9
	2231	7.6		● 2236	8.2
12	0542	1.5	27	0559	0.6
	1052	7.6		1102	8.2
SA	1758	1.5	SU	1820	0.8
	○ 2302	7.7		2320	8.3
13	0613	1.4	28	0642	0.7
	1122	7.7		1145	8.2
SU	1827	1.5	M	1902	0.8
	2334	7.8			
14	0641	1.4	29	0003	8.2
	1153	7.7		0721	0.9
M	1856	1.5	TU	1226	8.1
				1939	1.0
15	0005	7.7	30	0045	8.0
	0709	1.4		0756	1.2
TU	1223	7.6	W	1305	7.8
	1925	1.6		2013	1.4

OCTOBER

Day	Time	m	Day	Time	m
1	0126	7.6	16	0053	7.5
	0828	1.8		0750	1.9
TH	1343	7.5	F	1307	7.4
	2045	1.9		2011	1.9
2	0207	7.2	17	0135	7.3
	0859	2.3		0825	2.2
F	1423	7.1	SA	1349	7.2
	2119	2.4		2048	2.2
3	0253	6.7	18	0222	7.0
	0936	2.9		0906	2.6
SA	1513	6.6	SU	1439	6.9
	☽ 2204	2.9		2134	2.5
4	0356	6.3	19	0321	6.7
	1034	3.4		1000	2.9
SU	1626	6.3	M	1544	6.7
	2315	3.3		☾ 2240	2.8
5	0529	6.1	20	0447	6.6
	1204	3.6		1120	3.1
M	1800	6.2	TU	1717	6.6
6	0047	3.3	21	0013	2.8
	0658	6.2		0614	6.8
TU	1330	3.3	W	1257	2.8
	1920	6.4		1837	6.9
7	0202	2.9	22	0140	2.3
	0801	6.6		0722	7.1
W	1435	2.8	TH	1414	2.3
	2014	6.7		1942	7.3
8	0259	2.5	23	0249	1.8
	0843	7.0		0820	7.5
TH	1527	2.4	F	1518	1.8
	2054	7.1		2038	7.6
9	0348	2.1	24	0349	1.4
	0917	7.3		0910	7.9
F	1612	2.0	SA	1616	1.4
	2128	7.4		2128	7.9
10	0431	1.8	25	0444	1.1
	0948	7.5		0955	8.0
SA	1651	1.7	SU	1708	1.1
	2201	7.6		● 2215	8.0
11	0508	1.6	26	0532	1.0
	1020	7.6		1039	8.1
SU	1726	1.6	M	1754	1.0
	○ 2234	7.7		2259	8.1
12	0541	1.5	27	0614	1.1
	1052	7.7		1120	8.1
M	1758	1.5	TU	1835	1.1
	2307	7.7		2342	8.0
13	0611	1.5	28	0652	1.2
	1123	7.7		1201	8.0
TU	1829	1.5	W	1912	1.2
	2341	7.7			
14	0643	1.5	29	0024	7.8
	1156	7.7		0728	1.5
W	1902	1.5	TH	1240	7.8
				1947	1.5
15	0015	7.7	30	0105	7.5
	0716	1.6		0801	1.9
TH	1230	7.6	F	1318	7.5
	1936	1.6		2020	1.9
			31	0146	7.2
				0834	2.4
			SA	1358	7.1
				2054	2.4

NOVEMBER

Day	Time	m	Day	Time	m
1	0230	6.8	16	0217	7.2
	0912	2.9		0905	2.3
SU	1443	6.7	M	1432	7.2
	2135	2.8		2133	2.2
2	0323	6.5	17	0316	7.0
	1003	3.3		1000	2.6
M	1543	6.4	TU	1535	7.0
	☽ 2232	3.1		☾ 2236	2.4
3	0435	6.3	18	0430	6.9
	1113	3.5		1111	2.7
TU	1701	6.2	W	1653	6.9
	2347	3.3		2351	2.5
4	0554	6.3	19	0545	7.0
	1232	3.4		1229	2.6
W	1817	6.3	TH	1807	7.0
5	0102	3.1	20	0109	2.3
	0700	6.5		0652	7.2
TH	1341	3.1	F	1345	2.3
	1920	6.5		1914	7.2
6	0207	2.8	21	0219	2.0
	0752	6.8		0753	7.4
F	1439	2.7	SA	1451	2.0
	2009	6.9		2015	7.4
7	0301	2.4	22	0321	1.8
	0834	7.1		0846	7.7
SA	1529	2.3	SU	1550	1.7
	2051	7.2		2110	7.6
8	0348	2.1	23	0416	1.6
	0911	7.4		0934	7.8
SU	1613	2.0	M	1643	1.5
	2129	7.4		2159	7.7
9	0430	1.9	24	0505	1.5
	0947	7.6		1019	7.9
M	1652	1.8	TU	1730	1.4
	2206	7.6		● 2244	7.8
10	0507	1.7	25	0548	1.5
	1022	7.7		1101	7.9
TU	1729	1.6	W	1811	1.3
	○ 2243	7.7		2327	7.8
11	0544	1.6	26	0628	1.6
	1057	7.7		1141	7.8
W	1806	1.5	TH	1850	1.4
	2320	7.7			
12	0621	1.6	27	0008	7.7
	1134	7.8		0705	1.7
TH	1844	1.4	F	1220	7.7
	2359	7.7		1926	1.6
13	0700	1.6	28	0047	7.5
	1213	7.7		0741	2.0
F	1923	1.5	SA	1258	7.5
				2000	1.8
14	0041	7.6	29	0126	7.3
	0739	1.8		0816	2.3
SA	1255	7.6	SU	1336	7.3
	2003	1.7		2034	2.1
15	0127	7.4	30	0205	7.0
	0819	2.1		0852	2.6
SU	1341	7.4	M	1415	7.0
	2045	1.9		2110	2.5

DECEMBER

Day	Time	m	Day	Time	m
1	0246	6.7	16	0303	7.3
	0932	2.9		0956	2.1
TU	1458	6.7	W	1518	7.3
	2152	2.8		☾ 2224	2.0
2	0335	6.5	17	0402	7.1
	1020	3.2		1051	2.4
W	1552	6.4	TH	1622	7.1
	☽ 2243	3.0		2321	2.3
3	0438	6.4	18	0509	7.0
	1119	3.3		1154	2.5
TH	1701	6.3	F	1732	6.9
	2344	3.1			
4	0549	6.4	19	0030	2.4
	1224	3.3		0617	7.0
F	1813	6.4	SA	1308	2.5
				1845	6.9
5	0051	3.1	20	0145	2.4
	0652	6.6		0725	7.1
SA	1332	3.1	SU	1422	2.4
	1916	6.6		1956	7.0
6	0159	2.8	21	0254	2.3
	0746	6.8		0827	7.3
SU	1436	2.7	M	1527	2.1
	2010	6.8		2058	7.2
7	0259	2.5	22	0353	2.1
	0833	7.1		0920	7.5
M	1531	2.3	TU	1623	1.9
	2057	7.1		2150	7.4
8	0351	2.2	23	0445	1.9
	0916	7.4		1006	7.6
TU	1619	2.0	W	1711	1.7
	2140	7.4		2235	7.5
9	0437	1.9	24	0530	1.8
	0957	7.6		1048	7.7
W	1704	1.7	TH	1754	1.5
	○ 2222	7.5		● 2316	7.6
10	0522	1.7	25	0610	1.8
	1037	7.7		1126	7.7
TH	1748	1.4	F	1833	1.5
	2305	7.7		2353	7.6
11	0606	1.6	26	0648	1.8
	1118	7.8		1202	7.7
F	1833	1.3	SA	1909	1.5
	2348	7.7			
12	0651	1.5	27	0029	7.5
	1201	7.9		0724	1.8
SA	1918	1.2	SU	1238	7.6
				1943	1.6
13	0033	7.7	28	0103	7.4
	0736	1.5		0758	2.0
SU	1247	7.8	M	1313	7.5
	2003	1.3		2015	1.8
14	0120	7.7	29	0137	7.3
	0821	1.7		0830	2.2
M	1334	7.7	TU	1346	7.3
	2048	1.5		2045	2.1
15	0209	7.5	30	0211	7.1
	0907	1.9		0901	2.5
TU	1424	7.5	W	1419	7.1
	2134	1.7		2115	2.4
			31	0244	6.9
				0935	2.7
			TH	1456	6.8
				2150	2.6

Chart Datum: 4.72 metres below Lallemand System (Mean Sea Level, Marseilles)

LE HAVRE *continued*

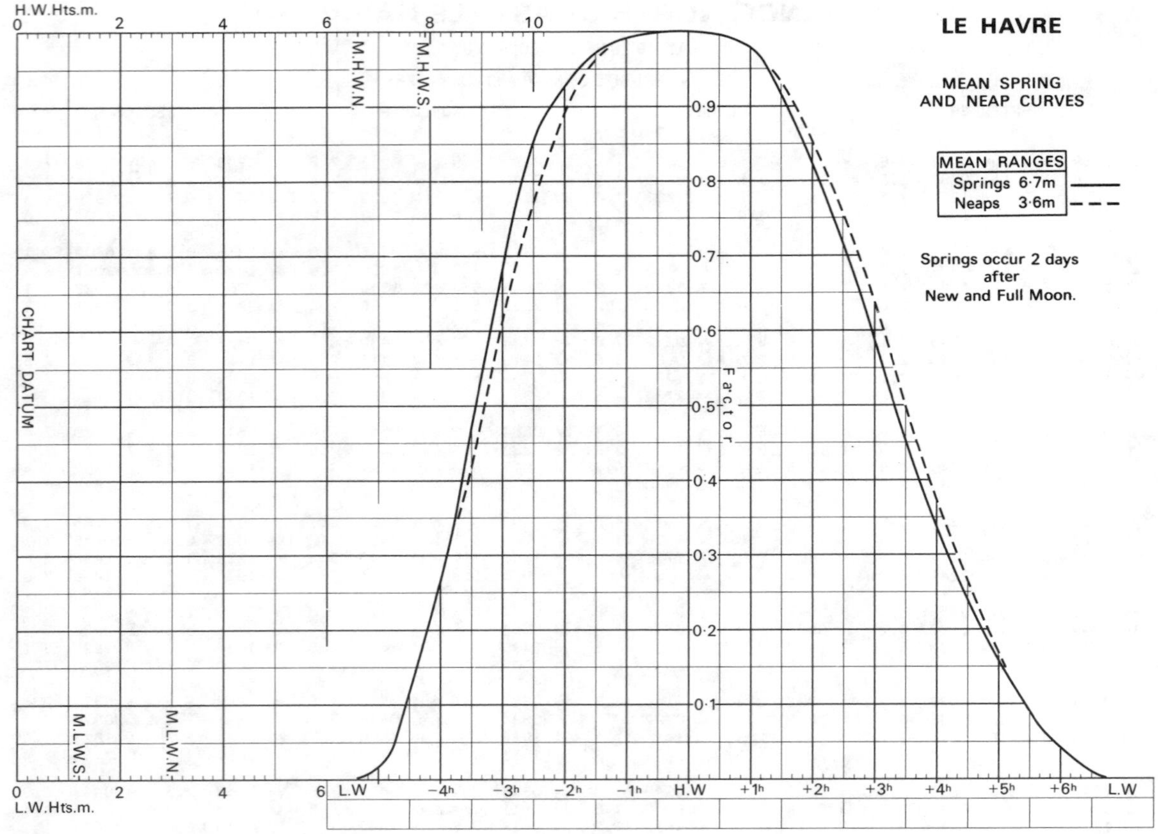
LE HAVRE
MEAN SPRING AND NEAP CURVES
MEAN RANGES
Springs 6·7m
Neaps 3·6m
Springs occur 2 days after New and Full Moon.
H.W.Hts.m.
L.W.Hts.m.
CHART DATUM
M.H.W.N.
M.H.W.S.
M.L.W.S.
M.L.W.N.
Factor
L.W -4h -3h -2h -1h H.W +1h +2h +3h +4h +5h +6h L.W

TELEPHONE (35)
Hr Mr 35.22.72.72; Hr Mr Port de Plaisance 35.21.23.95; Aff Mar 35.22.41.03; CROSS 33.52.72.13; SNSM 35.22.41.03; # 35.41.33.51; Meteo 35.42.21.06; Auto 35.21.16.11; Police 35.42.40.65; Dr 35.41.23.61; H 35.22.81.23; Brit Consul 35.42.27.47.

FACILITIES
Le Havre-Plaisance Marina (973+41 visitors) ☎ 35.21.23.95, Slip, AC, BH (16 ton), C (6 ton), CH, D, P, El, FW, Gas, Gaz, R, ◙, V, Access H24; **Accastillage Diffusion** ☎ 35.43.43.62, ME, Ⓔ, El, Sh, CH; **Marine Plus** ☎ 35.24.21.14, ME, El, Sh, CH; **Maintenance Plaisance** ☎ 35.46.48.50, ME, El, Sh; **YC – Société des Regates du Havre** ☎ 35.42.41.21, R, Bar; **Nautic-Service** ☎ 35.51.75.30 SHOM; **CRM** ☎ 35.26.61.53, Ⓔ; **Havre Voiles** Tel. 35.42.58.15, SM; **Town** ME, El, CH, V, Gaz, R, Bar. ✉; Ⓑ; ≷; ✈.
Ferry UK—Portsmouth.

FÉCAMP 10-19-20

Seine Maritime

CHARTS
Admiralty 1352, 2451; SHOM 932, 6765; ECM 1012; Stanford 1; Imray C31

TIDES
Dover −0036 (sp), −0053 (Np); ML 4·5; Duration 0550; Zone −0100

Standard Port DIEPPE (⟶)

Times				**Height (metres)**			
HW		LW		MHWS	MHWN	MLWN	MLWS
0100	0600	0100	0700	9·3	7·2	2·6	0·7
1300	1800	1300	1900				
Differences FÉCAMP							
−0022	−0018	−0034	−0043	−1·4	−0·7	0·0	+0·1
ANTIFER							
−0046	−0039	−0051	−0100	−1·3	−0·6	+0·4	+0·5

FECAMP *continued*

SHELTER
Excellent in basins but there is a scend in the Avant Port. Entry by boats of less than 1·2 m draught can be made at any tide and in most weathers. Even moderate W to NW winds make entrance and berthing in Avant Port (at marina-type pontoons) uncomfortable and a considerable surf runs off the entrance. Access best at HW+1. Yachts can lock into Berigny Basin (HW−2 to HW).

NAVIGATION
Waypoint 49°45′·90N 00°21′·00E, 265°/085° from/to Jetée Sud Lt, 0·58M. Beware the Charpentier Rks which run out from Pte Fagnet. Strong cross currents occur, depending on tides. Dredged channel subject to silting.

LIGHTS AND MARKS
Entrance can be identified by conspic church and signal station on Pte Fagnet, to the N.
Jetee Nord Fl (2) 10s 15m 16M; grey Tr, R top; Reed (2) 30s sounded HW−2½ to HW+2. Ldg Lts 085°. Front Jetée Sud, head, QG 14m 9M; vis 072°-217°. Rear QR. Normal entry signals on Tr by Avant Port show when dock gates of Bassin Bérigny and Bassin Freyeinet open. (HW−2 to HW)

RADIO TELEPHONE
VHF Ch **12** 16 20 (HW−2½ to HW+½). Yacht Hr Ch 09 (0800-2000 LT).

TELEPHONE (35)
Hr Mr (Marina) 35.28.13.58; Aff Mar 35.28.16.35; CROSS 21.87.21.87; SNSM 35.28.28.15; # 35.28.19.40; Meteo 35.42.21.06; Auto 35.21.16.11; Police 35.28.16.69; Ⓗ 35.28.05.13; Brit Consul 35.42.27.47.

FACILITIES
EC Monday (all day); **Marina (Avant Port)** (500+30 visitors) ☎ 35.28.11.25, D, L, FW, C (Mobile 36 ton); **Bassin Freyeinet** Slip, FW, Sh; **Bassin Bérigny** Slip, M, D, L, FW, CH, AB; **Moré (Chantier)** ☎ 35.28.28.15, Slip, ME, El, Ⓔ, Sh, Gaz, C (30 ton), AC, CH; **Société des Régates de Fécamp** ☎ 35.28.08.44, L, FW, AB; **Société Houvenaghel Le Grand** ME, El, Sh; **Villetard** ☎ 35.28.30.34, M, ME, El, Sh, CH. **Town** P, D, V, Gaz, R, Bar. ✉; Ⓑ; ⇌; ✈ (Le Havre).
Ferry UK — Le Havre—Portsmouth. Dieppe—Newhaven.

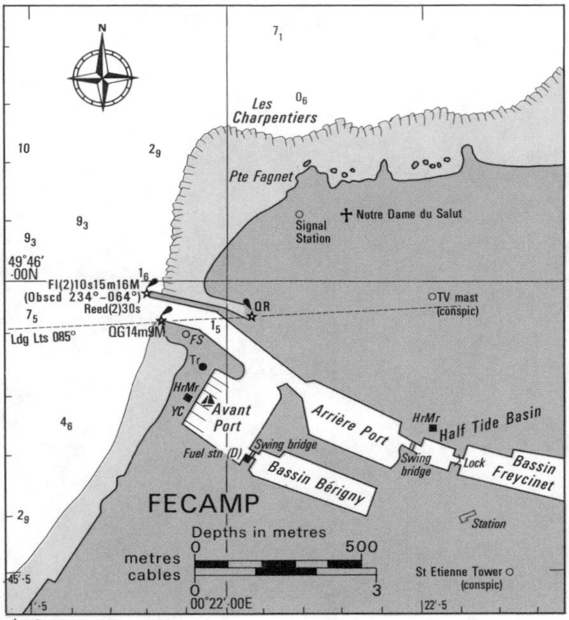
Les Charpentiers
Pte Fagnet
Notre Dame du Salut
Signal Station
Fl(2)10s15m16M
(Obscd 234°-064°)
Reed(2)30s
QR
TV mast (conspic)
Ldg Lts 085°
QG14m9M
FS
Tr
HrMr
YC
Avant Port
Arrière Port
HrMr
Half Tide Basin
Swing bridge
Fuel stn (D)
Bassin Bérigny
Swing bridge
Lock
Bassin Freycinet
FECAMP
Station
Depths in metres
metres
cables
St Etienne Tower (conspic)
49°46′·00N
00°22′·00E

▲ C pontoon

ST VALÉRY-EN-CAUX 10-19-21

Seine Maritime

CHARTS
Admiralty 2451; SHOM 6794; ECM 1012; Stanford 1; Imray C31

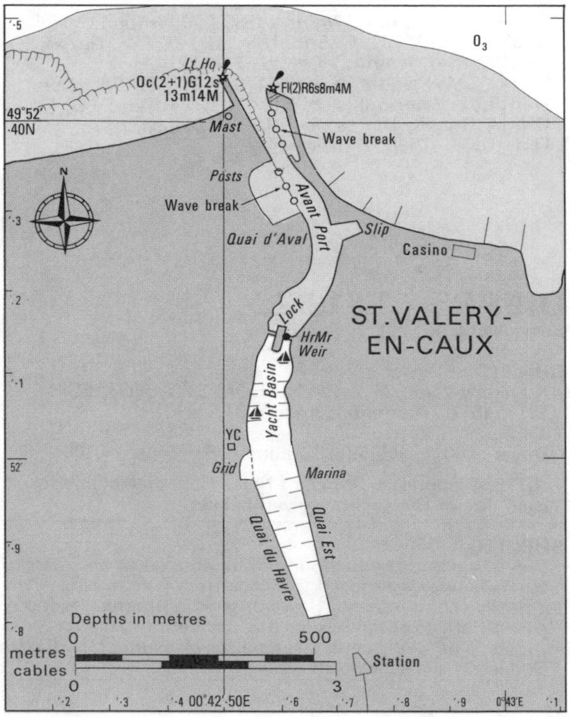
Lt Ho
Oc(2+1)G12s 13m14M
Fl(2)R6s8m4M
Mast
Wave break
Posts
Wave break
Avant Port
Slip
Quai d'Aval
Casino
Lock
HrMr
Weir
ST.VALERY-EN-CAUX
Yacht Basin
YC
Grid
Marina
Quai du Havre
Quai Est
Depths in metres
metres
cables
Station
49°52′·40N
00°42′·50E
0°43′E

TIDES
Dover −0044; ML 4·9; Duration 0530; Zone −0100

Standard Port DIEPPE (⟶)

Times				Height (metres)			
HW		LW		MHWS	MHWN	MLWN	MLWS
0100	0600	0100	0700	9·3	7·2	2·6	0·7
1300	1800	1300	1900				
Differences ST VALÉRY-EN-CAUX							
−0018	−0016	−0007	−0013	−0·4	−0·1	−0·1	+0·3

SHELTER
Good but outer harbour dries. Entry into outer harbour from HW−3. Marina access HW∓2. Bridge opens every half hour during the period, by day; at HW only at night.

NAVIGATION
Waypoint 49°53′·00N 00°42′·50E, 000°/180° from/to Jetée Ouest Lt, 0·50M. Entry is easy except in strong winds from E through N when seas break across entrance. Coast dries to approx 150 m off the pier heads. Inside the pier heads there are half-tide ramps to dampen the swell marked by posts each side. Shingle tends to build up against W wall.

LIGHTS AND MARKS
Harbour is difficult to identify between high chalk cliffs. Approaching from N or W the nuclear power station at Paluel is conspic 3 M W of entrance.
W pier head Lt Ho Oc (2+1) G 12s 13m 14M,
E pier head light structure Fl (2)R 6s. Bu flag indicates sluicing (at about LW−1). Traffic signals are shown on both sides of the bridge/lock
G Lt – Vessels may enter but not leave
R Lt – Vessels may leave but not enter
R+G – Vessels may not enter or leave

RADIO TELEPHONE
VHF Ch 09.

ST VALÉRY-EN-CAUX *continued*

TELEPHONE
Hr Mr 35.97.01.30; Aff Mar 35.28.16.35; CROSS 21.87.21.87; SNSM 35.97.09.03; # 35.28.19.40; Meteo 21.31.52.23; Auto 21.33.82.55; Police 35.97.05.27; Dr 35.97.20.13; Ⓗ 35.97.06.21; Brit Consul 35.42.27.47.

FACILITIES
EC Monday (all day); **Marina** (580+20 visitors) ☎ 35.97.01.30, AC, C (6 ton), V, CH, El, FW, Gaz, ME, Sh, SM, Bar; **Nautic 76** ☎ 35.97.04.22, CH, ME, El, Sh, M, Ⓔ, SM; **Prigent** ☎ 35.97.17.66, ME, El, Sh; **Club Nautique Valeriquais** ☎ 35.97.10.88. **Town** P, D, FW, CH, V, Gaz, R, Bar. ✉; Ⓑ; ⇌; ✈ (Dieppe).
Ferry UK — Dieppe—Newhaven.

DIEPPE 10-19-22

Seine Maritime

CHARTS
Admiralty 2147, 2612, 2451; SHOM 5927, 7083; ECM 1011, 1012; Stanford 1; Imray C31

TIDES
Dover −0011; ML 5.0; Duration 0535; Zone −0100

NOTE: Dieppe is a Standard Port. Tidal predictions for each day of the year are given below.

SHELTER
Very good and the harbour can be entered at any state of tide. Channel is exposed to winds from NW to NE, when a heavy scend renders. Beware work in progress in the Avant Port. Port de Plaisance is not comfortable for yachts. The SW part is reserved for pleasure craft. Bassin Duquesne is Yacht Basin.

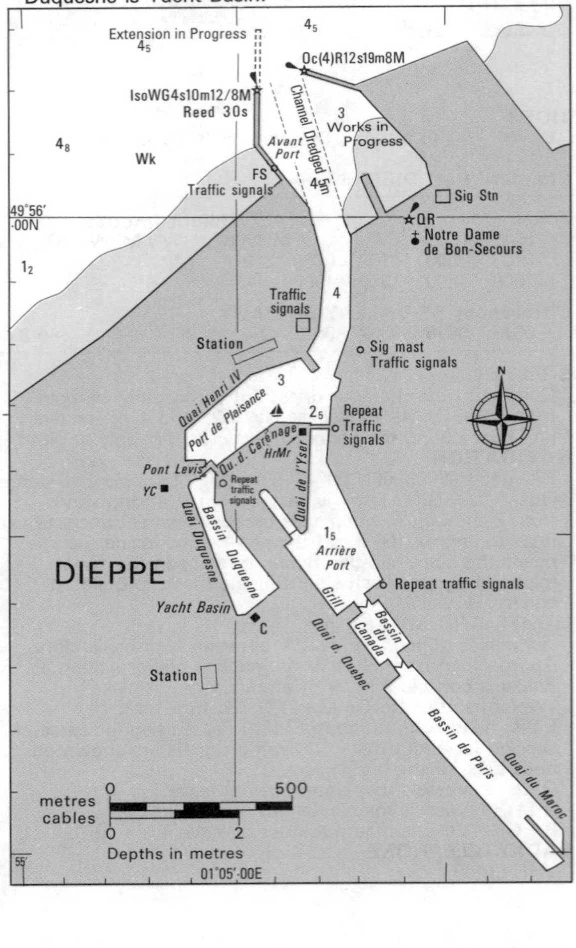
Extension in Progress
Oc(4)R12s19m8M
IsoWG4s10m12/8M
Reed 30s
Channel Dredged 5m
Works in Progress
Avant Port
Wk
FS
Traffic signals
Sig Stn
49°56′ ·00N
QR
Notre Dame de Bon-Secours
Traffic signals
Station
Sig mast
Traffic signals
Quai Henri IV
Port de Plaisance
Repeat Traffic signals
Qu. d. Carénage
HrMr
Pont Levis
YC
Repeat traffic signals
Quai de l'Yser
Quai Duquesne
Bassin Duquesne
Arrière Port
Repeat traffic signals
DIEPPE
Yacht Basin
C
Grill
Bassin du Canada
Quai d. Quebec
Station
Bassin de Paris
Quai du Maroc
metres
cables
500
Depths in metres
01°05′·00E
55′

NAVIGATION
Waypoint 49°56′.48N 01°04′.60E, 130°/310° from/to hbr ent 0.42M. Dieppe is a busy commercial and fishing port and both entry and exit are forbidden during shipping movements. Entry to harbour is simple and yachts normally lie in SW corner of Avant Port at pontoons and wait to pass through lock into Bassin Duquesne. Access HW−2 to HW+1. The bridge opens two or three times during each period. Beware strong stream setting across entrance. Yachts are forbidden in the Arrière Port. During work on the W jetty, yachts must request permission to enter 2M before reaching breakwaters on Ch 12; Also 10 minutes before leaving.

LIGHTS AND MARKS
W Jetty — Iso WG 4s 10m 12/8M W095°-164°, G 164°-095°
E Jetty — Oc (4) R 12s 19m 8M
Entry signals shown from Station at root of W jetty and from station on W side of harbour, 2½ ca (480m) S of former, (full code). Also repeated from repeating stations at entrances to Bassin Duquesne, Arriere Port and Bassin du Canada (simplified code). In low visibility a fog signal, 1 blast of 1 sec every 5 secs, is sounded from the head of Jettée Ouest to indicate 'Entry Prohibited'.
International signals combined with: —

FG to right	— Ferry entering
FR to right	— Ferry leaving
FW to left	— Lock gates open
2 FR (hor) to right	— Dredger in channel.

Signals are repeated with flags from the sig stn on the cliff top near church of Notre Dame de Bon-Secours.
Signals for Duquesne Basin: —
Bridge and lock gates to open — Sound 2 blasts
Vessels may enter but not leave — G Lt
Vessels may leave but not enter — R Lt
Request will not be met unless Flag P (W Lt at night) is flying from pier head and dock.

RADIO TELEPHONE
Call: *Dieppe Port* VHF Ch **12** 16 (H24).

TELEPHONE (35)
Hr Mr 35.84.10.55; Hr Mr (Port de Plaisance) 35.84.32.99; Aff Mar 35.82.59.40; CROSS 21.87.21.87; SNSM 35.84.30.76; # 35.82.24.47; Meteo 21.31.52.23; Auto 21.33.82.55; Police 35.84.87.32; Ⓗ 35.06.76.76; Brit Consul 35.42.27.47.

FACILITIES
Quai Duquesne M, L, FW, C (by arrangement with Hr Mr up to 30 ton), AB; **GAD-SA** ☎ 35.84.33.54 ME, El, Sh, CH; **Cercle de la Voile de Dieppe** ☎ 35.84.22.29, P, D, FW, C (3 ton), AB, R, Bar; **Thalassa** ☎ 35.82.16.08, ME, El, Ⓔ, Sh, CH; **Bassin Duquesne** (80+15 visitors) ☎ 35.84.34.95, FW, AC, BH (30 ton), Slip, C, P, D, CH; **Town** P, D, FW, V, Gaz, R, Bar. ✉; Ⓑ; ⇌; ✈.
Ferry UK—Newhaven.

TIME ZONE -0100
(French Standard Time)
Subtract 1 hour for GMT
For French Summer Time add ONE hour in non-shaded areas

FRANCE, NORTH COAST - DIEPPE

LAT 49°56'N LONG 1°05'E

TIMES AND HEIGHTS OF HIGH AND LOW WATERS

YEAR **1992**

JANUARY

Date	Day	Time	m	Time	m	Time	m	Time	m
1	W	0315	2.5	0900	7.7	1550	2.2	2132	7.6
2	TH	0418	2.3	0957	8.0	1647	1.9	2224	7.9
3	F	0509	2.0	1043	8.3	1734	1.7	2307	8.2
4	SA	0552	1.8	1122	8.5	1814	1.5	● 2344	8.4
5	SU	0631	1.6	1158	8.6	1852	1.3		
6	M	0019	8.6	0708	1.5	1232	8.7	1928	1.3
7	TU	0052	8.7	0742	1.5	1306	8.8	2001	1.3
8	W	0126	8.7	0814	1.5	1339	8.7	2032	1.3
9	TH	0158	8.6	0844	1.6	1411	8.6	2101	1.4
10	F	0230	8.5	0914	1.7	1443	8.4	2132	1.6
11	SA	0302	8.3	0947	1.9	1517	8.2	2205	1.8
12	SU	0338	8.1	1024	2.1	1556	7.9	2244	2.1
13	M	0419	7.8	1110	2.4	1643	7.5	☽ 2332	2.4
14	TU	0512	7.5	1207	2.6	1745	7.3		
15	W	0034	2.6	0623	7.4	1319	2.6	1909	7.2
16	TH	0153	2.6	0749	7.5	1443	2.4	2030	7.6
17	F	0318	2.3	0902	8.0	1559	1.9	2137	8.1
18	SA	0428	1.7	1004	8.5	1703	1.3	2237	8.7
19	SU	0530	1.3	1100	9.0	1804	0.9	○ 2331	9.1
20	M	0628	0.9	1153	9.4	1901	0.5		
21	TU	0022	9.5	0723	0.7	1242	9.7	1953	0.3
22	W	0110	9.6	0813	0.5	1329	9.8	2040	0.2
23	TH	0155	9.6	0858	0.6	1413	9.6	2121	0.4
24	F	0238	9.4	0939	0.8	1456	9.3	2159	0.8
25	SA	0320	9.0	1016	1.2	1538	8.8	2235	1.3
26	SU	0402	8.5	1054	1.7	1622	8.2	☾ 2313	1.9
27	M	0448	7.9	1139	2.2	1713	7.5		
28	TU	0001	2.5	0546	7.3	1237	2.7	1822	7.0
29	W	0109	2.9	0705	7.0	1355	2.9	1953	6.8
30	TH	0235	3.0	0834	7.1	1520	2.7	2114	7.1
31	F	0354	2.7	0940	7.5	1628	2.2	2210	7.6

FEBRUARY

Date	Day	Time	m	Time	m	Time	m	Time	m
1	SA	0453	2.2	1029	7.9	1719	1.8	2253	8.0
2	SU	0539	1.8	1107	8.3	1800	1.5	2329	8.4
3	M ●	0617	1.5	1142	8.6	1838	1.3		
4	TU	0001	8.6	0652	1.3	1215	8.8	1912	1.1
5	W	0033	8.8	0725	1.2	1247	9.0	1944	1.0
6	TH	0105	8.9	0756	1.2	1318	9.0	2014	1.0
7	F	0135	8.9	0825	1.2	1348	9.0	2042	1.1
8	SA	0205	8.9	0853	1.3	1419	8.8	2110	1.2
9	SU	0235	8.7	0923	1.5	1450	8.6	2138	1.5
10	M	0307	8.5	0955	1.7	1525	8.2	2211	1.8
11	TU	0344	8.2	1034	2.1	1607	7.8	☽ 2254	2.2
12	W	0430	7.7	1127	2.4	1704	7.3	2353	2.6
13	TH	0537	7.3	1238	2.6	1830	7.1		
14	F	0116	2.7	0715	7.2	1413	2.5	2008	7.3
15	SA	0254	2.4	0843	7.7	1540	2.0	2125	7.9
16	SU	0412	1.8	0952	8.4	1651	1.3	2227	8.6
17	M	0518	1.2	1050	9.0	1754	0.8	2320	9.2
18	TU ○	0618	0.8	1141	9.5	1850	0.3		
19	W	0008	9.6	0711	0.4	1227	9.8	1938	0.1
20	TH	0052	9.8	0757	0.3	1310	9.9	2021	0.1
21	F	0133	9.8	0838	0.4	1351	9.7	2058	0.3
22	SA	0212	9.5	0914	0.6	1430	9.4	2131	0.8
23	SU	0249	9.2	0946	1.1	1508	8.9	2200	1.3
24	M	0326	8.6	1017	1.6	1546	8.2	2231	1.9
25	TU	0405	7.9	1055	2.2	1630	7.4	☾ 2314	2.6
26	W	0454	7.2	1148	2.8	1733	6.7		
27	TH	0019	3.2	0614	6.6	1307	3.1	1914	6.4
28	F	0154	3.3	0802	6.6	1444	3.0	2050	6.8
29	SA	0326	2.9	0917	7.1	1601	2.5	2147	7.4

MARCH

Date	Day	Time	m	Time	m	Time	m	Time	m
1	SU	0429	2.3	1005	7.7	1654	1.9	2228	7.9
2	M	0515	1.8	1043	8.2	1737	1.5	2303	8.4
3	TU	0553	1.5	1118	8.6	1814	1.2	2336	8.7
4	W ●	0629	1.2	1150	8.9	1848	1.0		
5	TH	0008	8.9	0701	1.1	1222	9.0	1920	0.9
6	F	0039	9.0	0732	1.0	1253	9.1	1950	0.8
7	SA	0108	9.1	0803	0.9	1323	9.1	2019	0.9
8	SU	0139	9.1	0832	1.0	1355	9.0	2047	1.0
9	M	0210	9.0	0902	1.2	1428	8.8	2116	1.3
10	TU	0243	8.7	0934	1.5	1504	8.4	2149	1.7
11	W	0320	8.3	1013	1.8	1546	7.9	2232	2.1
12	TH	0406	7.8	1105	2.3	1644	7.4	☽ 2333	2.6
13	F	0515	7.3	1217	2.6	1815	7.0		
14	SA	0058	2.8	0659	7.1	1357	2.5	1956	7.3
15	SU	0239	2.4	0830	7.6	1526	1.9	2113	8.0
16	M	0358	1.7	0939	8.4	1637	1.2	2212	8.7
17	TU	0503	1.1	1034	9.0	1738	0.7	2302	9.2
18	W	0601	0.7	1122	9.5	1830	0.4	○ 2347	9.6
19	TH	0650	0.5	1206	9.7	1915	0.2		
20	F	0028	9.7	0734	0.4	1247	9.7	1955	0.3
21	SA	0107	9.7	0812	0.4	1326	9.6	2029	0.5
22	SU	0144	9.5	0845	0.7	1403	9.3	2100	0.9
23	M	0219	9.1	0916	1.1	1439	8.8	2128	1.4
24	TU	0254	8.6	0946	1.6	1516	8.2	2159	2.0
25	W	0330	7.9	1021	2.1	1556	7.4	2239	2.6
26	TH	0415	7.2	1109	2.7	1653	6.8	☾ 2338	3.2
27	F	0525	6.6	1220	3.1	1823	6.4		
28	SA	0107	3.4	0709	6.4	1355	3.1	2003	6.6
29	SU	0239	3.0	0833	6.9	1515	2.6	2106	7.2
30	M	0345	2.4	0926	7.5	1612	2.1	2150	7.8
31	TU	0435	1.9	1008	8.1	1658	1.6	2228	8.3

APRIL

Date	Day	Time	m	Time	m	Time	m	Time	m
1	W	0517	1.5	1045	8.5	1738	1.2	2303	8.7
2	TH	0555	1.2	1120	8.8	1815	1.0	2337	8.9
3	F ●	0631	1.1	1153	9.0	1849	0.9		
4	SA	0009	9.1	0705	0.9	1226	9.1	1923	0.8
5	SU	0041	9.2	0739	0.8	1259	9.1	1955	0.9
6	M	0114	9.2	0812	0.9	1334	9.1	2027	1.0
7	TU	0149	9.1	0846	1.0	1411	8.9	2101	1.2
8	W	0226	8.8	0922	1.3	1451	8.5	2138	1.6
9	TH	0307	8.3	1004	1.7	1538	8.0	2225	2.1
10	F	0358	7.8	1058	2.1	1641	7.5	☽ 2328	2.4
11	SA	0512	7.3	1212	2.4	1812	7.2		
12	SU	0053	2.6	0648	7.3	1346	2.2	1941	7.5
13	M	0225	2.2	0811	7.8	1508	1.7	2053	8.1
14	TU	0338	1.6	0918	8.3	1615	1.2	2150	8.7
15	W	0441	1.2	1013	8.9	1714	0.9	2239	9.1
16	TH	0537	0.9	1100	9.2	1804	0.7	2322	9.3
17	F ○	0624	0.7	1143	9.4	1847	0.6		
18	SA	0003	9.4	0706	0.7	1223	9.4	1925	0.7
19	SU	0040	9.4	0743	0.7	1301	9.3	2000	0.8
20	M	0117	9.2	0817	0.9	1338	9.0	2031	1.1
21	TU	0152	8.9	0849	1.1	1415	8.6	2102	1.5
22	W	0228	8.5	0921	1.6	1452	8.1	2134	2.0
23	TH	0305	7.9	0955	2.0	1532	7.6	2213	2.5
24	F	0347	7.3	1039	2.5	1622	7.0	☾ 2304	2.9
25	SA	0446	6.8	1138	2.9	1732	6.7		
26	SU	0016	3.2	0606	6.6	1256	3.0	1855	6.7
27	M	0137	3.0	0728	6.8	1413	2.7	2006	7.1
28	TU	0246	2.6	0832	7.3	1515	2.3	2100	7.6
29	W	0342	2.1	0922	7.8	1608	1.8	2145	8.1
30	TH	0430	1.7	1005	8.2	1654	1.5	2225	8.5

Chart Datum: 4.89 metres below Lallemand System (Mean Sea Level, Marseilles)

FRANCE, NORTH COAST - DIEPPE

TIME ZONE -0100
(French Standard Time)
Subtract 1 hour for GMT
For French Summer Time add ONE hour in non-shaded areas

LAT 49°56'N LONG 1°05'E

TIMES AND HEIGHTS OF HIGH AND LOW WATERS

YEAR **1992**

MAY

Day	Time	m	Time	m	Time	m	Time	m
1 F	0515	1.4	1045	8.6	1737	1.2	2303	8.8
2 SA	0557	1.2	1123	8.8	1817	1.1	● 2339	9.0
3 SU	0637	1.0	1200	9.0	1856	1.0		
4 M	0016	9.1	0716	0.9	1238	9.1	1934	0.9
5 TU	0054	9.2	0755	0.8	1318	9.1	2012	1.0
6 W	0134	9.1	0835	0.9	1401	8.9	2052	1.2
7 TH	0216	8.8	0917	1.1	1447	8.6	2136	1.5
8 F	0304	8.5	1004	1.4	1540	8.2	2227	1.8
9 SA	0400	8.0	1100	1.8	1644	7.8	☽ 2329	2.1
10 SU	0510	7.7	1210	2.0	1759	7.7		
11 M	0045	2.2	0628	7.6	1328	1.9	1914	7.8
12 TU	0201	2.0	0743	7.9	1440	1.7	2023	8.1
13 W	0310	1.7	0850	8.2	1546	1.4	2122	8.5
14 TH	0413	1.4	0947	8.5	1644	1.2	2213	8.8
15 F	0508	1.2	1036	8.8	1734	1.1	2258	8.9
16 SA	0556	1.1	1121	8.9	1817	1.1	○ 2339	9.0
17 SU	0638	1.0	1202	8.9	1856	1.1		
18 M	0017	9.0	0717	1.0	1240	8.9	1933	1.2
19 TU	0054	8.9	0753	1.0	1318	8.8	2009	1.3
20 W	0131	8.7	0829	1.2	1356	8.5	2043	1.6
21 TH	0208	8.4	0902	1.5	1433	8.2	2116	1.9
22 F	0245	8.1	0936	1.8	1512	7.9	2151	2.2
23 SA	0325	7.7	1014	2.2	1555	7.5	2234	2.5
24 SU	0411	7.3	1100	2.4	1646	7.2	☾ 2327	2.7
25 M	0509	7.0	1157	2.6	1748	7.1		
26 TU	0030	2.8	0617	7.0	1302	2.6	1856	7.1
27 W	0136	2.6	0726	7.1	1409	2.4	2001	7.4
28 TH	0241	2.3	0828	7.5	1511	2.1	2056	7.8
29 F	0339	2.0	0921	7.9	1607	1.8	2144	8.2
30 SA	0433	1.6	1009	8.3	1658	1.5	2229	8.6
31 SU	0523	1.3	1054	8.6	1746	1.3	2312	8.8

JUNE

Day	Time	m	Time	m	Time	m	Time	m
1 M	0611	1.1	1138	8.9	1832	1.1	● 2355	9.0
2 TU	0658	0.9	1223	9.1	1918	1.0		
3 W	0039	9.2	0744	0.8	1309	9.1	2003	0.9
4 TH	0125	9.2	0831	0.7	1356	9.1	2050	1.0
5 F	0213	9.1	0918	0.8	1446	8.9	2137	1.2
6 SA	0303	8.8	1007	1.1	1538	8.6	2228	1.4
7 SU	0357	8.5	1059	1.3	1633	8.3	☽ 2323	1.7
8 M	0455	8.2	1156	1.6	1734	8.1		
9 TU	0024	1.9	0559	7.9	1259	1.8	1839	7.9
10 W	0130	1.9	0708	7.8	1405	1.9	1947	8.0
11 TH	0237	1.9	0818	7.9	1512	1.8	2052	8.1
12 F	0342	1.7	0922	8.0	1613	1.7	2149	8.3
13 SA	0440	1.6	1017	8.2	1706	1.6	2238	8.5
14 SU	0531	1.4	1104	8.4	1752	1.5	2321	8.6
15 M	0615	1.3	1146	8.5	1834	1.4	○	
16 TU	0000	8.7	0656	1.2	1225	8.6	1913	1.4
17 W	0037	8.7	0734	1.2	1302	8.6	1950	1.4
18 TH	0114	8.7	0811	1.2	1338	8.6	2026	1.5
19 F	0150	8.5	0845	1.4	1414	8.4	2058	1.7
20 SA	0226	8.3	0917	1.6	1450	8.2	2130	1.9
21 SU	0301	8.1	0949	1.8	1525	8.0	2205	2.1
22 M	0338	7.8	1026	2.0	1604	7.7	2246	2.3
23 TU	0420	7.5	1109	2.2	1649	7.5	☾ 2334	2.5
24 W	0511	7.3	1201	2.4	1745	7.3		
25 TH	0032	2.6	0615	7.1	1302	2.5	1853	7.3
26 F	0138	2.5	0729	7.2	1412	2.4	2004	7.5
27 SA	0249	2.2	0837	7.6	1522	2.1	2105	7.9
28 SU	0355	1.9	0937	8.0	1624	1.8	2200	8.3
29 M	0454	1.5	1030	8.4	1720	1.4	2251	8.7
30 TU	0550	1.1	1121	8.8	1814	1.1	● 2340	9.1

JULY

Day	Time	m	Time	m	Time	m	Time	m
1 W	0645	0.8	1211	9.1	1907	0.9		
2 TH	0029	9.3	0738	0.6	1300	9.3	1958	0.8
3 F	0118	9.4	0828	0.5	1349	9.4	2047	0.7
4 SA	0206	9.4	0915	0.5	1436	9.3	2133	0.8
5 SU	0253	9.2	1000	0.7	1523	9.1	2218	1.0
6 M	0341	8.9	1044	1.0	1610	8.7	2304	1.4
7 TU	0430	8.5	1130	1.4	1702	8.3	☽ 2354	1.7
8 W	0526	8.0	1223	1.9	1801	7.9		
9 TH	0052	2.1	0631	7.6	1326	2.2	1910	7.6
10 F	0201	2.2	0748	7.4	1438	2.3	2025	7.6
11 SA	0313	2.2	0903	7.5	1547	2.2	2131	7.8
12 SU	0419	2.0	1004	7.8	1647	2.0	2225	8.1
13 M	0514	1.7	1054	8.1	1736	1.7	2309	8.4
14 TU	0600	1.5	1135	8.4	1819	1.5	○ 2347	8.5
15 W	0641	1.3	1211	8.6	1857	1.4		
16 TH	0022	8.7	0718	1.2	1245	8.7	1934	1.3
17 F	0056	8.8	0754	1.2	1318	8.7	2007	1.3
18 SA	0129	8.7	0826	1.2	1351	8.7	2037	1.4
19 SU	0202	8.7	0855	1.3	1423	8.6	2106	1.5
20 M	0233	8.5	0923	1.5	1453	8.4	2135	1.7
21 TU	0305	8.2	0954	1.7	1526	8.2	2210	2.0
22 W	0340	7.9	1029	2.0	1603	7.9	☾ 2250	2.2
23 TH	0422	7.6	1113	2.3	1649	7.6	2341	2.5
24 F	0516	7.3	1209	2.6	1750	7.3		
25 SA	0046	2.6	0632	7.1	1321	2.7	1914	7.3
26 SU	0206	2.5	0759	7.3	1446	2.4	2033	7.6
27 M	0325	2.1	0912	7.8	1559	1.9	2138	8.2
28 TU	0433	1.5	1013	8.4	1702	1.4	2235	8.7
29 W	0535	1.1	1108	8.9	1801	1.0	● 2328	9.2
30 TH	0634	0.7	1159	9.3	1857	0.7		
31 F	0017	9.5	0728	0.4	1247	9.6	1949	0.5

AUGUST

Day	Time	m	Time	m	Time	m	Time	m
1 SA	0105	9.7	0817	0.2	1333	9.7	2036	0.4
2 SU	0150	9.7	0901	0.3	1416	9.6	2118	0.6
3 M	0234	9.5	0941	0.5	1459	9.3	2157	0.9
4 TU	0317	9.1	1018	1.0	1541	8.9	2236	1.3
5 W	0400	8.5	1057	1.5	1626	8.3	☽ 2319	1.8
6 TH	0450	7.9	1143	2.2	1721	7.7		
7 F	0013	2.3	0553	7.3	1246	2.7	1833	7.2
8 SA	0125	2.7	0720	6.9	1407	2.8	2002	7.1
9 SU	0249	2.6	0849	7.1	1528	2.6	2117	7.5
10 M	0403	2.2	0953	7.6	1633	2.2	2211	7.9
11 TU	0501	1.8	1040	8.1	1723	1.8	2254	8.3
12 W	0546	1.5	1118	8.4	1803	1.5	2329	8.6
13 TH	0624	1.3	1151	8.7	1839	1.3	○	
14 F	0002	8.8	0659	1.1	1222	8.8	1913	1.2
15 SA	0033	8.9	0731	1.1	1253	8.9	1943	1.2
16 SU	0104	8.9	0801	1.1	1324	8.9	2012	1.2
17 M	0135	8.9	0829	1.1	1353	8.8	2040	1.3
18 TU	0204	8.7	0855	1.3	1422	8.7	2108	1.5
19 W	0234	8.5	0923	1.5	1452	8.5	2138	1.7
20 TH	0307	8.2	0954	1.9	1527	8.1	2214	2.1
21 F	0346	7.8	1034	2.3	1609	7.7	☾ 2302	2.4
22 SA	0437	7.4	1128	2.7	1707	7.3		
23 SU	0006	2.7	0552	7.0	1244	2.9	1836	7.1
24 M	0134	2.7	0733	7.2	1420	2.6	2010	7.5
25 TU	0305	2.2	0854	7.8	1541	2.0	2121	8.2
26 W	0417	1.5	0958	8.5	1646	1.4	2220	8.8
27 TH	0521	1.0	1053	9.1	1746	0.9	2312	9.4
28 F	0619	0.5	1142	9.5	1842	0.6	●	
29 SA	0000	9.7	0711	0.3	1227	9.8	1931	0.4
30 SU	0045	9.9	0757	0.2	1310	9.9	2015	0.4
31 M	0128	9.8	0838	0.3	1351	9.7	2055	0.6

Chart Datum: 4.89 metres below Lallemand System (Mean Sea Level, Marseilles)

TIME ZONE -0100
(French Standard Time)
Subtract 1 hour for GMT
For French Summer Time add ONE hour in non-shaded areas

FRANCE, NORTH COAST - DIEPPE

LAT 49°56′N LONG 1°05′E

TIMES AND HEIGHTS OF HIGH AND LOW WATERS

YEAR **1992**

SEPTEMBER

Day	Time	m	Time	m	Time	m	Time	m
1 TU	0209	9.6	0914	0.7	1431	9.4	2130	0.9
2 W	0249	9.1	0948	1.2	1510	8.9	2205	1.4
3 TH	0330	8.5	1022	1.8	1551	8.2	☽ 2243	2.0
4 F	0415	7.7	1105	2.5	1641	7.5	2334	2.6
5 SA	0516	7.0	1208	3.0	1754	6.9		
6 SU	0049	3.0	0649	6.6	1336	3.2	1935	6.8
7 M	0221	2.9	0829	6.9	1505	2.9	2056	7.2
8 TU	0340	2.5	0930	7.5	1610	2.3	2148	7.8
9 W	0436	1.9	1014	8.1	1658	1.8	2228	8.3
10 TH	0519	1.5	1050	8.5	1737	1.5	2303	8.6
11 F	0557	1.3	1123	8.8	1812	1.3	2335	8.9
12 SA ○	0631	1.1	1154	8.9	1845	1.2		
13 SU	0006	9.0	0703	1.1	1224	9.0	1916	1.1
14 M	0037	9.0	0732	1.0	1254	9.0	1945	1.1
15 TU	0106	9.0	0801	1.1	1323	9.0	2014	1.2
16 W	0136	8.9	0829	1.3	1352	8.9	2043	1.4
17 TH	0208	8.7	0857	1.5	1424	8.6	2113	1.6
18 F	0242	8.4	0928	1.9	1500	8.3	2149	2.0
19 SA	0322	7.9	1008	2.3	1543	7.8	☾ 2236	2.4
20 SU	0414	7.4	1104	2.7	1643	7.3	2343	2.7
21 M	0533	7.0	1223	2.9	1817	7.1		
22 TU	0115	2.7	0718	7.2	1404	2.6	1952	7.5
23 W	0249	2.2	0838	7.9	1524	2.0	2103	8.2
24 TH	0400	1.5	0940	8.6	1629	1.3	2201	8.9
25 F	0502	0.9	1033	9.2	1727	0.8	2252	9.4
26 SA	0558	0.5	1120	9.6	1820	0.6	● 2339	9.7
27 SU	0647	0.4	1203	9.8	1907	0.4		
28 M	0022	9.8	0731	0.4	1245	9.8	1950	0.5
29 TU	0103	9.7	0810	0.6	1324	9.6	2028	0.7
30 W	0143	9.4	0845	0.9	1403	9.3	2102	1.1

OCTOBER

Day	Time	m	Time	m	Time	m	Time	m
1 TH	0222	9.0	0917	1.4	1441	8.8	2135	1.5
2 F	0302	8.4	0950	2.0	1520	8.1	2211	2.1
3 SA	0345	7.7	1032	2.6	1608	7.4	☽ 2259	2.7
4 SU	0442	7.0	1131	3.2	1715	6.8		
5 M	0008	3.1	0606	6.6	1257	3.4	1848	6.6
6 TU	0138	3.1	0744	6.8	1423	3.0	2014	7.0
7 W	0256	2.7	0850	7.3	1529	2.5	2110	7.6
8 TH	0354	2.2	0936	7.9	1619	2.0	2152	8.1
9 F	0440	1.7	1014	8.4	1701	1.6	2229	8.5
10 SA	0520	1.4	1048	8.7	1738	1.4	2303	8.8
11 SU	0557	1.2	1121	8.9	1813	1.2	○ 2336	8.9
12 M	0630	1.2	1153	9.0	1847	1.2		
13 TU	0008	9.0	0703	1.1	1224	9.1	1919	1.1
14 W	0040	9.1	0734	1.2	1256	9.1	1951	1.1
15 TH	0113	9.0	0806	1.3	1329	9.0	2024	1.3
16 F	0148	8.8	0839	1.5	1404	8.8	2058	1.5
17 SA	0227	8.5	0915	1.9	1444	8.4	2137	1.9
18 SU	0310	8.0	0958	2.2	1531	7.9	2227	2.2
19 M	0406	7.6	1056	2.6	1635	7.5	☾ 2332	2.5
20 TU	0527	7.3	1213	2.8	1804	7.3		
21 W	0101	2.5	0659	7.5	1347	2.5	1930	7.7
22 TH	0229	2.1	0814	8.0	1503	1.9	2040	8.3
23 F	0338	1.5	0916	8.7	1607	1.3	2139	8.8
24 SA	0439	1.1	1008	9.2	1704	1.0	2230	9.2
25 SU	0532	0.8	1055	9.5	1755	0.8	● 2316	9.5
26 M	0620	0.7	1139	9.6	1841	0.7	2359	9.5
27 TU	0703	0.8	1220	9.6	1923	0.7		
28 W	0040	9.4	0741	0.9	1259	9.4	2001	0.9
29 TH	0120	9.2	0817	1.2	1337	9.1	2036	1.2
30 F	0159	8.8	0851	1.6	1416	8.7	2110	1.6
31 SA	0238	8.3	0925	2.1	1455	8.2	2145	2.1

NOVEMBER

Day	Time	m	Time	m	Time	m	Time	m
1 SU	0320	7.8	1005	2.6	1539	7.6	2227	2.6
2 M	0410	7.3	1055	3.0	1636	7.0	☽ 2324	3.0
3 TU	0515	6.9	1204	3.3	1748	6.8		
4 W	0038	3.1	0634	6.8	1322	3.2	1907	6.9
5 TH	0154	2.9	0747	7.1	1432	2.8	2014	7.3
6 F	0259	2.5	0844	7.6	1528	2.3	2105	7.7
7 SA	0352	2.1	0929	8.1	1617	1.9	2149	8.2
8 SU	0438	1.7	1010	8.5	1700	1.6	2229	8.5
9 M	0519	1.5	1047	8.8	1740	1.4	2306	8.8
10 TU	0558	1.3	1123	8.9	1818	1.2	○ 2342	8.9
11 W	0635	1.3	1158	9.1	1856	1.1		
12 TH	0018	9.0	0712	1.2	1234	9.1	1933	1.1
13 F	0056	9.0	0749	1.3	1312	9.1	2011	1.2
14 SA	0136	8.9	0828	1.4	1353	8.9	2051	1.3
15 SU	0220	8.7	0910	1.7	1438	8.6	2135	1.6
16 M	0308	8.3	0957	2.0	1529	8.2	2226	1.9
17 TU	0406	7.9	1054	2.3	1631	7.8	☾ 2327	2.2
18 W	0515	7.7	1203	2.4	1745	7.7		
19 TH	0042	2.2	0631	7.8	1322	2.3	1901	7.8
20 F	0200	2.0	0743	8.1	1435	1.9	2011	8.1
21 SA	0310	1.7	0848	8.5	1541	1.6	2113	8.5
22 SU	0412	1.4	0943	8.8	1639	1.3	2208	8.8
23 M	0506	1.2	1033	9.1	1731	1.1	2256	9.0
24 TU	0554	1.2	1118	9.2	1817	1.0	● 2340	9.1
25 W	0637	1.1	1159	9.2	1859	1.0		
26 TH	0022	9.1	0717	1.2	1239	9.2	1938	1.0
27 F	0102	9.0	0755	1.3	1318	9.0	2016	1.2
28 SA	0141	8.8	0831	1.6	1356	8.7	2051	1.5
29 SU	0219	8.5	0906	1.9	1434	8.3	2125	1.8
30 M	0258	8.1	0941	2.3	1514	7.9	2200	2.2

DECEMBER

Day	Time	m	Time	m	Time	m	Time	m
1 TU	0339	7.7	1021	2.6	1557	7.5	2241	2.5
2 W	0425	7.3	1109	2.9	1649	7.1	☽ 2333	2.8
3 TH	0522	7.1	1208	3.0	1752	7.0		
4 F	0036	2.9	0631	7.1	1316	3.0	1904	7.0
5 SA	0145	2.8	0740	7.3	1425	2.7	2010	7.3
6 SU	0252	2.5	0840	7.7	1527	2.3	2106	7.7
7 M	0351	2.2	0930	8.1	1620	1.9	2154	8.1
8 TU	0442	1.8	1015	8.5	1708	1.6	2238	8.5
9 W	0528	1.5	1057	8.8	1754	1.3	○ 2320	8.8
10 TH	0612	1.3	1138	9.0	1838	1.1		
11 F	0002	9.0	0656	1.2	1220	9.2	1922	0.9
12 SA	0045	9.1	0740	1.1	1303	9.3	2006	0.9
13 SU	0130	9.2	0825	1.1	1348	9.2	2051	1.0
14 M	0217	9.0	0910	1.3	1435	9.0	2136	1.1
15 TU	0305	8.8	0957	1.5	1525	8.7	2224	1.4
16 W	0356	8.5	1048	1.7	1618	8.4	☾ 2315	1.7
17 TH	0453	8.2	1144	2.0	1718	8.0		
18 F	0015	2.0	0557	8.0	1249	2.1	1827	7.8
19 SA	0123	2.1	0708	7.9	1401	2.1	1940	7.8
20 SU	0237	2.1	0819	8.0	1512	2.0	2050	8.0
21 M	0345	1.9	0922	8.3	1617	1.7	2151	8.2
22 TU	0444	1.7	1017	8.6	1712	1.5	2244	8.5
23 W	0535	1.5	1104	8.8	1800	1.3	2329	8.7
24 TH ●	0620	1.4	1147	8.9	1843	1.2		
25 F	0010	8.8	0700	1.3	1225	9.0	1922	1.1
26 SA	0048	8.9	0739	1.3	1302	9.0	2000	1.2
27 SU	0124	8.8	0815	1.4	1338	8.8	2034	1.3
28 M	0159	8.7	0848	1.6	1413	8.6	2105	1.5
29 TU	0234	8.5	0918	1.8	1447	8.3	2134	1.7
30 W	0307	8.2	0948	2.1	1521	8.0	2206	2.0
31 TH	0341	7.9	1024	2.4	1558	7.6	2244	2.3

Chart Datum: 4.89 metres below Lallemand System (Mean Sea Level, Marseilles)

DIEPPE *continued*

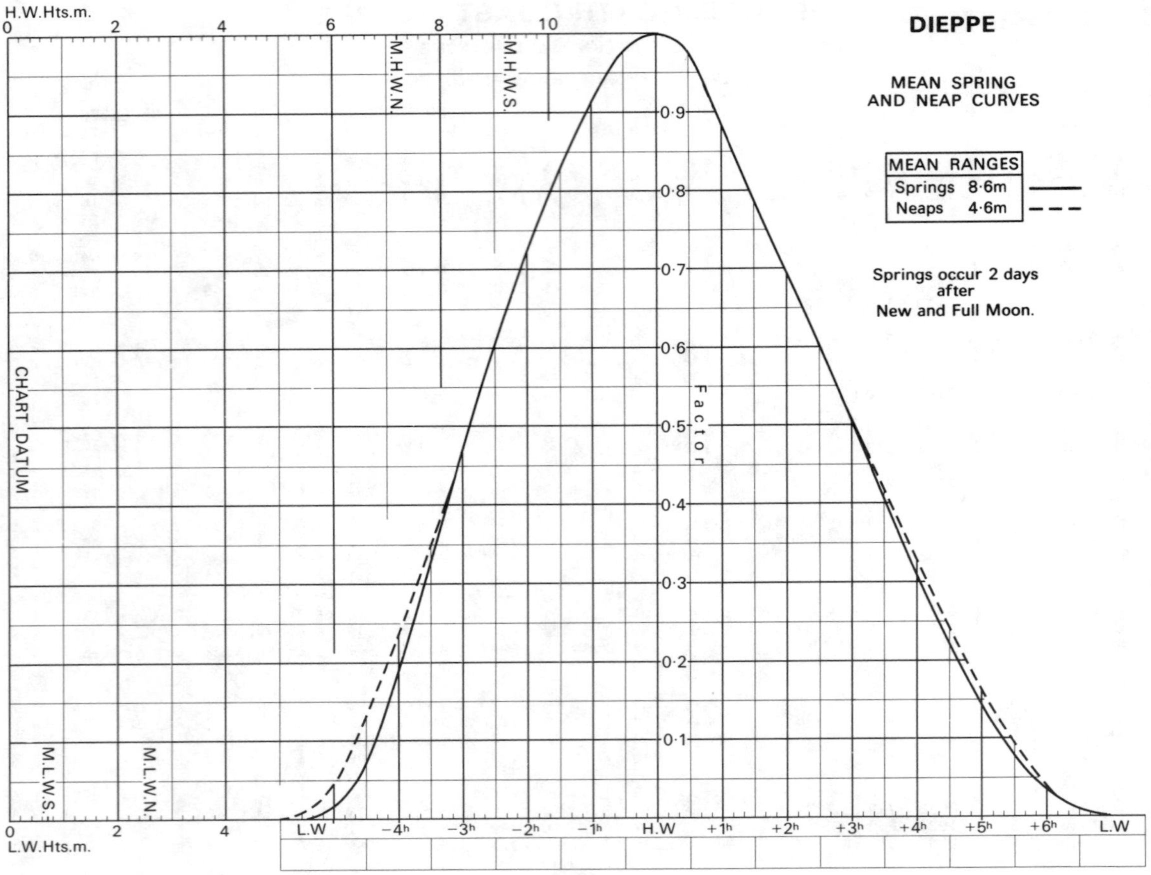
H.W.Hts.m.
0 2 4 6 8 10
M.H.W.N.
M.H.W.S.
CHART DATUM
M.L.W.S.
M.L.W.N.
0 2 4
L.W.Hts.m.
Factor
0·9 0·8 0·7 0·6 0·5 0·4 0·3 0·2 0·1
L.W −4h −3h −2h −1h H.W +1h +2h +3h +4h +5h +6h L.W
DIEPPE
MEAN SPRING AND NEAP CURVES
MEAN RANGES
Springs 8·6m
Neaps 4·6m
Springs occur 2 days after New and Full Moon.

LE TRÉPORT 10-19-23

Seine Maritime

CHARTS
Admiralty 1352, 2147, 2612, 2451; SHOM 5928, 7083; ECM 1011; Stanford 1; Imray C31

TIDES
Dover −0025; ML 5·0; Duration 0530; Zone −0100

Standard Port DIEPPE (←)

Times				Height (metres)			
HW		LW		MHWS	MHWN	MLWN	MLWS
0100	0600	0100	0700	9·3	7·2	2·6	0·7
1300	1800	1300	1900				
Differences LE TRÉPORT							
+0001	+0005	+0005	+0011	+0·1	+0·2	−0·1	0·0

SHELTER
Shelter good but harbour dries. Access difficult in strong on-shore winds. Entry channel dries — only usable from HW ∓ 1½. Wet basin opens from HW − 1½ to HW. Signal for opening of swing bridge — three blasts on passing heads of jetties. Yachts lie along NE wall (Quai Bellot) to await lock opening. In Arrière Port yachts lie on pontoons in NW corner.

NAVIGATION
Waypoint 50°04′·30N 01°21′·70E, 315°/135° from/to entrance, 0·52M. Coast dries to approx 300m off the pier heads. No navigational dangers. Entrance difficult in strong winds: scend is caused in the Avant Port.

LIGHTS AND MARKS
Le Treport can be difficult to identify. ''P'' flag or W Lt indicates entrance open. No Ldg Lts or marks.
Traffic signals shown from E jetty and entrance to Arrière-Port.

RADIO TELEPHONE
Call: *Ovaro* VHF Ch 16; 12 (HW−2 to HW).

TELEPHONE (35)
Hr Mr 35.86.17.91; Aff Mar 35.86.08.88; CROSS 21.87.21.87; SNSM 35.86.33.71; # 35.86.15.34; Meteo 35.42.21.06; Auto 35.21.16.11; Police 35.86.08.88; Dr 35.86.16.23; Brit Consul 21.96.33.76.

FACILITIES
Outer Harbour M; **Arrière Port** AB, FW; **Chantier Naval du Tréport** ☎ 35.86.12.33, ME, El, Sh, C, CH, M; **Yacht Club de la Bresle** ☎ 35.86.19.93, C (3 ton), AB, Bar; **Intermer Services** ☎ 35.50.26.42 ME, EL, Ⓔ, Sh, CH; **Loisirs Yachting** ☎ 35.50.16.70, ME, CH, Ⓔ. **Town** P, D, V, Gaz, R, Bar. ✉; Ⓑ; ⇌; ✈ (Dieppe).
Ferry UK — Dieppe—Newhaven.

LE TRÉPORT *continued*

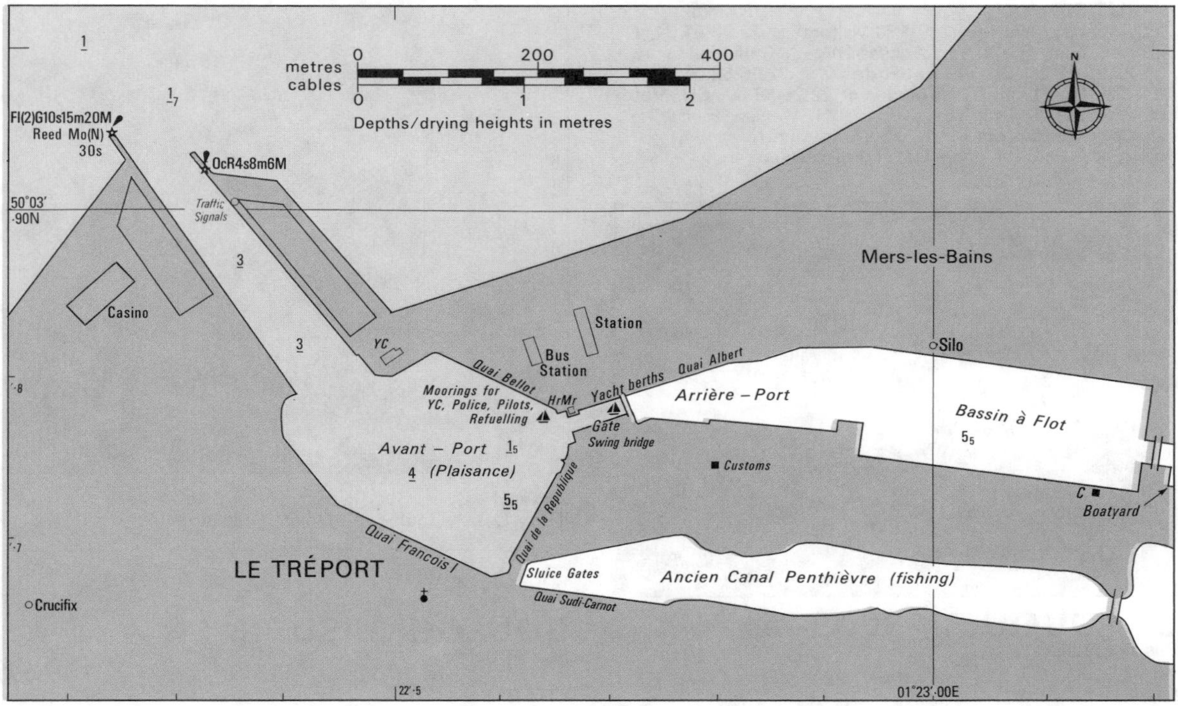

metres
cables
0
200
400
0
1
2
Depths/drying heights in metres
Fl(2)G10s15m20M
Reed Mo(N)
30s
OcR4s8m6M
Traffic Signals
50°03'
·90N
Casino
YC
Quai Bellot
Moorings for YC, Police, Pilots, Refuelling
HrMr
Station
Bus Station
Yacht berths
Quai Albert
Gate
Swing bridge
Arrière – Port
Mers-les-Bains
Silo
Bassin à Flot
Avant – Port
(Plaisance)
Customs
Boatyard
Quai de la République
Quai François I
LE TRÉPORT
Sluice Gates
Ancien Canal Penthièvre (fishing)
Quai Sudi-Carnot
Crucifix
22'·5
01°23'·00E

ST VALÉRY-SUR-SOMME

Somme

10-19-24

CHARTS

Admiralty 2451; SHOM 7084; ECM 1011; Stanford 1; Imray C31

TIDES

Dover –0020; ML —; Duration —; Zone –0100

Standard Port DIEPPE (←)

Times				Height (metres)			
HW		LW		MHWS	MHWN	MLWN	MLWS
0100	0600	0100	0700	9·3	7·2	2·6	0·7
1300	1800	1300	1900				
Differences ST VALÉRY-SUR-SOMME							
+0028	+0040	No data		+0·7	+0·8	No data	
LE HOURDEL and LE CROTOY							
+0021	+0026	No data		+0·7	+0·7	+0·1	+0·4

SHELTER

The bay is open to W and can be dangerous in onshore winds over force 6.

The three harbours, St Valéry-sur-Somme, Le Crotoy and Le Hourdel, are very well protected. Yachts can

(1) dry out on hard sand or moor alongside at Le Hourdel
(2) go into marina at St Valéry (max. draught 2·5 m). Access HW∓2
(3) go into marina at Le Crotoy when tidal range at Dover exceeds 4·4 m (max. draught 1·6 m). See 10.19.29.
(4) go into Abbeville Canal at St. Valéry (max. draught 3·3 m). Entry by prior arrangement and in daylight only.

NAVIGATION

Waypoint 'ATSO' N cardinal buoy, VQ, 50°14'·00N 01°28'·50E, about 1M W of buoyed channel (shifts). The whole estuary dries up to 3 M seaward from Le Hourdel. The landfall buoy N cardinal VQ 'ATSO' should be closed and entrance commenced at HW–2. Departure at HW–1. Channels are constantly changing but buoys are moved as necessary. The sands build up in ridges offshore but inside Pt du Hourdel are generally flat except where the River Somme and minor streams scour their way to the sea. If range of tide exceeds 4·1 m Dover there is sufficient water over the sands inside Pt du Hourdel from HW–1 to HW+½ for vessels with less than 1·5 m draught. At all other times buoys marking the channels must be followed in strict sequence. There are fishing fleets based at all three harbours and small cargo vessels occasionally navigate to the commercial quay inside the lock to the Abbeville Canal.

LIGHTS AND MARKS

Lt Ho Cayeux-sur-Mer FlR 6s 32m 22M (off chartlet). Numerous numbered buoys mark twisting channel marked S1, S2 up to approximately S50; starboard hand green cone buoys (odd numbers), port hand red can buoys (even numbers). Some buoys are lit. At a variable point NE off Pt du Hourdel there is a Division Buoy YBY from where buoys C1 to C10 run N and E to Le Crotoy; buoys prefixed S continue to St. Valery-sur-Somme.

LE HOURDEL Only landmark is Lt Ho Oc(3) WG 12s 19m. Channel unmarked. Follow St Valéry channel buoys until Lt Ho bears 270°, then head in.

ST VALERY-SUR-SOMME From Division Buoy, buoyed channel continues with stbd hand marks becoming beacons on submerged training wall the end of which is lit, Iso G 4s 9m 9M; then four Bns on end of groynes. Hut on lattice Tr Iso G 4s marks beginning of tree lined promenade with port hand beacons marking submerged training wall.

W Tr on beginning of Digue du Large Fl R 4s 9m 9M.

LE CROTOY – See 10.19.29.

RADIO TELEPHONE

VHF Ch 09 HW∓2.

TELEPHONE (22)

St Valery Hr Mr 22.26.91.64; Aff Mar 21.31.53.23; # 22.24.04.75; Lock (canal) 22.60.80.23; CROSS 21.92.86.66; Meteo 21.31.52.23; Auto 21.33.82.55; Police 22.60.82.08; Dr 22.26.92.25; Brit Consul 21.96.33.76.

ST VALÉRY-SUR-SOMME *continued*

FACILITIES
EC Monday. **Marina** (280+30 visitors) ☎ 22.26.91.64, C (6 ton), Slip, R, ◙, Bar; Access HW±2; **CNMF** ☎ 22.26.82.20, Sh, Ⓔ; **Latitude 50** ☎ 22.26.82.06, ME, El, CH, Ⓔ, charts; **Grandsaier** ☎ 22.26.88.80, CH; **Valois** ☎ 22.60.81.36, ME; **Town** P, D, CH, V, Gaz, R, Bar, ✉; Ⓑ; ⇄ (Noyelles-sur-Mer); ✈ (Le Touquet).
Ferry UK — Boulogne—Dover/Folkestone.

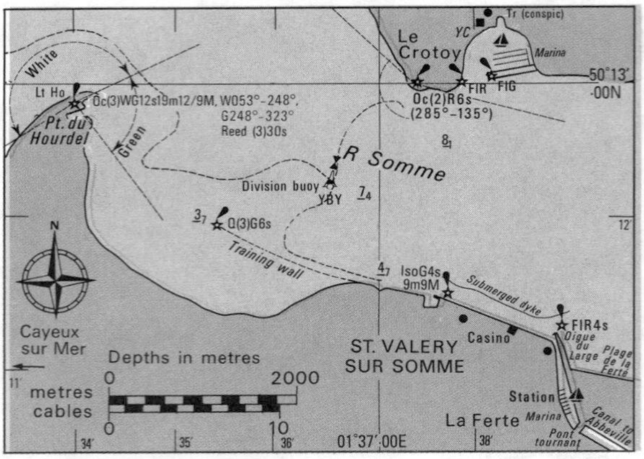
White
Lt Ho
Oc(3)WG12s19m12/9M, W053°-248°, G248°-323°
Reed (3)30s
Pt du Hourdel
Green
Le Crotoy
YC
Marina
Tr (conspic)
FlR
FlG
Oc(2)R6s (285°-135°)
50°13'·00N
R Somme
Division buoy
YBY
O(3)G6s
Training wall
IsoG4s 9m9M
Submerged dyke
FlR4s
Digue du Large
Plage de la Ferté
Casino
ST. VALERY SUR SOMME
Station
La Ferte
Marina
Pont tournant
Canal to Abbeville
Cayeux sur Mer
Depths in metres
metres
cables
0
2000
10
01°37'·00E

LE TOUQUET 10-19-25

Pas de Calais

CHARTS
Admiralty 2451; SHOM 6795; ECM 1011; Stanford 1, 9; Imray C31

TIDES
Dover −0010; ML 4·8; Duration 0520; Zone −0100

Standard Port DIEPPE (⟵)

Times				Height (metres)			
HW		LW		MHWS	MHWN	MLWN	MLWS
0100	0600	0100	0700	9·3	7·2	2·6	0·7
1300	1800	1300	1900				
Differences LE TOUQUET (ETAPLES)							
+0012	No data			−0·3	0·0	+0·2	+0·3

SHELTER
Good except in strong W winds. Yacht moorings, which dry, are to stbd after passing Pt de Touquet. There are plans to build a dam across the mouth of the R Canche, with locks. Marina at Étaples — see 10.19.29.

NAVIGATION
Waypoint 50°35'·00N 01°31'·80E, 308°/128° from/to Camiers Lt, 3·8M. Entrance is not easy — local pilots or fishermen are available. Best entrance is at HW−1. In W winds the sea breaks heavily a long way out and entry should not be attempted. The channel is always changing and buoys are moved accordingly. Beware stranded wreck 2M NW of Le Touquet-Paris Plage Lt Ho, marked by Lt buoy.

LIGHTS AND MARKS
Good landmarks are the Terres de Tourmont, a conspic range 175m high, visible for 25 miles. Le Touquet is at the S end of this range. Entrance between Pt de Lornel and Pt de Touquet. Pick up buoyed channel in R section of Camiers Lt. Pt du Touquet light is Y tower, Brown band, W & G top — Fl (2) 10s 54m 25M.

RADIO TELEPHONE
VHF Ch 21; 16.

TELEPHONE (21)
Hr Mr 21.05.12.77; Aff Mar Etaples 21.94.61.50; Auto 21.05.13.55; # 21.05.01.72; CROSS 21.87.21.87; Police 21.94.60.17; Dr 21.05.14.42; Brit Consul 21.96.33.76.

FACILITIES
Cercle Nautique du Touquet ☎ 21.05.12.77, Slip, M, P, ME, D, FW, C, CH, R, Bar; **Marina** (Etaples — see 10.19.29), AB, FW, P, D, AC; **Demoury** ☎ 21.84.51.76, Sh, SM; **Technical Composite** ☎ 21.05.62.97, BY.

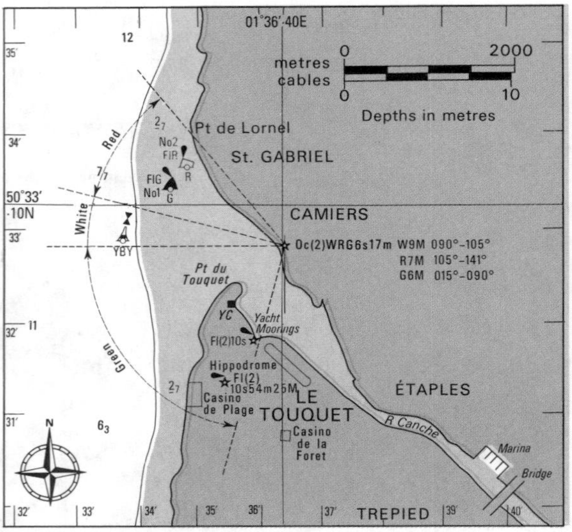
01°36'·40E
metres
cables
0
2000
10
Depths in metres
Pt de Lornel
St. GABRIEL
No2 FlR
FlG No1
Red
White
50°33'·10N
CAMIERS
YBY
Oc(2)WRG6s17m W9M 090°-105° R7M 105°-141° G6M 015°-090°
Pt du Touquet
YC
Yacht Moorings
Fl(2)10s
Hippodrome
Fl(2) 10s54m25M
Casino de Plage
LE TOUQUET
Casino de la Foret
ÉTAPLES
R Canche
Marina
Bridge
Green
TREPIED

Town P, D, V, Gaz, R, Bar. ✉; Ⓑ; ⇄; ✈.
Ferry UK — Boulogne—Dover/Folkestone.

BOULOGNE-SUR-MER 10-19-26

Pas de Calais

CHARTS
Admiralty 438, 1892, 2451; SHOM 6436, 6682, 6795; ECM 1010, 1011; Stanford 1, 9; Imray C31, C8

TIDES
Dover 0000; ML 5·0; Duration 0515; Zone −0100

Standard Port DIEPPE (⟵)

Times				Height (metres)			
HW		LW		MHWS	MHWN	MLWN	MLWS
0100	0600	0100	0700	9·3	7·2	2·6	0·7
1300	1800	1300	1900	−0·4	0·0	+0·2	+0·4
Differences BOULOGNE							
+0015	+0026	+0037	+0036	−1·8	−0·9	−0·5	+0·5

SHELTER
Good except in strong NE winds. Turbulent water when R Liane in spate; proceed with great care. Entrance possible in most weathers and at any state of tide. Yachts secure to pontoons in SW side of tidal basin alongside Quai Chanzy. Max length 10 m (over 10 m apply before arrival). Yacht berths tend to silt up.

NAVIGATION
Waypoint 50°44'·50N 01°33'·00E, 270°/090° from/to Digue Carnot Lt, 0·72M. Very busy commercial passenger and fishing port. Respect warnings and instructions given by harbour lights. There are no navigational dangers and entrance is easily identified and is well marked. Beware heavy wash from fishing boats. Also beware Digue Nord which partially covers at HW. Keep W and S of N light tower, Fl(2)R 6s.

LIGHTS AND MARKS
Ldg Lts 123° lead towards R Liane and marina. Besides normal traffic signals, special signals apply as follows: —

*G W G R	Movement suspended except for vessels with special permission to enter
*G W R R	Movement suspended except for vessels with special permission to leave inner and outer harbour
*G W R R R	Movement suspended except for vessels with special permission to leave inner harbour

*Normal light signal prohibiting entry and departure.
Two Bu Lts (hor) mean sluicing from R Liane.

RADIO TELEPHONE
VHF Ch 12 16 (H24).

BOULOGNE *continued*

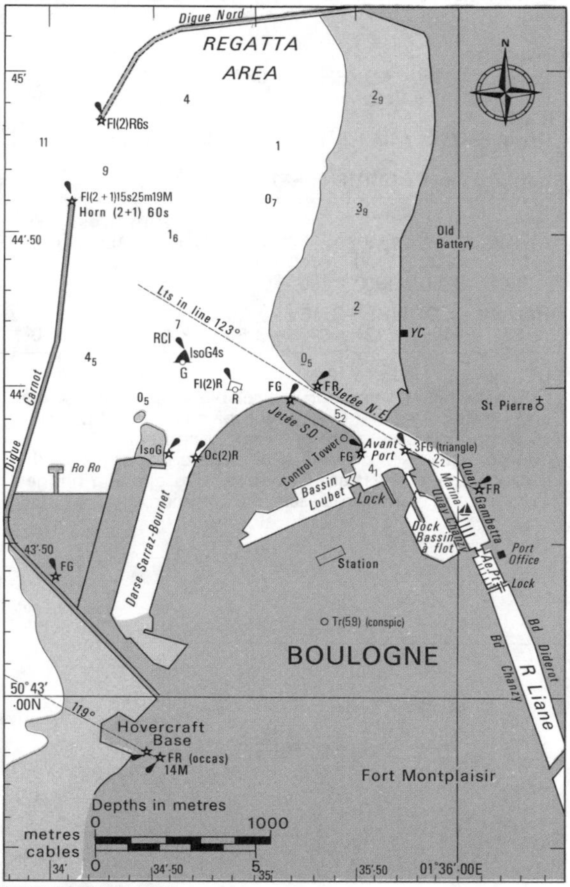
Digue Nord
REGATTA AREA
Fl(2)R6s
Fl(2+1)15s25m19M
Horn (2+1) 60s
Old Battery
Lts in line 123°
YC
RCl
IsoG4s
Fl(2)R
FG
Jetée N.E.
Jetée S.O.
St Pierre
IsoG
Oc(2)R
Ro Ro
Control Tower
Avant Port
3FG (triangle)
Bassin Loubet
Lock
Marina
Quai Gambetta
FR
Dock Bassin à flot
Port Office
Station
Lock
Digue Carnot
Darse Sarraz-Bournet
Tr(59) (conspic)
BOULOGNE
Bd Diderot
Bd Chanzy
R Liane
119°
Hovercraft Base
FR (occas) 14M
Fort Montplaisir
Depths in metres
metres
cables
1000
45'
44'·50
44'
43'·50
50°43'·00N
34'
34'·50
35'
35'·50
01°36'·00E

SHELTER

Shelter is very good especially in the marina. Bar is dredged to 4·5m but is liable to build up in heavy weather. Entrance is difficult in strong NW to NE winds. Enter Bassin Carnot if headed for the French canals otherwise use Bassin de l'Ouest, the marina.

NAVIGATION

Waypoint 50°58'·50N 01°49'·90E, 298°/118° from/to Jetée Ouest Lt, 0·43M. Entrance is relatively easy but beware the Ridens de la Rade, about 1 M N of entrance, a sandbank which shoals in places to about 0·75m and seas break on it. Entrance is well marked but there is a great deal of shipping, including ferries, which can be hazardous. Yachts are required to enter/leave under power. It is forbidden to tack in entrance channel.

LIGHTS AND MARKS

From a point ¼M SE of CA 10 buoy, Fl(2) R 6s, the main Lt Ho, Fl(4) 15s, bearing 140° leads through entrance. Normal entry signals with following additions.

R Lt = indicates ferry leaving — movements
G Lt = ferry entering — prohibited

Lights on Tr of Gare Maritime are for car ferries and cargo vessels only. Yachts may not enter or leave when at least three Lts are on. They may follow a car ferry entering or leaving but must keep to the stbd side of the fairway. One R Lt denotes the presence of a dredger and does not mean movement is forbidden.

Bassin Carnot

Lock signals, gates open HW−1½ to HW+¾.

2 G Lt hor = entry from Arrière Port permitted.
2 R Lt hor = entry from Arrière Port prohibited.
1 G Lt = entry from basin to Arrière Port permitted.
1 R Lt = entry from basin to Arrière Port prohibited.
2 blasts = request permission to enter Bassin Carnot.
4 blasts = request permission to enter Bassin de l'Ouest.

Bassin de l'Ouest

Or Lt = 10 mins before opening of lock.
R Lt = All movement prohibited.
G Lt = Movement authorised.

Dock gates and bridge open HW−1½, HW and HW+½. (Sat and Sun HW−2 and HW+1).

TELEPHONE (21)

Hr Mr 21.30.10.00; Hr Mr Plaisance 21.31.70.01; Harbour office 21.30.90.46; Aff Mar 21.30.53.23; CROSS 21.87.21.87; SNSM 21.31.42.59; # 21.30.14.24; Meteo 21.31.52.23; Auto 21.33.82.55; Police 21.31.75.17; Ⓗ 21.31.92.13; Brit Consul 21.30.25.11.

FACILITIES

Marina (350+50 visitors) ☎ 21.31.70.01, FW, Slip, AC, P, D, C (20 ton); **Quai Gambetta** M, P*, D*, L, FW, AB, V, R, Bar; **Baude Electronique** ☎ 21.30.01.15, Ⓔ; **Opale Marine** ☎ 21.30.36.19, ME, El, Sh, M, CH, Divers; **Angelo** ☎ 21.31.37.61, CH; **Librairie Duminy** ☎ 21.30.06.75, SHOM; **YC Boulonnais** ☎ 21.31.80.68, C, Bar. **Town** P, D, FW, ME, El, Sh, CH, V, Gaz, R, Bar. ✉; Ⓑ; ⇌; ✈ (Le Touquet/Calais).

Ferry UK—Dover/Folkestone.

*Obtainable from Societé Maritime Carburante Liquide.

CALAIS 10-19-27

Pas de Calais

CHARTS

Admiralty 1352, 1892; SHOM 6474, 6651, 6681; ECM 1010; Stanford 1, 19; Imray C8

TIDES

Dover +0048; ML 4·1; Duration 0525; Zone −0100

Standard Port DIEPPE (⟵)

Times				Height (metres)			
HW		LW		MHWS	MHWN	MLWN	MLWS
0100	0600	0100	0700	9·3	7·2	2·5	0·7
1300	1800	1300	1900				
Differences CALAIS							
+0043	+0057	+0105	+0054	−2·2	−1·3	−0·5	+0·2

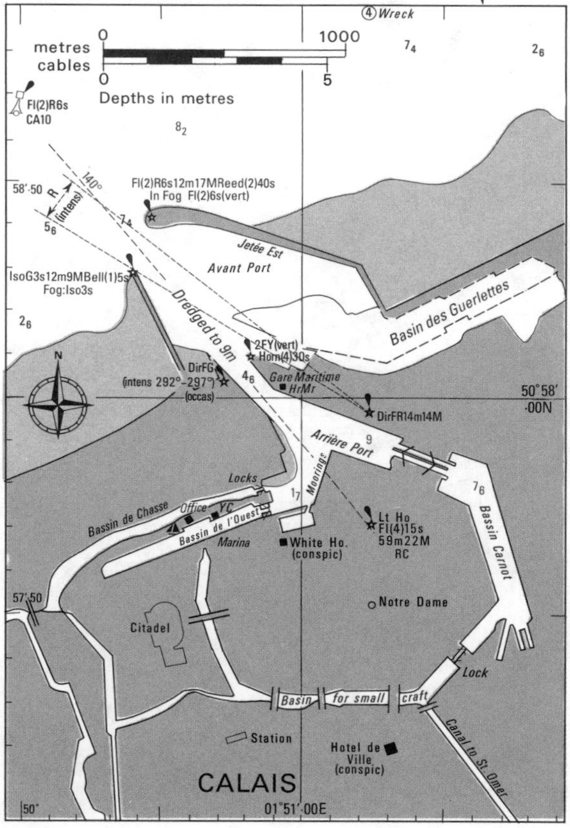
Wreck
metres
cables
1000
Depths in metres
Fl(2)R6s CA10
Fl(2)R6s12m17MReed(2)40s In Fog Fl(2)6s(vert)
140°
R (intens)
Jetée Est
Avant Port
IsoG3s12m9MBell(1)5s Fog:Iso3s
Dredged to 9m
Basin des Guerlettes
2FY(vert) Horn(4)30s
DirFG (intens 292°-297°) (occas)
Gare Maritime
HrMr
DirFR14m14M
Arrière Port
Locks
Moorings
Bassin de Chasse
Office
YC
Bassin de l'Ouest
Marina
White Ho. (conspic)
Lt Ho Fl(4)15s 59m22M RC
Bassin Carnot
Notre Dame
Citadel
Lock
Basin for small craft
Canal to St Omer
Station
Hotel de Ville (conspic)
CALAIS
58'·50
50°58'·00N
57'·50
50'
01°51'·00E

19

CALAIS *continued*

RADIO TELEPHONE
VHF Ch 12 16 (H24). Hoverport Ch 20 (occas). Carnot Lock Ch 12 (occas). Cap Gris Nez, Channel Navigation Information Service (CNIS), call: *Gris Nez Traffic* Ch 16 **69** 79 (H24). Information broadcasts in English and French on Ch 11, at H+10, and also at H+25 when visibility is less than 2 M.

TELEPHONE (21)
Hr Mr 21.96.31.20; Aff Mar 21.34.52.70; Pilot (Quai de la Gare Maritime) 21.96.40.18; CROSS 21.87.21.87; SNSM 21.96.40.18; Port de Plaisance 21.34.55.23; # 21.34.75.40; Meteo 21.31.52.23; Auto 21.33.82.55; Police 21.96.74.17; Dr 21.96.31.20; Ⓗ 21.97.99.60; Brit Consul 21.96.33.76.

FACILITIES
Marina (350+400 visitors) ☎ 21.34.55.23, D, FW, C (6 ton), BH (3 ton), AC, CH, Gaz, R, ⊡, Sh, SM, V, Bar; Access HW−1½ to HW+½. **YC de Calais** ☎ 21.97.02.34, M, P, Bar; **Ebaine** ☎ 21.34.69.01, CH, SM; **Godin Moteurs** ☎ 21.96.29.97, ME; **Marinerie** ☎ 21.34.47.83, CH. **Town** CH, V, Gaz, R, Bar. ✉; Ⓑ; ⇌; ✈.
Ferry UK—Dover.

DUNKERQUE 10-19-28
Nord

CHARTS
Admiralty 1350, 323; SHOM 7057, 6651; ECM 1010; Stanford 1, 19; Imray C30

TIDES
Dover +0050; ML 3·2; Duration 0530; Zone −0100

Standard Port DIEPPE (⟵)

Times				Height (metres)			
HW		LW		MHWS	MHWN	MLWN	MLWS
0100	0600	0100	0700	9·3	7·2	2·5	0·7
1300	1800	1300	1900				
Differences DUNKERQUE							
+0059	+0122	+0121	+0108	−3·5	−2·4	−1·1	−0·1

SHELTER
Good shelter and harbour is available at all states of tide and weather. Yachts must use E of harbour; all pleasure craft are prohibited from entering W harbour. YC pontoons are ¾M down E side of harbour, or proceed through Ecluse Trystram and under two opening bridges to municipal marina in Bassin du Commerce

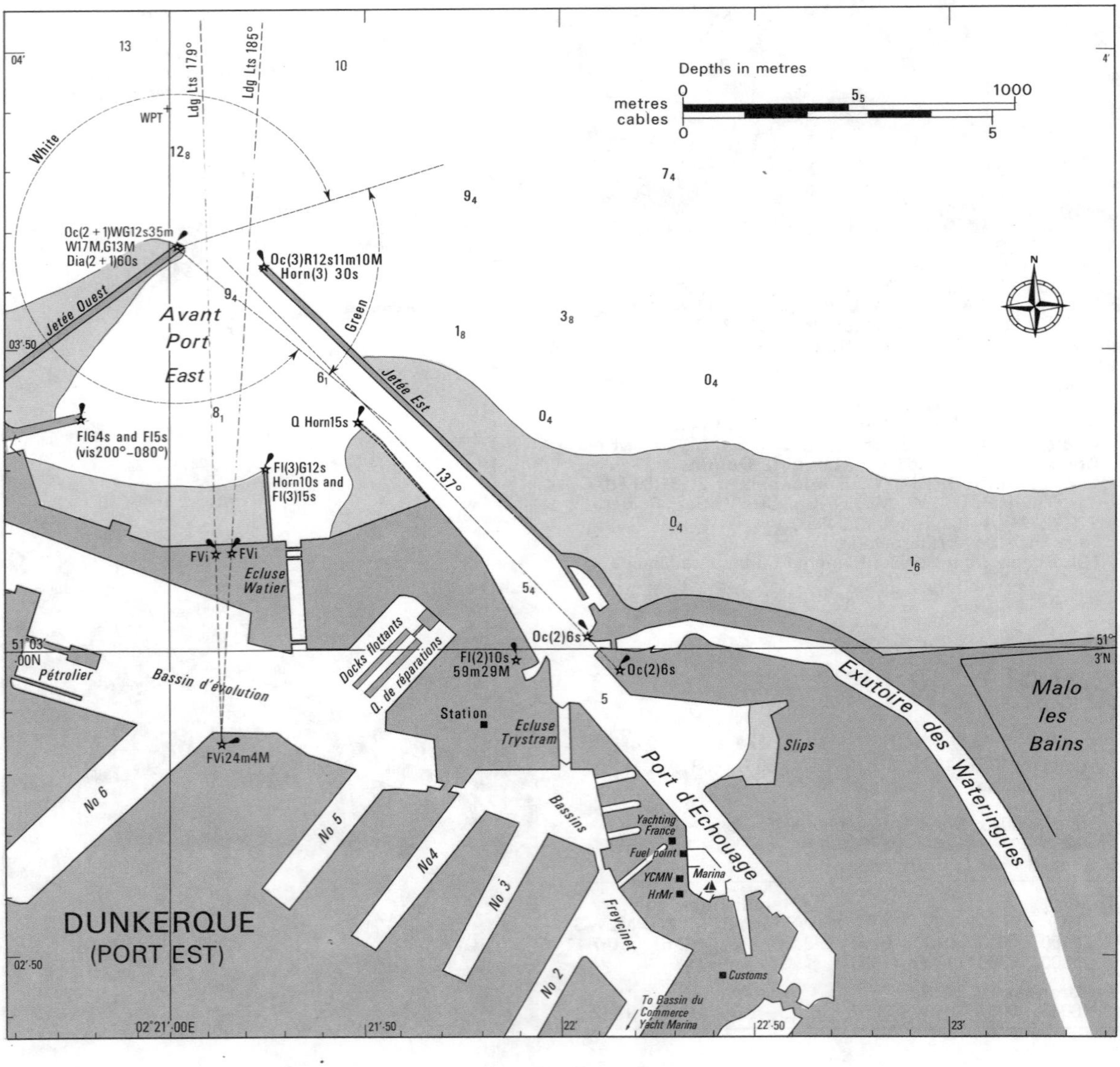

Depths in metres
metres
cables
0
1000
5
Ldg Lts 179°
Ldg Lts 185°
WPT
White
Green
Oc(2+1)WG12s35m
W17M,G13M
Dia(2+1)60s
Oc(3)R12s11m10M
Horn(3) 30s
Jetée Ouest
Jetée Est
Avant Port East
137°
Q Horn15s
FlG4s and Fl5s
(vis200°-080°)
Fl(3)G12s
Horn10s and
Fl(3)15s
FVi
FVi
Ecluse Watier
Oc(2)6s
Oc(2)6s
Fl(2)10s
59m29M
Docks flottants
Q. de réparations
Pétrolier
Bassin d'évolution
FVi24m4M
Station
Ecluse Trystram
Exutoire des Wateringues
Malo les Bains
Slips
Port d'Echouage
Bassins
Yachting France
Fuel point
YCMN
HrMr
Marina
Freycinet
Customs
To Bassin du Commerce Yacht Marina
No 6
No 5
No4
No 3
No 2
DUNKERQUE
(PORT EST)
04'
03'.50
51°03'
.00N
02'.50
02°21'.00E
21'.50
22'
22'.50
23'
4'
51°
3'N

DUNKERQUE *continued*

NAVIGATION

Waypoint Port Est 51°03'·90N 02°21'·00E, 355°/175° from/to Jetée Ouest Lt, 0·20M. From the W, fetch the Dunkerque Lanby 5M N of Calais, thence to DKA safe water pillar Lt Buoy, and then follow series of DW Lt buoys past Dunkerque Ouest to buoy DW 29, ½M WNW of ent. From the E, the series of E Lt buoys lead S of Banc Hills from the Nieuwpoort Bank W Cardinal Lt buoy. There is no bar. Strong currents reach about 3½ kn. This is a busy commercial port. Entrance is easy in most weathers, but fresh winds from NW to NE cause heavy seas at entrance to Avant Port and scend in harbour.

LIGHTS AND MARKS

Two sets of Ldg Lts (there are others in the Commercial Port):—

(1) Two Lts 179° (F Vi) giving entrance line between the E and W jetties. A second pair, with common rear, lead 185°.

(2) Two Lts in line at 137° (Oc(2) 6s) lead down to Port d'Echouage.

Normal entry signals with following additions, shown from head of Jetée Ouest

R W R W	Prohibition does not apply to tugs, warships or fishing vessels
R R W R	Prohibition does not apply to tankers or vessels with dangerous cargoes.

Lock signals (H24) are shown at Ecluse Watier and consist of three horizontal pairs disposed vertically. Middle pair refer to Ecluse Watier and lower pair to Ecluse Trystram:

2FG(hor) = lock open
2FR(hor) = lock closed

Lock signals at each lock:

2FG(hor) = lock ready
2FR(hor) = lock in use, no entry
FG FlG = enter and secure on side of flashing light
FW over 2FG(hor) = slack water, both gates open; enter lock.

RADIO TELEPHONE

VHF Ch 12 16 **73** (H24). Ecluse Trystram Ch 73.
YC Ch 09.

TELEPHONE (28)

Hr Mr 28.29.72.82; Port Control 28.29.72.87; Aff Mar 28.66.56.14; CROSS 21.87.21.87; SNSM 28.63.23.60; # 28.65.14.73; Meteo 28.66.45.25; Auto 28.63.44.44; Police 28.64.51.09; Ⓗ 28.66.70.01; Brit Consul 28.66.11.98.

FACILITIES

YC Mer du Nord Marina (320 + 70 visitors) ☎ 28.66.79.90, Slip, D, P, FW, C (4½ ton), BH (15 ton), AC, ME, SM, R, Bar, Access H24. **Bassin du Commerce** ☎ 28.66.11.06, M, D, L, FW, CH, AB; **Port de Pêche** Slip, P, D, FW, ME, El, Sh, CH, V, R, Bar; **FMC** ☎ 28.59.32.32, SHOM; **Leroy Garage** ☎ 28.66.82.37, P, D; **Flandre-Chantier** ☎ 28.66.49.62, M, ME, El, Ⓔ, Sh, CH; **Norbert-Peche** ☎ 28.24.35.14, ME, El, Sh, CH; **Bleu Marine** ☎ 28.63.93.33 ME, El, Ⓔ, Sh, CH; **Marine Diffusion** ☎ 25.59.18.19 ME, El, Sh, M, CH; **Nord Marine** ☎ 28.66.98.75 ME, Ⓔ; **Town** P, D, V, Gaz, R, Bar. ✉; Ⓑ; ≹, ✈ (Lille).
Ferry UK — Ramsgate/Dover.

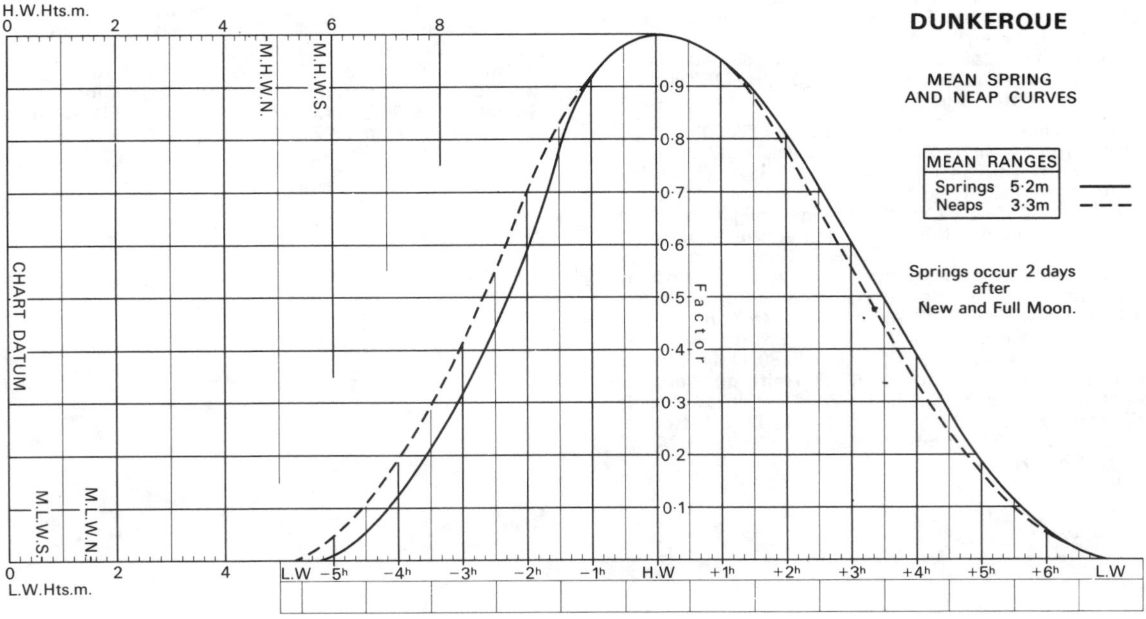
H.W.Hts.m.
0 2 4 6 8
M.H.W.N.
M.H.W.S.
CHART DATUM
M.L.W.S.
M.L.W.N.
0 2 4
L.W.Hts.m.
0·9 0·8 0·7 0·6 0·5 0·4 0·3 0·2 0·1
Factor
L.W −5h −4h −3h −2h −1h H.W +1h +2h +3h +4h +5h +6h L.W
DUNKERQUE
MEAN SPRING AND NEAP CURVES
MEAN RANGES
Springs 5·2m
Neaps 3·3m
Springs occur 2 days after New and Full Moon.

MINOR HARBOURS AND ANCHORAGES 10-19-29

ILES St MARCOUF, Manche, 49°30′·00N, 01°09′·00W, Zone −0100, Admty chart 2613; SHOM 7056. For tides, see 10.19.11. There are two islands, Ile de Terre and to the N, Ile du Large. The former is a bird sanctuary and is closed to the public; the latter has a small dinghy harbour on the W side. Anchor SW or SE of Ile du Large or SE or NE of the Ile de Terre. Both islands surrounded by drying rocks. Ile du Large Lt, VQ(3) 5s 18m 9M. Both islands are uninhabited and there are no facilities.

ISIGNY-SUR-MER, Calvados, 49°19′·00N, 01°06′·00W, Zone −0100, Admty chart 2613, SHOM 7056. HW −0230 on Dover (GMT), −0025 on Le Havre (zone −0100). See 10.19.11. The channel is buoyed from the RWVS buoy NW of the Roches de Grandcamp to breakwaters (marked by Bns); best to start from outer buoy HW−2½. Where channel divides, take E leg up to Isigny. Ldg Lts 173° lead up between the breakwaters, front Oc(2+1) 12s 7m 18M, intens 171°-175°. Rear, 600m from front, Oc(2+1) 12s 19m 18M, intens 171°-175°, synchronised with front. Access difficult with strong NW winds. Berth on SW side ¼M N of town. Facilities: Hr Mr ☎ 31.22.00.40; Aff.Mar. ☎ 31.22.03.11. **Quay** D, FW, P, Slip; **Club Nautique d'Isigny** AB, C (2, 5, 7 ton) Bar, R; **Isigny Garage** ☎ 31.22.02.33. El, ME, Sh; **Miquelot Marine** ☎ 31.22.10.67 ME, El, Sh; **Town** Ⓑ, Bar, ✉, R, V.

CAEN, Calvados, 49°10′·00N, 00°19′·00W, Zone −0100, Admty chart 1349, SHOM 7055. HW depths sp 7·2m, np 5·8m. Proceed up Caen Canal from Ouistreham, 8M see 10.19.15. Report to lock control Tr at Ouistreham to pay and arrange. Speed limit 7 kn; passage only possible by day. Three bridges, at Bénouville (2½M from locks), Hérouville (5M) and Calix (6½M), each show G Lt when passage clear. Seaward bound vessels have right of way. Marina at Bassin St Pierre near city centre. VHF Ch 12 68. Facilities: Hr Mr ☎ 31.52.12.88. Aff Mar. ☎ 31.85.40.55. # ☎ 31.86.61.50; **Marina** (64 visitors) ☎ 31.93.74.47, P, D, ME, Sh, El, AB, FW; **Clinique du Bateau** ☎ 31.84.48.63 ME, El, Sh, SM, CH; **Quay** FW; **City** Ⓑ, Bar, Ⓗ, ✉, R, ⇌, V.

CABOURG, Calvados, 49°19′·00N, 00°07′·00W, Zone −0100, Admty chart 2146,, SHOM 6928. Tides for Dives-sur-Mer. See 10.19.15. HW −0135 on Dover (GMT), −0032 on Le Havre (zone −0100); HW height −0·4m on Le Havre; ML 4·1m. Shelter good but entrance rough in winds from NW to NE. Entrance Lt, between Dives and Houlgate, Oc(2+1) WRG 12s 6m 12/9M G124°-150°, W150°-157°, R157°-193°. Entrance buoys, R can and G conical are moved according to shifting channel. There is a landing place at Dives at Société des Régates de la Dive. Channel from Dives to Cabourg is buoyed and accessible approx HW∓2. Yachts can go alongside jetty in front of Cabourg YC. Facilities: Aff Mar 31.91.23.55; Harbour run by **Cabourg YC** ☎ 31.91.23.55, AB, Bar, M, Slip; **Cabourg Marine** ☎ 31.91.69.08, CH, ME, El, Sh, M, Ⓔ, BY; **Town** Bar, Ⓑ, ✉, R, V.

ROUEN, Seine Maritime, 49°29′·00N, 01°05′·00E, Zone −0100. Admty charts 2880, 2994; SHOM 6117. HW +0330 on Dover (GMT), +0430 on Le Havre (zone −0100); HW height −0·1m on Le Havre; ML 6·2m; Duration 0400. See 10.19.18 for Seine navigation. Yacht navigation forbidden from ½ hr after sunset to ½ hr before sunrise. Yachts use Bassin St Gervais, on N bank, berth SE side for mast removal or replacements (max stay 48 hrs); berth in La Halte de Plaisance de Rouen NE side of Ile Lacroix. VHF 11 13 73 74 call *Rouen Port Capitainerie*. Facilities: Hr Mr 35.88.81.55; Aff Mar 35.98.53.98; # 35.98.27.60; Meteo 35.80.11.44; **Bassin St Gervais** C (3 to 25 ton), FW; **La Halte de Plaisance de Rouen** (50) ☎ 35.88.00.00, FW, AC, Slip, C (4 ton); **Villetard** ☎ 35.88.00.00, ME, El, Sh, P, D, CH; **Rouen YC** ☎ 35.66.52.52; **Eponville Nautic** ☎ 35.72.28.24, ME, El, Ⓔ, Sh, CH.

LE CROTOY, Somme, 50°13′·00N, 01°37′·00E, Zone −0100, Admty chart 2612, SHOM 7084. HW −0020 on Dover (GMT), −0035 on Dieppe (zone −0100); HW height +0·7m on Dieppe. See 10.19.24. It is on the N side of R Somme estuary, which dries. Access when tidal range at Dover exceeds 4·4m. Max draught 1·6m. Follow buoyed channel for St Valery-sur-Somme until the Division Buoy YBY, from where Le Crotoy channel runs N and E marked by small R and G buoys numbered C1 to C10. Pass very close to fishing boat stages entering yacht hr. Hr is tidal but scoured by two sluices. Severe silting leaves many pontoons dry. Secure at last stage and check with YC. Moor to the S side of S pontoon and check with YC. Access to non-tidal basin HW−1½ to HW+1½. Le Crotoy Lt, Oc(2)R 6s 19m 9M, vis 285°-135°. Yacht harbour W side, Fl R 2s 4m 2M. E side Fl G 2s 4m 2M. Facilities: Hr Mr ☎ 22.27.81.59. # ☎ 22.27.50.36. **Quay** FW, C (3.5 ton); **YC Nautique de la Baie de Somme** ☎ 22.27.83.11, M, FW, Slip, Bar; **Marina Plaisance Baie de Somme** (280) ☎ 22.27.86.05, FW, CH, El, M, ME, Sh; **Nautique Côté d'Opale** ☎ 22.27.86.47 ME, El, Ⓔ, Sh, CH; **Town** Ⓑ, Bar, D, P, ✉, R, ⇌, V.

ÉTAPLES, Pas de Calais, 50°32′·00N, 01°38′·00E, Zone −0100, Admty chart 2451, SHOM 6795. HW 0000 on Dover (GMT), +0012 on Dieppe (zone −0100); HW height −0·3m on Dieppe; ML 4·8m; Duration 0520. See 10.19.25. Very good shelter but entry to R Canche should not be attempted in strong on-shore winds. Access HW∓2. Channel in river marked by posts between sunken training walls to Étaples, where shoal draft boats can lie afloat on pontoons at small marina just below the bridge. Alternatively yachts which can take the ground can dry out on sand opposite the YC at Le Touquet. Whole estuary dries. Camiers Lt Oc(2) WRG 6s 17m 9/6M. Facilities: Hr Mr ☎ 21.94.74.26; Aff Mar. ☎ 21.94.61.50. **Marina** (115+15 visitors), FW, C (3 ton), AC; **Quay** C (3 ton), FW, Slip; **Centre Nautique YC** ☎ 21.94.74.26. Bar, Slip; **Agence Nautique du Nord** ☎ 21.94.26.55. CH, El, Ⓔ, M, ME, Sh; **ETS Lamour** ☎ 21.94.61.21, D; **Town** Ⓑ, Bar, D, P, ✉, R, ⇌, V.

GRAVELINES, Nord, 51°01′·00N, 02°06′·00E, Zone −0100, Admty chart 323, SHOM 7057, 6651. HW +0045 on Dover (GMT), +0100 on Dieppe (zone −0100); HW height −2·8m on Dieppe; ML 3·1m; Duration 0520. See 10.19.27. Good shelter but bar dries; entry should not be attempted in strong on-shore winds. Entrance between Grand Fort Philippe and Petit Fort Philippe. Beware strong tidal stream across ent to the E, at HW. Safest entry HW−1. Keep to W entering and to E when inside. Yachts may take the bottom or go into the yacht harbour to W of town, available HW∓1. Harbour dries but is soft mud. E Jetty Lt Fl(3)R 12s 5m 4M. W jetty Fl(2)WG 6s 14m 9/6M; vis W317°-327°, G078°-085°, W085°-244°. Facilities: Aff Mar. ☎ 28.23.06.12. **Bassin Vaubin** ☎ 28.23.06.12, C (1.5 ton to 15 ton); **Yacht Club Gravelines** ☎ 28.23.14.68 M, C (10 ton); **MER (Marine et Reparations)** ☎ 28.23.14.68. CH, El, M, ME, Sh; **Town** Ⓑ, Bar, D, P, ✉, R, ⇌, V.

Area 20

Belgium and the Netherlands
Nieuwpoort to Delfzijl

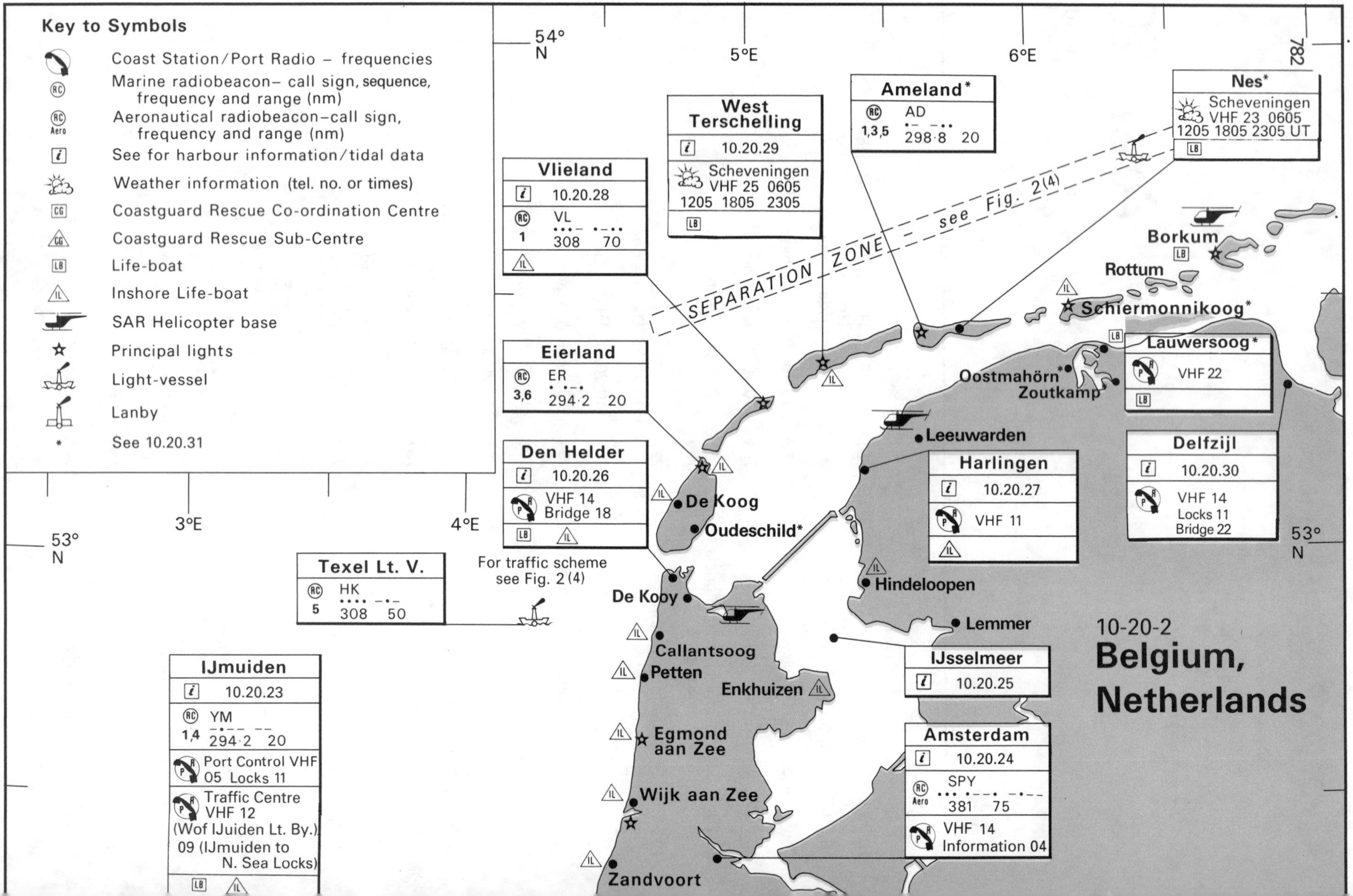

Key to Symbols
Coast Station/Port Radio – frequencies
Marine radiobeacon– call sign, sequence, frequency and range (nm)
Aeronautical radiobeacon–call sign, frequency and range (nm)
See for harbour information/tidal data
Weather information (tel. no. or times)
Coastguard Rescue Co-ordination Centre
Coastguard Rescue Sub-Centre
Life-boat
Inshore Life-boat
SAR Helicopter base
Principal lights
Light-vessel
Lanby
* See 10.20.31
54° N
5°E
6°E
3°E
4°E
53° N
Vlieland
10.20.28
VL
1 308 70
West Terschelling
10.20.29
Scheveningen VHF 25 0605 1205 1805 2305
Ameland*
AD
1,3,5 298·8 20
Nes*
Scheveningen VHF 23 0605 1205 1805 2305 UT
SEPARATION ZONE – see Fig. 2(4)
Borkum
Rottum
Schiermonnikoog*
Lauwersoog*
VHF 22
Oostmahörn*
Zoutkamp*
Eierland
ER
3,6 294·2 20
Den Helder
10.20.26
VHF 14 Bridge 18
Leeuwarden
Harlingen
10.20.27
VHF 11
Delfzijl
10.20.30
VHF 14 Locks 11 Bridge 22
De Koog
Oudeschild*
Texel Lt. V.
HK
5 308 50
For traffic scheme see Fig. 2 (4)
De Kooy
Hindeloopen
Lemmer
Callantsoog
Petten
Enkhuizen
IJsselmeer
10.20.25
IJmuiden
10.20.23
YM
1,4 294·2 20
Port Control VHF 05 Locks 11
Traffic Centre VHF 12 (W of IJuiden Lt. By.) 09 (IJmuiden to N. Sea Locks)
Egmond aan Zee
Wijk aan Zee
Zandvoort
Amsterdam
10.20.24
SPY
381 75
VHF 14 Information 04
10-20-2
Belgium, Netherlands

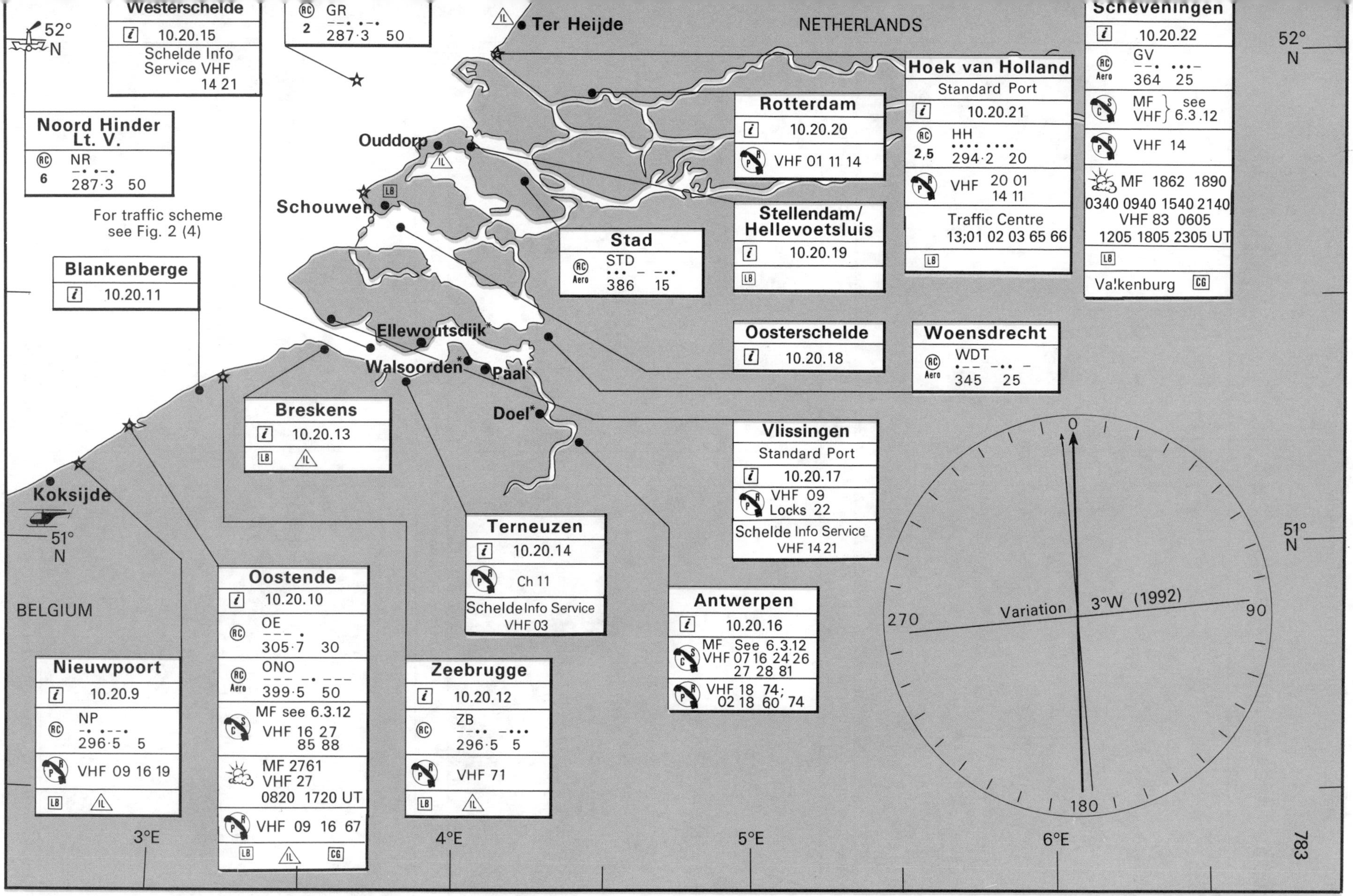
NETHERLANDS
BELGIUM
52° N
51° N
3°E
4°E
5°E
6°E
Ter Heijde
Ouddorp
Schouwen
Ellewoutsdijk*
Walsoorden*
Paal*
Doel*
Koksijde
Westerschelde
10.20.15
Schelde Info Service VHF 14 21
GR
2
287·3 50
Noord Hinder Lt. V.
NR
6
287·3 50
For traffic scheme see Fig. 2 (4)
Blankenberge
10.20.11
Breskens
10.20.13
Nieuwpoort
10.20.9
NP
296·5 5
VHF 09 16 19
Oostende
10.20.10
OE
305·7 30
ONO
399·5 50
MF see 6.3.12
VHF 16 27 85 88
MF 2761
VHF 27
0820 1720 UT
VHF 09 16 67
Zeebrugge
10.20.12
ZB
296·5 5
VHF 71
Terneuzen
10.20.14
Ch 11
Schelde Info Service VHF 03
Antwerpen
10.20.16
MF See 6.3.12
VHF 07 16 24 26 27 28 81
VHF 18 74; 02 18 60 74
Vlissingen
Standard Port
10.20.17
VHF 09
Locks 22
Schelde Info Service VHF 14 21
Oosterschelde
10.20.18
Woensdrecht
WDT
345 25
Stad
STD
386 15
Stellendam/ Hellevoetsluis
10.20.19
Rotterdam
10.20.20
VHF 01 11 14
Hoek van Holland
Standard Port
10.20.21
HH
2,5
294·2 20
VHF 20 01 14 11
Traffic Centre 13;01 02 03 65 66
Scheveningen
10.20.22
GV
364 25
MF VHF see 6.3.12
VHF 14
MF 1862 1890
0340 0940 1540 2140
VHF 83 0605
1205 1805 2305 UT
Valkenburg
Variation 3°W (1992)
0
90
180
270

10.20.3 AREA 20 TIDAL STREAMS

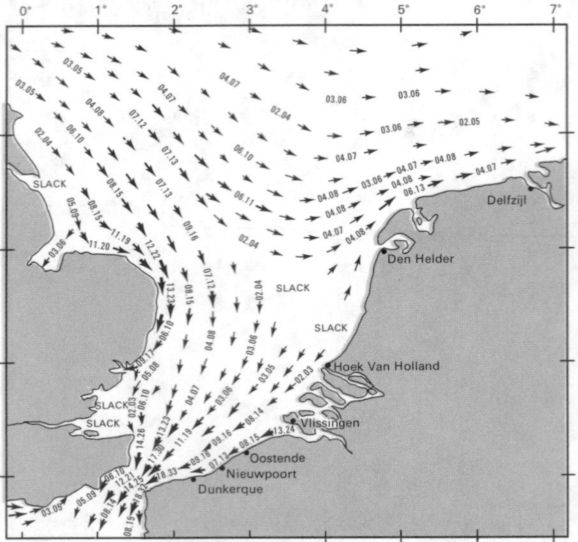
Den Helder
Delfzijl
Hoek Van Holland
Vlissingen
Oostende
Nieuwpoort
Dunkerque
SLACK

5 Hours before HW Dover (0420 after HW H van Holland)

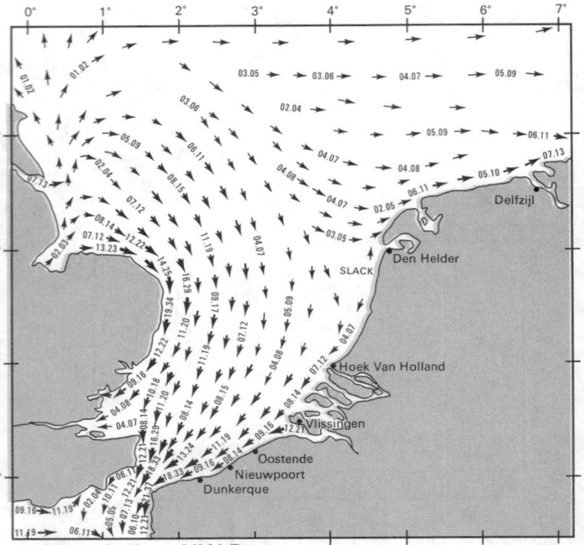
Den Helder
Delfzijl
Hoek Van Holland
Vlissingen
Oostende
Nieuwpoort
Dunkerque
SLACK

4 Hours before HW Dover (0520 after HW H van Holland)

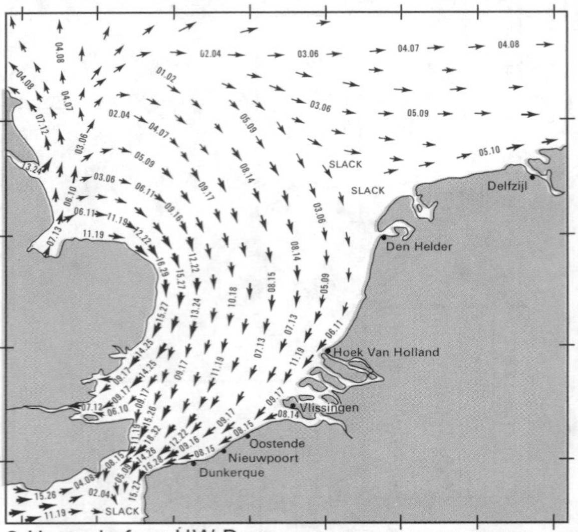
Den Helder
Delfzijl
Hoek Van Holland
Vlissingen
Oostende
Nieuwpoort
Dunkerque
SLACK

3 Hours before HW Dover (0605 before HW H van Holland)

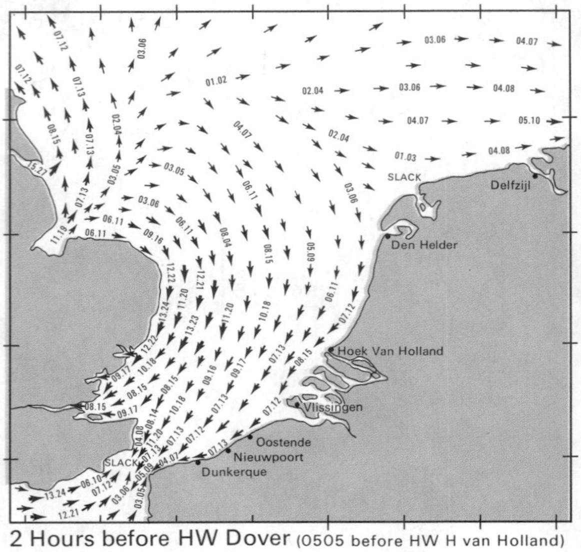
Den Helder
Delfzijl
Hoek Van Holland
Vlissingen
Oostende
Nieuwpoort
Dunkerque
SLACK

2 Hours before HW Dover (0505 before HW H van Holland)

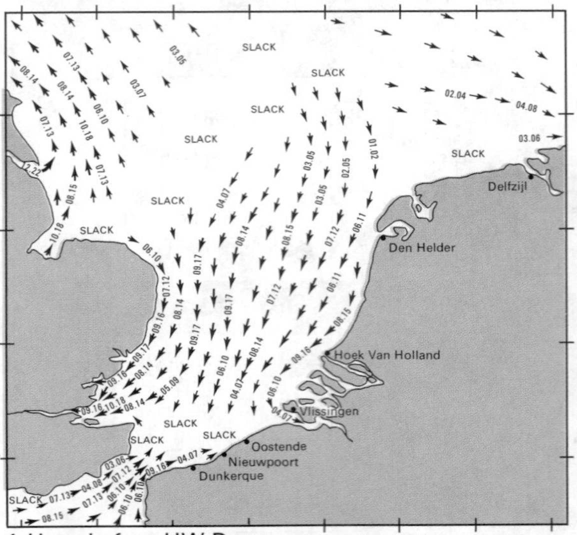
Den Helder
Delfzijl
Hoek Van Holland
Vlissingen
Oostende
Nieuwpoort
Dunkerque
SLACK

1 Hour before HW Dover (0405 before HW H van Holland)

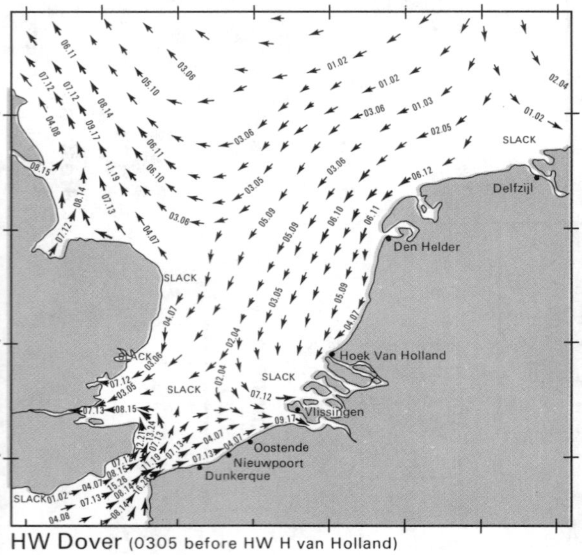
Den Helder
Delfzijl
Hoek Van Holland
Vlissingen
Oostende
Nieuwpoort
Dunkerque
SLACK

HW Dover (0305 before HW H van Holland)

North-eastward 10.21.3. North-westward 10.4.3.,10.5.3.

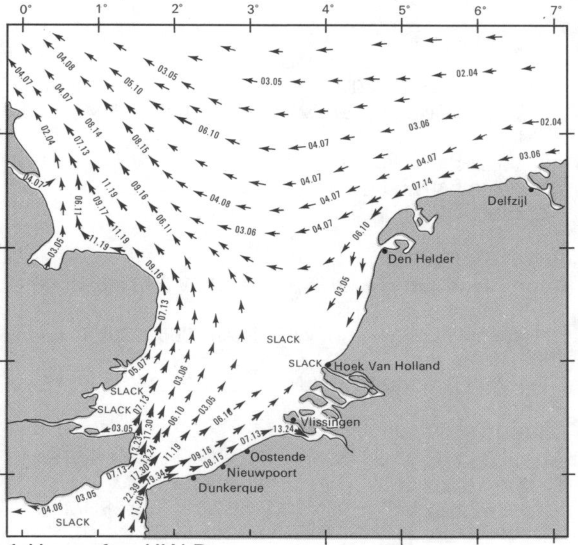
SLACK
Den Helder
Delfzijl
Hoek Van Holland
Vlissingen
Oostende
Nieuwpoort
Dunkerque

1 Hour after HW Dover (0205 before HW H van Holland)

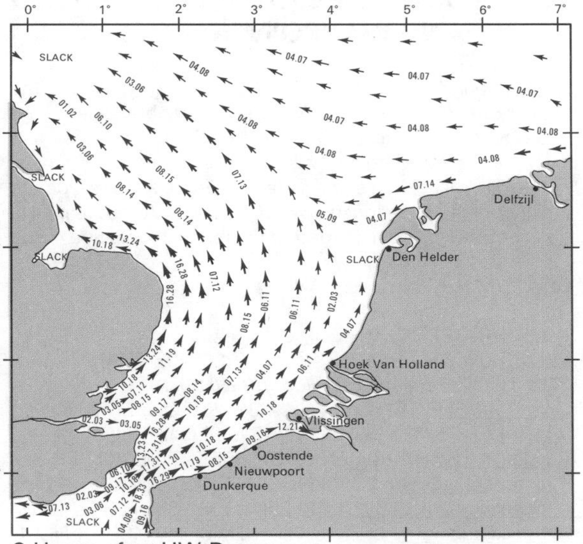
SLACK
Den Helder
Delfzijl
Hoek Van Holland
Vlissingen
Oostende
Nieuwpoort
Dunkerque

2 Hours after HW Dover (0105 before HW H van Holland)

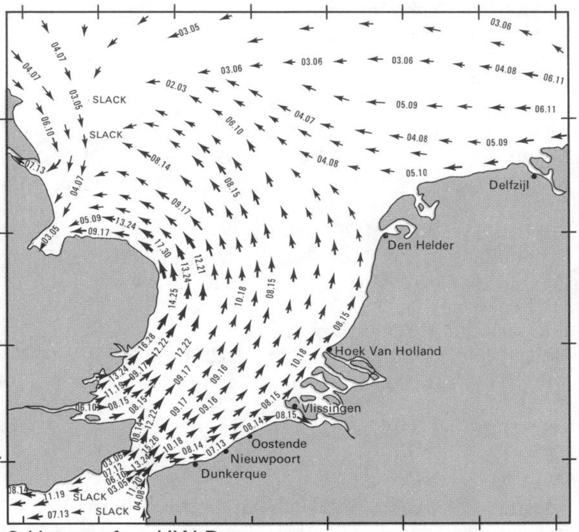
SLACK
Den Helder
Delfzijl
Hoek Van Holland
Vlissingen
Oostende
Nieuwpoort
Dunkerque

3 Hours after HW Dover (0005 before HW H van Holland)

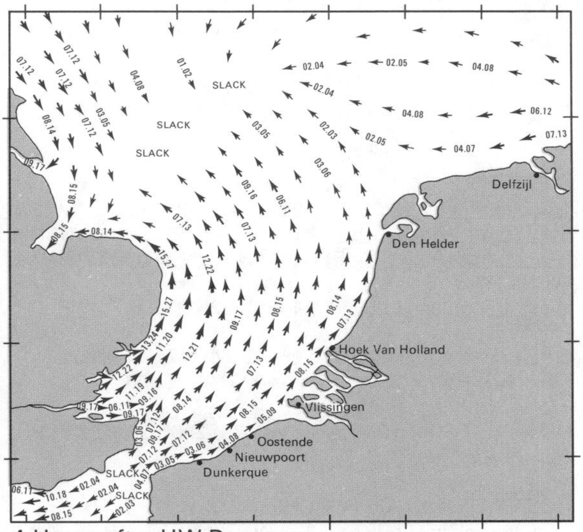
SLACK
Den Helder
Delfzijl
Hoek Van Holland
Vlissingen
Oostende
Nieuwpoort
Dunkerque

4 Hours after HW Dover (0055 after HW H van Holland)

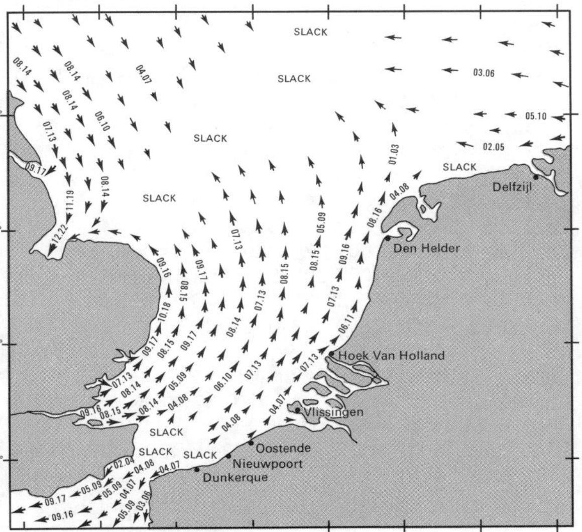
SLACK
Den Helder
Delfzijl
Hoek Van Holland
Vlissingen
Oostende
Nieuwpoort
Dunkerque

5 Hours after HW Dover (0155 after HW H van Holland)

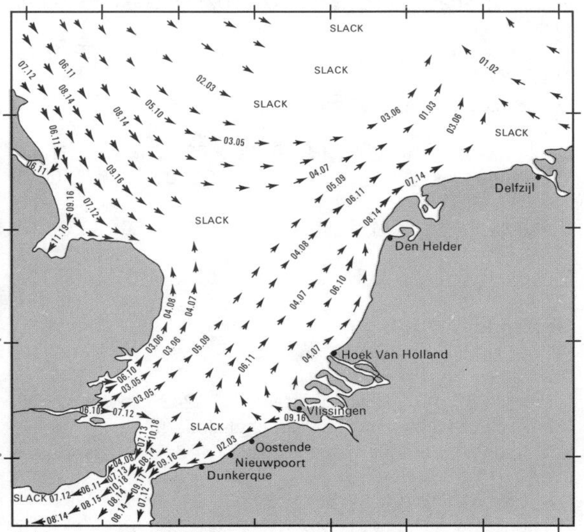
SLACK
Den Helder
Delfzijl
Hoek Van Holland
Vlissingen
Oostende
Nieuwpoort
Dunkerque

6 Hours after HW Dover (0255 after HW H van Holland)

10.20.4 COASTAL LIGHTS, FOG SIGNALS AND WAYPOINTS

Abbreviations used below are given in 1.4.1. Principal lights are in **bold** print, places in CAPITALS, and light-vessels, light floats and Lanbys in *CAPITAL ITALICS*. Unless otherwise stated lights are white. m—elevation in metres; M—nominal range in n. miles. Fog signals are in *italics*. Useful waypoints are underlined – use those on land with care. All geographical positions should be assumed to be approximate. See 4.2.2.

BELGIUM AND NETHERLANDS

WEST HINDER TO SCHEUR CHANNEL.
WEST HINDER LT V 51°23'·08N 02°26'·40E Fl (4) 30s 14m **17M**; R hull, 2 masts; RC; *Horn Mo(U) 30s.*
Oost-Dyck Lt By 51°21'·55N 02°31'·20E QG; SHM; *Whis* .
A-Zuid Lt By 51°21'·50N 02°37'·00E Fl (3)G 10s; SHM.
A-Noord Lt By 51°23'·50N 02°37'·00E Fl (4) R 20s; PHM.
Kwintebank Lt By 51°21'·75N 02°43'·00E Q; NCM; *Whis.*
Middelkirkebank Lt By 51°18'·25N 02°42'·80E Fl G 5s; SHM.
Middelkirkebank N Lt By 51°20'·87N 02°46'·40E Q; NCM.
Akkaert SW Lt By 51°22'·30N 02°46'·40E Q (9) 15s; WCM; *Whis* .
Midden Akkaert Lt By 51°24'·23N 02°53'·50E VQ (3) 5s; ECM.
Scheur 1 Lt By 51°23'·18N 03°00'·15E Fl G 5s; SHM.
Goote Bank Lt By 51°27'·00N 02°52'·70E Q (3)10s; ECM; *Whis.*

NIEUWPOORT AND APPROACHES.
Trapegeer Lt By 51°08'·45N 02°34'·45E Fl G 10s; SHM; *Bell*
Den Oever Wreck Lt By 51°09'·20N 02°39'·50E Q; NCM.
Nieuwpoortbank Lt By 51°10'·21N 02°36'·16E Q (9) 15s; WCM; *Whis.*
Weststroombank Lt By 51°11'·39N 02°43'·15E Fl (4) R 20s; PHM.
E Pier near root Fl (2) R 14s 26m **21M**; R Tr, W bands.
E Pier Hd FR 11m 10M; W Tr; vis 025°-250°, 307°-347°; H*orn Mo(K) 30s.*
W Pier Hd FG 11m 9M; W Tr; vis 025°-250°, 284°-324°; RC; *Bell (2) 10s.*

OOSTENDE AND APPROACHES.
Zuidstroombank Lt By 51°12'·33N 02°47'·50E Fl R 5s; PHM.
Middelkirkebank S Lt By 51°14'·78N 02°42'·00E Q (9) R 15s; PHM.
Oostendebank West Lt By 51°16'·25N 02°44'·85E Q (9) 15s; WCM; *Whis.*
Oostendebank Oost Lt By 51°17'·36N 02°52'·00E Fl (4) R 20s; PHM.
Nautica Ena Wreck Lt By 51°18'·12N 02°52'·85E Q; NCM.
Wenduinebank West Lt By 51°17'·30N 02°52'·87E Q (9) 15s; WCM; *Whis.*
Buitenstroombank Lt By 51°15'·20N 02°51'·80E Q; NCM; *Whis.*
Binnenstroombank Lt By 51°14'·50N 02°53'·73E Q (3) 10s; ECM.
Oostende Fl (3) 10s 63m **27M**; W Tr; obsc 069°-071°; RC.
W Pier Hd 51°14'·36N 02°55'·12E FG 12m 10M; W col; vis 057°-327°; Be*ll (1) 4s.*
E Pier Hd FR 13m 12M; W Tr; vis 333°-243°; *Horn Mo(OE) 30s.* QY Lt at signal mast when chnl closed.
Ldg Lts 128°, both FR 4M on W framework Trs, R bands; vis 051°-201°.
A1 Lt By 51°21'·70N 02°58'·10E L Fl 10s; SWM; *Whis.*
Oostendebank Noord Lt By 51°21'·25N 02°53'·00E Q; NCM; *Whis.*

A1 bis Lt By 51°21'·70N 02°58'·10E L Fl 10s; SWM; *Whis.*
SW Wandelaar Lt By 51°22'·00N 03°01'·00E Fl (4) R 20s; PHM.
Wenduine Bank N Lt By 51°21'·50N 03°02'·70E QG; SHM.
Wenduine Bank E Lt By 51°18'·85N 03°01'·70E QR; PHM.
A2 Lt By 51°22'·50N 03°07'·05E Iso 8s; SWM; *Whis.*

BLANKENBERGE.
Comte Jean Jetty Oc (2) 8s 30m **20M**; W Tr, B top; vis 065°-245°.
W Mole Hd FG 14m 11M; W Tr; intens 065°-290°, unintens 290°-335°.
E Pier Hd FR 12m 11M; W Tr; vis 290°-245°; *Bell (2) 15s.*

SCHEUR CHANNEL.
Scheur 2 Lt By 51°23'·38N 02°58'·20E Fl (4) R 15s; PHM.
Scheur 3 Lt By 51°24'·35N 03°02'·90E Q; NCM; *Whis.*
Scheur 4 Lt By 51°25'·05N 03°03'·10E Fl R 5s; PHM.
Scheur 5 Lt By 51°23'·73N 03°05'·90E Fl G 5s; SHM.
Scheur 6 Lt By 51°24'·25N 03°05'·90E Fl (4) R 20s; PHM.
Droogte van Schooneveld 51°25'·50N 03°09'·00E Fl (5) Y 20s 12m 2M; measuring Bn with platform; Ra refl.
Scheur 7 Lt By 51°24'·00N 03°10'·50E Fl G 5s; SHM.
Scheur 8 Lt By 51°24'·45N 03°10'·45E Fl R 5s; PHM.
Scheur 9 Lt By 51°24'·45N 03°15'·05E QG; SHM.
Scheur 10 Lt By 51°24'·90N 03°15'·05E Fl (4) R 15s; PHM.
Scheur 12 Lt By 51°24'·70N 03°18'·50E Fl R 5s; PHM.
Scheur- Wielingen Lt By 51°24'·26N 03°18'·00E Q; NCM.

ZEEBRUGGE AND APPROACHES.
Scheur-Zand Lt By 51°23'·70N 03°07'·68E Q (3) 10s; ECM.
Zand Lt By 51°22'·50N 03°10'·12E QG; SHM.
W Breakwater Oc G 7s 31m 7M.
E Breakwater Oc R 7s 31m 7M.
Heist, Mole Hd Oc WR 15s 22m , **R20M**; Gy Tr; vis W068°-145°, R145°-212°, W212°-296°; RC; Ho*rn (3+1) 90s.*

WESTERSCHELDE

WIELINGEN CHANNEL.
Wielingen Zand Lt By 51°22'·60N 03°10'·80E Q (9) 15s; WCM.
Bol van Heist Lt By 51°23'·15N 03°12'·05E Q (6) +LFIR 15s; PHM.
MOW3 Tide Gauge 51°23'·45N 03°12'·00E Fl (5) Y 20s; SPM; *Whis*; Racon.
Wielingen Lt By 51°23'·00N 03°14'·10E Fl (3) G 15s; SHM.
W1 Lt By 51°23'·50N 03°18'·00E Fl G 5s; SHM.
W2 Lt By 51°24'·64N 03°21'·58E Iso R 8s; PHM.
W3 Lt By 51°24'·03N 03°21'·58E Iso G 8s; SHM.
W4 Lt By 51°24'·92N 03°24'·48E L Fl R 5s; PHM.
W5 Lt By 51°24'·33N 03°24'·48E L Fl G 5s; SHM.
W6 Lt By 51°25'·15N 03°27'·25E L Fl R 8s; PHM.
W7 Lt By 51°24'·65N 03°27'·30E L Fl G 8s; SHM.
W8 Lt By 51°25'·48N 03°30'·15E L Fl R 5s; PHM.
W9 Lt By 51°24'·97N 03°30'·13E L Fl G 5s; SHM.
W10 Lt By 51°25'·80N 03°33'·00E QR; PHM.

Wave observation post 51°22'·84N 03°22'·82E Fl (5) Y 20s.
Kruishoofd 51°23'·73N 03°28'·36E Iso WRG 8s 14m W8M, R6M, G5M; W ■ Tr, B post; vis R074°-091°, W091°-100°, G100°-118°, W118°-153°, R153°-179°, W179°-198°, G198°-205°, W205°-074°.

<u>Nieuwe Sluis</u>, on embankment 51°24'·49N 03°30'·33E *Horn (3) 30s*. 51°24'·48N 03°31'·38E Oc WRG 10s 27m W14M, R11M, G10M; B 8-sided Tr, W bands; vis R055°-084°, W084°-091°, G091°-132°, W132°-238°, G238°-244°, W244°-258°, G258°-264°, R264°-292°, W292°-055°.

APPROACHES TO BRESKENS.
<u>Songa Lt By</u> 51°25'·34N 03°34'·78E QG; SHM.
<u>SS-VH Lt By</u> 51°24'·75N 03°34'·00E Q; NCM.

BRESKENS FERRY HARBOUR.
W Mole Hd 51°24'·40N 03°33'·23E FG 8m 4M; B & W mast; in fog FY; Ra refl; Fog Det Lt.
E Mole Hd FR 8m 5M; B & W mast; in fog FY.

BRESKENS.
<u>W Mole Hd</u> 51°24'·09N 03°34'·12E F WRG 6m; Gy mast; vis vis R090°-128°, W128°-157°, R157°-172°, W172°-175°, G175°-296°, W296°-300°, R300°-008°, G008°-090°; in fog FY; *Horn Mo(U) 30s*.
E Mole Hd FR 5m; Ra refl.

WESTKAPELLE TO VLISSINGEN.
Noorderhoofd Ldg Lts 149°, NW Hd of dyke. Front, 0·73M from rear Oc WRG 10s 18m W13M, R10M, G10M; R Tr, W band; vis R353°-008°, G008°-029°, W029°-169°.
Westkapelle, Common rear Fl 3s 48m **28M**; Tr, R top; obsc on certain brgs.
Zoutelande Ldg Lts 326°, Front 1·8M from rear FR 21m 12M; R ■ Tr; vis 321°-352°.
<u>Molenhoofd</u> 51°31'·61N 03°26'·07E Oc WRG 6s 9m; W mast R bands; vis R306°-328°, W328°-347°, R347°-008°, G008°-031°, W031°-035°, G035°-140°, W140°-169°, R169°-198°.
Kaapduinen, Ldg Lts 130°. Front 51°28'·5N 03°31'·0E Oc 5s 26m 13M; Y ■ Tr, R bands; vis 115°-145°. Rear 220m from front Oc 5s 36m 13M; Y ■ Tr, R bands; synchronised with front; vis 108°-152°.
<u>Fort de Nolle</u> 51°27'·00N 03°33'·20E Fl WRG 2·5s 11m W6M, R4M, G4M; W column, R bands; vis R293°-309°, W309°-333°, G333°-351°, R351°-013°, G013°-062°, R062°-086°, W086°-093°, G093°-110°, W110°-130°.

VLISSINGEN.
Ldg Lts 117°. Leugenaar causeway, front Oc R 5s 5m 7M; W&R pile; intens 108°-126°. Sardijngeul, rear 550m from front Oc WRG 5s 8m W12M, R9M, G8M; R ▲ with W bands on R and W mast; synchronised; vis R245°-271°, G271°-285°, W285°-123°, R123°-147°.
Koopmanshaven, <u>W Mole root</u> 51°26'·40N 03°34'·58E Iso WRG 3s 15m W12M, R10M, G9M; R pylon; vis R253°-270°, W270°-059°, G059°-071°, W071°-077°, R077°-101°, G101°-110°, W110°-114°.
E Mole Hd FG 7m
Buitenhaven E Mole Hd FG 4M; Gy mast on post; in fog FY.
<u>Buitenhaven, W Mole Hd</u> 51°26'·44N 03°36'·12E Iso WRG 4s 10m 5M; B mast; vis W072°-021°, G021°-042°, W042°-056°, R056°-072°; tfc sigs; Horn 15*s*.

<u>Schone Waardin</u> 51°26'·60N 0337'·95E Oc WRG 9s 10m W13M, R10M, G9M; R mast, W bands; vis R248°-260°, G260°-270°, W270°-282°, G282°-325°, W325°-341°, G341°-023°, W023°-024°, G024°-054°, R054°-066°, W066°-076°, G076°-094°, W094°-248°.

VLISSINGEN OOST.
W Mole Hd FR 8m 5M; W col; in fog FY; Ho*rn (2) 20s*.
E Mole Hd FG 8m 4M; W col.
Ldg Lts 023°. Front Oc R 8s 7m 8M; G post. Rear 100m from front Oc R 8s 12m 8M; G mast; synchronised with front, both vis 015°-031°.
Flushing E Hbr 51°27'·93N 03°40'·62E Dir F WRG; vis 303·5°-304·9°. W304·9°-305·1°, G305·1°-306·5°.

BORSSELE-NOORDNOL.
<u>Pier Hd</u> 51°25'·55N 03°42'·80E Oc WRG 5s; 9m; R mast, W bands; vis R305°-331°, W331°-341°, G341°-000°, W000°-007°, R007°-023°, G023°-054°, W054°-057°, G057°-113°, W113°-128°, R128°-155°, W155°-305°.
FR on chimney 0·4M NNE.
Borssele, <u>Total Jetty NW end</u> 51°24'·85N 03°43'·61E Oc WR 10s; vis R135°-160°, W160°-135°.
<u>Borssele-Everingen</u> 51°24'·73N 03°44'·20E Iso WRG 4s 9m; W structure, R band; vis R021°-026°, G026°-080°, W080°-100°, R100°-137°, W137°-293°, R293°-308°, W308°-344°, G344°-357°, W357°-021°.

ELLEWOUTSDIJK.
<u>W Pier Hd</u> (unlit) 51°23'·14N 03°49'·12E.

BRAAKMANHAVEN.
Ldg Lts 191°. Front 51°20'·3N 03°45'·8E Iso 4s 10m; B pile, W bands. Rear, 60m from front, Iso 4s 14m; B pile, W bands; synchronised with front, showing over hbr mouth.
Ldg Lts 211°, both Oc G 4s, synchronised, showing middle of turning basin.
W side 51°21'·0N 03°45'·9E FG; G pile, W bands; Ra refl.
E side 51°21'·1N 03°46'·3E FR; R mast, W bands; Ra refl, tfc signals.
<u>Braakman</u> 51°21'·03N 03°46'·31E Oc WRG 8s 7m W7M, R5M, G4M; B pedestal, W band; vis R116°-132°, W132°-140°, G140°-202°, W202°-116°.

TERNEUZEN.
Nieuw Neuzenpolder Ldg Lts 125°. Front Oc 5s 5m 13/9M; W col, B bands; intens 117°-133°. Rear 365m from front Oc 5s 16m 13/9M; B&W Tr; synchronised with front; intens 117°-133°.
Dow Chemical jetty, 4 dolphins showing Fl 3s and Fl R 3s; *Horn 15s*.
Veerhaven W jetty Oc WRG 5s 13m W9M, R7M, G6M; B and W Tr; vis R092°-115°, W115°-238°, G238°-248°, W248°-277°, R277°-309°, W309°-003°.
<u>W Mole Hd</u> 51°20'·62N 03°49'·7E FG 6m; Gy mast; in fog FY.
E Mole Hd FR 7m; Tfc signals.

HOEDEKENSKERKE.
<u>De Val</u> 51°25'·20N 03°55'·08E Iso WRG 2s 5m W8M, R5M, G4M; R Tr, W band; vis R008°-034°, W034°-201°, R201°-206°, W206°-209°, G209°-329°, W328°-008°.

HANSWEERT.
<u>W Mole Hd</u> 51°26'·45N 04°00'·50E Oc WRG 10s 9m W9M, R7M, G6M; R Tr, W band; vis R288°-310°, W310°-334°, G334°-356·5°, W356·5°-044°, R044°-061·5°, W061·5°-073°, G073°-089°, R089°-101·5°, G101·5°-109°, W109°-114·5°, R114·5°-127·5°W127·5°-288°; in fog FY; also Iso R 4s SS(traffic).
E side Pier Hd FG 6m; Gy col; Horn (4) 30*s*.

WALSOORDEN.
Ent N Mole Hd FG 5m; Gy col; in fog FY.
Ent S <u>Mole Hd</u> 51°22'·96N 04°02'·18E FR 5m; Gy col.

PAAL APPROACHES.
Speelmansgat Lt Bn 51°22'·03N 04°06'·26E Fl (5) Y 20s.

ZANDVLIET.
Ldg Lts 118°. Front 51°20'·70N 04°16'·40E Oc WRG 5s 11m W9M, R7M, G6M; vis R shore-350°, W350°-017°, G017°-019°, W019°-088°, G088°-109°, W109°-125°, R125°-shore. Rear, 200m from front, Oc 5s 18m 9M.

DOEL.
Ldg Lts 185·5°. Front 51°18'·5N 04°16'·2E Fl WRG 3s 5m W9M, R7M, G6M; vis R shore-175°, W175°-202°, G202°-304°, W304°-330°, R330°-shore. Rear, 260m from front, Fl 3s 14m 9M; synchronised with front.
Jetty Hd 51°18'·72N 04°16'·18E Oc WR 5s 9m W9M, R7M; Y ■, B stripes on Tr; vis R downstream-185°, W185°-334°, R334°-upstream shore.

LILLO.
Pier SE end 58°18'·20N 04°17'·28E Oc WRG 10s 5m W9M, R7M, G6M; R n, W band on B Bn; vis R shore-304°, W304°-322°, G322°-099°, W099°-148°, R148°-shore. **(TE 1989).**

ANTWERPEN.

OOSTERSCHELDE.

OUTER APPROACHES.
Wave observation post VR 51°30'·35N 03°14'·53E Fl Y 5s
SW Thornton Lt By 51°31'·01N 02°51'·00E Iso 8s; SWM.
Thornton Bank B Lt By 51°34'·45N 02°59'·15E Q; NCM.
Westpit Lt By 51°33'·70N 03°10'·00E Iso 8s; SWM.
Rabsbank Lt By 51°38'30N 03°10'·05E Iso 4s; SWM.
Middelbank Lt By 51°40'·90N 03°18'·30E Iso 8s; SWM.
Schouwenbank Lt By 51°45'·00N 03°14'·40E Mo (A) 8s; SWM; Racon.
Buitenbank Lt By 51°51'·20N 03°25'·80E Iso 4s; SWM.

WESTGAT/OUDE ROOMPOT (selected marks).
WG1 Lt By 51°38'·05N 03°26'·30E QG; SHM.
WG Lt By 51°38'·25N 03°28'·90E Q; NCM.
WG4 Lt By 51°38'·60N 03°28'·80E Iso R 8s; PHM.
Wave observation post OS11 51°38'·63N 03°28'·95E Fl Y 5s; Y pile.
WG7 Lt By 51°39'·45N 03°32'·75E Iso G 4s; SHM.
WG 8/OR Lt By 51°39'·75N 03°32'·60E VQ (6) + LFl 10s; SCM.
OR2 Lt By 51°39'·48N 03°33'·70E L Fl R 8s; PHM.
OR5 Lt By 51°38'·60N 03°35'·60E QG; SHM.
OR11 Lt By 51°37'·05N 03°38·40E Iso G 2s; SHM.
OR12 Lt By 51°37'·35N 03°39'·30E Iso R 2s; PHM.
Roompotsluis Ldg Lts 073°. Front Oc G 5s. Rear, 280m from front, Oc G 5s; synchronised.
N Breakwater Hd FR 6m; *Horn(2) 30s.*
S Breakwater Hd FG 6m.
Inner Mole Hd QR.

COLIJNSPLAAT.
E Jetty Hd 51°36'·25N 03°51'·15E FR 3m 3M; *Horn.*
W Jetty Hd FG 5m 3M.
Zeeland Bridge. N and S passages marked by FY Lts, 14m.

KATS.
N Jetty Hd FG 5m 5M.
S Jetty Hd 51°34'·44N 03°53'·72E Oc WRG 8s 5m 5M; vis W344°-153°, R153°-165°, G165°-200°, W200°-214°, G214°-258°, W258°-260°, G260°-313°, W313°-331°.

SAS VAN GOES.
S Mole Hd 51°32'·34N 03°55'·95E FR.
N Mole Hd FG.

WEMELDINGE.
W Jetty Hd 51°31'·34N 04°00'·25E Oc WRG 5s 7m W9M, R7M, G6M; B mast, W band; vis R shore-116°, W116°-123°, G123°-151°, W151°-153°, R153°-262°, W262°-266°, R266°-shore; in fog Oc Y 4s; tfc signals.
EJetty Hd FR; Horn*(4) 30s.*

YERSEKE.
Ldg Lts 155° (through Schaar van Yerseke). Front Iso 4s 8m; in fog FY. Rear, 180m from front, Iso 4s 13m; synchronised; in fog 2FY. FG and FR mark mole Hds.

Tholensche Gat. Strijenham 51°31'·40N 04°08'·91E Oc WRG 5s 9m W8M, R5M, G5M; R n, W bands, on mast; vis W shore-298°, R298°-320°, W320°-052°, G052°-069°, W069°-085°, R085°-095°, W095°-shore.
Gorishoek'51°31'·57N 04°04'·68E Iso WRG 8s 7m W6M, R4M, G4M; R pedestal, W bands; vis R260°-278°, W278°-021°, G021°-025°, W025°- 071°, G071°-085°, W085°-103°, R103°-120°, W120°-260°.

STAVENISSE.
E Mole Hd 51°35'·73N 04°00'·35E Oc WRG 5s 10m W12M, R9M, G8M; B pylon; W075°-090°, R090°-105·5°, W105·5°-108°, G108°-118·5°, W118·5°-124°, G124°-155°, W155°-158°, G158°-231°, W231°-238·5°, R238·5°-253°, W253°-350°.

ST ANNALAND.
Entrance W side 51°36'·32N 04°06'·60E FG.
E side FR.

ZIJPE. ANNA JACOBAPOLDER.
N Mole Hd Iso G 4s.
St Philipsland, on dyke Oc WRG 4s 9m W8M, R5M, G4M; pylon on B ● col; vis W051°-100°, R100°-144°, W144°-146°, G146°-173°.
Zijpsche Bout Oc WRG 10s 9m W12M, R9M, G8M; mast on R col; vis R208°-211°, W211°-025°, G025°-030°, W030°-040°, R040°-066°.
Tramweghaven S mole Iso R 4s 7m; Gy Bn.
N Mole FG.
Stoofpolder Iso WRG 4s 10m W12M, R9M, G8M; B Tr, W bands; vis W147°-154°, R154°-226·5°, G226·5°-243°, W243°-253°, G253°-259°, W259°-263°, G263°-270°, R270°-283°, W283°-008°.
Hoek Van Ouwerkerk 51°36'·92N 03°58'·27E Iso WRG 6s; vis R268°-305°, W305°-313°, G313°-008°, W008°-011°, G011°-059°, W059°-065°, R065°-088°, W088°-098°, G098°-112°, R112°-125°, W125°-268°.

DE VAL.
Engelsche Vaarwater Ldg Lts 019°. Front 51°37'·74N 03°55'·60E Iso WRG 3s 7m W6M, R4M, G4M; R pedestal, W band; vis R290°-306°, W306°-317°, G317°-334°, W334°-336°, G336°-017°, W017°-026°, G026°-090°, R090°-108°, W108°-290°. Rear, 300m from front, Iso 3s 15m 6M; R ■ on W mast, R bands.

ZIERIKZEE.
W Jetty Hd 51°37'·95N 03°53'·45E Oc WRG 6s 10m W6M, R4M, G4M; R pedestal, W band; vis G060°-107°, W107°-133°, R133°-156°, W156°-278°, R278°-304°, G304°-314°, W314°-331°, R331°-354°, W354°-060°.
W Mole Hd FR.
E Mole Hd FG.

FLAUWERSPOLDER.
W Mole Hd 51°40'·70N 03°50'·86E Iso WRG 4s 7m W6M, R4M, G4M; W daymark, B band on pylon; vis R303°-344°, W344°-347°, G347°-083°, W083°-086°, G086°-103°, W103°-110°, R110°-128°, W128°-303°.

HAMMEN.
E Breakwater Hd 51°41'·28N 03°48'·79E Fl (2) 10s 8m.

BURGHSLUIS,
S mole Hd 51°40'·59N 03°45'·56E F WRG 9m W8M, R5M, G4M; mast on R col; vis W218°-230°, R230°-245°, W245°-253·5°, G253·5°-293°, W293°-000°, G000°-025·5°, W025·5°-032°, G032°-041°, R041°-070°, W070°-095°.

APPROACHES TO EUROPOORT
West Schouwen 51°42'·58N 03°41'·60E Fl (2+1)15s 57m **30M**; Gy Tr, R diagonal stripes on upper part.
Verklikker 51°43'·58N 03°42'·39E F WR 13m W9M, R7M; Tr with R lantern; vis R115°-127°, W127°-169°, R169°-175°, W175°-115°.
Wave observation posts.
OS13 51°44'·00N 03°33'·40E Fl Y 5s; Y pile.
OS14 51°43'·30N 03°40'·60E Fl Y 5s; Y pile.
BG2 51°46'·10N 03°37'·20E Fl Y 5s; Y pile.
BG5 51°49'·50N 03°45'·70E Fl Y 5s; Y pile.
Ha10 51°51'·80N 03°51'·70E Fl Y 5s; Y pile.

Buitenbank Lt By 51°51'·20N 03°25'·80E Iso 4s; SWM.

Westhoofd 51°48'·83N 03°51'·90E Fl (3) 15s 55m **30M**; R ■ Tr.
Kwade Hock 51°50'·3N 03°59'·1E Iso WRG 4s 8m W12M, R9M, G8M; B mast, W bands; vis W 235°-068°, R068°-088°, G088°-108°, W108°-111°, R111°-142°, W142°-228°, R228°-235°. FR on radio mast 4·2M NE.
Slijkgat SG Lt By 51°52'·00N 03°51'·50E Iso 4s; SWM.
Hinder Lt By 51°54'·60N 03°55'·50E Q (9) 15s; WCM.

HARINGVLIET.
Heliushaven, W Jetty 51°49'·3N 04°07'·2E FR 7m 4M.
E Jetty FG 7m 3M; *Horn (3) 20s.*

HELLEVOETSLUIS.
51 49'·2N 04°07'·7E Iso WRG 10s 16m W11M, R8M, G7M; W Tr, R cupola; vis G shore-275°, W275°-294°, R294°-316°, W316°-036°, G036°-058°, W058°-095°, R095°-shore.
W Mole Hd FR 6m.
E Mole Hd FG 6m; in fog FY.
Hoornsche Hoofden, watchhouse on dyke, 51°48'·3N 04°11'·0E Oc WRG 5s 7m W7M, R5M, G4M; vis W288°-297°, G297°-313°, W313°-325°, R325°-335°, G335°-345°, W345°-045°, G045°-055°, W055°-131°, R131°-shore.

MIDDELHARNIS.
W Pier Hd F WRG 5m W8M, R5M, G4M; vis W144°-164°, R164°-176°, G176°-144°.
E Pier Hd FR 5m 5M; in fog FY.

Nieuwendijk. Ldg Lts 303°. Front 51°45'·1N 04°19'·5E Iso WRG 6s 8m W9M, R7M, G6M; B framework Tr; vis G093°-100°, W100°-103°, R103°-113°, W113°-093°. Rear, 450m from front F 11m 9M; B framework Tr.

VOLKERAK.
Noorder Voorhaven. W Mole Hd 51°42'·08N 04°25'·88E FG 6m 4M; R lantern on pedestal; in fog FY.

NOORD HINDER LT V 52°00'·15N 02° 51'·20E Fl (2) 10s 16m **27M**; R hull, W upperworks; RC; Racon; *Horn(2) 30s.*
Euro Platform 51°59'·9N 03°16'·6E Mo (U) 15s; W structure, R bands; helicopter platform; *Horn Mo(U) 30s.*
Goeree 51°55'·53N 03°40'·18E Fl(4) 20s 31m **28M**; R and W chequered Tr on platform; RC; helicopter platform; Racon; *Horn (4) 30s.*
Adriana Lt By 51°56'·13N 03°50'·65E VQ (9)10s; WCM.
Maas Center Lt By 52°01'·18N 03°53'·57E Iso 4s; SWM; Racon.
Indusbank N Lt By 52°02'·92N 04°03'·73E Q; NCM.

HOEK VAN HOLLAND.
Maasvlakte 51°58'·2N 04°00'·9E Fl(5) 20s 66m **28M**; B 8-sided Tr, Y bands.
Nieuwe Noorderdam Hd 51°59'·71N 04°02'·92E FR 24m 10M; Y Tr, B bands; Helicopter platform; in fog Al Fl WR 6s, vis 278°-255°.
Nieuwe Zuiderdam Hd 51°59'·19N 04°02'·58E FG 24m 10M; Y Tr, B bands; Helicopter platform; in fog Al Fl WG 6s, vis 330°-307°; *Horn 10s.*
Maasmond Ldg Lts 112° for very deep draught vessels. Front 51°58'·9N 04°04'·9E Iso 4s 29m 21M; W Tr, B bands; vis 101°-123°. **Rear**, 0.6M from front Iso 4s 46m **21M**; W Tr, B bands; synchronised with front. Ldg Lts 107° for other vessels. **Front** 51°58'·6N 04°07'·6E Iso R 6s 29m **18M**; R Tr, W bands; vis 100°-115°. **Rear** 450m from front Iso R 6s 43m **18M**; vis 100°-115°, synchronised.

EUROPOORT.
Calandkanaal Entrance Ldg Lts 116°. **Front** Oc G 6s 29m ; W Tr, R bands; vis 108°-124°, synchronised with **Rear** Lt 550m from front Oc G 6s 43m **16M**; W Tr, R bands; vis 108°-124°.
R Lts on Chimney 1·63M SW.
Beerkanaal Ldg Lts 192°. Front Iso G 3s. Rear, 50m from front, Iso G 3s.

SCHEVENINGEN.
SCH Lt By 52°07'·80N 04°14'·20E Iso 4s; SWM.
Scheveningen 52°06'·3N 04°16'·2E Fl (2) 10s 48m **29M**; brown Tr; vis 014°-244°.
Ldg Lts 156°. Front Iso 4s 17m 14M. Rear 100m from front Iso 4s 21m 14M; synchronised with front.
SW Mole Hd 52°06'·28N 04°15'·22E FG 11m 9M; B 6-sided Tr, Y bands, R lantern; *Horn (3) 30s.*
NE Mole Hd FR 11m 9M; B 6-sided Tr, Y bands, R lantern.

Noordwijk-aan-Zee 52°15'·00N 04°26'·10E Oc (3) 20s 32m **18M**; W ■ Tr.
Survey platform 52°16'·4N 04°17'·9E FR and Mo (U) 15s; *Horn Mo(U) 20s.*

IJMUIDEN.
IJmuiden Lt By (IJM) 52°28'·50N 04°23'·87E Mo (A) 8s; SWM; Racon. (also known as Verkenningston).
Ldg Lts 100°. **Front** F WR 30m **W16M**, R13M; dark R Tr; vis W050°-122°, R122°-145°, W145°-160°; RC. **Rear** 560m from front Fl 5s 52m **29M**; dark R Tr; vis 019°-199°.

S Breakwater Hd 52°27'·86N 04°32'·00E FG 15m 10M; in fog Fl 3s, *Horn (2) 30s.*
N Breakwater Hd FR 14m 10M.
N Pier Hd QR 11m 9M; vis 263°-096°; in fog FW.
S Pier Hd QG 11m 9M; vis 096°-295°; in fog FW.

NOORDZEE KANAL.
Ø Km mark 52°27'·86N 04°35'·64E.
20 Km mark 52°25'·21N 04°51'·94E

AMSTERDAM.
Yacht Hbr 52°23'·02N 04°53'·77E F & FR.

IJMUIDEN TO TEXEL.

Egmond-aan-Zee 52°37'·20N 04°37'·40E Iso WR 10s 36m **W18M**, R14M; W Tr; vis W010°-175°, R175°-188°. FR Lts on chy 10·2M N.

ZEEGAT VAN TEXEL.
TEXEL LT V. 52°47'·10N 04°06'·60E Fl (3+1) 20s 16m **26M**; R hull, W band; RC; Racon; *Horn (3) 30s.* During maintenance replaced by RW By Oc 10s; Racon.
ZH (Zuider Haaks) Lt By 52°54'·70N 04°34'·84E VQ (6) + LFl 10s; SCM.
MR (Middelrug) Lt By 52°56'·80N 04°33'·90E Q (9) 15s; WCM.
NH (Noorder Haaks) Lt By 53°00'·30N 04°35'·45E VQ; NCM.
Grote Kaap Oc WRG 10s 31m W11M, R8M, G8M; vis G041°-088°, W088°-094°, R094°-131°.
Schulpengat. Ldg Lts 026°. **Front** 53°00'·9N 04°44'·5E Iso 4s **18M**; vis 024°-028°. Rear, **Den Hoorn** 0·83M from front Oc 8s **18M**; church spire; vis 024°-028°.
Huisduinen 52°57'·20N 04°43'·37E F WR 27m W14M, R11M; ■ Tr; vis W070°-113°, R113°-158°, W158°-208°.
Kijkduin, Rear 52°57'·35N 04°43'·60E Fl (4) 20s 56m **30M**; brown Tr; vis except where obsc by dunes on Texel.
Ldg Lt 253° with Den Helder, Harssens Is (QG).

SCHULPENGAT.
SG Lt By 52°52'·95N 04°38'·00E Mo(A) 8s; SWM.
S1 Lt By 52°53'·74N 04°39'·25E Iso G 4s; SHM.
S2 Lt By 52°54'·05N 04°38'·20E Iso R 4s; PHM.
S3 Lt By 52°54'·60N 04°39'·80E Iso G 8s; SHM.
S4 Lt By 52°54'·70N 04°39'·30E Iso R 8s; PHM.
S5 Lt By 52°55'·40N 04°40'·30E Iso G 4s; SHM.
S6 Lt By 52°55'·50N 04°39'·95E Iso R 4s; PHM.
S7 Lt By 52°56'·20N 04°40'·80E Iso G 8s; SHM.
S6A Lt By 52°56'·55N 04°40'·50E QR; PHM.
S8 By 52°57'·10N 04°41'·14E (unlit); PHM.
S9 By 52°56'·90N 04°42'·15E (unlit); SHM.
S10 Lt By 52°57'·65N 04°41'·65E Iso R 8s; PHM.
S11 Lt By 52°57'·60N 04°43'·35E Iso G 4s; SHM.

MOLENGAT.
MG Lt By 53°03'·42N 04°39·10E Mo (A) 8s; SWM.
MG1 Lt By 53°02'·05N 04°41'·46E Iso G 8s; SHM.
MG2 Lt By 53°02'·18N 04°41'·87E Iso R 8s; PHM.
MG6 Lt By 53°01'·08N 04°41'·83E Iso R 4s; PHM.
MG5 Lt By 53°01'·08N 04°41'·52E Iso G 4s; SHM.
MG9 Lt By 53°00'·07N 04°41'·50E QG; SHM.
MG10 Lt By 53°00'·13N 04°41'·83E Iso R 8s; PHM.
MG13 Lt By 52°59'·17N 04°42'·30E Iso G 8s; SHM.
MG16 Lt By 52°59'·10N 04°42'·37E QR 4s; PHM.
MG 18 Lt By 52°58'·67N 04°43'·70E Iso R 4s; PHM.
S14/MG17 Lt By 52°58'·42N 04°43'·40E VQ (6) + L Fl 10s; SCM.

MARSDIEP.
DEN HELDER.
Marinehaven, W Breakwater Hd (Harssens Is) 52°58'·00N 04°46'·84E QG 12m 8M; *Horn 20s.*
MH6, E side of ent, QR 9m 4M; R pile; Ra refl.
Ent W side, Fl G 5s 9m 4M; vis 180°-067° (H24).
Ent E side, QR 9m 4M; (H24).
Ldg Lts 191°. Front Oc G 5s 15m 14M; B s on bldg; vis 161°-221°. Rear, 275m from front, Oc G 5s 25m 14M; B ▲ on bldg; vis 161°-247°, synchronised.

Schilbolsnol 53°00'·6N 04°45'·8E F WRG 27m **W15M**, R12M, G11M; G Tr; vis W338°-002°, G002°-035°, W035°-038° (leading sector for Schulpengat), R038°-051°, W051°-068°.

MOK.
Mok 53°00'·25N 04°46'·85E Oc WRG 10s 10m W10M, R7M, G6M; vis R229°-317°, W317°-337°, G337°-112°.
Ldg Lts 284°30'. Front Iso 2s 7m 6M. Rear, 245m from front, Iso 8s 10m 6M; both vis 224°-344°.

WADDENZEE.
Malzwin KM/RA1 52°58'·70N 04°49'·46E Fl (5) Y 20s; post.
Malzwin M5 52°58'·3N 04°49'·9E Iso G 4s; G pile; Ra refl.
Wierbalg W3A 52°58'·1N 04°57'·1E QG; G pile.
Pile 01 52°57'·0N 05°00'·6E Iso G 8s; G pile.
Pile 05 52°56'·9N 05°01'·9E Iso G 4s; G pile.

DEN OEVER.
Ldg Lts 132°. Front and rear both Oc 10s 7M; vis 127°-137°.
Detached Breakwater N Hd, L Fl R 10s.
Stevinsluizen, E wall, Iso WRG 5s 15m W10, R7, G7; vis G226°-231°, W231°-235°, R235°-290°, G290°-327°, W327°-335°, R335°-345°.
W wall, 80m from Hd, Iso WRG 2s; vis G195°-213°, W213°-227°, R227°-245°.

TEXELSTROOM.
T5/MH2 Lt By 52°58'·38N 04°47'·80E Fl (2+1) G 12s; preferred chan to port.
T11/GvS2 Lt By 52°59'·95N 04°49'·20E Fl (2+1) G 12s; preferred chan to port.
T17 Lt By 53°01'·20N 04°51'50E Iso G 8s; SHM.
T14 Lt By 53°02'·27N 04°51'·50E Iso R 8s; PHM. Note: Bys being renumbered.

OUDESCHILD.
S Mole Hd 53°02'·37N 04°51'·26E FR 7m; *Horn (2) 30s* (sounded 0600-2300).
N Mole Hd FG.
Oc 6s 7m Lt seen between FR and FG leads into hbr.
T23 Lt By 53°03'·45N 04°55'·70E Fl G 4s; SHM.

DOOVE BALG.
D4 53°02'·7N 05°04'·1E Iso R 8s; R pile; Ra refl.
D3A/J2 53°02'·1N 05°07'·0E Fl (2+1) G 12s; G post, R band.
D14 53°02'·5N 05°09'·2E Iso R 4s; R pile; Ra refl.
D11 53°02'9N 05°12'·0E Iso G 8s; G pile; Ra refl.

KORNWERDERZAND.
W side, 53°04'·0N 05°17'·6E Iso R 4s 9m 4M; Gy pedestal, R lantern; vis 049°-229°.
Buitenhaven, W Mole Hd FG 9m 7M; *Horn Mo(N) 30s.*
E Mole Hd FR.
Spuihaven Noord, W Mole Hd LFIG 10s 7m 7M.

BOONTJES/APPROACHES TO HARLINGEN.
BO11/K2/2 53°05'·0N 05°20'·3E Q; NCM.
BO28 53°07'·9N 05°22'·6E Iso R 8s; R pile.
BO34 53°08'·9N 05°23'·0E Iso R 2s; R pile.
BO39 53°10'·0N 05°23'·4E Iso G 4s; G pile.
BO40 53°10'·0N 05°23'·3E Iso R 4s; R pile.

TEXEL TO TERSCHELLING.
Eierland N Pt of Texel 53°10'·97N 04°51'·40E Fl (2) 10s 52m **29M**; R Tr; RC.
Tide gauge 53°11'·33N 04°48'05E Fl (5) Y 20s 5M.
Off Vlieland TSS. *VL CENTER LANBY* 53°27'·00N 04°40'·00E Fl 5s; Racon; *Horn(2) 30s.*
Oost Vlieland 53°17'·8N 05°03'·6E Iso 4s 53m **20M**; brown Tr; RC.

TERSCHELLING.
VSM Lt By 53°19'·05N 04°55'·73E Iso 4s; SWM.
TG Lt By 53°24'·22N 05°02'·40E Q (9) 15s; WCM.
A Otto Lt By 53°24'·68N 05°06'·50E VQ (3) 5s; ECM.

APPROACH TO WADDENZEE.

ZUIDER STORTEMELK (selected marks)
ZS-bank Lt By 53°18'·85N 04°57'·95E VQ; NCM.
ZS1 Lt By 53°18'·75N 04°59'·56E Fl G 5s; SHM.
ZS13/VS2 Lt By 53°18'·80N 05°05'·93E Fl (2+1) G 12s; preferred chan to port.
ZS14 Lt By 53°19'·00N 05°05'·55E L Fl R 8s; PHM.
ZS15 Lt By 53°18'·97N 05°07'·10E L Fl G 5s; SHM.
ZS18 Lt By 53°19'·36N 05°06'·95E L FlR 5s; PHM.

WEST TERSCHELLING.
Brandaris Tr 53°21'·67N 05°12'·99E Fl 5s 55m **29M**; Y ■ Tr; vis except where obsc by dunes on Vlieland and Terschelling.
Ldg Lts 053°, W harbour mole Hd, front 53°21'·3N 05°13'·1E FR 5m W8M, R5M; R post, W bands, vis W049°-055°, R055°-252°, W252°-263°, R263°-049°; *Horn 15s 3* ***(TD 1989)***. **Rear**, on dyke, 1·1M from front Iso 5s 14m **19M**; vis 045°-061°, intens 045°-052°.
E Pier Hd FG 5m 4M.

VLIELAND.
E Mole Hd 53°17'·73N 05°05'·59E FG

WADDENZEE.
VLIESTROOM (selected marks).
VL1 Lt By 53°19'·00N 05°08'·80E QG; SHM.
VL2/SG1 Lt By 53°19'·30N 05°09'·80E Fl (2+1) R 12s; preferred chan to stbd.
VL5 Lt By 53°18'·60N 05°09'·55E L Fl G 8s; SHM.
VL6 Lt By 53°18'·60N 05°11'·00E L Fl R 8s; PHM.
VL9 Lt By 53°17'·65N 05°10'·10E Iso G 4s; SHM.
VL12/WM1 Lt By 53°17'·20N 05°11'·25E VQ (9) 10s; WCM.
VL14 Lt By 53°15'·90N 05°10'·72E L Fl R 8s; PHM.
VL15 Lt By 53°16·05N 05°09'·80E L Fl G 8s; SHM.

APPROACH TO HARLINGEN.

BLAUWE SLENK (selected marks).
BS1/IN2 Lt By 53°14'·74N 05°10'·05E Fl 2+1) G 12s; preferred chan to port.
BS2 Lt By 53°14.70N 05°10'·20E QR; PHM.
BS3 Lt By 53°14'·40N 05°10'·20E L Fl G 5s; SHM.
BS4 Lt By 53°14'·50N 05°10'·40E L Fl R 5s; PHM.
BS7 Lt By 53°13'·85N 05°11'·45E L Fl G 8s; SHM.
BS8 Lt By 53°14'·05N 05°11'·54E L Fl R 8s; PHM.
BS11 Lt By 53°13'·63N 05°13'·30E Iso G 4s; SHM.
BS12 Lt By 53°13'·80N 05°13'·30E Iso R 4s; PHM.
BS19 Lt By 53°13'·40N 05°17'·00E QG; SHM.
BS20 Lt By 53°13'·55N 05°17'·10E QR; PHM.
BS27 Lt By 53°11'·95N 05°18'·25E QG; SHM.
BS28 Lt By 53°12'·10N 05°18'·42E QR; PHM.
BS31 Bn 53°11'·60N 05°19'·70E L Fl G 8s; G pile, SHM.
BS32 Lt By 53°11'·72N 05°19'·75E L Fl R 8s; PHM.

POLLENDAM.
SHM's: P1 Fl G 2s; P3 Iso G 4s; P5 Fl G 2s.
PHM's: P2 Fl R 2s 7m; P4 Iso R 4s 7m; P6 Fl R 2s 7m;
BS54 Bn 53°10'·80N 05°23'·50E VQ R; R pile, PHM.

HARLINGEN.
Ldg Lts 112°. Front 53°10°·56N 05°24'·42E Iso 6s 8m 4M; vis 097°-127°; and FG 9m 7 Rear 500m from front Iso 6s 19m 13M; both on B masts, W bands; vis 104·5°-119·5° (H24).
N Mole Hd 53°10'·57N 05°24'·42E Iso R 5s 8m 4M; R pedestal.
S Mole Hd ; *Horn(3) 30s.*

TERSCHELLING TO AMELAND.
TS Lt By 53°28'·20N 05°21'·60E VQ; NCM.

AMELAND
Ameland, W end 53°27'·02N 05°37'·60E Fl (3) 15s 57m **30M**; brown Tr, W bands; RC.

NES.
Niewue Veerdam Mole Hd 53°26'·02N 05°46'·53E Iso 6s 2m 8M

AMELAND TO SCHIERMONNICOOG.
BR Lt By 53°30'·75N 05°33'·60E Q Fl; NCM.
AM Lt By 53°31'·00N 05°44'·80E VQ; NCM.
NAM 21 Lt By 53°31'·18N 05°55'·50E Fl Y.
WRG Lt By 53°32'·78N 06°01'·75E Q; NCM.
VWG Lt By 53°32'·27N 06°05'·57E Iso 8s; SWM.
Schiermonnikoog 53°29'·20N 06°08'·90E Fl (4) 20s 43m **28M**; ● Tr, dark R Tr. F WR 28m W15M, R12M; (same Tr) F WR **W15M** R12M; vis W210°-221°, R221°-230°.

SCHIERMONNIKOOG.
Ferry Pier Hd 53°28'·17N 06°12'·21E 2 Fl (5) Y 20s.

LAUWERSOOG.
E Mole Hd 53°24'·72N 06°12'·14E FR 4M.
W Mole Hd FG 3M; in fog FY; *Horn (2) 30s.*

OOSTMAHORN.
Ent 53°23'·00N 06°09'·72E FG

ZOUTKAMP.
Ent (unlit) 53°20'·42N 06°17'·66E.

(For Die Ems see 10.21.4).

10.20.5 PASSAGE INFORMATION

CROSSING SOUTHERN NORTH SEA (charts 1610, 1872)

From Crouch, Blackwater or Orwell the first stage is to make Long Sand Head Lt By — from Crouch via Whitaker chan and East Swin; from Blackwater via the Wallet and N of Gunfleet Bn to Wallet No 2 Lt By; and from Orwell via Roughs Tower and Sunk Lt F. From Long Sand Head Lt By proceed to Gallop Lt By and thence to W Hinder Lt V, crossing the TSS at right angles. Care must be taken throughout with tidal streams, which may be setting across the yacht's track. The area is relatively shallow, and in bad weather seas are steep and short.

BELGIUM (chart1872)

Features of this coast are the long shoals lying roughly parallel to it. Mostly the deeper, buoyed chans run within 3M of shore, where the outer shoals give some protection in strong onshore winds. Approaching from seaward it is essential to fix position from one of the many marks, so that the required chan is identified before shoal water is reached. Shipping is another hazard, but it helps to identify the main routes.

From the W, the natural entry to the buoyed chans is at Dunkerque Lanby: from the Thames, bound for Oostende (10.20.10) or the Schelde (10.20.15), identify W Hinder Lt V, or the N Hinder Lt V if bound from the N. ForTraffic Schemes see Fig. 2(3) and 2(4). *North Sea Harbours and Pilotage* (Adlard Coles Nautical) is recommended for the coast of Belgium and of the Netherlands to Den Helder.

Off the Belgian coast the E-going stream begins at HW Vlissingen –0320 (HW Dover –0120), and the W-going at HW Vlissingen +0240 (HW Dover +0440), sp rates 2 kn. Mostly the streams run parallel with the coast. Nieuwpoort lies 8M from the French border. From the W (Dunkerque), approach through Passe de Zuydcoote (buoyed with least depth 3·3m) and West Diep. From ENE app through Kleine Rede, the inner road off Oostende which carries a depth of 6m. There are other apprs through the chans and over the banks offshore, but they need care in bad weather.

Off Oostende the E-going stream begins at HW Vlissingen –0245 (HW Dover –0045), sp rate 2·5 kn; the W-going stream begins at HW Vlissingen +0245 (HW Dover +0445), sp rate 1·5 kn. So sailing E from Oostende, leave about HW Vlissingen –0300 to catch the E-going stream. If bound for Blankenberge (10.20.11) it is only necessary to keep a mile or two offshore, but if heading E of Zeebrugge (10.20.12) it is advisable to clear the new hbr extension by 1M or more. The main route to Zeebrugge for commercial shipping is through Scheur (the deep water chan of the Westerschelde) as far as Scheur-Zand Lt By, about 3M NW of hbr ent. There is much commercial traffic, and yachts should keep clear (S of) the buoyed chan so far as possible. Beware strong tidal stream and possibly dangerous seas in approaches to Zeebrugge.

NETHERLANDS (charts 325, 110, 2322)

The main approach chans to Westerschelde are Wielingen and Oostgat, but yachts are required to keep clear of these. Coming from Zeebrugge keep close to S side of estuary until past Breskens (10.20.13) when, if proceeding to Vlissingen (10.20.17), cross close W of By H-SS. From N, use Deurloo/ Spleet chans to S side of estuary. The tide runs hard in the estuary, causing a bad sea in chans and overfalls on some banks in strong winds. Vessels under 20m must give way to larger craft; and yachts under 12m are requested to stay clear of main buoyed chan, and any buoyed chan between Walsoorden and Antwerpen (10.20.16) if navigation permits.

The final stages of the barrage across the Oosterschelde (10.20.18 & chart 192) are now completed, and entry must be made through Roompotsluis in the S part of the barrage. Several banks (e.g. Schaar, Schouwenbank, Middelbank, Steenbank) lie in the W approaches to Oosterschelde, and the main channel runs through Westgat and Oude Roompot, which are well marked. Oude Roompot would also be used if appr from the N.

Coming from the S, Oostgat runs close to the Walcheren shore. Westkapelle Lt Ho is conspic near the W end of Walcheren. There are two lesser Lts nearby – Molenhoofd 0·5M WSW and Noorderhoofd 0·75M NNW. Having passed the latter the coast runs NE past Domburg but becomes shallower as Roompot is approached, so it is necessary to keep near the Roompot chan which here is marked by Bys (unlit). It is important to have updated information on the buoyage and the chans.

From here to Hoek van Holland (10.20.21) banks extend 7M W of Schouwen and WSW of Goeree. Shipping is very concentrated at the ent to Europoort and Rotterdam (10.20.20). Traffic schemes must be noted and regulations for yachts (see 10.20.21) obeyed.

The coast N to Den Helder (10.20.26) is low, and not easily visible from seaward, like most of the Dutch coast. Conspic landmarks include Noordwijk aan Zee Lt, chys of steelworks N of IJmuiden, Egmond aan Zee Lt, and chys of nuclear power station 1·5M NNE of Petten. For TrafficSchemes see Figs. 2(3)-2(4). 3M W of IJmuiden (10.20.23) the N-going stream begins at HW Hoek van Holland –0120, and the S-going at HW Hoek van Holland +0430, sp rates about 1·5 kn. Off ent to IJmuiden the stream turns about 1h earlier and is stronger, and in heavy weather there may be a dangerous sea.

THE DUTCH FRISIAN ISLANDS (charts 2593)

N from Den Helder (10.20.26), and then running E for nearly 150M along the N coasts of Netherlands and Germany, is the chain of Frisian Is. The Dutch Is are in general larger and further offshore, but the great majority of Frisian Is have similar characteristics – being low, long and narrow, with the major axis parallel to the coast.

Between the Is, narrow chans (zeegat in Dutch, seegat in German) give access to/from the North Sea. Most of these chans are shallow for at least part of their length, and in these shoal areas a dangerous sea builds up in strong winds between W and N on the outgoing (ebb) tide. In onshore winds there are occasions when safe entry is possible on the flood tide, but departure is dangerous.

The flood stream along this coast is E-going, so it starts to run in through the zeegaten progressively from W to E. Where the tide meets behind each Is, as it flows in first at the W end and a little later at the E end, is formed a bank called a wad (Dutch) or watt (German). These banks between the Is and the coast are major obstacles to E/W progress inside the Is. The chans are narrow and winding, marked by Bys or by withies in the shallower parts, and they mostly dry – so that it is essential to time the tide correctly.

This is an area most suited to shallow-draught yachts, particularly with bilge keels or centreboards, that can take the ground easily. While the main zeegaten are described very briefly below, no attempt has been made to mention the many chans inside the Is. Reference should be made to *Frisian Pilot* (Adlard Coles Nautical).

While British Admiralty charts are adequate for through passages, coastal navigation, and entry to the main ports, Dutch charts are essential for any yacht exploring the cruising grounds along this coast or using the smaller hbrs. In non-tidal waters chart datum usually refers to the level at which the water is kept. In the Netherlands this may be Kanaalpeil, which in turn is related to Normaal Amsterdams Peil (NAP), which is about Mean Sea Level (MSL). In the North Sea shoal waters are liable to change due to gales and tidal streams. Changes in sea level due to special meteorological conditions may also be encountered.

It should be realised that there are numerous wrecks and obstructions which lie offshore and in coastal areas. Some of these are marked, but many are not. The Texel Traffic Scheme extends NNE from the Texel Lt V – see Fig.2(4): the separation zone incorporates the Helder gas field. Some 20–30M N lie the Placid and Petroland fields with production platforms. For general notes on N Sea oil and gas installations see 10.5.5.

TEXEL TO TERSCHELLING

Zeegat van Texel (chart 191) lies between Den Helder and the Is of Texel, and gives access to the Waddenzee, the tidal part of the former Zuider Zee. Haaksgronden shoals extend 5M seaward, with three chans: Schulpengat on S side, leading into Breewijd; Westgat through centre of shoals, where the stream sets across the chan but suitable for passage in good weather and in daylight; and Molengat near the Texel shore. Schulpengat is the main chan, and is well marked, Bys being prefixed with letter 'S'; but strong SW winds cause rough sea against the SW-going (ebb) stream which begins at HW Helgoland –0330, while the NE-going (flood) stream begins at HW Helgoland +0325, sp rates 1·5 kn. In Molengat the NW-going (ebb) stream begins at HW Helgoland –0145, and the SE-going (flood) stream at HW Helgoland +0425, sp rates 1·25 kn. Molengat is marked by Bys prefixed by letters 'MG', but strong winds between W and N cause a bad sea, and in such conditions Schulpengat should be used.

E of Zeegat van Texel the flood stream runs in three main directions: to E and SE through Malzwin, Wierbalg and Den Oever (where there is a lock into IJsselmeer), NE along the Afsluitdijk, and then N towards Harlingen (10.20.27); to NE and E through Texelstroom, Doove Balg towards the Pollen flats; and to NE through Texelstroom, Scheurrak, Omdraai and Oude Vlie, where it meets the flood stream from Zeegat van Terschelling. The ebb stream runs the other way. The locks at Kornwerderzand, near NE end of Afsluitdijk, also give access to the IJsselmeer (10.20.25). For Oudeschild see 10.20.31.

Eierlandsche Gat, between Texel and Vlieland, is a dangerous unmarked chan, only used by fishermen.

Zeegat van Terschelling (chart 112) is the chan between Vlieland (10.20.28) and Terschelling, leading to the harbs of Oost Vlieland, West Terschelling (10.20.29) and Harlingen (10.20.27), and also to the locks at Kornwerderzand. Terschellinger Gronden are shallow banks extending more than 3M seaward; the main chan (buoyed) through them is Zuider Stortemelk passing close N of Vlieland. In this chan the Bys are prefixed by letters 'ZS', and the E-going (flood) stream begins at HW Helogland +0325, while the W-going (ebb) stream begins at HW Helgoland –0230, sp rates 2·5 kn. Zuider Stortemelk leads into Vliesloot, and thence to Oost Vlieland where there is a yacht hbr, and on to Vliestroom. Vliestroom is a deep, well buoyed chan (By numbers prefixed by letters 'VL') which runs S about 4M until its junction with Blauwe Slenk and Inschot. The latter leads to Kornwerderzand and the IJsselmeer, while Blauwe Slenk runs SE to Harlingen. At the N end of Vliestroom, Schuitengat is a buoyed chan leading to W Terschelling.

Other chans through Terschellinger Gronden are, from W to E: Stortemelk, Thomas Smit Gat and Noordgat. The first two are unmarked, and are dangerous with an ebb tide and strong wind from W or N.

AMELAND TO BORKUM

Zeegat van Ameland is the chan between Terschelling and Ameland, fronted by the sandbank of Bornrif extending 3M seaward. Westgat is the main entrance, with buoys prefixed by letters 'WG'. In Westgat the flood stream begins at HW Helgoland +0425, and the ebb stream at HW Helgoland –0150, sp rates 2 kn. The chan runs close to the Terschelling shore: a dangerous sea develops in strong onshore winds. For Ameland see 10.20.31.

Between Ameland and Schiermonnikoog (10.20.31) is Friesche Zeegat, with the main chan also called Westgat and Bys also marked 'WG'. In strong winds the sea breaks across the whole passage. Westgat leads SE through Wierumer Gronden, and then past Engelsmanplaat (a prominent sandbank in mid-chan) into Zoutkamperlaag which is the main chan (marked by Bys prefixed 'Z') to Lauwersoog (10.20.31), where locks give access to the inland waterways.

Going E, the next main chan through the Is is Westerems (chart 3509), which runs SW of the German island of Borkum (10.21.10) and leads to Delfzijl (10.20.30) and Emden (10.21.23). Hubertgat, which runs S of the main Westerems chan, is more useful when bound to or from the W, but in both these chans there is a dangerous sea on the ebb stream in strong NW winds. The E-going (flood) stream begins at HW Helgoland +0530, and the W-going (ebb) stream begins at HW Helgoland –0030, sp rates 1·5 kn.

10.20.6 DISTANCE TABLE

Approximate distances in nautical miles are by the most direct route while avoiding dangers and allowing for traffic separation schemes etc. Places in *italics* are in adjoining areas.

1 *North Foreland*	**1**																			
2 *Dunkerque*	40	**2**																		
3 *Burnham-on-Crouch*	36	75	**3**																	
4 *Great Yarmouth*	77	101	76	**4**																
5 *Grimsby*	169	194	168	94	**5**															
6 Oostende	58	26	91	93	194	**6**														
7 Breskens	80	54	103	101	191	28	**7**													
8 Vlissingen	82	56	104	101	191	30	3	**8**												
9 Goeree Tower	91	73	108	83	169	51	40	40	**9**											
10 IJmuiden	137	119	151	102	182	97	86	86	46	**10**										
11 Amsterdam	150	132	164	115	195	110	99	99	59	13	**11**									
12 Den Helder	171	153	169	115	180	131	120	120	80	38	51	**12**								
13 West Terschelling	187	185	196	135	193	163	152	152	112	70	83	39	**13**							
14 Westerems Lt Buoy	226	224	235	174	232	202	191	191	151	109	122	78	47	**14**						
15 Delzijl	263	261	272	211	269	239	228	228	188	146	159	115	84	33	**15**					
16 *Norderney*	259	257	268	207	265	235	224	224	184	142	155	111	80	34	41	**16**				
17 *Wangerooge*	283	281	292	231	289	259	248	248	208	166	179	135	104	58	65	29	**17**			
18 *Wilhelmshaven*	307	305	316	255	313	283	272	272	232	190	203	159	128	82	89	53	27	**18**		
19 *Helgoland*	300	298	309	241	285	276	265	265	225	183	196	152	121	68	81	44	24	43	**19**	
20 *Brunsbüttel*	337	336	342	287	332	314	303	303	263	221	234	190	159	113	120	84	55	70	51	**20**

SPECIAL FACTORS AFFECTING BELGIUM AND THE NETHERLANDS 10-20-7

BELGIUM

TIME ZONE is −0100, which is allowed for in tidal predictions but no provision is made for daylight saving schemes which are indicated by the non-shaded areas on the tide tables (see 9.1.2).

SIGNALS International Port Traffic Signals (see colour plate 8) are shown at Nieuwpoort, Oostende and Zeebrugge. Small craft warnings (shown when wind from seaward is Force 4 or over) remain in force at Nieuwpoort, Oostende, Blankenberge and Zeebrugge as follows: –
By day: two black cones, points together
By night: blue flashing light.

CHARTS The chart most widely used is the 'Vlaamse Banken' issued by the Hydrografische Dienst der Kust. Admiralty, Stanford and Imray chart numbers are quoted.

PROVINCES In place of 'counties' in the UK, Provinces are given for Belgian ports.

MARINE RESCUE CO-ORDINATION CENTRES Sea Rescue Co- ordination Centre, Oostende, Tel. 70.10.00, 70.11.00, 70.77.01 or 70.77.02. Coast station, Oostende Radio Tel. 70.24.38.
In emergency Tel. 900, or call *Oostende Radio* VHF Ch 16. For medical advice call *Radiomédical Oostende* on Ch 16.

PUBLIC HOLIDAYS New Year's Day, Easter Monday, Labour Day (1 May), Ascension Day, Whit Monday, National Day (21 July), Feast of the Assumption (15 August), All Saints' Day (1 November), Armistice Day (11 November), King's Birthday or Fete de la Dynastie (15 November), Christmas Day.

TELEPHONE To call UK from Belgium, dial 00 (pause for new tone to be heard) 44. Then dial the full UK area code but omitting the prefix 0, followed by the number required. To call Belgium from UK, dial 010-32 followed by the code and number.
Emergencies Police – dial 101
Fire – dial 100

NOTE 1: Although the Hr Mr's tel no is given for Belgian ports, he is not the key figure for yachtsmen that he is in British ports. Berths and moorings are always administered by the local yacht clubs. British yachtsmen are very welcome in Belgian ports and YCs.
NOTE 2: Belgian harbour police are very strict about yachts using their engines entering harbour. If sails are used as well, display a black cone. Yachts may not navigate within 200m of shore (MLWS).
NOTE 3: Ports of entry are Nieuwpoort, Oostende and Zeebrugge.
NOTE 4: Further information can be obtained from The Belgian National Tourist Office, 38 Dover St., London, W1X 3RB, Tel. 071 499 5379 or Federation Royale Belge du Yachting, FRYB/KBJV, PB No 241 Boechontlaan, 1020 Brussels, Belgium.

NETHERLANDS

TIME ZONE is −0100, which is allowed for in tidal predictions but no provision is made for daylight saving schemes which are indicated by the non-shaded areas (see 9.1.2).

SIGNALS Traffic signals The standard French/Belgian system is not used in the Netherlands. Where possible the local system is given.
Sluicing signals In the Netherlands the following sluicing signals may be shown:
By day: A blue board, with the word 'SPUIEN' on it, often in addition to the night signal, of three red lights in a triangle, point up.
Visual storm signals Light signals only, shown day and night, in accordance with the International System (see 10.14.7) are shown at the following harbours: Vlissingen, Hoek van Holland, Amsterdam, IJmuiden, Den Helder, West Terschelling, Texel Lt V, Harlingen, Eierland, Ameland, Oostmahorn, Schiermonnikoog, Zoutkamp and Delfzijl.
Inland waterways
Bridge signals

Y –	You may pass under this arch
R each side –	Bridge closed (opens on request)
R one side G other side	Bridge about to open
G each side –	Bridge open
2 R (vert) –	Bridge out of use
2 G (vert) each side –	Bridge open but not in use (you may pass)

To request bridges to open sound 'long, short, long'.
Railway bridges
Opening times of railway bridges in the Netherlands are given in a leaflet 'Openingstijden Spoorwegbruggen' published annually by ANWB and available free (send A5 self addressed envelope with international reply coupon) from ANWB, L & A/Wat, Postbus 93200, 2509BA, Den Hag.
Buoyage
In certain inland waters, including the whole of the IJsselmeer, a buoyage system known as SIGNI is used. The main features are:
(1) Channel buoyage as for IALA (Region A).
(2) Supplementary port and starboard hand buoys may be red and white or green and white respectively.
(3) At division of channel, a spherical buoy with following characteristics:
a. Channels of equal importance – red and green bands; topmark red and green sphere;
b. Main channel to port – green above red; topmark green cone or green cone above a green sphere;
c. Main channel to starboard – red above green; topmark red can or red can above a red sphere.
Offshore buoys are often marked with abbreviations of the banks or channels which they mark (e.g. ZS – Zuider Stortemelk). A separation buoy has the abbreviations of both channels meeting there.
Some channels are marked with perches, starboard hand bound, port hand unbound. On tidal flats (e.g. Friesland) where the direction of main flood stream is uncertain, bound perches are on the S side of a channel and unbound on the N side.
In minor channels the buoyage may be moved without notice to accommodate changes.

CHARTS Chart numbers are printed in the following order: – Admiralty; Zeekaarten (equivalent to Admiralty, issued by the Hydrographer, Royal Netherlands Navy and up-dated by Dutch Notices to Mariners available from Dutch chart agents); Dutch Yacht Charts (Kaarten voor Zeil en Motorjachten, also issued by the Hydrographer of the Royal Netherlands Navy. A new edition comes out each year in March and is updated in Dutch Notices to Mariners); the letters of the ANWB Waterkaarten are quoted, lettered from A in the north to O in the South; Stanford (where applicable); Imray (where applicable). All vessels are required to carry a copy of all waterway regulations as given in ANWB publication 'Almanak voor Watertoerisme – deel 1.

PROVINCES In place of 'counties' in the UK, Provinces are given for Netherlands ports.

MARINE RESCUE CO-ORDINATION CENTRES Coast station Scheveningen Radio Tel. 550.19104. In emergency call *Scheveningen Radio* VHF Ch 16. For medical advice call *Radiomédical Scheveningen* on Ch 16.

PUBLIC HOLIDAYS New Year's Day, Easter Monday, Queen's Birthday (30 April), Liberation Day (5 May), Ascension Day, Whit Monday, Christmas Day and Boxing Day.

BROADCASTS Information broadcasts by VTS centres and associated communications, see Chapter 2.

TELEPHONE To call UK from the Netherlands, dial 09 (pause for new tone to be heard) 44. Then dial the full UK area code but omitting the prefix 0, followed by the number required.
To call the Netherlands from UK dial 010-31 followed by the area code and number.
Emergencies – Police, Ambulance, Fire dial 06-11.
CUSTOMS Main customs ports are Breskens, Vlissingen, Roompotsluis, Hoek van Holland, Scheveningen, IJmuiden, Den Helder, Harlingen, Oost Vlieland, West Terschelling, Lauwersoog, Delfzijl, Maassluis, Vlaardingen, Rotterdam and Schiedam. No entry/customs facilities at Stellendam, Den Oever or Kornwerderzand.
Note Further information, including a useful publication '*Watersports Paradise*' can be obtained from the Netherlands Board of Tourism, 25 Buckingham Gate, London, SW1E 6LD, Tel. (071) 630 0451. Royal Netherland Embassy, 12a Kensington Palace Gdns, London W8 4QU (071) 229 1594.

DUTCH GLOSSARY 10.20.8

Dutch	English
Aanlegplaats	Alongside berth (AB)
Ankerplaats	Anchorage (⚓)
Blauw	Blue (Bu)
Baken	Beacon (Bn)
Benzine	Petrol (P)
Beton	Concrete
Botenlift	Boat hoist (BH)
Diafoon	Diaphone
Dieselbrandstof	Diesel (D)
Dokter	Doctor (Dr)
Douane	Customs (⌗)
Driehoekig	Triangular
Drinkwater	Fresh water (FW)
Dukdalf	Dolphin
Electricien	Electrical repairs (El)
Facultatief	Occasional
Geblokt	Chequered
Gedoofd	Extinguished
Geel	Yellow (Y)
Oranje	Orange (Or)
GO	Group Occulting (2)
Grijs	Grey
GS	Group quick flashing (3)
Havenmeester	Harbour master (HrMr)
Haventrappen	Landing (L)
Hijskraan	Crane (C)
Horizontaal gestreept	Band
Houten	Wooden
Huis	House
Huisarts	Doctor (Dr)
Int F	Interrupted quick flashing
Jacht Club	Yacht Club (YC)
Jachthaven	Yacht harbour/marina
Kegel	Cone
Kegelvormig	Conical
Knalmistsein	Explosive
Kustwacht	Coast Guard (CG)
Lantaarnpaal	Column
Licht	Light
Lichtschip	Lightship
Lichtvlot	Light float
Loodsstation	Pilot station
Meerboei	Moorings (M)
Meerpaal	Dolphin
Metalen	Metal
Mistbel	Bell
Mistfluit	Reed/Whistle
Mistgong	Gong
Mistkanon	Explosive
Mistklok	Bell
Mistsirene	Siren
Monteur	Marine engineering (ME)
Nautofoon	Horn
Occ.	Occulting (Oc)
Petroleum	Paraffin
Postkantoor	Post office (PO)
(Q) Fl.	Quick flashing (Q)
Rood	Red (R)
Radiobaken	Radiobeacon
Reddingsboot	Lifeboat (LB)
Rond	Round
Ruitvormig	Diamond
Scheepshelling	Slipway (Slip)
Scheepswerf	Shipright/hull repairs (Sh)
Sluis	Lock
Smeerolie	Lubricating Oil
Stenen	Stone
Tijden winkelsluiting	Early closing (EC)
Tudeluk	Temporary
Topteken	Topmark
Toren	Tower (Tr)
Tyfoon	Horn
Uzeren	Iron
Vakwerktoren	Framework Tower
Verkeersseinen	Traffic signals
Vertikaal gestreept	Stripe
Vernield	Destroyed
vi(olet)	Violet (Vi)
Vierkant	Square
Vlaggestok	Flagstaff (FS)
Vliegveld	Airport (✈)
Vuurtoren	Lighthouse (Lt Ho)
W(it)	White (W)
Zeilmaker	Sailmaker (SM)
Ziekenhuis	Hospital 🄷
Zwart	Black (B)

NIEUWPOORT (NIEUPORT) 10-20-9

West Flanders

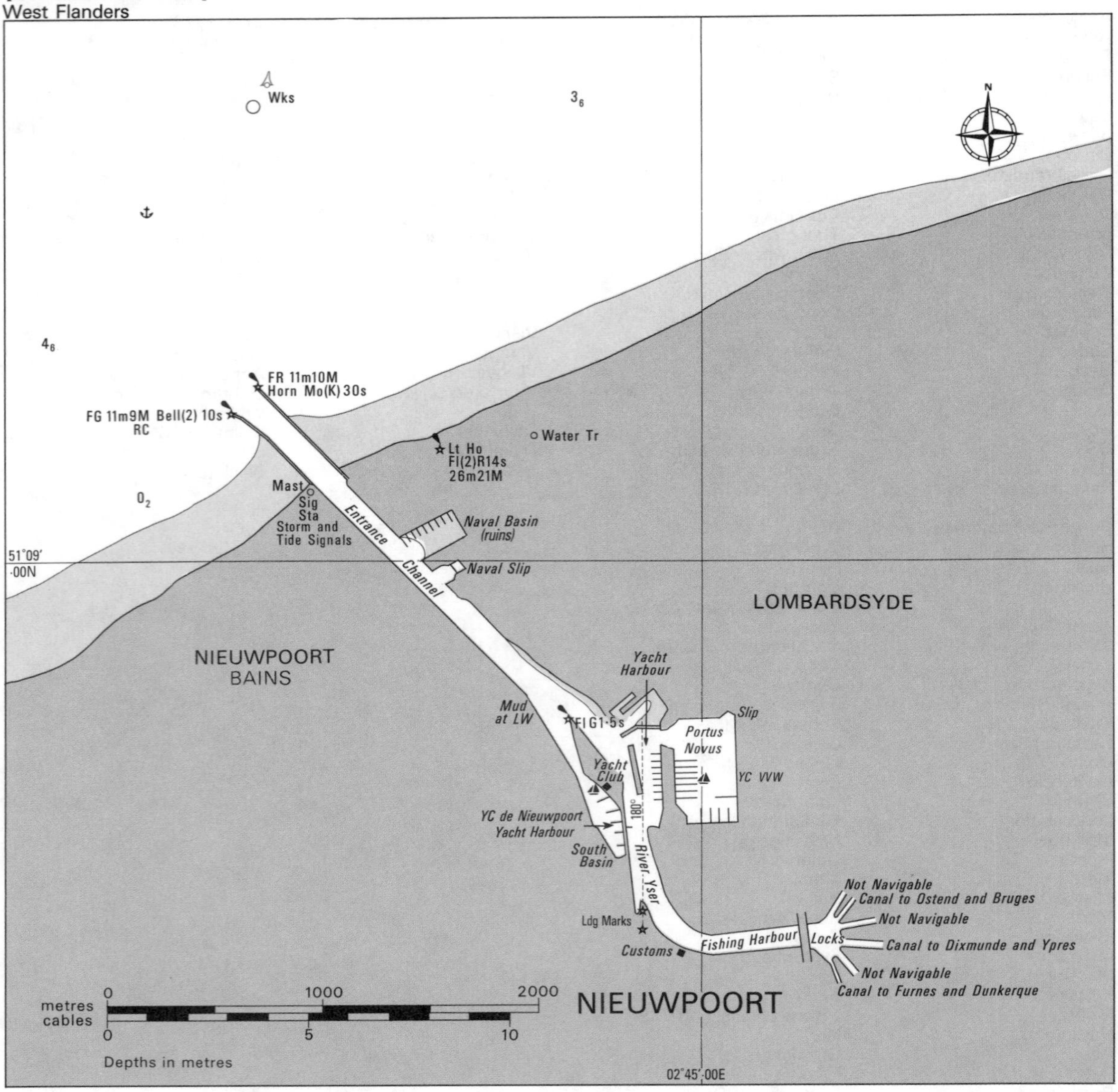
Wks
3_6
N
4_6
FR 11m10M
Horn Mo(K) 30s
FG 11m9M Bell(2) 10s
RC
Lt Ho
Fl(2)R14s
26m21M
Water Tr
Mast
0_2
Sig
Sta
Storm and
Tide Signals
Entrance
Channel
Naval Basin
(ruins)
51°09′
·00N
Naval Slip
LOMBARDSYDE
NIEUWPOORT
BAINS
Yacht
Harbour
Mud
at LW
Fl G1·5s
Slip
Portus
Novus
Yacht
Club
YC VVW
180°
YC de Nieuwpoort
Yacht Harbour
South
Basin
River Yser
Not Navigable
Canal to Ostend and Bruges
Not Navigable
Ldg Marks
Fishing Harbour
Locks
Canal to Dixmunde and Ypres
Customs
Not Navigable
Canal to Furnes and Dunkerque
metres
cables
0
1000
2000
0
5
10
NIEUWPOORT
Depths in metres
02°45′·00E

CHARTS

Admiralty 125, 1872; Belgian 101, D11; SHOM 7214; Stanford 1, 19; Imray C30

TIDES

Dover +0105; ML 2·4; Duration 0515; Zone −0100

Standard Port VLISSINGEN (⟶)

Times				Height (metres)			
HW		LW		MHWS	MHWN	MLWN	MLWS
0300	0900	0400	1000	4·7	3·9	0·8	0·3
1500	2100	1600	2200				
Differences NIEUWPOORT							
−0110	−0050	−0035	−0045	+0·6	+0·4	+0·4	+0·1

SHELTER

Shelter is good except for strong winds from the NW. There are two yacht harbours, both with good shelter. The YC of Nieuwpoort gets very full but there is always ample room in the Portus Novus.

NAVIGATION

Waypoint 51°10′·00N 02°42′·00E, 308°/128° from/to entrance, 0·90M. The bar is liable to silt up but there is usually sufficient water for yachts. Entrance and channels to both yacht harbours are dredged, although channel to both yacht harbours can drop to about 2m. At springs there is a strong stream across the entrance. The firing range E of Nieuwpoort is not used mid-June to end of September. At other times, contact range officer on Ch 67.

LIGHTS AND MARKS

Lt Ho Fl(2)R 14s 26m 21M; R Tr, W bands. E pier, head FR 11m 10M; W Tr; vis 025°-250°, 307°-347°; Horn Mo(K) 30s. W pier, head FG 11m 9M; W Tr; vis 025°-250°, 284°-324°; Bell(2) 10s; RC. International Port Traffic Signals from root of W pier, with addition of:

⧗ or Fl Bu Lt — Departure prohibited for craft under 6m length.

RADIO TELEPHONE

VHF Ch 09 19 16 (H24)

TELEPHONE (051 or 058)

Hr Mr 233000; CG 233045; Sea Rescue Helicopter 311714; # 233451; Duty Free Store 233433; Police 233002; Ⓗ (Oostende) 707631; Dr 233089; Brit Consul (02) 2179000.

NIEUWPOORT *continued*

FACILITIES
Koninklijke Yacht Club (400+80 visitors) ☎ 234413, Slip, M, L, FW, C (10 ton), CH, AB, R, Bar, Gas, ME, El, Sh, V, P, D, ⊡, Access; H24 **Novus Portus** (1,900+500 visitors) ☎ 235232, Slip, FW, BH (30 ton), C (15 ton), AC, CH, D, R, Bar; **YC Militair** ☎ 233433, M, L, FW, C (2 ton mobile), CH; **Belgian Boat Service** ☎ 234473, P, D, L, ME, El, Sh, C (15 ton), Gaz, CH; **West Diep** ☎ 234061, ME, El, Sh, C (6 ton), SM, CH; **Ship Shop** ☎ 235032, L, ME, El, Sh, C (6 ton), CH.
Town P, D, V, R, Bar. ✉; Ⓑ; ⇌; ✈ (Ostend).
Ferry UK — Ostend—Dover.
(Fuel can be bought on the harbour by arrangement).

OOSTENDE (OSTEND) 10-20-10

West Flanders

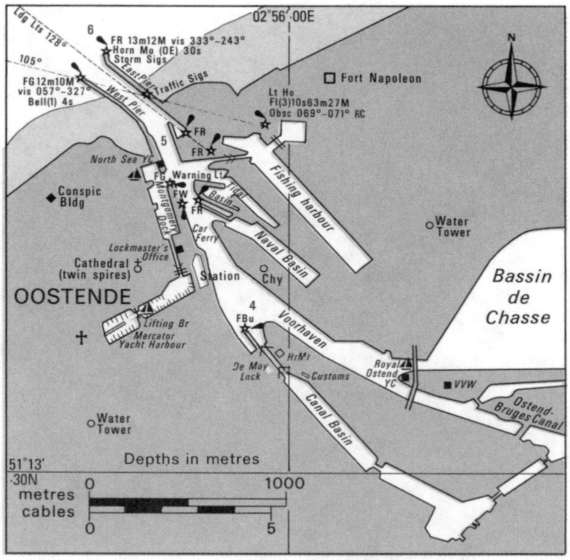

02°56'·00E
Ldg Lts 128°
6
FR 13m12M vis 333°-243°
Horn Mo (OE) 30s
Storm Sigs
105°
FG 12m10M vis 057°-327° Bell(1) 4s
East Pier
Traffic Sigs
West Pier
Fort Napoleon
Lt Ho Fl(3)10s63m27M Obsc 069°-071° RC
N
FR
FR
5
North Sea YC
FG Warning Lt
Montgomery Dock
FW
FR
Basin
Tidal
Fishing harbour
Conspic Bldg
Water Tower
Car Ferry
Naval Basin
Lockmaster's Office
Cathedral (twin spires)
Station
Chy
Bassin de Chasse
OOSTENDE
4
FBu
Voorhaven
Lifting Br
Mercator Yacht Harbour
HrMr
De Mey Lock
Customs
Royal Ostend YC
VVW
Ostend-Bruges Canal
Canal Basin
Water Tower
Depths in metres
51°13'·30N
metres
cables
0
1000
0
5

CHARTS
Admiralty 125, 325, 1872; SHOM 7214; Dutch Yacht Chart 1801; Stanford 1, 19; Imray C30
TIDES
Dover +0120; ML 2·4; Duration 0530; Zone −0100

Standard Port VLISSINGEN (⟶)

Times				Height (metres)			
HW		LW		MHWS	MHWN	MLWN	MLWS
0300	0900	0400	1000	4·7	3·9	0·8	0·3
1500	2100	1600	2200				
Differences OOSTENDE							
−0055	−0040	−0030	−0045	+0·3	+0·3	+0·3	+0·1

SHELTER
Very good shelter especially in the Town and Mercator Yacht Harbour (entered via the Montgomery Dock). Quiet berths may be found further up harbour in the Voorhaven by the VVW and Royal Oostende YCs.
NAVIGATION
Waypoint 51°15'·00N 02°53'·97E, 308°/128° from/to entrance, 0·98M. Approaching Oostende beware crossing the Stroombank and avoid altogether in rough weather; then approach by channel inside the bank or through the buoyed channel.
LIGHTS AND MARKS
Oostende Fl(3) 10s 63m 27M; W Tr; RC. W pier head FG 12m 10M: W Tr; vis 057°-327°; Bell(1) 4s. E pier head FR 13m 12M; W Tr; vis 333°-243°; Horn Mo(OE) 30s. Ldg Lts 128° both FR 12/18m 4M; both X on W pylons, R bands; vis 051°-201°.
International Port Traffic Signals are shown from head of E pier, with addition of following signals from S side of entrance to Montgomery dock:—

⧗ or Fl Bu Lt — Departure of craft under 6m length prohibited.

RADIO TELEPHONE
VHF Ch 09 16 67 (H24). Mercator Marina Ch 14 (H24).
TELEPHONE (059)
Hr Mr 705762; Life Saving Service 701100; Weather 991; # 702009; Police 500925; ⊞ 707637; Brit Consul (02) 2179000.
FACILITIES
Mercator Yacht Harbour (450+50 visitors) ☎ 705762, FW, AC, P, D, C, Slip; **North Sea YC** ☎ 702754, L, FW, AB, R, Bar; **Royal YC of Oostende** (160+40 visitors) ☎ 321452, Slip, M, C (½ ton), L, V, FW, AB, R, Bar; **Montgomery Dock** (70+50 visitors) YC, Bar, R, FW, Slip; **Compas** ☎ 700057, ME, CH; **Maritime Bureau Hindery CKT** ☎ 707261, ME, Sh, CH; **N end of Fishing harbour** D; **North Sea Marine** ☎ 320688, ME, El, Sh, SM; **Marina Yachting Centre** ☎ 320028, CH.
Town P and D (cans), CH, V, R, Bar. ✉; Ⓑ; ⇌; ✈.
Ferry UK—Dover.

BLANKENBERGE 10-20-11

West Flanders

CHARTS
Admiralty 325, 1872; Dutch Yacht Chart 1801; Stanford 1, 19; Imray C30
TIDES
Dover +0130; ML 2·5; Duration 0535; Zone −0100

Standard Port VLISSINGEN (⟶)

Times		Height (metres)			
HW	LW	MHWS	MHWN	MLWN	MLWS
All times	All times	4·7	3·9	0·8	0·3
Differences BLANKENBERGE					
−0040	−0040	−0·3	−0·1	+0·3	+0·1

SHELTER
Good shelter in the basin in the town and in the yacht harbour. There are also berths by the floating pontoons or alongside the quay. No yachts berths in Fishing Hr. Entrance channel between moles subject to silting, but dredged in summer months. Access HW∓2.
NAVIGATION
Waypoint Wenduine Bank N (stbd-hand) buoy, QG, 51°21'·55N 03°02'·67E, 317°/137° from/to entrance, 3·6M. Entry should not be attempted when strong winds are from the NW. Beware strong tides across entrance.
LIGHTS AND MARKS
Ldg Lts 134°, Front (Red X on column) FR 3M, Rear (Red X on concrete post) FR, 3M, show the best water.
FS by Lt Ho shows

⧗ or Fl Bu Lt — Departure of craft under 6m length prohibited.

RADIO TELEPHONE
Private volunteer VHF service, Ch 08 (or relay via Ostend or Zeebrugge). Blankenberg Safety Ch 16 (H24).
TELEPHONE (050)
Hr Mr 411420; # Zeebrugge 544223; Police 429842; Dr 333668; ⊞ 413701; Brit Consul (02) 2179000.
FACILITIES
Marine Centre ☎ 413560, ME, El, Sh, C (15 ton), CH; **Agemex** ☎ 414938, Slip, ME, El, Sh, C (15 ton), CH; **Yacht Harbour** Slip, FW, C (10 ton); **Scarphout YC** ☎ 411420, Bar, R, M, C (2½ ton), D, P, CH, FW, L, Slip; **Wittervrongel Sails** ☎ 411863, SM, CH; **N.V. Internautic on Sea** ☎ 413178, Slip, P, D, L, ME, El, Sh, C (22 ton), CH; **Marine Yachting Centre** ☎ 415712, CH; **YC Vrije Noordzeezeilers (VNZ)** ☎ 429150, M, Bar, FW, L; **YC VVW** ☎ 417536, Bar, M, D, P, FW, ⊡, Slip; **Town** V, R, Gaz, Bar. ✉; Ⓑ; ⇌; ✈ (Ostend).
Ferry UK — Zeebrugge—Dover/Hull/Felixstowe.

BLANKENBERGE *continued*

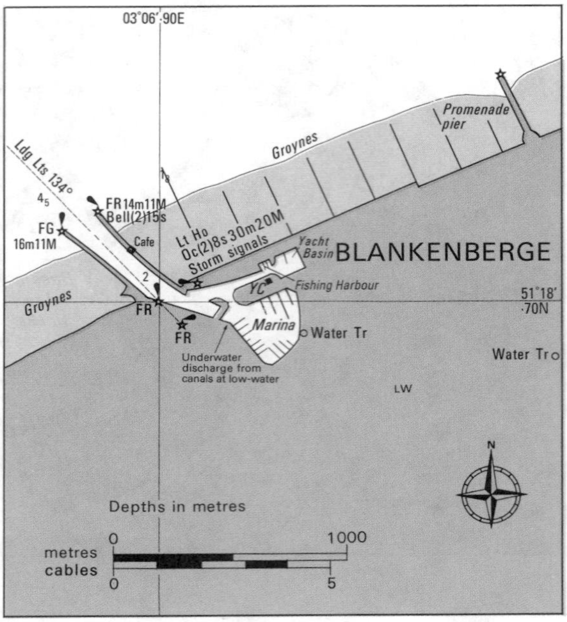

03°06'.90E
Promenade pier
Groynes
Ldg Lts 134°
FR14m11M
Bell(2)15s
FG
16m11M
Cafe
Lt Ho
Oc(2)8s30m20M
Storm signals
Yacht Basin
BLANKENBERGE
Fishing Harbour
YC
Groynes
FR
FR
Marina
Water Tr
51°18'
.70N
Underwater discharge from canals at low-water
Water Tr
LW
N
Depths in metres
0
1000
metres
cables
0
5

ZEEBRUGGE 10-20-12

West Flanders

CHARTS
Admiralty 97, 325, 1872; Zeekaart 1441; Dutch Yacht Chart 1801, 1803; Stanford 1, 19; Imray C30

TIDES
Dover +0110; ML 2·4; Duration 0535; Zone −0100

Standard Port VLISSINGEN (⟶)

Times				Height (metres)			
HW		LW		MHWS	MHWN	MLWN	MLWS
0300	0900	0400	1000	4·7	3·9	0·8	0·3
1500	2100	1600	2200				
Differences ZEEBRUGGE							
−0035	−0015	−0020	−0035	+0·1	0·0	+0·3	+0·1

SHELTER
Shelter in Zeebrugge is very good and harbour is always available. Zeebrugge is the port of Brugge (Zee Brugge) and the canal up to Brugge (or Bruges) is 6 M long. The yacht harbour is very well protected except in strong NE winds.

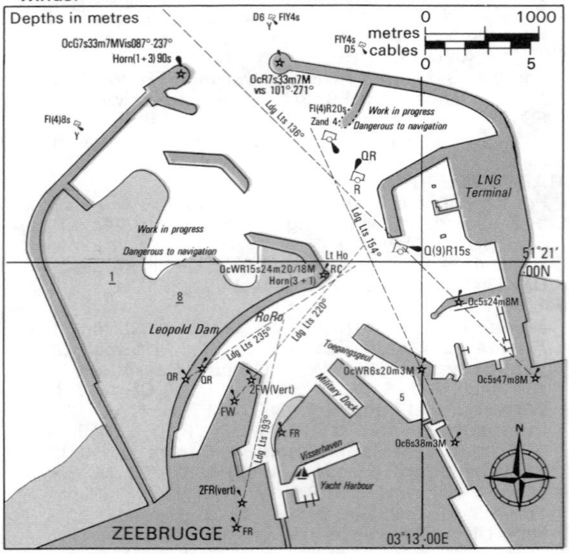

Depths in metres
0
1000
metres
cables
0
5
OcG7s33m7MVis087°-237°
Horn(1+3)90s
OcR7s33m7M
vis 101°-271°
Fl(4)R20s
Work in progress
Dangerous to navigation
Ldg Lts 136°
QR
R
LNG Terminal
Fl(4)8s
Work in progress
Dangerous to navigation
Ldg Lts 154°
Lt Ho
OcWR15s24m20/18M
Horn(3+1)
Q(9)R15s
51°21'
.00N
Oc5s24m8M
Leopold Dam
RoRo
Ldg Lts 235°
Ldg Lts 220°
Toegangsgeul
OcWR6s20m3M
Military Dock
Oc5s47m8M
QR
QR
2FW(Vert)
FW
FR
Ldg Lts 193°
Visserhaven
Oc6s38m3M
N
Yacht Harbour
2FR(vert)
ZEEBRUGGE
FR
03°13'.00E

NAVIGATION
Waypoint Scheur-Zand E cardinal buoy, Q(3) 10s, 51°23'·70N 03°07'·68E, 309°/129° from/to entrance, 3·1M. There are no hazards approaching the harbour mouth. Beware strong currents in harbour approaches (up to 4 kn at HW−1). Zeebrugge is the main fishing port of Belgium and is a ferry terminal, so keep clear of fishing boats and ferries. Call Harbour Control Ch 71 before entry.

LIGHTS AND MARKS
(1) Ldg Lts 136°. Oc 5s 8M, vis 131°-141° synchronised (H24).
(2) Ldg Lts 154°. Front Oc WR 6s. Rear Oc 6s synchronised (H24).
(3) Ldg Lts 235°. Both QR 5M, synchronised.
(4) Ldg Lts 220°, Front 2FW(vert) 30/22m. Rear FW 30m. Both W concrete columns, B bands.
(5) Ldg Lts 193°. Front 2FR(vert) 30/22m. Rear FR 29m. Both W concrete columns, R bands.

International Port Traffic Signals are shown at NE end of Leopold II Dam (old Zeebrugge mole). A QY Lt at S side of Visserhaven prohibits entry/departure to/from Visserhaven.

RADIO TELEPHONE
VHF Port Entrance and Port Control Ch 71 (H24).

TELEPHONE (050)
Hr Mr 543241; Port Control 546867; Lock Mr 543231; CG 545072; Sea Saving Service 544007; # 54.54.55; Police 544148; Dr 544590; Ⓗ 320832; Brit Consul (02) 2179000.

FACILITIES
Yacht Harbour (100) ☎ 544903, Slip, Sh, CH, D, AB, R, Bar; **Pontoon** L, FW; **Alberta (bar/restaurant of Royal Belgian SC)** ☎ 544197, R, Bar; **Royal Belgian SC** ☎ 544903, M, AB; **Brugge Marine** ☎ 353375, ME, El; **Hennion Luc Yachting** ☎ 544829, CH.
Town P, D, FW, ME, El, Sh, CH, Gaz, V, R, Bar. ✉; Ⓑ; ⇌; Tram to Oostende; ✈ (Ostend).
Ferry UK—Dover/Hull/Folkestone.

BRESKENS 10-20-13

Zeeland

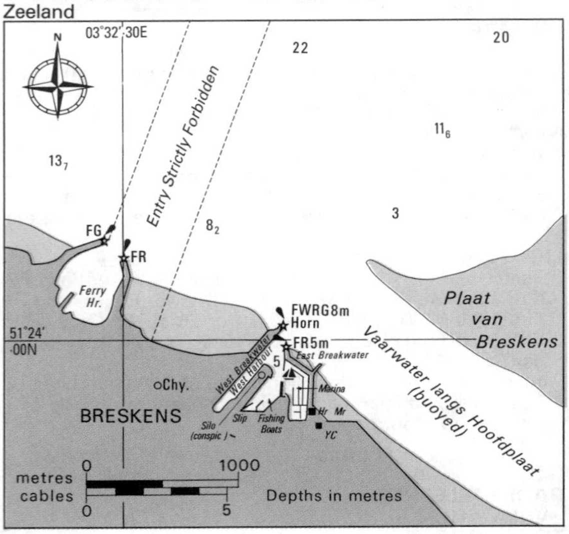

N
03°32'.30E
22
20
Entry Strictly Forbidden
11₆
13₇
3
8₂
FG
FR
Ferry Hr.
FWRG8m
Horn
Plaat van Breskens
51°24'
.00N
FR5m
East Breakwater
West Breakwater
West Harbour
Vaarwater langs Hoofdplaat (buoyed)
5
Chy.
Marina
BRESKENS
Silo (conspic)
Slip
Fishing Boats
Hr Mr
YC
0
1000
metres
cables
0
5
Depths in metres

CHARTS
Admiralty 325, 120; Zeekaart 1444, 1483; Dutch Yacht Chart 1801, 1803; Stanford 1,19; Imray C30

TIDES
Dover +0210; ML 2·5; Duration 0600; Zone −0100

Standard Port VLISSINGEN (⟶)

Times				Height (metres)			
HW		LW		MHWS	MHWN	MLWN	MLWS
0300	0900	0400	1000	4·7	3·9	0·8	0·3
1500	2100	1600	2200				
Differences BRESKENS							
−0005	−0005	−0002	−0002	+0·1	0·0	0·0	0·0

BREKENS *continued*

SHELTER
Good shelter in all winds. The North finger of the marina is for visiting yachts. Marina operated by Jachthaven Breskens BV. Anchor off Plaat van Breskens, in fine weather, not in harbour.

NAVIGATION
Waypoint SS-VH N cardinal buoy, Q, 51°24'·75N 03°34'·00E, 357°/177° from/to W breakwater Lt, 0·69M. Beware strong tides across the entrance. There is a shoal just to port after passing the entrance. Make sure the entrance is not confused with that of the ferry port 1000m WNW, where yachts are forbidden.

LIGHTS AND MARKS
West mole head F WRG 6m; vis R090°-128°, W128°-157°, R157°-172°, W172°-175°, G175°-296°, W296°-300°, R300°-008°, G008°-090°; Horn Mo(U) 30s. E mole head FR 5m. Nieuwe Sluis Lt Oc WRG 10s 14/10M is 1·2M W of Ferry Hr.

RADIO TELEPHONE
VHF Ch 14 (Flushing Traffic Control).

TELEPHONE (01172)
Hr Mr 1902; # 2610; Police (01170) 3156; Dr 1566; Ⓗ (01170) 53355; Brit Consul (020) 764343.

FACILITIES
Marina ☎ 1902, FW, ⊡; **YC Breskens** ☎ 3278, R, Bar; **Neil Pryde** ☎ 2101, SM; **C. Kosten** ☎ 1257, CH, D, Gaz, P, chart agent; **Standfast** ☎ 1797, BY, C (15 ton), El, ME, Sh, Slip; **Proctor** ☎ 1397 masts; **Jachtwerf Delta** ☎ 2440, BY, C (18 ton), El, ME, Sh; **M D Meeusen** ☎ 1996, Sh; **Tronik Shop** ☎ 3031, El, Ⓔ; **Town** V, R, Bar, ✉; Ⓑ; Gas, ⇄ (Flushing); ✈ (Ghent or Brussels). Ferry UK — Flushing—Sheerness.

TERNEUZEN 10-20-14
Zeeland

CHARTS
Admiralty 120; Zeekaart 1443; Dutch Yacht Chart 1803; Stanford 19; Imray C30

TIDES
Dover +0230; ML 2·6; Duration 0555; Zone −0100

Standard Port VLISSINGEN (⟶)

Times				Height (metres)			
HW		LW		MHWS	MHWN	MLWN	MLWS
0300	0900	0400	1000	4·7	3·9	0·8	0·3
1500	2100	1600	2200				
Differences TERNEUZEN							
+0021	+0022	+0022	+0033	+0·3	+0·3	0·0	0·0

SHELTER
Very good except in strong NW winds. The Veerhaven is tidal and exposed to NE. Yachts can find shelter through the East Lock (Oostsluis); see Lockmaster for berth. Yachts are prohibited in West Lock (Westsluis) and Western Harbour.

NAVIGATION
Waypoint No 23A (stbd-hand) buoy, IsoG 4s, 51°21'·37N 03°45'·66E, 285°/105° from/to Veerhaven entrance, 2·6M. Westerschelde (see 10.20.15) is a mass of sand-banks but well marked. It is the waterway to Antwerpen and Ghent, very full of shipping and also of barges (which do not normally conform to the rules). The Ghent canal is 17M long with three bridges, minimum clearance 6·5m when closed; VHF Ch 11 is compulsory.

LIGHTS AND MARKS
For the Veerhaven, the water Tr to SE and the Oc WRG Lt on W mole are conspic. When entry prohibited, a R flag is shown at W mole head by day, or a second R Lt below FR on E mole by night.
Signals for Oostsluis: R Lts each side of lock — entry prohibited; G Lts each side — entry permitted.

RADIO TELEPHONE
Call: *Havendienst Terneuzen* VHF Ch 11 (H24). Information broadcasts every H+00. For Terneuzen-Ghent canal call on Ch 11 and keep watch during transit. Contact Zelzate Bridge (call: *Uitkijk Zelzate*) direct on Ch 11, other bridges through Terneuzen. See also 10.20.15 for Schelde Information Service. Other stations: Ghent (call *Havendienst Ghent*) Ch 05 11 (H24); Antwerpen (call: *Antwerpen Havendienst*) Ch 18 (H24).

TELEPHONE (01150)
Hr Mr 96331; CG 13017 (H24); # 12377; Police 13017; Ⓗ 88000; Dr 12200; Brit Consul (020) 764343.

FACILITIES
Yacht harbour (120) ☎ 97089, Slip, ME, El, Sh, BH (15 ton), FW, AB; **de Honte YC** ☎ 17633, L, FW, ⊡, AB; **Neuzen YC** ☎ 96331, M, L, FW, AB; **D. Hamelink** ☎ 97240, ME, El; **Vermeulen's Jachtwerf** (inside locks) ☎ 12716, P, D, L, FW, ME, El, C (40 ton), AB; **Pontoon** L, FW, AB (see Hr Mr); **Sluiskil** Sh; **A. Dam** ☎ 13774 Gaz. **Town** P, D, CH, V, R, Bar. ✉; Ⓑ; ⇄; ✈ (Ghent). Ferry UK — Flushing—Sheerness.

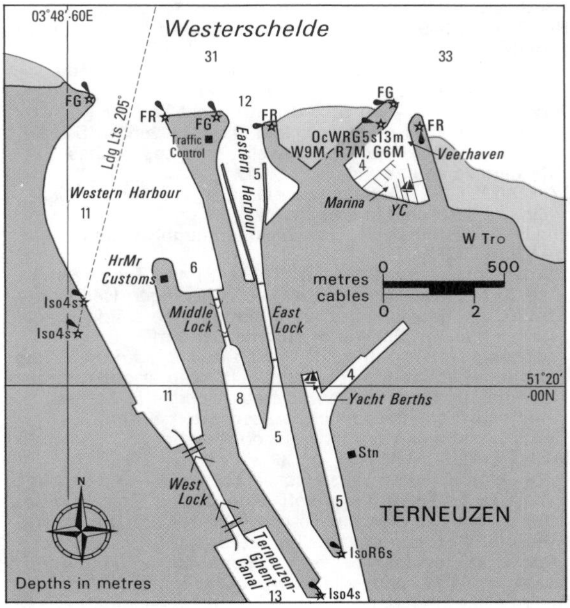

03°48'·60E
Westerschelde
31
33
12
FG
FR
FG
FR
FG
FR
Ldg Lts 205°
Traffic Control
Eastern Harbour
OcWRG5s13m W9M, R7M, G6M
Veerhaven
Western Harbour
Marina
YC
W Tr
HrMr Customs
Middle Lock
East Lock
metres
cables
0
500
0
2
Iso4s
Iso4s
51°20'·00N
Yacht Berths
Stn
West Lock
Terneuzen-Ghent Canal
TERNEUZEN
IsoR6s
Iso4s
N
Depths in metres

WESTERSCHELDE 10-20-15
Zeeland

CHARTS
Admiralty 120, 139, 325; Zeekaart 1443; Dutch Yacht Chart 1803; Stanford 19; Imray C30

TIDES
Dover +0200; ML (Hansweert) 2·7; Duration 0555; Zone −0100

Standard Port VLISSINGEN (⟶)

Times				Height (metres)			
HW		LW		MHWS	MHWN	MLWN	MLWS
0300	0900	0400	1000	4·7	3·9	0·8	0·3
1500	2100	1600	2200				
Differences WESTKAPELLE							
−0024	−0014	−0012	−0023	−0·6	−0·5	−0·1	0·0
HANSWEERT							
+0114	+0054	+0040	+0100	+0·5	+0·6	0·0	−0·1
BATH							
+0126	+0117	+0117	+0144	+0·8	+0·9	0·0	0·0

WESTERSCHELDE *continued*

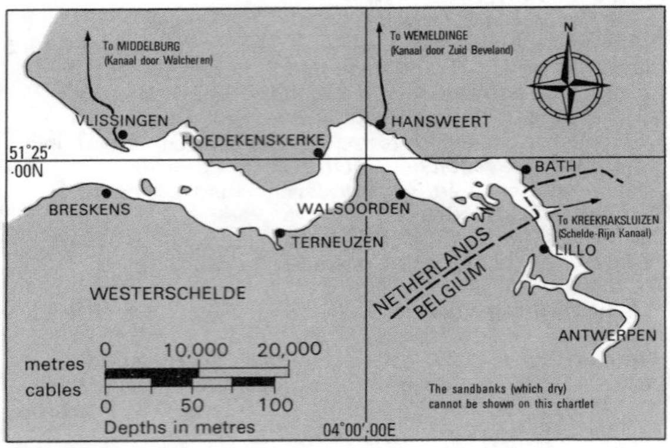

To MIDDELBURG (Kanaal door Walcheren)
To WEMELDINGE (Kanaal door Zuid Beveland)
N
VLISSINGEN
HOEDEKENSKERKE
HANSWEERT
51°25'·00N
BATH
BRESKENS
WALSOORDEN
To KREEKRAKSLUIZEN (Schelde-Rijn Kanaal)
TERNEUZEN
LILLO
NETHERLANDS
BELGIUM
WESTERSCHELDE
ANTWERPEN
0 10,000 20,000
metres
cables
0 50 100
Depths in metres
04°00'·00E
The sandbanks (which dry) cannot be shown on this chartlet

SHELTER
There are few harbours in the 38M from Terneuzen to Antwerpen. The following are possible for yachts:
HOEDEKENSKERKE — on N bank, disused ferry harbour (dries).
HANSWEERT — can be used temporarily, but it is the busy entrance to Zuid Beveland canal.
WALSOORDEN — on S bank with yacht harbour (Tijhaven, dries) on N side, and Diepe Haven on S side (depth 3m, but exposed to swell), both approached through same entrance.
ZANDVLIET — in Belgium, on N bank, is a commercial harbour; use only in emergency.
LILLO — customs post, for shallow-draught boats only.

NAVIGATION
Waypoints — see Breskens (10.20.13) and Terneuzen (10.20.14). Note traffic scheme off Vlissingen (see 10.20.5). The winding channel through the shifting banks is well marked, but full of commercial traffic. It is necessary to work the tide, which runs 2½ kn on average and more at springs. Yachts should keep at edge of main channel, and beware unpredictable actions of barges. Alternative channels must be used with caution, particularly going downstream on the ebb.

LIGHTS AND MARKS
The approaches to Westerschelde are well lit — on the S shore by Lt Trs at Kruishoofd and Nieuwe Sluis, and on the N shore at Westkapelle and Kaapduinen. Details of these and other important Lts are in 10.20.4. The main fairway is, for the most part, covered by the narrow white sectors of the various lights along the shore.

RADIO TELEPHONE
The following shore stations comprise the Schelde Information Service (all H24):
(1) Vlissingen.
A. Scheldemonding area, seaward of Kaapduinen and Kruishoofd Lts, call *Vlissingen Radio* VHF Ch 14.
B. Vlissingen area call *Post Vlissingen* Ch 21.
(2) Terneuzen area, call *Post Terneuzen* Ch **03** 14
(3) Hansweert area, call *Hansweert Radio* Ch 71
(4) Zandvliet area, call *Zandvliet Radio* Ch 12 14
Information broadcasts in Dutch and English every H+05 on Ch 03 by Terneuzen; every H+35 on Ch 12 by Zandvliet; Every H+20 on Ch 71 by Hansweert and every H+50 on Ch 14 by Vlissingen.
For other stations see harbour concerned.

FACILITIES
TERNEUZEN — see 10.20.14
HOEDEKENSKERKE (01193) — visitors berths, P, D, Gaz, FW; **W. Bek** ☎ 309 ME; **YC WV Hoedekenskerke** ☎ 259. **Town** ✉; Ⓑ; ≠ (Goes); ✈ (Antwerpen)
HANSWEERT (01130) — visitors berths, ME, C (17 ton) R, P, D; **Ribbens** ☎ 1371 CH; **Scheepswerf Reimerswaal** ☎ 3021, BY. **Town** ✉; Ⓑ; ≠ (Goes); ✈ (Antwerpen)
WALSOORDEN — visitors berths; **Havenmeester** ☎ 1235, P, D, Gaz; **De Klerk Scheepsbouw** ☎ 1614, BY. **Town** ✉; ≠; ✈ (Antwerpen).

ANTWERPEN (ANTWERP) 10-20-16

Antwerpen

CHARTS
Admiralty 139; Stanford 19; Zeekaart 1443; Dutch Yacht Chart 1803;

TIDES
Dover +0342; ML 2·7; Duration 0605; Zone −0100

Standard Port VLISSINGEN (⟶)

Times				Height (metres)			
HW		LW		MHWS	MHWN	MLWN	MLWS
0300	0900	0400	1000	4·7	3·9	0·8	0·3
1500	2100	1600	2200				
Differences ANTWERPEN							
+0128	+0116	+0121	+0144	+1·1	+0·9	0·0	0·0

SHELTER
Excellent in Imalso marina on W bank, 4ca (750m) SW of Kattendijksluis and ½M from city centre which can be reached through two tunnels. Access by lock HW$\mp$1 (0600-2000). Lock closed in winter except by arrangement.

NAVIGATION
For Westerschelde see 10.20.13/14/15. On river bend before marina is a windmill, and G conical buoy Iso G 8s. Two unlit Y buoys N and S of lock can be used if entrance is closed.

LIGHTS AND MARKS
(marina signals)

R flag or R Lt	— Entrance prohibited
G flag or G Lt	— Departure prohibited
Bu cone/flag or Bu Lt	— Approach channel closed
B ball or FW Lt	— Depth over sill 2·5–3·0m
2 B balls or 2 FW Lts	— Depth over sill 3·0–3·5m
3 B balls or 3 FW Lts	— Depth over sill 3·5–3·8m

Yachts should make following Int Code signals:
UH — I wish to enter marina under power
UP — I have an emergency; request priority entry
Z — Request tug assistance for entry
P — I wish to leave harbour

RADIO TELEPHONE
Call: *Antwerpen Havendienst* VHF Ch 18 (H24). Imalso Marina, (call *Bolleke*) Ch 72.

TELEPHONE (03)
Marina Lock Keeper 2190895; # 2340840; Police 321840; Ⓗ 2177111.

FACILITIES
Imalso Marina ☎ 2190895, FW, P, D, R, V, Gaz, El, Sh, AC, C (1·5 ton), Slip; **Royal YC van België** ☎ 2192788 Bar, R, M, C (5 ton), D, P, CH, FW, L, Slip; **Kon. Liberty YC** ☎ 2191147; **Martin & Co** ☎ 2250383, ACA, Dutch Chart Agent; **Bogerd Navtec** ☎ 8476 ACA; **Landtmeters** ☎ 2333131; **City** All facilities including ✉; Ⓑ; ≠; ✈. Ferry UK — Flushing-Sheerness.

ANTWERPEN *continued*

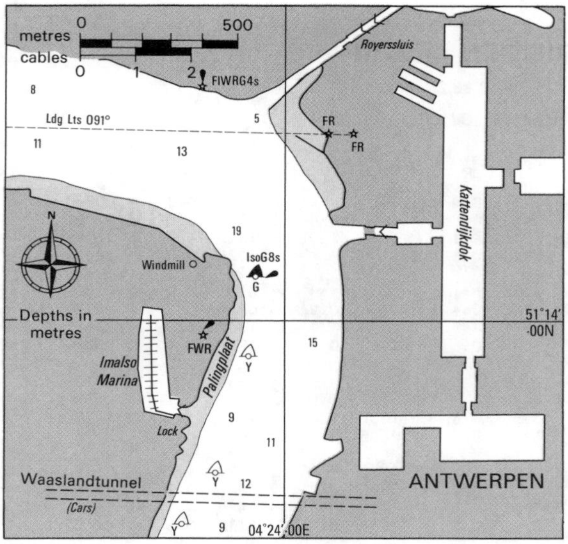
metres
cables
0
500
0
1
2
FIWRG4s
Royerssluis
8
Ldg Lts 091°
5
FR
FR
11
13
Kattendijkdok
19
Windmill
IsoG8s
G
Depths in metres
51°14'·00N
FWR
Y
15
Imalso Marina
Palingplaat
9
Lock
11
Waaslandtunnel
Y
12
ANTWERPEN
(Cars)
Y
9
04°24'·00E

VLISSINGEN (FLUSHING) 10-20-17

Zeeland

CHARTS
Admiralty 325, 120, 1872; Zeekaart 1444, 1443, 1533; Dutch Yacht Chart 1803; Stanford 19; Imray C30

TIDES
Dover +0215; ML 2·4; Duration 0555; Zone −0100

NOTE: Flushing is a Standard Port and the tidal predictions for each day of the year are given below.

SHELTER
Very good shelter, in both yacht harbours, one being near the entrance to the lock to Walcheren canal. The Old Harbour to the W has storm barrier (opens 1 Apr–1 Oct) leading to Michiel de Ruyter marina. Storm barrier has sill 0·9m below CD. Check gauge m barrier wall.

NAVIGATION
Waypoint H-SS N cardinal buoy, Q, 51°25'·97N 03°37'·54E, 125°/305° from/to Buitenhaven entrance, 0·95M. Approaching from the SW there are no dangers. Yachts are forbidden to sail in the main fairways. From Zeebrugge, keep S of Wielingen channel past Breskens, and cross to Flushing near buoy H-SS. From N use Deurloo/Spleet channels to S side of estuary, then as above. Heavy ocean-going traffic, often taking on or dropping pilots, off the town. In the harbour, frequent ferries berth at terminals near the locks and enter and leave at speed. See Westerschelde Traffic lanes Fig 2(3).

LIGHTS AND MARKS
The Lt Ho at the root of the W breakwater of Koopmanshaven is brown metal framework Tr, Iso WRG 3s 15m 12/9M.
Ldg Lts 117°. Front Leugenaar causeway, near head, OcR 5s 5m 7M. Rear Sardijngeul, 550m from front Oc WRG 5s 10m 12/8M, R Δ, W bands on R and W mast.
Entry signals from pier W side of Buitenhaven entrance:

R flag	or	Additional R Lt near R harbour Lt	Entry prohibited
R flag over G flag	or	Additional R and G Lt near R harbour Lt	Entry prohibited if over 6m draught

Two R Lts (vert) from lock indicate 'lock closed'.

RADIO TELEPHONE
Vlissingen Port Ch 21. Flushing – East Port Ch 09. Lock information Ch 22.
See also Westerschelde (10.20.15).

TELEPHONE (01184)
Hr Mr 68080; East Harbour Port Authority 68080; Buitenhaven Lock Keeper 12372; # 60000; Police 15050; H 25000; Dr 12233; Brit Consul (020) 764343.

FACILITIES
Michiel de Ruyter (60+40 visitors) ☎ 14498 D, P, FW, AC, Bar, R, YC; **Jachthaven 'VVW Schelde'** (85+40 visitors) ☎ 65912 AC, Bar, C (10 ton), D, FW, R, ⊡, M, Slip, (Access H24); **Royal Schelde Repair Yard** Sh; **Bureau Kramer** ☎ 16364, ME, Sh; **Gerb van de Gruiter** ☎ 65961, SM. **Town** P, D, CH, V, R, Bar. ✉; Ⓑ; ⇌; ✈ (Antwerpen).
Ferry UK—Sheerness.

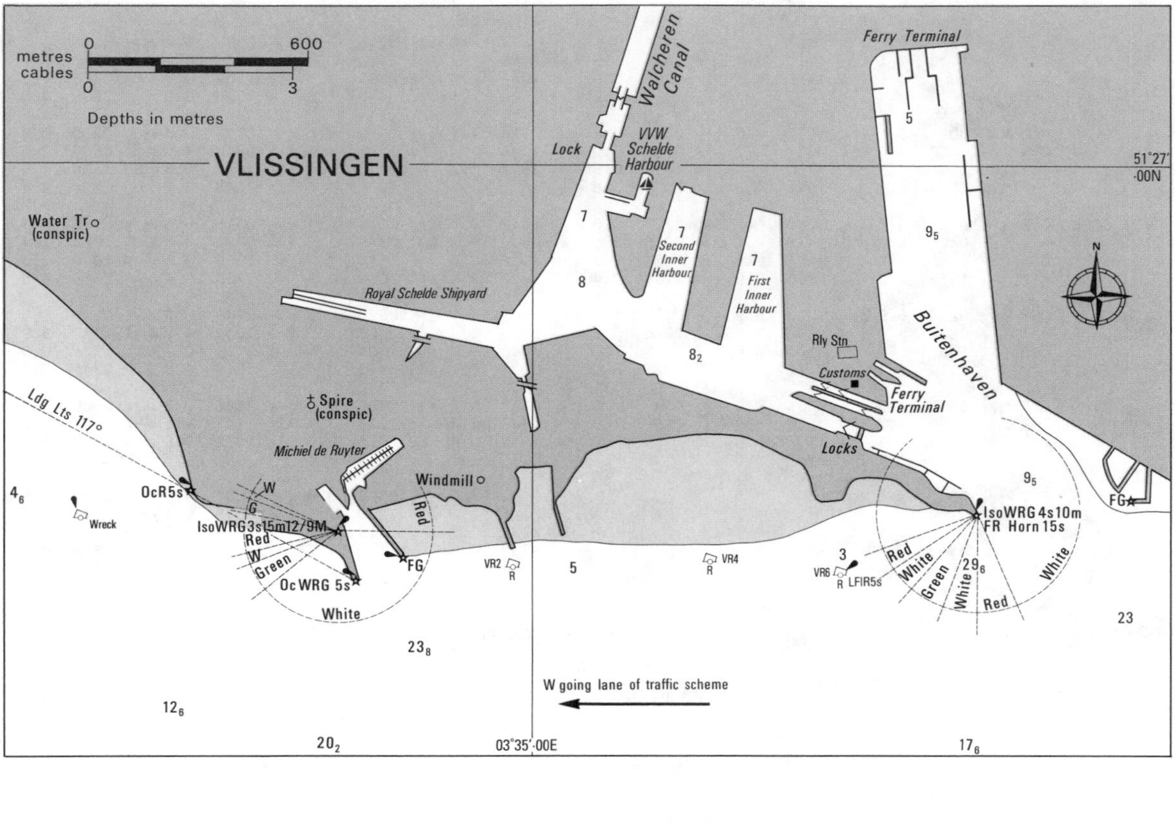
metres
cables
0
600
0
3
Depths in metres
VLISSINGEN
Walcheren Canal
Ferry Terminal
Lock
VVW Schelde Harbour
5
51°27'·00N
Water Tr (conspic)
7
7
Second Inner Harbour
9₅
7
First Inner Harbour
8
Royal Schelde Shipyard
Buitenhaven
Rly Stn
8₂
Customs
Ferry Terminal
Ldg Lts 117°
Spire (conspic)
Michiel de Ruyter
Locks
9₅
4₆
OcR5s
Windmill
FG
Wreck
IsoWRG3s15m12/9M
Red
IsoWRG 4s10m
FR Horn 15s
Red
W
G
Green
FG
VR2
R
5
VR4
R
3
VR6
R
LFIR5s
Red
White
Green
White
29₆
Red
White
Oc WRG 5s
White
23
23₈
W going lane of traffic scheme
12₆
20₂
03°35'·00E
17₆

TIME ZONE -0100
(Dutch Standard Time)
Subtract 1 hour for GMT
For Dutch Summer Time add ONE hour in non-shaded areas

NETHERLANDS - VLISSINGEN (FLUSHING)

LAT 51°27′N LONG 3°36′E

TIMES AND HEIGHTS OF HIGH AND LOW WATERS

YEAR **1992**

JANUARY

Day	Time	m	Time	m	Time	m	Time	m
1 W	0535	0.9	1129	4.0	1806	0.8		
2 TH	0005	4.1	0625	0.8	1225	4.1	1845	0.8
3 F	0055	4.2	0715	0.7	1320	4.3	1925	0.8
4 SA	0146	4.3	0755	0.6	1354	4.3	● 2006	0.8
5 SU	0220	4.3	0829	0.5	1436	4.4	2036	0.7
6 M	0252	4.4	0905	0.4	1505	4.5	2110	0.7
7 TU	0326	4.5	0946	0.3	1539	4.6	2145	0.7
8 W	0356	4.5	1019	0.3	1610	4.6	2225	0.7
9 TH	0428	4.5	1056	0.3	1645	4.5	2255	0.7
10 F	0502	4.4	1130	0.4	1719	4.4	2325	0.8
11 SA	0535	4.3	1154	0.4	1756	4.3		
12 SU	0006	0.8	0616	4.2	1235	0.5	1835	4.2
13 M	0045	0.8	0655	4.1	1326	0.6	☽ 1935	4.0
14 TU	0140	0.9	0806	3.9	1426	0.7	2051	4.0
15 W	0244	1.0	0921	3.9	1541	0.8	2200	3.9
16 TH	0404	1.0	1036	4.0	1650	0.7	2309	4.1
17 F	0526	0.8	1137	4.2	1755	0.6		
18 SA	0008	4.3	0636	0.6	1235	4.4	1858	0.5
19 SU	0102	4.5	0726	0.4	1322	4.7	○ 1948	0.4
20 M	0149	4.7	0820	0.1	1409	4.9	2036	0.3
21 TU	0235	4.8	0908	0.0	1453	5.0	2122	0.3
22 W	0318	4.9	0956	-0.1	1540	5.1	2208	0.3
23 TH	0405	4.9	1046	-0.1	1626	5.0	2251	0.4
24 F	0450	4.8	1128	0.0	1716	4.8	2336	0.5
25 SA	0537	4.7	1216	0.1	1807	4.6		
26 SU	0019	0.6	0629	4.5	1255	0.3	☾ 1901	4.3
27 M	0110	0.7	0725	4.2	1350	0.5	1959	4.0
28 TU	0210	0.9	0825	3.9	1456	0.8	2116	3.7
29 W	0336	1.0	0950	3.7	1615	0.9	2235	3.7
30 TH	0500	1.0	1110	3.8	1724	0.9	2346	3.8
31 F	0610	0.8	1215	4.0	1830	0.9		

FEBRUARY

Day	Time	m	Time	m	Time	m	Time	m
1 SA	0046	4.0	0659	0.7	1310	4.2	1909	0.8
2 SU	0125	4.2	0745	0.5	1350	4.3	1945	0.7
3 M	0205	4.3	0816	0.4	1415	4.4	● 2020	0.7
4 TU	0231	4.4	0849	0.3	1447	4.6	2056	0.6
5 W	0301	4.6	0926	0.2	1517	4.6	2128	0.5
6 TH	0331	4.6	1000	0.2	1549	4.7	2159	0.5
7 F	0402	4.6	1032	0.2	1618	4.6	2236	0.5
8 SA	0432	4.6	1106	0.2	1649	4.6	2306	0.6
9 SU	0506	4.5	1136	0.3	1721	4.5	2335	0.6
10 M	0537	4.5	1211	0.4	1758	4.4		
11 TU	0016	0.6	0617	4.3	1250	0.4	☽ 1848	4.2
12 W	0059	0.7	0716	4.1	1345	0.6	2006	3.9
13 TH	0210	0.9	0836	3.9	1500	0.8	2125	3.8
14 F	0335	0.9	1006	3.9	1626	0.8	2246	3.8
15 SA	0506	0.8	1118	4.1	1746	0.7	2358	4.1
16 SU	0620	0.5	1218	4.4	1846	0.5		
17 M	0047	4.4	0716	0.3	1312	4.7	1935	0.4
18 TU	0136	4.6	0808	0.0	1356	4.9	○ 2022	0.3
19 W	0216	4.8	0856	-0.1	1436	5.0	2106	0.2
20 TH	0258	4.9	0938	-0.2	1518	5.0	2148	0.2
21 F	0343	5.0	1019	-0.2	1605	5.0	2229	0.3
22 SA	0425	4.9	1106	0.0	1649	4.8	2309	0.4
23 SU	0506	4.8	1142	0.1	1735	4.5	2352	0.5
24 M	0555	4.5	1222	0.4	1825	4.2		
25 TU	0036	0.6	0646	4.2	1305	0.6	☾ 1915	3.9
26 W	0124	0.8	0745	3.9	1410	0.9	2014	3.5
27 TH	0255	1.0	0916	3.5	1524	1.1	2206	3.4
28 F	0415	1.0	1046	3.6	1655	1.1	2326	3.6
29 SA	0535	0.8	1155	3.8	1754	0.9		

MARCH

Day	Time	m	Time	m	Time	m	Time	m
1 SU	0015	3.9	0636	0.6	1245	4.1	1844	0.8
2 M	0106	4.1	0726	0.4	1321	4.3	1925	0.6
3 TU	0138	4.3	0756	0.3	1355	4.5	1956	0.6
4 W	0206	4.5	0825	0.2	1421	4.6	● 2030	0.5
5 TH	0235	4.6	0858	0.1	1448	4.7	2102	0.4
6 F	0302	4.7	0932	0.1	1517	4.7	2136	0.4
7 SA	0336	4.7	1005	0.1	1549	4.7	2210	0.4
8 SU	0403	4.7	1036	0.2	1620	4.6	2239	0.4
9 M	0435	4.7	1111	0.2	1656	4.6	2316	0.4
10 TU	0513	4.6	1146	0.3	1735	4.4	2356	0.5
11 W	0556	4.5	1226	0.4	1822	4.2		
12 TH	0046	0.6	0648	4.2	1326	0.6	☽ 1936	3.9
13 F	0149	0.7	0810	3.9	1440	0.8	2100	3.7
14 SA	0314	0.8	0945	3.9	1605	0.8	2225	3.7
15 SU	0455	0.7	1105	4.1	1736	0.7	2339	4.0
16 M	0605	0.4	1208	4.4	1832	0.5		
17 TU	0031	4.3	0706	0.2	1252	4.7	1922	0.3
18 W	0116	4.6	0749	0.0	1335	4.8	○ 2006	0.2
19 TH	0156	4.8	0836	-0.1	1416	4.9	2047	0.2
20 F	0236	4.9	0915	-0.1	1455	4.9	2128	0.2
21 SA	0317	4.9	0955	-0.1	1540	4.8	2208	0.2
22 SU	0358	4.9	1035	0.1	1623	4.7	2248	0.3
23 M	0443	4.7	1116	0.3	1705	4.4	2325	0.4
24 TU	0526	4.5	1150	0.5	1750	4.2		
25 W	0006	0.5	0609	4.2	1230	0.7	1835	3.8
26 TH	0055	0.7	0706	3.8	1330	1.0	☾ 1936	3.5
27 F	0215	0.9	0826	3.5	1444	1.1	2054	3.3
28 SA	0336	0.9	1006	3.5	1604	1.1	2246	3.4
29 SU	0450	0.8	1121	3.7	1714	0.9	2345	3.7
30 M	0606	0.6	1210	4.0	1816	0.7		
31 TU	0025	4.0	0646	0.4	1248	4.3	1855	0.6

APRIL

Day	Time	m	Time	m	Time	m	Time	m
1 W	0101	4.3	0722	0.3	1319	4.5	1926	0.5
2 TH	0131	4.4	0756	0.2	1349	4.6	1959	0.4
3 F	0159	4.6	0825	0.1	1417	4.7	● 2035	0.3
4 SA	0230	4.7	0902	0.1	1449	4.7	2110	0.3
5 SU	0305	4.8	0935	0.1	1522	4.7	2145	0.3
6 M	0336	4.8	1012	0.2	1556	4.7	2222	0.3
7 TU	0413	4.8	1048	0.2	1636	4.6	2306	0.3
8 W	0452	4.7	1126	0.3	1717	4.4	2346	0.3
9 TH	0537	4.5	1212	0.4	1809	4.1		
10 F	0035	0.4	0635	4.2	1304	0.6	☽ 1926	3.8
11 SA	0145	0.6	0806	4.0	1426	0.8	2048	3.7
12 SU	0315	0.6	0930	4.0	1555	0.8	2205	3.8
13 M	0440	0.5	1048	4.2	1726	0.7	2318	4.0
14 TU	0556	0.3	1145	4.4	1818	0.5		
15 W	0009	4.3	0645	0.1	1235	4.6	1902	0.3
16 TH	0053	4.5	0729	0.0	1316	4.7	1945	0.3
17 F	0135	4.7	0812	0.0	1356	4.8	○ 2026	0.2
18 SA	0215	4.8	0852	0.0	1436	4.7	2106	0.2
19 SU	0256	4.8	0930	0.1	1519	4.7	2145	0.2
20 M	0336	4.8	1008	0.2	1601	4.5	2226	0.2
21 TU	0420	4.6	1045	0.4	1638	4.3	2302	0.3
22 W	0458	4.4	1119	0.6	1718	4.1	2345	0.4
23 TH	0545	4.2	1200	0.7	1805	3.9		
24 F	0036	0.6	0636	3.9	1256	0.9	☾ 1856	3.7
25 SA	0146	0.7	0746	3.7	1416	1.1	2000	3.5
26 SU	0255	0.8	0906	3.5	1526	1.0	2124	3.4
27 M	0355	0.7	1026	3.7	1630	0.9	2256	3.6
28 TU	0506	0.6	1122	3.9	1725	0.8	2342	3.9
29 W	0606	0.5	1205	4.2	1816	0.6		
30 TH	0020	4.2	0646	0.3	1239	4.4	1856	0.5

Chart Datum: 2.32 metres below Normaal Amsterdams Peil

TIME ZONE **-0100**
(Dutch Standard Time)
Subtract 1 hour for GMT
For Dutch Summer Time add ONE hour in non-shaded areas

NETHERLANDS - VLISSINGEN (FLUSHING)

LAT 51°27'N LONG 3°36'E

TIMES AND HEIGHTS OF HIGH AND LOW WATERS

YEAR **1992**

MAY

Day	Time	m	Day	Time	m
1	0055	4.4	**16**	0115	4.5
	0716	0.3		0751	0.2
F	1315	4.6	SA	1340	4.5
	1928	0.4	○	2005	0.3
2	0127	4.5	**17**	0157	4.6
	0756	0.2		0825	0.2
SA	1347	4.7	**SU**	1426	4.5
●	2006	0.3		2048	0.2
3	0202	4.7	**18**	0239	4.6
	0830	0.2		0906	0.3
SU	1422	4.7	M	1506	4.5
	2046	0.3		2126	0.2
4	0236	4.8	**19**	0321	4.6
	0908	0.2		0942	0.4
M	1459	4.7	TU	1542	4.4
	2125	0.2		2206	0.2
5	0315	4.8	**20**	0401	4.6
	0951	0.2		1020	0.5
TU	1538	4.6	W	1625	4.3
	2208	0.2		2248	0.3
6	0355	4.8	**21**	0441	4.4
	1030	0.3		1056	0.6
W	1620	4.5	TH	1658	4.2
	2255	0.2		2330	0.3
7	0441	4.7	**22**	0528	4.3
	1112	0.3		1136	0.7
TH	1707	4.4	F	1742	4.1
	2342	0.2			
8	0530	4.6	**23**	0004	0.4
	1206	0.5		0616	4.1
F	1806	4.1	SA	1214	0.9
				1831	3.9
9	0040	0.3	**24**	0111	0.5
	0635	4.3		0706	3.9
SA	1259	0.6	**SU**	1315	1.0
☽	1916	4.0	☾	1926	3.7
10	0146	0.3	**25**	0216	0.6
	0755	4.2		0806	3.8
SU	1416	0.7	M	1446	1.0
	2030	3.9		2025	3.6
11	0255	0.4	**26**	0310	0.6
	0910	4.2		0909	3.8
M	1541	0.7	TU	1546	0.9
	2142	3.9		2135	3.7
12	0415	0.3	**27**	0405	0.6
	1025	4.3		1020	3.9
TU	1649	0.6	W	1638	0.8
	2250	4.1		2246	3.8
13	0530	0.3	**28**	0505	0.5
	1121	4.4		1115	4.1
W	1756	0.5	TH	1726	0.7
	2345	4.3		2336	4.0
14	0622	0.2	**29**	0556	0.5
	1215	4.5		1200	4.3
TH	1842	0.4	F	1809	0.6
15	0030	4.4	**30**	0017	4.3
	0708	0.2		0641	0.4
F	1257	4.5	SA	1238	4.5
	1926	0.3		1856	0.5
			31	0057	4.5
				0720	0.3
			SU	1322	4.6
				1940	0.4

JUNE

Day	Time	m	Day	Time	m
1	0135	4.6	**16**	0231	4.5
	0802	0.2		0841	0.5
M	1401	4.7	TU	1451	4.4
●	2026	0.3		2109	0.3
2	0216	4.7	**17**	0311	4.5
	0847	0.2		0919	0.6
TU	1443	4.7	W	1529	4.4
	2112	0.2		2156	0.2
3	0300	4.8	**18**	0347	4.5
	0932	0.3		0956	0.6
W	1526	4.6	TH	1605	4.4
	2158	0.1		2230	0.2
4	0345	4.8	**19**	0426	4.5
	1016	0.3		1035	0.6
TH	1613	4.6	F	1641	4.4
	2248	0.1		2316	0.2
5	0433	4.8	**20**	0505	4.4
	1106	0.4		1116	0.7
F	1702	4.5	SA	1719	4.3
	2335	0.1		2350	0.3
6	0525	4.7	**21**	0545	4.3
	1155	0.5		1144	0.8
SA	1759	4.3	**SU**	1800	4.2
7	0036	0.1	**22**	0025	0.4
	0629	4.5		0625	4.1
SU	1244	0.5	M	1229	0.8
☽	1902	4.2		1845	4.0
8	0129	0.1	**23**	0105	0.5
	0738	4.4		0720	4.0
M	1355	0.6	TU	1314	0.9
	2005	4.1	☾	1936	3.9
9	0235	0.2	**24**	0205	0.6
	0841	4.3		0816	3.9
TU	1506	0.7	W	1425	1.0
	2109	4.1		2041	3.8
10	0346	0.3	**25**	0316	0.6
	0949	4.3		0916	3.9
W	1620	0.7	TH	1535	0.9
	2218	4.1		2139	3.8
11	0455	0.4	**26**	0405	0.6
	1058	4.3		1020	4.0
TH	1726	0.6	F	1646	0.9
	2319	4.2		2246	3.9
12	0558	0.4	**27**	0505	0.6
	1151	4.3		1120	4.1
F	1819	0.5	SA	1735	0.7
				2346	4.1
13	0016	4.3	**28**	0559	0.5
	0646	0.4		1211	4.3
SA	1246	4.3	**SU**	1831	0.6
	1905	0.4			
14	0106	4.4	**29**	0033	4.4
	0728	0.4		0656	0.4
SU	1328	4.4	M	1259	4.5
	1949	0.4		1920	0.4
15	0149	4.4	**30**	0118	4.6
	0805	0.5		0742	0.3
M	1416	4.4	TU	1346	4.6
○	2032	0.3	●	2010	0.2

JULY

Day	Time	m	Day	Time	m
1	0203	4.8	**16**	0256	4.5
	0828	0.3		0900	0.6
W	1428	4.7	TH	1511	4.5
	2058	0.1		2132	0.2
2	0248	4.9	**17**	0332	4.6
	0917	0.3		0936	0.6
TH	1516	4.7	F	1545	4.5
	2150	0.0		2209	0.2
3	0336	5.0	**18**	0406	4.6
	1003	0.3		1012	0.6
F	1558	4.7	SA	1617	4.5
	2236	-0.1		2246	0.2
4	0422	4.9	**19**	0439	4.6
	1049	0.4		1045	0.6
SA	1647	4.7	**SU**	1656	4.5
	2328	-0.1		2322	0.3
5	0512	4.9	**20**	0515	4.5
	1140	0.4		1119	0.7
SU	1739	4.6	M	1726	4.4
				2356	0.4
6	0018	-0.1	**21**	0545	4.3
	0609	4.7		1156	0.7
M	1230	0.5	TU	1758	4.3
	1835	4.5			
7	0111	0.1	**22**	0026	0.4
	0707	4.5		0626	4.2
TU	1322	0.6	W	1224	0.8
☽	1935	4.3	☾	1839	4.1
8	0206	0.2	**23**	0106	0.5
	0809	4.3		0716	4.1
W	1426	0.7	TH	1315	0.9
	2036	4.2		1936	4.0
9	0306	0.4	**24**	0155	0.7
	0916	4.1		0820	4.0
TH	1535	0.8	F	1420	0.9
	2145	4.0		2051	3.9
10	0425	0.6	**25**	0305	0.8
	1030	4.1		0929	3.9
F	1655	0.8	SA	1535	1.0
	2300	4.0		2206	3.9
11	0536	0.6	**26**	0426	0.8
	1138	4.1		1046	4.0
SA	1800	0.7	**SU**	1700	0.8
				2311	4.0
12	0001	4.1	**27**	0535	0.7
	0626	0.6		1148	4.2
SU	1236	4.2	M	1806	0.6
	1855	0.5			
13	0059	4.3	**28**	0016	4.3
	0715	0.7		0636	0.5
M	1326	4.3	TU	1245	4.4
	1939	0.4		1906	0.4
14	0146	4.4	**29**	0105	4.6
	0749	0.7		0726	0.4
TU	1406	4.3	W	1329	4.6
○	2020	0.4	●	1955	0.2
15	0225	4.5	**30**	0146	4.9
	0825	0.7		0816	0.3
W	1440	4.4	TH	1413	4.8
	2055	0.3		2046	0.0
			31	0233	5.0
				0900	0.3
			F	1456	4.9
				2136	-0.1

AUGUST

Day	Time	m	Day	Time	m
1	0316	5.1	**16**	0338	4.7
	0946	0.3		0946	0.6
SA	1543	4.9	**SU**	1549	4.7
	2219	-0.1		2220	0.2
2	0403	5.1	**17**	0407	4.7
	1032	0.3		1026	0.6
SU	1625	4.9	M	1618	4.6
	2308	-0.1		2249	0.3
3	0448	5.0	**18**	0438	4.6
	1115	0.4		1049	0.6
M	1712	4.8	TU	1649	4.6
	2349	0.0		2320	0.4
4	0541	4.8	**19**	0506	4.5
	1159	0.5		1115	0.7
TU	1802	4.6	W	1719	4.5
				2351	0.5
5	0038	0.2	**20**	0538	4.4
	0636	4.5		1156	0.7
W	1245	0.6	TH	1757	4.4
☽	1858	4.4			
6	0125	0.4	**21**	0025	0.5
	0736	4.2		0621	4.3
TH	1345	0.8	F	1241	0.8
	2000	4.1	☾	1845	4.2
7	0226	0.7	**22**	0116	0.7
	0840	3.9		0725	4.0
F	1500	0.9	SA	1335	0.9
	2115	3.9		1949	3.9
8	0346	0.9	**23**	0226	0.9
	1006	3.8		0845	3.8
SA	1625	0.9	**SU**	1500	1.0
	2240	3.8		2126	3.8
9	0511	0.9	**24**	0350	0.9
	1125	3.9		1016	3.8
SU	1746	0.8	M	1636	0.9
	2351	4.0		2250	4.0
10	0616	0.9	**25**	0515	0.8
	1225	4.1		1128	4.0
M	1846	0.6	TU	1745	0.7
				2355	4.3
11	0050	4.3	**26**	0618	0.6
	0655	0.8		1225	4.4
TU	1310	4.3	W	1850	0.4
	1931	0.5			
12	0136	4.4	**27**	0047	4.7
	0735	0.8		0710	0.5
W	1348	4.4	TH	1309	4.6
	2006	0.4		1946	0.2
13	0208	4.5	**28**	0130	4.9
	0808	0.7		0757	0.4
TH	1419	4.5	F	1353	4.8
○	2038	0.3	●	2025	0.0
14	0238	4.6	**29**	0215	5.1
	0838	0.6		0842	0.3
F	1447	4.6	SA	1434	5.0
	2110	0.2		2113	-0.1
15	0305	4.7	**30**	0256	5.1
	0916	0.6		0927	0.3
SA	1519	4.7	**SU**	1515	5.1
	2145	0.2		2158	-0.1
			31	0337	5.1
				1008	0.3
			M	1558	5.0
				2239	0.0

Chart Datum: 2.32 metres below Normaal Amsterdams Peil

NETHERLANDS - VLISSINGEN (FLUSHING)

TIME ZONE -0100
(Dutch Standard Time)
Subtract 1 hour for GMT
For Dutch Summer Time add ONE hour in non-shaded areas

LAT 51°27'N LONG 3°36'E

TIMES AND HEIGHTS OF HIGH AND LOW WATERS

YEAR **1992**

SEPTEMBER

Day	Time	m	Day	Time	m
1 TU	0423 1052 1646 2322	4.9 0.4 4.9 0.2	16 W	0406 1026 1616 2245	4.7 0.6 4.7 0.4
2 W	0509 1135 1727	4.7 0.5 4.7	17 TH	0437 1056 1652 2321	4.6 0.6 4.7 0.5
3 TH	0005 0559 1216 ☽ 1819	0.4 4.4 0.7 4.4	18 F	0511 1126 1728 2356	4.5 0.6 4.6 0.6
4 F	0045 0656 1304 1920	0.7 4.1 0.8 4.1	19 SA ☾	0556 1212 1815	4.3 0.7 4.4
5 SA	0145 0800 1425 2040	0.9 3.8 1.0 3.8	20 SU	0048 0649 1316 1922	0.7 4.0 0.8 4.0
6 SU	0305 0924 1556 2215	1.1 3.5 1.0 3.7	21 M	0156 0821 1440 2106	1.0 3.8 0.9 3.9
7 M	0445 1055 1726 2336	1.2 3.7 0.9 3.9	22 TU	0336 0945 1610 2230	1.0 3.8 0.9 4.1
8 TU	0545 1200 1826	1.0 4.0 0.7	23 W	0444 1105 1736 2335	0.9 4.0 0.6 4.4
9 W	0025 0636 1245 1906	4.2 0.9 4.2 0.5	24 TH	0606 1201 1835	0.7 4.3 0.4
10 TH	0108 0709 1326 1940	4.4 0.8 4.4 0.4	25 F	0025 0655 1247 1926	4.7 0.5 4.6 0.2
11 F	0139 0746 1356 2012	4.6 0.7 4.5 0.3	26 SA	0109 0738 1329 ● 2008	4.9 0.4 4.8 0.1
12 SA	0210 0811 1419 ○ 2046	4.6 0.6 4.6 0.3	27 SU	0151 0822 1411 2050	5.0 0.4 5.0 0.0
13 SU	0237 0846 1447 2116	4.7 0.6 4.7 0.3	28 M	0233 0903 1454 2132	5.1 0.3 5.1 0.1
14 M	0306 0921 1517 2148	4.8 0.5 4.8 0.3	29 TU	0316 0945 1535 2216	5.0 0.4 5.0 0.2
15 TU	0335 0956 1547 2218	4.8 0.6 4.7 0.4	30 W	0359 1025 1616 2252	4.8 0.4 4.9 0.4

OCTOBER

Day	Time	m	Day	Time	m
1 TH	0442 1108 1702 2330	4.6 0.5 4.7 0.6	16 F	0413 1035 1629 2256	4.6 0.6 4.8 0.6
2 F	0529 1150 1749	4.3 0.7 4.4	17 SA	0455 1116 1712 2341	4.5 0.6 4.6 0.7
3 SA	0009 0618 1235 ☽ 1846	0.9 4.0 0.8 4.0	18 SU	0537 1206 1801	4.3 0.6 4.4
4 SU	0106 0716 1344 2000	1.1 3.7 1.0 3.7	19 M	0030 0638 1306 ☾ 1916	0.8 4.0 0.7 4.1
5 M	0225 0835 1504 2146	1.3 3.5 1.1 3.6	20 TU	0146 0759 1425 2046	1.0 3.8 0.8 4.0
6 TU	0350 1026 1630 2255	1.3 3.5 1.0 3.8	21 W	0316 0926 1544 2205	1.1 3.8 0.8 4.2
7 W	0506 1125 1734 2355	1.2 3.8 0.8 4.1	22 TH	0436 1040 1716 2311	1.0 4.0 0.6 4.4
8 TH	0600 1209 1824	1.0 4.1 0.6	23 F	0540 1138 1815	0.8 4.3 0.4
9 F	0035 0640 1246 1906	4.4 0.8 4.3 0.5	24 SA	0006 0636 1225 1902	4.6 0.6 4.6 0.3
10 SA	0105 0716 1317 1935	4.5 0.7 4.5 0.4	25 SU	0048 0715 1308 ● 1947	4.8 0.5 4.8 0.2
11 SU	0136 0746 1345 ○ 2010	4.6 0.6 4.6 0.4	26 M	0132 0800 1349 2026	4.9 0.4 4.9 0.2
12 M	0202 0815 1416 2039	4.7 0.6 4.7 0.4	27 TU	0213 0846 1432 2107	4.9 0.4 4.9 0.3
13 TU	0235 0850 1446 2116	4.8 0.5 4.8 0.4	28 W	0256 0925 1516 2146	4.8 0.4 4.9 0.4
14 W	0306 0926 1519 2151	4.8 0.5 4.8 0.4	29 TH	0339 1006 1557 2225	4.7 0.4 4.8 0.6
15 TH	0338 1000 1553 2226	4.7 0.6 4.8 0.5	30 F	0422 1046 1641 2302	4.5 0.5 4.6 0.8
			31 SA	0502 1125 1728 2346	4.3 0.6 4.4 1.0

NOVEMBER

Day	Time	m	Day	Time	m
1 SU	0550 1216 1820	4.1 0.8 4.1	16 M	0531 1202 1758	4.3 0.5 4.5
2 M	0030 0640 1315 ☽ 1915	1.1 3.8 0.9 3.8	17 TU	0022 0635 1305 ☾ 1905	0.8 4.1 0.6 4.3
3 TU	0146 0735 1425 2024	1.3 3.6 1.0 3.7	18 W	0125 0745 1416 2026	0.9 4.0 0.6 4.2
4 W	0255 0900 1536 2200	1.3 3.5 0.9 3.7	19 TH	0239 0858 1530 2135	1.0 4.0 0.6 4.2
5 TH	0406 1036 1634 2301	1.2 3.7 0.9 3.9	20 F	0400 1005 1646 2245	1.0 4.1 0.6 4.3
6 F	0516 1126 1745 2350	1.1 3.9 0.7 4.2	21 SA	0516 1107 1756 2346	0.9 4.2 0.5 4.5
7 SA	0555 1206 1826	0.9 4.1 0.6	22 SU	0616 1201 1840	0.7 4.4 0.4
8 SU	0025 0635 1239 1905	4.4 0.8 4.3 0.5	23 M	0031 0701 1247 1926	4.6 0.6 4.6 0.4
9 M	0058 0709 1312 1936	4.5 0.7 4.5 0.5	24 TU	0117 0746 1335 ● 2006	4.6 0.5 4.7 0.4
10 TU	0132 0746 1347 ○ 2011	4.7 0.6 4.7 0.4	25 W	0200 0828 1418 2046	4.6 0.4 4.7 0.5
11 W	0207 0826 1420 2045	4.7 0.6 4.8 0.4	26 TH	0242 0908 1501 2126	4.6 0.4 4.7 0.6
12 TH	0243 0905 1458 2122	4.7 0.5 4.8 0.5	27 F	0326 0948 1542 2159	4.5 0.4 4.7 0.7
13 F	0319 0945 1536 2202	4.7 0.5 4.8 0.5	28 SA	0406 1030 1626 2235	4.5 0.4 4.6 0.8
14 SA	0358 1025 1616 2246	4.6 0.5 4.8 0.6	29 SU	0445 1110 1709 2315	4.3 0.5 4.4 0.9
15 SU	0443 1109 1702 2330	4.5 0.5 4.7 0.7	30 M	0525 1156 1756	4.2 0.6 4.2

DECEMBER

Day	Time	m	Day	Time	m
1 TU	0000 0610 1247 1842	1.0 4.1 0.7 4.0	16 W	0012 0619 1255 ☾ 1856	0.7 4.3 0.3 4.5
2 W	0056 0700 1346 ☽ 1940	1.1 3.9 0.8 3.9	17 TH	0110 0726 1356 2002	0.8 4.2 0.4 4.4
3 TH	0205 0756 1434 2034	1.2 3.7 0.9 3.8	18 F	0216 0826 1456 2106	0.9 4.1 0.5 4.2
4 F	0310 0859 1539 2155	1.2 3.7 0.9 3.8	19 SA	0326 0935 1604 2215	0.9 4.1 0.6 4.2
5 SA	0404 1016 1639 2255	1.2 3.7 0.8 4.0	20 SU	0446 1041 1726 2321	0.9 4.1 0.6 4.2
6 SU	0506 1115 1736 2346	1.0 3.9 0.8 4.2	21 M	0550 1142 1820	0.8 4.2 0.6
7 M	0555 1159 1826	0.9 4.1 0.7	22 TU	0019 0645 1239 1905	4.3 0.7 4.3 0.6
8 TU	0025 0634 1241 1906	4.3 0.8 4.3 0.6	23 W	0107 0729 1325 1951	4.4 0.5 4.4 0.6
9 W	0106 0726 1321 ○ 1942	4.5 0.7 4.5 0.5	24 TH	0156 0815 1410 ● 2025	4.4 0.5 4.5 0.7
10 TH	0145 0805 1400 2026	4.6 0.5 4.7 0.5	25 F	0236 0856 1452 2106	4.4 0.4 4.6 0.7
11 F	0226 0845 1442 2109	4.7 0.4 4.8 0.5	26 SA	0316 0935 1531 2140	4.5 0.3 4.6 0.7
12 SA	0305 0933 1523 2150	4.7 0.3 4.9 0.5	27 SU	0348 1011 1608 2216	4.5 0.3 4.6 0.7
13 SU	0348 1026 1608 2238	4.7 0.3 4.9 0.5	28 M	0428 1049 1647 2256	4.5 0.3 4.5 0.8
14 M	0435 1110 1655 2325	4.6 0.3 4.8 0.6	29 TU	0505 1124 1726 2330	4.4 0.4 4.4 0.8
15 TU	0526 1159 1752	4.5 0.3 4.6	30 W	0542 1206 1808	4.3 0.5 4.2
			31 TH	0005 0619 1246 1849	0.9 4.2 0.6 4.1

Chart Datum: 2.32 metres below Normaal Amsterdams Peil

VLISSINGEN (FLUSHING) *continued*

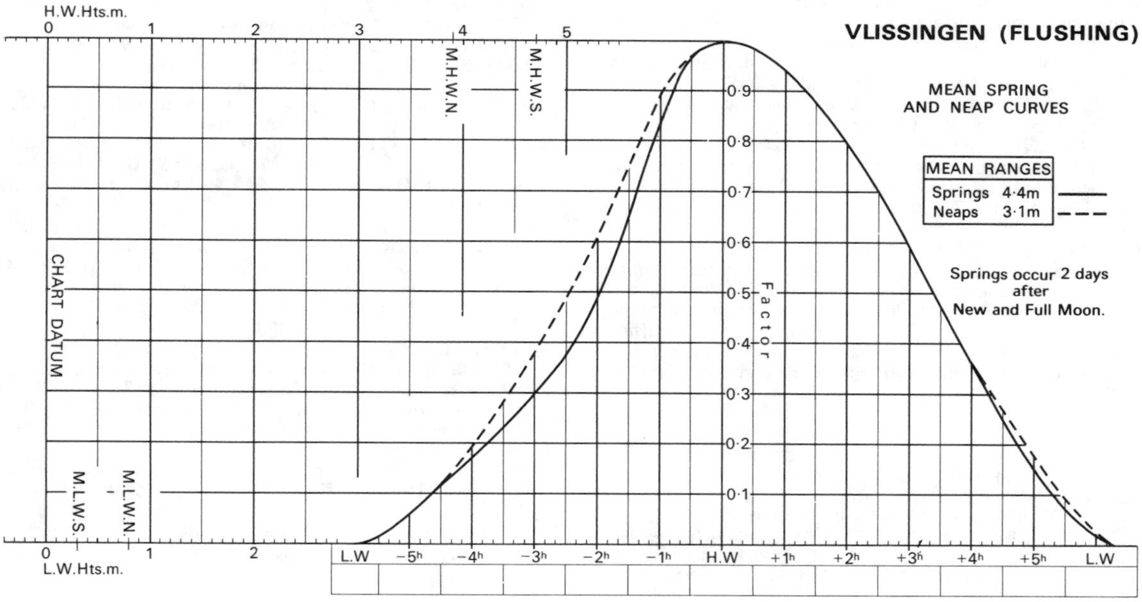
VLISSINGEN (FLUSHING)
MEAN SPRING AND NEAP CURVES
MEAN RANGES
Springs 4·4m
Neaps 3·1m
Springs occur 2 days after New and Full Moon.
H.W.Hts.m.
L.W.Hts.m.
CHART DATUM
M.H.W.N.
M.H.W.S.
M.L.W.S.
M.L.W.N.
Factor
L.W −5h −4h −3h −2h −1h H.W +1h +2h +3h +4h +5h L.W

OOSTERSCHELDE 10-20-18

Zeeland

CHARTS
Admiralty 192, 120, 110; Zeekaart 1448; Dutch Yacht Charts 1805, 1807; Stanford 19; Imray C30

TIDES
Dover +0230; ML Sas van Goes 2·0; Zierikzee 1·8
Duration Sas van Goes 0615; Zierikzee 0640; Zone −0100

Standard Port VLISSINGEN (←)

Times				Height (metres)			
HW		LW		MHWS	MHWN	MLWN	MLWS
0300	0900	0400	1000	4·7	3·9	0·8	0·3
1500	2100	1600	2200				
Differences ROOMPOT (outside)							
+0002	+0002	−0004	−0004	No data		No data	
ROOMPOT (inside)							
+0019	+0119	+0101	+0101	No data		No data	
WEMELDINGE							
+0134	+0134	+0110	+0110	No data		No data	
KRAMMER LOCKS							
+0135	+0135	+0105	+0105	No data		No data	
BERGSEDIEP LOCK							
+0133	+0133	+0113	+0113	No data		No data	

SHELTER
Inside the barrier good shelter is found in several harbours – for example Colijnsplaat and Zierikzee, which are both west of Zeelandbrug (bridge connecting Noord Beveland and Duiveland) and accessible at any tide. Veerse Meer is a non-tidal waterway with mooring places for yachts: access from Oosterschelde at Zandkreekdam lock, or through Kanaal door Walcheren via Vlissingen and Middelburg from Westerschelde. Access can be made via Bergsediepsluis, near Tholen to the Schelde-Rijn Canal and to the South Beveland canal at Wemeldinge.

NAVIGATION
Waypoint WG1 (stbd-hand) buoy, QG, 51°38′·00N 03°26′·30E at entrance to Westgat/Oude Roompot buoyed channel. Not advisable to enter in strong W to NW winds, and only from HW−6 to HW+1½ Zierikzee. There are several offshore banks, see 10.20.5. All vessels

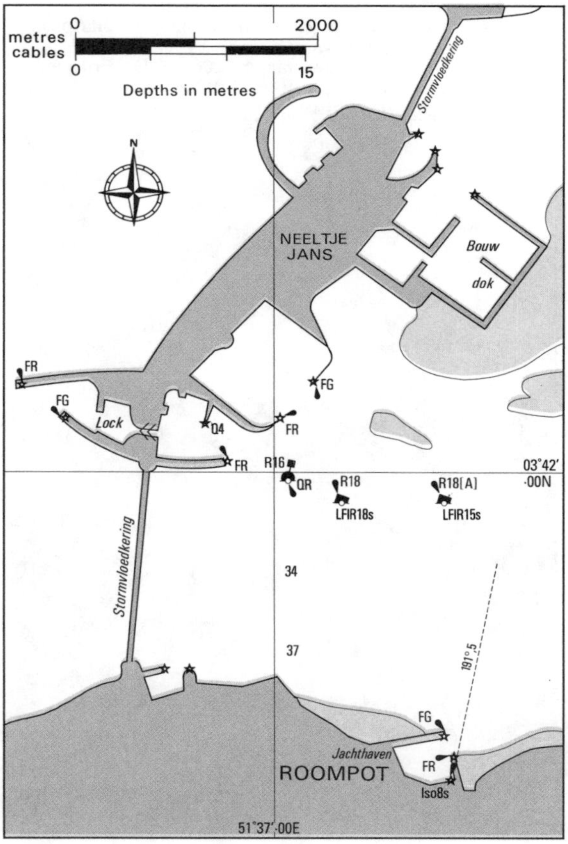
metres
cables
0
2000
15
Depths in metres
N
Stormvloedkering
NEELTJE JANS
Bouw
dok
FR
FG
Lock
Q4
FG
FR
FR
R16
QR
R18
LFIR18s
R18(A)
LFIR15s
03°42′·00N
34
37
191°5
Stormvloedkering
FG
Jachthaven
ROOMPOT
FR
Iso8s
51°37′·00E

20

OOSTERSCHELDE *continued*

must use the Roompotsluis (lock). The areas each side of the barrier are very dangerous due to strong tidal streams and many obstructions. Passage is prohibited west of Roggenplaat. Zeelandbrug clearance 11·5m at centre of arch in buoyed channels. Clearance is indicated on some of bridge supports, in metres. Bascule bridge near N end lifts except when wind in excess of Force 7.

LIGHTS AND MARKS

There are few prominent marks in the approaches. For principal lights and waypoints see 10.20.4. Roompot Marina Ldg Lts 070°30′ both Oc G 5s Entrance, W side FG, E side FR; depth 5m.

RADIO TELEPHONE

Zeelandbrug VHF Ch 18. Roompotsluis Ch 18. Krammer Locks. Call *Krammersluizen* Ch 22 (H24). Wemeldinge Locks Ch 68. Zandreek lock. Zandkneeksluis Wemeldinge Ch 18, Bruinisse lock Sluis Grevelingen Ch 20, Traffic control (Wemeldinge) (MUST be called if entering Wemeldinge or canal entrance) Verkeerspost Wemeldinge Ch 68, 18.

There are numerous ports to visit and the following is a selection of the more important ones (working anti-clockwise, starting from the Roompotsluis).

ROOMPOT MARINA (150+80 visitors) ☎ (01117) 4225, AC, D, P, Slip, FW, Gas, Gaz, ⊡, R, V, Bar, Ⓑ (Dr ☎ 2565).

COLIJNSPLAAT Hr Mr ☎ 762; YC ☎ 806, ⊡; Dr ☎ 304; **Marina WV Noord YC Beveland** AC, Slip, FW, berth N side of mole or W side of basin; **Delta Yacht** ☎ 776, P, D, BH (35 ton), ME, SM; **De Koster** ME; **Town** V, R, Gaz, ✉; Ⓑ; ≷ (Goes), ✈ (Antwerpen).

KATS. **Marina Jachtwerf. Rest Nautic BV** ☎ 270, D, ME, BH (35 ton), FW; **Lion Sails Holland** ☎ 291, SM.

GOES The canal up to Goes starts at Sas van Goes where there is a marina; there are no facilities at Wilhelminadorp half way up the canal. At Goes Hr Mr ☎ 27257; Dr ☎ 27451; Ⓗ ☎ 27000; **Marina WV 'De Werf'** ☎ 16572, FW, C (3½ ton), P, D; **Beekman** ☎ 27383 ME, El, Sh; **Jachtwerf Goes** ☎ 23944, Slip; **Sporthuis Olympia** ☎ 16008, Gaz; **Delta** ☎ 27338, ⊡. **Town** V, R, ✉; Ⓑ; ≷; ✈ (Antwerpen).

WEMELDINGE Hr Mr ☎ 2093; Dr ☎ 1438; Yachts pass through Westsluis locks and berth W side of Binnenhaven. **A. Wagenaar** ☎ 1286, P, D; **Florusse** ☎ 1253, ME, SM, AC, C (6.5 ton) ME; **Town**, V, R, ✉; Ⓑ; ≷ (Goes); ✈ (Antwerpen).

YERSEKE Hr Mr ☎ 1726 (VHF Ch 09); Dr ☎ 1444; **Marina Prins Willem-Alexanderhaven** FW, P, D, C; **Prins Beatrixhaven** Slip, FW, P, D; **J. Zoetewey** ☎ 1390, Gaz, SM; **W. Bakker** ☎ 1521, ME; **Town** V, BY, R, ✉; Ⓑ; ≷ (Kruiningen); ✈ (Antwerpen).

ST ANNALAND Dr ☎ 2400, ⊡; **Marina** Hr Mr ☎ 2463, Slip, BH (30 ton), AC, FW; **YC** ☎ 2634, ⊡, Bar, R; **J. Keur** ☎ 2454, P, D; **Jacht en Metaalbouw** ☎ 2282, Sh, El, CH, BH (25 ton), ME, Gaz, BY; **C. Bal** ☎ 2440, ME; **Town** Gaz, V, R, Ⓑ; ✉; ≷ (Bergen op Zoom); ✈ (Antwerpen).

BRUINISSE **Vissershaven** not for yachts; Hr Mr ☎ (01113) 1451 office, Dr ☎ (01113) 1280; **Marina WV 'Bru'** Hr Mr ☎ (01113) 1506, FW; **Aqua Delta** Hr Mr ☎ (01113) 1485, FW, AC, Slip, P, D, ⊡, Gaz, Bar, V; **Rowi Watersportservice** ☎ (01113) 2195, ME, C (16 ton), Sh. **Town** ✉, Ⓑ, ≷, ✈ (Rotterdam)

ZIERIKZEE Hr Mr ☎ (01110) 13174, Dr 12080, Ⓗ 16900; **Marina 't Luitje** and **Nieuwe Haven: WV Zierikzee** Hr Mr ☎ 14877, FW, AC; **Bouwman & Zn** ☎ 12966, P, D, Gaz; **Vrijland Watersport** C (18 ton), ME, Sh; **'t Loefje** ☎ 13403, SM, CH. **Town** ⊡, V, R, ✉, Ⓑ; ≷, ✈ (Rotterdam).

NIEUWE HAVEN AB, FW; **W. Bouwman** ☎ 2966, P, D, Gaz, AC; **Town** V, R, ✉; Ⓑ; ≷; ✈ (Rotterdam).

BURGHSLUIS Hr Mr ☎ 1302; **Marina** FW, AC, C (6 ton), **Blom** ☎ 2020, ME, AC; Facilities at Burg-Haamstede P, D, Gaz, ✉; Ⓑ; ≷; ✈ (Rotterdam)

TOWNS IN THE VEERSE MEER (non-tidal)

MIDDELBURG Dr ☎ 12637; Ⓗ ☎ 25555; **Marina WV 'Arne'** in the Dockhaven, ☎ 27180, FW, AC, ME, El, Sh, SM, ⊡; **J. Boone** ☎ 29913, D, Gaz, CH; **Jachtwerf Jansen** ☎ 13925, AC, Sh, Slip; **Town** V, R, Bar, ✉; Ⓑ; ≷; ✈ (Rotterdam). Note: No mooring in Kanaal door Walcheren.

VEERE Dr ☎ 1271; Yachts can berth in the Stadshaven or in the Buitenhaven. **Jachtwerf Veere** ☎ 1246, FW, AC, **Jachtclub Veere** ☎ 246, FW, M; **Jachthaven Oostwatering** ☎ 484, Slip, FW; **Town** V, R, Bar, ✉; Ⓑ; ≷ (Middelburg); ✈ (Rotterdam).

KORTGENE **Delta Marina** ☎ (01108) 1315 C (16 ton), P, D, FW, AC, CH, El, ⊡, ME, R, Sh, SM, V; **Town** V, R, Bar, Dr (tel 13 19), ✉, Ⓑ, ≷ (Goes), Air (Rotterdam).

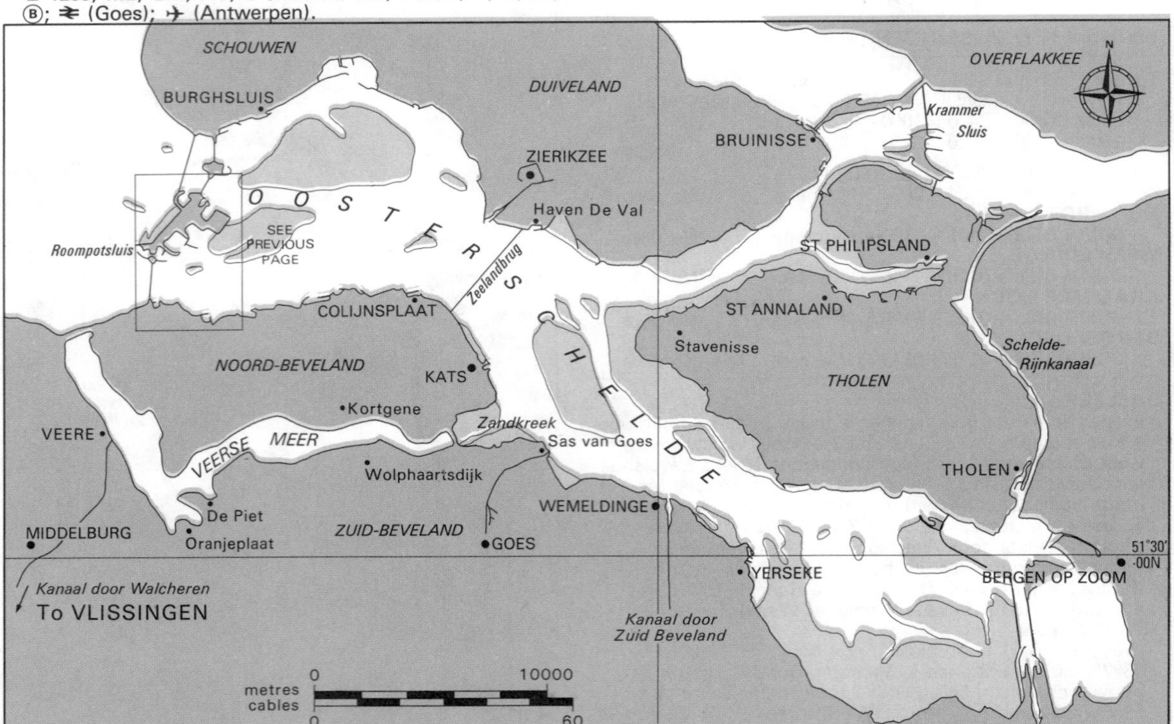
SCHOUWEN
DUIVELAND
OVERFLAKKEE
N
BURGHSLUIS
Krammer
Sluis
BRUINISSE
ZIERIKZEE
O O S T E R S C H E L D E
Haven De Val
SEE PREVIOUS PAGE
Roompotsluis
Zeelandbrug
ST PHILIPSLAND
COLIJNSPLAAT
ST ANNALAND
Stavenisse
Schelde-Rijnkanaal
NOORD-BEVELAND
KATS
THOLEN
Kortgene
VEERE
VEERSE MEER
Zandkreek
Sas van Goes
Wolphaartsdijk
THOLEN
De Piet
WEMELDINGE
MIDDELBURG
Oranjeplaat
ZUID-BEVELAND
GOES
51°30′·00N
YERSEKE
BERGEN OP ZOOM
Kanaal door Walcheren
To VLISSINGEN
Kanaal door Zuid Beveland
metres
cables
0
10000
0
60
04°00′·00E

STELLENDAM (HELLEVOETSLUIS) 10-20-19

Zuid Holland

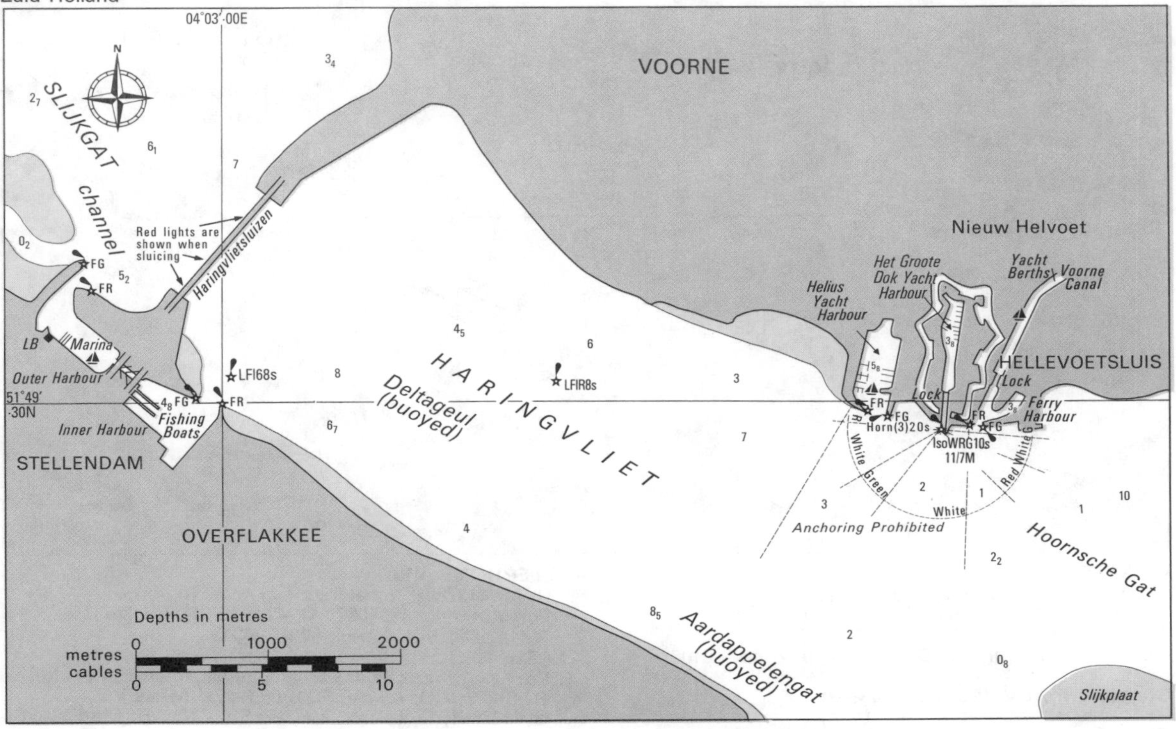
04°03'·00E
VOORNE
SLIJKGAT channel
Red lights are shown when sluicing
Haringvlietsluizen
FG
FR
LB
Marina
Outer Harbour
51°49'·30N
Inner Harbour
Fishing Boats
STELLENDAM
LFl68s
FR
Deltageul (buoyed)
HARINGVLIET
LFlR8s
Nieuw Helvoet
Het Groote Dok Yacht Harbour
Helius Yacht Harbour
Yacht Berths
Voorne Canal
HELLEVOETSLUIS
Lock
Ferry Harbour
Horn(3)20s
IsoWRG10s 11/7M
White
Green
Red
Anchoring Prohibited
Hoornsche Gat
OVERFLAKKEE
Depths in metres
metres
cables
Aardappelengat (buoyed)
Slijkplaat

CHARTS

Admiralty 2322; Zeekaart 1448; Dutch Yacht Chart: 1801, 1807; Stanford 19; Imray C30

TIDES

Dover +0300; ML 1·2; Duration 0510; Zone −0100

Standard Port VLISSINGEN (⟵)

Times				Height (metres)			
HW		LW		MHWS	MHWN	MLWN	MLWS
0300	0900	0400	1000	4·7	3·9	0·8	0·3
1500	2100	1600	2200				
Differences HARINGVLIETSLUIZEN							
+0016	+0014	+0006	−0026	−1·8	−1·7	−0·5	0·0

NOTE: Double LWs occur — The rise after the first LW is called Agger — Predictions for Hoek van Holland are for the lower LW which is usually the second. Time differences for Secondary Ports referred to Hoek van Holland are approximate — Water levels on this coast are considerably affected by the weather. Strong NW gales can raise levels up to 3m.

SHELTER

There are pontoons exclusively for yachts in the Aqua Pesch Marina in the Outer Harbour. Dangerous to enter Slijkgat with strong NW to W winds. Once through the lock, shelter in fishing harbour just inside lock or at one of the three yacht harbours at Hellevoetsluis (4M), the Industriehaven, the old harbour to the W or in the Voorne canal.

NAVIGATION

Waypoint Slijkgat SG safe water buoy, Iso 4s, 51°52'·00N 03°51'·50E, 290°/110° from/to Kwade Hoek Lt, 5·0M. The N passage to the Stellendam Lock, the Gat van de Hawk is no longer buoyed. It is therefore advisable to take the Slijkgat passage along the Goeree Shore. This is well buoyed and lit but beware a shoal about 5 ca from the lock, marked by G conical buoys. Keep clear of dam during sluicing.

LIGHTS AND MARKS

Hellevoetsluis Lt Iso WRG 10s 16m 11/7M, W stone Tr, R cupola. G Shore-275°, W275°-294°, R294°-316°, W316°-036°, G036°-058°, W058°-095°, R096°-shore
Sluicing signals — 3 R Lts in triangle shown from pillar heads on dam. Danger area marked with small R buoys.

RADIO TELEPHONE

Call: *Goereesesluis* VHF Ch 20.

TELEPHONE (01879)

Hr Mr Stellendam 1000; Hellevoetsluis 30911; ⊞ Rotterdam 298088 or Flushing 60000
Police 2444; Dr 1425; Dr Hellevoetsluis 12435;
Brit Consul (020) 764343.

FACILITIES

STELLENDAM **Aqua Pesch Marina** ☎ 2600, Slip, P, D, FW, C (8 ton); **Het Dumppaleis** ☎ 1529 Gaz; **Town** V, R, Bar, ✉ (2½ km); ⇌ (Hellevoetsluis); ✈ (Rotterdam).
HELLEVOETSLUIS **Het Groote Dok** ☎ 12166, P, D, L, El, Ⓔ, Gaz, FW, ME, CH, AB; **Helius Haven YC** ☎ 15868, P, D, FW, AB; **Voorne Canal YC** ☎ 12870, P, D, FW, AB; **Town** P, D, V, R, Bar, ✉; Ⓑ; ⇌; ✈ (Rotterdam).
Ferry UK — Hook of Holland—Harwich or Rotterdam—Hull.
Note. Voorne canal is dammed 4½M above entrance. An alternative port is Middelharnis, 4M upstream of Hellevoetsluis. Bound for Rotterdam, proceed by canals via Spui or Dordrecht.

ROTTERDAM 10-20-20

Zuid Holland

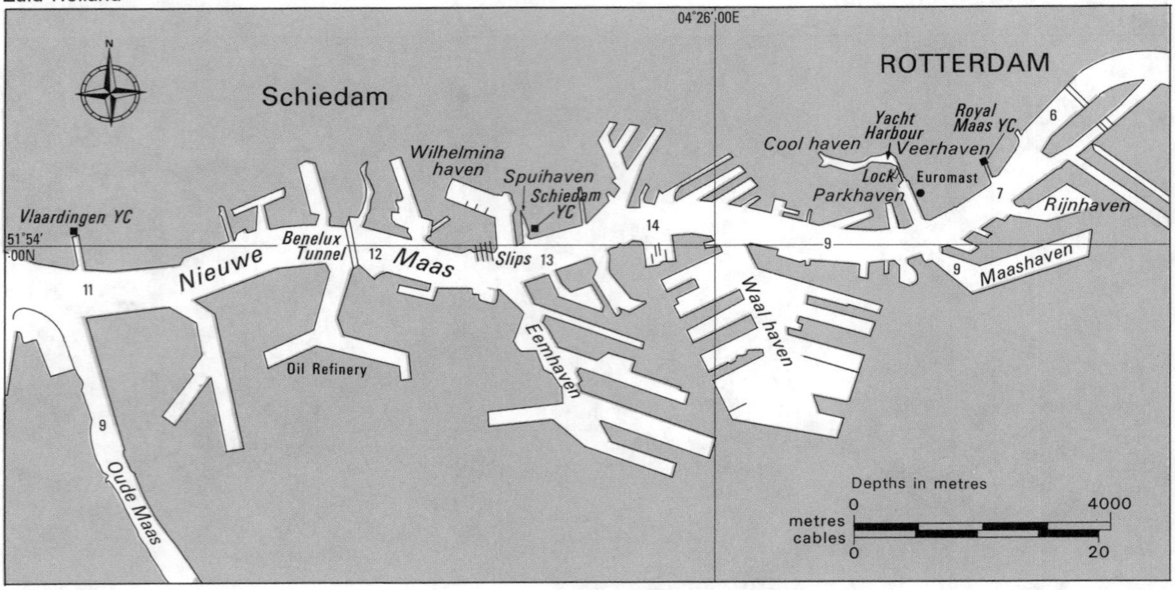
04°26'.00E
ROTTERDAM
Schiedam
N
Yacht Harbour
Royal Maas YC
6
Cool haven
Veerhaven
Wilhelmina haven
Spuihaven
Schiedam YC
Lock
Euromast
Parkhaven
7
Rijnhaven
Vlaardingen YC
51°54'.00N
14
Benelux Tunnel
12
Maas
Slips
13
9
Maashaven
Nieuwe
11
Waal haven
Eemhaven
Oil Refinery
9
Oude Maas
Depths in metres
0
4000
metres
cables
0
20

CHARTS
Admiralty 133, 132 122; Zeekaart 1540/1/2; Dutch Yacht Chart 1809; Stanford 19

TIDES
Dover +0414; ML 1.1; Duration 0440; Zone −0100

Standard Port VLISSINGEN (⟵)

Times				Height (metres)			
HW		LW		MHWS	MHWN	MLWN	MLWS
0300	0900	0400	1000	4.7	3.9	0.8	0.3
1500	2100	1600	2200				
Differences ROTTERDAM							
+0202	+0156	+0313	+0400	−2.7	−2.2	−0.6	−0.1

NOTE: Double LWs occur — The rise after the first LW is called the Agger — Predictions for Hoek van Holland are for the lower LW which is usually the second. Time differences for Secondary Ports referred to Hoek van Holland are approximate — Water levels on this coast are considerably affected by the weather. Strong NW gales can raise levels by up to 3m.

SHELTER
Shelter is good in the various yacht harbours but in the river there is always a very considerable sea and swell due to constant heavy traffic (Rotterdam/Europoort is the world's largest port complex). From Berghaven to Rotterdam is about 19 M. All but local yachts are actively discouraged from using the Nieuwe Maas.

NAVIGATION
See 10.20.21. There are no navigational dangers other than the amount of heavy sea-going traffic. 7 M before the centre of Rotterdam, the Oude Maas joins; from here to Dordrecht, sailing is prohibited. Speed limit – 6 kn.

LIGHTS AND MARKS
Marks to locate Yacht Harbours:
(1) Where Oude Maas enters from S, on N bank by Delta Hotel, between kilometre posts 1010-1011 entrance to Vlaardingen YC.
(2) 2 M further up, just above the entrance to Wilhelmina Haven at Schiedam is the Spuihaven.
(3) Parkhaven and the lock through to Coolhaven are clearly marked on the N bank by the huge Euromast in the park.
(4) The Royal Maas YC at the Veerhaven is less than one M further up on the N bank. The Veerhaven is a normal yacht harbour, mainly for traditional yachts.

RADIO TELEPHONE
There is a comprehensive Traffic Management and Information Service. See details under Hook of Holland 10.20.21.

TELEPHONE (010)
Hr Mr 4137681; Local Rijn Pilot 4659110; Port Authority 4894062; # 4298088; Police 4143144; Ⓗ 4112800; Brit Consul (020) 764343.

FACILITIES
Yacht Harbour ☎ 4138514, Slip, M, P, D, L, FW, ME, El, Sh, C, CH, AB, V, R, Bar; **Royal Maas YC** ☎ 4137681, D, L, FW, ME, El, Sh, CH, AB; **Maassluis** AB, By, ME, SM, FW, P, D, Gaz; **Schiedam YC** ☎ 4267765, D, L, FW, ME, El, Sh, CH, AB; **A.L. Valkhof** ☎ 4131226, P, D; **Watersport BV** ☎ 4841937, ME; **Vlaardingen YC** M, By, ME, SM, FW, P, D, Gaz; **Observator** ☎ 4130060, ACA; **Handelsmij Leeflang** ☎ 4181860, Gaz; **L. J. Harri** ☎ 4290333 Dutch Chart Agent; **Datema Delfzigl** ☎ 4366188 Dutch Chart Agent; **Sestrel Observator** ☎ 4130060 Dutch Chart Agent;
Town all facilities. ✉; Ⓑ; ⇌; ✈. Ferry UK — Hull.
Note: Special regulations apply to yachts in the Rhine. These are given in a French booklet '*Service de la Navigation du Rhin*' obtainable from 25 Rue de la Nuée Bleu, 6700, Strasbourg.

HOEK VAN HOLLAND 10-20-21 (HOOK OF HOLLAND)

Zuid Holland

CHARTS
Admiralty 132, 122; Zeekaart 1540, 1349, 1350, 1449; Dutch Yacht Chart 1809, 1801; Stanford 19; Imray C30, Y5

TIDES
Dover +0251; ML 1·1; Duration 0505; Zone −0100

Standard Port VLISSINGEN (←)

Times				Height (metres)			
HW		LW		MHWS	MHWN	MLWN	MLWS
0300	0900	0400	1000	4·7	3·9	0·8	0·3
1500	2100	1600	2200				
Differences HOEK VAN HOLLAND							
+0033	+0038	+0118	+0107	−2·4	−2·1	−0·5	+0·1
MAASSLUIS							
+0201	+0136	+0040	0000	−2·8	−2·2	−0·6	0·0

NOTE: Hook of Holland is a Standard Port and tidal predictions for each day of the year are given below. Double LWs occur — The rise after the first LW is called The Agger — Predictions for Hoek van Holland are for the lower LW which is usually the second. Time differences for Secondary Ports referred to Hoek van Holland are approximate — Water levels on this coast are considerably affected by the weather. Strong NW gales can raise the levels by up to 3m.

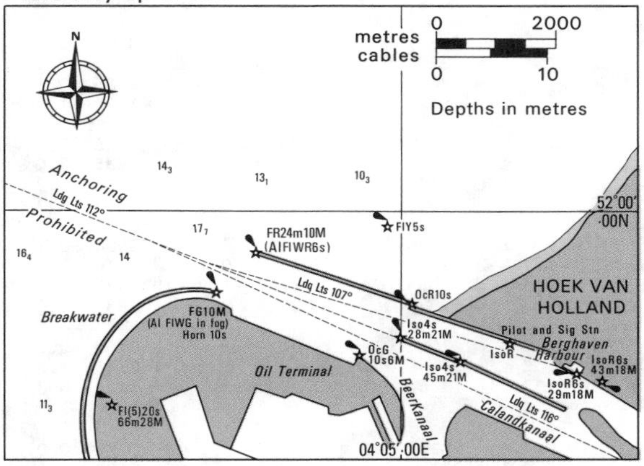

metres
cables
0
2000
0
10
Depths in metres
N
Anchoring
Prohibited
Ldg Lts 112°
FR24m10M (AlFlWR6s)
FlY5s
52°00'·00N
Ldg Lts 107°
OcR10s
HOEK VAN HOLLAND
Breakwater
FG10M (Al FlWG in fog) Horn 10s
Iso4s 28m21M
Pilot and Sig Stn
Berghaven
Harbour
OcG 10s6M
Iso4s 45m21M
IsoR6s 43m18M
IsoR6s 29m18M
Oil Terminal
Beerkanaal
Calandkanaal
Ldg Lts 116°
Fl(5)20s 66m28M
04°05'·00E

SHELTER
Entrance safe except in strong on-shore winds when heavy seas develop. Berghaven harbour not open to yachts. Better shelter at Maassluis, 10M up river.

NAVIGATION
Waypoints From S: MV-N N cardinal buoy, Q, 51°59'·65N 04°00'·30E, 288°/108° from/to Nieuwe Zuiderdam Lt, 1·5M. From N: Indusbank N cardinal buoy, Q, 52°02'·93N 04°03'·72E, 010°/190° from/to Nieuwe Noorderdam Lt, 3·2M. There are no real navigational dangers but care should be taken of the strong tidal set across the entrance. The river is a very busy waterway and the stream of ocean-going and local shipping is constant. See Maas Traffic Scheme Fig 2(4). Neither the Calandkanaal nor the Beerkanaal may be used by pleasure craft. Yachts crossing the Hook of Holland roadstead are recommended to call Maas Entrance on Ch 03, reporting yacht's name, position and course, and maintain watch on Ch 03. Yachts should cross under power on a track close W of line joining buoys MV (51°57'·5N, 3°58'·5E), MVN (51°59'·7N, 4°00'·3E) and Indusbank N (52°03'·0N, 4°03'·7E).

LIGHTS AND MARKS
Maasvlakte Fl(5) 20s 66m 28M; B 8-sided Tr, Or bands; vis 340°-267° (H24). Nieuwe Noorderdam, head FR 24m 10M; Or Tr, B bands, helicopter platform; in fog Al Fl WR 6s. Nieuwe Zuiderdam, head FG 24m 10M; Or Tr, B bands, helicopter platform; in fog Al Fl WG 6s; Horn 10s. Ldg Lts 107° (for Rotterdamsche Waterweg). Front Iso R 6s 29m 18M; R Tr, W bands; vis 100°-114° (H24). Rear Iso R 6s 43m 18M; R Tr, W bands; vis 100°-114° (H24), synchronized with front.
Traffic signals from Pilot and Signal Station:
Visible to seaward
R R
W } Entry to Rotterdamsche Waterweg prohibited
R R
Traffic signals from S side of Rotterdamsche Waterweg, opposite Berghaven:
Visible from landward
R R
W } Navigation to sea prohibited
R R
Patrol vessels show a Fl Bu Lt. If such vessels show a Fl R Lt, it means 'Stop'.

RADIO TELEPHONE
A comprehensive Traffic Management and Information Service operates in the Rotterdam waterway. Four Traffic Centres are manned H24: Haven Coordinatie Centrum (HCC) VHF Ch 11 14; Traffic Centre, Hoek van Holland (TCH) Ch 13; Traffic Centre Botlek (VCB) Ch 13; Traffic Centre Stad (VCS) Ch 13. The area is divided into sectors as below; vessels should listen on the assigned frequency and use it for messages unless otherwise directed.
Maas Approach Ch 01, TCH (Outer approaches to W boundary of Precautionary Area); *Pilot Mass* Ch 02, TCH (outer part of Precautionary Area); *Maas Entrance* Ch 03, TCH (inner part of Precautionary Area); *Waterweg* Ch 65, TCH (Nieuwe Waterweg to Kruitsteiger); *Europoort* Ch 66, TCH (Calandkanaal); *Maassluis* Ch 80, VCB (kp 1023 to kp 1017); *Botlek* Ch 61, VCB (kp 1017 to kp 1011); *Eemhaven* Ch 63, VCS (kp 1011 to kp 1007); *Waalhaven* Ch 60, VCS (kp 1007 to kp 1003); *Massbruggen* Ch 81, VCS (kp 1003 to kp 998); *Brienenoord* Ch 21, VCS (kp 998 to kp 993).
Yachts should report to Maas Approach or Pilot Maas (or to Maas Entrance if using the Inshore Traffic Zone) and follow instructions. Information broadcasts by Maas Approach and HCC on Ch 01. Weather on Ch 14 every H+00.
Other stations: Oude Maas (call: *RHD Post Hartel*) Ch 10; 13. Botlekbrug Ch 13; Spijkenisserbrug Ch 18.
Dordrecht (call: *Post Dordrecht*) Ch 08 10 13 14 71 (H24).

TELEPHONE (01747)
Hr Mr Rotterdam 896911; Rotterdam Port Authority 894062; Pilot Hook of Holland 4840; CG 2579; # 2418; Police 13444; H Rotterdam 112800;
Brit Consul (020) 764343.

FACILITIES
Schoemeyer ☎ 3464, ME, Sh; **N.C. Ruygers** ☎ 2487., FW; **Maassluis** AB, BY, CH, El, ME, P, ✉; R, Sh, V, ≹.
Town P, D, V, R, Bar. ✉; Ⓑ; ≹; ✈ (Rotterdam).
Ferry UK—Harwich.

HOEK VAN HOLLAND
MEAN SPRING AND NEAP CURVES

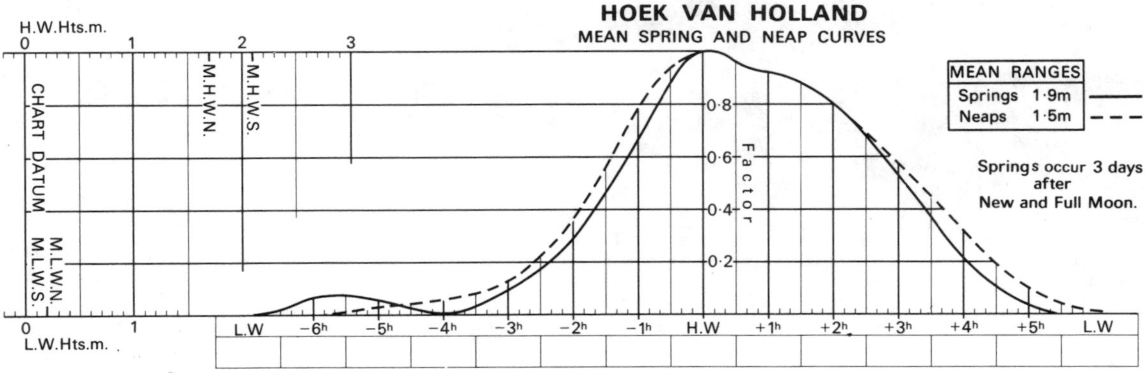

H.W.Hts.m.
0
1
2
3
CHART DATUM
M.H.W.N.
M.H.W.S.
M.L.W.N.
M.L.W.S.
0
1
L.W.Hts.m.
0·8
0·6
0·4
0·2
Factor
MEAN RANGES
Springs 1·9m
Neaps 1·5m
Springs occur 3 days after New and Full Moon.
L.W
−6h
−5h
−4h
−3h
−2h
−1h
H.W
+1h
+2h
+3h
+4h
+5h
L.W

20

TIME ZONE -0100
(Dutch Standard Time)
Subtract 1 hour for GMT
For Dutch Summer Time add ONE hour in non-shaded areas

NETHERLANDS - HOEK VAN HOLLAND

LAT 51°59'N LONG 4°07'E

TIMES AND HEIGHTS OF HIGH AND LOW WATERS

YEAR **1992**

JANUARY

Day	Time	m	Day	Time	m
1 W	0740	0.4	16 TH	0450	0.4
	1158	1.8		1109	1.8
	1946	0.3		1654	0.2
				2345	1.8
2 TH	0039	1.9	17 F	0534	0.4
	0905	0.3		1215	1.9
	1253	1.9		1753	0.3
	2117	0.4			
3 F	0134	1.9	18 SA	0045	1.9
	0934	0.3		0625	0.3
	1348	1.9		1304	2.0
	1935	0.4		1843	0.3
4 SA	0213	1.9	19 SU	0134	1.9
	1020	0.3		0705	0.2
	1434	2.0		1354	2.1
	● 2015	0.5		○ 1929	0.3
5 SU	0314	1.9	20 M	0224	2.0
	0824	0.2		0745	0.2
	1503	2.0		1436	2.2
	2055	0.5		2245	0.4
6 M	0339	1.9	21 TU	0307	2.0
	0854	0.2		0825	0.1
	1538	2.1		1525	2.3
	2156	0.5		2346	0.4
7 TU	0353	2.0	22 W	0355	2.0
	0914	0.1		0901	0.0
	1615	2.1		1607	2.3
	2330	0.5			
8 W	0434	2.0	23 TH	0030	0.4
	0944	0.1		0437	2.1
	1644	2.1		0949	0.0
				1654	2.3
9 TH	0010	0.4	24 F	0126	0.4
	0502	2.0		0525	2.0
	1025	0.1		1355	0.0
	1725	2.1		1741	2.2
10 F	0045	0.4	25 SA	0204	0.4
	0533	1.9		0614	2.0
	1105	0.1		1444	0.0
	1754	2.0		1837	2.1
11 SA	0135	0.4	26 SU	0305	0.4
	0608	1.9		0704	2.0
	1145	0.1		1244	0.1
	1828	2.0		☾ 1935	2.0
12 SU	0157	0.4	27 M	0145	0.4
	0643	1.9		0758	1.9
	1225	0.1		1354	0.1
	1914	2.0		2035	1.8
13 M	0204	0.4	28 TU	0235	0.4
	0738	1.8		0905	1.8
	1325	0.1		1504	0.2
	☽ 2019	1.9		2144	1.7
14 TU	0235	0.4	29 W	0355	0.4
	0844	1.8		1024	1.7
	1434	0.1		1624	0.3
	2135	1.8		2319	1.6
15 W	0325	0.4	30 TH	0505	0.3
	0959	1.7		1133	1.7
	1535	0.2		1745	0.3
	2245	1.8			
			31 F	0024	1.7
				0604	0.3
				1249	1.8
				1850	0.4

FEBRUARY

Day	Time	m	Day	Time	m
1 SA	0125	1.8	16 SU	0035	1.7
	0930	0.2		0554	0.2
	1338	1.9		1255	2.0
	2145	0.4		2107	0.3
2 SU	0208	1.9	17 M	0124	1.8
	1004	0.2		0646	0.2
	1418	2.0		1337	2.1
	2230	0.4		2145	0.3
3 M	0256	1.9	18 TU	0203	1.9
	0810	0.2		0725	0.1
	1443	2.0		1425	2.2
	● 2047	0.4		○ 2235	0.3
4 TU	0313	1.9	19 W	0250	2.0
	0834	0.1		0759	0.0
	1513	2.1		1506	2.3
	2147	0.4		2315	0.3
5 W	0355	2.0	20 TH	0335	2.0
	0855	0.1		0838	0.0
	1554	2.1		1548	2.3
	2310	0.4			
6 TH	0410	2.0	21 F	0016	0.3
	1144	0.1		0414	2.1
	1624	2.1		1250	0.0
	2345	0.4		1635	2.2
7 F	0437	2.0	22 SA	0106	0.3
	1235	0.0		0456	2.1
	1654	2.1		1346	0.0
				1718	2.1
8 SA	0046	0.3	23 SU	0156	0.3
	0508	2.0		0545	2.1
	1316	0.0		1425	0.0
	1724	2.1		1804	2.0
9 SU	0115	0.3	24 M	0224	0.3
	0538	2.0		0624	2.0
	1059	0.0		1250	0.1
	1754	2.0		1854	1.9
10 M	0135	0.4	25 TU	0107	0.3
	0614	2.0		0713	1.9
	1145	0.0		1335	0.1
	1839	2.0		☾ 1943	1.7
11 TU	0004	0.3	26 W	0210	0.2
	0654	1.9		0819	1.8
	1234	0.0		1445	0.2
	☽ 1924	1.9		2054	1.5
12 W	0150	0.3	27 TH	0325	0.3
	0755	1.9		0939	1.6
	1415	0.1		1604	0.3
	2045	1.8		2254	1.4
13 TH	0245	0.3	28 F	0445	0.2
	0914	1.7		1119	1.6
	1530	0.2		1715	0.3
	2153	1.7			
14 F	0404	0.3	29 SA	0005	1.5
	1033	1.7		0540	0.2
	1644	0.2		1224	1.7
	2325	1.6		1815	0.3
15 SA	0520	0.3			
	1155	1.8			
	1744	0.3			

MARCH

Day	Time	m	Day	Time	m
1 SU	0053	1.7	16 M	0019	1.6
	0624	0.2		0826	0.1
	1314	1.8		1238	2.0
	2117	0.3		2045	0.2
2 M	0144	1.8	17 TU	0103	1.7
	0956	0.1		0926	0.1
	1355	1.9		1325	2.1
	2155	0.3		2125	0.2
3 TU	0218	1.9	18 W	0155	1.9
	1014	0.1		0655	0.0
	1425	2.0		1405	2.1
	2225	0.3		○ 2210	0.3
4 W	0243	1.9	19 TH	0230	2.0
	0804	0.1		0738	0.0
	1454	2.1		1445	2.2
	● 2217	0.3		2256	0.3
5 TH	0314	2.0	20 F	0310	2.0
	1047	0.1		0819	0.0
	1520	2.1		1524	2.2
	2250	0.3		2339	0.2
6 F	0344	2.0	21 SA	0350	2.1
	1124	0.1		1226	0.0
	1549	2.1		1608	2.1
	2324	0.3			
7 SA	0407	2.0	22 SU	0036	0.2
	1216	0.0		0434	2.1
	1625	2.1		1316	0.0
	2355	0.3		1651	2.0
8 SU	0440	2.0	23 M	0126	0.2
	0951	0.1		0514	2.1
	1657	2.1		1355	0.1
	2215	0.3		1734	1.9
9 M	0510	2.0	24 TU	0205	0.2
	1029	0.0		0554	2.0
	1730	2.0		1430	0.2
	2244	0.2		1818	1.8
10 TU	0547	2.1	25 W	0027	0.2
	1115	0.0		0644	1.9
	1815	2.0		1340	0.2
	2335	0.2		1903	1.6
11 W	0628	2.0	26 TH	0140	0.1
	1204	0.1		0739	1.7
	1858	1.8		1440	0.2
				☾ 2003	1.5
12 TH	0050	0.2	27 F	0305	0.1
	0718	1.9		0854	1.6
	1415	0.1		1545	0.3
	☽ 2004	1.7		2129	1.3
13 F	0236	0.2	28 SA	0420	0.1
	0834	1.8		1044	1.5
	1514	0.2		1654	0.3
	2145	1.5		2323	1.4
14 SA	0335	0.2	29 SU	0515	0.1
	1013	1.7		1143	1.7
	1640	0.2		1744	0.3
	2315	1.5			
15 SU	0444	0.2	30 M	0024	1.6
	1133	1.8		0604	0.1
	1950	0.2		1233	1.8
				2020	0.3
			31 TU	0103	1.7
				0644	0.1
				1319	1.9
				2124	0.2

APRIL

Day	Time	m	Day	Time	m
1 W	0144	1.8	16 TH	0128	1.8
	0930	0.1		0940	0.0
	1348	2.0		1344	2.1
	2210	0.2		2145	0.2
2 TH	0208	1.9	17 F	0207	1.9
	1010	0.1		0715	0.1
	1418	2.0		1425	2.0
	2240	0.3		○ 2236	0.2
3 F	0234	1.9	18 SA	0246	2.0
	1040	0.1		1100	0.1
	1447	2.1		1504	2.0
	● 2240	0.3		2326	0.2
4 SA	0305	2.0	19 SU	0327	2.1
	0819	0.1		1155	0.1
	1520	2.1		1546	2.0
	2314	0.2			
5 SU	0337	2.0	20 M	0017	0.1
	1144	0.1		0408	2.1
	1557	2.1		1246	0.1
	2114	0.2		1627	1.9
6 M	0411	2.1	21 TU	0101	0.1
	0925	0.1		0450	2.1
	1630	2.0		1325	0.1
	2145	0.2		1710	1.8
7 TU	0446	2.1	22 W	0145	0.1
	1009	0.1		0535	2.0
	1711	2.0		1405	0.2
	2229	0.1		1755	1.7
8 W	0527	2.1	23 TH	0000	0.1
	1055	0.1		0614	1.9
	1754	1.9		1330	0.3
	2314	0.1		1832	1.6
9 TH	0610	2.1	24 F	0108	0.0
	1330	0.1		0703	1.8
	1845	1.7		1420	0.3
				☾ 1929	1.5
10 F	0035	0.1	25 SA	0240	0.0
	0704	1.9		0820	1.6
	1410	0.1		1535	0.3
	☽ 2005	1.6		2034	1.4
11 SA	0155	0.1	26 SU	0355	0.0
	0822	1.8		0923	1.6
	1505	0.2		1624	0.3
	2134	1.5		2159	1.3
12 SU	0304	0.1	27 M	0445	0.0
	1015	1.8		1053	1.6
	1800	0.2		1714	0.3
	2243	1.5		2334	1.5
13 M	0415	0.1	28 TU	0534	0.0
	1125	1.9		1154	1.8
	1930	0.2		1930	0.2
	2354	1.6			
14 TU	0744	0.1	29 W	0019	1.6
	1214	2.0		0647	0.1
	2027	0.2		1234	1.9
				2055	0.2
15 W	0044	1.7	30 TH	0052	1.7
	0844	0.0		0845	0.1
	1300	2.0		1315	1.9
	2110	0.2		2135	0.2

LOW WATERS - IMPORTANT NOTE. DOUBLE LOW WATERS OFTEN OCCUR. PREDICTIONS ARE FOR THE LOWER LOW WATER WHICH IS USUALLY THE SECOND.

Chart datum: 0.84 metres below Normaal Amsterdams Peil

TIME ZONE -0100
(Dutch Standard Time)
Subtract 1 hour for GMT
For Dutch Summer Time add ONE hour in non-shaded areas

NETHERLANDS - HOEK VAN HOLLAND

LAT 51°59'N LONG 4°07'E

TIMES AND HEIGHTS OF HIGH AND LOW WATERS

YEAR **1992**

MAY

Date	Day	Moon	Time	m	Time	m	Time	m	Time	m
1	F		0128	1.8	0946	0.1	1345	2.0	2225	0.2
2	SA	●	0200	1.9	1025	0.1	1414	2.0	2235	0.2
3	SU		0235	2.0	0756	0.1	1451	2.1	2023	0.2
4	M		0314	2.1	0835	0.2	1535	2.0	2055	0.2
5	TU		0348	2.1	0909	0.2	1611	2.0	2129	0.1
6	W		0428	2.1	1235	0.2	1654	1.9	2213	0.1
7	TH		0514	2.1	1320	0.2	1740	1.8	2309	0.0
8	F		0600	2.1	1346	0.2	1834	1.7		
9	SA	☽	0024	0.0	0700	2.0	1436	0.2	1959	1.6
10	SU		0134	0.0	0823	1.9	1607	0.2	2102	1.5
11	M		0245	0.0	0945	1.9	1744	0.2	2213	1.6
12	TU		0614	0.0	1054	1.9	1904	0.2	2324	1.6
13	W		0736	0.0	1154	2.0	2004	0.2		
14	TH		0018	1.7	0836	0.0	1237	2.0	2055	0.2
15	F		0105	1.8	0910	0.1	1325	2.0	2115	0.2
16	SA	○	0144	1.9	0950	0.2	1407	1.9	2155	0.2
17	SU		0227	2.0	1030	0.2	1455	1.9	2255	0.2
18	M		0310	2.0	1117	0.2	1534	1.8	2355	0.1
19	TU		0350	2.0	1204	0.2	1615	1.8		
20	W		0036	0.0	0435	2.0	1301	0.3	1655	1.8
21	TH		0104	0.0	0515	2.0	1335	0.3	1730	1.7
22	F		0137	0.0	0559	1.9	1330	0.3	1814	1.7
23	SA		0020	0.0	0644	1.8	1400	0.3	1905	1.6
24	SU	☾	0120	0.0	0745	1.8	1445	0.3	1959	1.5
25	M		0325	0.0	0833	1.7	1555	0.3	2059	1.5
26	TU		0414	0.0	0955	1.7	1634	0.3	2204	1.5
27	W		0505	0.1	1055	1.7	1735	0.2	2314	1.6
28	TH		0616	0.1	1144	1.8	1950	0.2		
29	F		0015	1.7	0805	0.1	1228	1.9	2106	0.2
30	SA		0048	1.8	0905	0.1	1315	2.0	2156	0.2
31	SU		0128	1.9	0654	0.2	1355	2.0	1929	0.2

JUNE

Date	Day	Moon	Time	m	Time	m	Time	m	Time	m
1	M	●	0211	2.0	0740	0.2	1434	2.0	2005	0.2
2	TU		0250	2.1	0815	0.2	1515	2.0	2035	0.1
3	W		0334	2.1	1206	0.2	1556	1.9	2120	0.1
4	TH		0417	2.2	1235	0.2	1644	1.8	2201	0.0
5	F		0505	2.2	1325	0.2	1734	1.8	2255	0.0
6	SA		0554	2.1	1405	0.2	1833	1.7		
7	SU	☽	0005	0.0	0659	2.1	1500	0.2	1945	1.7
8	M		0105	0.0	0802	2.0	1557	0.3	2045	1.7
9	TU		0214	0.0	0914	2.0	1715	0.2	2149	1.7
10	W		0325	0.0	1025	1.9	1825	0.2	2254	1.7
11	TH		0655	0.1	1135	1.9	1927	0.2	2354	1.8
12	F		0745	0.1	1224	1.9	2030	0.2		
13	SA		0044	1.8	0854	0.2	1310	1.9	2120	0.2
14	SU		0135	1.9	0838	0.3	1405	1.8	2205	0.2
15	M	○	0213	1.9	0827	0.3	1443	1.8	2005	0.2
16	TU		0257	2.0	0930	0.4	1528	1.8	2044	0.1
17	W		0337	2.0	1150	0.4	1604	1.8	2124	0.1
18	TH		0414	2.0	1235	0.4	1645	1.8	2154	0.0
19	F		0458	2.0	1250	0.4	1719	1.8	2244	0.0
20	SA		0534	2.0	1320	0.4	1755	1.8	2340	0.0
21	SU		0613	1.9	1337	0.3	1823	1.7		
22	M		0025	0.0	0653	1.9	1420	0.3	1924	1.7
23	TU	☾	0115	0.0	0748	1.8	1510	0.3	2020	1.6
24	W		0205	0.1	0854	1.8	1600	0.3	2115	1.6
25	TH		0255	0.1	0943	1.8	1654	0.3	2225	1.6
26	F		0410	0.2	1043	1.8	1737	0.3	2313	1.7
27	SA		0514	0.2	1148	1.9	1820	0.3		
28	SU		0015	1.8	0554	0.2	1245	1.9	1835	0.2
29	M		0104	1.9	0645	0.2	1334	1.9	1903	0.2
30	TU	●	0148	2.0	0725	0.2	1414	1.9	1945	0.1

JULY

Date	Day	Moon	Time	m	Time	m	Time	m	Time	m
1	W		0234	2.1	0805	0.3	1504	1.9	2019	0.1
2	TH		0316	2.2	1124	0.3	1544	1.9	2105	0.0
3	F		0401	2.2	1214	0.3	1629	1.9	2145	0.0
4	SA		0450	2.2	1316	0.3	1724	1.9	2236	0.0
5	SU		0540	2.2	1355	0.3	1814	1.9	2336	0.0
6	M		0634	2.1	1455	0.3	1915	1.8		
7	TU	☽	0035	0.0	0734	2.1	1540	0.3	2008	1.8
8	W		0145	0.0	0833	2.0	1655	0.3	2115	1.8
9	TH		0300	0.1	0949	1.9	1755	0.3	2224	1.7
10	F		0404	0.2	1105	1.8	1844	0.3	2329	1.7
11	SA		0700	0.2	1208	1.8	2007	0.3		
12	SU		0028	1.8	0905	0.3	1309	1.8	2126	0.2
13	M		0128	1.9	1005	0.4	1353	1.8	1915	0.2
14	TU	○	0213	1.9	0755	0.4	1449	1.8	1953	0.1
15	W		0254	2.0	0840	0.5	1535	1.9	2035	0.1
16	TH		0323	2.0	0916	0.5	1554	1.9	2054	0.1
17	F		0358	2.1	1128	0.5	1624	1.9	2129	0.0
18	SA		0434	2.1	1220	0.4	1654	1.9	2204	0.0
19	SU		0508	2.1	1250	0.4	1723	1.9	2254	0.0
20	M		0544	2.0	1325	0.4	1758	1.9	2325	0.1
21	TU		0619	2.0	1347	0.4	1834	1.8		
22	W	☾	0020	0.1	0655	1.9	1400	0.4	1904	1.8
23	TH		0105	0.1	0744	1.9	1415	0.4	2014	1.7
24	F		0205	0.1	0904	1.8	1505	0.4	2135	1.7
25	SA		0325	0.2	1004	1.8	1615	0.4	2233	1.7
26	SU		0435	0.2	1115	1.8	1736	0.3	2355	1.8
27	M		0545	0.3	1218	1.8	1804	0.3		
28	TU		0044	1.9	0625	0.3	1315	1.9	1845	0.2
29	W	●	0134	2.1	0704	0.3	1405	1.9	1925	0.1
30	TH		0216	2.2	0745	0.4	1444	2.0	1959	0.1
31	F		0259	2.3	1115	0.4	1528	2.0	2037	0.0

AUGUST

Date	Day	Moon	Time	m	Time	m	Time	m	Time	m
1	SA		0345	2.3	1155	0.4	1615	2.0	2121	0.0
2	SU		0430	2.3	1250	0.4	1656	2.0	2209	0.0
3	M		0514	2.3	1334	0.4	1745	2.0	2258	0.1
4	TU		0606	2.2	1424	0.4	1834	2.0		
5	W	☽	0004	0.1	0704	2.0	1520	0.4	1928	1.9
6	TH		0124	0.1	0805	1.9	1415	0.4	2023	1.8
7	F		0234	0.2	0904	1.7	1524	0.3	2149	1.7
8	SA		0344	0.3	1039	1.6	1640	0.3	2309	1.7
9	SU		0505	0.4	1159	1.7	1740	0.3		
10	M		0018	1.8	0627	0.4	1259	1.8	1825	0.2
11	TU		0124	1.9	0944	0.4	1343	1.8	2144	0.2
12	W		0204	2.0	1030	0.4	1435	1.9	1934	0.2
13	TH	○	0233	2.0	0814	0.5	1505	1.9	2005	0.1
14	F		0304	2.1	0835	0.5	1528	2.0	2029	0.1
15	SA		0337	2.1	0854	0.5	1559	2.0	2105	0.1
16	SU		0408	2.2	1140	0.5	1624	2.0	2136	0.1
17	M		0438	2.1	1225	0.4	1654	2.0	2205	0.1
18	TU		0508	2.1	1254	0.4	1725	2.0	2246	0.1
19	W		0538	2.1	1327	0.4	1754	2.0	2319	0.1
20	TH		0614	2.0	1145	0.4	1834	2.0	2354	0.1
21	F	☾	0654	2.0	1235	0.4	1914	1.9		
22	SA		0127	0.2	0754	1.8	1414	0.4	2035	1.8
23	SU		0254	0.3	0914	1.7	1525	0.4	2204	1.7
24	M		0414	0.3	1044	1.7	1650	0.4	2324	1.8
25	TU		0525	0.4	1205	1.7	1745	0.3		
26	W		0029	2.0	0609	0.4	1254	1.8	1819	0.2
27	TH		0117	2.1	0935	0.4	1346	1.9	1855	0.1
28	F	●	0157	2.3	0725	0.4	1424	2.0	1938	0.1
29	SA		0239	2.3	0806	0.4	1506	2.1	2015	0.0
30	SU		0322	2.4	1140	0.4	1546	2.1	2058	0.0
31	M		0405	2.3	1236	0.4	1634	2.2	2141	0.1

LOW WATERS - IMPORTANT NOTE. DOUBLE LOW WATERS OFTEN OCCUR. PREDICTIONS ARE FOR THE LOWER LOW WATER WHICH IS USUALLY THE SECOND.

Chart Datum: 0.84 metres below Normaal Amsterdams Peil

NETHERLANDS - HOEK VAN HOLLAND

TIME ZONE -0100
(Dutch Standard Time)
Subtract 1 hour for GMT
For Dutch Summer Time add ONE hour in non-shaded areas

LAT 51°59′N LONG 4°07′E

TIMES AND HEIGHTS OF HIGH AND LOW WATERS

YEAR **1992**

SEPTEMBER

Day	Time	m	Day	Time	m
1 TU	0455	2.2	16 W	0436	2.2
	1325	0.4		0955	0.4
	1714	2.1		1650	2.1
				2210	0.2
2 W	0200	0.2	17 TH	0511	2.1
	0534	2.1		1030	0.4
	1404	0.4		1724	2.1
	1800	2.1		2245	0.2
3 TH	0250	0.2	18 F	0547	2.1
	0624	2.0		1104	0.3
	1227	0.4		1805	2.1
☽	1848	2.0		2335	0.2
4 F	0107	0.3	19 SA	0628	2.0
	0714	1.8		1200	0.3
	1340	0.4		1848	2.1
	1948	1.9	☾		
5 SA	0214	0.3	20 SU	0106	0.3
	0823	1.6		0724	1.8
	1445	0.3		1340	0.3
	2103	1.7		1948	1.9
6 SU	0340	0.4	21 M	0234	0.4
	1014	1.5		0849	1.7
	1614	0.3		1455	0.3
	2254	1.7		2133	1.8
7 M	0449	0.5	22 TU	0344	0.4
	1134	1.6		1025	1.6
	1715	0.3		1604	0.3
				2315	1.9
8 TU	0003	1.8	23 W	0657	0.4
	0555	0.5		1145	1.7
	1234	1.7		1705	0.3
	1754	0.3			
9 W	0052	1.9	24 TH	0008	2.0
	0920	0.4		0815	0.4
	1325	1.8		1238	1.8
	2124	0.2		1749	0.2
10 TH	0133	2.0	25 F	0054	2.2
	0954	0.4		0905	0.4
	1404	1.9		1320	1.9
	1915	0.2		1829	0.2
11 F	0203	2.1	26 SA	0136	2.3
	1015	0.5		0950	0.4
	1435	2.0		1401	2.1
	1944	0.2	●	1915	0.1
12 SA	0238	2.1	27 SU	0218	2.3
	0815	0.5		0738	0.5
	1458	2.0		1442	2.1
○	2005	0.2		1951	0.1
13 SU	0304	2.2	28 M	0301	2.3
	0829	0.5		0815	0.5
	1525	2.1		1524	2.2
	2024	0.2		2035	0.2
14 M	0337	2.2	29 TU	0344	2.3
	0855	0.5		1210	0.4
	1554	2.1		1606	2.2
	2105	0.2		2119	0.2
15 TU	0404	2.2	30 W	0426	2.2
	1145	0.4		1306	0.4
	1625	2.1		1648	2.2
	2131	0.2			

OCTOBER

Day	Time	m	Day	Time	m
1 TH	0135	0.3	16 F	0446	2.1
	0510	2.1		1010	0.3
	1351	0.4		1704	2.2
	1730	2.2		2230	0.3
2 F	0205	0.4	17 SA	0524	2.0
	0554	1.9		1056	0.3
	1140	0.4		1745	2.2
	1818	2.1		2325	0.3
3 SA	0045	0.4	18 SU	0614	1.9
	0642	1.8		1144	0.2
	1254	0.3		1835	2.1
☽	1914	1.9			
4 SU	0154	0.5	19 M	0130	0.4
	0738	1.6		0709	1.8
	1418	0.3		1310	0.3
	2023	1.7	☾	1933	2.0
5 M	0305	0.5	20 TU	0230	0.4
	0853	1.5		0834	1.6
	1550	0.3		1430	0.3
	2219	1.7		2125	1.9
6 TU	0430	0.5	21 W	0335	0.5
	1114	1.5		0953	1.6
	1644	0.3		1535	0.3
	2344	1.8		2233	1.9
7 W	0525	0.5	22 TH	0647	0.4
	1205	1.7		1114	1.7
	1734	0.3		1914	0.3
				2345	2.1
8 TH	0024	1.9	23 F	0810	0.4
	0820	0.5		1210	1.8
	1254	1.8		2025	0.2
	1830	0.2			
9 F	0104	2.0	24 SA	0034	2.2
	0915	0.4		0855	0.4
	1323	1.9		1258	1.9
	1854	0.3		1809	0.2
10 SA	0134	2.1	25 SU	0116	2.2
	0955	0.4		0915	0.4
	1354	2.0		1340	2.1
	1930	0.3	●	1852	0.2
11 SU	0205	2.1	26 M	0200	2.2
	1035	0.5		1005	0.4
	1425	2.0		1421	2.1
○	1933	0.3		1936	0.2
12 M	0234	2.2	27 TU	0245	2.2
	0754	0.5		0755	0.4
	1450	2.1		1505	2.2
	2006	0.3		2020	0.3
13 TU	0304	2.2	28 W	0324	2.2
	0824	0.4		1151	0.4
	1520	2.2		1544	2.2
	2036	0.3			
14 W	0338	2.2	29 TH	0021	0.4
	0854	0.4		0406	2.1
	1555	2.2		1235	0.3
	2110	0.3		1626	2.2
15 TH	0415	2.2	30 F	0105	0.4
	0930	0.4		0450	2.0
	1629	2.2		1326	0.3
	2145	0.3		1714	2.2
			31 SA	0155	0.5
				0534	1.9
				1109	0.3
				1759	2.1

NOVEMBER

Day	Time	m	Day	Time	m
1 SU	0040	0.5	16 M	0120	0.4
	0618	1.8		0605	1.9
	1215	0.2		1139	0.2
	1843	1.9		1827	2.1
2 M	0130	0.5	17 TU	0137	0.5
	0715	1.7		0709	1.8
	1324	0.2		1244	0.2
☽	1955	1.8	☾	1932	2.0
3 TU	0235	0.6	18 W	0230	0.5
	0803	1.6		0834	1.7
	1520	0.2		1406	0.2
	2054	1.7		2059	2.0
4 W	0354	0.6	19 TH	0500	0.5
	0913	1.5		0934	1.7
	1614	0.2		1459	0.2
	2244	1.7		2208	2.0
5 TH	0500	0.5	20 F	0630	0.5
	1104	1.6		1045	1.7
	1715	0.2		1901	0.2
	2333	1.9		2314	2.0
6 F	0707	0.5	21 SA	0735	0.4
	1204	1.7		1145	1.8
	1810	0.3		1944	0.2
7 SA	0025	2.0	22 SU	0015	2.1
	0815	0.4		0824	0.4
	1238	1.8		1235	1.9
	2007	0.3		2055	0.3
8 SU	0053	2.0	23 M	0104	2.1
	0914	0.4		0904	0.4
	1315	1.9		1320	2.0
	2114	0.3		1846	0.3
9 M	0130	2.1	24 TU	0147	2.1
	0954	0.4		0950	0.4
	1344	2.0		1407	2.1
	1914	0.3	●	1924	0.4
10 TU	0204	2.2	25 W	0227	2.1
	1040	0.4		1046	0.4
	1417	2.1		1447	2.1
○	1945	0.3		2015	0.4
11 W	0236	2.2	26 TH	0311	2.0
	0809	0.4		1135	0.3
	1455	2.2		1530	2.2
	2015	0.3		2355	0.5
12 TH	0314	2.2	27 F	0354	2.0
	0840	0.4		1226	0.2
	1530	2.2		1614	2.2
	2049	0.3			
13 F	0354	2.1	28 SA	0034	0.5
	0916	0.3		0438	2.0
	1608	2.2		1300	0.2
	2135	0.4		1654	2.1
14 SA	0434	2.1	29 SU	0125	0.5
	0956	0.2		0514	1.9
	1651	2.2		1045	0.2
	2219	0.4		1733	2.1
15 SU	0517	2.0	30 M	0017	0.6
	1039	0.2		0558	1.9
	1736	2.2		1144	0.1
				1829	2.0

DECEMBER

Day	Time	m	Day	Time	m
1 TU	0110	0.5	16 W	0214	0.4
	0645	1.8		0653	1.8
	1244	0.1		1236	0.1
	1914	1.9	☾	1925	2.1
2 W	0157	0.5	17 TH	0258	0.5
	0745	1.7		0805	1.8
	1350	0.2		1335	0.1
☽	2014	1.8		2035	2.0
3 TH	0314	0.5	18 F	0300	0.5
	0829	1.7		0904	1.8
	1555	0.2		1434	0.1
	2114	1.8		2144	2.0
4 F	0414	0.5	19 SA	0547	0.5
	0923	1.6		1014	1.8
	1635	0.2		1545	0.2
	2223	1.8		2243	1.9
5 SA	0505	0.5	20 SU	0655	0.4
	1043	1.6		1119	1.8
	1740	0.3		1924	0.2
	2329	1.9		2355	1.9
6 SU	0607	0.5	21 M	0807	0.4
	1149	1.7		1214	1.9
	1910	0.3		2034	0.3
7 M	0014	1.9	22 TU	0048	1.9
	0846	0.4		0855	0.4
	1235	1.8		1308	1.9
	2034	0.3		2130	0.4
8 TU	0059	2.0	23 W	0137	1.9
	0936	0.4		0944	0.3
	1315	1.9		1353	2.0
	2146	0.3		1950	0.4
9 W	0138	2.1	24 TH	0234	1.9
	1010	0.4		1036	0.3
	1355	2.0		1444	2.1
○	1925	0.4	●	2046	0.5
10 TH	0216	2.1	25 F	0312	1.9
	0744	0.4		0829	0.2
	1434	2.1		1520	2.1
	2006	0.4		2330	0.5
11 F	0256	2.1	26 SA	0405	1.9
	0826	0.3		0910	0.2
	1514	2.2		1604	2.1
	2035	0.4			
12 SA	0337	2.1	27 SU	0004	0.5
	0859	0.2		0423	2.0
	1554	2.3		0944	0.1
	2126	0.4		1644	2.1
13 SU	0425	2.0	28 M	0106	0.5
	0939	0.2		0505	2.0
	1637	2.3		1024	0.1
				1725	2.1
14 M	0044	0.4	29 TU	0120	0.5
	0507	2.0		0538	1.9
	1025	0.1		1105	0.1
	1726	2.2		1804	2.0
15 TU	0124	0.4	30 W	0057	0.5
	0557	1.9		0614	1.9
	1125	0.1		1204	0.1
	1820	2.2		1834	2.0
			31 TH	0130	0.5
				0652	1.8
				1254	0.1
				1923	1.9

LOW WATERS - IMPORTANT NOTE. DOUBLE LOW WATERS OFTEN OCCUR. PREDICTIONS ARE FOR THE LOWER LOW WATER WHICH IS USUALLY THE SECOND.

Chart Datum: 0.84 metres below Normaal Amsterdams Peil

SCHEVENINGEN 10-20-22

Zuid Holland

CHARTS
Admiralty 122, 2322; Zeekaart 1035, 1349, 1350, 1449; Dutch Yacht Chart 1801; Dutch Waterkaarts ANWB H/J; Stanford 19; Imray Y5

TIDES
Dover +0320; ML No data; Duration 0445; Zone −0100

Standard Port VLISSINGEN (⟵)

Times				Height (metres)			
HW		LW		MHWS	MHWN	MLWN	MLWS
0300	0900	0400	1000	4·7	3·9	0·8	0·3
1500	2100	1600	2200				
Differences SCHEVENINGEN							
+0105	+0102	+0226	+0246	−2·6	−2·2	−0·6	−0·1

NOTE: Double LWs occur — The rise after the first LW is called The Agger — Predictions for Hoek van Holland are for the lower LW which is usually the second. Time differences for Secondary Ports referred to Hoek van Holland are approximate — Water levels on this coast are considerably affected by the weather. Strong NW gales can raise levels by up to 3m, whereas strong E winds can lower levels by 1m.

SHELTER
Entrance can be difficult in on-shore NW winds over force 6 but once in the Buitenhaven, shelter is good. The yacht marina in the Second Harbour gives very good shelter. Access H24.

NAVIGATION
Waypoint SCH safe water buoy, Iso 4s, 52°07′·80N 04°14′·20E, 336°/156° from/to entrance, 1·6M. Strong tidal streams running NE/SW across the entrance can cause problems. Strong winds from SW through NW to N cause a scend in the outer harbour. Beware large ships entering and leaving.

LIGHTS AND MARKS
Ldg Lts 156° to outer basin, 131° to inner basin.
Entry signals (from Semaphore Mast)
R over W Lts — Entry prohibited.
W over R Lts — Exit prohibited.
Fl Y Lt — entry difficult due to vessels leaving.
A QY Lt is shown by entrance to First Harbour (W side) when vessels are entering or leaving port.
Tide signals:
G over W Lts — tide rising.
W over G Lts — tide falling.
R Lt — less than 5m in entry channel.

RADIO TELEPHONE
Call: *Traffic Centre Scheveningen* VHF Ch 14 (H24). Yachts must get permission from Traffic Centre before entering.

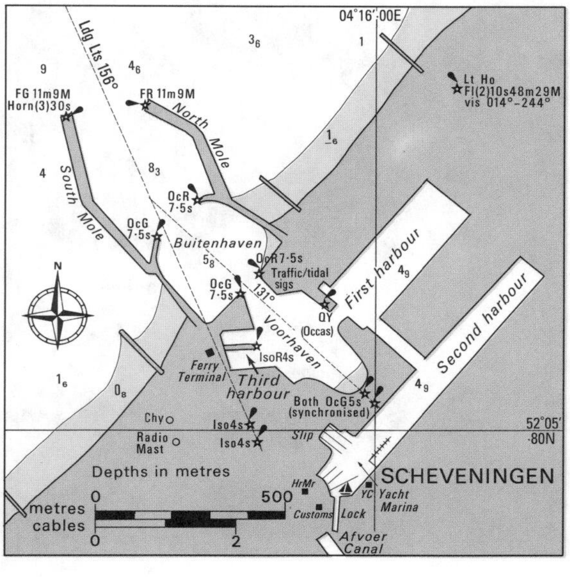
04°16′·00E
Ldg Lts 156°
FG 11m9M
Horn(3)30s
FR 11m9M
North Mole
South Mole
Lt Ho
Fl(2)10s48m29M
vis 014°-244°
OcR
7·5s
OcG
7·5s
Buitenhaven
OcR7·5s
Traffic/tidal sigs
OcG
7·5s
131°
QY
(Occas)
First harbour
Second harbour
Voorhaven
IsoR4s
Ferry Terminal
Third harbour
Both OcG5s
(synchronised)
Chy
Radio Mast
Iso4s
Iso4s
Slip
52°05′
·80N
N
Depths in metres
SCHEVENINGEN
HrMr
YC
Yacht Marina
Customs
Lock
Afvoer Canal
0 500
metres
cables
0 2

TELEPHONE (070)
Hr Mr 3527701, Marina Hr Mr 3520017, Traffic Centre (semaphore) 3527721, Pilot Hook of Holland (01740) 38811, # Scheveningen 3514481, Police 3104911, Dr. 3455300, Ambulance 3222111, Brit Consul (020) 764343.

FACILITIES
Marina Scheveningen (223+100 visitors) ☎ 3520017, AC, Bar, C (15 ton), CH, D, El, FW, ME, R, ⊡, Sh, SM; **Harbour** Slip, FW, ME, Sh, C (60 ton), CH, R, Bar; **Hoogenraad & Kuyt**, ME, El, Sh, CH; **Yachtclub Scheveningen** ☎ 3520308; **Vrolyk** ☎ 3554957 SM; **L. J. Harri** ☎ 3546292, ACA, Ⓔ, **Town** P, D, V, R, Bar. ✉; Ⓑ; ≋; ✈ (Rotterdam). Ferry UK — Rotterdam—Hull; Hook of Holland—Harwich.

IJMUIDEN 10-20-23

Noord Holland

CHARTS
Admiralty 2322, 124; Zeekaart 1450, 1543, 1035, 1350; Dutch Yacht Chart 1801; Stanford 19; Imray Y5

TIDES
Dover +0400; ML 1·1; Zone −0100

Standard Port VLISSINGEN (⟵)

Times				Height (metres)			
HW		LW		MHWS	MHWN	MLWN	MLWS
0300	0900	0400	1000	4·7	3·9	0·8	0·3
1500	2100	1600	2200				
Differences IJMUIDEN							
+0145	+0143	+0304	+0321	−2·7	−2·2	−0·6	−0·1

NOTE: Water levels on this coast can be considerably affected by the weather. Strong NW gales can raise the levels by up to 3m.

SHELTER
Good shelter especially on the S quay on the canal side of the small S locks. It is noteworthy that the canal level may be above or below the sea level. Yachts can stay in the Haringhaven for short periods but are not advised to stay at the sea side of the locks longer than necessary. There are marinas at IJmond (under lift bridge in Zijkanaal, 6M from IJmuiden and at Nauerna 7M from IJmuiden.

NAVIGATION
Waypoint IJmuiden Lt buoy, Mo(A) 8s, Racon, 52°28′·70N 04°23′·93E, 275°/095° from/to entrance, 5·0M. Beware strong tidal streams across the harbour entrance and heavy merchant traffic. Yachts normally use S lock.

LIGHTS AND MARKS
Ldg Lts 100° (front is the Lt Ho showing FWR 30m 16/13M, W050°-122°, R122°-145°, W145°-160°. RC, storm, tidal & traffic signals; rear Fl 5s 52m 29M). Both display a FW Lt by day. This line leads into the Buitenhaven and the Zuider Buitenkanaal.

RADIO TELEPHONE
IJmuiden Port Operations Centre. (1) IJmuiden. Call *IJmuiden Port Control* (or *IJmuiden Port Control Locks* for direct contact with locks) Ch 09, in area from North Sea to North Sea Locks. (2) Hemtunnel. Call IJmuiden Locks Ch 11 in area North Sea locks to Hembrug. (3) Amsterdam Ch 14, in area of Amsterdam port basins, E and W of Hembrug. Harbour Radar. Traffic Centre IJmuiden Ch 12 (W of IJmuiden Lt buoy) and IJmuiden Port Control. (All H24).
Reports on visibility, when less than 1000m, every H+00 on Ch 12 by Coastguard IJmuiden, every H+30 on Ch 05 and 11 by IJmuiden, every H+00 on Ch 14 by Amsterdam.
Vessels in the roads area, the Buitenhaven and the Noordzeekanaal should keep watch on the appropriate Ch, and report to Port Operations Centre on departure from or arrival in a port in Noordzeekanaal.

TELEPHONE (02550)
Hr Mr 19027; Traffic Centre IJmuiden (DGSM) 19027; Pilot 19027; # 23309; Police 35035; Ⓗ 65100; Brit Consul (020) 764343.

FACILITIES
IJmuiden YC ☎ 384457 AB, AC, Bar, BY, C (20 ton), ⊡, V, R, D; **Hermans** ☎ 12963, Gaz;
Town P, D, V, R, Bar. ✉; Ⓑ; ≋ (bus to Beverwijk); ✈ (Amsterdam).
Ferry UK — Hook of Holland—Harwich.

IJMUIDEN *continued*

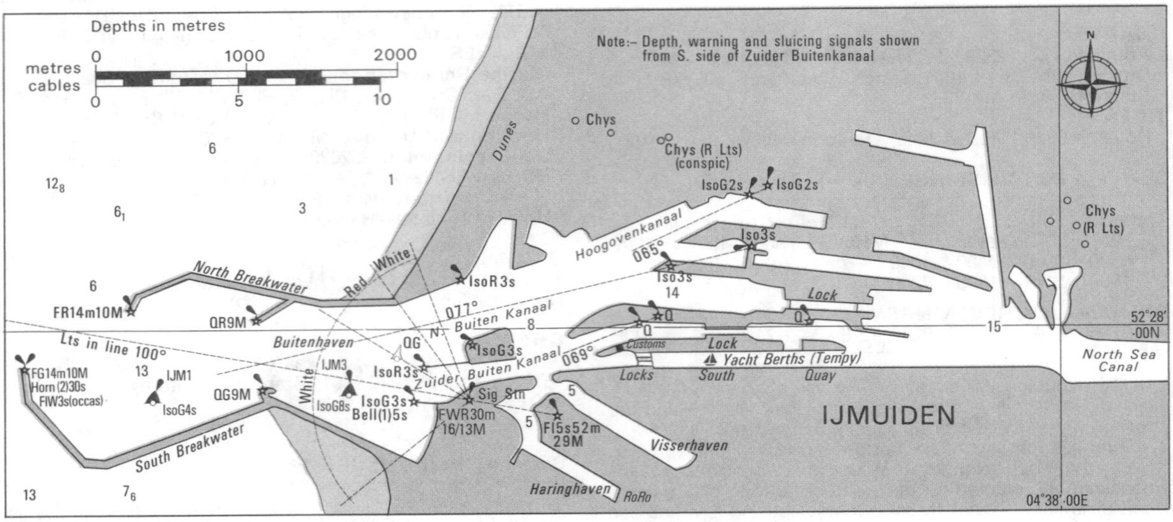

Depths in metres
0 1000 2000
metres
cables
0 5 10
Note:– Depth, warning and sluicing signals shown from S. side of Zuider Buitenkanaal
Dunes
Chys
Chys (R Lts) (conspic)
IsoG2s
IsoG2s
Chys (R Lts)
Hoogovenkanaal
Iso3s
065°
Iso3s
North Breakwater
Red
White
IsoR3s
FR14m10M
QR9M
077°
N. Buiten Kanaal
Lock
Q
Q
52°28'·00N
Lts in line 100°
Buitenhaven
QG
IsoG3s
069°
Customs
Lock
Yacht Berths (Tempy)
North Sea Canal
FG14m10M Horn(2)30s FIW3s(occas)
IJM1
IsoG4s
QG9M
IJM3
IsoG8s
White
IsoR3s
Zuider Buiten Kanaal
IsoG3s Bell(1)5s
Sig Stn
FWR30m 16/13M
Locks
South
Quay
IJMUIDEN
Fl5s52m 29M
Visserhaven
South Breakwater
Haringhaven
RoRo
04°38'·00E

AMSTERDAM 10-20-24

Noord Holland

CHARTS

Admiralty 124; Zeekaart 1543; Dutch Yacht Chart 1801, 1810; ANWB G, I

TIDES

Amsterdam is between the Noordzeekanaal and the IJsselmeer, both of which are non-tidal; Zone −0100.

SHELTER

Shelter is complete. There are several yacht harbours/marinas. The principal one is Sixhaven, on the N bank, NE of the railway station (conspic). Another is on the S bank, close NW of the Harbour Building (conspic), but beware of swell from passing ships. Amsterdam gives access to canals running to N and S and also, via the Oranjesluizen, to the IJsselmeer.

NAVIGATION

See 10.20.23. The transit of the Noordzeekanaal is straightforward, apart from the volume of commercial traffic. The speed limit for yachts is 9 kn. There is a slight set to the W during sluicing.

LIGHTS AND MARKS

Lights are shown along both banks of the canal at the entrances to branch canals and basins. The continuation E towards the Oranjesluizen and the Amsterdam-Rijn canal is marked by Lt buoys.

RADIO TELEPHONE

VHF Ch 14. See also 10.20.23.

TELEPHONE (020)

Port Control: 6221201; # 5867511; Police: 5599111; Dr: 5555555; Brit Consul: 6764343.

FACILITIES

Sixhaven Marina (60 + some visitors) ☎ 6370892, AC, Bar (weekends), FW; **L. J. Harri** ☎ 6248052, ACA, Dutch Chart Agent; **Jachthaven de Hoop** ☎ 6445817, Gaz.
City: All facilities, Ⓑ; ✉; ≠; ✈.
Ferry UK — Hook of Holland—Harwich.

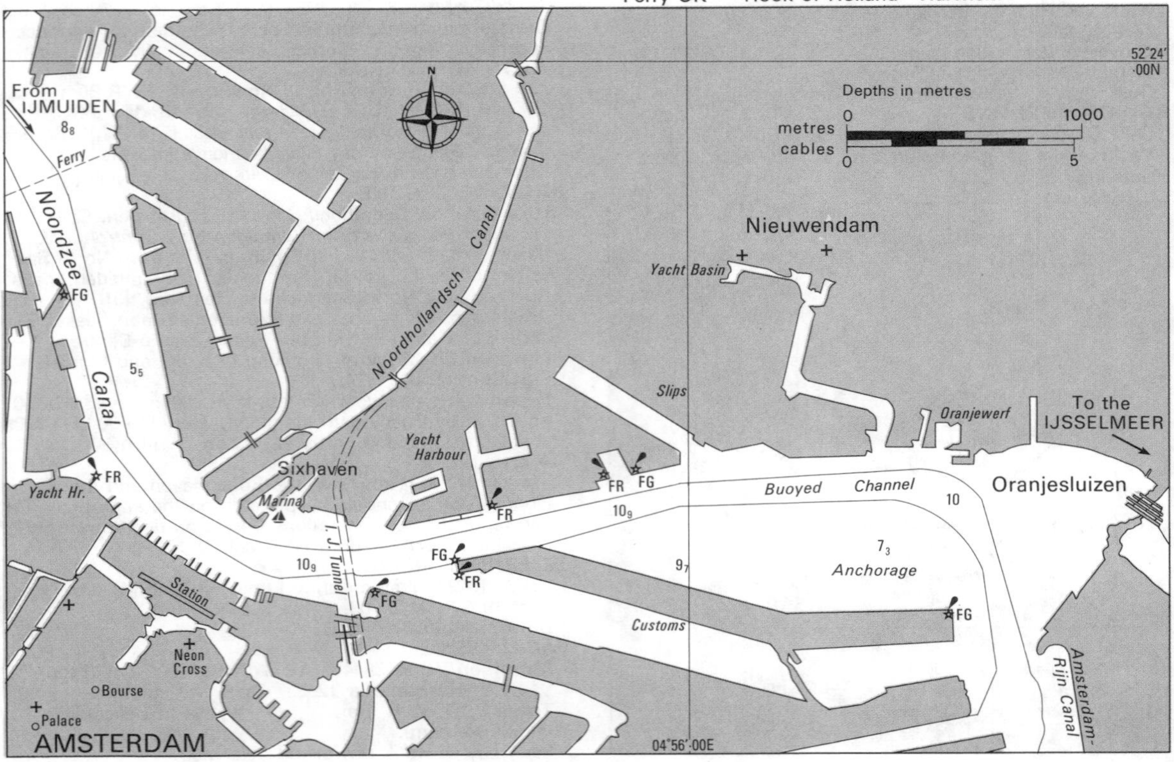

52°24'·00N
From IJMUIDEN
Depths in metres
0 1000
metres
cables
0 5
Ferry
Noordzee Canal
FG
Noordhollandsch Canal
Nieuwendam
Yacht Basin
Slips
Oranjewerf
To the IJSSELMEER
Oranjesluizen
Yacht Harbour
Sixhaven
Marina
FR
Yacht Hr.
FR
FG
FR
Buoyed Channel
L. J. Tunnel
FG
FR
Anchorage
FG
Station
FG
Customs
Neon Cross
Bourse
Palace
AMSTERDAM
Amsterdam-Rijn Canal
04°56'·00E

IJSSELMEER 10-20-25

CHARTS
Admiralty 1408, 2593; Zeekaart 1351, 1454; Dutch Yacht Chart 1810

TIDES
IJsselmeer is non-tidal. Tides at lock at Kornwerderzand Dover −0230; ML 1·2; Zone −0100.

Standard Port HELGOLAND (⟶)

Times				Height (metres)			
HW		LW		MHWS	MHWN	MLWN	MLWS
0200	0700	0200	0800	2·7	2·3	0·4	0·0
1400	1900	1400	2000				
Differences KORNWERDERZAND							
−0200	−0305	−0250	−0210	−0·5	−0·5	0·0	+0·2

SHELTER
IJsselmeer is the name for the un-reclaimed part of the Zuiderzee. Shelter is excellent in the many marinas, some of which are listed below. It is divided into two parts, the SW part being called the Markerwaard (20M × 15M, 2 to 4·5m deep) divided from the rest by a dyke with two locks, Enkhuizen in the N and Houtribhaven in the S. The rest of the IJsselmeer is 30M × 20M.

NAVIGATION
Three entrances
(1) via IJmuiden and Noordzeekanaal.
(2) via Stevinsluizen (Den Oever) at the W end of the Afsluitdijk which operates during working hrs.
(3) via the Kornwerderzand lock at the E end of the Afsluitdijk which operates 24 hrs.
Yacht charts are essential to avoid shoals, traps, fishing areas, nets etc which are well marked on the charts. Strong winds get up very quickly and short seas are frequently encountered. Strong winds can raise water level on lee shore, or lower it on weather shore, by 1m or more. Most harbours have water level gauges which should be checked in bad weather. Speed restrictions: in buoyed channels 8·5kn; outside 4·8kn. Between sunset and 0800 4·8kn everywhere. The Signi buoyage system is in use (see 10.20.7).

RADIO TELEPHONES
The following channels are used
Oranjesluizen Ch 18; den Oeversluizen Ch 20; Kornwerder Zandsluizen Ch 18; Lemmer Ch 20; Enkhuizen Ch 22; Houtribsluizen Ch 20; Emergency Ch 16.

There are numerous ports to visit and the following is a selection of the more important: (working clockwise from the Waddenzee).

MAKKUM. Approx 2M SE of the Kornwerderzand breakwaters, there is a buoyed channel approx 2000m long from buoy MA7, Iso G4s. Ldg Lts FR and FG at 092° leading between breakwaters into Makkum harbour. Hr Mr ☎ 1450. **Vissershaven** ☎ Hr Mr 2127, AB, BY, ME, C, FW, P, D, SM, Gaz. **Town** Ⓑ, Dr, V, R, ≷.

WORKUM, 2.5M, N of Hindeloopen, with buoyed channel leading to **"It Soal" Marina Hr Mr** ☎ 2927. Facilities: AB, BY, ME, C, FW, P, D, Gaz.

HINDELOOPEN has two marinas, one in town and one 180m to N. **Jachthaven Hindeloopen** (500) Hr Mr ☎ (05142) 1866 P, D, FW, AC, ⊡, CH, R, Bar. **Old Harbour** D, P, FW, ME, El, Sh; **Jachthaven Hr Mr** ☎ 2009, P, D, FW, ME, El, Sh.

STAVOREN. Entrance between FR and FG on line 048° Iso 4s Dir Lt. Yacht berths S of entrance by Rly Stn in Buitenhaven. Stavoren has several marinas after passing lock. Lock entrance between FR and FG Fl 5s Dir Lt approx 1000m S of entrance to Buitenhaven. Hr Mr ☎ (05149) 1216. **Stavoren Marina** ☎ 1469, AB, BY, ME, C, FW, P, D, SM, Gaz. **Town** Ⓑ, Dr, V, R, ≷

LEMMER has some 14 marinas. Ldg Lts into Prinses Margrietkanaal both Iso 8s at 038°. Ldg Lts into town and marinas both Iso 8s at 083° and FG and Iso G 4s at 065°. **Gemeente Jachthaven** Hr Mr ☎ (05146) 3343. Tacozijl ☎ 2003, AB, BY, ME, C, FW, P, D, Gaz, SM. **Town** Ⓑ, Dr, V, R, ✉.

URK Hr Ent ½M SE of Lt Ho Fl 5s 27m 18M. Harbour ent FR & FG dir Ldg Lt Iso 4s. Harbour in four parts – yachts go into Nieuwe Haven or the Oosthaven (3·3 m). Hr Mr ☎ (05277) 1394. FW; **Westhaven** P, D, SM. **Oosthaven** ME, El, Sh, Ⓔ, CH. **Town** EC Tuesday, V, R, Ⓑ, ✉, Dr.

KETELHAVEN From buoy WK1 IsoG 4s keep to buoyed channel. No Lts on marina ent. **Ketelmeer Marina** (200) FW, AC, R. Hr Mr (03210) 12271.

LELYSTAD has two marinas. **Houtribhaven** (560) Hr Mr ☎ (03200) 60198, D, CH, V, R, Bar, C; **Flevo Marina** (550) ☎ (03200) 21000 D, CH, V, R, C, M, Ⓔ, El. Both FR and FG on breakwaters.
Facilities: AB, BY, ME, C, FW, P, D, Gaz, ⊡, BH, R, Bar.

MUIDEN, home of the Royal Netherlands YC. Ldg Lts Q at 181° lead into Yacht Hr to W of entrance. **KNZ & RV Marina** (150) Hr Mr ☎ (02942) 1450 D, CH; **Stichting Jachthaven Muiden** (70) ☎ (02942) 1223 P.

MARKEN (picturesque show piece). Hr Ent FR and FG, Dir FW Lt. Approach from N. Lt Ho (conspic), Oc 8s 16m 9M Hr Mr (02996) 1305.

MONNICKENDAM has three marinas with all facilities. Ldg Lts FR at 236°. Hr Mr ☎ (02995) 1616.
Facilities: ME, C, FW, P, D, Gaz, AC, CH.

VOLENDAM; several yacht berths. Ldg Dir Lts Fl 5s at 313°. Hr Mr ☎ (02993) 69620.
Facilities: AB, ME, FW, C, P, D, Gaz, SM.

EDAM Enter keeping Iso W 8s between FG and FR at entrance. Narrow ent; beware commercial traffic. Yacht berth on N side or pass through lock to the Oorgat – at fork take S canal into Nieuwe Haven. Hr Mr ☎ (02993) 71092. Few facilities **T.D. Sails Oorgat** SM; **Ruud van Drunen** ME, el, Sh, **Town** V, R, Bar, ⊡, ✉, Gaz, Ⓑ. Hr Mr (02993) 71092.

HOORN W harbour ent has Iso W4s 15m 10M and FR and FG. Yachts have four choices – **Stichting Jachthaven Hoorn** (700) Hr Mr ☎ (02993) 15208, FW, AC, ⊡, CH, V, ME, El, Sh, C; **Buitenhaven** FW, D, Gas, **Vluchthaven marina** run by WV Hoorn (100) ☎ (02290) 13540 FW; **Binnenhaven** through Buitenhaven and lock (always open) FW, Gaz. **Town** V, CH, ✉, R, Dr, P, D, Ⓑ.

ENKHUIZEN. Approaching from SW, the Krabbersgat Ldg Lts Iso 4s at 039°; from NE Ldg Lts Iso 8s at 230° and the FR and FG at breakwaters lead to Knabbersgat lock and Hr of Enkhinzen. Call lock on Ch 22. Signals – RR = No entry; RG = Stand by; GG = enter. There are two marinas and the main harbour. **Compagnieshaver** (500) Hr Mr (02280) 13353 P, D, FW, AC, CH, Gaz; **Buyshaven** (195) ☎ (02280) 15660 FW, AC; **Town Harbour** ☎ (02280) 12444 FW. **Town** C, Slip, CH, SM, ME, El, Sh, Ⓑ, V, R, Bar, P, D, Dr, ✉, ≷.

ANDIJK. Has two marinas. But visitors use **Stichting Jachthaven Andijk.** (600) ☎ (02289) 3075. Ent between FR and FG Lts on 015°. ME, C, SM, Gaz, ⊡, D, CH,.

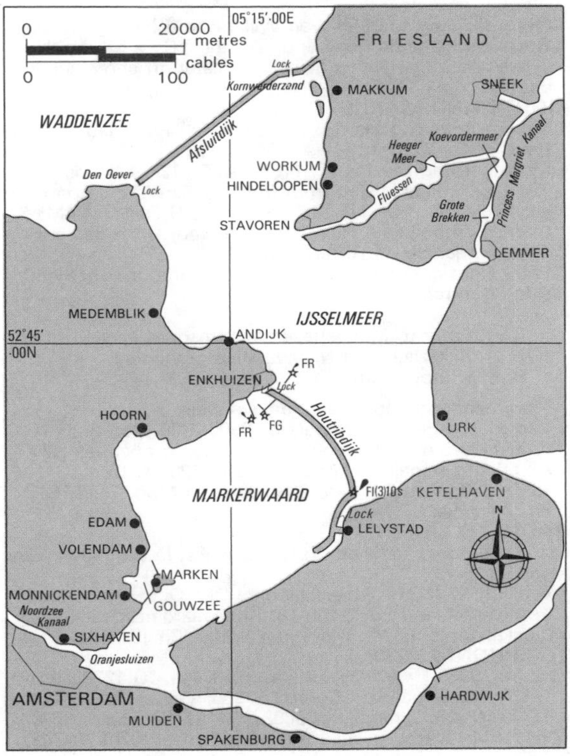
0
20000
metres
0
100
cables
05°15'·00E
FRIESLAND
Lock
Kornwerderzand
MAKKUM
SNEEK
WADDENZEE
Afsluitdijk
Heeger Meer
Koevordermeer
Princess Margriet Kanaal
Den Oever
Lock
WORKUM
HINDELOOPEN
Fluessen
Grote Brekken
STAVOREN
LEMMER
MEDEMBLIK
IJSSELMEER
52°45'·00N
ANDIJK
FR
ENKHUIZEN
Lock
Houtribdijk
HOORN
FR
FG
URK
MARKERWAARD
Fl(3)10s
KETELHAVEN
Lock
LELYSTAD
N
EDAM
VOLENDAM
MARKEN
MONNICKENDAM
Noordzee Kanaal
GOUWZEE
SIXHAVEN
Oranjesluizen
AMSTERDAM
HARDWIJK
MUIDEN
SPAKENBURG

IJSSELMEER *continued*

MEDEMBLIK. Entrance between FR and FG on line 232° Oc 5s Dir Lt. Visitors pass through Oosterhaven into 2 marinas and town harbour. **Pekelharinghaven** Hr Mr ☎ 2175, S of Oosterhaven; **Stichting Jachthaven** Hr Mr ☎ 1861 in Westerhaven, FW, AC, ◙, P, D, ME, El, Sh, C; **Middenhaven** Hr Mr ☎ 1686, CH, FW: Fuel in Oosterhaven. **Town** Ⓑ, CH, Dr, Bar, ◙, ME, El, C, ✉, R, SM, Sh, V.

DEN HELDER 10-20-26

Noord Holland

CHARTS
Admiralty 191, 2322, 2593; Zeekaart 1454, 1546; Dutch Yacht Chart 1811, 1801; ANWB F; Imray Y5

TIDES
Dover −0430; ML 1·1; Duration No data; Zone −0100

Standard Port HELGOLAND (⟶)

Times				Height (metres)			
HW		LW		MHWS	MHWN	MLWN	MLWS
0200	0700	0200	0800	2·7	2·3	0·4	0·0
1400	1900	1400	2000				
Differences DEN HELDER							
−0350	−0500	−0515	−0425	−0·9	−0·8	0·0	+0·2
OUDESCHILD							
−0300	−0430	−0435	−0355	−0·9	−0·8	0·0	+0·2
DEN OEVER							
−0245	−0420	−0355	−0300	−0·8	−0·7	0·0	+0·2

SHELTER
There is good shelter in the Naval Harbour, the YC and yacht harbour being immediately to stbd on entering. Yachts can lock into the Koopvaarders Binnenhaven Yacht Harbour or the Den Helder Yacht Haven, in Westoever.

NAVIGATION
Waypoint Schulpengat SG safe water buoy, Mo(A) 8s, 52°52'·95N 04°38'·00E (on leading line), 206·5°/026·5° from/to Kaap Hoofd, 6·0M.
There are two channels to the harbour entrance:—
(1) Molengat is good except in strong winds from NW when heavy breakers occur at this entrance.
(2) Schulpengat is well marked and well lit. Beware very strong tidal streams through the Marsdiep across the harbour entrance.
Note: the port Marinehaven Willemsoord belongs to the Royal Netherlands Navy and, like the YC, is run by them. There is a large fishing fleet, and many off shore service vessels.

LIGHTS AND MARKS
Schulpengat Ldg Lts 026 30° on Texel. Front Iso 4s 18M. Rear Oc 8s 18M. Both vis 025°-028°.
Molengat Ldg Lts 141·7°. Front Iso 5s 13m 8M; vis 124°-157°. Rear, 650m from front, F 22m 8M; Tr on hosp; vis 124°-157°. Ldg Lts 191°. Front Oc G 5s 16m 14M; B triangle on building. Rear (synchronised) Oc G 5s 25m 14M; B triangle on B framework Tr.
Entry signals, shown from Harssens Harbour Office on W side of entrance:—

R
W } Entry to Marinehaven Willemsoord and Rijkszeehaven Nieuwe Diep prohibited without permission
R

Moormanbridge operates 7 days a week H24.
Van Kinsbergenbridge operates 0500-2300 Mon-Fri; 0700-1400 Sat. Burgemeester Vissersbrug operates H24.
All bridges remain closed 0715-0810, 1200-1215, 1245-1300, Mon-Fri. Also 0830-0910 on Mon, 1545-1645 on Fri. All times LT.

RADIO TELEPHONE
It is obligatory to listen on Ch 12 whilst in the fairway and port.
VHF Ch 14 (H24). Other stations: Den Oever Lock Ch 20. Kornwerderzand Locks Ch 18. Koopvaardersschutsluis (Locks) Ch 22 (H24). Moorman Bridge Ch 18 (H24).

TELEPHONE (02230)
Hr Mr 13955 Hr Mr (Yacht Haven) 37444 CG 12732; Pilot 17424; Municipal Port Control 13955; Vessel Traffic Centre 52770, Naval Commander 56822; # 15182; Police 55700; Ⓗ 11414; Water Police 16767; Brit Consul (020) 764343.

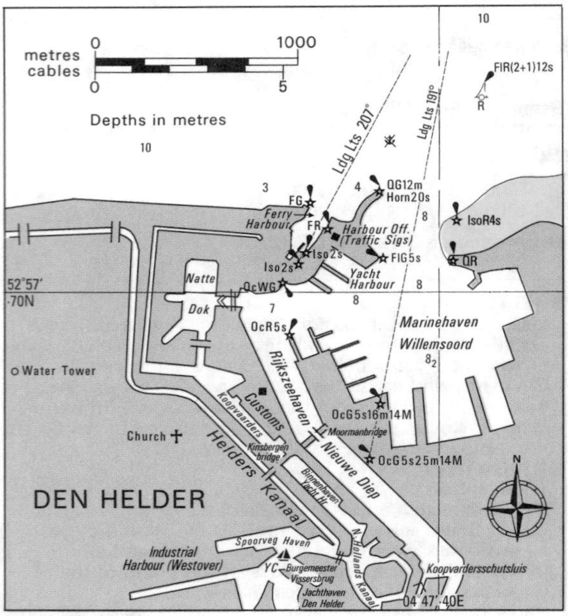

metres
cables
0
1000
0
5
Depths in metres
10
Ldg Lts 207°
Ldg Lts 191°
FlR(2+1)12s
R
QG12m
Horn20s
FG
Ferry Harbour
FR
Harbour Off. (Traffic Sigs)
Iso2s
Iso2s
FlG5s
IsoR4s
QR
Yacht Harbour
52°57'·70N
Watte
Dok
OcWG
OcR5s
Marinehaven Willemsoord
Water Tower
Rijkszeehaven
Customs
Koopvaarders
Kinsbergen bridge
Moormanbridge
OcG5s16m14M
OcG5s25m14M
Church
Helders Kanaal
Nieuwe Diep
Binnenhaven Yacht Hr
DEN HELDER
N
Spoorweg Haven
Industrial Harbour (Westover)
YC
Burgemeester Vissersbrug
Jachthaven Den Helder
N. Hollands Kanaal
Koopvaardersschutsluis
04°47'·40E

FACILITIES
Yacht Harbours KMYC ☎ 56645, FW, D, Bar, R; **MWY YC** (Binnenhaven) ☎ 17076, P (at garage), D, L, FW, AB; **YC WSOV** ☎ 52173; **YC HWN** ☎ 24422; **W. Visser & Son** ME, El, Sh, Floating dock; **Binnenhaven** ☎ 16641, L, FW, CH, AB, SM; **Yacht Haven** ☎ 37444, AB, ME, El, Sh, C, CH, Slip, FW, R, Bar; **W. Bakker** ☎ 17356, Gaz. **Town** P, CH, V, R, Bar. ✉; Ⓑ; ⇌; ✈ (Amsterdam). Ferry UK — Hook of Holland—Harwich.

HARLINGEN 10-20-27

Friesland

CHARTS
Admiralty 112, 2593; Zeekaart 1454, 1456; Dutch Yacht Chart 1811; ANWB B; Imray Y5

TIDES
Dover −0210; ML 1.2; Duration 0520; Zone −0100

Standard Port HELGOLAND (⟶)

Times				Height (metres)			
HW		LW		MHWS	MHWN	MLWN	MLWS
0200	0700	0200	0800	2.7	2.3	0.4	0.0
1400	1900	1400	2000				
Differences HARLINGEN							
−0145	−0245	−0155	−0115	−0.4	−0.4	−0.1	+0.2

SHELTER
Good shelter, but entrance can be rough at HW with winds in W or SW. Coming in with flood, beware strong current across entrance. Very good shelter in yacht harbour in Noorderhaven and also inside the lock into the Van Harinxma canal in the yacht harbour (immediately to stbd on leaving the locks). There is limited room here and only advisable if proceeding on to the lakes.

NAVIGATION
Waypoint BS1-IN2 buoy, GRG, Fl(2+1)G 12s, 53°14′.46N 05°09′.54E, at Blauwe Slenk/Inschot junction. Approach via the Vliestroom and Blauwe Slenk, both buoyed and lit, but channel is narrow for the last 2½ M. Beware the Pollendam, marked with port and stbd beacons; when covered, strong tidal stream sweeps across the Pollendam. Hanerak, a second buoyed channel, runs about 600m S of the Pollendam. At particularly high tides, the outer yacht harbour may be closed off by flood gates from up to HW−1½ to HW+1½.

LIGHTS AND MARKS
Ldg Lts 112° Front Iso 6s, rear Iso 6s. Entry signals for locks in Nieuwe Voorhaven (at signal station):
2 FR (vert) = Arrival or departure of large vessel — all other movement prohibited.
Bu Flag = Sluicing, entry prohibited.

RADIO TELEPHONE
VHF Ch 11 (Mon 0000 to Sat 2200 LT). Port Authority VHF Ch 4 CG; VHF Ch 22 Harinxma Canal locks.

TELEPHONE (05178)
Hr Mr 13041; CG (Brandaris) (05620) 3100; Port Authority 3041; # 18750; Police 13333; Ⓗ 99999; Brit Consul (020) 764343.

FACILITIES
EC Monday; **Noorderhaven Yacht Harbour** ☎ 15666, FW, El, CH, V, R, Bar, ⊡; **Yacht Harbour Van Harinxma Canal** ☎ 16898, FW, ⊡, C (6 ton); **'Het Anker' Watersport** ☎ 14030, CH, El, E, Gaz, Diving and salvage; **'Leeuwenbrug' watersport** ☎ 15666, El (by arrangement), CH, ME (by arrangement); **Post, Zuiderhaven 39**, D, P; **'Welgelegen' Scheepsw** ☎ 127444, big ship firm — emergency only.
Town LB, D, P, V, R, Bar, SM ☎ 12104, ✉, Ⓑ, ⇌, ✈ (Amsterdam). Ferry UK — Hook of Holland—Harwich.

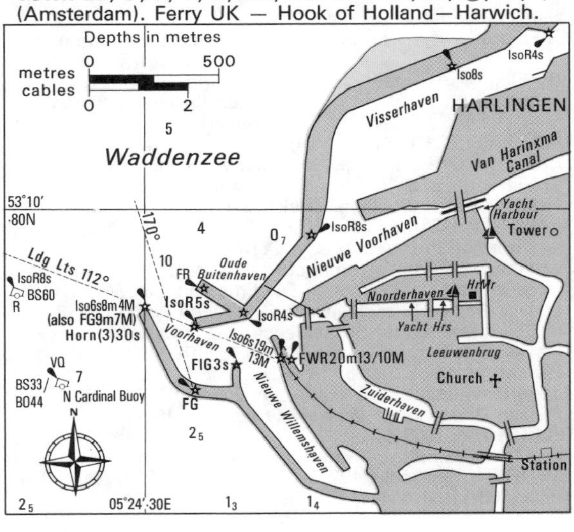
Depths in metres
metres
cables
500
Waddenzee
HARLINGEN
Visserhaven
Van Harinxma Canal
Yacht Harbour
Tower
Nieuwe Voorhaven
Oude Buitenhaven
Noorderhaven
HrMr
Yacht Hrs
Leeuwenbrug
Church
Zuiderhaven
Nieuwe Willemshaven
Voorhaven
Station
Ldg Lts 112°
170°
IsoR8s
IsoR4s
Iso8s
IsoR5s
Iso6s8m4M
(also FG9m7M)
Horn(3)30s
Iso6s19m13M
FWR20m13/10M
FlG3s
FG
FR
BS60
BS33/B044
N Cardinal Buoy
VQ
53°10′·80N
05°24′·30E

VLIELAND 10-20-28

WEST FRISIAN ISLANDS
Friesland

CHARTS
Admiralty 112, 2593; Zeekaart 1456; Dutch Yacht Chart 1811; Imray Y5

TIDES
Dover −0300; Duration Rising 0600 Falling 0620; Zone −0100

Standard Port HELGOLAND (⟶)

Times				Height (metres)			
HW		LW		MHWS	MHWN	MLWN	MLWS
0200	0700	0200	0800	2·7	2·3	0·4	0·0
1400	1900	1400	2000				
Differences VLIELAND—HAVEN							
−0255	−0320	−0350	−0330	−0·4	−0·3	+0·1	+0·2

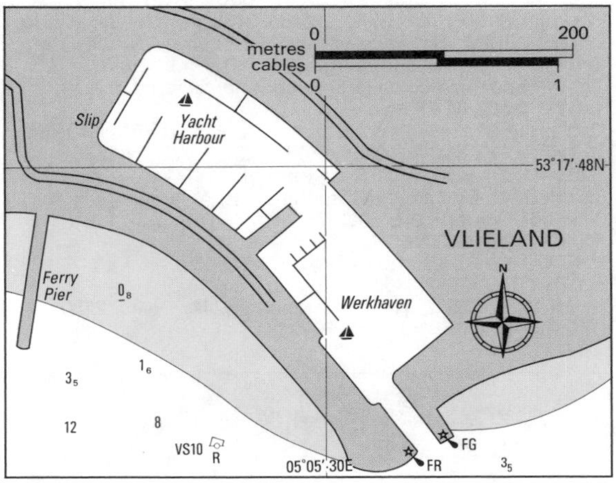
metres
cables
200
Slip
Yacht Harbour
53°17′·48N
VLIELAND
Ferry Pier
Werkhaven
VS10
R
FG
FR
05°05′·30E

SHELTER
Shelter is good, but yacht harbour becomes very crowded in high season. Anchorage about 1600m W of the harbour is good except in S to SW winds, and it is near the village. Yachts are forbidden to anchor in buoyed channel or berth at pier ½M W of harbour.

NAVIGATION
Waypoint VSM safe water buoy, Iso 4s, 53°19′·08N 04°55′·74E, 274°/094° from/to ZS1 and ZS2 buoys at Zuider Stortemelk entrance, 2·3M. Only safe approach is through the Zuider Stortemelk which is deep and well marked and lit. This leads to Vliesloot. There is an alternative entrance from the S via Fransche Gaatje but it is very much shallower and can even dry out at very LW.

LIGHTS AND MARKS
Ldg Lts 277°. Front FW 8M — Rear Oc W 10s.
Main Lt Ho Iso 4s 53m 20M; brown Tr, W lantern; RC.
Entry signals: R Flag or two R Lts on the pier indicates harbour closed.

RADIO TELEPHONE
VHF CG Ch 02 (Brandaris—W. Terschelling).

TELEPHONE (05621)
Hr Mr 1563; Hr Mr (Yacht Hr) 1729; CG 1326; # 1522; Police 1312; Dr 201307; Brit Consul (020) 764343.

FACILITIES
Yacht Harbour ☎ 1729, P, D, L, FW, AB; **Harbour** C (12 ton); **North Shore W of Ferry Pier** M; **D.W. Floor** ☎ 1558 El, Ⓔ, **B. H. Iedema** ☎ 1336, Gaz; **C. D. Hoogland** ☎ 1352, P, D; **Town** P, D, ME, El, CH, V, R, Bar. ✉; Ⓑ; ⇌ (ferry to Harlingen); ✈ (Amsterdam). Ferry UK — Hook of Holland—Harwich.

TERSCHELLING 10-20-29

WEST FRISIAN ISLANDS
Friesland

CHARTS
Admiralty 112, 2593; Zeekaart 1456; Dutch Yacht Chart 1811; Imray Y5

TIDES
Dover −0300; ML 1·3; Duration No data; Zone −0100

Standard Port HELGOLAND (⟶)

Times				Height (metres)			
HW		LW		MHWS	MHWN	MLWN	MLWS
0200	0700	0200	0800	2·7	2·3	0·4	0·0
1400	1900	1400	2000				
Differences WEST TERSCHELLING							
−0220	−0250	−0330	−0305	−0·4	−0·3	+0·1	+0·2

SHELTER
Good shelter especially in marina in N corner of harbour. Very crowded in season. Yachts may go alongside near Hr Mr's office.

NAVIGATION
See 10.20.28. Waypoint VL2-SG1 buoy, RGR, Fl(2+1)R 12s, 53°19'·30N 05°09'·80E, 225°/045° from/to front Ldg Lt 053°, 2·9M. Entrance via the Schuitengat Noord; the channel is narrow and shifts but it is well buoyed. The harbour has considerable commercial traffic.

LIGHTS AND MARKS
Ldg Lts 053°. Front (West mole) FWR 5m 8/5M; R post, W bands; vis W049°-055°, R055°-252°, W252°-263°, R263°-049°; Horn 15s. Rear (on dyke 1·1M from front, off chartlet) Iso 5s 14m 19M; metal mast, Y lantern; vis 045°-061° (intens 045°-052°).

RADIO TELEPHONE
VHF CG Ch 02 (Brandaris—W. Terschellig).

TELEPHONE (05620)
Hr Mr 2235; CG 2341; ⊞ Harlingen 5241; Police 2280; Dr 2181; Brit Consul (020) 764343.

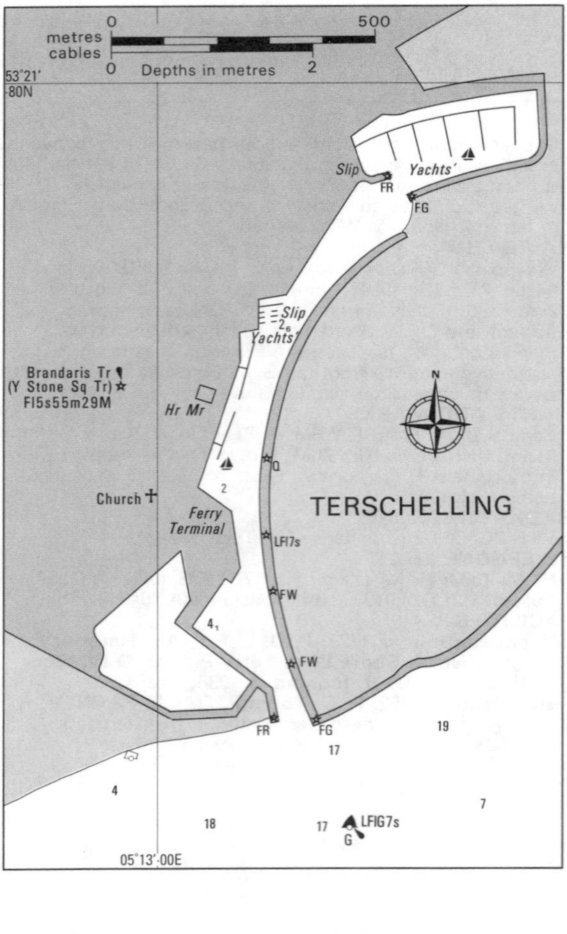

0
500
metres
cables
0
Depths in metres
2
53°21'·80N
Slip
FR
Yachts'
FG
Slip
Yachts'
Brandaris Tr
(Y Stone Sq Tr)
Fl5s55m29M
Hr Mr
Q
Church
Ferry Terminal
TERSCHELLING
LFl7s
FW
FW
FR
FG
19
17
4
18
17
LFlG7s
G
7
05°13'·00E

FACILITIES
EC Wednesday; **Marina – "Stichting Passantenhaven Terschelling"** (500) ☎ 3337, Hr Mr, C, FW; **Harbour** Slip, M, FW (in cans), ME, AB; **W. Bloem** ☎ 2076, ME; **L. G. Schiepstra** ☎ 2694, ME; **C Bloem** ☎ 2178, SM; **Village** P, D, FW, CH, V, R, Bar. ✉; Ⓑ (W. Terschelling); ⇌ (ferry to Harlingen); ✈ (Groningen). Ferry UK — Hook of Holland—Harwich.

DELFZIJL 10-20-30

Groningen

CHARTS
Admiralty 3510, 3509; Zeekaart 1555; Dutch Yacht Chart 1812; Dutch ANWB A

TIDES
Dover −0025; ML 2·0; Duration 0605; Zone −0100

Standard Port HELGOLAND (⟶)

Times				Height (metres)			
HW		LW		MHWS	MHWN	MLWN	MLWS
0200	0700	0200	0800	2·7	2·3	0·4	0·0
1400	1900	1400	2000				
Differences DELFZIJL							
+0020	−0005	−0035	+0005	+0·8	+0·9	+0·1	+0·2
EEMSHAVEN							
−0025	−0045	−0115	−0035	+0·3	+0·4	+0·2	+0·2
LAUWERSOOG							
−0130	−0150	−0230	−0225	+0·1	+0·2	+0·2	+0·2

SHELTER
Good shelter. Yacht harbour in Balkenhaven gives good protection. Yachts can lock through into the Eemskanaal and berth in Farmsumerhaven (1 day only) or at the end of the old Eemskanaal near the obsolete lock, in new yacht harbour.

NAVIGATION
Waypoint Hubertgat safe water buoy, Iso 8s, Whis, 53°34'·90N 06°14'·32E, 270°/090° from/to Borkum Kleiner Lt, 15·5M. Westerems safe water buoy, Iso 4s, Racon, 53°36'·97N, 06°19'·48E, 272°/092° from/to Nos 1 and 2 Westerems channel buoys, 1·9M. See also 10.21.9. Channels in the Ems are well buoyed and lit. The entrance is 3 M ESE of the town of Delfzijl. Beware strong tides across the entrance, as these can be dangerous.

LIGHTS AND MARKS
Harbour entrance, FG on W arm and FR on E arm with Horn 15s and FY (occasl). Ldg Lts 203°, Front QR No 2A, W pedestal on dolphin; Rear FR. The channel from the entrance has G Fl Lts to N and R Fl Lts to S.

Entry signals:—

2 R Flags or 2 R Lts —	All movement prohibited except as directed by Hr Mr.

Sluicing signals:—

R Flag or 3 R Lts in triangle —	Sluicing at Eemskanaal Lock through gates.
Bu Flag or 3 R Lts in triangle over G Lt —	Sluicing at Eemskanaal Lock through draining sluices.

RADIO TELEPHONE
Call: *Port Office Delfzijl/Eemshaven* VHF Ch 14 (H24). Traffic reports on Ch 14 every 10 min from H+00 when visibility less than 500m. Locks (Eemskanaalsluizen) Ch 11 (Mon-Sat, H24). Die Ems (Ems Revier) Ch 18 20 21 (H24) — information broadcasts in German every H+50 with weather and tidal information, including storm warnings for coastal waters between Die Ems and Die Weser. Locks: Grosse Seeschleuse (call: *Emden Lock*) Ch 13 16 (H24). Nesserlander Seeschleuse (call: *Nesserland Lock*) Ch 13 16 (H24). Leer Lock Ch 16 13 (0700-2300 LT). Papenburg Lock Ch 16; 13 (H24). Jann-Berghaus Bridge (call: *Leer Bridge*) Ch 15. Friesen Bridge (call: *Weener Bridge*) Ch 15.

TELEPHONE (05960)
Hr Mr (Delfzijl Port Authorities) 40477; Neptunus Yacht Hr Mr 15004; Sea locks 13293; CG (Police) 13831; ⊞ 15060; Police 06-11; Ⓗ 44444; Brit Consul (020) 764343.

DELFZIJL *continued*

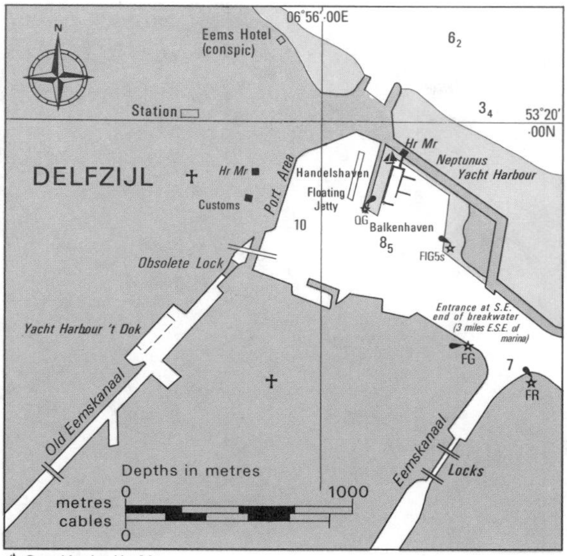
06°56'·00E
Eems Hotel (conspic)
Station
53°20'·00N
DELFZIJL
Hr Mr
Handelshaven
Port Area
Floating Jetty
Customs
QG
Balkenhaven
FlG5s
Hr Mr
Neptunus Yacht Harbour
Obsolete Lock
Entrance at S.E. end of breakwater (3 miles E.S.E. of marina)
Yacht Harbour 't Dok
FG
FR
Old Eemskanaal
Eemskanaal
Locks
Depths in metres
metres
cables
0
1000
0

⛵ See Yacht Hr Mr

FACILITIES

Neptunus Yacht Harbour ☎ 15004, D, Bar, M, L, FW; **Yacht Harbour 't Dok** D, FW, AB; **Datema** ☎ 13810, CH, ACA, Dutch Chart Agent; **P. Dinges** ☎ 15010, ME, El; **H. S. Hunfeld** ☎ 13446, ME, El; **Ems Canal** L, FW, AB; **IJzerhandel Delken** ☎ 30200, Gaz; **Motor Boat Club Abel Tasman** ☎ 16560 Bar, M, D, FW, L, ⊡, V; **Town** P, D, V, R, Bar. ⊠; Ⓑ; ≢; ✈ (Groningen). Ferry UK — Hook of Holland—Harwich.

MINOR HARBOURS AND ANCHORAGES 10-20-31

WALSOORDEN Zeeland 51° 23' ·00N, 04° 02' ·00E. Zone −0100 Admty chart 120, Zeekaart 1443. Dutch Yacht Chart 1803 HW +0300 on Dover (GMT), +0110 on Vlissingen (zone −0100); HW height +0·7m on Vlissingen, ML 2·6m Ldg Lts 220° both Oc W 3s. Hr ent marked with FG and FR. Zandvliet Radio VHF Ch 12. Yacht basin dead ahead on entering harbour depth 2·3 to 3·4m. ☎ (01148) Hr Mr ☎ 1235 FW, Slip; **P Burm** ☎ 1504, Gas, P, D; **L Hemelaar** ☎ 1359 P, D; **Jachtwerf Moed en Trouw** ☎ 1205 ME, El, **Town,** R, Bar, ⊠.

PAAL Zeeland 51° 21' ·00N, 04°07' ·00E Zone −0100 Admty Charts 120, 139 Zeekaart 1443. Dutch Yacht Chart 1803; HW +0310 on Dover (GMT); +0120 on Vlissingen (zone −0100); HW height +0·8m on Vlissingen. ML 2·7m. Zandvliet Radio VHF Ch 12. Yacht harbour entrance on W side at river mouth, marked by withy. No lights. Harbour dries ☎ (01143) Hr Mr 346 **Jachthaven** AC, FW, **EPW Staal** ☎ 277 V, P, D, Gaz; **J J Verras** ☎ 264 ME, El, R.

DOEL Antwerpen 51° 19' ·00N, 04° 16' ·00E Zone −0100 Admty Chart 139, Zeekaart 1443 Dutch Yacht Chart 1803 HW +0310 on Dover (GMT); +0100 on Vlissingen (zone −0100); HW height +0·7m Vlissingen Lt on N pierhead Oc W5s ☎ (03) Hr Mr 7733072 **YC de Noord** ☎ 7733669 R, Bar, FW.

ELLEWOUTSDIJK Zeeland 51° 23' ·00N, 03° 49' ·00E. Zone −0100. Admty Chart 120 Zeekaart 1443 Dutch Yacht Chart 1803. HW+0230 on Dover (GMT), +0020 on Vlissingen (zone −0100); HW height +0·3m on Vlissingen; ML2·6m. Small harbour on the N bank. No lights. Entry HW∓3. ☎ (01104) Hr Mr ☎ 248 FW, D. **YC Ellewoutsdijk** ☎ 446. **M.P. de Broekert** ☎ 302 Gaz.

OUDESCHILD, Texel, Noord Holland, 53°02' ·00N, 04°51' ·00E, Zone −0100, Admty charts 191, 2593, Zeekaart 1546, 1454, Dutch Yacht 1811. HW −0355 on Dover (GMT), −0425 on Helgoland (zone −0100); HW height −0·7m on Helgoland; ML 1·1m; Duration 0625. On SE side of Texel, Hr gives good shelter and has Yacht Harbour in the Werkhaven, NNE of ent. Beware strong cross tides across ent. Keep Ldg Lt, Oc 6s 14m between harbour entrance Lts, FR and FG on course of 291°. VHF Ch 09, 0730−1500 LT. Facilities: ☎ (02220) Hr Mr ☎ 12710; **Marina** ☎ 3608, Slip, Gaz, Bar, D, Dr, FW, M, R; **YC W. V. Texel**; **Boom Shiprepairs** ☎ 12661, Sh, Dry dock, ME, C.

NES, AMELAND, Friesland, 53°26' ·00N, 05°45' ·00E, Zone −0100, Admty chart 2593, Zeekaart 1458, Dutch Yacht 1811, 1812. HW −0055 on Dover (GMT), −0108 on Helgoland (zone −0100); HW height +0·4m on Helgoland; ML 1·3m; Duration 0625. Harbour at Nes, mid S of the island; no proper yacht hr but sheltered from all but winds from E to S. Much of harbour dries but fin keels sink into mud. Beware sandbanks in the Zeegat van Ameland. Lt at W end of Ameland Fl(3) 15s 57m 30M, RC. Nes Nieuwe Veerdam head Iso 6s 2m 8M. Facilities are very limited; Gaz. Hr Mr (05191) 2304.

OOSTMAHORN, Friesland, 53°23' ·00N, 06°09' ·00E, Zone −0100, Admty chart 3509, Zeekaarten 1458, Dutch Yacht Chart 1812; non tidal. Harbour on W side of Lauwersmeer; lock in from the Zoutkamperlaag to W of Lauwersoog. Main harbour with FR and FG Lts at entrance has yacht haven (2·5m to 3·4m). Approx 450m to the SSE there is another yacht haven, the Voorm Veerhaven (1·5m). Floating beacons with Y flags mark fishing areas. Facilities: Hr Mr (05193) 1331; most normal facilities in the Yacht Haven.

ZOUTKAMP, Friesland, 53°20' ·00N, 06°18' ·00E, Zone −0100. Admty chart 3509, Zeekaarten 1458, Dutch Yacht Chart 1812; non tidal. Approach down the Zoutkamperril (3 to 4·5m); Approx 400m before the bridge, the yacht haven 'Hunzegat' (1·4 to 2·2m) is on the NE side. There is another yacht haven, the Oude Binnenhaven (2m), further SE. Pass through lock, Provinciale Sluis, and yacht haven is immediately to NE. FW and FR Lts shown from lock. Facilities: **Gruno BY** ☎ 2057, ME, El, Sh, C (20 ton), BH; **Oude-Binnenhaven** AC, C, FW; **Hunzegat** ☎ 2588, AC, FW, SC, Slip; **Town** BY, C, D, Dr, El, Gaz, ME, P, ⊠, R, Sh, SM, V.

LAUWERSOOG, Friesland, 53°25' ·00N, 06°12' ·00E, Zone −0100, Admty charts 3509, 3761, Zeekaart 1458, Dutch Yacht 1812. HW −0150 on Dover (GMT), −0120 on Helgoland (zone −0100); HW height +0·5m on Helgoland; ML 1·3m. See 10.20.30. Good shelter in all conditions in inner harbour. Outer harbour has swell in bad weather. Yachts lock into inner harbour, the Lauwersmeer, 0400−2100 weekdays, 0400−1800 Saturdays, 0900−1000 and 1630−1830 Sundays LT. Yacht harbour to SE of lock; visitors mooring on first pontoon. Lts, N of N jetty. W of entrance FG 3M. E of entrance FR 4M. Locks, lead-in jetty Iso 4s. VHF Ch 09 (Mon−0000−1700LT, Tue−Wed 0800−1700LT, Thur−Sat 0700−1500LT. Locks VHF CH 22 May−Sept: Mon−Fri 0700−2000LT, Sat 0700−1900LT, Sun 0900−1200 & 1400−1830LT. Oct−Apr: Mon−Fri 0700−1800LT, Sat 0700−1700LT. Hr Mr ☎ (05193) 9023. Lockmaster ☎ (05193) 9043. Facilities: Gaz, BY, **Pontoons** AB, D, FW; **Near ferry terminal** P; **W end of harbour**, Bar, R, V, YC.

SCHIERMONNIKOOG, Friesland, 53°28' ·00N, 06°12' ·00E, Zone −0100. Admty charts 3509, 3761, Zeekaart 1458, Dutch Yacht 1812 HW (Lauwersoog) −0150 on Dover (GMT), −0120 on Helgoland (zone −0100); HW height +0·5m on Helgoland. Entrance via Friesche Zeegat (Westgat), buoyed but dangerous in bad weather due to the bar across the harbour mouth. Gat van Schiermonnikoog (buoyed) runs E from Zoutkamperlaag over bar (depth variable). Groote Siege (marked) leads NE from a point 2·5M SSE of Lt Ho to the ferry pier. Access to Ferry Pier at all states of tide, a natural sill keeping 1 to 1·5m in harbour. Ent only 15m wide. Yachts may not go alongside Ferrypier. About 1M before the pier there is a small yacht harbour, entrance marked by perches. Access HW−2 to HW+1. Picturesque, but very full in high season and also expensive. Lights: near W end of island, Lt Ho Fl(4) 20s; Ferry Pier head Lt, FW. Facilities: Hr Mr ☎ (05195) 544 (May-Sept), FW.

TERMUNTERZIJL Gronigen, 53°18' ·00N, 07°02' ·00E Zone -0100 Admty chart 3510, Zeekaart 1555 Dutch Yacht chart 1812 HW −0025 on Dover (GMT); +0015 on Helgoland; HW height +0·8m on Helgoland. Entrance marked by seven R and seven G bns. No lights. Yachts go to yacht berths SW of entrance or to small pontoons to SE of entrance. ☎ (05962) Hr Mr 2168 (Apr-Sept) VHF09, FW, AC, Bar, R.

Area 21

Germany
Borkum to Danish border

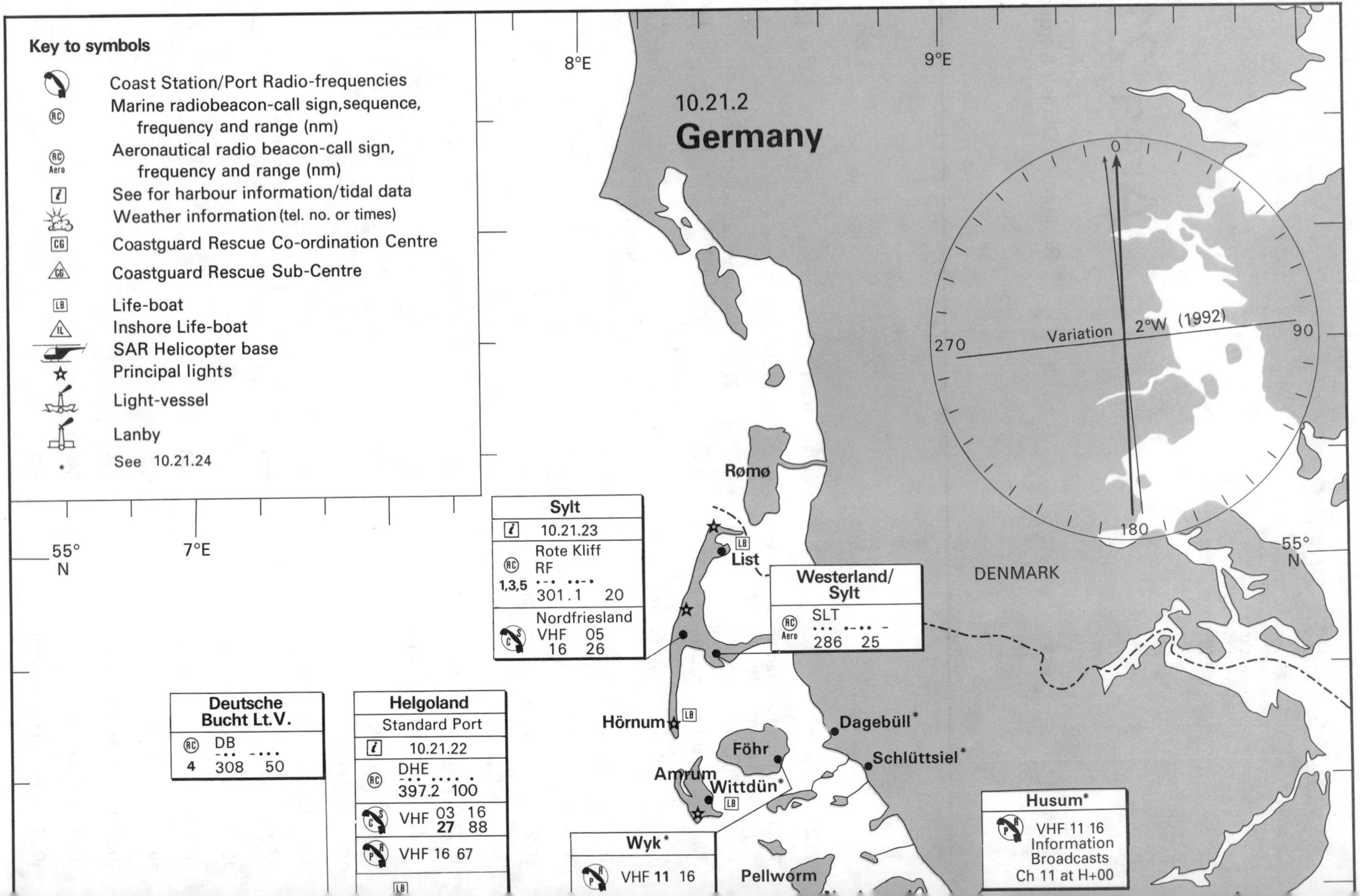

10.21.2
Germany
Key to symbols
Coast Station/Port Radio-frequencies
Marine radiobeacon-call sign, sequence, frequency and range (nm)
Aeronautical radio beacon-call sign, frequency and range (nm)
See for harbour information/tidal data
Weather information (tel. no. or times)
Coastguard Rescue Co-ordination Centre
Coastguard Rescue Sub-Centre
Life-boat
Inshore Life-boat
SAR Helicopter base
Principal lights
Light-vessel
Lanby
* See 10.21.24
8°E
9°E
7°E
55° N
Variation 2°W (1992)
0
90
180
270
DENMARK
Rømø
List
Hörnum
Föhr
Amrum
Wittdün*
Dagebüll*
Schlüttsiel*
Pellworm
Sylt
10.21.23
Rote Kliff
RF
1,3,5 301.1 20
Nordfriesland
VHF 05 16 26
Westerland/Sylt
SLT
286 25
Deutsche Bucht Lt.V.
DB
4 308 50
Helgoland
Standard Port
10.21.22
DHE
397.2 100
VHF 03 16 27 88
VHF 16 67
Wyk*
VHF 11 16
Husum*
VHF 11 16
Information Broadcasts
Ch 11 at H+00

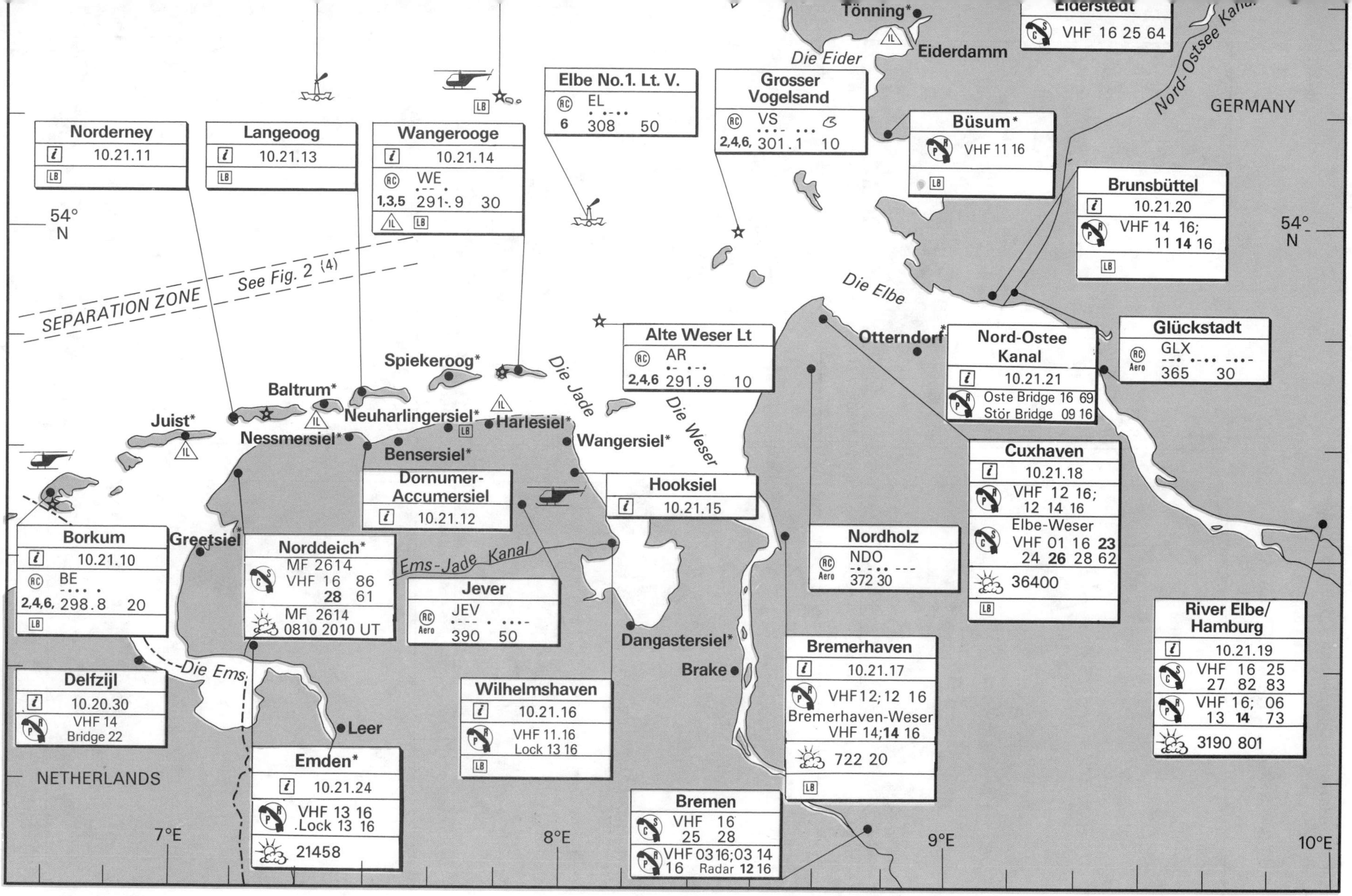

Eiderstedt
VHF 16 25 64
Tönning*
Eiderdamm
Die Eider
Nord-Ostsee Kanal
GERMANY
Norderney
10.21.11
LB
Langeoog
10.21.13
LB
Wangerooge
10.21.14
WE
1,3,5 291.9 30
IL LB
Elbe No.1. Lt. V.
EL
6 308 50
Grosser Vogelsand
VS
2,4,6, 301.1 10
Büsum*
VHF 11 16
LB
Brunsbüttel
10.21.20
VHF 14 16; 11 14 16
LB
54° N
SEPARATION ZONE
See Fig. 2 (4)
Die Elbe
Alte Weser Lt
AR
2,4,6 291.9 10
Otterndorf*
Nord-Ostee Kanal
10.21.21
Oste Bridge 16 69
Stör Bridge 09 16
Glückstadt
GLX
Aero
365 30
Spiekeroog*
Baltrum*
Juist*
Neuharlingersiel*
Harlesiel*
Nessmersiel*
Bensersiel*
Wangersiel*
Die Jade
Die Weser
Dornumer-Accumersiel
10.21.12
Hooksiel
10.21.15
Cuxhaven
10.21.18
VHF 12 16; 12 14 16
Elbe-Weser
VHF 01 16 23 24 26 28 62
36400
LB
Borkum
10.21.10
BE
2,4,6, 298.8 20
LB
Greetsiel*
Norddeich*
MF 2614
VHF 16 86 28 61
MF 2614
0810 2010 UT
Ems-Jade Kanal
Jever
JEV
Aero
390 50
Nordholz
NDO
Aero
372 30
Dangastersiel*
Brake
Bremerhaven
10.21.17
VHF 12; 12 16
Bremerhaven-Weser
VHF 14; 14 16
722 20
LB
River Elbe/Hamburg
10.21.19
VHF 16 25 27 82 83
VHF 16; 06 13 14 73
3190 801
Delfzijl
10.20.30
VHF 14
Bridge 22
Die Ems
Leer
Emden*
10.21.24
VHF 13 16
Lock 13 16
21458
Wilhelmshaven
10.21.16
VHF 11.16
Lock 13 16
LB
Bremen
VHF 16 25 28
VHF 03 16; 03 14 16
Radar 12 16
NETHERLANDS
7°E
8°E
9°E
10°E

10.21.3 AREA 21 TIDAL STREAMS

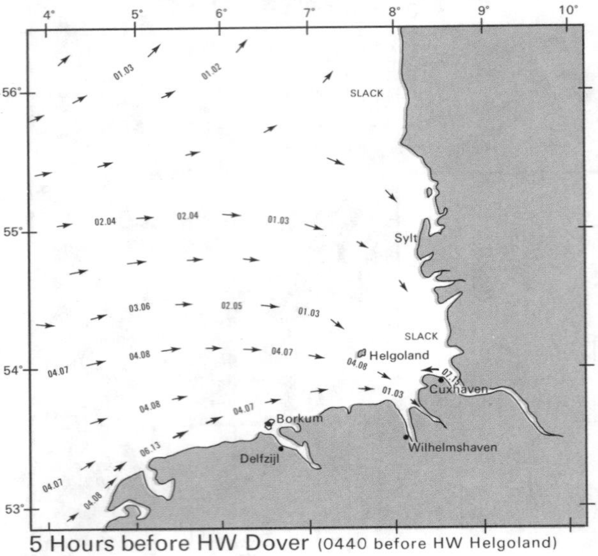
SLACK
Sylt
Helgoland
Cuxhaven
Borkum
Delfzijl
Wilhelmshaven

5 Hours before HW Dover (0440 before HW Helgoland)

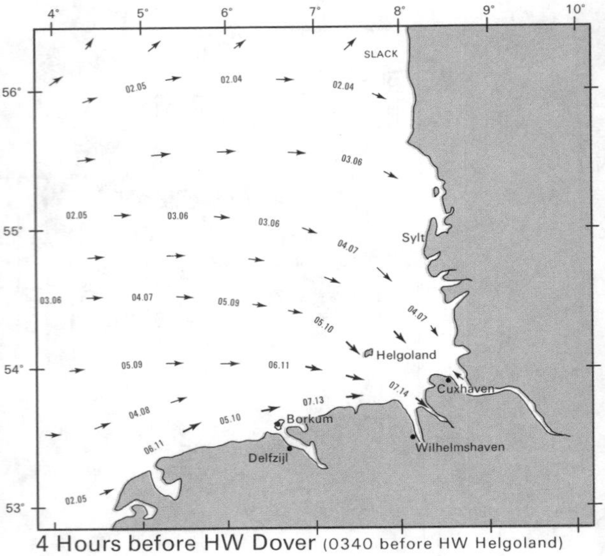
SLACK
Sylt
Helgoland
Cuxhaven
Borkum
Delfzijl
Wilhelmshaven

4 Hours before HW Dover (0340 before HW Helgoland)

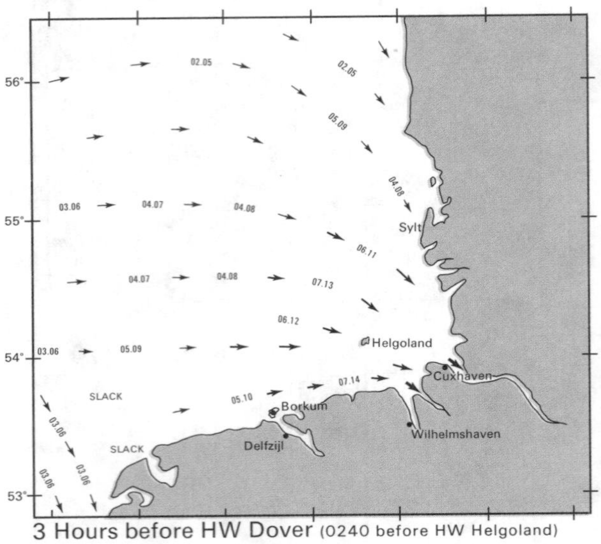
SLACK
Sylt
Helgoland
Cuxhaven
Borkum
Delfzijl
Wilhelmshaven

3 Hours before HW Dover (0240 before HW Helgoland)

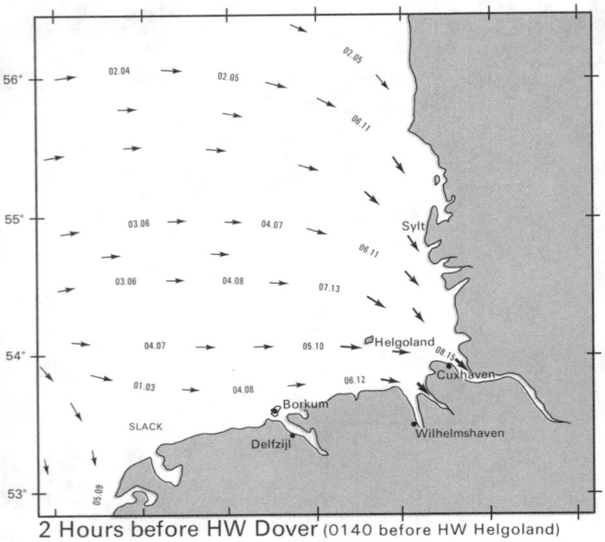
SLACK
Sylt
Helgoland
Cuxhaven
Borkum
Delfzijl
Wilhelmshaven

2 Hours before HW Dover (0140 before HW Helgoland)

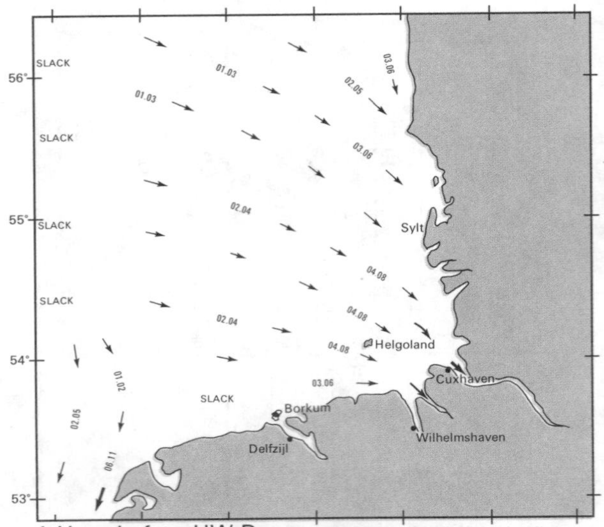
SLACK
Sylt
Helgoland
Cuxhaven
Borkum
Delfzijl
Wilhelmshaven

1 Hour before HW Dover (0040 before HW Helgoland)

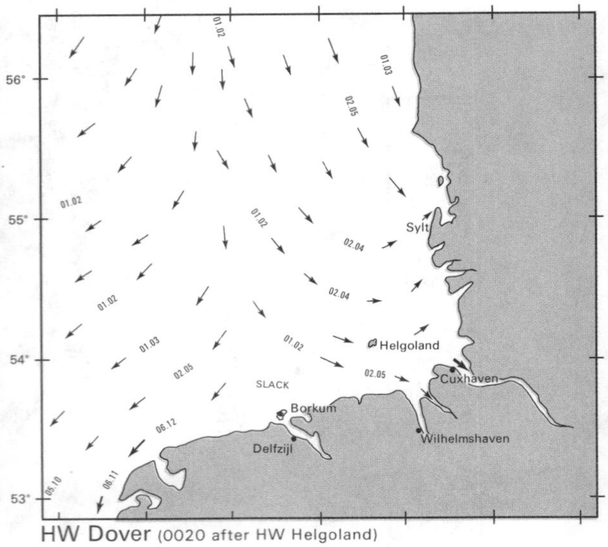
SLACK
Sylt
Helgoland
Cuxhaven
Borkum
Delfzijl
Wilhelmshaven

HW Dover (0020 after HW Helgoland)

South-westward 10.20.3.

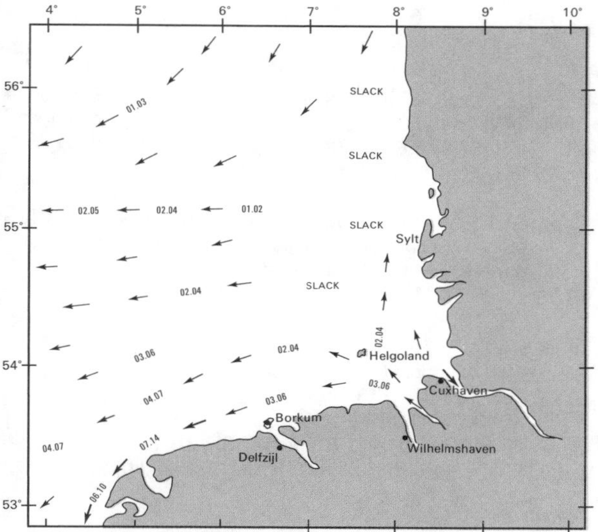
4°
5°
6°
7°
8°
9°
10°
56°
55°
54°
53°
SLACK
SLACK
SLACK
SLACK
Sylt
Helgoland
Cuxhaven
Borkum
Delfzijl
Wilhelmshaven

1 Hour after HW Dover (0120 after HW Helgoland)

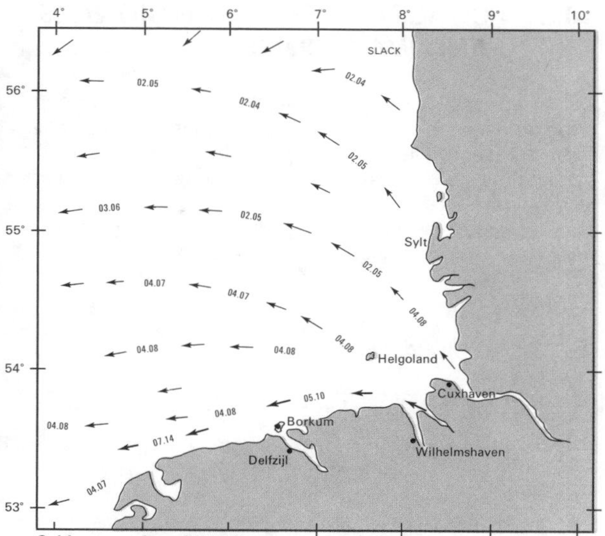
4°
5°
6°
7°
8°
9°
10°
56°
55°
54°
53°
SLACK
Sylt
Helgoland
Cuxhaven
Borkum
Delfzijl
Wilhelmshaven

2 Hours after HW Dover (0220 after HW Helgoland)

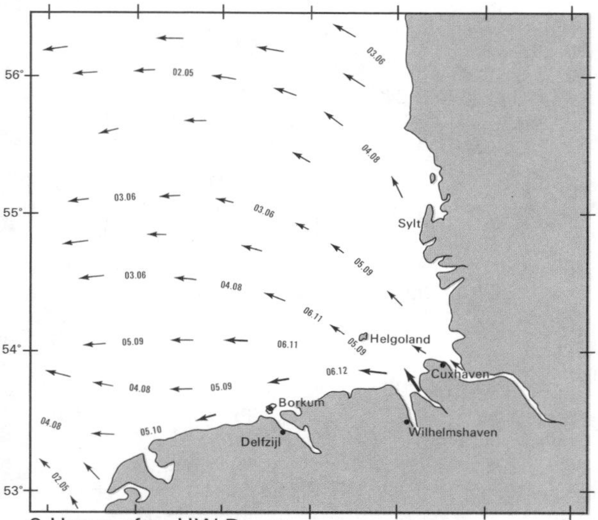
56°
55°
54°
53°
Sylt
Helgoland
Cuxhaven
Borkum
Delfzijl
Wilhelmshaven

3 Hours after HW Dover (0320 after HW Helgoland)

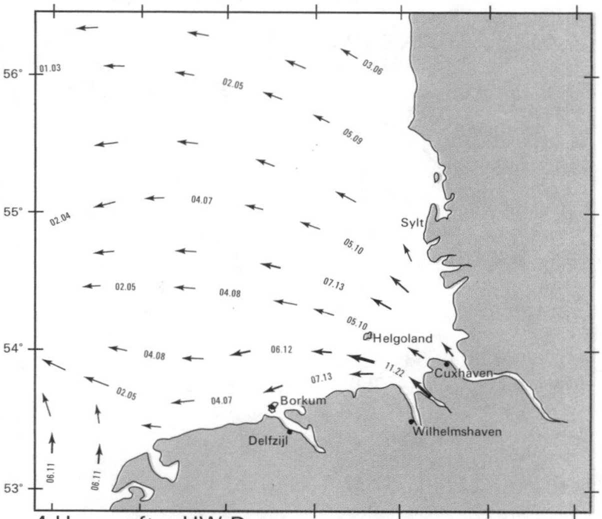
56°
55°
54°
53°
Sylt
Helgoland
Cuxhaven
Borkum
Delfzijl
Wilhelmshaven

4 Hours after HW Dover (0420 after HW Helgoland)

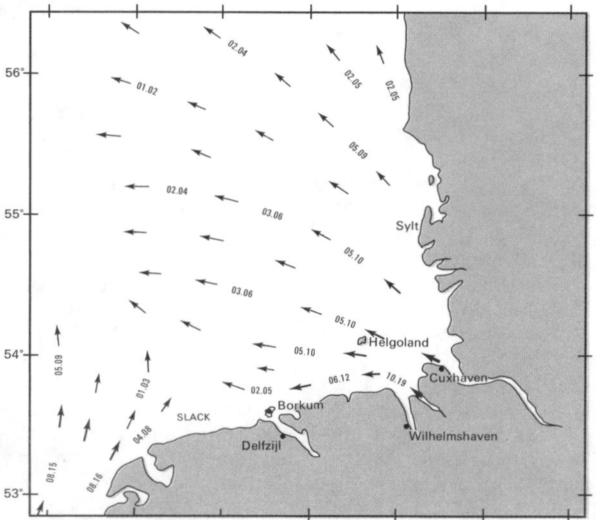
56°
55°
54°
53°
SLACK
Sylt
Helgoland
Cuxhaven
Borkum
Delfzijl
Wilhelmshaven

5 Hours after HW Dover (0520 after HW Helgoland)

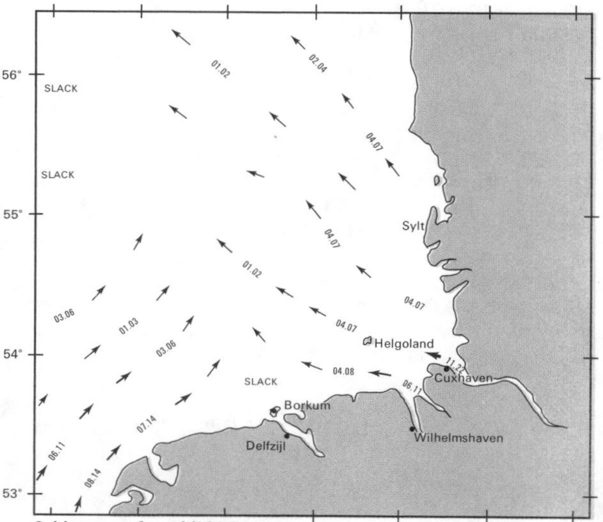
56°
55°
54°
53°
SLACK
SLACK
SLACK
Sylt
Helgoland
Cuxhaven
Borkum
Delfzijl
Wilhelmshaven

6 Hours after HW Dover (0620 after HW Helgoland)

10.21.4 COASTAL LIGHTS, FOG SIGNALS AND WAYPOINTS

Abbreviations used below are given in 1.4.1. Principal lights are in **bold** print, places in CAPITALS, and light vessels, light floats and Lanbys in *CAPITAL ITALICS*. Unless otherwise stated lights are white. m - elevation in metres; M - nominal range in n. miles. Fog signals are in *italics*. Useful waypoints are underlined - use those on land with care. All geographical positions should be assumed to be approximate. See 4.2.2.

GERMANY

DIE EMS TO DIE JADE

LIMIT OF INSHORE TRAFFIC ZONE.

DB1/Ems Lt By 53°43'·35N 06°22'·40E IQ. G 13s; SHM.
DB3/Lt By 53°44'·65N 06°31'·20E Fl (2) G 9s; SHM.
DB5/ Lt By 53°45'·69N 06°40'·10E Oc (3) G 12s; SHM.
DB7/ Lt By 53°47'·35N 06°49'·75E Fl (2) G 9s; SHM.
DB9/ Lt By 53°48'·45N 06°57'·80E Oc (3) G 12s; SHM.
DB11/Lt By 53°49'·72N 07°06'·60E Fl (2) G 9s; SHM.
DB13/Lt By 53°51'·00N 07°15'·50E Oc (3) G 12s; SHM.
DB15/Lt By 53°52'·20N 07°24'·35E Fl (2) G 9s; SHM.
DB17/Lt By 53°53'·47N 07°33'·22E Oc (3) G 12s; SHM.
DB19/Jade Lt By 53°54'·70N 07°42'·20E IQ. G 13s; SHM.

BORKUMRIFF LT BY 53°47'·50N 06°22'·13E Oc (3) 15s; SWM Racon.

INSHORE ROUTE EMS TO JADE.
Riffgat Lt By 53°38'·90N 06°27'·10E Iso 8s; SWM.
Oosterems Lt By 53°42'·00N 06°36'·20E Iso 4s; *Whis*; SWM.
Juisterriff -N Lt By 53°42'·90N 06°45'·80E Q; NCM.
Juist-N Lt By 53°43'·90N 06°55'·50E VQ; NCM.
53°40'·95N 07°03'·50E Aero Fl 5s 14m (occas).
Schluchter Lt By 53°44'·90N 07°05'·30E Iso 8s; SWM.
Dovetief Lt By 53°45'·50N 07°11'·30E Iso 4s; SWM.
Platform 54°42'·1N 07°10'·0E Mo(u) 15s 24m 9M; R platform, Y stripes; *Horn Mo(U) 30s*.
Norderney N Lt By 53°46'·15N 07°17'·22E Q; NCM.
Accumer Ee Lt By 53°47'·10N 07°26'·65E Iso 8s; SWM; *Bell*; (frequently moved).
Otzumer Balje Lt By 53°48'·13N 07°37'·23E Iso 4s; SWM (frequently moved).
Harle Lt By 53°49'·28N 07°49'·00E Iso 8s; SWM.

DIE EMS.
Westerems Lt By 53°36'·98N 06°19'·40E Iso 4s; SWM; Racon (G).
Hubert Gat Lt By 53°34'·90N 06°14'·32E Iso 8s; *Whis*; SWM.
Borkum Grosser 53°35'·4N 06°39'·8E Fl (2) 12s 63m **24M**; brown Tr. F RWG 46m **W19M**, R15m, G15M; vis G107·4°-109°, W109°-111·2°, R111·2°-112·6°.

Borkum Kleiner 53°34'·78N 06°40'·08N FW 32m **30M**; R Tr, W bands; FW (intens) 089·9°-090·9° (Ldg sector for Hubertgat); Fl 3s; vis 088°-089·9°; Q (4) 10s; vis 090·9°-093°; RC; Iso Y 4s on tide gauge 420m SW.

BORKUM.
Fischerbalje 53°33'·21N 06°43'·00E Oc (2) WRG 16s 15m **W16M**, R12M, G11M; W l Tr, R top and lantern, on tripod; vis R260°-313°, G313°-014°, W014°-068°, (Ldg sector to Fischerbalje), R068°-123°. Fog Det Lt.
Schutzhafen Ent FR 8m 4M and FG 10m 4M.

Binnen-Randzel 53°30'·20N 06°49'·95E F WRG 14m W7M, R5M, G4M; B and grey framework Tr, W tank; vis W 318°-345°, R345°-015·8°, W015·8-033·5°, R033·5°-077·3°, W077·3°-098°, G098°-122°.

Campen 53°24'·39N 07°01'·00E F 62m **30M**; R framework Tr, 2 galleries, W central col, G cupola; vis 126·5°-127°. Fl 5s (same Tr); vis 126°-127°. Fl (4) 15s (same Tr) vis 127·3°-127·8°.

ALTE EMS.
H11 By 53°34'·65N 06°33'·62E (unlit); SHM.
A2a By 53°32'·93N 06°39'·53E (unlit); PHM.
A3 By 53°32'·85N 06°39'·25E (unlit); SHM.
A5 By 53°30'·95N 06°40'·70E (unlit); SHM.
33/ Alte Ems II By 53°27'·80N 06°51'·38E (unlit); SHM.

EEMSHAVEN.
W Pier 53°27'·80N 06°50·15E FG 8m 3M; *Horn (2) 20s*.

DUKE GAT
No. 35 Lt By 53°27'·08N 06°52'·88E Fl G 4s; SHM.
No. 37 Lt By 53°26'·00N 06°55'·00E QG; SHM.
No. 41 Lt By 53°24'·32N 06°56'·80E Fl (2) G 9s; SHM.
No. 45 By 53°22'·05N 06°58'·57E (unlit); SHM.
No. 49 Lt By 53°20'·02N 06°59'·75E Oc (2) G 9s; SHM.

KNOCK
K4 Lt Buoy 53°19'·87N 07°00'·82E QR; PHM.
Knock 53°20'·37N 07°01'·50E F WRG 28m W12M, R9M, G8M; Gy Tr, four galleries, broad top, radar antenna; vis W270°-299°, R299-008·3°, G008·3°-023°, W023°-026·8°, R026·8°-039°, W039°-073°, R073°-119°, W119°-154°; Fog Det Lt.

DELFZIJL ENTRANCE.
Westerhoofd 53°19'·07N 07°00'·35E FG 3M; Ra Refl.
Oosterhoofd FR 3m; *Horn 15s*; Ra Refl; In fog FY (occas).
Ldg Lts 203°. Rear 575m from front, FR. Common Front, No. 2A 53°18'·8N 07°00'·3E QR; W pedestal on dolphin; Ra Refl.
Ldg Lts 012°. Rear 500m fron front FR 6m; vis 087°-117°; Ra Refl.
Zeehavenkannaal, N side (odd numbered posts); 2 QG; 3 Fl G 2s, 5 Fl G 5s; R Refl.
Zeehavenkannaal, S side (even numbered posts); 1 Fl R 2s; 5 Fl R 5s; R Refl.
E side ent No. 21 (Marina ent) Fl G 5s; W post on dolphin.

TERMUNTERZIJL.
BW 13 Lt By 53°18'·70N 07°02'·37E Fl G 5s; SHM.
Wybelsum 53°20'·20N 07°06'·57E F WR 16m W6M, R5M; W framework Tr, R bands; radar antenna; vis W295°-320°, R320°-024°, W024°-049°; Fog Det Lt.
Logum Ldg Lts 075°. Front 53°20'·17N 07°08'·05E Oc (2) 12s 16m 12M; W mast, R bands. Rear, 630m from front, Oc (2) 12s 28m 12M; W mast, R bands; syncronised with front.

EMDEN.
Ldg Lts 087·6°. Front 53°20'·07N 07°12'·15E Oc 5s 14m 14M; intens on Ldg line. Rear, 0·8M from front, Oc 5s 30m 14M; syncronised with front, intens on Ldg line.
Outer Hbr E pier Hd FG 7m 5M: Ra Refl.
W Pier Hd 53°20'·10N 07°10'·57E FR 10m 4M; Ra Refl; *Horn Mo (ED) 30s*.

DIE EMS TO DIE JADE

JUIST.
Training Wall, S end 53°39'·70N 06°59'·92E; pile; SCM.
Juist 53°41'·9N 07°03'·5E Aero Fl 5s 14m.

NORDDEICH.
W training wall, Hd 53°38'·7N 07°09'·0E FG 8m 4M; G framework Tr, W lantern; vis 021°-327°.
E training wall Hd FR 8m 4M; R & W s on R Tr; vis 327°-237°. Fog Lt.
Ldg Lts 144°. Front Iso WR 6s 6m W6M, R4M; B mast; vis 078°-122°, W122°-150°. Rear, 140m from front, Iso 6s 9m 6M; B mast; synchronised with front.

NORDERNEY.
Norderney 53°42'·6N 07°13'·8E Fl (3) 12s 59m **23M**; R 8 sided Tr; unintens 067°-077° and 270°-280°.
Fish Hbr Ldg Lts 274°30'. Front, W Mole Hd 53°41'·9N 07°09'·9E Oc WR 4s 10m W7M, R4M; R&W Tr; vis W062°-093°, R093°-25·5°, W259·°-289·5°, R289·5°-062°. Rear. 460m from front, Oc 4s 18m 7M; Gy mast; synchronised with front.

BALTRUM.
Baltrum groyne Hd 53°43'·3N 07°21'·7E Oc WRG 6s 7m W6M, R4M, G3M; vis G 082·5°-098°, W098°-103°, R103°-082·5°.

NESSMERSIEL
Mole N Hd 53°41'·9N 07°21'·7E Oc 4s 6m 5M; G mast.

LANGEOOG.
W Mole Hd 53°43'·5N 07°30'·1E Oc WRG 6s 8m W7M, R5M, G4M; R basket on R mast; vis G 064°-070°, W070°-074°, R074°-326°, W326°-330°, G330°-335°, R335°-064°; Horn *Mo (L) 30s* (0730-1800LT).

DORNUMER-ACCUMERSIEL.
W breakwater Hd 53°41'·25N 07°29'·40E.

BENSERSIEL.
W training wall Hd 53° 41'·62N 07°32'·95E.

NEUHARLINGERSIEL.
Training wall Hd 53°43'·22N 07°42'·30E Oc 6s 6m 5M; G mast.
Carolinensieler Balje. Leitdamm 53°44'·1N 07°50'·1E L Fl 8s 7m 6M; G mast.

HARLESIEL.
Harlesiel 53°42'·63N 07°48'·70E Iso R 4s 6m 7M.

SPIEKEROOG.
Spiekeroog 53°45'·0N 07°41'·3E FR 6m 4M; R mast; vis 197°-114°.

WANGEROOGE.
Wangerooge W end 53°47'·45N 07°51'·52E Fl R 5s 60m **23M**; R Tr, 2 W bands; same Tr; F WRG 24m **W22M**, **W15M**, **R17M,** R11M, **G18M**, G10M;vis R002°-011°, W011°-023°, G023°-055°, W055°-060·5°, R060·5°-065·5°, W065·5°—71°, G(18M) 137°-142·5°, W(22M) 142·5°-152°, Ldg sector, R (17M) 152°-157·5°; RC.

DEUTSCHE BUCHT

DEUTSCHE BUCHT LT F 54°10'·70N 07°26'·01E Oc (3) 15s 12m **17M**; R hull marked D-B; RC; Racon; *Horn Mo (DB) 30s.*
D-B Weser Lt By 54°02'·42N 07°43'·05E Oc (3) R 12s; PHM; Racon.

DIE JADE.
DB 19/Jade Lt By 53°54'·74N 07°42'·10E IQ. G 13s; SHM.
Mellumplate 53°46'·35N 08°05'·60E F 27m **24M**; R n Tr, W band; vis 115·7°-116°; Ldg sector for outer part of Wangerooger Fahrwasser. The following Lts are shown from the same Tr over sectors indicated. Fl 4s **23M**; vis 113·7°-114·9°. Fl (4) 15s; vis 116·9°-118·1°. Oc WRG 29m **W14M**, R11M, G10M; vis R000°-006°, W006°-037·6°, G037·6°-113·7°, R118·1°-168°, W168°-183·5°, R183·5°-212°, W212°-266°, R266°-280°, W280°-000°. Mo(A) 7·5s; vis 114·9°-115·7° Ldg sector. Mo(N) 7·5s; vis116°-116·9°; Ldg sector. Helicopter platform.

No. 1A/Lt By 53°52'·04N 07°45'·56E QG; SHM.
No. 7/Lt By 53°50'·30N 07°51'·24E Oc (3) G 12s; SHM.
No.11/Lt By 53°49'·23N 07°55'·08E Fl G 4s; SHM.
No.15/Blaue Balje Lt By 53°48'·13N 07°58'·88E IQ. G 13s; SHM.
No.19 Lt By 53°47'·08N 08°01'·95E QG; SHM.
No.23 Lt By 53°45'·21N 08°02'·81E Oc (3) G 12s; SHM.
Minsener Oog, Buhne A N end 53°47'·30N 08°00'·45E F WRG 16m W13M, R10M, G9M; n Tr; vis R050°-055°, W055°-130°, G130°-138°, W138°-158°, R158°-176°, W176°-268°, G268°-303°, W303°-050°.
Oldoog, Buhne C 53°45'·40N 08°01'·35E Oc WRG 4s 25m W13M, R10M, G9M; B column, W bands, platform; visW153°-180°, G180°-203°, W203°-232°, R232°-274°, W274°-033°; Fog Det Lt.
Schillig 53°41'·8N 08°01'·7E Oc WR 6s 15m **W15M**, R12M; B pylon, W band; vis W195·8°-221°, R221°-254·5°, W254·5°-278.3°.
Hooksielplate Cross Lt 53°40'·20N 08°09'·00E Oc WRG 3s 25m W7M, R5M, G4M, W Tr, R bands; vis R345°-358·8°, W358·8°-001·8°, G001·8°-012·4°, W012·4°-020·5°, R020·5°-047·3°, W047·3°-061·9°, G061·9°-079·7°, W079·7°-092·5°, R092·5°-110.5°; Fog Det Lt.
No. 31/Reede/W Siel 1 Lt By 53°41'·59N 08°04'·50E Oc (3) G 12s; SHM.

WANGERSIEL.
No.37/Hooksiel Lt By 53°39'·38N 08°06'·63E Oc (2) G 9s; SHM.

HOOKSIEL.
H3 By 53°38'·68N 08°05'·42E (unlit); SHM.
Voslap Ldg Lts 164°35'. **Front** 53°37'·19N 08°06'·88E Iso 6s 15m **24M**; R Tr, W bands, R lantern; R Refl; intens on Ldg line. **Rear**, 2·35M from front Iso 6s 60m **27M**; W Tr, R bands. Same structure, Cross light F RWG 20m W9M, R6M, G5M; vis W200°-228°, G228°-248°, W248°-269°, R269°-310°.
Tossens. Ldg Lts 146°. **Front** 53°34'·56N 08°12'·42E Oc 6s 15m **20M**; B Tr, W stripes, R lantern. **Rear**, 2M from front, Oc 6s 51m **20M;** R Tr, W stripes, 3 galleries; Helicopter platform.

21

WILHELMSHAVEN.
Eckwarden Ldg Lts 154°. **Front, Solthörner Watt** 53°32'·45N 08°13'·09E Iso WRG 3s 15m **W19M**, W12M, R9M, G8M; R Tr, W bands; vis R346°-348°, W348°-028°, R028°-052°.; W (intens) 052°-054° Ldg sector, G054°-067·5°, W067·5°-110°, G110°-152·6°; W (intens) 152·6° across fairway, with undefined limit on E side of Ldg line.
Rear, 1·27M from front, Iso 3s 41m **21M;** R Tr & lantern; synchronised with front.
Neuer Vorhaven Ldg Lts 207°48'. Front Iso 4s 17m 11M; B mast, R lantern. Rear, 180m from front, Iso 4s 23m 11M; Y bldg; intens on Ldg line.
W Mole Hd Oc G 6s 15m 4M.
E Mole Hd Oc R 6s 5M.
Fluthaffen N Mole Hd 53°30'·91N 08°09'·40E F WG 9m W6M, G3M; G Tr; vis W216°-280°, G280°-010°, W010°-020°, G020°-130°.
Flutmole Hd FR 6m 5M
Arngast Dir Lt 53°28'·91N 08°10'·97E F WRG 30m **W21M,** W10, R16M**,** G17M**, G7M**; R I Tr, W bands; vis: W135°-142°, G142°-150°, W150°-152°, G152°-160·3°, G168·8-174·6°, R180·5°-191°, W191°-198·3°, W198·8°-213°, R213°-225°, W(10M) 286°-303°, G(7M) 303°-314°. Same structure Fl WG 3s **W20M**, vis: G174·6°-175·5°, W175·5°-176·4°. Same structure Fl (2) W 9s; vis: 177·4°-180·5°. Same structure Oc 6s; vis: 176·4°-177·4°

DANGAST.
Lock 53°26'·85N 08°06'·60E.

VARELER SIEL.
Lock 53°24'·65N 08°11'·40E

DIE WESER.

Weser Lt By 53°54'·25N 07°50'·00E Iso 5s 12m **17M**; SWM; Racon.
Alte Weser 53°51'·85N 08°07'·72E F WRG 33m **W22M**, **R19M**, **G17M**; R Tr, 2 W bands, B base, floodlit; vis W288°-352°, R352°-003°, W003°-017°, Ldg sector for Alte Weser, G017°-045°, W045°-074°, G074°-118°, W118°-123°, Ldg sector for Alte Weser, R123°-140°, G140°-175°, W175°-183°, R183°-196°, W196°-238°; Fog Det Lt; RC; *Horn Mo (AL) 60s.*
Tegeler Plate, N end 53°47'·90N 08°11'·50E F WRG 21m **W27M**, **R17M**, **G16M**; R Tr, gallery, W lantern, R roof; vis W329°-340°, R340°-014°, W014°-100°, G100°-116°, R119°-123°, G123°-144°, R147°-264°; same structure, Oc 6s **21M**; vis 116°-119°; Ldg sector for Neue Weser; Ldg sector for Alte Weser 144°-147°.
Hohe Weg, NE part 53°42'·80N 08°14'·65E F WRG 29m **W19M**, **R16M**, **G15M**; R 8 sided Tr, 2 galleries, G lantern; visW102°-138·5°, G138·5°-142·5°, W142·5°-145·5°, R145·5°-184°, W184°-278·5°; Fog Det Lt.
Robbennordsteert 53°42'·20N 08°20'·45E 11m W10M, R7M; R column on tripod; vis W324°-356°, R356°-089°, W089°-121°.
Robbenplate Ldg Lts 122·3°. **Front**, Oc 15m **17M**; R tripod; intens on Ldg line. **Rear**, 0·54M from front, Oc 6s 37m **18M;** R Tr, 3 galleries, G lantern; vis 116°-125·5°; synchronised with front; Fog Det Lt.
Wremer Loch Ldg Lts 140·8°. Front Iso WRG 15m W12M, R9M, G8M; vis G131°-139°, W139°-142·5°, R142·5°-183°, W183°-300°, G300°-303°. Rear, 0·57M from front, Iso 6s 31m 14M; synchronised with front; Ra Refl.

Dwarsgat Ldg Lts 320·8°. Front Iso 6s 16m **15M**. **Rear** Iso 6s 35m **17M;** synchronised with front (same Ldg Line as Wremer Loch).
Langlütjen Ldg Lts 304·6°. Front Oc WRG 6s 15m W12M, R9M, G8M; B mast, B & W gallery; vis G141°-145°, W145°-211°, R299°-303°, W303°-306°, G306°-309°; Ra Refl. Rear Oc 6s 35m **17M**; synchronised with front.
Imsum Ldg Lts 124°36'. Front Oc 6s 15m 13M; R tripod with gallery; **Rear,** 1·02M from front, Oc 6s 39m **16M**; synchronised with front.

BREMERHAVEN.
Vorhafen N pier Hd 53°32'·19N 08°34'·57E FR 15m 5M; *Horn Mo (GG) 60s.*
S pier Hd 53°32'·14N 08°34'·57E FG 15m 5M.

BREMEN.
Hasenbüren Sporthafen 53°07'·51N 08°40'·02E 2 FY (vert).

HELGOLAND.
Restricted area Helgoland W By 54°10'·65N 07°48'·25E (unlit); W CM.
Helgoland Lt By 54°09'·00N 07°53'·57E Q (3) 5s; ECM; *Whis.*
Helgoland Lt Ho Fl 5s 82m **28M**; brown n Tr, B lantern, W balcony; RC;. FR on radio masts 180m SSE and 740m NNW.
Cable Area Oc (3) WRG 8s 18m W6M, R4M, G4M; W mast, R bands; vis W179°-185°, R185°-190°, W190°-196°, W239°-244°, G244°-280°, W280°-285°.
Vorhafen. Ostmole, S elbow Oc WG 6s 5m W7M, G4M; G post; vis W203°-250°, G250°-109°; Fog Det Lt.
Ostmole Hd FG 7m 4M; vis 289°-180°; *Horn (3) 30s.*
Sudmole Hd Oc (2) R 12s 7m 4M; Gy post, R lantern; vis 101°-334°.
Binnenhafen Ldg Lts 302°. W Pier, Front Oc R 6s 8m 7M. Rear, 50m from front, Oc R 6s 10m 7M; synchronised with front.

DÜNE.
Ldg Lts 020°. Front Iso 4s 11m 8M; intens on Ldg line. Rear, 120m from front, Iso WRG 17M W11M, R10M, G10M; synchronised with front; vis G010°-018·5°, W018·5°-021°, R210°-030°, G106°-125°, W125°-130°, R130°-144°.
Sellebrunn Lt By 54°14'·43N 07°49'·83E VQ (9) 10s; WCM; *Whis.*

DIE WESER TO DIE ELBE

Schlüsseltonne Lt By 53°56'·28N 07°54'·85E Iso 8s; SWM.
Nordergründe-N Lt By 53°57'·08N 08°00'·17W VQ; NCM.
Westertill-N Lt By 53°58'·18N 08°06'·82E Q; NCM.
Scharnhörnriff-W Lt By 53°58'·53N 08°08'·80E Q (9) 15s; WCM.
Scharnhörnriff-N Lt By 53°58'·99N 08°11'·25E Q; NCM.

DIE ELBE.
ELBE 1 LT FLOAT 54°00'·00N 08°06'·58E Iso 10s 12m **17M**; R hull and Lt Tr; RC; Racon; *Horn Mo(EL) 31s.*
Grosser Vogelsand 53°59'·78N 08°28'·68E Fl (3) 12s 39m **25M**; helicopter platform on R Tr, W bands; vis 085·1°-087·1°. Same Tr, Iso 3s **26M**; vis 087·1°-091·1°. Oc 6s **26M**; vis 091·1°-095·1°. Fl (4) 15s **19M**; vis 095·1°-101·9°. Fl (4) R 15s 12M; vis 101·9°-105·1°. Fl R 3s **15M**; vis 113°-270°. Oc (4) R 18s 9M; vis 322·5°-012°; Fog Det Lt; RC; *Horn Mo (VS) 30s.*

No.1 Lt By 53°59'·27N 08°13'·30E QG; SHM.
No.5 Lt Boy 53°59'·35N 08°19'·08E QG; SHM.
No.19 Lt By 53°57'·83N 08°34'·48E QG; SHM.
No.25 Lt By 53°56'·67N 08°38'·32W QG; SHM.
No.35 Lt By 50°50'·73N 08°45'·86E Oc (2) G; SHM
No.43 Lt By 53°50'·27N 08°52'·30E Oc (2) G 9s; SHM.
No.51 Lt By 53°51'·07N 09°00'·22E QG; SHM.
No.57 Lt By 53°52'·55N 09°06'·38E QG SHM.
Neuwerk, S side 53°55'·0N 08°29'·8E L Fl (3) WRG 20s 39m **W16M**, R12M, G11M; vis G165·3°-215·3°, W215·3°-238·8°, R238·8°-321°, R343°-100°.

CUXHAVEN.
Ldg Lts 151·2°. **Baumrönne**, front 1·55M from rear, Fl 3s 25m **17M**; W Tr, B band on gallery; vis 143·8°-149·2°. Same Tr, Iso 4s **17M**; vis 149·2°-154·2°. Fl (2) 9s **17M**; vis 154·2°-156·7°. **Altenbruch**, Common rear, Iso 4s 58m **21M**; intens on Ldg line; synchronised with front. Same structure, Iso 8s 51m **22M**; synchronised with front. Crosslight Oc WR 44m W7M, R5M; vis 201·9°-232·8°, R232·8°-247·2°, W247·2°-254·6°.
Altenbruch Ldg Lts 261°. **Common front**, Iso 8s 19m **19M**; W Tr, B bands. Same structure, Iso WRG 8s W8M, R9M, G8M; vis G117·5°-124°, W124°-135°, R135°-140°. Rear, Wehldorf Iso 8s 31m 11M; W Tr, B bands; synchronised with front.
Balje Ldg Lts 130°48'. **Front** 53°51'·4N 09°02'·7E Iso WG 8s 24m **W17M**, **G15M**; W Tr, R bands; vis G shore-080·5°, W080·5°-shore. **Rear** 1·35M from front, Iso 8s 54m **21M**; W Tr, R bands; intens on Ldg line; synchronised with front. Same structure Oc WR 3s 24m **16M**; vis W180°-195°, R195°215°, W215°-223°.
Zweidorf 53°53'·5N 09°05'·7E Oc R 5s 9m 3M; R n on W pylon; vis 287°-107°.

BRUNSBÜTTEL.
Ldg Lts 065·5°'. Front **Schleuseninsel** Iso 3s 24m **16M; R Tr, W bands;** vis North of 063·3°. Same structure Fl 3s; vis South of 063·5°. Rear **Industriegebiet**, 0·9M from front, Iso 3s 46m **21M**; R Tr, W bands; synchronised with front.
Alterhaven N Mole (Mole 4) Hd 53°53'·29N 09°07'·59E F WR (vert) 15m W10M, R8M; vis R275·5°-079°, W079°-084°.

NORD-OSTSEE KANAL (KIEL CANAL)

RENDSBURG.
No. 2/Obereider 1 Lt By 54°18'·95N 09°42'·71E Fl (2+1) R 15s; PHM.

KIEL/HOLTENAU.
Nordmole 54°21'·83N 10°09'·18E Oc (2) WR 9s 23m.

FRIEBURG
Entrance Bn (unlit) 53°50'·25N 09°18'·90E; SHM.
Rhinplatte Nord 53°48'·09N 09°23'·36E Oc WRG 6s 11m W6M. R4M, G3M; vis: G122°-144°, W144°-150°, R150°-177°, W177°-122°; Ra refl.

GLÜCKSTADT.
Glückstad Ldg Lts 131·8° Iso 8s 15m **19M**; W Tr, R bands; intens on Ldg line. Rear, 0·68M from front, Iso 8s 30m **21M**; W Tr, R bands; intens on Ldg line.
N mole Oc WRG 6s 9m W8M R6M, G5M; W Tr with gallery; vis R330°-343°, W343°-346°, G346°145°, W145°-150°, R150°170°.
N Pier Hd 53°47'·15N 09°24'·58E FR 5m 4M. (FG on S Mole Hd).

Pagensand Ldg Lts 134·2° 53°42'·15N 09°30'·30E. Front Oc WRG 4s 18m W12M, W9M, R6M, G5M; W Tr, R bands; vis: R345°-356·5°, W356·5°-020°, G020°-075°. Rear, 500m from front, Oc 4s 35m 13M; Synchronised with front; intens on Ldg line.

STADE.
Stadersand 53°37'·74N 09°31'·72E Iso 8s 20m 14M.

WEDEL.
E ent, E Pier Hd 53°34'·30N 09°40'·87E FG.

HAMBURG

NESSKANAL.
Ent 53°32'·75N 09°50'·53E Oc (3) Y 12s 6m.

RÜSCHKANAL.
Ent 53°32'·63N 09°51'·10E FR 8m.

TEUFELSBRÜCK.
Breakwater Hd 53°32'·88N 09°52'·12E (unmarked).

INSHORE ROUTE ELBE TO SYLT

Süderpiep Lt By 54°06'·55N 08°18'·85E Iso 8s; SWM.
Ausseneider Lt By 54°14'·10N 08°18'·30E Iso 4s; SWM.
Hever Lt By 54°20'·45N 08°18'·90E Oc 4s; SWM; *Whis.*
Rütergat Lt By 54°31'·00N 08°12'·05E Iso 8s; SWM.
Vortrapptief Lt By 54°34'·95N 08°11'·30E Oc 4s; SWM.
Theeknobs West Lt By 54°43'·52N 08°10'·00E Q (9) 15s; WCM.
Lister Tief Lt By 55°05'·40N 08°16'·85E Iso 8s; SWM.

BÜSUM.
Büsum 54°07'·65N 08°51'·55E Oc (2) WRG 16s 22m **W16M**, R14M, G13M; vis W248°-317°, R317°-024°, W024°-084°, G084°-091·5°, W091·5°-093·2° Ldg sector for Süder Piep, R093·5°-097°, W097°-148°.
W Mole Hd Oc (3) R 12s 10m 4M; R Tr; FW Fog Det Lt.
E Mole Hd Oc (3) G 12s 10m 4M; G Tr; vis 260°-168°.
Ldg Lts 355°. Front Iso 4s 9m 13M; B mast, W bands. Rear, 110m from front, Iso 4s 12m 13M; synchronised with front.

DIE EDER.
St Peter 54°17'·30N 08°39'·15E L Fl (2) WRG 15s 23m **W15M**, R13M, G11M; R Tr, B lantern; vis R271°-294°, W294°-325°, R325°-344°, W344°-035°, G035°-056·5°, W056·5°-068°, R068°-091°, W091°-113°, G113°-115°, W115°-116°, Ldg sector for Mittelhever, R116°-130°.
Eiderdamm Lock, N Mole, W end Oc (2) R 12s 8m 5M; W Tr.
S Mole, W end Oc G 6s 8m 5M: W Tr, grey top.

TÖNNING.
W Mole Hd FR 5m 4M; R col.
Quay FG 5m 4M; G col.

DIE HEVER.
Westerheversand 54°22'·5N 08°38'·5E Oc (3) WR 15s 41m **W21M**, **R16M**; R Tr, W bands; vis W012·2°-089°, R089°-107°, W107°-155·5°, R155·5°-169°, W169°-206·5°, R206·5°-218·5°, W218.5°-233°, R233°-248°.

HUSUM.
Husumer Al Outer Ldg Lts 106°30'. Front 54°28'·6N 09°00'·8E Iso R 8s 8m 5M; R mast, W bands; intens on Ldg line. Rear, 0·52M from front, Iso R 8s 17m 6M; Y mast; syncronised with front.
Inner Ldg Lts 090°. Front Iso G 8s 7m 3M; R mast, W bands; intens on Ldg line. Rear, 40m from front, Iso G 8s 9m 3M; intens on Ldg line; synchronised with front.

NORDSTRAND.
Strucklahnungshörn, W Mole Hd 54°30'·00N 08°48'·5E Oc G 6s 8m 2M.

PELLWORM.
Pellworm S side Ldg Lts 041°. **Front** Oc WR 5s 14m **W20M**, W11M, R8M. Intens on Ldg line; vis W303·5°-313·5°, R313.5°-316·5°. **Rear**, 0·8M from front, Oc 5s 38m **20M**; R Tr, W band; synchronised with front. Same Tr as rear Lt, Cross Light Oc WR 5s 38m W14M, W9M, R11M, R6M.; vis R(11M) 122·6°140°, W(14M) 140°-161·5°, R(11M) 161·5°-179·5°, W(14M) 179·5°-210·2°, R(6)M 255°-265·5°, W9M 265·5°-276°, R(6)M 276°-297°, W(9)M 297°-307°.

AMRUM.
Amrum Hafen Ldg Lts 272·9°. Front 54°37'·9N 08°22'·9E Iso R 4s 11m 10M; W mast, R stripe; intens on Ldg Line. **Rear**, 0·9M from front, Fl (3) 30s 63m **23M**; R Tr, W bands. Same structure Iso R 4s 33m **15M**.
Wriakhorn Cross light L Fl (2) WR 15s 26m W9M, R7M; vis W297·5°-319°, R319°-343°, W343°-014°, R014°-034°.
Nebel 54°38'·8N 08°21'·7E Oc WRG 5s 16m **W20M**, **R15M**; **G15M**; R Tr, W band; vis R255·5°-258·5°, W258·5°-260·5°, G260·5°-263·5°.
Norddorf 54°40'·3N 08°16'·6E Oc WRG 6s 22m **W15M**, R12M, G11M; W Tr, R lantern; vis W009-035°, G035-037°, Ldg sector, R038·5°-090°, W090°-156°, R156°-176·5°, W176·5-178·5°, G178·5°-188°, G(unintens) 188°-202°, W(partially obscured) 202°-230°.

LANGENESS.
Nordmarsch 54°37'·6N 08°31'·8E F WRG 13m W14M, R11M, G10M; Dark Brown Tr; vis W268°-279°, R279°-311°, W311°350°, G350°-033°, W033°-045°, R045°-064°, W064°-123°, R123°-127°, W127°-218°.

OLAND.
Near W Pt 54°40'·5N 08°41'·3E F WRG 12m W13M, R10M, G9M; R Tr; G086°-093°, W093°-160°, R160°-172°.

SCHLUTTSIEL.
Harbour ent 54°40'·9N 08°45'·0E (approx) (unlit).

FÖHR.
Nieblum 54°41'·1N 08°29'·2E Oc (2) WRG 10s 11m **W19M**, **R15M, G15M**; R Tr, W band; vis G028°-031°, W031°-032·5°, R032·5°-035·5°.

DAGEBÜLL.
53°43'·9N 08°41'·4E Iso WRG 8s 23m **W18M**, **R15M**, **G15M**; G mast; vis G042°-043°, W043°-044·5°, R044·5°-047°.
FW Lts shown on N and S mole Hd

SYLT.
Hörnum Ldg Lts 012·5°. Front 54°44'·8N 08°17'·4E Iso 8s 20m 14M; R Tr, W band; intens on Ldg line. **Rear** Iso 8s 45m **15M**; R Tr, W band; synchronised with front; intens on Ldg line.
Hörnum Fl (2) 9s 48m **20M**.
N Pier Hd FG 6m 3M; vis 024°-260°.
Schutzmole Hd FR 7m 4M; R mast; mole floodlit.
Kampen, Rote Kliff 54°56'·87N 08°20'·50E Oc (4) WR 15s 62m **W20M**, 3R16M, W Tr, B band; vis W193°-260°, W(unintens) 260°-339°, W339°-165°, R165°-193°.
Ellenbogen N end, List W 55°03'·25N 08°24'·19E Oc WRG 6s 19m W14M, R11M, G10M; W Tr, R lantern; vis R040°-133°, W133°-196°, R196°-210°, W210°-227°, R227°-266·4°, W266·4°-268°, G268°-285°, W285°-310°, W(unintens) 310°-040°.
N side, List ost Iso WRG 3s 13m W12M, R9M, G9M; W Tr, R band; vis W(unintens) 010·5°-098°, G098°-112°, W112°-114°, R114°-122°, W122°-262°, R262°-278°, W278°-296°, R296°-323·3°, W323·3°-324·5°, G324·5°-350°, W350°-010·5°.
List Land Oc WRG 3s 13m W12M, R9M, G8M; W mast, R band; vis W170°-203°, G203°-212°, W212°-215·5°, R215·5°-232·5°, W232·5°234°, G234°-243°, W243°-050°.
List Hafen N Mole Hd 55°01'·0N 08°26'·5E FG 5m 3M; G mast; vis 218°-038°.
S mole FR 5m 4M; R mast; vis 218°353°.

10.21.5 PASSAGE INFORMATION

DIE EMS TO DIE JADE (chart 3761)

The coastal route from the Hubertgat entrance of Die Ems to the Wangerooger Fahrwasser at the ent to Die Jade (see below) is about 60 miles. The route leads along the Inshore Traffic Zone, S of the Terschellinger-Deutsche Bucht Traffic Scheme Fig 2(4), the E-going lane of which is marked on its S side by SHMs with the letters DB (DB1, DB3, DB5 etc). About 4M S of this line of Bys the landward side of the Inshore Traffic Zone is marked by Bys showing the apprs to the various zeegaten between the German Frisian Is (see below). There are major Lts on Borkum, Norderney and Wangerooge. Near the traffic scheme the E-going stream begins at HW Helgoland –0500, and the W-going at HW Helgoland +0100, sp rates 1·2 kn. Inshore the stream is influenced by the flow through the zeegaten.

DIE EMS (charts 3509, 3510)

Die Ems forms the boundary between Netherlands and Germany, and is a major thoroughfare leading to ports such as Eemshaven, Delfzijl (10.20.30), Emden (10.21.24), Leer and Papenburg. Approach is made through Hubertgat or Westerems, which join W of Borkum. Both are well buoyed but can be dangerous with an ebb stream and a strong W or NW wind. The flood begins at HW Helgoland +0530, and the ebb at HW Helgoland –0030, sp rates 1·5 kn.

From close SW of Borkum the chan divides into two — Randzel Gat to the N and Alte Ems running parallel to it to the S – as far as Eemshaven on the S bank. About 3M further on the chan again divides. Bocht van Watum is always varying so keep in main chan, Ostfriesisches Gatje, for Delfzijl (10.20.30) and beyond. Off Eemshaven the stream runs 2-3 kn.

Osterems is the E branch of the estuary of Die Ems, passing between Borkum and Memmert. It is not lit, but is a useful chan in daylight and good weather if bound to/from the E, although much shallower than Westerems. It also gives access to the Ley chan, leading to the hbr of Greetsiel.

THE GERMAN FRISIAN ISLANDS (chart 3761)

The German Is to the E of Die Ems have fewer facilities for yachtsmen than the Dutch Is to the W, and most of them are closer to the mainland. For general notes on the Frisian Islands see 10.20.5 and 10.21.9. For navigating inside the Is, in the so-called watt chans, it is essential to have the appropriate German charts and to understand the system of chan marking. Withies, unbound (with twigs pointing up) are used as PHMs, and withies which are bound (with twigs pointing down) as SHM's. Inshore of the Is the **conventional direction of buoyage is always from W to E**, even though this may conflict with the actual direction of the flood stream in places.

Borkum (10.21.10 and chart 3509) is the first of the German Is. It lies between Westerems and Osterems, with high dunes each end so that at a distance it looks like two separate Is. Round the W end of Borkum are unmarked groynes, some extending 0·25M offshore. Conspic landmarks include Grosse Bn and Neue Bn, a water Tr, Borkum Grosser Lt Ho, Borkum Kleiner Lt Ho, and a disused Lt Ho — all of which are near the W end of the Is.

Memmert on the E side of Osterems is a bird sanctuary, and landing is prohibited. Juist (10.21.24) is the first of the chain of similar, long and narrow Is which lie in an E/W line between the estuaries of Die Ems and Die Jade. Most have groynes and sea defences on their W and NW sides. Their bare sand dunes are not easy to identify, and shoals extend seaward for 2M or more in places. The zeegaten between the islands vary in position and depth, and all of them are dangerous on the ebb tide — even in a moderate onshore wind. There are Nature Reserves (entry prohibited) inshore of Baltrum, Langeoog and the W end of Spiekeroog (chart 1875).

Norderneyer Seegat is a deep chan close W of Norderney, but there are dangerous shoals offshore, through which lead two shallow chans, Dovetief and Schluchter. Both are buoyed. The chans vary considerably and on occasions are silted up. Dovetief is the main chan, but Schluchter is more protected from the NE. Neither should be used in strong winds. Further inward Norderneyer Seegat leads round the W end of the island to Hafen von Norderney (10.21.11). Beware groynes and other obstructions along the shore.

SW of Norderney, Busetief leads in a general S direction to the tidal hbr of Norddeich (see 10.21.24), which can also be approached with sufficient rise of tide from Osterems through the Norddeich Wattfahrwasser with a depth of about 2m at HW. Busetief is deeper than Dovetief and Schluchter, and is marked by Bys and Lt Bys. The flood begins at HW Helgoland –0605, and the ebb at HW Helgoland –0040, sp rates 1 kn.

Baltrum (10.21.24) is an Is about 2·5M long, very low in the E and only rising to dunes about 15m high in the W. With local knowledge and only in good weather it can be approached through Wichter Ee, a narrow chan obstructed by a bar between Norderney and Baltrum. There is a small pier alongside a groyne which extends about 0·2M from the SW corner of Baltrum. The little hbr dries, and is exposed to the S and SW. Continuing southwards from Wichter Ee is Nessmersiel Balje, with Bys on its W side prefixed by the letter 'N', leading to the sheltered hbr of Nessmersiel (see 10.21.24).

Proceeding E, the next major chan through the Is is Acummer Ee between Baltrum and Langeoog. Shoals extend 2M to N, depths in chan vary considerably and it sometimes silts up. In onshore winds the sea breaks on the bar. Chan is marked by Bys prefixed with letter 'A', moved as necessary. Apart from Langeoog (10.21.13), Accumer Ee gives access to the mainland hbrs of Dornumer-Accumersiel (10.21.12) and Bensersiel (10.21.24).

Westerbalje and Otzumer Balje are both buoyed and lead inward between Langeoog and Spiekeroog. Otzumer Balje is normally the deeper (0·7m-2·0m) but both chans may silt up and should be used only in good weather and on a rising tide.

Harle chan (Bys prefixed by letter 'H') leads W of Wangerooge (10.21.14), but beware Buhne H groyne which extends 0·75M WSW from end of Is to edge of fairway. Dove Harle (Bys prefixed by letter 'D') leads to the hbr. In bad weather Harlesiel, 4M S on the mainland shore, is a more comfortable berth. See 10.21.24.

Blau Balje leads between the E end of Wangerooge and Minsener Oog. Although marked by Bys (lettered 'B' and moved as requisite) this chan is dangerous in N winds and there is a prohib area (15 May–31 Aug) S of the E end of Wangerooge for the protection of seals.

DIE JADE (charts 3368, 3369)

To the E of Wangerooge and Minsener Oog lie the est of Die Jade and Die Weser. Die Jade is entered through the Wangerooger Fahrwasser (buoyed) and then leads SSE past Wangersiel and the yachting centre of Hooksiel (10.21.15) to Wilhelmshaven (10.21.16). S of Wilhelmshaven is a large but shallow area of water called Die Jadebusen, through which chans run to the small hbrs of Dangastersiel (10.21.24) and Vareler Siel. Although not so dangerous as Die Elbe (see below), the outer parts of both Die Jade and Die Weser become very rough with wind against tide, and are dangerous on the ebb in strong NW winds.

DIE WESER (charts 3368, 3405, 3406, 3407)

Die Weser is an important waterway leading to the ports of Bremerhaven, Nordenham, Brake and Bremen which in turn connect with the inland waterways. From Bremen to Bremerhaven (10.21.17) the river is called Die Unterweser, and below Bremerhaven it is Die Aussenweser flowing into a wide est through which pass two main chans — Neue Weser and Alte Weser. The position and extent of sandbanks vary: on the W side they tend to be steep-to, but on the E side there are extensive shoals (e.g. Tegeler Plate).

Weser Lt By marks the approach from NW to Neue Weser (the main fairway) and Alte Weser which are separated by Roter Sand and Roter Grund, marked by the disused Roter Sand Lt Tr (conspic). Both chans are well marked and they join about 3M S of Alte Weser Lt Tr (conspic). From this junction Hohewegrinne (buoyed) leads inward in a SE direction past Tegeler Plate Lt Tr (conspic) on the E side to the Fedderwarder Fahrwasser, which passes N of Hohe Weg Lt Tr (conspic). In Die Aussenweser the stream, which runs over 3 kn at sp, often sets towards the banks and the branch chans which pass through them.

Das Weser-Elbe Wattfahrwasser is a useful inshore pass between Die Weser and Die Elbe. It leads in a general NE direction from the Wurster Arm, part of the Weser which runs N of the N leitdamm, and keeps about 3M offshore. The normal yacht will take two tides to traverse it, but there are suitable anchs. Like other inshore pass behind the Is, it is well described in *Frisian Pilot* by Mark Brackenbury (Adlard Coles Nautical).

DIE ELBE (charts 3261, 3262, 3266, 3268)

Yachts using the Elbe (see 10.21.19) are probably bound for the Nord-Ostee Kanal ent at Brunsbüttel (10.21.20). Commercial traffic is very heavy. At Elbe 1 Lt F the E-going (flood) stream begins at HW Helgoland −0500, and the W-going (ebb) stream at HW Helgoland +0500, sp rates 2 kn. The stream runs harder N of Scharnhörn, up to 3·5 kn on the ebb, when the Elbe est is dangerous in strong W or NW winds. From E end of traffic scheme the chan is well marked by Bys and Bn Trs.

DIE ELBE TO DANISH BORDER (charts 1875, 3767)

The W coast of Schleswig-Holstein is low and marshy, with extensive offshore banks which partly dry and on which are low offshore Is (Die Nordfriesischen Inseln). Between the banks and Is are many chans which change frequently. Süderpiep and Norderpiep are two chans (both buoyed, but the latter unlit) S of Die Eider, which join S of Blauort and lead to Büsum (10.21.24) and Meldorfer Hafen. Norderpiep has a bar (depth 3m) while Süderpiep does not and is preferable in W winds. Landmarks from seaward are Tertius Bn and Blauwortsand Bn, and a conspic silo at Büsum.

Die Eider is merged with much of its length with Der Nord-Ostsee Kanal, with which it connects at Gieselau. Below Tönning (10.21.24) it winds into an est, separated from Die Hever further N by the Eiderstedt Peninsula. About 5M below Tönning the est is closed by Eiderdamm — a storm barrage with a lock and sluices. The lock operates H24. Approaching from seaward, locate the Ausseneider Lt By, about 6M W of the buoyed ent chan. St Peter Lt Ho is conspic on N shore. The ent is rough in W winds, and dangerous in onshore gales.

Die Hever consists of several chans on the N side of Eiderstedt Peninsula, and S of the Is of Süderoogsand and Pellworm. Mittelhever is the most important of the three buoyed chans through the outer grounds, all of which meet SE of Süderoogsand before they separate once more into Heverstrom leading to Husum (10.21.24), and Noderhever which runs NE between Pellworm and Nordstrand into a number of watt channels. Schmaltief leads S of Amrun to Amrun Hafen, to Wyk on E side of Fohr, and to Dagebüll (see 10.21.24).

Sylt (10.21.23) is the largest of Die Nordfriesischen Inseln, and is some 20M from N to S. It has a straight coast facing the sea, and a peninsula on the E side connected to the mainland by Hindenburgerdamm. Vortrapptief is the chan inward between Amrum and Sylt, leading to Hörnum-Reede and Hafen von Hörnum. It has a depth of about 4m (subject to frequent change) and is marked by Bys and Lt Bys. The area should not be approached in strong W winds. The flood (ESE-going) stream begins at HW Helgoland −0350, and the ebb (WNW-going) at HW Helgoland +0110, sp rates 2·5 kn.

Lister Tief, which marks the German-Danish border, leads between the N end of Sylt and Romo, and gives access to List Roadstead and Hafen von List as well as to Danish hbrs. Lister Tief is well marked by Bys and Lt Bys, with a least depth over the bar of about 4m. After Süderpiep it is the safest chan on this coast, available for yachts seeking anch under the lee of Sylt in strong W winds (when however there will be a big swell over the bar on the ebb). Beware obstructions (ODAS) marked by Lt Bys, 18M WSW of List West Lt Ho.

10.21.6 DISTANCE TABLE

Approximate distances in nautical miles are by the most direct route while avoiding dangers and allowing for traffic separation schemes etc. Places in *italics* are in adjoining areas.

1 *North Foreland*	**1**																			
2 *Dunkerque*	40	**2**																		
3 *Burnham-on-Crouch*	36	75	**3**																	
4 *Grimsby*	169	194	168	**4**																
5 *Goeree Tower*	91	73	108	169	**5**															
6 *Den Helder*	171	153	169	180	80	**6**														
7 Borkum	243	241	252	249	168	95	**7**													
8 Norderney	259	257	268	265	184	111	31	**8**												
9 Wangerooge	283	281	292	289	208	135	55	29	**9**											
10 Bremerhaven	316	314	325	322	241	168	88	62	38	**10**										
11 Helgoland	300	298	309	285	225	152	67	44	24	44	**11**									
12 Brunsbüttel	337	335	347	332	263	190	110	84	55	78	51	**12**								
13 Holtenau	390	388	400	385	316	243	163	137	108	131	104	53	**13**							
14 Hamburg	374	372	384	369	300	189	104	81	61	81	88	37	90	**14**						
15 Husum	339	337	348	327	265	190	105	85	52	82	47	76	129	113	**15**					
16 Hörnum Lt (Sylt)	325	323	334	301	251	177	97	77	60	80	38	75	128	112	48	**16**				
17 *Esbjerg*	355	353	360	322	281	207	133	123	109	127	83	126	179	163	95	47	**17**			
18 *Thyboron*	393	390	400	348	329	256	200	186	178	201	154	196	249	233	163	120	90	**18**		
19 *Skagen*	501	499	507	442	437	364	305	291	283	306	259	301	—	338	268	225	195	104	**19**	
20 *Oksoy Lt (Norway)*	466	468	470	391	398	332	272	268	260	283	236	278	—	315	245	203	172	83	84	**20**

SPECIAL FACTORS AFFECTING GERMANY 10-21-7

TIME ZONE is −0100, which is allowed for in the tidal predictions but no provision is made for daylight saving schemes which are indicated by the non-shaded areas on the tide tables (see 9.1.2).

SIGNALS Local port, tidal, distress and traffic signals are given where possible.

Light signals

R		R	— Passage or entry forbidden.
	R		— Be prepared to pass or enter.
W R		 R	Bridge closed or down; vessels which can pass under the available clearance may proceed, but beware of oncoming traffic which have right of way.
W R		W R	Lift bridge will remain at first step; vessels which can pass under the available vertical clearance may proceed.
G		G	Passage or entry permitted; oncoming traffic stopped.
W G		 G	Passage permitted, but beware of oncoming traffic which may have right of way.
	R R		Bridge, lock or flood barrage closed to navigation.
	R		— Exit from lock forbidden.
	G		— Exit from lock permitted.

Visual storm signals in accordance with the International System (see 10.14.7) are shown at: Borkum, Norderney, Norddeich, Accumersiel, Bensersiel, Bremerhaven, Brunsbüttel, Die Oste, Glückstadt, Stadersand, Hamburg, Büsum, Tönning, Husum, Wyk, List and Helgoland.

Lights In coastal waters particular use is made of light sectors. A leading sector (usually white, and often intensified) may be flanked by warning sectors to show the side on which the vessel has deviated. If to port — a red fixed light or a white group flashing light with an even number of flashes. If to starboard — a green fixed light or a white group flashing light with an odd number of flashes. Cross lights with red, white and green sectors may indicate the limits of roadsteads, turning points in channels etc.

Signals hoisted at masts

By day	By night	Meaning
Red cylinder	W R W	Reduce speed to minimize wash
Two black balls over cone point down	R R G	Fairway obstructed
Black ball over two cones points together (or red board with white band)	R G W	Channel permanently closed

When motoring always display motoring cone apex down.

CHARTS Where possible the Admiralty, Stanford, Imray and Dutch chart numbers are quoted. The German chart numbers are those of the charts issued by the Deutsches Hydrografisches Institut in Hamburg.

LANDS In place of the 'counties' in the UK, Lands are given.

MARINE RESCUE CO-ORDINATION CENTRES Coast station, Elbe- Weser Radio ☎ (04721) 22066. Kiel Radio, ☎ (0431) 39011. Norddeich Radio, ☎ (04931) 1831.

PUBLIC HOLIDAYS New Year's Day, Good Friday, Easter Monday, Labour Day (1 May), Ascension Day, Whit Monday, Day of German Unity (17 June), Christmas Day and Boxing Day.

BROADCASTS Information broadcasts by VTS centres and associated communications, see Chapter 2.

TELEPHONES To call UK from West Germany, dial 0044. Then dial the full UK area code, but omitting the prefix 0, followed by the number required.
To call Germany from UK, dial 010-49.

EMERGENCIES Police – dial 110
Fire, Ambulance – dial 112

Note: Two National Water Parks have been declared; one the Watten Sea area of Lower Saxony excluding the Jade and Weser rivers and the Ems-Dollard estuary; the other the west coast of Schleswig-Holstein. The rules for yachting in these areas have not yet been published other than a ban on leaving grounded boats unattended except in harbours. It is hoped that more detailed rules, due to be published by the Federal Ministry of Transport, will be available for the Supplements.

CUSTOMS Entry ports are Borkum, Norderney, Norddeich, Wilhelmshaven, Bremerhaven, Cuxhaven. Not Helgoland. Yachts passing through Kiel Canal without visiting Germany fly the third substitute pendant.

GAS Sometimes Calor gas bottles can be re-filled. German "Flussig" gas can be used with calor regulators.

CURRENCY 1 Deutch Mark = 100 Pfennigs

USEFUL ADDRESSES German Embassy, 23 Belgrave Sq, Chesham Place, London SW1X 8PX (Tel 071.235.5033). German National Tourist Office, 61 Conduit St, London W1 (Tel 071.734.2600).

AGENTS WANTED
Ploumanac'h
Trébeurden
Le Touquet
Norderney
Dornumersiel
Langeoog
Wangerooge
Hooksiel
Bremerhaven

If you are interested in becoming our agent please write to the Editors and get your free copy annually. You do not have to be a resident in a port to be the agent but at least a fairly regular visitor.

GERMAN GLOSSARY 10.21.8

Ankerplatz	Anchorage (⚓)
Arzt	Doctor (Dr)
Bahnhof	Railway Station (⇌)
Bake	Beacon (Bn)
Benzin	Petrol (P)
Beschläge	Fittings
betoniert	concrete
bl (blau)	blue (Bu)
Blz (Blitz)	Flashing (Fl)
Blitzknallsignal	Explosive
Elektroreparatur	Electrical repairs (El)
Dalben	Dolphin
dreieckig	triangular
eisern	iron
Elektronik	Electronics (Ⓔ)
f (fest)	fixed (F)
Feuerschiff	Light-vessel
Fkl (Funkel)	quick flashing (Q)
Fkl unt (Funkelfeuer unterbrochen)	interrupted quick flashing
Flughafen	Airport (✈)
früher Ladenschluß	early closing (EC)
Funkfeuer	Radiobeacon
g (gelb)	yellow (Y)
Gas	Gas
gelöscht	extinguished
gewürfelt	chequered
Gittermast	Framework Tower
Glt (Gleichtakt)	Isophase (Iso)
Glocke	Bell
gn (grün)	green (G)
Hafenkapitän	Harbour Captain
Hafenmeister	Harbour Master (Hr Mr)
Heulboje	Whistling Buoy
hölzerner	wooden
Ingenieur	Engineer (ME)
Kaitreppe	Landing place (L)
Kanone	gun
Kegel	Cone
kegelförmig	conical
Kran	Crane (C)
Krankenhaus	Hospital ⊞
Küstenwache, Seenotwache	Coastguard (CG)
Laternenträger	Column
Lebensmittel	Food, Victuals (V)
Leuchtfeuer, Licht	Light (Lt)
Leuchtfloß	Light-float
Leuchtturm	Lighthouse (Lt Ho)
Lotsenstation	Pilotstation
Nebel	Fog
Nebelhorn	Foghorn
or (orange)	orange (Or)
Petroleum	Paraffin
Pfahl	Pile
Pfosten	Post
Postamt	Post Office (✉)
Propangas	Popangas
Quadrat	Square
r (rot)	red (R)
Raute, rautenförmig	Diamond, diamond-shaped
Reisepaß	Passport
Rettungsboot	Lifeboat (LB)
rundum	round
s (schwarz)	black (B)
Schiffswerft	Shipyard (BY)
Schilf	Reed
Schleuse	Lock
Segelmacher	Sailmaker (SM)
senkrecht gestreift	Stripe
Stegplatz	Alongside berth (AB)
Stein, steinern	Stone, stone
Toppzeichen	Topmark
Trinkwasser	Fresh water (FW)
Turm	Tower (Tr)
Tyfon, Typhon	Horn
ubr (unterbrochen)	occulting (Oc)
ubr Gr (unterbrochene Gruppe)	Group occulting
Verkehrssignale	Traffic signals
Viereck	Square
violett, lila	violet (Vi)
vorübergehend	temporary
w (weiß)	white (W)
waagerecht gestreift	Band
Waschsalon, Wäscherei	Laundrette ◙
wchs (wechselnd)	alternating (Alt)
Yachthafen, Jachthafen	Yacht Harbour
Yachtwerft, Jachtwerft	Boatyard (BY)
zeitweise	occasional, temporary (Occas)
zerstört	destroyed
Zoll	Customs (#)

GERMAN FRISIAN ISLANDS 10-21-9

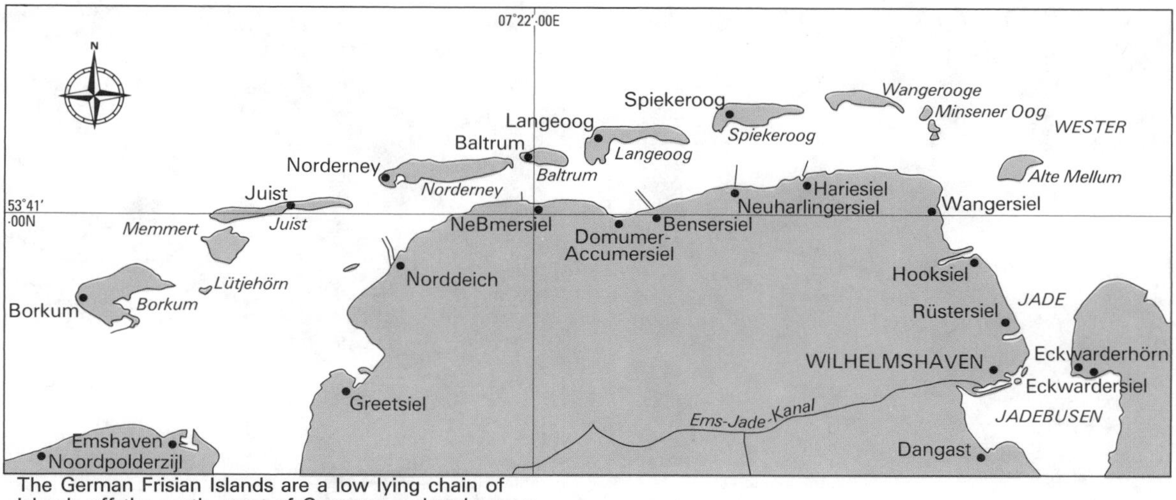
07°22'·00E
N
53°41'·00N
Wangerooge
Spiekeroog
Minsener Oog
WESTER
Langeoog
Spiekeroog
Baltrum
Langeoog
Norderney
Baltrum
Alte Mellum
Norderney
Hariesiel
Juist
Neuharlingersiel
Wangersiel
Memmert
Juist
Neßmersiel
Bensersiel
Domumer-Accumersiel
Norddeich
Hooksiel
Lütjehörn
Borkum
Borkum
JADE
Rüstersiel
WILHELMSHAVEN
Eckwarderhörn
Eckwardersiel
Greetsiel
Ems-Jade-Kanal
JADEBUSEN
Emshaven
Noordpolderzijl
Dangast

The German Frisian Islands are a low lying chain of Islands off the north coast of Germany and make up a chain of Islands comprising the West Frisian Islands off the Netherlands, the East Frisian Islands off Germany and the North Frisian Islands off Schleswig-Holstein and Denmark. They lie between 3 and 20 miles off-shore and were, at one time, the north coast. The area between the islands and the present coastline which is now flooded by the sea is called the Watten. The German Frisian Islands run from the Ems estuary to the Jade Bay with two small islands in the Elbe estuary. The islands are known locally as the Ostfriesland and the inhabitants speak a patois known as Fries, a language with a close resemblance to English. The gaps between the islands are known as Seegats and the watersheds (where the tide meets having swept both ways round the island, usually about ⅓ the way from the E end of the S side) are known as Watts. Tidal streams are very slack over the watts but very strong in the Seegats. Deep water channels are buoyed but shallow channels are marked by withies (pricken in German). Withies the natural way up ↡ are to be taken as port-hand lateral marks and withies inverted thus ↟ are to be taken as starboard-hand lateral marks. As stated in 10.21.5, the conventional direction of buoyage is always from West to East inside the islands, so leave port-hand marks to the North whichever way the stream is flowing. With strong W or NW winds, the sea level rises over 0.25 m.

BORKUM (14 sq. miles), the largest, see 10.21.10.

LUTJEHORN – bird sanctuary; landing prohibited.

MEMMERT, bird sanctuary; landing prohibited. Lt on stone Tr with G cupola, Oc (2) WRG 14s 15m 17/12 M.

JUIST (6½ sq. miles). No yacht harbour. See 10.21.24

NORDERNEY (10 sq. miles) Lt on R octagonal Tr, Fl (3) W 12s 59m 23M see 10.21.11.

BALTRUM (3 sq. miles). Pretty island with small town and harbour at W end. See 10.21.24.

LANGEOOG (7 sq. miles). See 10.21.13.

SPIEKEROOG (5 sq. miles). See 10.21.24.

WANGEROOGE (2 sq. miles). See 10.21.14.

MINSENER OOG Large Bn. Beware groynes and overfalls in strong NW winds

ALTE MELLUM Bird sanctuary; landing prohibited

SCHARNHÖRN (2 sq. miles) between Alte Mellum and Neu Werk; off charlet, in Elbe estuary. Uninhabited.

GROSSES KNECHTSAND between Alte Mellum and Neu Werk; Bird sanctuary; landing prohibited.

NEU WERK – off chartlet, in Elbe estuary. Only inhabited by Lifeboat Crew and Lighthouse men. Lt in square brick Tr with B cupola LFl (3) WRG 20s 38m 18/12M. On W side there is a conspic W radar Tr and landing stage. Ferry to Cuxhaven.

BORKUM 10-21-10

EAST FRISIAN ISLANDS
Niedersachsen

CHARTS
Admiralty 3509, 3761; German D3012; Dutch Yacht Chart 1812; ANWB A

TIDES
Dover –0105; ML 1·3; Duration 0610; Zone –0100

Standard Port HELGOLAND (⟶)

Times				Height (metres)			
HW		LW		MHWS	MHWN	MLWN	MLWS
0200	0700	0200	0800	2·7	2·3	0·4	0·0
1400	1900	1400	2000				
Differences BORKUM (FISCHERBALJE)							
–0045	–0049	–0123	–0105	0·0	+0·1	0·0	0·0
NORDDEICH HAFEN							
–0015	–0018	–0032	–0010	+0·2	+0·2	0·0	0·0

SHELTER
The shelter is reasonable in the Schutzhafen but it dries at LW. To the W there is a yacht harbour; access H24 with good shelter and facilities. There is another small harbour to the NE, the triangular Kleinbahnhafen (Light Railway Harbour) whose entrance is 65m wide. None give good protection in really bad weather, but the Yacht Harbour is best.

NAVIGATION
Waypoint Riffgat (safe water) buoy, Iso 8s, 53°38'·90N 06°27'·10E, 302°/122° from/to Fischerbalje Lt, 11M. See also 10.20.30. There are many groynes extending up to 2¾ ca (500 m) off shore. Approaching from any direction, pick up the Fischerbalje Lt at the end of the Leitdamm. Beware strong cross currents across the Fischerbalje channel. Speed limit in harbours 5 kn.
Note:— The S part of the island is a Nature Reserve. Borkum town is 7 km away.

LIGHTS AND MARKS
Landmarks — Water Tower, Grosse Beacon and 2 ca to the SW, Neve Beacon.
From the Fischerbalje to the channel up to the harbour is well buoyed.
Schutzhafen harbour ent shows FR on W and FG on E moles.
Fischerbalje Lt, Oc (2) WRG 16s 15m 16/11M, W Tr with R top and lantern on tripod; R260°-313°, G313°-014°, W014°-068°. Ldg sector for Fischerbalje R068°-123°, Fog Det Lt.

RADIO TELEPHONE
Hr Mr VHF Ch 16. See also Delfzijl, 10.20.30.

TELEPHONE (04922)
Hr Mr 2420; CG Borkum Kleiner Lt Tr; # 2287; Police 3950; H 813; Brit Consul (040) 446071.

21

FACILITIES

Yacht Harbour (30 + 170 visitors) ☎ 3880, AB, FW, Slip, D, R, Bar, AC, C (6 ton), V, R; **Kleinbahnhof** C (hand), AB; **F. Hellman** ☎ 2576, Gaz.

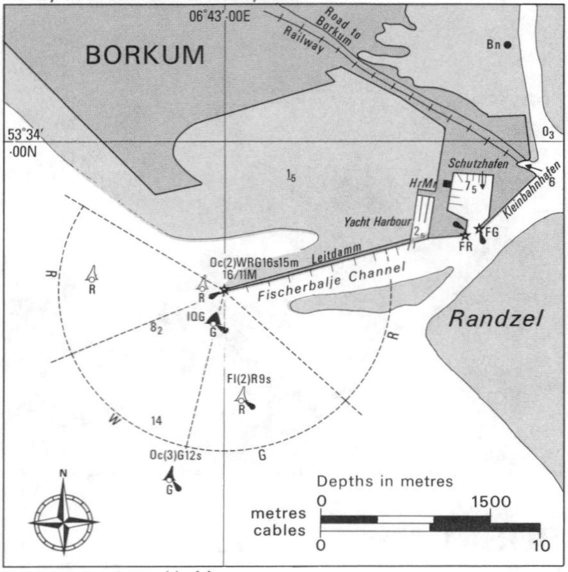

06°43'·00E
BORKUM
Road to Borkum
Railway
Bn
53°34'·00N
Schutzhafen
Kleinbahnhafen
HrMr
Yacht Harbour
FG
FR
Oc(2)WRG16s15m 16/11M
Leitdamm
Fischerbalje Channel
Randzel
IQG
Fl(2)R9s
Oc(3)G12s
R
W
G
Depths in metres
metres
cables
0
1500
10
N

⛵ – report to Hr Mr

Town P, ME, El, Gaz, V, R, Bar. ✉; Ⓑ; ⇌ (ferry to Emden); ✈ (services to Emden and Bremen).
Ferry UK – Hamburg–Harwich.

NORDERNEY 10-21-11

EAST FRISIAN ISLANDS
Niedersachsen

CHARTS

Admiralty 3761; Dutch Yacht Chart 1812; German D3012

TIDES

Dover −0042; ML 1·4; Duration 0605; Zone −0100

Standard Port HELGOLAND (⟶)

Times				Height (metres)			
HW		LW		MHWS	MHWN	MLWN	MLWS
0200	0700	0200	0800	2·7	2·3	0·4	0·0
1400	1900	1400	2000				
Differences NORDERNEY (RIFFGAT)							
−0025	−0030	−0055	−0040	+0·1	+0·1	+0·1	0·0

SHELTER

Good shelter and the harbour is always available. Yacht harbour is at the NE of the harbour, where yachts lie bow to pontoon, stern to posts.

NAVIGATION

Waypoint Schlu (safe water) buoy, Iso 8s, 53°44'·90N 07°05'·30E, 325°/145° from/to W point of Norderney, 3·0M. Entrance through the Dovetief (see 10.21.5) is well buoyed but the bar is dangerous in on-shore winds and seas break on it, especially on an ebb tide. Beware also that tidal streams run across the Dovetief and not up and down it. Beware merchant shipping. Harbour speed limit 3kn.

LIGHTS AND MARKS

Land marks – Norderney Light in centre of island – tall octagonal red brick tower, Fl (3) 12s 59m 23M. Water tower in town (conspic). Storm signal mast 4 ca NW of water tower.

Ldg Lts in line at 274°, synchronised.

RADIO TELEPHONE

None.

TELEPHONE (04932)

Hr Mr 793; CG 2293; # 3386; Weather Emden 21458; Police 788; Ⓗ 477 & 416; Brit Consul (040) 446071.

FACILITIES

Segler-Verein (SVN) ☎ 2850, M, L, FW, C (10 ton), V, R; **W. Visser** ☎ 2207, CH, SM; **Dübbel & Jesse** ☎ 2928, Slip, ME, El, Sh; **Aral** ☎ 2913, P, D; **Shell** (in harbour) ☎ 2468, P; **Yacht Club** Bar; **A. Berghaus** ☎ 1689 Gaz; **Pontoon/Quay** P, D, FW;

Town V, R, Bar. ✉; Ⓑ; ⇌ (ferry to Norddeich); ✈ (services to Bremen).
Ferry UK – Hamburg–Harwich.

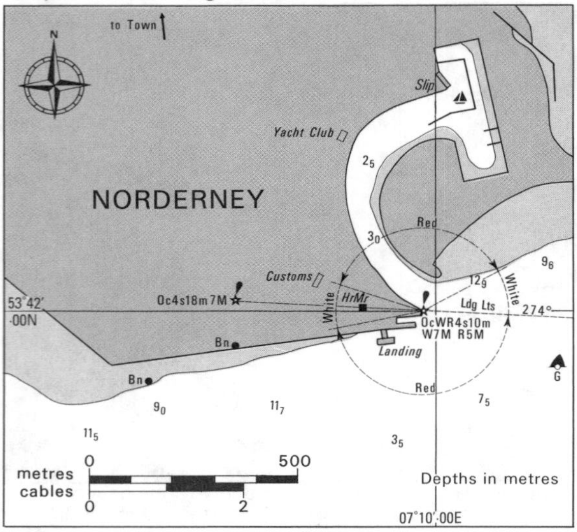

to Town
N
Slip
Yacht Club
NORDERNEY
Red
White
Customs
HrMr
Oc4s18m7M
Ldg Lts
274°
OcWR4s10m W7M R5M
Landing
Bn
53°42'·00N
G
metres
cables
0
500
2
Depths in metres
07°10'·00E

DORNUMER-ACCUMERSIEL 10-21-12

Niedersachsen

CHARTS

Admiralty 1875, 3761; German D3014, D89

TIDES

−0040 Dover; ML 1·4; Duration 0600; Zone −0100

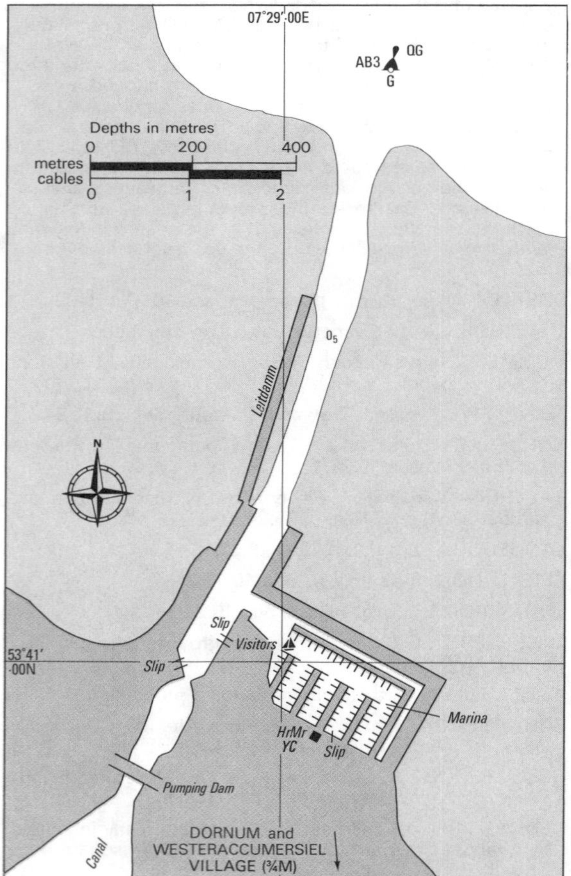

07°29'·00E
AB3
QG
G
Depths in metres
0
200
400
metres
cables
1
2
Leitdamm
N
Slip
Visitors
53°41'·00N
Marina
HrMr
YC
Slip
Pumping Dam
Canal
DORNUM and WESTERACCUMERSIEL VILLAGE (¾M)

DORNUMER-ACCUMERSIEL *continued*

Standard Port HELGOLAND (→)

Times				Height (metres)			
HW		LW		MHWS	MHWN	MLWN	MLWS
0200	0700	0200	0800	2·7	2·3	0·4	0·0
1400	1900	1400	2000				
Differences LANGEOOG OSTMOLE							
+0005	+0005	−0030	−0020	+0·4	+0·4	+0·1	0·0

SHELTER
The marina provides complete shelter in all winds. Marina depth 3m, access HW∓4. Marina entrance is narrow; keep to W of channel on entering. Marina is fenced so obtain a key before leaving.

NAVIGATION
Approach through Accumer Ee (see 10.21.5 and 10.21.13) leading into Accumersieler Balje and to AB3 buoy, (stbd-hand), QG. From here keep four withies (downturned brooms) to stbd, clear of the Leitdamm. Note warnings on German chart D89.

LIGHTS AND MARKS
None.

RADIO TELEPHONE
None.

TELEPHONE (04933)
Hr Mr 1732; Deputy Hr Mr 441; ⌗ (04971) 7184; Lifeboat (04972) 247; Weather Emden 21458; Police 2218; Ⓗ 011502; Brit Consul (040) 446071.

FACILITIES
Dornumer Yacht Haven (250) All facilities and all pontoons removed out of season: FW, R, Slip, Gaz, D; **YC Dornumersiel** ☎ 622; **Rinjes** ☎ 712 ME, El, Sh; **Town** V, R, Bar, ✉; Ⓑ; ⇌ (Harlesiel); ✈ (Bremen or Hamburg).
Ferry UK — Hamburg—Harwich.

LANGEOOG 10-21-13

EAST FRISIAN ISLANDS
Niedersachsen

CHARTS
Admiralty 1875, 3761; Dutch Yacht Chart 1812; ANWB A; German D014

TIDES
Dover −0010; ML No data; Duration 0600; Zone −0100

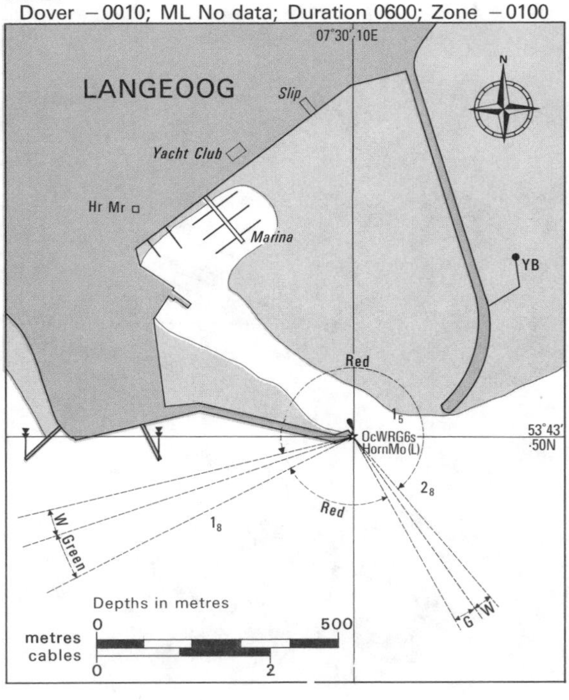
07°30'·10E
LANGEOOG
Slip
Yacht Club
Hr Mr
Marina
YB
Red
1_5
OcWRG6s
HornMo(L)
53°43'
·50N
2_8
Red
1_8
W
Green
G
W
Depths in metres
0
500
metres
cables
0
2

Standard Port HELGOLAND (→)

Times				Height (metres)			
HW		LW		MHWS	MHWN	MLWN	MLWS
0200	0700	0200	0800	2·7	2·3	0·4	0·0
1400	1900	1400	2000				
Differences LANGEOOG OSTMOLE							
+0003	−0002	−0036	−0019	+0·3	+0·3	0·0	0·0
SPIEKEROOG REEDE							
+0001	+0005	−0031	−0013	+0·4	+0·4	+0·1	0·0

SHELTER
At SW corner of the island, the harbour gives good shelter but it is open to the S. Sand dunes, 20m high, give considerable protection from winds.

NAVIGATION
Waypoint Accumer Ee (see 10.21.5) (safe water) buoy, Iso 8s, Bell, 53°46'·95N 07°25'·22E, 334°/154° from/to SW point of Langeoog, 5·3M. The E side of harbour dries and channel to yacht pontoons is marked by withies. Ice protectors extend about 40m E of E mole, awash at HW, marked by withies.

LIGHTS AND MARKS
Lt Bn on W pier Oc WRG 6s 8m 7/4M.
G064°-070°, W070°-074°, R074°-326°, W326°-330°, G330°-335°, R335°-064°, Horn Mo (L) 30s.
(0730—1800 LT)
Landmarks:— Langeoog church, Esens church spire and Water Tower 2 ca WNW of Langeoog church.

RADIO TELEPHONE
None.

TELEPHONE (04971)
Hr Mr 301; Lifeboat CG 247; ⌗ 275; Weather Emden 21458; Police 810; Dr 589; Brit Consul (040) 446071.

FACILITIES
Langeoog Marina (70+130 visitors) ☎ 552, Slip, FW, C, (12 ton), El, Bar, R; **Segelverein Langeoog YC; Village** (1½ M) P, D, V, R, Gaz, Bar. ✉; Ⓑ; ⇌ (ferry to Norddeich); ✈ (services to Bremen).
Ferry UK — Hamburg—Harwich.
NOTE: Motor vehicles are prohibited on this island. Village is 1½ M away — go by foot, pony and trap or train. Train connects with ferries to Bensersiel.

WANGEROOGE 10-21-14

EAST FRISIAN ISLANDS
Niedersachsen

CHARTS
Admiralty 3368, 1875; German D2, D3011, D3014/5; Imray B B 70B

TIDES
E Wangerooge, Dover -0009, ML 1·9
W Wangerooge, Dover −0014, ML 1·5
Duration 0600; Zone −0100

Standard Port HELGOLAND (→)

Times		Height (metres)			
HW	LW	MHWS	MHWN	MLWN	MLWS
All Times	All Times	2·7	2·3	0·4	0·0
Differences WEST WANGEROOGE					
+0003	−0019	+0·5	+0·4	+0·1	0·0

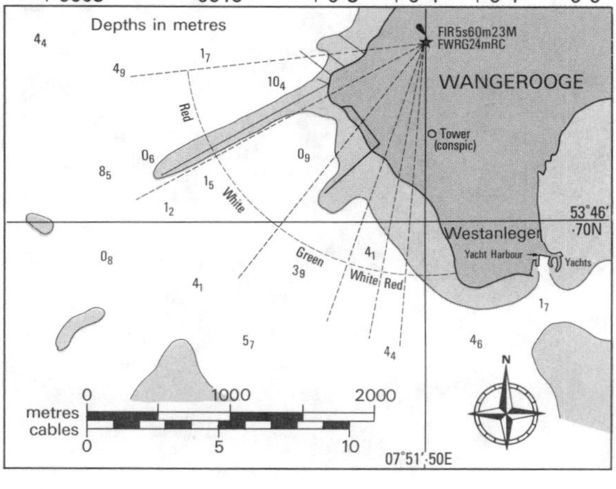
Depths in metres
FlR5s60m23M
FWRG24mRC
WANGEROOGE
Tower
(conspic)
Red
White
Green
White
Red
Westanleger
Yacht Harbour
Yachts
53°46'
·70N
4_4
4_9
1_7
10_4
0_6
8_5
0_9
1_5
1_2
0_8
4_1
3_9
4_1
5_7
4_4
4_6
1_7
0
1000
2000
metres
cables
0
5
10
07°51'·50E

21

WANGEROOGE *continued*

SHELTER
Not good shelter except in N winds. Winds from all other directions make the harbour uncomfortable and, if strong, dangerous. Yachts lie against the E pier. In bad weather, yachts should make for Harlesiel, 4 M SSW.

NAVIGATION
Waypoint Harle (safe water) buoy, Iso 8s, 53°49′·28N 07°49′·00E, 321°/141° from/to Wangerooge Lt, 2·4M. From seaward the Harle channel (see 10.21.5) leads inward between Spiekeroog and Wangerooge: it varies in depth and position, and care is needed. Beware Buhne H groyne, extending 7½ ca (1390 m).
Yachts are forbidden to use the W jetty which is reserved for ferries. Beware protrusions on the E jetty.

LIGHTS AND MARKS
Wangerooge Lt Ho Fl R 5s 60m 23M; R Tr with two W bands. Also FWRG 24m 15/10M R002°-011°, W011°-023°, G023°-055°, W055°-060·5°, R060·5°-065·5°, W065·5°-071°, G137°-142°. W142°-152° Leading sector R152°-157·5° RC.

RADIO TELEPHONE
None.

TELEPHONE (04469)
Hr Mr 630; # 223; Weather Bremerhaven 72220; Police 205; Ambulance 588; Brit Consul (040) 446071.

FACILITIES
Wangerooge YC ☎ 364, FW, L, El, M; **Grunemann** ☎ 258, Gaz. **Village** El, V, R. ✉, R, P and D (cans), CH, ◎; Ⓑ; ⇌ (ferry to Harlesiel); ✈ (services to Bremen, Bremerhaven and Helgoland).
Ferry UK — Hamburg—Harwich.

HOOKSIEL 10-21-15

Niedersachsen

CHARTS
Admiralty 3369; German D3011, D7

TIDES
Dover +0034; ML 1·8; Duration 0605; Zone −0100

Standard Port HELGOLAND (→)

Times		Height (metres)			
HW	LW	MHWS	MHWN	MLWN	MLWS
All Times	All Times	2·7	2·3	0·4	0·0
Differences HOOKSIEL					
+0039	+0012	+1·0	+1·0	No data	

SHELTER
Yachts can lie alongside in the Vorhafen (approx 1m at MLWS) but it is very commercial and uncomfortable in E winds. Inside the lock there is complete shelter in a lake 2M long and approx 2·8m deep. Best berths for yachts are in Visitor Yacht Harbour at the far end, in the town. (Max draught 2m – bigger yachts go to YCs – see Lockmaster).

NAVIGATION
Waypoint No 37/Hooksiel 1 (stbd-hand) buoy, Oc (2) G 9s, 53°39′, 38N, 08°06′·63E 227°/047° from/to entrance 1·1M. See also 10.21.16. Entrance is marked by H3 stbd-hand buoy, approx 1M W of main Innenjade channel. Approach to lock through Vorhafen, enclosed by two moles. Depth in channel 2·5m. Lock opens weekdays 0800-1900 (LT), Sundays 0900-2000 (LT), actual times on board at lock. Report to lock office. Secure well in lock. Beware tanker pier and restricted area to SE of entrance.

LIGHTS AND MARKS
Conspic chimneys of oil refinery 1·7M S of lock, which is in the W047°-062° sector of the Hooksielplate Cross Lt, Oc WRG 3s. There is a street lamp on the N mole and a pile with R dayglo paint on S mole. Ordinary traffic signals at lock.

RADIO TELEPHONE
VHF Ch 63.

TELEPHONE (04425)
Hr Mr 565; Lockmaster 430; # (0441) 42031; CG (0421) 5550555; Weather Bremerhaven 72220; Police Wilhelmshaven; Ⓗ (04421) 2080; Dr 1080; Brit Consul (040) 446071.

FACILITIES
Visitors Yacht Hr (50) AC, FW, BH (25 ton), Slip, Bar; **Alter Hafen** AB, FW, V, R, Bar; **Wilhelmshaven YC** ☎ 285; **Boot-Stove-North** Gaz; **Town** BY, SM, ME, El, CH, P, D, Gaz, V, R, Bar, Ⓑ; ✉; ⇌ (Wilhelmshaven); ✈ (Wilhelmshaven or Bremen).
Ferry UK — Hamburg—Harwich.

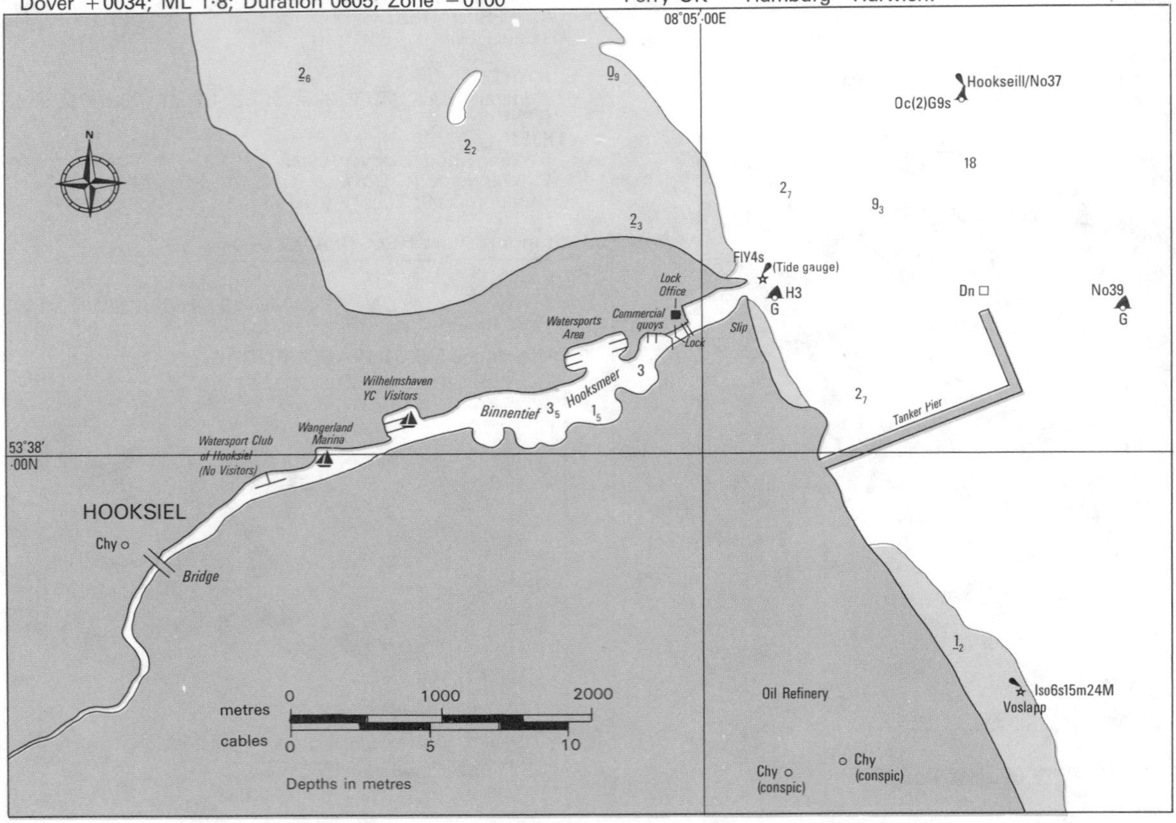
08°05′·00E
53°38′·00N
N
Hookseill/No37
Oc(2)G9s
18
FlY4s
(Tide gauge)
H3
G
Dn
No39
G
Lock Office
Commercial quays
Lock
Slip
Watersports Area
Wilhelmshaven YC Visitors
Binnentief
Hooksmeer
Wangerland Marina
Watersport Club of Hooksiel (No Visitors)
Tanker Pier
HOOKSIEL
Chy
Bridge
Oil Refinery
Iso6s15m24M
Voslapp
Chy (conspic)
metres
0
1000
2000
cables
0
5
10
Depths in metres

WILHELMSHAVEN 10-21-16

Niedersachsen

CHARTS
Admiralty 3369; German D3011, D8

TIDES
Dover +0050; ML 2·0; Duration 0615; Zone −0100

Standard Port HELGOLAND (⟶)

Times		Height (metres)			
HW	LW	MHWS	MHWN	MLWN	MLWS
All Times	All Times	2·7	2·3	0·4	0·0
Differences WILHELMSHAVEN					
+0109	+0034	+1·6	+1·5	+0·2	0·0

SHELTER
The yacht harbour, on E side of Ausrustungshafen inside the locks is sheltered, but unattractive and remote. Locks operate Mon-Fri: 0600-1830, Sat: 0630-1600, Sun and holidays: 0800-1600 (all LT). The tidal yacht harbour in Nassauhafen is better for a short stay.

NAVIGATION
Waypoint Die Jade. Wangerooge Fahrwasser No 3 (stbd-hand) buoy, QG, 53°52′·00N 07°45′·58E, 296°/116° from/to Mellumplate Lt, 13M. The fairway is deep and wide to Wilhelmshaven, a busy commercial port. The Ems-Jade canal, 35M long, is usable by yachts with lowering masts with max draught 1·7m. Min bridge clearance 3·75m. There are six locks. Speed limit 4 kn.

LIGHTS AND MARKS
Die Jade is well marked and lit; for principal Lts see 10.21.4. Ldg Lts 208° into Neuer Vorhafen both Iso 4s. Fluthafen N mole FWG 9m 6/3M (for sectors see chartlet); S arm, head FR. Audio signals for bridge openings (VHF Ch 11 09).
Kaiser Wilhelm —···
Deich Bridge ——···
Ruestringer ——····

RADIO TELEPHONE
VHF Ch 11 16 (H24). Wilhelmshaven Lock Ch 13 16 (Mon-Fri: 0600-1830. Sat: 0630-1600. Sun and Public Holidays: 0800-1600 LT). Bridges Ch 11. Other stations: Die Jade (call: *Jade Revier*) Ch 20 63 (H24) gives information broadcasts in German every H+10.

TELEPHONE (04421)
Hr Mr 61552; Port Authority 26311; Lock 33404; # 43136; Weather Bremerhaven 72220; Police 43031; Ⓗ 8011; Brit Consul (040) 446071.

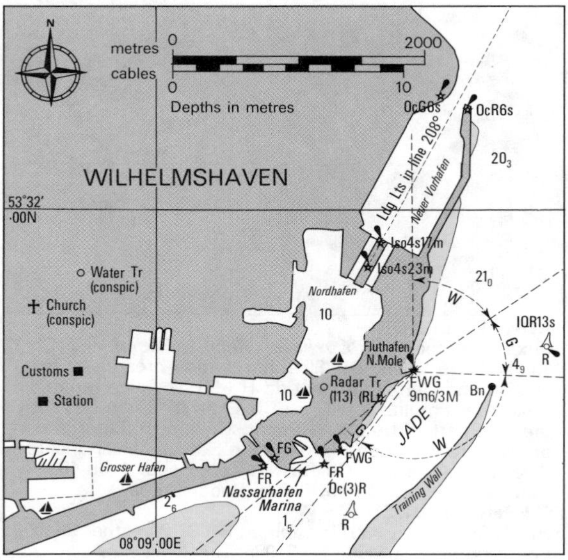
N
metres 0 2000
cables 0 10
Depths in metres
WILHELMSHAVEN
53°32′·00N
Water Tr (conspic)
Church (conspic)
Customs
Station
Nordhafen
Ldg Lts in-line 208°
Neuer Vorhafen
OcG6s
OcR6s
Iso4s17m
Iso4s23m
Fluthafen N.Mole
Radar Tr (113) (RLt)
FWG 9m6/3M
IQR13s
Bn
JADE
Grosser Hafen
FG
FR
FWG
Oc(3)R
Nassauhafen Marina
Training Wall
08°09′·00E

FACILITIES
Nassauhafen Marina (28+100 visitors) ☎ 41439 Slip, BY, ME, P, D, AC, Bar, FW, SM, R; **Wiking Sportsboothafen** (30) ☎ 41301 AC, Bar, CH, El, FW, Gaz, ME, R, SM, V; **Turbo-Technik** ☎ 44061, ME, El, Sh; **Farymann** ☎ 23058, ME; **Hochsee YC Germania** ☎ 44121; **Ship-Shop** ☎ 26011 Gaz.
Town BY, SM, ME, CH, El, P, D, Gaz, V, ✉; Ⓑ; ≹; ✈.
Ferry UK — Hamburg—Harwich.

BREMERHAVEN 10-21-17

Federal State of Bremen

CHARTS
Admiralty 3406, 3405; German D3011, D4

TIDES
Dover +0051; ML 2·0; Duration 0600; Zone −0100.

Standard Port HELGOLAND (⟶)

Times				Height (metres)			
HW		LW		MHWS	MHWN	MLWN	MLWS
0200	0800	0200	0800	2·7	2·3	0·4	0·0
1400	2000	1400	2000				
Differences BREMERHAVEN							
+0136	+0144	+0119	+0129	+1·5	+1·4	+0·1	0·0

SHELTER
The fishing and yacht harbours are in the S-most basin, entered through Vorhafen, close S of conspic Radar Tr (112m). Yachts may go into R Geeste (uncomfortable in SW-W winds) or to one of the three YC/marinas. The Nordseeyachting Marina (NYC or Bremerhaven Marina) in Fischereihafen II, 1·3M S of locks on W side (3m); the Wassersportverein Wulsdorf Marina (WVW) 0·5M beyond; the Weser Yacht Club Yacht Haven to E of Handelshafen. There are also Yacht Harbours up the R Weser at Nordenham, Rodenkirchen, Brake and at Elsfleth.

NAVIGATION
Waypoint Alte Weser. Schlüsseltonne (safe water) buoy, Iso 8s, 53°56′·30N 07°54′·87E, 300°/120° from/to Alte Weser Lt, 9M. For The Weser, see 10.21.5. R Weser is very well marked. Beware large amounts of commercial shipping and ferries using R Geeste. Leave R Weser at Lt Buoy 61.

LIGHTS AND MARKS
Ldg Lts 151° lead down main channel (R Weser). Front Oc 6s 17m 18M. Rear 0·68M from front, Oc 6s 45m 18M synchronised. Vorhafen N mole head FR 15m 5M. To enter Schleusenhafen sound Q and enter when G Lt is shown.

RADIO TELEPHONE
Bremerhaven Port VHF Ch 12; 12 16 (H24). Bremerhaven Weser Ch 14; **14** 16 (H24). Brake Lock Ch 10 (H24). The Weser Radar Information Service broadcasts information in German every H+20 from Alte Weser Radar Ch 22, Hohe Weg Radar I Ch 02, Hohe Weg Radar II Ch 02, Robbenplate Radar I Ch 04, Robbenplate Radar II Ch 04 and Blexen Radar Ch 07; also from Bremen-Weser-Revier at H+30 on Ch 19 and by Hunte-Revier on Ch 17. Hunte Bridge Ch 10 (daylight hours). Oslebshausen Lock, Bremen, Ch 12. Bremen Port Ch 03 16; 03 14 16 (H24).

TELEPHONE (0471)
Hr Mr 481260; Bremerhaven Marina (NYC) 77555; Weser YC Yacht Hafen 23531; Wassersportverein Wulsdorf (WVW) 73268; Weather 72220; Fischereihafen Lock 4811; Police 47011; Ⓗ 42028; Brit Consul (040) 446071.

FACILITIES
Bremerhaven Fischereihafen Hauptkanal (WeserYC) ☎ 23531 C, AC, FW, **Bremerhaven Fischereihafen 2** ☎ 73268 C, Slip, El, P, D, FW **Marina Bremerhaven** ☎ 77555 C, Slip, AC, FW; **Weser YC** ☎ 23531, R, Bar, AB; **Yachting Club Wulsdorf** ☎ 23268, AB, FW, Slip; **W. G. Janssen** ☎ 25095 Gaz. **Nordsee Yachting** ☎ 77555 **Town** all facilities, V, R, Bar, ✉; Ⓑ; ≹; ✈.
Ferry UK — Hamburg—Harwich.

BREMERHAVEN *continued*

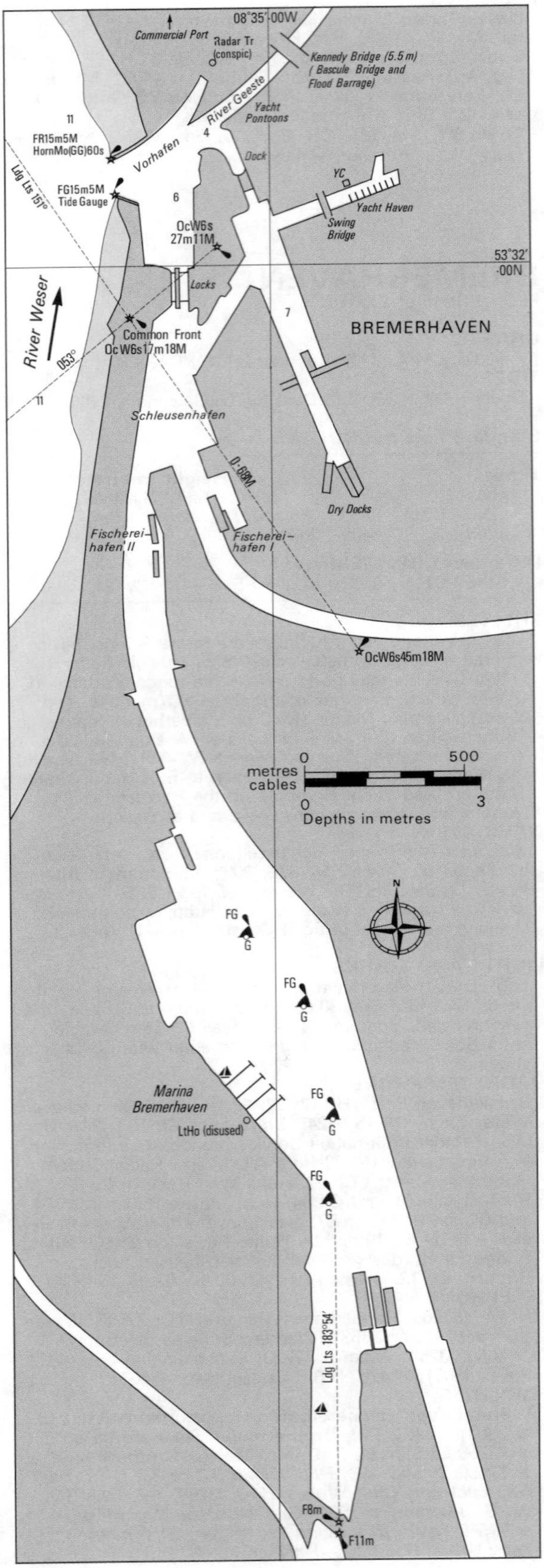

08°35'·00W
Commercial Port
Radar Tr (conspic)
Kennedy Bridge (5.5 m) (Bascule Bridge and Flood Barrage)
River Geeste
Yacht Pontoons
Vorhafen
FR15m5M HornMo(GG)60s
Ldg Lts 151°
FG15m5M Tide Gauge
Dock
YC
Yacht Haven
Swing Bridge
OcW6s 27m11M
53°32' ·00N
Locks
River Weser
053°
Common Front OcW6s17m18M
BREMERHAVEN
Schleusenhafen
Dry Docks
Fischerei-hafen II
Fischerei-hafen I
OcW6s45m18M
metres
cables
0
500
3
Depths in metres
FG
G
Marina Bremerhaven
LtHo (disused)
Ldg Lts 183°54'
F8m
F11m

CUXHAVEN 10-21-18

Niedersachsen

CHARTS

Admiralty 3261; German D3010

TIDES

Dover +0103; ML 1·5; Duration 0535; Zone −0100

Standard Port HELGOLAND (⟶)

Times		Height (metres)			
HW	LW	MHWS	MHWN	MLWN	MLWS
All Times	All Times	2·7	2·3	0·4	0·0
Differences CUXHAVEN					
+0119	+0116	+0·6	+0·5	−0·1	−0·1
SCHARNHÖRN					
+0024	+0019	+0·7	+0·7	0·0	0·0

SHELTER

Good shelter both in the Alter Hafen and in the Yacht Harbours to the NW. Apply to Cuxhaven YC for moorings. Yachts over 20m may be allowed in Alter Fischereihafen.

NAVIGATION

Waypoint Elbe Lt buoy, Iso 10s, Horn, RC, Racon, 54°00'·00N 08°06'·6E, 271°/091° from/to Grosser Vogelsand Lt, 13M. Channel well marked by buoys and beacons, see 10.21.4 and 10.21.5. Tide is strong, up to 5 kn off Cuxhaven on the ebb. Much commercial shipping.

LIGHTS AND MARKS

Entrance to S Yacht Harbour is close NW of conspic radar Tr, and N of main Cuxhaven Lt Tr (dark R with copper cupola) FWR, Fl(4) 12s, Oc 6s and Fl(5) 12s (for sectors see chartlet).

Luminous tide signals (G by day, Y at night) from radar Tr. Top panel: chevron point up — tide rising; chevron point down — tide falling; horizontal line below chevron — level below CD. Lower panel: two figures show difference in decimetres between level and CD. S Yacht Harbour entrance, N side FWG, G108°-340°, W340°-108°. S side FWR, W056°-120°, R120°-272°, W272°-295°.

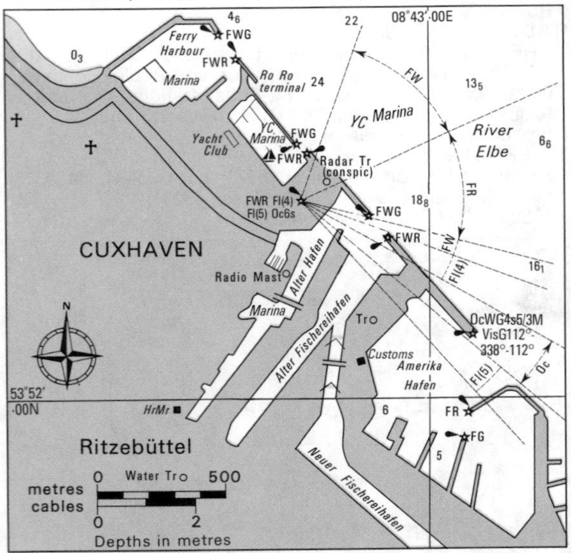

08°43'·00E
Ferry Harbour
FWG
FWR
Marina
Ro Ro terminal
YC Marina
Yacht Club
Radar Tr (conspic)
River Elbe
FW
FWR Fl(4) Fl(5) Oc6s
FWG
FWR
CUXHAVEN
Radio Mast
Alter Hafen
Marina
Alter Fischereihafen
Tr
Customs
Amerika Hafen
OcWG4s5/3M VisG112°-338°-112°
Fl(4)
Fl(5)
Oc
53°52' ·00N
HrMr
FR
FG
Ritzebüttel
Water Tr
metres
cables
0
500
2
Depths in metres
Neuer Fischereihafen

RADIO TELEPHONE

Cuxhaven Elbe. Call: *Cuxhaven Report (Radio)* VHF Ch 12 16; 12 14 16 (H24). Die Elbe information broadcasts in English and German every odd H+55 by *Revierzentrale Cuxhaven* simultaneously on Ch 19 18 05 21 and 03 for the East part of Deutsche Bucht. Cuxhaven Radar is part of Die Elbe Radar and Information Service which includes River Elbe Approach Ch 19, Neuwerk Radar 1 Ch 18, Neuwerk Radar 2 Ch 05, Belum Radar Ch 03.

TELEPHONE (04721)

Hr Mr 34111; CG 38011; Lifeboat 34622; Weather 36400; Port Authority 501450; ⌗ 21085; Brit Cruising Assn 35820; Police 22071; Dr 23411; Brit Consul (040) 446071.

FACILITIES
Cuxhaven YC Marina ☎ 34111 (summer only), Slip, M, L, FW, C, AB, R, Bar; **Cuxhavener Bootswerft** ☎ 22132, Slip, ME, El, Sh; **Glüsing** ☎ 24017, P, D, Gaz; **Ferry Harbour Marina** No tel, no visitors, no facilities; **Herbert Krause** ☎ 22197, CH, El; **Rauschenplath-Buchhandlung** ☎ 37137, chart agent; **Euromar** ☎ 32929, CH; **Krause Wilhelmi** ☎ 22197, Ⓔ, El; **Little Ship Club** ☎ 35820; **B Hein** ☎ 24069, CH, SM; **Segler-Vereingung Cuxhaven** ☎ 04725; **Town** All facilities, R, V, Bar, ✉; Ⓑ; ⇌; ✈ (Bremen, Hamburg, Hanover).
Ferry UK — Hamburg—Harwich.

RIVER ELBE/HAMBURG 10-21-19

Niedersachsen/Schleswig Holstein

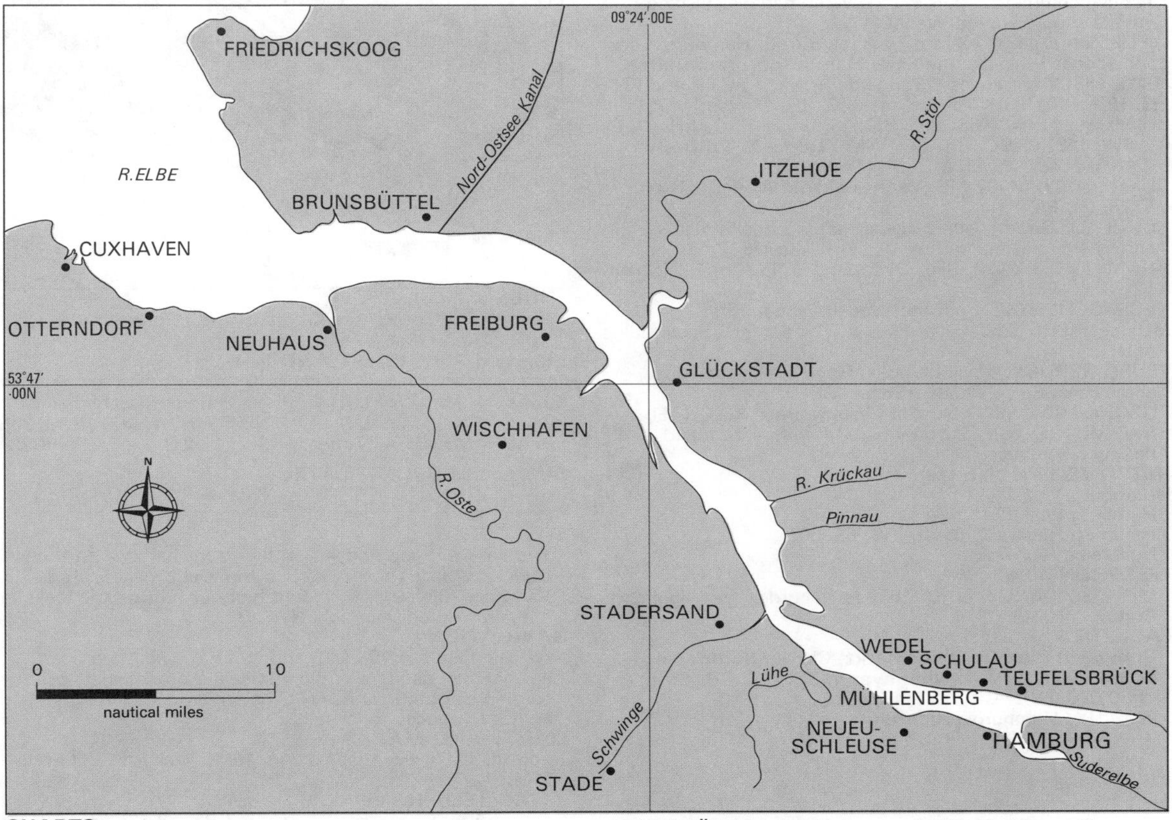
09°24'·00E
FRIEDRICHSKOOG
Nord-Ostsee Kanal
R. Stör
R.ELBE
ITZEHOE
BRUNSBÜTTEL
CUXHAVEN
OTTERNDORF
NEUHAUS
FREIBURG
GLÜCKSTADT
53°47'·00N
WISCHHAFEN
N
R. Krückau
R. Oste
Pinnau
STADERSAND
WEDEL
SCHULAU
TEUFELSBRÜCK
0
10
nautical miles
Lühe
MÜHLENBERG
NEUEU-SCHLEUSE
HAMBURG
Schwinge
Suderelbe
STADE

CHARTS
Admiralty 3262, 3266, 3268; German D3010 Sheet 1 to 16, D46, D47, D48.

TIDES

Glückstadt	ML 1·2	Duration 0515	Zone −0100
Brunshausen	ML 1·1	Duration 0510	
Hamburg	ML 1·3	Duration 0435	
Bunthaus	ML 1·4	Duration 0435	

Standard Port HELGOLAND (⟶)

HW	LW	MHWS	MHWN	MLWN	MLWS
All Times	All Times	2·7	2·3	0·4	0·0
Differences GLÜCKSTADT					
+0322	+0329	+0·3	+0·3	−0·3	−0·1
STADERSAND					
+0359	+0413	+0·4	+0·4	−0·3	0·0
SCHULAU					
+0459	+0443	+0·6	+0·5	−0·3	−0·1
HAMBURG					
+0459	+0532	+0·8	+0·7	−0·4	−0·1
BUNTHAUS					
+0522	+0614	+0·6	+0·5	−0·4	0·0

The river is tidal up to Geesthacht, 24 M above Hamburg, and Hamburg is 78 M from the Elbe 1 Light Vessel. It is a very busy waterway and there are so many lights that at night it can be very confusing. Yachts should keep to starboard, preferably just outside the marked channel. The river is 13m deep all the way to Hamburg. Strong W winds can raise the level in the river by as much as 4m.

There are a number of places with good shelter and facilities but it is not a particularly salubrious yachting area. (Chart is D3010 and sheet numbers are shown below).

BRUNSBÜTTEL alter Hafen see 10.21.20. (Sheet 7).

ST. MARGARETHEN (Sheet 8). Depth HW 10m. No facilities.

FREIBURG (7 M above Brunsbüttel) on the SW bank. The river here is ½m wide. Small vessels can enter Freiburg harbour at HW and there is excellent shelter at Freiburg Reede. ML 2·2m. ☎ Hr Mr (04779) 8314. Facilities ME, El, Sh, C, FW, Slip, YC **Jugendheim** and **YC Klubheim** V, R, Bar. (Sheet 8).

STÖRLOCH/BORSFLETH Entrance approx 600 m above locks on E bank. ML 2·8m. Facilities. Hr Mr ☎ (04124) 71437 FW, YC. (Sheet 9).

STÖR/BEIDENFLETH Ml 2·8m (Sheet 9). **Stör/Langes Rack YC**

GLÜCKSTADT, on the NE bank 2½ M up-stream from entrance to the Stör River. Good shelter both inner and outer harbours having min depth of 2·0 m. Hr Mr ☎ (04124) 2087; Customs ☎ (04124) 2171. YC, FW, C, D, V, R, ⊡, Bar. (Sheet 9).

WISCHHAFEN Hr Mr ☎ (04770) 334; Customs (04770) 3014 FW, M, Slip, P, D, ML 2·7 m. (Sheet 9)·

RUTHENSTROM ldg marks into harbour, two Bns with triangular topmarks on 197°. ML 2·6 m. Hr Mr ☎ (04143) 5282; C, Slip, FW, ME, El, Sh. (Sheet 10).

KRÜCKAUMÜNDUNG JACHTHAFEN ☎ (04121) 20945 Slip, FW. ML 2·7 m. Customs 20551. (Sheet 10).

PINNAUMÜNDUNG JACHTHAFEN Entrance via lock gate on N bank after passing through main locks. ML 2·5 m. Hr Mr ☎ (04101) 22447 Slip, M, FW, YC, C. (Sheet 10).

PINNAU-NEUENDEICH Marina 1½M up the Pinnau from main locks and another at approx. 2M. (Sheet 10).

ABBENFLETH Entrance maked by two Bns in line 221° with triangular topmarks. (Sheet 11).

HASELDORF Hafen. Hr Mr ☎ (04129) 268 Slip, FW, V, YC.

RIVER ELBE/HAMBURG *continued*

SCHWINGE – BRUNSHAUSEN (04141) 3085
HÖRNE/WÖHRDEN ML 2·8m
STADE (04141) 101275 C, YC, V on SW bank, 12M up-stream from Glückstadt. Access HW∓2. Yachts lock into inner basin. Customs ☎ 3014. (Sheet 11/12).

LÜHE Hafen in town of Lühe. (Sheet 12).

HAMBURG
A busy commercial port with several marinas. Visiting yachts should stay in Wedel.

WEDEL on E bank, 12 M downstream from Hamburg, very good shelter available any time; **Hamburger Yachthafen** (1800) with 2 entrances (23 m wide) marked by FR and FG Lts. Hr Mr (04103) 4438 (office), 5632 (Hr Mr east), 7751 (Hr Mr west); # 2688; Bar, BH (16 ton), BY, C, CH, D, El, Ⓔ, FW, ME, P, SC, Sh, Slip, SM, **Bülow & Partner** (04103) 88492 Ⓔ, El, ME, Sh (Sheet 12);

BUKH (04103) 84402 ME, **Yachtelektrik Wedel** (04103) 87273 Ⓔ, El;

SCHULAU. Good shelter. Beware strong tidal streams across ent. Ent marked by Oc (2) R and Oc (2) G Lts. Hr Mr (04103) 2422, Slip, C, P, D, ME, El, Ch, SC (Sheet 12);

NEUENSCHLEUSE, opposite Wedel, (Sheet 13);

MÜHLENBERG (250), Slip, FW, SC (Sheet 13). Small boats only;

TEUFELSBRÜCK, small harbour. Good shelter, sandbar across ent. Bar, FW, SC (Sheet 13);

RÜSCHKANAL, on S bank in Finkenwerder, C, CH, El, FW, ME, Slip, Sh, SC new harbour with 4 SCs and nearby resort area

RADIO TELEPHONE
Hamburg Port 14,17
Hamburg Elbe 12
Hamburg Radar 03, 05, 07, 19, 63, 80
Süderelbe Revier 13

TELEPHONE (040)
Met 3190 826/827, or (0)11509 for recorded message; Brit. Consul 446071

FACILITIES
Subwaystation 'Rödingsmarkt' CH; **B. Schmeding** ☎ 353646 Gaz, **A.W. Niemeyer** ☎ 3614140 CH, **Möhrer** ☎ 366300 Ⓔ, El **City** all facilities ✉, Ⓑ, ⇌, ✈
Ferry UK. Hamburg – Harwich

HAMBURGER YACHTHAFEN, WEDEL

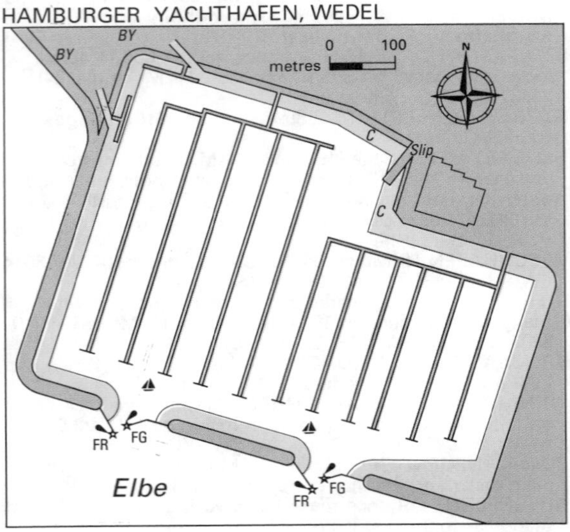

BY
BY
0 100
metres
N
C
Slip
C
FR
FG
Elbe
FR
FG

BRUNSBÜTTEL 10-21-20

Schleswig-Holstein

CHARTS
Admiralty 2469, 3262; German D3010 Sheet 6

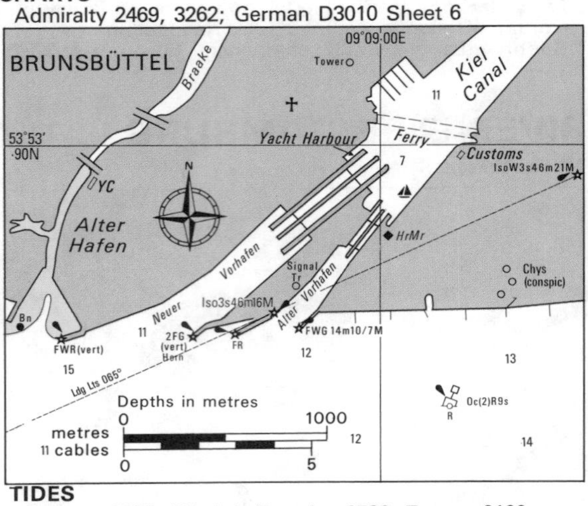

BRUNSBÜTTEL
09°09·00E
Braake
Tower
Kiel Canal
53°53'·90N
Yacht Harbour
Ferry
Customs
IsoW3s46m21M
YC
Alter Hafen
N
HrMr
Signal Tr
Neuer Vorhafen
Alter Vorhafen
Iso3s46m16M
Chys (conspic)
Bn
FWR(vert)
2FG (vert) Hern
FR
FWG 14m10/7M
Ldg Lts 065°
Depths in metres
metres 0 1000
cables 0 5
Oc(2)R9s
R

TIDES
Dover +0203; ML 1.4; Duration 0520; Zone −0100

Standard Port HELGOLAND (⟶)

Times		Height (metres)			
HW	LW	MHWS	MHWN	MLWN	MLWS
All Times	All Times	2.7	2.3	0.4	0.0
Differences BRUNSBÜTTEL					
+0221	+0234	+0.3	+0.3	−0.1	0.0

SHELTER
There is very good shelter in the yacht harbour on the N bank, just inside the locks into the Kiel canal. There is also good shelter in the yacht harbour outside the locks in the Alter Hafen, available HW∓3.

NAVIGATION
For Die Elbe see 10.21.19 and 10.21.5. There are no navigational dangers in the immediate approaches, but commercial traffic is heavy. The stream sets strongly across entrances to locks.

LIGHTS AND MARKS
Ldg Lts 065°, front Iso 3s 24m 16M; Rear Iso 3s 46m 21M.

RADIO TELEPHONE
Brunsbüttel Elbe. Call: *Brunsbüttel Report (Radio)* VHF Ch 14 16; 11 **14** 16 (H24). Die Elbe information broadcasts in English and German every odd H+05 by Revierzentrale Brunsbüttel Ch 04 67 18 22 05 and 21 (see also Cuxhaven 10.21.18). Nord-Ostsee Kanal: Ports — Ostermoor (Brunsbüttel to Burg) Ch 73 (H24), Breiholz (Breiholz to Nübbel) Ch 73 (H24). Canal — Kiel Kanal I (Brunsbüttel entrance and locks) Ch 13 (H24), Kiel Kanal II (Brunsbüttel to Breiholz) Ch 02 (H24), Kiel Kanal III (Breiholz to Holtenau) Ch 03 (H24). Kiel Kanal IV (Holtenau entrance and locks) Ch 12 (H24). Information broadcasts by Kiel Kanal II on Ch 02 at H+15, H+45 and by Kiel Kanal III on Ch 03 at H+20, H+50. Vessels should monitor these broadcasts and not call the station if this can be avoided. Other stations: Oste Bridge Ch 16 69. Este Lock Ch 10 16. Stör Bridge Ch 09 16. Stadersand Elbe. Call: *Stadersand Report (Radio)* Ch 11 16; **11** 12 16 (H24). Hamburg Elbe Port Ch **12** 16; 12 14 (H24). Hamburg Port. Call: *Hamburg Report (Radio)* Ch 16; 06 13 **14** 73 (H24). Hamburg Control Vessel Ch 14 16. Rethe Revier Ch 16 13 (Mon-Sat: 0600-2100 LT, Sun and Public Holidays on request). Süderelbe Revier (at Kattwyk bridge) Ch 16 13 (H24). Harburg Lock Ch 13 16 (H24). See also Cuxhaven 10.21.18.

TELEPHONE (04852)
Hr Mr 8011 ex 360; CG 8444; # 87241; Weather Cuxhaven 36400; Police 1012; Ⓗ 601; Brit Consul (040) 446071.

FACILITIES
Alter hafen ☎ 3107, Slip, SC, AC, C (20 ton), FW, R; **Kanal-Yachthafen** ☎ 8011, FW, AC, #, Bar; **P. Lützen** ☎ 51016, Gaz;
Town P, D, ME, El, Sh, V, R, LB, Ⓗ, Bar. ✉; Ⓑ; ⇌; ✈ (Hamburg).
Ferry UK — Hamburg—Harwich.

NORD-OSTSEE KANAL (Kiel Canal) 10-21-21

Schleswig Holstein

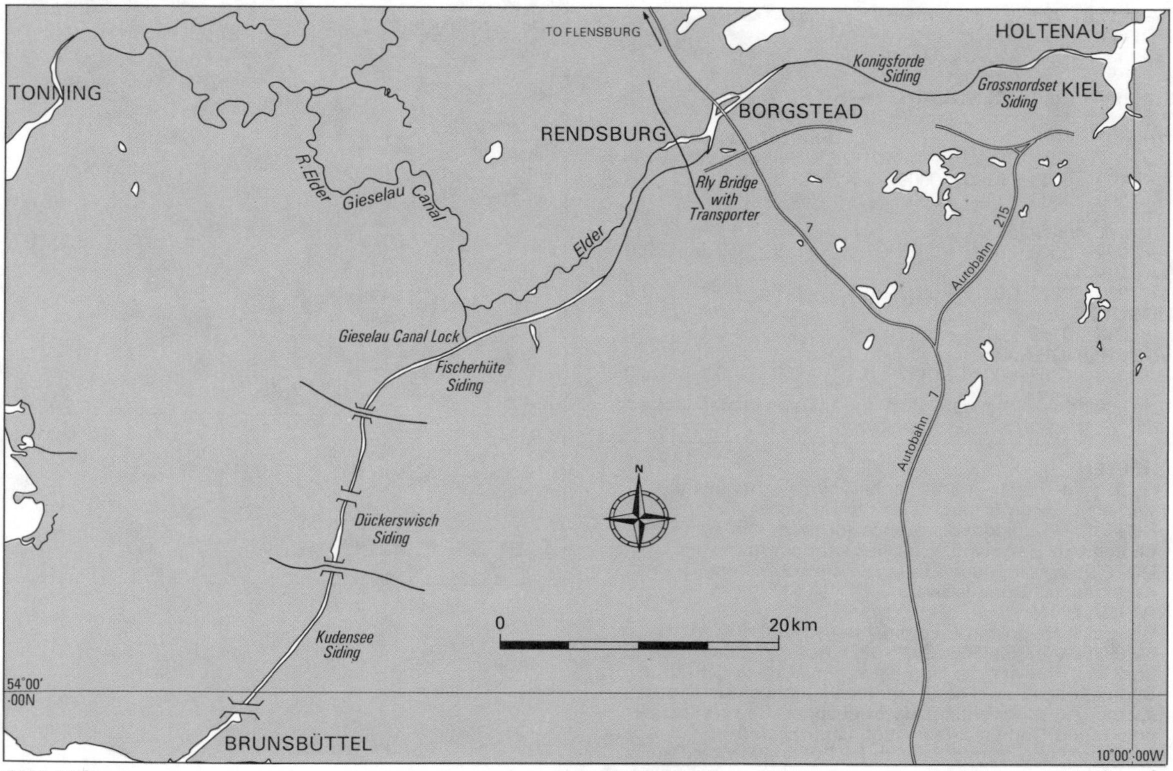
TO FLENSBURG
HOLTENAU
TONNING
Konigsforde Siding
Grossnordset Siding
KIEL
BORGSTEAD
RENDSBURG
R. Elder
Gieselau Canal
Rly Bridge with Transporter
Elder
Autobahn 215
Gieselau Canal Lock
Fischerhüte Siding
Autobahn 7
Dückerswisch Siding
Kudensee Siding
0
20km
54°00'·00N
BRUNSBÜTTEL
10°00'·00W

CHARTS

Admty 2469 German D 3010

Yachts are only permitted to use the Kiel Canal and the entrances thereto during the hours of daylight and in good visibility. This does not apply to craft proceeding to the yacht berths at Kiel-Holtenau, to the Inner Harbour at Brunsbüttel and the Old Harbour at Brunsbüttel.

Nord-Ostsee Kanal is 53·3M long (98·7 km) running from Brunsbüttel to Kiel-Holtenau. Width 103 to 162m on the surface, 44 to 90m on the bottom, with a depth of 11m. Kilometre marks start at Brunsbüttel; there are ten passing places (sidings or weichen) and seven bridges with 40m clearance. The speed limit is 8 kn. Sailing, except motor sailing is forbidden. Yachts must then display a B cone, apex down, or a B flag, cone shaped. Yachts should report before entering as follows: at Brunsbüttel through Kiel Kanal I on VHF Ch 13; at Holtenau through Kiel Kanal IV on VHF Ch 12.

Canal dues can be paid at either end of the canal at the 'Dues Office'.

Yachts purely in transit are not usually troubled by the Customs Authority and transiting yachts should fly the third substitute of the International Code.

Yachts are to regulate their transit so as to reach the intended berthing places during the day. These are:

1) Yacht Harbour at Kiel-Holtenau (km 0)
2) The Borgstedt Narrows (km 28·5)
3) The Ober Eider Lake (km 32·5)
4) Berthing place outside the Gieselau Canal Lock (km 58)
5) Berthing place at the jetty in Dückerswisch Siding (km 77)
6) Brunsbüttel (km 98·5)

Entrance Area: Signals shown from Canal Pilots House.

R – No entry

W/R – Prepare to enter

G – enter with pilot

W/G – enter without pilot (yachts follow coasters flying Flag N)

Lock signals

R – No entry

W/R – Prepare to enter

G – enter with pilot; secure to middle wall

W/G – without pilot – enter; secure to middle wall

W/W G – with pilot enter and secure by W Lt

W – Yachts may enter

Other signals

In canal:—

3FR (vert) — all movement prohibited

Other signals — not relevant to yachts.

Other ports in the canal, Ostermoor Ch 73 (H24) and Breiholz Ch 73 (H24). The traffic signal of most concern to yachts is 3FR(vert) meaning 'STOP' and usually means the approach of a big ship. Yachts keep to starboard side. Speed limit in canal is 15 kilometres/hour; in the Gieselau Canal 10 and in the Achterwehr Shipping Canal 8 kilometres/hr.

The principal port along the canal is Rensburg, situated between kilometre posts 60 and 67. There are all facilities at Rensburg including dry docks and several shipyards. The Eider Canal connects Rensburg with Tonning (see 10.21.21). At the Baltic end of the canal is Kiel-Holtenau, a major port with all facilities. Here two pairs of locks lead into the Kieler Förde which is practically tideless and almost the same level as the canal.

21

HELGOLAND 10-21-22

Schleswig-Holstein

CHARTS
Admiralty 126, 1875; German D88, D3010, D3013/4

TIDES
Dover −0030; ML 1.4; Duration 0540; Zone −0100

Standard Port HELGOLAND (⟶)

Times				Height (metres)			
HW		LW		MHWS	MHWN	MLWN	MLWS
0100	0600	0100	0800	2.7	2.3	0.4	0.0
1300	1800	1300	2000				
Differences BÜSUM							
+0054	+0049	0000	+0028	+1.0	+0.9	+0.1	0.0
DAGEBULL							
+0230	+0222	+0217	+0231	+0.5	+0.6	−0.1	0.0
HUSUM							
+0213	+0159	+0128	+0212	+1.1	+1.1	+0.1	0.0
SUDEROOGSAND							
+0116	+0102	+0038	+0122	+0.3	+0.3	+0.1	0.0

Helgoland is a Standard Port and tidal predictions for each day of the year are given below.

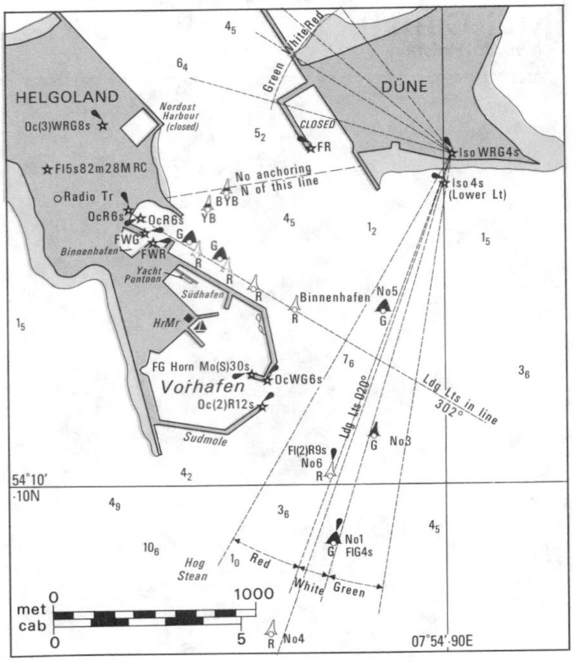

HELGOLAND
DÜNE
Nordost Harbour (closed)
CLOSED
Oc(3)WRG8s
Fl5s82m28M RC
Radio Tr
OcR6s
OcR6s
FWG
FWR
Binnenhafen
Yacht Pontoon
Südhafen
HrMr
FR
Iso WRG4s
Iso 4s (Lower Lt)
No anchoring N of this line
BYB
YB
Binnenhafen
No5
FG Horn Mo(S)30s
OcWG6s
Vorhafen
Oc(2)R12s
Sudmole
Ldg Lts 302° in line
Ldg Lts 020°
No3
Fl(2)R9s No6
No1 FlG4s
Hog Stean
Red
White
Green
Green
White
Red
54°10′ ·10N
met cab
0
1000
5
No4
07°54′·90E

SHELTER
Good safe shelter in artificial harbour; yachts use the Vorhafen, or go through into the Südhafen.
NOTE 1. No customs clearance for entry into Germany. Customs in Helgoland is for passport control.
NOTE 2. It is forbidden to land from yachts on neighbouring Düne Island.

NAVIGATION
Waypoint Helgoland E cardinal buoy, Q(3) 10s, Whis, 54°09′.00N 07°53′.56E, 202°/022° from/to Düne front Ldg Lt, 2.1M. Beware the Hog Stean shoal, 4 ca (740 m) S of Sudmole head Lt. The S entrance is dangerous due to submerged rocks either side of channel. Beware lobster pots round Düne Is. Navigation is prohibited from 1 April to 12 July and from 1 Sept to 31 Dec in restricted areas. See Admty chart 3761.

LIGHTS AND MARKS
Helgoland Lt Ho, Fl 5s 82m 28M; brown sq Tr, B lantern, W balcony; RC.
Binnenhafen Ldg Lts 302°, both Oc R 6s, synchronised.

RADIO TELEPHONE
Helgoland Port Radio VHF Ch 16 67 (Mon-Sat: 0700-2100 LT): Coast Radio VHF Ch 03 16 27 88 (H24).
Information broadcasts in English and German every H+00 and H+30 on Ch 80 by Deutsche Bucht Revier (at Helgoland Lt Ho) for area within 26M of Helgoland.

TELEPHONE (04725)
Hr Mr 504; CG 210; # 304; Met (04725) 606; Police 607; Dr 7345; Ⓗ 8030; Brit Consul (040) 446071.

FACILITIES
Wasser Sport Club Helgolard ☎ 585 Bar, R, M, C (12 ton), D, P, CH, ME, El, Sh, FW, ⊡, V; **Südhafen** ☎ 504, D, FW, ME, C (mobile 12 ton), CH, AB, V, R, Bar; **Binnenhafen** ☎ 504, P, D, FW, ME, C (mobile 12 ton), CH, AB, V, R, Bar; **Vorhafen** L, AB; **Rickmers** ☎ 585, Gaz;
Town V, R, Bar. ✉; Ⓑ; ⇌ (ferry Cuxhaven); ✈ (services to Bremen or Hamburg).
Ferry UK — Hamburg—Harwich.

HELGOLAND
MEAN SPRING AND NEAP CURVES

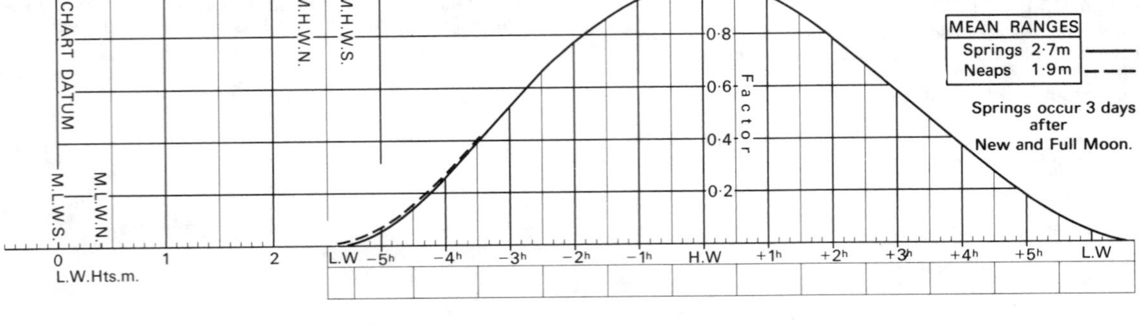

H.W.Hts.m.
0
1
2
3
CHART DATUM
M.H.W.N.
M.H.W.S.
M.L.W.S.
M.L.W.N.
0·8
0·6
0·4
0·2
Factor
0
1
2
L.W.Hts.m.
L.W
−5h
−4h
−3h
−2h
−1h
H.W
+1h
+2h
+3h
+4h
+5h
L.W
MEAN RANGES
Springs 2·7m
Neaps 1·9m
Springs occur 3 days after New and Full Moon.

TIME ZONE -0100
(German Standard Time)
Subtract 1 hour for GMT

For German Summer Time add ONE hour in non-shaded areas

GERMANY - HELGOLAND

LAT 54°11'N LONG 7°54'E

TIMES AND HEIGHTS OF HIGH AND LOW WATERS

YEAR **1992**

JANUARY

Day	Time	m	Time	m	Time	m	Time	m
1 W	0301	0.4	0850	2.5	1534	0.4	2122	2.5
2 TH	0409	0.4	0954	2.5	1633	0.4	2219	2.6
3 F	0506	0.4	1050	2.6	1724	0.4	2309	2.7
4 SA ●	0556	0.3	1137	2.6	1809	0.4	2352	2.7
5 SU	0640	0.2	1217	2.5	1847	0.3		
6 M	0029	2.8	0717	0.2	1252	2.5	1922	0.2
7 TU	0103	2.8	0751	0.1	1326	2.5	1954	0.2
8 W	0137	2.8	0822	0.1	1359	2.5	2024	0.2
9 TH	0208	2.8	0851	0.2	1428	2.5	2053	0.2
10 F	0237	2.7	0921	0.2	1459	2.4	2124	0.2
11 SA	0310	2.7	0954	0.2	1533	2.4	2157	0.2
12 SU	0346	2.6	1027	0.2	1608	2.4	2233	0.3
13 M ☽	0423	2.6	1102	0.3	1649	2.3	2317	0.4
14 TU	0510	2.5	1149	0.4	1744	2.3		
15 W	0020	0.5	0614	2.4	1258	0.4	1854	2.3
16 TH	0139	0.5	0732	2.4	1417	0.4	2012	2.4
17 F	0302	0.4	0852	2.5	1536	0.4	2127	2.5
18 SA	0418	0.3	1005	2.5	1647	0.2	2232	2.7
19 SU ○	0526	0.1	1108	2.6	1749	0.1	2328	2.8
20 M	0626	0.0	1203	2.6	1844	0.1		
21 TU	0020	2.8	0721	-0.1	1253	2.6	1935	0.0
22 W	0111	2.9	0812	-0.2	1343	2.6	2024	-0.1
23 TH	0200	2.9	0859	-0.2	1429	2.6	2107	-0.1
24 F	0243	2.9	0939	-0.1	1512	2.6	2146	0.0
25 SA	0323	2.9	1017	0.0	1553	2.5	2225	0.1
26 SU ☾	0406	2.8	1055	0.1	1635	2.5	2307	0.2
27 M	0452	2.7	1135	0.3	1720	2.4	2354	0.3
28 TU	0544	2.5	1225	0.4	1815	2.3		
29 W	0056	0.4	0650	2.3	1332	0.5	1925	2.3
30 TH	0217	0.4	0809	2.3	1453	0.4	2045	2.3
31 F	0341	0.3	0927	2.3	1608	0.4	2156	2.4

FEBRUARY

Day	Time	m	Time	m	Time	m	Time	m
1 SA	0451	0.2	1032	2.3	1708	0.3	2251	2.5
2 SU	0543	0.1	1122	2.4	1754	0.2	2335	2.6
3 M ●	0625	0.1	1201	2.4	1833	0.1		
4 TU	0013	2.6	0702	0.0	1235	2.4	1908	0.0
5 W	0046	2.7	0735	0.0	1307	2.4	1939	0.0
6 TH	0117	2.7	0804	0.0	1337	2.5	2006	0.0
7 F	0146	2.7	0830	0.0	1404	2.5	2034	0.0
8 SA	0214	2.7	0858	0.0	1432	2.4	2105	0.0
9 SU	0245	2.6	0930	0.0	1505	2.4	2138	0.0
10 M	0319	2.6	1001	0.1	1537	2.4	2208	0.1
11 TU ☽	0352	2.5	1028	0.2	1610	2.4	2243	0.2
12 W	0431	2.4	1106	0.3	1655	2.3	2338	0.3
13 TH	0531	2.3	1212	0.4	1806	2.2		
14 F	0101	0.3	0655	2.2	1342	0.4	1936	2.3
15 SA	0237	0.2	0828	2.2	1516	0.3	2104	2.4
16 SU	0406	0.1	0951	2.3	1636	0.1	2218	2.6
17 M	0519	-0.1	1059	2.4	1741	0.0	2318	2.7
18 TU ○	0618	-0.2	1153	2.5	1835	-0.1		
19 W	0008	2.8	0710	-0.3	1239	2.5	1923	-0.2
20 TH	0055	2.8	0756	-0.3	1322	2.5	2008	-0.2
21 F	0140	2.8	0838	-0.3	1405	2.5	2049	-0.2
22 SA	0221	2.8	0915	-0.2	1445	2.5	2125	-0.2
23 SU	0259	2.8	0950	-0.1	1522	2.5	2200	-0.1
24 M	0337	2.7	1021	0.1	1558	2.5	2235	0.0
25 TU ☾	0417	2.5	1054	0.2	1637	2.4	2315	0.1
26 W	0502	2.3	1136	0.4	1725	2.3		
27 TH	0012	0.3	0603	2.1	1241	0.4	1835	2.2
28 F	0133	0.3	0725	2.0	1408	0.4	2002	2.2
29 SA	0308	0.2	0854	2.0	1538	0.3	2126	2.3

MARCH

Day	Time	m	Time	m	Time	m	Time	m
1 SU	0428	0.1	1009	2.1	1647	0.2	2228	2.4
2 M	0523	0.0	1101	2.3	1735	0.1	2312	2.5
3 TU	0603	-0.1	1138	2.3	1812	0.0	2348	2.5
4 W ●	0638	-0.1	1210	2.4	1846	-0.1		
5 TH	0020	2.6	0709	-0.2	1240	2.4	1917	-0.2
6 F	0050	2.6	0738	-0.2	1308	2.4	1945	-0.2
7 SA	0119	2.6	0805	-0.2	1336	2.4	2014	-0.2
8 SU	0149	2.6	0834	-0.1	1406	2.5	2047	-0.1
9 M	0222	2.6	0907	0.0	1439	2.5	2121	-0.1
10 TU	0257	2.5	0939	0.0	1513	2.4	2154	-0.1
11 W	0332	2.4	1008	0.1	1545	2.4	2228	0.0
12 TH ☽	0412	2.3	1045	0.2	1630	2.3	2322	0.1
13 F	0512	2.2	1151	0.3	1741	2.2		
14 SA	0046	0.1	0638	2.1	1325	0.3	1915	2.3
15 SU	0226	0.1	0815	2.1	1504	0.2	2048	2.4
16 M	0357	-0.1	0939	2.3	1625	0.1	2204	2.5
17 TU	0507	-0.2	1044	2.4	1727	-0.1	2302	2.6
18 W ○	0602	-0.3	1135	2.4	1819	-0.2	2350	2.7
19 TH	0650	-0.3	1218	2.5	1905	-0.3		
20 F	0034	2.7	0732	-0.3	1258	2.5	1947	-0.3
21 SA	0116	2.7	0811	-0.3	1337	2.5	2026	-0.3
22 SU	0156	2.7	0847	-0.2	1415	2.6	2102	-0.2
23 M	0235	2.7	0919	-0.1	1451	2.6	2135	-0.1
24 TU	0311	2.6	0950	0.1	1526	2.5	2209	0.0
25 W	0348	2.4	1020	0.2	1602	2.4	2247	0.0
26 TH ☾	0429	2.2	1058	0.3	1647	2.3	2337	0.1
27 F	0523	2.0	1156	0.4	1751	2.2		
28 SA	0051	0.2	0641	1.9	1321	0.4	1916	2.1
29 SU	0223	0.2	0811	1.9	1454	0.3	2043	2.2
30 M	0348	0.1	0930	2.1	1610	0.2	2150	2.3
31 TU	0447	0.0	1025	2.2	1701	0.1	2235	2.4

APRIL

Day	Time	m	Time	m	Time	m	Time	m
1 W	0526	-0.1	1102	2.3	1739	0.0	2312	2.5
2 TH	0601	-0.2	1134	2.3	1814	-0.1	2346	2.5
3 F ●	0635	-0.2	1206	2.4	1849	-0.2		
4 SA	0019	2.5	0706	-0.2	1237	2.4	1921	-0.2
5 SU	0051	2.5	0736	-0.2	1308	2.5	1954	-0.2
6 M	0126	2.6	0810	-0.1	1342	2.5	2030	-0.2
7 TU	0202	2.5	0846	-0.1	1418	2.5	2109	-0.2
8 W	0241	2.5	0923	0.0	1455	2.5	2147	-0.2
9 TH	0323	2.4	0959	0.0	1535	2.4	2229	-0.1
10 F ☽	0410	2.3	1043	0.1	1625	2.4	2326	0.0
11 SA	0512	2.2	1149	0.2	1736	2.4		
12 SU	0046	0.1	0634	2.1	1318	0.3	1905	2.4
13 M	0219	0.0	0804	2.2	1452	0.2	2033	2.5
14 TU	0343	-0.1	0921	2.3	1608	0.0	2143	2.6
15 W	0445	-0.2	1020	2.4	1705	-0.1	2238	2.6
16 TH	0534	-0.3	1108	2.4	1755	-0.2	2326	2.6
17 F ○	0621	-0.3	1153	2.5	1842	-0.2		
18 SA	0012	2.7	0705	-0.2	1233	2.6	1924	-0.2
19 SU	0054	2.7	0743	-0.1	1311	2.6	2001	-0.2
20 M	0133	2.7	0817	0.0	1348	2.6	2038	-0.1
21 TU	0211	2.6	0850	0.0	1424	2.6	2113	-0.1
22 W	0248	2.5	0922	0.1	1459	2.5	2148	-0.1
23 TH	0325	2.3	0954	0.1	1536	2.4	2225	0.0
24 F ☾	0405	2.1	1030	0.2	1618	2.4	2310	0.1
25 SA	0453	2.0	1120	0.3	1714	2.3		
26 SU	0011	0.2	0558	1.9	1231	0.3	1826	2.2
27 M	0129	0.2	0717	2.0	1356	0.3	1946	2.2
28 TU	0249	0.1	0834	2.1	1513	0.2	2055	2.3
29 W	0352	0.0	0932	2.2	1611	0.1	2146	2.4
30 TH	0437	-0.1	1015	2.3	1655	0.0	2228	2.5

Chart Datum: 1.76 metres below Normal Null (German reference Level)

TIME ZONE -0100
(German Standard Time)
Subtract 1 hour for GMT
For German Summer Time add ONE hour in non-shaded areas

GERMANY - HELGOLAND

LAT 54°11'N LONG 7°54'E

TIMES AND HEIGHTS OF HIGH AND LOW WATERS

YEAR 1992

MAY

Day	Time	m	Time	m	Time	m	Time	m
1 F	0516	-0.1	1053	2.4	1736	-0.1	2308	2.5
2 SA ●	0555	-0.2	1129	2.5	1816	-0.1	2347	2.5
3 SU	0632	-0.2	1205	2.5	1855	-0.2		
4 M	0025	2.6	0709	-0.1	1242	2.6	1935	-0.2
5 TU	0106	2.6	0750	-0.1	1323	2.6	2018	-0.2
6 W	0149	2.5	0832	-0.1	1404	2.6	2102	-0.2
7 TH	0233	2.5	0914	0.0	1447	2.6	2147	-0.2
8 F	0320	2.4	0957	0.0	1533	2.6	2235	-0.2
9 SA ☽	0413	2.3	1048	0.1	1628	2.5	2333	-0.1
10 SU	0515	2.2	1151	0.2	1735	2.6		
11 M	0044	0.0	0628	2.3	1309	0.3	1854	2.6
12 TU	0204	0.0	0745	2.3	1431	0.2	2011	2.6
13 W	0316	0.0	0854	2.4	1541	0.1	2116	2.6
14 TH	0414	-0.1	0949	2.4	1636	0.0	2210	2.6
15 F	0502	-0.1	1038	2.5	1727	-0.1	2302	2.6
16 SA ○	0551	-0.1	1126	2.6	1818	-0.1	2351	2.6
17 SU	0637	0.0	1211	2.6	1902	-0.1		
18 M	0034	2.7	0717	0.1	1249	2.7	1941	-0.1
19 TU	0112	2.6	0752	0.1	1325	2.7	2017	-0.1
20 W	0150	2.5	0825	0.1	1402	2.7	2054	0.0
21 TH	0227	2.4	0859	0.1	1438	2.6	2130	0.0
22 F	0305	2.3	0933	0.1	1515	2.6	2206	0.0
23 SA	0343	2.2	1008	0.2	1555	2.5	2245	0.1
24 SU ☾	0426	2.1	1050	0.2	1641	2.5	2332	0.2
25 M	0516	2.1	1144	0.3	1736	2.4		
26 TU	0031	0.2	0617	2.1	1251	0.3	1842	2.3
27 W	0138	0.2	0725	2.1	1405	0.3	1950	2.4
28 TH	0244	0.1	0828	2.2	1510	0.2	2049	2.4
29 F	0339	0.1	0922	2.4	1605	0.1	2141	2.5
30 SA	0428	0.0	1010	2.5	1656	0.1	2230	2.5
31 SU	0516	0.0	1055	2.6	1744	0.0	2318	2.6

JUNE

Day	Time	m	Time	m	Time	m	Time	m
1 M ●	0602	0.0	1138	2.6	1831	-0.1		
2 TU	0004	2.6	0647	0.0	1222	2.7	1919	-0.1
3 W	0052	2.6	0735	0.0	1309	2.7	2009	-0.2
4 TH	0141	2.5	0824	-0.1	1357	2.7	2058	-0.2
5 F	0228	2.5	0909	0.0	1443	2.7	2145	-0.2
6 SA	0316	2.4	0955	0.0	1531	2.7	2235	-0.1
7 SU ☽	0409	2.4	1046	0.1	1626	2.7	2329	0.0
8 M	0508	2.4	1144	0.2	1727	2.7		
9 TU	0030	0.1	0611	2.4	1249	0.3	1833	2.7
10 W	0134	0.1	0716	2.4	1359	0.2	1941	2.6
11 TH	0240	0.1	0820	2.4	1507	0.2	2045	2.6
12 F	0339	0.1	0918	2.5	1608	0.1	2144	2.6
13 SA	0433	0.1	1011	2.5	1703	0.1	2241	2.6
14 SU	0525	0.1	1103	2.6	1757	0.1	2333	2.6
15 M ○	0614	0.1	1151	2.7	1844	0.0		
16 TU	0017	2.6	0656	0.1	1232	2.7	1924	0.0
17 W	0055	2.6	0732	0.1	1308	2.7	2000	0.0
18 TH	0132	2.5	0806	0.1	1345	2.7	2036	0.0
19 F	0209	2.4	0840	0.0	1420	2.7	2109	0.0
20 SA	0244	2.4	0912	0.1	1454	2.7	2142	0.1
21 SU	0319	2.3	0945	0.1	1530	2.6	2218	0.1
22 M	0356	2.3	1021	0.2	1609	2.6	2256	0.2
23 TU ☾	0436	2.3	1101	0.3	1651	2.5	2337	0.2
24 W	0521	2.3	1152	0.4	1742	2.5		
25 TH	0029	0.3	0617	2.3	1256	0.4	1844	2.4
26 F	0133	0.3	0722	2.3	1407	0.3	1951	2.4
27 SA	0239	0.2	0828	2.4	1516	0.3	2056	2.5
28 SU	0343	0.2	0929	2.5	1619	0.2	2158	2.5
29 M	0443	0.1	1026	2.6	1719	0.1	2256	2.6
30 TU ●	0540	0.1	1118	2.7	1815	0.0	2350	2.6

JULY

Day	Time	m	Time	m	Time	m	Time	m
1 W	0633	0.0	1208	2.8	1909	-0.1		
2 TH	0041	2.6	0724	0.0	1259	2.8	2002	-0.2
3 F	0132	2.6	0815	-0.1	1349	2.8	2052	-0.2
4 SA	0220	2.6	0901	-0.1	1435	2.9	2137	-0.2
5 SU	0306	2.5	0945	0.0	1520	2.9	2222	-0.1
6 M	0354	2.5	1032	0.0	1610	2.8	2310	0.0
7 TU ☽	0446	2.5	1123	0.2	1705	2.8		
8 W	0000	0.1	0540	2.5	1217	0.3	1802	2.7
9 TH	0054	0.2	0636	2.4	1318	0.3	1905	2.6
10 F	0156	0.3	0740	2.4	1429	0.3	2014	2.5
11 SA	0304	0.3	0847	2.5	1542	0.2	2123	2.5
12 SU	0409	0.3	0950	2.6	1647	0.2	2225	2.5
13 M	0506	0.3	1046	2.6	1742	0.1	2318	2.5
14 TU ○	0556	0.2	1134	2.7	1829	0.1		
15 W	0003	2.5	0639	0.1	1216	2.7	1909	0.0
16 TH	0040	2.5	0716	0.1	1253	2.7	1944	0.0
17 F	0115	2.5	0750	0.0	1328	2.7	2016	0.0
18 SA	0149	2.5	0820	0.0	1400	2.7	2046	0.0
19 SU	0219	2.5	0849	0.1	1429	2.7	2114	0.1
20 M	0250	2.4	0920	0.1	1501	2.7	2147	0.1
21 TU	0324	2.4	0953	0.2	1537	2.7	2221	0.2
22 W ☾	0359	2.4	1027	0.2	1613	2.6	2253	0.3
23 TH	0435	2.4	1104	0.3	1652	2.5	2331	0.3
24 F	0519	2.4	1157	0.4	1747	2.4		
25 SA	0030	0.4	0622	2.3	1310	0.4	1859	2.4
26 SU	0147	0.4	0738	2.4	1433	0.3	2019	2.4
27 M	0307	0.3	0855	2.5	1552	0.2	2134	2.5
28 TU	0421	0.2	1005	2.6	1702	0.1	2241	2.5
29 W ●	0525	0.1	1104	2.7	1804	0.0	2339	2.6
30 TH	0622	0.1	1157	2.8	1859	-0.1		
31 F	0030	2.6	0713	0.0	1247	2.9	1950	-0.2

AUGUST

Day	Time	m	Time	m	Time	m	Time	m
1 SA	0118	2.6	0802	-0.1	1336	2.9	2037	-0.2
2 SU	0204	2.6	0847	-0.1	1420	2.9	2119	-0.2
3 M	0247	2.6	0928	-0.1	1502	2.9	2159	-0.1
4 TU	0329	2.6	1009	0.0	1546	2.8	2240	0.1
5 W ☽	0414	2.5	1053	0.1	1635	2.7	2322	0.2
6 TH	0501	2.5	1139	0.3	1726	2.6		
7 F	0008	0.4	0553	2.4	1235	0.4	1826	2.5
8 SA	0110	0.5	0658	2.4	1351	0.4	1941	2.3
9 SU	0228	0.5	0816	2.4	1517	0.3	2102	2.3
10 M	0348	0.4	0932	2.5	1633	0.2	2212	2.4
11 TU	0453	0.3	1032	2.6	1729	0.1	2306	2.4
12 W	0541	0.2	1118	2.7	1812	0.1	2347	2.5
13 TH ○	0621	0.2	1157	2.7	1849	0.0		
14 F	0022	2.5	0657	0.1	1233	2.7	1922	0.0
15 SA	0054	2.5	0729	0.0	1305	2.7	1951	0.0
16 SU	0124	2.5	0757	0.0	1335	2.7	2017	0.0
17 M	0151	2.5	0824	0.0	1403	2.7	2044	0.1
18 TU	0219	2.5	0854	0.1	1433	2.7	2115	0.2
19 W	0251	2.5	0927	0.1	1507	2.7	2147	0.2
20 TH	0326	2.5	0959	0.2	1541	2.6	2217	0.3
21 F ☾	0358	2.5	1031	0.3	1616	2.5	2249	0.4
22 SA	0436	2.5	1117	0.4	1707	2.4	2344	0.5
23 SU	0537	2.4	1231	0.4	1823	2.3		
24 M	0108	0.5	0701	2.4	1405	0.3	1954	2.3
25 TU	0242	0.4	0831	2.5	1536	0.2	2119	2.4
26 W	0405	0.3	0949	2.6	1651	0.1	2229	2.5
27 TH	0513	0.2	1051	2.8	1751	0.0	2326	2.6
28 F ●	0608	0.1	1143	2.9	1843	-0.1		
29 SA	0014	2.7	0657	0.0	1230	2.9	1930	-0.1
30 SU	0058	2.7	0743	-0.1	1315	2.9	2013	-0.2
31 M	0141	2.7	0826	-0.1	1359	2.9	2053	-0.1

Chart Datum: 1.76 metres below Normal Null (German reference Level)

TIME ZONE -0100
(German Standard Time)
Subtract 1 hour for GMT
For German Summer Time add ONE hour in non-shaded areas

GERMANY - HELGOLAND

LAT 54°11′N LONG 7°54′E

TIMES AND HEIGHTS OF HIGH AND LOW WATERS

YEAR **1992**

SEPTEMBER

Day	Time	m	Day	Time	m
1 TU	0222	2.7	16 W	0150	2.6
	0905	-0.1		0830	0.1
	1439	2.9		1407	2.7
	2131	0.0		2044	0.2
2 W	0301	2.7	17 TH	0222	2.6
	0943	0.0		0904	0.2
	1520	2.8		1441	2.7
	2207	0.2		2117	0.3
3 TH	0341	2.6	18 F	0256	2.6
	1021	0.1		0937	0.2
	1604	2.7		1516	2.6
	☽ 2243	0.3		2149	0.3
4 F	0422	2.5	19 SA	0330	2.6
	1103	0.3		1011	0.3
	1651	2.5		1554	2.5
	2324	0.5		☾ 2224	0.4
5 SA	0511	2.4	20 SU	0410	2.5
	1157	0.4		1057	0.4
	1749	2.3		1646	2.3
				2320	0.5
6 SU	0024	0.6	21 M	0512	2.4
	0616	2.4		1211	0.4
	1313	0.4		1804	2.2
	1906	2.2			
7 M	0148	0.6	22 TU	0046	0.5
	0741	2.3		0640	2.4
	1446	0.4		1348	0.4
	2035	2.2		1938	2.3
8 TU	0318	0.5	23 W	0225	0.5
	0907	2.4		0814	2.5
	1611	0.3		1522	0.2
	2153	2.3		2106	2.4
9 W	0432	0.4	24 TH	0350	0.4
	1013	2.6		0933	2.7
	1709	0.2		1635	0.1
	2248	2.4		2214	2.5
10 TH	0521	0.3	25 F	0456	0.2
	1057	2.7		1033	2.8
	1747	0.1		1731	0.0
	2324	2.5		2306	2.6
11 F	0556	0.2	26 SA	0548	0.1
	1131	2.7		1123	2.9
	1820	0.1		1819	-0.1
	2354	2.5		● 2352	2.7
12 SA ○	0629	0.1	27 SU	0636	0.0
	1204	2.7		1209	2.9
	1852	0.0		1904	-0.1
13 SU	0024	2.5	28 M	0034	2.7
	0702	0.0		0719	0.0
	1236	2.7		1253	2.9
	1920	0.0		1945	0.0
14 M	0053	2.5	29 TU	0114	2.7
	0731	0.0		0801	0.0
	1306	2.7		1336	2.9
	1946	0.1		2024	0.1
15 TU	0121	2.6	30 W	0155	2.8
	0759	0.0		0841	0.0
	1336	2.7		1417	2.8
	2013	0.1		2100	0.2

OCTOBER

Day	Time	m	Day	Time	m
1 TH	0234	2.8	16 F	0159	2.7
	0918	0.1		0846	0.2
	1456	2.8		1422	2.6
	2134	0.3		2056	0.3
2 F	0310	2.7	17 SA	0235	2.7
	0954	0.2		0923	0.2
	1536	2.6		1501	2.5
	2208	0.4		2132	0.3
3 SA	0349	2.6	18 SU	0314	2.6
	1034	0.3		1003	0.2
	1619	2.4		1545	2.4
	☽ 2247	0.5		2214	0.4
4 SU	0435	2.5	19 M	0400	2.6
	1124	0.4		1053	0.3
	1714	2.2		1641	2.3
	2342	0.6		☾ 2312	0.5
5 M	0537	2.4	20 TU	0503	2.5
	1233	0.5		1205	0.4
	1827	2.1		1756	2.3
6 TU	0101	0.7	21 W	0033	0.6
	0658	2.3		0627	2.6
	1401	0.5		1334	0.4
	1955	2.1		1924	2.3
7 W	0233	0.6	22 TH	0207	0.5
	0826	2.4		0756	2.6
	1528	0.4		1502	0.3
	2116	2.2		2047	2.4
8 TH	0352	0.5	23 F	0329	0.4
	0937	2.5		0911	2.7
	1630	0.3		1611	0.2
	2213	2.4		2150	2.6
9 F	0445	0.4	24 SA	0431	0.3
	1023	2.6		1009	2.8
	1709	0.2		1703	0.1
	2249	2.5		2240	2.6
10 SA	0521	0.3	25 SU	0523	0.2
	1056	2.7		1100	2.8
	1741	0.1		1750	0.1
	2319	2.5		● 2326	2.7
11 SU	0555	0.2	26 M	0611	0.1
	1129	2.7		1148	2.8
	1814	0.1		1836	0.1
	○ 2350	2.5			
12 M	0630	0.1	27 TU	0010	2.8
	1203	2.7		0656	0.1
	1845	0.1		1232	2.9
				1917	0.2
13 TU	0021	2.6	28 W	0050	2.8
	0703	0.1		0737	0.2
	1237	2.7		1314	2.9
	1915	0.1		1955	0.3
14 W	0053	2.6	29 TH	0130	2.9
	0735	0.1		0817	0.2
	1311	2.7		1355	2.8
	1947	0.2		2031	0.3
15 TH	0125	2.7	30 F	0209	2.8
	0809	0.1		0855	0.2
	1346	2.7		1434	2.7
	2020	0.3		2105	0.4
			31 SA	0246	2.8
				0932	0.2
				1512	2.5
				2139	0.4

NOVEMBER

Day	Time	m	Day	Time	m
1 SU	0323	2.7	16 M	0306	2.7
	1010	0.3		1001	0.2
	1553	2.3		1542	2.5
	2217	0.5		2211	0.4
2 M	0406	2.5	17 TU	0356	2.7
	1054	0.4		1053	0.2
	1642	2.2		1639	2.4
	☽ 2305	0.6		☾ 2308	0.5
3 TU	0500	2.5	18 W	0458	2.7
	1151	0.5		1158	0.3
	1744	2.1		1746	2.4
4 W	0010	0.7	19 TH	0020	0.6
	0609	2.4		0612	2.7
	1304	0.5		1314	0.4
	1859	2.1		1902	2.4
5 TH	0131	0.7	20 F	0142	0.5
	0728	2.4		0730	2.7
	1423	0.5		1431	0.3
	2016	2.2		2016	2.5
6 F	0250	0.6	21 SA	0258	0.4
	0840	2.5		0842	2.7
	1530	0.4		1537	0.2
	2118	2.4		2119	2.5
7 SA	0352	0.5	22 SU	0402	0.3
	0934	2.6		0942	2.7
	1617	0.4		1631	0.2
	2202	2.5		2212	2.6
8 SU	0437	0.4	23 M	0456	0.3
	1015	2.6		1037	2.7
	1655	0.3		1721	0.2
	2238	2.6		2302	2.7
9 M	0516	0.3	24 TU	0549	0.2
	1053	2.6		1129	2.8
	1733	0.2		1810	0.3
	2315	2.6		● 2349	2.8
10 TU	0556	0.2	25 W	0637	0.2
	1131	2.6		1215	2.8
	1811	0.2		1854	0.3
	○ 2351	2.7			
11 W	0635	0.2	26 TH	0031	2.9
	1210	2.7		0718	0.2
	1847	0.2		1256	2.8
				1931	0.4
12 TH	0027	2.7	27 F	0109	2.9
	0714	0.2		0757	0.2
	1250	2.7		1335	2.7
	1926	0.2		2007	0.3
13 F	0106	2.8	28 SA	0148	2.9
	0754	0.2		0836	0.2
	1331	2.7		1414	2.6
	2006	0.3		2042	0.3
14 SA	0145	2.8	29 SU	0226	2.8
	0836	0.2		0913	0.2
	1413	2.6		1452	2.5
	2044	0.3		2117	0.3
15 SU	0224	2.8	30 M	0302	2.7
	0917	0.2		0948	0.3
	1455	2.5		1530	2.4
	2124	0.3		2151	0.4

DECEMBER

Day	Time	m	Day	Time	m
1 TU	0341	2.7	16 W	0350	2.8
	1026	0.3		1046	0.2
	1611	2.3		1629	2.5
	2230	0.5		☾ 2300	0.4
2 W	0425	2.6	17 TH	0446	2.8
	1110	0.4		1142	0.3
	1658	2.2		1728	2.5
	☽ 2319	0.6			
3 TH	0517	2.5	18 F	0000	0.5
	1202	0.5		0549	2.8
	1755	2.2		1243	0.3
				1830	2.4
4 F	0021	0.6	19 SA	0108	0.5
	0620	2.4		0657	2.7
	1306	0.5		1351	0.4
	1901	2.2		1938	2.5
5 SA	0134	0.6	20 SU	0221	0.4
	0729	2.4		0808	2.6
	1413	0.5		1459	0.3
	2008	2.3		2045	2.5
6 SU	0244	0.6	21 M	0331	0.4
	0833	2.5		0915	2.6
	1514	0.5		1602	0.3
	2106	2.5		2146	2.6
7 M	0344	0.5	22 TU	0435	0.3
	0928	2.6		1017	2.6
	1606	0.4		1659	0.3
	2156	2.6		2242	2.6
8 TU	0436	0.4	23 W	0532	0.3
	1016	2.6		1114	2.6
	1655	0.3		1751	0.3
	2241	2.6		2333	2.7
9 W	0524	0.3	24 TH ●	0622	0.2
	1103	2.6		1201	2.6
	1741	0.2		1836	0.3
	○ 2324	2.7			
10 TH	0611	0.2	25 F	0016	2.8
	1148	2.6		0704	0.2
	1826	0.2		1241	2.6
				1914	0.3
11 F	0006	2.8	26 SA	0054	2.8
	0657	0.1		0742	0.2
	1233	2.6		1319	2.6
	1911	0.2		1949	0.3
12 SA	0051	2.8	27 SU	0131	2.8
	0744	0.1		0820	0.2
	1321	2.6		1356	2.5
	1957	0.2		2023	0.2
13 SU	0137	2.8	28 M	0208	2.8
	0831	0.1		0854	0.2
	1406	2.6		1432	2.5
	2040	0.2		2056	0.2
14 M	0219	2.9	29 TU	0241	2.8
	0914	0.1		0925	0.2
	1450	2.6		1504	2.4
	2121	0.2		2127	0.2
15 TU	0302	2.8	30 W	0315	2.7
	0958	0.1		0957	0.3
	1536	2.5		1538	2.3
	2206	0.3		2159	0.3
			31 TH	0350	2.6
				1031	0.3
				1614	2.3
				2235	0.4

Chart Datum: 1.76 metres below Normal Null (German reference Level)

SYLT 10-21-23

Schleswig-Holstein

CHARTS
Admiralty 3767; German D107, D108, 3013 Sheet 4 (List)

TIDES
Dover +0110; ML 1·8; Duration 0540; Zone −0100

Standard Port HELGOLAND (⟵)

Times				Height (metres)			
HW		LW		MHWS	MHWN	MLWN	MLWS
0100	0600	0100	0800	2·7	2·3	0·4	0·0
1300	1800	1300	2000				
Differences LIST							
+0256	+0246	+0207	+0213	−0·8	−0·6	−0·2	0·0
HÖRNUM							
+0225	+0221	+0134	+0143	−0·5	−0·3	−0·2	0·0
AMRUM-HAFEN							
+0144	+0140	+0129	+0140	+0·2	+0·3	+0·1	0·0

The island of Sylt is about 20M long, has its capital Westerland in the centre, Hornum in the S and List in the N. It is connected to the mainland by the Hindenburgdamm.

SHELTER
HÖRNUM Good in the small harbour, approx 370m × 90m, protected by outer mole on the S side and by two inner moles. Yachts secure on the N side. Good anchorage in Hörnum Reede in W and N winds and in Hörnumtief in E and S winds.
LIST The small harbour is sheltered except in NE to E winds. Entrance is 25m wide and harbour 3m deep.

There are two other harbours; Rantum and Munkmarsch which both dry; access HW∓3.

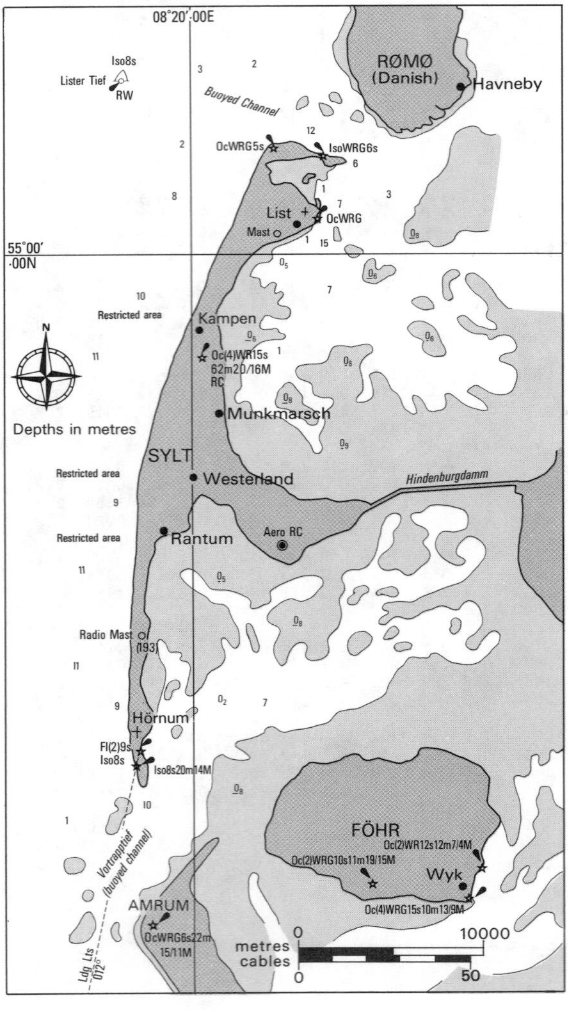

08°20'·00E
55°00'·00N
Iso8s
Lister Tief
RW
Buoyed Channel
RØMØ
(Danish)
Havneby
OcWRG5s
IsoWRG6s
List
OcWRG
Mast
Restricted area
Kampen
Oc(4)WR15s
62m20/16M
RC
Munkmarsch
Depths in metres
SYLT
Westerland
Hindenburgdamm
Restricted area
Restricted area
Rantum
Aero RC
Radio Mast
(193)
Hörnum
Fl(2)9s
Iso8s
Iso8s20m14M
Vortrapptief
(buoyed channel)
FÖHR
Oc(2)WR12s12m7/4M
Oc(2)WRG10s11m19/15M
Wyk
Oc(4)WRG15s10m13/9M
AMRUM
OcWRG6s22m
15/11M
Ldg Lts 012°
metres
cables
0
10000
0
50

NAVIGATION
HÖRNUM Waypoint Westvortrapptief (safe water) buoy, Oc 4s, 54°35′·00N 08°11′·30E, 222°/042° from/to Norddorf Lt (Amrum), 6·7M. Access through Vortrapptief buoyed channel (see below) inside drying banks. In strong W winds the sea breaks on off-lying banks and in the channel. Keep mid-channel in harbour entrance, approached from NE. Access at all tides. Large sections of the area to landward of Sylt are nature reserves and landing prohibited.
LIST Waypoint Lister Tief safe water buoy, Iso 8s, 55°05′·37N 08°16′·87E, 298°/118° from/to List West Lt, 4·7M. Lister Tief (see 10.21.5) is well marked. In strong W or NW winds expect a big swell on the bar (depth 4m) on the ebb, which sets on to Salzsand. NE quay is open construction and not suitable for yachts. Channel buoys through roadstead lead to harbour.Access at all tides, but beware strong tidal streams across entrance.

LIGHTS AND MARKS
HÖRNUM Conspic radio mast 3M N of harbour. Follow W041°-043° sector of Norddorf Lt (Oc WRG 6s) to line of Hörnum Ldg Lts 012°, both Iso 8s. N pier head FG, vis 024°-260°, S pier head FR. Outer mole head FR (mole floodlit).
LIST Kampen Lt, List West Lt, List Ost Lt and Romo church are prominent. For Lts see 10.21.4. N mole head FG, vis 218°-038°. S mole head FR, vis 218°-353°.

RADIO TELEPHONE
None.

TELEPHONE Hörnum (04653)
List (04652)
Westerland (04651)
HÖRNUM Hr Mr 1027, Dr 1016, Ⓗ (04651) 841; Police 1510; CG 1256.
LIST Hr Mr 374; Police 510 Ⓗ (04651) 841, # 413.

FACILITIES
HÖRNUM **Sylter YC** ☎ 274, AB, Bar, AC, FW, ◻; **Town** V, R, Bar, ME, ✉; Ⓑ.
LIST **Harbour** SC, AB, FW, #, C (3½ ton), Slip; **Village** V, R, Bar, P and D (cans), CG 365; Dr 350; Ferry to Römö (Denmark).
WESTERLAND **HB Jensen** ☎ 7017, Gaz; CG 85199 Police 7047; **Town** V, R, Bar, P and D (cans), #, ✉; Ⓑ; ≠; ✈.

MINOR HARBOURS AND ANCHORAGES 10-21-24

EMDEN, Ostfriesland, 53°21′·00N, 07°12′·00E, Zone −0100. Admty chart 3510, German D91 3012 Sheet 4. HW +0022 on Dover (GMT), +0040 on Helgoland (zone −0100); HW height +0·8m on Helgoland; ML 1·9m. Ldg Lts 088°, both Oc 5s 12M, lead to Vorhafen entrance, marked by FR and FG Lts. Proceed up Aussenhafen to yacht harbour on E side before Nesserland Lock. Good shelter except in SW winds. If no room there, go through lock into inner harbour, and round to Jarssumer Hafen in SE corner of port. Locks operate 0600-2200 (0800-2000 Sundays) LT. Sound NV (—· ···—) for opening. Jarssumer Hafen is also approached through Grosse Seeschleuse (H24). Both lock-keepers on VHF Ch 13 (H24). Facilities: Hr Mr 29034 Weather 21458; Yacht Hafen ☎ 26020 FW; # ☎ 20371; all facilities in city (1M). Ferry to Borkum.

GREETSIEL Niedersachsen, 53°30′·00N, 07°06′·00E, Zone−0100 Admty charts 3509, 3761. German D89. HW −0040 on Dover (GMT), −0010 on Helgoland (zone−0100); ML2·6m. Watt channel marked by perches, leads 2M SE over flats of Leysand. Breakwater extends a mile NNW from coast to near Greetsiel Buoy. Harbour access HW+1½. Yachts berth in Yacht Hr on pontoons. Harbour dries. A canal connects Greetsiel to Emden. There are a few facilities. **Village** R, V, ⇌, # ☎ (04931) 2764. Hr Mr ☎ (04926) 760.

JUIST, Niedersachsen, 53°41′·00N, 07°00′·00E, Zone −0100. Admty chart 3509, German D90. HW −0105 on Dover (GMT), −0035 on Helgoland (zone −0100); HW height +0·1 on Helgoland (latter two readings taken at Memmert). Entrance through narrow channel running N in the centre of the S side of island, marked by withies to the W. To the W of these is the long (5 ca) landing pier. West Beacon, on Haakdünen at W end of island, Juist water tower (conspic) in centre and East Beacon, 1M from E end of island. Aero Lt Fl W 5s 14m (occas) at the airfield. There is no yacht harbour. Anchor a cable S of W part of town ½M E of Steamer Pier or at E end of island. Facilities: Hr Mr ☎ 724; # ☎ 351; Harbour FW, Slip, C; villages of Oosdorp, Westdorp and Loog in centre of island have limited facilities, V, R, Bar, Gaz. Train runs from Juist pier to Oosdorp. Ferry – Norddeich.

NORDDEICH, Niedersachsen, 53°37′·00N, 07°09′·00E, Zone −0100, Admty chart 3761, German D3014. HW −0030 on Dover (GMT), −0020 on Helgoland (zone −0100); HW height +0·2m on Helgoland. See 10.21.10. Very good shelter in harbour, reached by channel 50m wide, 2m deep and over 1M long between two training walls which cover at HW and are marked by stakes. Hr divided by central mole; yachts berth in West Hr. Lts on W training wall head FG 8m 4M, vis 021°−327°. On E training wall head FR 8m 4M, vis 327°−237°. Ldg Lts 144°, Front, Iso WR 6s 6m 6/4M, Rear, 140m from front, Iso W 6s 9m 6M synchronised. Ldg Lts 350°, Front Iso WR 3s 5m 6/4M, Rear, 95m from front, Iso W 3s 8m 6M. Ldg Lts 170°, Front Iso W 3s 12m 10M, Rear, 420m from front, Iso W 3s 23m 10M, synchronised. Facilities: Hr Mr ☎ 8060; **Fuel Stn** ☎ 2721; # ☎ 2735; **YC** ☎ 3560; **Fritz H. Venske** CH, German Chart Agent; **M. Wagner** Gaz; **Town** AB, Ⓑ, Bar, C (5 ton), D, Dr, FW, ✉, R, ⇌, Slip, V, Gaz. Ferry to Juist and Norderney.

BALTRUM, Niedersachsen, 53°43′·00N, 07°23′·00E, Zone −0100. Admty charts 1875, 3761, German D3012. HW −0040 on Dover (GMT), −0005 on Helgoland (zone −0100), HW height +0·4m on Helgoland (latter two readings taken at Langeoog Ostmole). Shelter is good except in SW winds. Without local knowledge, the approach via Wichter Ee Seegat is not recommended. Entrance channel marked by withies to be left approx 10m to the W. Harbour partly dries. Yacht moorings in the Bootshafen at the E end of harbour. Lt at the groyne head Oc WRG 6s 7m 6/3M G082·5°-098°, W098°-103°, R103°-082·5°. Facilities; Hr Mr ☎ (04939) 448; **Harbour** AB, FW: **Baltrumer Bootsclub YC; Village** (¼M NNE) V, R, Bar. There is no fuel. Ferry from Nessmersiel.

NESSMERSIEL, Niedersachsen, 53°41′·00N, 07°22′·00E, Zone −0100. Admty charts 1875, 3761, German D3012, D89; HW −0040 on Dover (GMT), −0020 on Helgoland (zone −0100); HW height −0·2m on Helgoland. Good shelter in all weathers. Approach down the Nessmersieler Balje, channel marked by stbd buoys and beacons leading to end of Leitdamm. End of Leitdamm has Bn, Oc W, which, together with other unlit Bns mark the course of the Leitdamm on W; withies mark the E side of channel. Leitdamm covers at HW. Beyond ferry berth is a Yachthafen (1½M); secure to catamarans S of Ferry Quay. Harbour dries (2m at HW). Facilities: Hr Mr ☎ 2981; # ☎ 2735; **Nordsee Yachtclub Nessmersiel**; no supplies except FW: **Village** (1M to S) has limited facilities. Ferry to Baltrum.

BENSERSIEL, Niedersachsen, 53°41′·00N, 07°35′·00E, Zone −0100, Admty charts 1875, 3761, German D3012. HW −0024 on Dover (GMT), +0005 on Helgoland (zone −0100); HW height +0·4m on Helgoland. Very good shelter in the yacht harbour (dries). Entrance channel from Rute 1·5M between training walls with depth of 1·5m. Walls submerge at HW. Yacht Hr to SW just before harbour ent (2m). Yachts can also berth in the SW side of main hr. Lights: E training wall head Oc WRG 6s 6m 5/2M G110°−119°, W119°−121°, R121°−110°. W mole head FG, E mole head FR. Ldg Lts 138° Front Iso W 6s 7m 9M (intens on line), Rear, 167m from front, Iso W 6s 11m 9M, synchronised with front. Facilities: Hr Mr ☎ (04971) 2502, # ☎ (04421) 42031, Slip, C (8 ton), D (on E pier), FW, P (from garage); **Harle-Yachtbau** ☎ (04971) 1760, El, ME, Sh; **Kerkau** ☎ 2401, Gaz; **Town** Ⓑ, Bar, ✉, R, ⇌, V, Gaz. Ferry to Langeoog.

NEUHARLINGERSIEL, Niedersachsen, 53°42′·00N, 07°42′·00E, Zone −0100. Admty charts 3368, 1875, 3761, German D3012. HW 0000 on Dover (GMT), +0015 on Helgoland (zone −0100); HW height +0·5m on Helgoland. Approach channel well marked from Baklegde N end of Leitdamm, Oc 6s. Beware strong tidal streams across the entrance. Channel runs close E of Leitdamm which is marked by stakes with downturned brooms. It covers at HW. Yachts lie in NE corner of harbour; where there are numerous poles. Visitors berths very limited. Facilities: Hr Mr (04974) 289 **Quay** FW, D; **Village** V, R, Bar. Very picturesque place. Ferry to Spiekeroog (35 mins).

SPIEKEROOG, Niedersachsen, 53°45′·00N, 07°41′·00E, Zone −0100, Admty charts 3368, 1875, 3761 (GMT), German D89, D3015. HW −0008 on Dover, −0007 on Helgoland (zone −0100); HW height +0·5m on Helgoland; ML 1·3m; Duration 0555. See 10.21.13. Good shelter except in winds from S to SW when heavy swell builds up. Small harbour which dries. There is a harbour on S side of Spiekeroog used by ferries and yachts. Lt on rectangular structure FR 6m 4M, vis 197°−114°. There are no facilities except a 5 ton crane but the town can be reached by light railway. Hr Mr ☎ (04976) 217. Ferry from Nieuharlingersiel.

HARLESIEL , Niedersachsen, 53°43′·00N, 07°49′·00E; zone −0100. Admty chart 3369, 3368; German D3012. HW −0100 on Dover (GMT), −0005 on Helgoland (zone −0100) HW height +0·5m on Helgoland. Excellent shelter S of lock. Lock opens approx HW∓1. Yachts lie at pontoons to W by village or at BY to E after passing through lock on W side of 'pumping barrier'. River navigable up to Carolinensiel. Air and ferry to Wangerooge. Facilities: Hr Mr ☎ (04464) 472; # ≢ 249; **YC Harle** ☎ (04464) 1473; **Harbour** BY, C, V, R, Slip, P, D, FW **Town** El, ME, Gaz, ✉, V.

WANGERSIEL, Niedersachsen, (also known as Horumersiel) 53°41′·00N, 08°01′·00E, Zone −0100. Admty chart 3369, German D3011. HW −0100 on Dover (GMT), −0030 on Wilhelmshaven (zone −0100); HW height −0·6m on Wilhelmshaven; ML 3·3m. From buoy W3 (G conical) besom perches mark the N side of the channel to the harbour. Best water 10 to 20m from perches. Depth at ent, 1·3m. Channel keeps shifting especially at E end. Boats drawing 1·5m can cross the bar HW∓2½. Most of harbour dries. Secure on N quay. In NW corner is the YC and FW. Facilities: Hr Mr ☎ 238. No fuel. At Horumersiel (¼M) V, R, Bar.

DANGAST, Niedersachsen, 53°27′·00N, 08°07′·00E, Zone −0100, Admty chart 3369, German D3011. HW +0055 on Dover (GMT), −0007 on Helgoland (zone −0100). S of Wilhelmshaven in the wide bay of Jadebusen, which mostly dries: the Hr dries. Ent via Dangaster Aussentief (0·5m at LWS) leading SW from Stenkentief, marked on NW side by stakes. There are no lights other than Arngast Lt in the middle of Jadebusen. Yacht Hr on W side just before lock into Dangaster Tief, access HW∓2. Facilities: Very limited but usual facilities can be found in the seaside town of Dangast.

MINOR HARBOURS *continued*

OTTERNDORF , Niedersachsen, 53°49′ ·00N, 08°54′ ·00E, Zone – 0100, Admty charts 3261, 3262; German D3010 Sheet 5. HW +0100 on Dover (GMT), +0120 on Helgoland (zone –0100); HW height +0·5 on Helgoland; ML 2·9m; Duration 0525. Channel from sea (0·6m) divides and yachts can take the W branch to Kutherhafen (0·9m) or go up the canal to E, pass through lock then turn sharp S, then W to yacht harbour. Entrance marked by the Buoy on N side. Ldg Lts 245° 30′, Front Iso W94s 23m 18/10M; W Tr, R bands, R conical roof; Vis G to S of 091° W to N or 091°; Rear Iso W4s 52 m 21 M; W Tr R bands, R conical roof. Lockmaster ☎ (04751) 2190. **Yacht harbour** ☎ 2213 C, AC, FW, Bar. **Town** (3km) ME, Gaz, V, PO. Hr Mr (04926) 760. The canal from Ottendorf goes to Bederkesa and Bremerhaven.

BÜSUM, Schleswig Holstein, 54°07′ ·00N, 08°51′ ·00E, Zone –0100, Admty charts 1875, 3767, German D105, 3013 Sheet 16. HW +0036 on Dover (GMT), +0051 on Helgoland (zone –0100); HW height +0·1m on Helgoland; ML 1·8m; Duration 0625. Very good shelter. Two fairways, Suderpiep and Norderpiep, marked by R and G buoys, each approx 17M, lead into the port. Beware strong tidal streams across ent and sudden winds over the moles. Yachts pass through lock at N of Vorhafen, turn to SE into Yacht harbour. Lock controlled by R and G Lts and manned H24. Signal for opening, one long blast on entering approach chan; two long blasts on reaching lock if not already open. VHF Ch 11 16; Call *Büsum Port*. Facilities: (04834) Hr Mr ☎ 2183; CG ☎ 2025; # ☎ 2376; Dr ☎ 2088; **Büsum YC** ☎ 2997; **Yacht harbour** AB, AC, El, FW, M, ME, C, P, D, ◙**Town** CH, V, R, Bar, ✉, Ⓑ, ≷, Ⓗ ✈ (Hamburg).

TÖNNING, Schleswig Holstein, 54°19′ ·00N, 08°57′ ·00E, Zone –0100; Admty chart 3767, German D104, D3013 Sheet 18. HW +0216 on Dover (GMT), +0246 on Helgoland (zone –0100); HW height +0·5m on Helgoland; ML 2·7m. Eiderdamm lock, 5M seawards, operates H24. R. Eider with the Gieselau Kanal connects Tonning with the Kiel Canal (see 10.21.21). VHF Ch 14 16; N mole Oc(2)R 12s, S mole Oc G 6s. Above the dam, Die Eider is tidal, depending on operation of sluices HW+3 to HW+½ (beware strong currents). Secure on S quay of middle section of harbour. If proceeding up river, bridge clearance 5·6m, opened on request Mon-Sat 0600 to sunset. Facilities: (04861) Hr Mr ☎ 1400; **Tönning YC** ☎ 754 (all welcome); Dr ☎ 389; Ⓗ ☎ 706; **Jetty** FW, P, D; **BY** C (5 ton), D, FW, Slip; **Hamkens** Gaz; **Town** Bar, Ⓑ,Ⓗ (☎ 706), ✉, R, ≷, V.

HUSUM, Schleswig Holstein, 54°29′ ·00N, 09°03′ ·00E, Zone –0100. Admty chart 3767, German D105; 3013 Sheet 13. HW +0036 on Dover (GMT), +0205 on Helgoland (zone –0100), ML 1·9m; Duration 0555. See 10.21.22. Yachts can either anchor W of Rly bridge near YC on S bank or pass through bridge (clearance 5m when unopened) to Inner Harbour by SC Nordsee. Both dry. There is a sluice/lock 650m downstream from YC which is shut when level exceeds 0·3m over MHW. A R Lt is shown when closed. Beware the canal effect when passing big ships in the narrows. VHF call *Husum Port* on Ch 11. Traffic reports on Ch 11 every H+00 from HW–4 to HW+2. Outer Ldg Lts 106° both Iso R 8s, synchronised and intens on leading line. Inner Ldg Lts 090° both Iso G 8s, synchronised and intens on leading line. Facilities: (04841) Most facilities available in town. P, D, in harbour. Hr Mr ☎ 667217; Sluice ☎ 2565; **Husum YC** ☎ 65670; **SC Nordsee** ☎ 3436; # ☎ 61759.

WITTDÜN, Amrum, 54°38′ ·00N, 08°23′ ·00E; Zone –0100. Admty chart 3767; German D107; 3013 Sheet 7. HW +0107 on Dover (GMT), +0137 on Helgoland (zone –0100); ML 2·7m; Duration 0540. See 10.21.23. Wittdün is the main harbour of Amrum; Yachts berth on yacht bridge S of stone quay, lying bows to pontoon, stern to posts. Good shelter except in E winds. The quay 800m to the E is reserved for ferries only. Channel is 2m. Ldg Lts 273°. Front Iso R 4s 11m 10M; W mast, R stripe; intens on Ldg line. Rear, 0·9M from front, Iso R 4s 33m 15M and Fl(3) 30s 63m 23M; R Tr, W bands. It is not advisable to enter at night. Channel into harbour marked by withies left to port. Wriakhörn Cross Lt to W of town LFl(2) WR 15s 26m 9/7M; W297°-319°, R319°-343°, W343°-014°, R014°-034°. Facilities: (04682) Hr Mr ☎ 2294; # ☎ 2026, Dr ☎ 2612. P and D (in cans) at Nebel. **Amrum YC** ☎ 2054.

SCHLÜTTSIEL, Schleswig Holstein, 54°41′ ·00N, 08°45′ ·00E; Zone –0100. Admty chart 3767; German D107; 3013 sheets 7, 9. HW +0156 on Dover (GMT), +0026 on Helgoland (zone –0100). Approach between Langeness/Oland and Gröde-Appelland. Channel 2-3m deep, harbour 2m. Turn into harbour at buoy SCHL 20, proceed between groynes 300m long, ends marked by S and N cardinal beacons. Small harbour mainly used by ferries with no special places for yachts. Moor alongside north walls of the quay. In W winds a swell runs into the harbour. Beware warps across harbour from local boats. There are no lights. Facilities: there are very few facilities. Hr Mr ☎ 3301. **Dagebüll YC** ☎ 1463.

WYK, Island of Föhr, 54°42′ ·00N, 08°35′ ·00E, Zone –0100. Admty chart 3767, German D107; 3013 sheet 7. HW +0107 on Dover (GMT), +0137 on Helgoland (zone –0100); ML 2·8. Good yacht harbour to N of entrance, sheltered in all winds, or yachts can berth on E quay of Old Harbour. Yacht harbour (1·5m) Visitors go to seaward side of Pontoon 1. Access H24; Commercial harbour (4m). Lights – Oldenhorn (SE point of Föhr), R tower, Oc(4) WRG 15s 10m 13/9M; W208°-250°, R250°-281°, W281°-290°, G290°-333°, W333°-058°, R058°-080°. S mole head Oc(2) WR 12s 12m 7/4M; W220°-322°, R322°-220°. Facilities: (04681) Yacht harbour Hr Mr ☎ 3030; Commercial Hr Mr ☎ 2852; **YC** ☎ 1280; Dr ☎ 8998; # ☎ 2594; **Harbour road** (500m), CH, ◙, P and D (cans); **Yacht Harbour** R, V. **W Quay** D.

DAGEBÜLL, Schleswig Holstein, 54°44′ ·00N, 08°42′ ·00E, Zone –0100. Admty chart 3767; German D107; 3013 Sheet 7. HW +0211 on Dover (GMT), +0026 on Helgoland (zone –0100) ML 2·9m. Small harbour mainly for ferries; there are no special yacht berths. Yachts berth on outer side of N mole. Iso WRG 8s 23m 18/15M; G042°-043°, W043°-044·5°, R044·5°-047° on G mast. Keep in W sector up to 1.3M from harbour. Ldg Lts 053°, Front Iso R 4s 7m 9M; R mast, W bands; vis 346°-121°. Rear, 50m from front, Iso R 4s 10m 9M; R mast, W bands; synchronised. FW Lts on N and S moles. Depth in basin 2·8m. Facilities: Hr Mr ☎ 233; Slip ☎ 209; **Village** R, V, P and D (cans), ≷.

TIDAL INFORMATION FOR WEST COAST OF DENMARK 10-21-25

The following figures are average values and so are approximate and should be used with caution
Standard Port HELGOLAND (⟵)

Times				Height (metres)			
HW		LW		MHWS	MHWN	MLWN	MLWS
0300	0700	0100	0800	2·7	2·3	0·4	0·0
1500	1900	1300	2000				
Differences HOJER SLUICE							
+0247	+0322	No data		–0·3	–0·2	0·0	0·0
ROMO HAVN							
+0227	+0302	+0221	+0201	–0·8	–0·7	–0·1	0·0
GRADYB BAR							
+0137	+0152	No data		–1·2	–1·1	–0·1	0·0
ESBJERG							
+0307	+0307	+0221	+0221	–1·1	–0·9	–0·2	–0·1
BLAAVANDS HUK							
+0147	+0157	+0131	+0121	–0·9	–0·9	–0·1	0·0
TORSMINDE							
+0337	+0357	+0301	+0231	–1·8	–1·6	–0·3	0·0
THYBORON							
+0427	+0537	+0631	+0431	–2·3	–2·0	–0·3	0·0
HANSTHOLM							
+0407	+0647	+0601	+0351	–2·4	–2·0	–0·3	0·0
HIRTSHALS							
+0402	+0627	+0601	+0321	–2·4	–2·0	–0·3	0·0

Advertisers' Index

Enquiries about advertising in this book should be addressed to:

Communications Management International
Chiltern House
120 Eskdale Avenue
Chesham
Bucks
HP5 3BD

Late corrections

(up to and including Admiralty Notices to Mariners, weekly edition No. 19/91).

Important navigational information in the body of this Almanac is corrected up to Weekly Edition No.14/1991 of *Admiralty Notices to Mariners*. For ease of reference each correction is sequentially numbered, followed by the page number.

Chapter 4 – Radio Navigation Aids

01.46 RADIOBEACONS.
Delete: No. 73 **Outer Gabbard Lt V**.
Delete all details of No. 63 listed under No. 77 Smith's Knoll Lt V. Also delete No. 73 from map on page 47.

02.50 RADIOBEACONS.
Delete: No. 201 **Douglas Victoria Pier Lt.**
Delete all details of No. 201 listed under No. 209 Walney Island Lt on page 52. Also delete No. 201 from map on page 51.

03.62 RADIO BEACON CALLSIGNS.
Delete: DG Douglas 201, and GA Outer Gabbard Lt V 73.

04.67 RADAR BEACONS.
No. 43 **Winterton Old Lighthouse**.
Amend col 2 to read 3 & 10 cm*.
No. 39 **Outer Gabbard Lt V**.
Amend to read **Outer Gabbard Lt By** and form of flash to read **O**.

05.68 RADAR BEACONS.
No. 97 **Ve Skerries Lt**.
Amend form of flash to read **M**.
No. 157 **East Channel Lt F**.
Amend to read: Lt By.
No. 201 **Mizen Hd**.
Amend col 2 to read: 3 & 10 cm*.

Chapter 6 – Communications

06.139 UK Coast Radio Stations.
North Foreland Radio, MF frequencies.
Channel T withdrawn. Station transmits on 1848 kHz, receives on 2016 kHz (unchanged).

07.141 **Stonehaven Radio**, MF frequencies.
Add: Ch T. Station transmits on 2698 kHz, receives on 2016 kHz. A new channel opened, known as Channel 1 (one). Station transmits 1722 kHz, receives 2066 kHz (for Autolink RT equipped vessels only).

08.141 **Wick Radio**. Channel G, amend to read 1755 and 2099 kHz.

09.141 **Shetland Radio**. Channel C, amend to read 2604 and 2013 kHz. Channel D, amend to read 1659 and 2084 kHz.

10.145 Continental Coast Radio Stations.
Pont l'Abbé Radio.
In col 2 add: See Note (a) below. In remaining cols, amend Ch 27 to read Ch 86.

11.145 **Brest- Le Conquet Radio.**
Gale Warning col, lines 1 - 2. Delete: 1673 kHz and 1876 kHz. Insert: 1806 kHz.

12.145 **Ouessant, Plougasnou, Paimpol and St Malo Radios**.
The data shown in cols 5 and 6 should each be moved one col to the right, and refer to Weather Bulletins and Gale Warnings respectively.

13.145 **Plougasnou Radio**.
In col 2 add: See Note (a) below. In remaining cols amend Ch 83 to read Ch 81.

14.146 **Boulogne Radio**. Gale Warnings.
Line 1. Delete: 1694. Insert: 1771.
Line 3. Delete: 1694 and.

Chapter 7 – Weather

15.154 7.2.2 BBC Inshore Waters Forecast.
RH column. Line 9.
Delete: Blackpool.
Insert: Liverpool (Crosby).

Chapter 10 – Harbour, Coastal and Tidal Information.

Area 2 – Central Southern England

16.231 LIGHTS, FOG SIGNALS & WAYPOINTS.
RIVER HAMBLE. RH column. Line 14.
Ldg Lts 026° Warsash shore. Amend vis to read: 010°-040°.

Area 3 – SE England

17.282 LIGHTS, FOG SIGNALS & WAYPOINTS.
LH column. Line 1.
Before Mixon Bn, insert: Boulder Lt By 50°41'·53N 00°49'·00W Fl G 2·5s; PHM.

18.284 LIGHTS, FOG SIGNALS & WAYPOINTS.
OAZE DEEP. LH column. Line 10.
Medway Lt By. Amend characteristic to read: Mo (A) 6s.

19.287 S.E. ENGLAND WAYPOINTS.
Insert:
Boulder Lt By 50°41'·53N 00°49'·00W.
Street By 50°41'·65N 00°48'·80W.

20.305 RIVER MEDWAY (SHEERNESS).
NAVIGATION.
Amend characteristic of Medway Lt By to read: Mo (A) 6s.

21.317 SOUTHEND - ON - SEA/LEIGH - ON - SEA.
NAVIGATION. Lines 3/4.
Amend to read: outside the W Shoebury Lt By (SHM) Fl G 2·5s.

Area 4 – East England

22.327 LIGHTS, FOG SIGNALS & WAYPOINTS.
OUTER GABBARD Lt V.
Delete: All present details.
Insert: Outer Gabbard Lt By
51°59'·38N 02°04'·63E Q (3) 10s; ECM; *Whis;* Racon.

23.328 *NEWARP Lt F.*
Amend to read: *NEWARP LANBY*
52°48'·35N 01°55'·80E Fl 10s 12m **21M** (H24); R hull with Lt Tr; *Horn 20s*; Racon.

24.340 RIVER DEBEN.
NAVIGATION.
Line 2 to read: "51°58'·47N 01°24'·35E 114°/294° approx from/to buoyed".

Area 5 – North–East England

25.356 LIGHTS, FOG SIGNALS & WAYPOINTS.
RH column. Line 49.
Bull Sand Fort. Amend to: *Horn 30s*.

26.362 RIVER HUMBER.
CHARTLET.
Bull Sand Fort. Amend to: *Horn 30s*.

Area 6 – SE Scotland

27.398 RIVER TAY.
CHARTLET.
Delete: Lt By Fl G 2s SHM located approx 4 ca S of Tay road bridge & SE of Middle Bank.

Area 8 – N.W. Scotland

28.446 ULLAPOOL.
CHARTLET.
The values on the Latitude and Longitude grids should be amended to 57°52'·7N 05°09'·5W.

29.452 LOCH ALINE.
CHARTLET.
Amend values of scales to read 500 metres (instead of 1000) and 2·5 ca (instead of 5).
Delete: Bogha Lurcain Lt By QG SHM.
(Note: There is a drying rock lying half a cable off Bolorkle Pt in the same position as the SHM mentioned above).

Area 11 – South Wales & Bristol Channel

30.522 LIGHTS, FOG SIGNALS & WAYPOINTS.
BARMOUTH. LH column.
N Bank Y perch.
Delete: 2 M, TE 1986. Insert: 5M.
Ynys y Brawd SE end. Add: 5M.

31.525 LIGHTS, FOG SIGNALS & WAYPOINTS.
LUNDY. RH column.
Near North Pt. Amend to read: 48m **15M.**

32.529 BARMOUTH.
CHARTLET.
Y perch. Amend Lt range to 5M.

33.550 MINOR HARBOURS & ANCHORAGES.
LUNDY ISLAND. Line 12.
Near North Pt Lt. Amend to read: 48m 15M.

Area 15 – South Brittany

34.662 VANNES.
FACILITIES. Line 5.
Delete: Gas.

35.665 LORIENT.
NAVIGATION. Lines 8/9.
Delete: (see inset).

36.668 BÉNODET.
TELEPHONE. Line 1.
Amend Hr Mr ☎ to 98.56.38.72.

37.672 MINOR HARBOURS & ANCHORAGES.
PORT D'ARZAL.
Line 9. Insert: CH, P.
Line 11. Delete: C (15 ton), CH, P, D, El, Gas, Gaz, ME, Sh.

Area 16 – North Brittany

38.673 AREA 16 INDEX PAGE.
10.16.25. Delete: Pontrieux.

38.692 PERROS-GUIREC.
TIDES. Last two lines.
Delete: Ploumanach and Time/Height differences.

Index

Explanation

Significant place names are shown in **bold** type without the definite article.

Abbreviations are entered under the full word and not the abbreviation.

For example, St Abb's comes under Saint and not St.

Page numbers in **bold** type indicate harbour and tidal information.

Page numbers in *italics* indicate tidal information (only).

The prefix C before a page number indicates a Coast Radio Station.

The prefix L before a page number indicates an entry in the lists of Lights, Fog Signals and Waypoints.

The prefix R before a page number indicates a Radio Navigational Aid.

A

B

C

D

E

F

G

H

I

M

N

Q

R

S

T

U